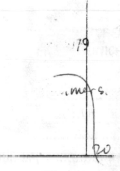

ORGANIC
CHEMISTRY

LOUIS F. FIESER
and MARY FIESER

Department of Chemistry, Harvard University

THIRD EDITION

REINHOLD PUBLISHING CORPORATION

NEW YORK

CHAPMAN & HALL, LTD., LONDON

1956

Copyright 1956 by
REINHOLD PUBLISHING CORPORATION

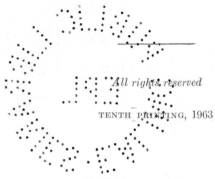

TENTH PRINTING, 1963

D. C. Heath and Company
Publishers of Textbook Edition

Chapman & Hall, Ltd., London
British Distributors

Library of Congress Catalog Card Number 56-6691

REINHOLD PUBLISHING CORPORATION

Publishers of Chemical Engineering Catalog, Chemical Materials Catalog, "Automatic
Control," "Materials & Design Engineering," "Progressive Architecture,"
Advertising Management of the American Chemical Society

Printed in the U.S.A. by
THE WAVERLY PRESS, Baltimore, Md.

PREFACE

The period between the first (1944) and second (1950) editions of this book did not compare in richness of new developments with that of the years 1950–1956, a period which has seen elucidation of structures and total syntheses of important fatty acids, carbohydrates, peptides, enzymes, alkaloids, isoprenoids, tropolones, steroids, and antibiotics. In some areas the new developments have so altered the previous concepts as to call for almost complete rewriting. Use of isotopic tracers and of microbiological techniques has so accelerated elucidation of pathways of biogenesis as to necessitate complete revision of chapters on the metabolism of fats, carbohydrates, and proteins; these chapters now incorporate some topics that seemed out of place in a previous chapter on microbiological processes.

Advances in theory have been no less important. The concepts of conformational analysis are developed in Chapter 12 (Ring Formation and Stability) and used in discussions of sugars, terpenes, alkaloids, and steroids. The molecular orbital theory, now generally recognized as contributing importantly to the understanding of organic phenomena, is introduced in Chapter 3. More mechanisms are included than before, of both ionic and free radical reactions, and they are cited throughout the text, as the reactions are encountered. Mechanisms of ionic reactions are further reviewed and extended in an integrated exposition.

Changes aimed at making the book more useful as a student text include considerable rearrangement of material and rewriting. Resonance is introduced much earlier than before, in a section in Chapter 3 on conjugated dienes, and thereafter is used extensively. Problems are given at the end of chapters, even some of the advanced ones, and answers to them are included at the end of the book.

In appreciation of the friendly reception of our book in countries other than the United States and of its use by readers of a variety of professions and interests, we have deleted nonessential details of technological processes, production figures, and trade names, particularly as they reflect practice in our own country. These deletions have saved space for inclusion of new material and helped restrict the book to a reasonable length.

The idea of including brief biographical sketches of past and present chemists associated with developments cited was introduced by Dr. Hans Hensel in his German translation of our second edition. The list of biographies is now increased to 454 entries, each of which gives the person's full name and vital statistics, the university at which he earned a higher degree

or studied, the professor under whom he worked, and the university or
company of his major service. Nobel Prize awards are indicated, and references are given to memorial lectures and biographical sketches. Names and
dates in the text may aid location of papers cited; author's initials not given
in the text are to be found in the author index.

Cambridge, Massachusetts   LOUIS F. FIESER
April 15, 1956   MARY FIESER

CONTENTS

CHAPTER | PAGE

1 THE NATURE OF ORGANIC COMPOUNDS............ 1

2 SATURATED HYDROCARBONS (Alkanes)......... 25

3 ETHYLENIC HYDROCARBONS (Alkenes).............. 49

4 ACETYLENIC HYDROCARBONS (Alkynes)......... 84

5 PETROLEUM............. 94

6 ALCOHOLS.............. 111

7 HALOGEN COMPOUNDS.... 145

8 CARBOXYLIC ACIDS....... 161

9 ALDEHYDES AND KETONES. 191

10 AMINES................ 224

11 STEREOCHEMISTRY....... 249

12 RING FORMATION AND STABILITY.............. 295

13 REACTION MECHANISMS... 326

14 CARBOHYDRATES........ 350

15 FATS................. 399

16 PROTEINS............. 417

17 CARBOHYDRATE METABOLISM................ 472

18 FAT METABOLISM........ 488

19 PROTEIN METABOLISM.... 497

CHAPTER | PAGE

20 STRUCTURE OF BENZENE.. 514

21 AROMATIC HYDROCARBONS. 527

22 AROMATIC SUBSTITUTIONS. 556

23 NITRO COMPOUNDS...... 571

24 SULFONIC ACIDS......... 588

25 ARYL AMINES........... 595

26 PHENOLS.............. 623

27 ARYL HALIDES.......... 644

28 AROMATIC CARBOXYLIC ACIDS................. 656

29 AROMATIC ALDEHYDES AND KETONES............... 674

30 QUINONES............. 709

31 NAPHTHALENE.......... 732

32 POLYNUCLEAR HYDROCARBONS.................. 753

33 HETEROCYCLES......... 796

34 ALKALOIDS............ 826

35 POLYMERS............. 847

36 DYES................. 880

37 ISOPRENOIDS.... 935

38 STEROIDS............. 961

39 VITAMINS............. 997

40 CHEMOTHERAPY......... 1021

ANSWERS TO PROBLEMS...... 1039

INDEXES................ 1051

CHAPTER 1

THE NATURE OF ORGANIC COMPOUNDS

The designation "organic," which means pertaining to plant or animal organisms, was introduced into chemical terminology as a convenient classification of substances derived from plant or animal sources. A few such substances had been known since earliest antiquity. Prehistoric peoples were familiar with sugar, with the fermentation of the sweet principle of grape (sugar) and the production of wine, and with the souring of wine under the agency of *Acetobacter* to produce vinegar, a dilute solution of acetic acid (L. *acetum*, vinegar). The process of rectifying alcoholic beverages by distillation, as a means of increasing the proportion of alcohol, was discovered as early as A.D. 900, and a crude mode of distillation had previously been applied to the production of oil of turpentine from pine resin. Vegetable oils and animal fats, and the process of making soap from these substances, have been known for centuries. Methods of applying the beautiful vegetable dye indigo and of dyeing with madder root (alizarin) were developed by ancient Romans and Egyptians, and for many centuries these natural pigments were the chief dyes for fabrics. Tyrian purple was a prized dye extracted by the Phoenicians from a rare species of mollusk.

The Middle Ages afforded but few additions to the list of chemical compounds of organic origin. During the 16th and 17th centuries some advances resulted from application of the method of pyrolysis, or heat treatment, to plant products. Dry distillation of wood afforded a crude substance called pyroligneous acid (1661), now known to contain methyl alcohol, acetone, and acetic acid. Succinic acid was obtained by destructive distillation of amber, and benzoic acid was isolated as a product of pyrolysis of gum benzoin (1608). Toward the end of the 18th century a start was made on the more significant problem of examining plant and animal products in the native state, that is, as obtained by solvent extraction and without alterations attendant upon the brutal process of destructive distillation. In the years 1769-85 the gifted Swedish chemist Scheele[1] conducted a series of investigations that constituted a forerunner of modern studies of the chemistry of biological products. He isolated tartaric acid as the sour principle of the grape, citric acid from lemon, malic acid from apples, gallic acid from nut galls, lactic acid from sour milk, uric acid from urine, and oxalic acid from wood sorrel. Scheele further prepared oxalic acid by oxidation of sugar with nitric acid; he discovered glycerol and characterized it as the sweet principle common to animal fats and vegetable oils. Other early

---

[1] Carl Wilhelm Scheele. 1742-86; b. Stalsund; apothecary in Stockholm, Uppsala, Köping

chemists isolated urea from human urine (Rouelle, 1773), hippuric acid from horse urine (Liebig, 1829), cholesterol from animal fats (Chevreul,[2] 1815) morphine from opium (Sertürner, 1805), and the alkaloidal drugs quinine, strychnine, brucine, and cinchonine (Pelletier and Caventou, 1820).

Nothing was known of the chemical nature of these substances derived from living organisms until Lavoisier's classic investigations of the process of combustion (1772–77). Lavoisier[3] established that air is composed of oxygen, discovered by Scheele and by Priestley[4] in 1772–74, and of a second inert gas that he termed "azote" (nitrogen); he was the first to recognize that combustion consists in interaction of the burning substance with oxygen of the air. He proved that sulfur, phosphorus, and carbon combine with oxygen on burning to yield products that, in the presence of moisture, appear as sulfuric, phosphoric, and carbonic acid. Metals were found to afford bases on oxidation. Turning to the as yet unexplored organic substances, Lavoisier devised a method for burning them in a small lamp floating on mercury in a bell jar containing air or oxygen. All the compounds examined yielded carbon dioxide and water, and hence must contain the elements carbon and hydrogen. Lavoisier determined the amount of carbon dioxide formed on combustion by absorption in potassium hydroxide solution, and by a first crude technique of quantitative analysis made an approximate estimation of the amounts of carbon and hydrogen present.

By application and elaboration of Lavoisier's scheme of combustion analysis, certain compounds of organic origin were shown to be composed of carbon and hydrogen alone (hydrocarbons). In a considerable number of others the combined carbon and hydrogen content was too low to account for the whole, and yet the sole products of combustion were carbon dioxide and water. These compounds therefore must be composed of carbon, hydrogen, and oxygen (e.g., sugar, alcohol, acetic acid). A certain few of the organic compounds known at the time also yielded nitrogen, when burned in an atmosphere of oxygen, and this element was thereby recognized as a further constituent (e.g., urea, hippuric acid, morphine). As more and more examples of the rapidly expanding list of plant and animal products were investigated, the surprising conclusion became inescapable that the great majority of these natural products of widely diversified properties and types are made up of combinations of the same small group of elements consisting of carbon, hydrogen, oxygen, and nitrogen. Different combinations of the first three of these elements give rise to solid, liquid, and gaseous substances, to materials that are sour and to those that are sweet, to blue and to red dyes, and to substances essential to the human diet, as well as to plant products poisonous to the animal organism.

In sharp contrast with this situation was the status of the results of

[2] Michel Eugéne Chevreul, 1786–1899; Paris

[3] Antoine Lavoisier, 1743–94; b. Paris; guillotined; see D. McKie, "Antoine Lavoisier" (Lippincott)

[4] Joseph Priestley, 1733–1804; b. Yorkshire, England

parallel investigations of substances of mineral or inorganic origin. Discoveries in this field were made in abundance in the early part of the 19th century, particularly under the leadership of a succession of able Swedish and Finnish chemists and mineralogists working with supplies of rare ores found in Sweden. Here diversification in elemental composition proved to be the rule, and the investigator who succeeded in achieving the first chemical analysis of a mineral was often rewarded with the discovery of a new element. By 1807 thirty-six elements were known, and by 1830 the list had mounted to fifty-three.

The fact that substances associated with living organisms were all derived from a selected few of the large number of known elements was only one of the seemingly mysterious attributes of these compounds, the study of which was first referred to as organic chemistry by Berzelius[5] in 1807. In contrast with most mineral substances, the organic compounds are as a rule easily combustible, and often are destroyed or damaged by even moderate application of heat. They tend to be delicate and sensitive, and certain of them resemble actual plant and animal tissues. Since all the first-known members of the group had been isolated as products of the life process, the belief was current for a time that organic compounds could arise only through operation of a vital force inherent in the living cell. Although inorganic compounds had been prepared artificially in the laboratory, Berzelius, a leading figure of the period, held that the chemical synthesis of organic substances was beyond the realm of possibility.

The doctrine of an essential vital force remained unchallenged until Wöhler[6] was led, through a chance observation reported in 1828, to the discovery that organic compounds can arise without the agency of any organism. In experimenting with ammonium cyanate, a substance of purely mineral or inorganic character, this early German chemist discovered to his surprise that evaporation of an aqueous solution of the salt resulted in production of urea, a representative compound of the organic type excreted in human urine. The result was so contrary to the thought of the period

$$NH_4OCN \longrightarrow CO(NH_2)_2$$
Ammonium cyanate   Urea

that Wöhler repeated the experiment many times before publication of his results. When fully satisfied with the experimental evidence, Wöhler saw that it constituted a refutation of the postulated "vital force," and in a letter to Berzelius he stated, "I must tell you that I can prepare urea without requiring a kidney or an animal, either man or dog." Although Berzelius, Gerhardt,[7] and other contemporary chemists would not at first concede the evidence of this initial experiment, the discovery eventually led to abandonment of the idea of a vital force. The preparation of organic compounds

[5] Jöns Jacob Freiherr von Berzelius, 1779–1848, Stockholm

[6] Friedrich Wöhler, 1800–82; b. Germany; Göttingen

[7] Charles Frédéric Gerhardt, 1816–56; b. France; Strasbourg

presents no special mystery but is merely a matter of knowledge and experimental skill.

The designation organic has persisted as a convenient and reasonably descriptive classification of a group of chemical compounds having a number of characteristics in common. Most of them contain hydrogen, a large number contain oxygen as well, many contain nitrogen, and some contain halogen, sulfur, phosphorus, and other elements. Since they all contain carbon, organic chemistry can be defined as the chemistry of carbon compounds.

Distinguishing Characteristics of Organic Compounds. — Although carbon compounds are so varied and extensive that broad generalizations concerning their properties are almost inevitably subject to exceptions, several general characteristics differentiate organic from inorganic compounds. Organic compounds, with very few exceptions (e.g., CCl_4), are combustible, and this property constitutes the basis of the chief methods for their analysis. Inorganic salts, as a rule, do not burn. Such salts are solid substances, and they are either infusible or difficultly fusible. By contrast, organic compounds usually exist as gases, liquids, or low-melting solids. The great bulk of solid substances have melting points in the relatively low temperature range between room temperature and 400° C.

Although alcohol, acetic acid, sugar, and a number of other organic compounds are readily soluble in water, water solubility is the exception rather than the rule. Hydrocarbons of petroleum do not dissolve in water, and neither do animal fats and vegetable oils, coal tar, rubber, indigo, or turpentine oil. These solubility relationships are understandable in the light of the useful generalization that like dissolves like. Alcohol, acetic acid, and sugar dissolve in water because, like water, they contain the hydroxyl group (OH); the conventional symbol AcOH for acetic acid emphasizes this fact. The organic compounds cited above as being insoluble in water do not contain hydroxyl groups and are unlike water.

That many inorganic acids, bases, and salts dissolve in water is attributable to their ionic character. In an electric field, water molecules acquire an orientation disclosing the presence of a negative end and a positive end that together constitute a dipole. This arises because oxygen is more electronegative than hydrogen (see Table, p. 50) and tends to draw the bonding electrons closer to it than they are to the hydrogen atoms. No polarization could result if the water molecule were linear, but physical evidence shows that it is not. Actually the two O—H bonds are at an angle of 105° to each other, and the electron displacement produces a fractional positive charge (δ-) at the oxygen end balanced by an equal fractional positive charge distributed between the two hydrogens at the other end. When hydrogen chloride dissolves in water the proton (hydrogen ion) is attracted to the negative oxygen and forms the hydronium ion, H_3O^+. A larger cation, for example Na^+, can attract and hold many molecules of water to form a polyhydrate ion. Anions are solvated by attraction of the positive end of

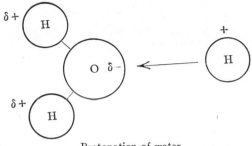

Protonation of water

the water molecule.   The lack of water-solubility of nonhydroxylic organic compounds (CH_4, CCl_4) is thus explained by the fact that they are non-ionic.

The nonionic character of typical carbon compounds is a feature inherent in the carbon atom.   In the periodic table carbon occupies a central position halfway between the positive alkali metals and the negative halogens.   The atoms of lithium and sodium readily donate the lone valence electron that

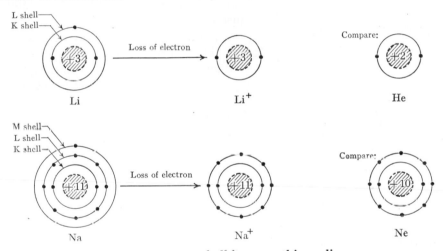

makes up a beginning of an outer shell because this peeling process uncovers an electron shell having the stable arrangement of a noble gas.   Since in the original atom the total complement of negative electrons balances the positive charge of the nucleus, removal of an electron results in formation of a positively charged particle, a cation.   Fluorine and chlorine, at the other extreme of the periodic table, have seven electrons in the outer shell, and thus need a single electron to conform to the stable octet arrangement characteristic of all noble gases beyond helium.   A halogen atom consequently has a tendency to gain an electron and acquire the noble gas configuration, and the result is formation of an anion.   In contrast with these electron donor and acceptor elements, the carbon atom has four electrons in the outer shell (L orbit) and could acquire the noble gas condition either by

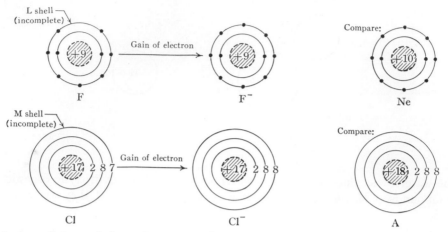

L shell (incomplete)

Gain of electron

Compare:

F   F⁻   Ne

M shell (incomplete)

Gain of electron

Compare:

Cl   Cl⁻   A

losing all four of these electrons or by gaining a total of four additional ones to complete the octet. Either process would be difficult. When, for

C

example, an atom acquires successive electrons, the second is taken up less readily than the first, and the third less readily than the second, because the increasingly negative net charge repels the incoming electron. Thus carbon, being midway between the stable electron states of helium and neon and remote in type from either noble gas, has less tendency than most other atoms to either lose or gain electrons. Carbon even occupies a unique place in the series of elements in the fourth group of the periodic table. Lead, a higher member of the series, also has an external shell of four valence electrons, but two of these can be transferred readily to other elements with formation of the bivalent lead ion. This difference in behavior is understandable, for the valence electrons in the lead atom are so far away from the positive nucleus that they are bound by a relatively weak electrostatic force. In carbon the external electrons are close to the nucleus, and consequently are held firmly in the atomic sphere.

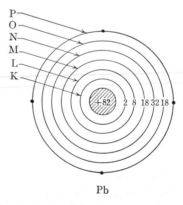

Pb

Some organic substances are subject to ionization of a degree comparable to that typical of the inorganic compounds, but the dissociation usually occurs at some site in the molecule other than a carbon atom; for example, at an attached oxygen or nitrogen atom. When acetic acid ionizes, the ionic charge is acquired by oxygen: $AcOH \rightleftharpoons AcO^- + H^+$. Certain organic compounds of special structural types do form carbonium ions (cations) or even carbanions (negative) of appreciable stability, but these represent an exception and not the rule (as with ammonium compounds).

However, it is now recognized that although the more typical organic compounds do not form stable ions, many of the reactions of these substances proceed through ionic intermediate phases that have not been isolated but nevertheless have been shown by physicochemical studies and reaction rates (kinetics) to have transient existence. If a transient ionic intermediate is an essential requirement for a reaction, the reaction will not occur unless the experimental conditions promote its formation.

Thus certain characteristics of organic reactions are attributable to the resistance of carbon to acquisition of an ionic charge. One is the requirement of an appreciable time interval. There is no time lag in the neutralization of sodium hydroxide by hydrochloric acid or in the precipitation of silver chloride because the essential interactions are between small, stable, mobile, oppositely charged ions that are drawn together by electrostatic attraction. Hydrochloric acid and sodium hydroxide are both largely ionized in aqueous solution, as the resulting sodium chloride is, and the essential process involved in neutralization is combination of hydrogen and hydroxide ions to form the relatively slightly ionized water molecule:

$$H^+ \text{ (from HCl)} \quad + \quad OH^- \text{ (from NaOH)} \quad \rightleftharpoons \quad HOH$$

If two typical organic compounds are brought together there is no comparable attraction between oppositely charged particles; interaction between the relatively large, uncharged, molecular bodies may occur merely as the result of random collisions, only a certain proportion of which are fruitful, and several hours or days may be required for completion of a reaction conducted at room temperature. Some reactions of organic compounds with bromine or chlorine proceed through formation of a minute amount of a transient ionic phase, and addition of an inorganic acid or base may be required as catalyst to promote production of an ionic complex and so cause reaction to occur at a practical rate. Other halogenation reactions involve a nonionic organic intermediate (free radical) and require special conditions, for example irradiation, to promote transient formation of halogen atoms that attack the uncharged organic molecules; again a time interval is involved.

The random motion of neutral molecules in solution or in the gaseous state becomes progressively greater as the temperature is raised; this effect results in a greater number of collisions and, consequently, in an increased rate of reaction. The reaction rate is approximately doubled for each $10°$ rise in temperature, and the cumulative effect of a substantial increase in reaction temperature is therefore appreciable. Reactions proceed about 256 times as fast at $100°$ as they do at $20°$. Organic chemistry laboratories are equipped with steam baths, which provide a safe means of accelerating reactions involving flammable materials. Application of heat to promote reactions is seldom necessary in inorganic chemistry.

Another significant difference is that organic reactions are rarely quantitative. Inorganic reactions involving precipitation, neutralization, oxidation, or reduction follow exact stoichiometric relationships, which form the basis of methods of quantitative analysis. Organic reactions proceed less smoothly, and the yield of product seldom approaches the theoretically possible amount, even in the hands of a skilled operator. A yield of 85–90% of the theory usually is considered very satisfactory. In industry, where a yield differential of only a few percent may spell the success or failure of a manufacturing process, all efforts of chemists in the research and development laboratories may serve to raise the yield in a given reaction to no more than 50–60%. A number of factors contribute to loss of material. The heat treatment usually required to accelerate interaction between nonionic molecules frequently leads to damage of some of the sensitive organic reactants, with the result that the reaction mixture contains tarry, resinous, dark-colored materials. Such substances not only represent a direct loss but constitute contaminants that have to be separated from the main reaction product through a sometimes elaborate and wasteful process of purification by distillation, crystallization, or chromatography. The carrying out of a reaction is often a small part of the chemist's work, and the main task is freeing the reaction product from contaminates.

Side reactions also detract from the yield of the desired product. A slow reaction provides opportunity for side reactions leading to by-products. If molecules of A and of B form C only in the course of a few hours, there may be opportunity for some of the A molecules to react with one another to produce the by-product D, for B molecules to form by-product E, or for either A or B to combine with the solvent, the catalyst, or oxygen of the atmosphere.

The Covalent Bond. — Although the carbon atom has little tendency either to gain or to lose electrons and hence to form ionic compounds, it can combine with other elements by electron sharing. Thus carbon, with its four valence electrons (dots), can form a stable compound with four hydrogen atoms, each of which brings one external electron (cross) into the molecular sphere of the resulting methane, CH_4. The carbon atom is thereby surrounded by four electrons of its own and four derived from the hydrogens; the resultant stable octet conforms to the neon pattern. Each hydrogen atom now is associated with two electrons, and hence is electronically comparable to helium. Since every atom conforms in electron arrangement to

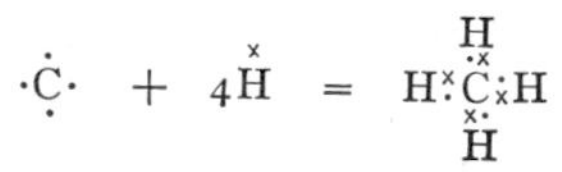

$$\cdot \overset{\cdot}{\underset{\cdot}{C}} \cdot \ + \ 4\overset{x}{H} \ = \ H \overset{\cdot\cdot}{\underset{x \cdot}{\overset{x}{C}}} \overset{x}{H}$$

Methane

a noble gas, the union affords a stable molecule. Since all the electrons are still within the original atomic spheres and are still neutralized by the respective atomic nuclei, the molecule is completely nonionic, or nonpolar. The pair of shared electrons linking each hydrogen to carbon constitutes a covalent bond. Methane represents a union of carbon with an element that in many of its other compounds is an electron donor. Electron-acceptor atoms can also form stable carbon compounds. In carbon tetrachloride (CCl_4), for example, each of the four electrons of carbon fills a gap in the nearly complete external shell of a chlorine atom and gives a cluster of eight

$$\cdot\overset{\cdot}{\underset{\cdot}{C}}\cdot \;+\; 4\,{}^{x}_{x}\overset{xx}{\underset{xx}{Cl}}{}^{x}_{x} \;=\; {}^{x}_{x}\overset{xx}{\underset{xx}{Cl}}{}^{x}_{x}\overset{\overset{xx}{{}^{x}_{x}Cl{}^{x}_{x}}}{\underset{\underset{xx}{{}^{x}_{x}Cl{}^{x}_{x}}}{C}}{}^{x}_{x}\overset{xx}{\underset{xx}{Cl}}{}^{x}_{x}$$

around the halogen. Electron sharing results also in surrounding of the carbon atom with an octet of electrons without electron transfer and consequent development of an ionic charge.

Combustion Analysis. — Pioneer chemists were confronted with the problem of isolating a given organic compound in a state of purity and determination of the empirical formula, that is, the kind and number of the different atoms in the molecule. Lavoisier's method of burning a compound in oxygen sufficed for establishment of the nature of the elements present, but did not prove sufficiently accurate for determination of the relative atomic proportions. Successive attempts were made to develop the combustion method into a precise technique of quantitative analysis, and this goal was achieved by Liebig[8] in 1831. For nearly a century Liebig's combustion technique, essentially unmodified save for improvements in materials, constituted the standard method for determination of carbon and hydrogen. A combustion conducted in an atmosphere of oxygen is not easily controlled and may be either incomplete or explosive. Liebig, however, took advantage of an earlier observation that organic vapors are burned effectively on contact with red-hot copper oxide, for example:

$$C_2H_6 \;+\; 7\,CuO \;\longrightarrow\; 2\,CO_2 \;+\; 3\,H_2O \;+\; 7\,Cu$$
$$C_4H_{10}O \;+\; 12\,CuO \;\longrightarrow\; 4\,CO_2 \;+\; 5\,H_2O \;+\; 12\,Cu$$

In Liebig's method the sample is burned in oxygen in a tube packed with copper oxide as an auxiliary source of oxygen to insure complete combustion. The tube is swept with a slow stream of oxygen which effects direct combustion of a part of the sample and eventually oxidizes any metallic copper formed. The original supply of copper oxide is thus replenished. The stream of oxygen, which is freed from traces of moisture and carbon dioxide before entering the combustion tube, carries the products of combustion into a calcium chloride tube, which retains the water formed, and then into a bubbler containing potassium hydroxide solution to absorb the carbon dioxide. Prior to analysis each absorption unit is weighed separately and then mounted in position. The sample is weighed into a small porcelain or platinum boat inserted with a wire hook into a rear position in the combustion tube before this has been heated. The front section, packed with copper oxide wire, is brought to a red glow before introducing the sample. When the boat is in place, burners under the rear part of the tube are

---

[8] Justus von Liebig, 1803–73; b. Darmstadt, Germany; Giessen, Munich; *Ber.*, **23**, 785 (1890)

lighted progressively, and eventually the whole tube is brought to a dull red heat. Oxygen is passed through the hot tube for a sufficient period to sweep the products of combustion into the absorption train.

At the end of the combustion the absorption tubes are weighed; the gain in weight of the calcium chloride tube gives the amount of water produced and that of the potassium hydroxide bubbler the weight of carbon dioxide. Calculation of the percentage composition then follows from the proportion of hydrogen in water and of carbon in carbon dioxide, using the atomic weights H = 1.008 and C = 12.01.

$$\text{Wt. of hydrogen} = \text{Wt. of water} \times \frac{2.016\ (H_2)}{18.016\ (H_2O)}$$

$$\%\ H = \frac{\text{Wt. of hydrogen}}{\text{Wt. of sample}} \times 100$$

$$\text{Wt. of carbon} = \text{Wt. of carbon dioxide} \times \frac{12.01\ (C)}{44.01\ (CO_2)}$$

$$\%\ C = \frac{\text{Wt. of carbon}}{\text{Wt. of sample}} \times 100$$

If the percentages of carbon and hydrogen do not add up to 100 and no other element is detected, the deficiency is taken as the percentage of oxygen.

For interpretation of the results of an analysis in terms of an empirical formula, the first step is to divide the percentage of each element by its atomic weight; the next is to divide the resulting numbers by the smallest one of the group and so ascertain the atomic ratios. An ideal analysis for ethyl alcohol would give 52.14% C and 13.13% H, whence the oxygen content by difference is 34.73%. The calculations are then:

	Percent		Atomic weight					Atomic ratio
C	52.14	÷	12.01	=	4.3			2
H	13.13	÷	1.008	=	13.03	$\times \dfrac{1}{2.17} =$		6
O	34.73	÷	16	=	2.17			1

Ethyl alcohol contains two carbon and six hydrogen atoms for every oxygen atom. A molecule cannot contain less than one of the least abundant species of atom, which in this case is oxygen, but it might contain two or more such atoms. From the analysis alone, ethyl alcohol might be C_2H_6O or $C_4H_{12}O_2$ or $(C_2H_6O)_n$, where n is any integer, for these formulas all have the same percentage composition. A choice between the different possibilities is made possible by knowledge of the molecular weight; even an experimental value recognized as only a rough approximation may suffice. Thus the unit C_2H_6O has the molecular weight (rounded) of 46, and a choice would be required between 46, 92, 138, etc. Molecular weight determinations accurate to no better than 20% and falling in the range from 37 to 55 units would suffice. The molecular weight of a gas or of an easily vaporized substance can be determined by the vapor density method, which consists in weighing a measured volume of the gaseous substance and calculating the number of grams that would occupy a volume of 22.4 liters at standard conditions (N.P.T.). Methods applicable to solid compounds utilize the fact that a dissolved substance raises the boiling point or lowers the freezing point of a solvent to an extent directly dependent on the proportion of the dissolved to the total molecules. These ebullioscopic and cryoscopic methods are widely applicable and are precise. Organic chemists frequently use a rapid, approximate cryoscopic method (Rast), in which the solid substance camphor is used as solvent and determination of the lowering of the melting point is made with use of only a few milligrams of the mixture and an ordinary thermometer. The method succeeds because the melting or freezing point of camphor is lowered to an extraordinary extent by a small amount of a dissolved substance. A rapid boiling point method which gives reasonably accurate results is illustrated in Fig. 1.1.

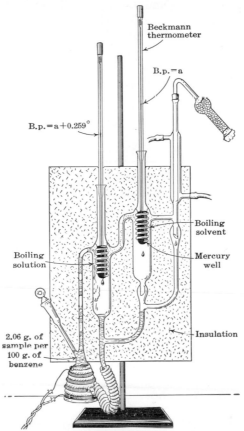

FIG. 1.1 — Ebullioscopic Determination of the Molecular Weight of a Nonvolatile Solid
This determination is made by direct measurement of the difference in the boiling point of a solution of the substance in benzene and of pure benzene (Swietoslawski apparatus).

$$\text{Mol. wt.} = \frac{\text{Wt. of sample} \times 1000 \times k}{\text{Wt. of solvent} \times \Delta t}$$

where the constant k is the elevation in boiling point produced by 1 mole of substance in 1000 g. of solvent (for benzene, $k = 2.53°$), and Δt is the observed elevation in boiling point.

Because of experimental error associated with an actual analysis, the atomic ratios calculated may deviate appreciably from integral values; therefore careful judgment must be exercised to decide which of possibly two or three of the nearest sets of integral values is the most likely. The best way of making such a decision is to calculate the theoretical percentages of carbon and hydrogen for each possible formula and see how closely they correspond to the experimentally determined values. An illustrative example is taken from a series of analyses carried out by Liebig in 1838 and interpreted by him on the basis of the atomic weights accepted at the time. Since the same values figure in the calculation of both experimental and theoretical percentages, the inaccuracy in early atomic weights did not seriously distort the picture, and Liebig usually arrived at formulas that have stood the test of time. In the following example the results are recalculated on the basis of modern atomic weights. Liebig's combustion of a 0.533-g. sample of gallic acid afforded 0.969 g. of carbon dioxide and 0.172 g. of water, and calculations of the percentage composition and the ratio of carbon, hydrogen, and oxygen are as follows:

	Percent		Atomic weight					Atomic ratio
C	49.61	÷	12.01	=	4.13			1.41
H	3.61	÷	1.008	=	3.58	$\times \dfrac{1}{2.92}$ =		1.22
O	46.78	÷	16	=	2.92			1

The result indicates that the compound contains approximately 1.4 carbon atoms and 1.2 hydrogen atoms for every oxygen atom. If 2 oxygen atoms were present there would be 2.4 hydrogen atoms, but this figure is too far from an integral value for serious consideration. Multiplication of the atomic ratio values by 3 and 5, however, gives figures not far from integral, namely $C_{4.2}H_{3.7}O_3$, and $C_{7.1}H_{6.1}O_5$. It would seem possible, then, that the substance is either $C_4H_4O_3$ or $C_7H_6O_5$, or a higher multiple of one of these formulas, and although the second appears to be a better fit than the first, a decision can be made from comparison of the experimentally determined values for carbon and hydrogen with those calculated for the possible alternative formulas:

	% C	% H
Found..........................	49.61	3.61
Calculated for $C_4H_4O_3$............	48.01	4.03
Calculated for $C_7H_6O_5$............	49.42	3.56

The percentage of hydrogen found is in fair agreement with that required for the first formula, but the carbon value is 1.6% too high, and this deviation is considerably greater than the experimental error of some 0.3–.4%. The analytical values check very well, however, with the calculated percentages for $C_7H_6O_5$, and hence this minimal formula is correct for gallic acid. Liebig interpreted the analysis in this way and his formula was substantiated in subsequent work.

Since the valence numbers of carbon and oxygen are both even, compounds containing only C, H, and O, as well as hydrocarbons, invariably contain an even number of hydrogen atoms. Thus formulas such as C_6H_{11} or $C_7H_7O_5$ are at once recognized as fallacious.

That Liebig was able to obtain remarkably accurate results with the comparatively crude laboratory equipment and analytical balances of the day is attributable both to his skill and to his use of a sample sufficiently large to offset error (o.5–.9 g.). Improvements in the instrumental facilities in the ensuing hundred-year period made it possible to reduce the size of the sample to 100–120 mg. and still maintain an adequate degree of accuracy. Although this would appear to be a trivial amount of an abundantly available material such as sugar, acetic acid, or alcohol, many interesting organic compounds of both natural and synthetic origin have been encountered that, initially at least, were obtainable in only minute amounts. Butenandt's discovery in 1931 of the male sex hormone androsterone, for example, was the result of the processing of 15,000 liters of urine, which afforded a total of 15 mg. of the physiologically active principle. This difficult feat of isolation would have been rather pointless, and might not have been undertaken, had there not been available a modification of Liebig's method of analysis applicable to such minute quantities of material. The procedure of microanalysis was introduced in 1911 by Pregl,[9] whose own research experience had convinced him of the serious limitations to a method of analysis requiring for a single combustion an amount of sample considerably greater than that which the chemist may be able to secure. With the aid of special manipulative techniques, a skilled chemist can carry out a reaction with no more than 5–10 mg. of material and can purify the product for analysis by crystallization or, in some instances, even by distillation. Pregl reinvestigated every detail of the existing analytical method with regard to refinement. The chief determining factor was the accuracy of the balance, and under Pregl's leadership a microbalance was developed with which minute samples can be weighed with extraordinary precision. Microbalances now available, when operated in an air-conditioned room on a vibration-free mounting, can weigh to a precision of about 1 microgram (0.001 mg., or 0.000001 g.). With the aid of a precision instrument and by redesigning the combustion tube, absorption train, and all accessories, Pregl was able to work out a scheme of microanalysis by which the carbon and hydrogen content of a 3–4 mg. sample of material can be determined accurately. By application of the micro method, which was duly recognized as one of the achievements of modern science by the award to Pregl of the Nobel Prize, Butenandt's 15-mg. sample of androsterone sufficed for two analyses and for preparation and analysis of a derivative. The analytical results, coupled with keen observations and inferences, led in 1932 to an initial postulate of the chemical nature of the hormone that proved to be correct.

---

[9] Fritz Pregl, 1869–1930; b. Laibach, Austria; Ph.D. Graz; Innsbruck, Graz; Nobel Prize 1923; *Ber.*, **64A**, 113 (1931)

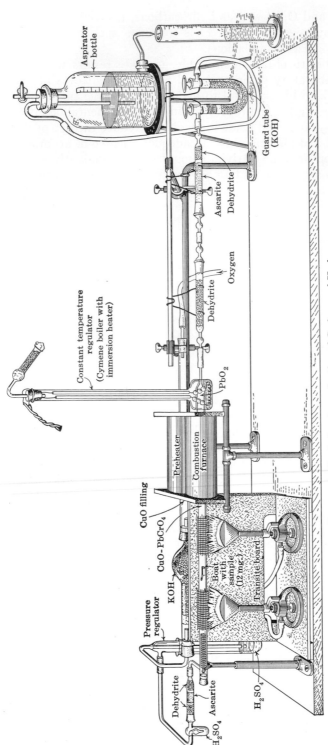

FIG. 1.2. — Semimicrodetermination of Carbon and Hydrogen

Oxygen from a low-pressure tank passes first through a preheater to burn any traces of organic matter, and then through a large tube of solid potassium hydroxide to absorb water and carbon dioxide, and a small unit to condition the gas exactly as it will be discharged from the absorption train. The first tube in this train contains solid Dehydrite (magnesium perchlorate trihydrate) to absorb water, and the second is filled with Ascarite (sodium hydroxide on asbestos) for the absorption of carbon dioxide and with an end section of Dehydrite to maintain the same condition of the gas on exit as on entrance. The oxygen is delivered to the combustion tube at a slight positive pressure and is drawn through the system at an adjustable, measured rate by the aspirator. The combustion furnace and preheater are heated with electric resistance units connected in series. The part of the combustion tube heated in the furnace is filled largely with copper oxide, but contains, at the exit end, a charge of lead chromate to combine with and retain oxides of sulfur. The end section of the tube contains lead peroxide to combine with oxides of nitrogen; this reagent must be maintained at a critical temperature different from that of the furnace, provided by the use of a boiler containing liquid of proper boiling point (cymene, $C_{10}H_{14}$). Silver wool or wire is introduced at the extreme end of the tube to retain halogen.

A compromise method requiring a less elaborate outlay of equipment but employing several of the refinements introduced by Pregl, known as semimicroanalysis, is often employed. Adequate precision in the determination of carbon and hydrogen is achieved with a sample weighing from 10 to 50 mg. A typical assembly of apparatus is illustrated in Fig. 1.2.

Determination of Nitrogen. — The most widely used method of determining nitrogen in organic compounds was introduced in 1830 by Dumas.[10] The sample is mixed with fine copper oxide and placed in a tube packed with coarse copper oxide. The tube is swept with a stream of carbon dioxide until all the air has been displaced, and then gradually brought to a dull red heat, when the sample is oxidized by the copper oxide to carbon dioxide, water, and elementary nitrogen containing oxides of nitrogen. The gaseous products are swept by a slow stream of carbon dioxide over a roll of hot copper gauze at the end of the tube which reduces oxides of nitrogen to nitrogen. The effluent gas passes into the base of an inverted, graduated glass tube filled with potassium hydroxide solution, which absorbs the carbon dioxide. The volume of the residual nitrogen is measured after adjustment of the pressure to that of the atmosphere with a leveling bulb.

Since nitrogen has a valence of three in typical organic substances. compounds containing carbon, hydrogen, oxygen, and one atom of nitrogen always have an odd number of hydrogen atoms; if two nitrogen atoms are present, the number of hydrogen atoms is even.

A second method of analysis was introduced in 1883 by Kjeldahl.[11] The sample is digested with concentrated sulfuric acid, usually with addition of an oxidizing agent ($KMnO_4$, $HClO_4$), to decompose the substance and convert the nitrogen into ammonium sulfate. The solution is diluted, excess alkali is added, and the ammonia is distilled with steam into a known amount of standard acid and estimated by titration of the excess acid. The Kjeldahl method is less general than that of Dumas, but it is useful for the rapid analysis of specific groups of compounds of low nitrogen content, for example proteins.

Complexity of Organic Compounds. — The substances of natural origin analyzed by Liebig, Dumas, Chevreul, Pelletier and Caventou, Robiquet, and contemporaries were mainly compounds of a complex character, and some of the problems uncovered in these pioneer investigations were eventually solved only in extended researches by succeeding generations of chemists. Thus Liebig in 1831 analyzed such compounds as the following series of physiologically active alkaloids (alkali-like):

Morphine	$C_{17}H_{19}O_3N$
Cinchonine	$C_{19}H_{22}ON_2$
Quinine	$C_{20}H_{24}O_2N_2$
Strychnine	$C_{21}H_{22}O_2N_2$
Brucine	$C_{23}H_{26}O_4N_2$

[10] Jean Baptiste André Dumas, 1800–84; b. Alais; Paris; *Ber.*, **17**, 629 (1884).

[11] Johan Kjeldahl, 1849–1900; b. Denmark; Carlsberg Laborat., Copenhagen; *Ber.*, **33**, 3881 (1900)

In this series the molecules are made up of as many as 55 atoms, of which the majority are carbon and hydrogen in varying numbers. The oxygen content varies from one to four atoms, and one substance contains a single atom of nitrogen whereas the others contain two. No regularity is discernible, and the formulas alone reveal little concerning the chemical individualities of the compounds or the nature of their divergent action on the animal organism. Why does $C_{17}H_{19}O_3N$ represent an alkali-soluble base that is a powerful analgesic agent of great use in medicine (alleviation of pain)? Why is the compound $C_{20}H_{24}O_2N_2$ an alkali-insoluble base of value as an antimalarial drug? The early chemists were confronted with particularly complicated problems. Wöhler, in a letter written to Berzelius in 1835, said: "Organic chemistry just now is enough to drive one mad. It gives me an impression of a primeval tropical forest, full of the most remarkable things, a monstrous and boundless thicket, with no way to escape, into which one may well dread to enter."

Another complication in the interpretation of analytical data had been encountered in 1823 by Liebig, who discovered that silver fulminate has the same composition as silver cyanate, characterized previously by Wöhler. The substances are different chemical entities possessing distinctive properties; for example, the fulminate is a powerful explosive and the cyanate is not. Yet both compounds have the same empirical formula, AgCNO. This observation proved to be no isolated case but merely the first established example of a phenomenon that was soon to be regarded as general. Berzelius found that tartaric acid and racemic acid have the formula $C_4H_6O_6$, and he introduced the term isomerism for the phenomenon (Greek isos, the same; meros, parts). Silver fulminate and silver cyanate are isomers. Many other pairs of isomers exist, and numerous instances of isomerism of a much higher degree can be cited. There are four isomers of the formula $C_3H_6Br_2$, four corresponding to $C_4H_{10}O$, and seven represented by $C_6H_{12}O$. As many as 150 isomers of the formula $C_{10}H_{12}O_2$ are known, and more may be discoverable.

Comparable difficulties are almost never encountered in the inorganic field. There is only one compound of the formula $KMnO_4$ and only one corresponding to $K_2Cr_2O_7$, and generally no thought need be given to the phenomenon of isomerism. Furthermore, once the empirical formula is established, it is an essentially complete chemical characterization. When qualitative and quantitative analyses have established the formula for potassium permanganate as $KMnO_4$, it is evident that the manganese atom is utilizing eight negative valences of oxygen and one positive valence of the potassium atom and hence is exhibiting a positive valence of seven corresponding to its position in the periodic table.

With even simple organic compounds, the valence balance is not always clear from the formulas. The first few members of the series of hydrocarbons are as follows:

$$\text{Methane} \ldots \ldots \ldots \ldots \ldots \quad CH_4$$
$$\text{Ethane} \ldots \ldots \ldots \ldots \ldots \quad C_2H_6$$
$$\text{Propane} \ldots \ldots \ldots \ldots \ldots \quad C_3H_8$$

Two isomers $\begin{cases} \text{Butane} \ldots \ldots \ldots \ldots \ldots \\ \text{Isobutane} \ldots \ldots \ldots \ldots \ldots \end{cases} \Bigg\} C_4H_{10}$

The carbon atom of methane obviously has a valence of four, but with ethane the usual method of dividing the number of attached atoms by the number of carbon atoms would seem to indicate a valence of three, which, however, is inconsistent with the fact that ethane exhibits almost exactly the same chemical properties as methane. Application of the same system of calculation would indicate a fractional carbon valence for propane, which again closely resembles the other two hydrocarbons. With an increase in carbon content, the phenomenon of isomerism is encountered, for C_4H_{10} describes two chemical individuals, butane and isobutane. That the combination of four carbon and ten hydrogen atoms can give rise to two different hydrocarbons, differing in boiling point, density, and other properties, must mean that two modes of combination between these fourteen atoms are possible. Isomerism must result from a difference in the arrangement of atoms within the molecule.

Kekulé Theory of Structure. — Chemists of the early analytical period appreciated the importance of discovering the manner in which atoms are arranged in individual molecules, that is, of determining the structures, but they saw no way of doing it. The problem remained at a standstill for a number of years, but in 1859 a remarkably simple solution was envisioned by Kekulé,[12] a German chemist of keen intuitive faculties and endowed with such a combination of energy and personal charm that he became a leading and dominant figure in the rationalization of existing empirical data. Kekulé's first premise was that carbon has the same normal valence of four in complicated organic compounds as it has in such simple compounds as CH_4, CCl_4, CO_2, Na_2CO_3. He saw that a graphical representation of valence would be helpful, and introduced the convention of affixing to the symbol for an element one short line for every valence available for combination:

$$-\overset{|}{\underset{|}{C}}- \qquad =C= \qquad -C\equiv \qquad -O- \qquad =O \qquad -H$$

When two elements are joined together in a molecule, a full line between them means that one valence of each atom has been utilized to establish a valence bond or linkage, as illustrated by the Kekulé formulas for methane, carbon dioxide, ammonia, and hydrogen cyanide. The number of bonds

$$H-\overset{\overset{\displaystyle H}{|}}{\underset{\underset{\displaystyle H}{|}}{C}}-H \qquad O=C=O \qquad H-\overset{\overset{\displaystyle H}{|}}{N}-H \qquad H-C\equiv N$$

---

[12] August Kekulé, 1829–96; b. Darmstadt, Germany; Bonn; *Ber.*, **23**, 1265 (1890); **29**, 1971 (1896)

extending from a given atom provides a simple, graphical indication of the valence. In modern terms the Kekulé bond is a pair of shared electrons, a covalent bond. Thus Kekulé's formulation can be regarded as an intuitive forerunner of a concept of structure based upon physical actualities. The electronic counterparts of the above formulas are as follows:

$$\begin{array}{ccccc} \text{H} & & & & \text{H} \\ \text{H:}\overset{\cdot\cdot}{\text{C}}\text{:H} & & \text{:}\overset{\cdot\cdot}{\text{O}}\text{::C::}\overset{\cdot\cdot}{\text{O}}\text{:} & & \text{H:}\overset{\cdot\cdot}{\text{N}}\text{:H} & & \text{H:C}\overset{\cdot\cdot}{\;\;}\text{N:} \\ \text{H} & & & & \end{array}$$

The nitrogen atom has five valence electrons, and combination of one nitrogen and three hydrogen atoms gives a structure with a cluster of eight electrons surrounding the nitrogen. Methane and ammonia contain four and three covalent bonds, respectively, but the compounds differ in that the nitrogen atom of ammonia carries one unshared pair of electrons and hence can combine with a proton by sharing the extra electron pair with hydrogen to give the ammonium ion, which carries the charge derived from the proton. Oxygen, with six valence electrons, completes its octet on combination with two atoms of hydrogen (see formula for water). Since two unshared pairs of electrons are available, water, like ammonia, combines with

$$\text{H:}\overset{\cdot\cdot}{\text{O}}\text{:H} \quad + \quad \text{H}^+ \quad \longrightarrow \quad \text{H:}\overset{\cdot\cdot+}{\text{O}}\text{:H}$$
$$\qquad\qquad\qquad\qquad\qquad\qquad\qquad\qquad\qquad\text{H}$$

Water   Hydronium ion

a proton; the product is a hydrated proton or hydronium ion. Carbon dioxide contains two double bonds, each made up of two pairs of shared electrons; hydrogen cyanide possesses a triple covalent bond, three electron pairs.

The idea that carbon is normally tetravalent, coupled with the concept of valence bonds, led Kekulé to a simple interpretation of the nature of ethane and propane that involves merely the linking together of two and of three carbon atoms. In the formulas shown, the carbon atoms are joined

$$\begin{array}{cc} \text{H} \;\; \text{H} & \text{H} \;\; \text{H} \;\; \text{H} \\ | \;\;\;\; | & | \;\;\;\; | \;\;\;\; | \\ \text{H—C—C—H} & \text{H—C—C—C—H} \\ | \;\;\;\; | & | \;\;\;\; | \;\;\;\; | \\ \text{H} \;\; \text{H} & \text{H} \;\; \text{H} \;\; \text{H} \\ \text{Ethane, C}_2\text{H}_6 & \text{Propane, C}_3\text{H}_8 \end{array}$$

by a valence bond (electron pair); there are four bonds extending from each carbon atom and one from each hydrogen, corresponding to valences of four and of one. The existence of two butanes of the formula C_4H_{10} can be explained, for the four carbon atoms can be joined either in a straight-chain or in a branched-chain arrangement: if hydrogen atoms are supplied where required to give each carbon atom the valence of four, formulas are obtained that conform to the required C_4H_{10} and are reasonable representations for butane and isobutane. (In the formula for isobutane three valence bonds are indicated, for convenience, by a conventional abbreviation consisting

```
C—C—C—C                              C—C—C
                                         |
                                         C
```

```
    H  H  H  H                      H   H   H
    |  |  |  |                      |   |   |
H—C—C—C—C—H                  H—C——C——C—H
    |  |  |  |                      |   |   |
    H  H  H  H                      H  H·C·H  H
      Butane                               |
                                           H
                                      Isobutane
```

in a dot; where there can be no ambiguity, the symbol for a connecting union is sometimes omitted.)

Kekulé applied to formulas arrived at by deduction a critical test that is a further important part of his general theory of structure, namely, consideration of the chemical properties. The fact that hydrocarbons of the methane series are identical in their chemical reactions and behavior affords experimental evidence that the carbon atoms have the same valence and thus validates the theory. Structural determinations in general embody analysis of the empirical formula to discover what structure or structures can be written with maintenance of the normal valences of all atoms, and consideration of the properties, either to check a theoretically deduced formula that appears to represent the only possibility, or, where more than one formula can be written, to make a selection. After all theoretically possible formulations have been considered, the problem is referred to experimentation. It usually is found that only one of the possible formulas is consistent with specific chemical characteristics, and hence that a decision can be made on the basis of properties alone. Sometimes this is not possible. Butane and isobutane are so generally inert chemically and enter into so few reactions that differentiation between the two formulas cannot be made easily or securely from consideration of subtle differences in the meager chemical properties. In this instance the problem can be solved by synthesis. Both the straight-chain and branched-chain structures corresponding to C_4H_{10} can be synthesized by methods that are consistent only with either one or the other formula. The Kekulé principle, then, is to determine by experiment which one of all theoretically possible formulas is consistent with the properties and reactions of the compound and (or) with the mode of formation by synthesis.

Ethyl alcohol and dimethyl ether are isomers of the empirical formula C_2H_6O. There are only two ways in which two tetravalent carbon atoms can be joined with six atoms of hydrogen and one of oxygen; the two carbons must be either linked directly to each other, as in I, or linked through oxygen, II. It is necessary, then, to determine which formula reflects the prop-

```
    H  H                              H       H
    |  |                              |       |
H—C—C—O—H                    H—C—O—C—H
    |  |                              |       |
    H  H                              H       H
      I                                   II
```

erties of the alcohol and which fits those of the ether. Ethyl alcohol, b.p. 78°, enters into a number of reactions, of which two can be selected for illustration. The substance reacts with hydrogen iodide on application of moderate heat, and analysis of the reaction product establishes the following equation:

$$C_2H_6O \quad + \quad HI \quad \longrightarrow \quad C_2H_5I \quad + \quad H_2O$$
Ethyl alcohol   Ethyl iodide

The iodine of the reagent displaces an oxygen and a hydrogen atom, and these appear as a hydroxyl group (OH) in the molecule of water produced. The elements apparently were present originally as a hydroxyl group, and since formula I contains such a group and II does not, the observation points to the former formulation for the alcohol:

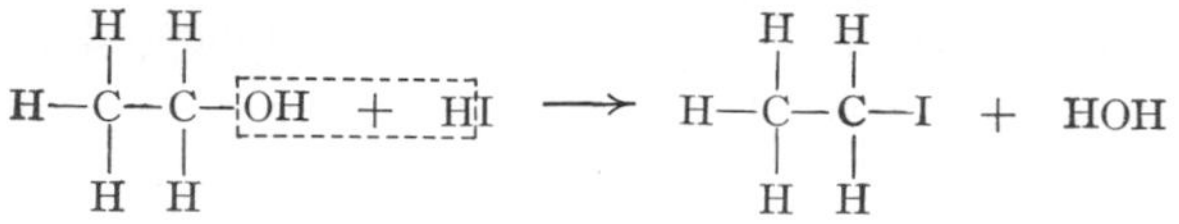

Moreover, dimethyl ether (b.p. $-25°$) behaves differently; it reacts with hydrogen iodide, but at a higher temperature, and the molecule is split into two one-carbon units, with consumption of two molecules of reagent for one of the ether:

$$C_2H_6O \quad + \quad 2\,HI \quad \longrightarrow \quad 2\,CH_3I \quad + \quad H_2O$$
Dimethyl ether   Methyl iodide

No hydroxyl group is removed from the molecule or is indicated as having been present, for all six hydrogen atoms are retained in the two molecules of the product. The reaction is not understandable in terms of formula I, but can be interpreted with the alternate formula:

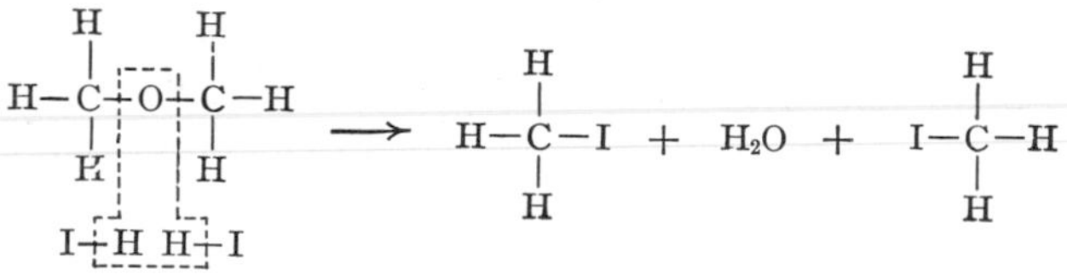

The hydrogen atoms of the reagent combine with the oxygen atom, with severance of the bridge between the carbon residues, which are left free to unite separately with iodine.

A second diagnostic test for distinguishing between the formulas consists in treatment with sodium. Ethyl alcohol reacts readily, with liberation of hydrogen, and the reaction is similar to that of water but less violent. The reaction involves displacement of one hydrogen atom by sodium, and

$$C_2H_6O \quad + \quad Na \quad \longrightarrow \quad C_2H_5ONa \quad + \quad \tfrac{1}{2}\,H_2$$
Ethyl alcohol

Compare: $HOH + Na \longrightarrow NaOH + \tfrac{1}{2}\,H_2$

once this change has been accomplished, the reaction stops and the other five hydrogen atoms remain unattacked. Since sodium does not react with methane and ethane, hydrogen atoms attached to carbon in similar combinations are evidently inert, and hence a rational interpretation of the behavior of ethyl alcohol in terms of formula I is that the five hydrogens connected directly to carbon remain unscathed, while the one occupying a unique position on oxygen is replaceable by sodium. One would predict that a substance of formula II would be inert to the reagent, since all six hydrogens conform exactly to the environment of those in ethane, and indeed dimethyl ether is resistant to attack by sodium. Properties of the alcohol and of the ether thus decisively indicate formula I for the former and II for the latter. Both structures have been verified by synthesis.

The same deductive reasoning is applicable alike to simple and complex compounds. With a substance of elaborate structure, the problem may become difficult because of a multiplicity of possible isomeric formulas and because of the extensive investigation required to distinguish between the formulas, but the principle is the same. Evidence of the validity of the vast body of structural theory built upon the principles discovered by Kekulé is that the number of isomers found experimentally corresponds with predictions of the theory.

Although several hundred thousand organic compounds are known, these fall into a reasonably small number of groups, the members of which exhibit many common characteristics. This natural classification makes possible a comprehensive understanding of a very extensive subject matter from a consideration of properties, reactions, and methods of preparation of typical members of each group and from knowledge of limits of variation within a series. Furthermore, such close interrelationships exist between different series that the whole subject of organic chemistry acquires the aspect of orderly systematization.

The series of hydrocarbons of which methane, ethane, and propane are the initial members has fundamental importance because compounds belonging to several other series can be regarded as derivatives of the hydro-

$$
\begin{array}{cccc}
\text{H} & \text{H} & \text{H} & \text{H} \\
| & | & | & | \\
\text{H—C H} & \text{H—C—OH} & \text{H—C—Cl} & \text{H—C—NH}_2 \\
| & | & | & | \\
\text{H} & \text{H} & \text{H} & \text{H} \\
\\
\text{Methane} & \text{Methyl} & \text{Methyl} & \text{Methyl} \\
 & \text{alcohol} & \text{chloride} & \text{amine}
\end{array}
$$

carbons. Replacement of one hydrogen atom in the methane formula by a hydroxyl, a halo, or an amino (NH_2) group gives the formulas for the first members of the series of alcohols, halides, and amines, respectively. Similar replacement as applied to ethane or propane gives the corresponding ethyl or propyl compounds, while substitution of a hydrogen of methane by a methyl group (—CH_3) gives the formula of ethane. Methane is a key or parent substance from which are derivable a vast number of compounds belonging to one broad group of organic substances that are designated aliphatic compounds. The second broad group comprises derivatives of the

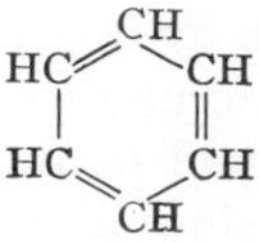

Benzene 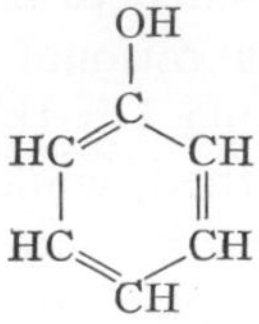   Phenol 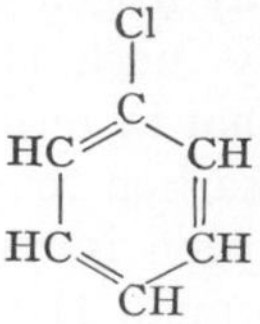   Chlorobenzene 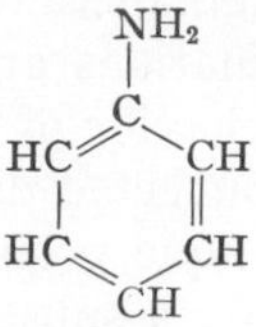   Aniline

Aromatic Compounds

parent hydrocarbon benzene, and these substances are called aromatic compounds. The peculiar ring structure of benzene and the special characteristics of aromatic substances will be considered later. Higher aromatic hydrocarbons are derivable from benzene just as ethane and propane are from methane; replacement of one hydrogen by a methyl group gives the formula of toluene. The aromatic hydrocarbon group, $-C_6H_5$, common to all the compounds mentioned, is called the phenyl group.

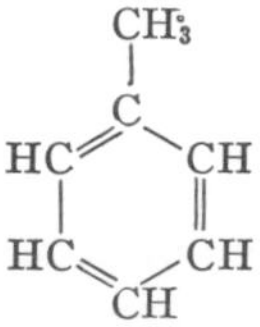

Toluene

PROBLEMS

(Answers in back of book)

1. Write the Kekulé formulas for the following compounds (only one formula is possible for each): hydrazine, N_2H_4 (trivalent nitrogen); formic acid, CH_2O_2.
2. There are two isomers of the formula $C_2H_4Br_2$ and two of the formula $C_2H_3Br_3$. Write the four structural formulas.
3. Write an electronic formulation for the reaction of ammonia with hydrogen chloride (see p. 18).
4. Write electronic formulas for $CHBr_3$, CH_3OH, and C_2H_4 (ethylene).
5. A semimicroanalysis of an 11.25-mg. sample of an unknown substance gave 26.99 mg. of CO_2 and 6.77 mg. of H_2O. Calculate the percentage composition.
6. The following two compounds containing only C, H, and O were analyzed and the molecular weights determined, with the results recorded. Calculate the empirical formulas.

     (a) % C = 65.55; 65.25   (b) % C = 70.31; 69.95
          % H = 5.65; 5.35   % H = 4.08; 4.18
          Mol. wt. = 111; 115   Mol. wt. = 185, 187

7. Which of the following formulas represent possible compounds and which are false: $C_{10}H_{22}O$, $C_{20}H_{41}$, $C_{14}H_8O_4$, $C_{21}H_{31}O_3$, $C_{21}H_{31}O_3N$, $C_8H_{14}ON$, $C_{20}H_{32}OSN_2$, $C_{10}H_{20}Br_3$?
8. An analysis of a substance that is a gas at room temperature gave the results 83.06% C, 16.85% H; 1 liter of gas at N.P.T. was found to weigh 3.20 g. What is the most likely empirical formula?
9 A crystalline yellow substance occurring in the grain of certain tropical woods and found to be composed of C, H, and O gave the analysis: C, 74.11%; H. 5.90%. Determinations of the molecular weight by the Rast method gave the results 240

and 255. Calculate the empirical formula and the theoretical percentage composition.

10. A liquid vitamin factor extracted from green plants gave no test for nitrogen or sulfur, and the results of a microanalysis were: 82.64% C, 10.20% H. Calculate the minimal empirical formula.

11. A derivative of morphine contains 72.27% C, 7.13% H, and 4.60% N. No other element except oxygen is present, and the molecular weight is in the range 250–350. Calculate the empirical formula.

12 The determination of molecular weight illustrated in Fig. 1.1 was carried out with the substance benzil, $C_6H_5COCOC_6H_5$. Calculate the result of the determination and compare it with the theoretical value.

READING REFERENCES

F. J. Moore, "A History of Chemistry," 3rd Ed., 175–246, McGraw-Hill, New York (1939)

J. R. Partington, "A Short History of Chemistry," 216–239, Macmillan, London (1937)

C. Schorlemmer, "The Rise and Development of Organic Chemistry," Macmillan, London (1894)

A. W. v. Hofmann, Faraday Lecture for 1875, "The Life and Work of Liebig," Macmillan, London (1876)

F. R. Japp, "Kekulé Memorial Lecture," *J. Chem. Soc.*, **73**, 97–138 (1898)

CHAPTER 2

SATURATED HYDROCARBONS
(ALKANES)

Compounds of the methane-ethane-propane series are called saturated hydrocarbons because the carbon valences are all saturated with hydrogen. An alternate designation, based upon the fact that the substances are characteristically inert and have little tendency to combine with many reagents, is paraffin hydrocarbons (L. *parum affinis*, slight affinity). Alkane is a systematic designation, the significance of which will become apparent.

Derivatives of Methane. — It can be taken as axiomatic that the four hydrogen atoms of methane are equivalent. There is only one monochloro derivative of methane and only one monobromo or monohydroxy or other monosubstitution product, and hence it does not matter which of the four hydrogens has been replaced by a substituent. Only one dichloro derivative has been discovered, even though different preparative methods have been tried and different starting materials used; consequently formulas I and II are equivalent and equally satisfactory representations of the dichloro compound. They both indicate a molecule composed of a carbon atom to which two hydrogen and two chlorine atoms are joined; structural

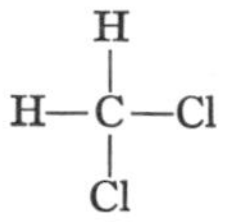

$$
\begin{array}{cc}
\begin{array}{c}
\text{H} \\
| \\
\text{H}-\text{C}-\text{Cl} \\
| \\
\text{Cl}
\end{array}
&
\begin{array}{c}
\text{H} \\
| \\
\text{Cl}-\text{C}-\text{Cl} \\
| \\
\text{H}
\end{array} \\
\text{I} & \text{II}
\end{array}
$$

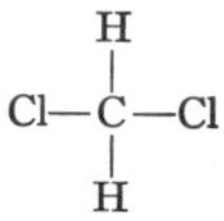

formulas are intended to indicate which atoms are bonded with one another and nothing more. The Kekulé formula for methane, for example, makes no implication regarding the shape of the molecule or the manner in which the radial hydrogen atoms are projected into space. The abbreviated formula CH_2Cl_2 is just as satisfactory a representation of dichloromethane (or methylene chloride) as I or II, for it indicates the arrangement of atoms in the molecule and is free from any suggestion of spatial characterization. Inspection of the formula $CHCl_3$ for trichloromethane (chloroform) and of CCl_4 for the tetrachloro derivative (carbon tetrachloride) shows that isomerism is impossible also in these instances.

Derivatives of Ethane. — In ethane all six hydrogen atoms are identically situated and hence equivalent, and only one monosubstitution product is possible. The monochloro derivative, which can be described as monochloroethane but which is more generally known as ethyl chloride, is represented correctly by any one of the formulas shown, for each conveys the same information.

$$H-\underset{\underset{H}{|}}{\overset{\overset{H}{|}}{C}}-\underset{\underset{H}{|}}{\overset{\overset{H}{|}}{C}}-Cl \qquad H-\underset{\underset{Cl}{|}}{\overset{\overset{H}{|}}{C}}-\underset{\underset{H}{|}}{\overset{\overset{H}{|}}{C}}-H \qquad CH_3CH_2Cl$$

Ethyl chloride

Isomerism becomes possible whenever two substituents are introduced into the ethane molecule, for these can either be located on the same carbon atom or distributed between the two. If two chlorine atoms are linked to one of the two carbon atoms, as in the formula below on the left, the compound represented can be distinguished from the isomer on the right by

$$H-\underset{\underset{H}{|}}{\overset{\overset{H}{|}}{C}}-\underset{\underset{Cl}{|}}{\overset{\overset{H}{|}}{C}}-Cl \quad (CH_3CHCl_2) \qquad H-\underset{\underset{Cl}{|}}{\overset{\overset{H}{|}}{C}}-\underset{\underset{Cl}{|}}{\overset{\overset{H}{|}}{C}}-H \quad (ClCH_2CH_2Cl)$$

1,1-Dichloroethane · · · 1,2-Dichloroethane

numbering the carbon atoms and indicating the position of each chlorine atom by citing the number of the carbon atom to which it is joined. In the first compound both chlorines are attached to carbon atom No. 1 (or C_1), and hence the compound is 1,1-dichloroethane. The name 1-dichloroethane is incomplete and therefore incorrect; it would leave unspecified the location of one of the chlorine atoms. The name 1,1-chloroethane is incorrect because it implies 1-monochloroethane. The second dichloroethane is the 1,2-derivative. In this case the molecule is symmetrical and it makes no difference whether the carbon atoms are numbered from right to left, as shown, or in the reverse order. In the case of the isomer, left-to-right counting would give the alternate name 2,2-dichloroethane, but a choice between the prefixes 1,1- and 2,2- is afforded by the rule that the numbers be kept as low as possible. However a formula is written, one should try all possible methods of counting the carbon atoms and select the one which gives the smallest numbers for the positions of the substituent groups.

Three chlorine atoms or three other substituents can be introduced into the ethane molecule in the following two ways:

$$H-\underset{\underset{H}{|}}{\overset{\overset{H}{|}}{C}}-\underset{\underset{Cl}{|}}{\overset{\overset{Cl}{|}}{C}}-Cl \quad (CH_3CCl_3) \qquad H-\underset{\underset{Cl}{|}}{\overset{\overset{H}{|}}{C}}-\underset{\underset{Cl}{|}}{\overset{\overset{H}{|}}{C}}-Cl \quad (ClCH_2CHCl_2)$$

1,1,1-Trichloroethane · · · 1,1,2-Trichloroethane

Note that with the second isomer the numbering of the carbon atoms from right to left, as the formula is written, gives smaller numbers (1,1,2-) than the alternate counting (1,2,2-). The two possible types of tetrasubstitution products are illustrated as follows:

CH_2ClCCl_3 $CHCl_2CHCl_2$
(1,1,1,2-)   (1,1,2,2-)

Only one pentachloro and one hexachloro derivative are possible, for the situation is the same as with the penta- and hexahydrogen compounds.

Derivatives of Propane. — The propane molecule presents a different situation because the eight hydrogen atoms are not all similarly located. The six hydrogens attached to the two terminal carbon atoms are equivalent (dotted lines), but the environment is different from that of the two hydrogens located on the central carbon atom of the chain. There is thus a differentiation between end and middle positions in the molecule; one result is that two isomeric monosubstitution products are possible, as exemplified by the monochloro derivatives:

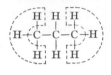

```
    H   H   H                         H   H   H
    |   |   |                         |   |   |
H — C — C — C — Cl               H — C — C — C — H
    |   |   |                         |   |   |
    H   H   H                         H   Cl  H
  (CH₃CH₂CH₂Cl)                     (CH₃CHClCH₃)
```

$(CH_3CH_2CH_2Cl)$ .... $(CH_3CHClCH_3)$
1-Chloropropane, or .... 2-Chloropropane, or
n-propyl chloride .... isopropyl chloride

These can be described as the 1-chloro and 2-chloro derivatives of propane but are more commonly called normal (n-) propyl chloride and isopropyl chloride. Although there is only one form of a methyl (CH_3—) or ethyl (C_2H_5—) group, the next higher hydrocarbon radical exists as either the n-propyl group, $CH_3CH_2CH_2$—, or the isopropyl group, $(CH_3)_2CH$—.

Polysubstitution in propane presents opportunity for isomerism of a still higher degree, as can be seen from the following tabulation:

Dichloropropanes:		Trichloropropanes:	
$CH_3CH_2CHCl_2$	1,1-	$CH_3CH_2CCl_3$	1,1,1-
$CH_3CHClCH_2Cl$	1,2-	$CH_3CHClCHCl_2$	1,1,2-
$ClCH_2CH_2CH_2Cl$	1,3-	$ClCH_2CH_2CHCl_2$	1,1,3-
$CH_3C(Cl_2)CH_3$	2,2-	$CH_3CCl_2CH_2Cl$	1,2,2-
		$ClCH_2CHClCH_2Cl$	1,2,3-

Butanes. — The formula of ethane can be derived from that of methane by replacing one hydrogen atom by a methyl group, and the propane formula can be built up similarly. This systematic method of derivation serves a useful purpose, for if all modes of substitution are considered, no isomers can be missed. Propane has two different types of hydrogen atoms, the type on the ends (a) and that in the middle (b), and hence in the derivation of butanes substitution of each by methyl must be tried:

$$\overset{a}{\text{C}}\text{H}_3\overset{b}{\text{C}}\text{H}_2\overset{a}{\text{C}}\text{H}_3$$
Methyl substitution in propane,   gives:

a. CH₃CH₂CH₂CH₃
n-Butane
(b.p. −0.5°)

b. CH₃CHCH₃
|
CH₃
Isobutane
(b.p. −12°)

Replacement of any one of the terminal hydrogens by a methyl group gives a straight-chain hydrocarbon of the formula C_4H_{10}, namely, normal butane. A similar operation on a centrally located hydrogen affords the isomeric, branched-chain hydrocarbon isobutane. The formula shown is a more compact representation than that given in Chapter 1, but it is lucid. Further simplication can be accomplished by pooling the three methyl groups attached to the central carbon atom: $(CH_3)_3CH$. This formula suggests an alternate and descriptive name. The substance is seen to be a derivative of methane in which only one of the original hydrogens remains and the other three have been replaced by methyl groups; isobutane therefore can be defined as trimethylmethane, just as $CHCl_3$ is described as trichloromethane.

Pentanes. — Structural formulas of the C_5-hydrocarbons can be derived by the same systematic procedure of making all possible methyl substitutions in both butanes, and the only added operation necessary is to inspect the resulting formulas and eliminate duplicates:

From the butanes,

$$\overset{a}{\text{C}}\text{H}_3\overset{b}{\text{C}}\text{H}_2\overset{b}{\text{C}}\text{H}_2\overset{a}{\text{C}}\text{H}_3, \quad \overset{c}{\text{C}}\text{H}_3\overset{d}{\text{C}}\text{H}\overset{c}{\text{C}}\text{H}_3,$$

CH₃
c

are derived:

a. CH₃CH₂CH₂CH₂CH₃
b. CH₃CH₂CHCH₃
|
CH₃

[c. CH₃CHCH₂CH₃   same as b
|
CH₃]

d.   CH₃
|
CH₃CCH₃
|
CH₃

It is seen that the third substitution tried (c) gives a formula identical with the second (b) and merely written in a different manner. Three distinct formulas remain and, since all possibilities have been investigated, the conclusion is reached that three pentanes can exist. The branched-chain isomers can be represented by simplified formulas and named as derivatives of methane; the three pentanes are as follows:

	B.P.	NAME
CH₃CH₂CH₂CH₂CH₃	36.1°	n-Pentane
CH₃CH₂CH(CH₃)₂	27.9°	Dimethylethylmethane
(CH₃)₄C	9.5°	Tetramethylmethane

The scheme of naming a compound as a derivative of some simpler parent substance is frequently employed because it affords a convenient method of focusing attention on a special feature of structure. The name tetramethylmethane for the third pentane emphasizes that the substance has a central carbon atom to which four methyl groups are attached. The tabulation of boiling points indicates that this most highly branched isomer is the most volatile of the pentanes and also that dimethylethylmethane has a lower boiling point than the normal, straight-chain hydrocarbon. Comparison of the boiling points of butane and isobutane shows that the branched-chain isomer is the more volatile. This relationship is rather general. On suitable cooling substances that are gases at ordinary temperatures pass through the liquid to the solid state. Melting points are useful identifying constants, but they usually bear no relationship to the boiling points and often show wider variation from member to member. A frequent relationship is that the more symmetrical isomers tend to have higher melting points. n-Pentane melts at $-129.7°$, dimethylethylmethane at $-159.6°$, and the symmetrical tetramethylmethane at the much higher temperature of $-16.6°$. The boiling point is generally correlated closely with the molecular weight, whereas the melting point is sensitive to differences in structure.

Hexanes. — By application of the process of systematic methyl substitution to the three pentanes it can be ascertained that, according to the Kekulé theory, five hexanes should exist. Five, and only five, isomers have been discovered; formulas and physical constants are listed in Table 2.1. The names assigned conform to a system (Geneva system) that is better adapted to higher hydrocarbons than the system of considering the substances as derivatives of methane. A given compound is regarded as a derivative of that parent hydrocarbon which corresponds to the longest chain of carbon atoms in the molecule. Methyl groups attached to such a chain are substituents, comparable to chlorine atoms. Isomer II has a straight chain of five carbon atoms and is considered to be a pentane with a methyl substituent; since right-to-left counting gives a smaller number than

TABLE 2.1. HEXANES, C_6H_{14}

ISOMER	FORMULA	NAME	M.P., °C.	B.P., °C.
I	$CH_3CH_2CH_2CH_2CH_2CH_3$	n-Hexane	-94.0	68.7
II	$CH_3CH_2CH_2CHCH_3$ $\quad\quad\quad\quad$ | $\quad\quad\quad\quad CH_3$	2-Methylpentane	-153.7	60.3
III	$CH_3CH_2CHCH_2CH_3$ $\quad\quad\quad$ | $\quad\quad\quad CH_3$	3-Methylpentane	(-118)	63.3
IV	$\quad\quad\quad CH_3$ $\quad\quad\quad$ | $CH_3CH_2CCH_3$ $\quad\quad\quad$ | $\quad\quad\quad CH_3$	2,2-Dimethylbutane	-98.2	49.7
V	$CH_3CH-CHCH_3$ $\quad\quad$ | $\quad$ | $\quad\quad CH_3 \quad CH_3$	2,3-Dimethylbutane	-128.8	58.0

left-to-right, this isomer is 2-methylpentane.   It is also proper and for some purposes desirable to employ the methane-derivative system, illustrated in the following list in which simplified formulas are employed.   Melting points

ISOMER	FORMULA	METHANE DERIVATIVE
II	$CH_3CH_2CH_2CH(CH_3)_2$	Dimethyl-n-propylmethane
III	$(CH_3CH_2)_2CHCH_3$	Methyldiethylmethane
IV	$CH_3CH_2C(CH_3)_3$	Trimethylethylmethane
V	$(CH_3)_2CHCH(CH_3)_2$	Dimethylisopropylmethane

are scattered and irregular in the hexane series.   There is less spread in boiling points than in the pentane series of lower molecular weight, and n-hexane is less volatile than the branched-chain isomers.

Heptanes. — The formulas and Geneva-system names of the nine known isomers are given in Table 2.2.   Again, the straight-chain hydrocarbon boils

TABLE 2.2.   HEPTANES, C_7H_{16}

ISOMER	FORMULA	NAME	M.P., °C.	B.P., °C.
I	$CH_3(CH_2)_5CH_3$	n-Heptane	-90.5	98.4
II	$CH_3CH_2CH_2CH_2CHCH_3$ CH_3	2-Methylhexane	-118.2	90.0
III	$CH_3CH_2CH_2CHCH_2CH_3$ CH_3	3-Methylhexane	-119	92.0
IV	CH_3 $CH_3CH_2CH_2CCH_3$ CH_3	2,2-Dimethylpentane	-125.0	78.9
V	CH_3CH_2CH—$CHCH_3$ CH_3 CH_3	2,3-Dimethylpentane	. . . .	89.7
VI	$CH_3CHCH_2CHCH_3$ CH_3 CH_3	2,4-Dimethylpentane	-119.3	80.8
VII	CH_3 $CH_3CH_2CCH_2CH_3$ CH_3	3,3-Dimethylpentane	-134.9	86.0
VIII	$CH_3CH_2CHCH_2CH_3$ CH_2 CH_3	3-Ethylpentane	-119	93.3
IX	CH_3 CH_3CH—CCH_3 CH_3 CH_3	2,2,3-Trimethylbutane	-25.0	80.8

at a slightly higher temperature than branched-chain isomers, but differences between isomers have become progressively less as the molecular weight has increased. The highly branched isomer IX, of tightly knit structure, has the highest melting point.

Heptanes can be named as derivatives of methane, but this method of nomenclature is scarcely practical for hydrocarbons containing more than seven carbon atoms. The point of greatest branching ordinarily is taken as the focus of the substituted methane molecule. Isomer II can be described as dimethyl-n-butylmethane, III as methylethyl-n-propylmethane, IV as trimethyl-n-propylmethane. Isomer VI cannot be named according to this scheme on the basis of the information at hand, but can be called diisopropylmethane. Similarly, the hexane listed in Table 2.1 as isomer V can be described adequately as diisopropyl. The heptane V (Table 2.2) can be named methylethylisopropylmethane.

Isomers of Higher Hydrocarbons. — The nine isomeric heptanes demanded by theory are all known (Table 2.2). It can be ascertained by writing the formulas that eighteen octanes can exist, and that thirty-five nonanes are possible. No direct mathematical relationship has been discovered between the carbon content and the total number of isomers, but a relationship has been established between a given carbon content and the total number of isomeric alcohols having a lesser carbon content (H. R. Henze and C. M. Blair, 1931). By means of a mathematical formula of a finite recursive type the number of isomeric hydrocarbons of a given C_n value can be calculated from knowledge of the number of isomeric alcohols of n/2 and of all lesser carbon contents. Results of the calculations included in Table 2.3 have been checked through the tetradecanes by actual writing.

TABLE 2.3. NUMBER OF ISOMERS

CARBON CONTENT	ISOMERS
C_8	18
C_9	35
C_{10}	75
C_{11}	159
C_{12}	355
C_{13}	802
C_{14}	1,858
C_{15}	4,347
C_{20}	366,319
C_{25}	36,797,588
C_{30}	4,111,846,763
C_{40}	62,491,178,805,831

Normal Hydrocarbons. — Successive members of the series (Table 2.4) differ in composition by the increment CH_2 and are said to form a homologous series. Thus heptane and octane are homologous hydrocarbons; eicosane is a higher homolog of methane. The formulas conform to the type C_nH_{2n+2}. Names of the hydrocarbons beyond butane are derived largely from the Greek numerals, although Latin prefixes are used in some instances (undecane).

The hydrocarbons having from one to four carbon atoms are gases, the C_5- to C_{17}-homologs are liquids, and the higher members of the series are solids. A similar relationship in a series of progressively increasing molecu-

TABLE 2.4. NORMAL SATURATED HYDROCARBONS

NAME	FORMULA, C_nH_{2n+2}	M.P., °C.	B.P., °C.	SP. GR. (AS LIQUIDS) [1]	
Methane	CH_4	−182.6	−161.7	0.4240	gases
Ethane	C_2H_6	−172.0	−88.6	.5462	
Propane	C_3H_8	−187.1	−42.2	.5824	
n-Butane	C_4H_{10}	−135.0	−0.5	.5788	
n-Pentane	C_5H_{12}	−129.7	36.1	.6264	liquids
n-Hexane	C_6H_{14}	−94.0	68.7	.6594	
n-Heptane	C_7H_{16}	−90.5	98.4	.6837	
n-Octane	C_8H_{18}	−56.8	125.6	.7028	
n-Nonane	C_9H_{20}	−53.7	150.7	.7179	
n-Decane	$C_{10}H_{22}$	−29.7	174.0	.7298	
n-Undecane	$C_{11}H_{24}$	−25.6	195.8	.7404	
n-Dodecane	$C_{12}H_{26}$	−9.6	216.3	.7493	
n-Tridecane	$C_{13}H_{28}$	−6	(230)	.7568	
n-Tetradecane	$C_{14}H_{30}$	5.5	251	.7636	
n-Pentadecane	$C_{15}H_{32}$	10	268	.7688	
n-Hexadecane	$C_{16}H_{34}$	18.1	280	.7749	
n-Heptadecane	$C_{17}H_{36}$	22.0	303	.7767	
n-Octadecane	$C_{18}H_{38}$	28.0	308	.7767	solids
n-Nonadecane	$C_{19}H_{40}$	32	330	.7776	
n-Eicosane	$C_{20}H_{42}$	36.4		.7777	
n-Heneicosane	$C_{21}H_{44}$	40.4		.7782	
n-Docosane	$C_{22}H_{46}$	44.4		.7778	
n-Tricosane	$C_{23}H_{48}$	47.4		.7797	
n-Tetracosane	$C_{24}H_{50}$	51.1		.7786	
n-Pentacosane	$C_{25}H_{52}$	53.3			
n-Triacontane	$C_{30}H_{62}$	66			
n-Pentatriacontane	$C_{35}H_{72}$	74.6		.7814	
n-Tetracontane	$C_{40}H_{82}$	81			
n-Pentacontane	$C_{50}H_{102}$	92		.7940	
n-Hexacontane	$C_{60}H_{122}$	99			
n-Dohexacontane	$C_{62}H_{126}$	101			
n-Tetrahexacontane	$C_{64}H_{130}$	102			
n-Heptacontane	$C_{70}H_{142}$	105	300 at 0.00001 mm.		

[1] Specific gravities reported in this and subsequent tables refer to the liquid state. With substances liquid at 20°, values for this temperature are given where available. The data given for more volatile substances are for temperatures close to the boiling point, those for less volatile compounds for temperatures just above the melting points.

lar weight is found in the halogens: chlorine, bromine, and iodine. Melting points of the hydrocarbons show an initial irregularity but tend to rise steadily as the molecules become larger. The boiling point increases with increasing molecular weight, and the increment is particularly prominent in the first few members of the series, where the increase in molecular weight represents a large proportion of the total. Ethane boils at a temperature 73° higher than methane and has a molecular weight (30) that is 87% greater than that of methane (16). n-Decane has a boiling point 23° higher than that of the next lower homolog, and the increment of 14 units cor-

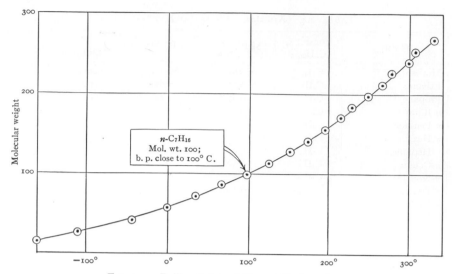

FIG. 2.1 — Boiling Points of Normal Hydrocarbons

responding to CH_2 represents an increase in molecular weight of only 10%. From decane on, the average increase in boiling point for successive CH_2-units is about 20°. The relationship of boiling point to molecular weight is shown in Fig. 2.1. It is useful to remember that the normal alkane (C_7H_{16}) of molecular weight 100 has a boiling point close to 100° (98.4°), for the relationship is that generally found for substances that do not associate to form molecular aggregates.

A practical consequence of the relationship is that lower members of the series are more easily separated by distillation than higher members. Processes of fractional distillation, now refined to a state of almost miraculous effectiveness, are applicable to hydrocarbons of all ranges of volatility. Gaseous hydrocarbons can be liquefied and then fractionally distilled at temperatures far below 0°, and precision stills are operated in the industry to effect separations. Extraordinarily efficient units of several types have been perfected for precision fractionation at atmospheric pressure. The apparatus illustrated in Fig. 2.2, though not a precision fractionator, represents a type of still useful in general laboratory practice; it is shown in use for distillation at atmospheric pressure, but with a suitable adapter can be employed for fractional distillation at pressures obtainable with an oil pump (1–2 mm.). Substances of low vapor pressure can be fractionated by high-vacuum distillation, or molecular distillation, utilizing a mercury-diffusion pump or a pump operating on the diffusion principle but employing a high-boiling organic liquid for expulsion of gas molecules (Fig. 2.3).

Specific gravities of the hydrocarbons in the liquid phase are given in the last column of Table 2.4. The hydrocarbons are all lighter than water and, being insoluble, float on water. Methane is less than half as heavy as

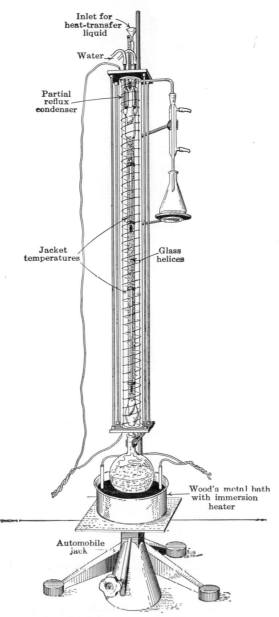

Inlet for
heat-transfer
liquid

Water

Partial
reflux
condenser

Jacket
temperatures

Glass
helices

Wood's metal bath
with immersion
heater

Automobile
jack

FIG. 2.2. — Distillation at Atmospheric Pressure

water; with succeeding members the density increases rapidly for a time and then, in $C_{15}H_{32}$, reaches a limiting value of 0.77–0.78.

Occurrence. — Natural gas and petroleum are made up in large part of mixtures of saturated hydrocarbons. The only abundant sources of natural gas for industrial utilization are in the United States, and the gas from these

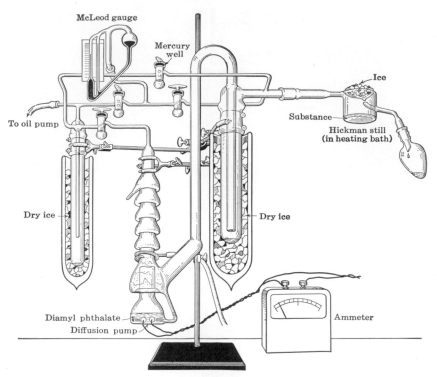

FIG. 2.3. — High-Vacuum Distillation

wells contains chiefly methane. Petroleum consists chiefly of a mixture of homologs of methane ranging in carbon content from C_1 to C_{30}–C_{40} (Chapter 5).

Methane occurs as the sole hydrocarbon constituent of marsh gas, which is formed by anaerobic (absence of oxygen) fermentation of cellulose by microorganisms. In swamps and marshlands where plant parts have become covered with water, bacterial fermentation of cellulose constituents $(C_6H_{10}O_5)_n$ of the vegetation results in production of a flammable gas that rises to the surface and that consists principally of methane, together with small amounts of hydrogen, carbon dioxide, and nitrogen. Sewage sludge on fermentation affords a similar gas, which has been utilized in some cities as a fuel.

Saturated hydrocarbons have been isolated in small amounts from the waxy constituents of certain plants. n-Heptane occurs in the wood turpentine of two pines found in the western part of the United States, *Pinus jeffreyi* and *P. sabiniani*, and can be extracted easily. All natural wax paraffins contain an odd number of carbon atoms ranging from 27 to 37. They probably arise through decarboxylation of higher fatty acids, since the natural acids all have an even number of carbon atoms. n-Nonacosane $(C_{29}H_{60})$, m.p. 62.7–62.8°, has been extracted from cabbage leaves (1.5 g. from 220 kg.), and the cuticle of the apple contains C_{27}- and C_{29}-paraffin hydrocarbons. Beeswax contains heptacosane ($C_{27}H_{56}$) and hentriacontane ($C_{31}H_{64}$).

SYNTHETIC PREPARATION

From Alcohols. — Alcohols are one group of available starting materials that can be utilized for synthesis of saturated hydrocarbons. In certain methods the alcohol is first converted into the corresponding halide. As noted in Chapter 1, ethyl alcohol is converted by hydrogen iodide or constant-boiling hydriodic acid into ethyl iodide. The reaction is general and can be used for the preparation of typical halides: methyl, *n*-propyl, and

$$CH_3CH_2OH + HI \longrightarrow CH_3CH_2I + H_2O$$
$$\text{Ethyl iodide}$$

isopropyl iodide. Hydrogen bromide, as the dry gas or in the form of constant-boiling 47% aqueous solution, reacts similarly, for example:

$$\begin{array}{c} CH_3 \\ CHOH \\ CH_3 \end{array} + HBr \longrightarrow \begin{array}{c} CH_3 \\ CHBr \\ CH_3 \end{array} + H_2O$$
$$\text{Isopropyl bromide}$$

Except in special cases, hydrochloric acid is not reactive enough for practical purposes, but other methods are available for preparing the chlorides from alcohols. Halides derived from alcohols are designated by the generic name alkyl halide, and the conventional general formula is RX, where X stands for fluorine, chlorine, bromine, or iodine, and R indicates any hydrocarbon residue, or alkyl group (derived from an alcohol), for example the methyl, ethyl, *n*- or *i*-propyl group or a $C_{16}H_{33}$- or $C_{30}H_{61}$-group. The symbol R stands for the group (C_nH_{2n+1})—, and since RH is the general formula for hydrocarbons of the methane series, these substances can be called alkanes. The hydrogen halide (HX) method of preparing alkyl halides can be represented by the general formulation:

$$ROH + HX \longrightarrow RX + H_2O$$
$$\text{Alcohol} \quad \text{(except HCl)} \quad \text{Alkyl halide}$$

Wurtz Reaction. — A method of synthesizing hydrocarbons discovered by Wurtz[1] (1855) consists in treatment of an alkyl halide with metallic sodium, which has a strong affinity for bound halogen and acts on methyl iodide in such a way as to strip iodine from the molecule and produce sodium iodide. The reaction involves two molecules of methyl iodide and two atoms of sodium:

$$\begin{array}{c} H \\ | \\ H-C+I \\ | \\ H \end{array} + 2Na + \begin{array}{c} H \\ | \\ I+C-H \\ | \\ H \end{array} \longrightarrow \begin{array}{cc} H & H \\ | & | \\ H-C-C-H \\ | & | \\ H & H \end{array} + 2NaI$$

---

[1] Adolphe Wurtz, 1817–84; b. Strasbourg; Paris; *Ber.*, **20**, 815 (1887)

Actually, the reaction probably proceeds through the formation of methyl-sodium, which interacts with methyl iodide:

$$CH_3I \xrightarrow{Na} CH_3Na \xrightarrow{CH_3I} CH_3CH_3$$

The Wurtz reaction can be applied generally to synthesis of hydrocarbons by the joining together of hydrocarbon residues of two molecules of an alkyl halide (usually the bromide or iodide). With halides of high molecular weight the yields are often good, and the reaction has been serviceable in the synthesis of higher hydrocarbons starting with alcohols found in nature. for example:

$$\underset{\text{Dihydrophytyl bromide}}{2\,C_{20}H_{41}Br} \xrightarrow[31\% \text{ yield}]{Na} \underset{\text{Perhydrolycopene}}{C_{40}H_{82}}$$

$$\underset{\text{Cetyl iodide}}{2\,n\text{-}C_{16}H_{33}I} \xrightarrow[70\text{-}80\% \text{ yield}]{Mg \text{ (ether)}} \underset{n\text{-Dotriacontane}}{C_{32}H_{66}}$$

Cetyl iodide (from the alcohol of spermaceti wax) has been converted into the C_{32}-hydrocarbon both by the action of sodium amalgam in alcohol—ether and, as shown in the equation, with use of magnesium in place of sodium.

A general expression for the Wurtz synthesis is:

$$\underset{\text{Alkyl halide}}{2\,RX} \;+\; 2\,Na \longrightarrow \underset{\text{Alkane}}{R \cdot R} \;+\; 2\,NaX$$

It might appear that the synthesis could be varied by use of two different alkyl halides, with the linking together of the two hydrocarbon fragments, for example:

$$\underset{n\text{-Butyl iodide}}{CH_3CH_2CH_2CH_2I} + \underset{n\text{-Propyl iodide}}{ICH_2CH_2CH_3} \xrightarrow{2\,Na} \underset{n\text{-Heptane}}{CH_3CH_2CH_2CH_2CH_2CH_3}$$

The reaction mixture, however, contains many millions of molecules of each halide, and there is nearly as much opportunity for interaction of like as of unlike molecules. Some butyl iodide molecules will react with molecules of propyl iodide and yield heptane as pictured, but some will combine with other molecules of the same kind and product octane. The total result can be represented as follows:

$$CH_3CH_2CH_2CH_2I + CH_3CH_2CH_2I \xrightarrow{2\,Na} \begin{cases} n\text{-}C_6H_{14}, \text{ b.p. } 69° \\ n\text{-}C_7H_{16}, \text{ b.p. } 98° \\ n\text{-}C_8H_{18}, \text{ b.p. } 126° \end{cases}$$

The reaction affords a mixture of which the unsymmetrical product n-heptane can be expected to constitute no more than one half, and since the three hydrocarbon components are similar and do not differ greatly in boiling point, isolation of even a small amount of n-heptane in a moderately homogeneous condition would obviously be difficult. It is therefore impracticable to utilize an unsymmetrical Wurtz reaction in synthesis, for the inevitable result is:

$$RX \;+\; R'X \longrightarrow RR' \;+\; RR \;+\; R'R'$$

Reduction; the Grignard Reaction. — Alkyl halides in some instances can be reduced directly to hydrocarbons:

$$RX \;+\; 2H \text{ (reducing agent)} \longrightarrow RH \;+\; HX$$

Reductions have been accomplished with zinc and hydrochloric acid, with the zinc—copper couple in alcohol, with magnesium amalgam and water, with hydrogen in the presence of palladium catalyst, and by heating the iodide with hydriodic acid in a sealed tube. Examples are as follows:

$$C_2H_5I \;+\; HI \xrightarrow{\text{High temp.}} C_2H_6 \;+\; I_2$$

$$CH_3CH_2CH_2CH_2I \xrightarrow[\text{nearly quantitative}]{\text{Mg(Hg), ROH}} CH_3CH_2CH_2CH_3$$

$$C_{26}H_{53}I \xrightarrow[68\%]{\text{Zn—HCl}} C_{26}H_{54}$$

Ceryl iodide   Cerane
(alcohol from Chinese wax)

An alternate method that usually proceeds in good yield utilizes a reactive organometallic compound of a type discovered by Grignard[2] in 1901. Grignard found that methyl iodide, as an example, reacts with metallic magnesium suspended in ether (diethyl ether) to give the ether-soluble substance

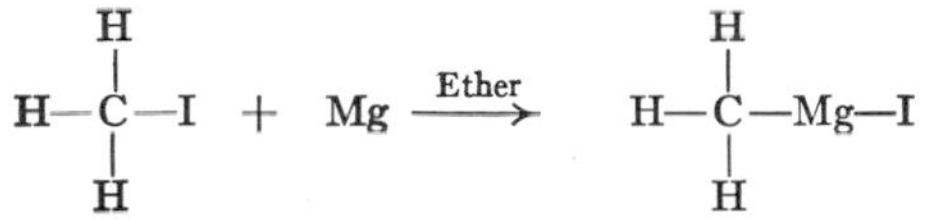

$$\begin{array}{ccccc} \text{H} & & & & \text{H} \\ | & & & & | \\ \text{H—C—I} & + & \text{Mg} & \xrightarrow{\text{Ether}} & \text{H—C—Mg—I} \\ | & & & & | \\ \text{H} & & & & \text{H} \end{array}$$

Methylmagnesium iodide

methylmagnesium iodide. The magnesium is employed in the form of thin turnings or granules, and the ether must be pure and free from traces of moisture. Even special drying of the glass reaction flask and condenser may be necessary to eliminate a slight moisture film that otherwise might inhibit the reaction; but with suitable technique the reaction can be initiated easily and then proceeds briskly, even under ice cooling; the magnesium metal is soon etched and then disintegrated, and a cloudy solution results. The reaction proceeds satisfactorily with methyl, ethyl, and higher alkyl halides, and can be conducted with a chloride, a bromide, or an iodide. The general formulation is:

$$RX \;+\; Mg \longrightarrow RMgX$$

Alkylmagnesium halide
(Grignard reagent)

---

[2] Victor Grignard, 1871–1935; b. Cherbourg; Nancy, Lyon; Nobel Prize 1912; *J. Chem. Soc.*, 171 (1937)

Ether is not merely a convenient solvent but forms a complex (etherate) essential to the reaction. The etherate has the composition $RMgX \cdot 2(C_2H_5)_2O$ and is represented by an electronic formulation indicating that magnesium completes its octet by accepting electrons from the ether oxygens (coordinate covalent bonds, see p. 51):

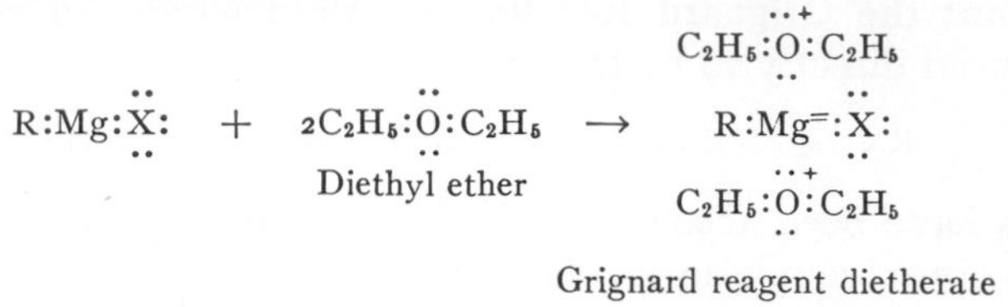

$$R:Mg:X: \quad + \quad 2C_2H_5:\overset{..}{O}:C_2H_5 \quad \rightarrow \quad
\begin{array}{c}
C_2H_5:\overset{..+}{O}:C_2H_5 \\
R:Mg^=:X: \\
C_2H_5:\overset{..+}{O}:C_2H_5
\end{array}$$

$$\text{Diethyl ether}$$

$$\text{Grignard reagent dietherate}$$

Alkylmagnesium halides, or Grignard reagents, are highly reactive and versatile substances capable of entering into many useful reactions. The broad significance of this valuable synthetic tool is reflected in the award to Grignard of the Nobel Prize. The active agent, having a hydrocarbon group and a halogen atom linked to magnesium, is sensitive, but fortunately can be employed for a reaction in the ethereal solution in which it is produced and need not be isolated. Conversion into a hydrocarbon of the alkane series is accomplished merely by adding slowly to the ethereal solution an equivalent quantity of water. Methylmagnesium iodide gives methane:

$$\underset{H}{\overset{H}{H-\underset{|}{\overset{|}{C}}-MgI}} \; + \; HOH \; \longrightarrow \; \underset{H}{\overset{H}{H-\underset{|}{\overset{|}{C}}-H}} \; + \; HO-Mg-I$$

Methane gas is liberated at once in amount equivalent to the actual Grignard reagent present. Side reactions occur to a slight extent in production of the reagent, but yields in the order of 85–90% are usual, and hence satisfactory overall yields are obtained in the series of reactions:

$$RX \xrightarrow{\;Mg\;} RMgX \xrightarrow{\;HOH\;} RH \; + \; Mg\overset{\displaystyle X}{\underset{\displaystyle OH}{\Big\langle}} \cdot$$

The basic magnesium halide tends to separate from the ether—water mixture as a white precipitate, but can be kept in solution in the water by addition of hydrochloric acid, which forms the normal halide. A dilute solution of mineral acid is often used to effect hydrolytic decomposition of the organometallic halide. Alcohols, organic acids, and any substance containing a hydroxyl group will react as readily as water, for example:

$$CH_3CH_2CH_2MgBr \; + \; CH_3OH \; \longrightarrow \; CH_3CH_2CH_3 \; + \; Mg\overset{\displaystyle OCH_3}{\underset{\displaystyle Br}{\Big\langle}}$$

The propane produced, like methane, appears as a gas.   A higher hydrocarbon such as *n*-decane would be retained in the ether layer, from which it could be isolated by removal of the low-boiling ether (b.p. 35°) by distillation.   *n*-Pentane (b.p. 36°) boils at practically the same temperature as ether and cannot be separated from the solvent by distillation, and in the preparation of this hydrocarbon, one of the higher homologs of ether is used.

From Acids. — Typical organic acids contain the combination known as the carboxyl group —C(=O)OH as a functional group responsible for the acidity.   For convenience in writing this is often abbreviated to —COOH or —CO$_2$H, but such formulas should be read with the understanding that one oxygen is present as a hydroxyl group and that the other is doubly bound to carbon.   The structures and names of typical carboxylic acids are:

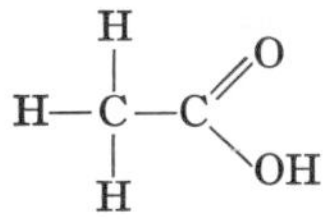

$$H-\overset{\displaystyle H}{\underset{\displaystyle H}{C}}-C\overset{\displaystyle O}{\underset{\displaystyle OH}{\Large\diagup}}\quad \text{or}\quad CH_3COOH$$

Acetic acid

CH_3CH_2COOH
Propionic acid
(cf. propane)

$CH_3CH_2CH_2COOH$
n-Butyric acid
(cf. butane)

The type formula is RCOOH, and the ionization can be represented thus:

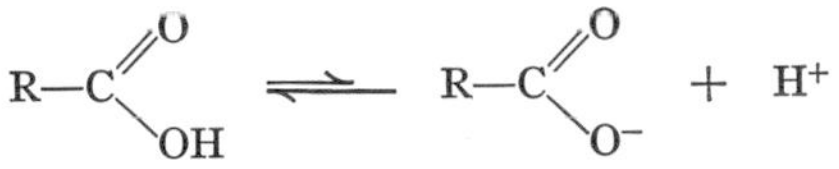

$$R-C\overset{\displaystyle O}{\underset{\displaystyle OH}{\Large\diagup}} \rightleftharpoons R-C\overset{\displaystyle O}{\underset{\displaystyle O^-}{\Large\diagup}} + H^+$$

In comparison with mineral acids, the organic substances are only weakly acidic, but they react with sodium bicarbonate, as well as with sodium carbonate and sodium hydroxide, and form ionic salts, for example sodium acetate, CH_3COONa.

By Decarboxylation. — One way of converting carboxylic acids into alkanes is pyrolytic elimination of carbon dioxide from the carboxyl group, using a metal salt of the acid.   When solid sodium acetate is mixed with sodium hydroxide, or better with the less easily fusible soda lime, and the mixture is heated to a sufficiently high temperature, breakdown occurs and methane is liberated:

$$CH_3COONa + NaOH \xrightarrow{\text{Fuse}} CH_4 + Na_2CO_3$$

The reaction is somewhat analogous to the thermal decomposition of sodium bicarbonate with loss of carbon dioxide and formation of the more stable sodium carbonate.   Sodium carbonate evidently is also more stable than sodium acetate, in combination with alkali. An example of the preparation of a higher hydrocarbon from a natural acid is as follows:

$$(C_{17}H_{35}COO)_2Ba \xrightarrow[\text{Dry distillation}]{\text{NaOH, CH}_3\text{ONa}} 2\, C_{17}H_{36}$$

Barium stearate n-Heptadecane

The general reaction $RCOONa + NaOH \rightarrow R \cdot H$ represents a degradative method of preparing hydrocarbons (loss of carbon); it is not so useful as methods involving true synthesis.

Kolbe Synthesis. — A hydrocarbon synthesis discovered by Kolbe[3] in 1849 consists in electrolysis of an aqueous solution of the salt of an acid. Sodium acetate on electrolysis yields ethane, and the net reaction can be formulated as follows:

$$2\, CH_3COONa + 2\, H_2O \xrightarrow{\text{Electrolysis}} \underbrace{C_2H_6 + 2\, CO_2}_{\text{Anode}} + \underbrace{2\, NaOH + H_2}_{\text{Cathode}}$$

Under the influence of the electric current sodium ions migrate to the cathode, pick up electrons from the inflowing stream, and yield sodium hydroxide and hydrogen. The acetate anion is impelled to the anode, where it gives up the ionic charge and possibly exists in a transient phase as an acetate radical having an odd electron. The radical at once loses carbon dioxide

$$2\, CH_3C\!\!\begin{array}{c}{}^{\nearrow O}\\{}_{\searrow O^-}\end{array} \; -2e \longrightarrow 2\left[CH_3C\!\!\begin{array}{c}{}^{\nearrow O}\\{}_{\searrow O\cdot}\end{array}\right] \longrightarrow 2[CH_3\cdot] \longrightarrow CH_3CH_3$$

Acetate ion   Acetate radical   Methyl radical   Ethane

and gives an equally transient trivalent carbon radical, and this finally achieves stabilization by doubling up to form the tetravalent carbon compound ethane.

Sodium propionate on electrolysis affords n-butane, and sodium or potassium n-butyrate yields n-hexane:

$$\begin{array}{l} CH_3CH_2CH_2COOK \\ CH_3CH_2CH_2COOK \end{array} \xrightarrow{\text{Electrolysis}} \begin{array}{l} CH_3CH_2CH_2 \\ \;\;\;\;\;\;\;| \\ CH_3CH_2CH_2 \end{array}$$

Potassium n-butyrate n-Hexane

Acids derived from fats provide starting materials for synthesis of higher homologs:

$$\begin{array}{c} C_{11}H_{23}COO\diagdown \\ \qquad\qquad\diagup Ca \\ C_{11}H_{23}COO\diagup \end{array} \xrightarrow[86\%]{\text{0.8 Amp., 45}^\circ} C_{22}H_{46}$$

Calcium laurate n-Docosane

Summary. — The synthetic methods just described can be summarized

---

[3] Hermann Kolbe, 1818–84; b. Germany; Ph.D. Göttingen; Marburg, Leipzig

in generalized terms as follows:

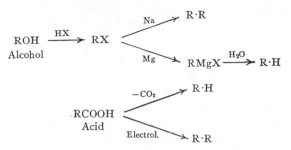

Other useful syntheses of alkanes will become apparent in considering the chemistry of certain further series of compounds.

PROPERTIES

Hydrocarbons of the methane series are, in general, decidedly inert. The normal, or straight-chain members are particularly resistant to attack by powerful chemical reagents that react with, and often destroy, organic compounds of many other types.   n-Hexane, for example, passes unscathed through treatment with concentrated sulfuric acid, boiling nitric acid, molten sodium hydroxide, or through attempted oxidation with potassium dichromate or permanganate.   Such reactions as have been realized are dependent upon special structures, high reaction temperatures, or methods of catalysis.

Chlorination. — Mixtures of methane and chlorine when prepared and kept in the dark do not react.   Exposure to sunlight results in rapid reaction which, at appropriate concentrations of the two gases, may assume explosive proportions.   The photochemical, or light-induced chlorination of methane involves in the initial step substitution of one of the hydrogen atoms by chlorine and liberation of hydrogen chloride.   The reaction does not terminate at this initial stage but gives the higher products: methylene chloride (CH_2Cl_2), chloroform ($CHCl_3$), and carbon tetrachloride (CCl_4).

$$CH_4 + Cl_2 \xrightarrow{\text{Light}} HCl + CH_3Cl \rightarrow CH_2Cl_2 \rightarrow CHCl_3 \rightarrow CCl_4$$

Higher substitution products are found in the mixture even though considerable methane is still present, which shows that introduction of chlorine renders the molecule more vulnerable than before to the reagent.   The photochemical process is not well adapted to laboratory-scale operation, for it does not afford single, easily purified products.   In technological practice, however, the reaction has been employed to produce mixtures of chlorinated hydrocarbons of use as solvents.   Bromine reacts with hydrocarbons under the influence of light in the same way as chlorine but less vigorously.   Iodine is too inert to effect substitution, and indeed the reverse reaction can be realized: $RI + HI \rightarrow RH + I_2$.

The photochemical activation of the reagents can be simulated by use of chemical catalysts, for alkanes have been chlorinated at low temperatures by the action of sulfuryl chloride catalyzed by benzoyl peroxide (Kharasch,[4] 1939):

$$RH + SO_2Cl_2 \xrightarrow[40-80°]{\text{Peroxide}} RCl + HCl + SO_2$$

n-Heptane yields 12.5% of 1-chloroheptane and 76.5% of 2-chloroheptane; n-propyl chloride on similar treatment affords 45% of 1,2-dichloropropane and 34% of 1,3-dichloropropane.

The peroxide-catalyzed process proceeds through a series of reactions involving transient free radicals, which are fragments containing an odd, or unpaired, electron formed by dissociation of a covalent bond: $A{:}B \rightarrow A{\cdot} + B{\cdot}$. Such dissociation requires a large input of energy (energy of dissociation), but a radical once formed is highly reactive because of the pronounced tendency of atoms to attain their normal valence shell. Benzoyl peroxide functions as a catalyst because it readily decomposes according to equations 1 and 2 to give the phenyl radical, which reacts as in 3 with sulfuryl chloride to give the radical $SO_2Cl{\cdot}$. The latter radical then initiates a chain reaction involving steps 4–6, in which the radicals required in the initial step 4 are continually regenerated during the course of transformation of the hydrocarbon into the chloride (5–6). Ideally, a single chain-initiating

Chain-initiating reactions
1. $C_6H_5COO{-}OOCC_6H_5 \longrightarrow C_6H_5COO{\cdot} + CO_2 + C_6H_5{\cdot}$
   Dibenzoyl peroxide   Benzoate radical   Phenyl radical
2. $C_6H_5COO{\cdot} \longrightarrow C_6H_5{\cdot} + CO_2$
3. $C_6H_5{\cdot} + SO_2Cl_2 \longrightarrow C_6H_5Cl + SO_2Cl{\cdot}$

Chain reaction
4. $SO_2Cl{\cdot} \longrightarrow SO_2 + Cl{\cdot}$
5. $Cl{\cdot} + RH \longrightarrow HCl + R{\cdot}$
6. $R{\cdot} + SO_2Cl_2 \longrightarrow RCl + SO_2Cl{\cdot}$

radical derived from the decomposition of benzoyl peroxide would suffice for the chlorination, and actually only a catalytic amount of peroxide is required. However, such a reaction is markedly sensitive to traces of impurities that can react with one of the free-radical intermediates and so break the chain. The photochemical chlorination of hydrocarbons probably involves dissociation of chlorine molecules to chlorine atoms under actinic radiation, followed by a chain process consisting in the steps:

$$Cl{\cdot} + RH \longrightarrow HCl + R{\cdot}$$
$$R{\cdot} + Cl_2 \longrightarrow RCl + Cl{\cdot}$$

Chlorosulfonation. — In the presence of actinic radiation ($h\nu$) in a weakly basic medium the reaction of an alkane with sulfuryl chloride results in introduction of the chlorosulfonyl group:

$$RH + SO_2Cl_2 \xrightarrow[50\%]{h\nu \ (\text{pyridine})} RSO_2Cl + HCl$$

---

[4] Morris S. Kharasch, b. 1895 Kremenetz, Ukrainia; Ph.D. Chicago (Piccard); Chicago

The same reaction can be accomplished by use of sulfur dioxide and chlorine under illumination. As the formulation indicates, propane affords about equal amounts of the two possible isomers. The symmetrical hydrocarbon

$$CH_3CH_2CH_3 \xrightarrow{SO_2,\ Cl_2,\ h\nu,\ 50°} CH_3CH_2CH_2SO_2Cl + (CH_3)_2CHSO_2Cl$$

$$48\% \qquad\qquad\qquad 52\%$$

cyclohexane, formulated below, yields a single product. The conversion of single hydrocarbons or of mixtures into sulfonyl chlorides affords one method for the commercial production of synthetic detergents.

A related reaction, introduction of the —COCl group by reaction of an alkane with phosgene, $COCl_2$, or with oxalyl chloride, $(COCl)_2$, is induced by either light or a peroxide. The reaction proceeds more readily with cycloparaffins, for example cyclohexane, than with straight-chain paraffins.

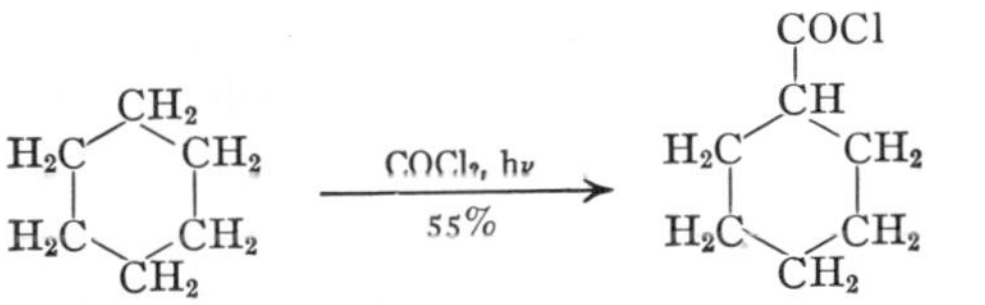

Cyclohexane   Cyclohexanecarboxylic acid chloride

The process likewise involves a chain mechanism and is formulated by Kharasch as in 1–4.

1. $(COCl)_2 \longrightarrow 2\,CO + 2\,Cl\cdot$
2. $RH + Cl\cdot \longrightarrow R\cdot + HCl$
3. $R\cdot + (COCl)_2 \longrightarrow RCOCl + \cdot COCl$
4. $\cdot COCl \longrightarrow CO + Cl\cdot$

Cracking. — When the vapor of a higher homolog of methane is passed through a hot (500–700°) metal tube, a process of thermal decomposition (pyrolysis), or cracking, takes place which consists in rupture of carbon-to-carbon linkages and cleavage of a large molecule into two or more fragments. Partial carbonization occurs, elementary hydrogen may be produced by rupture of carbon–hydrogen bonds, and some of the resulting hydrocarbons contain a lower proportion of hydrogen than the starting materials and belong to the series of unsaturated hydrocarbons. Some of the possible courses of the process are illustrated as follows:

$$C_8H_{18} \xrightarrow{\text{Pyrolysis}} \begin{cases} C_4H_{10} + C_4H_8\ (\text{unsaturated}) \\ C_6H_{14} + C_2H_4\ (\text{unsaturated}) \\ C_4H_{10} + CH_4 + C_2H_4 + C \\ C_8H_{16} + H_2 \end{cases}$$

Although the cracking process is complex and gives a diversified mixture of products, modern technology has turned it into an extremely useful method of producing superior motor fuels and valuable synthetic intermediates, as will be described later. Cracking proceeds by a free-radical mechanism.

TABLE 2.5. HEATS OF COMBUSTION

HYDROCARBON		KG.-CAL. PER MOLE	KG.-CAL. PER GRAM	% H	KG.-CAL. PER ML.
NAME	FORMULA				
Methane	CH₄	210.9	13.14	25.1	5.57
Ethane	C₂H₆	368.4	12.24	20.1	6.68
Propane	C₃H₈	526.3	11.94	18.3	6.95
Isobutane	C₄H₁₀	683.4	11.76	17.3	6.81
n-Pentane	C₅H₁₂	838.3	11.62	16.8	7.28
n-Hexane	C₆H₁₄	990.6	11.50	16.4	7.58
n-Heptane	C₇H₁₆	1149.9	11.48	16.1	7.85
n-Octane	C₈H₁₈	1305	11.43	15.9	8.03
n-Decane	C₁₀H₂₂	1610	11.32	15.6	8.26
n-Hexadecane	C₁₆H₃₄	2559	11.30	15.1	8.76
n-Eicosane	C₂₀H₄₂	3183	11.27	15.0	8.76

Oxidation. — The reaction of saturated hydrocarbons with oxygen with the output of energy is the basis for use of gasoline as fuel in internal combustion engines. The energy release on burning a given hydrocarbon is expressed as the heat of combustion in terms of kg.-cal.*/mole, as in the third column of Table 2.5. The heat release per mole increases regularly with increasing size of the molecule, and in the series shown the average increment for the CH_2 unit is 156 kg.-cal. The fourth column of the table gives a comparison on the basis of equal weights of fuel; methane has the highest heat of combustion per gram and the value falls off fairly sharply at first and then becomes essentially constant starting with the C_8-hydrocarbon. This relationship is correlated with the hydrogen content (fifth column), which is also greatest with methane and then drops to a fairly constant value. The explanation is that the heat of combustion of hydrogen is 33.9 kg.-cal./g., whereas the value for carbon is only 8.08 kg.-cal./g.; hydrocarbons of highest hydrogen content therefore have the advantage. If the weight of a given fuel charge were the only consideration, liquid methane or ethane would appear to represent more efficient fuels than higher hydrocarbons. The volume capacity of a fuel tank, however, is usually a more important limiting factor than the weight, and low molecular weight substances are light and bulky. Figures for the heats of combustion per ml. (last column) show that in the higher members of the series the increased density more than compensates for a somewhat lower heat value on the weight basis. The homologous hydrocarbons containing sixteen to twenty carbon atoms release 57% more heat per ml. than methane does. A fuel tank or an incendiary bomb of a given volume capacity obviously will carry a greater fuel load if charged with higher hydrocarbons than with the lighter members of the series, though a balance must be struck between the fuel load and the particular ignition characteristics required.

Incomplete combustion of gaseous hydrocarbons is important in industry in the manufacture of carbon blacks, particularly lampblack, a pig-

---

* One kg.-cal. = 1000 calories = 3.968 B.T.U. (British thermal units)

ment for ink, and channel black, used as a filler in rubber compounding. Natural gas is used because of its cheapness and availability; the yield of black varies with the type of gas and the manufacturing process but usually is in the range of 2–6% of the theoretical amount.

Partial air oxidation of a more limited extent is a means for production of specific oxygenated substances. Controlled air oxidation of high-boiling mineral oils and waxes from petroleum affords mixtures of higher carboxylic acids similar to those derived from fats (fatty acids) and suitable for use in making soaps: $RCH_2CH_2R' \xrightarrow{O_2} RCO_2H + HO_2CR'$.

Oxidation of paraffin hydrocarbons by chemical reagents in special cases has only theoretical interest. Normal hydrocarbons are resistant to attack by potassium permanganate, but the hydrocarbon $(CH_3CH_2)_2CHCH_3$ can be oxidized rather readily by the reagent, probably with initial production of $(CH_3CH_2)_2C(OH)CH_3$. The lone hydrogen on the carbon atom to which three alkyl groups are attached (tertiary hydrogen) is the vulnerable point. Hydrocarbons of this type (R_3CH) are in general susceptible to oxidation, though the reactions are not clear-cut and the products are usually subject to secondary reactions.

Nitration. — Treatment of branched hydrocarbons with nitric acid at an elevated temperature results not only in oxidation but in nitration, as in the following example:

$$\underset{\text{Isobutane}}{CH_3-\overset{\displaystyle H}{\underset{\displaystyle CH_3}{C}}-CH_3} \xrightarrow[\text{22\% yield}]{HNO_3 \text{ (sealed tube, } 150°)} \underset{\text{2-Nitro-2-methylpropane}}{CH_3-\overset{\displaystyle NO_2}{\underset{\displaystyle CH_3}{C}}-CH_3} + H_2O$$

Since such nitrations are troublesome to carry out and give only low yields, the nitrated hydrocarbons, or nitroparaffins, until recently were more readily obtainable by other methods. The first known nitroparaffin was prepared by Victor Meyer[5] (1872) by interaction of an alkyl halide with silver nitrite: $RBr + AgNO_2 \rightarrow RNO_2 + AgBr$. An improved procedure applicable to primary and secondary halides involves reaction with sodium nitrite in dimethylformamide solution containing urea to increase the solubility of the nitrite (N. Kornblum, 1955). A method of preparing nitromethane giving yields up to 50% is illustrated as follows (Kolbe):

$$CH_2ClCOOH \xrightarrow{NaNO_2, CaCO_3} \left[\overset{\displaystyle CH_2COOH}{\underset{\displaystyle NO_2}{|}} \right] \longrightarrow CH_3NO_2$$

A modern development consists in preparation of the nitro derivatives of either straight-chain or branched hydrocarbons by vapor-phase nitration (H. B. Hass, 1936). When a gaseous mixture of two moles of hydrocarbon and one mole of nitric acid vapor is passed through a narrow reactor tube at

---

[5] Victor Meyer, 1848–97; b. Berlin; Geneva, Zurich ETH, Heidelberg; *Ber.*, **30**, 2157 (1897)

420° (760 mm. pressure), ethane, propane, and *n*-butane react rapidly. Methane is attacked only slowly at this temperature, but at 475° some 13% of the material is converted in each pass through the reactor into nitromethane, and the recovered hydrocarbon can be recycled. Ethane and the higher homologs on vapor-phase nitration behave abnormally in that they afford mixtures containing nitro compounds having fewer carbon atoms than the original hydrocarbon. Ethane yields not only nitroethane (9 parts, b.p. 114.5°) but nitromethane (1 part, b.p. 101.9°), and propane affords a complex mixture also containing nitromethane:

$$CH_3CH_2CH_3 \xrightarrow{HNO_3,\ 420°}
\begin{cases}
CH_3CH_2CH_2NO_2\ (32\ parts) \\
CH_3CHCH_3\ (33\ parts) \\
\quad | \\
\quad NO_2 \\
CH_3CH_2NO_2\ (26\ parts) \\
CH_3NO_2\ (9\ parts)
\end{cases}
\begin{array}{l} total \\ yield, \\ 21\% \end{array}$$

The degradative reaction is generally considered to be associated with a process of cracking at the elevated temperature and to involve free radicals as intermediates. Certain lower nitroparaffins are made commercially by the vapor-phase process; nitromethane is produced chiefly as a by-product in the nitration of propane. Nitro compounds are nontoxic, stable, and noncorrosive, and have found use as solvents, primary fuels, and as starting materials in synthesis.

Urea Complexes. — Straight-chain alkanes containing at least six carbon atoms combine with urea to form complexes, which are decomposed by water

$$\underset{\text{Urea}}{H_2N-\overset{\displaystyle O}{\overset{\|}{C}}-NH_2} \qquad \underset{\text{Thiourea}}{H_2N-\overset{\displaystyle S}{\overset{\|}{C}}-NH_2}$$

to the components (M. F. Bengen, 1940). The molar ratio of urea to hydrocarbon is proportional to the chain length, being 6:1 with *n*-heptane and 21:1 with the *n*-C_{28}-alkane. The complexes are useful for separation of straight-chain from branched-chain hydrocarbons. Thiourea also forms complexes but the structural requirements are not so specific, since a variety of branched- as well as straight-chain C_{14} and higher hydrocarbons complex with this reagent.

CYCLOPARAFFINS

Cycloparaffins (cycloalkanes) bear a close resemblance to paraffins (Table 2.6). As a consequence of the ring structure, the carbon valences are saturated even though the hydrocarbons contain two hydrogen atoms less than the corresponding open-chain alkanes. In chemical properties, cyclopentane, cyclohexane, and all higher homologs closely resemble normal alkanes and are hardly distinguishable from them; cyclopropane and cyclo-

TABLE 2.6.   CYCLOPARAFFINS

NAME	FORMULA C_nH_{2n}	STRUCTURE	M.P., °C.	B.P., °C.	SP. GR. (AS LIQUIDS)
Cyclopropane	C_3H_6	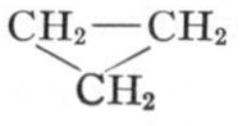 CH$_2$—CH$_2$ CH$_2$	-127	-32.9	0.688
Cyclobutane	C_4H_8	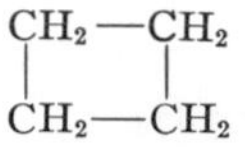 CH$_2$—CH$_2$ CH$_2$—CH$_2$	-80	11	.7038
Cyclopentane	C_5H_{10}	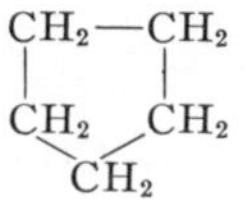 CH$_2$—CH$_2$ CH$_2$ CH$_2$ CH$_2$	-94	49.5	.7460
Cyclohexane	C_6H_{12}	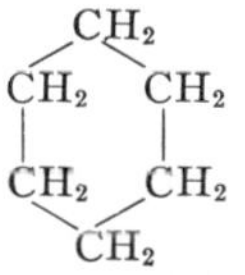 CH$_2$ CH$_2$ CH$_2$ CH$_2$ CH$_2$ CH$_2$	6.4	80.8	.7781
Cycloheptane	C_7H_{14}	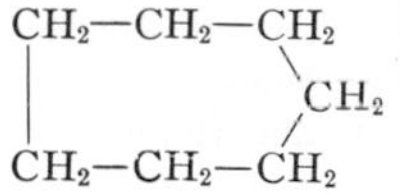 CH$_2$—CH$_2$—CH$_2$ CH$_2$ CH$_2$—CH$_2$—CH$_2$	-13	117	.8100
Cyclooctane	C_8H_{16}	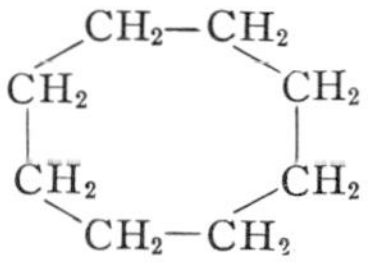 CH$_2$—CH$_2$ CH$_2$ CH$_2$ CH$_2$ CH$_2$ CH$_2$—CH$_2$	14	147	.8304

butane are exceptional, and the former hydrocarbon in particular is endowed with considerable chemical reactivity.

Cyclic hydrocarbons boil 10–20° higher than normal alkanes of the same carbon content (and of only slightly higher molecular weight). The most noteworthy contrast in physical properties between the cyclic and noncyclic alkanes is that the former have densities some 20% greater than the latter. The heat of combustion of cyclohexane on a weight basis is slightly lower than that of n-hexane, namely 939 kg.-cal./mole, or 11.16 kg.-cal./g.; owing to the distinctly greater density, the heat of combustion on a volume basis, 8.68 kg.-cal./ml., is considerably higher than the value (7.58) for the straight-chain hydrocarbon

PROBLEMS

1. Formulate and name all possible dibromo derivatives of isobutane (3 isomers) and n-butane (6 isomers).
2. Write formulas for all heptanes derived from $CH_3CH(CH_3)CH_2CH_2CH_3$ and name them as derivatives of methane.

3. Write structural formulas for:

 (a) 1-Bromo-2-chlorononane
 (b) 2,2,3-Trichloroheptane
 (c) 2-Hydroxy-2-methylbutane
 (d) Dimethylisopropylmethane
 (e) Tetraethylmethane
 (f) n-Hexylmagnesium iodide

4. Name the following compounds as derivatives of methane:

 (a) CCl_2F_2
 (b) $(CH_3)_2C(CH_2CH_3)_2$
 (c) $(CH_3)_3CCH_2CH_2CH_2CH_3$
 (d) $(CH_3CH_2CH_2)_2CHCH(CH_3)_2$

5. Give Geneva names for:

 (a) $CH_3CH(CH_3)CH_2CH_2CH(CH_3)CH_2CH_3$
 (b) Isobutane
 (c) $CH_3CH_2CH_2CH(C_2H_5)CH_3$
 (d) $(CH_3)_2CHCH(C_2H_5)CH_2CH(CH_3)_2$

6. What octanes can be derived from the heptane $CH_3CH_2CH_2C(CH_3)_3$? Give the Geneva names.

READING REFERENCES

"Definitive Report of the Committee for the Reform of Nomenclature in Organic Chemistry,"
 J. Chem. Soc., 1607 (1931)
E. E. Gilbert, "The Reactive Paraffins," J. Chem. Ed., 18, 435 (1941)
G. Edgar, G. Calingaert and R. E. Marker, "The Preparation and Properties of the Isomeric Heptanes," J. Am. Chem. Soc. 51, 1483 (1929)
D. H. Hey and W. A. Waters, "Free Radicals and Homolytic Reactions," Chemistry of Carbon Compounds (E. H. Rodd, Ed.), IA, 195-217, Elsevier (1951)

CHAPTER 3

ETHYLENIC HYDROCARBONS
(ALKENES)

Hydrocarbons of this series differ relatively little from alkanes in physical constants but contrast with them in chemical properties. The first member is ethylene, C_2H_4, and there is no one-carbon member corresponding to methane. Ethylene has two hydrogens less than the corresponding C_2-alkane and is hence unsaturated; the same is true of propylene (C_3H_6), butylene (C_4H_8), and the others. In contrast with alkanes, these unsaturated substances are highly reactive. They combine with bromine in the dark, and with mineral acids and with oxidizing agents. The reactions are of a different type; they are not substitutions, as encountered in the methane series, but additions. Thus ethylene and bromine combine to form ethylene dibromide; there is no exchange or replacement but merely addition of the two reactants to form a new molecule.

$$C_2H_4 \quad + \quad Br_2 \quad \longrightarrow \quad C_2H_4Br_2$$
Ethylene $\qquad\qquad\qquad$ Ethylene dibromide

The structure for ethylene suggested by the Kekulé theory is that in which two valences of each carbon atom are utilized to form a connecting double bond, or ethylenic linkage. In terms of the electronic theory, the double bond consists of two pairs of shared electrons. Since a single bond is sufficient to provide a firm link between the carbon atoms, the presence of an extra bond, or pair of electrons, represents latent combining capacity, which comes into play in and determines the characteristic addition reactions. Initial and final stages in the addition of bromine to ethylene can be represented by formulas showing merely the electrons involved in the process:

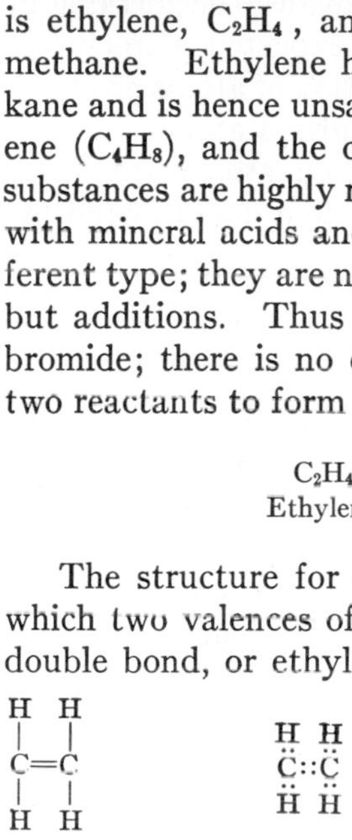

$$CH_2::CH_2 \quad + \quad Br:Br \quad \longrightarrow \quad Br:CH_2:CH_2:Br$$

The course of addition reactions of higher hydrocarbons of the series substantiates the double-bond formulation. Propylene readily adds a molecule of bromine to give 1,2-dibromopropane, and the appearance of

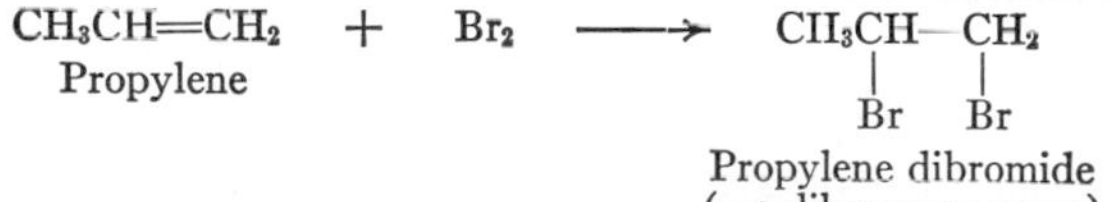

$$CH_3CH{=}CH_2 \quad + \quad Br_2 \quad \longrightarrow \quad CH_3CH{-}CH_2$$
Propylene $\qquad\qquad\qquad\qquad$ Br $\quad$ Br
Propylene dibromide
(1,2-dibromopropane)

49

bromine atoms in the 1- and 2-positions locates the original centers of unsaturation as adjacent to each other, as in the double-bond formulation.
Of the two isomeric butylenes, one yields a 1,2-dibromide and the other
a 2,3-dibromide; indeed ethylenic hydrocarbons invariably form addition
products in which the added groups appear on adjacent carbon atoms. No
formulation other than that based upon the concept of the double bond explains this experimental observation. If propylene contained two trivalent
carbon atoms, these centers of reactivity could be distributed in both the
1,2- and the 1,3-combinations, and not exclusively in one way, and an
initial member of the series would exist having a single trivalent carbon.
Conversely, a double bond in an organic formula provides considerable information concerning the chemical properties to be expected, namely, (1)
reactivity, (2) ability to enter into additions, (3) addition of atoms or groups
in pairs, and (4) attachment of groups to adjacent carbon atoms.

Double Bond Types. — In ethylene the two carbon atoms are linked
by two pairs of shared electrons that constitute a **covalent double bond** (a).

$$H_2C::CH_2 \qquad {>}C::C{<} \qquad {>}C{=}C{<} \qquad \overset{\delta^+ \ \ \delta^-}{{>}C{=}C{<}} \qquad \overset{\delta^+ \ \ \delta^-}{{>}C{=}O}$$

$$\text{(a)} \qquad\qquad \text{(b)} \qquad\qquad \text{(c)} \qquad\qquad \text{(d)} \qquad\qquad \text{(e)}$$

Since the molecule is symmetrical, the four electrons concerned in the bonding must occupy a median position between the two carbon atoms. In an
unsymmetrical derivative of ethylene, however, a difference in the electron-
attracting power of atoms or groups attached to the two carbon atoms may
result in some displacement of the shared electrons toward one of the two
doubly-bonded carbon atoms, as indicated in formulas (b) and (c) with a
curved arrow. No full electron-transfer to produce a stable ion is implied,
but merely somewhat unequal sharing of the electrons. The displacements
pictured tend to produce partial polarization in the sense that the carbon
atom written to the right has the higher electron density or carries a fractional negative charge, indicated in formula (d) by the symbol δ^-; the other
carbon atom then must have a fractional positive charge of the same magnitude (δ^+). Thus formulas (b), (c), and (d) are alternate conventions for
representation of a **partially polarized covalent double bond**. A double
bond between two unlike atoms, for example the carbon–oxygen double
bond of a carbonyl group ($C{=}O$), is usually partially polarized, since unlike
atoms differ in relative electronegativity. Estimated relative electronega-
tivities are as follows:

F	4.0	Cl	3.0	S	2.5
O	3.5	Br	2.8	C	2.5
N	3.0	I	2.5	H	2.1

Oxygen is more electronegative than carbon, and hence the carbonyl group
is partially polarized in the sense indicated in formula (e).

The doubly bound atoms in an unsymmetrical ethylene or in a carbonyl compound are not polarized to anything like the extent that the atoms of sodium chloride are polarized, and the net charges, positive for one atom and negative for the other, actually are not far from the limiting charge of zero, which is defined as the formal charge. In sodium chloride the formal charge on sodium is +1 and that on chlorine is −1, but there appears to be some electron-sharing to give the bond between the two atoms a minor covalent character, and hence the net charge on each atom approximates but does not quite equal the formal charge. Thus a formula written with either plus and minus charges or with no charges represents merely an approximation to the actual condition of polarization, which may be at some stage intermediate between complete electron transfer and equal sharing.

Another type of double bond is exemplified by one of two kinds of nitrogen–oxygen linkages in nitric acid. If the usual concept of electron-sharing is applied to the linking together of one atom of hydrogen (1 e), one atom of nitrogen (5 e), and three atoms of oxygen (6 e), the result (f) is seen to represent an electronically unstable structure because the nitrogen atom is

$$H:\overset{..}{\overset{..}{O}}:N::\overset{..}{O}: \qquad H:\overset{..}{\overset{..}{O}}:\overset{+}{N}:\overset{\bar{..}}{O}: \qquad H{-}O{-}\overset{+}{N}{-}\overset{-}{O}$$
$$\overset{..}{\underset{..}{:O:}} \qquad\qquad \overset{..}{\underset{..}{:O:}} \qquad\qquad \overset{\|}{O}$$

(f) (g) (h)

surrounded by ten electrons. It is thus supposed that two of the four electrons between nitrogen and, say, the oxygen written to the right move into the exclusive sphere of this oxygen atom to give structure (g). In this structure each oxygen and nitrogen atom is surrounded by an electron octet, and the nitrogen and one oxygen atom bear positive and negative formal charges, since one of the two electrons that was moved from a shared position originally belonged to nitrogen and hence is donated by nitrogen to oxygen. The two atoms concerned are thus linked by the concerted action of a covalent bond and a polar bond, and the combination is defined as a **coordinate covalent bond**, or a **semipolar bond**. Formula (h) is the equivalent counterpart written with Kekulé bonds.

The validity of an electronic formula such as (g) can be tested by conformation of the charge for a given atom to the following equation:

$$F \text{ (formal charge)} = Z - s/2 - p$$

where Z is the positive charge in the kernel (balancing the valence electrons of the atom), s is the number of shared electrons, and p is the number of unshared electrons. Thus for the nitrogen atom in (g), $F = 5 - 8/2 - 0 = +1$; for the charged oxygen atom, $F = 6 - 2/2 - 6 = -1$; for the uncharged oxygen atom, $F = 6 - 4/2 - 4 = 0$.

Structures and Names. — The first few members of the series usually are referred to by the common names: ethylene, propylene, butylene, and amylene (C_5H_{10}). Amylene, with the same carbon content as pentane, is so named because it can be obtained from certain amyl alcohols. Where the structures are not too complicated, unsaturated hydrocarbons are sometimes named as derivatives of ethylene; this scheme, which is illustrated in the accompanying examples, is used for derivatives substituted with the phenyl group, C_6H_5—.

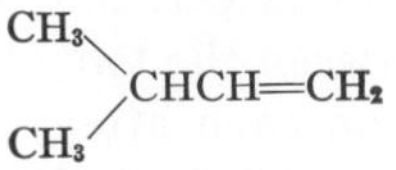

$$\begin{array}{c} CH_3 \\ \diagdown \\ CHCH{=}CH_2 \\ \diagup \\ CH_3 \end{array}$$
Isopropylethylene

$CH_3CH{=}CHCH_3$
s-Dimethylethylene
(s = symmetrical)

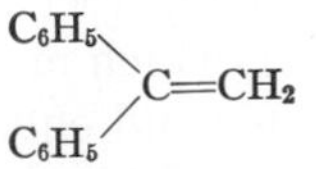

$$\begin{array}{c} C_6H_5 \\ \diagdown \\ C{=}CH_2 \\ \diagup \\ C_6H_5 \end{array}$$
1,1(or α,α)-Diphenylethylene

$C_6H_5CH{=}CHC_6H_5$
1,2(or α,β)-Diphenylethylene

In the Geneva system of nomenclature, an ethylenic hydrocarbon is indicated by changing the end of the name from -ane, for a paraffin, to -ene. Ethylene is called ethene, propylene propene, and the ethylenic hydrocarbon corresponding to octane is an octene. Branched-chain compounds are assigned a basic name corresponding to the longest straight carbon chain, and alkyl groups attached to the chain are considered as substituent groups, with the positions indicated by prefix numbers. The double bond is not a substituent but a functional group, conferring specific reaction functions. The position of the double-bond (or -ene) functional group is indicated by a number, included usually at the end of the name, to show the position in the carbon chain of the first of the two unsaturated carbon atoms. In case of a choice, the number is made as small as possible, as illustrated in the fourth of the examples shown. A hydrocarbon having two double bonds is a diene.

$CH_3CH_2CH{=}CH_2$
Butene-1

$CH_3CH{=}CHCH_3$
Butene-2

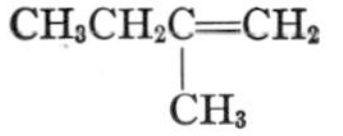

$$\begin{array}{c} CH_3CH_2C{=}CH_2 \\ | \\ CH_3 \end{array}$$
2-Methylbutene-1

$CH_3CH_2CH_2CH{=}CHCH_2CH_3$
Heptene-3 (not -4)

An alcohol is indicated in the Geneva system by change in the suffix from -ane to -anol; for example, methyl alcohol is methanol and ethyl alcohol is ethanol. The designation -ol for the functional hydroxyl group thus again appears at the end, and where necessary the position is indicated by a suffixed number. Examples:

$CH_3CH_2CH_2CH_2OH$
Butanol-1

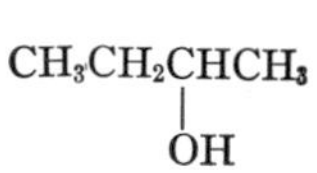

$$\begin{array}{c} CH_3CH_2CHCH_3 \\ | \\ OH \end{array}$$
Butanol-2

The Geneva system provides the convenient generic term alkene, which designates hydrocarbons of the series comprising ethylene and its homologs. A much earlier term that still finds use is olefin (oil-forming substance),

TABLE 3.1. PHYSICAL CONSTANTS OF ALKENES

NAME	FORMULA C_nH_{2n}	CARBON STRUCTURE	M.P., °C.	B.P., °C.	SP. GR., LIQUID
Ethylene	C_2H_4	C=C	−169.4	−102.4	0.6100
Propylene	C_3H_6	C·C=C	−185	−47.7	.6104
Butene-1	C_4H_8	C·C·C=C		−6.5	.6255
Butene-2 (cis[1])	C_4H_8	C·C=C·C	−139.3	−3.7	
Isobutylene	C_4H_8	C·C=C· C	−140.7	−6.6	.6266
Pentene-1	C_5H_{10}	C·C·C·C=C		30.1	.6429
2-Methylbutene-1	C_5H_{10}	C·C·C=C C		31	.6501
3-Methylbutene-1	C_5H_{10}	C·C·C=C C		20.1	.6340
Hexene-1	C_6H_{12}	C·C·C·C·C=C	−138	63.5	.6747
Heptene-1	C_7H_{14}	C·C·C·C·C·C=C	−119	93.1	.6976
Octene-1	C_8H_{16}	C·C·C·C·C·C·C=C	(−104)	122.5	.7159

[1] This designation will be explained in Chapter 11.

based on the fact that gaseous members of the series combine with chlorine to form oily addition products. The ethylenic hydrocarbons, or alkenes, thus are sometimes referred to as olefins or as olefinic hydrocarbons.

Physical Properties. — In the three physical properties listed in Table 3.1 alkenes are hardly distinguishable from the corresponding saturated hydrocarbons. The boiling points are no more than a few degrees below those of alkanes of slightly higher molecular weight, and the densities are a few percent higher; in the first few members of the two series there is even a marked correspondence in the melting points. Cycloalkanes (p. 47) differ more from alkanes than alkenes do, and hence ring formation influences physical properties more than introduction of an ethylene linkage. Hexene and cyclohexane both conform to the type C_nH_{2n}. The formula C_nH_{2n-2} represents either an open-chain diene, a saturated hydrocarbon with two rings, or a hydrocarbon with one double bond and one ring. The heat of combustion of hexene-1 is practically the same as that of *n*-hexane on either a weight or volume basis: 952.6 kg.-cal./mole, 11.32 kg.-cal./g., 7.64 kg.-cal./ml.

SYNTHETIC PREPARATION

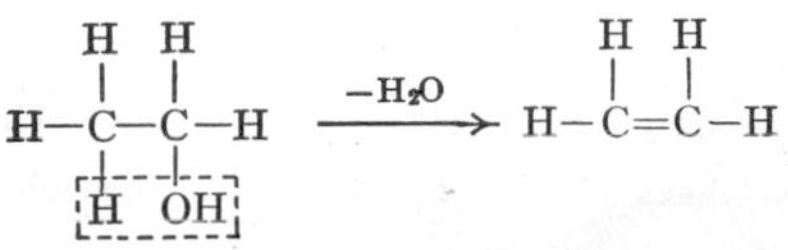

From Alcohols. — The most generally useful method of synthesis of alkenes or olefinic hydrocarbons utilizes an alcohol as a starting material. The hydroxyl group presents a point of vulnerability, as shown by the reaction with hydrobromic or hydriodic acid already cited, in which the original functional group is replaced by halogen. Conversion of an alcohol into an alkene requires simultaneous elimination of the hydroxyl group with a hydrogen from an adjacent carbon atom. By loss of —OH from one carbon and of H— from another ethyl alcohol yields ethylene.

One practicable procedure of catalytic dehydration consists in passing vaporized alcohol through a tube packed with coarse granules of alumina and maintained at a temperature of 350–400° in an electrically heated furnace. The reaction resembles pyrolysis of an alkane, since it involves production of an unsaturated product from a saturated one at an elevated temperature, but the pyrolysis temperature for the alcohol is distinctly lower, and the process is simpler and more uniform. The alcohol can be introduced into the tube at an appropriate rate by distillation; a partial vacuum is sometimes advantageous in providing for removal of the olefin before secondary changes can occur (Fig. 3.1).

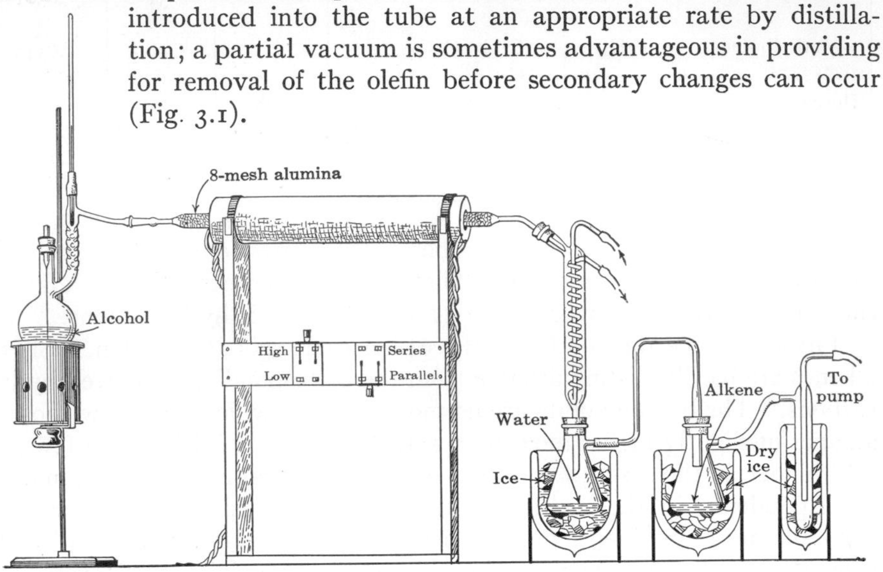

FIG. 3.1. — Apparatus for Dehydration of an Alcohol over Alumina at Reduced Pressure

Examples illustrating results obtainable by catalytic dehydration are as follows:

1. CH_3CH_2OH $\xrightarrow[98\%]{\text{Kaolin or alumina, 350–360°}}$ $CH_2=CH_2$

(Used during the first World War as a source of ethylene for mustard gas)

2.
$$CH_3-\underset{\underset{\displaystyle OH}{|}}{\overset{\overset{\displaystyle CH_3}{|}}{C}}-\underset{\underset{\displaystyle OH}{|}}{\overset{\overset{\displaystyle CH_3}{|}}{C}}-CH_3 \quad \xrightarrow[79-86\%]{Al_2O_3,\ 420-470°} \quad CH_2=\underset{\overset{\displaystyle CH_3}{|}}{C}-\underset{\overset{\displaystyle CH_3}{|}}{C}=CH_2$$

Pinacol   2,3-Dimethylbutadiene-1,3

3. $\xrightarrow[89\%]{Al_2O_3,\ 380-450°}$

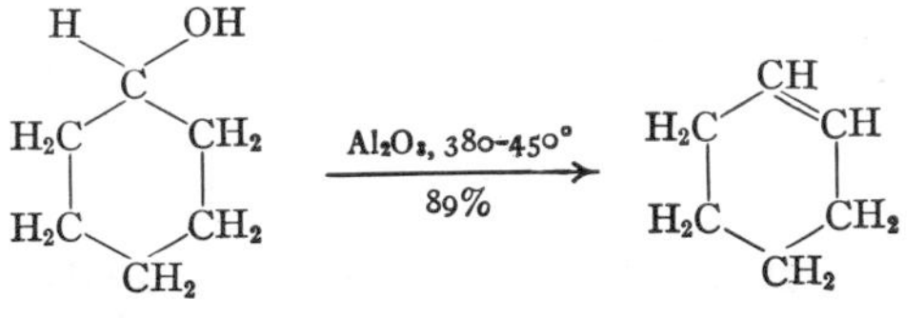

Cyclohexanol   Cyclohexene

Alcohols can be dehydrated at lower temperatures by chemical dehydrating agents, one of the commonest being sulfuric acid. Ethylene can be produced from a mixture of ethyl alcohol and sulfuric acid heated at a temperature of 170°. The yield is not high, owing to by-product formation, and the reaction may involve an intermediate whose presence can be demonstrated at a lower temperature. Sulfuric acid, a component of the intermediate, is a dihydroxy acid conveniently represented by formula I.

$$HO-SO_2-OH \qquad HO-\overset{\overset{\displaystyle O^-}{|}}{\underset{\underset{\displaystyle O}{\|}}{S^+}}-OH$$

$$\text{I} \qquad\qquad \text{II}$$

The representation given in formula II expresses the postulate that the sixth valence of sulfur is polar; the bond S^+—O^- is a semipolar bond. When chilled sulfuric acid is added slowly to alcohol at ice-bath temperature, water is eliminated from the two reactants, and ethylsulfuric acid is formed. The reaction proceeds to completion with

$$CH_3CH_2OH \;+\; HOSO_2OH \underset{\text{Excess } H_2O}{\overset{\text{concd. } H_2SO_4}{\rightleftharpoons}} CH_3CH_2OSO_2OH \;+\; H_2O$$

Ethylsulfuric
acid

use of excess concentrated sulfuric acid at 0°, for the acid absorbs the water formed; the process, however, is an equilibrium, and the conversion can be reversed by use of a large excess of water.

Ethylsulfuric acid, in which one of the hydroxylic hydrogens of sulfuric acid is replaced by an ethyl group, is stable at low temperatures but undergoes decomposition when heated. At an optimum temperature of 170°, the

$$H-\overset{\overset{\displaystyle H}{|}}{\underset{\underset{\displaystyle H}{|}}{C}}-\overset{\overset{\displaystyle H}{|}}{\underset{\underset{\displaystyle H}{|}}{C}}-OSO_2OH \;\xrightarrow{170°}\; CH_2{=}CH_2 \;+\; HOSO_2OH$$

chief organic product of the decomposition is ethylene, formed by loss of the radical —OSO_2OH from one carbon atom and of hydrogen from the adjacent position to produce sulfuric acid. A side reaction consists in formation of diethyl ether (ordinary ether) by the action of alcohol on ethylsulfuric

$$\begin{array}{c} CH_3CH_2OSO_2OH(C_2H_5) \\ + \\ CH_3CH_2OH \end{array} \;\xrightarrow{140°}\; \begin{array}{c} CH_3CH_2 \\ \diagdown \\ \diagup \qquad O \\ CH_3CH_2 \end{array}$$

acid. This reaction can be operated practicably for the preparation of ether by adjusting the proportions of reagents and maintaining a temperature of 140°. The difference in the optimum temperatures for ethylene and ether formation is so slight that each product is a by-product of the production of the other. A third product, diethyl sulfate (b.p. 210°), can be prepared by heating ethylsulfuric acid at a temperature below 140° at a pressure sufficiently reduced to cause diethyl sulfate to distil from the non-volatile acids.

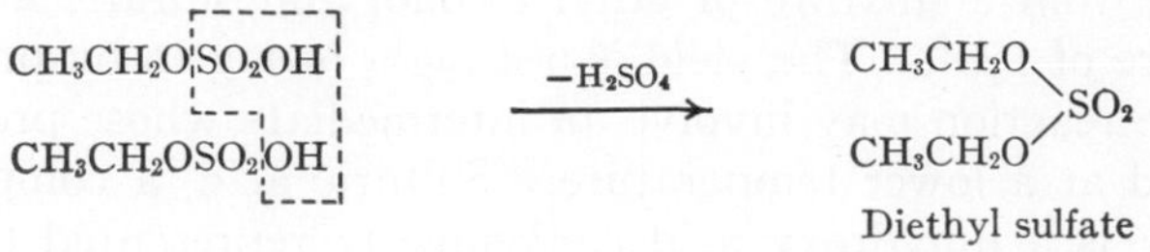

$$CH_3CH_2OSO_2OH$$
$$CH_3CH_2OSO_2OH \xrightarrow{-H_2SO_4} \begin{array}{c} CH_3CH_2O \\ CH_3CH_2O \end{array} SO_2$$

Diethyl sulfate

Dehydration can be effected with phosphorus pentoxide or with strong acids other than sulfuric. An acid like hydrochloric cannot form an intermediate analagous to an alkylsulfuric acid and probably functions as cat-

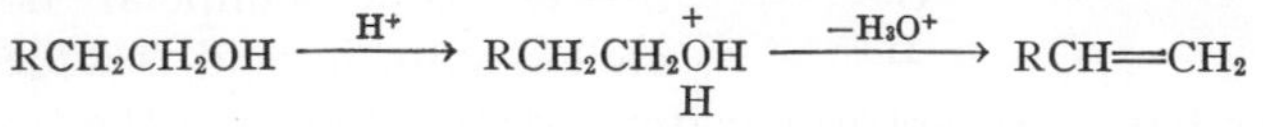

$$RCH_2CH_2OH \xrightarrow{H^+} RCH_2CH_2OH \xrightarrow{-H_3O^+} RCH=CH_2$$
$$\underset{H}{\overset{+}{}}$$

alyst by protonation of the alcoholic oxygen to form an oxonium ion from which the hydronium ion is eliminated.

Alcohols vary in the ease with which they undergo dehydration to alkenes, those of highly branched-chain structure being particularly susceptible. Alcohols are classified as primary, secondary, or tertiary, depending on the number of alkyl groups attached to the carbon atom carrying the hydroxyl group:

RCH₂OH   R₂CHOH   R₃COH

$$RCH_2OH \qquad R_2CHOH \qquad R_3COH$$
Primary alcohol   Secondary alcohol   Tertiary alcohol

Tertiary alcohols are dehydrated most easily, secondary are next, and primary alcohols are least easily converted into alkenes. These differences are illustrated in the accompanying examples. The secondary alcohol shown in

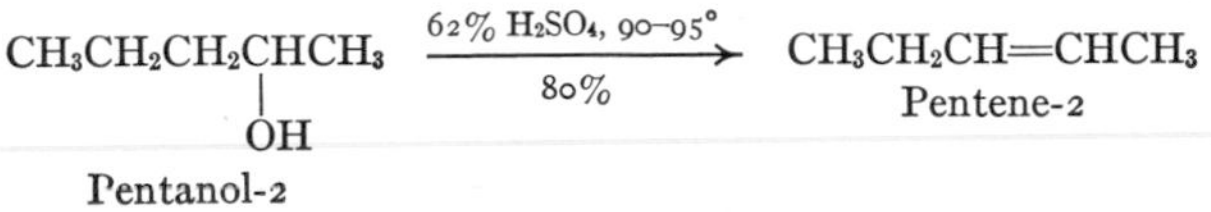

$$CH_3CH_2CH_2CHCH_3 \xrightarrow[80\%]{62\% \ H_2SO_4, \ 90-95°} CH_3CH_2CH=CHCH_3$$
$$|$$
$$OH$$
Pentanol-2   Pentene-2

2.
$$\underset{OH}{\underset{|}{CH_3CH_2\overset{\overset{\displaystyle CH_3}{|}}{C}CH_3}} \xrightarrow[84\%]{46\% \ H_2SO_4, \ 90-95°} CH_3CH=\overset{\overset{\displaystyle CH_3}{|}}{C}CH_3$$
2-Methylbutanol-2   2-Methylbutene-2

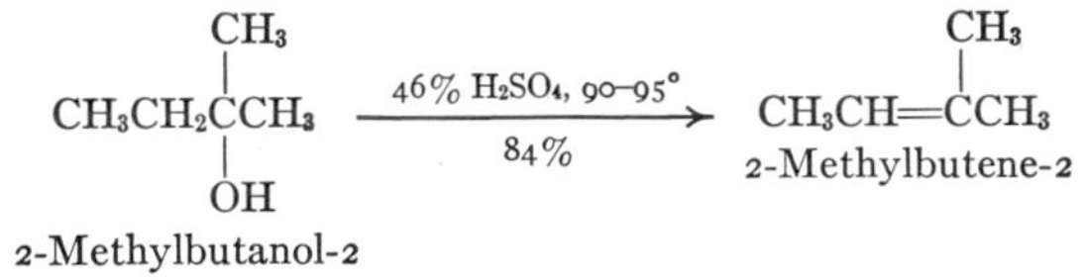

3. 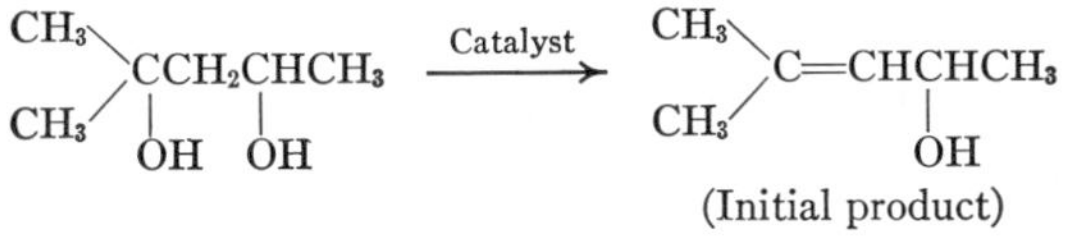
$$\begin{array}{c} CH_3 \\ \diagdown \\ CH_3 \diagup \end{array} \underset{OH \ \ OH}{\underset{|\ \ \ |}{CCH_2CHCH_3}} \xrightarrow{Catalyst} \begin{array}{c} CH_3 \\ \diagdown \\ CH_3 \diagup \end{array} \underset{OH}{\underset{|}{C=CHCHCH_3}}$$
(Initial product)

4.   Cyclohexanol $\xrightarrow[83\%]{95\% \ H_2SO_4, \ 130-140°}$ Cyclohexene

example 1 is dehydrated in 80% yield at the temperature of the steam bath by 62% sulfuric acid, whereas the tertiary alcohol of example 2 affords an olefin in comparable yield at the same temperature by the action of acid

of only 46% strength.   The case of ethyl alcohol, cited above, is representative of the behavior of a primary alcohol; the best results are obtained with
use of 96% sulfuric acid at the higher temperature of 170°.   That a tertiary
alcohol undergoes dehydration more easily than a secondary alcohol is
further demonstrated by the behavior of the dihydroxy compound shown
in example 3.   This substance contains both a tertiary and a secondary
alcoholic group, and on partial dehydration the former is preferentially
eliminated.   Example 4 shows that cyclohexanol can be dehydrated to cyclohexene by sulfuric acid as well as by the catalytic method cited above,
although in slightly lower yield.   This dehydration has been accomplished
also with use of potassium bisulfate ($KHSO_4$), phosphoric acid, iodine, and
oxalic acid, an organic dibasic acid of acidic strength nearly comparable to
that of a mineral acid.

   Dehydrohalogenation. — Introduction of a double bond can be accomplished by treating an alkyl halide with a basic reagent capable of
splitting out the elements of hydrogen halide from adjacent carbon atoms:

$$-\overset{\underset{\displaystyle H}{|}}{\underset{}{C}}-\overset{\underset{\displaystyle X}{|}}{\underset{}{C}}- \;+\; Base \;\longrightarrow\; -\overset{|}{C}=\overset{|}{C}- \;+\; Salt$$

An acid-binding reagent commonly employed is an alcoholic solution of
potassium hydroxide.   Aqueous alkali is less suitable because of lack of
solubility of the alkyl halide in water; alcohol has a satisfactory solvent
action on the organic reagent and also dissolves potassium hydroxide.   The
preparation of an alkene by this method is illustrated by the conversion of
both *n*-propyl and isopropyl iodide into propylene; the yield is notably
better with the secondary than with the primary iodide (temperature in

$$CH_3CH_2CH_2I \qquad\qquad\qquad \overset{\displaystyle I}{\underset{}{CH_3CHCH_3}}$$

alc. KOH | 1. $\longrightarrow CH_3CH{=}CH_2\longleftarrow$ 2. | alc. KOH

36%*   94%

each case, 80–100°).   The tertiary iodide shown in example 3 reacts so
readily that the alkene is obtained simply by addition of the halide dropwise
to boiling water, which retains the hydrogen iodide formed.   The order of
reactivity of halides of primary, secondary, and tertiary structure is thus
the same as that of alcohols.

3.

$$\begin{matrix} CH_3\diagdown \\ C-CH_3 \\ CH_3\diagup\;| \\ I \end{matrix} \;\xrightarrow{H_2O,\;100°}\; \begin{matrix} CH_3\diagdown \\ C{=}CH_2 \\ CH_3\diagup \end{matrix}$$

Isobutylene

   The method finds little use in preparation of ethylenic hydrocarbons

_____

   * The loss in yield is due to the formation of an ether: $CH_3CH_2CH_2I + KOC_2H_5 \rightarrow$
$CH_3CH_2CH_2OC_2H_5$.

themselves, for the required alkyl halides are best obtained from the corresponding alcohols and a shorter route from the alcohol to the alkene is direct dehydration. The occasion for introducing a double bond, however, arises in other series of compounds, and a halogen-containing compound frequently is the most readily available intermediate for preparation of the desired unsaturated substance; for example, a double bond can be introduced into isobutyric acid by bromination, followed by elimination of hydrogen bromide.

$$
\begin{array}{ccc}
\underset{\text{CH}_3}{\overset{\text{CH}_3}{>}}\text{C—COOH} & \xrightarrow[\text{78–80\%}]{\text{25\% aq. NaOH}} & \underset{}{\overset{\text{CH}_3}{|}} \\
\quad\;\;| & & \text{CH}_2\!\!=\!\!\text{C—COOH} \\
\quad\;\text{Br} & & \text{Methacrylic acid} \\
\alpha\text{-Bromoisobutyric acid} & & \text{(m.p. } 15°\text{)}
\end{array}
$$

From a *vicinal*-Dihalide. — A compound in which two halogen atoms are situated on adjacent positions in the carbon chain, and are hence in the same vicinity, is described as a vicinal (or *vic*-) dihalide. The halogen atoms in such a compound can be eliminated simultaneously by treatment with a bivalent metal, particularly zinc. Zinc is capable of stripping off the two

$$
\underset{\substack{|\;\;| \\ \text{Br Br} \\ \textit{vic}\text{-Dibromide}}}{>\!\text{C—C}\!<} \xrightarrow{\;\text{Zn}\;} \underset{\text{Alkene}}{>\!\text{C}\!=\!\text{C}\!<}
$$

halogen atoms at the same time, whereas sodium could react initially with one halogen and give rise to a Wurtz type of coupling. The reaction is not of much use in the actual synthesis of alkenes because the required *vic*-dihalides are not sufficiently available, but it is frequently employed in purification of ethylenic compounds. An alkene can be converted into its bromine-addition product and subsequently regenerated by debromination with zinc dust, with advantages that can be appreciated from consideration of an example. A sample of trimethylethylene contaminated with the corresponding saturated hydrocarbon, 2-methylbutane (isopentane), could not be separated effectively from this substance by distillation because the boil-

$$
\begin{array}{ccc}
\underset{\text{CH}_3}{\overset{\text{CH}_3}{>}}\text{C}\!=\!\text{CHCH}_3 & & \underset{\text{CH}_3}{\overset{\text{CH}_3}{>}}\text{C—CHCH}_3 \\
\text{Trimethylethylene (b.p. 38.6°)} & & \quad\;\;\text{Br Br} \\
 & \xrightarrow{\text{Br}_2} & \text{(b.p. 170–175°; 64–66° at 16 mm.)} \\
\underset{\text{CH}_3}{\overset{\text{CH}_3}{>}}\text{CHCH}_2\text{CH}_3 & & \underset{\text{CH}_3}{\overset{\text{CH}_3}{>}}\text{CHCH}_2\text{CH}_3 \\
\text{2-Methylbutane (b.p. 27.9°)} & & \text{(unchanged)}
\end{array}
$$

ing points lie too close together. If the mixture is treated with bromine without undue exposure to light, the alkene reacts selectively and is converted into a derivative heavier by some 160 units of molecular weight and **consequently having a much higher boiling point. Trimethylethylene di-**

bromide boils at a temperature 140–145° higher than 2-methylbutane, and can be separated easily by distillation; the distillation is conducted in vacuum, for slight decomposition of the halide at the higher temperature is thereby obviated. By treatment of the distilled addition product with zinc dust in alcoholic solution, pure trimethylethylene is regenerated. A similar procedure is applicable to the purification of ethylenic substances that are solids. Thus cholesterol $(C_{27}H_{46}O)$, an unsaturated alcohol found in animal fats, is purified by formation of the sparingly soluble dibromide, crystallization to eliminate more soluble contaminants that do not form dibromides, and regeneration by debromination with zinc dust and acetic acid or with sodium iodide in ethanol:

$$>C-C< \ + \ 2\,NaI \ \longrightarrow \ >C=C< \ + \ 2\,NaBr \ + \ I_2$$
$$\;\;\;\; \overset{|}{Br}\;\overset{|}{Br}$$

REACTIONS

Halogenation. — Ethylene readily adds chlorine or bromine, but not the less reactive iodine. Addition of bromine to a double bond to give a *vic*-dibromide is a general reaction, characteristic of the great majority of compounds containing the ethylenic linkage and employed as a test for

$$>C=C< \ + \ Br_2 \ \longrightarrow \ >C-C<$$
$$\overset{|}{Br}\;\overset{|}{Br}$$
$$\textit{vic-Dibromide}$$

unsaturation. The reaction can be conducted with a solution of bromine in carbon tetrachloride or chloroform, and a positive test is indicated by discharge of the red color due to bromine. Halogenation proceeds readily without illumination or deliberate introduction of a catalyst. Exceptions to the generality of bromine addition are encountered in rare instances with substances of specialized structure. Thus tetraphenylethylene fails to absorb bromine and takes up the more reactive chlorine only to a small extent in an equilibrium reaction:

$$\begin{matrix} C_6H_5 \\ C_6H_5 \end{matrix} C=C \begin{matrix} C_6H_5 \\ C_6H_5 \end{matrix} \ + \ Cl_2 \ \rightleftharpoons \ \begin{matrix} C_6H_5 \\ C_6H_5 \end{matrix} \overset{|}{C}-\overset{|}{C} \begin{matrix} C_6H_5 \\ C_6H_5 \end{matrix}$$
$$\text{Tetraphenylethylene} \qquad\qquad\qquad \overset{}{Cl}\;\;\overset{}{Cl}$$

Evidence cited in Chapter 13 shows that addition of halogen to an ethylene in a polar solvent is not a simple one-step process involving opening of the double bond with simultaneous affixment of halogen atoms to the adjacent free positions but that the halogen atoms are affixed one at a time, for example, by the following mechanism:

1. $\quad >C::C< \ + \ Br:Br \longrightarrow \ >\overset{Br}{C}:C< \ + \ :Br: \ \longrightarrow \ >\overset{Br}{C}:\underset{Br}{C}<$

$$\qquad\qquad\qquad\qquad (a) \qquad\qquad (b) \qquad\qquad (c)$$

In the initial step one bromine atom of the bromine molecule retains the covalent pair of electrons and becomes a bromide ion (b), while the other, defined as an electrophilic agent, accepts a pair of electrons from the double bond and becomes bonded to one of the carbon atoms. One electron of the pair accepted by bromine originally belonged to the second double-bonded carbon atom, and hence this atom acquires a positive charge and the intermediate is a carbonium ion (a). This ion (a) then combines with bromide ion, which is believed to approach on the side opposite to that occupied by the first bromine atom, with formation of the dibromide (c). In a simple hydrocarbon such as propylene the reaction product would be the same whether the approach is on the same or opposite side, since both structures represent one and the same substance. However, in olefins of certain types

$$
\begin{array}{ccc}
& \text{Br} & \\
& | & \\
\text{CH}_3\text{—CH—CH}_2 & = & \text{CH}_3\text{—CH—CH}_2 \\
| & & | \quad | \\
\text{Br} & & \text{Br} \quad \text{Br}
\end{array}
$$

two addition products are possible of different orientation in space, and the one actually formed is that with the bromine atoms in opposite orientation. The same mechanism probably represents the true path of reaction in the simpler instances where the two modes of reaction are not distinguishable.

The electronic formula for the intermediate carbonium ion shows that the positively charged carbon atom is surrounded by only six electrons. A carbon atom with only an electron sextet seeks two electrons for completion of the octet. A charge on a carbon atom also represents a condition of instability; hence a carbonium ion ordinarily is a highly reactive species of fleeting existence.

$$
\begin{array}{c}
:\overset{..}{\text{Br}}:_+ \\
\text{H}:\overset{..}{\text{C}}:\text{C}:\text{H} \\
\overset{..}{\text{H}}\ \text{H}
\end{array}
$$
Carbonium ion

The initial step in bromine addition as formulated in 1 is often represented for convenience as an attack of the ethylene by a bromine cation, as in 2, but this should be regarded as an abbreviation of a concept that is expressed more adequately by equation 1. The reaction involves molecular bromine and, if the bromine atom within the dotted lines accepts the pair of electrons from carbon synchronously with separation of the second bromine atom with the pair of bromine-shared electrons, Br^+ may have no actual existence. The symbol Br^+ in equation 2 thus represents merely a possible transient phase of the electrophilic (electron-seeking) agent. If the groups R and R' attached to the double bond attract electrons from the doubly

$$
2. \qquad R_2C{=}CR_2' \ + \ \underset{\substack{\text{Bromonium} \\ \text{ion}}}{Br^+} \ \longrightarrow \ \underset{\substack{\text{Carbonium} \\ \text{ion}}}{\overset{\displaystyle \text{Br}}{\underset{|}{R_2C}}{-}CR_2'{}^+}
$$

bound carbons and produce an electron drift away from these centers, combination with positive bromine would occur less readily; if the attached groups are electron-repelling, the process would be accelerated. Propylene, with one methyl substituent, adds bromine twice as fast as ethylene, and the rate of bromination of tetramethylethylene ($R = R' = CH_3$) is fourteen times that of ethylene. Thus methyl is electron-repelling as compared with hydrogen. The fact that acrylic acid, $CH_2=CHCOOH$, reacts very slowly with bromine shows that the carboxyl group is electron-attracting.

Addition of Hydrogen Halides. — Hydrogen halides add to alkenes with attachment of hydrogen to one of the unsaturated carbon atoms and halogen to the other. The order of reactivity of the halides is the reverse

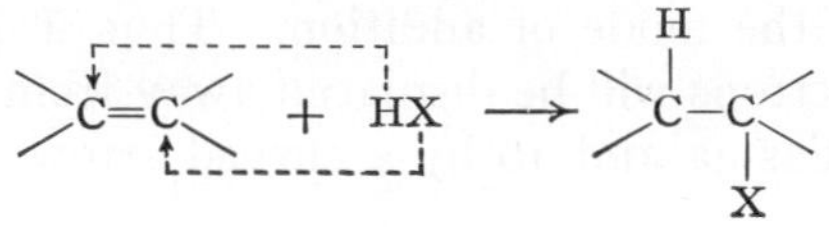

of that of the corresponding halogens, namely: HI > HBr > HCl. That chlorine has pronounced affinity for other reagents means that the compound which it forms with hydrogen is a comparatively stable one in which the chlorine–hydrogen bond is not easily severed; the relatively inert iodine forms with hydrogen a looser combination in which the constituent elements can part company more readily and enter into either additions or substitutions. Ethylene gas is not absorbed by concentrated hydrochloric acid but reacts with both hydrogen bromide and hydrogen iodide in concentrated aqueous solutions; higher homologs of ethylene are more reactive and usually add hydrogen chloride.

With an unsymmetrical olefin, where two possible modes of addition are available, the reaction ordinarily follows a course defined by an empirical generalization known as the **Markownikoff[1] rule**, which states that, in a normal addition, the hydrogen becomes affixed to the carbon carrying the greater number of hydrogen atoms. Propylene adds hydrogen bromide to give isopropyl bromide as the preponderant product, accompanied by a few percent of the alternate product *n*-propyl bromide. Isobutylene adds in

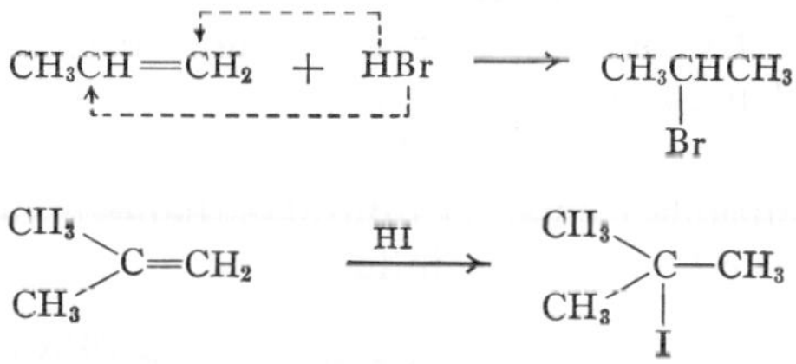

such a way that the halogen of the hydrogen halide becomes attached to the carbon carrying two methyl groups.

The facts cited find a simple explanation in the modern theory of the reaction mechanism. Like the addition of bromine, the addition of hydrogen halide is believed to be a two-step process consisting in an electrophilic

---

[1] Vladimir W. Markownikoff, 1838–1904; b. Russia; Kasan, Odessa, Moscow; *Ber.*, **38**, 4249 (1905); *J. Chem. Soc.*, **87**, 597 (1905)

attack of one carbon atom by a proton with production of an intermediate ion (3). In an unsymmetrical ethylene, say one having the group R on

3.
$$\text{>C=C<} \; + \; H^+ \; \longrightarrow \; \underset{\underset{H}{|}}{\text{>C^+-C<}} \; \xrightarrow{Br^-} \; \underset{\underset{H}{|}}{\overset{\overset{Br}{|}}{\text{>C-C<}}}$$

Carbonium ion

carbon atom C_1 and the group R' on C_2, if one group has a greater tendency to attract or repel electrons than the other a displacement of electrons may occur and determine the mode of addition. Thus if R is more electron-repelling than R', electrons will be displaced away from C_1 and toward C_2, as indicated in formulas 4a and 4b by a curved arrow. The displacement

4.
$$\underset{1 \quad \;\; 2}{RCH\!:\!:\!CHR'} \qquad \underset{1 \quad \;\; 2}{RCH\!=\!\!CHR'} \qquad \underset{1 \quad \;\; 2}{\overset{+}{RCH}\!-\!\overset{-}{CHR'}}$$
$$\quad (a) \qquad\qquad\qquad (b) \qquad\qquad\qquad (c)$$

may not reach the complete stage of polarization, pictured in (c), but the tendency is in this direction and C_2 is relatively negative. Since the methyl group of propylene is electron-repelling, as compared with hydrogen, the electron displacement in this case causes the unsubstituted carbon atom to be the more negative of the pair (5), and hence this is the point of attack by

5.
$$CH_3CH\!=\!\!CH_2 \xrightarrow{H^+} CH_3\overset{+}{CH}\!-\!CH_3 \xrightarrow{Br^-} \underset{\underset{Br}{|}}{CH_3CHCH_3}$$

the proton. The addition thus proceeds according to the Markownikoff rule because of the electron displacement produced by the methyl group. The electron-repelling effect of methyl and higher alkyl substituents further accounts for the fact, noted above, that homologs of ethylene add hydrogen halides more readily than ethylene itself does.

In 1933 Kharasch discovered that the normal mode of addition of hydrogen bromide frequently can be reversed in the presence of a peroxide catalyst. Thus propylene, when treated with hydrogen bromide in the presence of a trace of benzoyl peroxide, yields n-propyl bromide. Vinyl bromide under ordinary conditions yields 1,1-dibromoethane, in accordance with the Markownikoff rule, but under the influence of a peroxide catalyst affords

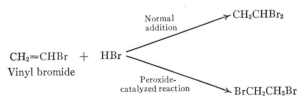

the 1,2-isomer. Unlike the ordinary reaction, the peroxide-catalyzed addition does not proceed by an ionic mechanism but rather involves free-radical intermediates. Thus factors other than electron-displacements determine the direction of addition. Whereas the addition of hydrogen bromide is usually subject to reversal of direction in the presence of peroxide, most other unsymmetrical reagents (hydrogen chloride, hydrogen iodide, sulfuric acid, hypochlorite) add in the same way (normal) whether a peroxide is present or absent.

Sulfuric Acid. — Whereas liquid alkanes when shaken with concentrated sulfuric acid in the cold are unaffected and separate from the acid in an upper layer, alkenes combine with the acid and dissolve in the acid layer. This differentiation provides a convenient method of freeing saturated hydrocarbons from traces of unsaturated substances. The reaction with an alkene is an addition, in which a proton from the acid combines with one center of unsaturation and the anion of the acid becomes joined to the other. Ethylene yields ethylsulfuric acid, also obtainable, as described above, by treatment of ethyl alcohol with cold concentrated sulfuric acid. Since the latter reaction is reversible, ethylene can be converted through formation

$$CH_2\!\!=\!\!CH_2 \ + \ HOSO_2OH \ \xrightarrow{\text{o-15}^\circ} \ CH_3CH_2OSO_2OH$$
$$\text{Ethylsulfuric acid}$$

and hydrolysis of the ethylsulfuric acid into ethyl alcohol. This procedure represents the reverse of reactions applicable to the preparation of ethylene,

$$CH_2\!\!=\!\!CH_2 \ \underset{170^\circ}{\overset{H_2SO_4,\ \text{o-15}^\circ}{\rightleftharpoons}} \ C_2H_5OSO_2OH \ \underset{H_2SO_4,\ \text{o-15}^\circ}{\overset{H_2O}{\rightleftharpoons}} \ C_2H_5OH$$

and this example of a complete cyclic process illustrates the importance of temperature and concentration in the course of reactions.

The net result of addition of sulfuric acid to an alkene and hydrolysis of the product is hydration of the double bond, and this reaction is an important route to alcohols. Sulfuric acid, an unsymmetrical reagent, reacts with an unsymmetrical alkene in accordance with the Markownikoff rule, that is, the anionic fragment (like Br of HBr) adds to the carbon poorer in hydrogen. An interesting consequence of this fact is that primary alcohols can be

$$\begin{array}{c} CH_3 \\ \diagdown \\ CH_3 \diagup \end{array}\!\!C\!\!=\!\!CHCH_3 \ \xrightarrow{HOSO_2OH} \ \begin{array}{c} CH_3 \\ \diagdown \\ CH_3 \diagup \end{array}\!\!\underset{OSO_2OH}{\overset{}{C}}CH_2CH_3$$

isomerized to the corresponding secondary alcohols by suitable application of the sulfuric acid reactions, as illustrated for n-propyl alcohol.

$$CH_3CH_2CH_2OH \ \xrightarrow{H_2SO_4,\ \text{heat}} \ CH_3CH\!\!=\!\!CH_2 \ \xrightarrow{H_2SO_4} \ \underset{OSO_2OH}{CH_3CHCH_3} \ \xrightarrow{\text{Hydrol.}} \ \underset{OH}{CH_3CHCH_3}$$
n-Propyl alcohol

$$\text{Isopropyl alcohol}$$

Hypohalite Additions. — Ethylene reacts with an alkaline solution of chlorine to give ethylene chlorohydrin: $ClCH_2CH_2OH$. The reaction was once thought to involve addition of hypochlorous acid, formed in the equilibrium:

$$Cl_2 + HOH \; \overset{CH^-}{\rightleftharpoons} \; HCl + HOCl$$

However, evidence cited in Chapter 13 shows that the reaction is a two-step process in which chlorine cation attacks one of the carbon atoms to produce an ionic intermediate, which in the alkaline medium combines with hydroxide

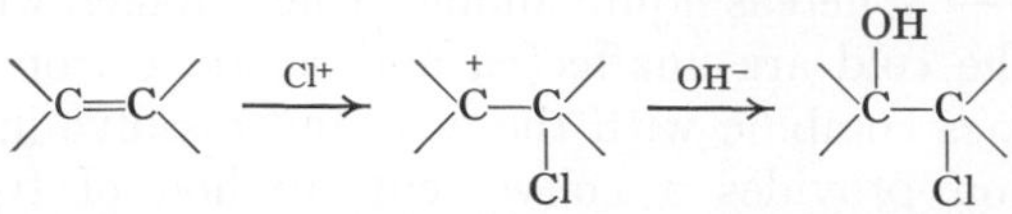

$$\underset{}{>}C=C\underset{}{<} \; \xrightarrow{Cl^+} \; \underset{\underset{Cl}{|}}{>}C-C\underset{}{<} \; \xrightarrow{OH^-} \; \underset{\underset{Cl}{|}}{\overset{\overset{OH}{|}}{>C-C<}}$$

Chlorohydrin

ion. This mechanism explains why in an addition to an unsymmetrical olefin the hydroxyl group, like the bromine of hydrogen bromide, becomes affixed to the carbon poorer in hydrogen. In propylene the displacement produced by the electron-repelling methyl group renders the terminal carbon susceptible to attack by positive chlorine, and the hydroxyl group thus appears on the central carbon atom.

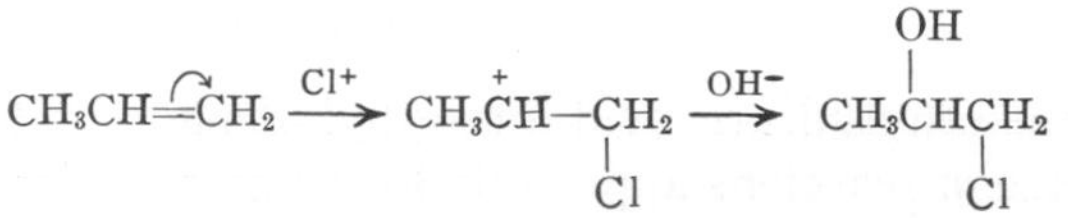

$$CH_3CH \overset{\frown}{=} CH_2 \; \xrightarrow{Cl^+} \; \underset{\underset{Cl}{|}}{CH_3\overset{+}{C}H-CH_2} \; \xrightarrow{OH^-} \; \underset{\underset{Cl}{|}}{\overset{\overset{OH}{|}}{CH_3CHCH_2}}$$

Propylene chlorohydrin

Hypobromous acid adds similarly to give bromohydrins. The halohydrins have certain uses in synthetic operations because they contain two reactive functional groups. Treatment of ethylene chlorohydrin with strong alkali results in elimination of the elements of hydrogen chloride between

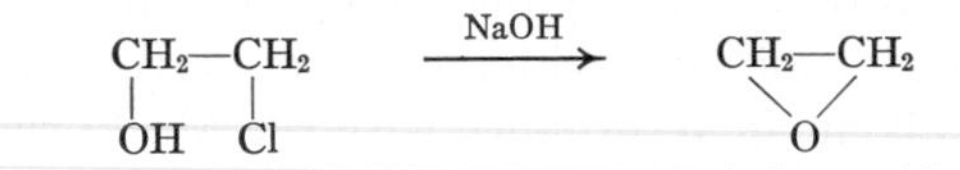

$$\underset{\underset{OH \;\; Cl}{|\;\;\;\;\;\;|}}{CH_2-CH_2} \; \xrightarrow{NaOH} \; \underset{\underset{O}{\diagdown\diagup}}{CH_2-CH_2}$$

Ethylene chlorohydrin   Ethylene oxide

the two functional groups with the production of ethylene oxide. Homologous alkylene oxides are obtainable from the corresponding chlorohydrins; bromohydrins react similarly.

Hydrogenation. — Ethylenic hydrocarbons add hydrogen under the influence of a suitable catalyst, and the process of saturating a double bond with hydrogen is called catalytic hydrogenation. Ethylene and hydrogen

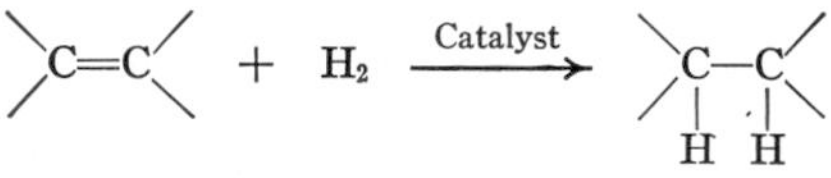

$$\underset{}{>}C=C\underset{}{<} \; + \; H_2 \; \xrightarrow{Catalyst} \; \underset{\underset{H \;\; H}{|\;\;\;\; \cdot |}}{>C-C<}$$

show no tendency to combine in the absence of a catalyst and indeed constitute products of the cracking of ethane at high temperatures. Certain metals in a finely divided condition function as catalysts capable of activating both the olefin and the hydrogen gas to the point of promoting an inter-

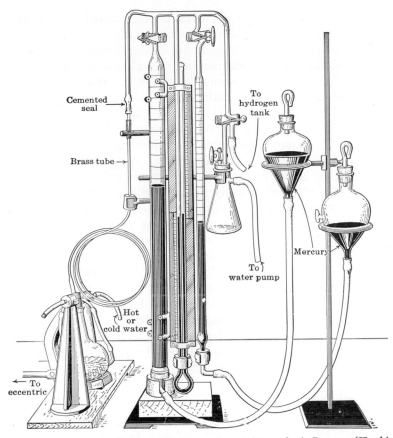

FIG. 3.2. — Apparatus for Catalytic Hydrogenation at Atmospheric Pressure (Hershberg)

Hydrogen, introduced to the shaker flask through a flexible tube, is taken from either the large or the small burette; the volume of reserve gas present at any time is read on the burette after adjusting the appropriate leveling bulb to a point where the mercury is at the same level in the two arms of the central manometer tube.

action.   Combination between the reactants appears to be dependent upon their adsorption on the active surface of the catalyst, and the activity of a given metal increases with increased surface area per unit of weight.   The most potent hydrogenation catalysts are prepared from the noble metals platinum and palladium.   In one procedure (R. Adams[2]) chloroplatinic acid is fused with sodium nitrate; the resulting brown platinum oxide catalyst is added to a solution of the compound to be hydrogenated, and the mixture is shaken with hydrogen; the oxide is first reduced to a very fine black suspension of platinum, which then functions as catalyst for the addition of hydrogen to the double bond.   Another method is addition of a reducing agent to an aqueous solution of platinum or palladium chloride in which finely

[2] Roger Adams, b. 1889 Boston; Ph.D. Harvard (Torrey, Richards); Univ. Illinois

divided charcoal is suspended; the metal is precipitated in an active condition on the surface of the minute charcoal particles.

Platinum and palladium catalysts are active enough to promote hydrogenation in solution at temperatures from 0–90° and with a hydrogen pressure only slightly above one atmosphere; the reaction is conducted in a shaking apparatus capable of maintaining intimate contact between the gaseous, liquid, and solid phases (Fig. 3.2). Catalysts of a less active type are obtainable from the base metals chromium and nickel, and the lower degree of activity is compensated for by conducting the reactions at elevated temperatures and high pressures (Ipatieff[3]). An efficient copper—chromium oxide catalyst is widely used in high-pressure hydrogenations conducted in a special alloy-steel, electrically heated bomb mounted in a mechanical rocker (Adkins[4]); hydrogenations ordinarily are conducted at temperatures of 150 to 250° and pressures of 3000 to 5000 lbs. per sq. in. A special nickel catalyst discovered by M. Raney (1927) possesses such remarkable activity that it will promote many hydrogenations at room temperature and at pressures of no more than 50–100 lbs. per sq. in. Raney nickel catalyst is prepared by treating a nickel—aluminum alloy with warm sodium hydroxide solution, which dissolves the aluminum and leaves the nickel as a black pyrophoric suspension. In the industry hydrogenations usually are conducted in the vapor phase (Sabatier[5]), for this technique lends itself to continuous processes; a mixture of the vaporized unsaturated compound with hydrogen is passed over a base-metal catalyst (Ni) at high temperatures (300°).

Hydrogenation is applicable to almost all ethylenic compounds, including unsaturated alcohols, acids, etc., as well as to alkenes, and finds many useful applications. The conversion of alkenes into alkanes is an important step in synthesis. An alcohol can be converted into an alkane of the same carbon content via the alkyl halide by methods described in Chapter 2, but an often preferred route is dehydration to the alkene and catalytic

$$CH_3CH_2CH_2CHCH_2CH_3 \xrightarrow{-H_2O} \begin{Bmatrix} CH_3CH_2CH{=}CHCH_2CH_3 \\ CH_3CH_2CH_2CH{=}CHCH_3 \end{Bmatrix} \xrightarrow{H_2,\ Pt} CH_3CH_2CH_2CH_2CH_2CH_3$$

$$\underset{\substack{| \\ OH \\ \text{Hexanol-3}}}{} \qquad\qquad\qquad\qquad\qquad\qquad\qquad\qquad\qquad\qquad\qquad \text{\textit{n}-Hexane}$$

hydrogenation, as illustrated in the example (it is immaterial that dehydration gives a mixture of hexene-2 and hexene-3, for they both yield n-hexane on hydrogenation).

Quantitative microhydrogenation is used for determination of the number of double bonds in unsaturated compounds. If a hydrocarbon of the

---

[3] Vladimir N. Ipatieff, 1867–1952; b. Moscow; St. Petersburg, Northwestern Univ; *Nature*, **171**, 151 (1953)

[4] Homer Adkins, 1892–1949; b. Newport, Ohio; Ph.D. Ohio State Univ. (Evans); Univ. Wisconsin

[5] Paul Sabatier, 1854–1941; Ph.D. Paris; Toulouse; Nobel Prize 1912; *J. Am. Chem. Soc.* **66**, 1615 (1944)

formula C_nH_m contains x double bonds, the number of rings (y) can be calculated from the expression: $y = n - m/2 - x + 1$.

Oxidation. — Alkenes are so sensitive to oxidizing agents that a simple qualitative test based upon the rapid decoloration of a dilute aqueous solution of potassium permanganate and sulfuric acid provides a useful method of characterizing ethylenic hydrocarbons and other unsaturated substances or of detecting traces of alkenes in samples of alkanes. The initial reaction has been established in experiments conducted at 0° with alkaline permanganate, which is more mild in action than permanganate in an acidic medium. By operating under these controlled conditions and avoiding excess reagent it is possible to isolate as the primary reaction product a saturated dihydroxy compound, or glycol. Ethylene gives ethylene glycol, propylene

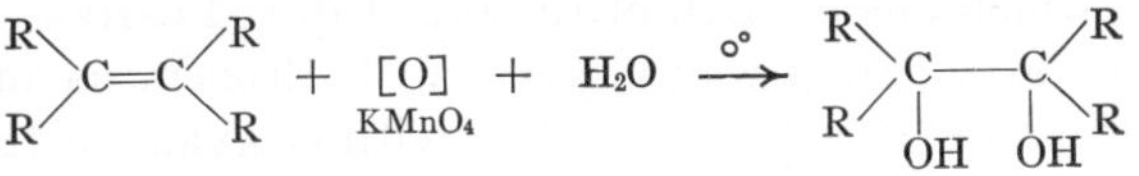

$$\begin{array}{c}R \\ R\end{array}C=C\begin{array}{c}R \\ R\end{array} + \underset{KMnO_4}{[O]} + H_2O \xrightarrow{0°} \begin{array}{c}R \\ R\end{array}\underset{OH}{C}-\underset{OH}{C}\begin{array}{c}R \\ R\end{array}$$

Glycol

gives propylene glycol. The process involves addition to the double bond of two hydroxyl groups, derived from the combination of an oxygen atom supplied by the permanganate with a molecule of water. Hydroxylation of the double bond also can be accomplished in many instances by warming the unsaturated compound in acetic acid solution with hydrogen peroxide, and this reagent has the advantage of being without further action on the initial

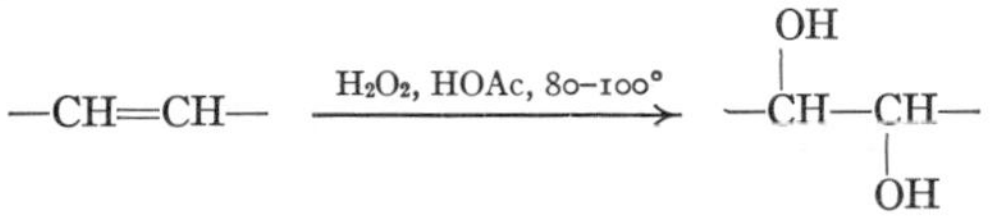

$$-CH=CH- \xrightarrow{H_2O_2,\ HOAc,\ 80-100°} \underset{OH}{-CH}-\underset{OH}{CH}-$$

product. Glycols are readily attacked further by permanganate, and hence this reagent must be used in limited amounts. Glycols also arise by hydrolysis of oxides, which in turn can be made by the action of perbenzoic acid on an alkene.

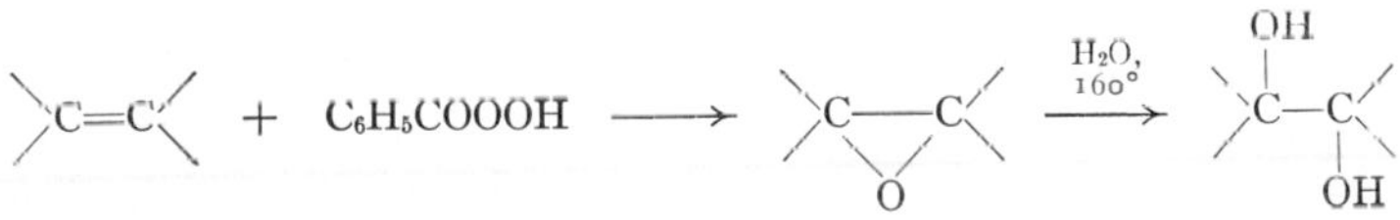

$$C=C + C_6H_5COOOH \longrightarrow \underset{O}{C-C} \xrightarrow[160°]{H_2O,} \underset{OH}{C-C}$$

Perbenzoic acid   Oxide

When an alkene is oxidized without cooling with all the alkaline permanganate that it will consume or when it is oxidized exhaustively with acidified permanganate, with chromic acid in acetic acid solution, or with potassium dichromate and sulfuric acid, the intermediary glycol is destroyed, and the end result is severance of the carbon linkage at the point of the original double bond with production of two oxidized fragments. A symmetrical alkene (I) affords two identical fragments having a carboxyl group,

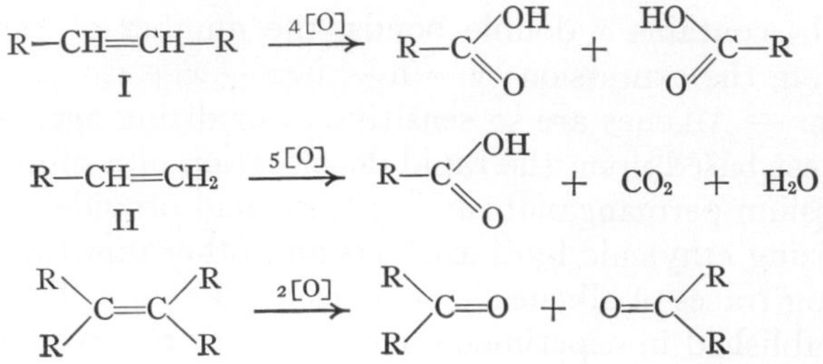

$$R-CH=CH-R \xrightarrow{4[O]} R-C\diagdown_{O}^{OH} + \diagup_{O}^{HO}C-R$$

$$\text{I}$$

$$R-CH=CH_2 \xrightarrow{5[O]} R-C\diagdown_{O}^{OH} + CO_2 + H_2O$$

$$\text{II}$$

$$\diagup_{R}^{R}C=C\diagup_{R}^{R} \xrightarrow{2[O]} \diagup_{R}^{R}C=O + O=C\diagup_{R}^{R}$$

$$\text{III}$$

for the limit of oxidation of the group —C(H)= is —C(OH)=O. If the alkene has a terminal double bond (II), exhaustive oxidation of the end unit containing a lone carbon atom gives carbon dioxide. A third structural type is that in which one or both of the unsaturated carbon atoms are substituted by two alkyl groups and carry no hydrogen, as in III. Here a terminal point in the oxidation is reached with cleavage of the double bond and production of a substance having doubly bound oxygen attached to the originally ethylenic carbon; such a compound, $R_2C=O$, is a ketone.

Exhaustive oxidation, involving as it does fission of an unsaturated compound between the unsaturated centers, provides an experimental method of locating these centers and hence of determining the structures of unsaturated substances. The three butylenes IV–VI, for example, give characteristic oxidation products that not only locate the positions of the double bonds but also fix the nature of the carbon chains. The first isomer (IV) yields a three-carbon acid and carbon dioxide, a result indicative of a chain

$$CH_3CH_2CH=CH_2 \xrightarrow{[O]} CH_3CH_2COOH + CO_2$$

$$\text{IV}$$

$$CH_3CH=CHCH_3 \xrightarrow{[O]} 2\,CH_3COOH$$

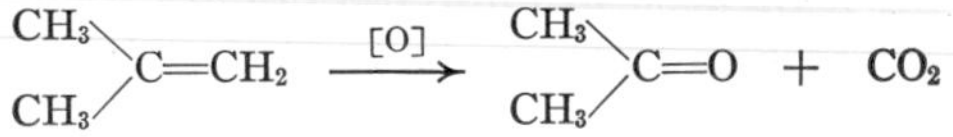

$$\text{V}$$

$$\diagup_{CH_3}^{CH_3}C=CH_2 \xrightarrow{[O]} \diagup_{CH_3}^{CH_3}C=O + CO_2$$

$$\text{VI}$$

of four carbons with a terminal double bond, C·C·C:C. Production of a single two-carbon acid identifies the structure V, and formation, in the last instance, of the three-carbon ketone acetone along with carbon dioxide fixes the structure as having a branched chain and a terminal doubly bound methylene group.

Oxidation with excess permanganate or chromic acid is subject to some limitation, as applied to determination of structure, because it is not entirely selective. Thus primary and secondary alcohols are readily oxidized by the same reagents. A more selective method of characterizing ethylenic compounds is ozonization. Ozone, produced in amounts up to 6–8% by passing a stream of oxygen through a generator in which it is submitted to an electric discharge (Fig. 3.3), adds quantitatively to the double bond of an

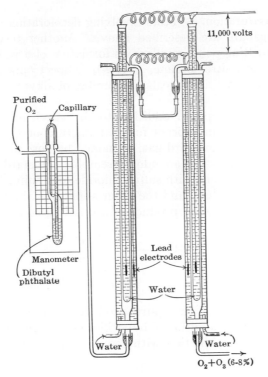

FIG. 3.3. — Ozone Generator, with Flowmeter for the Entering Oxygen

alkene to give an ozonide. The ozonides usually are not isolated, for they

are for the most part viscous oils or glasses, sometimes of explosive properties, but they can be characterized adequately by identifying the products of their decomposition by water or by catalytic hydrogenation. Ozone is a more specific reagent for the double bond than the above-mentioned oxidizing agents and does not attack alcohols. The normal mode of action involves addition, and is not accompanied by subsequent secondary oxidation. Thus hydrogen atoms attached to the unsaturated centers are undisturbed, and it is possible to isolate reaction products having the —CH=O, or aldehyde group; with permanganate such substances are converted into acids

Tests for Unsaturation. — Tests involving decoloration of bromine and of acid permanganate are described above. Another test, conveniently conducted in a melting point capillary, is formation of a yellow complex of an alkene with tetranitromethane, $C(NO_2)_4$. Spectrophotometric determination of the color density reveals the number of alkyl substituents on an isolated double bond.

Mustard Gas. — A special addition to the ethylenic double bond is utilized in the Levinstein process for manufacture of the highly potent combat agent known as mustard gas, so named because in high concentrations the crude product has an odor resembling mustard. The process consists in treating ethylene with sulfur chloride; one sulfur becomes linked to two hydrocarbon residues, and the other appears in the free form and is retained in the crude reaction product in a colloidal state.

$$\begin{matrix} CH_2{=}CH_2 \\ CH_2{=}CH_2 \end{matrix} \ + \ S_2Cl_2 \ \longrightarrow \ \begin{matrix} ClCH_2CH_2 \\ ClCH_2CH_2 \end{matrix}\!\!\Big\rangle S \ + \ S$$

Mustard gas
(β,β'-dichloroethyl sulfide)

In a second process, which gives a purer product that is less readily detected, ethylene is converted by addition of hypochlorous acid into ethylene chlorohydrin, and this on combination with sodium sulfide yields β-thiodiglycol

$$\begin{matrix} HOCH_2CH_2Cl \\ HOCH_2CH_2Cl \end{matrix} \ + \ Na_2S \ \longrightarrow \ \begin{matrix} HOCH_2CH_2 \\ HOCH_2CH_2 \end{matrix}\!\!\Big\rangle S \ \xrightarrow{HCl} \ \text{Mustard gas}$$

β-Thiodiglycol

(β,β'-dihydroxyethyl sulfide). This intermediate, being nontoxic, can be prepared and handled with safety prior to conversion to mustard gas in a final step consisting in treatment with dry hydrogen chloride gas.

β,β'-Dichloroethyl sulfide is a high-boiling vesicant liquid with low vapor pressure; it is not a true gas, but is so designated because low concentrations in the air over a battle area can be highly effective. The constants reported for pure mustard gas are: b.p. 217.5°, m.p. 14.4°, sp. gr. 1.27. The substance made its first appearance in warfare in a prolonged series of artillery bombardments against the British front at Ypres, Flanders, in July, 1917, and for a time took a heavy toll of casualties.

RESONANCE THEORY

Conjugated Dienes. — Compounds such as pentadiene-1,4 ($CH_2{=}CHCH_2CH{=}CH_2$) and hexadiene-1,5 ($CH_2{=}CHCH_2CH_2CH{=}CH_2$), in which two equivalent double bonds are separated by one or more saturated carbon atoms, present no novel features and behave as expected from analogy with monoolefins. The two double bonds would be expected to absorb bromine, hydrogen, or hydrogen bromide at the same rate, and such is the case. A different situation is encountered in butadiene-1,3, which has a pair of doubly bonded carbon atoms adjacent to each other. Buta-diene is known as a conjugated diene, because in characteristic addition reactions the two centers of unsaturation function as a unit rather than as isolated double bonds. When butadiene is treated with bromine, the first molecular equivalent of reagent is taken up so much more rapidly than the second that a dibromide fraction is easily isolated. The 1,2-dibromide is a minor component of this fraction; the principal component carries bromine atoms not on adjacent carbon atoms but at the terminal positions 1 and 4.

$$CH_2{=}CHCH{=}CH_2 \xrightarrow{\text{Br}_2} BrCH_2CH{=}CHCH_2Br + CH_2{=}CHCHBrCH_2Br$$

1,4-addition   1,2,-addition

(major product)   (minor product)

The main reaction is thus a 1,4-addition to the conjugated system and in-volves disappearance of both original double bonds with establishment of a new double bond at the 2,3-position.

The special mode of addition of butadiene is associated with special characteristics of the molecule disclosed by physical measurements. Ther-mochemical data show that butadiene is significantly more stable, in the sense of having a lower energy content, than dienes with isolated (non-conjugated) double bonds; and electron-diffraction measurements reveal an abnormality in bond length, defined as the distance between atomic centers. The normal bond length for the C—C link is 1.54 Å and for the isolated C=C link the distance is 1.34 Å. In butadiene the central bond in the molecule, represented in the ordinary formula as a single link, is found actually to have a bond distance of 1.46 Å, intermediate between a double and a single bond; the two terminal bonds are somewhat longer than an isolated double bond. The evidence suggests that the three bonds linking the carbon atoms are neither true double nor true single bonds but some-thing of an intermediate character.

The resonance theory accounts for the facts cited on the postulate of certain redistributions of electrons. Thus redistribution of the electrons

$$CH_2\!:\!CH\!:\!CH\!:\!CH_2 \leftrightarrow CH_2\!:\!CH\!:\!:\!CH\!:\!CH_2 \leftrightarrow \overset{+}{C}H_2\!:\!CH\!:\!:\!CH\!:\!\overset{-}{C}H_2 \leftrightarrow \overset{-}{C}H_2\!:\!CH\!:\!:\!CH\!:\!\overset{+}{C}H_2$$

(a)   (b)   (c)   (d)

in formula (a) in the directions indicated by the dotted lines (one electron of each double bond moved to the center) would give structure (b), which has a central double bond, two terminal single bonds, and terminal carbon atoms each having an unpaired electron. An electron transfer in (b) from one terminal carbon atom to the other could give a polarized species, (c) or (d), depending upon the direction of transfer. These four structures differ merely in the positions of the electrons. According to the resonance theory, when a substance can have two or more structures that are equiva-lent or nearly equivalent to one another and that are interconvertible by mere redistribution of valence electrons of unsaturated or ionized centers, the actual molecule does not conform to any one of the structures but exists as a resonance hybrid of them all. In the formulation, resonance is indicated by a double-headed arrow. It is sometimes possible to infer that certain structures make greater contributions than others in determining the average character or ground state of the molecule. A structure that contributes to a minor extent is called an excited structure.

The concept of butadiene as a resonance hybrid of structures formulated as a–d, or as the equivalent a′–d′, explains why the central linkage partakes

$$CH_2{=}CHCH{=}CH_2 \longleftrightarrow \overset{.}{C}H_2CH{=}CH\overset{.}{C}H_2 \longleftrightarrow \overset{+}{C}H_2CH{=}CH\overset{-}{C}H_2 \longleftrightarrow \overset{-}{C}H_2CH{=}CH\overset{+}{C}H_2$$

$$\quad\;\; (a') \qquad\qquad\qquad (b') \qquad\qquad\qquad (c') \qquad\qquad\qquad (d')$$

of the character of both a single and a double bond. Quantum mechanics calculations have shown that bond shortening is a necessary consequence of such a resonance effect, as is the lengthening of the terminal linkages in consequence of their partial single-bond character.

A further consequence of resonance is dissipation of energy, or thermodynamic stabilization. Conversely, thermodynamic data afford a measure of the magnitude of resonance stabilization. The average heat of hydrogenation of propylene, butene-1, and other olefins having the terminal-bond structure of butadiene is 30.3 kg.-cal./mole. The heats of hydrogenation of the nonconjugated pentadiene-1,4 and hexadiene-1,5, namely 60.8 and 60.5 kg.-cal./mole, are almost exactly twice that of the monoolefins. The value observed for butadiene, however, is only 57.1 kg.-cal./mole, and hence this hydrocarbon has a lower energy content than that corresponding to two isolated double bonds. The difference of 3.5 kg.-cal./mole represents the resonance stabilization, or resonance energy, of butadiene. The stabilization is appreciable but only a fraction of that in the molecule of benzene, where resonance in a closed conjugated triene system is attended with stabilization amounting to a resonance energy of 39 kg.-cal./mole.

Any structure contributing to a resonance hybrid may participate in a reaction such as bromination, even an excited structure. If structure (a′) of butadiene is attacked by a bromonium ion, the resulting carbonium ion would be a resonant hybrid of structures (e′) and (f′); attack of the polarized structure (c′) would afford the same hybrid ion. The combination of this hybrid with bromide ion can give either the 1,2- or the 1,4-addition product; the preponderance of the 1,4-product suggests that structure (f′) is the major contributor or the more reactive species of the carbonium ion hybrid.

$$\left.\begin{array}{c} CH_2{=}CHCH{=}CH_2 \\ (a') \\ \updownarrow \\ \overset{+}{C}H_2CH{=}CH\overset{-}{C}H_2 \\ (c') \end{array}\right\} \xrightarrow{Br^+} \left\{\begin{array}{c} CH_2{=}CH{-}\overset{+}{C}HCH_2Br \\ (e') \\ \updownarrow \\ \overset{+}{C}H_2{-}CH{=}CHCH_2Br \\ (f') \end{array}\right\} \xrightarrow{Br^-} \left\{\begin{array}{l} CH_2{=}CHCHBrCH_2Br \\ (1,2\text{-product}) \\[1em] BrCH_2CH{=}CHCH_2Br \\ (1,4\text{-product}) \end{array}\right.$$

Resonance of a further type probably contributes to the stability of ionic intermediates, even those involved in the addition of bromine to monoolefins.   Thus the intermediate ion resulting from electrophilic attack of ethylene by bromine is regarded as a resonance hybrid of the carbonium ions (g) and (i) and the bromonium ion (h).

$$CH_2{=}CH_2 \xrightarrow{Br^+} \overset{+}{C}H_2{-}CH_2 \longleftrightarrow CH_2{-}CH_2 \longleftrightarrow CH_2{-}\overset{+}{C}H_2$$

$$\qquad\qquad\qquad Br \qquad\qquad Br^+ \qquad\qquad Br$$

$$\qquad\qquad\qquad (g) \qquad\qquad (h) \qquad\qquad (i)$$

ORBITAL THEORY

Atomic Orbitals. — The orbital concept for describing molecular structure, which both supplements the resonance theory and offers certain alternative interpretations, is based on quantum mechanics, developed in 1925 in different forms by Heisenberg and by Schrödinger.   In contrast to the older quantum theory of Bohr in which the orbit of an electron about a nucleus appeared as simple as the orbit of a planet around the sun, quantum mechanics, more realistically, provides a method for calculation of the probable position of an electron in relation to the nucleus from consideration of the energy relationships.   It describes statistically the behavior of an electron in terms of a wave function, ψ, which defines the region, or orbit, within which the electron is, in probability, largely located.   In the case of the hydrogen atom, with one electron, the orbit is spherically symmetrical and is called a $1s$ orbital (1 = quantum number, s = state).   The $1s$ orbital can be represented (Fig. 3.4) as a cloud, or charge-cloud, where most of the negative charge resides; the density at any point in this cloud is proportional to ψ^2.   The charge-cloud is symmetrical with respect to the x, y, and z axes in both the $1s$ orbital and when a $1s$-orbital is surrounded by a $2s$ orbital (Fig. 3.4b).   The $2s$-state contains an interior spherical node in which $\psi = 0$, that is, the probability of finding an electron at this site is zero.

A second type of orbital, the p-type, is not spherical but directional. Here the electron is practically confined to two merging regions or clouds that, together, form a sort of dumbbell (Fig. 3.5).   A $2p$ orbital is oriented along a particular axis and is defined as a $2p_x$, $2p_y$, or $2p_z$ orbital.   In one half of the dumbbell the sign of ψ is positive and in the other half it is nega-

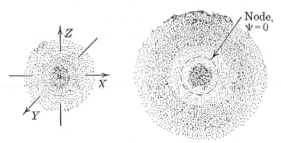

FIG. 3.4. — Atomic $1s$ and $2s$ Orbitals

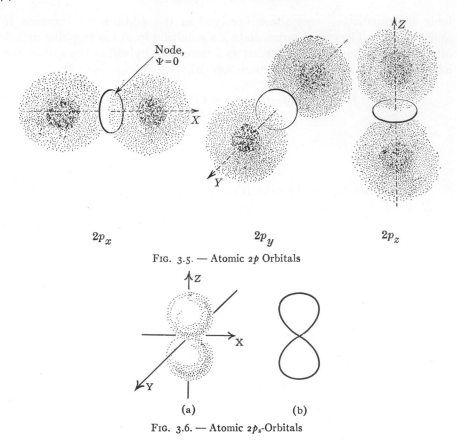

FIG. 3.5. — Atomic $2p$ Orbitals

FIG. 3.6. — Atomic $2p_z$-Orbitals

tive, and hence the two regions are separated by a nodal plane, represented in Fig. 3.5 by a disc, over which $\psi = 0$. For brevity, the dumbbell is sometimes represented by two balls (Fig. 3.6a) or by a symbol (Fig. 3.6b) that does not even depict the three-dimensional character of the region defining the probable location of the electron.

An orbital can be occupied by one electron or by two, but no more. The pairing of two electrons in a single orbital is possible only if the electron spins are suitably aligned. The property of spin (Uhlenbeck and Goudsmit, 1925) gives to an electron angular momentum and a magnetic moment such that, in a magnetic field, the orientation is either with or against the field. According to the Pauli exclusion principle (1925), two electrons can occupy the same orbital only if their magnetic moments of spin are opposed. The helium atom in the normal state contains two electrons in the s-orbital. The L-shell of other elements, when completely filled with 8 electrons, consists of four orbitals each containing two electrons. One of these is the spherical $2s$ orbital, and the others are dumbbell-type orbitals, $2p_x$, $2p_y$, and $2p_z$. Because of the attraction of the positively charged nucleus, the $1s$ orbital is filled before a $2s$ orbital, which in turn is filled before a $2p$

TABLE 3.2. ELECTRONIC CONFIGURATIONS OF THE K AND L SHELLS
(An arrow designates an electron and indicates the sense of spin)

ELEMENT	K SHELL	L SHELL			
	$1s$	$2s$	$2p_x$	$2p_y$	$2p_z$
H	↓				
He	↑ ↓				
Li	↑ ↓	↓			
Be	↑ ↓	↑ ↓			
B	↑ ↓	↑ ↓	↓		
C	↑ ↓	↑ ↓	↓	↓	
N	↑ ↓	↑ ↓	↓	↓	↓
O	↑ ↓	↑ ↓	↑ ↓	↓	↓
F	↑ ↓	↑ ↓	↑ ↓	↑ ↓	↓
Ne	↑ ↓	↑ ↓	↑ ↓	↑ ↓	↑ ↓

orbital. The order for filling the three $2p$ orbitals is further determined by the rule (F. Hund) that two electrons do not occupy any p orbital of the shell until all p orbitals of the shell have one electron. The normal electronic configurations of the first ten atoms of the periodic series are shown in Table 3.2 (each doublet contains electrons of opposed spins).

It will be noted from the table that application of the Hund rule implies that carbon, with two unpaired electrons in the $2p$ orbitals, should be bivalent. However, for purposes of bond formation, atoms tend to make use of all possible orbitals by a process of mixing that results in hybridization. In the case of carbon it is postulated that the $2s$ orbital mixes with the two $2p$ orbitals to form four equivalent hybrid orbitals (Fig. 3.7) called sp^3 hybrid orbitals (the superscript indicates that three original orbitals are utilized). The hybrid sp orbitals are directional and resemble the p orbital components more than the s. The four species together comprise an electron cloud that is directed tetrahedrally and permits utilization of four, now equivalent, valence electrons (Fig. 3.8). Through hybridization, the carbon atom is thus prepared for symmetrical bonding through four equivalent t orbitals (t = tetrahedral).

Molecular Orbitals. — The electronic distribution in a molecule is described by an extension of the principles used in the case of atoms. Thus each molecular orbital is compounded out of atomic orbitals and retains the characteristics of the components. When two hydrogen atoms bond to

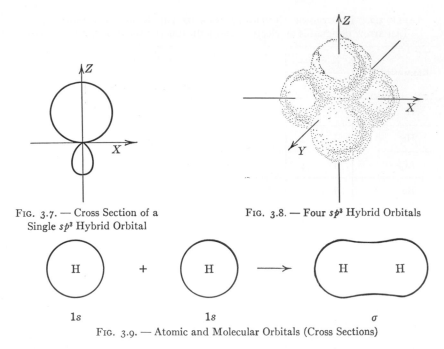

FIG. 3.7. — Cross Section of a
Single sp^3 Hybrid Orbital

FIG. 3.8. — Four sp^3 Hybrid Orbitals

FIG. 3.9. — Atomic and Molecular Orbitals (Cross Sections)

form a hydrogen molecule the two $1s$ orbitals coalesce to form a molecular orbital occupied by two electrons of opposed spins and encompassing the two nuclei. This orbital is symmetrical about a line connecting the two nuclei, and hence has the same symmetrical character as an atomic s orbital and is known as a σ (sigma) molecular orbital. The energy of a molecular orbital is lowest, and consequently the binding energy is highest, when the component atomic orbitals overlap to the highest degree, since overlapping facilitates electron exchange. Two s orbitals overlap efficiently, and hence the covalent bond, or σ-bonded link, of the hydrogen molecule is strong. The same is true of the C—H bonds of methane, in which, according to the theory, four σ molecular orbitals are formed, with maximum overlapping, by linear combination of each of the four carbon t orbitals with a hydrogen $1s$ orbital; it is described as $[C(t) + H(1s), \sigma]^8$, where 8 is the number of electrons involved. Methane thus should have a tetrahedral configuration with valence angles of $109° 28'$. The covalent carbon–carbon bond of ethane is similarly characterized by a σ orbital.

Combination of p atomic orbitals can lead to a molecular orbital of a different type, illustrated in Fig. 3.10, for simplicity, for combination of hypothetical elements A and B, each of which has a $2p_z$ atomic orbital (Fig. 3.6, more easily pictured than the equivalent $2p_x$ and $2p_y$ orbitals). The resulting molecular orbital is not spherically symmetrical but has a dumbbell-like character resembling an atomic p-orbital, and hence is described as a π (pi) molecular orbital. The dumbbell arrangement here consists in one doughnut-like cloud structure (a) overlying another (b). The most stable

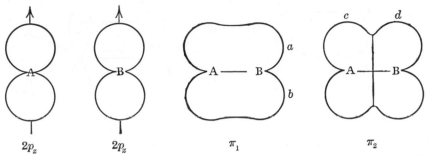

$$2p_z \qquad\qquad 2p_z \qquad\qquad \pi_1 \qquad\qquad\qquad \pi_2$$

FIG. 3.10. — Formation of π Molecular Orbitals from $2p_z$ Atomic Orbitals (Cross Sections)

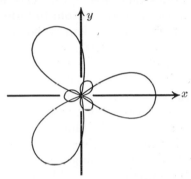

FIG. 3.11. — Trigonal Orbitals (sp^2 Hybridization)

state, or ground state (π_1), is that in which the nodal planes (low electron density) of the atomic orbital contributors are aligned with the σ-bond linking A to B.   In consequence of the Pauli exclusion principle, only two electrons can occupy a given π orbital such as that pictured (π_1), but in case additional electrons require accommodation the cloud charge can take the form π_2 (Fig. 3.10), in which a new nodular plane perpendicular to the A—B σ bond separates the cloud into two vertically oriented doughnut-like areas (c and d) that, together, form a dumbbell.   Since stability is greatest when the number of nodular planes is at a minimum, the π_1 orbital is more stable than the π_2 orbital.

Ethylene. — Quantum mechanics has established fully the electronic structure of the hydrogen molecule, but for molecules more complex the mathematical task has proved of too great complexity for exact solution. Approximations, based upon simplifying assumptions, have led to plausible interpretations with respect to methane and ethane, as outlined above.   A further plausible interpretation applies to ethylene.   A form of hybridization different from the tetrahedral type (Fig. 3.8) is postulated, namely sp^2 or trigonal hybridization (Fig. 3.11).   Each carbon atom has available four electrons: a $2s$ pair, and two other electrons listed in Table 3.2 as a $2p_x$ and a $2p_y$, but actually $2p_x$, $2p_y$, and $2p_z$ are all equivalent.   The three orbitals comprising these four electrons are hybridized to give three equivalent trigonal orbitals and one undistributed $2p$ orbital, described as a $2p_z$ orbital

a   b

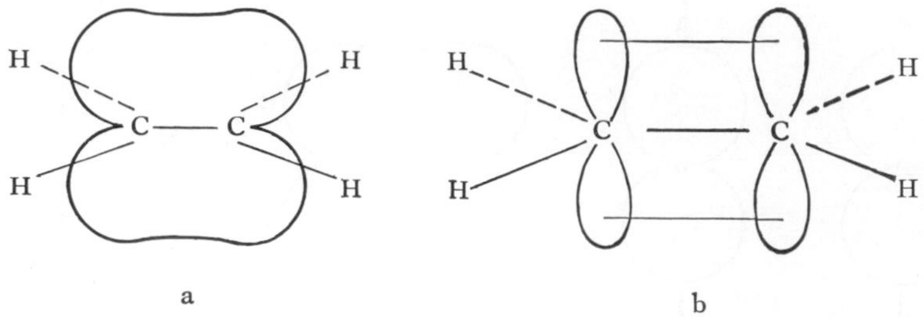

FIG. 3.12. — Ethylene (Cross Section of π Orbital)

for simplification of formulation (Fig. 3.6). One hybrid trigonal orbital merges with that of the second carbon atom to form a σ orbital linking the two carbon atoms together by a covalent, σ bond, comparable to that of ethane. The other two form σ orbitals with two hydrogen atoms. The six atoms of the ethane molecule thus all lie in the same plane, and the σ bonds linking each carbon with two hydrogens are at angles of 120° from each other. In Fig. 3.12 the five σ bonds are indicated by conventional bars. The $2p_z$ orbitals of the two carbon atoms merge to form a π molecular orbital, represented in (a) as a two-doughnut cloud and in (b) by two figure eight loops, corresponding to the original atomic p-orbitals, but with lines joining them to indicate the overlapping involved in the formation of the molecular orbital. The concept of a double bond as two pairs of shared electrons is thus extended, in the orbital theory, to the concept of two kinds of two-electron bonds: a σ bond, stabilized by efficient overlapping of symmetrical atomic orbitals, and a π bond, compounded with poor overlapping and hence of higher energy content and greater reactivity. The loop representation (Fig. 3.11b) has the advantage of emphasizing the point that π electrons, that is the two electrons occupying the π orbital, retain some character of the original p orbitals and that the plane of vibration of a π electron is perpendicular to the plane of the σ bond. The reactivity of ethylene, particularly in additions, is thus attributable to lack of stability of the π electrons and hence their availability for formation of more stable σ bonds with other atoms. The overlap in formation of the π orbital although weak is not without significant consequence. Thus the carbon–carbon bond distance in ethane of 1.54 Å is, in ethylene, shortened to 1.34 Å, evidently because the additional π orbital surrounding the two nuclei draws them together more strongly.

Conjugated Dienes. — The case of butadiene is an extension of that of ethylene but presents an additional feature. In a polyatomic molecule such as methane the bonds are all localized, that is, each separately resembles the bond in the diatomic hydrogen molecule, since the tetrahedral arrangement isolates each molecular orbital present from the others and so prevents them from interacting. The π orbital of ethylene is also isolated and localized. In butadiene, however, a molecular orbital is compounded out of four $2p_z$ orbitals on four adjacent and coplanar carbon atoms, and these orbitals are parallel to one another and at right angles to the common nuclear axis

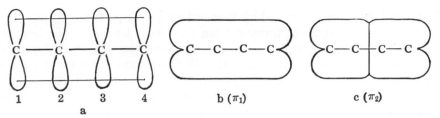

FIG. 3.13. — Butadiene (Carbon Skeleton)

(Fig. 3.13a). Hence it is clear that C_2 and C_3 overlap each other as much as they overlap C_1 and C_4 and hence that formation of two localized π orbitals is impossible. Instead, all four wave functions coalesce to form a π orbital that encompasses all four nuclei (b). This initial orbital (b), designated π_1, is particularly stable because it possesses only one nodal plane, but, in accordance with the Pauli exclusion principle, only two of the four electrons can occupy it. The second pair of electrons is accommodated in a further orbital, π_2 (c), having a second nodal plane perpendicular to the first and hence less stable than π_1. The electrons thus swarm over the complete molecule, and hence an electrical influence at one part of the molecule is transmitted throughout the system. The electrons have more room in which to move and have lower total energy and therefore greater binding energy than when paired in localized double bonds. Energy postulated in the orbital theory to be derived from delocalization is quantitatively identical with energy postulated in the resonance theory to be derived from resonance. It is obvious from the orbital theory that the stability and other special properties of conjugated systems requires coplanarity of the unsaturated centers but not colinearity. Thus one would expect even more delocalization in cyclohexatriene (benzene) than in butadiene.

GENEVA SYSTEM OF NOMENCLATURE

The systematic naming of hydrocarbons calls for further consideration of the rules of nomenclature evolved at an International Congress of chemists held in Geneva in 1892. The basic name is derived from that of the alkane corresponding to the longest chain in the molecule, irrespective of the manner in which the formula is written. Formula I has a chain of five carbon

$$
\begin{array}{cc}
CH_3 \;\; CH_3 & CH_3 \;\; CH_3 \\
| \quad\;\; | & | \qquad\;\; | \\
CH_3CCH_2CCH_3 \;\; = \;\; & CH_3CH_2CCH_2CCH_2CH_3 \\
| \quad\;\; | & | \qquad\;\; | \\
CH_2 \;\; CH_2 & CH_3 \;\; CH_3 \\
| \quad\;\; | & \\
CH_3 \;\; CH_3 & \\
\quad\quad I & Ia
\end{array}
$$

atoms on a horizontal line, but on counting around the corners it is seen that a longer chain of seven carbon atoms is present. The hydrocarbon is 3,3,5,5-tetramethylheptane. The formula can be written equally well as in Ia, and this is the way in which it would appear on performing the reverse operation of evolving the formula from the Geneva name. The best procedure in performing this operation is to write the carbon skeleton corresponding to the basic name, affix the alkyl and other substituents, and fill in hydrogen atoms where required to conform to the normal valence.

A general tenet of the Geneva system is to pick the simpler of two possible alternatives. If substituent group numbers alone are concerned, counting is done in such a way as to provide the smallest numbers; the same rule applies to a choice between alternative methods of locating positions of functional groups. Frequently there is a conflict between substituent group numbers and functional group numbers, as in the case of isooctene (II), which might be called 2,2,4-trimethylpentene-4 or 2,4,4-trimethylpentene-1. The Geneva ruling is that the number indicating the position of the functional group takes precedence over substituent group

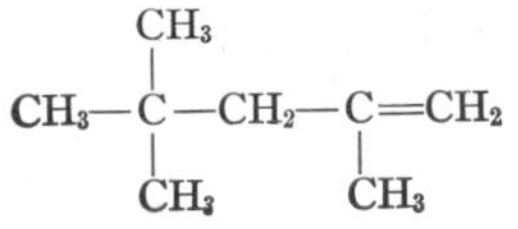

$$CH_3-\underset{\underset{CH_2}{|}}{\overset{\overset{CH_3}{|}}{C}}-CH_2-\underset{\underset{CH_3}{|}}{C}=CH_2$$

II

numbers, and hence the second alternative is selected and the hydrocarbon is described as a pentene-1 derivative. Similarly, III is named 5-chloropentanol-1 and not 1-chloropentanol-5.

$$ClCH_2CH_2CH_2CH_2CH_2OH$$

III

When a number of different substituent groups are present, the preferred practice is to list them in order of increasing complexity rather than in alphabetical order. Thus IV is 5-methyl-6-ethyl-4-n-propyloctene-3.

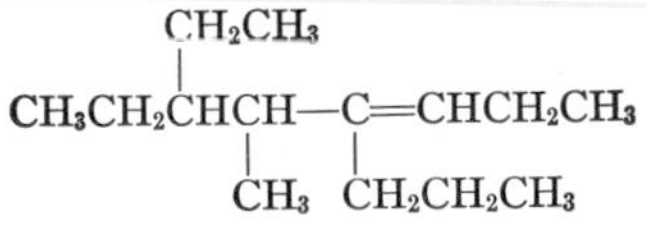

$$CH_3CH_2\underset{\underset{CH_3}{|}}{C}HCH-\underset{\underset{CH_2CH_2CH_3}{|}}{\overset{\overset{CH_2CH_3}{|}}{C}}=CHCH_2CH_3$$

IV

Compounds containing more than one functional group are adequately designated by an appropriate modification of the ending. Thus V is hexatriene-1,3,5, and VI is pentanediol-1,5. Allyl alcohol (VII) in the

$$CH_2=CHCH=CHCH=CH_2 \qquad\qquad HOCH_2CH_2CH_2CH_2CH_2OH$$
$$\text{V} \qquad\qquad\qquad\qquad\qquad \text{VI}$$

$$CH_2=CHCH_2OH \qquad\qquad\qquad -CH=\underset{\underset{OH}{|}}{C}-$$

$$\text{VII} \qquad\qquad\qquad\qquad\qquad \text{VIII}$$

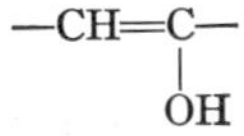

Geneva system is propene-2-ol-1, and compounds having the functional ethylenic (-ene) and alcoholic (-ol) groups in combination, as in VIII, are described as enols.

In case the longest carbon chain in the molecule does not include such functional groups as may be present, the rule is to select as the basis of the name the next longest chain that includes the maximum number of such groups. The alcohol IX has a 6-carbon chain to which the group —CH_2OH is attached, but it would be contrary to the Geneva system to

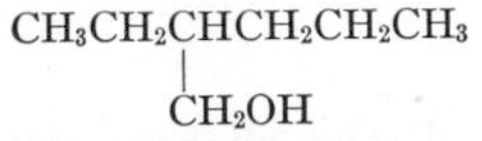

$$CH_3CH_2CHCH_2CH_2CH_3$$
$$|$$
$$CH_2OH$$
IX

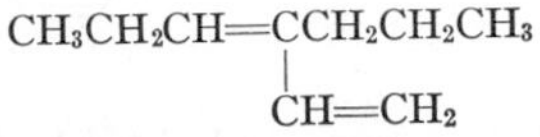

$$CH_3CH_2CH{=}CCH_2CH_2CH_3$$
$$|$$
$$CH{=}CH_2$$
X

regard this group as a substituent unless there were no way of indicating its functional character. This, however, can be done by picking the 5-carbon chain that includes the hydroxylated carbon, and the substance thus is 2-ethylpentanol-1. Again, the hydrocarbon X has an ethylenic 7-carbon chain and might be regarded as a vinyl ($CH_2{=}CH—$) heptene. The substance would then be classified as a monoolefin, or ene, whereas actually it is a diolefin, or diene. The correct name is 3-*n*-propylhexadiene-1,3.

The basic name for cycloparaffins is that of the ring, and ring atoms are numbered in such a way as to assign minimal numbers to the functional group and then to the substituent groups. Compound XI is 1,2-dimethyl-

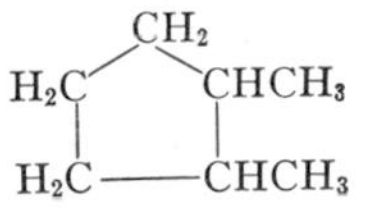

$$\begin{array}{c} CH_2 \\ H_2C \diagup \quad \diagdown CHCH_3 \\ | \qquad\qquad | \\ H_2C{-}{-}{-}CHCH_3 \\ XI \end{array}$$

$$\begin{array}{c} CHOH \\ H_2C \diagup \quad \diagdown CHC_2H_5 \\ | \qquad\qquad | \\ H_2C \diagdown \quad \diagup CH_2 \\ CHOH \\ XII \end{array}$$

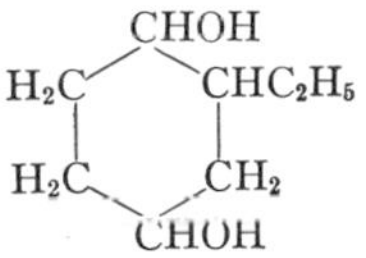

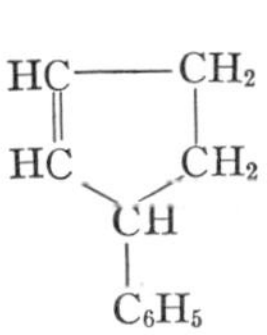

$$\begin{array}{c} HC{-}{-}{-}CH_2 \\ \| \qquad\qquad | \\ HC \qquad CH_2 \\ \diagdown CH \diagup \\ | \\ C_6H_5 \\ XIII \end{array}$$

cyclopentane (not the 2,3- or 1,5-derivative). Substance XII is 2-ethyl-cyclohexanediol-1,4, and XIII is 3-phenylcyclopentene-1.

In the aromatic series, positions of substituents in the benzene ring, which is usually abbreviated by a plain hexagon with the carbon and hydrogen atoms omitted, are indicated either by numbers or by the specific designation *ortho* (normal), *meta* (beyond), and *para* (across), or by the prefixes *o*-, *m*-, and *p*-. It should be emphasized that the double bonds in the benzene ring are of a special inert character and that aromatic hydro-

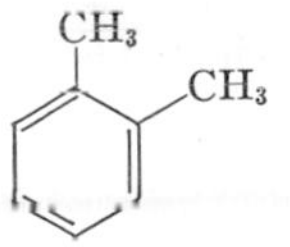

1,2-
(ortho)

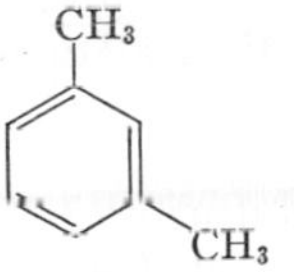

1,3-
(meta)

1,4-
(para)

Dimethylbenzenes (xylenes)

carbons do not exhibit the characteristic reactivity associated with alkenes. They do not add hydrogen halides or hypochlorous acid, and they react with bromine, hydrogen and a catalyst, or oxidizing agents so much less readily than an olefin that olefin additions can be conducted in the presence of benzene without the latter being attacked. Allylbenzene can react ex-

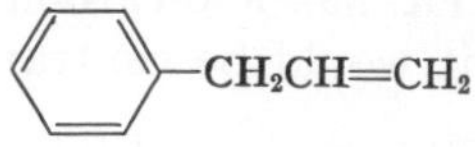

Allylbenzene

clusively at the terminal double bond with all the characteristic reagents for alkenes without disturbance of the aromatic ring.

PROBLEMS

1. Calculate the formal charges on the magnesium and oxygen atoms of the Grignard reagent dietherate (p. 38).
2. Write an electronic formula for sulfuric acid corresponding to II (p. 55), and check it by calculation of the formal charges.
3. Give Geneva names for:
   (a) Propylene glycol
   (b) Dimethylisopropylmethane
   (c) Citronellol, $CH_3C(CH_3)=CHCH_2CH_2CH(CH_3)CH_2CH_2OH$
   (d) $(CH_3)_2CHCHCH(CH_3)CH_2OH$
   $\qquad\qquad |$
   $\qquad\ \ CH_2CH=CH_2$
   (e) $CH_3CHCH_2CHCH_2CH_3$
   $\qquad\ \ |\qquad\ \ |$
   $\quad CH_3CHCH_2CH_2$
   (f) $(CH_3)_2C=CHCH=C(CH_3)_2$
   (g) Benzene

4. Write formulas for:
   (a) 2-Methyl-3-ethylpentanol-1   (d) Butanediol-2,3
   (b) 1,4-Diphenylbutadiene-1,3   (e) 5-Chloro-4-methylpentene-1
   (c) Trimethylethylene   (f) 1,2-Butylene oxide

5. By what methods can each of the following hydrocarbon samples be purified?
   (a) n-Hexane, contaminated with hexene-3
   (b) n-Hexane, contaminated with hexanol-1
   (c) Hexene-3, contaminated with n-hexane

6. In what way can the following isomers be distinguished?
   $$CH_3CH_2CH=C(CH_3)_2 \text{ and } CH_3CH_2C(CH_3)=CHCH_3$$

7. A hydrocarbon C_7H_{10} on drastic oxidation gives the products $O=CCH_2C=O$ and
   $\qquad\qquad\qquad\qquad\qquad\qquad\qquad\qquad\quad |\qquad\ |$
   $\qquad\qquad\qquad\qquad\qquad\qquad\qquad\qquad\ CH_3\ CH_3$
   HOOC—COOH. What is its structure?

8. A pure hydrocarbon of the formula C_6H_{12} decolorizes bromine solution, dissolves in concentrated sulfuric acid, yields n-hexane on hydrogenation, and on oxidation with excess potassium permanganate affords a mixture of two acids of the type RCOOH. What is the structure?

9. Devise a method of preparing adipic acid, $HOOC(CH_2)_4COOH$, from cyclohexanol.

10. A hydrocarbon $C_{11}H_{20}$, which on catalytic hydrogenation absorbs two moles of hydrogen, gives on oxidation the products

$$CH_3CH_2COCH_3 , HOOCCH_2CH_2COOH, and CH_3CH_2COOH$$

What is its structure?

11. (a) A hydrocarbon of the formula $C_{10}H_{14}$ absorbs two moles of hydrogen on catalytic hydrogenation and gives a product inert to acid permanganate. How many rings does it contain?

(b) If a compound with the formula $C_{27}H_{46}$ absorbs just one mole of hydrogen, how many rings are present?

12. A hydrocarbon $C_{10}H_{16}$ absorbs one mole of hydrogen, is known to contain no methyl, ethyl, or other alkyl groups, and on ozonization gives a symmetrical diketone of the formula $C_{10}H_{16}O_2$. What is its structure?

READING REFERENCES

G. Egloff, "Physical Constants of Hydrocarbons," Vols. I and II, Reinhold, New York (1939, 1940)

H. Adkins, "Role of the Catalyst," *Ind. Eng. Chem.*, **32**, 1189 (1940)

R. C. Huston, "A Correlation of Some Physical Properties of Alkanes and Alkenes," Michigan State College Press, East Lansing (1947)

F. R. Mayo and C. Walling, "The Peroxide Effect in the Addition of Reagents to Unsaturated Compounds and in Rearrangement Reactions," *Chem. Rev.*, **27**, 351 (1940)

L. Pauling, "The Nature of the Chemical Bond," Cornell University Press, Ithaca (1940)

G. W. Wheland, "Resonance in Organic Chemistry," Wiley, New York (1955)

C. A. Coulson, "Molecular Orbitals," *Quart. Rev.*, **1**, 144 (1947); "The Contributions of Wave Mechanics to Chemistry," *J. Chem. Soc.*, 2069 (1955)

CHAPTER 4

ACETYLENIC HYDROCARBONS
(ALKYNES)

The simplest member of this series of unsaturated hydrocarbons is acetylene, C_2H_2. The substance has two hydrogens less than ethylene and thus bears the same relationship to ethylene as ethylene does to ethane. Valency requirements are satisfied by a triple-bond formulation for acetylene, and the properties and reactions are consistent with this structure

$$H—C\equiv C—H \qquad HC:::CH$$

Acetylene

The chemistry of acetylenic hydrocarbons is similar to that of alkenes. The electronic equivalent of the Kekulé triple-bond formula indicates that the two unsaturated carbon atoms share three pairs of electrons.

Other members of the series are often named as derivatives of the parent hydrocarbon, for example:

I. $CH_3C\equiv CH$, Methylacetylene
II. $CH_3CH_2C\equiv CH$, Ethylacetylene

III. $CH_3C\equiv CCH_3$, Dimethylacetylene
IV. $CH_2\equiv CHCH_2CH_2C\equiv CH$

In the Geneva system of nomenclature an acetylenic hydrocarbon is indicated by the ending -yne (or -ine), and hence I can be described as propyne, II is butyne-1, and III is butyne-2. The generic name for the series is alkyne. Hydrocarbons having a combination of double and triple bonds are termed enynes, or dienynes, enediynes, etc.; the substance IV, for example, is hexene-5-yne-1.

Properties of some members of the alkyne series are given in Table 4.1. It is noteworthy that acetylene boils at a temperature very close to the melting point. Acetylenic hydrocarbons distil at temperatures some 10–20° higher than the corresponding ethylenes, and the boiling points are somewhat closer to those of saturated hydrocarbons having the same number of carbon atoms than to those of alkenes. The triple-bond compounds are slightly denser in the liquid state than the double-bond analogs.

GENERAL METHODS OF PREPARATION

From *vic*-Dihalides. — Hydrocarbon derivatives having halogen atoms in adjacent positions in the chain, or *vic*-dihalides, are readily available

TABLE 4.1. PROPERTIES OF ACETYLENIC HYDROCARBONS

NAME	FORMULA C_nH_{2n-2}	CARBON SKELETON	M.P., °C.	B.P., °C.	SP. GR. (LIQ.)
Acetylene	C_2H_2	C≡C	−81.8*	−83.4	0.6179
Methylacetylene	C_3H_4	C·C≡C	−101.5	−23.3	.6714
Ethylacetylene	C_4H_6	C·C·C≡C	−122.5	8.6	.6682
Dimethylacetylene	C_4H_6	C·C≡C C	−28	27.2	.6937
Pentyne-1	C_5H_8	C·C·C·C≡C	−98	39.7	.695
Pentyne-2	C_5H_8	C·C·C≡C·C	−101	55.5	.7127
3-Methylbutyne-1	C_5H_8	C·C·C≡C · C		28	.665
Hexyne-1	C_6H_{10}	C·C·C·C·C≡C	−124	71	.7195
Hexyne-2	C_6H_{10}	C·C·C·C≡C·C	−92	84	.7305
Hexyne-3	C_6H_{10}	C·C·C≡C·C·C C	−51	82	.7255
3,3-Dimethylbutyne-1	C_6H_{10}	· C·C·C≡C · C	−81	38	.6686
Octadecyne-1	$C_{18}H_{24}$	C·(C)$_{15}$·C≡C	28	180 at 15 mm.	.8025

* At 891 mm.

by addition of halogens to alkenes and can be converted into acetylenic hydrocarbons through elimination of two molecules of hydrogen halide by treatment with alcoholic potassium hydroxide. Thus one method for introduction of the triple bond is the sequence of reactions:

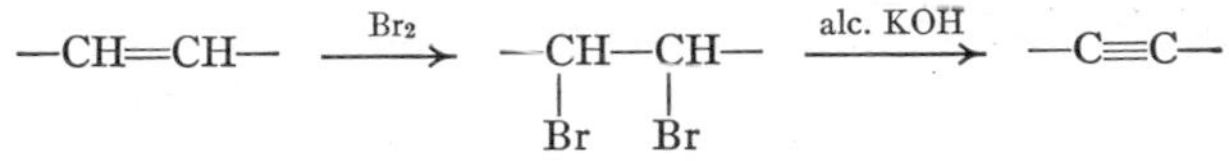

$$-CH=CH- \xrightarrow{Br_2} \underset{\underset{Br\ \ Br}{|\ \ |}}{-CH-CH-} \xrightarrow{alc.\ KOH} -C≡C-$$

When bromine is added to the double bond of propylene and the product is treated with potassium hydroxide in alcohol, the unsaturated hydrocarbon produced is essentially pure methylacetylene. A possible alternative

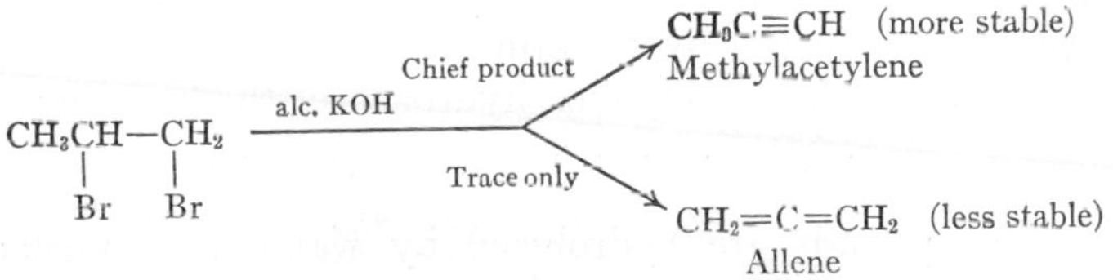

$$\underset{\underset{Br\ \ Br}{|\ \ |}}{CH_3CH-CH_2} \xrightarrow{alc.\ KOH} \begin{cases} \text{Chief product} \nearrow CH_3C≡CH \text{ (more stable)} \\ \qquad\qquad\qquad \text{Methylacetylene} \\ \text{Trace only} \searrow CH_2=C=CH_2 \text{ (less stable)} \\ \qquad\qquad\qquad \text{Allene} \end{cases}$$

course of the reaction would involve elimination of hydrogen bromide between the 2-bromo atom and a hydrogen of the adjacent methyl group to give allene, $CH_2=C=CH_2$. This diene, however, appears in no more than traces; allenes are labile and show a marked tendency to rearrange to the more stable acetylenic isomers. A dibromide of the type $RCH_2CHBrCHBrCH_2R$ can yield either an acetylene or a conjugated diene or a mixture.

From *gem*-Dihalides. — An alternate method of introducing a triple bond consists in elimination of two molecules of hydrogen bromide from a substance having two halogens on the same carbon atom, a twinned (*L. gemini*), or *gem*-dihalide:

$$-CH_2-CBr_2- \xrightarrow{\text{alc. KOH}} -C{\equiv}C-$$

gem-Dihalides are obtainable by the action of phosphorus tribromide or trichloride on compounds having oxygen doubly bound to carbon, namely aldehydes, $RCH{=}O$, and ketones, $R_2C{=}O$. Preparative processes are illustrated in the formulas. An alternate procedure of eliminating hydrogen

$$CH_3CH_2C{\diagdown}^{\diagup H}_{\diagdown O} \xrightarrow{PBr_3} CH_3CH_2CHBr_2 \xrightarrow{\text{alc. KOH}} CH_3C{\equiv}CH$$

Propionaldehyde

$$CH_3CH_2CCH_2CH_3 \xrightarrow{PCl_3} CH_3CH_2CCl_2CH_2CH_3 \xrightarrow{\text{alc. KOH}} CH_3CH_2C{\equiv}CCH_3$$
$$\overset{\|}{O}$$

Diethyl ketone

bromide involving use of sodamide has the advantage that it can be conducted in an anhydrous medium, with avoidance of side reactions:

$$-CH_2CCl_2- + 2\,NaNH_2 \longrightarrow -C{\equiv}C- + 2\,NaCl + 2\,NH_3$$

By Alkylation of Acetylene. — Acetylene and the monoalkylacetylenes ($RC{\equiv}CH$) are unique among hydrocarbons in that the hydrogen atom attached to triply bound carbon is acidic and replaceable by metals. In its weakly acidic character, acetylene ($H{-}C{\equiv}CH$) is analogous to hydrogen cyanide ($H{-}C{\equiv}N$). Acetylene when passed into the blue solution of one equivalent of sodium in liquid ammonia is converted into a monosodio derivative; under more drastic conditions a disodio derivative can

$$HC{\equiv}CH + Na \xrightarrow{\text{(liq. NH}_3)} HC{\equiv}CNa + \tfrac{1}{2}H_2$$
$$\text{Sodium acetylide}$$

be produced (acetylene gas over warm sodium). Sodamide is employed for replacement of the lone acetylenic hydrogen of the homologs $RC{\equiv}CH$:

$$RC{\equiv}CH + NaNH_2 \longrightarrow RC{\equiv}CNa$$

The sodium compounds are hydrolyzed by water with regeneration of hydrocarbon: $\equiv CNa + HOH \rightarrow \equiv CH + NaOH$. They also enter into a metathetical reaction with methyl iodide and can be used for synthesis of methyl homologs of the original hydrocarbons, thus:

$$HC{\equiv}CNa + CH_3I \longrightarrow HC{\equiv}CCH_3$$
$$RC{\equiv}CNa + CH_3I \longrightarrow RC{\equiv}CCH_3$$

For introduction of higher alkyl groups, the dialkyl sulfate, R_2SO_4, is preferred to the alkyl iodide, since the latter is liable to conversion to the alkene.

Sodium acetylide can be used for introduction of the acetylene residue into certain other compounds (ketones), and another derivative having practically the same synthetic applications is the Grignard reagent, obtainable by a replacement reaction:

$$HC\equiv CH \quad + \quad C_2H_5MgBr \quad \longrightarrow \quad HC\equiv CMgBr \quad + \quad C_2H_6$$

Acetylenemagnesium
bromide

The Grignard reagent reacts similarly to the sodio derivative with water or with methyl iodide, for example:

$$HC\equiv CMgBr \quad + \quad CH_3I \quad \longrightarrow \quad HC\equiv CCH_3 \quad + \quad MgBrI$$

With two equivalents of ethylmagnesium bromide acetylene yields the disubstituted derivative $BrMgC\equiv CMgBr$.

ACETYLENE

Although acetylenic hydrocarbons in general are comparatively rare, acetylene itself is a key chemical in the synthetic production of a number of strategic materials. This importance is a consequence of unique chemical properties, coupled with the fact that acetylene has long been available from coal, limestone, and water by a process applicable to quantity production. Calcium carbide is first prepared by fusion of coke with quicklime in an electric furnace; the crude product consists of hard gray lumps with a crystalline fracture. When treated with water, it affords acetylene (compare the behavior of the other metal derivatives mentioned above). Prob-

$$\underset{\text{Quicklime}}{CaO} \quad + \quad \underset{\text{Coke}}{3\,C} \quad \xrightarrow{2500-3000°} \quad \underset{\text{Calcium carbide}}{CaC_2} \quad + \quad CO$$

$$CaC_2 \quad + \quad 2\,H_2O \quad \longrightarrow \quad Ca(OH)_2 \quad + \quad HC\equiv CH$$

ably unsaturation is attained in the thermal reaction and not in the subsequent low-temperature reaction of calcium carbide with water. Acetylene manufactured by this method has a characteristic odor due to the presence of hydrogen sulfide and phosphine; these contaminants can be removed by passing the gas through a solution of mercuric chloride in dilute hydrochloric acid; the purified material is practically odorless. Acetylene is also manufactured by the cracking of methane in an electric arc; the process was introduced in Germany during World War II.

Acetylene burns with a highly luminous flame, probably because at the combustion temperature the hydrocarbon is in part broken down to finely divided carbon particles that become incandescent. Because of this luminosity, acetylene was employed as an illuminating gas prior to the advent of the electric lamp, particularly for transportation vehicles. A few decades ago the usual bicycle lamp was a small acetylene generator consisting of a calcium carbide canister into which water could be dripped as desired through a setscrew valve. It is not feasible to prepare supplies of preformed acetylene for transportation by liquefying the gas under pressure in steel cylinders because in this condition the substance is sensitive to shock and may explode. This instability is associated with the high energy content of acetylene, as shown by a high negative value for the heat of formation:

$$2C + H_2 \rightarrow C_2H_2 - 54.8 \text{ kg.-cal.}$$

The substance is endothermic, in contrast to ethane, for which the heat of formation is positive. A safe method of storage consists in absorbing the gas at a moderate pressure (12 atmospheres) in acetone, which is capable of dissolving 300 times its volume of acetylene. The solution is prepared in a steel cylinder containing asbestos or other porous solid that absorbs the liquid and prevents its slushing about in transit. An important use for preformed acetylene is as a fuel in welding and cutting of metals. The oxyacetylene flame reaches temperatures as high as 2700°; the high heat value is derived in part from the endothermic character of the hydrocarbon.

REACTIONS

Electrophilic Additions. — Acetylene adds two moles of chlorine (1), but the intermediate dichloride can be isolated without difficulty. A triple

1.　　　$CH{\equiv}CH \xrightarrow{Cl_2} ClCH{=}CHCl \xrightarrow{Cl_2} Cl_2CHCHCl_2$

　　　　　　　　Acetylene dichloride　　　s-Tetrachloroethane

2.　　　$CH_2{=}CHCH_2C{\equiv}CH \xrightarrow{Br_2} CH_2BrCHBrCH_2C{\equiv}CH$

3.　　　$CH{\equiv}CH \xrightarrow{HI} CH_2{=}CHI \xrightarrow{HI} CH_3CHI_2$

　　　　　　　　Vinyl iodide　　　Ethylidene iodide

bond actually is less reactive than a double bond, as shown by the selective bromination formulated in (2). Hydrogen halides also add more slowly to triple than to double bonds. The addition proceeds in two stages (3) and, in the absence of a peroxide, the second step follows the Markownikoff rule. Alkynes are much less reactive than alkenes to peracids. Acetylene itself is attacked at an immeasurably slow rate; dialkyl acetylenes are somewhat more reactive and give a variety of products. Like the reactions formulated above, which involve attack by Cl^+, Br^+, H^+, the reaction of an alkene with perbenzoic acid to give an oxide is an electrophilic addition involving attack by $\overset{+}{O}H$ (4) to give a transient oxonium ion. The triple bond

4.　$R_2C{=}CR_2 + C_6H_5CO\overset{-\ +}{O}OH \rightarrow R_2C{-}CR_2 + C_6H_5COO^- \rightarrow$

　　　　　　　　　　　　　　　　　　　$\diagdown \diagup$
　　　　　　　　　　　　　　　　　　　　^+OH

　　　　　　　　　　　　　　　$R_2C{-}CR_2 + C_6H_5COOH$
　　　　　　　　　　　　　　　　$\diagdown \diagup$
　　　　　　　　　　　　　　　　　　O

also shows less reactivity than the double bond in chromic acid oxidation, as demonstrated by reaction (5). Also, alkynes do not form colored com-

5. $$CH\equiv C(CH_2)_7CH=C(CH_3)_2 \xrightarrow[40\%]{CrO_3} CH\equiv C(CH_2)_7CO_2H$$

plexes with tetranitromethane.

Nucleophilic Additions. — Since acetylene has less affinity for positive fragments than ethylene, it would be expected to have greater affinity for negative ions or fragments, termed nucleophilic, and it does indeed enter into nucleophilic additions not applicable to alkenes. One (6), addition of hydrogen cyanide in the presence of a catalyst to form acrylonitrile (80%), affords a starting material of value in the production of synthetic polymers.

6. $$CH\equiv CH \xrightarrow{CN^-} \bar{C}H=CHCN \xrightarrow{H^+} CH_2=CHCN$$
$$\text{Acrylonitrile}$$

The addition is represented as initating in attack by cyanide anion. A comparable reaction is hydration. Alkenes can be hydrated to alcohols, but only by stepwise addition of sulfuric acid and hydrolysis. Alkynes, however, add water directly under catalysis by hot dilute sulfuric acid containing a little mercuric sulfate. The reaction probably initiates in attack by OH^-, analogous to (6). The initial product from acetylene (7), vinyl alcohol, is not stable and isomerizes to acetaldehyde by migration of hydrogen from oxygen to carbon with simultaneous shift of the double bond. The hypothetical vinyl alcohol is an unstable enol; the same lability and tendency to isomerize is generally characteristic of ordinary enols, though highly un-

7. $$CH\equiv CH + HOH \xrightarrow{42\% H_2SO_4, HgSO_4} \left[CH_2=CH-OH\right] \longrightarrow CH_3-CH=O$$
$$\text{Vinyl alcohol} \qquad\qquad \text{Acetaldehyde}$$
$$\text{(hypothetical)}$$

saturated groups attached to the unit $-CH=C(OH)-$ can effect stabilization. Derivatives of vinyl alcohol in which the mobile hydrogen is replaced by alkyl groups or acid residues (acyl groups) exist as chemical entities and do not isomerize. Methanol adds similarly to acetylene to give methyl vinyl ether. The reaction, known as vinylation, is the basis for a German

8. $$CH_3OH + CH\equiv CH \xrightarrow[80-95\%]{KOH} CH_3OCH=CH_2 \xrightarrow{dil. H_2SO_4} CH_3CHO$$
$$\text{Methyl vinyl}$$
$$\text{ether}$$

process for manufacture of acetaldehyde; acid hydrolysis of methyl vinyl ether affords acetaldehyde and methanol, which is recovered and reused.

Acetic acid adds to acetylene in the presence of mercuric salts or acetyl-sulfuric acid as catalyst to give vinyl acetate, an ester. Vinyl acetate,

9. $$\underset{\text{O}}{CH_3-\overset{\displaystyle\text{O}}{\overset{\|}{C}}-OH} + CH\equiv CH \xrightarrow[80\%]{\text{Acetylsulfuric acid}} CH_3-\overset{\displaystyle\text{O}}{\overset{\|}{C}}-O-CH=CH_2$$
$$\text{Vinyl acetate}$$

manufactured by this method, is a key material for production of the vinyl resins, used as synthetic rubbers and as plastics. The chief technological utilization of the conversion of acetylene into acetaldehyde is the manufacture of acetic acid. The acetaldehyde is separated from unchanged acetylene, which is recycled, and is oxidized catalytically with air in the

10.
$$CH_3-C{\overset{H}{\underset{O}{}}} \xrightarrow{[O]} CH_3-C{\overset{OH}{\underset{O}{}}}$$

Acetaldehyde   Acetic acid

presence of manganese acetate. The hydration reaction is applicable to other members of the series; methylacetylene, for example, yields acetone. The initial addition follows the Markownikoff rule.

11.
$$CH_3C{\equiv}CH \xrightarrow{H_2O, \text{ catalyst}} \left[CH_3\underset{OH}{C}{=}CH_2 \right] \longrightarrow CH_3\underset{O}{C}CH_3$$

Methylacetylene   Acetone

Reduction. — The triple bond is sufficiently more reactive than the double bond that selective hydrogenation is feasible and is frequently used in synthesis (12). A particularly useful catalyst for the purpose is a form

12.
$$RC{\equiv}C(CH_2)_nCH{=}CHR' \xrightarrow{2H} RC{\overset{H}{=}}\overset{H}{C}(CH_2)_nCH{=}CHR'$$

of palladium partially inactivated with heavy metal salt and quinoline (H. Lindlar, 1952). Alkynes are also reducible chemically to alkenes. The most useful technique is reduction with sodium or lithium in liquid ammonia; since alkenes are inert to this mode of reduction there is no problem of over-reduction. Since the reaction involves nucleophilic attack, the greater reactivity of the triple bond is in line with observations in the preceding section.

Additions of Acetylene. — Some special reactions of acetylene involve its functioning as the entity H—A in additions to unsaturated compounds. One is addition of acetylene to itself to form vinylacetylene, a dimerization.

13.
$$HC{\equiv}CH + HC{\equiv}CH \longrightarrow CH_2{=}CHC{\equiv}CH$$
Vinylacetylene

This is effected by absorption of acetylene in a solution of cuprous chloride and ammonium chloride in hydrochloric acid. Vinylacetylene is a key intermediate in production of the synthetic rubber Neoprene. The reaction is analogous to addition of hydrogen cyanide to acetylene (6), and since the structures H—C≡N and H—C≡CH are similar (and the compounds similarly acidic), the reaction (13) probably involves attack by $\overline{C}{\equiv}CH$. Another analogy is that both hydrogen cyanide and acetylene add to the carbonyl group (C=O), as in (14). The reaction with formaldehyde yields

14. $$CH\equiv CH + H_2C=O \longrightarrow CH\equiv CCH_2OH$$
Propargyl alcohol

$$O=CH_2 + CH\equiv CH + CH_2=O \longrightarrow HOCH_2C\equiv CCH_2OH$$
Butyne-2-diol-1.4

the mono-addition product propargyl alcohol and the di-addition product butyne-2-diol-1,4. Propargyl alcohol can be hydrogenated to allyl alcohol, $CH_2=CHCH_2OH$, and butyne-2-diol-1,4 is the starting material for a German process for the manufacture of butadiene, $CH_2=CHCH=CH_2$, an important precursor of synthetic rubbers. The catalyzed reaction of carbon monoxide with acetylene and an alcohol to produce an ester of acrylic acid (15) may be analogous, but the mechanism is not known. The three

15. $$CH\equiv CH + CO + ROH \xrightarrow{Ni(CO)_4} CH_2=CHC\overset{\displaystyle O}{\underset{\displaystyle OR}{\big\langle}}$$
Acrylate ester

processes just described were developed by Reppe[1] at the I. G. Farbenindustrie in the period 1925–45. They require high pressure, and Reppe's key discovery was recognition of this fact and development of methods for handling acetylene safely at pressures up to 30 atmospheres. The striking effect of changing conditions is shown by the fact that acetylene yields a dimer in an aqueous medium (as described above), the trimer benzene at elevated temperatures in the gaseous phase, and the tetramer cyclooctatetraene (p. 524) under high pressure (Reppe).

A reaction that supplements the Reppe addition of acetylene to aldehydes is the addition of the hydrocarbon to acetone in the presence of powdered potassium hydroxide in a solvent containing the O—C—O or O—C—C—O group; the reaction is the basis of an efficient method for manufacture of isoprene (Weizmann), which is obtained by partial hydrogenation of the addition product and vapor-phase dehydration.

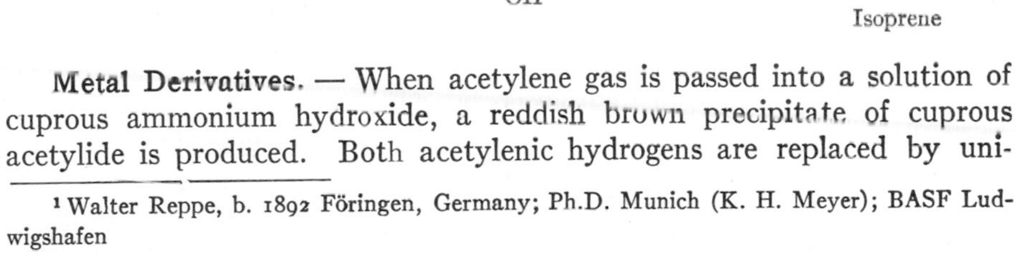

$$\underset{CH_3}{\overset{CH_3}{>}}C=O + HC\equiv CH \xrightarrow{KOH} \underset{CH_3}{\overset{CH_3}{>}}\underset{OH}{\overset{|}{C}}-C\equiv CH \xrightarrow{H_2, Pd}$$
3-Methylbutyne-1-ol-3

$$\underset{CH_3}{\overset{CH_3}{>}}\underset{OH}{\overset{|}{C}}-CH=CH_2 \xrightarrow{Al_2O_3} \underset{CH_2}{\overset{CH_3}{>}}C-CH=CH_2$$
Isoprene

Metal Derivatives. — When acetylene gas is passed into a solution of cuprous ammonium hydroxide, a reddish brown precipitate of cuprous acetylide is produced. Both acetylenic hydrogens are replaced by uni-

---

[1] Walter Reppe, b. 1892 Föringen, Germany; Ph.D. Munich (K. H. Meyer); BASF Ludwigshafen

$$HC\equiv CH \ + \ 2\,Cu(NH_3)_2OH \ \longrightarrow \ CuC\equiv CCu \ + \ 4\,NH_3 \ + \ 2\,H_2O$$
$$\text{Cuprous acetylide}$$

valent copper atoms; an alkyne of the type $RC\equiv CH$ gives a monocopper derivative. Since the reaction is specific to hydrocarbons containing an acetylenic hydrogen and is not shown by alkanes, alkenes, or alkynes of the type $RC\equiv CR'$, it is used as a diagnostic test for recognition of the unit $\equiv CH$. Silver acetylides are similarly precipitated from an ammoniacal solution of silver nitrate, for example: $CH\equiv CH \rightarrow AgC\equiv CAg$. The heavy-metal acetylides differ from light-metal derivatives in that they are not hydrolyzed by water and, in the dry state, are explosive and highly sensitive to shock. Copper acetylide on explosion produces copper and carbon and no gaseous products. An occasional use for the heavy-metal acetylides is in the purification of acetylene or of alkynes of the type $RC\equiv CH$; the metal derivative is precipitated, collected, washed, and treated in the moist condition with dilute hydrochloric acid, or better with aqueous potassium cyanide, with regeneration of the purified alkyne.

Lewisite (β-Chlorovinyldichloroarsine). — β-Chlorovinyldichloroarsine, or lewisite, is a war gas developed in 1917 by W. Lee Lewis, an American, to meet the demand for a nonpersistent vesicant that would produce immediate casualties and thus be applicable to offensive combat. A method of manufacture was worked out consisting in addition of arsenic trichloride to acetylene in the presence of anhydrous aluminum chloride as catalyst. The

$$CH\equiv CH \ + \ ClAsCl_2 \ \xrightarrow{AlCl_3} \ ClCH=CHAsCl_2$$
$$\text{Lewisite}$$

first lot was ready for shipment overseas only in November, 1918, and after declaration of the Armistice, was destroyed at sea.

Lewisite (b.p. 190°) combines a vesicant action similar to that of mustard gas with the systemic poisoning effect of arsenic, and it is also a lung injurant and a lachrymator. Inhalation of the vapor for ten minutes at a concentration of 0.12 mg. per liter of air is fatal. Like mustard gas, lewisite rapidly penetrates clothing and body tissue. Lewisite is about four times as quick in acting as mustard gas and it is much less persistent. The two halogen atoms attached to arsenic are highly reactive, and the substance is hydrolyzed rapidly in moist air to β-chlorovinylarsine oxide. This hydrolysis product is itself a potent vesicant but it is nonvolatile. Be-

$$ClCH=CHAsCl_2 \ \xrightarrow{H_2O} \ ClCH=CHAsO$$
$$\beta\text{-Chlorovinylarsine oxide}$$

cause of susceptibility to hydrolysis, by which one toxic agent is transformed into another, the tactical uses of lewisite are dependent upon the humidity and temperature of the terrain.

An antidote to lewisite, developed by an English group during World War II, is known as BAL (British anti-lewisite). The discovery is based upon recognition that lewisite exerts its lethal action by combination with sulfhydryl groups (—SH) of proteins.   The substance contains two sulf-

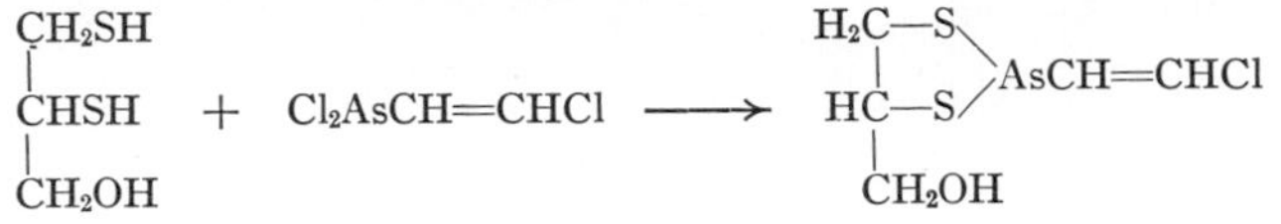

$$
\begin{array}{ccc}
\text{CH}_2\text{SH} & & \text{H}_2\text{C—S} \\
| & & \quad\diagdown \\
\text{CHSH} \quad + \quad \text{Cl}_2\text{AsCH=CHCl} \quad \longrightarrow \quad & \text{HC—S}\quad\diagup\text{AsCH=CHCl} \\
| & & | \\
\text{CH}_2\text{OH} & & \text{CH}_2\text{OH}
\end{array}
$$

BAL (2,3-dimercaptopropanol-1)

hydryl groups and combines with lewisite to form a stable, cyclic, nontoxic compound.

PROBLEMS

1. Indicate methods by which the following syntheses could be effected:
   (a) Methylacetylene from acetone
   (b) Pentyne-2 from pentanol-2
   (c) 4-Methylpentyne-2 from isopropylacetylene
   (d) n-Butane from acetylene

2. Vinylacetylene can be hydrated under the catalytic influence of a mercuric salt.   Predict the structure of the product.
3. A hydrocarbon of the formula C_6H_{10} yields 2-methylpentane on hydrogenation; it combines with the elements of water when treated with mercuric sulfate and dilute sulfuric acid but does not react with ammoniacal cuprous chloride solution.   What is the structure?
4. Describe a simple test that would prove that benzene (C_6H_6) does not have the structure CH≡CCH=CHCH=CH₂ .

READING REFERENCES

R. A. Peters, "British Anti-Lewisite," *J. Chem. Soc.*, **26**, 85 (1949)

W. Reppe, "Chemie des Acetylens," *Experientia*, **5**, 93 (1949)

F. D. Bergmann, "The Chemistry of Acetylene and Related Compounds," Interscience, New York (1948)

R. A. Raphael, "Acetylenic Compounds in Organic Synthesis," Butterworths, London (1955)

CHAPTER 5

PETROLEUM

Natural gas and petroleum, probably formed by decomposition of organic material of marine origin, occur in pockets in the upper strata of the earth entrapped by an overlying rock structure (L. *petra*, rock + *oleum*, oil). When a well is drilled through the cap, oil for a time is forced to the surface under pressure from the gas, and after the pressure has subsided oil is removed by pump. Natural gas as it flows from a well consists largely of methane and gaseous homologs, but dissolved in it are significant amounts of C_5-C_7 hydrocarbons, which are normally liquid and which are valuable as gasoline components. Consequently the raw gas is processed for recovery of this material, known as natural gasoline, either by compression sufficient to liquify the less volatile constituents or by passage of the gas through a scrubber in which the natural gasoline is absorbed in an oil from which it can be removed by distillation. Natural gasoline accounts for about 10% of the gasoline manufactured; it is blended with refinery gasoline to increase vapor pressure. The residual natural gas is used for production of carbon black (p. 44) or is carried by pipeline to industrial areas for use as fuel.

Petroleum, a dark brown or greenish, viscous oil, is refined near the oil field if labor and transportation are available, or is shipped by tanker or pipeline to suitably located refineries. Refining involves separation into fractions of different boiling ranges by distillation, followed by reprocessing of specific fractions, as required. The principal fractions are: petroleum ether (b.p. 20–60°, pentanes and hexanes), ligroin or light naphtha (b.p. 60–100°, hexanes, heptanes), gasoline (b.p. 40–205°), kerosene (b.p. 175–325°), gas oil (b.p. above 275°).

Finally, vacuum distillation affords lubricating oil, and leaves a residuum that is either asphalt or petroleum coke, depending upon the nature of the petroleum.

CONSTITUENTS

Hydrocarbons. — Natural gas, freed of natural gasoline by compressors or oil scrubbers, contains methane as the chief hydrocarbon constituent, together with decreasing amounts of ethane, propane, butane, and isobutane; varying amounts of carbon dioxide, nitrogen, or sometimes helium, are also present. Since the lower paraffins differ considerably in boiling point from one another and from nitrogen and helium, the components of a given natural gas can be separated efficiently by liquification and fractional distillation under pressure at low temperatures. Pure methane (b.p. $-162°$), ethane (b.p. $-89°$), propane (b.p. $-42°$), and helium (b.p. $-269°$) are produced from this source; propane, and a butane-isobutane mixture are available as compressed gases in cylinders and are used for heating and as motor fuels.

Natural gasoline, extracted from raw natural gas either by compression or by absorption in oil, contains paraffins ranging from C_3 to C_8, for example: C_3-C_4, 20%; C_5, 30%; C_6, 24%; C_7, 20%; C_8, 4%; residue, 2%. The more volatile portion is easily separated by distillation into propane, butanes, and a fraction known as the C_5-cut, which contains n-pentane and isopentane in approximately equal amounts and a negligible quantity of neopentane. This fraction is separated easily, since the least volatile C_4-

$CH_3CH_2CH_2CH_2CH_3$	$(CH_3)_2CHCH_2CH_3$	$C(CH_3)_4$ (minor component)
n-Pentane (b.p. 36.1°)	Isopentane (b.p. 27.9°)	Neopentane (b.p. 9.5°)

C_5-cut

hydrocarbon, n-butane, boils at $-0.5°$, and the most volatile C_6-hydrocarbon, trimethylethylmethane, boils at $49.7°$.

Isolation of hydrocarbons of more than six carbon atoms from petroleum is difficult, since the number of isomers increases tremendously and the difference between the boiling points decreases rapidly as the chain length is increased (p. 31). Since 1927 a group at the National Bureau of Standards (Rossini,[1] et al.) has made an extensive investigation of the lighter distillates of a Midcontinent petroleum, and has isolated about seventy hydrocarbons. By use of highly efficient columns it is possible to separate hydrocarbons whose boiling points differ by as little as 1°, especially if the distillation is carried out alternately at normal and at reduced pressures or with an added azeotrope-forming substance. Other valuable methods include extraction, adsorption, and crystallization from such solvents as liquid methane, propane, and dichlorodifluoromethane. A total of twenty-eight paraffin hydrocarbons have been isolated from the gasoline fraction. These include the ten straight-chain hydrocarbons from methane to n-decane, and eighteen branched-chain hydrocarbons, ranging from isobutane to methylnonanes.

In addition to the open-type hydrocarbons, petroleum contains varying amounts of cycloparaffins known in petroleum technology as naphthenes. Seventeen of these have been isolated from the gasoline fraction discussed above; they are alkyl derivatives of cyclopentane and cyclohexane, both of which are also present. Typical naphthenes are shown in the formulas:

---

[1] Frederick D. Rossini; b. 1912 Buffalo, Iowa; Ph.D. California; Bureau of Standards, Carnegie Inst. Techn.

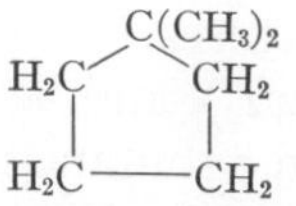

$$\begin{array}{cc} & C(CH_3)_2 \\ H_2C & CH_2 \\ | & | \\ H_2C & ---CH_2 \end{array}$$

1,1-Dimethylcyclopentane
(b. p. 87.5°)

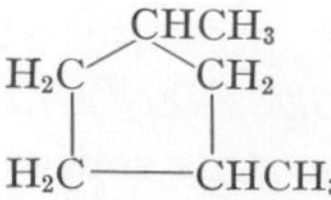

$$\begin{array}{cc} & CHCH_3 \\ H_2C & CH_2 \\ | & | \\ H_2C & ---CHCH_3 \end{array}$$

1,3-Dimethylcyclopentane
(b. p. 90.9°)

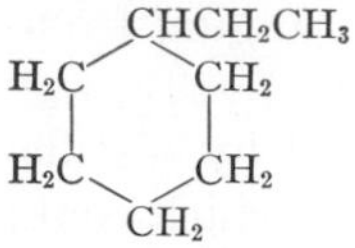

$$\begin{array}{cc} & CHCH_2CH_3 \\ H_2C & CH_2 \\ | & | \\ H_2C & CH_2 \\ & CH_2 \end{array}$$

Ethylcyclohexane
(b. p. 131.8°)

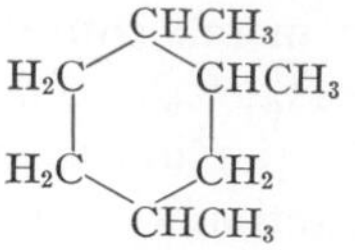

$$\begin{array}{cc} & CHCH_3 \\ H_2C & CHCH_3 \\ | & | \\ H_2C & CH_2 \\ & CHCH_3 \end{array}$$

1,2,4-Trimethylcyclohexane
(b. p. 141.2°)

Most petroleums also contain aromatic hydrocarbons. The total aromatic content of Borneo crudes is estimated at 39%, and in World War I this petroleum was an important source of toluene, a strategic material for the preparation of the high explosive trinitrotoluene (TNT). Nineteen aromatics have been isolated by the Bureau of Standards group from the gasoline fraction, and these are alkyl derivatives of benzene, which is also present. Typical ones are formulated:

Benzene
(b. p. 80.1°)

CH_3

Toluene
(b. p. 110.6°)

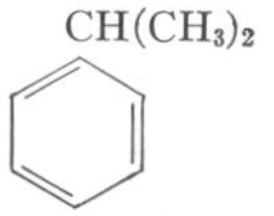

$CH(CH_3)_2$

Cumene
(isopropylbenzene,
b. p. 152.4°)

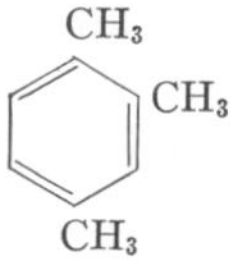

CH_3
CH_3
CH_3

Pseudocumene
(b. p. 169.2°)

The relative proportion of the three types of hydrocarbons varies in different crude gasolines, even from the same general locality; the content of naphthenes and aromatics may vary from a few percent to as much as 40%. The aniline point, defined as the temperature at which a given gasoline is miscible with an equal volume of aniline, has been used as an indication of the approximate hydrocarbon composition. Since aniline, C_6H_5-NH_2, is a derivative of benzene, aromatic hydrocarbons dissolve even at temperatures as low as $-30°$. Naphthenes have higher aniline points (35–$55°$), and paraffins, which are most dissimilar to aniline, the highest (70–$76°$). The specific gravities have been used also as a similar index of composition; aromatic hydrocarbons have the highest values (benzene = 0.89), straight-chain paraffins the lowest (n-hexane = 0.66), and cyclic hydrocarbons intermediate values (cyclohexane = 0.78). A method of analysis developed by the Bureau of Standards group takes advantage of the fact that aromatics can be separated fairly readily from paraffins and naphthenes by adsorption, which depends upon differences in chemical properties rather than differences in the molecular size. In another method the aromatic content is determined from the percent absorbed by sulfuric acid:

$$C_6H_6 + H_2SO_4 \xrightarrow{P_2O_5} C_6H_5SO_3H + H_2O$$

and the amounts of paraffins and naphthenes in the residue are determined from the density and refractive index.

Eleven hydrocarbons have been isolated by the Bureau of Standards group from the kerosene fraction of the above Midcontinent crude. These include one paraffin, n-dodecane (b.p. 216.3°), three alkyl derivatives of benzene, naphthalene (a bicyclic aromatic, b.p. 218.0°), and two alkyl

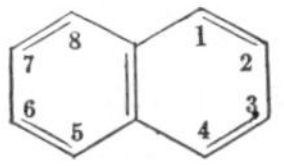

Naphthalene

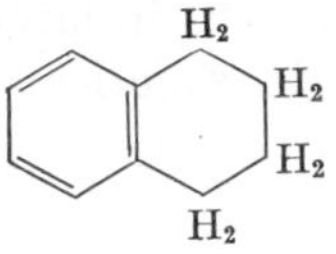

Tetralin

derivatives, α- and β- (or 1- and 2-) methylnaphthalene, which had been isolated previously by virtue of the less soluble complexes that they form with picric acid, $HOC_6H_2(NO_2)_3$. The additional four substances contain a benzene ring fused to a cycloparaffin ring, such as tetralin (1,2,3,4-tetrahydronaphthalene, b.p. 207.6°) and two alkyl derivatives, 1- and 2-methyl-5,6,7,8-tetrahydronaphthalene (b.p. 234°, 229°).

Naphthenic Acid. — Extraction of petroleum with alkali and acidification of the alkaline solution gives a black viscous tar known as naphthenic acid, since the constituents are mainly cycloparaffin acids derived from naphthene components. Investigations by Markownikoff (1899) and by v. Braun[2] (1931–33) showed that only minor amounts of paraffinic acids are present (e.g., $(CH_3)_2CHCH_2CH_2CH_2CO_2H$ and n-$C_{15}H_{31}CO_2H$), and that the lowest-boiling fractions contains C_8–C_{12} acids of the general formula I, in which n, the number of methylene groups, is 1 to 5. Acids whose analyses indicate the presence of two and three rings were also encountered. The further naphthenic

I (R=H or alkyl)

acids II-IV were isolated by Nenitzescu (1938); acids V–VII, two of which are cyclohexane derivatives, were isolated and characterized by a group at the University of Texas. Analysis of fractions from the high-boiling naphthenic acids of lubricating oils indicate that they are monobasic C_{14}–C_{19} acids with an average of 2.6 rings.

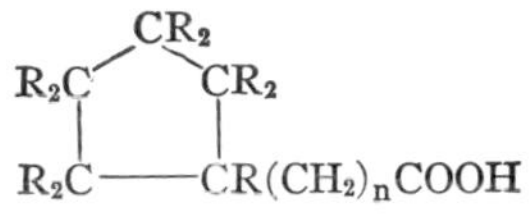

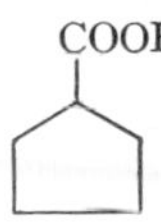

Cyclopentane-carboxylic acid
II

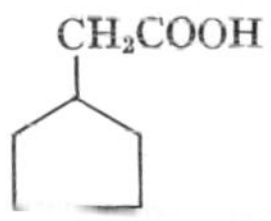

Cyclopentyl-acetic acid
III

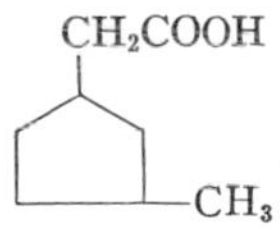

3-Methylcyclopentyl-acetic acid
IV

[2] Julius von Braun, 1875–1939 b. Warsaw; Ph.D. Göttingen (Wallach); Frankfurt, Germany

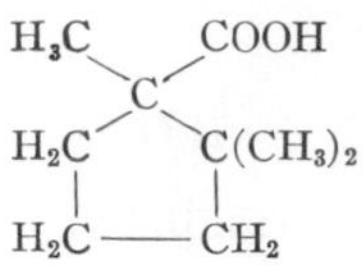

H₃C   COOH
    \   /
     C
H₂C⁄   \C(CH₃)₂
 | |
H₂C —— CH₂

Camphonanic acid
(m.p. 194–195°)

V

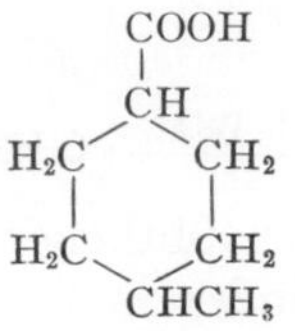

COOH
 |
 CH
H₂C⁄ \CH₂
 | |
H₂C⎣ ⎤CH₂
   CHCH₃

4-Methylcyclohexane-
carboxylic acid
(m.p. 110–111°)

VI

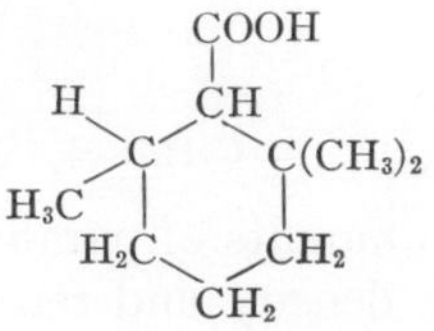

COOH
 |
H   CH
 \ |
  C \C(CH₃)₂
H₃C|
H₂C⎣ ⎤CH₂
   CH₂

2,2,6-Trimethylcyclo-
hexanecarboxylic acid
(m.p. 83°)

VII

Naphthenic acids occur in larger amounts (3%) in Russian, Rumanian, and Polish oils than in American oils (0.1–0.3%), but since extraction of petroleum with alkali is a usual part of the refining operations and since the volume of U. S. production is enormous, naphthenic acid is available for technical uses in large quantity. Most uses require conversion into a water-insoluble metallic salt, or soap, of aluminum or of a heavy metal, either by precipitation from an alkaline solution or, in the case of aluminum, by fusion with an aqueous aluminum hydroxide gel. These soaps are amorphous solids or tough gums; in contrast to sodium soaps of paraffinic acids, they are soluble in hydrocarbon solvents.

A certain amount of naphthenic acid goes into the manufacture of the lead, cobalt, and manganese soaps for use as driers (oxidation catalysts) in paint and varnish formulations. Copper naphthenate is used for mildew-proofing sandbags, rope for use at sea, and other wood, cotton, jute, and hemp products. The fungicidal action is associated with the copper present, but copper naphthenate is a preferred agent because it is taken up by the fiber from an oil solution more readily than other copper soaps. Another use is in the compounding of special lubricants required where high pressures are encountered. Napalm, a coprecipitated aluminum soap from naphthenic acid and the fatty acids of coconut oil developed in 1942 (Fieser and Hershberg), was used in the war for preparation of gasoline gels for incendiary munitions.

Sulfur and Nitrogen Compounds. — Petroleums contain sulfur compounds in amounts up to about one percent. These are objectionable because of a disagreeable odor and because even the combined sulfur in gasoline is oxidized during combustion to sulfur dioxide, which is corrosive in the presence of moisture (sulfurous acid). Specifications for government purchases allow 0.10% as the maximum sulfur content of gasoline. A certain

(CH₃)₂CHCH₂SH
Isobutyl mercaptan

CH₃SC₂H₅
Methyl ethyl sulfide

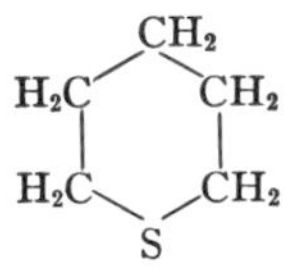

        CH₂
H₂C⁄ \CH₂
 | |
H₂C⎣ ⎤CH₂
   S

Pentamethylene sulfide

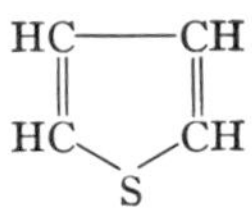

HC —— CH
 ‖   ‖
HC⎣ ⎤CH
   S

Thiophene

number of the sulfur compounds have been identified and they are of the three types corresponding to the paraffins, naphthenes, and aromatics of the hydrocarbon constituents.

The nitrogen content of most petroleums is very low, for instance, 0.008% for Pennsylvanian oils. Some of the nitrogen compounds are basic and can be extracted with sulfur dioxide or mineral acids. The only nitrogen bases of known structure are quinoline derivatives, formulas VIII–X (J. R. Bailey).

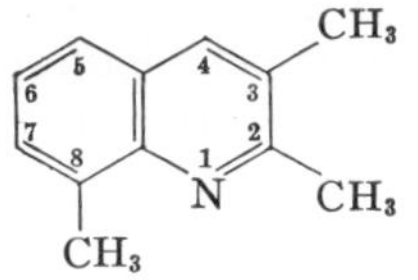

2,3,8-Trimethyl-quinoline

VIII

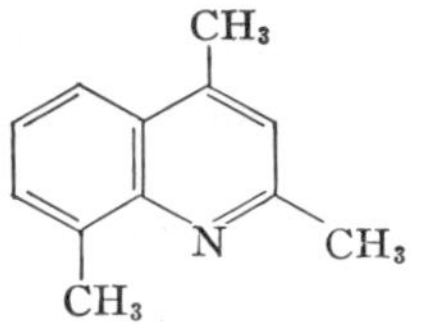

2,4,8-Trimethyl-quinoline

IX

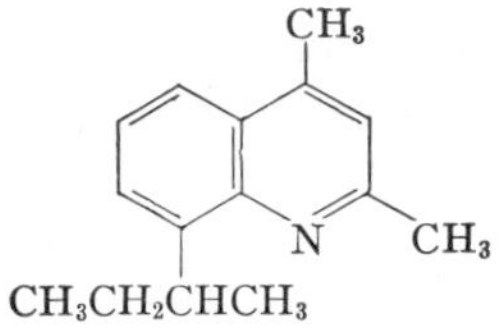

2,4-Dimethyl-8-sec-butylquinoline

X

MOTOR FUELS

Fuel Knock and Octane Rating. — The knock (or ping) heard when an automobile engine under stress is accelerated too rapidly is a warning that conditions for efficient performance of the engine with the particular gasoline used have been exceeded. In the down-stroke of the piston a mixture of air and gasoline vapor and droplets is drawn from the carburetor into the cylinder, and on the up-stroke the mixture is compressed; the ratio of the initial volume to the final volume is the compression ratio. At the end of the up-stroke a spark from the ignition system ignites the compressed air-gasoline mixture in the immediate vicinity of the spark plug and, in normal operation, the gases expand and a flame-front travels at a regular and orderly rate through the remainder of the fuel mixture to give a power thrust transmitted by the piston to the crankshaft. If the stress is excessive, however, the major portion of the fuel mixture burns in an orderly fashion but in doing so compresses the end gas, that is, the gas furthest from the point of ignition, and produces in it a preflame reaction which lowers its ignition temperature. In consequence, the end gas burns in an explosive and disorderly fashion ahead of the flame front and so produces the sound of knocking. Knocking increases with increasing compression ratio, and since an engine develops more power and requires less fuel with increasing compression ratio, the development of efficient high-compression engines was dependent upon the knocking tendencies of available gasolines.

With recognition that gasolines vary greatly in this property, standards were introduced for rating fuels (1927). Isooctane (2,2,4-trimethylpentane), which detonates only at high compression and which was superior to any gasoline known at the time, was assigned the octane rating of 100, and n-heptane, which is particularly prone to knocking, was given the octane number of 0. The octane number of a given fuel is the percent of isooctane in a blend with n-heptane that has the same knocking characteristics of the fuel under examination in a standard one-cylinder engine operated under specific conditions. Determination of the octane ratings of a large number of synthetic hydrocarbons has shown that in the alkane series octane number decreases as the carbon chain is lengthened and increases with branching of the chain. Alkenes have higher ratings than the corresponding alkanes, and the octane number increases as the double bond is shifted to the center of the molecule. Cycloparaffins are less prone to knock than normal paraffins, and aromatic hydrocarbons have exceptionally high octane numbers.

The straight-run gasolines provided by distillation of petroleum consist mainly of alkanes, and as a result the octane rating varies from as high as 73 to as low as 20 (Michigan). However, technological improvements have so increased octane ratings that engines of the nineteen twenties with a compression ratio of some 4:1 have given place to models of superior efficiency of ratios of 8–9 to 1.

In Diesel engines the air alone is compressed, with the result that the temperature is increased to 290–340°. The fuel is injected almost at the end of the compression stroke and is spontaneously ignited. Diesel fuel need not be volatile, and generally consists of the fraction boiling between kerosene and the heavier lubricating oils. Owing to differences in engine construction, high octane fuels are much less efficient than low ones. The ignition quality is expressed in terms of the cetane number, which refers to a mixture of cetane (n-hexadecane, value = 100) and α-methylnaphthalene (value = 0); most automotive Diesel engines require a fuel of cetane number greater than 45; that is, the desirability of hydrocarbons is exactly reversed for the Diesel as compared with the ordinary engine.

Antiknock Compound. — The steady improvement in antiknock characteristics of gasoline is due in part to new technological processes, but the first major advance was the discovery that knocking can be inhibited by addition of certain chemicals, the most important of which is tetraethyllead (TEL), developed by T. Midgley and T. A. Boyd (1922). After the initial observation that iodine, aniline, and selenium oxychloride are somewhat effective in decreasing knock, study of innumerable substances led to the organometallic compound, which still retains its supremacy. About 88% of all American gasolines contain tetraethyllead; gasolines leaded to the point of an octane rating of 80 or more are known to the trade as Ethyl or premium gasoline. An early synthesis utilized the Grignard reaction:

$$4\,C_2H_5MgBr \;+\; 2\,PbCl_2 \longrightarrow Pb(C_2H_5)_4 \;+\; 4\,MgClBr \;+\; Pb$$

The commercial process now consists in interaction of a sodium–lead alloy with ethyl chloride at moderate temperatures and pressures:

$$4\,PbNa \;+\; 4\,C_2H_5Cl \longrightarrow Pb(C_2H_5)_4 \;+\; 4\,NaCl \;+\; 3\,Pb$$

The lead derivative is separated by steam distillation, and the lead sludge is smelted into pig lead.

Ethyl fluid contains not only tetraethyllead (63%), but also ethylene dibromide (26%), ethylene dichloride (9%), and a dye (2%). Ethylene dibromide is an essential constituent since it reacts with the lead oxide produced during combustion to form volatile lead bromide, which is swept from the cylinders in the exhaust gases. The manufacture of large amounts of ethylene dibromide presented a problem, since bromine was not available in sufficient quantity. The difficulty was solved by extraction of bromine from sea water, 7.5 tons of which contain one pound of bromine. An early process, operated on board the S.S. "Ethyl," extracted bromine by adding aniline to chlorinated sea water, and recovering bromine from the filtered precipitate. In the modern process, bromine is liberated from natural bromine-containing brines by oxidation with chlorine, entrained in a cur-

$$3\,Na_2CO_3 \;+\; 3\,Br_2 \longrightarrow 5\,NaBr \;+\; NaBrO_3 \;+\; 3\,CO_2$$

rent of air, and absorbed in sodium carbonate solution, from which it can be recovered easily. The efficiency is 95%.

The amount of tetraethyllead in motor gasoline ranges from 0.75 to 3 ml. per gal., the legal maximum; aviation gasolines are more heavily leaded. The susceptibility of various gasolines depends upon the initial octane number and the hydrocarbon composition. The response is greater for low-octane gasolines, and hence tetraethyllead decreases in effectiveness with increasing concentration. The effect on a specific straight-run gasoline with an original octane number of 73 is shown by the following results: 1 ml. per gal. increases the rating to 82, 2 ml. to 86, 3 ml. to 89, and 6 ml. to 93.

Cracked Gasolines. — The perfection of practicable processes for conducting the controlled pyrolytic decomposition, or cracking, of paraffinic hydrocarbons has had the important result of more than doubling the amount of motor gasoline obtainable from petroleum. The large and relatively nonvolatile hydrocarbons of otherwise practically unutilized fractions can be broken down by suitable thermal treatment into mixtures of smaller molecules having the desired volatility. Cracking processes are conducted in the temperature range from 400 to 700° and at pressures which vary from atmospheric (vapor-phase cracking) to as much as 1200 lbs. per sq. in. (liquid-phase cracking). The widely used mixed-phase processes are conducted at moderate temperatures (400–500°) and high pressures. Owing to the complex nature of the usual petroleum distillates, it is generally advantageous to crack fractions boiling over a narrow range. Optimum conditions can be attained, and therefore increased yields of gasoline of higher octane rating are obtained by selective cracking. The olefinic hydrocarbons formed during pyrolysis were at first assumed to be objectionable and were removed, with high resultant loss, but it was subsequently found that olefins actually increase the octane rating and that cracked gasolines generally have superior antiknock characteristics.

Thermal Reactions of Gaseous Hydrocarbons. — Studies of the pyrolysis of the gaseous hydrocarbons available from natural gas and natural gasoline have provided information concerning the reactions involved in cracking and have led to development of several synthetic intermediates of great technical importance. Methane is exceptionally stable but decomposes into carbon and hydrogen at temperatures above 1000° (carbon black, p. 44). Ethane yields ethylene as an initial product of pyrolysis (1), and this olefin can be produced in high yield. The higher alkanes undergo both dehydrogenation and rupture of the chain, usually with formation of methane. Propane (2) affords both propylene, by dehydrogenation, and

1. $CH_3CH_3 \xrightarrow{485°} CH_2{=}CH_2 + H_2$

2. $CH_3CH_2CH_3 \xrightarrow{460°}$
$\begin{cases} CH_3CH{=}CH_2 + H_2 \\ \quad \text{(45 parts)} \\ CH_2{=}CH_2 + CH_4 \\ \quad \text{(55 parts)} \end{cases}$

ethylene, by methane splitting; the velocity of the pyrolytic reaction increases with increasing temperature, but the relative proportion of the products is not materially affected by the conditions of temperature or pressure. In the pyrolysis of n-butane (3), dehydrogenation to butene occurs to a minor extent and the predominating reactions consist in fission

3. $CH_3CH_2CH_2CH_3 \xrightarrow{435°}$
$\quad n$-Butane
$\begin{cases} CH_3CH_2CH{=}CH_2 + CH_3CH{=}CHCH_3 + H_2 \\ \quad \text{(12 parts)} \\ CH_3CH{=}CH_2 + CH_4 \\ \quad \text{(50 parts)} \\ CH_2{=}CH_2 + CH_3CH_3 \\ \quad \text{(38 parts)} \end{cases}$

of the chain with elimination of methane and ethane. It is generally found that as the chain length increases carbon-to-carbon rupture predominates over dehydrogenation. In the industry cracking of the propane—n-butane refinery cut provides a practicable method for production of ethylene and propylene.

The branched-chain hydrocarbon isobutane (4) suffers both dehydrogenation and elimination of methane, and with the still more highly branched neopentane (5) the latter is the sole reaction. Although neopentane occurs in petroleum only in small amounts, the isobutane fraction is often considerable and is employed for production of the valuable synthetic intermediate isobutene (isobutylene) and of isooctane (p. 105).

4. $\begin{array}{c} CH_3 \\ \\ CH_3 \end{array}\!\!\Big\rangle CHCH_3 \xrightarrow{435°}$
Isobutane
$\begin{cases} \dfrac{CH_3}{CH_3}\!\Big\rangle C{=}CH_2 + H_2 \\ \quad \text{(60 parts)} \\ CH_3CH{=}CH_2 + CH_4 \\ \quad \text{(40 parts)} \end{cases}$

5. $\begin{array}{cc} CH_3 & CH_3 \\ & \\ CH_3 & CH_3 \end{array}\!C\! \longrightarrow \dfrac{CH_3}{CH_3}\!\Big\rangle C{=}CH_2 + CH_4$
Neopentane   Isobutene

Olefins generally are more stable than the corresponding paraffins, and the thermal resistance increases as the double bond is moved nearer the center of the molecule but decreases as the chain is lengthened or branched. Products have been isolated that result from four types of reactions: dehydrogenation, polymerization, carbon-to-carbon fission, and rearrangement. Products ranging from carbon to naphthalene have been reported for the pyrolysis of even the simplest olefin, ethylene. The chart (6) shows some of the many substances that have been isolated as products of the pyrolysis of ethylene and indicates possible alternative mechanisms of the eventual polymerization to long-chain olefins (and their hydrogenation products), cyclization to naphthenes, and conversion to aromatic hydrocarbons. Both acetylene and butene-1 have been postulated as the initial products.

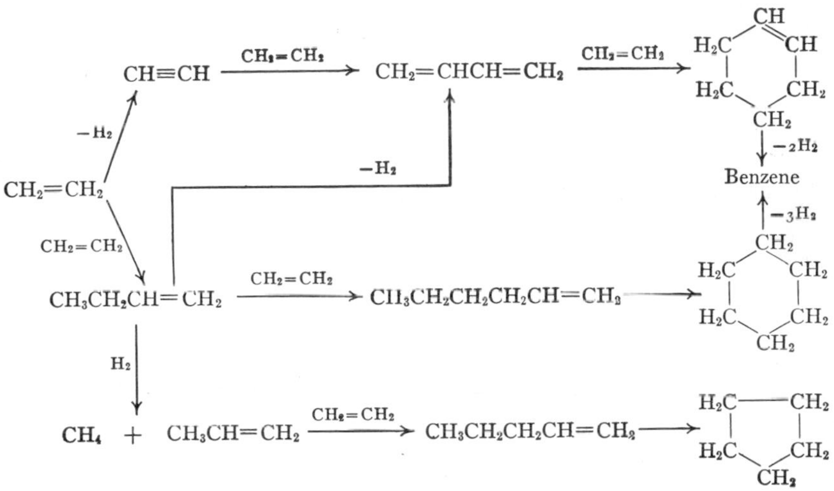

Catalytic Cracking. — The first successful catalytic process was developed by Houdry (1934). The catalyst consists of silica and alumina in a ratio of 4:1 and about 1% of manganese oxide. The cost of the original catalyst for a plant with a capacity of 15,000 bbl. per day has been estimated at $35,000. The activity is markedly decreased during use, owing to deposition of carbon, but is restored on oxidation, and the catalyst can be used about a year. In comparison with thermal cracking the conditions are comparatively mild (500°, 30 lbs. per sq. in.), and gas formation is only 4-7% by weight. The main effect of the catalyst is probably on the olefins produced by cracking, since Houdry gasoline contains only a small amount of olefins, known to undergo ready isomerization, polymerization, and condensation under the influence of various catalysts. The high octane value (around 80) is attributed principally to branched paraffins and aromatics formed from olefins. Houdry gasolines are comparatively stable, and the sulfur content is slight (0.2% for gasoline from a charging stock containing as much as 2%). The yield of liquid products is much higher per pass than in ordinary cracking, 40-50% by volume of gasoline and 50-55% of gas oil; but the total yield is less, since the gas-oil fraction cannot be recycled economically. It is used as furnace oil or more often is cracked thermally at high temperatures.

Reforming. — Thermal treatment of gasoline for the purpose of increasing the octane number is known as reforming, which is essentially a cracking process carried out at high pressure for a very short time, ten to twenty seconds. The reaction is promoted by a variety of catalysts (Houdry type, bauxite, chromium oxide), which increase formation of aromatics and branched-chain compounds, with resultant high-octane values and improved lead susceptibility. Yields of gasoline are 85–95% by volume and the octane numbers are often increased by as much as 20 units; for instance, specific naphthas of the ratings 43, 53, and 57 are reformed to 62, 64, and 77, respectively.

Polymer Gasoline. — The unsaturated gaseous hydrocarbons produced in cracking are valuable starting materials for the production not only of synthetic alcohols and derived products but also of high-octane motor fuels. The first large-scale use involved polymerization of a cracked fraction rich in gaseous olefins to a liquid product known as polymer gasoline, of octane number 78–83. The process of polymerization, usually induced by phosphoric or sulfuric acid (Ipatieff, 1935), is actually one of dimerization.

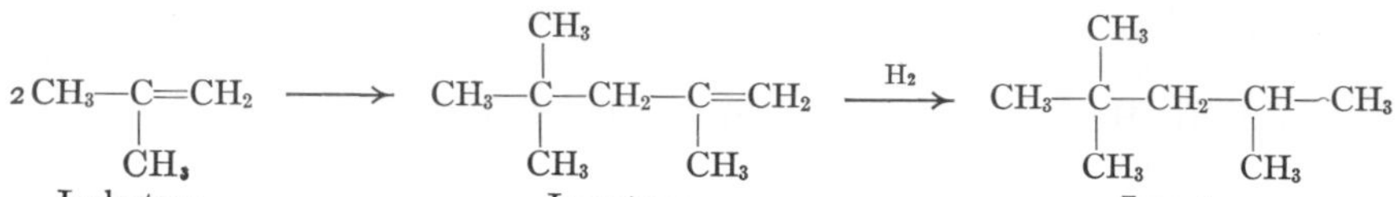

$$2\,CH_3-\underset{\underset{CH_3}{|}}{\overset{\overset{CH_3}{|}}{C}}=CH_2 \longrightarrow CH_3-\underset{\underset{CH_3}{|}}{\overset{\overset{CH_3}{|}}{C}}-CH_2-\underset{\underset{CH_3}{|}}{C}=CH_2 \xrightarrow{H_2} CH_3-\underset{\underset{CH_3}{|}}{\overset{\overset{CH_3}{|}}{C}}-CH_2-\underset{\underset{CH_3}{|}}{CH}-CH_3$$

Isobutene   Isooctene   Isooctane
                                 (diisobutylene)

Thus isobutene yields the dimer isooctene, which consists mainly of 2,4,4-trimethylpentene-1 but contains about 20% of 2,4,4-trimethylpentene-2. Both isomers on hydrogenation yield isooctane, which in a pure form has an octane number of 100. The acid-catalyzed polymerization can be interpreted by the following reaction mechanism: (a) a proton attacks the more negative of the two unsaturated carbon atoms to give trimethylcarbonium

(a) $(CH_3)_2C\overset{\frown}{=}CH_2 \xrightarrow{H^+} (CH_3)_2\overset{+}{C}CH_3 \; [or \; (CH_3)_3\overset{+}{C}]$

(b) $(CH_3)_3C^+ + \overset{\curvearrowleft}{CH_2}=C(CH_3)_2 \longrightarrow (CH_3)_3C-CH_2\overset{+}{C}(CH_3)_2$

(c) $(CH_3)_3CCH_2\overset{+}{C}(CH_3)_2 \xrightarrow{-H^+} (CH_3)_3CCH_2C(CH_3)=CH_2$

ion; (b) this ion attacks the more negative center of a second molecule of isobutene; (c) the resulting dimer ion expels a proton to form isooctene.

In practice isobutene is available in mixtures, for example as a component of the C_4-cut of cracked gasoline, which also contains butenes (-1 and -2) and butanes (n- and i-). Isobutene, however, has greater affinity for sulfuric acid than the butenes, and when the fraction is passed into 65% sulfuric acid at 20–35°, isobutene is selectively absorbed. The acid solution is then heated at 100° for about a minute, after which polymerization is complete. The isooctene obtained is about 85% pure and on hydrogenation affords isooctane of an octane rating of 91–97. The product as such is too high-boiling for aviation fuel and is blended with more volatile hydrocarbons. A typical 100-octane aviation gasoline contains about 40% isooctane, 25% isopentane, 35% depentanized base stock, and 4 ml. per gal. of tetraethyllead. Cumene is an excellent blending fuel in high-octane gasoline.

Alkylation. — A second reaction of considerable technological importance can be represented as an addition of an alkane to the double bond of an olefin but is usually described as the alkylation of an alkane with an

$$(CH_3)_3C \cdot H \ + \ CH_2{=}C(CH_3)_2 \xrightarrow{H_2SO_4} \ \underset{\underset{CH_3}{|}}{\overset{\overset{CH_3}{|}}{CH_3{-}C{-}CH_2}}{-}\underset{\underset{CH_3}{|}}{CHCH_3}$$

Isobutane	Isobutylene	Isooctane (2,2,4-trimethylpentane)

olefin. The alkylation of isobutane with isobutene gives isooctane, and hence this important hydrocarbon is obtained in one step from the C_4-cut of cracked gasoline, which contains both components. Alkylation can be induced with catalysts (sulfuric acid, boron fluoride, anhydrous hydrogen fluoride, aluminum chloride) or by thermal treatment. A mechanism for acid-catalyzed alkylation postulates (a) addition of a proton to the olefin

(a) $(CH_3)_2C{=}CH_2 + H^+ \rightleftharpoons (CH_3)_3\overset{+}{C}$

(b) $(CH_3)_3\overset{+}{C} + CH_2{=}C(CH_3)_2 \rightleftharpoons (CH_3)_3CCH_2\overset{+}{C}(CH_3)_2$

(c) $(CH_3)_3CCH_2\overset{+}{C}(CH_3)_2 + (CH_3)_3CH \rightarrow (CH_3)_3CCH_2CH(CH_3)_2 + (CH_3)_3\overset{+}{C}$

to form a carbonium ion (b), addition of this ion to another molecule of olefin to form a dimeric carbonium ion, and (c) reaction of this with the alkane to form the final product, with regeneration of the original carbonium ion. The reaction is not limited to isoparaffins or to an olefin of special structure. Thus propane is alkylated with ethylene to give the products

$$CH_2{=}CH_2 \ + \ H_2C\underset{CH_3}{\overset{CH_3}{<}} \quad \overset{55\%}{\nearrow} \quad CH_3CH_2CH\underset{CH_3}{\overset{CH_3}{<}}$$

Ethylene / Propane

Isopentane

$$\underset{16\%}{\searrow} \quad CH_3CH_2CH_2CH_2CH_3$$

n-Pentane

shown; the course of the reaction demonstrates that the hydrogen atoms of a methylene group are more reactive than those of a methyl group. Alkylation of isobutane with propylene leads to three products: 2,2-dimethylpentane (60–80%), 2-methylhexane (10–30%), and 2,2,3-trimethylbutane or

$$(CH_3)_3CH \ + \ CH_2{=}CHCH_3 \longrightarrow \begin{cases} (CH_3)_3CCH_2CH_2CH_3 \ (2,2\text{-Dimethylpentane}) \\ (CH_3)_2CHCH_2CH_2CH_2CH_3 \ (2\text{-Methylhexane}) \\ (CH_3)_3CCH(CH_3)_2 \ (2,2,3\text{-Trimethylbutane}) \end{cases}$$

triptane $(7-11\%)$. The last hydrocarbon has a particularly high octane rating, $(100) + 1.8$.

Isomerization. — At the same time that isobutane became a key compound in the manufacture of high-octane fuel, a method for its preparation on a large scale fortunately became available. *n*-Butane occurs in greater concentration than isobutane in both natural and thermally cracked gas. Isobutane has never been detected as a pyrolysis product of butane, and it has been calculated that an equilibrium mixture of the butanes at 527° would contain only 13% of isobutane. The point of equilibrium however is tremendously influenced by the temperature. In the presence of aluminum bromide an equilibrium mixture is obtained at 27° that contains

$$CH_3CH_2CH_2CH_3 \rightleftharpoons (CH_3)_3CH$$
$$\text{Butane} \qquad\qquad \text{Isobutane}$$

75–80% of isobutane. Isomerization of straight-chain paraffins is important commercially since the octane number is increased considerably with branching. Isomerization undoubtedly occurs during catalytic cracking and reforming, and is partly responsible for the superior quality of the products.

Olefins also can undergo isomerization. In some instances only the double bond is shifted; butene-1, for example, is converted into butene-2 merely by heating in a quartz tube at 550° (87% conversion) or in a lime-filled porcelain tube at 420° (92% conversion):

$$CH_3CH_2CH=CH_2 \underset{}{\overset{\text{Heat}}{\rightleftharpoons}} CH_3CH=CHCH_3$$
$$\text{Butene-1} \qquad\qquad\qquad \text{Butene-2}$$

$$\Big\updownarrow \text{Catalyst}$$

$$CH_3C=CH_2$$
$$\underset{}{|}$$
$$CH_3$$
$$\text{Isobutene}$$

Partial isomerization of the butenes to isobutene can be accomplished by alumina, aluminum sulfate, or phosphoric acid as catalyst.

Dehydrogenation of Paraffins and Olefins. — Since carbon-to-carbon fission occurs more readily than carbon-to-hydrogen fission, at least with heavier paraffins, commercial dehydrogenation processes (1939) depend upon suitable catalysts, such as oxides of chromium, molybdenum, vanadium, or zinc, deposited on alumina, silica gel, or active carbon carriers. Conversions of 80–95% are achieved (recycle) in the dehydrogenation of ethane, propane, and the butanes (600°, atmospheric pressure). Olefins are dehydrogenated further by the same catalysts to diolefins and not to acetylenes. The double bonds of the diolefins produced are always adjacent to each other (conjugated). This reaction provides an important method for the preparation of butadiene, a strategic raw material for one group of synthetic rubbers.

$$CH_2=CHCH_2CH_3 \longrightarrow CH_2=CHCH=CH_2 + H_2$$

Butene-1   Butadiene

Hydrogenation of Petroleum. — Hydrogenation of high-boiling petroleum fractions for conversion into gasoline is an outgrowth of the Bergius process for production of fuels from coal by destructive hydrogenation (p. 108); the large molecules first undergo pyrolytic fission, and then the fragments are saturated with hydrogen. Since petroleum contains sulfur, which poisons the usual hydrogenation catalysts, special sulfur-resistant types have been developed. These are derived from the following metals: tin, lead, titanium, molybdenum, and germanium. Hydrogen is generated in a two-stage process from methane:

$$CH_4 + H_2O \xrightarrow{\text{Catalyst, } 870°} CO + 3H_2$$

$$CO + H_2O \xrightarrow{\text{Catalyst, } 450°} CO_2 + H_2$$

High-grade gasolines (octane number 75–90) can be obtained by the high-temperature hydrogenation of petroleum oils.

Nondestructive hydrogenation at lower temperatures is used in refining straight-run or cracked gasolines. Olefins are converted into the more stable paraffins, and the sulfur and nitrogen content is reduced considerably, thereby increasing the lead susceptibility.

Aromatization. — Toluene is normally obtained from coal tar, the production of which is geared to coke requirements. A new process for production of toluene, announced in 1940, is based on the conversion of *n*-heptane. The reaction proceeds through intermediate formation of heptene-1, which is converted to methylcyclohexane by intramolecular alkylation. The reaction is catalyzed by oxides of chromium or molybdenum carried on alumina or magnesia. Yields are excellent: about 72% in one pass and 90% on recycling.

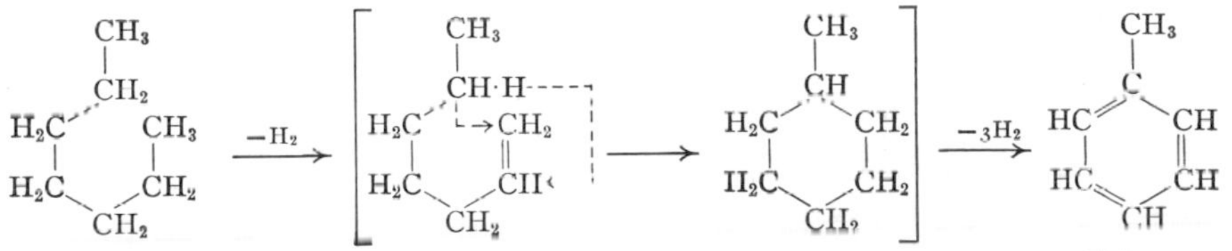

n-Heptane   Toluene

Aromatization plays an important role in a catalytic refining process known as **hydroforming** (1941). The process is based on an early observation (Zelinsky, 1911) that dehydrogenation of cyclohexane derivatives with palladium catalyst occurs readily in the presence of excess hydrogen, which even exerts a favorable effect, presumably by maintaining the activity of the catalyst. The process was operated on a large scale during World War II for production of toluene from methylcyclohexane. *o*-Xylene is now made commercially in this way from 1,2-dimethylcyclohexane. However, the major current use of hydroforming is for production of high-octane gasoline.

SYNTHETIC FUELS FROM COAL

Bergius Process. — The production of fuels by destructive hydrogenation of coal was developed in Germany during World War I by Bergius,[3] and has been operated on a large scale (Leuna plant). Coal probably is an elaborate network of carbon rings, which are cleaved during the process into fragments that are hydrogenated to open-chain and cyclic hydrocarbons. One ton of gasoline is obtained from 1.5–2 tons of coal. In the early process powdered coal was mixed with heavy tar (bottom from previous operation) and 5% of iron oxide, originally added for the purpose of fixing sulfur present in coal but actually a catalyst, and the pasty mass was heated with hydrogen at 450–490° for about two hours at a pressure of 3000 lbs. per sq. in. In the modern process more active catalysts are employed (tin, lead, etc.), and the reaction is carried out in liquid phase and finally in vapor phase. The product is separated by distillation into gasoline (b.p. to 200°), gas oil (b.p. 200–300°), and a residue that is recycled with fresh coal. A typical gasoline fraction contains 74% paraffins, 22% aromatics, and 4% olefins. Octane numbers of 75–80 are reported.

Fischer-Tropsch Process. — Synthetic motor fuel known as Kogasin was made in Germany in large amounts by hydrogenation of water gas, which is a mixture of carbon monoxide and hydrogen formed by treating coke with steam at high temperatures:

$$C + H_2O \longrightarrow CO + H_2$$

The pioneering experiments of Sabatier demonstrated that carbon monoxide can be hydrogenated at high temperatures to methane in the presence of nickel or iron catalysts:

$$CO + 3H_2 \longrightarrow CH_4 + H_2O$$

F. Fischer[4] and Tropsch[5] (1933) showed that the hydrogenation can be modified further by certain catalysts for production of a complex mixture of

$$nCO + 2nH_2 \longrightarrow C_nH_{2n} + nH_2O$$
$$nCO + (2n+1)H_2 \longrightarrow C_nH_{2n+2} + nH_2O$$

aliphatic products. Hydrogen is added to water gas so that the approximate ratio to carbon monoxide is 2:1; the mixture is treated with an iron oxide catalyst to remove sulfur and finally passed over a cobalt catalyst at

---

[3] Friederich Bergius, 1884–1949; b. Goldschmieden bei Breslau; Ph.D. Leipzig (Hantzsch); Hannover, Essen, Heidelberg; Nobel Prize 1931

[4] Franz Fischer, 1877–1947; b. Freiburg; Ph.D. Giessen (Elbs); Berlin, Mülheim/Ruhr, Kaiser-Wilhelm Inst. Coal Research

[5] Hans Tropsch, 1889–1935; b. Plan (Bohemia); Ph.D. Prague; Coal Research Inst.. Prague· Univ. Chicago; *Ber.*, **68A**, 169 (1935)

200°. The reaction is believed to involve formation of cobalt carbide (Co_2C) and cleavage of the carbide by hydrogen to cobalt and methylene radicals, which polymerize to give straight-chain alkanes and alkenes. One cubic meter of gas yields 130–140 g. of a hydrocarbon fraction (theory = 209 g.), more than half of which boils in the gasoline range. Because of the preponderance of straight-chain hydrocarbons, the octane rating is only 40, so reforming and leading are required. The higher-boiling fraction (Kogasin II) has a cetane rating of 85 and is eminently suited for Diesel engines. The Fischer-Tropsch hydrocarbon fraction is accompanied by a smaller but appreciable fraction rich in oxygenated compounds, particularly straight-chain alcohols, aldehydes, and ketones. An American plant utilizing natural gas as starting material has a potential capacity for conversion of 100,000,000 cubic feet of gas per day into 6000 barrels of gasoline 1000 barrels of Diesel fuel, and 400,000 lbs. of oxygenated paraffins.

LUBRICATING OILS

By use of the same methods as had been developed for the lighter fractions of petroleum, the Bureau of Standards group has obtained numerous fractions from an Oklahoma lubricating oil, homogeneous as to size and type of constituent. Although no single compound has been isolated, it is possible from the chemical and physical properties of the various fractions to draw the following conclusions concerning the composition of the very complex mixture in the oil: approximately 18–26% is composed of straight-chain and possibly branched-chain paraffins; 43–51% of alkylated naphthenes containing 1, 2, or 3 rings; 23% of alkylated naphthene—aromatic hydrocarbons containing 2, 3, or 4 rings; and 8% of "asphaltic" substances, which are considered to be largely aromatic.

The natural fluorescence of certain oils, notably Pennsylvanian, is considered to be due to aromatic ring systems, and although fluorescence is actually of no importance, dyes are often added to nonfluorescent oils to match the appearance of prominent types. The proportion and character of cyclic and open-chain structures determine the physical properties. Paraffin-base lubricating oils consist largely of long chains probably attached to cyclic structures. Lubricating oils are refined to improve the viscosity and viscosity index, which is a measure of the change of viscosity with temperature. Since lubricating oils are submitted to a wide variety of temperatures, a high viscosity index is desirable. Another important characteristic is the solidifying tendency, measured by the pour-point test or cold test. Substances that crystallize from the oil on chilling are known as petroleum waxes and their removal decreases the pour-point temperature, and generally the viscosity, but lowers the viscosity index. The presence of wax is not necessarily harmful in engines operated at temperatures at which the wax remains in solution, but at low temperatures crystallization prevents normal circulation of oil. Orginally dewaxing was accomplished by allowing the crude oil to settle during the winter months, and the wax-free layer was poured off or sometimes filtered. In more recent processes solvents are used to increase the rate of filtration and also to permit better separation. Unfortunately no solvents are known that differentiate completely between the waxes and the oil at temperatures above the melting point of the wax, but many solvents are available that completely dissolve the oil at temperatures at which the waxes are crystalline. The usual solvents are liquid propane, benzene–acetone, and chlorinated hydrocarbons such as trichloroethylene and ethylene dichloride. Vaseline is a mixture of paraffin waxes and added oils, but usually waxes for commercial uses (candles, etc.) are freed from residual traces of oil by sweating (gradual application of heat) or by solvents and subsequent pressing.

Greases are solid or semisolid gels prepared by the addition to mineral oils of hydrocarbon-soluble metal soaps or salts of higher fatty acids, for example, calcium stearate, lithium stearate, aluminum naphthenate. The soap content may vary from less than one to as much as thirty percent. Calcium soaps of the rosin acids are used as the gelator in the lubricants known as sett greases. In addition greases contain a certain amount of water as a stabilizer.

READING REFERENCES

B. T. Brooks, "Petroleum Research and Wars," *Ind. Eng. Chem.*, **34**, 798 (1942)
G. Egloff, "Modern Motor Fuels," *J. Chem. Educ.*, **18**, 582 (1941)
W. G. Lovell, "Knocking Characteristics of Hydrocarbons," *Ind. Eng. Chem.*, **40**, 2388 (1948)
"The Science of Petroleum," Oxford University Press (1938)
S. F. Birch, "Chemicals from Petroleum," *Prog. Org. Chem.*, **1**, 83 (1952).

CHAPTER 6

ALCOHOLS

Alcohols can be regarded either as hydroxyl derivatives of paraffinic hydrocarbons or as alkyl derivatives of water, and similarities to both

R·H	R·OH	H·OH
Hydrocarbon	Alcohol	Water

parent substances exist. Methyl alcohol has a boiling point not far below that of water, and is miscible with water in all proportions. In respect to the generalization that like dissolves like, methyl alcohol is like water in that the hydroxyl group constitutes a considerable part of the total molecule. n-Hexyl alcohol, $CH_3CH_2CH_2CH_2CH_2CH_2OH$, which is preponderantly hydrocarbon in character, is only slightly soluble in water and bears more resemblance to n-hexane. Methyl, ethyl, and n-propyl alcohol are all infinitely soluble in water; the next higher homologs have the following solubilities in water at 20°, expressed as grams dissolved by 100 grams of water: n-butyl alcohol, 8.3 g.; n-amyl alcohol (n-$C_5H_{11}OH$), 2.6 g.; n-hexyl alcohol, 1 g.

The simpler members of the series are known both by their common and Geneva names. At an early period when the sole practical sources of methyl and ethyl alcohol were destructive distillation of hardwood and fermentation of corn or rye these alcohols were called wood alcohol (or wood spirits) and grain alcohol, respectively. Of the two propyl alcohols, one is primary and the other secondary (two alkyl groups attached to the hydroxylated carbon): $CH_3CH_2CH_2OH$ and $(CH_3)_2CHOH$.

The structures of the four butyl alcohols are shown in Table 6.1. The prefixes n, sec, and t in the common names indicate the alcohol type. Since two of the isomers are primary, the one of branched chain is called isobutyl alcohol; higher alkyl groups such as amyl or hexyl are called isoamyl or isohexyl if they contain the $(CH_3)_2CH$— group. Alcohols are also named as derivatives of carbinol (carbine-alcohol), that is CH_3OH. The carbinol system, as applied to secondary and tertiary alcohols, has the advantage of both indicating the alcohol type and describing the structure. The substance $(C_6H_5)_3COH$ is invariably called triphenylcarbinol.

Eight isomeric alcohols of the formula $C_5H_{11}OH$ are theoretically possible, and they are all known. The name amyl alcohol arose because the first isomer to be discovered was obtained as a by-product of fermentation of crude potato starch to ethyl alcohol (L. *amylum*, starch, fine meal). Actually two amyl alcohols are constituents of the by-product material

TABLE 6.1. BUTYL ALCOHOLS

FORMULA	TYPE	COMMON NAME	CARBINOL NAME
$CH_3CH_2CH_2CH_2OH$	Primary	n-Butyl alcohol	n-Propylcarbinol
CH_3 CHCH$_2$OH CH_3	Primary	Isobutyl alcohol	Isopropylcarbinol
$CH_3CH_2CHCH_3$ $\quad\ \ $OH	Secondary	sec-Butyl alcohol	Methylethylcarbinol
CH_3 CH_3—COH CH_3	Tertiary	t-Butyl alcohol	Trimethylcarbinol

known as fusel oil, which is formed in the fermentation process but which is derived not from starch but from accompanying proteins. The more abundant constituent is isoamyl alcohol, $(CH_3)_2CHCH_2CH_2OH$, and a second major constituent has the formula $CH_3CH_2CH(CH_3)CH_2OH$ and is commonly called active amyl alcohol for reasons that will become apparent. Another isomer is named t-amyl alcohol because it is the only one of the eight isomers having a tertiary structure: $CH_3CH_2C(OH)(CH_3)_2$.

Table 6.2 lists all saturated monohydric alcohols having from one to four carbon atoms, and includes most of the other monohydric alcohols available for use as starting materials in laboratory syntheses. With the

TABLE 6.2. MONOHYDRIC ALCOHOLS

NAME	FORMULA	M.P., °C.	B.P., °C.	SP. GR.
Methyl alcohol	CH_3OH	−97	64.7	0.792
Ethyl alcohol	CH_3CH_2OH	−114	78.3	.789
n-Propyl alcohol	$n\text{-}C_3H_7OH$	−126	97.2	.804
Isopropyl alcohol	$i\text{-}C_3H_7OH$	−88.5	82.3	.786
Allyl alcohol	$CH_2{=}CHCH_2OH$	−129	97.0	.855
n-Butyl alcohol	$n\text{-}C_4H_9OH$	−90	117.7	.810
Isobutyl alcohol	$(CH_3)_2CHCH_2OH$	−108	107.9	.802
sec-Butyl alcohol	$CH_3CH_2CH(OH)CH_3$		99.5	.808
t-Butyl alcohol	$(CH_3)_3COH$	25	82.5	.789
n-Amyl alcohol	$n\text{-}C_5H_{11}OH$	−78.5	138.0	.817
Isoamyl alcohol	$(CH_3)_2CHCH_2CH_2OH$	−117	131.5	.812
t-Amyl alcohol	$CH_3CH_2C(OH)(CH_3)_2$	−12	101.8	.809
n-Hexyl alcohol	$n\text{-}C_6H_{13}OH$	−52	155.8	.820
Cyclohexanol	$C_6H_{11}OH$	−24	161.5	.962
n-Octyl alcohol	$n\text{-}C_8H_{17}OH$	−16	194.0	.827
Capryl alcohol (octanol-2)	$n\text{-}C_6H_{13}CH(OH)CH_3$	−39	179.0	.819
n-Decyl alcohol	$n\text{-}C_{10}H_{21}OH$	6	232.9	.829
Lauryl alcohol	$n\text{-}C_{12}H_{25}OH$	24	259	.831
Myristyl alcohol	$n\text{-}C_{14}H_{29}OH$	38	167/15 mm.	.824
Cetyl alcohol	$n\text{-}C_{16}H_{33}OH$	49	189/15 mm.	.798
Stearyl alcohol	$n\text{-}C_{18}H_{37}OH$	58.5	210.5/15 mm.	.812
Benzyl alcohol	$C_6H_5CH_2OH$	−15.3	205.4	1.046

exception of myristyl alcohol, all the substances listed can be purchased in practical grades at prices not over \$3.50 per kg., and often much less. Most of the higher paraffinic alcohols are straight-chain compounds having an even number of carbon atoms; they are obtained from acids of the same skeletal structure, which occur as components of animal and vegetable

$$n\text{-}C_{11}H_{23}COOH \xrightarrow{\text{2 steps}} n\text{-}C_{11}H_{23}CH_2OH$$

$$\text{Lauric acid} \qquad\qquad \text{Lauryl alcohol}$$

fats.   Higher acids with an odd number of carbon atoms do not occur in nature, and the corresponding alcohols are not available except by synthesis.

A few higher alcohols occur in nature in the form of esters.   An ester is derived from an acid by replacement of an acidic hydrogen atom by an alkyl residue, and on hydrolysis it affords an acid and an alcohol:

$$R-C\overset{\displaystyle O}{\underset{\displaystyle OR'}{<}} \xrightarrow{\text{Hydrolysis}} R-C\overset{\displaystyle O}{\underset{\displaystyle OH}{<}} \;+\; HOR'$$

$$\text{Ester} \qquad\qquad\qquad \text{Acid} \qquad\quad \text{Alcohol}$$

Cetyl alcohol, $n\text{-}C_{16}H_{33}OH$, is obtained by hydrolysis of spermaceti, a waxy solid that separates from sperm whale oil and consists largely of the ester cetyl palmitate, $n\text{-}C_{15}H_{31}COOC_{16}H_{33}$.   Capryl alcohol, or octanol-2, is one of two main products resulting from pyrolytic decomposition of the sodium salt of ricinoleic acid, which results from the action of alkali on castor oil.

$$CH_3(CH_2)_5CHCH_2CH{=}CH(CH_2)_7COONa \xrightarrow{\text{NaOH, heat, air}}$$
$$\quad\;\; |$$
$$\quad\; OH$$

Sodium salt of ricinoleic acid

$$CH_3(CH_2)_5CHCH_3 \;+\; HOOC(CH_2)_8COOH$$
$$\qquad\quad |$$
$$\qquad\; OH \qquad\qquad\quad \text{Sebacic acid (as Na salt)}$$

Capryl alcohol, or octanol-2
(40–42% yield)

Table 6.2 includes a common unsaturated alcohol (allyl), a cycloparaffin alcohol (cyclohexanol), and an alcohol containing a phenyl group (benzyl alcohol).   Ethylene glycol, CH_2OHCH_2OH, and the *vic*-glycols generally obtainable by controlled oxidation of alkenes typify known dihydric alcohols; hexamethylene glycol, $HO(CH_2)_6OH$ (b.p. 250°, m.p. 42°), is another example.   Glycerol, $CH_2OHCHOHCH_2OH$, is a trihydric alcohol, and erythritol, $CH_2OHCHOHCHOHCH_2OH$ (m.p. 120°), tetrahydric.   In these and all other known instances, there is no more than one hydroxyl group on any one carbon atom; Erlenmeyer recognized that the grouping —$C(OH)_2$— is unstable and that *gem*-dihydroxy compounds ordinarily are incapable of existence (Erlenmeyer rule).

Hydrogen Bonding. — Boiling points of monohydric alcohols are much higher (100–200°) than those of corresponding alkanes; ethyl alcohol is a liquid, b.p. 78.3°, whereas ethane is a gas, b.p. −88.6°.   The relatively low volatility of alcohols is due to the fact that in the liquid state the molecules are associated. Liquid water is also associated, and contrasts with unassociated hydrogen compounds of comparable molecular weight that are gases at ordinary temperature: H_2, H_2S, HCl, NH_3; water vapor is monomeric. The association of alcohol and water molecules is due to the phenomenon of hydrogen bonding. The electronic formulation of an alcohol dimer shows that the hydroxylic hydrogen atom of one monomer molecule is attracted by the strongly electronegative oxygen of a second

$$:\ddot{O}:H \;+\; :\ddot{O}:H \;\rightleftharpoons\; :\ddot{O}:H \;:\ddot{O}:H \text{ or } O\!-\!H\!\leftarrow\!O\!-\!H$$

| Alcohol monomer (vapor) | Alcohol dimer (liquid) |

molecule with the result that the hydrogen forms a bridge, or hydrogen bond, linking the two oxygen atoms. The bonding of oxygen to hydrogen through an unshared pair of electrons is often represented by an arrow pointing to hydrogen, as in the alternate formula for the alcohol dimer. In electronegativity, defined as the tendency of an atom to gain electrons, fluorine surpasses oxygen and all other atoms, and hydrogen fluoride dimer contains a particularly stable hydrogen bond. That the boiling point of methanol is lower than that of water, even though it has a higher molecular weight, is because it is not so highly associated as water.

The presence in a compound of an unbonded hydroxyl group can be recognized by the appearance in the infrared spectrum of an absorption band of characteristic wave length, and the disappearance of this band is evidence of hydrogen bonding. The high boiling points of water and of alcohols are attributable to the fact that heat energy is required to break the hydrogen bonds. Energy required to dissociate a given covalent bond in a gaseous molecule is the bond energy of that linkage and is accurately determinable (Pauling). Typical bond energies of covalent compounds are given in Table 6.3. The hydrogen bond energy is about 5 kg.-cal./mole; the energy is distinctly less than that of covalent single and double bonds but is still appreciable. The marked effect on boiling point is seen from

TABLE 6.3. BOND ENERGIES

BOND	BOND ENERGY, KG.-CAL./MOLE	BOND	BOND ENERGY, KG.-CAL./MOLE
H—H	103.4	O—H	110.2
O—O	118.2	S—H	87.5
S—S	63.8	C—H	87.3
Cl—Cl	57.8	C—C	58.6
Br—Br	46.1	C=C	100
H—Cl	102.7	C≡C	123
H—Br	87.3	C=O	149
		(aldehyde)	
H—I	71.4	Hydrogen bond	5

comparison of n-heptane (unassociated), mol. wt. 100, b.p. 98.4°, with n-hexyl alcohol (hydrogen-bonded), mol. wt. 102, b.p. 155.8°.

Other Properties. — Paraffinic alcohols have somewhat higher densities than the corresponding paraffins but are still lighter than water. The alcohols derived from methane, ethane, and propane are miscible with water, as noted above, and those having six or more carbon atoms are but sparingly soluble in this solvent. t-Butyl alcohol is completely soluble in water, whereas the other three butyl alcohols are only moderately soluble. Tertiary alcohols have boiling points significantly below those of the primary and secondary isomers.

Since, in comparison with hydrocarbons, alcohols are in an already partly oxidized condition, the heat release on combustion is lower. The heat of combustion of ethyl alcohol is 328 kg.-cal./mole, or 5.62 kg.-cal./ml. of liquid. The substance thus has a relatively low fuel value in comparison with hydrocarbons in the same boiling range: n-hexane (b.p. 69°), 7.58 kg.-cal./ml.; n-heptane (b.p. 98°), 7.85 kg.-cal./ml.

METHODS OF SYNTHESIS

Hydrolysis of Alkyl Halides. — The reaction of an alcohol with a hydrogen halide to give an alkyl halide and water is an equilibrium process and can be conducted in the reverse sense as a means of preparing an alcohol:

$$RX + HOH \longrightarrow ROH + HX$$

Water alone acts only slowly at ordinary temperatures, except upon the particularly reactive tertiary halides, for example t-butyl chloride, $(CH_3)_3CCl$, but hydrolysis can be promoted by use of a basic reagent to bind the acid produced. Since ethyl, propyl, and higher halides can also yield alkenes when treated with bases, experimental conditions have to be sought by which the hydrolytic reaction gains precedence over elimination of the elements of hydrogen halide from adjacent positions. This requirement is met by use of silver hydroxide, as obtained from a suspension of silver oxide in moist ether:

$$RCH_2I + AgOH \longrightarrow RCH_2OH + AgI$$

This method has limited application because alcohols are usually more accessible than the corresponding alkyl halides.

Hydration of Alkenes. — Conversion of alkenes into alcohols by addition of sulfuric acid to the double bond and hydrolysis of the resulting alkylsulfuric acid has been discussed in Chapter 3. The course of addition, and

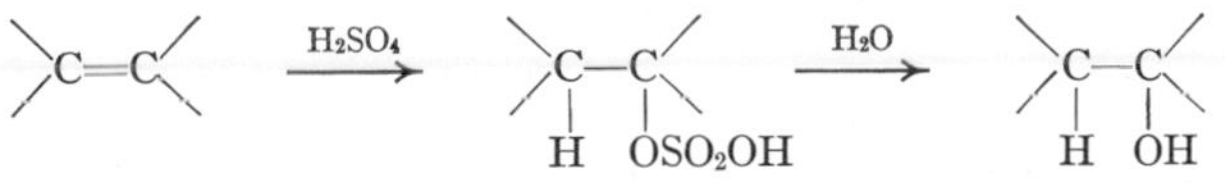

consequently the structure of the alcohol, can be predicted from the electronic concept of the reaction mechanism.

Reduction of Carbonyl Compounds. — Aldehydes and ketones contain the carbonyl group, which, like the ethylenic linkage, can enter into additions, in some instances with reagents that add to alkenes. Hydrogen adds to both the carbonyl group and the ethylenic double bond, but under different conditions. An aldehyde affords a primary alcohol on reduction. A ketone of necessity gives a secondary alcohol.

$$R-C \overset{H}{\underset{O}{\diagdown}} \xrightarrow{2 H} \text{RCH}_2\text{OH} \qquad \overset{R\diagdown}{\underset{R'\diagup}{}}C=O \xrightarrow{2 H} \overset{R\diagdown}{\underset{R'\diagup}{}}CHOH$$

Aldehyde   Primary alcohol   Ketone   Secondary alcohol

One application of the method is the preparation of *n*-heptyl alcohol. The starting material, *n*-heptaldehyde, is readily available as one of two useful products resulting from pyrolysis of castor oil, consisting in large part of the glyceride of ricinoleic acid.

$$\text{CH}_3(\text{CH}_2)_5\text{CH}\,\text{CH}_2\text{CH}=\text{CH}(\text{CH}_2)_7\text{COOH} \xrightarrow{\text{Heated in vacuum}}$$
$$|$$
$$\text{OH}$$

Ricinoleic acid (as glyceride)

$$\text{CH}_3(\text{CH}_2)_5\text{C} \overset{H}{\underset{O}{\diagdown}} \;+\; \text{CH}_2=\text{CHCH}_2(\text{CH}_2)_7\text{COOH}$$

n-Heptaldehyde   Undecylenic acid

$$\text{CH}_3(\text{CH}_2)_5\text{CHO} \xrightarrow[75-81\%]{\text{Fe, aq. HOAc}} \text{CH}_3(\text{CH}_2)_5\text{CH}_2\text{OH}$$
n-Heptaldehyde   *n*-Heptyl alcohol

An example of the preparation of a secondary alcohol is reduction of the aromatic ketone benzophenone:

$$\overset{\text{C}_6\text{H}_5\diagdown}{\underset{\text{C}_6\text{H}_5\diagup}{}}C=O \xrightarrow[68-69\%]{\text{Zn, alc. NaOH}} \overset{\text{C}_6\text{H}_5\diagdown}{\underset{\text{C}_6\text{H}_5\diagup}{}}CHOH$$

Benzophenone   Benzhydrol

A new route to alcohols was provided by the discovery of the ether-soluble lithium aluminum hydride (Finholt, Bond, and Schlesinger,[1] 1947):

$$4\,\text{LiH} + \text{AlCl}_3 \longrightarrow \text{LiAlH}_4 + 3\,\text{LiCl}$$

This substance reacts at room temperature with a carbonyl compound to form an alcoholate, which on hydrolysis yields the alcohol (Nystrom and W. G. Brown); the solvent must be free from water and alcohol, both of

$$4\,\text{R}_2\text{C}=O + \text{LiAlH}_4 \longrightarrow (\text{R}_2\text{CHO})_4\text{LiAl} \xrightarrow{4\,\text{H}_2\text{O}} 4\,\text{R}_2\text{CHOH} + \text{LiOH} + \text{Al(OH)}_3$$

which liberate hydrogen from the reagent. One advantage is that the reagent ordinarily does not attack ethylenic bonds. Aldehydes, ketones, and esters can be reduced.

[1] Hermann I. Schlesinger, b. 1882 Minneapolis; Ph.D. Chicago; Chicago

$$CH_3(CH_2)_5CHO \xrightarrow[86\%]{LiAlH_4} CH_3(CH_2)_5CH_2OH$$

$$CH_3CH_2COCH_3 \xrightarrow[80\%]{LiAlH_4} CH_3CH_2CH(OH)CH_3$$

$$\underset{\text{Crotonaldehyde}}{CH_3CH=CHCHO} \xrightarrow[70\%]{LiAlH_4} \underset{\text{Crotyl alcohol}}{CH_3CH=CHCH_2OH}$$

$$\underset{\text{Ethyl benzoate}}{C_6H_5COOC_2H_5} \xrightarrow[90\%]{LiAlH_4} \underset{\text{Benzyl alcohol}}{C_6H_5CH_2OH}$$

One of the most novel applications of lithium aluminum hydride is preparation of alcohols by reduction of carboxylic acids, which are resistant to most other reducing agents:

$$\underset{\text{Trimethylacetic acid}}{(CH_3)_3CCOOH} \xrightarrow[92\%]{LiAlH_4} \underset{\text{Neopentyl alcohol}}{(CH_3)_3CCH_2OH}$$

$$\underset{\text{Sebacic acid}}{HOOC(CH_2)_8COOH} \xrightarrow[97\%]{LiAlH_4} \underset{\text{Decanediol-1,10}}{HOCH_2(CH_2)_8CH_2OH}$$

Another complex hydride, sodium borohydride ($NaBH_4$), is insoluble in ether but soluble in water without decomposition. It can be used for effecting reduction in water or methanol of aldehydes and ketones (not acids):

$$\underset{\text{Acetonylacetone}}{CH_3COCH_2CH_2COCH_3} \xrightarrow[86\%]{NaBH_4} \underset{\text{Hexanediol-2,5}}{CH_3CH(OH)CH_2CH_2CH(OH)CH_3}$$

$$CH_3CH=CHCHO \xrightarrow[85\%]{NaBH_4} CH_3CH=CHCH_2OH$$

Lithium borohydride ($LiBH_4$) is soluble in ether and decomposed by water; solutions in ether (0.5 M) or in tetrahydrofuran (3.5 M; p. 134) can be employed. The reagent is milder than lithium aluminum hydride and particularly suited to selective reduction of the more reactive of two groups. Aldehydes and ketones are reduced rapidly at 0°; esters are reduced when the solution is refluxed for several hours, and acids are even more resistant:

$$\underset{\text{n-Butyl palmitate}}{n\text{-}C_{15}H_{31}COOC_4H_{9}\text{-}n} \xrightarrow[95\%]{LiBH_4} \underset{\text{n-Hexadecanol}}{n\text{-}C_{15}H_{71}CH_2OH}$$

$$\underset{\text{β-Benzoylpropionic acid}}{C_6H_5COCH_2CH_2COOH} \xrightarrow[78\%]{LiBH_4} \underset{\text{(as the lactone, p. 317)}}{C_6H_5CH(OH)CH_2CH_2COOH}$$

$$\underset{\text{m-Nitroacetophenone}}{m\text{-}NO_2C_6H_4COCH_3} \xrightarrow[93\%]{LiBH_4} \underset{\text{α-(m-Nitrophenyl)-ethanol}}{m\text{-}NO_2C_6H_4CH(OH)CH_3}$$

Grignard Synthesis. — The most important method of synthesizing alcohols is a widely variable application of the Grignard reaction. The essential step consists in addition of an alkylmagnesium halide to the carbonyl group of a second component, followed by hydrolysis:

$$\text{\Large$>$}C{=}O \;+\; RMgX \;\longrightarrow\; \text{\Large$>$}\underset{\underset{R}{|}}{C}{-}OMgX \;\xrightarrow{\text{HOH}}\; \text{\Large$>$}\underset{\underset{R}{|}}{C}{-}OH \;+\; HOMgX$$

Carbonyl   Grignard
compound   reagent   Alcohol

That the MgX-radical becomes affixed to the oxygen atom accords with
the marked affinity of magnesium metal for oxygen (magnesium incendi-
aries). The alkyl group of the Grignard reagent becomes linked to the
carbon of the carbonyl group, and in the final product appears on the carbon
carrying the alcoholic hydroxyl group. Alcohols of all three classes,
primary, secondary, and tertiary, can be synthesized by suitable selection of
the carbonyl component. With an aldehyde, which has one alkyl group
initially joined to the carbonyl function, the Grignard addition results in a

1. $R{-}C\underset{\searrow O}{\overset{\nearrow H}{}}\;\xrightarrow{R'MgX}\;\underset{R'}{\overset{R}{>}}CHOMgX\;\xrightarrow{H_2O}\;\underset{R'}{\overset{R}{>}}CHOH$

             Aldehyde   Secondary alcohol

Example: 1. Addition
                                     2. Hydrolysis

$$CH_3CH_2CH_2CH{=}O \;+\; CH_3CH_2MgI \;\xrightarrow{\quad}\; \underset{\underset{CH_3CH_2}{|}}{CH_3CH_2CH_2CHOH}$$

   n-Butyraldehyde   Ethylmagnesium   Ethyl-n-propylcarbinol
                      iodide   (hexanol-3)

secondary alcohol (1). A ketone, which has two alkyl groups initially
joined to the carbonyl group, is converted into a tertiary alcohol (2).

2. $\underset{R'}{\overset{R}{>}}C{=}O\;\xrightarrow{R''MgX}\;\underset{R''}{\overset{R}{\underset{R'}{>}}}C{-}OMgX\;\xrightarrow{H_2O}\;\underset{R''}{\overset{R}{\underset{R'}{>}}}COH$

             Ketone   Tertiary alcohol

Example:

$$\underset{CH_3}{\overset{CH_3}{>}}CHMgBr \;+\; O{=}C\underset{\searrow CH_3}{\overset{\nearrow CH_3}{}} \;\xrightarrow{(\text{2 steps})}\; \underset{CH_3}{\overset{CH_3}{>}}CH{-}\underset{\underset{OH}{}}{C}\underset{\nwarrow CH_3}{\overset{\nearrow CH_3}{}}$$

                                                   Dimethylisopropylcarbinol
                                                   (2,3-dimethylbutanol-2)

Tertiary alcohols can be synthesized also by the action of two molecules

3. $R{-}\underset{\underset{}{\|}}{\overset{\overset{OC_2H_5}{|}}{C}}{=}O\;\xrightarrow{CH_3MgBr}\;R{-}\underset{\underset{CH_3}{|}}{\overset{\overset{OC_2H_5}{|}}{C}}{-}OMgBr\;\longrightarrow\;R{-}\underset{\underset{CH_3}{|}}{C}{=}O\;\xrightarrow{CH_3MgBr}$

     Ester   Ketone

$$R{-}\underset{\underset{CH_3}{|}}{\overset{\overset{CH_3}{|}}{C}}{-}OMgBr\;\xrightarrow{H_2O}\;R{-}\underset{\underset{CH_3}{|}}{\overset{\overset{CH_3}{|}}{C}}{-}OH$$

                                                  Tertiary alcohol

of Grignard reagent on an ester. The reaction involves initial addition to the carbonyl group of the ester to give an intermediate which has two oxygen substituents on the same carbon and which is no more stable than a corresponding *gem*-diol. If, for example, a methyl Grignard reagent acts on an ethyl ester (3), an unstable addition product is formed and at once decomposes with elimination of C_2H_5OMgBr and formation of a ketone; this substance then adds a further molecule of Grignard reagent and affords, after hydrolysis, a tertiary alcohol. In the general case, the overall reaction is:

$$RCOOR' \xrightarrow{\text{2 R''MgX, hydrolysis}} \begin{array}{c} R \\ R''-COH \\ R'' \end{array}$$

Whereas in the synthesis from ketones tertiary carbinols having three different constituents can be prepared, the synthesis from esters can be applied only to the preparation of products in which two of the three alkyl groups are identical. Dimethylisopropylcarbinol, given above as an example of reaction 2, can be prepared by the action of two equivalents of methylmagnesium bromide on methyl isobutyrate, $(CH_3)_2CHCOOCH_3$. Triphenylcarbinol is prepared in a similar reaction from ethyl benzoate, the ethyl ester of benzoic acid.

$$C_6H_5COOC_2H_5 + 2\,C_6H_5MgBr \longrightarrow (C_6H_5)_3COMgBr \xrightarrow[91\%]{H_2O} (C_6H_5)_3COH$$
Ethyl benzoate   Phenylmagnesium   Triphenylcarbinol
                      bromide

Synthesis of a primary alcohol by the Grignard reaction can be accomplished by employing a carbonyl component having no attached alkyl substituents, namely formaldehyde, $HCH=O$. The type reaction (4) is generally applicable, and increases the carbon chain by one unit. A reagent

4. $RMgX + CH_2=O \longrightarrow RCH_2OMgX \xrightarrow{H_2O} RCH_2OH$

Example:

$$\begin{array}{c} CH_2CH_2 \\ CH_2 \qquad CHMgCl \\ CH_2CH_2 \end{array} \xrightarrow[64-69\%]{\substack{1.\ CH_2=O \\ 2.\ H_2O}} \begin{array}{c} CH_2CH_2 \\ CH_2 \qquad CHCH_2OH \\ CH_2CH_2 \end{array}$$

Cyclohexylmagnesium   Cyclohexylcarbinol
chloride

that also gives primary alcohols, and with which the chain is lengthened by two carbon atoms, is ethylene oxide. This substance possesses reactivity akin to that of formaldehyde, for the three-membered ring tends to open with ease comparable to that noted for the carbonyl group (two-membered ring). In the reaction with a Grignard reagent (5) the oxide ring is ruptured and the alkyl group adds to carbon while the magnesium halide residue adds to oxygen.

$$RMgX + \underset{O}{CH_2-CH_2} \longrightarrow RCH_2CH_2OMgX \xrightarrow{H_2O} RCH_2CH_2OH$$

Ethylene oxide   Primary alcohol

Example:

$$CH_3CH_2CH_2CH_2MgBr \xrightarrow[60-62\%]{\substack{1.\ \text{Ethylene oxide} \\ 2.\ \text{Hydrolysis}}} CH_3CH_2CH_2CH_2CH_2OH$$

n-Butylmagnesium bromide   *n*-Hexyl alcohol

Trimethylene oxide (b.p. 48°), available in moderate yield by the reactions formulated reacts in an analogous manner and affords the means of introducing a three-carbon chain with a terminal primary alcohol group.

$$\underset{CH_2OH}{CH_2CH_2OH} \xrightarrow{HCl} \underset{CH_2OH}{CH_2CH_2Cl} \xrightarrow{CH_3CO_2H} \underset{CH_2OCOCH_3}{CH_2CH_2Cl} \xrightarrow{KOH} \underset{CH_2-O}{CH_2-CH_2}$$

Trimethylene oxide

Because of the many variations possible in the type of the carbonyl component or cyclic oxide and in the choice of both specific oxygen-containing compounds and alkylmagnesium halides, the Grignard synthesis provides an invaluable means of preparing alcohols of all types, whose structures can be foretold with assurance from the method of synthesis. When a meticulous technique is employed throughout, including use of pure reagents and dry ether, pure reaction products are obtainable in satisfactory overall yields.

INDUSTRIAL PREPARATION OF ALCOHOLS

Methanol. — Until 1923 methanol was prepared by destructive distillation of wood, which consists of the carbohydrate cellulose, $(C_6H_{10}O_5)_n$, together with some 20–30% of lignin, a polymeric substance containing aromatic rings bearing methoxyl groups ($-OCH_3$). Methanol derived from wood arises from the lignin component. When wood is heated without access of air to temperatures above 250°, it decomposes into charcoal and a volatile fraction that partly condenses on cooling to a liquor, pyroligneous acid. A dark heavy oil separates from the condensate, and the supernatant aqueous layer contains methanol, acetic acid, traces of acetone and allyl alcohol, and contaminants with a disagreeable odor. Acetic acid can be neutralized with calcium hydroxide, and methanol separated by distillation. At the present time methanol is made largely synthetically in nearly quantitative yield by hydrogenation of carbon monoxide:

$$2\,H_2 + CO \rightleftharpoons CH_3OH.$$

Formation of methanol is accompanied by a decrease in volume, and hence pressures of 3000 lbs./sq. in. are commonly employed to promote the conversion. The usual temperature range is 350–400°. The hydrogenation is catalyzed by chromic oxide in combination with zinc oxide.

Ethanol. — Production of ethyl alcohol by fermentation of sugars under the influence of yeast has been known since antiquity. Yeast contains biological catalysts, enzymes, which promote a lengthy sequence of reactions that effect, in about 95% yield, the following overall reaction: $C_6H_{12}O_6 \rightarrow$ 2 C_2H_5OH + 2 CO_2 . Elucidation of all the steps was a major triumph of biochemistry (p. 479). Ethanol is also manufactured from ethylene, available from coke-oven gas and by cracking of petroleum fractions, by absorption in sulfuric acid and hydrolysis of the ethylsulfuric acid formed.

Ordinary commercial alcohol is a constant-boiling mixture of alcohol (95.57% by weight) and water (4.43%), and since this mixture boils at 78.2°, a temperature slightly lower than the boiling point of absolute ethyl alcohol, 78.3°, separation cannot be effected by ordinary distillation. Absolute alcohol can be prepared by chemical methods, for example with use of quicklime, which combines with water but not with alcohol, but it is prepared commercially by azeotropic distillation. When a mixture of 95% alcohol and benzene is distilled, the initial fraction consists of benzene—alcohol—water (64.8°), followed by alcohol—benzene (68.2°), and the final fraction consists of absolute alcohol.

Isopropyl Alcohol. — Isopropyl alcohol is made by hydrogenation of

$$CH_3COCH_3 \xrightarrow{\text{H}_2\ (Ni)} CH_3CHOHCH_3$$
$$\text{Acetone} \qquad\qquad \text{Isopropyl alcohol}$$

acetone and by hydration of propylene (petroleum); diisopropyl alcohol, a by-product, is valued because it has an octane rating of 98.

Butyl Alcohols. — n-Butyl alcohol is made along with acetone by bacterial fermentation of carbohydrates. The process (utilizing *Clostridium acetobutylicum* Weizmann) was developed by Weizmann[2] in 1911 to provide acetone, required for compounding the explosive Cordite; after the war, its major function was to supply n-butyl alcohol, required for quick-drying automobile lacquers. sec-Butyl alcohol, or butanol-2, is made from the mixture of butene-1 and -2 present to the extent of 30–32% in the C_4-cut of gas obtained on vapor-phase cracking. Isobutene is selectively absorbed

$$\left.\begin{array}{c} CH_3CH{=}CHCH_3 \\ \text{Butene-2} \\ \\ CH_3CH_2CH{=}CH_2 \\ \text{Butene-1} \end{array}\right\} \xrightarrow[\text{80\%}]{\text{H}_2SO_4,\ H_2O} \begin{array}{c} CH_3CH_2CHOHCH_3 \\ \text{Butanol-2} \end{array}$$

in 65% sulfuric acid at 5–10°, and butadiene is removed by treatment with cuprous chloride—ammonium chloride. The butenes are then extracted from butane and isobutane by absorption in concentrated sulfuric acid, and the alcohol is obtained on hydrolysis of the acid solution.

Amyl Alcohols. — A mixture of amyl alcohols is prepared by chlorination of the C_5-cut of natural gasolines, consisting of approximately equal amounts of n-pentane and isopentane, and by hydrolysis of the mixture of halides. Chlorination is carried out in vapor phase at 200° in the absence of catalysts

[2] Chaim Weizmann, 1874–1952; b. Russia; Ph.D. Berlin, Germany, and Freiburg, Switzerland (Bistrzycki); Univ. Manchester, Weizmann Inst. Sci., Israel; *J. Chem. Soc.*, 2840 (1953)

and in darkness. In the Sharples plant chlorine is continuously fed at the rate of 22 tons per day into a 60-mile per hour stream of hot pentane vapor (100,000 gal. per day of pentane cut, b.p. 28–39°). In strictly thermal chlorination the course of substitution seems to be governed by probability, as can be seen from the approximate proportions of the reactants indicated in the chart. The mixture of monochloropentanes cannot be separated, partly because the secondary and tertiary chlorides on heating easily form amylenes by loss of hydrogen chloride. Hydrolysis by aqueous sodium

$$CH_3CH_2CH_2CH_2CH_3 \xrightarrow{Cl_2}$$
n-Pentane
(b.p. 36°)

24% $\longrightarrow CH_3CH_2CH_2CH_2CH_2Cl \xrightarrow{NaOH} CH_3CH_2CH_2CH_2CH_2OH$
(b.p. 107°) — n-Amyl alcohol (b.p. 138.0°)

15% $\longrightarrow CH_3CH_2CH_2CHClCH_3 \xrightarrow{NaOH} CH_3CH_2CH_2CHOHCH_3$
(b.p. 97°) — Methyl-n-propylcarbinol (b.p. 119.5°)

19% $\longrightarrow CH_3CH_2CHClCH_2CH_3 \xrightarrow{NaOH} (CH_3CH_2)_2CHOH$
(b.p. 96°) — Diethylcarbinol (b.p. 115.6°)

$$(CH_3)_2CHCH_2CH_3 \xrightarrow{Cl_2}$$
Isopentane
(b.p. 28°)

14% $\longrightarrow CH_3CH_2CH(CH_3)CH_2Cl \xrightarrow{NaOH} CH_3CH_2CH(CH_3)CH_2OH$
(b.p. 99°) — sec-Butylcarbinol (b.p. 128°)

19% $\longrightarrow (CH_3)_2CHCH_2CH_2Cl \xrightarrow{NaOH} (CH_3)_2CHCH_2CH_2OH$
(b.p. 101°) — Isoamyl alcohol (b.p. 131.5°)

9% { $(CH_3)_2CClCH_2CH_3$ (b.p. 86°) / $(CH_3)_2CHCHClCH_3$ (b.p. 91°) } yield traces of alcohols

hydroxide is facilitated by addition of a sodium stearate soap, which provides more intimate contact by emulsifying the two immiscible layers. The total mixture of alcohols and the segregated primary and secondary alcohol cuts are used as solvents and plasticizers, particularly for production of the important lacquer solvent amyl acetate. The chloride mixture is useful in the preparation of various synthetic products.

Commercial sec-amyl alcohol is a mixture made by the sulfuric acid method from pentene-1 and pentene-2, present to an extent of about 30% in the pentane—pentene fraction from gasoline. Pure pentene-1 forms pentanol-2; pentene-2, a mixture of pentanol-2 (65%) and pentanol-3 (35%). The commercial product contains about 80% of pentanol-2 and 20% of pentanol-3.

Ethylene Glycol. — Ethylene glycol (glycol) was prepared originally by hydrolysis of ethylene dichloride. Preparation from ethylene chlorohydrin

$$CH_2=CH_2 + Cl_2 \longrightarrow ClCH_2CH_2Cl \xrightarrow{Na_2CO_3} HOCH_2CH_2OH$$
Ethylene glycol
(b.p. 197.5°)

is an improvement because of the greater rate of hydrolysis and because, since only half the amount of soda is required, separation of sodium chloride from the product is facilitated. This operation can be avoided by conversion of the chlorohydrin into ethylene oxide, which is rapidly hydrolyzed

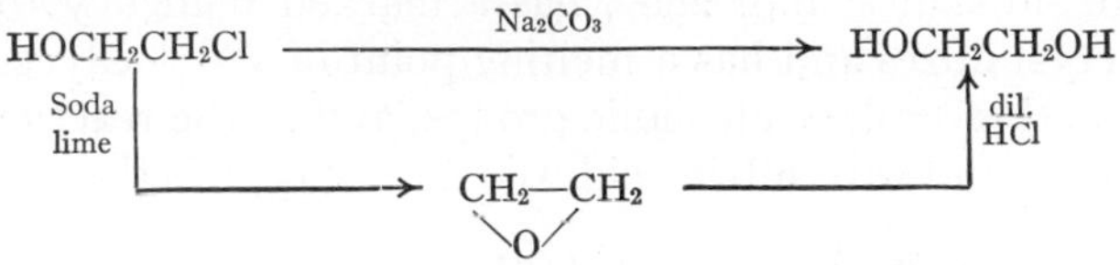

$$\text{HOCH}_2\text{CH}_2\text{Cl} \xrightarrow{\text{Na}_2\text{CO}_3} \text{HOCH}_2\text{CH}_2\text{OH}$$

Soda lime $\qquad$ dil. HCl

$$\text{CH}_2\text{—CH}_2 \quad \underset{\text{O}}{\diagdown}$$

by dilute acid. Ethylene oxide is made more usually by direct combination of ethylene and oxygen at a high temperature in the presence of silver catalysts. Ethylene glycol is an antifreeze agent; an aqueous mixture containing 60% of glycol freezes at −40°.

A series of useful monoalkyl ethers, marketed under the trade name of Cellosolve, are obtained by alcoholysis of ethylene oxide:

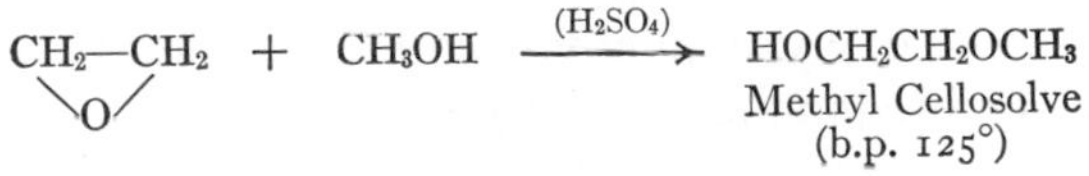

$$\text{CH}_2\text{—CH}_2 + \text{CH}_3\text{OH} \xrightarrow{(\text{H}_2\text{SO}_4)} \text{HOCH}_2\text{CH}_2\text{OCH}_3$$

Methyl Cellosolve
(b.p. 125°)

Cellosolves are widely used as solvents in varnishes and lacquers. Dioxan is made by polymerization of ethylene oxide:

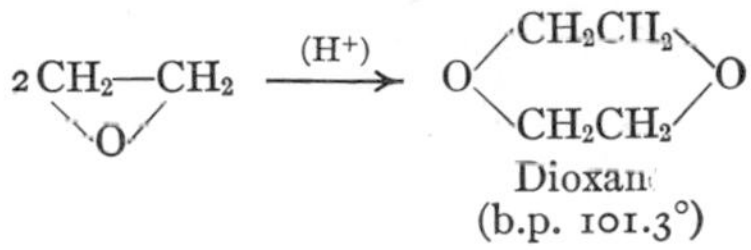

$$2\,\text{CH}_2\text{—CH}_2 \xrightarrow{(\text{H}^+)} \text{O} \underset{\text{CH}_2\text{CH}_2}{\overset{\text{CH}_2\text{CH}_2}{\diagup}} \text{O}$$

Dioxan
(b.p. 101.3°)

Dioxan is an excellent solvent for many organic compounds and is also miscible with water; this property is shown by methyl, ethyl, and even n-butyl Cellosolve.

Propylene Glycol. — This glycol is made from propylene (oil gas):

$$\text{CH}_3\text{CH}=\text{CH}_2 \longrightarrow \underset{\text{OH}}{\text{CH}_3\text{CHCH}_2\text{Cl}} \longrightarrow \underset{\text{O}}{\text{CH}_3\text{CHCH}_2} \longrightarrow \text{CH}_3\text{CHOHCH}_2\text{OH}$$

Propylene $\qquad\qquad\qquad\qquad\qquad\qquad\qquad\qquad\qquad$ Propylene glycol

Glycerol. — Glycerol is produced as a by-product in the manufacture of soap in amounts sufficient except in time of war (nitroglycerin). During World War I additional quantities were made by fermentation. Production was announced in 1938 of synthetic glycerol from petroleum (propylene) by the following reactions:

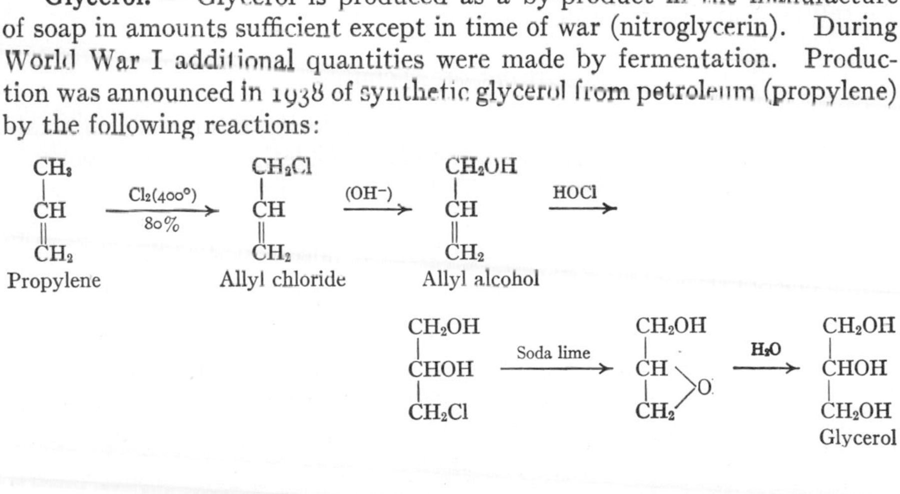

$$\underset{\text{Propylene}}{\overset{\text{CH}_3}{\underset{\text{CH}_2}{\overset{|}{\underset{\|}{\text{CH}}}}}} \xrightarrow[80\%]{\text{Cl}_2(400°)} \underset{\text{Allyl chloride}}{\overset{\text{CH}_2\text{Cl}}{\underset{\text{CH}_2}{\overset{|}{\underset{\|}{\text{CH}}}}}} \xrightarrow{(\text{OH}^-)} \underset{\text{Allyl alcohol}}{\overset{\text{CH}_2\text{OH}}{\underset{\text{CH}_2}{\overset{|}{\underset{\|}{\text{CH}}}}}} \xrightarrow{\text{HOCl}}$$

$$\underset{\text{CH}_2\text{Cl}}{\overset{\text{CH}_2\text{OH}}{\overset{|}{\underset{|}{\text{CHOH}}}}} \xrightarrow{\text{Soda lime}} \underset{\text{CH}_2}{\overset{\text{CH}_2\text{OH}}{\overset{|}{\underset{\diagdown}{\text{CH}}}}}\text{O} \xrightarrow{\text{H}_2\text{O}} \underset{\text{Glycerol}}{\overset{\text{CH}_2\text{OH}}{\underset{\text{CH}_2\text{OH}}{\overset{|}{\underset{|}{\text{CHOH}}}}}}$$

Glycerol (Gr. *glykys*, sweet), a viscous, hygroscopic liquid with a sweet taste, was discovered by Scheele in 1779 as a product of hydrolysis of olive oil. The pure substance, b.p. 290°, has a marked tendency to supercool, but it slowly crystallizes and has a melting point of 18°. Glycerol contains both primary and secondary alcoholic groups, and in the reactions with dry hydrogen chloride and with nitric acid, the former type is the more reactive:

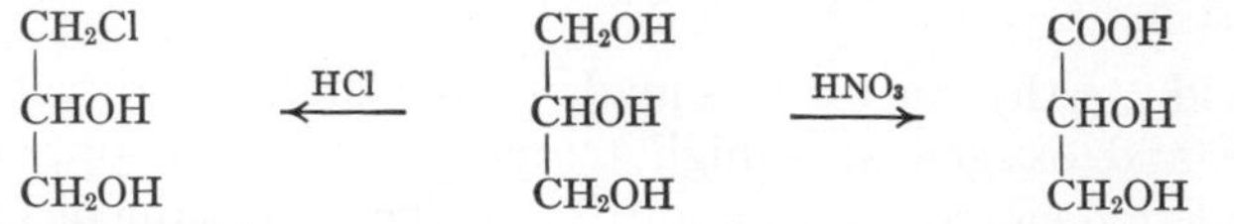

$$
\begin{array}{ccccc}
CH_2Cl & & CH_2OH & & COOH \\
| & \xleftarrow{\;HCl\;} & | & \xrightarrow{\;HNO_3\;} & | \\
CHOH & & CHOH & & CHOH \\
| & & | & & | \\
CH_2OH & & CH_2OH & & CH_2OH
\end{array}
$$

α-Monochlorohydrin   Glyceric acid
(with some β-isomer)   (chief product)

Oxidation of glycerol under milder conditions, for example with hydrogen peroxide and a ferrous salt as catalyst or with sodium hypobromite, gives an equilibrium mixture of glyceraldehyde and the isomeric dihydroxyacetone in which the former predominates. These substances are interconvertible through a common enediol resulting from migration of hydrogen (Lobry de Bruyn–van Ekenstein rearrangement). These three-carbon hydroxy carbonyl compounds are structurally related to sugars.

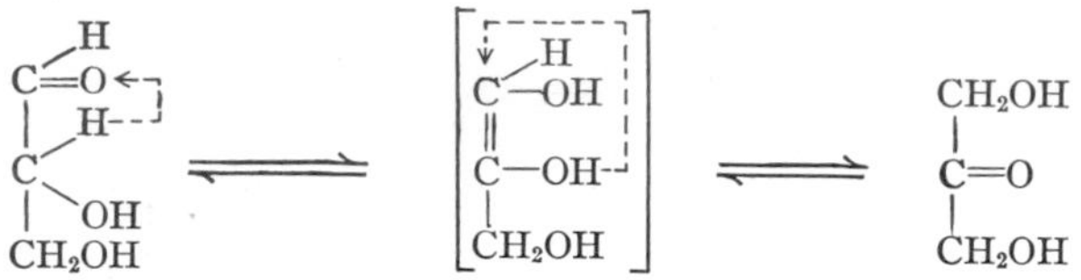

Glyceraldehyde   Enediol   Dihydroxyacetone

Trimethylene Glycol ($HOCH_2CH_2CH_2OH$, b.p. 214° dec., sp. gr. 1.055). —This glycol, propanediol-1,3, is a product of bacterial fermentation of glycerol. In the course of the large-scale production of glycerol from fats in World War I, some batches were found to contain sufficient trimethylene glycol to lower the specific gravity below the tolerance value for material required for nitroglycerin manufacture. By deliberate fermentation glycerol can be converted into the glycol in 45% yield.

REACTIONS OF ALCOHOLS

With Metals. — When metallic sodium is added continuously in small pieces to excess methanol, the metal rapidly dissolves, hydrogen is evolved, and there is a considerable heat effect, although not sufficient to cause ignition of hydrogen as in the parallel reaction with water. The resulting solution contains sodium methoxide, CH_3ONa (also called sodium methylate). The substance can be obtained as a dry white solid by preparing a suspension of powdered sodium in absolute ether and adding in portions one

$$CH_3OH \quad + \quad Na \quad \longrightarrow \quad CH_3ONa \quad + \quad \tfrac{1}{2}H_2$$

Sodium methoxide

molecular equivalent of methanol. Sodium methoxide and ethoxide are reactive substances having applications in synthesis. They are subject to hydrolysis, and with a limited amount of water an equilibrium mixture is obtained, for example:

$$C_2H_5ONa \ + \ H_2O \ \rightleftharpoons \ C_2H_5OH \ + \ NaOH$$
Sodium ethoxide

Conversely, a solution prepared from sodium or potassium hydroxide in alcohol, (alcoholic sodium or potassium hydroxide) is not merely a solution of the reagent, but contains a certain amount of sodium or potassium ethoxide in an equilibrium mixture. The reaction of an alkyl halide with alcoholic potassium hydroxide involves attack by the alkoxide ion RO^-), which functions as an electron-donating or nucleophilic agent. An alkoxide ion is a more powerful nucleophilic agent than the hydroxide ion because the inductive drift of electrons away from the alkyl group increases the electron density on oxygen: $CH_3 \rightarrow O^-$.

Higher alcohols react with sodium to give sodium alkoxides, but the reaction proceeds with decreasing readiness as the molecular weight increases; as the hydrocarbon residue increases in size, the functional hydroxyl group responsible for the reaction becomes a minor part of the whole and offers a more elusive target for sodium atoms. Aluminum isopropoxide, $Al[OCH(CH_3)_2]_3$, and aluminum t-butoxide, $Al[OC(CH_3)_3]_3$, have specific synthetic uses and are prepared by interaction of the anhydrous alcohol with amalgamated aluminum.

Dehydration. — Elimination of water from adjacent positions in an alcohol, either by pyrolysis over alumina or by use of mineral acids, constitutes a valuable path to alkenes. Examples given in Chapter 3 illustrate the generalization that tertiary alcohols suffer dehydration more readily than secondary ones, which in turn react more readily than primary alcohols. These relationships are significant not only in fixing the conditions required to convert a given alcohol into an alkene but also in determining the course of partial dehydration of a polyhydric alcohol. Thus a tertiary alcoholic group usually can be eliminated from a substance having secondary and primary groups without disturbance of these less labile hydroxyls.

A further differentiation can be made with respect to the direction of dehydration when two routes are open. In pentanol-2 hydrogen atoms adjacent to the hydroxylated carbon are available at both positions 1 and 3, but actually the latter hydrogen is utilized almost exclusively, and the chief product of dehydration is pentene-2. An alkene having a terminal

$$CH_3CH_2\overset{3}{C}H_2CH(OH)\overset{1}{C}H_3 \ \xrightarrow{-H_2O} \ CH_3CH_2CH=CHCH_3$$
Pentanol-2   Pentene-2

double bond (pentene-1) is a less preferred product than an isomer with the ethylenic linkage in an interior position (pentene-2). In the case of 2-methylpentanol-3 removal of hydrogen from either of the alternate positions 2 or 4 would give an internal double bond, but nevertheless a definite

$$
\begin{array}{cc}
\underset{CH_3}{\overset{CH_3}{\diagup}}\!\!\!\!\!\!\!\overset{2}{\diagdown}\underset{\underset{OH}{|}}{CHCHCH_2CH_3} \xrightarrow{-H_2O} & \underset{CH_3}{\overset{CH_3}{\diagup}}\!\!\!\!\!\!\!\overset{}{\diagdown}C{=}CHCH_2CH_3
\end{array}
$$

2-Methylpentanol-3   2-Methylpentene-2

preference exists, and the chief product is that resulting from utilization of hydrogen in the 2-position. The carbon atom at this position is tertiarily substituted and carried but one hydrogen, whereas at the alternate (second-ary) position there are two. In the dehydration of pentanol-2 cited above the hydrogen eliminated comes from a secondarily, rather than a primarily substituted carbon atom. These examples are representative and illustrate an empirical rule due to Saytzeff[3] (1875) that, in dehydration of alcohols, hydrogen is eliminated preferentially from the adjacent carbon atom that is poorer in hydrogen.[*] This relationship means that the tertiarily bound hydrogen of the structure R_3CH is more reactive than the hydrogen of a methylene group, R_2CH_2, and the latter surpasses in reactivity the hydro-gen of the primary carbon of a methyl group, RCH_3. The relationship is exactly the same as that noted for relative reactivities of alkanes in the catalytic addition to ethylenic hydrocarbons (p. 105). The Saytzeff rule applies also to elimination of hydrogen halide from an alkyl halide (Chapter 13).

Wagner[4]-Meerwein[5] Rearrangement. — Molecular rearrangements sometimes occur on acid-catalyzed dehydration of alcohols having a tertiary carbon atom adjacent to that carrying the hydroxyl group. In 1901 N. Zelinsky and J. Zelikow heated methyl-*t*-butylcarbinol (I) with oxalic acid in expectation of producing *t*-butylethylene (II), but found the product to

$$
\begin{array}{ccc}
\underset{\underset{CH_3}{|}}{\overset{\overset{CH_3}{|}}{CH_3{-}C}}{-}\!\!\!\!\!\!\overset{\overset{OH}{|}}{CH}{-}CH_3 & \underset{\underset{CH_3}{|}}{\overset{\overset{CH_2}{\|}}{CH_3{-}C}}{-}CH{=}CH_2 & \underset{\underset{CH_3\ \ CH_3}{|\ \ \ \ |}}{CH_3{-}C{=\!\!=}C{-}CH_3}
\end{array}
$$

I   II   III

be tetramethylethylene, III. Many years later other workers found that dehydration of I over alumina gives chiefly the normal product II. This and many other acid-catalyzed rearrangements were eventually elucidated through investigations by Wagner in the field of the terpenes, and by Meer-wein in a broader field. The reaction is now interpreted as follows. A proton abstracts hydroxyl to form the carbonium ion (a), which is unstable because the charged carbon has only a sextet of electrons. Hence a methyl

---

[3] Alexander M. Saytzeff, 1841–1910; b. Kasan; stud. Marburg, Paris; Kasan

[*] S. Matthew, XXV, 29, " . . . but from him that hath not shall be taken away even that which he hath."

[4] Georg Wagner, b. Russia; Univ. Warsaw

[5] Hans Meerwein, b. 1879 Hamburg, Germany; Ph.D. Bonn (Schroeter); Marburg

$$CH_3 : \overset{CH_3}{\underset{H}{C}} : \overset{\overset{+}{\boxed{OH \quad + \quad H}}}{\underset{}{C : CH_3}} \longrightarrow \boxed{CH_3 : \overset{\overset{\boxed{CH_3}}{+}}{\underset{CH_3 \quad H}{C}} : C : CH_3} \longrightarrow CH_3 : \overset{\overset{\boxed{+}}{C}}{\underset{CH_3 \quad CH_3}{C}} : \overset{\boxed{H}}{C : CH_3} \xrightarrow{-H} \overset{+}{}$$

I   (a)   (b)

$$CH_3 : \overset{CH_3}{C} : : \overset{CH_3}{C} : CH_3$$

III

group on an adjacent carbon migrates with its pair of electrons and attacks the charged carbon to produce a more stable tertiary carbonium ion (b). This also has an open electron sextet, but stabilization is achieved by expulsion of a hydrogen atom and the charge, as a proton, and utilization of the electron pair released for formation of a double bond (III).

Oxidation. — Methyl, ethyl, and many higher alcohols are susceptible to oxidation by chromic acid, potassium dichromate, or potassium permanganate. Since methane and ethane are resistant to the same reagents, the presence of oxygen in a molecule confers susceptibility to further oxidation. In ethyl alcohol one of the two carbon atoms is linked to oxygen, and hence is already oxidized, while the other is joined to hydrogen and carbon and corresponds to the carbon atoms of the inert ethane; hence oxidizing agents attack the molecule at the former, rather than the latter position. The initial oxidation product is acetaldehyde, which on further oxidation is attacked in the already oxidized part of the molecule and yields

$$\underset{\text{Ethyl alcohol}}{H-\overset{\overset{H}{|}}{\underset{\underset{H}{|}}{C}}-\overset{\overset{H}{|}}{\underset{\underset{H}{|}}{C}}-OH} \xrightarrow{[O]} \underset{\text{Acetaldehyde}}{H-\overset{\overset{H}{|}}{\underset{\underset{H}{|}}{C}}-\overset{\overset{H}{|}}{C}=O} \xrightarrow{[O]} \underset{\text{Acetic acid}}{H-\overset{\overset{H}{|}}{\underset{\underset{H}{|}}{C}}-\overset{\overset{OH}{|}}{C}=O}$$

acetic acid as an end product resistant to further attack. The first step in the overall process can be regarded as dehydrogenation rather than oxidation, involving elimination of a hydroxylic hydrogen together with a hydrogen of the hydroxylated carbon atom, with direct establishment of a carbon-oxygen double bond. The reagent employed to effect the reaction functions as a hydrogen acceptor. The second step leading to acetic acid also can be interpreted as dehydrogenation if it is supposed that the reaction

$$CH_3-C\overset{\overset{H}{\diagup}}{\diagdown_O} + HOH \longrightarrow \left[CH_3-\overset{\overset{\boxed{H}}{|}}{\underset{\underset{OH}{|}}{C}}-\boxed{OH} \right] \xrightarrow{-2H} CH_3-\overset{}{\underset{\underset{OH}{|}}{C}}=O$$

proceeds through the transient formation of an unstable hydrate of acetaldehyde (Wieland). Indeed, aldehydes are resistant to oxidation by silver oxide in an anhydrous state but are capable of conversion into acids by this reagent in the presence of water. The dehydrogenation mechanism thus probably represents at least one path for oxidation of an aldehyde.

An alternate empirical statement of the oxidation is that a hydrogen atom on an oxidized carbon of acetaldehyde becomes converted into a hydroxyl group. That such hydroxylation can occur in the absence of a carbonyl group capable of forming an intermediate hydrate is demonstrated by the ready oxidation of triphenylmethane to triphenylcarbinol: $(C_6H_5)_3CH \xrightarrow{[O]} (C_6H_5)_3COH$. The concept of hydroxylation provides a basis for predicting the outcome of many oxidation reactions. If, in ethyl alcohol, one of the hydrogen atoms attached to the already oxidized carbon were to become hydroxylated, the product would be an unstable *gem*-diol and would lose water to form acetaldehyde. Acetic acid is stable to

$$CH_3CH_2OH \xrightarrow{[O]} \left[CH_3CH \overset{O H}{\underset{OH}{<}} \right] \xrightarrow{-H_2O} CH_2CH=O$$

oxidation though it contains a highly oxidized carbon atom, because this atom carries no hydrogen. Oxidation of methanol may proceed to the stage of formaldehyde through an intermediate *gem*-diol; the next product is formic acid, HCOOH, and this, unlike acetic acid, still possesses a hydro-

$$\underset{\text{Methanol}}{H-\overset{\displaystyle H}{\underset{\displaystyle H}{C}}-OH} \xrightarrow{[O]} \left[H-\overset{\displaystyle OH}{\underset{\displaystyle H}{C}}-OH \right] \xrightarrow{-H_2O} \underset{\text{Formaldehyde}}{H-\overset{\displaystyle}{\underset{\displaystyle H}{C}}=O} \xrightarrow{[O]}$$

$$\underset{\text{Formic acid}}{H-\overset{\displaystyle}{\underset{\displaystyle OH}{C}}=O} \xrightarrow{[O]} \left[HO-\overset{\displaystyle}{\underset{\displaystyle OH}{C}}=O \right] \xrightarrow{-H_2O} O=C=O$$

gen atom on the oxidized carbon and is oxidized further. Hydroxylation of the specially situated hydrogen would give carbonic acid, which is an unstable diol that decomposes to carbon dioxide and water.

The behavior of ethyl rather than methyl alcohol is generally typical of primary alcohols, for such alcohols on oxidation yield aldehydes initially and then acids. A secondary alcohol can undergo hydroxylation of the

$$\underset{\text{Primary alcohol}}{RCH_2OH} \xrightarrow{[O]} \underset{\text{Aldehyde}}{RCHO} \xrightarrow{[O]} \underset{\text{Acid}}{RCOOH}$$

lone hydrogen on the oxidized carbon followed by loss of water, with production of a ketone, and this product represents a stopping point for normal oxidation. Thus isopropyl alcohol yields acetone; diethylcarbinol affords

$$\underset{\text{Secondary alcohol}}{\overset{R}{\underset{R'}{>}}C\overset{H}{\underset{OH}{<}}} \xrightarrow{[O]} \underset{\text{Ketone}}{\overset{R}{\underset{R'}{>}}C=O}$$

diethyl ketone, $CH_3CH_2COCH_2CH_3$. Acetone is sufficiently resistant to oxidation to be employed as a solvent in permanganate oxidation of other substances, and ketones are normal end products of oxidation even though, under special conditions, they can undergo oxidative degradation.

A tertiary alcohol, R_3COH, contains a hydroxylated carbon atom but this carries no hydrogen, and hence the alcohol should be resistant to oxidation. Under ordinary conditions of oxidation in a neutral or alkaline medium tertiary alcohols are indeed inert and hence can be distinguished from primary and secondary alcohols (alkaline permanganate test). Acid oxidation occurs under special conditions but is attended with rupture of the carbon chain (p. 669). Primary and secondary alcohols are capable of oxidation to aldehydes, acids, or ketones, in which the original carbon skeleton is intact. The oxidation reaction therefore has diagnostic value, since qualitative tests can distinguish between aldehydes and ketones and identify a carboxylic acid. An alcohol that on oxidation yields either an aldehyde or an acid of the same carbon chain is a primary alcohol; one that affords a ketone is a secondary alcohol; and an alcohol that is resistant to attack under neutral conditions must have a tertiary structure.

As noted in Chapter 3, an alkene on oxidation with alkaline permanganate under controlled conditions or on treatment with hydrogen peroxide in acetic acid yields initially a *vic*-glycol, which is readily oxidized further. A glycol such as II, derived from an alkene (I), offers various possibilities for oxidation. Two hydrogens on oxidized carbon atoms are available for

$$
RCH{=}CHR' \xrightarrow{\ [O]\ } \underset{\substack{|\quad|\\ OH\ OH \\ II}}{RCH{-}CHR'} \quad \begin{array}{l} \xrightarrow{KMnO_4} RCOOH\ +\ HOOCR' \\ \\ \xrightarrow{Pb(OAc)_4} RCHO\ +\ OCHR' \end{array}
$$

hydroxylation, and furthermore a bond extending between two oxidized carbon atoms is weak and subject to oxidative severance. Thus excess permanganate or dichromate converts the glycol II into a mixture of the acids RCOOH and R'COOH, either by cleavage of the connecting bond and oxidation of the fragments or by oxidation of the secondary alcoholic groups followed by oxidative cleavage. The selective cleavage of the weakened connecting bond of a *vic*-glycol can be accomplished with either lead tetraacetate in acetic acid solution (Criegee[6]) or with periodic acid in aqueous solution. With either of these specific reagents the outcome of glycol cleavage can be visualized as fission of the bond between the oxidized carbons and addition of a hydroxyl group to each fragment:

$$
\underset{\substack{|\quad|\\ OH\ OH}}{RCH{-}CHR} \xrightarrow[\text{Pb(OAc)}_4\text{ or HIO}_4]{2[OH]} \left[2RCHO\underset{OH}{H} \right] \longrightarrow 2RCH{=}O
$$

$$
\underset{\substack{|\quad|\\ OH\ OH}}{RCH{-}CR_2} \xrightarrow{2[OH]} \left[\underset{OH}{RCHOH}\ +\ \underset{OH}{HOCR_2} \right] \longrightarrow RCH{=}O\ +\ O{=}CR_2
$$

* Rudolf Criegee, b. 1902; Ph.D. Würzburg (Dimroth); Düsseldorf, Karlsruhe

ESTER DERIVATIVES

An ester is the organic equivalent of an inorganic salt, since it is derived by elimination of water from an acid and an alcohol:

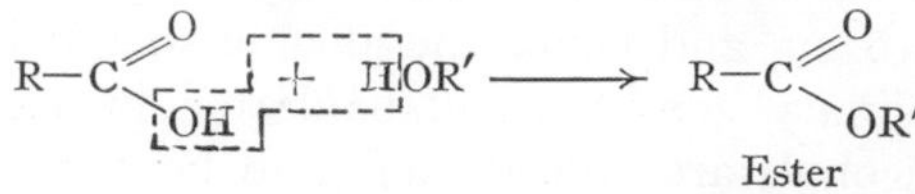

$$R-C{\overset{O}{\underset{OH}{<}}} + HOR' \longrightarrow R-C{\overset{O}{\underset{OR'}{<}}}$$

Ester

The analogy is superficial, since esters are typically organic in character; they are nonionic and, with the exception of the initial members, sparingly soluble in water. Formation of an ester from the components, known as esterification, can be accomplished by refluxing a mixture of the acid and the alcohol in the presence of a trace of mineral acid as catalyst (method of E. Fischer). The process is an equilibrium reaction, and attainment of equilibrium is hastened by a trace of hydrogen ion. Pure acetic acid reacts very slowly with an equivalent amount of pure ethanol to give the ester ethyl acetate, and equilibrium is attained only after a period of refluxing amounting to several days. If about 3% of dry hydrogen chloride, con-

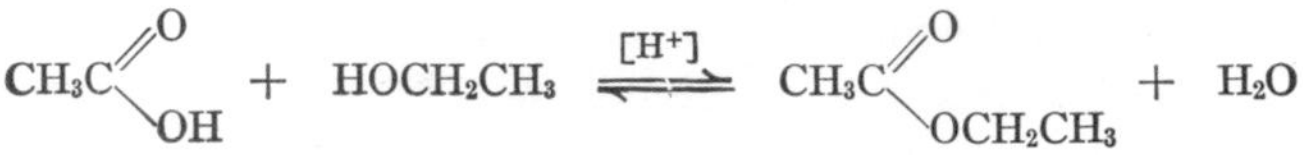

$$CH_3C{\overset{O}{\underset{OH}{<}}} + HOCH_2CH_3 \overset{[H^+]}{\rightleftharpoons} CH_3C{\overset{O}{\underset{OCH_2CH_3}{<}}} + H_2O$$

Ethyl acetate

centrated sulfuric acid, or boron fluoride is added to the original mixture, the same equilibrium can be reached in a period of a few hours; the mechanism of the reaction is discussed on page 174. With equivalent quantities of reactants conversion into the ester amounts to only about two thirds of that theoretically possible before the reverse reaction of hydrolysis is proceeding at the same rate as the esterification reaction and equilibrium is reached. In accordance with the mass-action law the equilibrium is displaced in favor of the ester by an excess of one component, and in practice it is expedient to employ a large excess of alcohol for efficient esterification of a valuable acid.

Esterification of an alcohol with an inorganic acid is favored both by the strongly acidic character of the inorganic component and by the fact that such acids are dehydrating agents. Concentrated sulfuric acid effects

$$ROH + HOSO_2OH \rightleftharpoons ROSO_2OH + H_2O$$
Alkylsulfuric acid

$$CH_3CH_2OH + HONO_2 \rightleftharpoons CH_3CH_2ONO_2 + H_2O$$
Ethyl nitrate
(b.p. 87.5°)

$$CH_3CH_2OH + HONO \rightleftharpoons CH_3CH_2ONO + H_2O$$
Ethyl nitrite
(b.p. 17°)

complete conversion of an alcohol into an alkylsulfuric acid because it is highly ionized and absorbs the water formed in esterification. Ethyl alcohol similarly combines with nitric acid and with nitrous acid to form ethyl nitrate and ethyl nitrite, respectively.

Nitroglycerin. — The powerful explosive commonly known as nitroglycerin is more accurately defined as the trinitrate ester of glycerol, or glycerol trinitrate. It is made by cautious addition of anhydrous glycerol to a stirred mixture of concentrated nitric acid and fuming sulfuric acid at a temperature maintained at 10–20° by efficient cooling (exothermic reaction). The nitration is conducted in lead vessels with cooling coils, and agitation

$$
\begin{array}{c}
CH_2OH \\
| \\
CHOH \\
| \\
CH_2OH \\
\text{Glycerol}
\end{array}
\quad + \quad 3\,HONO_2
\quad \xrightarrow[94\%]{H_2SO_4} \quad
\begin{array}{c}
CH_2ONO_2 \\
| \\
CHONO_2 \\
| \\
CH_2ONO_2 \\
\text{Nitroglycerin}
\end{array}
$$

is accomplished with compressed air. The sulfuric acid absorbs the water liberated and promotes formation of the fully esterified product.

Nitroglycerin is a colorless oily liquid (sp. gr. 1.6) with a sweet burning taste. It is very slightly soluble in water but readily soluble in alcohol or ether. It supercools to a marked degree but crystallizes in two forms, one labile (m.p. 2.9°) and the other stable (m.p. 13.2°). The substance has some use for treatment of angina pectoris, usually in the form of a dilute alcoholic solution (which can be handled safely if care is taken to prevent evaporation of solvent).

The most significant property of the nitrate ester is violent detonation on slight shock. More than enough oxygen is present to convert the carbon and hydrogen into the corresponding oxides, with liberation of elemental nitrogen:

$$
C_3H_5(ONO_2)_3 \longrightarrow \tfrac{3}{2}N_2 + 3\,CO_2 + \tfrac{5}{2}H_2O + \tfrac{1}{4}O_2
$$

The sudden liberation of this large volume of gas in a space initially occupied by the liquid substance gives an explosion wave of enormous pressure. Nitroglycerin was first prepared in 1846, and some years later Alfred Nobel in Sweden undertook its manufacture. The great sensitivity introduced considerable hazard, and the expedient of transporting the product in the frozen condition, in which state nitroglycerin is somewhat less sensitive to shock than in the liquid form, reduced but did not eliminate accidents. The experience, however, provided a clue that materialized in Nobel's discovery in 1866 of the practical explosive dynamite. Kieselguhr, a diatomaceous earth, will absorb up to three times its weight of nitroglycerin and still remain dry; the absorbed nitroglycerin in this solid form retains explosive properties but shows greatly diminished sensitivity. Commercial dynamites often contain sodium or ammonium nitrate to aid in burning an organic absorbent. Dynamite usually is molded as sticks encased in paraffined paper wrappers. It is sufficiently insensitive to shock to be handled and shipped with comparative safety, and it is exploded with use of a percussion cap, or detonator, containing mercuric fulminate, $Hg(ONC)_2$, or lead azide, PbN_6.

In 1875 Nobel made the further discovery that guncotton can be gelatinized with nitroglycerin to give a jelly of satisfactory stability and powerful explosive properties. Guncotton has much the same appearance as ordinary cotton and consists largely of cellulose trinitrate (nitrocellulose), a polymeric substance of the formula $[C_6H_7O_2(ONO_2)_3]_n$; the substance is a nitric acid ester structurally similar to nitroglycerin, $C_3H_5(ONO_2)_3$, and this similarity may account for the solubility of the solid of high molecular weight in the liquid ester. Nobel's first formulation, called Blasting Gelatin, contained 92% of nitroglycerin and 8% of guncotton; it is one of the most powerful and brisant (shattering) explosives known and is employed for blasting rocks. By greatly reducing the proportion of nitroglycerin to guncotton formulations are obtainable of slow-burning characteristics suitable for use as propellants in shells. A rifled arm requires a particularly slow-burning powder to impart a substantial push to the projectile without building up an excessive pressure in the almost gas-tight space confined by a lead bullet or shell fitting snugly into the spiral grooves of the barrel. Cordite, a superior smokeless powder introduced as the British Service propellant in 1889, has the composition: nitroglycerin, 30%; guncotton, 65%; mineral jelly (crude vaseline), 5%. With this high proportion of guncotton, gelatinization cannot be accomplished by nitroglycerin alone, and acetone is employed as a mutual solvent adapted to the production of a homogeneous gel. A paste of the ingredients, moistened with the solvent, is incorporated in a kneading machine into a stiff dough that is then extruded through a die in the form of cords (hence Cordite) of various sizes, usually having carefully spaced perforations to provide for even burning from within as well as from without. The cords are cut into lengths and dried thoroughly to evaporate the acetone, the bulk of which is recovered.

Pentaerythritol Tetranitrate (PETN) is a related high explosive prepared by esterification of the alcohol with mixed acid. The substance has considerable brisance, but is more sensitive to shock than other common high

$$HOCH_2-\underset{\underset{CH_2OH}{|}}{\overset{\overset{CH_2OH}{|}}{C}}-CH_2OH \xrightarrow{HNO_3,\ H_2SO_4} O_2NOCH_2-\underset{\underset{CH_2ONO_2}{|}}{\overset{\overset{CH_2ONO_2}{|}}{C}}-CH_2ONO_2$$

Pentaerythritol (m.p. 260°)   PETN (m.p. 138–140°)

explosives, such as TNT, and usually is detonated by impact of a rifle bullet. The substance is used chiefly in manufacture of detonating fuse (Primacord), a waterproof textile filled with powdered PETN.

ETHERS

The type formula for an ether can be derived by replacement of the two hydrogens of water by alkyl groups, but ethers are regarded more appropriately as derivatives of alcohols, from which they usually are prepared. The physical properties of some better known ethers are listed in Table 6.4. Usage varies with respect to nomenclature of symmetrical

HOH	ROH	ROR′ or R:$\ddot{\mathrm{O}}$:R′
Water	Alcohol	Ether

ethers, and some chemists omit the prefix "di–," e.g., "isopropyl ether" instead of "diisopropyl ether." Ethers boil at temperatures much lower than the alcohols from which they are derived or than alcohols of similar molecular weight, but the boiling points correspond closely to those of comparably constituted alkanes of similar molecular complexity. Since an oxygen atom (16) is nearly the equivalent of a methylene group (14), it is appropriate to compare diethyl ether (b.p. 34.6°) with *n*-pentane (b.p. 36.1°); methyl *n*-butyl ether (b.p. 70.3°) with *n*-hexane (b.p. 68.7°); or di-*n*-butyl ether (b.p. 140.9°) with *n*-nonane (b.p. 150.7°). Ethers, like alkanes, are unassociated in the liquid form and hence wholly different from the high-boiling, hydrogen-bonded alcohols.

Diethyl ether, known simply as ether, is the most important member of the series and is used extensively as a solvent and as an anesthetic. The combination of two hydrocarbon residues linked through an inert oxygen atom confers marked solvent power for organic compounds of most types other than those of a highly hydroxylic character. Ether is an excellent

TABLE 6.4. ETHERS

NAME	FORMULA	M.P., °C.	B.P., °C.	SP. GR. (LIQ.)
Dimethyl ether	CH_3OCH_3	− 140	− 24.9	0.661
Methyl ethyl ether	$CH_3OCH_2CH_3$		7.9	.697
Diethyl ether	$CH_3CH_2OCH_2CH_3$	$\begin{cases} -116 & (\alpha) \\ -123.5 & (\beta) \end{cases}$	34.6	.714
Di-*n*-propyl ether	$(CH_3CH_2CH_2)_2O$	− 122	90.5	.736
Diisopropyl ether	$(CH_3)_2CHOCH(CH_3)_2$		68	.735
Methyl *n*-butyl ether	$CH_3OCH_2CH_2CH_2CH_3$	− 116	70.3	.744
Ethyl *n*-butyl ether	$CH_3CH_2OCH_2CH_2CH_2CH_3$		92	.752
Di-*n*-butyl ether	$(CH_3CH_2CH_2CH_2)_2O$		141	.769
Di-*n*-amyl ether	$(n\text{-}C_5H_{11})_2O$	− 69	187.5	.774
Diisoamyl ether	$[(CH_3)_2CHCH_2CH_2]_2O$		172.2	.777
Di-*n*-hexyl ether	$(n\text{-}C_6H_{13})_2O$		208.8	
s-Di-(chloromethyl) ether	$ClCH_2OCH_2Cl$		106	1.315
α,β-Dichloroethyl ethyl ether	$CH_3CH_2OCHClCH_2Cl$		145	1.174
Di-(β-chloroethyl) ether	$CH_2ClCH_2OCH_2CH_2Cl$		178	1.213
Ethylene glycol dimethyl ether	$CH_3OCH_2CH_2OCH_3$		83	.863
Divinyl ether	$CH_2{=}CHOCH{=}CH_2$		35	
Diallyl ether	$(CH_2{=}CHCH_2)_2O$		94	.826
Tetrahydrofuran	$\begin{array}{c} CH_2CH_2 \\ \diagdown \\ \quad\quad O \\ \diagup \\ CH_2CH_2 \end{array}$	− 108	65.4	.888
Diphenyl ether	$C_6H_5OC_6H_5$	26.9	259	1.072
Anisole	$C_6H_5OCH_3$	− 37.3	154	.994

extraction medium because it is a good solvent for organic compounds and dissolves but few inorganic substances, because it is not miscible with water and separates as a discrete upper layer, and because its high volatility (b.p. 34.6°) permits rapid removal from an extract by distillation at a temperature so low as to avoid damage to sensitive substances. Dimethyl ether would not be suitable because it is a gas at room temperature (Table 6.4), and the higher homologs are less volatile and are not so readily available. Ether falls short of being an ideal extraction solvent because it is not completely insoluble in water; at room temperature ether dissolves 1–1.5% of water and water dissolves 7.5% of ether; hence considerable solvent is lost in extraction operations. The volatile solvent is also highly flammable, and ether vapor, being about two and one half times as heavy as air, tends to settle on bench surfaces and catch fire. Another property calling for caution in handling ether is that on standing for some time in contact with air the substance is partly oxidized to a nonvolatile peroxide, which is left as a residue on evaporation of the solvent and which may explode violently in a distillation carried to dryness with consequent overheating. Ether peroxide is a mixture of which the following constituents have been identified:

$$CH_3CHO\cdot OCHCH_3 \atop \textstyle \underset{OH}{|} \quad \underset{OH}{|}$$
Dihydroxyethyl peroxide

$$\left(CH_3CH{\Big\langle}{O \atop O}{\Big|} \right)_n$$
Ethylidene peroxide polymer

Ether that has been kept under conditions permitting oxidation should be shaken with ferrous sulfate solution prior to distillation to destroy any peroxide present. Iron wire is introduced into glass-bottled commercial ether to inhibit peroxide formation in storage.

Tetrahydrofuran (Table 6.4), now available commercially, has extraordinary solvent properties, is less volatile than diethyl ether, and is miscible with water but recoverable from an aqueous solution as an azeotropic distillate containing 4.3% of water. The solvent is frequently added to Grignard reaction mixtures to dissolve a complex that separates when ether alone is used.

Ether as an Anesthetic. — Ether was first used in surgical anesthesia by Long in Georgia in 1842, but the results were not published and did not influence medical practice. The safe abolition of pain by inhalation of ether for a period long enough for a surgical operation was rediscovered by the Boston dentist Morton, and introduction of ether anesthesia into surgical practice resulted from a successful demonstration by Morton at the Massachusetts General Hospital in 1846. The term anesthesia (insensibility) was suggested to Morton by Oliver Wendell Holmes. Inhalation of ether vapor produces unconsciousness by depressing activity of the central nervous system. The effect appears to be associated with affinity of ether for cell surfaces, possibly with alteration in the permeability of cells.

Anesthesia with ethylene was employed successfully in clinical surgery in 1923 (Luckhardt and Lewis), but although the hydrocarbon produces a rapid and pleasant induction of unconsciousness, with prompt recovery, the explosiveness of certain mixtures of ethylene and air imposes difficulties, and the method has been little used. Divinyl ether, suggested as an anesthetic by Leake and Chen (1930) and made available in a satisfactory form by Ruigh and Major, is characterized by a potency about seven times that of ether and by greater rapidity of action, but these advantages are offset by danger of rapidly reaching a too deep plane of anesthesia. The commercial preparation Vinethene contains 3.5% of absolute alcohol to retard evaporation leading to frosting of the anesthetic mask and a trace of an antioxidant (0.01% of phenyl-α-naphthylamine). Cyclopropane, first used clinically at the University of Wisconsin General Hospital in 1934, is the most potent anesthetic gas, and in very low concentrations can produce insensibility to pain without unconsciousness. However, the hydrocarbon is expensive, and mixtures with air over the entire anesthetic range are explosive and flammable; an experienced anesthetist with access to special equipment is required. Nitrous oxide was suggested for use in surgical operations by Sir Humphry Davy in 1799, but was investi-gated for this purpose only subsequent to the American discovery of the similar use of ether. The oxide has found some use in dentistry but not in general surgery, for even undiluted nitrous oxide has only a weak depressant action on the central nervous system, and in an operation lasting more than a minute or two oxygen must be given to prevent anoxemia (insufficient aeration of the blood); this dilution of the anesthetic reduces potency to a low level. Chloroform, formerly employed to some extent as an anesthetic, possesses significant liver toxicity and is now little used except in the tropics, where the low boiling point of ether presents difficulties. Ether thus continues to be the safest and the most widely used general anesthetic.

Preparation of Ethers. — Diethyl ether can be produced from ethanol, either by the sulfuric acid method or by dehydration over aluminum oxide or sulfate catalysts at high pressure and at temperatures of 240–260°. The sulfuric acid process consists in preparing an initial mixture of alcohol and sulfuric acid, heating it to a temperature of about 140°, and running in a large additional quantity of alcohol at the rate at which the ether produced distils from the reaction mixture p. (55). The competitive reaction of dehydration to an alkene limits applicability of the method to the preparation of ethers from alcohols that are not easily dehydrated. The results are best with primary alcohols; dimethyl and di-n-propyl ether can be prepared satisfactorily by the action of sulfuric acid on the corresponding alcohol. Ethylene chlorohydrin on treatment with sulfuric acid yields di-(β-chloroethyl) ether, a nonvesicant oxygen analog of mustard gas. The dichloro compound is employed as an intermediate in production of divinyl ether:

$$2\,HOCH_2CH_2Cl \xrightarrow[\substack{75\%}]{H_2SO_4} \underset{\substack{\text{Di-}(\beta\text{-chloroethyl})\\ \text{ether}}}{O(CH_2CH_2Cl)_2} \xrightarrow[\substack{25\%}]{\text{Fused KOH, 200–240°, stream of NH}_3} \underset{\substack{\text{Divinyl ether}}}{O(CH=CH_2)_2}$$

Isoamyl alcohol can be converted into the ether in 45–50% yield by treatment with one tenth part of sulfuric acid at a temperature of 140°, which is above the boiling point of the alcohol and below that of the ether. In this case the alcohol that distils in the initial stages is returned to the reaction flask, and at the end of a suitable period, the diisoamyl ether that has accumulated in the flask is separated from sulfuric acid and charred material by steam distillation. Secondary and tertiary alcohols are so readily dehydrated to alkenes by mineral acids that their conversion into ethers by the sulfuric acid method often presents difficulties. Diisopropyl ether is a by-product of the production of isopropyl alcohol from propylene.

A generally applicable method of preparing either simple or mixed ethers is the **Williamson[7] synthesis,** which involves interaction of a sodium alkoxide with an alkyl halide. A given alcohol can be transformed into the cor-

$$RONa + R'X \rightarrow ROR' + NaX$$

responding simple ether by converting one part of it into the sodio derivative and another into the bromide or iodide, and bringing these two components into reaction. Examples of the preparation of mixed ethers are:

$$CH_3CH_2CH_2ONa \quad + \quad CH_3CH_2I \xrightarrow{70\%} CH_3CH_2CH_2OCH_2CH_3$$
Sodium n-propoxide   Ethyl n-propyl ether

$$CH_3CH_2ONa \quad + \quad BrCH_2CH_2CH_2CH_3 \xrightarrow{110°} CH_3CH_2OCH_2CH_2CH_2CH_3$$
Ethyl n-butyl ether

The alkyl halide in the Williamson synthesis can be replaced by a dialkyl sulfate. This method of alkylation has particular importance in the aro-

$$(CH_3)_2SO_4 \quad + \quad NaOCH_2CH(CH_3)_2 \longrightarrow CH_3OCH_2CH(CH_3)_2 \quad + \quad CH_3NaSO_4$$
Methyl isobutyl ether

matic series and is widely employed for preparation of methyl and ethyl ethers of phenols, for example:

Phenol   Anisole

Properties of Ethers. — Ethers are inert substances in comparison with alcohols, and approach saturated hydrocarbons in general lack of pronounced chemical affinity. They do not react with sodium and are undamaged by treatment at moderate temperatures with strong acids or bases. Although ethers slowly undergo some peroxidation on prolonged contact with air, an ether group in a complex molecule is resistant to attack by chemical oxidizing agents and will survive oxidation of a double bond or of a primary or secondary alcoholic group. An alkoxy group likewise is indifferent to a Grignard reagent, and, unlike hydroxyl, does not decompose the

---

[7] Alexander W. Williamson, 1824–1904; b. Wandsworth, England; Ph.D. Giessen (Liebig); London; *J. Chem. Soc.*, **87**, 605 (1905)

reagent with formation of the hydrocarbon. Thus hydroxyl groups are often protected during synthetic operations by methylation. That ethers are more reactive than paraffinic hydrocarbons is indicated by the fact that diethyl ether can be chlorinated readily at ordinary temperatures without illumination; the product, α,β-dichloroethyl ethyl ether, $CH_3CH_2OCHCl-CH_2Cl$, is obtained in about 24% yield.

The ether linkage between hydrocarbon residues can be split fairly readily by halogen acids, particularly hydrogen iodide. Moderate treatment with one equivalent of this reagent brings about hydrolysis of an aliphatic ether to a mixture of alkyl halides and alcohols; if one group attached to oxygen is methyl and the other is a higher residue other than a tertiary group, cleavage chiefly produces methyl iodide, for example:

$$CH_3OCH_2CH_2CH_3 \xrightarrow{HI} CH_3I + HOCH_2CH_2CH_3$$

With excess hydrogen iodide an ether suffers fission to two molecules of alkyl halide. Hydrobromic acid acts similarly at a higher temperature, and

$$R-O-R' + 2HI \longrightarrow RI + R'I + H_2O$$

a frequently used method of demethylating nonvolatile methoxy compounds consists in refluxing with constant-boiling hydrobromic acid in acetic acid solution. Such a process is useful for removal of a masking methyl group introduced to provide protection for a reactive hydroxyl group, which then can be regenerated by treatment of the halide with silver hydroxide. The cleavage of methoxy compounds by hydrogen iodide is the basis of the Zeisel method for quantitative determination of the methoxyl content of substances other than mixed ethers of low molecular weight. A weighed sample is boiled with excess hydriodic acid, the volatile methyl iodide formed (b.p. 42.3°) is distilled into an alcoholic solution of silver nitrate, and the resulting precipitate of silver iodide is weighed. Titrimetric methods of determination are used in microanalysis. The other cleavage product must be relatively nonvolatile. An example is the alkaloid papaverine, which was found by Zeisel determination to contain four methoxyl groups. The free

$$C_{16}H_9N(OCH_3)_4 \xrightarrow{HI} C_{16}H_9N(OH)_4 + 4CH_3I$$
$$\text{Papaverine} \qquad \text{Nonvolatile residue} \qquad \text{Distillate}$$

hydroxyl groups present in the nonvolatile fragment are attached to benzene rings; such groups are not subject to ready replacement by iodine in the manner characteristic of aliphatic hydroxyl groups.

Basic Properties. — Ethers are basic in that they are able to combine with strong mineral acids to form oxonium salts, $[R_2OH]^+X^-$, comparable to ammonium salts, $[NH_4]^+X^-$. Thus dimethyl ether combines with hydrogen chloride by attachment of a proton to oxygen by one of the unshared electron pairs to produce a cation that is bound to the chloride ion by elec-

$$CH_3:\overset{..}{O}: + H^+Cl^- \longrightarrow \left[CH_3:\overset{..}{O}:H \right]^+ Cl^-$$
$$\qquad CH_3 \qquad\qquad\qquad\qquad CH_3$$
$$\text{Oxonium salt}$$

trostatic forces.   The salt exists only in a strongly acidic medium and is decomposed to the components by water.   Ethers dissolve in cold concentrated sulfuric acid owing to formation of oxonium salts, $[R_2OH]^+OSO_2OH^-$, and they are thereby readily distinguishable and separable from paraffinic hydrocarbons and alkyl halides.   If the sulfuric acid solution of the oxonium salt is diluted carefully by ice, the ether can be liberated in unchanged condition; if cooling is not sufficient to compensate for the heat of dilution of sulfuric acid, some hydrolysis may occur.

Formation of nonpolar complexes of an ether with a Grignard reagent and with substances such as mercuric bromide, magnesium bromide, boron fluoride, or aluminum chloride is best understood in terms of the G. N. Lewis[8] concept of acids and bases.   Lewis defined an acid as an electron acceptor and a base as an electron donor.   In formation of an oxonium salt from an ether, the proton of the mineral acid accepts an electron pair from oxygen and thus functions as a Lewis acid; the electron-donating ether is a base.

$$\begin{array}{ccccc} R:\overset{..}{\underset{..}{O}}: & + & H^+ & \longrightarrow & \left[R:\overset{..}{O}:H\right]^+ \\ R & & & & R \end{array}$$

Lewis base   Lewis acid   Oxonium ion

Boron fluoride is a Lewis acid because the boron atom, with an original sextet of electrons, can form an octet by accepting electrons; ether serves as an electron donor, or base, and the two reactants form a stable, coordinate covalent complex, boron fluoride etherate, which distils without decomposition.   Boron fluoride, a gas, is an excellent catalyst for esterification

$$\begin{array}{ccccc} & & F & & F \\ C_2H_5:\overset{..}{\underset{..}{O}}: & + & \overset{..}{\underset{..}{B}}:F & \longrightarrow & C_2H_5:\overset{..}{\underset{..}{O}}\overset{+}{:}\overset{-}{B}:F \\ C_2H_5 & & F & & H_5C_2 \; F \end{array}$$

Lewis base   Lewis acid   Boron fluoride etherate
                                                                (b.p. 126°)

$R':\overset{..+}{\underset{..}{O}}:R'$ and acylation, and for this purpose it is conveniently employed as the etherate.   An alkylmagnesium halide, $R:Mg:X$, is a Lewis

$R:\overset{-}{Mg}:X$ acid, and the magnesium atom completes its octet by accepting a

$R':\overset{..+}{\underset{..}{O}}:R'$ pair of electrons from each of two ether oxygen atoms to form a dietherate (p. 38).   Neutralization can be regarded as the combination of a proton (Lewis acid) with hydroxide ion, as Lewis base.   The

$$\begin{array}{ccccccc} \left[H:\overset{..}{\underset{..}{O}}:\right]^- & + & H^+ & \longrightarrow & H:\overset{..}{\underset{..}{O}}: & \xrightarrow{+\,H^+} & \left[H:\overset{..}{O}:H\right]^+ \\ & & & & H & & H \end{array}$$

Lewis base   Lewis acid   Water   Hydronium ion

resulting water molecule has an electronic structure like that of an ether; it is a Lewis base and combines with a proton to form a hydronium ion, the active species in reactions of mineral acids in aqueous solution.

---

[8] Gilbert N. Lewis, 1875–1946; b. Weymouth, Mass.; Ph.D. Harvard (Richards); Univ. Calif., Berkeley

SULFUR ANALOGS

Mercaptans. — Sulfur is in the same group as oxygen in the periodic table and forms similar compounds. The sulfur analogs of alcohols, RSH, are known both as mercaptans and as alkane thiols. The —SH group is called the mercapto-, thiol-, or sulfhydryl group. The boiling points are much lower than those of the corresponding alcohols, for example: CH_3SH, 6°; CH_3CH_2SH, 36°; $CH_3CH_2CH_2SH$, 68°; $CH_3(CH_2)_3SH$, 98°. The boiling point of the last compound, n-butyl mercaptan, is that characteristic of a normal alkane of molecular weight 100, and the molecular weight of the mercaptan is almost the same (90). That mercaptans are thus only slightly associated is because, since sulfur is much less negative than oxygen, mercaptans are unable to form hydrogen bonds. Inability to form hydrogen bonds with water accounts for the fact that mercaptans are much less soluble in water than alcohols. A distinguishing feature of volatile mercaptans is their disagreeable odor. Mercaptans, unlike alcohols, are acidic and form water-soluble salts with alkalis and insoluble salts with heavy metals (mercury, lead, zinc). The name is derived from this property (*L. mercurium captans*, seizing mercury).

Primary mercaptans can be prepared by reaction of an alkyl halide with sodium or potassium hydrosulfide: $RX + Na(K)SH \rightarrow RSH + Na(K)X$. The yields are satisfactory, however, only if the alkyl group is primary. A method that generally gives high yields involves reaction of either an alkyl halide or a dialkyl sulfate with thiourea (a) to form the S-alkylthiuronium salt (b), which is hydrolyzed by alkali to the mercaptan (c) and cyanamide

$$n\text{-}C_{12}H_{25}Br \;+\; S{=}C(NH_2)_2 \longrightarrow n\text{-}C_{12}H_{25}SC\overset{\displaystyle +}{\underset{\textstyle NH_2}{\diagup}}\overset{NH_2Br^-}{} \xrightarrow[\text{80\% overall}]{NaOH}$$

$$\text{(a)} \qquad\qquad\qquad\qquad\qquad \text{(b)}$$

$$n\text{-}C_{12}H_{25}SH \;+\; NaBr \;+\; H_2NC{\equiv}N \;+\; H_2O$$

$$\text{(c)} \qquad\qquad\qquad\qquad \text{(d)}$$

(d). Another convenient method is reaction of an alkyl halide with potassium thiolacetate to give an acetyl mercaptan, which is hydrolyzed: $RX + CH_3COSK \rightarrow RSCOCH_3 \rightarrow RSH$.

The most characteristic chemical property of mercaptans is that they are reducing agents; they are readily oxidized by hydrogen peroxide or sodium hypohalite to disulfides, from which they can be regenerated by reduction (zinc dust and acid). A natural product required for growth of

$$2\,RSH + H_2O_2 \rightarrow RSSR + H_2O$$

certain microorganisms known as thioctic acid (or lipoic acid) is a fairly simple cyclic disulfide (3), which has been synthesized from ethyl 6,8-dibromooctanate (1) through the 6,8-dimercapto acid (2), followed by oxidative ring closure (overall yield 64%). Nitric acid oxidizes either a mercaptan or the corresponding disulfide to the alkylsulfonic acid, RSO_2OH.

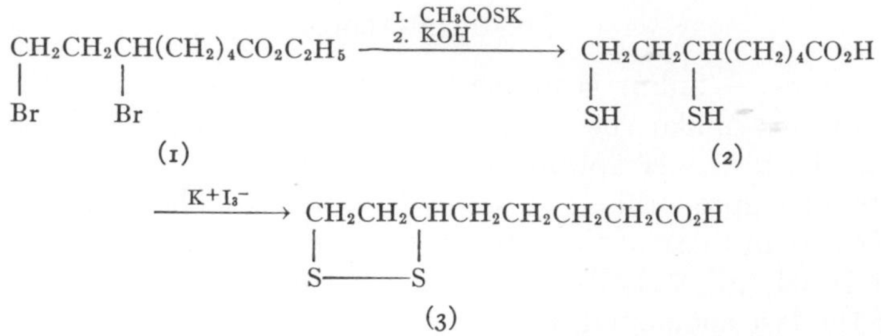

$$\underset{\underset{(1)}{\overset{|}{\underset{Br}{}}\quad\overset{|}{\underset{Br}{}}}{CH_2CH_2CH(CH_2)_4CO_2C_2H_5} \xrightarrow[\text{2. KOH}]{\text{1. CH}_3\text{COSK}} \underset{\underset{(2)}{\overset{|}{\underset{SH}{}}\quad\overset{|}{\underset{SH}{}}}{CH_2CH_2CH(CH_2)_4CO_2H}$$

$$\xrightarrow{\text{K}^+\text{I}_3^-} \underset{\underset{(3)}{\underset{S\text{———}S}{|\qquad|}}}{CH_2CH_2CHCH_2CH_2CH_2CH_2CO_2H}$$

Sulfides. — These analogs of ethers can be prepared by a method (1) analogous to the Williamson synthesis.   A symmetrical disulfide is obtained

1. $C_2H_5Br + NaSCH_3 \rightarrow CH_3CH_2SCH_3$
        Methyl ethyl sulfide, b.p. 67°

2. $2\ C_2H_5Br + Na_2S \rightarrow CH_3CH_2SCH_2CH_3$
        Diethyl sulfide, b.p. 92°

most readily by the action of sodium sulfide on an alkyl halide (2).

Sulfides combine with alkyl halides to form crystalline sulfonium salts (a), comparable to oxonium salts, and they react with chlorine, bromine, or iodine to form dihalides that are similarly constituted. On oxidation (HNO_3 ,

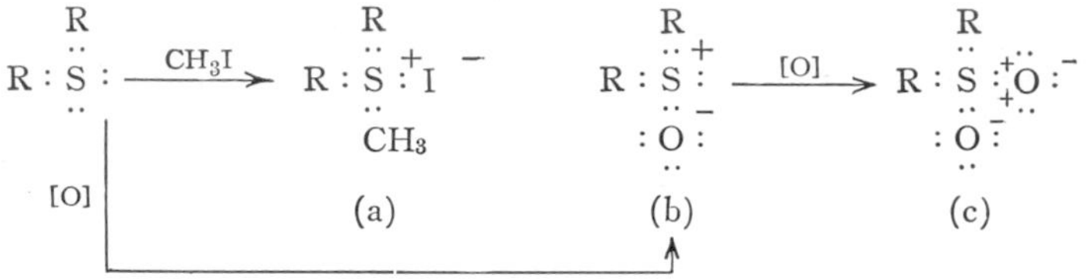

H_2O_2 , etc.), one oxygen equivalent of reagent converts a sulfide into a sulfoxide (b) and a second produces the sulfone (c).   If sulfur, like carbon, nitrogen, and oxygen, can have only eight electrons in the valence shell, these derivatives contain one and two semipolar bonds, respectively.

PROBLEMS IN SYNTHESIS

Several reactions described in this chapter are serviceable in the synthetic preparation of compounds of predictable structure, and an important phase of an organic chemist's assignment is application of the knowledge of such synthetic reactions to the preparation of desired end products.   To attain competency the student should not stop with an understanding of a given set of reactions and an ability to reproduce type formulations and illustrative examples, but should seek to acquire facility in applying this information to the solution of specific problems in synthesis.   Although even a complicated synthesis may be comprehended easily when viewed in a completed form, the working out of an original plan of synthesizing a desired compound is a more difficult task, and facility usually comes only with considerable practice.

It is of assistance to have a grasp of the scope and limitations of different reactions and of the types of both starting materials and products involved. In planning syntheses of alcohols, for instance, it is useful to recall that in the Grignard process formaldehyde and ethylene oxide give primary alcohols, aldehydes afford secondary alcohols, and both ketones and esters yield tertiary alcohols. Although the reaction has wide scope, a limitation is that neither component may contain functional groups capable of reaction with the reagent. Allyl chloride forms a Grignard reagent satisfactorily, since the ethylenic linkage is inert to an alkylmagnesium halide, but chloroacetone, CH_3COCH_2Cl, possesses a carbonyl group capable of adding RMgX and hence fails to yield a Grignard reagent. Ethylene chlorohydrin similarly is unsuitable for production of a Grignard reagent because the hydroxyl and MgCl groups are incompatible.

Generalizations such as the Markownikoff rule are also useful. Rules pertaining to the relative ease of dehydration of primary, secondary, and teritary alcohols, and to the direction of dehydration where alternate paths are open are equally applicable to reactions in which an alkene is produced by elimination of HX from an alkyl halide. The course of oxidation of alcohols and of alkenes also can be predicted on the basis of empirical generalizations, and an oxidation reaction may be useful at either an initial or a terminal stage of synthesis. Alcohols listed in Table 6.2 are key starting materials available for many syntheses, for these substances can be converted by oxidation into aldehydes, ketones, or acids, which serve as synthetic intermediates. Association of one reaction with another is of further assistance. Dehydration of an alcohol to an alkene can be followed by catalytic hydrogenation to an alkane, and the alcohol required in the first step may be obtainable by a Grignard reaction. A primary alcohol can be oxidized to a carboxylic acid, which can be decarboxylated to an alkane having one carbon atom less than the alcohol. A Grignard synthesis leading to a secondary alcohol also makes available the ketone obtainable from such an alcohol by oxidation. The sulfuric acid hydration of an alkene having the grouping —CH=CH— also provides an alcohol capable of being transformed into a ketone: $-CH_2CH(OH)- \rightarrow -CH_2CO-$.

Specific problems in synthesis usually are attacked advantageously by working back from the final product to available starting materials, rather than by centering attention on starting materials. A typical requirement would be to synthesize 2-methylbutanol-2, utilizing as starting materials any alcohol having not more than three carbon atoms; this requirement would include the saturated C_1-, C_2-, and C_3-monohydric alcohols, ethylene glycol, and glycerol, but of course these substances constitute potential sources of formaldehyde, acetaldehyde, propionaldehyde, acetone, and formic, acetic, and propionic acid (also the esters of these substances), as well as of allyl alcohol (glycerol, formic acid) and ethylene oxide (from ethanol, through ethylene and ethylene chlorohydrin). If the suggested process of deductive reasoning is followed, the formula of 2-methylbutanol-2 is first examined.   This tertiary alcohol contains the hydroxyl group at a

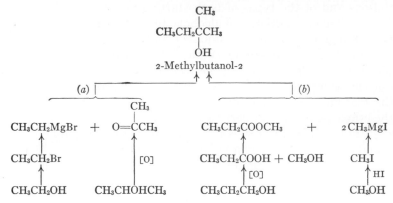

2-Methylbutanol-2

branching point in the carbon chain, as would result from a Grignard synthesis.   Tertiary alcohols are obtainable by the action of alkylmagnesium halides on either ketones or esters, and the desired alcohol can evidently be synthesized either from ethylmagnesium bromide and acetone (a), or from methyl propionate and a methylmagnesium halide (b).   Both sets of intermediates are obtainable from simple C_1- to C_3-alcohols, and hence two satisfactory solutions of the problem are at hand.

Another problem is the synthesis of 3-methylhexene-3 (I) from alcohols having not more than four carbon atoms.   Two possible precursors come to mind, one with the hydroxyl at the 3-position (III) and the other with this group at position 4 (II).   Structure III is disadvantageous because the hydroxylated carbon atom is flanked on each side by a methylene group (—CH₂—) and dehydration would probably occur to about the same extent

$$CH_3CH_2CH\text{—}CHCH_2CH_3 \rightarrow \underset{CH_3}{\overset{3\quad 4}{CH_3CH_2C\text{=}CHCH_2CH_3}} \qquad \underset{CH_3}{\overset{OH}{CH_3CH_2CCH_2CH_2CH_3}}$$

$$\underset{CH_3\quad OH}{}$$

II   III

$$CH_3CH_2CHMgBr + O\text{=}CHCH_2CH_3$$

$$\underset{CH_3}{}$$

IV   V

in each of the two possible directions.   In the alcohol II, however, one carbon adjacent to the hydroxylated carbon carries a lone hydrogen atom whereas the alternate position carries two, and hence, in analogy with known cases, dehydration can be expected to yield the desired alkene I. Synthesis of the intermediate alcohol II can be accomplished by interaction of sec-butylmagnesium bromide (IV) with propionaldehyde (V), and these substances in turn are obtainable from sec-butyl alcohol and n-propyl alcohol, respectively.

The synthesis of 4-methyloctane (VI) from C_1- to C_4-alcohols obviously calls for a process more elaborate than the union of two parts, for the hydro-carbon contains nine carbon atoms. It could be obtained from the alcohol VII either by dehydration and catalytic hydrogenation or by conversion

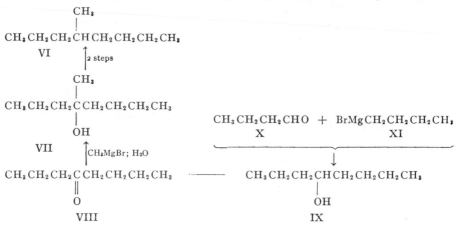

into the bromide, preparation of the Grignard reagent, and treatment with water. The alcohol VII could be synthesized, in turn, by addition of methyl Grignard reagent to the ketone VIII, and this substance would result from oxidation of the secondary alcohol IX, obtainable by interaction of n-butyraldehyde (X) with n-butylmagnesium bromide (XI).

PROBLEMS

1. Predict the chief products of the following reactions:

   (a) Methyldiethylcarbinol on dehydration
   (b) $(CH_3)_2CHCHBrCH_2CH(CH_3)_2$ + alcoholic KOH
   (c) $(CH_3)_2COHCH_2CH_2CH_2OH$ on partial dehydration (elimination of one molecule of H_2O)
   (d) $CH_3CH_2CH_2COH(CH_3)_2$ + $K_2Cr_2O_7$ in a hot solution of dilute sulfuric acid
   (e) Cyclohexene, heated in acetic acid with hydrogen peroxide, followed by the addition of lead tetraacetate
   (f) Ethylene oxide + n-amyl alcohol, in the presence of dry hydrogen chloride
   (g) Ethylene oxide + ammonia

2. Indicate Grignard syntheses of the following substances from n-propylmagnesium bromide and any second component desired:

   (a) 2-Methylpentanol-2   (d) n-Amyl alcohol
   (b) 4-Methylheptanol-4   (e) Methylethyl-n-propylcarbinol
   (c) n-Butyl alcohol

3. Devise syntheses of the following compounds, starting with any alcohols having not more than three carbon atoms and any desired components readily obtainable from these alcohols (the list of available starting materials thus includes C_3-compounds of the types RX, RMgX, RCHO, RCOR, RCO_2H; also ethylene oxide, allyl alcohol):

   (a) $(CH_3)_2CHCH_2OH$ (f) 4-Methylpentene-1
   (b) $(CH_3)_2C(OH)CH_2CH_3$ (g) 2,3-Dimethylbutene-2
   (c) $(CH_3CH_2)_3COH$ (h) Isobutane
   (d) $CH_3CH_2CH_2CH_2CH_2OH$ (i) 2-Methylpentane
   (e) 2-Methylbutene-2   (j) 2,3,4-Trimethylpentane

4. Give syntheses of the following compounds from the starting materials of (3):

   (a) 4-Ethylheptane
   (b) 4-Methylpentadiene-1,3
   (c) Neopentyl alcohol, $(CH_3)_3CCH_2OH$

5. Devise syntheses of the following compounds starting with alcohols and derived substances having no more than four carbons:

   (a) 2,4-Dimethylpentene-2   (c) 2-Methylhexane
   (b) 3-Methylhexanol-3   (d) 2,2-Dimethylpentane

6. A hydrocarbon C_5H_{10} yields 2-methylbutane on catalytic hydrogenation and adds HBr to form a compound that on reaction with silver hydroxide affords an alcohol. The latter on oxidation gives a ketone. What is the structure of the hydrocarbon?

7. An alcohol $C_5H_{11}OH$ gives a ketone on oxidation, and when it is dehydrated and the resulting alkene is oxidized, a mixture of a ketone and an acid results. What is the structure of the alcohol?

8. Plan a synthesis of octadiene-2,6, starting with cyclohexene.

9. How could you distinguish experimentally between the following isomers?

10. Starting with a natural product that has been formulated, plan a synthesis of:

$$CH_3(CH_2)_5CH(OH)CH_2CHOHCHOH(CH_2)_7CH_2OH$$

READING REFERENCES

R. W. Cairns, "Industrial and Military Explosives," *J. Chem. Ed.*, **19**, 109 (1942)

C. A. Thomas, "Chemicals Derived from Pentanes," *Science of Petroleum*, IV, 2795, Oxford University Press, London (1938)

L. Pauling, "The Nature of the Chemical Bond," Chapter IX Cornell University Press (1939).

CHAPTER 7

HALOGEN COMPOUNDS

In the series of alkyl halides (Table 7.1), bromides boil at temperatures distinctly higher than the corresponding chlorides, and iodides are higher boiling than bromides. There is also a rise in boiling point in each series of homologs, and thus an increase in molecular weight due to either a heavier halogen atom or a larger alkyl group results in an increase in boiling point. The chlorides are much less volatile than the alkanes from which they are derived but do not differ greatly from alkanes of comparable molecular weight. Iodides boil at about the same temperatures as alcohols of corresponding structure. Among the initial members of the series, methyl chloride, ethyl chloride, and methyl bromide are gases at laboratory temperature; liquefied methyl chloride is obtainable commercially in steel cylinders and the other two in sealed glass ampules, which are chilled prior to being opened or resealed. When a small quantity of a methyl or an ethyl halide is required, convenience in measuring may dictate selection of methyl iodide or ethyl bromide, but the chlorides are cheaper and usually preferable for large-scale operations. The boiling point of ethyl chloride is such that a fine stream of the liquid sprayed on the skin freezes tissues in a localized area by abstraction of heat required for evaporation. Because of the resulting insensitization to pain, ethyl chloride has found some use as a local anesthetic for minor operations of short duration (e.g., incision of boils).

Alkyl halides are practically insoluble in water and separate from water in layers. Chlorides are slightly lighter than water, and bromides and particularly iodides are much heavier. Like alkanes, halogen compounds are insoluble in and inert to cold concentrated sulfuric acid, and extraction with this reagent removes contaminants such as alkenes, alcohols, and ethers.

Preparation. — A method applicable to the preparation of many alkyl bromides and iodides consists in treatment of the appropriate alcohol with constant-boiling hydrobromic or hydriodic acid. In the preparation of primary bromides the yield is increased by conducting the reaction in the presence of sulfuric acid, and the most economical procedure is either to prepare the required hydrobromic—sulfuric acid solution by reduction of bromine with aqueous sulfur dioxide or to treat the alcohol with a mixture of aqueous sodium bromide and sulfuric acid. Yields of 90–95% are realized in the preparation of ethyl, n-butyl, isoamyl, n-octyl, lauryl, and allyl bromide. Since secondary alcohols are more subject to the interfering reaction of dehydration, the presence of sulfuric acid is to be avoided; a useful

TABLE 7.1. ALKYL HALIDES

NAME	FORMULA	M.P., °C.	B.P., °C.	SP. GR. (LIQ.)
Methyl chloride	CH_3Cl	−97	−23.7	0.920
Methyl bromide	CH_3Br	−93	4.6	1.732
Methyl iodide	CH_3I	−64	42.3	2.279
Ethyl chloride	C_2H_5Cl	−139	13.1	0.910
Ethyl bromide	C_2H_5Br	−119	38.4	1.430
Ethyl iodide	C_2H_5I	−111	72.3	1.933
n-Propyl chloride	$CH_3CH_2CH_2Cl$	−123	46.4	0.890
n-Propyl bromide	$CH_3CH_2CH_2Br$	−110	71	1.353
n-Propyl iodide	$CH_3CH_2CH_2I$	−101	102	1.747
Isopropyl chloride	$(CH_3)_2CHCl$	−117	36.5	0.860
Isopropyl bromide	$(CH_3)_2CHBr$	−89	59.5	1.310
Isopropyl iodide	$(CH_3)_2CHI$	−91	89.4	1.703
n-Butyl chloride	$CH_3(CH_2)_3Cl$	−123	78.1	0.884
n-Butyl bromide	$CH_3(CH_2)_3Br$	−112	101.6	1.275
Isobutyl chloride	$(CH_3)_2CHCH_2Cl$	−131	68.9	0.866
Isobutyl bromide	$(CH_3)_2CHCH_2Br$	−120	91.3	1.250
sec-Butyl chloride	$CH_3CH_2CHClCH_3$		68	0.871
sec-Butyl bromide	$CH_3CH_2CHBrCH_3$		91.3	1.251
t-Butyl chloride	$(CH_3)_3CCl$	−28.5	51.0	0.851
t-Butyl bromide	$(CH_3)_3CBr$	−20	73.3	1.222
n-Amyl bromide	$CH_3(CH_2)_4Br$	−95	129.7	1.223
Isoamyl bromide	$(CH_3)_2CHCH_2CH_2Br$	−112	120.7	1.215
t-Amyl bromide	$(CH_3)_2CBrCH_2CH_3$		109.2	1.190
n-Hexyl bromide	$CH_3(CH_2)_5Br$		156	1.173
n-Octadecyl bromide	$CH_3(CH_2)_{17}Br$	34	170 at 0.5 mm.	
Vinyl chloride	$CH_2{=}CHCl$	−160	−14	
Vinyl bromide	$CH_2{=}CHBr$	−138	15.8	1.517
Allyl chloride	$CH_2{=}CHCH_2Cl$	−136	45.7	0.938
Allyl bromide	$CH_2{=}CHCH_2Br$	−119	70.0	
Allyl iodide	$CH_2{=}CHCH_2I$	−99	102.0	1.848

alternate method is the reaction of phosphorus tribromide with an alcohol:

$$3\,ROH \;+\; PBr_3 \;\longrightarrow\; 3\,RBr \;+\; P(OH)_3$$

The reaction can be conducted with preformed phosphorus tribromide (isopropyl bromide, 68% yield, sec-butyl bromide, 80% yield) or with a mixture of red and yellow phosphorus and bromine (isopropyl bromide, 69–73% yield, sec-butyl bromide, 84–85% yield). Alkyl iodides can be prepared satisfactorily with phosphorus triiodide, which need not be prepared in advance but is generated by addition of iodine to a suspension of red phosphorus in the alcohol (yields above 90% for methyl, ethyl, n-propyl, n-butyl, and n-amyl iodide). A special method for the preparation of methyl iodide consists in interaction of dimethyl sulfate with aqueous potassium iodide in the presence of calcium carbonate (90–94% yield).

Since hydrochloric acid is less active than hydrobromic or hydriodic acid, alcohols are not convertible into chlorides so readily as into bromides or iodides. Zinc chloride serves as an activator of the acid, and with mixtures of concentrated hydrochloric acid and zinc chloride, n-propyl, n-butyl, and sec-butyl alcohol can be converted into the chlorides at temperatures of 130–150° in yields of 70–80%. Alkyl chlorides are obtainable also with phosphorus trichloride, phosphorus pentachloride, or thionyl chloride ($SOCl_2$). The latter two reagents function as follows:

$$ROH + PCl_5 \longrightarrow RCl + HCl + POCl_3$$
$$ROH + SOCl_2 \longrightarrow RCl + HCl + SO_2$$

A newer method for preparation of halides employs triphenylphosphite and a halogen (H. N. Rydon, 1954). These react (a) to form the triphenyl-

(a) $(C_6H_5O)_3P + X_2(Cl_2, Br_2$ or $I_2) \rightarrow (C_6H_5O)_3PX_2$

(b) $ROH + (C_6H_5O)_3PX_2 \rightarrow RX + (C_6H_5O)_2P(=O)X + C_6H_5OH$

phosphite dihalide, which in turn reacts with an alcohol as shown (b). Actually, except for the case of unsaturated alcohols, the reaction is usually carried out in one step by mixing the three components. The reaction proceeds to completion at room temperature within an hour or so and yields are in the range of 65–95%.

Alcohols of the types represented by t-butyl alcohol and allyl alcohol possess special reactivity to hydrogen halides and are convertible into the chlorides by aqueous hydrochloric acid without catalyst and at moderate temperatures. t-Butyl chloride can be prepared by merely shaking the

$$(CH_3)_3COH \xrightarrow[94\%]{\text{concd. HCl, 25°}} (CH_3)_3CCl$$
t-Butyl alcohol   t-Butyl chloride

$$CH_2{=}CHCH_2OH \xrightarrow[]{\text{concd. HCl, 100°}} CH_2{=}CHCH_2Cl$$
Allyl alcohol   Allyl chloride

alcohol with concentrated hydrochloric acid for a few minutes in a separatory funnel at room temperature. In the second reaction replacement of hydroxyl by halogen proceeds readily in an aqueous medium under conditions not adequate for addition of hydrogen chloride to the double bond.

Alkyl halides are also available from carboxylic acids by the reaction of bromine or chlorine with the silver, mercury, or potassium salt of the acid. The carboxyl group is eliminated as carbon dioxide and is replaced by halogen. The reaction has been used mainly for preparation of long-chain

$$CH_3(CH_2)_6COOK \xrightarrow[45\%]{Br_2} CH_3(CH_2)_6Br$$
Potassium caprylate   Heptyl bromide

$$CH_3(CH_2)_{10}COOH \xrightarrow[67\%]{\substack{1.\ AgNO_2 \\ 2.\ Br_2}} CH_3(CH_2)_{10}Br$$
Lauric acid   Undecyl bromide

halides where the starting materials are the natural fatty acids; it also provides a useful method of degradation.

Reactivity. — The instances already discussed in which alkyl halides react with magnesium (Grignard), reducing agents, sodium (Wurtz), sodium alkoxides (Williamson), alcoholic potassium hydroxide (alkenes), and silver hydroxide (alcohols), illustrate the general reactivity of these substances. Quantitative investigations of the relative reactivities of different halides have been made by determination of the amount of material entering into a given reaction after varying periods of time (reaction rate). Although minor variations are observable from one type of replacement reaction to another and in experiments at different temperatures and in different solvents, certain striking differences have been recognized. One is that in the series of normal saturated chlorides, bromides, and iodides, the methyl homolog is distinctly more reactive (from 5 to 20 times) than the ethyl, *n*-propyl, *n*-butyl, and higher halides, and that the reactivity remains essentially constant from the ethyl homolog on:

$$CH_3X > C_2H_5X, \; n\text{-}C_3H_7X, \; n\text{-}C_4H_9X, \text{ etc.}$$

A second generalization is that a given iodide is more reactive than the corresponding bromide, which in turn surpasses the chloride:

$$RI > RBr > RCl$$

The differences here are even more pronounced than between a methyl and and ethyl halide and are observable, for example, in the speed of reaction with magnesium in the presence of ether; methyl iodide usually begins to react within a minute or two, and the production of the Grignard reagent proceeds with vigorous ebullition, whereas with methyl chloride there is often a prolonged induction period, followed by slow conversion, even with external application of heat. In the reaction of alkyl chlorides with potassium iodide in acetone solution, $RCl + KI \rightarrow RI + KCl$, secondary chlorides ($R_2CHCl$) are only about 0.05 as reactive as primary chlorides.

Mechanism of Substitution. — Whereas secondary halides invariably are less reactive in substitution reactions than primary halides, tertiary halides under most conditions are more reactive than secondary or even than primary halides. Hydrolysis of a halide is the counterpart of displacement of the hydroxyl group of an alcohol by halogen, and it was noted above that tertiary alcohols differ from primary and secondary alcohols in the great facility with which they react with hydrochloric acid to yield chlorides. Kinetic studies, or physical-chemical determination of rates of reactions in homogeneous solution with standardization of temperature, solvent, and concentrations, have accounted for the apparent inconsistency (see fuller discussion in Chapter 13). In nucleophilic substitutions or displacements, for example hydrolysis of alkyl bromides by hydroxide ion (nucleophilic agent), hydrolysis of methyl, ethyl, or isopropyl bromide is predominantly a bimolecular reaction, or a reaction of second order, that is, the rate of

$$\boxed{HO^- + R} : Br \longrightarrow HOR + Br^-$$

reaction is dependent upon the concentration of both the alkyl bromide and hydroxide ion. The hydrolysis is thus described as an S_N2 reaction (nucleophilic substitution of second-order kinetics). The key step must involve collisions between molecules of alkyl bromide and the nucleophilic hydroxide ions. A generally accepted interpretation advanced by Ingold and Hughes postulates an intermediate complex or transition state. The bromine atom of methyl bromide is electronegative and must repel the negative hydroxide ion, and hence the latter is pictured as attacking the opposite side of the carbon, or the back side. In the transition state the three hydrogen atoms

S_{N2} Mechanism:

$$HO^- + H-\overset{\overset{\displaystyle H}{|}}{\underset{\underset{\displaystyle H}{|}}{C}}-Br \longrightarrow \left[\overset{\overset{\displaystyle H \quad H}{\diagdown \diagup}}{HO\overset{\delta^-}{\cdots}\underset{\underset{\displaystyle H}{|}}{C}\overset{\delta^-}{\cdots}Br} \right] \longrightarrow HO-\overset{\overset{\displaystyle H}{|}}{\underset{\underset{\displaystyle H}{|}}{C}}-H + Br^-$$

Transition state

are bound to carbon by the original covalent bonds and hydroxyl and bromine are bound by fractional ionic links, since the original charge of the hydroxide ion is distributed evenly between the entering and departing groups. Attack of hydroxide ion and expulsion of bromide ion from the complex are synchronous processes.

Table 7.2 shows that methyl, ethyl, and isopropyl bromide undergo hydrolysis to all but a negligible extent bimolecularly, and that the reactiv-

TABLE 7.2. RATE OF HYDROLYSIS OF ALKYL BROMIDES

(80% ETHANOL AT 55°)

ALKYL BROMIDE	FIRST-ORDER REACTION CONSTANT sec.$^{-1}$ $k_1 \times 10^5$	SECOND-ORDER REACTION CONSTANT sec.$^{-1}$/(g. mol./l.) $k_2 \times 10^5$
CH_3Br	0.349	2140
CH_3CH_2Br	0.139	171
$(CH_3)_2CHBr$	0.237	4.75
$(CH_3)_3CBr$	1010	—

ity, as measured by the second-order rate constants, decreases markedly in the order of listing. The progressive decrease in reactivity of ethyl and

$$CH_3 \rightarrow CH_2Br \qquad \overset{\displaystyle CH_3}{\underset{\displaystyle CH_3}{\diagdown\hspace{-0.3em}\diagup}} CHBr$$

isopropyl bromide is attributable to the electron-releasing effect of the one and two methyl groups, respectively, joined to the carbon atom undergoing substitution, which should inhibit approach of the hydroxide ion.

In tertiary butyl bromide the combined inductive effect of three methyl groups completely suppresses the bimolecular reaction and hydrolysis proceeds unimolecularly (Table 7.2); that is, the reaction rate is dependent only on the concentration of alkyl bromide and is not increased by an increase in concentration of hydroxide ion. In the unimolecular reaction the rate-determining step is considered to be ionization of the halide to form a carbonium ion, which then combines with hydroxide ion as rapidly

as it is formed.   Ionization is promoted by the combined electron release
of the three alkyl groups; strongly ionizing solvents further favor unimolecular substitutions.

S_{NI} Mechanism:

$$(CH_3)_3C\!-\!Br \longrightarrow (CH_3)_3C^+ + Br^- \text{ (relatively slow)}$$
$$(CH_3)_3C^+ + OH^- \longrightarrow (CH_3)_3COH \text{ (fast)}$$

Allyl-Type Halides. — A remarkable enhancement in reactivity is encountered in the allyl halides, $CH_2\!=\!CHCH_2X$, and in all similarly unsaturated halides.   In a typical replacement reaction allyl chloride reacts
79 times as fast as the saturated halide *n*-propyl chloride.   Allyl bromide
and iodide show correspondingly enhanced reactivity.   The position of the
double bond with respect to the halogen is critical, for if it is moved to a
more distant location, the special reactivity vanishes and there is little differentiation from the saturated compounds:

$$CH_2\!=\!CHCH_2Br > \begin{cases} CH_3CH_2CH_2Br \\ CH_2\!=\!CHCH_2CH_2Br \\ CH_2\!=\!CHCH_2CH_2CH_2Br \\ CH_3CH_2CH_2CH_2CH_2Br \end{cases} \begin{array}{c} \text{Same degree} \\ \text{of} \\ \text{reactivity} \end{array}$$

A double bond adjacent to the carbon carrying the halogen exerts a marked
activating influence on the halogen atom.   If the atoms in the chain are
numbered starting with the halogen atom, the bromine atom at position 1
in allyl bromide is activated by the unsaturated linkage at the 3,4-position:

$$\underset{4321}{H_2C\!=\!C\!-\!C\!-\!\boxed{Br}}$$
$$\overset{H}{}\;\overset{H_2}{}$$

That the bromine atom possesses a special reactivity or lability means that
the 1,2-link is relatively weak, and hence a directly correlated phenomenon
is the ready replacement of the hydroxyl group of allyl alcohol by chlorine,
noted above.   Here the hydroxyl group and not the hydrogen occupies the

$$\underset{4321}{H_2C\!=\!C\!-\!C\!-\!\boxed{OH}} \xrightarrow{\text{HCl}} H_2C\!=\!C\!-\!C\!-\!Cl$$

1-position in the chain, and the bond linking this group to carbon is weakened by the adjacent double bond.   Enhanced reactivity invariably is
found in compounds of the allyl-halide or allyl-alcohol type.   Among
numerous other instances of the activating influence of an adjacent double
bond are the following previously mentioned but hitherto uncorrelated reactions:

$$\left[\underset{4321}{H_2C\!=\!C\!-\!O\!-\!\boxed{H}} \right] \longrightarrow \underset{}{H_3C\!-\!C\!=\!O}$$

Vinyl alcohol (unstable)   Acetaldehyde

$$\underset{}{H_2C\!=\!C\!-\!C\!-\!\boxed{H}} \xrightarrow{Cl_2,\ 400°} H_2C\!=\!C\!-\!C\!-\!Cl$$

Propylene   Allyl chloride

Rearrangement of the hypothetical vinyl alcohol to acetaldehyde involves shift of an activated hydrogen atom at the 1-position, and the high-temperature chlorination of propylene with production of allyl chloride, in preference to addition to the double bond, is ascribable to the activated character of the hydrogen atom that suffers replacement. The high temperature apparently favors dissociation of the normal addition compound. Ziegler[1] (1942) discovered that unsaturated compounds can be brominated in the allyl position even at a low temperature by use of N-bromosuccinimide (p. 243). Allylic bromination is promoted by peroxides and by illumination, and hence involves free radicals. Cyclohexene (a) is converted into 3-bromocyclohexene-1 in about 80% yield. A methylene group adjacent

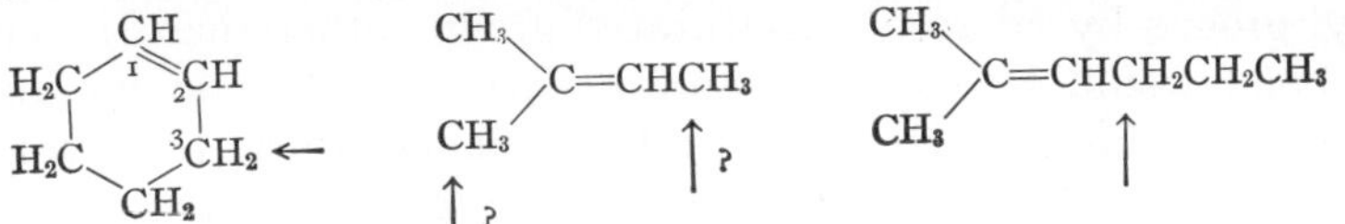

(a)   (b)   (c)

to a double bond is attacked more rapidly than a methyl group; the hydrocarbon (b) consumes an equivalent amount of reagent only after sixteen hours, whereas (c) reacts in ten minutes.

The resonance theory explains the reactivity of allyl compounds. If hydrolysis of allyl bromide involves a transient phase of ionization, the carbonium ion is a resonance hybrid, and resonance stabilizes the ion and

$$CH_2=CH-CH_2Br \xrightarrow{-Br^-} CH_2=CH-\overset{+}{C}H_2 \longleftrightarrow \overset{+}{C}H_2-CH=CH_2$$

resonance hybrid

$$\downarrow OH^-$$

$$CH_2=CH-CH_2OH$$

promotes its formation, and hence promotes hydrolysis. The double bond in the 3,4-position has an activating effect because it affords opportunity for resonance. In the case of a substituted allyl halide, for example cinnamyl bromide, the two resonance forms are not identical; in one the positive charge is on the α-carbon and in the other it is on the γ-carbon:

$$\overset{\gamma}{C_6H_5}CH=\overset{\beta}{CH}\overset{\alpha}{CH_2}Br \xrightarrow{-Br^-} C_6H_5CH=CH\overset{+}{C}H_2 \longleftrightarrow C_6H_5\overset{+}{C}HCH=CH_2$$

Cinnamyl bromide

Such halides usually react to give both the normal replacement product and the product of allylic rearrangement, in which the entering group is linked to the γ-carbon atom:

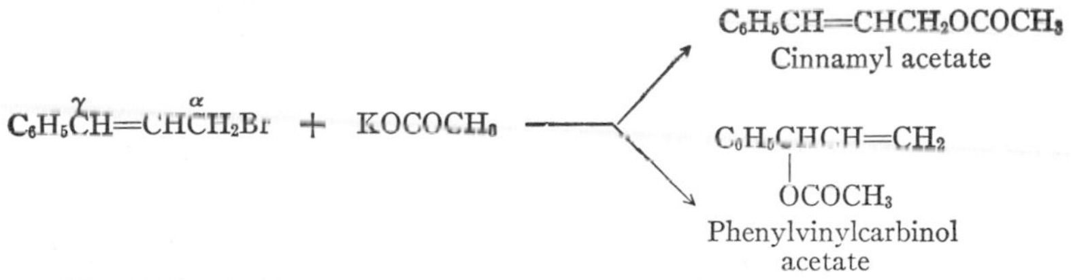

$$\overset{\gamma}{C_6H_5}CH=\overset{\alpha}{CH}CH_2Br + KOCOCH_3 \longrightarrow$$

C₆H₅CH=CHCH₂OCOCH₃
Cinnamyl acetate

C₆H₅CHCH=CH₂
|
OCOCH₃
Phenylvinylcarbinol
acetate

[1] Karl Ziegler, b. 1898 Kassel, Germany; Ph.D. Marburg (von Auwers); Heidelberg, KWI for Coal Res., Mülheim/Ruhr

The reactivity invariably associated with allyl-type compounds is utilized in a special hydrocarbon synthesis. When an allyl halide is added to an ethereal solution of the Grignard reagent from an ordinary alkyl halide, a coupling of the hydrocarbon residues occurs to give an alkene having a terminal double bond:

$$CH_2=CHCH_2X + RMgX \longrightarrow CH_2=CHCH_2R + MgX_2$$

This coupling reaction is not unique to allyl-type halides and is often observed as a minor side reaction in the preparation of Grignard reagents, but it finds practicable application as a direct synthetic method particularly in the specially reactive allyl-type compounds. Activation of halogen and hydroxyl groups by adjacent unsaturated groups other than the ethylenic double bond would be expected and is encountered in many instances. An adjacent methoxyl group also results in enhanced reactivity, for chloromethyl ether (CH_3OCH_2Cl) is 918 times more reactive to potassium iodide than *n*-butyl chloride; the oxygen atom, bearing unshared electrons, exerts a function comparable to that of a double bond.

Vinyl-Type Halides. — In contrast with allyl bromide, vinyl bromide is peculiarly unreactive. A halogen atom directly attached to an ethylenic carbon atom displays definitely diminished reactivity as compared with

$$CH_2=CHBr$$
Vinyl bromide

$$\begin{matrix} \diagdown \\ \diagup \end{matrix}C=C- \\ \qquad\qquad | \\ \qquad\qquad X$$
Vinyl halide type

the halogen of the corresponding saturated alkyl halide. Even vinyl iodide is so unamenable to replacement reactions that it does not react satisfactorily with magnesium to produce a Grignard reagent, and vinyl-magnesium halides are ordinarily unavailable.* One consequence of the re-

$$BrCH_2CH_2Br \xrightarrow{\text{alc. KOH}} CH_2=CHBr$$
Ethylene dibromide $\qquad\qquad\qquad$ Vinyl bromide

lationship is that vinyl halides can be prepared in good yield by selective elimination of one molecule of hydrogen halide from a *vic*-dihalide; the product of initial transformation is so much less reactive than the starting material that there is no difficulty in stopping the reaction at the first stage, without production of an acetylene.

The inert character of the bromine atom in vinyl bromide (*a*) is interpreted as due to resonance involving the polarized structure (*b*). The cor-

$$CH_2=CH-Br \longleftrightarrow \bar{C}H_2-CH=\overset{+}{Br}$$
$$(a) \qquad\qquad\qquad (b)$$

$$H:C::C:\overset{..}{B}r: \longleftrightarrow H:\overset{-}{C}:C::\overset{+}{B}r:$$
$$\;\;\overset{..}{H}\;\overset{..}{H}\qquad\qquad\quad \overset{..}{H}\;\overset{..}{H}$$
$$(c) \qquad\qquad\qquad\qquad (d)$$

---

* Substituted vinyl halides of the type $(C_6H_5)_2C=CHBr$ and $(C_6H_5)_2C=C(C_6H_5)Br$ form Grignard reagents.

responding electronic formulations are (c) and (d). In consequence of the resonance effect, bromine is held to carbon by a linkage that has a certain double-bond character and that is therefore shorter than the normal C—Br bond and less labile.

The following synthesis of 3-cyclohexylpropyne-1 illustrates the coupling of a Grignard reagent with an allyl-type halide and the relative reactivity of halogen atoms adjacent to and attached to an ethylenic carbon atom:

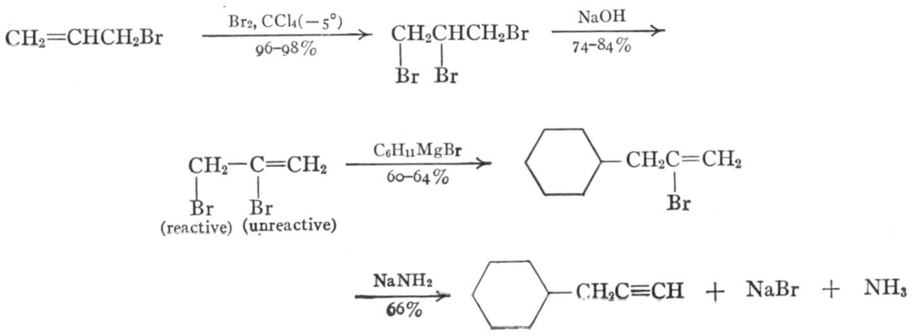

$$CH_2=CHCH_2Br \xrightarrow[96-98\%]{Br_2,\ CCl_4(-5°)} \underset{\underset{Br\ Br}{|\ \ \ |}}{CH_2CHCH_2Br} \xrightarrow[74-84\%]{NaOH}$$

3-Cyclohexylpropyne-1

The diminished reactivity of vinyl halides finds a parallel in the character of halides of the aromatic series, or aryl halides (ArX). In chlorobenzene and bromobenzene the halogen is attached to an unsaturated carbon atom, and the compounds are distinctly less reactive than corresponding alkyl halides but not so inert as vinyl chloride and bromide. Bromobenzene is reactive enough to combine with magnesium to give a Grignard reagent, but chlorobenzene does not react similarly.

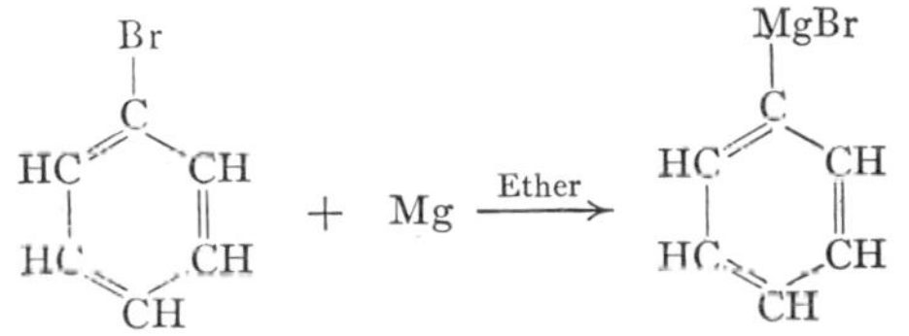

Bromobenzene   Phenylmagnesium bromide

Methylene Halides. — Methylene chloride (CH_2Cl_2) is a low-boiling liquid heavier than water (Table 7.3), and it finds use as an extraction solvent immiscible with water. It is prepared technically as one of the products of chlorination of methane. Methylene bromide and methylene iodide are prepared most readily by reduction of the corresponding trihalomethane derivatives with sodium arsenite in alkaline solution:

$$\underset{\substack{Iodoform\\(bromoform)}}{CHI_3(CHBr_3)} + Na_3AsO_3 + NaOH \xrightarrow[88-97\%]{} \underset{\substack{Methylene\ iodide\\(bromide)}}{CH_2I_2(CH_2Br_2)} + NaI(Br) + Na_3AsO_4$$

Methylene halides yield formaldehyde on hydrolysis and are sometimes

TABLE 7.3. POLYHALOGEN COMPOUNDS

NAME	FORMULA*	M.P., °C.	B.P., °C.	SP. GR.
Methylene chloride	CH_2Cl_2	−96	40.8	1.336
Methylene bromide	CH_2Br_2	−53	98.2	2.46
Methylene iodide	CH_2I_2	5	180 dec.	3.322
Chloroform	$CHCl_3$	−63.5	61.2	1.489
Bromoform	$CHBr_3$	7.8	149.6	2.865
Iodoform	CHI_3	119	....	4.1
Carbon tetrafluoride	CF_4	....	−128	....
Carbon tetrachloride	CCl_4	−23	76.8	1.575
Carbon tetrabromide	CBr_4	92.5	189.5	3.42
Dichlorodifluoromethane	CCl_2F_2	−155	−29.8	1.4
Ethylene dichloride (ethylene chloride)	$ClCH_2CH_2Cl$	−35.5	83.8	1.238
Ethylene dibromide	$BrCH_2CH_2Br$	10	131.7	2.182
Ethylidene chloride	CH_3CHCl_2	−97	57.3	1.174
Ethylidene bromide	CH_3CHBr_2	....	110	2.056
s-Tetrachloroethane (acetylene tetrachloride)	$CHCl_2CHCl_2$	−43	146.3	1.600
Hexachloroethane	CCl_3CCl_3	189	185	2.091
s-Dichloroethylene [1] (acetylene dichloride)	$ClCH{=}CHCl$	−50	48.4	1.259
Trichloroethylene	$CHCl{=}CCl_2$	−86	87	1.477
Trimethylene bromide	$Br(CH_2)_3Br$	−36	167	1.979
Tetramethylene bromide	$Br(CH_2)_4Br$	−21	198 dec.	1.79
Pentamethylene bromide	$Br(CH_2)_5Br$	−40	221	1.706
Hexamethylene bromide	$Br(CH_2)_6Br$	....	240 dec.	1.599

[1] *trans* form; *cis* form: m.p. −80.5°, b.p. 60.3°, sp. gr. 1.265.

employed as a potential source of this reagent:

$$CH_2X_2 \xrightarrow{H_2O} \left[CH_2{\diagup}^{OH}_{\diagdown}{}_{OH} \right] \longrightarrow CH_2{=}O$$

The Haloform Reaction. — The trihalomethanes, chloroform, bromoform, and iodoform, are obtained easily by a process known as the haloform reaction (chloroform is so named because the structure is derivable from that of formic acid, HCOOH, by replacement of all oxygen substituents by chlorine atoms). This process consists in treatment of acetone with bleaching powder or with a solution of sodium hypochlorite. In the first phase of

(a) $CH_3C{-}C{-}H$ (Acetone) $+$ 3NaOCl $\longrightarrow$ CH_3CCCl_3 (Trichloroacetone) $+$ 3NaOH

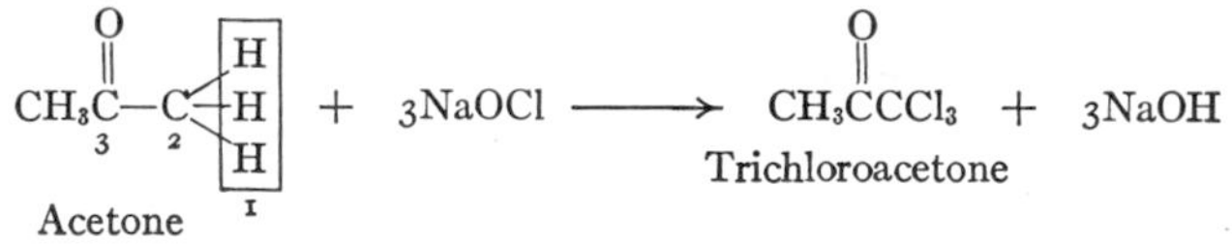

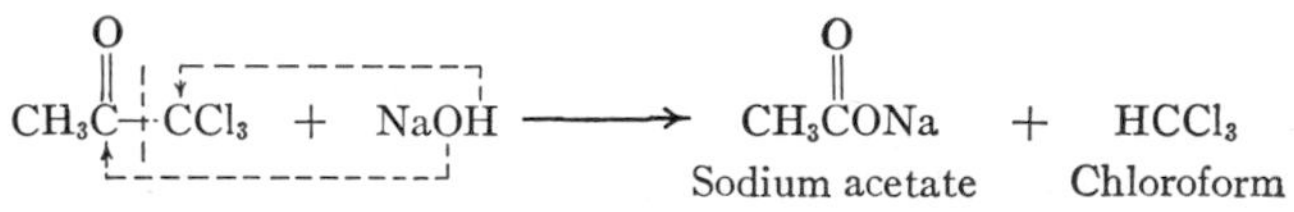

(b) $CH_3C{+}CCl_3$ $+$ NaOH $\longrightarrow$ CH_3CONa (Sodium acetate) $+$ $HCCl_3$ (Chloroform)

the reaction (*a*) one methyl group is fully substituted by chlorine, and in the second (*b*) alkaline cleavage of trichloroacetone occurs with production of sodium acetate and chloroform. Since sufficient alkali to bring about the cleavage is produced in the initial chlorination, the reactions proceed together and require a single operation. Both reactions have points in common with phenomena already discussed. The hydrogen atoms in acetone that suffer replacement are in a position (1) to be activated by the adjacent carbon–oxygen double bond (3, 4). A simple interpretation of the activating effect is that the ketone is in equilibrium with a trace of the enol (*c*). which adds chlorine to give a transient intermediate that loses hydrogen

$$
(c) \quad \underset{\text{O}}{\overset{\text{O}}{\parallel}} \quad -\text{C}-\text{CH}_3 \rightleftharpoons -\underset{\text{OH}}{\overset{|}{\text{C}}}=\text{CH}_2 \xrightarrow{\text{Cl}_2} -\underset{\substack{|\\ \text{Cl}}}{\overset{\text{OH}}{\underset{|}{\text{C}}}}-\text{CH}_2\text{Cl} \xrightarrow{-\text{HCl}} -\overset{\text{O}}{\overset{\parallel}{\text{C}}}-\text{CH}_2\text{Cl}
$$

chloride and gives the substitution product. After the first halogen has entered the acetone molecule, a choice is open between further substitution in the same methyl group or in the one that is still intact, for both are equally activated by the carbonyl group. Since chlorine is a close neighbor of oxygen in the periodic table, analogy between the process of chlorination and that of oxidation is expected, and it has been noted (p. 127) that an already oxidized site is more susceptible to further oxidation than unoxidized sites. Thus chlorine is more prone to attack the already partly chlorinated carbon atom than the intact methyl group. The cleavage reaction (*b*) finds some analogy in the oxidative cleavage of *vic*-glycols (p. 129), described as rupture of a weak bond connecting two oxidized carbon atoms. In the present instance the bond between the oxidized and the chlorinated carbon evidently is weak, or labile, and suffers easy rupture.

Chloroform is also obtainable in good yield by the action of a hypochlorite on ethyl alcohol, for the reagent has oxidizing properties and acts initially by oxidizing the alcohol to acetaldehyde (*d*); the reactions of halo-

$$(d) \quad \text{CH}_3\text{CH}_2\text{OH} + \text{NaOCl} \rightarrow \text{CH}_3\text{CHO} + \text{NaCl} + \text{H}_2\text{O}$$

gen substitution (*e*) and cleavage (*f*) then follow the same course as before:

$$(e) \quad \text{CH}_3\text{C}\overset{\text{H}}{\underset{\text{O}}{\diagdown}} + 3\text{NaOCl} \longrightarrow \text{CCl}_3\text{C}\overset{\text{H}}{\underset{\text{O}}{\diagdown}} + 3\text{NaOH}$$

$$(f) \quad \text{CCl}_3\text{C}\overset{\text{H}}{\underset{\text{O}}{\diagdown}} + \text{NaOH} \longrightarrow \underset{\text{Chloroform}}{\text{CHCl}_3} + \underset{\substack{\text{Sodium}\\ \text{formate}}}{\text{HC}\overset{\text{O}}{\underset{\text{ONa}}{\diagdown}}}$$

Either acetone or alcohol can be employed for technical production of chloroform; at the end of the reaction the halide is removed by distillation from the alkaline solution of sodium acetate or formate. Sodium hypobromite and hypoiodite react in the same manner and yield bromoform ($CHBr_3$) and iodoform (CHI_3), respectively. The iodoform reaction is particularly well adapted to test purposes because this substance has properties that make it easily recognized and identified. The substane separates as fine yellow crystals from an aqueous medium and can be identified by melting-point and mixed melting-point determinations. One application of the test is in distinguishing ethyl from methyl alcohol; ethyl alcohol gives a positive test, but methyl alcohol is converted into formaldehyde, which cannot afford iodoform.

Acetaldehyde is the only aldehyde that gives the iodoform test, but all ketones that, like acetone, have at least one methyl radical joined to the carbonyl group yield iodoform on reaction with iodine in sodium hydroxide solution. Thus all methyl ketones give a positive response in the test.

$$RCOCH_3 \xrightarrow{NaOI} RCOCI_3 \xrightarrow{NaOH} RCOONa + CHI_3$$

Secondary alcohols undergo oxidation by sodium hypoiodite to ketones, and those that yield methyl ketones likewise give a positive result. Thus the

$$RCHOHCH_3 \xrightarrow{NaOI} RCOCH_3 \xrightarrow{NaOI} CHI_3$$

iodoform reaction is exhibited by acetaldehyde, by methyl ketones, and by such alcohols as can yield acetaldehyde or a methyl ketone on oxidation. The test has important uses in the diagnosis of structure. In the series of isomers pentanol-1 (I), pentanol-2 (II), and pentanol-3 (III), the first substance on oxidation with potassium dichromate gives an aldehyde, and the other two give ketones, the latter two compounds are distinguished by the fact that II yields iodoform on treatment with sodium hypoiodite and III does not.

$$CH_3CH_2CH_2CH_2CH_2OH \qquad CH_3CH_2CH_2\underset{\underset{OH}{|}}{C}HCH_3 \qquad CH_3CH_2\underset{\underset{OH}{|}}{C}HCH_2CH_3$$

$$I \qquad\qquad II \qquad\qquad III$$

Chloroform is a sweet-smelling liquid having anesthetic properties and uses as an extraction solvent. The liquid is not flammable but the vapor can burn. On exposure to air and sunlight, chloroform suffers slow oxidation to the highly toxic phosgene. The lone hydrogen on the highly chlorinated carbon atom evidently is comparable in susceptibility to oxidation to hydrogen affixed to an oxidized carbon atom, and the reaction may proceed through initial hydroxylation:

$$Cl_3CH \xrightarrow{O_2,\ light} \left[Cl-\underset{\underset{Cl}{|}}{\overset{\overset{Cl}{|}}{C}}-OH \right] \longrightarrow Cl-\underset{\underset{Cl}{|}}{C}=O + HCl$$

Phosgene

Commercial preparations are stored in brown bottles and contain 0.6–1%

of alcohol, which destroys traces of phosgene that may be formed in storage. Chloroform is made industrially both by the haloform reaction and by the reduction of carbon tetrachloride with iron and water:

$$CCl_4 \ + \ 2H(Fe, H_2O) \ \longrightarrow \ CHCl_3 \ + \ HCl$$

Bromoform, being a liquid of unusually high density, is used as a component in flotation methods of mineral analysis. **Iodoform,** in addition to the characteristic properties already noted, functions as an antiseptic agent as the result of slow release of elemental iodine, but it is not very effective.

Carbon tetrachloride is manufactured by chlorination of carbon disulfide, obtained by heating sulfur with coke in an electric furnace. Antimony pentachloride, aluminum chloride, or ferric chloride is employed as a catalyst, or halogen carrier:

$$CS_2 \ + \ 3Cl_2 \ \xrightarrow{SbCl_5} \ CCl_4 \ + \ S_2Cl_2$$
$$\text{Sulfur}$$
$$\text{monochloride}$$

Having no hydrogen atoms, carbon tetrachloride is one of the rare instances of a noncombustible organic compound, and it is used in fire extinguishers (e.g., Pyrene). It has a low boiling point (76.8°) and volatilizes readily when sprayed on a fire, and the heavy vapor settles over the flame and smothers it by excluding oxygen; some phosgene is formed, and hence adequate ventilation is essential. The substance is used in the laboratory as a heavier than water extraction solvent. It is a powerful solvent for greases and is preferred for use in commercial dry cleaning and as a household cleaning fluid (Carbona) because of the freedom from fire hazard.

Ethane Derivatives. — **Ethylene dichloride,** $ClCH_2CH_2Cl$, is made by addition of chlorine to ethylene, and **s-tetrachloroethane,** $Cl_2CHCHCl_2$, is produced by addition of two moles of chlorine to acetylene. The dichloro compound is an excellent extraction solvent of moderate boiling point (83.8°), and the tetrachloro derivative is a powerful, higher-boiling (146.3°) solvent. **Ethylidene chloride,** CH_3CHCl_2, is less used; it can be prepared by the action of phosphorus pentachloride on acetaldehyde and by addition of hydrogen chloride to vinyl chloride. **Hexachloroethane** can be prepared by the action of amalgamated aluminum on carbon tetrachloride, but is produced industrially as a by-product in the reaction of acetylene with chlorine or by chlorination of s-tetrachloroethane in the presence of aluminum chloride. It is a crystalline solid of camphorlike odor having a marked tendency to sublime. The melting point, determined by heating the substance in a sealed capillary tube, is practically the same as the boiling point. Hexachloroethane is a component of a mixture used in smoke candles and smoke pots, consisting of zinc dust (36%), hexachloroethane (44%), ammonium perchlorate (10%), and ammonium chloride (10%). When started with a suitable igniter, the reaction between zinc dust and the organic halide proceeds with liberation of sufficient heat (tempera-

$$3Zn \ + \ C_2Cl_6 \ \longrightarrow \ 3ZnCl_2 \ + \ 2C$$

ture of 1200°) to volatilize the zinc chloride formed and produces a dense smoke having nearly half the obscuring power of the smoke from the burning of white phosphorus.

Ethylene Derivatives. — *s*-Dichloroethylene, $ClCH=CHCl$, is prepared in the industry by abstraction of a molecule of chlorine from *s*-tetrachloroethane by the action of zinc dust; **trichloroethylene** is obtained by elimination of hydrogen chloride from the same starting material:

$$CHCl_2CHCl_2 \underset{Ca(OH)_2}{\overset{Zn}{\diagup\diagdown}} \begin{matrix} CHCl=CHCl \\ \\ CHCl=CCl_2 \end{matrix}$$

Both these unsaturated compounds are of the vinyl-halide type and are chemically inert; they are nonflammable and noncorrosive to metals in the presence of water, and are employed as solvents for fats, oils, and resins.

Polymethylene Halides. — Halides containing two functional groups, $X—(CH_2)_n—X$, are useful in synthesis because of the opportunity for conducting simultaneous operations at the ends of the carbon chain. The dibromides of the series are obtainable in yields of 75–90% by the action of dry hydrogen bromide at 135° on the corresponding glycols, where these starting materials are available. Trimethylene glycol is available as a fermentation product (p. 124), and tetramethylene and hexamethylene glycol can be produced satisfactorily from the corresponding dibasic acids (p. 177); hence the derived bromides $Br(CH_2)_3Br$, $Br(CH_2)_4Br$, $Br(CH_2)_6Br$ are useful synthetic starting materials. Pentamethylene bromide can be produced efficiently by a process utilizing a fairly readily accessible intermediate (von Braun reaction):

$$
\begin{matrix}
& CH_2 & \\
H_2C & & CH_2 \\
| & & | \\
H_2C & & CH_2 \\
& N & \\
& | & \\
& C_6H_5C=O &
\end{matrix}
\quad \xrightarrow[65-72\%]{PBr_5} \quad
\underset{\text{Pentamethylene bromide}}{BrCH_2CH_2CH_2CH_2CH_2Br} \; + \; C_6H_5CN \; + \; POBr_3
$$

Benzoylpiperidine

Pentamethylene bromide can be obtained also by an efficient four-step process starting with the abundantly available furfural (Table 9.1).

One use of polymethylene halides in syntheses involves temporarily protecting one of the two functional groups by conversion into an ether group so that the other can be utilized selectively. The half-ether can be obtained by interaction of a sodium alkoxide with an excess of the halide.

$$\underset{\text{Sodium phenoxide}}{C_6H_5ONa} \; + \; BrCH_2CH_2CH_2Br \; \xrightarrow{84-85\%} \; \underset{\gamma\text{-Phenoxypropyl bromide}}{C_6H_5OCH_2CH_2CH_2Br}$$

The monohalide can be used in Grignard or other syntheses and the ether group subsequently cleaved with hydrogen bromide to the bromo derivative.

FLUORO COMPOUNDS

Fluorinated hydrocarbons are not readily obtainable by interaction of an alcohol with concentrated or even anhydrous hydrogen fluoride, since the position of equilibrium favors hydrolysis, and the reaction cannot be promoted satisfactorily by use of sulfuric acid, which causes formation of alkenes from fluorides. One route to fluorides is addition of hydrogen fluoride to a double bond, (1) and (2), even though the reverse reaction is prone to occur. A second method consists in metathesis of an organic halide with an inorganic fluoride, usually mercuric fluoride or antimony trifluoride, (3) and (4).

1. $$CH_2{=}CH_2 + HF \xrightarrow[81\%]{90°} CH_3CH_2F$$
$$M.p. - 143°, \; b.p. - 38°$$

2. $$CH_3CH{=}CH_2 + HF \xrightarrow[61\%]{0°} CH_3CHFCH_3$$
$$M.p. - 133°, \; b.p. - 10°$$

3. $$2\,CH_3CH_2Br + HgF_2 \xrightarrow[(quant.)]{0°} 2\,CH_3CH_2F + HgBr_2$$

4. $$2\,CHBrF_2 + HgF_2 \xrightarrow[80\%]{50°} 2\,CHF_3 + HgBr_2$$
$$B.p. - 14.5° \qquad\qquad M.p. - 163°, \; b.p. \; 82°$$

Although monofluorides are markedly unstable, polyfluorides in which more than one fluorine atom is situated on the same carbon atom are chemically inert; for example, as-difluoroethylene. $CH_2{-}CF_2$, is stable to air oxidation, in contrast with the corresponding dichloro compound, which under the same conditions is rapidly attacked. The stabilizing effect of fluorine atoms extends to other halogen atoms situated on the same or on an adjacent carbon atom, for dichlorodifluoromethane, CCl_2F_2, is completely impervious to hydrolysis and to molten sodium. One explanation of the inertness of polyfluorides (Brockway, 1937) is based upon the observation that the normal carbon–fluorine bond distance of $1.42\mathring{A}$ in monofluorides is decreased to $1.35\mathring{A}$ in polyfluorides and that the carbon–chlorine bond distance in mixed chloropolyfluorides is also shortened by 0.03–0.07$\mathring{A}$; no comparable shortening of bond length is observed with polychlorides.

Dichlorodifluoromethane has ideal properties for use as a refrigerant liquid for domestic refrigerators and for air-conditioning units and has been employed widely for this purpose since its introduction (Midgley and Henne,[2] 1930). It is nonflammable, nontoxic, noncorrosive, nearly odorless, and stable up to 550°. The boiling point (−29.8°), indicative of the desired degree of volatility, is not far from that of the earlier, flammable refrigerant methyl chloride (b.p. −23.7°). Preparation is accomplished by replacement of two chlorine atoms of carbon tetrachloride by fluorine by the action of antimony trifluoride containing antimony pentahalide as catalyst. The industrial process utilizes liquid hydrogen fluoride as a cheap source of the fluorine substituents and involves continuous regeneration of a small initial

---

[2] Albert L. Henne, b. 1901 Brussels, Belg.; Ph.D. Brussels; Ohio State Univ.

batch of antimony trifluoride containing pentahalide:

$$3\,CCl_4 \ + \ 2\,SbF_3 \ \xrightarrow{\ (SbCl_5)\ } \ 3\,CCl_2F_2 \ + \ 2\,SbCl_3$$

$$6\,HF \ + \ 2\,SbCl_3 \ \text{--}\cdot\!\longrightarrow \ 2\,SbF_3 \ + \ 6\,HCl$$

The dichlorodifluoro compound and hydrogen chloride (b.p. $-85°$, insoluble in liquid HF) liberated are taken off through a column that easily separates and returns to the mixture the partially fluorinated substance CCl_3F (b.p. $25°$). The mixed halides (Freons) $CClF_2CClF_2$, b.p. $3.8°$, and $CHClF_2$, b.p. $-40°$, are used in household refrigerators and in deepfreeze units, respectively.

PROBLEMS

1. Suggest methods suitable for the preparation of each of the following halides from the corresponding alcohol:

   (a) n-$C_{18}H_{37}Cl$
   (b) $CH_3CH_2CCl(CH_3)_2$

   (c) $CH_3CH_2CH_2CHBrCH_3$
   (d) n-$C_6H_{13}I$

2. Arrange the following compounds in the expected order of decreasing activity:

   (a) $CH_3CHBrCH_2CH_2CH_3$
   (b) $(CH_3)_2CHCH_2CH_2Br$

   (c) $(CH_3)_2C\!=\!CBrCH_2CH_3$
   (d) $(CH_3)_2C\!=\!CHCH_2Br$

3. Which of the following substances would be expected to give a positive iodoform test?

   (a) $CH_3CH_2CH_2CH(CH_3)CH_2OH$
   (b) $CH_3CH_2CH_2CHOHCH_3$
   (c) $CH_3CH(CH_3)CHOHCH_2CH_3$
   (d) CH_2OHCH_2OH

   (e) $CH_3COCH_2CH_2CH_2COOH$
   (f) CH_3COOH
   (g) $C_6H_5CHOHCH_3$
   (h) $(CH_3)_3COH$

4. Starting with allyl bromide and any other components desired, suggest syntheses for:

   (a) 4-Methylpentene-1
   (b) 1,2,3-Tribromopropane

   (c) 1,2-Dibromopropane
   (d) 2,3-Dibromopropene-1

5. Glycerol on treatment with concd. sulfuric acid yields the substance C_3H_4O. Predict the structure of the product.

READING REFERENCES

E. H. Huntress, "Organic Chlorine Compounds," Wiley, New York (1948)
A. E. Remick, "Electronic Interpretations of Organic Chemistry," Wiley, New York, (1949)
A. L. Henne, "The Preparation of Aliphatic Fluorine Compounds," *Organic Reactions*, **2**, 49 (1944)

CHAPTER 8

CARBOXYLIC ACIDS

The combination of a carbonyl and a hydroxyl group is a carboxyl function and has acidic characteristics. Acetic acid, a typical member of the
series, has a dissociation constant (k_a) of 1.75×10^{-5}, which means that

$$k_a = [H^+][OAc^-]/[HOAc]$$

it is a weak or sparingly dissociated acid. A 1N aqueous solution is dissociated only to the extent of 0.4%. In contrast, 1N solutions of the
mineral acids, hydrochloric, hydrobromic, and sulfuric acid, are about 62%
ionized and show apparent dissociation constants greater than 1. Carbonic
acid is still more feebly acidic than acetic acid; the apparent dissociation
constant for separation of the first proton is 3.4×10^{-7}. The intermediate position of acetic acid is illustrated by the fact that the acid is liberated
from sodium acetate by hydrochloric acid but in turn liberates carbonic acid
from sodium bicarbonate. The classical dissociation constant of an acid,
k_a, does not provide a convenient basis for comparison of different acids,
and in this book acidic strength is expressed as the negative logarithm of
the dissociation constant, pK_a. Thus $pK_a = -\log k_a$; for acetic
acid ($k_a = 1.75 \times 10^{-5}$), $pK_a = -(-5 + 0.24) = 4.76$. For separation
of the first proton of carbonic acid, $pK_a = 6.5$. Mineral acids are so highly
ionized that pK_a is not measurable.

Acetic acid and ethyl alcohol are both two-carbon hydroxy compounds,
and the fact that the former tends to liberate the hydroxylic hydrogen as
an ion, whereas the latter does not, is attributable to its unsaturated character. The double bond is in the 3,4-position with respect to the hydrogen
at position 1 and hence is able to activate the hydrogen. Allyl alcohol is an
unsaturated compound, but the double bond is so located as to activate the

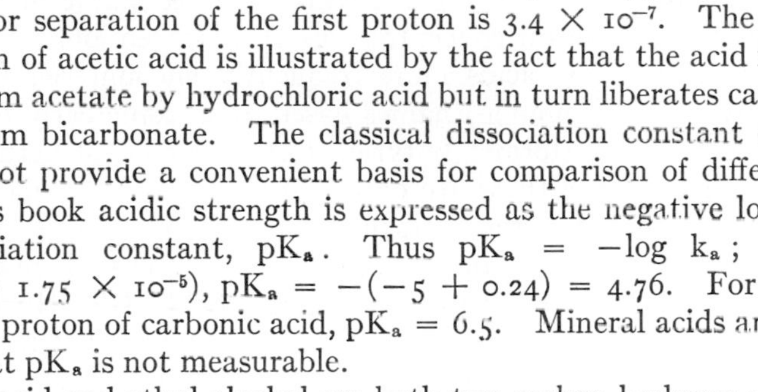

hydroxyl group rather than the hydrogen atom, and the substance is not
acidic. The acidity of carboxylic acids is thus ascribable to the presence of
a hydroxyl group on an unsaturated carbon atom.

Many inorganic acids possess one or more hydroxyl groups attached to
an unsaturated atom. In the weakly acidic nitrous acid a hydroxyl group
is joined to an unsaturated nitrogen atom; nitric acid is more highly unsaturated and is a strong acid. A similar relationship exists between sulfu-

$$O=N-OH$$
Nitrous acid

$$O \diagdown \atop \overline{O} \diagup N^+-OH$$
Nitric acid

rous and sulfuric acid, $(HO)_2S=O$ and $(HO)_2SO_2$. In the series of hydroxy acids derived from chlorine, the acidic strength increases progressively with increasing unsaturation, with consequent activation of the hydrogen atom. The degree of acidity is dependent on the nature of the unsaturated element joined to oxygen as well as on the degree of unsaturation. Carbonic acid is structurally comparable to a carboxylic acid in that it possesses a hydroxy-ated carbonyl group, and the fact that it is much more feebly acidic is as-

$$\underset{\text{(unstable)}}{\overset{\overset{\displaystyle OH}{|}}{O=C-OH}} \qquad\qquad \underset{\text{(stable)}}{\overset{\overset{\displaystyle R}{|}}{O=C-OH}}$$

cribable to its comparative instability. Carbonic acid is a *gem*-diol and exists as such to only a slight extent in aqueous solution in equilibrium with carbon dioxide and water.* The carboxylic acids are stable in water solution and can give significant concentrations of hydrogen ion.

Nomenclature. — The acids more frequently encountered (Table 8.1) are known by trivial (common) names based upon some early observed or special source in nature (formic, butyric, etc.) or upon a structural feature (trimethylacetic). Since there are only two C_4-acids, the name isobutyric acid is unambiguous for the branched-chain isomer, $(CH_3)_2CHCOOH$; among higher homologs, substances similar to isobutyric acid are also termed *iso* compounds, for example: isovaleric acid, $(CH_3)_2CHCH_2COOH$, iso-caproic acid, $(CH_3)_2CHCH_2CH_2COOH$. In the Geneva system the carbon of the carboxyl group is taken as the first atom in the longest carbon chain in the molecule; thus pelargonic acid, the straight-chain C_9-acid, is nonanoic acid. The position adjacent to the carboxyl group is known as the α-position and more distant positions are defined as β, γ, δ, etc. For example, $CH_3CHBrCOOH$ is α-bromopropionic acid; $HOCH_2CH_2CH_2COOH$ is γ-hydroxybutyric acid.

Acidic Strength. — The pK_a values of a number of carboxylic acids are listed in Table 8.1. In the series of normal acids from acetic (C_2) to pel-argonic (C_9), the values all fall in the range pK_a 4.8–5, and the effect of branching the chain is minor. Formic acid, the first member of the series, is exceptional and is distinctly more strongly acidic (pK_a 3.77) than any of the homologs (RCOOH) having an alkyl group rather than hydrogen attached to the carboxyl group. Values for the second and third series of acids listed in the table show that substitution of halogen, hydroxyl, and other groups often produces a profound increase in acidic strength.

A rational explanation of the effect of substituents on the ionization of

---

* Calculation indicates that if carbonic acid were stable in water solution it would be a stronger acid than acetic acid.

TABLE 8.1. CARBOXYLIC ACIDS

ACID	FORMULA	M.P., °C.	B.P., °C.	SP. GR.	$pK_a^{25°}$
Formic	HCOOH	8.4	100.5	1.220	3.77
Acetic	CH_3COOH	16.6	118	1.049	4.76
Propionic	CH_3CH_2COOH	− 22	141	0.992	4.88
n-Butyric	$CH_3CH_2CH_2COOH$	− 4.7	162.5	.959	4.82
Isobutyric	$(CH_3)_2CHCOOH$	− 47	154.4	.949	4.85
n-Valeric	$CH_3(CH_2)_3COOH$	− 34.5	187	.939	4.81
Trimethylacetic	$(CH_3)_3CCOOH$	35.5	163.8	.905	5.02
Caproic	$CH_3(CH_2)_4COOH$	− 1.5	205	.929	4.85
n-Heptylic	$CH_3(CH_2)_5COOH$	− 11	223.5	.922	4.89
Caprylic	$CH_3(CH_2)_6COOH$	16	237	.910	4.85
Pelargonic	$CH_3(CH_2)_7COOH$	12.5	254	.907	4.96
Fluoroacetic	CH_2FCOOH	33	165	.....	2.66
Chloroacetic	$CH_2ClCOOH$	63	189.5	1.37	2.81
Bromoacetic	$CH_2BrCOOH$	50	208	1.934	2.87
Iodoacetic	CH_2ICOOH	82	......	.....	3.13
Dichloroacetic	$CHCl_2COOH$	10	193.5	1.563	1.29
Trichloroacetic	CCl_3COOH	58	196	1.617	0.08*
α-Chloropropionic	$CH_3CHClCOOH$	......	186	1.306	2.8
β-Chloropropionic	CH_2ClCH_2COOH	39	204	.....	4.1
Glycolic	$HOCH_2COOH$	79	......	.....	3.83
Lactic	$CH_3CHOHCOOH$	18	$122^{15mm.}$	1.249	3.87
Methoxyacetic	CH_3OCH_2COOH	......	204	1.777	3.48
Thioglycolic	$HSCH_2COOH$	− 16.5	$123^{29mm.}$	1.325	3.55
Cyanoacetic	$N{\equiv}CCH_2COOH$	66	dec.	.....	2.44
Glyoxylic	$O{=}CHCOOH$	......	......	.....	3.3
Malonic	$HOOCCH_2COOH$	135	......	1.631	2.80
Acrylic	$CH_2{=}CHCOOH$	13	141	.....	4.26
Vinylacetic	$CH_2{=}CHCH_2COOH$	− 39	163	1.013	4.35
Phenylacetic	$C_6H_5CH_2COOH$	78	265	.....	4.31

* A 0.03 M solution is 89.5% ionized; comparable solutions of acetic acid and the mono- and dichloro derivatives are ionized to the extent of 2.4%, 22.5%, and 70%.

acids was advanced by G. N. Lewis (1923). In a symmetrical molecule such as CH_3:CH_3 or Cl:Cl, the pair of electrons constituting the covalent bond is shared equally by the two atomic centers. In an unsymmetrical molecule, however, one center may have a greater attraction for electrons than the other, and hence the electron pair will be displaced toward that center. Such a displacement, described by Ingold as an inductive effect (I), can be represented by an arrow pointing in the direction of the drift of electrons, B→A. If, in an acid A—COOH, the group A attracts electrons, the inductive displacement of the electron pair between C and A in the direction of A will cause secondary displacements of electrons of the C:O and O:H bonds and hence facilitate separation of the hydroxylic hydrogen as a proton:

$$A{\leftarrow}\overset{\overset{O}{\|}}{C}{:}\ddot{O}{:}H \rightleftharpoons A{-}\overset{\overset{O}{\|}}{C}{:}\ddot{O}{:}^- + H^+$$

A group B that repels electrons will produce a displacement in the opposite direction and decrease the extent of ionization:

$$\overset{O}{\underset{\longrightarrow}{\underset{\longrightarrow}{B{\rightarrow}C:\ddot{O}:H}}} \;\rightleftharpoons\; \overset{O}{B{-}C:\ddot{O}:^{-}} + H^{+}$$

The fact that acetic acid is a weaker acid than formic acid means that the methyl group has less attraction for electrons than a hydrogen atom, or is relatively electron-repelling: $CH_3{\rightarrow}COOH$. The conclusion agrees with that inferred from the effect of methyl substituents on the rate of bromination of ethylenes (p. 62). The higher normal homologs are so close to acetic acid in pK_a values that any difference in electron-release between methyl, ethyl, and higher n-alkyl groups must be so slight as to be obscured in the transmissal of the inductive effect through two covalent links.

Substitution of one of the α-hydrogen atoms of acetic acid by chlorine greatly increases the acidic strength: $CH_2ClCOOH$, pK_a 2.81. Chlorine, therefore, is strongly electron-attracting and produces displacements of the type $Cl{\leftarrow}C({=}O){\leftarrow}O{\leftarrow}H$. Bromine is less effective than chlorine, and iodine is less effective than bromine; the order of electron-attraction, as measured by the inductive effect, corresponds with the order of decreasing electronegativity. That the inductive effect of a substituent decreases rapidly with increasing distance from the hydroxylic hydrogen is shown by comparison of α- and β-chloropropionic acid. The α-chloro acid is much more acidic than the parent acid, whereas the β-chloro isomer is only a little

CH₃CH₂COOH	CH₃CHCOOH | Cl	CH₂CH₂COOH | Cl
Propionic acid pK_a 4.88	α-Chloropropionic acid pK_a 2.8	β-Chloropropionic acid pK_a 4.1

more acidic. Substitution in acetic acid of one, two, and three α-chlorine atoms produces progressive shifts to greater acidic strength, and trichloroacetic acid almost reaches the acidic strength of mineral acids.

The pK_a values of the acids listed in the third series of Table 8.1 indicate that the following groups, like halogen, are electron-attracting: hydroxyl, methoxyl, sulfhydryl ($-SH$), cyano ($-C{\equiv}N$), aldehydo ($-CH{=}O$), carboxyl, vinyl ($-CH{=}CH_2$), phenyl ($-C_6H_5$); the last five groups are unsaturated. The order of inductive effect of substituent groups, deduced partly from the effect on the strength of acids and bases, is as follows:

$$Cl > Br > I > OCH_3 > OH > C_6H_5 > CH{=}CH_2 > H < CH_3 < CH_2CH_3 < CH(CH_3)_2 < C(CH_3)_3$$

Decreasing electron attraction ($+$ I groups)	Decreasing electron release ($-$ I groups)

Boiling Points. — Boiling points of carboxylic acids are not far from those of alcohols of comparable molecular weight and are much higher than those of alkanes or alkyl halides of similar molecular size. As in the case of alcohols, the relatively low volatility is attributed to association of the hydroxylic molecules through hydrogen bonding. The ester derivatives of acids are nonhydroxylic and show no evidence of association. Relationships are illustrated by the typical data of Table 8.2. Cryoscopic determinations in hydrocarbon solvents and X-ray crystallographic measurements

TABLE 8.2. BOILING POINTS

FORMULA	MOL. WT.	B.P., °C.	
$CH_3CH_2CH_2CH_2CH_2CH_2CH_3$	100.20	98.4	
$HCOOCH_2CH_2CH_2CH_3$	102.13	106.8	
$CH_3COOCH_2CH_2CH_3$	102.13	101.7	unassociated
$CH_3CH_2COOCH_2CH_3$	102.13	99.1	
$CH_3CH_2CH_2COOCH_3$	102.13	102.3	
$CH_3CH_2CH_2CH_2CH_2Cl$	106.60	105.7	
$CH_3CH_2CH_2CH_2COOH$	102.13	187	associated
$CH_3CH_2CH_2CH_2CH_2CH_2OH$	102.17	155.8	

both indicate that carboxylic acids exist largely in a dimeric form, formulated as shown. The boiling point of formic acid (100.5°) is about that characteristic of unassociated substances of molecular weight comparable to that of formic acid dimer (92).

$$R-C \begin{matrix} O{\rightarrow}H{-}O \\ \\ O{-}H{\leftarrow}O \end{matrix} C{-}R$$

Solubility relationships of carboxylic acids conform to the usual rule for hydroxylic compounds. Formic, acetic, propionic, and n-butyric acid are miscible with water in all proportions, the next few members of the series are partially soluble, and the C_9-acids and higher homologs are practically insoluble in water.

Occurrence and Special Sources. — Formic acid, a vesicatory liquid of pungent odor, was so named because it is a constituent of certain ants (L. *formica*, ant). It occurs also in several plants, including the nettle, and the irritating effect resulting from contact with the plant is due in part to injection of the acid under the skin. On macerating ants or nettles with water and distilling, a dilute aqueous solution of formic acid passes into the distillate. The method of manufacture involves combination of

$$NaOH + CO \xrightarrow[\text{100 lbs./sq. in.}]{120-150°} H-C\begin{matrix} O \\ \\ ONa \end{matrix}$$

Sodium formate

carbon monoxide with pulverized sodium hydroxide at moderate temperatures and pressures; the resulting sodium formate when treated with sulfuric acid yields free formic acid.

Acetic acid is the sour principle of vinegar resulting from air oxidation of ethanol present in wine or hard cider under the influence of specific bacteria (e.g., in mother of vinegar), which provide enzymes that promote oxidation. If not deliberately added, microorganisms from the atmosphere find access to exposed solutions. The fortified wines port and sherry do not turn sour on standing in opened bottles because the delicate enzyme is inactivated by ethanol in any but very dilute solutions. Dilute solutions of pure ethanol in water fail to undergo microbiological oxidation because the microorganism requires for normal growth nitrogenous substances and mineral salts such as are present in beers and wines. It has never been practicable to produce concentrated or pure acetic acid from crude vinegars. Formerly the chief source was pyroligneous acid, the dilute aqueous solution of methanol and acetic acid resulting from destructive distillation of wood, for this yielded the two products methanol and calcium acetate, and distillation of the dry salt with sulfuric acid afforded substantially pure, acetic acid. Pure acetic acid, m.p. 16.6°, is called glacial because it freezes at temperatures frequently encountered in the laboratory, and the melting point is depressed to such an extent by small amounts of water that samples observed to remain liquid on cooling are readily recognized as impure. Modern processes of manufacture involve air oxidation of ethanol over a metal catalyst and hydration of acetylene and oxidation of the resulting acetaldehyde (p. 89).

Many of the homologous acids from propionic (C_3) to caproic (C_6) occur in plant or animal products, either as such or as esters of glycerol (glycerides). Thus n-butyric acid, in the form of the glyceride, is a characteristic component of butter; caproic acid occurs similarly in goat's milk and coconut oil. The C_3- to C_6-acids possess characteristically pungent and disagreeable odors. n-Butyric acid is responsible for the odor of rancid butter and stale perspiration; it can be produced by bacterial fermentation of sugars. Acids having an even number of carbon atoms in the series from C_{12} to C_{18} occur as glycerides in animal and vegetable fats and oils, which contain also smaller amounts of the C_8-, C_{10}-, C_{20}-, and C_{22}-acid derivatives (Chapter 15). The acids propionic, n-butyric, isobutyric, n-valeric, and isovaleric, $(CH_3)_2CHCH_2COOH$, are available either by fermentation processes or by oxidation of the corresponding alcohols. Normal acids with an even number of carbon atoms from C_{12} to C_{18} are abundantly available in cheap commercial grades of about 90% purity.

METHODS OF PREPARATION

Oxidation Reactions. — Acids can be obtained by oxidation of primary alcohols or aldehydes. Thus n-heptaldehyde, obtainable from castor oil, provides a source of n-heptylic acid, and β-chloropropionic acid can be prepared by a synthesis utilizing oxidation of a primary alcohol:

1. $n\text{-}C_6H_{13}CHO \xrightarrow[95-97\%]{KMnO_4, H_2SO_4 (20°)} n\text{-}C_6H_{13}COOH$
   n-Heptaldehyde   n-Heptylic acid

2. $HOCH_2CH_2CH_2OH \xrightarrow[50-60\%]{dry\ HCl} ClCH_2CH_2CH_2OH \xrightarrow[78-79\%]{HNO_3 (25-30°)} ClCH_2CH_2COOH$
   Trimethylene glycol   Trimethylene chlorohydrin   β-Chloropropionic acid

Oxidation of ethylenic compounds having the grouping RCH= also affords carboxylic acids, and the method has applications to unsaturated substances derived from fats. Acids are also obtainable by hypohalite oxidation of methyl ketones or of alcohols of the type $RCHOHCH_3$. The reaction has wide application in the aromatic series where a general method is available for preparation of the methyl ketone derivatives. In isolated instances suitable aliphatic starting materials are also available, for example:

$$(CH_3)_3CCOCH_3 \xrightarrow[71-74\%]{NaOBr} (CH_3)_3CCOOH$$
Pinacolone · · · · · · · · · · · · · · · · Trimethylacetic acid

Grignard and Nitrile Syntheses. — Replacement of the halogen atom of an alkyl halide by a carboxyl group can be accomplished by two alternate synthetic methods. One is addition of a Grignard reagent to the carbonyl group of carbon dioxide and hydrolysis of the magnesiohalide derivative:

$$(CH_3)_3CCl \xrightarrow{Mg,\ ether} (CH_3)_3CMgCl + C\!\!\!\begin{array}{c}O\\O\end{array} \longrightarrow$$

$$(CH_3)_3CC\!\!\!\begin{array}{c}O\\OMgCl\end{array} \xrightarrow[60-70\%\ overall]{H_2O} (CH_3)_3CCOOH$$
Trimethylacetic acid

The carbonation of an alkylmagnesium halide can be accomplished by bubbling carbon dioxide into a solution of the Grignard reagent or by pouring the solution on dry ice.

The second synthesis consists in preparation and hydrolysis of a substance of the type $RC\!\equiv\!N$, known both as an alkyl cyanide and as a nitrile. This is obtained by interaction of an alkyl halide with sodium or potassium cyanide in aqueous-alcoholic solution, and complete hydrolysis is accomplished under catalysis with either an acid or a base:

$$RX + KCN \longrightarrow RC\!\equiv\!N + KX$$
Alkyl cyanide
(nitrile)

$$RC\!\equiv\!N + 2H_2O \xrightarrow{H^+\ or\ OH^-} RCOOH + NH_3$$

If hydrochloric acid is employed for hydrolysis, the ammonia is bound as ammonium chloride, whereas on alkaline hydrolysis ammonia is liberated and the carboxylic acid is obtained by acidification of the reaction mixture containing the alkali salt. Typical applications to synthesis are:

1. $Br(CH_2)_3Br \xrightarrow[77-86\%]{2NaCN} NC(CH_2)_3CN \xrightarrow[83-85\%]{HCl} HOOC(CH_2)_3COOH$
   Glutaric acid

2. $HOCH_2CH_2Cl \xrightarrow[79-80\%]{NaCN} HOCH_2CH_2CN \xrightarrow[75-80\%]{NaOH} HOCH_2CH_2COOH$
   Ethylene · · · · · · Ethylene cyanohydrin · · · · · · β-Hydroxypropionic acid
   chlorohydrin

The intermediate alkyl cyanides are called nitriles when it is desired to emphasize the structural relation to the acids which they yield on hydrolysis; thus methyl cyanide, CH_3CN, is the nitrile of acetic acid, or acetonitrile; ethyl cyanide, CH_3CH_2CN, is propionitrile.

Cyanides are stable substances boiling at temperatures some 60–80° higher than the chlorides from which they can be prepared, for example capronitrile, or *n*-amyl cyanide (n-$C_5H_{11}CN$): b.p. 162–163°, sp. gr. 0.809, mol. wt. 97.16 (compare data on p. 165). The triple bond between carbon and nitrogen can enter into various additions. Hydrolysis can be conducted

$$R-C{\equiv}N \xrightarrow{OH^-} \left[R-\underset{\overset{|}{OH}}{C}{=}N^- \xrightarrow{H^+} R-\underset{\overset{|}{OH^-}}{\overset{|}{C}}{=}NH \right] \longrightarrow R-\underset{\overset{\|}{O}}{C}-NH_2$$

Amide

in two steps, the first of which affords an amide. Nucleophilic attack of the triple bond and rearrangement of an activated hydrogen atom of the intermediate find analogy in the hydration of acetylene. Amides can be prepared as products of mild hydrolysis and can be hydrolyzed to acids under more drastic conditions:

$$R-\overset{\overset{O}{\|}}{C}-NH_2 \ + \ H{\mid}OH \longrightarrow R-\overset{\overset{O}{\|}}{C}-OH \ + \ NH_3$$

Of the two methods available for conversion of alkyl halides into acids, the Grignard synthesis is the more generally applicable. The alternate cyanide procedure usually gives good results as applied to primary halides, but the reagent is so strongly basic that with secondary and tertiary halides some alkene formation is inevitable. Thus *t*-butyl bromide is converted by sodium cyanide largely into isobutylene.

PROPERTIES AND REACTIONS

Unique Properties of Formic Acid. — Formic acid is different in chemical behavior from typical carboxylic acids, in which the carboxyl group is linked to a hydrocarbon residue rather than to a lone hydrogen atom. Formic acid has the structure of both an acid and an aldehyde:

$$H{\mid}\overset{\overset{O}{\|}}{C}-OH \qquad\qquad H-\overset{\overset{O}{\|}}{C}{\mid}OH$$

Acid   Aldehyde

By virtue of its aldehydic character the substance is susceptible to ready oxidation, whereas the other carboxylic acids are not; it reduces ammoniacal silver hydroxide solution to metallic silver (silver-mirror test). The acid is employed also in certain reductions, for example:

$$\underset{\text{Triphenylcarbinol}}{(C_6H_5)_3COH} \ + \ HCOOH \longrightarrow \underset{\text{Triphenylmethane}}{(C_6H_5)_3CH} \ + \ H_2O \ + \ CO_2$$

Formic acid has a strong bactericidal action (used in disinfection of wine casks) resembling that of formaldehyde.

The exceptional acidity of formic acid has been mentioned. A technical water-containing grade is used in the textile and rubber industries as a cheap acidifying agent in place of acetic or sulfuric acid. In concentrated form, the acid is a pungent-smelling, highly corrosive liquid capable of raising blisters on the skin. In further contrast with typical acids, formic acid undergoes decomposition when heated in a closed system at moderately elevated temperatures somewhat above the boiling point. This decarboxylation, or decomposition to carbon dioxide and hydrogen, can be brought

$$H{\mid}COO{\mid}H \xrightarrow{\;160°\;} CO_2 + H_2$$

about even at room temperature under the influence of a palladium catalyst.

Preparation of anhydrous formic acid presents difficulties. The boiling point (100.5°) is very close to that of water; hence a concentration beyond about 75% cannot be achieved by distillation. Addition of concentrated sulfuric acid to dry sodium formate liberates the anhydrous organic acid, but precautions have to be taken to avoid a secondary reaction in which formic acid is dehydrated to carbon monoxide:

$$H{\mid}CO{\mid}OH \xrightarrow{\;H_2SO_4\;} CO + H_2O$$

This reaction, which is a reversal of the technical synthesis of sodium formate from carbon monoxide and alkali, proceeds so rapidly on moderate heating that it is utilized in the standard laboratory process for generation of carbon monoxide. The technical method of producing 85–90% formic acid with minimum loss by decomposition consists in adding concentrated sulfuric acid to a slurry of powdered sodium formate in a sufficient quantity of preformed 85–90% acid to moderate the reaction and promote rapid conversion of all the sulfuric acid into sodium sulfate. Anhydrous acid can be prepared in the laboratory by the action of dry hydrogen sulfide on lead formate at 100°.

Metal Salts. — The characteristic acidity and ability to form salts with bases is a distinctive property by which carboxylic acids are differentiated from alcohols, aldehydes, ketones, ethers, and esters. Carboxylic acids, whether soluble in water or not, liberate carbon dioxide from a sodium carbonate or bicarbonate solution, and on titration with standard sodium hydroxide solution consume an equivalent amount of base. Simple methods of qualitative and quantitative analysis are thus available.

The sodium and potassium salts are very different in physical properties from the free acids, for they are partly inorganic and are ionic. They are all solid substances even if the parent acid is a liquid, and they dissolve in water even though the free acid is insoluble. Because of the ionic character, they are not soluble in ether or in a hydrocarbon solvent. For example, caproic acid ($C_5H_{11}COOH$) is a liquid sparingly soluble in water, soluble in ether, capable of being distilled, and showing a characteristic melting point of $-1.5°$; sodium caproate ($C_5H_{11}COONa$) is a solid substance soluble in water but insoluble in ether, and it is nonvolatile and fusible only at a temperature above 300°. The differentiation in properties provides a useful basis for separation of acids from mixtures with other organic compounds. Such a mixture can be dissolved in ether and the acidic component quantitatively extracted by shaking the solution with aqueous alkali; the separated alkaline layer can be extracted with fresh ether to remove traces of suspended neutral substances and then acidified, and the uncontaminated acid is then obtained either as a precipitate or by ether extraction.

Decarboxylation and **Kolbe electrolysis** of salts of carboxylic acids have been described in Chapter 2.

Halogenation. — Acetic acid can be chlorinated in the presence of a trace of iodine, red phosphorus, or with exposure to sunlight, and yields in succession chloroacetic acid, di-, and trichloroacetic acid. In contrast with the photochemical chlorination of methane, halogen substitution

$$CH_3COOH \xrightarrow{Cl_2(I_2)} CH_2ClCOOH \xrightarrow{Higher\ temp.} CHCl_2COOH \xrightarrow{Higher\ temp.} CCl_3COOH$$

can be conducted in discrete stages, and either the mono- or the dichloro compound can be prepared in good yield and in satisfactory purity by merely introducing chlorine slowly until the proper increase in weight is observed. Fortunately no separation of mixtures is required, for the three chlorinated acids all boil at nearly the same temperature (Table 8.1). Trichloroacetic acid is obtained most conveniently by oxidation of chloral, CCl_3CHO (p. 197), with concentrated nitric acid. The iodine catalyst is described as a halogen carrier, and probably iodine trichloride is the effective chlorinating agent:

$$I_2 + 3\,Cl_2 \longrightarrow 2\,ICl_3$$
$$ICl_3 + 2\,CH_3COOH \longrightarrow ICl + 2\,CH_2ClCOOH$$
$$ICl + Cl_2 \longrightarrow ICl_3$$

Bromination of acids also can be effected readily, for example with use of a small amount of phosphorus trichloride as catalyst:

$$CH_3CH_2CH_2CH_2CH_2CO_2H \xrightarrow[83-89\%]{Br_2(PCl_3),\ 65-70°} CH_3CH_2CH_2CH_2CHCO_2H$$

Caproic acid (α) → α-Bromocaproic acid (Br)

Bromine enters exclusively the activated α-position adjacent to the unsaturated carbonyl group, and activation by $C{=}O$ can be understood as

$$RCH{-}C{=}O \rightleftharpoons RCH{=}C{-}OH \xrightarrow{Br_2} RCHC{-}OH \xrightarrow{-HBr} RCHC{=}O$$

affording opportunity for formation of an enol, through which the α-bromo acid can be formed by a process of addition-elimination. Indeed the catalyst used in the above example is effective because it converts the acid into the acid chloride, $RCOCl$, which is more prone to enolization than the free acid and which is regenerated by interchange. This is the Hell-Volhard-

$$RCHBrCOCl + RCH_2CO_2H \rightarrow RCHBrCO_2H + RCH_2COCl$$

Zelinsky procedure. An acid $RCH_2CH_2CO_2H$ yields first the α-bromo acid and then the α,α-dibromo acid but, as expected, β- or other positions in the chain are not attacked. The acid $(CH_3)_3CCO_2H$ has no hydrogen on the α-carbon and it does not yield a halo-substitution product. Information regarding the structure of an unknown mono or polycarboxylic acid can sometimes be gained by determination of the number of α-bromine atoms that can be introduced.

α-Iodo acids cannot be prepared by direct halogenation but can be obtained by metathesis from the bromo compounds:

$$RCHBrCOOH + KI \longrightarrow RCHICOOH + KBr$$

Inertness to Additions. — Although the carboxyl group is unsaturated to the same degree as a carbonyl group, acids and their salts generally do not enter into addition reactions characteristic of aldehydes and ketones. A free acid reacts initially with a Grignard reagent to produce a magnesio-halide salt and a hydrocarbon, but the salt fails to respond to a further molecule of Grignard reagent in the manner of carbonyl compounds; the

$$R-C\overset{O}{\underset{OH}{<}} + CH_3MgI \longrightarrow R-C\overset{O}{\underset{OMgI}{<}} + CH_4$$

sole product is the original acid. A carboxyl group, however, does not necessarily interfere with Grignard addition to a carbonyl group present in the same molecule, except to the extent that the initially formed —COOMgX group may decrease the solubility in ether, and frequently a successful result is obtained by using two equivalents of Grignard reagent. The carbonyl group of acids is resistant to methods of reduction that are applicable to the corresponding esters. Thus esters can be reduced with sodium and alcohol or catalytically (see below), whereas acids fail to react except under special conditions. The only general method of reducing free acids to alcohols, $RCOOH \rightarrow RCH_2OH$, is by use of the remarkable reducing agent lithium aluminum hydride. With this one exception, acids are distinctly less reactive than their esters.

An early interpretation by Hantzsch of the lower degree of reactivity of the carbonyl group in an acid or salt, in comparison to that in an ester, was based upon observation that acids and salts when examined spectrographically are distinctly weaker than esters in their power to absorb ultraviolet light; since absorption of light is indicative of unsaturation, esters were regarded as true carbonyl compounds, and acids and salts as substances in which the hydrogen or metal atom (ionic charge) is linked equally to both oxygen atoms, with obliteration of the carbonyl characteristics:

$$R-C\overset{O}{\underset{OR'}{<}} \qquad R-C\overset{O}{\underset{O}{<}}\Big\} H(Na)$$

Ester   Acid or salt

Resonance. — According to the resonance theory (p. 70), when a substance can have two or more structures that are equivalent or nearly equivalent to one another and that are interconvertible by mere redistribution of the valency electrons of unsaturated or ionized centers, the actual molecule does not conform to any one of the structures but exists as a resonance hybrid of them all. Since a carboxylate ion can assume two identical forms, it is a resonance hybrid of these forms:

$$R-C\overset{O}{\underset{O^-}{\big<}} \longleftrightarrow R-C\overset{O^-}{\underset{O}{\big<}} \quad \text{or} \quad :\!\ddot{O}\!:\!C\!::\!\ddot{O}\!: \longleftrightarrow :\!\ddot{O}\!::\!C\!:\!\ddot{O}\!:$$

The carbonate ion is a resonance hybrid described by three equivalent structures, and X-ray analyses of crystalline carbonates have shown that all

$$O\!=\!C\overset{O^-}{\underset{O^-}{\big<}} \longleftrightarrow {}^-O\!-\!C\overset{O}{\underset{O^-}{\big<}} \longleftrightarrow {}^-O\!-\!C\overset{O^-}{\underset{O}{\big<}}$$

three oxygen atoms are equidistant from the carbon atom and from one another, and lie in a plane with the carbon atom. Planar configuration is a necessary condition for resonance, for the change of one nonplanar form to another would require movement of atoms and not merely redistribution of electrons. X-ray data also establish the important fact that in this symmetrical system the interatomic distances are distinctly smaller than would be expected for an average of one double and two single bonds. The distance between the atomic center of the carbon atom and any one of the oxygen atoms of the carbonate ion is 1.30 Å, whereas in nonresonating systems the interatomic distance corresponding to the C—O bond is 1.43 Å, and the double bond distance in the normal C=O link is 1.28 Å. Shortened bond distances are a characteristic result of resonance; in a resonant molecule bonding energy of the atoms is increased by resonance, the atoms are brought closer together, and dissipation of energy through resonance confers stability. The thermal reaction $RCOONa + NaOH \rightarrow RH + Na_2CO_3$ shows that the carbonate is more stable to heat than the carboxylate; the difference may be due to opportunity for resonance among three structures, rather than only two.

The special stability of a resonance ion also provides the driving force for ionization, and hence the fundamental reason for the acidity of substances having a hydroxyl group attached to an unsaturated atom is that the separation of a proton from this structure gives a system that is stabilized by resonance. The diminished reactivity of the carbonyl group of a carboxylic acid in any reactions involving the carboxylate ion is understandable, since the ion contains no actual double bond but a hybrid partaking of the character of both a single and a double bond. The carbonyl group in a free acid also appears to be inert, probably in consequence of hydrogen bonding in the dimer. An ester is incapable of either resonance or hydrogen bonding and hence behaves as a true carbonyl compound.

ESTERS

Esters are one of three common types of derivatives of carboxylic acids. They are readily obtainable by acid-catalyzed esterification or by one of the alternate methods described below, and they can be reconverted efficiently into the acids by alkaline hydrolysis.   Because of the ready interconversion and because esters possess certain advantageous physical characteristics, it is frequently expedient to esterify an acid or acid mixture in order to effect purification, separation, or characterization.   Methyl and ethyl esters are unassociated liquids and distil at temperatures lower than the corresponding associated acids, even though the molecular weights are higher.   The comparative data of Table 8.3 show that methyl esters

TABLE 8.3.   BOILING POINTS OF ACIDS AND ESTERS, °C.

	ACID	METHYL ESTER	DIFFERENCE
Formic	100.5	32	68.5
Acetic	118	57	61
Propionic	141	79.7	61.3
n-Butyric	162.5	102.3	60.2
n-Valeric	187	127.3	59.7

boil an average of 62° below the acids; the ethyl esters boil some 42° below the acids.   Both methyl and ethyl formate boil at temperatures lower than the component acid and alcohols.   The more volatile esters are also more stable to heat than the free acids and can be distilled satisfactorily in cases where the acid undergoes decomposition.   Esters of solid acids melt at lower temperatures than the acids and often more sharply and without decomposition; they are more soluble in organic solvents and crystallize more satisfactorily.   A methyl ester invariably has a higher melting point than the corresponding ethyl ester.

Volatile esters are liquids of characteristic fruity odors.   The disagreeable-smelling acids butyric and valeric are converted by esterification into pleasantly fragrant derivatives.   Esters, usually in the form of mixtures, are responsible for the flavor and fragrance of many fruits and flowers, and artificial flavoring essences are mixtures of synthetic esters empirically compounded to reproduce the flavor and aroma of natural fruits and extracts (apple, raspberry, cherry, rum, etc.).   The ester mixtures are usually prepared in an alcoholic solution containing glycerol, chloroform, or acetaldehyde as fixatives to retain the fragrant principles, and organic acids are added to simulate the tartness of fruits.   The esters most extensively employed are ethyl formate, ethyl and isoamyl acetate, ethyl and isoamyl n-butyrate, ethyl and isoamyl n-valerate, and ethyl heptylate.   One formulation for artificial raspberry flavor utilizes nine esters, two organic acids, acetaldehyde, glycerol, and alcohol.

The esters listed in Table 8.4 are all slightly lighter than water, and all but those of low molecular weight are practically insoluble.   At room tem-

TABLE 8.4.　ESTERS (ALL LIQUIDS)

NAME	FORMULA	B.P., °C.	SP. GR.
Methyl formate	HCO_2CH_3	32	0.974
Ethyl formate	$HCO_2C_2H_5$	54	.906
Methyl acetate	$CH_3CO_2CH_3$	57	.924
Ethyl acetate	$CH_3CO_2C_2H_5$	77.1	.901
n-Propyl acetate	$CH_3CO_2C_3H_7(n)$	101.7	.886
n-Butyl acetate	$CH_3CO_2C_4H_9(n)$	126.5	.882
n-Amyl acetate	$CH_3CO_2C_5H_{11}(n)$	147.6	.879
Isobutyl acetate	$CH_3CO_2C_4H_9(i)$	118	.871
t-Butyl acetate	$CH_3CO_2C(CH_3)_3$	97	.896
Isoamyl acetate	$CH_3CO_2C_5H_{11}(i)$	142	.876
n-Octyl acetate	$CH_3CO_2C_8H_{17}(n)$	210	.885
Methyl propionate	$C_2H_5CO_2CH_3$	79.7	.915
Ethyl propionate	$C_2H_5CO_2C_2H_5$	99.1	.891
Methyl n-butyrate	$n\text{-}C_3H_7CO_2CH_3$	102.3	.898
Ethyl n-butyrate	$n\text{-}C_3H_7CO_2C_2H_5$	121	.879
Isoamyl n-butyrate	$n\text{-}C_3H_7CO_2C_5H_{11}(i)$	178.6	.866
Methyl n-valerate	$n\text{-}C_4H_9CO_2CH_3$	127.3	.910
Ethyl n-valerate	$n\text{-}C_4H_9CO_2C_2H_5$	145.5	.877
Methyl isovalerate	$i\text{-}C_4H_9CO_2CH_3$	117	.881
Isoamyl isovalerate	$i\text{-}C_4H_9CO_2C_5H_{11}(i)$	194	.858
Ethyl n-heptylate	$n\text{-}C_6H_{13}CO_2C_2H_5$	187	.872
Ethyl pelargonate	$n\text{-}C_8H_{17}CO_2C_2H_5$	228	.866

perature, 100 g. of water dissolves 30 g. of methyl formate, 33 g. of methyl acetate, 8.5 g. of ethyl acetate, or 6.5 g. of methyl propionate.

Preparation.　(a) **Fischer Esterification.** — The method of esterification introduced by E. Fischer consists in refluxing the acid with excess alcohol in the presence of about 3% of hydrogen chloride, sulfuric acid, or boron fluoride etherate. The operation is simple, and when an unbranched acid is esterified with a primary alcohol the yield of pure ester is usually high. However, alkyl groups attached to either the α-carbon atom of the

$$RCH_2COOH \ + \ HOCH_2R' \ \overset{H^+}{\rightleftharpoons} \ RCH_2COOCH_2R' \ + \ H_2O$$

acid or the carbinol carbon atom of the alcohol exert a blocking effect, or steric hindrance, that may retard the reaction and cause the equilibrium to be less favorable to the ester. Thus the rate of esterification of acetic acid with isopropyl alcohol is just half that of esterification of the acid with methanol or ethanol. The highly branched trimethylacetic acid when heated with isobutyl alcohol at 155° for one hour gives only 8% of the ester, as compared with 33% for n-butyric acid.

Surprisingly, the rate of esterification of t-butyl alcohol with acetic acid is slightly greater than the rate of reaction of methanol with the same acid. Studies employing isotopic tracer elements have established that esterification of a tertiary alcohol proceeds by a mechanism different from that involved in the case of a primary or secondary alcohol. When ordinary benzoic acid containing the O^{16}-isotope is esterified with heavy methanol,

$CH_3O^{18}H$, in the presence of hydrogen chloride, the water formed has the ordinary isotopic composition, and hence the reaction proceeds as follows:

$$C_6H_5C\overset{O}{\diagdown}\underset{}{OH} + \overline{H}O^{18}CH_3 \xrightarrow{H^+} C_6H_5C\overset{O}{\diagdown}O^{18}CH_3 + H_2O$$

The hydroxyl group eliminated thus comes from the acid rather than from the primary alcohol. This fact, as well as the role of the acid catalyst, can be interpreted in terms of a mechanism of esterification applicable to primary and secondary alcohols. A proton from the mineral acid accepts a pair

$$\text{(a)} \quad R-\overset{O}{\overset{\|}{C}}-OH + H^+ \longrightarrow R-\overset{O}{\overset{\|}{C}}-\overset{+}{\underset{H}{O}H}$$

$$\text{(b)} \quad H\overset{+}{\underset{H}{O}} -\overset{O}{\underset{R}{\overset{\|}{C}}} + HOR' \longrightarrow H_2O + \overset{O}{\underset{R}{\overset{\|}{C}}}-\overset{+}{\underset{H}{O}R'}$$

$$\text{(c)} \quad R-\overset{O}{\overset{\|}{C}}-\overset{+}{\underset{H}{O}R'} - H^+ \longrightarrow R-\overset{O}{\overset{\|}{C}}-OR'$$

of unshared electrons from the hydroxylic oxygen atom of the organic acid to form an oxonium ion (a), similar to the hydronium ion from water; this is attacked from the rear by the alcohol with expulsion of water to form the substituted oxonium ion (b), which loses a proton to give the ester (c). The proton required in the first step is regenerated in the last step. That the proton functions in the sense of a Lewis acid, or electron acceptor, explains why the reaction is also catalyzed effectively by boron fluoride, which is also a powerful electron acceptor. In the esterification of a tertiary alcohol with a carboxylic acid the hydroxyl group of the alcohol, rather than of the acid, is eliminated. The following mechanism appears applicable:

$$(CH_3)_3COH \xrightarrow{H^+} \underset{\text{(a)}}{(CH_3)_3C\overset{+}{O}H} \xrightarrow{-H_2O} \underset{\text{(b)}}{(CH_3)_3C^+} \xrightarrow{R-\overset{O}{\overset{\|}{C}}-OH}$$

$$\underset{\text{(c)}}{R-\overset{O}{\overset{\|}{C}}-\overset{+}{O}C(CH_3)_3} \xrightarrow{-H^+} \underset{\text{(d)}}{R-\overset{O}{\overset{\|}{C}}-OC(CH_3)_3}$$

The product of initial addition of a proton is an oxonium ion (a) that loses water to form a carbonium ion (b) because of the combined election-releasing power of the three methyl groups. The carbonium ion combines with the acid to form a substituted oxonium ion (c) that expels a proton to form the ester (d). The catalytic role of the proton is accounted for, and the differing behavior of the tertiary alcohol is interpreted as due to the inductive effect of the three alkyl groups in promoting formation of a carbonium ion.

Acid hydrolysis is the reverse of acid esterification. The rates of alkaline hydrolysis of esters of primary and secondary alcohols are the same as the rates of acid-catalyzed esterifications. However, esters of tertiary alcohols are resistant to alkaline hydrolysis for the reason that a basic medium does not promote formation of the carbonium ion intermediate.

(b) **Silver Salt Method.** — In those instances where direct acid-catalyzed esterification is slow or inefficient, satisfactory results can be obtained by treatment of the dry silver salt of the acid with an alkyl halide:

$$RCOOAg + XR' \longrightarrow RCOOR' + AgX$$

The reaction, analogous to the Williamson synthesis of ethers, apparently proceeds through simple metathesis involving fission of the O—Ag bond, for it is not materially impeded by the presence of branching alkyl groups. The silver salt often can be precipitated by dissolving the acid in dilute aqueous ammonia, boiling off the excess, and adding silver nitrate solution. The method has the objection of being lengthy and expensive.

(c) **With Diazomethane.** — An elegant route to methyl esters consists in treatment of the acid with an etheral solution of diazomethane:

$$RCOOH + CH_2N_2 \longrightarrow RCOOCH_3 + N_2$$

$$ \text{Diazomethane} \qquad \text{Methyl ester}$$

The reagent is a yellow gas, and small quantities can be prepared conveniently, prior to use, in the form of a solution in ether. When the yellow ethereal solution is added in portions to a solution or suspension of the acid in ether at room temperature, nitrogen is evolved at once and the yellow color is discharged; when the yellow color persists, an indication that excess diazomethane has been added, the solution is warmed on the steam bath to expel excess reagent and, since the only by-product is a gas, a solution of the desired ester in ether results. The method is generally applicable and is not subject to hindrance effects. Diazomethane is probably a resonance hybrid of several forms: $\overset{-}{C}H_2N\equiv\overset{+}{N} \leftrightarrow CH_2=\overset{+}{N}=\overset{-}{N} \leftrightarrow \overset{+}{C}H_2-\overset{-}{N}=N$. It is prepared most conveniently by the action of alkali on the precursor (a) of A. F. McKay (1948) or the comparable precursor (b)

$$CH_3NH_3^+Cl^- + H_2NCNHNO_2 \xrightarrow[84\%]{KOH} CH_3NHCNHNO_2 \xrightarrow[90\%]{HNO_2}$$

$$ \underset{\text{Nitroguanidine}}{} \qquad$$

with NH above each of the C groups.

$$CH_3NCNHNO_2 \xrightarrow{KOH} CH_2=\overset{+}{N}=\overset{-}{N} \leftarrow CH_3NSO_2C_6H_4CH_3\text{-}p$$

with NH above the C; NO below the first structure's N; NO below the last structure's N.

(a) N-Methyl-N-nitroso-   (b) p-Tolylsulfonyl-
    N'-nitroguanidine   methylnitrosamide

of Th. J. deBoer and H. J. Backer (1954). The reagent is toxic and explosive and hence requires special handling.

Reactions. (a) **Grignard Synthesis.** — Esters contain a carbonyl group capable of Grignard additions but less reactive than that of aldehydes and ketones. The practical application of the Grignard synthesis is limited to the reaction: $RCOOR' + 2R''MgX$ (and hydrolysis) $\rightarrow R''_2RCOH$; the reaction cannot be stopped readily at the ketone stage because the ketone is more reactive than the ester.

(b) **Reduction to Alcohols.** — Esters are easily reducible and usually can be converted into two alcohols, one having the carbon content of the acid residue and the other of the alcoholic component. The Bouveault[1]-

$$RCOOR' + 4H \rightarrow RCH_2OH + HOR'$$

Blanc method of reduction, consists in refluxing the ester with metallic sodium and an alcohol. Ethyl alcohol is commonly used to furnish hydrogen, but butyl alcohol is sometimes employed in reduction of higher esters to provide a higher refluxing temperature. Practical examples are as follows:

1.
$$(CH_2)_8\underset{\diagdown CO_2C_2H_5}{\overset{\diagup CO_2C_2H_5}{}} \xrightarrow[73-76\%]{C_2H_5OH,\ Na} (CH_2)_8\underset{\diagdown CH_2OH}{\overset{\diagup CH_2OH}{}}$$

Diethyl sebacate — Decamethylene glycol (m.p. 72°)

2.
$$CH_3(CH_2)_7CH=CH(CH_2)_7CO_2C_4H_9 \xrightarrow[82-84\%]{C_4H_9OH,\ Na} CH_3(CH_2)_7CH=CH(CH_2)_7CH_2OH$$

Butyl oleate — Oleyl alcohol (liq., b.p. 195°/8 mm.)

A second experimental method is high-pressure hydrogenation over copper chromite catalyst, for example:

$$(CH_2)_4\underset{\diagdown CO_2C_2H_5}{\overset{\diagup CO_2C_2H_5}{}} \xrightarrow[85-90\%]{H_2,\ CuCr_2O_4\ (255°,\ 15-20\ atm.)} (CH_2)_4\underset{\diagdown CH_2OH}{\overset{\diagup CH_2OH}{}}$$

Diethyl adipate — Hexamethylene glycol (m.p. 42°, b.p. 250°)

Tetramethylene glycol, $HO(CH_2)_4OH$ (m.p. 16°, b.p. 230°), can be prepared in the same way from diethyl succinate, $C_2H_5OCOCH_2CH_2COOC_2H_5$. Some of the higher monohydric alcohols are produced technically from even-carbon acids abundantly available from vegetable oils and animal fats by hydrogenation of the esters. Thus lauryl alcohol, $n\text{-}C_{12}H_{25}OH$, is produced from coconut oil and other nut oils rich in the glyceride of lauric acid; direct hydrogenation of the glyceride yields lauryl alcohol with destruction of the glycerol, and when the recovery of this material is imperative the glyceride is converted into the methyl ester, with separation of the glycerol, and the simple ester is hydrogenated. A third method, reduction with lithium aluminum hydride, is illustrated on page 117.

---

[1] Louis Bouveault, 1864–1909; b. Nevers, France; Ph.D. Paris (Hanriot); Lyon, Lille, Nancy, Paris; *Ber.*, **42**, 3561 (1909)

(c) **Hydrolysis.** — The hydrogen-ion catalyzed reaction of an acid with an alcohol to give an ester is reversible, and the same equilibrium state can be reached starting with the products of the reaction, the ester and water. The acid catalysts suitable for esterification are just as effective in bringing about hydrolysis, and one method of hydrolyzing an ester consists in re-fluxing the substance with excess water containing hydrochloric or sulfuric acid:

$$RCOOR' + HOH \text{ (excess)} \xrightleftharpoons{H^+} RCOOH + R'OH$$

The mechanism and intermediates of the hydrolytic reaction are the same as those for esterification. Esterification is catalyzed by hydroxide ions as well as by protons, and though base-catalyzed esterification is not a practicable process, bases have advantages as applied to the reverse reaction. When an ester is heated with water containing slightly more than one equivalent of sodium hydroxide, hydrolysis to the alcohol and the organic acid is followed by combination of the acid with alkali, and the equilibrium is displaced:

$$RCOOR' + H_2O \xrightleftharpoons{OH^-} R'OH + RCOOH \xrightarrow{NaOH} RCOONa$$

The combination of a reversible reaction followed by an irreversible step insures completeness of reaction, and hence alkaline hydrolysis (saponification) is the more efficient   method of cleaving esters.

(d) **Alcoholysis, or Ester Interchange.** — When the methyl ester of an acid is refluxed with excess ethyl alcohol containing a few percent of hydrogen chloride or sulfuric acid, it is converted to a large extent into the ethyl ester. An equilibrium is set up, and the extent of conversion is dependent upon the relative amounts of methyl and ethyl alcohol present in either the free or combined form:

$$RCOOCH_3 + \underset{\text{(excess)}}{C_2H_5OH} \xrightleftharpoons{H^+} RCOOC_2H_5 + CH_3OH$$

An ethyl ester can be transformed similarly into the methyl derivative by ester-interchange. Rapid interchange of alkyl groups also can be brought about with a catalytic amount of sodium alkoxide, and this fact is the basis for the statement in the preceding section that the esterification reaction is subject to basic catalysis. A technical application of ester interchange is the production of lauryl alcohol from the glyceride trilaurin with recovery of glycerol. Refluxing the glyceride with methanol and sulfuric acid affords the methyl ester, which separates as an oil on addition of water; the glycerol is recovered from the aqueous solution:

$$
\begin{array}{c}
C_{11}H_{23}COOCH_2 \\
| \\
C_{11}H_{23}COOCH \\
| \\
C_{11}H_{23}COOCH_2 \\
\text{Trilaurin} \\
\text{(m.p. 46°)}
\end{array}
\ + \ 3\,CH_3OH \xrightarrow{H_2SO_4}
\begin{array}{c}
3\,C_{11}H_{23}COOCH_3 \\
\text{Methyl laurate} \\
\text{(m.p. 5°)}
\end{array}
\ + \
\begin{array}{c}
CH_2OH \\
| \\
CHOH \\
| \\
CH_2OH \\
\text{Glycerol}
\end{array}
$$

(e) **Ammonolysis.** — Esters are converted by interaction with ammonia into amides, neutral derivatives of acids already encountered as products of partial hydrolysis of nitriles. The reagents H—OH, H—OR, and H—NH$_2$ thus all act upon esters in the same manner, with elimination of the original alkoxyl group, possibly through initial addition to the double bond. The reactions of hydrolysis and alcoholysis require an acidic or a basic catalyst; ammonia itself provides basic conditions favorable for the transformation. Ammonolysis of an ester usually is carried out with either

$$RCO \fbox{OR'} + \fbox{H} NH_2 \longrightarrow RC \underset{NH_2}{\overset{O}{\diagup}} + R'OH$$

Amide

aqueous or alcoholic ammonia at room temperature; sometimes the mixture is cooled in order to avoid attack of another reactive group in the molecule, for example:

$$ClCH_2COOC_2H_5 + aq.\ NH_3 \xrightarrow[62-87\%]{0-5°} ClCH_2CONH_2$$

Ethyl chloroacetate — Chloroacetamide (m.p. 120°)

With the exception of formamide, the amides are crystalline solids at room temperature, and they are frequently prepared from liquid acids or esters for purposes of identification by mixed melting-point determinations. The data of Table 8.5, however, show that among the amide derivatives of

TABLE 8.5. AMIDES

NAME	FORMULA	M.P., °C.	B.P., °C.	SP. GR.	SOLUBILITY IN WATER
Formamide	HCONH$_2$	2	193	1.139	sol.
Acetamide	CH$_3$CONH$_2$	82	222	1.159	sol.
Propionamide	C$_2$H$_5$CONH$_2$	80	213	1.042	sol.
n-Butyramide	n-C$_3$H$_7$CONH$_2$	116	216	1.032	sol.
n-Valeramide	n-C$_4$H$_9$CONH$_2$	106		1.023	sol.
n-Caproamide	n-C$_5$H$_{11}$CONH$_2$	101		0.999	sol. hot
Stearamide	n-C$_{17}$H$_{35}$CONH$_2$	109	251$^{12\,mm.}$		insol.

straight-chain aliphatic acids there is little change in the melting point from the C$_5$-compound on. The amides boil at temperatures higher than the acids from which they are derived, and the boiling points are less regular than usual and show less increase with increasing molecular weight, a relationship which suggests that in the liquid state amides are associated to varying degrees. Dimethylformamide, HCON(CH$_3$)$_2$ (b.p. 153°), is a useful solvent.

Other substances derived from ammonia react with esters in an analogous manner; hydrazine, for example, reacts as follows:

$$CH_3C \underset{OC_2H_5}{\overset{O}{\diagup}} + H_2NNH_2 \xrightarrow{Reflux} CH_3C \underset{NHNH_2}{\overset{O}{\diagup}} + C_2H_5OH$$

Hydrazine — Acethydrazide (m.p. 67°)

ACYL HALIDES

Acyl halides are reactive, low-boiling derivatives in which the hydroxyl group of an acid is replaced by a halogen atom.   They bear the same rela-

$$R-C{\overset{\displaystyle O}{\diagdown}}_X \qquad\qquad R-C{\overset{\displaystyle O}{\diagdown}}$$

Acyl halide   Acyl radical

tionship to acids as alkyl halides do to alcohols, and replacement of hydroxyl by halogen has a similar effect on the boiling point in each case·

$n\text{-}C_3H_7CO\boxed{OH}$, b.p. 162.5° $n\text{-}C_5H_{11}\boxed{OH}$, b.p. 138.0°

$n\text{-}C_3H_7CO\boxed{Cl}$, b.p. 102° $n\text{-}C_5H_{11}\boxed{Cl}$, b.p. 105.7°

(mol. wt. 106.55)   (mol. wt. 106.60)

The acyl chloride and alkyl chloride selected for illustration have practically the same molecular weights, and the boiling points are very close to each other and to that of n-heptane (unassociated liquids).   Properties of other acyl halides are recorded in Table 8.6.   The initial member, the chloride of formic acid, does not exist as such, but in some reactions a mixture of carbon monoxide and hydrogen chloride functions as though the substance is produced in a transient phase:

$$\overset{\displaystyle H}{\underset{\displaystyle Cl}{|}} \;+\; C{=}O \;\rightleftharpoons\; \overset{\displaystyle H}{\underset{\displaystyle Cl}{\diagup}}{\diagdown}C{=}O$$

TABLE 8.6.   ACYL HALIDES[1]

NAME	FORMULA	B.P., °C.	SP. GR.
Acetyl fluoride	CH_3COF	20.5	0.993
Acetyl chloride	CH_3COCl	52	1.104
Acetyl bromide	CH_3COBr	76.7	1.52
Acetyl iodide	CH_3COI	108	1.98
Chloroacetyl chloride	$CH_2ClCOCl$	105	1.495
Bromoacetyl bromide	$CH_2BrCOBr$	150	2.317
Propionyl chloride	CH_3CH_2COCl	80	1.065
n-Butyryl chloride	$CH_3CH_2CH_2COCl$	102	1.028
Isobutyryl chloride	$(CH_3)_2CHCOCl$	92	1.017
n-Valeryl chloride	$CH_3CH_2CH_2CH_2COCl$	128	1.016
Isovaleryl chloride	$(CH_3)_2CHCH_2COCl$	113	
n-Caproyl chloride	$n\text{-}C_5H_{11}COCl$	153	
Capryl chloride	$CH_3(CH_2)_6COCl$	196	0.975
Stearoyl chloride	$CH_3(CH_2)_{16}COCl$	$215^{15\,\text{mm.}}$	
Benzoyl chloride	C_6H_5COCl	197.2	1.212

[1] All liquids except stearoyl chloride, m.p. 23°.

Preparation. — Replacement of the hydroxyl group of acids by chlorine can be accomplished with the reagents employed for bringing about the corresponding transformation of alcohols, namely phosphorus trichloride, phosphorus pentachloride, thionyl chloride.   The type reactions are:

$$3RCOOH + PCl_3 \longrightarrow 3RCOCl + H_3PO_3$$
$$RCOOH + PCl_5 \longrightarrow RCOCl + POCl_3 + HCl$$
$$RCOOH + SOCl_2 \longrightarrow RCOCl + SO_2 + HCl$$

Some considerations guiding the choice of reagent are indicated by the following combinations found satisfactory for preparative purposes:

1. CH_3COOH $\xrightarrow[70\%]{PCl_3}$ CH_3COCl (b.p. 52°) + H_3PO_3 (dec. 200°)
   Acetic acid   Acetyl chloride

2. C_6H_5COOH $\xrightarrow[90\%]{PCl_5}$ C_6H_5COCl (b.p. 197.2°) + $POCl_3$ (b.p. 107.2°)
   Benzoic acid   Benzoyl chloride

3. n-C_3H_7COOH $\xrightarrow[85\%]{SOCl_2 \text{ (b.p. } 77°)}$ n-C_3H_7COCl (b.p. 102°) + SO_2 + HCl
   n-Butyric acid n-Butyryl chloride

Acid chlorides are so sensitive to hydrolysis, particularly when liquid, that it is impracticable to separate the reaction products from accompanying inorganic materials by extraction of the latter with water, and the only method of purification available is distillation. Phosphorus trichloride is a satisfactory reagent in example (1) because the low-boiling acetyl chloride can be distilled from the nonvolatile residue of phosphorous acid. If phosphorus trichloride were used in the case of benzoic acid, however, benzoyl chloride could not be distilled from the reaction mixture because it boils at about the temperature at which phosphorous acid begins to decompose; phosphorus pentachloride is better in this case because the inorganic reactant is phosphorus oxychloride, which is more volatile than the organic product and can be removed by distillation prior to distillation of the benzoyl chloride (2). Phosphorus pentachloride would be a poor choice for the preparation of n-butyryl chloride because the boiling point of this substance is close to that of phosphorus oxychloride; thionyl chloride gives satisfactory results (3). It may be necessary to employ excess thionyl chloride, and hence the boiling point of the product must be sufficiently above or below that of thionyl chloride to permit separation. For some purposes the crude materials can be used without purification. Thus benzoic acid can be warmed with phosphorus trichloride, the mixture cooled, and the upper layer of the acid chloride decanted from a lower layer of phosphorous acid and employed directly.

Replacement Reactions. — Acetyl chloride fumes in moist air as the result of liberation of hydrogen chloride. The higher acid chlorides are somewhat more resistant to the action of water because they are less soluble in water. Alcohols and ammonia act upon acid chlorides in the same way.

Hydrolysis $RCOCl + HOH \rightarrow RCOOH + HCl$

Alcoholysis $RCOCl + HOR' \rightarrow RCOOR' + HCl$

Ammonolysis $RCOCl + HNH_2 \rightarrow RCONH_2 + HCl$

In these reactions resulting in replacement of halogen by a hydroxyl, alkoxyl, or amino group, acid chlorides are more reactive than alkyl chlorides or even than alkyl iodides. This reactivity seems surprising when it is considered that the chlorine atom is linked to an unsaturated carbonyl group, for unsaturated halides of the type of vinyl chloride, $CH_2=CHCl$, are notably unreactive. An explanation is based on the fact that the carbonyl group is endowed with specific additive power not shared by an ethylenic double bond. Probably all three of the apparent replacements proceed by an addition, with formation of an unstable intermediate from which hydrogen chloride is eliminated with the same ease that water separates from an unstable *gem*-diol, for example:

$$
\begin{array}{c}
\text{Cl} \\
| \\
\text{R—C=O}
\end{array}
+ \text{HOCH}_3 \rightleftharpoons
\left[
\begin{array}{c}
\overline{\text{Cl}} \\
| \\
\text{R—C—O}\!\!\text{H} \\
| \\
\text{OCH}_3
\end{array}
\right]
\longrightarrow
\begin{array}{c}
\text{R—C=O} \\
| \\
\text{OCH}_3
\end{array}
+ \text{HCl}
$$

The halogen atom is apparently susceptible to replacment not because it is actually labile but as a consequence of its being linked to a functional group capable of entering into additions; even if the addition reaction is an equilibrium proceeding to only a slight extent, the irreversible decomposition of the addition product can displace the equilibrium and lead to complete conversion.

Grignard Reaction. — In the reaction with a Grignard reagent an acid chloride, like an ester, yields first a ketone and then, with more reagent, a tertiary alcohol:

$$
\text{RCOCl} \xrightarrow{\text{R'MgX}} \text{RCOR'} \xrightarrow{\text{R'MgX, H}_2\text{O}}
\begin{array}{c}
\text{R} \\
\text{R'} \!\!\!\searrow\!\!\text{COH} \\
\text{R'}
\end{array}
$$

The initial step proceeds more rapidly than the corresponding reaction of an ester, and there is more differentiation between the first and second steps. Consequently ketones can be prepared in reasonable yield by using just one equivalent of Grignard reagent and adding it by portions to a solution of the acid chloride (inverse Grignard reaction), in order to avoid exposure of the ketone formed to the action of the reagent. Investigations of other organometallic compounds have established the cadmium derivatives as preferred reagents for conversion of acid chlorides into ketones (Gilman,[2] 1936). Addition of one equivalent of anhydrous cadmium chloride to an ethereal solution of a Grignard reagent affords the corresponding alkylcadmium halide:

$$
\text{RMgX} + \text{CdCl}_2 \longrightarrow \text{RCdCl} + \text{MgXCl}
$$

The cadmium derivative can combine with an acid chloride, but adds to the carbonyl group of the initially formed ketone less readily than a Grignard reagent, and hence the reaction is easily arrested at the ketone stage:

$$
\text{RCdX} + \text{R'COCl} \longrightarrow \text{RCOR'} + \text{CdXCl}
$$

Formation of a ketone in the reaction of an acyl halide with an organometallic halide can be interpreted as the result of either direct replacement or initial addition to the carbonyl group and subsequent elimination

[2] Henry Gilman, b. 1893, Boston; Ph.D. Harvard (Kohler); Iowa State College

of a metal dihalide, as follows:

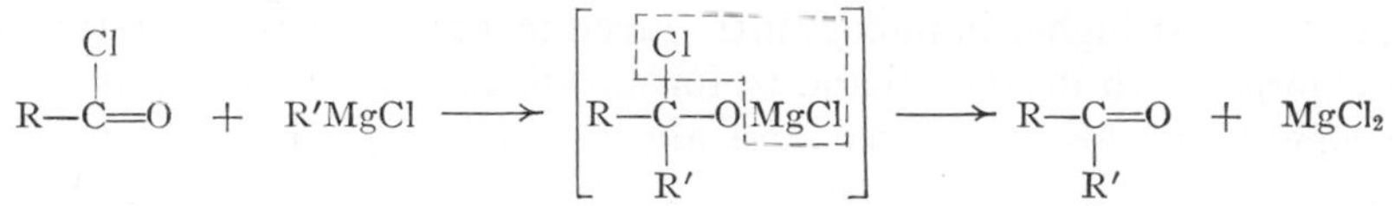

$$
\underset{\underset{R'}{\overset{Cl}{|}}}{R-C=O} + R'MgCl \longrightarrow \left[\underset{\underset{R'}{\overset{\overset{Cl}{|}}{|}}}{R-C-O\,MgCl} \right] \longrightarrow \underset{\overset{|}{R'}}{R-C=O} + MgCl_2
$$

Evidence permitting a decision between the two possibilities is available from a study of the reactivity of a series of acid fluorides, chlorides, and bromides to a given Grignard reagent as evaluated in competitive experiments (J. R. Johnson[3]). The order of reactivity is found to be RCOF > RCOCl > RCOBr, which is just the reverse of the order of lability of the carbon–halogen bonds in alkyl halides as determined in replacement reactions: C—Br > C—Cl > C—F. That the acid fluoride is the most, rather than the least, reactive member of the series indicates that the reaction can hardly involve direct severance of the carbon–halogen linkage, and suggests an initial addition to the carbonyl group. The halogen atom then influences the speed of the reaction merely to the extent that it modifies the additive power of the carbonyl group, and this effect may be partly a function of its size, a large atom tending to block free access of the Grignard reagent to the unsaturated center. The space factor can be evaluated from the interatomic distances given in Table 8.7; the differ-

TABLE 8.7. ATOMIC DIMENSIONS

BOND	DISTANCE BETWEEN ATOMIC CENTERS, Å	RADIUS OF THE HALOGEN ATOM, Å
C—C	1.54	....
C—F	1.41	0.64
C—Cl	1.76	.99
C—Br	1.91	1.14
C—I	2.10	1.33

ences between the halogens are very marked. The relationship between an acid fluoride and an acid bromide is indicated schematically as follows:

More reactive   Less reactive

A second factor is the relative electronegativity of the halogens, for the addition reaction may require partial polarization of the carbonyl group in the sense $>\overset{+}{C}-\overset{-}{O}$. Since fluorine is the most electronegative, or electron-accepting, of the halogens, the fluorine atom would cause a drift of electrons away from the carbon atom and hence increase the fractional positive charge to an extent greater than is realized in an acid chloride or bromide.

---

[3] John R. Johnson, b. 1900 Chicago; Ph.D. Illinois (Adams); Cornell Univ.

Arndt[4]-Eistert[5] Reaction. — This general method for conversion of an acid to the next higher homolog, introduced in 1935, involves reaction of an acid chloride with diazomethane to form a diazo ketone which, under suitable conditions, loses nitrogen and affords the acid. The decomposition

$$RCOCl + CH_2N_2 \xrightarrow{-HCl} RCOCHN_2 \xrightarrow{H_2O} RCH_2CO_2H + N_2$$

Diazoketone

can be effected with silver oxide catalyst in the presence of absolute methanol, in which case the product is the methyl ester. In an improved procedure (Wilds, 1948) a higher boiling alcohol (benzyl alcohol, octanol-2) is used and the reaction conducted at 160–180°; a catalyst is not essential, but addition of a tertiary amine (collidine) improves the yield. The key step (actually the previously known reaction of L. Wolff, 1912) proceeds through an intermediate ketene, which, in the absence of water, alcohols, primary or secondary amines, is isolable. The course of the reaction is illustrated for one of the resonance structures of the diazo ketone (a). Loss of nitrogen

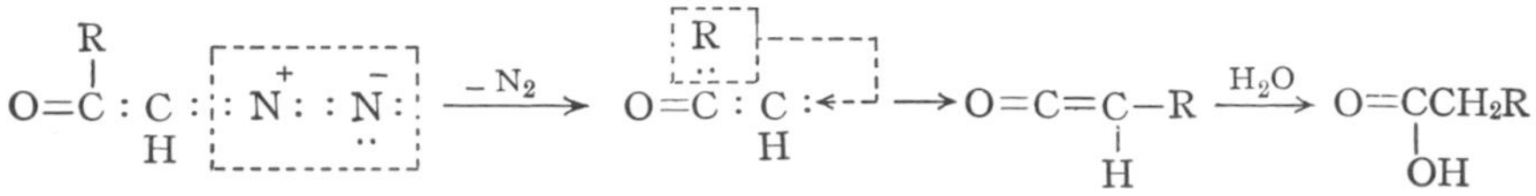

(a)   (b)   (c)   (d)

produces the bivalent carbon product (b), and the alkyl group migrates with its pair of electrons to fill the open sextet and produce the ketene (c). Evidence of group migration is that the labeled diazo ketone $C_6H_5C^{13}OCHN_2$ gives $C_6H_5CH_2C^{13}O_2H$.

Phosgene (COCl₂). — Phosgene was discovered by J. Davy (1812) as a product of the combination of carbon monoxide and chlorine under the influence of light (Gr. *phos*, light; L. *genere*, to be born), and it is now manufactured from these reagents with activated charcoal as catalyst.

Phosgene
(b.p. 8.3°)

The substance is a highly toxic gas having an odor resembling that of new-mown hay; it is available in the liquefied form in steel cylinders.

Phosgene is the diacid chloride of the unstable carbonic acid and is sometimes called carbonyl chloride. It enters into typical reactions of hydrolysis to carbonic acid and ammonolysis to urea:

Urea

---

[4] Fritz Arndt, b. 1885 Hamburg, Germany; Ph.D. Freiburg (Howitz); Breslau, Istanbul
[5] Bernd Eistert, b. 1902 Ohlau, Schleswig; Darmstadt, BASF Ludwigshafen

The reaction with an alcohol can be conducted in two stages, and either the mono- or dialkoxy derivative can be prepared:

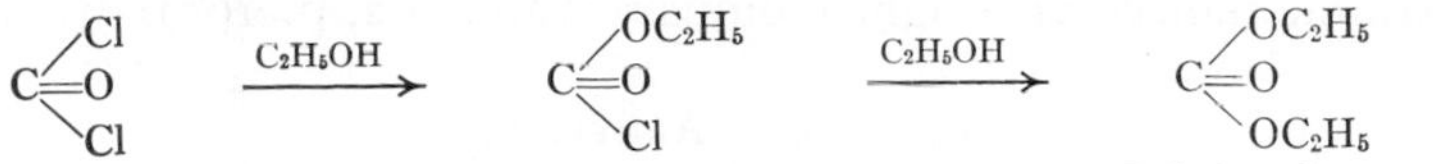

$$C{<}_{Cl}^{Cl}{=}O \xrightarrow{C_2H_5OH} C{<}_{Cl}^{OC_2H_5}{=}O \xrightarrow{C_2H_5OH} C{<}_{OC_2H_5}^{OC_2H_5}{=}O$$

Ethyl chlorocarbonate, or ethyl chloroformate (b.p. 95°)

Ethyl carbonate (b.p. 125.8°)

The initial product of the reaction with ethanol, ethyl chlorocarbonate or ethyl chloroformate, is the ethyl ester of the unknown chloro derivative of formic acid [ClCOOH]. It has the grouping —COCl characteristic of acid chlorides and is useful as a reagent with which to introduce the carbethoxy group ($COOC_2H_5$), for example, into ammonia:

$$ClCOOC_2H_5 \xrightarrow{NH_3} NH_2COOC_2H_5$$

Ethyl chlorocarbonate

Urethan, or ethyl carbamate (m.p. 48°, b.p. 184°)

Phosgene was introduced as a war gas by the Germans in 1915 and was responsible for about 80% of the gas casualties in World War I. It is a lung injurant similar to chlorine but about ten times as toxic; it is also more insidious in action, since it gives no warning symptoms for an hour or two. The irritant action is attributed to hydrolysis in the tissues to hydrochloric acid, which is the agent directly toxic to cells. Phosgene is nonpersistent and hence applicable as an attacking agent. It is ineffective in wet weather as the result of ready hydrolysis, and it is stopped effectively by modern gas masks. The substance diphosgene is convertible into phosgene and has also been used as a war gas. It is trichloromethyl chloroformate, $ClCOOCCl_3$, and is made by chlorination of methyl chloroformate, derived from phosgene and methanol:

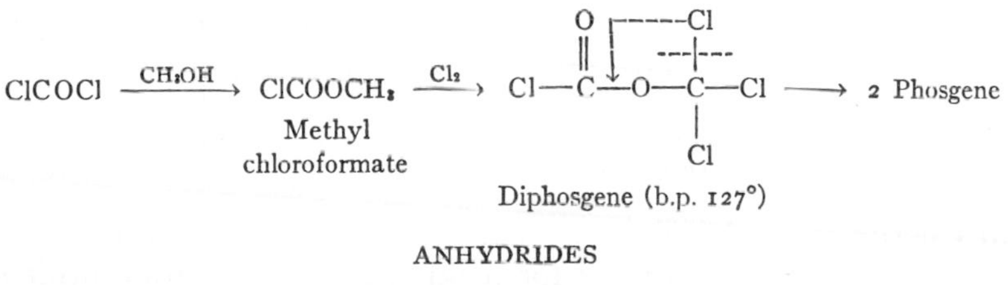

$$ClCOCl \xrightarrow{CH_3OH} ClCOOCH_3 \xrightarrow{Cl_2} Cl{-}\overset{\overset{O}{\|}}{C}{-}O{-}\overset{\overset{Cl}{|}}{\underset{\underset{Cl}{|}}{C}}{-}Cl \longrightarrow 2\ Phosgene$$

Methyl chloroformate

Diphosgene (b.p. 127°)

ANHYDRIDES

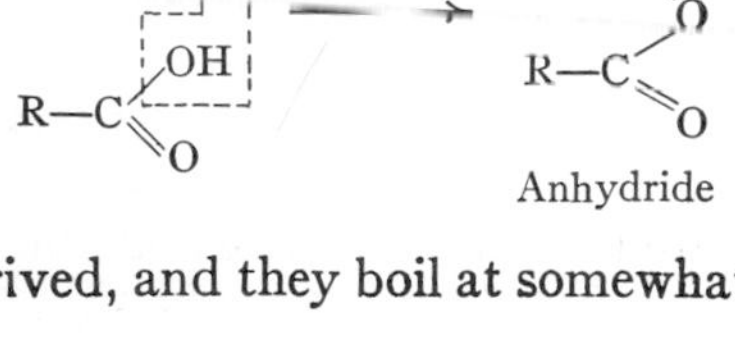

With the exception of formic acid, which on dehydration yields carbon monoxide, the carboxylic acids form anhydrides in which water is eliminated between two molecules of the acid. Anhydrides of normal acids up to C_{12} are liquids (Table 8.8); acetic anhydride is a mobile liquid with a pungent irritating odor. Anhydrides have nearly twice the molecular weights of the acids from which they are derived, and they boil at somewhat higher temperatures.   Acetic anhydride (b.p. 139.6°, mol. wt. 102.09) boils at a higher temperature than esters, halogen compounds, and hydrocarbons of comparable molecular weight (compare Table 8.2, p. 165).

TABLE 8.8. ANHYDRIDES

NAME	FORMULA	M.P., °C.	B.P., °C.	SP. GR.
Acetic anhydride	$(CH_3CO)_2O$	−73	139.6	1.082
Propionic anhydride	$(C_2H_5CO)_2O$	−45	168	1.012
n-Butyric anhydride	$(n\text{-}C_3H_7CO)_2O$	−75	198	0.969
n-Valeric anhydride	$(n\text{-}C_4H_9CO)_2O$		$218^{754mm.}$	.929
Stearic anhydride	$(n\text{-}C_{17}H_{35}CO)_2O$	72		
Succinic anhydride	$\begin{array}{c} CH_2CO \\ \;\;\;\; \rangle O \\ CH_2CO \end{array}$	119.6	261	1.104
Benzoic anhydride	$(C_6H_5CO)_2O$	42	360	1.199
Phthalic anhydride	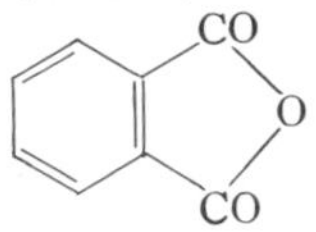 $\begin{array}{c} CO \\ \;\;\;\; \rangle O \\ CO \end{array}$	132	284.5	1.527

Preparation. — A laboratory method of preparing acetic anhydride is the reaction of acetyl chloride with anhydrous sodium acetate (compare the Williamson synthesis of an ether).   Several variations of this method

$$CH_3COO\,Na \atop + \atop CH_3CO\,Cl \longrightarrow {CH_3CO \atop CH_3CO} \rangle O + NaCl$$

have been used in production of the chemical on a scale which, in the United States, has been well over 100 million pounds per year.   For example, when phosphorus oxychloride acts upon excess sodium acetate, acetyl chloride is formed, and this then reacts with more sodium acetate as above, the net result being:

$$4\,CH_3COONa + POCl_3 \longrightarrow 2\,(CH_3CO)_2O + NaPO_3 + 3\,NaCl$$

Sulfur chloride is employed as the active halide in another procedure.

A modern industrial process for making acetic anhydride utilizes the highly unsaturated and reactive ketene, prepared by cracking acetone:

$$H\,CH_2\text{—}C\!\!=\!\!O \;\;{\overset{700\text{–}750°}{\xrightarrow{\hspace{1.2cm}}}}\;\; CH_2\!\!=\!\!C\!\!=\!\!O + CH_4$$
$$\text{Ketene (b.p.} - 56°)$$

with CH_3 above.

Methane results from the pyrolysis by elimination of the methyl group along with an activated hydrogen in the α-position.   Ketene can be prepared in the laboratory in the generator illustrated in Fig. 8.1.   Vapor of

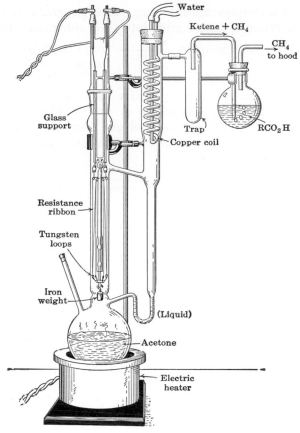

FIG. 8.1. — Ketene Generator

refluxing acetone comes in contact with a glowing grid of resistance wire and undergoes cracking; unchanged acetone is condensed and returned to the boiling flask, and the ketene evolved in the gas stream along with methane is absorbed directly by a liquid reagent or in a solution.

Ketene combines with most reagents containing either hydroxyl or amino ($-$ NH$_2$) groups; it reacts readily with acetic acid to give acetic anhydride, probably by addition to the carbonyl group and migration of the enolic hydrogen atom:

$$CH_3COOH \;+\; CH_2{=}C{=}O \longrightarrow \begin{bmatrix} CH_2{=}C{-}OH \\ \quad\quad O \\ CH_3C{=}O \end{bmatrix} \longrightarrow \begin{array}{c} CH_3C{=}O \\ \quad\quad O \\ CH_3C{=}O \end{array}$$

Mixed anhydrides of the type CH$_3$CO$\cdot$O$\cdot$COR can be prepared by addition of a higher acid, RCOOH, to ketene and distillation at a greatly reduced pressure, but unless the temperature is kept low the mixed anhydride rearranges and the more volatile acetic anhydride distils first.   By deliberate maintenance of a temperature favoring rearrangement, ketene can be employed for conversion of higher acids into their anhydrides, for example:

$$2\,CH_3(CH_2)_4CO_2H \ + \ CH_2=C=O \ \xrightarrow[80-87\%]{} \ [CH_3(CH_2)_4CO]_2O \ + \ CH_3CO_2H$$

Caproic anhydride
(b.p. 243°)

Higher anhydrides that are crystalline solids are prepared by heating the acid with either acetic anhydride or acetyl chloride; in either case acetic acid is formed and serves as a solvent from which the higher anhydride crystallizes on cooling. Example 2 illustrates the conversion of a dibasic acid into a cyclic anhydride.

1. $C_6H_5COOH \ \xrightarrow[72-74\%]{(CH_3CO)_2O \ + \ H_3PO_4 \ (trace)} \ (C_6H_5CO)_2O$

Benzoic acid   Benzoic anhydride

2.

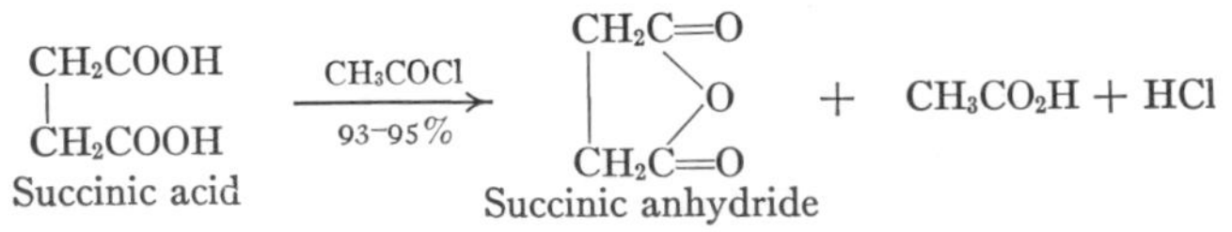

$$\begin{array}{c} CH_2COOH \\ | \\ CH_2COOH \end{array} \ \xrightarrow[93-95\%]{CH_3COCl} \ \begin{array}{c} CH_2C=O \\ | \quad\quad\ \diagdown O \\ CH_2C=O \end{array} \ + \ CH_3CO_2H + HCl$$

Succinic acid   Succinic anhydride

Hydrolysis and Ammonolysis. — Anhydrides are not so sensitive to water as acyl halides, but are more easily hydrolyzed than esters. Thus acetic anhydride can be hydrolyzed in a few minutes by boiling water. The anhydride dissolves in cold water to the extent of abou 12 g. per 100 g., and if the solution is kept at room temperature, the substance undergoes complete hydrolysis only after an hour or two, whereas acetyl chloride is

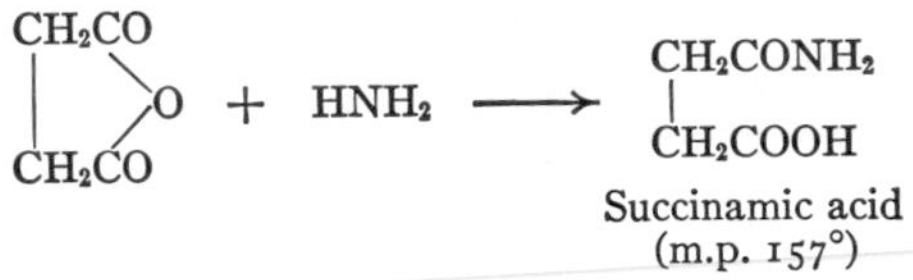

$$\begin{array}{c} CH_2CO \\ | \quad\quad\ \diagdown O \\ CH_2CO \end{array} \ + \ HNH_2 \ \longrightarrow \ \begin{array}{c} CH_2CONH_2 \\ | \\ CH_2COOH \end{array}$$

Succinamic acid
(m.p. 157°)

hydrolyzed at once. The reaction with ammonia parallels that with water and is used for preparation of the monoamides of dibasic acids.

Alcoholysis; Acetylation of Alcohols. — Anhydrides react with alcohol as with water and ammonia; succinic anhydride, for example, affords the monoester of the corresponding dibasic acid:

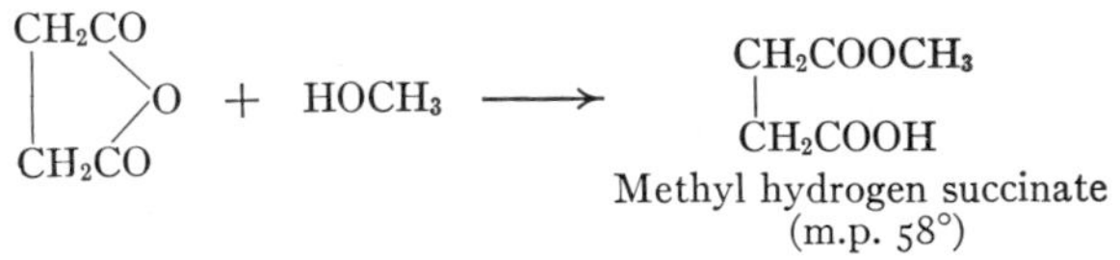

$$\begin{array}{c} CH_2CO \\ | \quad\quad\ \diagdown O \\ CH_2CO \end{array} \ + \ HOCH_3 \ \longrightarrow \ \begin{array}{c} CH_2COOCH_3 \\ | \\ CH_2COOH \end{array}$$

Methyl hydrogen succinate
(m.p. 58°)

The most important application of the general reaction is acetylation of primary and secondary alcohols, that is, conversion of these substances into their acetyl derivatives. Acetylation can be conducted by warming

$$RCH_2OH \ \xrightarrow{(CH_3CO)_2O} \ RCH_2OCOCH_3$$

$$R_2CHOH \ \xrightarrow{(CH_3CO)_2O} \ R_2CHOCOCH_3$$

the alcohol with acetic anhydride alone, but usually advantage is taken of the accelerating action of a small amount of concentrated sulfuric acid, boron fluoride, or a basic catalyst such as sodium acetate or pyridine (C_6H_5N). Under these conditions tertiary alcohols ordinarily do not react, and a tertiary hydroxyl group is thereby distinguishable from a primary or secondary group. The acetylation reaction is useful for investigation of polyhydroxy compounds, since the number of entering acetyl groups can be established both by elementary analysis of the purified reaction product and by an acetyl determination, consisting in alkaline hydrolysis of a weighed sample and acidification, distillation, and titration of the acetic acid in the distillate. Two acetyl groups can be introduced into ethylene glycol and three into glycerol, whereas a glycol of the type $R_2C(OH)CH_2CH_2OH$ gives only a monoacetyl derivative. Acetyl chloride is also used as an acetylating agent either alone or in pyridine solution.

PROBLEMS

1. Compare the acidity constants (pK_a) of acids of the type $A—CH_2CO_2H$, where $A = CH_3$, OH, I, and Cl. What are the relative positions in the periodic table of the key elements in the group A?
2. Which of the following substances would you expect to be the more strongly acidic?

    (a) Malonic acid, $HOOCCH_2COOH$
    (b) Succinic acid, $HOOCCH_2CH_2COOH$

3. Write formulas for:

    (a) Isovaleric acid   (c) Triethylacetic acid
    (b) α,β-Dibromobutyric acid   (d) Octanoic acid

4. Which synthesis, Grignard or nitrile, would you pick for effecting the following transformations:

    (a) $CH_3CH_2CHBrCH(CH_3)_2 \rightarrow$ Ethylisopropylacetic acid
    (b) $CH_3CHOHCH_2CH_2Cl \rightarrow \gamma$-Hydroxyvaleric acid

5. Devise a synthesis of succinic acid, $HO_2CCH_2CH_2CO_2H$, from ethanol.
6. How could $(CH_3)_2CHCH_2COCH_3$ be converted into isovaleric acid?
7. Outline a procedure for the isolation of n-butyric acid from a mixture of the substance with n-amyl alcohol, n-amyl chloride, and ethyl n-valerate.
8. What method of experimentation would distinguish between the following isomeric acids?

    (a) $CH_3CH_2CH(CH_3)CO_2H$ (c) $(CH_3)_3CCO_2H$
    (b) $(CH_3)_2CHCH_2CO_2H$

9. Write electronic formulas showing how a redistribution of electrons in one of the structures representing the resonant carbonate ion gives a second structure.
10. Write electronic formulas for allyl bromide and its resonance-hybrid ion. Calculate the formal charges. Does each carbon atom have an octet of electrons?
11. (a) Write the electronic formula for vinyl bromide and for the structure contributing to resonance, and test the formulas by calculation of formal charges. (b) How could you deduce, without such calculation, that the terminal carbon atom carries a negative charge? (c) Why does not the structure $\overset{+}{CH_2}—CH=Br^-$ contribute to the resonance?

12. Would you expect the hydrogen-bonded dimer of acetic acid to be subject to resonance stabilization? (See formula for alcohol dimer, p. 114; note that the bonding hydrogen is closer to one oxygen atom than to the other.)

13. Write an electronic representation of diazomethane.

14. Suggest methods for the preparation of the methyl esters of each of the following acids. If a catalyst is to be used, suggest a specific one.

    (a) $(CH_3)_3CCH_2CO_2H$
    (b) $CH_3CH_2C(CH_3)_2CO_2H$
    (c) $CH_3CH{=}CHCO_2H$
    (d) $n\text{-}C_{11}H_{23}COOH$, starting with $n\text{-}C_{11}H_{23}COOCH_2CH_2CH_3$

15. Write an electronic formulation showing the mechanism of the esterification of acetic acid with methanol, with boron fluoride as catalyst.

16. Indicate a synthesis of $(CH_3)_2CHCOCH_3$ from isobutyric acid.

17. How could bromoacetyl chloride be prepared from acetic acid?

18. What products would you expect to result from the interaction of ketene with water and with ethanol?

19. By what sequence of reactions could succinic acid be transformed into CH_3OCOCH_2-CH_2COCl?

20. A substance of the formula $C_4H_{10}O_4$ yields on acetylation with acetic anhydride a derivative of the formula $C_{12}H_{18}O_8$. How many hydroxyl groups are present in the substance? What is the probable structure?

21. Devise a synthesis of 2,5-dimethylhexadiene-2,4 starting with succinic acid.

22. Compare the reactivities of acid chlorides, anhydrides, esters, and ethers.

23. Indicate two reaction sequences by which n-heptylic acid can be prepared from castor oil (see pp. 113, 116).

READING REFERENCES

C. E. Entemann, Jr., and J. R. Johnson, "The Relative Reactivity of Various Functional Groups toward a Grignard Reagent," *J. Am. Chem. Soc.*, **55**, 2900 (1933)

J. F. G. Dippy, "Dissociation Constants of Monocarboxylic Acids," *Chem. Rev.*, **25**, 151 (1939)

CHAPTER 9

ALDEHYDES AND KETONES

Aldehydes and ketones are carbonyl compounds having, respectively, one and two alkyl residues joined to the carbonyl function:

R\
    C=O
H/
Aldehyde

R\
    C=O
R'/
Ketone

Formaldehyde is exceptional in that the carbonyl group carries two hydrogen atoms and no alkyl substituents, and it exhibits unique properties. Differences in the behavior of aldehydes and ketones in additions to the carbonyl group are determined by the number, size, and character of the R substituents.

Aldehydes are so named because they are obtainable by dehydrogenation of alcochols (alcohol dehydrogenated), and the generic name ketone is derived from that of the simplest member of the series, acetone. The group —CHO is called a formyl group. Common names of aldehydes are taken from those of the acids into which the substances are convertible by oxidation. Ketones can be designated according to the substituent groups, for example, diethyl ketone, methyl ethyl ketone. In the Geneva system the aldehydic and ketonic groups are indicated by the endings -al and -one, respectively. Thus propionaldehyde is propanal and acetone is propanone; positions of functional groups are indicated by numbers where there is ambiguity, for example, $2,5$-dimethylhexanone-3 for $(CH_3)_2CHCH_2COCH-(CH_3)_2$. Other examples are:

CH₃COCH₂COCH₃
Pentanedione-2,4
(acctylacetone)

$$CH_3C=CHCH_2CH_2C=CHCHO$$ with CH_3 groups
3,7-Dimethyloctadiene-2,6-al-1
(citral)

Physical constants of representative aldehydes and ketones are listed in Tables 9.1 and 9.2. In each series the first few members are soluble in water, and those from C_5 on are sparingly soluble or insoluble. The boiling points are slightly above those of paraffins and other unassociated liquids of comparable molecular weight:

COMPOUND	MOL. WT.	B.P., °C.
CH₃CH₂CH₂CH₂CH₂CHO	100.16	129
CH₃COCH₂CH₂CH₂CH₃	100.16	127.2
CH₃CH₂COCH₂CH₂CH₃	100.16	124
CH₃CH₂CH₂CH₂CH₂CH₂CH₃	100.20	98.4

(See also Table 8.2, p. 165)

TABLE 9.1. ALDEHYDES

NAME	FORMULA	M.P., °C.	B.P., °C.	SP. GR.
Formaldehyde	CH_2O	−92	−21	0.815
Acetaldehyde	CH_3CHO	−123	20.8	.781
Chloral	CCl_3CHO	−57.5	97.8	1.512
Glyoxal	$O{=}HC \cdot CH{=}O$	15	50.4	1.14
Propionaldehyde	CH_3CH_2CHO	−81	48.8	0.807
n-Butyraldehyde	$CH_3CH_2CH_2CHO$	−97	74.7	.817
Isobutyraldehyde	$(CH_3)_2CHCHO$	−66	61	.794
n-Valeraldehyde	$CH_3CH_2CH_2CH_2CHO$	−92	103.7	.819
Isovaleraldehyde	$(CH_3)_2CHCH_2CHO$	−51	92.5	.803
n-Caproaldehyde	$CH_3(CH_2)_4CHO$		129	.834
n-Heptaldehyde (enanthol)	$CH_3(CH_2)_5CHO$	−45	155	.850
Stearaldehyde	$CH_3(CH_2)_{16}CHO$	38		
Acrolein	$CH_2{=}CHCHO$	−88	52.5	.841
Crotonaldehyde	$CH_3CH{=}CHCHO$	−76.5	104	.859
Benzaldehyde	C_6H_5CHO	−56	179	1.046
Furfural	$\begin{array}{c} CH{-}CH \\ \| \quad\ \| \\ CH \quad CCHO \\ \diagdown\ O\ \diagup \end{array}$	−31	162	1.156

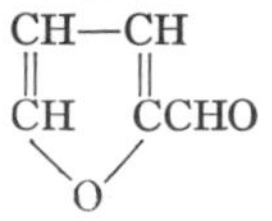

TABLE 9.2. KETONES

NAME	FORMULA	M.P., °C.	B.P., °C.	SP. GR.
Acetone	CH_3COCH_3	−95	56.1	0.7915
Methyl ethyl ketone	$CH_3COCH_2CH_3$	−86	79.6	.805
Methyl n-propyl ketone	$CH_3CH_2CH_2COCH_3$	−77.8	102.1	.812
Diethyl ketone	$CH_3CH_2COCH_2CH_3$	−42.0	101.7	.814
Hexanone-2	$CH_3CH_2CH_2CH_2COCH_3$	−56.9	127.2	.830
Hexanone-3	$CH_3CH_2CH_2COCH_2CH_3$		124	.818
Methyl t-butyl ketone (pinacolone)	$CH_3COC(CH_3)_3$	−52.5	106.3	.811
Di-n-propyl ketone	$(CH_3CH_2CH_2)_2CO$	−34	144.2	.821
Diisopropyl ketone	$[(CH_3)_2CH]_2CO$		125	.806
Diisobutyl ketone	$[(CH_3)_2CHCH_2]_2CO$		166	.833
Di-n-amyl ketone	$(n\text{-}C_5H_{11})_2CO$	14.6	228	.826
Stearone	$(n\text{-}C_{17}H_{35})_2CO$	88.5	345[12 mm.]	.793
Chloroacetone	CH_3COCH_2Cl	−44.5	119	1.162
s-Dichloroacetone	$ClCH_2COCH_2Cl$	45	173.4	1.383
Diacetyl	$CH_3COCOCH_3$		89	0.975
Acetylacetone	$CH_3COCH_2COCH_3$	−23.2	137	.976
Mesityl oxide	$(CH_3)_2C{=}CHCOCH_3$	−59.0	131	.863
Phorone	$[(CH_3)_2C{=}CH]_2CO$	28	198.2	.885
Cyclohexanone	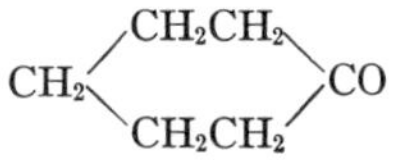 $CH_2 \begin{array}{c} \diagup CH_2CH_2 \diagdown \\ \\ \diagdown CH_2CH_2 \diagup \end{array} CO$		156.7	.949
Benzophenone	$C_6H_5COC_6H_5$	48	305.4	1.083

The slight elevation in boiling point may be attributable to a certain amount of association due to electrostatic attraction between contributing resonance forms polarized in the sense: $R_2\overset{+}{C}\!\!-\!\!\overset{-}{O}$, or $R_2\overset{\delta+}{C}\!\!=\!\!\overset{\delta-}{O}$.

METHODS OF PREPARATION

From Alcohols. (*a*) **By Oxidation.** — A primary alcohol on oxidation yields an aldehyde as the initial product, and this is convertible on further oxidation into an acid. The aldehyde initially formed is more susceptible

$$RCH_2OH \xrightarrow{[O]} RCHO \xrightarrow{[O]} RCOOH$$

to oxidation than the starting material, and if the outcome of an oxidation were dependent solely upon the relative reactivities, the oxidative process would not be practicable. Advantage can be taken however of the greater volatility of the aldehyde. Thus ethanol yields an aldehyde of boiling point some 55° lower. Because of the marked temperature differential, acetal-

$$CH_3CH_2OH \xrightarrow{K_2Cr_2O_7,\ dil.\ H_2SO_4,\ 50°} CH_3CHO$$
$$\text{(b.p. 78.3°)} \qquad\qquad\qquad\qquad \text{(b.p. 20.8°)}$$

dehyde can be distilled from the reaction mixture as it is formed: ethanol is added dropwise to a solution of potassium dichromate in dilute sulfuric acid maintained at a temperature (50°) below the boiling point of ethanol and above that of acetaldehyde. The alcohol is retained in the mixture until it undergoes oxidation, and acetaldehyde is removed by distillation and is thereby protected from further oxidation.

Ketones are more stable to oxidation than aldehydes and are obtained readily from secondary alcohols without protection of the initial reaction product. For example menthol, the chief constituent of oil of peppermint, can be oxidized by gradual addition of potassium dichromate in dilute sulfuric acid and the corresponding ketone extracted from the cooled reaction mixture with ether. A procedure often applied to secondary alcohols that

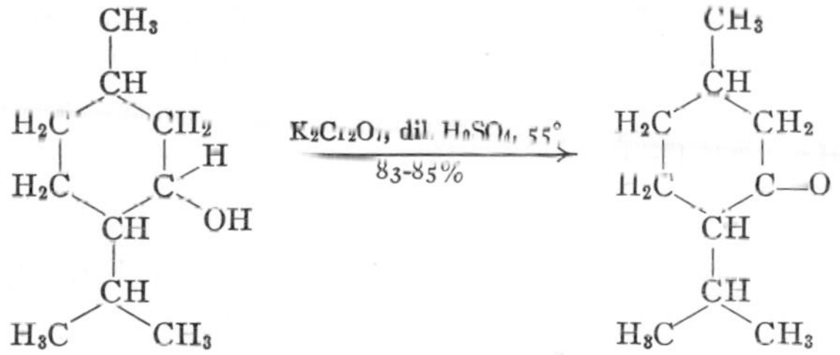

l-Menthol
(m.p. 42.5°)

l-Menthone
(b.p. 207°)

are water-insoluble solids is to dissolve the alcohol in acetic acid and add either anhydrous chromic anhydride or a solution prepared by dissolving chromic anhydride in one part of water and adding ten parts of acetic acid.

(b) **By Dehydrogenation.** — An alternate experimental procedure for conversion of an alcohol into an aldehyde or a ketone is passage of the vaporized substance over metallic copper in the temperature range 200–300°. Hydrogen is eliminated as such. The reaction can be conducted in an as-

$$
\underset{\text{Cyclohexanol}}{
\begin{array}{c}
\text{OH} \\
|\\
\text{CH} \\
\text{H}_2\text{C} \qquad \text{CH}_2 \\
| \qquad | \\
\text{H}_2\text{C} \qquad \text{CH}_2 \\
\text{CH}_2
\end{array}}
\quad \xrightarrow{\text{Cu, } 250°} \quad
\underset{\text{Cyclohexanone}}{
\begin{array}{c}
\text{O} \\
\|\\
\text{C} \\
\text{H}_2\text{C} \qquad \text{CH}_2 \\
| \qquad | \\
\text{H}_2\text{C} \qquad \text{CH}_2 \\
\text{CH}_2
\end{array}}
\quad + \quad \text{H}_2
$$

sembly similar to that shown in Fig. 8.1, page 187, except that the vapor space is provided with a heated copper grid or with a heated tube charged with reduced copper chromite, a particularly efficient catalyst. Excellent yields are obtainable, and the method is well adapted to the technical production of volatile aldehydes and ketones (formaldehyde, acetaldehyde, acetone, cyclohexanone). Formaldehyde is made by passing methanol vapor and air over heated silver or copper catalyst. The reaction probably

$$\text{CH}_3\text{OH} + \tfrac{1}{2}\text{O}_2 \xrightarrow{\text{Ag, } 250°} \text{CH}_2\text{O} + \text{H}_2\text{O}$$

consists in dehydrogenation followed by combustion of the hydrogen produced, and enough heat is liberated to maintain the required temperature. The oxidation is controlled to a point short of complete conversion, and the gaseous mixture is absorbed in water and marketed under the name formalin, a 40% solution of formaldehyde containing some methanol. Formalin is employed as a convenient source of formaldehyde for manufacture of synthetic resins, preserving anatomical specimens, hardening photographic film, embalming, etc.

(c) **Oxidation of Secondary Alcohols with Aluminum t-Butoxide.** — This elegant method (Oppenauer, 1937) consists in refluxing a secondary alcohol with aluminum t-butoxide and a large excess of acetone; the net result is dehydrogenation of the alcohol with transference of the hydrogen atoms to acetone as acceptor. The equilibrium actually involves the alumi-

$$
\begin{array}{c}
\text{R} \\
 \\
\text{R}'
\end{array}\!\!\text{CHOH} + (\text{CH}_3)_2\text{C}{=}\text{O} \underset{\text{(excess)}}{\xrightarrow{\text{Al[OC(CH}_3)_3]_3}}
\begin{array}{c}
\text{R} \\
 \\
\text{R}'
\end{array}\!\!\text{C}{=}\text{O} + (\text{CH}_3)_2\text{CHOH}
$$

num derivative of the secondary alcohol, formed by interchange with the aluminum derivative of t-butyl alcohol, which itself is stable to oxidation. The equilibrium is displaced in the desired direction by employing a large excess of acetone. The reaction usually proceeds in good yield, and it has the advantage of being specific to the alcoholic group and hence applicable to alcohols having unsaturated centers that would be attacked by ordinary oxidizing agents.

(d) **Aldehydes from Glycols and Alkenes.** — In special instances preparative use can be made of the cleavage of *vic*-glycols by lead tetraacetate or periodic acid (p. 130) and of the formation of aldehydes by ozonolysis of alkenes (p. 68):

$$\underset{\substack{| \quad |\\ OH \quad OH}}{RCH\text{—}CHR} \xrightarrow{Pb(OCOCH_3)_4 \text{ or } HIO_4} 2\,RCHO$$

$$RCH\text{=}CHR \xrightarrow{O_3} Ozonide \xrightarrow{H_2,\,Pt} 2\,RCHO$$

From Acids. (*a*) **Pyrolysis of Metal Salts.** — When calcium acetate is heated strongly it undergoes decomposition to acetone and calcium carbonate. The reaction is like the thermal decomposition of sodium acetate in

$$\begin{array}{c} CH_3CO\,O \\ CH_3\,COO \end{array}\!\!Ca \xrightarrow{Heat} \begin{array}{c} CH_3 \\ CH_3 \end{array}\!\!C\text{=}O + CaCO_3$$

the presence of sodium hydroxide to give the more stable carbonate and methane. The reaction illustrated once constituted the chief method of manufacturing acetone; the required calcium acetate, known as gray acetate of lime, was obtained from pyroligneous acid. The reaction has general application for synthesis of symmetrical ketones. In some instances im-

$$(RCOO)_2Ca \xrightarrow{Heat} R_2CO + CaCO_3$$

proved results have been obtained with the barium, manganese, or thorium salts. Instead of preparing the salt as a dry solid prior to pyrolysis, the acid can be distilled through a heated tube packed with the metal oxide. Thus manganous oxide impregnated on pumice is employed in a catalytic process for conversion of acetic acid into acetone; the vaporized acid passing

$$2\,CH_3COOH \xrightarrow{MnO,\,300°} (CH_3)_2CO + H_2O + CO_2$$

through the catalyst tube forms manganous carbonate, which breaks down to the oxide and carbon dioxide.

If a mixture of the calcium salts of two different acids is pyrolyzed, three reaction products are possible because each salt can decompose independently or interact with the other one. Such a reaction inevitably gives mix-

$$\begin{array}{c} (RCO\,O)_2Ca \\ (R'COO)_2Ca \end{array} \longrightarrow \begin{array}{c} R \\ R' \end{array}\!\!C\text{=}O + \begin{array}{c} R \\ R \end{array}\!\!C\text{=}O + \begin{array}{c} R' \\ R' \end{array}\!\!C\text{=}O$$

tures and is practicable in the preparation of unsymmetrical ketones only when an easy method of separation is at hand. For example, methyl benzyl ketone can be obtained by dropping a mixture of phenylacetic acid and two equivalents of acetic acid through a heated tube of thorium oxide catalyst deposited on pumice. The cheaper reagent, acetic acid, is taken

$$\underset{\text{Phenylacetic acid}}{C_6H_5CH_2COOH} + CH_3COOH \xrightarrow[55-65\%]{ThO_2,\,430-450°} \underset{\text{Methyl benzyl ketone}}{C_6H_5CH_2COCH_3}$$

in excess in order to allow for formation of acetone as an easily eliminated by-product. The other by-product is dibenzyl ketone, $C_6H_5CH_2COCH_2$-C_6H_5, which has a much higher molecular weight than the desired product and is distinctly less volatile (b.p. about 200° at 21 mm.; methyl benzyl ketone, b.p. 110–115° at 21 mm.). Similarly, aldehydes can be synthesized by pyrolysis of a mixture of excess calcium formate with the salt of a higher

$$(RCO\;O)_2Ca \qquad\qquad \begin{array}{c} R \\ \diagdown \\ H \diagup \end{array}C{=}O \;+\; \begin{array}{c} R \\ \diagdown \\ R \diagup \end{array}C{=}O \;+\; \begin{array}{c} H \\ \diagdown \\ H \diagup \end{array}C{=}O$$
$$(H\;COO)_2Ca$$

homolog. A ketone is formed as a by-product, but aldehydes and ketones differ sufficiently in properties to allow fairly sharp separation.

An application of the pyrolytic method is used in the preparation of cyclic ketones from dibasic acids; for example, a mixture of adipic acid with about 5% of barium hydroxide is heated until distillation of the re-

$$\begin{array}{l} CH_2CH_2CO\;OH \\ | \\ CH_2CH_2\;COOH \end{array} \xrightarrow[\text{75–80\%}]{Ba(OH)_2,\ 285-295°} \begin{array}{l} CH_2{-}CH_2 \\ | \qquad\quad \diagdown \\ \qquad\qquad\;\; C{=}O \\ | \qquad\quad \diagup \\ CH_2{-}CH_2 \end{array}$$

Adipic acid

Cyclopentanone
(b.p. 130.6°)

action product is complete. The reaction proceeds best in the production of five- and six-membered ring compounds.

(b) **Rosenmund**[1] **Reaction.** — A useful method of transforming an acid into an aldehyde having the same carbon chain is the catalytic hydrogenation of the acid chloride. The success of the method depends upon differen-

$$R{-}C\!\!\begin{array}{c}\diagup O \\ \diagdown Cl\end{array} \;+\; H_2 \xrightarrow{\text{Catalyst}} R{-}C\!\!\begin{array}{c}\diagup O \\ \diagdown H\end{array} \;+\; HCl$$

tiation between the speed of replacement of halogen by hydrogen and that of hydrogenation of the resulting aldehyde. The technique introduced by Rosenmund consists in adding a small amount of a poisoning agent containing sulfur, which does not seriously inhibit the desired reduction of the highly reactive acid chloride but effectively stops hydrogenation of the aldehyde. A stream of hydrogen is passed through a boiling solution of the

COCl $\xrightarrow[\text{74–81\%}]{\text{H}_2,\ \text{Pd—BaSO}_4,\ \text{poison}}$ CHO $\;+\;$ HCl

β-Naphthoyl chloride

β-Naphthaldehyde

acid chloride in a hydrocarbon solvent, and the exit gas is passed into standard alkali; the course of the reaction is followed from the amount of hydrogen chloride absorbed.

---

[1] Karl W. Rosenmund, b. 1884 Berlin; Ph.D. Berlin (Diels); Kiel

Hydroformylation of Alkenes. — In this process, developed in Germany (1943) and investigated in this country by Adkins (1948–49), aldehydes are prepared by reaction of an alkene with carbon monoxide and hydrogen in the presence of a catalyst such as dicobalt octacarbonyl, $[Co(CO)_4]_2$:

$$RCH{=\!\!=}CH_2 + CO + H_2 \xrightarrow[\text{1000–6000 lbs./sq. in.}]{[Co(CO)_4]_2,\ 125^\circ,} \begin{cases} RCH_2CH_2CHO \ (a) \\ \underset{\underset{CHO}{|}}{RCHCH_3} \quad (b) \end{cases}$$

A mixture of the two possible aldehydes often results, but the primary aldehyde (a) generally predominates.

Examples:

1. $CH_3(CH_2)_3CH{=\!\!=}CH_2 \xrightarrow{CO,\ H_2} CH_3(CH_2)_5CHO + CH_3(CH_2)_3\underset{\underset{CH_3}{|}}{\overset{\overset{CHO}{|}}{C}}HCH_3$
    Hexene-1   32%   32%

2. $CH_3COOCH_2CH{=\!\!=}CH_2 \xrightarrow[69\%]{CO,\ H_2} CH_3COOCH_2CH_2CH_2CHO$
    Allyl acetate   γ-Acetoxybutyraldehyde

3.

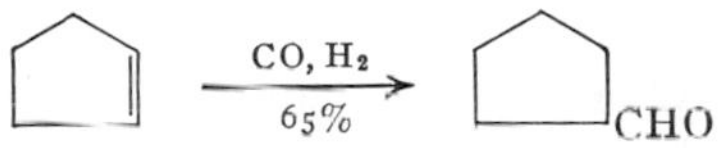

    Cyclopentene   Formylcyclopentane

4. $C_2H_5OCOCH{=\!\!=}CHCOOC_2H_5 \xrightarrow[51\%]{CO,\ H_2} C_2H_5OCO\underset{\underset{CHO}{|}}{C}HCH_2COOC_2H_5$
    Diethyl fumarate   Diethyl α-formylsuccinate

The process is similar to the oxo process for production of alcohols, in which the addition of one mole of carbon monoxide and two moles of hydrogen to an olefin is effected with a Fischer-Tropsch catalyst. A convenient route to normal paraffinic hydrocarbons involves reversal of the oxo process:

$$n\text{-}C_{16}H_{31}CH_2CH_2CH_2OH \xrightarrow[240\ atm.]{Ni,} [C_{16}H_{31}CH_2CH_2CHO \xrightarrow{CO}$$

$$C_{16}H_{31}CH{=\!\!=}CH_2] \xrightarrow{H_2} n\text{-}C_{17}H_{36}$$

Stearyl alcohol

n-Heptadecane (yield 95%)

Special Methods. — Production of **acetaldehyde** by catalyzed hydration of acetylene has been mentioned (p. 89); the preparation of **acetone** by bacterial fermentation of sugars is described on page 121. **Chloral** is made by the action of chlorine on ethanol; the alcoholic group is oxidized

$$CH_3CH_2OH + 4\,Cl_2 \longrightarrow CCl_3CHO + 5\,HCl$$
Chloral

by the halogen during the reaction. Chloral is an intermediate in the reaction of ethanol with sodium hypochlorite, and the material prepared under nonalkaline conditions is cleaved by alkali to chloroform and sodium formate.

The α,β-unsaturated aldehyde **acrolein** is obtained by dehydration of glycerol with acidic reagents. The reaction apparently involves preferential elimination of the secondary, rather than a primary, hydroxyl group, a hydrogen shift in the resulting enol, and elimination of water between an activated α-hydrogen atom and a hydroxyl group in the β-position.

$$\begin{array}{c} CH_2CH-CH_2 \\ |\quad|\quad\ | \\ OH\ OH\quad OH \end{array} \xrightarrow{KHSO_4,\ 215-230°} \left[\begin{array}{c} CH_2CH=CH \\ |\qquad\quad| \\ OH\qquad OH \end{array} \longrightarrow \begin{array}{c} \overset{\beta}{CH_2}\overset{\alpha}{CHC}\diagdown^H_O \\ OH\ H \end{array} \right]$$

$$\xrightarrow[33-48\%\ (overall)]{} \quad CH_2{=}CHCHO$$
$$\text{Acrolein}$$

Acrolein is a highly reactive, volatile liquid with a sharp irritating odor and a marked tendency to polymerize.

REACTIONS

Oxidation, Bromination. — Aldehydes, having a hydrogen atom on the oxidized carbon of the carbonyl group, are subject to ready oxidation, whereas ketones are not, and the two types of compounds can be distinguished by qualitative tests with oxidizing agents specific for aldehydes. One reagent is a solution of silver nitrate in excess ammonium hydroxide, containing the complex ion $Ag(NH_3)_2{}^+$. The aldehyde is oxidized to the

$$RCHO\ +\ 2\,Ag(NH_3)_2OH\ \longrightarrow\ RCOONH_4\ +\ 2\,Ag\ +\ 3\,NH_3\ +\ H_2O$$

acid, which forms the ammonium salt, and the complex metal ion is reduced to metallic silver, which is deposited on the walls of a test tube as an adherent film or mirror. A second test reagent, Fehling's solution, is made by mixing a solution of copper sulfate with an alkaline solution of a salt of tartaric acid ($HOOCCHOHCHOHCOOH$); this combination results in a deep blue solution containing a complex cupric ion, and on interaction with an aldehyde the copper is reduced to the univalent stage, and a red precipitate of cuprous oxide is indicative of a reaction. Thus aldehydes give a

$$\underset{\substack{\text{(Fehling's}\\ \text{solution)}}}{RCHO\ +\ 2\,Cu^{++}}\ +\ NaOH\ +\ H_2O\ \longrightarrow\ RCOONa\ +\ Cu_2O\ +\ 4H^+$$

positive silver-mirror test and reduce Fehling's solution, whereas ketones do not. These reagents are specific to aldehydes and do not attack alcohols or ethylenic compounds.

Although ketones, in contrast with aldehydes, are generally resistant to usual oxidizing agents, some ketones are subject to oxidative fission by a particularly powerful reagent such as hot nitric acid. The molecule can be ruptured on both sides of the carbonyl group, and several acid fragments may be formed. Such reactions are seldom of value. In a cyclic ketone,

$$RCH_2CO CH_2R' \xrightarrow{HNO_3} RCO_2H + RCH_2CO_2H + R'CO_2H + R'CH_2CO_2H$$

for example cyclopentanone, fission of a carbon–carbon linkage does not give two fragments but merely opens the ring to give a dibasic acid. The

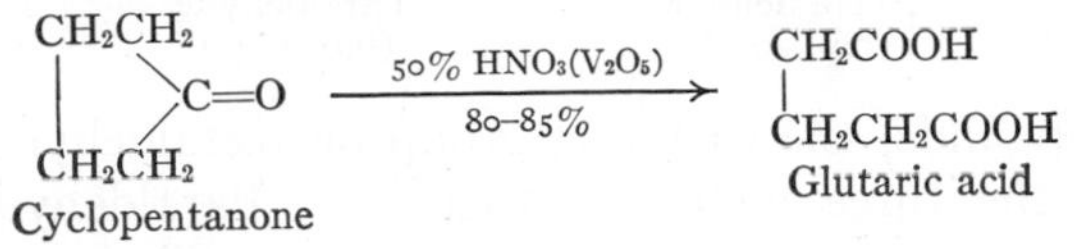

$$\begin{array}{c} CH_2CH_2 \\ | \quad \rangle C{=}O \\ CH_2CH_2 \end{array} \xrightarrow[80-85\%]{50\% \ HNO_3(V_2O_5)} \begin{array}{c} CH_2COOH \\ | \\ CH_2CH_2COOH \end{array}$$

Cyclopentanone   Glutaric acid

substance is symmetrical and the same acid results from fission of either connecting linkage. The next higher homolog, adipic acid, can be prepared by nitric acid oxidation of either cyclohexanone or its precursor, cyclohexanol. A ketone *per se* presents no point of vulnerability to oxidative

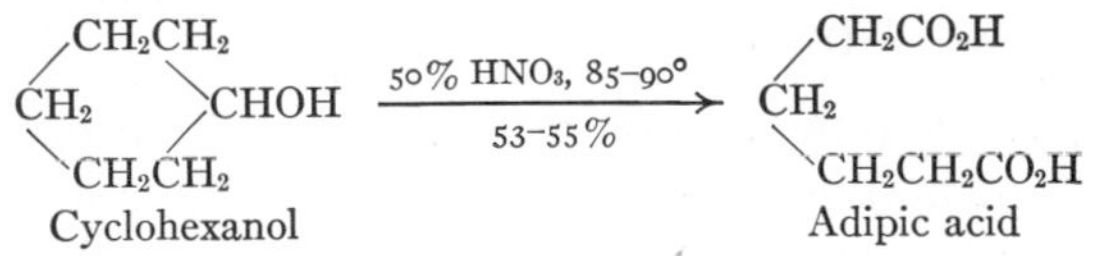

$$\begin{array}{c} CH_2CH_2 \\ CH_2 \quad CHOH \\ CH_2CH_2 \end{array} \xrightarrow[53-55\%]{50\% \ HNO_3, \ 85-90°} \begin{array}{c} CH_2CO_2H \\ CH_2 \\ CH_2CH_2CO_2H \end{array}$$

Cyclohexanol   Adipic acid

attack, and the reaction probably proceeds by oxidation of the enolic form present in equilibrium. The enol is removed continuously from the equi-

$$\begin{array}{ccc} -C-CH_2- & \rightleftharpoons & -C{=}CH- \xrightarrow{[O]} & -COOH + HOOC- \\ \| & & | \\ O & & OH \end{array}$$

Ketone   Enol

librium by irreversible oxidation, and eventually the entire lot of ketone is transformed through the enolic intermediate into the oxidation product or products. α-Bromination of a ketone, for example cyclohexanone (a), is known to proceed through the enol, since the same product is formed much

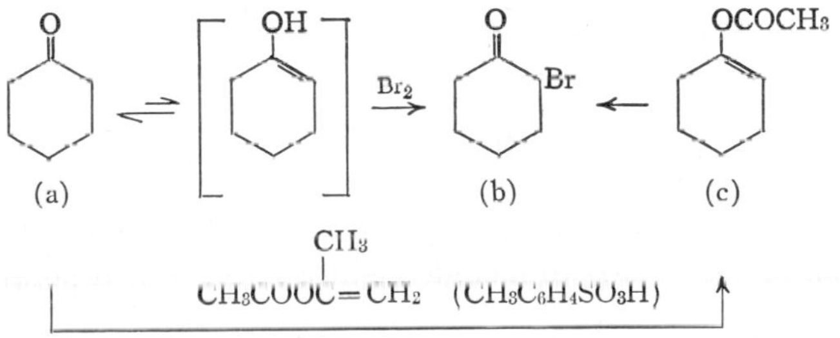

(a)   (b)   (c)

$$\begin{array}{c} CH_3 \\ | \\ CH_3COOC{=}CH_2 \quad (CH_3C_6H_4SO_3H) \end{array}$$

more rapidly from the enol acetate (c). Ketone enol acetates are prepared conveniently by acid catalyzed acetate exchange with isopropenyl acetate, a commercially available enol acetate made by reaction of ketene with acetone in the presence of sulfuric acid.

Polymerization of Aldehydes. — Acetaldehyde, a volatile liquid of pungent smell and marked reactivity, undergoes rapid polymerization under the influence of a trace of sulfuric acid to a less volatile and unreactive trimer, **paraldehyde.** The reaction is reversible but reaches equilibrium

when the conversion is about 95% complete. Since paraldehyde is inert
to oxidizing agents and shows none of the addition reactions characteristic

$$3\,CH_3CHO \xrightleftharpoons{\;H_2SO_4\;} (CH_3CHO)_3$$

Acetaldehyde　　　　　　　Paraldehyde
(b.p. 20.8°)　　　　　　　(b.p. 124°)

of carbonyl compounds, the carbonyl group of acetaldehyde must be utilized in linking the three molecules together. Paraldehyde is therefore
formulated as having a six-membered oxide ring. The conversion of ace-

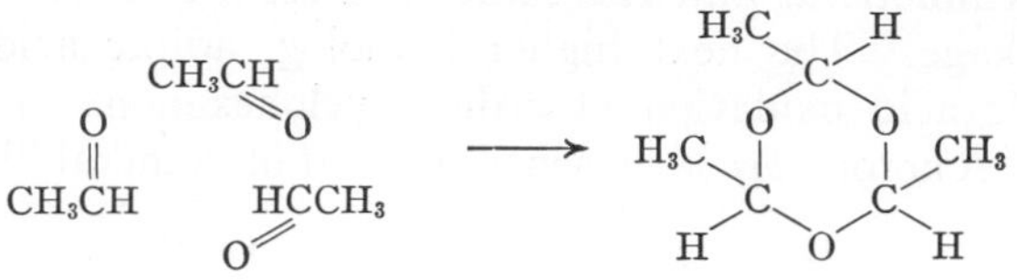

taldehyde into paraldehyde, as well as the regeneration of acetaldehyde, is
easily accomplished because the monomer is volatile and is miscible with
water, whereas the trimer has a higher boiling point and is sparingly soluble. The polymer is prepared by adding a small amount of sulfuric acid
to acetaldehyde, when the temperature rises owing to the exothermic reaction, and equilibrium is soon attained; the mixture is then washed with
water to remove the small amount of unconverted acetaldehyde and the
acid catalyst, and the undissolved paraldehyde is dried and distilled. In
the absence of an acid catalyst the trimer suffers no depolymerization on
distillation or on storage, and since the substance is inert, nonvolatile, and
not subject to oxidation, it is a convenient form in which to store potential
acetaldehyde. Depolymerization is accomplished by addition of a trace
of sulfuric acid, which gives an equilibrium mixture, and distillation of the
acetaldehyde; progressive amounts are produced under the influence of
the catalyst till regeneration is complete.

A second, crystalline polymer of acetaldehyde, metaldehyde, can be
obtained by the action of an acid catalyst at a temperature at or below 0°.
Metaldehyde is a tetramer, $(CH_3CHO)_4$; it undergoes depolymerization
when heated at temperatures somewhat above 100°, and contains no free
carbonyl groups. The structure assigned is similar to that of paraldehyde
but with the ring extended to include eight atoms by incorporation of one
more $—OCH(CH_3)—$ unit.

Formaldehyde, when distilled from a 60% solution containing 2% sulfuric acid, polymerizes to a crystalline trimer **trioxan**, which can be extracted with methylene chloride:

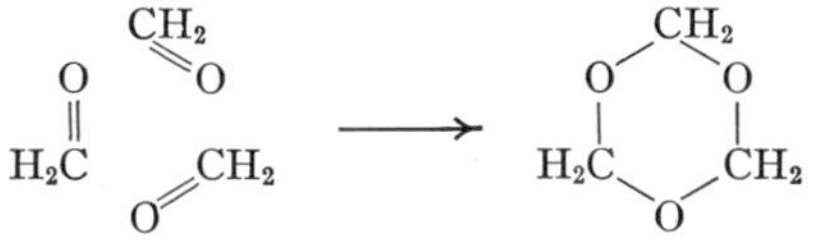

Trioxan
(m.p. 62°, b.p. 115°)

Trioxan is a stable substance that can be distilled without decomposition at atmospheric pressure. A chain polymer rather than the cyclic polymer is formed on evaporation of an aqueous solution of formaldehyde. Formaldehyde in aqueous solution does not display the sensitivity to air oxidation and general reactivity characteristic of the aldehyde in the gaseous state and hence is probably present to a considerable extent as the hydrate.

$$CH_2=O + HOH \rightleftharpoons CH_2\!\!\begin{array}{c} OH \\ OH \end{array}$$

Formaldehyde hydrate

Since the carbonyl group of formaldehyde has greater additive power than that of higher aldehydes, the equilibrium is probably particularly favorable to the *gem*-diol. This diol or hydrate has not been isolated, for evaporation of the aqueous solution gives a mixture of chain polymers of varying chain length, evidently arising from elimination of water between successive molecules of formaldehyde hydrate. The usual polymer mixture known as

$$HOCH_2OH + nHOCH_2OH + HOCH_2OH \longrightarrow HOCH_2(OCH_2)_nOCH_2OH$$

Paraformaldehyde

paraformaldehyde is an amorphous solid of high molecular weight that is insoluble in water. Depolymerization occurs at a temperature of 180–200°, and hence paraformaldehyde is a convenient source of anhydrous, gaseous formaldehyde.

Addition of Sodium Bisulfite. — A reaction characteristic of aldehydes and of some ketones is addition of sodium bisulfite, employed in a saturated (40%) aqueous solution. Equilibrium is reached, but the carbonyl component can be converted almost entirely into the addition product by use of excess bisulfite. The addition product is a crystalline salt and has the

$$RC\!\!\begin{array}{c} H \\ O \end{array} + \underset{\text{(large excess)}}{NaHSO_3} \rightleftharpoons RC\!\!\begin{array}{c} H \\ OH \\ SO_3Na \end{array}$$

Bisulfite-addition
compound

usual characteristics of an ionic metal compound; it is very soluble in water but subject to salting out by the common-ion effect, and it is insoluble in ether, infusible, and nonvolatile. Since the reaction is reversible, the aldehyde can be regenerated by adding to an aqueous solution of the product an amount of sodium carbonate or hydrochloric acid sufficient either to neutralize or to destroy the free sodium bisulfite present in equilibrium.

$$RC\!\!\begin{array}{c} H \\ OH \\ SO_3Na \end{array} \rightleftharpoons RCHO + NaHSO_3 \underset{HCl}{\overset{\frac{1}{2}Na_2CO_3}{\Bigg\langle}} \begin{array}{c} Na_2SO_3 + \frac{1}{2}CO_2 + \frac{1}{2}H_2O \\ NaCl + SO_2 + H_2O \end{array}$$

Because of their specific physical properties and ease of formation and decomposition, bisulfite-addition products are useful for separation and puri-

TABLE 9.3. REACTION OF CARBONYL COMPOUNDS WITH ALKALI BISULFITE
(ONE EQUIVALENT)

COMPOUND	PERCENTAGE OF BISULFITE COMPOUND	
	IN $\frac{1}{2}$ HR.	IN 1 HR.
$CH_3CO \cdot H$	88.0	88.7
$RCO \cdot H$		70–90
CH_3COCH_3	47.0	56.2
$CH_3CH_2COCH_3$	25.1	36.4
$CH_3CH_2CH_2COCH_3$	14.8	23.4
$(CH_3)_2CHCOCH_3$	7.5	12.3
$(CH_3)_3CCOCH_3$	5.6	5.6
$CH_3CH_2COCH_2CH_3$		2
$C_6H_5COCH_3$		1
$CH_2\begin{matrix}CH_2CH_2\\ \\CH_2CH_2\end{matrix}C{=}O$		35

fication of carbonyl compounds. To separate an aldehyde from an alcohol, for example, the mixture is shaken with excess saturated sodium bisulfite solution to form and to salt out the addition product; this is collected as a white solid and washed with bisulfite solution, ethanol, and then ether, to eliminate all traces of the original alcohol; the dried solid is dissolved in water and treated with sodium carbonate or hydrochloric acid; the liberated aldehyde is precipitated or obtained by distillation or by extraction with ether. Similar separations can be made from hydrocarbons, ethers, alkyl halides, carboxylic acids, and esters, since the carbonyl group of an ester is not sufficiently reactive to combine with sodium bisulfite. An aldehydic component that is insoluble in water often can be converted into an addition product by being dissolved in alcohol prior to treatment with aqueous bisulfite solution.

Although the reaction is general for aldehydes, only a limited number of ketones form bisulfite-addition products in practical amounts. Data are given in Table 9.3 for the extent of reaction of various carbonyl compounds with an equivalent amount of sodium or potassium bisulfite (at 0–25°). With acetaldehyde equilibrium is reached rapidly, and nearly complete conversion is obtained even in the absence of excess bisulfite. Higher aldehydes behave in much the same manner, regardless of the size of the lone alkyl group, presumably because the substances all have in common the formyl group, —CHO. Acetone reacts less rapidly and to a less extent, but still the conversion surpasses that observed with higher homologs. In the series of ketones having one methyl group the extent of reaction decreases as the second alkyl group increases either in size or extent of branching. Evidently a hydrogen atom imposes little obstacle to the addi-

$$\underset{RCH_2CH}{\overset{O}{\overset{\|}{}}} > \underset{CH_3CCH_3}{\overset{O}{\overset{\|}{}}} > \underset{RCH_2CCH_3}{\overset{O}{\overset{\|}{}}} > \underset{R_2CHCCH_3}{\overset{O}{\overset{\|}{}}} > \underset{R_3CCCH_3}{\overset{O}{\overset{\|}{}}}$$

tion of sodium bisulfite to the carbonyl group, a methyl group exerts some blocking action, and larger and more bulky groups further impede formation of the addition product. Diethyl ketone reacts to only a negligible extent, and unless a ketone of the type RCOR' contains at least one methyl group it is incapable of yielding a bisulfite-addition product. The behavior of the ketone $C_6H_5COCH_3$ (acetophenone) shows that a phenyl group inhibits bisulfite addition. Bisulfite-addition products can be prepared satisfactorily only from aldehydes and from methyl ketones other than those containing an aromatic group. The blocking, or hindering, effect is markedly reduced by ring formation, for cyclohexanone reacts about as readily as methyl ethyl ketone and to a greater extent than diethyl ketone.

The greater additive power of aldehydes is demonstrated in the Schiff test, a qualitative color reaction. A solution is made by treating the dye fuchsin (magenta) with sulfur dioxide, when it forms a colorless addition product. An aldehyde abstracts sulfurous acid from the Schiff reagent and restores a pink coloration; with a ketone the solution remains colorless.

Addition of Hydrogen Cyanide. — Hydrogen cyanide adds to carbonyl compounds by nucleophilic attack of the positively polarized carbon atom;

$$>C=O \xrightarrow{CN^-} \underset{CN}{\overset{O^-}{\underset{|}{\overset{|}{C}}}} \xrightarrow{H^+} \underset{CN}{\overset{OH}{\underset{|}{\overset{|}{C}}}}$$

the reaction product is a cyanohydrin. Anhydrous liquid hydrogen cyanide reacts satisfactorily, particularly under basic catalysis, but the reagent is volatile and so toxic that it is advantageously generated in the course of the reaction. One procedure is to mix the carbonyl compound with an aqueous solution of sodium or potassium cyanide and add a mineral acid. Another

$$(CH_3)_2CO \xrightarrow[77-78\%]{NaCN + H_2SO_4 \ (10-20°)} \underset{CH_3}{\overset{CH_3}{>}}C\underset{CN}{\overset{OH}{<}}$$

Acetone cyanohydrin
(b.p. 82° at 23 mm.)

is to convert the carbonyl compound into its bisulfite-addition product, which is then treated with an equivalent amount of sodium cyanide, as in the synthesis of mandelic acid. Sodium cyanide acts as a base and neu-

$$C_6H_5CHO \xrightarrow{NaHSO_3} C_6H_5CH(OH)SO_3Na \xrightarrow{NaCN}$$
Benzaldehyde

$$C_6H_5CH(OH)CN \xrightarrow[50-52\% \ (overall)]{Hydrolysis \ (HCl)} C_6H_5CH(OH)COOH$$
Mandelonitrile   Mandelic acid
(m.p. −10°)   (m.p. 118°)

tralizes the sodium bisulfite in equilibrium with the bisulfite compound with formation of sodium sulfite; the simultaneously liberated aldehyde and hydrogen cyanide then combine to give the cyanohydrin. The example cited, in which the intermediate cyanohydrin is converted into mandelic acid by acid hydrolysis, illustrates use of hydrogen cyanide addition for synthesis of α-hydroxy acids.

The reaction with hydrogen cyanide is an equilibrium, and the addition can be reversed by treatment of the cyanohydrin with moist silver oxide. The scope is nearly the same as that for the addition of sodium bisulfite, that is, cyanohydrin formation is applicable to aldehydes, to most methyl ketones other than those having a phenyl group, and to cyclic ketones. The carbonyl group of an ester is indifferent.

Grignard Reaction. — The useful synthetic reaction involving addition of an alkyl- or arylmagnesium halide to a carbonyl group is applicable with few exceptions to both aldehydes and ketones. Those limitations encountered are instances where the hydrocarbon residues in either the carbonyl component or the Grignard reagent are of such a highly branched or bulky nature as to restrict the free space available for formation of the addition complex and thus to impose hindrance. Diisopropyl ketone adds methylmagnesium iodide normally but with isopropylmagnesium bromide the addition reaction is repressed, and the ketone instead suffers reduction at the expense of the organometallic reagent with formation of the magnesiohalide derivative of diisopropylcarbinol and propylene:

$$
\begin{array}{c}
CH_3 \\
{}^{CH_3}\!\!\diagdown CHCCH \diagup^{CH_3}_{CH_3} + {}^{CH_3}\!\!\diagdown CHMgBr \longrightarrow {}^{CH_3}\!\!\diagdown CHCHCH\diagup^{OMgBr}_{CH_3} + CH_3CH=CH_2 \\
CH_3 \diagup \qquad CH_3 \diagup \qquad CH_3 \diagup \diagdown CH_3
\end{array}
$$

Again, di-t-butyl ketone adds methylmagnesium iodide but not phenylmagnesium bromide, and it is merely reduced to the carbinol by t-butyl-

$$
\begin{array}{ccc}
& CH_3\ \ O\ \ CH_3 & \\
CH_3-\overset{\displaystyle CH_3}{\underset{\displaystyle CH_3}{C}}-\overset{\displaystyle O}{C}-\overset{\displaystyle CH_3}{\underset{\displaystyle CH_3}{C}}-CH_3 & \qquad & CH_3-\overset{\displaystyle CH_3}{\underset{\displaystyle CH_3}{C}}-C\overset{H}{\diagup}_{\diagdown O}
\end{array}
$$

Di-t-butyl ketone　　　　　　　　Trimethylacetaldehyde

magnesium chloride. This tertiary Grignard reagent also reduces rather than adds to trimethylacetaldehyde.

Even though the carbonyl component may contain hydroxyl or carboxyl groups that rapidly destroy the Grignard reagent, just as water does, a satisfactory addition frequently can be accomplished by using sufficient excess reagent to allow for destruction of an amount equivalent to the hydroxyl groups present. For example, such substances as

$$RCO(CH_2)_nCH_2OH \qquad\qquad HOOC(CH_2)_nCHO$$

react with a first mole of methylmagnesium iodide with liberation of methane, and then add a second mole to form the derivatives:

$$
\overset{\displaystyle OMgI}{\underset{\displaystyle CH_3}{R\overset{|}{C}(CH_2)_nCH_2OMgI}} \qquad\qquad IMgOOC(CH_2)_n\overset{|}{\underset{\displaystyle CH_3}{C}HOMgI}
$$

Liberation of methane by compounds with hydroxyl or other active-hydrogen groups is the basis of a useful analytical method introduced by Zerewitinoff (1912) and elaborated by others, particularly Kohler[2] (1930). In the original method a weighed sample is treated with excess methyl Grignard reagent and the volume of evolved methane measured; the number of equivalents of gas liberated indicates the number of hydroxyl groups. The procedure can be modified to include determination of the amount of reagent that adds to the molecule by using a measured amount of Grignard solution of known content, measuring the methane evolved on reaction with the test sample, and then adding water and measuring the methane evolved from the remaining reagent not utilized for addition. A micro-apparatus (Kohler: Grignard machine) including technical improvements introduced by W. M. Lauer is illustrated in Fig. 9.1. A measured volume

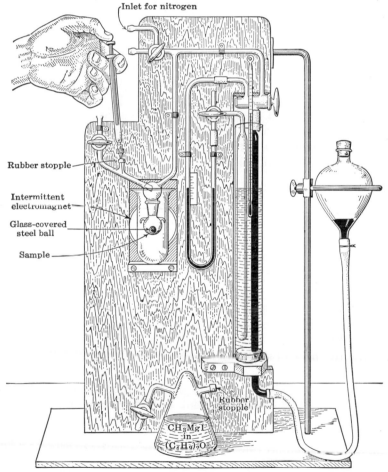

FIG. 9.1. — Grignard Machine for the Determination of Active Hydrogen Atoms and Carbonyl Groups

[2] Elmer Peter Kohler, 1865–1938; b. Egypt, Penna.; Ph.D. Johns Hopkins (Remsen); Bryn Mawr Coll., Harvard Univ.

of Grignard solution, withdrawn from a reservoir with a hypodermic syringe and introduced into the apparatus without exposure to moist air, is mixed with a weighed sample of the substance to be analyzed, and the mixture is agitated by oscillation of a glass-covered steel ball.

Reduction. — Most aldehydes and ketones can be reduced to the corresponding primary and secondary alcohols by **catalytic hydrogenation** in the presence of either platinum or Raney nickel catalyst. Chemical methods of reduction are usually applicable to aldehydes and in some instances give satisfactory results with ketones. Examples cited in Chapter 6 include the reduction of *n*-heptaldehyde with iron and acetic acid and of benzophenone with zinc dust and alcoholic sodium hydroxide (p. 116). More often, the reduction of a ketone by the combination of a metal with either an acid or a base (so-called nascent hydrogen) does not follow the normal course exclusively, but proceeds also by a process described as **bimolecular reduction** because the reduction product is derived from two molecules of the starting material. Thus acetone is reduced by metal combinations only in part to isopropyl alcohol and affords in addition a considerable amount of the product of bimolecular reduction, pinacol: $(CH_3)_2C(OH)C(OH)(CH_3)_2$. Pinacol is a useful synthetic intermediate and is prepared by the action of amalgamated magnesium on dry acetone in benzene solution, followed by hydrolysis of the magnesium derivative. The reaction probably involves attachment of magnesium to the oxygen atoms of two molecules of acetone to form a transient diradical and then magnesium pinacolate, which is

$$2(CH_3)_2CO \xrightarrow{\text{Mg}} \begin{matrix} (CH_3)_2C\!-\!O \\ \vdots \\ (CH_3)_2C\!-\!O \end{matrix}\!\!\Big\rangle Mg \longrightarrow \begin{matrix} (CH_3)_2C\!-\!O \\ | \\ (CH_3)_2C\!-\!O \end{matrix}\!\!\Big\rangle Mg \xrightarrow[43\text{-}50\%]{H_2O} \begin{matrix} (CH_3)_2COH \\ | \\ (CH_3)_2COH \end{matrix}$$

Pinacol

subsequently hydrolyzed to pinacol. Anhydrous pinacol is a liquid, b.p. 174.4°; it forms a crystalline hydrate containing six molecules of water. Pinacol hydrate, $C_6H_{12}(OH)_2 \cdot 6H_2O$ (named from *pinako-*, Gr., tabletlike, referring to the crystalline form of the hydrate), melts at 45°. Ketones generally undergo bimolecular reduction to a considerable extent with metal combinations such as zinc and acid, sodium, magnesium, or aluminum amalgam. With the same reagents aliphatic aldehydes are reduced unimolecularly to the corresponding alcohols, as they are on catalytic hydrogenation. The difference between aldehydes and ketones appears attributable to the greater availability of the carbonyl group of the former substances for the simultaneous addition to both carbon and oxygen. In a ketone the carbon of the carbonyl group is somewhat hindered by the two alkyl substituents, and evidently an initial attachment to the oxygen atom can open the double bond of the carbonyl group and yield a transient radical. The difference in behavior is thus in line with the relative reactivities of aldehydes and ketones in the bisulfite-addition reaction. Since a phenyl group depresses the additive ability of a carbonyl group to which it is joined, it is understandable that benzaldehyde, unlike aliphatic aldehydes, gives a considerable amount of the bimolecular reduction product on treatment with a metal combination.

A process for reduction of both aldehydes and ketones is the **Meerwein-Ponndorf method** (1925–26), which consists in heating a carbonyl compound in benzene or toluene solution with aluminum isopropoxide and distilling the acetone from the resulting equilibrium mixture. The reaction is the

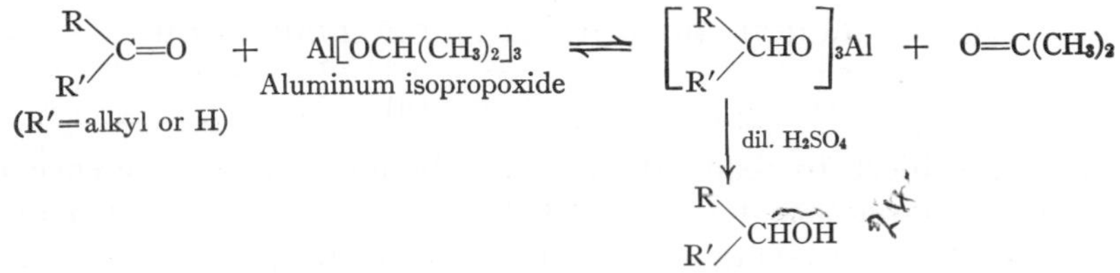

$$\underset{R'}{\overset{R}{>}}C=O \ + \ Al[OCH(CH_3)_2]_3 \ \rightleftharpoons \ \left[\underset{R'}{\overset{R}{>}}CHO\right]_3Al \ + \ O=C(CH_3)_2$$

Aluminum isopropoxide

$(R' = alkyl \ or \ H)$

$$\downarrow dil. \ H_2SO_4$$

$$\underset{R'}{\overset{R}{>}}CHOH$$

counterpart of the subsequently discovered Oppenauer oxidation of an alcohol with excess acetone (p. 194). Reduction with aluminum isopropoxide is generally applicable, and the yields are often good. The reaction is specific to the carbonyl group, and can be employed for reduction of unsaturated aldehydes and ketones, for example:

$$CH_3CH=CHCHO \ \xrightarrow[85–90\%]{Al(OC_3H_7)_3} \ CH_3CH=CHCH_2OH$$

Crotonaldehyde   Crotyl alcohol

Aldehydes and ketones, as well as esters and acids, can be reduced with lithium aluminum hydride or sodium borohydride (p. 116).

Aldol Condensation. — When acetaldehyde is treated with a small quantity of sodium hydroxide, two molecules combine in an equilibrium process and afford aldol, or β-hydroxy-n-butyraldehyde. The reaction in-

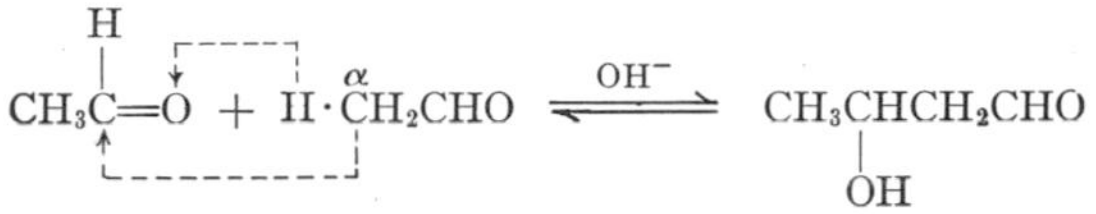

$$CH_3\overset{H}{\underset{}{C}}=O \ + \ H \cdot \overset{\alpha}{CH_2}CHO \ \xrightarrow{OH^-} \ CH_3\underset{\underset{OH}{|}}{CH}CH_2CHO$$

Aldol (b.p. 83°/20 mm.)

volves addition of one molecule of acetaldehyde to the carbonyl group of another molecule, and is dependent upon an activated hydrogen in the α-position to the carbonyl group of the adding molecule. Thus aldol condensation is shown only by aldehydes having at least one hydrogen in the α-position, and not by such substances as trimethylacetaldehyde, $(CH_3)_3CCHO$, or benzaldehyde, C_6H_5CHO. Propionaldehyde gives an aldol condensation product by utilization of one of the activated α-hydrogens, and not one of the hydrogens in the β-position:

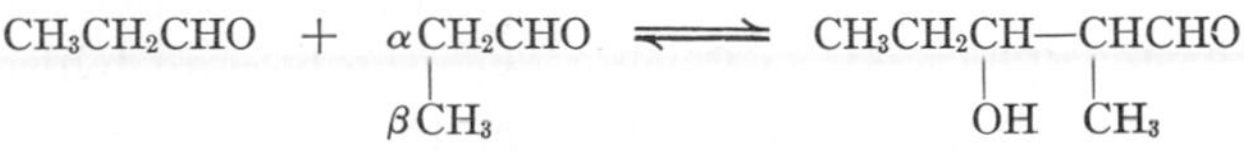

$$CH_3CH_2CHO \ + \ \alpha CH_2CHO \ \rightleftharpoons \ CH_3CH_2CH-CHCHO$$
$$\qquad\qquad\qquad \beta CH_3 \qquad\qquad\qquad OH \quad CH_3$$

Base-catalyzed aldolization, like cyanohydrin formation, involves nucleophilic addition. In an initial, slow step (a) the basic catalyst abstracts a proton from the aldehyde to give the anion required for the more rapid step of addition (b); the terminal step (c) regenerates the catalytic anion.

(a) $OH^- + HCH_2CHO \rightleftharpoons H_2O + \bar{C}H_2CHO$

(b) $CH_3CH{=}O + \bar{C}H_2CHO \rightleftharpoons CH_3CHCH_2CHO$
$$\qquad\qquad\qquad\qquad\qquad\qquad\qquad \underset{O^-}{|}$$

(c) $CH_3CHCH_2CHO + H_2O \rightleftharpoons CH_3CHCH_2CHO + OH^-$
$$\qquad\quad \underset{O^-}{|} \qquad\qquad\qquad\qquad\qquad \underset{OH}{|}$$

Aldol is subject to ready dehydration because of the presence of a β-hydroxyl group adjacent to an activated α-hydrogen atom. Conditions are thus particularly favorable for elimination of water, and aldol is converted into crotonaldehyde either by heating the isolated product alone or with a trace of mineral acid or by merely warming the aqueous solution of the equilibrium mixture resulting from aldolization. Crotonaldehyde is a

$$\underset{\substack{\lfloor\,\overline{OH}\ \ \overline{H}\,\rfloor\\ \text{Aldol}}}{\overset{\substack{\beta\qquad\alpha}}{CH_3CH{-}CHCHO}} \xrightarrow{-H_2O} \underset{\substack{\beta\qquad\alpha\\ \text{Crotonaldehyde}}}{CH_3CH{=}CHCHO}$$

representative α,β-unsaturated aldehyde available by aldol condensation and dehydration. If acetaldehyde is warmed with strong alkali, it is converted into a resinous product resulting from repeated aldol condensations among aldol, crotonaldehyde, and acetaldehyde.

The carbonyl group of acetone has less additive power than that of acetaldehyde, although comparably activated α-hydrogen atoms are present. Aldol condensation occurs under basic catalysis, but the position of equilibrium is very unfavorable to formation of the condensation product, diacetone alcohol. Even so, a special technique of conducting the reaction

$$\underset{\text{Acetone (b.p. 56.1°)}}{\overset{CH_3}{\underset{CH_3}{\diagup}}C{=}O} + H \cdot CH_2COCH_3 \underset{}{\overset{Ba(OH)_2}{\rightleftharpoons}} \underset{\text{Diacetone alcohol (b.p. 166°)}}{\overset{CH_3}{\underset{CH_3}{\diagup}}\underset{\underset{OH}{|}}{C}{-}CH_2COCH_3}$$

makes possible efficient preparation of the condensation product. Solid barium hydroxide is used as catalyst and promotes reaction on contact with acetone without dissolving in it. The catalyst is placed in a filter-paper thimble in an extraction apparatus (Soxhlet) in which acetone is distilled into a vertical condenser, the condensate trickles over the solid catalyst, and the liquid then filters by gravity through the thimble and is returned to the boiling flask. The acetone flowing over the barium hydroxide is converted into diacetone alcohol in small amounts approaching the equilibrium concentration, but once the resulting solution has passed through the filter and is out of contact with catalyst, the dimeric condensation product does not revert to acetone but accumulates in the boiling flask as the more volatile acetone is continually removed by distillation and recycled. By operation of such a unit for about four days, 1.5 liters of acetone can be converted into diacetone alcohol in 71% yield.

Diacetone alcohol can be dehydrated by adding a small amount of iodine as catalyst and slowly distilling the somewhat more volatile reaction product. The resulting substance, a colorless liquid having a peppermint-like odor and a burning taste, was assigned the name mesityl oxide at an early date

$$\underset{\substack{\text{Diacetone alcohol (b.p. 166°)}}}{\underset{\substack{| \\ \text{OH}}}{\overset{CH_3}{\underset{CH_3}{>}}C-CH_2COCH_3}} \xrightarrow{I_2} \underset{\substack{\text{Mesityl oxide (b.p. 131°)}}}{\overset{CH_3}{\underset{CH_3}{>}}C=CHCOCH_3}$$

because of an erroneous conception of its chemical nature; it is in no sense an oxide but is an α,β-unsaturated ketone. By the action of sodium hypochlorite it can be converted in good yield into β,β-dimethylacrylic acid, $(CH_3)_2C=CHCOOH$ (m.p. 70°, b.p. 195°). Mesityl oxide is also obtainable directly from acetone by the action of dry hydrogen chloride, but the yields are low, and the substance is accompanied by a product of further conden-

$$\overset{CH_3}{\underset{CH_3}{>}}C=\overline{\underline{|O}} + \overline{H_2|}CHCOCH_3 \xrightarrow{HCl} \underset{\text{Mesityl oxide}}{\overset{CH_3}{\underset{CH_3}{>}}C=CHCOCH_3} \xrightarrow{(CH_3)_2CO}$$

$$\underset{\text{Phorone}}{\overset{CH_3}{\underset{CH_3}{>}}C=CHCOCH=C\overset{CH_3}{\underset{CH_3}{<}}}$$

sation with another molecule of acetone, phorone. These reactions doubtless proceed through aldol-type products, which are dehydrated under the influence of the acidic condensing agent. Phorone, so named because of a chance correspondence of the empirical formula with that of a camphor derivative (camphor + acetone), is a yellow crystalline solid having a geranium odor.

Aldol condensation of two different aldehydes having reactive α-hydrogen atoms gives a mixture of all possible products and is seldom of preparative value. When an aldehyde and a ketone are condensed in an alkaline medium mixtures also result, though the ketone tends to add to the more reactive carbonyl group of the aldehyde in preference to the reverse process. One useful application of such mixed aldol condensations is to aromatic aldehydes, which have no α-hydrogen atoms, and this will be described later. Formaldehyde likewise has no α-hydrogen atoms and can be condensed with another aldehyde. Thus one commercial process for the preparation of acrolein depends upon the aldol condensation of equimolecular quantities of acetaldehyde and formaldehyde (yield 75%, based on acetaldehyde).

$$O=CH_2 + HCH_2CHO \longrightarrow [HOH_2CCH_2CHO] \xrightarrow{-H_2O} \underset{\text{Acrolein}}{H_2C=CHCHO}$$

Another application is the preparation of alcohols by aldol condensation, dehydration, and hydrogenation. Thus acetaldehyde is converted through aldol and crotonaldehyde into *n*-butyl alcohol; other applications are as follows:

$$CH_3CHO \ + \ CH_3CH_2CH_2CHO \ \xrightarrow{\ -H_2O;\ H_2\ } \ \begin{cases} CH_3CH_2CH_2CH_2CH_2CH_2OH \\ (CH_3CH_2)_2CHCH_2OH \end{cases}$$

$$2\,CH_3CH_2CH_2CHO \ \xrightarrow{\ -H_2O;\ H_2\ } \ CH_3CH_2CH_2CH_2\underset{\underset{C_2H_5}{|}}{C}HCH_2OH$$

Cannizzaro Reaction of Aldehydes. — Another reaction, characteristic of aldehydes having no α-hydrogen atoms and applicable chiefly in the aromatic series, is oxidation of one molecule of the aldehyde at the expense of another, which suffers reduction. The reaction, which bears the name of the discoverer, Cannizzaro[3] (1853), is brought about by the action of a concentrated solution of sodium or potassium hydroxide on an aldehyde of the type indicated, for example benzaldehyde:

$$2\,C_6H_5C\!\!\begin{array}{c}H\\ \\ O\end{array} \ + \ KOH \ \xrightarrow{\ 60\%\ KOH\ } \ C_6H_5C\!\!\begin{array}{c}OK\\ \\ O\end{array} \ + \ C_6H_5CH_2OH$$

Potassium   Benzyl alcohol
benzoate

The oxidation product, benzoic acid, can be isolated in 85–95% yield, and the reduction product, benzyl alcohol, in 80% yield. This type of compensated oxidation-reduction process is called disproportionation. The reaction is interpreted as involving (a) interaction of the aldehyde with hydroxide ion to produce an anion which, by virtue of the electron displacements

$$(a) \quad R-\underset{}{\overset{O}{\overset{\|}{C}}}-H \ + \ OH^- \ \longrightarrow \ R-\underset{\underset{OH}{|}}{\overset{\overset{O^-}{|}}{C}}-H$$

$$(b) \quad R-\underset{\underset{OH}{|}}{\overset{\overset{O^-}{|}}{C}}-H \ + \ R-\underset{\underset{H}{|}}{C}=O \ \longrightarrow \ R-\underset{\underset{OH}{|}}{\overset{\overset{O}{\|}}{C}} \ + \ R-\underset{\underset{H}{|}}{\overset{\overset{H}{|}}{C}}-O^-$$

$$\Big\downarrow H_2O$$

$$OH^- \ + \ RCH_2OH$$

indicated, has reducing properties and can donate a hydride ion (H⁻) as in (b) to a second molecule of aldehyde.

In the aliphatic series the reaction is encountered only in the rare instances of substances such as formaldehyde and trimethylacetaldehyde, which possess no activated hydrogen atom in the α-position and therefore are incapable of undergoing the more rapid aldol condensation. The Cannizzaro reaction is involved in the standard method for preparation of

---

[3] Stanislao Cannizzaro, 1826–1910; b. Palermo, Italy; stud. Pisa (Piria); Genoa, Palermo, Rome; *J. Chem. Soc.*, **111**, 1677 (1912)

pentaerythritol, a polyhydric alcohol employed as an intermediate in the manufacture of the explosive tetranitrate ester (PETN, p. 132). This method consists in treating acetaldehyde with about five equivalents of formaldehyde in an aqueous solution of calcium hydroxide at 15–45°. The initial step is an aldol condensation, and since formaldehyde possesses the

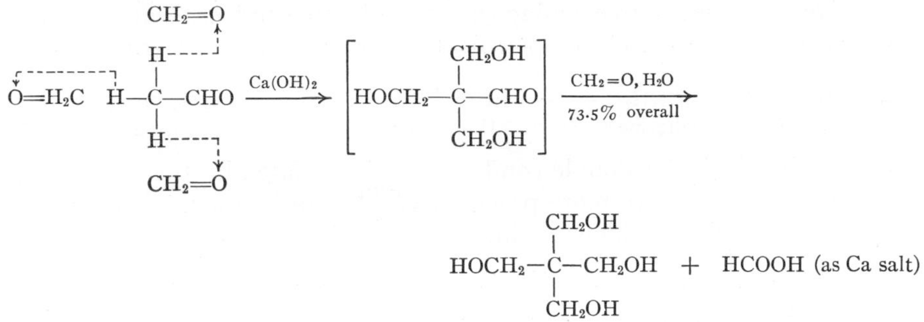

$$CH_2{=}O$$
$$H{----}$$
$$O{=}H_2C \quad H{-}\underset{\underset{CH_2{=}O}{\overset{|}{H}{----}}}{\overset{\overset{\uparrow}{|}}{C}}{-}CHO \xrightarrow{Ca(OH)_2} \left[HOCH_2{-}\underset{\overset{|}{CH_2OH}}{\overset{\overset{CH_2OH}{|}}{C}}{-}CHO \right] \xrightarrow[\text{73.5\% overall}]{CH_2{=}O,\ H_2O}$$

$$HOCH_2{-}\underset{\overset{|}{CH_2OH}}{\overset{\overset{CH_2OH}{|}}{C}}{-}CH_2OH \quad + \quad HCOOH \text{ (as Ca salt)}$$
Pentaerythritol (m.p. 260°)

more reactive carbonyl group of the two components and acetaldehyde alone contains activated α-hydrogen atoms, the reaction consists in addition of acetaldehyde to three formaldehyde molecules. The next step is a crossed Cannizzaro reaction consisting in disproportionation between the initially formed trihydroxyaldehyde and formaldehyde, and resulting in reduction of the former to pentaerythritol and oxidation of the latter to formic acid.

Condensation with Amines. — Among reagents for the carbonyl group are various amine derivatives of ammonia. The simplest are monoalkyl derivatives RNH_2. One useful reagent, hydroxylamine, represents a combination of the structures of water and of ammonia; another, hydrazine, is structurally comparable to hydrogen peroxide, to which it bears the same relation as ammonia does to water. These amine reagents condense with

$$\left. \begin{array}{l} H{\cdot}OH \\ H{\cdot}NH_2 \end{array} \right\} HO{\cdot}NH_2, \text{ Hydroxylamine}$$

$$HO{\cdot}OH \} H_2N{\cdot}NH_2, \text{ Hydrazine}$$

aldehydes and ketones with the net result that water is eliminated between the two molecules and an unsaturated nitrogen-containing derivative is

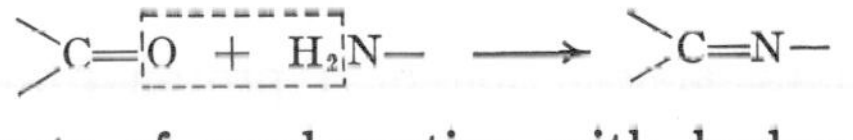

$$>\!C{=}O \ + \ H_2N{-} \ \longrightarrow \ >\!C{=}N{-}$$

formed. The products of condensation with hydroxylamine are called oximes, and can be designated as aldoximes or ketoximes, according to the nature of the carbonyl component. The condensations proceed readily on

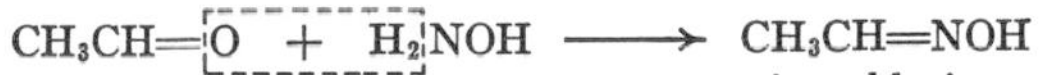

$$CH_3CH{=}O \ + \ H_2NOH \ \longrightarrow \ CH_3CH{=}NOH$$
Acetaldoxime
(m.p. 47°)

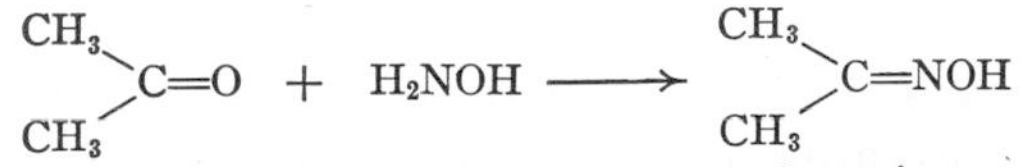

$$\underset{CH_3}{\overset{CH_3}{>}}C{=}O \ + \ H_2NOH \ \longrightarrow \ \underset{CH_3}{\overset{CH_3}{>}}C{=}NOH$$
Acetoxime
(m.p. 60°)

warming the components in aqueous or alcoholic solution, and the examples indicate that oximes are crystalline solids even though the carbonyl compounds from which they are derived are volatile liquids. Oximes are thus solid derivatives of service for identification.

Hydrazine reacts in a similar manner to form a hydrazone, but this derivative possesses a free amino group and can condense with another molecule of the carbonyl component to form an azine. Derivatives of

$$RCH{=}O \;+\; H_2NNH_2 \;\longrightarrow\; RCH{=}NNH_2 \;\xrightarrow{RCHO}\; RCH{=}NN{=}CHR$$
Aldehyde   Hydrazine   Hydrazone   Azine

hydrazine in which this double condensation is obviated by the presence of a substituent group have more practical value than hydrazine itself. One is phenylhydrazine, which yields phenylhydrazone derivatives. The

$$C_6H_5CHO \;\xrightarrow{H_2NNHC_6H_5}\; C_6H_5CH{=}NNHC_6H_5$$
Benzaldehyde   Benzaldehyde phenylhydrazone
(liquid)   (m.p. 156°)

phenylhydrazone of acetaldehyde is also a crystalline solid, m.p. 99°. Replacement of the oxygen atom of a carbonyl group by the residue $={NNHC_6H_5}$ is attended with decided increase in molecular weight and consequent decrease in solubility, and hence an aldehyde or a ketone often can be precipitated from a dilute solution as the phenylhydrazone and identified by the melting point of this derivative. Another reagent is semicarbazide, $H_2NNHCONH_2$; this generally gives derivatives that melt at higher temperatures than oximes or phenylhydrazones.

$$CH_3CHO \;+\; H_2NNHCONH_2 \;\longrightarrow\; CH_3CH{=}NNHCONH_2$$
Semicarbazide   Acetaldehyde semicarbazone
(m.p. 162°)

All the condensations cited are reversible, and oximes, phenylhydrazones, and semicarbazones can be hydrolyzed by boiling with dilute hydrochloric or sulfuric acid with regeneration of the free carbonyl compound. Aldehydes and ketones are isolated frequently from reaction mixtures in the form of one of these crystalline, sparingly soluble derivatives, and then recovered in a purified condition by acid hydrolysis.

These condensations appear to proceed by an addition-elimination mechanism initiated by abstraction of a proton from the reagent (e.g.,

$$OH^- + H_2NOH \rightarrow H_2O + H\bar{N}OH \xrightarrow{R_2C{=}O}$$
(a)

$$R_2C\overset{O^-}{\underset{NHOH}{\big<}} \;\xrightarrow[-OH^-]{H_2O}\; R_2C\overset{OH}{\underset{NHOH}{\big<}} \;\xrightarrow{-H_2O}\; R_2C{=}NOH$$
(b)   (c)   (d)

hydroxylamine) by hydroxide ion, and addition of the anion (a) to the carbonyl group, with eventual formation of (c) and dehydration to (d).

A solution of acetaldehyde in ether absorbs dry ammonia gas and gives a crystalline, white precipitate, aldehyde ammonia, which presumably is the addition product, for it yields acetaldehyde when neutralized with dilute mineral acid in the cold, but it is unstable and is not obtainable in pure condition. The trichloro derivative, chloral, has greater additive power and forms with ammonia and with hydroxylamine authentic addition products sufficiently stable to permit their isolation and characterization; the product from hydroxylamine slowly changes into the oxime on standing at room temperature:

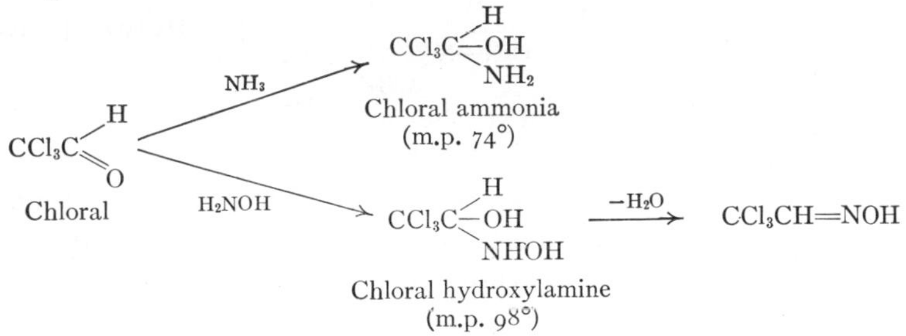

$$CCl_3C \overset{H}{\underset{O}{<}} \quad \begin{matrix} \overset{NH_3}{\nearrow} & CCl_3C \overset{H}{\underset{NH_2}{-}} OH \\ & \text{Chloral ammonia} \\ & \text{(m.p. 74°)} \\ \underset{H_2NOH}{\searrow} & CCl_3C \overset{H}{\underset{NHOH}{-}} OH \end{matrix} \xrightarrow{-H_2O} CCl_3CH{=}NOH$$

Chloral

Chloral hydroxylamine
(m.p. 98°)

The amine reagents also react with esters; for example, ammonia reacts to form amides (p. 178) and hydrazine gives acid hydrazides (p. 179). The condensations with esters, however, proceed much more slowly or require a considerably higher temperature. Thus in the preparation of acethydrazide from ethyl acetate and hydrazine hydrate, the mixture is refluxed for two days. The more reactive aldehydes and ketones combine with hydrazine or phenylhydrazine rapidly at room temperature.

Formaldehyde, which is particularly reactive, condenses with ammonia to give a crystalline solid of the formula $C_6H_{12}N_4$, hexamethylenetetramine. The substance, which can be prepared merely by allowing a mixture of formalin and concentrated ammonia solution to evaporate, has a polycyclic structure made up of methylene groups bridged by nitrogen atoms into a

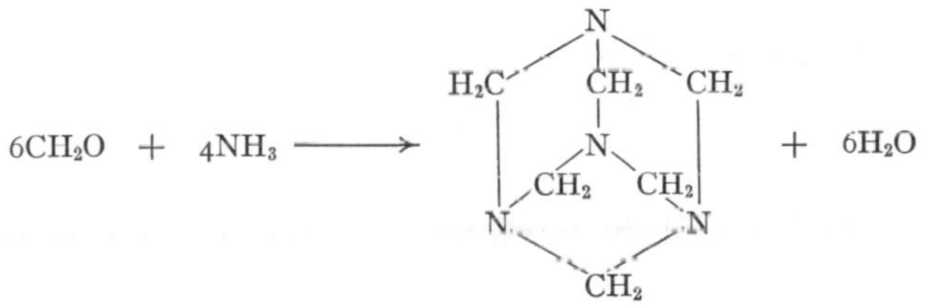

$$6CH_2O \; + \; 4NH_3 \longrightarrow \quad + \; 6H_2O$$

Hexamethylenetetramine

cross-linked six-membered ring. The product presumably arises as the result of a series of additions of ammonia or of ammonia-addition products to the carbonyl group of successive formaldehyde molecules. Hexamethylene-

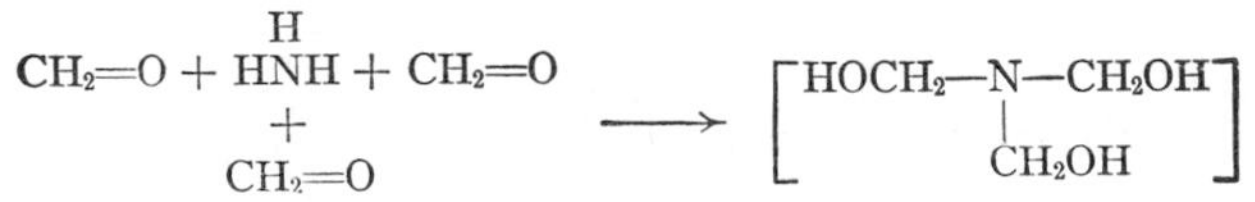

$$\begin{matrix} \overset{H}{} \\ CH_2{=}O + HNH + CH_2{=}O \\ + \\ CH_2{=}O \end{matrix} \longrightarrow \begin{bmatrix} HOCH_2{-}N{-}CH_2OH \\ | \\ CH_2OH \end{bmatrix}$$

tetramine (urotropin, renders urine basic) is employed in medicine as a urinary antiseptic, and is effective because it slowly releases formaldehyde by reversal of the reactions leading to its formation. Another use is the preparation of a powerful high explosive known as cyclonite, or RDX. This is made by treating hexamethylenetetramine with fuming nitric acid, when the inner bridge system is destroyed by oxidation and the peripheral nitrogen

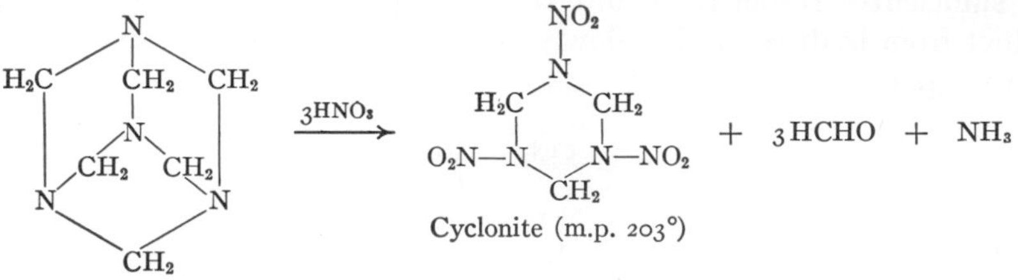

Cyclonite (m.p. 203°)

atoms are nitrated. The yield can be approximately doubled (that is, two moles of cyclonite can be obtained from one mole of hexamethylenetetramine) if ammonium nitrate and acetic anhydride are added (Bachmann and Sheehan, 1949):

$$C_6H_{12}N_4 + 4HNO_3 + 2NH_4NO_3 + 6(CH_3CO)_2O \xrightarrow[70\%]{} 2C_3H_6N_6O_6 + 12CH_3COOH$$

Cyclonite

Wolff-Kishner Reduction. — This method was discovered independently in Germany (Wolff,[4] 1912) and in Russia (Kishner,[5] 1911). A ketone (or aldehyde) is converted into the hydrazone, and this derivative is heated in a sealed tube or an autoclave with sodium ethoxide in absolute ethanol. After preliminary technical improvements (Soffer; Whitmore, 1945), Huang-

$$\text{\Large >}C{=}O \xrightarrow{H_2NNH_2} \text{\Large >}C{=}NNH_2 \xrightarrow{NaOC_2H_5,\ 200°} \text{\Large >}CH_2 + N_2$$

Minlon (1946) introduced a modified procedure by which the reduction is conducted on a large scale at atmospheric pressure with efficiency and economy. The ketone is refluxed in a high-boiling water-miscible solvent (usually di- or triethylene glycol) with aqueous hydrazine and sodium hydroxide to form the hydrazone; water is then allowed to distil from the mixture till the temperature rises to a point favorable for decomposition of the hydrazone (200°); and the mixture is refluxed for three or four hours to complete the reduction.

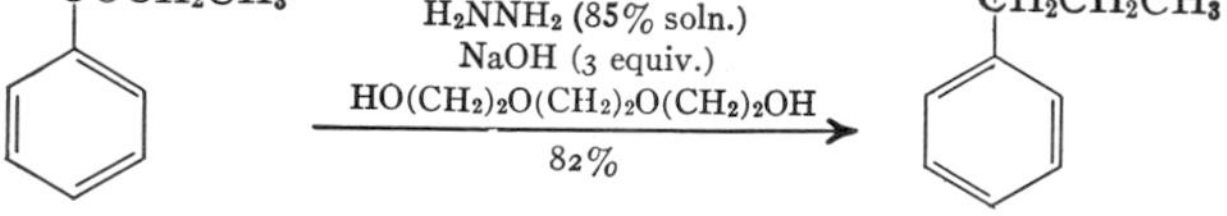

Propiophenone   n-Propylbenzene

[4] Ludwig Wolff, 1857–1919; b. Neustadt/Hardt; Ph.D. Strasbourg (Fittig); Jena; *Ber.*, **62A**, 145 (1929)

[5] N. M. Kishner, 1867–1935; b. Moscow; Ph.D. Moscow (Markownikoff); Tomsk, Moscow

Acetals and Ketals. — Under the catalytic influence of dry hydrogen chloride a typical aldehyde adds a molecule of ethyl alcohol to form a moderately stable addition product (hemiacetal), which combines with a second molecule of the alcohol and yields a stable derivative known as an

$$CH_3CH{=}O \ + \ HOC_2H_5 \ \xrightarrow{HCl} \ CH_3CH\begin{smallmatrix}OH\\OC_2H_5\end{smallmatrix} \ \xrightarrow{HOC_2H_5(H^+)} \ CH_3CH\begin{smallmatrix}OC_2H_5\\OC_2H_5\end{smallmatrix}$$

Hemiacetal   Acetal (b.p. 104°)

$$CH_2{=}O \ + \ 2\,HOCH_3 \ \xrightarrow{H^+} \ CH_2(OCH_3)_2$$

Methylal (b.p. 42°)

$$CH_2{=}O \ + \ 2\,HOC_2H_5 \ \xrightarrow{H^+} \ CH_2(OC_2H_5)_2$$

Ethylal (b.p. 88°)

acetal. Acetals are *gem*-diethers but, unlike the corresponding unstable *gem*-diols, can be obtained as pure, distillable liquids. Acetal formation is reversible, and acetals are hydrolyzed easily with water and a mineral acid catalyst (compare the acid-catalyzed depolymerization of paraldehyde). Acetals are considerably more stable to alkalis than to acids, and they are so much more stable than free aldehydes to basic reagents and oxidizing agents that aldehydic compounds are often converted into the acetals to protect the aldehydic function during synthetic operations involving other groups of the molecule. Acetals usually are prepared by passing about one percent of hydrogen chloride gas into a solution of the aldehyde in methanol or ethanol. The order of reactivity for the alcoholic component is: primary > secondary > tertiary, in the ratio of about 80:45:20. Ketones react so much less readily that preparation of ketals by the direct route may be difficult. An indirect method is reversible interaction with ethyl

$$\begin{smallmatrix}R\\R'\end{smallmatrix}{>}C{=}O \ + \ HC{\begin{smallmatrix}OC_2H_5\\OC_2H_5\\OC_2H_5\end{smallmatrix}} \ \rightleftharpoons \ \begin{smallmatrix}R\\R'\end{smallmatrix}{>}C{\begin{smallmatrix}OC_2H_5\\OC_2H_5\end{smallmatrix}} \ + \ HCOOC_2H_5$$

Ketone   Ethyl orthoformate   Ketal
(b.p. 146°)

orthoformate (from chloroform and sodium ethoxide). A protective derivative particularly useful in synthesis is the ethyleneketal, made by re-

$$\begin{smallmatrix}R\\R'\end{smallmatrix}{>}C{=}O \ + \ \begin{smallmatrix}HOCH_2\\|\\HOCH_2\end{smallmatrix} \ \xrightarrow{H^+} \ \begin{smallmatrix}R\\R'\end{smallmatrix}{>}C{\begin{smallmatrix}O-CH_2\\|\\O-CH_2\end{smallmatrix}} \ + \ H_2O$$

Ethyleneketal

fluxing a ketone in ethylene glycol in the presence of an acid catalyst under a take-off condenser for removal of the water formed.

Ketones react with mercaptans much more readily than with alcohols to form thioketals, $(RS)_2CR_2$. Ethanedithiol, analogous to ethylene glycol, is a favored reagent and gives cyclic ethylenethioketals which, like thioketals,

$$\begin{smallmatrix}R\\R'\end{smallmatrix}{>}C{=}O \ \xrightarrow[BF_3 \cdot HOAc]{HSCH_2CH_2SH} \ \begin{smallmatrix}R\\R'\end{smallmatrix}{>}C{\begin{smallmatrix}S-CH_2\\|\\S-CH_2\end{smallmatrix}} \ \xrightarrow{Ni,\ H_2} \ \begin{smallmatrix}R\\R'\end{smallmatrix}{>}CH_2$$

Ethylenethioketal

can be desulfurized by reaction with Raney nickel (with adsorbed hydrogen), with the result that the original carbonyl oxygen is replaced by two atoms of hydrogen (Bougault, 1938; Mozingo, 1943; Wolfrom, 1944). The condensation with ethanedithiol proceeds rapidly and in high yield at room temperature in the presence of boron fluoride etherate, alone or in acetic acid solution. Thioketals are hydrolyzed with too great difficulty to be useful as protective derivatives. Ethylenesemithioketals, made in the same way with β-mercaptoethanol, $HSCH_2CH_2OH$, are reconverted to the ketones by Raney nickel.

Stable Hydrates. — Ordinary aldehydes do not form stable addition products with water, although small amounts of the unstable *gem*-diols may exist in equilibrium with the aldehyde, just as carbonic acid is present in aqueous solutions of carbon dioxide. The tendency of formaldehyde to form chain polymers in aqueous solution indicates that the equilibrium is more favorable to formation of a hydrate than in the case of acetaldehyde and the higher homologs. A few aldehydes of specialized types surpass formaldehyde in additive power and form stable hydrates. One is chloral, a liquid substance which combines exothermally with water to form a stable

$$CCl_3C\begin{smallmatrix}H\\ \\O\end{smallmatrix} \quad + \quad HOH \longrightarrow \quad CCl_3C\begin{smallmatrix}H\\OH\\OH\end{smallmatrix}$$

Chloral   Chloral hydrate
(m.p. 51.7°)

crystalline hydrate. The reactivity of the carbonyl group of chloral is further shown by formation of products of addition with ammonia and with hydroxylamine, cited above. The modifying influence of the α-chloro atoms on the additive power of the carbonyl group finds a parallel in the effect of similar substitution on the acidic strength of acetic acid. In the present instance the effect is ascribable to the electron-attracting character of the three chlorine atoms; withdrawal of electrons from the carbon atom of the carbonyl group renders this center relatively positive and hence vulnerable to attack by hydroxide ion. Other examples of the formation of stable, isolable hydrates are as follows:

$$O{=}HC{\cdot}CH{=}O \xrightarrow{2H_2O} \begin{smallmatrix}HO\\HO\end{smallmatrix}{>}CHCH{<}\begin{smallmatrix}OH\\OH\end{smallmatrix}$$

Glyoxal   Hydrate

$$O{=}HC{\cdot}COOH \xrightarrow{H_2O} \begin{smallmatrix}HO\\HO\end{smallmatrix}{>}CHCOOH$$

Glyoxylic acid   Hydrate

$$\left[O{=}C{<}\begin{smallmatrix}COOH\\COOH\end{smallmatrix}\right] \xrightarrow{H_2O} \begin{smallmatrix}HO\\HO\end{smallmatrix}{>}C{<}\begin{smallmatrix}COOH\\COOH\end{smallmatrix}$$

Mesoxalic acid
(m.p. 121°)

ENOLS AND ENOLATES

Tautomerism. — The behavior of ketones on oxidation and on bromina-tion was interpreted above as proceeding through a minute amount of an enolic form present in equilibrium with the ketone in consequence of acti-vation of a hydrogen in the α-position to the unsaturated carbonyl group. When a second carbonyl group is present in such a position as to accentuate the activation by the first, the equilibrium may be sufficiently favorable to permit isolation of the enol. The classical example of a compound known in both ketonic and enolic forms is the β-keto ester ethyl acetoacetate, $CH_3COCH_2CO_2C_2H_5$, commonly known as acetoacetic ester, in which the hydrogens of the methylene group are activated both by a carbonyl group and an ester-carbonyl group. Analytical chemical reactions (K. H. Meyer,[6] 1911) and physical measurements (molecular refraction, von Auwers,[7] 1918) established that ordinary, liquid acetoacetic ester consists of an equilibrium mixture containing approximately 7% of the enol form. The phenomenon

$$CH_3C{-}CH_2C\underset{O\overset{\shortparallel}{{-}{-}}}{\overset{O}{\diagup\diagdown}}OC_2H_5 \quad \rightleftharpoons \quad CH_3C{=}CHC\underset{OH{-}}{\overset{O}{\diagup\diagdown}}OC_2H_5$$

Keto form (93%)   Enol form (7%)

Tautomeric system

of the reversible interconversion of isomers is known as tautomerism. An activated hydrogen atom migrates from carbon to oxygen to give the enol, and since in this substance the hydrogen also occupies an activated position, it can migrate back again. The tautomeric migration of hydrogen in either direction is called an α,γ-shift; in each case hydrogen attached to an α-atom adjacent to a β,γ-double bond migrates to the γ-position:

$$-\overset{\beta}{C}-\overset{\alpha}{C}H- \quad \rightleftharpoons \quad -\overset{\beta}{C}{=}\overset{\gamma}{C}H-$$
$$\underset{\gamma O\ \ H}{} \qquad\qquad \underset{\alpha OH}{}$$

The keto form has been isolated by cooling a solution of the equilibrium mixture, when the ketonic form eventually separates as a crystalline solid, m.p. 39°. The enolic tautomer has been obtained in a liquid but sub-stantially pure condition by passing hydrogen chloride gas into a suspension of sodioacetoacetic ester in petroleum ether at −78° (Knorr, 1911) or by acidification of an ice-cold alkaline solution of the ester with sulfuric acid (K. H. Meyer, 1911). Although the keto form predominates at equilibrium, establishment of equilibrium is slow at low temperatures.

At ordinary temperatures each form slowly reverts in part to the other to give the same equilibrium mixture. The interconversion is subject to

[6] Kurt Hans Meyer, 1883–1952; b. Dorpat, Germany; Ph.D. Leipzig; BASF Ludwigshaven, Univ. Geneva; *Angew. Chem.*, **64**, 521 (1952)

[7] Karl von Auwers, 1863–1939; b. Gotha, Germany; Ph.D. Berlin (Hofmann); Marburg *Ber.*, **72A**, 111 (1939)

catalysis by acids or bases, and equilibrium is established rapidly when either form is treated with a trace of alkali. The equilibrium mixture of the tautomeric forms responds to reagents specific to either component, and, as one form is removed from the equilibrium by conversion into a derivative, the other tautomerizes, and eventually the entire material is converted into the derivative. The position of equilibrium is different in different solvents and varies with temperature. Other β-keto esters form tautomeric systems of varying enol content; the similarly constituted 1,3-diketones are even more prone to enolize, whereas diesters of the malonic ester type are less enolic, as shown in the following comparison:

$C_2H_5OOCCH_2COOC_2H_5$	$CH_3COCH_2COOC_2H_5$	$CH_3COCH_2COCH_3$
Diethyl malonate	Ethyl acetoacetate	Acetylacetone
Trace	7%	72%

Enol content of the equilibrium mixture

The two moderately unsaturated carbethoxy groups of malonic ester do not provide sufficient activation to stabilize the enol form, whereas acetylacetone, with two powerful unsaturated carbonyl groups, exists largely in the enolic form. Acetoacetic ester has a combination of the two unsaturated groups and occupies an intermediate position.

When ordinary acetoacetic ester is distilled very slowly in a quartz apparatus, the distillate consists almost exclusively of the enolic form (K. H. Meyer, 1920). Quartz is required because glass has a sufficiently alkaline reaction to catalyze interconversion of the tautomers. The preferential distillation of one tautomer indicates that the hydroxylic enol form is more volatile than the keto form. The relationship is just the opposite of that noted with ordinary alcohols and ketones, for alcohols are highly associated in the liquid state and boil at temperatures about 30° higher than ketones of comparable molecular weight. The unusual volatility of the enolic form of acetoacetic ester indicates that the substance differs from ordinary alcohols in being unassociated, and a reasonable interpretation is that hydrogen bonding occurs between the hydroxyl group and the carbonyl group of the ester function. The coordinate link closes a labile six-membered ring of the type described as a chelate ring (Gr. *chēlē*, claw). The hydroxylic hydrogen atom is thus rendered unavailable for bonding with a second molecule, and the substance therefore is not associated.

Acetoacetic Ester in Synthesis. — The enolic β-keto ester is prepared by condensation of two molecules of ethyl acetate in the presence of sodium ethoxide; the reaction is reversible, but a high yield can be obtained by distillation of the alcohol formed and thereby displacing the equilibrium (McElvain,[8] 1937). The reaction is generally applicable to esters having

---

[8] Samuel M. McElvain. b. 1897 Duquoin, Ill.; Ph.D. Illinois (Adams); Wisconsin

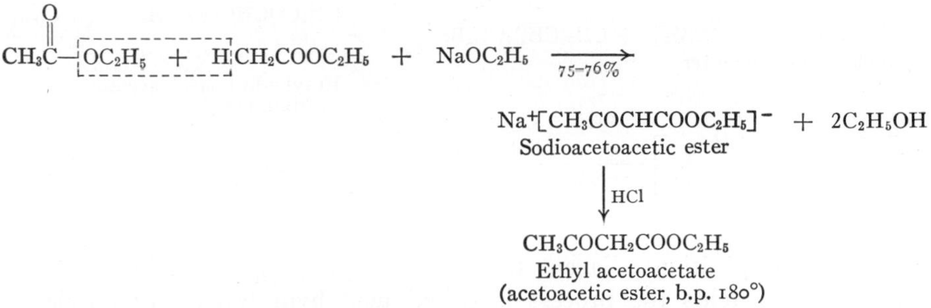

$$CH_3C-[OC_2H_5] + [H]CH_2COOC_2H_5 + NaOC_2H_5 \xrightarrow[75-76\%]{}$$

$$Na^+[CH_3COCHCOOC_2H_5]^- + 2C_2H_5OH$$
Sodioacetoacetic ester

$$\downarrow HCl$$

$$CH_3COCH_2COOC_2H_5$$
Ethyl acetoacetate
(acetoacetic ester, b.p. 180°)

an available activated hydrogen in the α-position, and is known as an **ester condensation.** Acetoacetic ester is liberated on acidification of the sodio derivative produced in the condensation and can be reconverted into this derivative by interaction with sodium ethoxide. The anion of the sodio derivative is a resonance hybrid, and the carbon atom of the original methylene group carries sufficient negative charge to be susceptible to alkylation

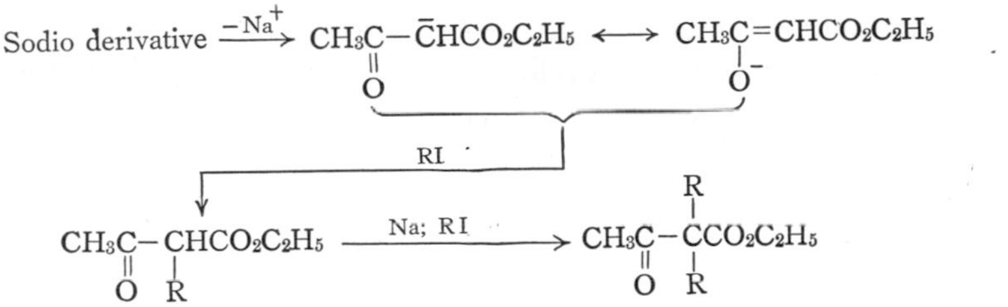

$$\text{Sodio derivative} \xrightarrow{-Na^+} CH_3C-\bar{C}HCO_2C_2H_5 \longleftrightarrow CH_3C=CHCO_2C_2H_5$$

$$CH_3C-CHCO_2C_2H_5 \xrightarrow{Na;\ RI} CH_3C-CCO_2C_2H_5$$

on reaction with an alkyl halide. The product still has an activated hydrogen and forms a sodio derivative, through which another alkyl group can be introduced. The significance of these reactions is that β-keto esters on hydrolysis with dilute alkali yield β-keto acids which, because the α-carbon atom carries both a carbonyl and a carboxyl group, undergo smooth decarboxylation at moderate temperature (e.g. 100°) to give ketones. **Ke-**

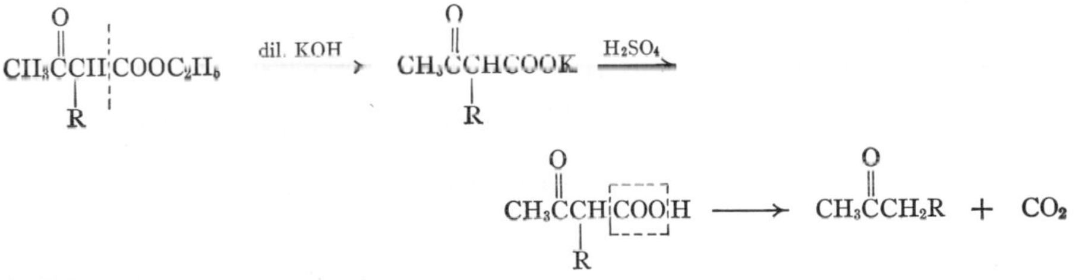

$$CH_3CCH[COOC_2H_5] \xrightarrow{dil.\ KOH} CH_3CCHCOOK \xrightarrow{H_2SO_4}$$

$$CH_3CCH[COOH] \longrightarrow CH_3CCH_2R + CO_2$$

tonic hydrolysis, as the process is called, coupled with mono or di alkylation, thus affords a useful synthetic sequence, as exemplified by the synthesis of methyl n-amyl ketone. Concentrated alkali cleaves β-keto

$$\text{Na}^+[\text{CH}_3\text{COCHCOOC}_2\text{H}_5]^- + \text{CH}_3(\text{CH}_2)_2\text{CH}_2\text{Br} \xrightarrow{69-72\%} \begin{array}{c}\text{CH}_3\text{COCHCOOC}_2\text{H}_5\\ |\\ \text{CH}_2(\text{CH}_2)_2\text{CH}_3\end{array} \xrightarrow{5\%\ \text{NaOH}}$$

Sodioacetoacetic ester

Ethyl *n*-butylacetoacetate
(b.p. 114°/16 mm.)

$$\left[\begin{array}{c}\text{CH}_3\text{COCHCOOH}\\ |\\ \text{CH}_2(\text{CH}_2)_2\text{CH}_3\end{array}\right] \xrightarrow[\text{52–61\%, overall from acetoacetic ester}]{\text{dil. H}_2\text{SO}_4} \text{CH}_3\text{CO(CH}_2)_4\text{CH}_3 \ + \ \text{CO}_2$$

Methyl *n*-amyl ketone
(b.p. 150°)

esters at the position adjacent to the carbonyl group, and since the two products are acids the process is called **acid hydrolysis.** By alkylation

$$\underset{\overset{|}{R}}{\overset{\overset{O}{\|}}{\text{CH}_3\text{C}}}\text{CHCOOC}_2\text{H}_5 \xrightarrow{\text{OH}^-(-\text{C}_2\text{H}_5\text{OH})} \text{CH}_3\overset{\overset{OH}{|}}{\text{C}}\!=\!\text{O} \ + \ \text{RCH}_2\text{COOH}$$

of acetoacetic ester and cleavage in this second way, acids of the types $\text{RCH}_2\text{CO}_2\text{H}$ and $\text{RR}'\text{CHCO}_2\text{H}$ can be synthesized. However the malonic ester synthesis described below accomplishes the same end and is more widely used.

Dieckmann[9] Reaction (1894). — Application of the ester condensation reaction affords a route to cyclic β-keto esters and cyclic ketones. The

Diethyl adipate

2-Carbethoxycyclopentanone
(b.p. 78–81°/3 mm.)

Cyclopentanone

cyclic β-keto ester shown in the example has an α-hydrogen replaceable by alkyl through the sodio enolate.

Malonic Ester Synthesis. — Diethyl malonate, commonly called malonic ester, is made by the action of ethanol and a mineral acid on sodium cyanoacetate. The carboxyl group is liberated and esterified, and addition of

$$\begin{array}{c}\text{CH}_2\text{CO}_2\text{Na}\\ |\\ \text{CN}\end{array} \xrightarrow{\text{C}_2\text{H}_5\text{OH, H}^+} \begin{array}{c}\text{CH}_2\text{CO}_2\text{C}_2\text{H}_5\\ |\\ \text{C}\!\equiv\!\text{N}\end{array} \xrightarrow{\text{C}_2\text{H}_5\text{OH, H}^+}$$

$$\begin{array}{c}\text{CH}_2\text{CO}_2\text{C}_2\text{H}_5\\ |\\ \text{HN}\!=\!\text{C}\!-\!\text{OC}_2\text{H}_5\end{array} \xrightarrow{\text{H}_2\text{O}} \begin{array}{c}\text{CH}_2\text{CO}_2\text{C}_2\text{H}_5\\ |\\ \text{CO}_2\text{C}_2\text{H}_5\end{array}$$

Imino ester

Diethyl malonate

---

[9] Walter Dieckmann, 1869–1925 b. Hamburg, Germany; Ph.D. Munich (Bamberger); Munich

ethanol to the nitrile group gives the imino ester, which is hydrolyzed on addition of water.

Unlike β-keto esters and β-diketones, malonic ester does not form an enolate that is isolable or present in any but trace amounts at equilibrium. It does, however, react with sodium like these substances to form an enolate ion, stabilized by resonance. The enolate, represented for convenience as

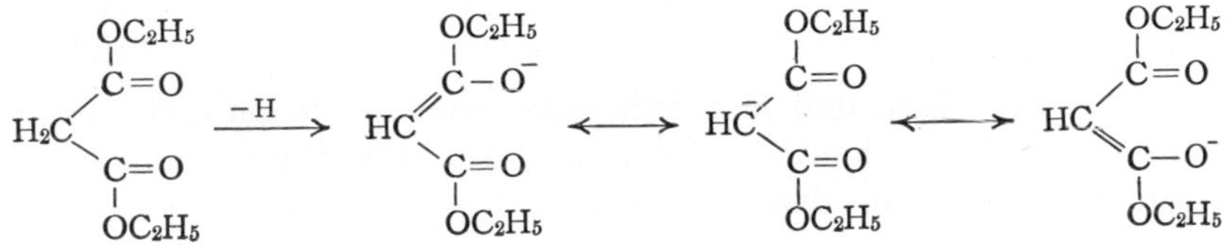

NaCH$(CO_2C_2H_5)_2$, can be alkylated to RCH$(CO_2C_2H_5)_2$, and when this is hydrolyzed the substituted malonic acid readily loses carbon dioxide and

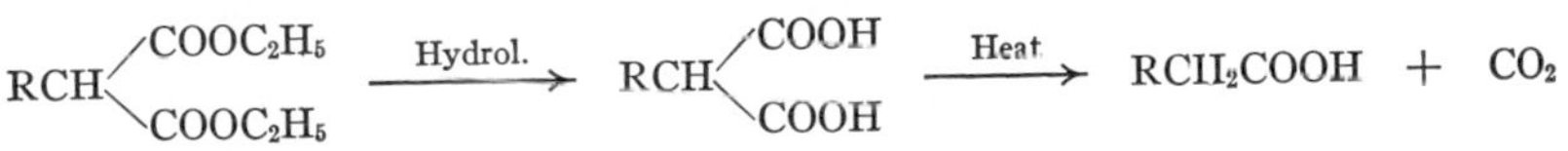

affords a substituted monocarboxylic acid. An example is the synthesis of caproic acid starting with n-butyl bromide. Metallic sodium is dissolved in ethanol to give a solution of sodium ethoxide, and malonic ester is slowly

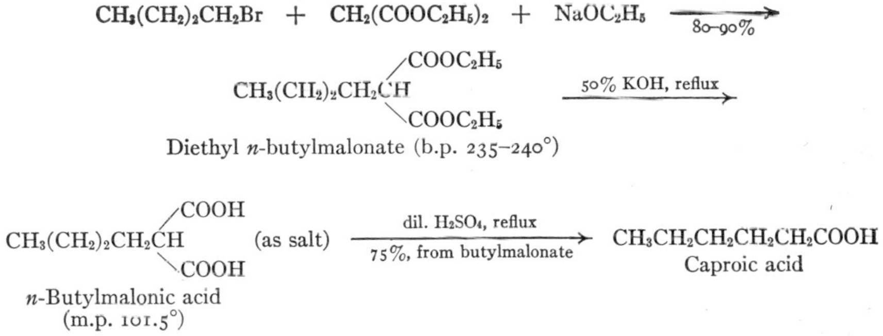

$$CH_3(CH_2)_2CH_2Br \ + \ CH_2(COOC_2H_5)_2 \ + \ NaOC_2H_5 \xrightarrow[80-90\%]{}$$

$$CH_3(CH_2)_2CH_2CH\begin{array}{l}COOC_2H_5\\COOC_2H_5\end{array} \xrightarrow{50\% \ KOH, \ reflux}$$

Diethyl n-butylmalonate (b.p. 235–240°)

$$CH_3(CH_2)_2CH_2CH\begin{array}{l}COOH\\COOH\end{array} \ (\text{as salt}) \xrightarrow[75\%, \ from \ butylmalonate]{dil. \ H_2SO_4, \ reflux} CH_3CH_2CH_2CH_2CH_2COOH$$

n-Butylmalonic acid   Caproic acid
(m.p. 101.5°)

introduced followed by an equivalent amount of n-butyl bromide. The substituted malonic ester is separated by removing the bulk of the alcohol and adding water, and it is hydrolyzed with boiling potassium hydroxide solution. The resulting n-butylmalonic acid can be isolated as a solid and the decarboxylation conducted by heating the molten material at 150°. A simpler method is to render the aqueous solution strongly acidic with sulfuric acid and reflux the mixture; the mineral acid catalyzes loss of carbon dioxide at a temperature not much above 100°.

A monosubstituted malonic ester still has a hydrogen atom replaceable by sodium and therefore available for a second alkylation. An example is the synthesis of diethylacetic acid. Malonic ester is either converted into the mono- and then the diethyl derivative or treated with two equivalents each of sodium ethoxide and ethyl iodide and so diethylated directly. The disubstituted malonic ester is hindered and hence more resistant to alkaline hydrolysis than a monosubstituted ester.

$$CH_2(CO_2C_2H_5)_2 \longrightarrow C_2H_5CH(CO_2C_2H_5)_2 \longrightarrow (C_2H_5)_2C(CO_2C_2H_5)_2 \longrightarrow$$

$$\underset{\substack{\text{Diethylmalonic acid}\\(\text{m.p. } 121°)}}{\underset{C_2H_5}{\overset{C_2H_5}{>}}C\underset{CO_2H}{\overset{CO_2H}{<}}} \xrightarrow{180°} \underset{\substack{\text{Diethylacetic acid}\\(\text{b.p. } 190°)}}{\underset{C_2H_5}{\overset{C_2H_5}{>}}CHCOOH}$$

A reaction that is related since it involves the enolate ion is the addition of malonic ester to acrylonitrile under catalysis by sodium ethoxide. The base can be assumed to abstract a proton from the ester to produce the

$$(C_2H_5OCO)_2\bar{C}H \ + \ \overset{\delta+}{CH_2}=CH\overset{\frown}{-}C\overset{\frown}{\equiv}\overset{\delta-}{N} \ \longrightarrow \ (C_2H_5OCO)_2CHCH_2CH=C=\bar{N}$$

$$\xrightarrow{CH_2(CO_2C_2H_5)_2} \ (C_2H_5OCO)_2CHCH_2CH_2CN \ + \ \bar{C}H(CO_2C_2H_5)_2$$

anion, which attacks the positively polarized center of the nitrile. The condensation is an example of the Michael reaction (p. 699). Condensations involving acrylonitrile are called cyanoethylations; the product in the example is diethyl cyanoethylmalonate.

PROBLEMS

1. Give the Geneva names for:

    (a) $CH_3CH(OH)COCH_2CH_3$
    (b) $(CH_3)_2CHCH_2CH_2CH_2C(CH_3)=CHCH_2OH$
    (c) $OHCC(CH_3)=CHCH=CHC(CH_3)=CHCHO$

2. Suggest an appropriate method for preparation of the following compounds from the starting materials indicated:

    (a) Methyl ethyl ketone from *sec*-butyl alcohol
    (b) Methyl *n*-hexyl ketone from capryl alcohol, $CH_3(CH_2)_5CH(OH)CH_3$
    (c) Methyl allyl ketone, starting with acetaldehyde and allyl bromide
    (d) Sebacic acid-half aldehyde, $O=CH(CH_2)_8COOH$, from undecylenic acid, $CH_2=CH(CH_2)_8COOH$
    (e) *n*-Valeraldehyde from *n*-valeric acid

3. Indicate the steps required for transformation of cyclohexanone into cyclopentanone. How could the reverse transformation be accomplished?

4. Summarize the quantitative and qualitative differences in reactions of aldehydes and ketones.

5. Cite specific comparisons that establish the order of reactivity of the carbonyl groups in the following compounds: acetone, diethyl ketone, acetaldehyde, chloral, diisopropyl ketone.

6. How could cinnamaldehyde, $C_6H_5CH=CHCHO$, be converted into cinnamyl alcohol, $C_6H_5CHCH=CH_2OH$?

7. Predict the result of the treatment of isobutyraldehyde with dilute aqueous sodium hydroxide solution in the cold.

8. Predict the result of the action of a concentrated solution of alkali on trimethylacetaldehyde.

9. Suggest a synthesis of β-hydroxyisovaleric acid, $(CH_3)_2C(OH)CH_2COOH$, starting with acetone.

10. Suggest a procedure by which the aldehydic group of the compound CH_3COCH_2-CH_2CHO could be protected and the substance converted into the aldehyde-acid $HOOCCH_2CH_2CHO$.

11. One commercial process for making n-butyl alcohol starts with an aldol condensation of acetaldehyde. Formulate the process.

12. Cite specific examples establishing the relative reactivity of the carbonyl group of ketones and esters.

13. A substance $C_6H_{12}O$ yields an oxidation product $C_6H_{10}O$ that reacts with phenyl-hydrazine and gives a positive iodoform test. The original substance also can be dehydrated with sulfuric acid to a hydrocarbon C_6H_{10}, and this on oxidation yields acetone. What is the structure of the substance?

14. A substance $C_6H_8O_2$ forms a dioxime, gives a positive iodoform test and a positive Schiff test, and can be converted into n-pentane. What is its structure?

15. Predict the result of the following reactions:

(a) Ethylene oxide + HCN

(b) CH_3COCH_3 + $(CH_3)_3CCHO$ (with a trace of alkali)

16. Starting with three-carbon components, devise syntheses for:

(a) Diethyl ketone (c) Isovaleric acid
(b) Hexanone-3

17. A hydrocarbon C_7H_{12} yields cyclopentanecarboxylic acid on chromic acid oxidation. On reaction with concentrated sulfuric acid followed by hydrolysis it yields an alcohol, $C_7H_{14}O$, that gives a positive iodoform test. What is the structure of the hydrocarbon?

18. A compound $C_7H_{14}O_2$ (I) reacts with acetic anhydride to give $C_7H_{13}O(OCOCH_3)$ (II); it does not react with phenylhydrazine. When treated with $Pb(OAc)_4$, I gives $C_7H_{12}O_2$ (III), which reacts with H_2NOH to give $C_7H_{12}(=NOH)_2$, reduces Fehling's solution, and on treatment with NaOI consumes 4 moles of the reagent to give iodoform and $HOOC(CH_2)_4COOH$. Give a brief interpretation of the significance of each of the observations recorded and deduce the structure of I.

19. What is the probable mechanism of the reaction of RMgX with R_2CO?

20. Suggest a method for reduction of $CH_3COCH_2CO_2C_2H_5$ to $CH_3CH_2CH_2CO_2C_2H_5$.

21. Phenylglyoxal, C_6H_5COCHO, under the influence of base, undergoes a Cannizzaro-like intramolecular reaction to form a substance $C_8H_8O_3$. What is the structure?

22. Formulate syntheses for the following compounds from malonic ester and any halogen compound desired:

(a) $(CH_3)_2CHCH_2CO_2H$ (b) $CH_3CH_2CH(CH_3)CO_2H$
(c) $HOOCCH_2CH_2CH_2CH_2CH_2CH_2CO_2H$

23. Predict the relative enol content of the C-methyl and C-acetyl derivatives of aceto-acetic ester:

$$CH_3COCH(CH_3)CO_2C_2H_5 \text{ and } CH_3COCH(COCH_3)CO_2C_2H_5$$

READING REFERENCES

L. C. Cooley, "Acetone," *Ind. Eng. Chem.*, **29**, 1399 (1937)

C. F. H. Allen and A. H. Blatt, "The Carbon-Oxygen Double Bond," in H. Gilman, "Organic Chemistry," 2nd Ed., I, 643–657, Wiley, New York (1943)

H. Adkins, "Equilibria and Rates in the Formation of Acetals and Semicarbazones," in H. Gilman, "Organic Chemistry," 2nd Ed., I, 1046–1052, Wiley, New York (1943)

C. R. Hauser and B. E. Hudson, Jr., "The Acetoacetic Ester Condensation and Certain Related Reactions," *Organic Reactions*, I, 266–302, Wiley, New York (1942)

CHAPTER 10

AMINES

Amines are derivatives of ammonia in which one or more hydrogen atoms are replaced by an alkyl radical, and they are called primary, secondary, and tertiary amines according to the number of such substitutions:

RNH_2	$\begin{matrix} R \\ \diagdown \\ R' \diagup \end{matrix} NH$	$\begin{matrix} R \\ \diagdown \\ R' \!\!-\!\! N \\ R'' \diagup \end{matrix}$
Primary amine	Secondary amine	Tertiary amine

If but one radical is introduced, the substance has a primary amino group (NH_2) and is a primary amine even though the alkyl substituent may have a secondary or tertiary structure, for example t-butylamine, $(CH_3)_3CNH_2$. Methyl- and ethylamine were discovered in 1849 by Wurtz, and a general

TABLE 10.1. AMINES

NAME	FORMULA	M.P., °C.	B.P., °C.	SP. GR.
Methylamine	CH_3NH_2	−92.5	−6.5	0.699
Dimethylamine	$(CH_3)_2NH$	−96.0	7.4	.680
Trimethylamine	$(CH_3)_3N$	−124.0	3.5	.662
Ethylamine	$CH_3CH_2NH_2$	−80.6	16.6	.689
Diethylamine	$(CH_3CH_2)_2NH$	−38.9	56.0	.711
Triethylamine	$(CH_3CH_2)_3N$	−114.8	89.5	.728
n-Propylamine	$CH_3CH_2CH_2NH_2$	−83.0	48.7	.719
Di-n-propylamine	$(CH_3CH_2CH_2)_2NH$	−39.6	110.7	.738
Tri-n-propylamine	$(CH_3CH_2CH_2)_3N$	−93.5	156	.757
n-Butylamine	$CH_3CH_2CH_2CH_2NH_2$	−50.5	76	.740
n-Amylamine	$CH_3CH_2CH_2CH_2CH_2NH_2$	−55.0	104	.766
n-Hexylamine	$CH_3(CH_2)_5NH_2$	−19	$130^{742mm.}$	
Laurylamine	$CH_3(CH_2)_{11}NH_2$	28	$135^{15mm.}$	
Ethylenediamine	$H_2NCH_2CH_2NH_2$	8.5	117	.892
Trimethylenediamine	$H_2NCH_2CH_2CH_2NH_2$		135.5	.884
Tetramethylenediamine	$H_2NCH_2CH_2CH_2CH_2NH_2$	27	158	
Pentamethylenediamine	$H_2NCH_2CH_2CH_2CH_2CH_2NH_2$	9	178	.855
Hexamethylenediamine	$H_2N(CH_2)_6NH_2$	39	196	
Ethanolamine	$HOCH_2CH_2NH_2$		171	1.022
Diethanolamine	$(HOCH_2CH_2)_2NH$	28	270	1.097
Triethanolamine	$(HOCH_2CH_2)_3N$	21	$279^{150mm.}$	1.124
Allylamine	$CH_2{=}CHCH_2NH_2$		53.2	0.761
Aniline	$C_6H_5NH_2$	−6	184	1.022

method of preparing secondary and tertiary as well as primary amines was discovered shortly by Hofmann[1] (1849).

Methylamine is a gas under ordinary conditions (Table 10.1) and has a boiling point somewhat higher than that of ammonia (b.p. $-33.3°$). The odor of the also volatile ethylamine is so similar to that of ammonia that when Wurtz first had the material in hand he did not recognize it as a new substance until, in the course of experimentation, the alkaline gas by chance came near a flame and took fire. In general, amines that are either gases or fairly volatile liquids of moderate molecular weight have a pronounced odor similar to that of ammonia but less pungent and more fishlike. Dimethylamine and trimethylamine are constituents of herring brine. The lower amines are very soluble in water; among compounds having normal alkyl groups the limiting members in the three series showing significant solubility are: n-amylamine, di-n-propylamine, and triethylamine.

Comparative data of isomeric compounds of molecular weight 101.19 show that straight-chain amines boil at temperatures only slightly above those characteristic of unassociated liquids of this molecular weight (b.p. about 100°) and that branching of the chain is attended by enhanced volatility. Diethanolamine (mol. wt. 105.14) has a much higher boiling point (270°), indicative of association attributable to the hydroxyl groups. Pentamethylenediamine (mol. wt.

COMPOUND (MOL. WT. 101.19)	B.P.
$CH_3CH_2CH_2CH_2CH_2CH_2NH_2$	130°/742mm.
$CH_3CH_2CH_2NHCH_2CH_2CH_3$	110.7°
CH_3 CH_3 $>$CHNHCH$<$ CH_3 CH_3	84°
CH_3CH_2 $>$N—CH_2CH_3 CH_3CH_2	89.5°

102.18) has a boiling point (178°) considerably above the normal value for unassociated liquids, and this property is in line with the fact that even monoamines show some tendency to exist in an associated condition. The association is attributable to hydrogen bonding; since nitrogen is less electronegative than oxygen, hydrogen bonding in primary and secondary amines is less pronounced than that in alcohols.

Basic Properties. – Amines, like ammonia, give an alkaline reaction in aqueous solution and form salts with acids. The essential process is combination of the amine, functioning as an electron donor or Lewis base,

$(CH_3)_3N:$ $+$ $\begin{cases} \text{(a) } H^+ & \longrightarrow (CH_3)_3\overset{+}{N}:H \\ \text{(b) } B(CH_3)_3 & \longrightarrow (CH_3)_3N^+:B^-(CH_3)_3 \end{cases}$

(Lewis acids)   Trimethylamine—Trimethylboron, m.p. 128°

with the electron-accepting proton (a), and analogous combination occurs with other Lewis acids, for example trimethylboron (b). The new bond formed in case (b) is a coordinate covalent bond. The alkaline reaction

---

[1] August Wilhelm von Hofmann, 1818–92; b. Giessen, Germany; Professor at Bonn, Royal Coll. of Chem., London (1845–64), Berlin; see reading ref., also *Ber.*, **25**, 3369 (1892); **35**, 4503 (1902)

noted when an amine is dissolved in water is due to the excess hydroxide ion concentration following withdrawal of hydrogen ions by the combination (a), and the overall result can be represented thus:

$$R_3N: + \overset{+}{H}OH^- \rightleftharpoons R_3\overset{+}{N}{:}H + OH^-$$

The amine may be present partly as the unstable hydrate, R_3NHOH. The basic dissociation constant of an amine (k_b) is expressed as the product of the concentrations of the ammonium and hydroxide ions divided by the total concentration of unionized material, $[CH_3NH_2]$, for example:

$$k_b = \frac{[CH_3NH_3^+][OH^-]}{[CH_3NH_2]}$$

Basic strength is conveniently expressed as the negative logarithm of the basic dissociation constant; thus $pK_b = -\log k_b$. A strong base has a low pK_b value, a weak one has a value approaching the limit $pK_b = 14$. The typical aliphatic amines listed in Table 10.2 are all more strongly basic

TABLE 10.2. BASIC DISSOCIATION, $pK_b^{25°}$

NH₃, 4.75	
CH_3NH_2, 3.37	$CH_3CH_2NH_2$, 3.27
$(CH_3)_2NH$, 3.22	$(CH_3CH_2)_2NH$, 2.89
$(CH_3)_3N$, 4.20	$(CH_3CH_2)_3N$, 3.36
$C_6H_5NH_2$ (Aniline), 9.30	

than ammonia; aromatic amines, typified by aniline, are much weaker bases. That methylamine and ethylamine are stronger bases than ammonia by 1.4–1.5 pK_b units is attributable to the electron release of the methyl or ethyl group, which increases the electron density on nitrogen and hence increases its affinity for a proton. That the effect of a second group is much less than that of the first is consistent with the effect of one and two chlorine atoms on the ionization of acetic acid (p. 164), but the marked and uneven decrease in basic strength in the tertiary series is difficult to understand. H. C. Brown (1944) has suggested an interpretation based on the assumption of strains (B- and F-strain) in the normally pyramidal ammonia molecule that influence attack by the proton.

Salts with mineral acids are analogous to ammonium salts, and are formed both in aqueous solution and under anhydrous conditions, for example by passing hydrogen chloride gas into an ethereal solution of the amine, in which case the amine salt separates quantitatively as a white solid. Alternate conventional methods of formulating and naming amine salts are illustrated for the salt of methylamine and hydrochloric acid:

CH_3NH_3Cl
Methylammonium chloride

$CH_3NH_2{\cdot}HCl$
Methylamine hydrochloride

Salt formation involves an increase in the valence of nitrogen from three to five, and the fifth linkage is polar; the reaction is represented as follows:

$$\underset{\substack{\text{Trimethylamine}}}{\overset{\displaystyle CH_3}{\underset{\displaystyle CH_3}{CH_3:\overset{..}{\underset{..}{N}}:}}} \quad + \quad H^+:\overset{..}{\underset{..}{Br}}:^- \quad \longrightarrow \quad \underset{\substack{\text{Trimethylammonium}\\\text{bromide (trimethyl-}\\\text{amine hydrobromide)}}}{\overset{\displaystyle CH_3}{\underset{\displaystyle CH_3}{CH_3:\overset{..}{\underset{..}{N}}:H^+:\overset{..}{\underset{..}{Br}}:^-}}}$$

The hydrogen ion accepts the unshared pair of electrons of the nitrogen atom with formation of a covalent bond, and the nitrogen-containing group thereby acquires a positive charge. Amine salts, owing to their ionic character, contrast with amines in physical properties. They are all odorless, nonvolatile solids, even though the amines from which they are derived are odoriferous gases or liquids, and they are insoluble in ether or in hydrocarbon solvents, which dissolve the typically organic amines. With the exception of substances of very high molecular weight, the salts are readily soluble in water and exist in the solution in ionized condition. The solubility in water is decreased by addition of excess of the appropriate mineral acid, and use is made of the common-ion effect in crystallization of amine salts. Ability to form salts is a property distinctive of amines and can be recognized easily by simple qualitative tests. An amine of low molecular weight may be substantially as soluble in water as it is in dilute hydrochloric acid, but if so it will be in the range of the odoriferous amines, and the fact of salt formation will be evident from obliteration of the odor on addition of excess acid. Odorless amines invariably are at most only partially soluble in water, and salt formation is apparent from the fact that they can be brought into solution by addition of a mineral acid. Similarly, an amine salt can be recognized by addition of sodium hydroxide to the aqueous solution. The alkali is a much stronger base than the amine, and liberation of the amine is evident either from the odor or from separation of an oil or solid. For recovery of an amine from a salt, the material set free by addition of alkali is collected by suction filtration of a solid or by extraction with ether or steam distillation of a volatile amine.

Amine salts of the halogen acids often possess characteristic melting points, or points of decomposition, as shown in Table 10.3. Amine hydro-

TABLE 10.3. AMINE SALTS

FORMULA	M.P.	FORMULA	M.P.
$CH_3NH_2 \cdot HCl$	226°	$(C_2H_5)_2NH \cdot HCl$	217°
$C_2H_5NH_2$ HCl	109°	$(C_2H_5)_3N \cdot HCl$	254°
$C_2H_5NH_2 \cdot HBr$	159.5°	$C_6H_5NH_2 \cdot HCl$	198°
$C_2H_5NH_2 \cdot HI$	188.5°	$C_6H_5NH_2 \cdot HBr$	286°

chlorides, although insoluble in ether, ligroin, or benzene, often are somewhat soluble in methanol or ethanol and can be separated from a mixture containing ammonium chloride by extraction with a lower alcohol. The sulfates usually are less fusible and less soluble in water. Acetic acid forms salts of slight stability, but strongly acidic organic acids (e.g., picric acid, oxalic acid) give stable salts which, being of more organic character than mineral acid salts, tend to be less soluble in water and more readily fusible and which are therefore useful for identification. Volatile amines are conveniently prepared for analysis in the form of their sparingly soluble salts with chloroplatinic acid, for example $(RNH_3)_2PtCl_6$.

Quaternary Ammonium Compounds. — Tertiary amines when heated with alkyl halides combine to form compounds similar to ammonium salts but having four alkyl groups attached to nitrogen and hence called quaternary ammonium salts. These salts are solid ionic substances readily soluble

$$(CH_3)_3N \xrightarrow{CH_3I} (CH_3)_4\overset{+}{N}I^-$$
Tetramethylammonium
iodide

in water and insoluble in ether and comparable to hydrochlorides and hydrobromides of the same tertiary amines. They are also difficultly fusible substances that when strongly heated decompose into a tertiary amine and an alkyl halide. The tetraalkylammonium salts contrast with amine hydrohalides and simple ammonium salts in behavior toward alkalis, for no free amine is liberated and instead there results an equilibrium mixture containing a stable quaternary ammonium hydroxide, for example:

$$(CH_3)_4\overset{+}{N}I^- + KOH \rightleftharpoons (CH_3)_4\overset{+}{N}OH^- + KI$$
Tetramethylammonium
hydroxide

The tetraalkyl derivative cannot decompose by loss of water in the manner characteristic of ammonium hydroxide and amine hydrates and therefore affords a high concentration of hydroxide ion. The substance is a strong base comparable to sodium or potassium hydroxide, which explains why the equilibrium constant in the above reaction is close to unity. The preparation of a quaternary ammonium base is accomplished by treatment of the halide in aqueous solution with silver hydroxide, for silver halide precipitates and the equilibrium is displaced. The filtered aqueous solution

$$(CH_3)_4\overset{+}{N}I^- + AgOH \longrightarrow (CH_3)_4\overset{+}{N}OH^- + AgI$$

can be evaporated without decomposition of the organic base, which can be obtained as a crystalline solid, usually as a deliquescent hydrate. Concentrated solutions of quaternary ammonium hydroxides have a caustic, corrosive action similar to alkalis and cannot be stored in glass vessels without contamination due to attack of the container.

PREPARATION OF AMINES

Alkylation of Ammonia. — One of several fundamental discoveries made by Hofmann in pioneering investigations of amines is that alkyl groups can be introduced directly into ammonia by interaction with an alkyl halide and subsequent treatment with alkali (1849). The reaction is general but is subject to the disadvantage that higher substitution inevitably occurs.

$$RX \xrightarrow{\text{HNH}_2} RNH_2 \cdot HX \xrightarrow{\text{NaOH}} RNH_2$$

When ethyl bromide reacts with ammonia, the halide initially adds to the trivalent nitrogen to give an ammonium salt, but this enters into equilibrium with ammonia still present with liberation of a certain amount of ethylamine. The primary amine then competes with ammonia for the alkyl halide and yields some of the secondary amine salt; repetition of the process affords the tertiary amine salt, and in the presence of excess alkyl halide the reaction may even continue to the production of the quaternary ammonium salt. A primary amine thus is not the exclusive product of a

$$C_2H_5Br + NH_3 \rightarrow C_2H_5\overset{+}{N}H_3Br^-$$

$$C_2H_5\overset{+}{N}H_3Br^- + NH_3 \rightleftharpoons C_2H_5NH_2 + NH_4Br$$

$$C_2H_5NH_2 + C_2H_5Br \rightarrow (C_2H_5)_2\overset{+}{N}H_2Br^-$$

$$(C_2H_5)_2\overset{+}{N}H_2Br^- + NH_3 \rightleftharpoons (C_2H_5)_2NH + NH_4Br$$

reaction conducted with equivalent amounts of reagents, but is contaminated with secondary and tertiary amines, and in the preparation of a secondary amine by the reaction $RNH_2 + R'Br$, some of the corresponding tertiary amine invariably is formed. Thus the method of alkylation is practicable for preparation of pure products only where an adequate method of separation is available. Mono-, di-, and triethylamine are prepared industrially by this method because the boiling points are separated sufficiently to permit fractionation of the mixture. The corresponding methyl homologs boil over such a narrow range that distillation technique is not applicable. Trimethylamine can be prepared by exhaustive methylation of ammonia to a mixture of the tertiary amine and the tetramethylammonium salt, which can be converted by thermal decomposition into trimethylamine and the alkyl halide. When the halogen atom of an expensive intermediate is to be replaced by a primary amino group, it is expedient to use a large excess of ammonia in order to suppress formation of disubstituted ammonia, as in the following preparation:

$$\underset{\overset{|}{Br}}{CH_3CHCO_2H} \xrightarrow[65-70\%]{\text{NH}_3 \text{ (70 equivalents)}} \underset{\overset{|}{NH_2}}{CH_3CHCO_2H}$$

Alanine

Reduction of Unsaturated Nitrogen Compounds. — **Nitriles** or **cyanides** are one of four types of unsaturated compounds yielding primary amines as the chief products of reduction. The reaction, which can be brought about by either chemical reducing agents or catalytic hydrogenation, involves addition of two pairs of hydrogen atoms to the triple bond: $RC \equiv N + 4H \rightarrow RCH_2NH_2$. The required nitriles are readily obtainable from alcohols by interaction of the halides with potassium cyanide. Reduction with zinc and sulfuric acid proceeds so slowly as to allow loss of starting material by hydrolysis; reduction with sodium and alcohol is only moderately satisfactory. Hydrogenation of nitriles proceeds readily

$$CH_3CH_2CH_2CH_2CH_2C \equiv N \xrightarrow[70\%]{Na,\ C_2H_5OH} CH_3CH_2CH_2CH_2CH_2CH_2NH_2$$
Capronitrile   n-Hexylamine

in the presence of nickel catalysts but yields, surprisingly, a considerable amount of the secondary amine, for example:

$$C_6H_5CH_2CN \xrightarrow{H_2,\ Raney\ Ni,\ 140°} \begin{cases} C_6H_5CH_2CH_2NH_2\ (71\%) \\ \beta\text{-Phenylethylamine} \\ (C_6H_5CH_2CH_2)_2NH\ (20\%) \\ Di\text{-}\beta\text{-phenylethylamine} \end{cases}$$
Benzyl cyanide

The by-product is regarded as resulting from addition of some of the primary amine to the initially produced imine (RCH=NH), followed by hydrogenative fission, or hydrogenolysis. Formation of the secondary

$$RCH_2NH_2 + RCH=NH \longrightarrow \underset{RCH_2}{\overset{RCH-NH_2}{>}}NH \xrightarrow{2H} \underset{RCH_2}{\overset{RCH_2}{>}}NH + NH_3$$

amine is suppressed by conducting the hydrogenation in either liquid ammonia or a solution of dry ammonia in methanol; under these conditions β-phenylethylamine is obtained in yields of 85–90%.

Reduction of nitriles by lithium aluminum hydride is one application of this useful reagent. A highly advantageous feature of this method is that secondary and tertiary amines are not formed. The yields in the reduction of aliphatic mononitriles are high (lauronitrile, 90%); reduction of dinitriles

$$2\ RC \equiv N + LiAlH_4 \longrightarrow (RCH_2N)_2LiAl \xrightarrow{H_2O} 2\ RCH_2NH_2$$

Examples:

$$C_6H_5C \equiv N \xrightarrow[72\%]{LiAlH_4} C_6H_5CH_2NH_2$$
Benzonitrile   Benzylamine

$$N \equiv C(CH_2)_8C \equiv N \xrightarrow[40\%]{LiAlH_4} H_2NCH_2(CH_2)_8CH_2NH_2$$
Sebaconitrile   1,10-Diaminodecane

proceeds with some difficulty. **Amides** of the types $RCONH_2$, $RCONHR'$, and $RCONR'R''$ are reduced by lithium aluminum hydride to primary, secondary, and tertiary amines, respectively. Amides are rather unreactive

Examples:

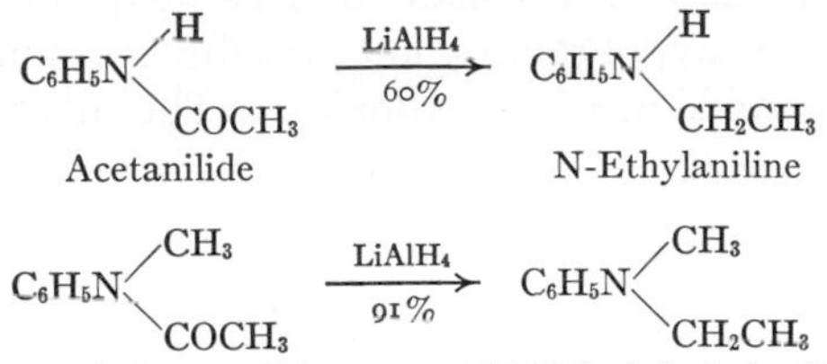

$$C_6H_5N\begin{matrix}H\\COCH_3\end{matrix} \xrightarrow[60\%]{LiAlH_4} C_6H_5N\begin{matrix}H\\CH_2CH_3\end{matrix}$$

Acetanilide   N-Ethylaniline

$$C_6H_5N\begin{matrix}CH_3\\COCH_3\end{matrix} \xrightarrow[91\%]{LiAlH_4} C_6H_5N\begin{matrix}CH_3\\CH_2CH_3\end{matrix}$$

N-Methylacetanilide   N,N-Methylethylaniline

substances and are not reducible by other chemical methods. Hydrogenation can be accomplished at high temperatures and pressures, but mixtures usually result; for example:

$$CH_3(CH_2)_9CH_2CONH_2 \xrightarrow[250°,\ 300\ atm.]{H_2,\ Cu—Cr,\ dioxan,} CH_3(CH_2)_9CH_2CH_2NH_2$$

Lauramide   Laurylamine
                             (with 49% of the
                             secondary amine)

Oximes resulting from condensation of hydroxylamine with aldehydes and ketones are also reducible to primary amines, presumably by addition of hydrogen to the double bond and replacement of the hydroxyl group by hydrogen:

$$RCH{=}NOH \xrightarrow{2H} \left[RCH_2N\begin{matrix}H\\OH\end{matrix}\right] \xrightarrow{2H} RCH_2NH_2 + H_2O$$

Such reductions are often accomplished successfully with sodium and alcohol or with sodium amalgam and dilute acetic acid, as in the example:

$$CH_3(CH_2)_5CH{=}NOH \xrightarrow[60-73\%]{Na,\ C_2H_5OH} CH_3(CH_2)_5CH_2NH_2$$

n-Heptaldoxime   n-Heptylamine

On hydrogenation of the same oxime over a nickel catalyst supported on kieselguhr, n heptylamine is obtained in 61% yield, accompanied by 20% of di-n-heptylamine; a further example of the method is as follows:

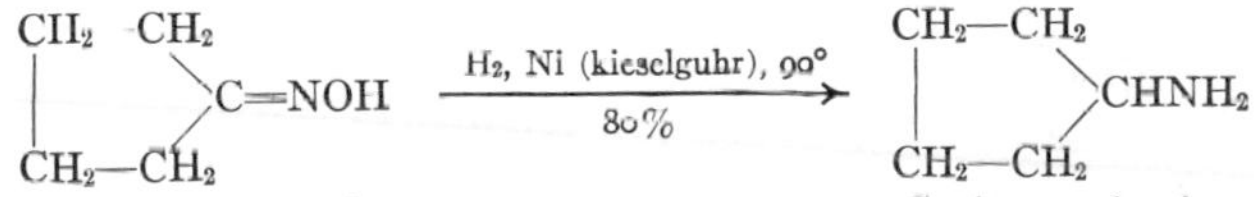

$$\begin{matrix}CH_2-CH_2\\ C{=}NOH\\CH_2-CH_2\end{matrix} \xrightarrow[80\%]{H_2,\ Ni\ (kieselguhr),\ 90°} \begin{matrix}CH_2-CH_2\\ \ \ \ \ \ \ \ \ \ \ \ \ \ \ \ \ CHNH_2\\CH_2-CH_2\end{matrix}$$

Cyclopentanone oxime   Cyclopentylamine
                                 (with 10% of the
                                 secondary amine)

Some secondary amine invariably is formed in the hydrogenation and may result from initial condensation of the primary amine with the starting material.

Nitroalkanes are reducible with lithium aluminum hydride to amines; for example, 2-nitrobutane gives sec-butylamine in 85% yield.

Hofmann Reaction. — A reaction discovered by Hofmann in 1881 affords primary amines in excellent yields uncontaminated with secondary amines. The method consists in treatment of an amide with sodium hypochlorite or hypobromite and results in elimination of the carbonyl group of the amide as carbon dioxide. The mechanism of this remarkable

$$R-C{\overset{O}{\underset{NH_2}{}}} + NaOBr \xrightarrow{NaOH} RNH_2 + NaBr + CO_2$$

transformation is well established. The reaction proceeds in two stages, of which the first consists in formation of a bromoamide by substitution of bromine for one of the hydrogen atoms that is attached to nitrogen and is in a position to be activated by the adjacent carbonyl group. Bromoamides are stable in the absence of excess alkali and can be prepared in good yield by adding sufficient dilute alkali to a mixture of equivalent amounts of the amide and of bromine to produce a corresponding amount of sodium hypobromite. The bromoamide when warmed with excess alkali decomposes to the primary amine and carbon dioxide as the result of elimination of hydrogen bromide and formation of a transient intermediate and rearrangement to an isocyanate by migration of the alkyl group from carbon to nitrogen.

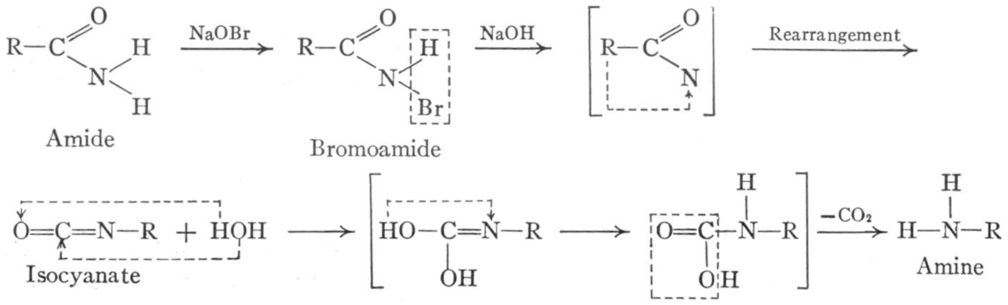

The electronic formulation shows that the nitrogen atom of the intermediate has only a sextet of electrons; this condition of instability induces migration

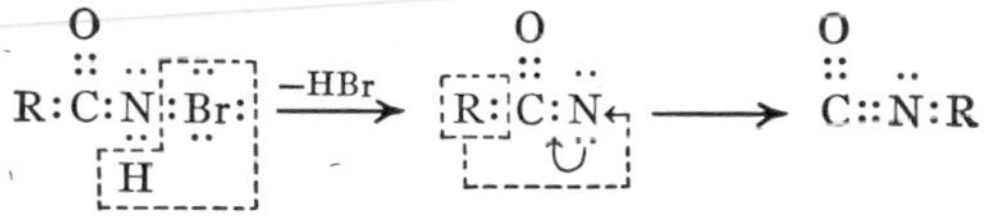

of the alkyl group with the pair of shared electrons from carbon to nitrogen, which completes the nitrogen octet. Isocyanates have been isolated in some instances and are well characterized compounds, usually prepared by condensation of amines with phosgene. Isocyanates are subject to hydroly-

$$RNH_2 + ClCOCl \longrightarrow RNHCOCl \longrightarrow RN{=}C{=}O + HCl$$

sis by alkalis; indeed this reaction was employed by Wurtz in the first preparation of an alkylamine. The hydrolysis step is formulated as involving addition of water to the carbonyl group, migration of hydrogen, and decarboxylation of a carboxyamine (carbamic acid), for which ample analogy exists. These many changes proceed efficiently, and in an actual preparation no intermediate need be isolated. Hofmann obtained excellent yields of pure primary amines from a number of amides, for example:

$$\underset{\text{Caproamide}}{CH_3CH_2CH_2CH_2CH_2CONH_2} \xrightarrow[88\%]{\text{NaOBr}} \underset{n\text{-Amylamine}}{CH_3CH_2CH_2CH_2CH_2NH_2}$$

The yields fall off somewhat on extending the reaction to amides of high molecular weight, but in this case satisfactory results are obtained by a modified procedure utilizing bromine and methyl alcoholic sodium methoxide.

The **Curtius reaction** (1894), also available for preparation of primary amines, utilizes an acyl azide prepared either from an acid chloride and sodium azide ($RCOCl + NaN_3$) or by the action of nitrous acid on an acyl hydrazide (from an ester and hydrazine, p. 179). When heated in a solvent, the acyl azide loses nitrogen with rearrangement to an isocyanate, as in the

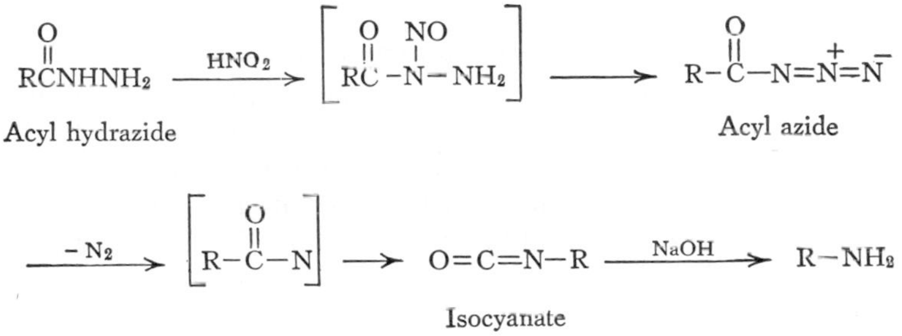

$$\underset{\text{Acyl hydrazide}}{\overset{O}{\overset{\|}{R}CNHNH_2}} \xrightarrow{HNO_2} \left[\overset{O}{\overset{\|}{RC}} \overset{NO}{\overset{\|}{-N}} -NH_2 \right] \longrightarrow \underset{\text{Acyl azide}}{\overset{O}{\overset{\|}{R-C}}-N=\overset{+}{N}=\overset{-}{N}}$$

$$\xrightarrow{-N_2} \left[R-\overset{O}{\overset{\|}{C}}-N \right] \longrightarrow \underset{\text{Isocyanate}}{O=C=N-R} \xrightarrow{NaOH} R-NH_2$$

Hofmann reaction. Loss of nitrogen (a) gives an electronically deficient nitrogen atom, which stabilizes itself by alkyl migration. In the **Schmidt modification** (1923) the carboxylic acid and hydrazoic acid are condensed

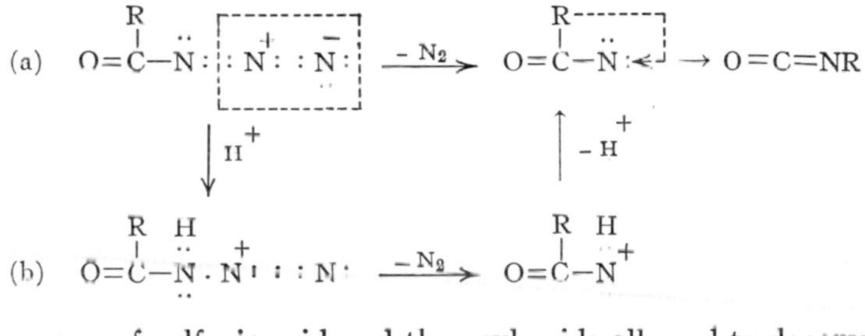

(a) $\quad O=\overset{R}{\overset{|}{C}}-\overset{..}{N}: [: \overset{+}{N} : : \overset{-}{N} :] \xrightarrow{-N_2} O=\overset{R}{\overset{|}{C}}-\overset{..}{N} : \longleftarrow \longrightarrow O=C=NR$

$\qquad \downarrow H^+ \qquad\qquad\qquad\qquad \uparrow -H^+$

(b) $\quad O=\overset{R\ \ H}{\overset{|\ \ |}{C}}-\overset{..}{N}\cdot\overset{+}{N}::N\cdot \xrightarrow{-N_2} O=\overset{R\ \ H}{\overset{|\ \ |}{C}}-\overset{..+}{N}$

in the presence of sulfuric acid and the acyl azide allowed to decompose and rearrange under the influence of the mineral acid; the conjugate acid (b) loses nitrogen more easily than the azide itself. The one-step procedure is convenient and yields are high, for example:

$$\underset{\text{Stearic acid}}{CH_3(CH_2)_{16}CO_2H} \xrightarrow[96\%]{HN_3,\ H^+,\ H_2O} \underset{\text{Heptadecylamine}}{CH_3(CH_2)_{16}NH_2 + CO_2 + N_2}$$

Gabriel Synthesis. — Gabriel, when working in Hofmann's laboratory, introduced in 1887 a useful method of preparing pure primary amines con-

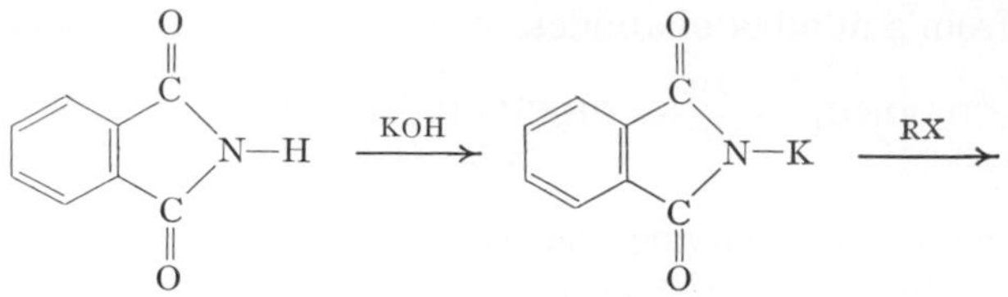

Phthalimide
(pK$_a$ 8.30)

Potassium phthalimide

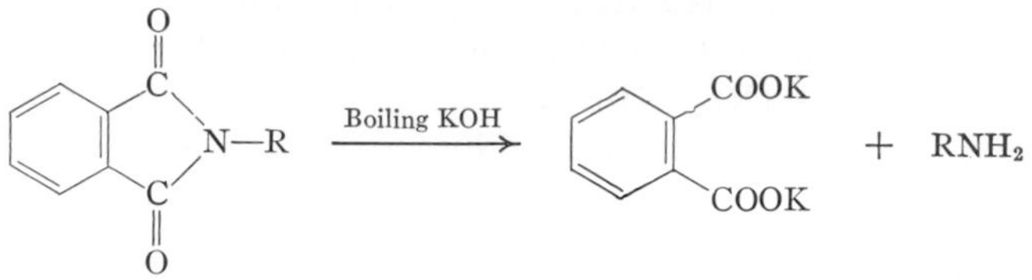

+ RNH$_2$

sisting in alkylation of a derivative of ammonia in which two of the positions are temporarily occupied by blocking groups to prevent introduction of more than a single alkyl substituent. The cyclic substance phthalimide, employed as the ammonia derivative, possesses a hydrogen atom doubly activated by the carbonyl groups and hence acidic and capable of forming metal salts, which react with alkyl halides. The alkylated phthalimide is then hydrolyzed with alkali and the liberated amine is removed from the alkaline mixture by steam distillation.

Special Methods. — Special processes for preparation of methylamine and trimethylamine depend upon the reactivity and reducing properties of formaldehyde. The monoalkylamine is obtained in the form of the hydrochloride as the chief product of interaction of ammonium chloride with two equivalents of formaldehyde (formalin solution) at a moderate temperature. Probably ammonia resulting from dissociation of ammonium chloride adds

$$2\,CH_2O \; + \; NH_4Cl \; \xrightarrow[45-51\%]{104°} \; CH_3NH_2 \cdot HCl \; + \; HCO_2H$$

to one molecule of formaldehyde, and the addition product, CH$_2$(OH)NH$_2$, is reduced by a second molecule of the aldehyde. When ammonium chloride is heated to a higher temperature with a large excess of anhydrous formaldehyde, derived from paraformaldehyde, the chief product is trimethylamine hydrochloride, which is isolated by addition of alkali and distillation of the liberated amine into hydrochloric acid solution. The reaction may proceed

$$3\,(CH_2O)_3 \; + \; 2\,NH_4Cl \; \xrightarrow[89\%]{160°} \; 2\,(CH_3)_3N \cdot HCl \; + \; 3\,CO_2 \; + \; 3\,H_2O$$

through addition of ammonia to three molecules of formaldehyde to give the trihydroxymethyl derivative (HOCH$_2$)$_3$N and its reduction by formaldehyde, which at the higher temperature is oxidized to carbon dioxide.

Another special process is utilized for technical production of ethanol-, diethanol-, and triethanolamine. In the initial step ammonia reacts with ethylene oxide by opening the oxide ring, and the primary amino compound produced reacts with more ethylene oxide in the same manner to give the higher substitution products:

$$CH_2\!-\!CH_2 \;+\; HNH_2 \longrightarrow HOCH_2CH_2NH_2 \xrightarrow{\;\;CH_2\!-\!CH_2\;(O)\;\;}$$

Ethanolamine

$$\begin{array}{c} HOCH_2CH_2 \\ NH \\ HOCH_2CH_2 \end{array} \xrightarrow{\;\;CH_2\!-\!CH_2\;(O)\;\;} \begin{array}{c} HOCH_2CH_2 \\ HOCH_2CH_2\!-\!N \\ HOCH_2CH_2 \end{array}$$

Diethanolamine   Triethanolamine

REACTIONS

Acylation. — Primary and secondary amines react with acetic anhydride or acetyl chloride to give acetyl derivatives in which a hydrogen atom of the amino group is replaced by an acetyl radical. Although a primary

$$(CH_3)_2CHCH_2NH_2 \xrightarrow{\;(CH_3CO)_2O\;} (CH_3)_2CHCH_2NHCOCH_3 \;+\; CH_3CO_2H$$

Primary amine   Acetylisobutylamine
                                  (m.p. 107°)

$$\begin{array}{c} (CH_3)_2CH \\ NH \\ (CH_3)_2CH \end{array} \xrightarrow{\;CH_3COCl\;} \begin{array}{c} (CH_3)_2CH \\ NCOCH_3 \;+\; HCl \\ (CH_3)_2CH \end{array}$$

Secondary amine   Acetyldiisopropylamine
                             (liq., b.p. 222–225°)

amine has two replaceable hydrogen atoms and can yield a diacetyl derivative under forcing conditions, the second substituent is introduced so much less readily than the first that diacetyl compounds are rarely encountered. The monoacetyl derivatives of primary and secondary amines are often useful for characterization and identification, particularly since acetylation often converts a liquid amine into a solid product. Furthermore, basic amines are converted by acetylation into neutral substances, for the acid-forming acetyl residue counterbalances the basic quality of trivalent nitrogen. Thus the acetyl compounds in the illustrations do not form salts with mineral acids and are not extracted from an ethereal solution by hydrochloric acid.

A tertiary amine has no replaceable hydrogen and is indifferent to acetic anhydride or acetyl chloride. The differentiation between amines that are easily acetylated and those that fail to react is useful both in classifying unknown compounds and in effecting separations and purifications. For example, a tertiary amine contaminated with primary and secondary amines can be freed from these materials by adding enough acetic anhydride to react with all acylable material and extracting a solution of the mixture in ether with dilute hydrochloric acid; the neutral acetyl derivatives of the primary and secondary amines remain in the ether layer, and the tertiary amine is selectively extracted and can be recovered from the aqueous acid layer by neutralization with alkali. Alternately, the crude tertiary amine is treated with a little acetic anhydride and distilled, when the less volatile acetylated products remain as a residue.

Other aliphatic acyl groups can be introduced in the same manner as acetyl, but the reagents are less available. An available and much used reagent of the aromatic series is benzoyl chloride, C_6H_5COCl, which reacts to give benzoyl derivatives of the types $RNHCOC_6H_5$ and $R_2NCOC_6H_5$. Another aromatic acid chloride, benzenesulfonyl chloride ($C_6H_5SO_2Cl$), is employed in the **Hinsberg test** for distinguishing between primary and secondary amines. A reaction of the usual type occurs in each case, but the products are distinguished by the fact that those from primary amines form water-soluble alkali salts whereas those from secondary amines do not; both types are insoluble in acid. Tertiary amines do not react with the

$$C_6H_5SO_2Cl \ + \ H_2NR \ \xrightarrow{-HCl} \ C_6H_5SO_2NR \ \xrightarrow{NaOH} \ C_6H_5SO_2\overset{-}{N}R \quad Na^+$$

$$\begin{array}{ccc} & \text{Primary} & \text{H} \\ & \text{amine} & \text{(soluble} \\ & & \text{in alkali)} \end{array}$$

$$C_6H_5SO_2Cl \ + \ HNR_2 \ \xrightarrow{-HCl} \ C_6H_5SO_2NR_2$$

$$\begin{array}{cc} \text{Secondary} & \text{(insoluble} \\ \text{amine} & \text{in alkali)} \end{array}$$

reagent. The salt-forming property of the benzenesulfonamide derivative of a primary amine is attributable to the presence of a remaining amino hydrogen atom so located as to be activated by the unsaturated sulfonyl group. The derivative of a secondary amine has no corresponding hydrogen atom, and hence is not acidic. Like other acyl derivatives, benzenesulfonamides of both types can be hydrolyzed, with regeneration of the amines. The benzenesulfonamide from a primary amine can be alkylated and the product hydrolyzed, and in this way the original amine can be converted into a pure N-alkyl derivative:

$$RNH_2 \ \xrightarrow{C_6H_5SO_2Cl,\ NaOH} \ \underset{Na^+}{\overset{-}{R}NSO_2C_6H_5} \ \xrightarrow{(CH_3)_2SO_4} \ \underset{CH_3}{RNSO_2C_6H_5} \ \xrightarrow{Hydrol.} \ \underset{CH_3}{RNH}$$

Reaction with Nitrous Acid. — The three types of amines respond differently to nitrous acid. A primary amine reacts with liberation of nitrogen and formation of an alcohol. A possible interpretation of the transfor-

$$R-N\overset{H}{\underset{H}{\big<}} \ + \ HO-N{=}O \ \longrightarrow \ \left[R-\overset{\overset{\text{H}\text{-}\text{-}\text{-}\text{-}\text{-}}{|}}{N}-N{=}\overset{\downarrow}{O} \ \longrightarrow \ R{-}\!\!\overset{\ }{N}{=}\!N\!{-}OH \right] \ \longrightarrow \ ROH + N_2$$

mation is indicated in the formulation. The nitrogen liberated is quantitatively equivalent to the primary amine employed, and since the gas can be collected and its volume measured accurately, the reaction provides a useful method of determining the amount of primary amino nitrogen present in a weighed sample of a given substance or mixture. If the reaction mixture is kept strongly acidic (pH 3) during treatment with nitrous acid, the amine may be convertible into the corresponding alcohol, though the high acidity may result in dehydration of a secondary or a tertiary alcohol. In a less acidic medium the alkyl group frequently suffers rearrangement; for example, *n*-propylamine gives isopropyl alcohol, propylene, and a trace of *n*-propyl alcohol; and methylamine gives no methanol.

Secondary amines combine with nitrous acid by elimination of water and consequent replacement of the lone amino hydrogen atom by a nitroso group (—NO); the products are nitrosoamines. The reaction corresponds to the first step postulated in the reaction of a primary amine and the

$$\begin{array}{c}R \\ \diagdown \\ \diagup \\ R'\end{array} N—H \;+\; HON{=}O \;\longrightarrow\; \begin{array}{c}R \\ \diagdown \\ \diagup \\ R'\end{array} N—N{=}O \;+\; H_2O$$

Secondary amine   Nitrosoamine

difference in the final outcome is that the product has no hydrogen available for migration and is stable. Nitrosoamines are somewhat comparable in structure to esters and to the acetyl derivatives of amines; like these substances they can be hydrolyzed by boiling dilute hydrochloric acid, and the original amine can be recovered by neutralization with alkali and steam distillation. The nitroso group has the same effect as an acetyl substituent of neutralizing the basic character of nitrogen, and these derivatives are likewise neutral substances. They usually are oily yellow liquids, sparingly soluble in water. Two typical nitrosoamines are shown in the formulas.

$$\begin{array}{c}CH_3 \\ \diagdown \\ \diagup \\ CH_3\end{array} N{\cdot}NO \qquad\qquad \begin{array}{c}(CH_3)_2CH \\ \diagdown \\ \diagup \\ (CH_3)_2CH\end{array} N{\cdot}NO$$

N-Nitrosodimethylamine   N-Nitrosodiisopropylamine
(yellow oil, b.p. 153°)   (volatile yellow solid, m.p. 46°)

Tertiary amines, having no replaceable hydrogen, neither liberate nitrogen nor form nitroso derivatives, and at most form with nitrous acid unstable salts that are destroyed on neutralization. The differing behavior of the three types of amines to the reagent affords a basis for a method of separating mixtures. When nitrous acid acts upon a mixture of amines of the three types, the primary amino component is destroyed by conversion into an alcohol, the secondary amine forms a neutral nitroso compound, and the unaltered tertiary amine can be removed from the mixture by extraction of an ethereal solution with mineral acid. The unextracted neutral material is then hydrolyzed with acid to regenerate the secondary amine from its nitroso derivative and the free base is liberated with alkali.

Thermal Decomposition of Quaternary Ammonium Hydroxides (Hofmann, 1851). — The mono-, di-, and trimethyl derivatives of ammonium hydroxide, like the parent substance, exist only in aqueous solution, and on evaporation of the solution lose the elements of water and revert to the free amines. The quaternary compound, tetramethylammonium hydroxide, has no hydrogen atom available for elimination of water and in aqueous solution is stable and strongly basic. When heated somewhat above the boiling point of water, however, the substance undergoes decomposition analogous to the more facile decomposition of the unstable hydrates and yields trimethylamine and methanol. Other quaternary bases likewise un-

$$[(CH_3)_4N]^+OH^- \xrightarrow{130-135°} (CH_3)_3N + CH_3OH$$

Tetramethylammonium
hydroxide (pentahydrate, m.p. 63°)

dergo thermal decomposition, but if the alkyl group eliminated in the process contains two or more carbon atoms the nitrogen-free reaction product is not the alcohol but the corresponding alkene. Thus tetraethylammonium hydroxide when heated breaks down into triethylamine, ethylene, and water. This behavior is typical of the bases as a class, and formation of an

$$[(CH_3CH_2)_4N]^+OH^- \xrightarrow{100°} (CH_3CH_2)_3N + CH_2{=}CH_2 + H_2O$$

(tetrahydrate, m.p. 50°)

alcohol in the one instance where production of an alkene is impossible represents a special case. Furthermore, elimination of a methyl group as methanol occurs less readily than the splitting off of any higher alkyl group as the alkene. If the hydroxide contains both methyl and ethyl groups, as in $[(CH_3)_3NCH_2CH_3]^+OH^-$ or $[(CH_3CH_2)_3NCH_3]^+OH^-$, decomposition invariably affords ethylene and not methanol. When a still higher group competes with methyl, the latter holds fast to nitrogen and the higher group is severed from the molecule with loss of a β-hydrogen and formation

$$(CH_3)_3\overset{+}{N}{-}\overset{|}{\underset{\beta}{C}}{-}\overset{|}{C}H{-} \longrightarrow (CH_3)_3N + \overset{|}{C}{=}\overset{|}{C} + H_2O$$
$$OH^-$$

of an alkene. The decomposition proceeds readily and in good yield at moderate temperatures, and the temperature of decomposition can be lowered by operation in vacuum. In some instances isolation of the hydroxide as a solid can be dispensed with and decomposition effected by merely boiling an aqueous solution of the substance.

Hofmann Degradation. — Hofmann saw in this smoothly occurring reaction and in the greater firmness of attachment of methyl than of other groups a general scheme applicable both to determination of the structures of amines and to preparation of ethylenic compounds. The first step consists in treating an amine with excess methyl iodide to replace all available amino hydrogens by methyl groups and then to produce the quaternary salt or methiodide by addition of the reagent to the tertiary amine (exhaustive methylation). Analysis reveals whether the starting material is a primary, secondary, or tertiary amine, for these types allow the introduction of three, two, or one methyl group, respectively. The iodide is then converted with moist silver oxide into the quaternary ammonium hydroxide and this is pyrolyzed. As applied to a primary amine, the process can be illustrated as follows:

$$RCH_2CH_2NH_2 \xrightarrow{CH_3I} RCH_2CH_2\overset{+}{N}(CH_3)_3 \xrightarrow{AgOH} RCH_2CH_2\overset{+}{N}(CH_3)_3 \xrightarrow{Heat} RCH=CH_2$$
$$\qquad\qquad\qquad\qquad\quad I^- \qquad\qquad\qquad\qquad OH^-$$

In special cases such a process is employed in preference to other methods for preparation of alkenes. If an amine of unknown structure is under investigation, it can be degraded by the Hofmann procedure into a simpler, nitrogen-free substance having a center of unsaturation of assistance in its further characterization. Many naturally occurring nitrogen bases of elaborate structure have been investigated by this method with profitable outcome. Several tertiary amines have been encountered in which the nitrogen atom is substituted by one methyl group and two higher groups that differ from each other and are both of a complex character. In this case exhaustive methylation and pyrolysis of the quaternary ammonium hydroxide (1) releases one of the large groups in a form suitable for characterization, and repetition of the process (2) releases the other:

$$\begin{matrix} RCH_2CH_2 \\ \diagdown \\ \diagup \quad N\cdot CH_3 \\ R'CH_2CH_2 \end{matrix} \longrightarrow \begin{matrix} RCH_2CH_2 \\ \diagdown \\ \overset{+}{N}(CH_3)_2 \\ \diagup \quad OH^- \\ R'CH_2CH_2 \end{matrix} \xrightarrow{(1)}$$

$$R'CH_2CH_2N(CH_3)_2 \ + \ RCH=CH_2$$

$$\downarrow$$

$$R'CH_2CH_2\overset{+}{N}(CH_3)_3 \xrightarrow{(2)} R'CH=CH_2 \ + \ (CH_3)_3N$$
$$OH^-$$

Amine Oxides. — Amines are resistant to oxidation in solutions of mineral acids by virtue of the stabilizing effect of salt formation, but free amines undergo ready oxidation, with initial attack on the nitrogen atom. The case of tertiary amines is the most significant and the simplest, for these substances are oxidized by hydrogen peroxide to amine oxides of the general formula R_3NO or to the hydrates, $R_3N(OH)_2$. Trimethylamine on reaction with aqueous hydrogen peroxide yields a hydrate, m.p. 98°, and this when warmed in vacuum affords anhydrous trimethylamine oxide, m.p. 208°. In accordance with the rule that the fifth valence of nitrogen is invariably polar, hydrates must be regarded as quaternary ammonium hydroxides, and this formulation accounts for both the usual preparative reaction (1) and an alternate synthesis (2). That the two hydroxyl groups

$$\overset{(1)}{\overbrace{\qquad\qquad\qquad}} \qquad\qquad \overset{(2)}{\overbrace{\qquad\qquad\qquad}}$$

$$\begin{matrix} R \\ \diagdown \\ R\!-\!N \\ \diagup \\ R \end{matrix} \xrightarrow{HO-OH} \begin{matrix} R \\ \diagdown \\ R\!-\!\overset{+}{N}OH^- \\ \diagup \quad | \\ R \quad \ OH \end{matrix} \xleftarrow[\;2.\ AgOH\;]{1.\ RI} \begin{matrix} R \\ \diagdown \\ N\!-\!OH \\ \diagup \\ R \end{matrix}$$

Tertiary amine   Amine oxide   Dialkylhydroxylamine
                        hydrate

actually are bound in different ways, namely one by a polar and the other by a covalent link, has been proved by the synthesis of two isomers containing a hydroxyl and a methoxyl group joined to the nitrogen of trimethylamine (Meisenheimer[2]); the isomers exhibit properties consistent with the structures I and II, as indicated by the course of the thermal decompositions:

$$\left[\begin{matrix} CH_3 \\ \\ CH_3 \end{matrix} \!\! >\!\! N\!\! <\!\! \begin{matrix} CH_3 \\ \\ OCH_3 \end{matrix} \right]^+ OH^- \longrightarrow (CH_3)_3N + CH_2O + H_2O$$

I

$$\left[\begin{matrix} CH_3 \\ \\ CH_3 \end{matrix} \!\! >\!\! N\!\! <\!\! \begin{matrix} CH_3 \\ \\ OH \end{matrix} \right]^+ OCH_3^- \longrightarrow (CH_3)_3NO + CH_3OH$$

II

The anhydrous amine oxide contains pentavalent nitrogen and likewise must have one polar link, and indeed a saltlike character can be inferred from the high melting point and the fact that the substance is soluble in water and insoluble in ether. One acceptable formulation (a) indicates the presence of a semipolar bond between nitrogen and oxygen. The representation of the disposition of the valence electrons of nitrogen and oxygen is

$$\begin{matrix} CH_3 \\ \\ CH_3\!-\!\overset{+}{N}\!-\!\overset{-}{O} \\ \\ CH_3 \end{matrix}$$

Trimethylamine oxide

(a)

$$R\!:\!\overset{..}{N}\!:\!\overset{\text{transfer}}{\cdots\cdots} \!\! \overset{\cdots}{\underset{R}{\longrightarrow}}\!\! \overset{..}{O}\!: \;=\; R\!:\!\overset{\overset{..+\cdots-}{}}{\underset{R}{N}}\!:\!\overset{..}{\underset{..}{O}}\!: \qquad \overset{R}{\underset{R}{>}}\!N\!\rightarrow\!O$$

(b)   (c)

shown in formula (b). Inspection of the electronic structures of the component parts shows that sharing of two pairs of electrons between nitrogen and oxygen (double bond) would give ten electrons in the outer shell of nitrogen, and since eight constitute the maximum consistent with stability, such sharing does not occur. Formula (b) indicates stable eight-electron shells for both nitrogen and oxygen and a single pair of electrons shared between them; the electron contributed by oxygen can be regarded as derived from nitrogen by a transfer, and hence the donor nitrogen atom becomes positive and the oxygen negative. The alternate formula (c) is often employed as an expression of an electron transfer in the direction of the arrow.

Nitrogen Mustards. — Tertiary amines of the general formula $RN(CH_2CH_2Cl)_2$ have vesicant properties similar to those of mustard gas, $S(CH_2CH_2Cl)_2$; hence they were investigated intensively during World War II as possible chemical warfare agents. They can be prepared by reaction of ethylene oxide with the appropriate amine followed by reaction

$$RNH_2 \xrightarrow{\;\; \overset{CH_2-CH_2}{\underset{O}{\diagdown\;\;\diagup}} \;\;} RN\!\! <\!\! \begin{matrix} CH_2CH_2OH \\ \\ CH_2CH_2OH \end{matrix} \xrightarrow{\;\; SOCl_2 \;\;} RN\!\! <\!\! \begin{matrix} CH_2CH_2Cl \\ \\ CH_2CH_2Cl \end{matrix}$$

[2] Jacob Meisenheimer, 1876–1934; b. Greisheim, Germany; Ph.D. Munich; Berlin, Greisswald, Tübingen; *Ber.*, 68 A, 32 (1935)

with thionyl chloride in boiling benzene.   Toxicity of the nitrogen mustards is believed to be due to reaction with tissue protcins, built up of amino acids of the formula $RCH(NH_2)COOH$, according to the general scheme:

$$RN\begin{matrix}CH_2CH_2Cl\\\\CH_2CH_2Cl\end{matrix} \quad + \quad 2\,NH_2CHRCOOH \quad \longrightarrow \quad RN\begin{matrix}CH_2CH_2NHCHRCOOH\\\\CH_2CH_2NHCHRCOOH\end{matrix}$$

Nitrogen mustards are all somewhat unstable and eventually are transformed even at room temperature into cyclic piperazinium dimers:

$$2\,RN\begin{matrix}CH_2CH_2Cl\\\\CH_2CH_2Cl\end{matrix} \quad \longrightarrow \quad ClCH_2CH_2{}^+N\begin{matrix}\overset{R}{|}\quad CH_2CH_2\quad \overset{R}{|}\\\\Cl^-\quad CH_2CH_2\end{matrix}N^+CH_2CH_2Cl \; Cl^-$$

AMIDES

Amides of the type $RCONH_2$ are related to acids in the same way that amines are related to alcohols, and they are also acyl derivatives of ammonia.   They are neutral, or at most feebly basic substances, owing to the combination of an acid-forming and a base-forming group.   Acetamide, CH_3CONH_2, is comparable in this respect to acetylmethylamine, $CH_3NHCOCH_3$, which is also defined as N-methylacetamide (the prefixed letter denotes that the substituent is attached to nitrogen).

Typical amides are crystalline solids, and since they are easily prepared from acids they are often employed for characterization of these frequently liquid substances.   The physical constants of representative amides are as follows (compare p. 179):

CH_3CONH_2	$CH_3CH_2CONH_2$	$CH_3(CH_2)_{16}CONH_2$	$C_6H_5CONH_2$
Acetamide	Propionamide	Stearamide	Benzamide
(m.p. 82.0°, b.p. 222°)	(m.p. 80°, b.p. 213°)	(m.p. 109°)	(m.p. 130°)

The substances have abnormally high boiling points; n-valeramide, of molecular weight 101.15, boils in the range 100–130° at 6 mm. pressure.

Preparation. — Acids can be converted into amides by the action of ammonia on their ester, acid chloride, or anhydride derivatives, as already noted; the route through the halide is usually the most convenient.   A useful technical method consists in pyrolysis of the ammonium salt of the

$$CH_3COONH_4 \xrightarrow[87\text{-}90\%]{\text{Slow distillation}} CH_3CONH_2 \; + \; H_2O$$
$$\text{[from } CH_3COOH + (NH_4)_2CO_3]$$

acid.   Amides also result from partial hydrolysis of nitriles (p. 168).   One improvement in the procedure for conversion of nitriles into amides consists in use of alkaline hydrogen peroxide at 45–55°.   Another is use as catalyst of an ion-exchange basic resin, for example, the commercial product

IRO–400, a water-insoluble polymer containing quaternary ammonium chloride groups. The resin is stirred with dilute alkali and the resulting resin base is washed free of sodium chloride and of excess alkali and added to a solution of the nitrile. Brief boiling (1 hr.) of the suspension effects hy-

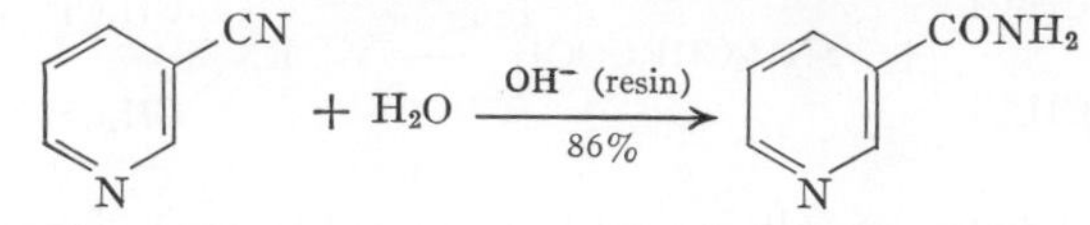

Nicotinonitrile   Nicotinamide

drolysis to the amide stage and no further, and the filtered solution of the amide is free from inorganic salts.

Reactions. — Hydrolysis of amides to acids proceeds smoothly but requires somewhat drastic conditions, for these substances are much less reactive than esters. Prolonged refluxing with a mixture of acetic and hydrochloric acid or with alcoholic alkali (in a copper flask) may be required, but the material is not damaged in the process, and the acid is usually obtainable in good yield. The primary amino group present is attacked by nitrous acid in the manner characteristic of primary amines, and this reaction has afforded a satisfactory method of hydrolysis in some instances:

Amides are convertible into nitriles by dehydration, usually accomplished by the action of phosphorus pentoxide or of boiling acetic anhydride. The reaction represents reversal of the partial hydrolysis of a nitrile and may proceed through the enolic form, present in small amounts in equilibrium

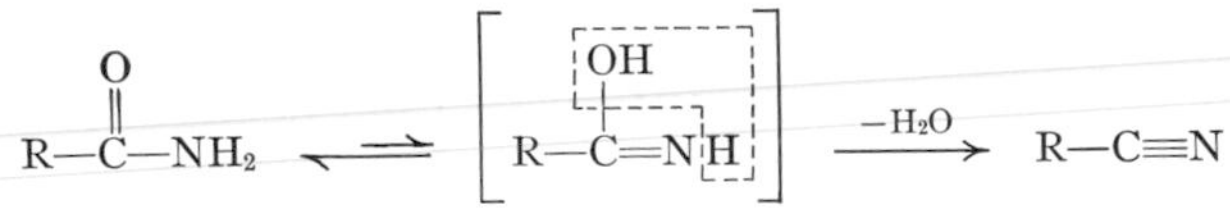

with the amide. The N-bromination of amides with neutral sodium hypobromite to the derivatives RCONHBr and the alkaline cleavage of these substances to amines have been described. Amides react with Grignard reagents in the same manner as acid chlorides; the reaction is most usefully applied in the aromatic series and is illustrated later.

Imides. — The dibasic succinic acid can be converted by usual methods into a neutral diamido derivative, succinamide. This substance when strongly heated could conceivably suffer dehydration to a nitrile, but instead it loses ammonia and yields a cyclic diacyl-substituted ammonia derivative, succinimide. Succinimide is a weak acid (pK$_a$ 10.52) capable of forming salts with alkalis. Phthalimide (p. 234), a substance of similar structure, is even more strongly acidic. Two acyl substituents more than compensate for the basic character inherent in the trivalent nitrogen atom; the imido hydrogen atom is activated by both carbonyl groups, and sepa-

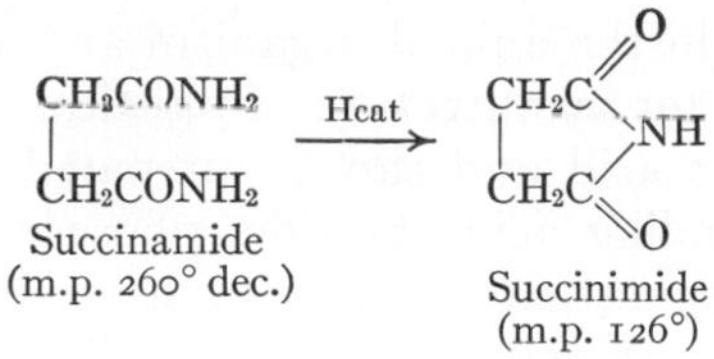

$$CH_2CONH_2 \xrightarrow{\text{Heat}} CH_2C\overset{\displaystyle O}{\underset{O}{<}}NH$$

CH_2CONH_2 (left) / CH_2C (right)

Succinamide
(m.p. 260° dec.)

Succinimide
(m.p. 126°)

rates as a proton. Imides are hydrolyzed more readily than the usual amides. Thus succinimide is convertible in good yield to the monoamido compound succinamic acid, $HOOCCH_2CH_2CONH_2$, m.p. 157°. This half-amide probably is an intermediate in the reaction of succinimide with sodium or potassium hypobromite, which is a useful application of the Hofmann reaction to the preparation of an amino acid:

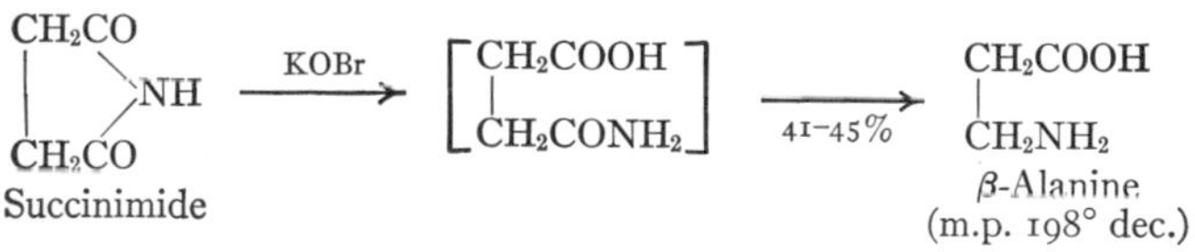

$$\begin{matrix} CH_2CO \\ | \quad\quad >NH \\ CH_2CO \end{matrix} \xrightarrow{KOBr} \begin{bmatrix} CH_2COOH \\ | \\ CH_2CONH_2 \end{bmatrix} \xrightarrow[41\text{-}45\%]{} \begin{matrix} CH_2COOH \\ | \\ CH_2NH_2 \end{matrix}$$

Succinimide

β-Alanine
(m.p. 198° dec.)

By adding bromine to an ice-cold solution of succinimide in alkali and quickly collecting the material that precipitates, N-bromosuccinimide of about 97% purity can be prepared in high yield. The bromine atom in

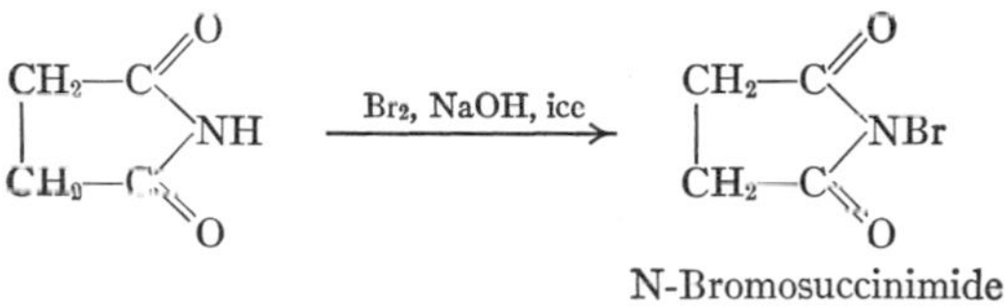

$$\begin{matrix} CH_2-C \\ | \quad\quad >NH \\ CH_2-C \end{matrix} \xrightarrow{Br_2,\ NaOH,\ ice} \begin{matrix} CH_2-C \\ | \quad\quad >NBr \\ CH_2-C \end{matrix}$$

N-Bromosuccinimide

this bromoimide is described as a positive halogen, since on hydrolysis it combines with the negative hydroxide ion to form hypobromous acid; an alkyl bromide affords hydrobromic acid. N-Bromosuccinimide is useful as a specific reagent for introduction into alkenes of a bromine atom in the allyl position adjacent to a double bond (Ziegler, 1942). The reaction is applicable not only to unsaturated hydrocarbons but to unsaturated esters.

$$CH_3CH=CHCOOCH_3 + \text{N-Bromosuccinimide} \xrightarrow[86\%]{\text{Boiling CCl}_4}$$

Methyl crotonate

$$BrCH_2CH=CHCOOCH_3 + \text{Succinimide}$$

Methyl γ-bromocrotonate

Allylic bromination is subject to catalysis by benzoyl peroxide and by light and therefore must proceed by a free-radical mechanism. In the presence of water N-bromosuccinimide functions as a mild oxidizing agent capable of effectively oxidizing certain specific secondary alcoholic groups and not others.

Urea: $(NH_2)_2C=O$, m.p. 132.7°. — Urea is important as a normal product of metabolism in the animal organism and as a synthetically produced starting material for manufacture of plastics. It can be regarded as the diamide of carbonic acid and can be prepared by the action of ammonia on the corresponding acid chloride, phosgene (ClCOCl). One industrial method of preparation consists in heating carbon dioxide with ammonia under pressure (1), and a second in partial hydrolysis of cyanamide (2).

1. $O=C=O + HNH_2 \rightleftharpoons O=C\begin{smallmatrix}OH\\NH_2\end{smallmatrix} \xrightarrow{NH_3} O=C\begin{smallmatrix}ONH_4\\NH_2\end{smallmatrix} \rightleftharpoons O=C\begin{smallmatrix}NH_2\\NH_2\end{smallmatrix} + H_2O$

Ammonium
carbamate

2. $H_2N-C\equiv N + HOH \longrightarrow \left[H_2N-C=NH \atop OH \right] \longrightarrow H_2N-\underset{O}{\overset{}{C}}-NH_2$

Cyanamide

The normal individual excretes in the urine 28–30 g. of urea per day, formed as a product of metabolism of proteins. The substance can be isolated from urine as the nitric acid salt, urea mononitrate, $H_2NCONH_2 \cdot HNO_3$. Because of the presence of two amino groups and only one acid-forming group, urea is more basic than an ordinary amide and forms mono salts.

Cyclic Ureides. — The urea molecule is often incorporated into a ring system, as in the cyclic ureide parabanic acid:

$$\begin{matrix}COOH\\COOH\end{matrix} + \begin{matrix}NH_2\\ \quad CO\\NH_2\end{matrix} \xrightarrow{PCl_3} \begin{matrix}CO-NH\\ \qquad\quad CO\\CO-NH\end{matrix}$$

Oxalic acid   Urea   Parabanic acid

As the name implies the substance is acidic and forms salts with alkalis. The acidic character is probably attributable to dissociation of the doubly activated imide hydrogen atoms (compare succinimide).

The most prominent natural cyclic ureide is uric acid, discovered by Scheele in 1776 as a constituent of human urinary calculi (pebbles). Wöhler and Liebig, in a paper published in 1838 reporting results of a comprehensive investigation of this substance, wrote: "There is in organic chemistry no substance that claims the attention of the physiologist and the chemist to such a high degree as uric acid." After the lapse of a century, the type of structure found in uric acid gained in interest with development of the synthetic ureides of the series of barbiturate drugs and with recognition that the physiologically important growth factors riboflavin and biotin are cyclic ureides. A structural relationship between uric acid and both thiamine (vitamin B_1) and sulfadiazine also exists.

Uric acid is represented in the classical literature by formula (a), in which one ureide grouping occupies the 1,2,3-position and a second the 7,8,9-position. It is even more acidic than parabanic acid, and hence the triketonic formula (a), which can be written as in (b), is not so truly descriptive as the dienolic formula (c).   In (c) the six-membered heterocyclic

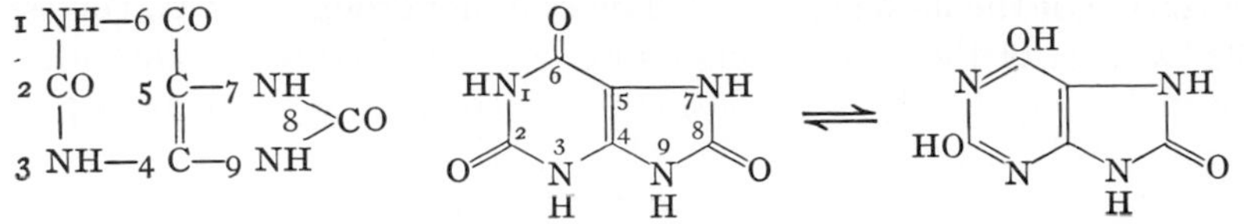

(a)   (b)   (c)

Uric acid

(pK$_a$ 5.7; solubility in water at 18°, 1:39,480)

ring, a pyrimidine ring, has the arrangement of alternating double bonds characteristic of benzene, and resonance in the aromatic ring stabilizes the molecule.   Hydroxy derivatives of benzene (phenols) are similarly acidic.

In addition to the original source, uric acid has been isolated from urine, from tissues of patients suffering from gout, and in quantity by extraction of excreta of snakes and birds (guano deposits).   The substance is a white crystalline solid sparingly soluble in water and decomposing above 400°. Wöhler and Liebig found it to be subject to oxidation, and they isolated and analyzed a number of products of oxidation and further transformation. The problem was taken up later by Baeyer (1863–64), who established the relationship between uric acid and the degradation products and paved the way for final elucidation and proof of structure by Emil Fischer in researches concluded in 1899.

The oxidative degradations shown in the chart establish the nature of the six-membered ring and of the five-membered ring, respectively.   Oxi-

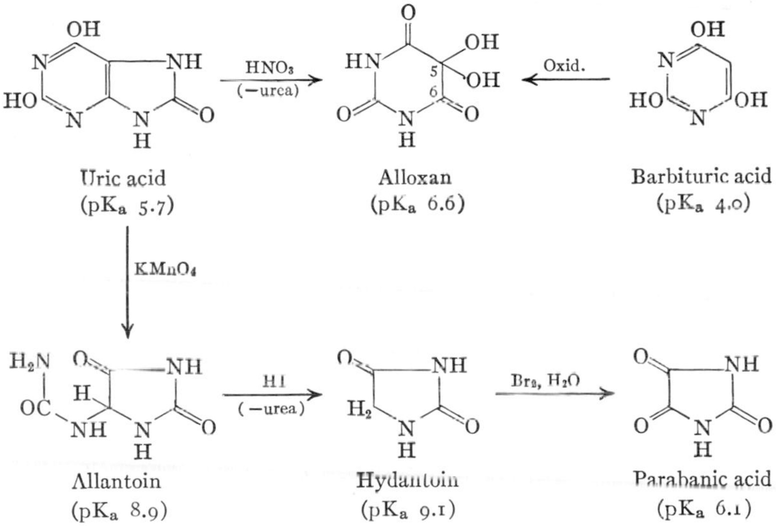

Uric acid   Alloxan   Barbituric acid
(pK$_a$ 5.7)   (pK$_a$ 6.6)   (pK$_a$ 4.0)

Allantoin   Hydantoin   Parabanic acid
(pK$_a$ 8.9)   (pK$_a$ 9.1)   (pK$_a$ 6.1)

dation with nitric acid attacks the smaller ring and affords urea and the six-membered ring compound alloxan.   The oxidation destroys the aromatic character of the pyrimidine ring, and alloxan is thus formulated as a diimide rather than as the dienol; the weakly acidic character is attributable to ionization of the imide groups. The *gem*-diol grouping at C_5 corresponds to the hydrate of the 5-keto compound, which indeed has been obtained as bright yellow crystals by sublimation of the colorless hydrate at 215° in high vacuum. Anhydrous alloxan has three carbonyl groups adjacent to one another; the central C_5-carbonyl group is influenced by the strong inductive effect of the two flanking groups, and therefore forms a stable hydrate. Alloxan was identified by comparison with material prepared by oxidation of barbituric acid, the synthesis of which is described below.

Oxidation of uric acid with alkaline permanganate opens the six-membered pyrimidine ring with loss of carbon atom 6 as carbon dioxide and formation of allantoin. The urea grouping, which in allantoin is linked at only one point, can be severed completely by reduction with hydrogen iodide, and the product, hydantoin, contains the isolated five-ring structure of the uric acid molecule. The further degradation product parabanic acid, identified by synthesis, can be obtained from hydantoin by bromination and hydrolysis or directly from uric acid by drastic oxidation with nitric acid. Allantoin and hydantoin are much weaker acids than the more highly unsaturated parabanic acid.

Barbituric acid is synthesized by condensation of urea with the diethyl ester of malonic acid in the presence of sodium ethoxide:

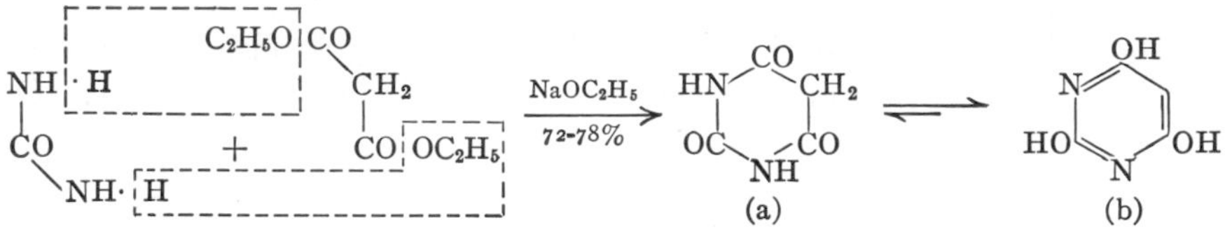

Diethyl malonate   Barbituric acid (m. p. 245°)

Barbituric acid is represented less accurately by the malonylurea formula (a) than by the aromatic trienolic structure (b); it is a stronger acid than acetic acid and is also soluble in dilute mineral acids.

Derivatives of barbituric acid are valuable in medicine as soporifics. The 5,5-diethyl derivative was introduced into therapy as the result of work by E. Fischer and von Mering (1903) and has been used widely under the name veronal or barbital to induce sleep and to some extent as a sedative

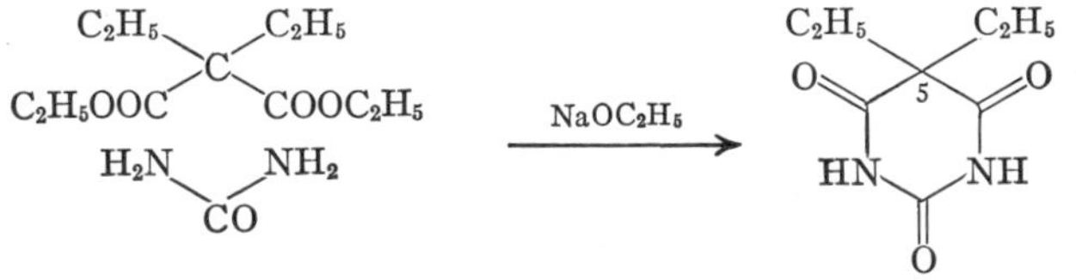

Diethylbarbituric acid
(veronal, m. p. 191°, pK_a 7.4)

and in anesthesia. It is synthesized from diethyl malonate and urea. The substance is similar in structure and degree of acidity to alloxan.

It is a curious fact that the alkaloids caffeine, theophylline, and theobromine bear a certain structural analogy to the barbiturates but have

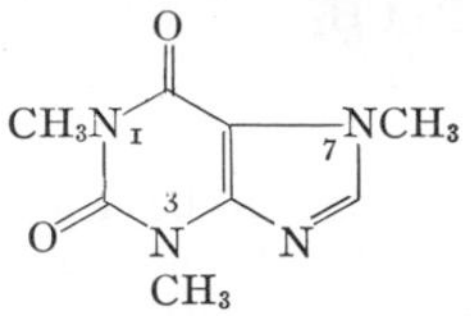

Caffeine 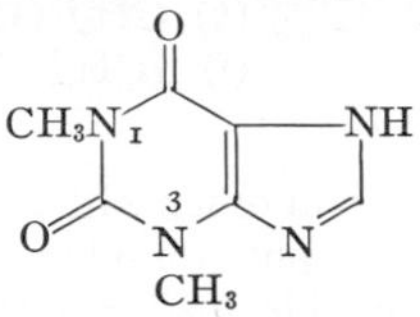   Theophylline 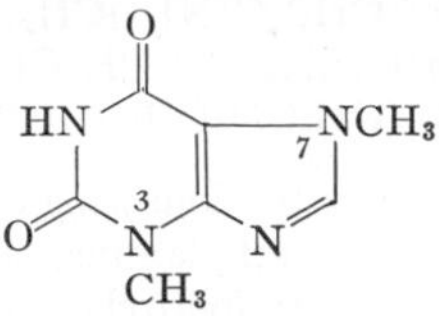   Theobromine

physiological activity of directly opposite type: they are stimulants. The coffee bean contains caffeine (1.5%); tea leaves contain caffeine (5%) and theophylline (trace); cocoa beans (*Theobroma cacao*) contain theobromine (1.8%). Caffeine, the most potent stimulant of the three, is a component of some popular American soft drinks. The alkaloids are methyl derivatives of the parent base xanthine, which differs from uric acid merely in the absence of oxygen at position 8; thus caffeine is 1,3,7-trimethylxanthine, and the other substances are the 1,3- and 3,7-dimethyl derivatives.

The picturesque names of the uric acid compounds for the most part were chosen by Wöhler and Liebig at a time when it was impossible to envision structures and when the analytical method used for determination of nitrogen was so subject to error as to give misleading results. The oxidation product allantoin was so named because it was identical with a substance isolated from the allantoic liquid of cows, and its product of reduction, or hydrogenation, was named hydantoin. The product of nitric acid oxidation, alloxan, was thought to contain the elements of allantoin and oxalic acid. The further oxidation product parabanic acid impressed Wöhler and Liebig as a "new and peculiar acid" both because of the unusually low hydrogen content and because it was converted by bases with great ease into another substance (oxaluric acid, $NH_2CONHCOCOOH$, the monoureide of oxalic acid); the name is derived from the Greek *parabainein*, to deviate. Baeyer's choice of the name barbituric acid is believed to have been motivated by gallantry to a friend, Barbara. In the systematic nomenclature subsequently introduced, substances having the skeletal structure of uric acid are defined as purines, from the name assigned by E. Fischer to the parent compound (**L.** *purum uricum*). The six-membered ring of

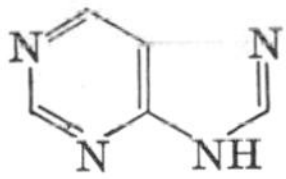

Purine
(m.p. 216°)

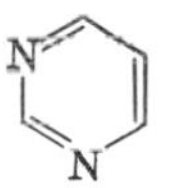

Pyrimidine, or
1,3-diazine
(m.p. 22°, b.p. 124°)

alloxan and barbituric acid is known both as a pyrimidine and as a 1,3-diazine ring.

PROBLEMS

1. Name the following compounds and indicate the class to which each belongs:
   - (a) $CH_3CH_2CH(CH_3)NH_2$
   - (b) $(CH_3CH_2)_2NCH(CH_3)_2$
   - (c) $(CH_3)_2C(NH_2)CH_2CH_3$
   - (d) $CH_3NHCH_2CH(CH_3)_2$
   - (e) $(CH_3CH_2CH_2)_2N(CH_3)\cdot HCl$
   - (f) $[(CH_3)_2CH]_4NBr$
   - (g) $CH_3CH_2CH_2N(NO)CH_2CH_3$
   - (h) $CH_3CONHCH_2CH_3$
   - (i) $(CH_3)_3CCONH_2$

2. Arrange the following compounds in order with respect to their acidic or basic properties: methylamine, acetamide, phthalimide, tetramethylammonium hydroxide, urea, acetylmethylamine, succinimide, β-alanine ($H_2NCH_2CH_2COOH$).

3. Suggest convenient chemical methods for isolating in a pure form the chief component of each of the following mixtures:
   - (a) Triethylamine, containing traces of ethylamine and diethylamine
   - (b) Diethylamine, contaminated with ethylamine and triethylamine
   - (c) Ethylamine, containing di- and triethylamine

4. How could n-propylamine and n-amylamine be prepared from n-butyl alcohol?

5. Suggest a method other than one proceeding through the halogen derivative for the preparation of sec-butylamine from sec-butyl alcohol.

6. If n-butyl bromide is to be converted into n-butylamine, what would be the advantage of using the Gabriel synthesis rather than direct ammonolysis? Comment on the practicability of converting the alcohol into the aldehyde, preparing the oxime, and reduction.

7. Indicate the steps involved in the transformation of a nitrile into an acid and of an acid into a nitrile. Would you expect an aldoxime to be convertible directly to a nitrile?

8. Formulate the Hofmann degradation as applied to cyclohexylamine.

9. How could the Hofmann degradation be applied to the determination of the structure of the following cyclic base:

10. Is there any similarity in electronic state between trimethylboron and the trimethylcarbonium ion?

11. What structures can contribute to the resonant hybrid anion from succinimide?

12. With the aid of electronic formulas, explain more fully the statement on page 243 that the bromine atom in N-bromosuccinimide is relatively positive since the substance on hydrolysis affords HOBr, whereas RBr yields HBr.

13. The thermal decomposition of quaternary ammonium hydroxides with the formation of alkenes is an example of the rather general phenomenon that high or moderately high temperatures favor the formation of unsaturated compounds. A number of other examples have been cited in earlier chapters; how many can you cite?

READING REFERENCE

Lord Playfair, Sir F. A. Abel, W. H. Perkin, and H. E. Armstrong, "Hofmann Memorial Lecture," *J. Chem. Soc.*, **69**, 575–732 (1896)

CHAPTER 11

STEREOCHEMISTRY

OPTICAL ISOMERISM

An important phase of organic chemistry is associated with the phenomenon of the polarization of light, discovered by Étienne Louis Malus in 1808. Ordinary white light consists of rays of different wave length vibrating in many different planes, and if selection is made of light of a single wave length, either with a special light source, such as a sodium lamp, or with filters, the resulting monochromatic light likewise consists of waves vibrating in many planes at right angles to the direction of propagation. Malus discovered that light transmitted by a crystal of Iceland spar, a transparent variety of the doubly refractive mineral calcite ($CaCO_3$) found in Iceland, differs from normal light in being polarized in a single plane determined by the orientation of the crystal, or polarizer. The character of the crystal is such that it permits passage of only those light waves vibrating in a specific plane and transmits two rays, ordinary and extraordinary, which are polarized in planes at right angles to each other. Experimentation with plane polarized light is simplified by use of the Nicol prism (William Nicol, Edinburgh), a device made by bisecting a rhombohedron of Iceland spar obliquely through the obtuse corners and uniting the parts with a cement (Canada balsam) of an index that allows complete reflection of the ordinary ray at the interface; this is thereby rejected from the field of vision, and the extraordinary ray of plane polarized light alone is transmitted. A rough analogy to the operation of a Nicol prism is that a closed book will permit easy insertion of a table knife between the pages only when the knife is held in a specific plane.

Although Malus' experiments were terminated by his premature death in 1812 at the age of 37, investigation of the interesting phenomenon was actively pursued by the French physicists D. F. Arago and J. B. Biot.[1] It was soon observed that a quartz crystal cut parallel to the axis and traversed by plane polarized light normal to the surface rotates the plane of polarization, and Biot ascertained that some quartz crystals turn the beam of light to the right whereas others turn it to the left. A few years later the mineralogist Haüy noticed that some specimens of quartz crystals exist in two hemihedral forms, each characterized by the presence of a set of faces arranged in either a right-handed or left-handed sense and constituting just half of the faces required to give a symmetrical crystal. Such

---

[1] Jean Baptiste Biot, 1774–1862; b. Paris; physicist, Collège de France

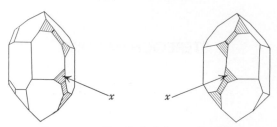

FIG. 11.1. — Hemihedral Quartz Crystals

crystals, illustrated in Fig. 11.1 are enantiomorphous, that is, related to each other as the right hand is to the left hand. The examples illustrated represent rare specimens; ordinarily evidence of hemihedry is discernible in but a small portion of the quartz crystals examined, and then only on careful scrutiny. Sir John Herschel in 1820 suggested a possible relationship between the crystallographic and optical properties of quartz, and experiment established that crystals with the faces inclined to the right and to the left rotate the plane of polarized light in opposite directions.

Biot in 1815 discovered that certain naturally occurring organic compounds rotate plane polarized light in either the liquid or the dissolved state. Oil of turpentine, solutions of sugar, of camphor, and of tartaric acid were found to exhibit this property and are described as possessing optical activity. The importance of the discovery was apparent to Biot, who pointed out that, whereas in the previously observed phenomena the optical activity was associated with a specific crystalline structure and disappeared with destruction of the crystalline form by either melting or dissolving the solid, the ability of the organic substances to rotate the plane of polarization in the noncrystalline state must be inherent in the molecules.

Polarimeter. — Subsequent experimentation showed that a number of organic compounds possess optical activity; those that rotate plane polarized light to the right, or in a clockwise direction, are defined as dextrorotatory (positive), whereas those rotating in the opposite sense are called levorotatory (negative). The extent of rotation for a given amount of material can be determined with a polarimeter (Fig. 11.2). This instrument contains two Nicol prisms traversed by a beam of monochromatic light. One, the polarizer, is mounted in a fixed position and transmits plane polarized light to a tube of known length with glass windows at the two ends, in which the solution to be examined is placed. The second Nicol prism, the analyzer, is mounted on a movable axis and can be rotated as desired; the angle of rotation is measured on a circular scale. The zero point on the scale is that which, with the polarimeter tube either empty or containing a solvent devoid of optical activity, permits maximum transmission of light, an indication that the analyzer has been oriented in the same optical plane as the polarizer; if the analyzer is now turned through an angle of 90°, a point of minimum light transmission is reached, and the Nicols are said to be crossed. When a solution of an optically active substance is placed in the polarimeter tube, light transmitted by the polarizer

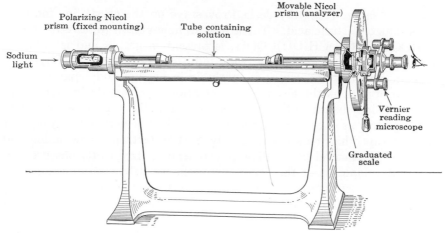

Sodium light

Polarizing Nicol prism (fixed mounting)

Tube containing solution

Movable Nicol prism (analyzer)

Vernier reading microscope

Graduated scale

FIG. 11.2. — Polarimeter

is rotated to a certain extent either to the right or to the left; light reaching the eyepiece is thus diminished in intensity, but by rotating the analyzer a point can be found where the original intensity is restored and at which the analyzer is aligned with the plane of light emerging from the polarimeter tube; the angle of rotation in either the dextro or levo sense is then read from the scale. The optical system shown in the illustration is of a simplified form; instruments ordinarily used contain two additional small Nicol prisms that provide segments in the light field permitting exact matching of light intensities and obviate necessity of estimating relative brightness.

Rotatory power of a given substance in the dissolved state is dependent on the concentration of the solution, the length of the polarimeter tube, the temperature of measurement, the wave length of light used, and the solvents. Results are reported in terms of the specific rotation, $[\alpha]$, defined as the rotation in degrees due to a solution containing 1 g. of substance in 1 ml. of solution as examined in a 1-decimeter polarimeter tube. The ro-

$$[\alpha] = \frac{\text{Observed rotation}}{\text{Length of tube in dm.} \times \text{concentration (g. per ml.)}}$$

tation value, which may be to the right (positive) or to the left (negative), is reported with a notation of the temperature of measurement and either the nature or wave length of the light source. Sodium light is usually employed and is indicated by the letter D (D line of the spectrum), for example, $[\alpha]_D^{25°}$; if the green line of mercury of wave length 5461 Å is used, the symbol is $[\alpha]_{5461}^T$. Thus the specific rotation of cane sugar in aqueous solution is $[\alpha]_D^{20°} = + 66.5°$.

Work of Pasteur. — Louis Pasteur,[2] on completion of the curriculum at the École Normale in Paris, sought to strengthen himself in the knowledge of crystallography by repeating a series of careful measurements published

[2] Louis Pasteur, 1822–95; b. Dôle, Dept. Jura; Dijon, Strasbourg, Lille, Paris (Sorbonne)

a few years earlier (1841) by de la Provostaye on the crystalline forms of various salts of tartaric acid. Tartaric acid, now known to have the structure HOOCCH(OH)CH(OH)COOH, is present in grapes and is obtained from tartar, a by-product of the wine industry; tartar consists largely of potassium acid tartrate, which is insoluble in alcohol and separates as a sludgy precipitate as the alcohol concentration increases during fermentation. Pasteur's determinations agreed substantially with those reported previously, but as the work proceeded he noticed a very interesting fact that had escaped his predecessor, namely, that all tartrates show undoubted evidence of hemihedral faces. The phenomenon is frequently obscured by irregular development of the crystals, by chance deformations, or by arrestment of the development of faces, but nevertheless Pasteur, by repeating crystallizations where necessary under modified conditions, established that every one of nineteen different tartrates investigated exhibits hemihedral faces. A further observation that seemed significant was that the tartrates are all hemihedral in the same sense. Since Biot had found the tartrates to be optically active in the same sense, and Herschel had suggested a correlation between the hemihedral and optical characteristics of quartz crystals, Pasteur was led to think that a relation might exist between the hemihedry of the tartrates and the property of deviating the plane of polarized light in the dissolved state.

This hypothesis, however, appeared to be invalidated by an observation reported in 1844 by the chemist and crystallographer Mitscherlich[3] concerning the sodium ammonium salt of racemic acid, a substance that had been observed by a wine manufacturer to be a by-product of the crystallization of tartaric acid, the main acidic product of alcoholic fermentation, and which was first studied by Berzelius in 1831 (L. *racemus*, grape). The substance was found to have the same chemical composition as tartaric acid but different physical properties; this early instance of isomerism led Berzelius to coin the name descriptive of the phenomenon. Biot examined racemic acid and its salts and found that they do not influence plane polarized light, or are optically inactive, in contrast with dextrorotatory tartaric acid. Mitscherlich then made a crystallographic comparison of the sodium ammonium salts of tartaric and racemic acid and reported that these two salts of the same chemical composition have the same crystalline form, the same double refraction, and consequently the same inclination of their optical axes, and in short differ only in that one is dextrorotatory and the other optically inactive. Since the existence of optically active and inactive isomers of identical crystalline form would be contradictory to the relationship tentatively postulated, Pasteur had the audacity to think that Mitscherlich might have overlooked the existence of hemihedry in the tartrate, and he reinvestigated the two salts in the hope of finding the tartrate hemihedral and the inactive racemate symmetrical. He found that sodium ammonium tartrate affords hemihedral crystals, like all other

---

[3] Eilhard A. Mitscherlich, 1794–1863; b. Neuerde, Ostfriedland; Berlin

tartrates previously studied, but discovered to his great surprise and in apparent contradiction to his hypothesis, that sodium ammonium racemate is hemihedral also. He then observed that "the hemihedral faces which in the tartrate were all turned the same way were in the racemate inclined sometimes to the right and sometimes to the left." Pasteur carefully picked out a quantity of crystals that were hemihedral to the right and a further quantity of those hemihedral to the left and examined their solutions separately in the polarimeter; he thereupon made the exciting observation that the former material rotated the plane of polarized light to the right and the latter to the left. When equal weights of the two kinds of crystals were dissolved in water, the solution of the mixture, like the starting material, was indifferent to polarized light. In this experiment, conducted in 1848, Pasteur had for the first time achieved the resolution of an optically inactive compound into the component, optically active parts. By precipitation of the lead or barium salts of each substance and digestion of these with sulfuric acid, the free acids were obtained. One proved identical with the natural, dextrorotatory tartaric acid, or d-tartaric acid, whereas the other was a heretofore unknown substance exhibiting rotation to the same extent in the opposite direction and hence called the *levo* acid, or l-tartaric acid.

Pasteur's striking discovery was referred to Biot for review before presentation to the Academy of Sciences, and this veteran worker required the young investigator to repeat the experiment before his eyes with a sample of racemic acid that he himself had studied and found to be optically inactive. Pasteur prepared a solution of the sodium ammonium salt with reagents that Biot likewise provided, and the solution was set aside for slow evaporation in one of the rooms at the Collège de France. In due course Pasteur was called in to collect and separate the crystals. Biot prepared the solutions and examined first the more interesting solution, that which Pasteur declared should show levorotation, and the discoverer of the phenomenon of optical activity in organic compounds was immensely impressed on observing that it was indeed levorotatory.

It was recognized only some time later that the resolution achieved by Pasteur is dependent upon a critical temperature factor. If sodium ammonium racemate is crystallized from a hot concentrated solution, the crystals have the same form and are symmetrical; they show no sign of hemihedrism. In this case each crystal contains equal parts of the *dextro* and the *levo* form and is optically inactive; the racemate salt is a molecular compound having the analysis of a monohydrate, $Na(NH_4)C_4H_4O_6 \cdot H_2O$. It is only when the crystals separate at a temperature below a critical transition point of 28° that hemihedral crystals composed respectively of molecules of the *dextro* and the *levo* salt separate to give a crystal mixture known as a conglomerate; this consists of crystals of sodium ammonium d-tartrate and sodium ammonium l-tartrate, both of which are tetrahydrates of the formula $Na(NH_4)C_4H_4O_6 \cdot 4H_2O$. Transition temperatures are often observed in inorganic chemistry between different hydrates of a given salt or between double and single salts. For example, a solution of sodium and magnesium sulfate deposits crystals of $Na_2SO_4 \cdot 10H_2O$ and $MgSO_4 \cdot 7H_2O$ at temperatures below $22°$, but yields the double salt $Na_2SO_4 \cdot MgSO_4 \cdot 4H_2O$ at higher temperatures. Pasteur adopted a technique of slow crystallization from a very dilute solution and thereby had the good fortune to operate at a temperature below the transition point, whereas previous investigators evidently had conducted crystallization at higher temperatures and had obtained only the inactive racemate. The initial resolution accomplished in 1848 is particularly remarkable because such instances are rare; in a century of subsequent research, only nine other examples have been encountered in which crystallization at any temperature affords a conglomerate of sufficiently large crystals displaying hemihedry to permit their segregation by hand picking under a lens. Fortunately, two other methods are now known for resolution of inactive molecular compounds composed of dextro- and levorotatory component parts, described as *dl*-compounds, or racemates, or racemic forms. Both of these other methods, one of which is widely applicable, were discovered by Pasteur in the period 1848–54, before he turned his attention to fermentation. He also discovered a fourth form of tartaric acid that is optically inactive and is called mesotartaric acid. These developments are discussed later.

Dextro- and *levo*-tartaric acid have the same melting point, solubility in a given solvent, dissociation constant, and density, and they exhibit the same chemical behavior. In fact the two substances are identical in every respect except that they rotate the plane of polarized light in opposite directions (but to the same extent) and that they form crystals that are hemihedral in the opposite sense. Pasteur, in view of the hypothesis that he had entertained on first examining the racemate, thought there must be a connection between the optical activity of the substances in solution and the hemihedral forms of the crystals. The relationship between the crystals of *d*- and *l*-tartaric acid is the same as that illustrated in Fig. 11.1 for right- and left-handed quartz crystals. The two are similar but not superposable, and the one is to the other as an object is to its mirror image; the crystals are thus asymmetric, for they possess no plane of symmetry. In a remarkably lucid interpretation of the new phenomenon, now described as optical isomerism, Pasteur concluded that tartaric acids must possess asymmetry within the molecule itself. Although the concept of structural formulas was developed only many years later, Pasteur had the vision to foresee the need of something beyond structural formulas for full understanding of organic compounds. He recognized that two substances identical in the nature and number of elements may differ in arrangement of the atoms in space and envisioned arrangements showing asymmetry in opposite senses. "Are the atoms of the *dextro* acid grouped on the spirals of a right-handed helix," questioned Pasteur in 1860, "or situated at the corners of an irregular tetrahedron, or have they some other asymmetric grouping? We cannot answer these questions. But it cannot be a subject of doubt that there exists an asymmetric arrangement having a nonsuperposable image. It is not less certain that the atoms of the *levo* acid possess precisely the inverse asymmetric arrangement."

Isomerism of the Lactic Acids. — Pasteur's brilliant deductions were so far ahead of the thought of the time that many years elapsed before any substantial advance was made in the understanding of optical isomerism. Although other optically active compounds were examined from time to time, the only investigations other than those of Pasteur that proved fruitful were those on the lactic acids. Scheele (1780) had discovered in sour milk a substance which he called lactic acid and which was subsequently found to arise as a product of bacterial fermentation of milk sugar (lactose). The structure is now known to be that of α-hydroxypropionic acid. Berzelius (1807) discovered a similar acidic substance as a constituent of muscle tissue extractable with water, and the substance was characterized by Liebig (1832) as having the same composition as the fermentation lactic acid. The acids have properties unfavorable for purposes of identification and comparison, for they are very soluble both in water and in organic

$$CH_3-\overset{\overset{\displaystyle H}{|}}{\underset{\underset{\displaystyle OH}{|}}{C}}-COOH$$

Lactic acid

solvents and are obtained only with considerable difficulty as low-melting, highly hygroscopic, and generally ill-defined solids (m.p. 26°). Thus a reliable conclusion regarding the relationship of the two acids was first reached by Engelhard (1848) on the basis of a comparison of a series of salts with respect to solubility, crystalline form, amount of water of crystallization, and course of dehydration. The comparison established that the lactic acids constitute two distinct chemical entities but have the same composition. It was also established that the acid from muscle is a dextrorotatory substance, which hereafter can be referred to as *d*-lactic acid. On the other hand fermentation lactic acid, at least as originally obtained, is optically inactive.

After the advent of the structural theory of Kekulé (1859), the problem of the structures of the interesting lactic acids received considerable attention, particularly in the hands of Wislicenus.[4] In a series of researches initiated at Zurich in 1863, Wislicenus applied the methods both of synthesis and of degradation, and though he encountered early difficulties and uncertainties in identification of materials of different origin, he eventually secured unequivocal evidence that the two natural acids have the same structure (1873). Thus they are both decomposed by hot sulfuric acid to acetaldehyde and formic acid, and they both yield acetic acid on

$$CH_3-\overset{\overset{\displaystyle H}{|}}{\underset{\underset{\displaystyle OH}{|}}{C}}-COOH \quad \begin{array}{c} \overset{H_2SO_4,\ 130°}{\nearrow} CH_3CHO\ +\ HCOOH \\[2ex] \underset{Oxid.}{\searrow} CH_3COOH\ +\ CO_2\ +\ H_2O \end{array}$$

---

[4] Johannes Wislicenus, 1835–1902; b. Germany; Zurich, Würzburg, Leipzig; *Ber.*, **37**, 4861 (1904)

oxidation. The alternate structure $HOCH_2CH_2COOH$ was thereby ex-cluded, for this could not yield products with an intact methyl group. Indeed Wislicenus synthesized this structural isomer from ethylene chloro-hydrin through the nitrile, and proved that it differs from either lactic acid. Synthesis of α-hydroxypropionic acid from acetaldehyde gave a product identical with the optically inactive fermentation lactic acid. At the con-

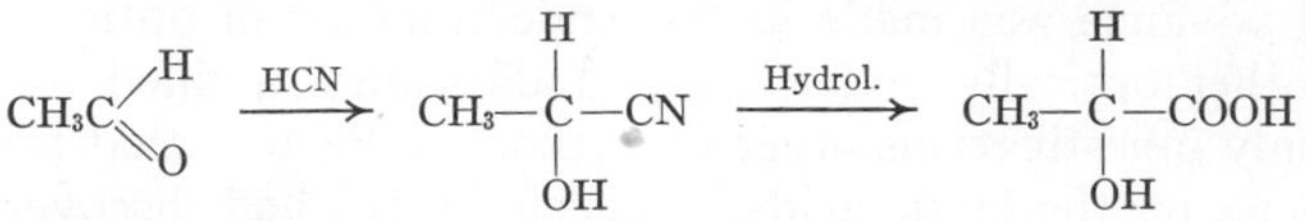

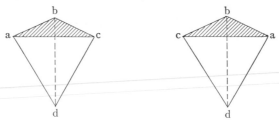

clusion of his experiments of 1873 which had established the identity of the structures, Wislicenus wrote: "If molecules can be structurally identical and yet possess dissimilar properties, this difference can be explained only on the ground that it is due to a different arrangement of the atoms in space."

Theory of van't Hoff and Le Bel. — A theory, beautiful in its simplicity, which met the requirements envisioned by Pasteur and set forth clearly by Wislicenus twenty-five years later with reference to simple compounds of established structures, was announced independently in 1874 by van't Hoff[5] in Holland (September) and by Le Bel[6] in France (November). The theory as stated by van't Hoff is that the four valences of carbon are directed to the corners of a tetrahedron, at the center of which the carbon atom is situated. If four different atoms or groups are attached at the four corners, then the molecule *Cabcd* is asymmetric and can exist in two forms:

The three-dimensional models cannot be superposed upon each other and hence are different, even though they represent the same structural arrange-ment of atoms. They bear a relationship to each other corresponding to that which exists between right- and left-handed quartz crystals, or be-tween an object and its mirror image. A tetrahedral carbon atom carrying four groups that are all different therefore must invariably constitute a center of asymmetry and permit two arrangements of the groups in space. This asymmetry calls for the existence of two isomers identical in all respects except optical properties. Asymmetry is possible only if all four valences of carbon are utilized by different groups; for example, if the substituent *c* in the above space formulas is replaced by a second *a* group, the formulas become identical.

[5] Jacobus Hendricus van't Hoff, 1852–1911; b. Rotterdam; Ph.D. Utrecht; Amsterdam; Nobel Prize 1901; *J. Chem. Soc.*, 1127 (1913)

[6] Joseph Achille Le Bel, 1847–1930; b. Péchelbronn, France; *J. Chem. Soc.*, 2789 (1930)

The young Dutch and French scientists (van't Hoff was 22, Le Bel, 27), who had met as students of Wurtz in Paris but who had not discussed the problem of isomerism, arrived at essentially the same theoretical concept by different reasoning. Le Bel was impressed by the correlation suggested by Pasteur between the rotatory power of the tartrates and the hemihedral character of the crystalline forms and saw that molecular asymmetry can exist if four different radicals are united to a single carbon atom, whatever the geometrical form of the molecule may be. Indeed a model consisting of a sphere with groups affixed at four points on the surface, or of an irregular, or off-centered tetrahedron, explains the facts of optical isomerism. van't Hoff, inspired to reflect on the problem by the publications of Wislicenus on lactic acid, reasoned that the four valences of the carbon atom cannot lie in a single plane at right angles to one another, or isomerism would be encountered in substances such as CH_2RR and $CH_2R_1R_2$, and proposed the tetrahedral arrangement as an explanation for both the nonexistence of such isomerism and the existence of optical isomers of the formula $CR_1R_2R_3R_4$. A regular tetrahedral arrangement is usually employed in formulations as a matter of convenience and is now accepted as representing the condition of a symmetrical molecule such as methane; this arrangement has been proved by X-ray measurements for tetramethylmethane and for pentaerythritol, $C(CH_2OH)_4$. The van't Hoff-Le Bel theory derived initial substantiation from the fact that at the time thirteen optically active compounds of established structure were known and they all contained at least one asymmetric carbon atom, designated C^* in the following examples:

Lactic acid,	$CH_3C^*H(OH)COOH$
Aspartic acid,	$HOOCC^*H(NH_2)CH_2COOH$
Asparagine,	$HOOCC^*H(NH_2)CH_2CONH_2$
Malic acid,	$HOOCC^*H(OH)CH_2COOH$
Active amyl alcohol,	$CH_3CH_2C^*H(CH_3)CH_2OH$

Wislicenus welcomed the theory as an answer to the problem that his own experiments had raised, and he sponsored van't Hoff's work to the extent of writing a supporting introduction to a German translation of the original Dutch pamphlet. Kolbe, who was reaching the end of his career, took an opposite view and wrote a scathing criticism of the "fanciful nonsense" and "supernatural explanations" of the two "unknown" chemists. Within a decade, however, those few observations that had appeared contradictory to the theory were shown to be in error (e.g., supposed activity of propyl alcohol, due to contamination with amyl alcohol), abundant new evidence was accumulated in substantiation of the concept, and the interpretation of optical activity in the dissolved state as due to the asymmetric character of the carbon atom gained general acceptance. Kolbe had died, and Wislicenus had been appointed to his post at Leipzig.

Compounds with One Asymmetric Carbon. — As predicted by the theory, the inactive lactic acid resulting from fermentation of carbohydrates was found to contain equal parts of d-lactic acid, identical with that found in muscle, and of the optical isomer l-lactic acid; indeed **fermentation can**

yield an excess of either the *d*- or the *l*-acid, depending on the microorganism. Spatial arrangement or configuration of the optical isomers is most conveniently represented by affixing to a regular tetrahedron the four groups H, CH_3, OH, COOH; this formulation can be done in two ways, as follows:

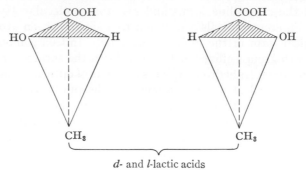

d- and *l*-lactic acids

The subtle problem of determining which specific configuration corresponds to the *d*- and to the *l*-form, respectively, is not settled in this or any other instance of optical isomerism. Certain conventions in representation, adopted where empirical correlations have been established between one series and another, are described later. A representation of the lactic acids with a simple three-dimensional model of convenience in interpretations of stereochemical phenomena is shown in Fig. 11.3. In such models the atoms and groups joined to the asymmetric carbon are represented by differently colored balls. These groups differ actually in the space that they occupy; a hydrogen atom, for example, is small in comparison to a carboxyl group (ratio of atomic weight units, 1:45). The unequal distribution of weight or of space requirement may give rise to an irregular tetrahedron. An approach to a more accurate representation of the molecular characteristics is afforded by Stuart models (1934), illustrated in Fig. 11.4. The atoms are represented by spheres of appropriate relative diameters and appropriate facings to indicate effective spheres of bound atoms on a scale of actual interatomic distances. These models give one of the best available representations of the spatial characteristics of actual molecules.

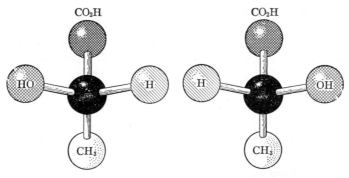

FIG. 11.3. — Models of the Mirror-Image Forms of Lactic Acid

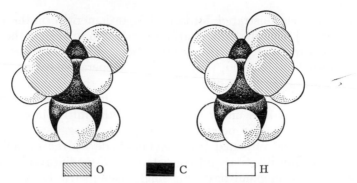

FIG. 11.4. — Stuart Models of d- and l-Lactic Acid

Whatever models or space formulas are used to represent the lactic acids, each form is seen to be asymmetric, since it possesses no plane of symmetry that will halve the molecule, or since the two forms are like right- and left-handed screws. Because such mirror-image isomers bear the relationship to each other of enantiomorphous crystals of quartz or of sodium ammonium racemate, they are described as a pair of enantiomers (Gr. *enantio-*, opposite). In all instances where the d- and l-forms have been isolated in satisfactory purity, the physical constants of enantiomers agree within experimental error. This concordance is illustrated by data given in Table 11.1 for the optically active mandelic acids. Such small deviations as are noted in solubilities and in angles of rotation can be attributed either to imperfect purification or to experimental error. Although the enantiomers melt at the same temperature, a mixture of a small amount of the d-acid depresses the melting point of the l-form, and vice versa; hence the method of mixed melting-point determination detects even a subtle difference. That the melting point of the dl-acid, or racemic form, is below the melting points of the component acids is purely fortuitous, for such molecular compounds can have properties not predictable from those of the component parts. Relative solubilities are likewise unforetellable. The acidic dissociation constant is a property of the dissolved molecules and the fact that the dl-acid has the same value as that found for the l-acid is evidence that the enantiomers correspond in acidity. Chemical properties are also independent of the physical form, and the d-, l-, and dl-acids exhibit the same chemical characteristics; they react in the same way with the same reagents, and the reactions proceed at the identical rate in the three cases. Correspondence in physical properties is accounted for by

TABLE 11.1. THE MANDELIC ACIDS, $C_6H_5CH(OH)COOH$

	M.P., ° C.	SOLUBILITY, G./100 G. $H_2O^{20°}$	ACIDIC DISSOCIATION, $pK_a^{25°}$	SPECIFIC ROTATION, $[\alpha]_D^{20°}$ 2% IN H_2O
d-Acid	132.8	8.54 g.		+ 155.5°
l-Acid	132.8	8.64 g.	3.37	− 154.4°
dl-Acid	118.5	15.97 g.	3.38	inactive

any of the models illustrated, for in each enantiomeric form the same groups are present and have the same spatial relationship to one another and to the asymmetric carbon atom. If any attractions or repulsions between groups are manifested in one form, they are equally operative in the other. That one acid rotates the plane of polarized light to the right is a phenomenon associated with asymmetry of the molecule in a manner not as yet fully interpretable, but it is understandable that the mirror-image counterpart shows an equal rotatory power in the opposite sense.

The lactic acid obtained from acetaldehyde by the cyanohydrin synthesis is optically inactive and consists of a *dl*-modification. Indeed any synthesis of a compound having a single asymmetric carbon atom yields a *dl*-form or racemate; that is, it affords exactly the same number of molecules of the *d*- and of the *l*-forms. A simple explanation of this observation is found in the van't Hoff-Le Bel theory. If acetaldehyde is represented by a space formula in which the carbon atom of the carbonyl group is indicated by a tetrahedron with methyl at one corner and hydrogen at another and with the other two corners united to oxygen by a double link, the molecule has a plane of symmetry bisecting the oxygen atom and the hydrogen and

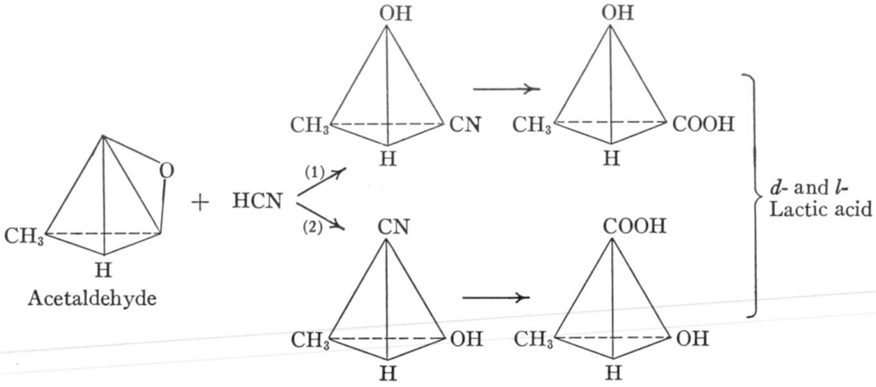

methyl substituents. This symmetry means that there is no difference in the two linkages of the carbonyl group, and hence that in the reaction with hydrogen cyanide, the same opportunity exists for opening of the one linkage as of the other, (1) and (2). Since an experiment on even a microscale involves many million molecules, the law of the probability of occurrence of two equally likely events is applicable with accuracy, and the carbonyl group must open, on the average, to an equal extent in the two possible directions. Asymmetry is established in the initial addition; the two enantiomeric cyanohydrins are formed in equal amounts, and equal amounts of the *d*- and *l*-acids result on hydrolysis.

Another reaction leading to production of an asymmetric center is the synthesis of α-hydroxybutyric acid starting with the α-bromination of butyric acid by the action of bromine and red phosphorus (Hell-Volhard-Zelinsky method); the initial reaction product is the acid bromide, which undergoes halogenation in the α-position more readily than the free acid.

$$CH_3CH_2CH_2COOH \xrightarrow{P, Br_2} \begin{bmatrix} CH_3CH_2\overset{*}{C}HCOBr \\ | \\ Br \end{bmatrix} \xrightarrow[77\%]{H_2O}$$

$$\begin{matrix} CH_3CH_2\overset{*}{C}HCOOH \\ | \\ Br \end{matrix} \xrightarrow[69\%]{K_2CO_3, H_2O, 100°} \begin{matrix} CH_3CH_2\overset{*}{C}HCOOH \\ | \\ OH \end{matrix}$$

dl-α-Bromobutyric acid   *dl*-α-Hydroxybutyric acid
(m.p. −4°)   (m.p. 42.5°)

The crude α-bromo acid bromide is not isolated, but is poured slowly into hot water to hydrolyze the more reactive halogen atom. The resulting x-bromo acid is then hydrolyzed to the hydroxy acid by boiling with water containing one molecular equivalent of potassium carbonate, and under these conditions there is little elimination of hydrogen bromide from the α,β-position to produce crotonic acid. Asymmetry is established with replacement of one of the two α-hydrogen atoms by bromine, and a space

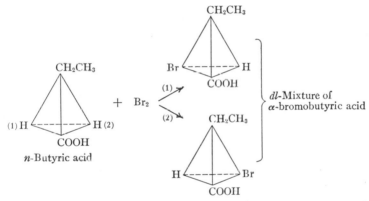

model shows that there is exactly the same opportunity for replacement of the one as of the other. Again the law of chance dictates formation of equal amounts of the two possible products, and hence a *dl*-mixture results. These two examples typify the general situation in the synthesis of compounds that can exist in mirror-image forms, for the production of an asymmetric carbon atom is invariably accomplished by either an addition reaction, in which either of two linkages of a double bond is utilized, or the substitution or replacement of one of two identical atoms or groups.

Correlations and Conventions. — The dextrorotatory lactic acid from muscle forms metallic salts that are all levorotatory. Actually both the acid and its salts are so weakly rotatory that the absolute difference in rotation between them is slight and the reversal in the sign of rotation therefore of little significance (see formulas). The salts, as well as the likewise

$\begin{matrix} CH_3CHCO_2H \\ | \\ OH \end{matrix}$	$\begin{matrix} (CH_3CHCO_2)_2Zn \\ | \\ OH \end{matrix}$	$\begin{matrix} CH_3CHCO_2CH_3 \\ | \\ OH \end{matrix}$	$\begin{matrix} CH_3CHCO_2H \\ | \\ OCH_3 \end{matrix}$	$\begin{matrix} CH_3CHCO_2H \\ | \\ OC_2H_5 \end{matrix}$
+3.3°	−6.0°	−8.2°	−75.5°	−66.4°

$[\alpha]_D$ of *d*-lactic acid and derivatives

weakly levorotatory methyl ester, are reconvertible into the weakly dextrorotatory free acid; these substances all have the same configuration, or
orientation of groups in space. The methyl and ethyl ethers of dextrorotatory lactic acid also belong to the same configurational series, even though
they are relatively strongly levorotatory. Thus the magnitude and even
the direction of rotation in a given stereochemical series is subject to considerable variation according to the groups attached to the asymmetric
center. Therefore the sign of rotation of one member of the series, for
example free d-lactic acid, does not constitute a satisfactory characterization
of the configurational feature common to all members of the series.

A suitable designation of configurational relationships that has gained
general acceptance was introduced by Emil Fischer (1891), slightly modified
by M. A. Rosanoff (1906), and fully interpreted by C. S. Hudson (1949).
Dextrorotatory glyceraldehyde, $HOCH_2CH(OH)CHO$, is taken as the
reference standard and is arbitrarily assigned a configuration that is defined
in terms of the perspective tetrahedral model (a) or the equivalent, symmetrically oriented model (b). In both (a) and (b) the solid line connecting

D-(+)-Glyceraldehyde

H and OH represents an edge of the tetrahedron that projects in front of or
above the plane of the paper, and the dotted line connecting CHO and
CH_2OH is an edge of the tetrahedron that would be unseen in an opaque
mechanical model. For convenience in writing and printing, Fischer defined the following convention for planar projection of the three-dimensional
model; the model is oriented as in (b) with the carbon chain vertical and to
the rear and the hydrogen and hydroxyl standing out in front; the model is
then imagined to be flattened and the groups are laid on the plane of the
paper in the order that they appear in the model, as in (c). The planar
projection (c) must be thought of in terms of the actual model that it
represents (H and OH extending toward the front); it can be turned around
in the plane of the paper, but must not be imagined to be lifted and inverted. If the carbon chain contains two or more adjacent asymmetric
carbon atoms (see tartaric acid, below), the projection is made in the same
way from a model oriented with CHO or equivalent group at the top,
CH_2OH or equivalent at the bottom, the carbon chain vertical and to the
rear, and H and OH groups extending to the front.

The second convention is that the configuration of dextrorotatory
glyceraldehyde is designated by the small capital Roman D; the opposite
configuration is designated L. The reference substance is thus D-glyceraldehyde; a fuller description is given by the name D-(d)-glyceraldehyde; in

which D indicates the configuration and *d* records the incidental fact that the substance is dextrorotatory. The same information is given by the name D-(+)-glyceraldehyde, which is less confusing and therefore preferable.

Any compound that has been shown experimentally to contain an asymmetric carbon atom of the same configuration as that of D-glyceraldehyde belongs to the D-series. This is true of the acid resulting from oxidation of the aldehydic function; the substance is levorotatory and is therefore fully described by the name D-(−)-glyceric acid. If the CHO group of

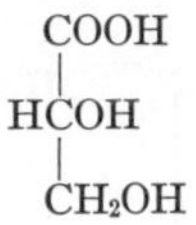

```
      COOH              COOH               COOH
       |                 |                  |
      HCOH              HCOH               HOCH
       |                 |                  |
      CH₂OH             CH₃                CH₂COOH
  D-(−)-Glyceric acid   D-(−)-Lactic acid   L-(−)-Malic acid
```

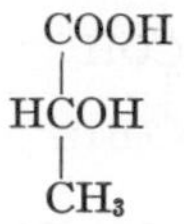

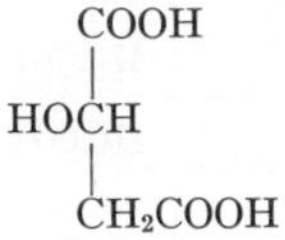

glyceraldehyde is oxidized and the CH_2OH group is reduced, the resulting substance is lactic acid. Experimental correlation has established the fact that levorotatory lactic acid, or *l*-lactic acid or (−)-lactic acid, corresponds in configuration to the reference standard and therefore is D-(−)-lactic acid. In the projection formula, hydroxyl is thus to the right and hydrogen to the left; this formula corresponds to the models shown at the right-hand side in Figs. 11.3 and 11.4 and in the corresponding tetrahedral diagrams. The designation of configuration eliminates confusion associated with the opposite sign of rotation of the lactic acids and their derivatives. Thus the statement that esterification of L-(+)-lactic acid gives the L-(−)-ester indicates that the direction of rotation changes but the configuration remains the same. Natural malic acid has been demonstrated to belong to the L-series; it is weakly levorotatory in dilute aqueous solution and becomes weakly dextrorotatory as the concentration is increased.

Natural *d*-tartaric acid has two similar asymmetric carbon atoms. When the asymmetric carbon atom written at the bottom in the formula is compared with that of D-glyceraldehyde and when CHOHCOOH is taken as equivalent to CHO and COOH is taken as equivalent to CH_2OH each equivalent center in *d*-tartaric acid is found to have the configuration opposite to that of the standard. The enantiomeric *l*-tartaric acid is thus the one that belongs to the D-series; it is D-(−)-tartaric acid and is formulated as shown.

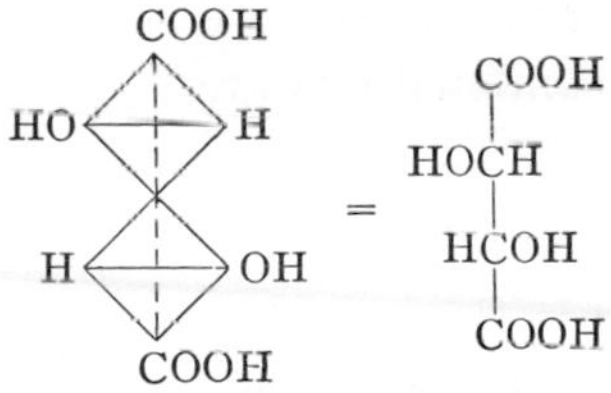

```
             COOH                COOH
              /\                   |
        HO <  +  > H            HOCH
              |           =       |
        H  <  +  > OH           HCOH
              \/                   |
             COOH                COOH
```

D-(−)-Tartaric acid

D-Glyceraldehyde was chosen as reference standard because it is the simplest member of the sugar series and corresponds in configuration to one of four asymmetric carbon atoms in the key sugar glucose. The complete series of related sugars includes the further members arabinose and erythrose, of projection formulas shown. The lowermost asymmetric center

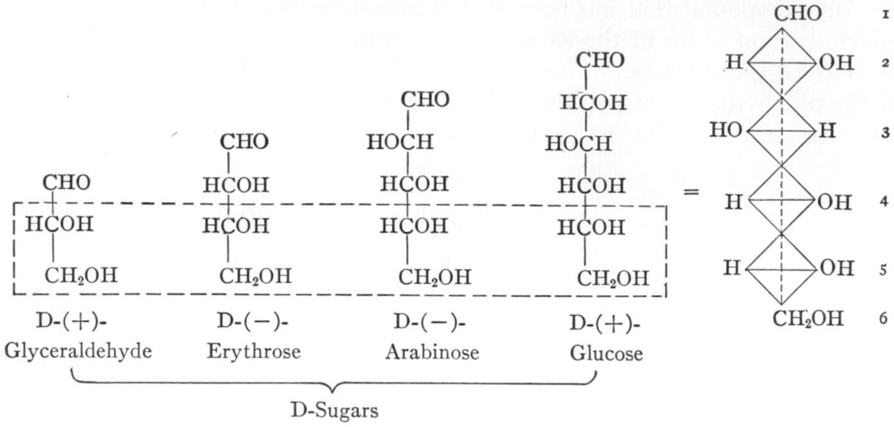

	CHO		CHO	CHO	CHO	1
D-(+)-	D-(−)-	D-(−)-	D-(+)-			
Glyceraldehyde	Erythrose	Arabinose	Glucose			

D-Sugars

of each of the higher sugars (C_5 in glucose) has the configuration of D-glyceraldehye, and hence the substances all belong to the D-series; it is incidental that D-glucose is dextrorotatory and the others levorotatory.

Compounds with Two Dissimilar Asymmetric Carbons. — Application of the ordinary addition reactions of olefins frequently gives rise to substances having two asymmetric carbon atoms, for example:

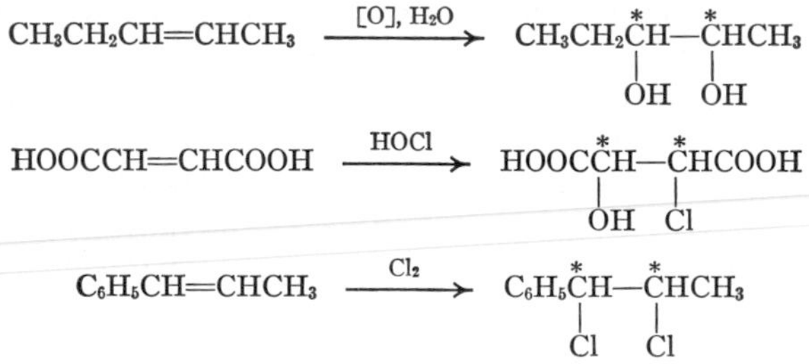

$$CH_3CH_2CH=CHCH_3 \xrightarrow{[O],\ H_2O} CH_3CH_2\overset{*}{C}H-\overset{*}{C}HCH_3$$
$$\underset{OH\ \ \ OH}{}$$

$$HOOCCH=CHCOOH \xrightarrow{HOCl} HOOC\overset{*}{C}H-\overset{*}{C}HCOOH$$
$$\underset{OH\ \ \ Cl}{}$$

$$C_6H_5CH=CHCH_3 \xrightarrow{Cl_2} C_6H_5\overset{*}{C}H-\overset{*}{C}HCH_3$$
$$\underset{Cl\ \ \ Cl}{}$$

In each of these examples the two asymmetric centers are dissimilar, and each therefore can contribute to a certain different extent to the rotatory power of the molecule as a whole in either a *dextro* or *levo* sense. If the contribution of one center of asymmetry is designated as ±a and the other as ±b, then the possible combinations are:

$$\begin{array}{cc} +a & -a \\ +b & -b \end{array} \qquad \begin{array}{cc} +a & -a \\ -b & +b \end{array}$$

dl-Form　　　　　*d'l'*-Form

The theory therefore predicts existence of four isomers, grouped in two pairs of enantiomeric modifications, or *dl*-mixtures, and this prediction has been verified. For example, two substances corresponding to the formula $C_6H_5\overset{*}{C}HBr\overset{*}{C}HBrCOOH$ are known; both are optically inactive but distinguished from each other by a profound difference in melting point, and both have been shown to constitute racemic mixtures. One, cinnamic acid dibromide, m.p. 201°, has been resolved into the active components of specific rotations +67.5° and −68.3°, and the other, allocinnamic acid dibromide, m.p. 90°, is capable of resolution, though the active forms have not been isolated in pure condition. Space formulas can be written to represent the four isomers, but since the configurations relative to glyceraldehyde are not known, a given formula cannot be identified as attributable to a particular isomer. A first formula is constructed by joining two tetrahedrons together and affixing appropriate groups to the free corners in an arbitrary manner, for example, as in I. This arbitrary formula can be taken as representing a d-acid, in which the upper half of the molecule

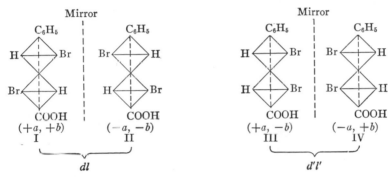

is a +a part and the lower half a +b part. Formula II, representing the enantiomer of I, is constructed by visualizing the image of I in a mirror, and the upper and lower halves are, by definition, −a and −b parts. Formula III is made up of the upper half of I (+a) and the lower half of II (−b), and IV is its mirror image. Projection formulas utilizing the simplification that the asymmetric carbons are represented merely as the intersections of the lines connecting substituents are as follows:

C_6H_5	C_6H_5	C_6H_5	C_6H_5
H——Br	Br——H	H——Br	Br——H
Br——H	H——Br	H——Br	Br——H
COOH	COOH	COOH	COOH

The two racemates are appropriately designated as dl- and d′l′-forms, and it is understandable that they should differ in melting point and other physical properties and indeed even in the rates at which they undergo reactions. The d acid I is composed of two different asymmetric molecular halves (+a, +b), and the combination is neither duplicated nor mirrored in either the d′-acid III (+a, −b) or the l′-acid IV (−a, +b). Stereoisomers that, like the d-, d′-, and l′-acids, are not identical and yet are not mirror images, are defined as **diastereoisomers** (Gr. dia, apart). The l-acid II is the enantiomer of I, but is a diastereoisomer of III and IV.

Orientation of the two tetrahedrons as shown in formula I does not permit easy visualization of the effect of rotation of the two asymmetric carbon atoms about the single bond connecting them. Formula Ia is another orientation that is equivalent to formula I; in Ia the corner of the upper tetrahedron that projects to the front carries hydrogen, and the projecting corner of the lower tetrahedron carries the carboxyl group. If the upper tetrahedron of Ia is rotated 120° clockwise, the bromine atom appears at the projecting position and formula Ib is obtained. This, like

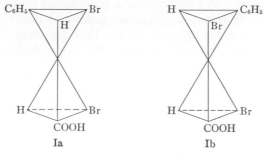

Ia, is made up of +a and +b halves and has a mirror-image counterpart, and is a satisfactory *alternative* to Ia. It does not, however, represent an *additional* isomer; if this were the case an infinite number of isomers could exist corresponding to the setting of the upper tetrahedron at any of an infinite number of angles from the original position. Furthermore, if the phenyl and carboxyl groups in Ia and Ib were replaced by hydrogen the formulas would stand for two stereoisomeric dibromoethanes, but no such isomerism exists. These facts indicate that carbon atoms ordinarily are free to rotate about a single bond. Exceptions to the principle of free rotation are known where molecules contain ring systems or bulky groups so situated as to prevent or restrict normal rotation.

An interesting series of isomers having two dissimilar asymmetric carbons is that of the chloromalic acids, HOOCCHClCHOHCOOH. The four isomers, corresponding to the projection formulas shown, have been isolated and characterized. The optically active components of the lower-melting *dl*-acid V both melt at 165–166° and have the low specific rotations

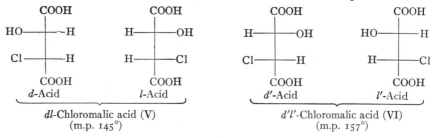

$[\alpha]_D^{20°}$ +7.1° and −7.5°, and by a coincidence, the components of acid VI also melt at 165–166° and have nearly the same rotations, $[\alpha]_D^{20°}$ −9.3°

and $-8.0°$.   The inactive acids V and VI nevertheless differ in their response to bases, resulting in elimination of hydrogen chloride and closure of an ethylene oxide ring, in the velocity of hydrolysis with boiling water, in the rate of reduction, and in their dissociation constants and other properties. By comparing various physical constants with those of isomers of the series HOOCĊHOHĊHOHCOOH and HOOCĊHClĊHClCOOH, R. Kuhn and T. Wagner-Jauregg (1928) established a relationship of d-chloromalic acid to l-tartaric acid (upper carbon) and to d-dichlorosuccinic acid (lower carbon):

l-Tartaric acid   d-Dichlorosuccinic acid

The specific configurations indicated in the projection formulas above were deduced on this basis.

Compounds with Several Dissimilar Asymmetric Carbons. — If three centers of asymmetry in a given molecule can contribute in either a positive or negative sense to the extent of a, b, and c to the rotatory power as a whole, then the possible combinations are:

$$
\begin{array}{cc\ \ \ cc\ \ \ cc\ \ \ cc}
|\,a & a & a & +a & +a & -a & +a & -a \\
+b & -b & +b & -b & -b & +b & +b & -b \\
+c & -c & +c & -c & +c & -c & -c & +c \\
\hline
dl & & d'l' & & d''l'' & & d'''l''' &
\end{array}
$$

Eight different optically active forms are possible, falling into four pairs of mirror-image isomers.   A general relationship by which the number of isomers can be calculated is: number of optically active forms = 2^n (where n is the number of dissimilar asymmetric carbon atoms).   When n = 4 the number of optically active forms possible is sixteen, and indeed an instance is known in the sugar series in which all sixteen isomers predicted by the van't Hoff-Le Bel theory have been obtained.

Tartaric Acids. — The tartaric acid series is the classical example of compounds possessing two similar asymmetric carbon atoms.   Pasteur had established that the inactive racemic acid can be resolved into d- and l-forms and is in fact dl-tartaric acid, and he had discovered another inactive isomer, mesotartaric acid.

*CH(OH)COOH
|
*CH(OH)COOH

This isomer, typical of other substances which are therefore described generally as *meso* modifications, is produced along with the dl-acid by heating d-tartaric acid with water at $165°$ and can be isolated from the mixture in the form of the sparingly soluble acid potassium salt.   The existence of two active and two inactive tartaric acids is readily explained. Since the rotatory contribution of each of two similar centers of asymmetry can be represented as $\pm a$, the following forms are predicted:

$$
\begin{array}{ccc}
+a & -a & +a \\
+a & -a & -a
\end{array}
$$

$$
\underbrace{}_{dl\text{-Form}} \qquad \underbrace{}_{meso\text{ Form}}
$$

The combination of equal parts of the d- and the l-acid constitutes one inactive form, and the second, or *meso* form is inactive because the molecule has a plane of symmetry. Mesotartaric acid is sometimes called an internally compensated inactive form, since there exists within each molecule a balancing of the right- and left-handed tendencies; dl-tartaric acid is inactive by virtue of compensation of an external nature: the presence of like numbers of two kinds of molecules. Pasteur's own researches afforded a proof that mesotartaric acid consists of symmetrical molecules, for he encountered evidence that this substance, unlike the dl-acid, is incapable of resolution into component, optically active forms (p. 274).

The space formula and relative configuration of d-tartaric acid, or D-(+)-tartaric acid, have been discussed (p. 263). The complete series is represented in both tetrahedral formulas and projections. The two asym-

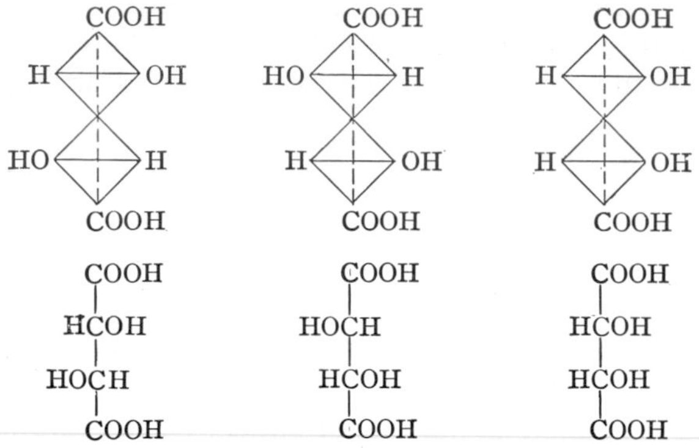

COOH	COOH	COOH
H〈〉OH	HO〈〉H	H〈〉OH
HO〈〉H	H〈〉OH	H〈〉OH
COOH	COOH	COOH

COOH	COOH	COOH
HCOH	HOCH	HCOH
HOCH	HCOH	HCOH
COOH	COOH	COOH
dextro (D)	*levo* (L)	*meso*

Tartaric acids

metric carbon atoms of d-tartaric acid make equal dextrorotatory contributions, and, as the formulas are written, the arrangement of the groups COOH, OH, and H is clockwise, or right-handed, in both the upper and lower centers. In the case of l-tartaric acid the arrangement is counterclockwise throughout, and in the *meso* acid the upper and lower centers are right- and left-handed, respectively.

Some properties of the two active and two inactive forms of tartaric acid are given in Table 11.2. A noteworthy point is that the dl-form, racemic acid, melts at a higher temperature than the optically active components. This property is not inconsistent with the observation, already noted, that the melting point of the d-acid is depressed by admixture with a *small* amount of the l-acid, and vice versa, for racemic acid is not a mixture of the active forms but a molecular compound having its own characteristics.

TABLE 11.2. PROPERTIES OF THE TARTARIC ACIDS

ACID	M.P., ° C.	$[\alpha]_D^{25°}$, 20% AQ. SOLUTION	SOLUBILITY, G. PER 100 G. H_2O	ACIDIC DISSOCIATION	
				pK_{a_1}	pK_{a_2}
dextro	170	$+12°$	139	2.93	4.23
levo	170	$-12°$	139	2.93	4.23
dl (racemic)	206	inactive	20.6	2.96	4.24
meso	140	inactive	125	3.11	4.80

The situation can be appreciated by consideration of diagrams giving the melting points (or freezing points) of mixtures of the *d*- and *l*-acids of compositions varying from 100 percent of the one to 100 percent of the other (Roozeboom,[7] 1899).   Figure 11.5, case A, gives the typical relationship to which the tartaric acids conform.   The melting point of the *d*-acid is depressed by successive additions of the *l*-form till a eutectic point is reached; the curve then rises to a maximum at the 50:50 point, corresponding to the melting point of the molecular (*dl*-) compound, which in this instance is higher than that of either component.   An equally characteristic relationship is shown in case B; here the diagram again consists of two complementary halves, each having a eutectic point, but the *dl*- compound has a lower melting point than the active forms.   In either case A or B, addition of a small amount of one of the active forms to the *dl*-compound depresses the melting point.   In those instances where equal parts of two enantiomers fail to combine to a molecular compound but afford a racemic mixture or conglomerate, this 50:50 mixture melts lower than mixtures of any other composition melt, and addition of an active isomer to the inactive form raises the melting point.   This difference provides a method of distinguishing racemic compounds from racemic mixtures.

Resolution of Racemic Modifications. — Resolution of an inactive substance into its optically active components can be accomplished only in rare instances by crystallization and mechanical separation, as in the

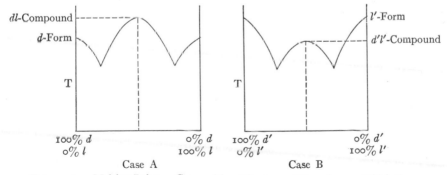

FIG. 11.5. — Melting Point — Composition Diagrams of Enantiomers Which Form Racemic Compounds

[7] Hendrick W. B. Roozeboom, 1854–1907; b. Alkman, Netherlands; Ph.D. Leiden: Amsterdam

classical experiment of Pasteur or by subsequently introduced modifications.   Pasteur's contributions, however, included the discovery of a method
of resolution that is practicable and capable of wide application.   Either
through scientific curiosity or because of an instinct for thorough investigation, the gifted experimentalist prepared and characterized all conceivable
salts derived from the combination of the tartaric acids with both inorganic
and organic bases, including naturally occurring, optically active amine
bases.   The salts of *d*- and *l*-tartaric acid with metals, ammonia, and aniline
were identical in solubility and other physical properties; but Pasteur observed that with the salts derived from asymmetric, optically active natural
bases such as asparagine, quinine, strychnine, or brucine "all is changed in
an instant.   The solubility is no longer the same and the properties all
differ as much as in the case of the most distantly related isomers."   The
reason is apparent from consideration of an example.   If a *dl*-acid is neutralized with a dextrorotatory (*d'*) base, one of the two salts produced is
composed of two right-handed parts (*dd'*), and the other is made up of right-

$$
\text{Enantiomers} \begin{Bmatrix} d\text{-Acid} \\ + \quad d'\text{-Base} \rightarrow \\ l\text{-Acid} \end{Bmatrix} \begin{matrix} dd'\text{-Salt} \\ \\ ld'\text{-Salt} \end{matrix} \Bigg\} \text{Diastereoisomers}
$$

and left-handed components (*ld'*).   The two salts obviously differ in rotatory
power and are in fact diasteroisomers.   If the acidic and basic components
are strongly rotatory, the *dd'*-salt probably will be dextrorotatory; the
ld'-salt is composed of oppositely acting but unbalanced parts and may
show either a positive or negative rotation.   In any case, the two salts
have different rotatory values, different solubilities, and different melting
points; they therefore are separable by fractional crystallization, and the
course of separation can be followed by determination of appropriate physical constants.   Once one salt has been secured pure, it can be treated with
sodium hydroxide, the resolving *d'*-base recovered, and the optically active
acid liberated by acidification of the alkaline solution.

The method is equally applicable to resolution of a synthetic *dl*-amine
with use of an optically active acid.   The resolving agents that are particularly useful are listed in Table 11.3.   Some are of natural occurrence, some
are obtained by modification of a natural product, and some are produced
by synthesis and resolution.   The alkaloidal bases cinchonine and cinchonidine have the same structures and are diastereoisomers, as the alkaloids quinine and quinidine are.   Brucine is a dimethoxy derivative of
strychnine.   The natural bases listed are tertiary amines, with the exception
of arginine, and an innovation consists in using as resolving agents the
quaternary ammonium hydroxides obtainable from them (R. T. Major,
1941).   Thus quinine is treated with methyl iodide, and the methiodide is
converted with silver oxide and water into quinine methohydroxide:

$$
\text{>N} \xrightarrow{CH_3I} \text{>N}^+\!\!\diagup^{CH_3} \;\; I^- \xrightarrow{AgOH} \text{>N}^+\!\!\diagup^{CH_3} \;\; OH^-
$$

Methohydroxide

TABLE 11.3. RESOLVING AGENTS

NAME	FORMULA	M.P., ° C.	$[\alpha]_D$
Bases			
Cinchonine	$C_{19}H_{21}N_2(OH)$	264	+223
Cinchonidine	$C_{19}H_{21}N_2(OH)$	207	−111
Quinine	$C_{19}H_{20}N_2(OH)OCH_3$	175	−158
Quinidine	$C_{19}H_{20}N_2(OH)OCH_3$	173	+243
Strychnine	$C_{21}H_{22}O_2N_2$	290	−110
Brucine	$C_{21}H_{20}O_2N_2(OCH_3)_2$	178	−80
Morphine	$C_{16}H_{14}ON(OH)_2CH_3$	254	−133
l-Menthylamine	$C_{10}H_{19}NH_2$	liq.	−36
d- and l-α-Phenylethylamine	$C_6H_5CH(NH_2)CH_3$	liq.	±39
d-2-Amino-1-hydroxyhydrindene	$C_9H_8(OH)NH_2$	142	+23
L-Arginine	$C_6H_{14}O_2N_4$	238° dec.	+12.5
Acids			
d-Tartaric acid	HOOCCHOHCHOHCOOH	170	+12
l-Malic acid	HOOCCHOHCH$_2$COOH	100	−2.3[1]
l-Mandelic acid	$C_6H_5CHOHCOOH$	133	−154
d-Camphorsulfonic acid	$C_{10}H_{15}OSO_3H$	196	+24
α-Bromocamphor-π-sulfonic acid	$C_{10}H_{14}OBrSO_3H$		+85[2]
l-Quinic acid[3]	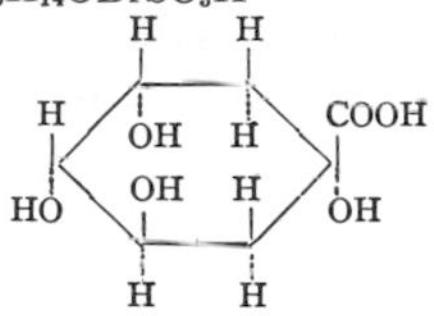 (ring structure, see p. 291)	162	−44
d- and l-6,6′-Dinitrodiphenic acid	see p. 292	231	±127

[1] The substance is levorotatory only in dilute aqueous solutions, and becomes dextrorotatory as the concentration is increased; thus the following specific rotations are noted at the concentrations indicated: 8.4%, −2.3°; 34%, ±0°; 70%, +3.3°.

[2] As the ammonium salt.

[3] For an explanation of the formula, see page 291.

The methohydroxides of quinine, quinidine, and cinchonine are much stronger bases than the tertiary amines and are excellent resolving agents. High rotatory power of the resolving agent facilitates following the separation by polarimetric examination of the crystallizates; in some instances the diastereoisomeric salts are best characterized by their melting points or by the crystalline form. Availability and cost of the reagent are considerations, though a reasonably stable substance can be recovered without undue loss.

Values for specific rotations given in Table 11.3 represent merely typical determinations in solvents usually employed and are not strictly comparable with respect to solvent, concentration, and temperature. With some compounds the specific rotation is independent of the concentration, whereas with others there is a noticeable variation; thus l-malic acid is weakly levo-

TABLE 11.4. OPTICALLY ACTIVE SALTS

		M.P., °C.	SOLUBILITY IN 100 G. H₂O AT 21.6°	$[\alpha]_D$
d-Cinchonine {	d-mandelate	80	1.08 g.	+152.4
	l-mandelate	165	2.05 g.	+92.1
l-Menthylamine {	d-tartrate	198		−12.6
	l-tartrate	194		−42.0
l-Menthylamine mesotartrate		218		−32.1

rotatory in dilute solutions but weakly dextrorotatory in concentrated solutions. The rotations of the two diastereoisomeric salts involved in a resolution are not predictable from specific rotations of the nonionized acids and bases involved; the molecular rotation (p. 371) of a salt is the sum of the molecular rotations of the component ions. Typical relationships between pairs of salts encountered in resolutions are given in Table 11.4 for the case of cinchonine (+223°) combined with the mandelic acids (±154°) and for that of l-menthylamine (−36°) combined with the tartaric acids (±12°). Rotatory values of the salts fall roughly in the order expected. The salt of l-menthylamine with the optically inactive mesotartaric acid has a specific rotation not far from that of the free base but falling between those of the other isomers. Of greatest practical significance is the fact that solubilities of the diastereoisomeric salts differ considerably; one of the mandelic acid salts is twice as soluble as the other.

When a pair of diastereoisomeric salts is fractionated, the less soluble isomer often can be obtained relatively easily, but isolation of the more soluble salt in pure form may present difficulties. Change to another resolving agent is sometimes advantageous, for with another pair of salts the solubility relationships may be reversed. Thus in an efficient procedure for resolution of dl-α-phenylethylamine, the d-form is obtained by fractionally crystallizing the salt formed with l-malic acid. treating the purified, less soluble salt with alkali, and isolating the free d-amine by steam distillation and extraction with benzene; yield 58–65%. The crude malate salt from the mother liquors is then converted into the free amine and this is crystallized with d-tartaric acid; l-α-phenylethylamine is obtained from the pure l-base-d-tartrate in overall yield of 53–70%.

The method of resolution by conversion into diastereoisomers has been applied in only a few instances involving formation of derivatives other than salts. Sometimes resolution of a neutral compound is accomplished most advantageously by conversion into a derivative capable of salt formation. For example, octanol-2 (capryl alcohol) is converted by treatment with phthalic anhydride into the acid phthalate, which is resolved by crystallization of the brucine salts. The separated salts are decomposed with hydrochloric acid and the brucine is recovered, and the two acid phthalates are then hydrolyzed with alkali; the d- and l-forms of the alcohol are thereby obtained in yields of about 66% in each case.

$$C_6H_{13}\underset{CH_3}{\overset{|}{C}}HOH \quad + \quad \text{Phthalic anhydride} \quad \longrightarrow \quad dl\text{-Acid phthalate} \quad \xrightarrow{\text{Brucine}}$$

Octanol-2   Phthalic anhydride   dl-Acid phthalate

$$\xrightarrow[\substack{\text{HCl} \\ \text{(removal of brucine} \\ \text{hydrochloride)}}]{} \quad d\text{- and }l\text{-Acid phthalates} \quad \xrightarrow[\substack{\text{NaOH} \\ \text{(removal of} \\ \text{phthalic acid)}}]{} \quad d\text{- and }l\text{-Octanol-2}$$

Two salts, separated

An often efficient modification (Pope,[8] 1912) consists in treating a dl-base with half the amount of a resolving organic acid required for neutralization, together with a further half equivalent of hydrochloric acid. Equilibrium is set up among the two pairs of salts, but those derived from the organic acid are distinctly less soluble than the hydrochlorides. Thus the less soluble of the two diastereoisomeric organic salts tends to crystallize, and the solution contains chiefly the hydrochloric acid salt of the enantiomeric amine.

Microbiological Separation of Racemic Modifications. — Pasteur discovered in 1858–1860 that when the microorganism *Penicillium glaucum*, the green mold found on aging cheese and rotted fruits, is grown in a dilute aqueous solution of nutrient salts (phosphates, ammonium salts) containing racemic acid, the originally optically inactive solution slowly becomes levorotatory. The microorganism preferentially assimilates the d-form of tartaric acid, and if the process is interrupted at an appropriate point the unnatural l-tartaric can be isolated. If the process is allowed to continue, the l-form eventually is consumed, but natural d-tartaric acid is attacked by the microorganism much more rapidly.

Many instances are known of preferential destruction of one of two enantiomers by molds or bacteria or even by higher organisms. The action probably is attributable to the enzyme systems of the organisms, for the same effect has been observed with isolated enzymes. Thus dl-mandelonitrile becomes levorotatory when acted on by the enzyme emulsin. Since the enzyme is optically active, the selective action may be associated with formation of an intermediate complex that plays a role analogous to that of the diastereoisomeric salts involved in the method of resolution described in the preceding section.

The microbiological method of separation is seldom of preparative value, particularly since one of the two forms, usually the more interesting natural one, is sacrificed. Also, the process must be conducted in very dilute solutions containing nutrient salts favorable to growth of the microorganism, and recovery of the optically active product is often difficult and inefficient. The chief value of the method is in determining whether or not a given sub-

[8] Sir William J. Pope, 1870–1939; b. London; Manchester, Cambridge; *Nature*, **144**, 810 (1939)

stance is resolvable. Whereas racemic acid is acted upon by *Penicillium glaucum* and gives a levorotatory solution, mesotartaric acid under the same conditions develops no optical activity, and this observation provides evidence that the *meso* acid is the internally compensated form. Isomers of *meso* and *dl*-types often can be distinguished without isolation of any products merely by examination of similarly processed solutions in a polarimeter tube.

Racemization. — Conversion of half of a given quantity of an optically active compound into the enantiomer, with resultant formation of the *dl*-modification, is defined as racemization. The experiment by Pasteur in which *d*-tartaric acid was converted by the action of water at 165° into a mixture of the *meso* and *dl*-acids involved racemization of a part of the material. The racemic (*dl*) acid occurring as a by-product of the production of *d*-tartaric acid in the wine industry probably arises by partial racemization of the *d*-acid during processing.

Racemization occurs especially readily with compounds having a carbonyl group adjacent to an asymmetric carbon carrying a hydrogen atom, for example tartaric acid, lactic acid, and glyceraldehyde. Where the specific grouping indicated is lacking, racemization usually proceeds with difficulty. Thus, in contrast with mandelic acid, $C_6H_5CHOHCOOH$, the C-methyl derivative atrolactic acid, $C_6H_5C(CH_3)OHCOOH$, does not undergo racemization. These facts suggest that the α-hydrogen atom plays a part and that enolization is involved. If the activated α-hydrogen

(a)   (b)   (c)

atom in (a) migrates to oxygen in an equilibrium process to give an enol (b), the center of asymmetry is destroyed temporarily by production of a double bond, and when the hydrogen migrates back to the carbon atom, the process can involve opening of either of the two linkages of the symmetrical double bond, and hence can afford either the original configuration (a) or the opposite configuration (c); the chances being equal, a mixture of equal parts of (a) and (c) must result. Since all the transformations are reversible, formation of only a minute amount of the enol would result in eventual racemization of the entire material. The interpretation is strengthened by the fact that racemization is promoted by acids and bases, reagents which catalyze enolization.

The phenomenon is general and has certain practical applications. One is illustrated by the procedure developed (Merck, 1940) for resolution of an intermediate required for synthesis of pantothenic acid. This intermediate, III, is obtained by aldol condensation of isobutyraldehyde with formaldehyde (more reactive carbonyl group) and application to the hydroxyaldehyde 1 of the cyanohydrin synthesis (as modified by Carter).

The initial product is a hydroxy acid, II, but this readily loses water intra-molecularly to form a lactone, III. The *dl*-lactone is resolved by dissolving it in one equivalent of alkali, when the sodium salt of the acid II is formed, and adding one-half equivalent of quinine hydrochloride (Pope procedure); the quinine salt of one enantiomer crystallizes selectively (86% yield) and affords the desired levorotatory form of the lactone III (m.p. 91°, yield

$$O=CH_2 \;+\; H-\underset{\underset{CH_3}{|}}{\overset{\overset{CH_3}{|}}{C}}-CHO \;\xrightarrow{K_2CO_3,\,20°}\; HOCH_2-\underset{\underset{CH_3}{|}}{\overset{\overset{CH_3}{|}}{C}}-CHO \;\xrightarrow{aq.KCN \text{ and } CaCl_2}$$

Isobutyraldehyde   α,α-Dimethyl-β-hydroxy-propionaldehyde, I
(m.p. 96–97°)

$$\left[HOCH_2-\underset{\underset{CH_3\;\;OH}{|\;\;\;\;\;|}}{\overset{\overset{CH_3}{|}}{C}}-CHCN \right] \longrightarrow$$

$$\left[\underset{\underset{CH_3\;\;OH}{|\;\;\;\;\;|}}{\overset{\overset{CH_3}{|}}{HOCH_2-C}}-CH-COOH \right] \xrightarrow{77–81\% \text{ from I}} CH_2-\underset{\underset{CH_3\;\;OH}{|\;\;\;\;\;|}}{\overset{\overset{CH_3}{|}}{C}}-CH-CO$$

II   *dl*-α-Hydroxy-β,β-dimethyl-butyrolactone, III
(m.p. about 80°)

71%). The other enantiomer, which is valueless for the synthesis of panto-thenic acid, is then racemized by heating an aqueous solution of its sodium salt at 150° for eighteen hours, and the resulting *dl*-product is added to the next batch of synthetic material submitted to resolution; in this manner the entire lot, rather than half, of the intermediate can be utilized.

In a compound having more than one asymmetric carbon atom, selective racemization of an asymmetric center adjacent to a carbonyl group and possessing a hydrogen atom available for enolization is possible, for example:

$$-\underset{\underset{OH}{|}}{\overset{\overset{H}{|}}{C^*}}-\underset{\underset{OH}{|}}{\overset{\overset{H}{|}}{C^*}}-C\begin{smallmatrix}O\\ \diagdown H\end{smallmatrix} \;\rightleftarrows\; \left[-\underset{\underset{OH}{|}}{\overset{\overset{H}{|}}{C^*}}\;C(OH)=C\begin{smallmatrix}OH\\ \diagdown H\end{smallmatrix} \right] \;\rightleftarrows\; -\underset{\underset{OH\;\;H}{|\;\;\;\;\;|}}{\overset{\overset{H\;\;\;OH}{|\;\;\;\;\;|}}{C^*-C^*}}-C\begin{smallmatrix}O\\ \diagdown H\end{smallmatrix}$$

(a)   (b)   (c)

The result is transformation of the original substance (a) partially into the isomer (c), which has been selectively inverted at a single asymmetric center and is described as an epimer of the first substance. The epimerization is not complete, for equilibrium between the isomers is reached; the point of equilibrium by no means corresponds to 50% conversion, but varies from compound to compound. The reason for this difference from an ordinary racemization is that the other center or centers of asymmetry in the molecule exert control over the course of ketonization of the enolic intermediate (b); opening of the double bond is not a purely fortuitous happening, but occurs under the directive influence of the stable asymmetric part of the molecule with preference for one or the other of the possible configurational arrangements of the labile center.

Asymmetric Synthesis. — The phenomenon of an asymmetric directive influence on the course of reactions is also applicable to processes of synthesis. One application is demonstrated by the following typical experiments on the reduction of esters of pyruvic acid, $CH_3COCOOH$ (McKenzie,[9] 1904–09). Reduction of the carbonyl group of the methyl or ethyl ester of this α-keto acid can proceed equally well in opposite steric directions and affords the methyl or ethyl ester of dl-lactic acid, $CH_3CHOHCOOH$. When, however, the acid is esterified with the optically active natural alcohol l-menthol, reduction does not proceed to an equal extent in the two possible ways but gives a mixture containing an excess of the ester of l-lactic acid; the product resulting on hydrolysis and removal of the l-menthol is

$$CH_3-\overset{\overset{O}{\|}}{C}-COOH \;+\; \text{HOHC*}\cdots \text{(l-Menthol, $C_{10}H_{19}OH$)} \longrightarrow CH_3-\overset{\overset{O}{\|}}{C}-COOC_{10}H_{19} \xrightarrow{\;Al(Hg)\;}$$

Pyruvic acid l-Menthyl pyruvate

$$CH_3-\overset{H}{\underset{OH}{C}}-COOC_{10}H_{19} \xrightarrow{\;KOH\;} CH_3-\overset{H}{\underset{OH}{C}}-COOH$$

{ l-Menthyl-d-lactate   { d-Lactic acid
{ l-Menthyl-l-lactate (excess)   { l-Lactic acid (excess)

optically active and consists of a mixture of dl- and l-lactic acid. The reduction proceeds to a greater degree in one steric sense than in the other.

The key step in such a process of asymmetric synthesis is production of a new center of asymmetry, and this affords two diastereoisomers, such as l-menthyl d-lactate and l-menthyl l-lactate. In the two molecules the corresponding groups are located at different distances from each other, and not in a mirror-image relationship, and the two substances differ not only in the rate with which they react with given reagents but also in the rate of their formation from a common starting material. Thus the control exercised by a center of asymmetry already present over the production of a new asymmetric center amounts to a preferential rate of formation of one of the two possible diastereoisomers. Neither the direction nor the extent of the preference is ordinarily predictable.

The principle of asymmetric synthesis is important in chemical transformations of compounds containing asymmetric carbon atoms. An aldehydic substance having the grouping I affords two products of the cyanohydrin

[9] Alexander McKenzie, 1869–1951; b. Dundee, Scotland; Ph.D. St. Andrews (Purdie); London, Dundee; *J. Chem. Soc.*, 270 (1952)

synthesis in *unequal* amounts (II and III), and often one product or the other is formed in greatly preponderant amount. The same is true of hydrogenation of an ethylenic compound having the partial structure **IV**; both saturated substances usually are formed, but often one is the chief product and the other is a by-product.

$$
\begin{array}{c}
\text{OH OH} \\
| \quad | \quad \quad \nearrow^{O} \\
-\text{C}^*-\text{C}^*-\text{C} \\
| \quad | \quad \quad \searrow_{\text{H}} \\
\text{H} \quad \text{H} \\
\text{I}
\end{array}
\xrightarrow{\text{HCN, hydrol.}}
\begin{array}{c}
\text{OH OH OH} \\
| \quad | \quad | \\
-\text{C}^*-\text{C}^*-\text{C}^*-\text{CO}_2\text{H} \\
| \quad | \quad | \\
\text{H} \quad \text{H} \quad \text{H} \\
\text{II}
\end{array}
+
\begin{array}{c}
\text{OH OH H} \\
| \quad | \quad | \\
-\text{C}^*-\text{C}^*-\text{C}^*-\text{CO}_2\text{H} \\
| \quad | \quad | \\
\text{H} \quad \text{H} \quad \text{OH} \\
\text{III}
\end{array}
$$

$$
\begin{array}{c}
\text{OH} \quad\quad \text{R} \\
| \quad\quad\quad | \\
-\text{C}^*-\text{CH}_2-\text{C}=\text{CH}- \\
| \\
\text{H} \\
\text{IV}
\end{array}
\xrightarrow{2\text{H}}
\begin{array}{c}
\text{OH} \quad\quad \text{R} \\
| \quad\quad\quad | \\
-\text{C}^*-\text{CH}_2-\text{C}^*-\text{CH}_2- \\
| \quad\quad\quad | \\
\text{H} \quad\quad\quad \text{H} \\
\text{V}
\end{array}
+
\begin{array}{c}
\text{OH} \quad\quad \text{H} \\
| \quad\quad\quad | \\
-\text{C}^*-\text{CH}_2-\text{C}^*-\text{CH}_2- \\
| \quad\quad\quad | \\
\text{H} \quad\quad\quad \text{R} \\
\text{VI}
\end{array}
$$

Walden Inversion. — A most interesting phenomenon discovered by Walden[10] (1896) is that when a substituent directly attached to an asymmetric carbon atom is replaced by another atom or group, the original center of asymmetry sometimes, but not always, becomes inverted in the process, with the result that its configuration in the product is the opposite of that in the starting material. The phenomenon is distinct from that of racemization, for one optically active compound is converted into another, rather than into a *dl*-mixture, and it is not a matter of change in direction of rotation, which may or may not follow and is coincidental, but rather a question of change in absolute configuration. Examples for illustration are the interconversions of optically active chlorosuccinic and malic acids shown in the chart with projection formulas giving configurations relative to the configuration of glyceraldehyde (*l*-malic acid = L-series). *l*-Chlorosuccinic acid on hydrolysis with potassium hydroxide affords a hydroxy

Inversion

$$
\left\{
\begin{array}{ccc}
\begin{array}{c}
\text{CH}_2\text{CO}_2\text{H} \\
| \\
\text{HCCl} \\
| \\
\text{CO}_2\text{H} \\
\textit{l}\text{-Chlorosuccinic acid}
\end{array}
&
\begin{array}{c}
\xrightarrow{\text{KOH}} \\
\xleftarrow{\text{PCl}_5}
\end{array}
&
\begin{array}{c}
\text{CH}_2\text{CO}_2\text{H} \\
| \\
\text{HOCH} \\
| \\
\text{CO}_2\text{H} \\
\textit{d}\text{-Malic acid}
\end{array}
\\[3em]
\text{Ag}_2\text{O} \downarrow & & \uparrow \text{Ag}_2\text{O}
\\[3em]
\begin{array}{c}
\text{CH}_2\text{CO}_2\text{H} \\
| \\
\text{HCOH} \\
| \\
\text{CO}_2\text{H} \\
\textit{l}\text{-Malic acid}
\end{array}
&
\begin{array}{c}
\xrightarrow{\text{PCl}_5} \\
\xleftarrow{\text{KOH}}
\end{array}
&
\begin{array}{c}
\text{CH}_2\text{CO}_2\text{H} \\
| \\
\text{ClCH} \\
| \\
\text{CO}_2\text{H} \\
\textit{d}\text{-Chlorosuccinic acid}
\end{array}
\end{array}
\right.
$$

No inversion (left) · No inversion (right)

Inversion

---

[10] Paul von Walden, 1863–1957; Livland, Russia; stud. Riga, Leipzig, Munich, Odessa; St. Petersburg, Rostock, Tübingen

acid of opposite configuration. That the dextrorotatory character of the product is fortuitous can be appreciated from the fact that the malic acids show but feeble rotatory power, with considerable dependence on the concentration. The evidence indicates, however, that a Walden inversion occurs in this reaction and in the reverse change brought about by phosphorus pentachloride. On the other hand, l-chlorosuccinic acid is hydrolyzed by silver oxide without inversion and d-chlorosuccinic acid affords d-malic acid on treatment with the same reagent.

Whether or not a given displacement proceeds with inversion, with retention of configuration, or with partial or total racemization is dependent upon the reagent, the conditions, and the specific characteristics of the substance undergoing reaction. The combination of these factors determines the particular mechanism by which the reaction proceeds, and the mechanism may differ from compound to compound or according to the reagent and the conditions. The relationship of mechanism to the steric course of displacements is discussed in Chapter 13. A partial statement of the accepted interpretation of the Walden inversion is as follows. If the hydrolysis of an alkyl bromide (I) is a bimolecular reaction, that is, if the reaction rate is dependent upon the concentrations of both the alkyl halide and the

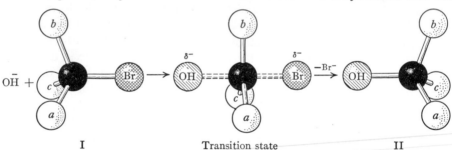

I   Transition state   II

hydroxide ion, then the anion does not react by frontal attack of the bromine atom with normal metathesis but attacks the molecule from the rear, or at the side opposite to the position of the negative bromine. This backside attack affords a transient ionic complex, or transition state, in which the hydroxide ion has given up part of its charge to bromine and in which neither group is fully joined to carbon or fully separated. In the transition state the fractionally charged (δ^-) OH and Br lie in a line and the groups a, b, and c lie in a plane perpendicular to this line. Bromine is then expelled as the anion from one side, with synchronous attachment of hydroxyl to the other side by a covalent link. The result is the alcohol II, of configuration opposite to that of I. The process of inversion is thus like the turning of an umbrella inside out in the wind.

GEOMETRICAL ISOMERISM

In his classical paper of 1874, van't Hoff not only developed the fundamental theory of optical isomerism but predicted the existence of a second form of stereoisomerism arising from the tetrahedral character of the carbon atom independent of asymmetry and not involving optical activity. He reasoned that two carbon atoms connected by a double bond can hardly rotate about the double linkage as they can about a single bond, and that the fixed union of the tetrahedrons at two common corners offers opportunity for two different spatial arrangements of the substituent groups, if the groups on each unsaturated carbon atom are different from each other (modern interpretations: π orbitals, p. 78). The two configurations corresponding to the formula are illustrated in Fig. 11.6 with a tetrahedral formulation, and in Fig. 11.7 with mechanical models. The two forms are different, for one is not superposable on the other. They are not asymmetric, for each possesses at least one plane of symmetry, and they therefore do not bear a mirror-image relationship. The four attached groups are in the same plane, in which the carbon atoms also lie, and an asymmetrical distribution in space is not possible even if all four groups are different.

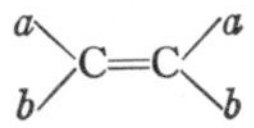

Although van't Hoff's conception of the double bond as a pair of tetrahedra joined at two corners has given place to the theory that the double bond consists of one σ and one π bond and that restriction of rotation is the result of overlap of p-atomic orbitals in formation of the π-orbital, the orbital theory has not extended the interpretations of the original mechanical concept. The concept of what has become known as geometrical isomerism

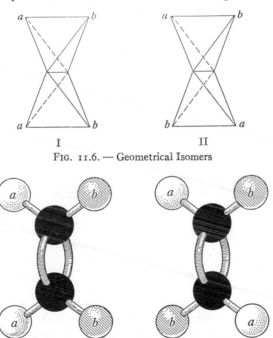

I　　　　　II

Fig. 11.6. — Geometrical Isomers

Ia　　　　　IIa

Fig. 11.7. — Models of Geometrical Isomers

was advanced by van't Hoff as a prediction, for at the time no instance of such isomerism could be cited as evidence. It had long been known that malic acid loses water readily when heated and affords two substances, maleic acid and fumaric acid, and Liebig in 1838 established that these have

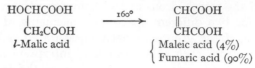

$$\begin{array}{ccc} \text{HOCHCOOH} & & \text{CHCOOH} \\ | & \xrightarrow{160°} & \| \\ \text{CH}_2\text{COOH} & & \text{CHCOOH} \\ \textit{l}\text{-Malic acid} & & \left\{ \begin{array}{l} \text{Maleic acid (4\%)} \\ \text{Fumaric acid (90\%)} \end{array} \right. \end{array}$$

the same composition and are both dibasic acids. Since maleic acid (m.p. 130°) can be converted in part into the much higher-melting fumaric acid (m.p. 287°) when heated at a temperature slightly above the melting point, Liebig and, later, Erlenmeyer (1870, 1886) considered fumaric acid to be a polymer of maleic acid, or a molecular compound containing units of this substance. The relationship of these acids remained unsettled for some time after van't Hoff's publication, but eventually the acids were shown to be monomeric isomers of identical structure. The recognition of the existence of ethylenic isomers of the same structure and constituting a pair of geometrical isomers as postulated by van't Hoff was due particularly to experimentation by Wislicenus (1887).

The space formulations and models of Figs. 11.6 and 11.7 show that in the molecule pictured on the left side of the page (I, Ia), the similar groups attached to the two carbon atoms lie on the same side of the molecule; in the geometrical isomer, the similar substituents lie on opposite sides or across the molecule from each other. That isomer in which the same or similar groups occupy adjacent positions in space is called the *cis* form (L., on this side); the second isomer is called the *trans* form (L., across). The general phenomenon is described as either geometrical or *cis-trans* isomerism. The space formulations are conveniently represented by pro-

$$\begin{array}{cc} a\text{—C—}b & a\text{—C—}b \\ \| & \| \\ a\text{—C—}b & b\text{—C—}a \\ \textit{cis} & \textit{trans} \end{array}$$

jection formulas, which should be used with remembrance that the two carbon atoms and the four substituents all lie in the same plane but that the double bond is in a plane perpendicular to the paper. The above formulas represent an ethylenic compound in which each of the doubly bound carbons carries the same two substituents, *a* and *b*. In a second general case each carbon atom is differently substituted. The isomerism

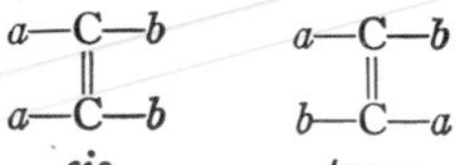

$$\begin{array}{cccc} a\text{—C—}b & a\text{—C—}b & a\text{—C—}a & a\text{—C—}b \\ \| & \| & \| & \| \\ x\text{—C—}y & y\text{—C—}x & a\text{—C—}b & x\text{—C—}x \\ \textit{cis and trans} & & \text{No isomerism} & \text{No isomerism} \end{array}$$

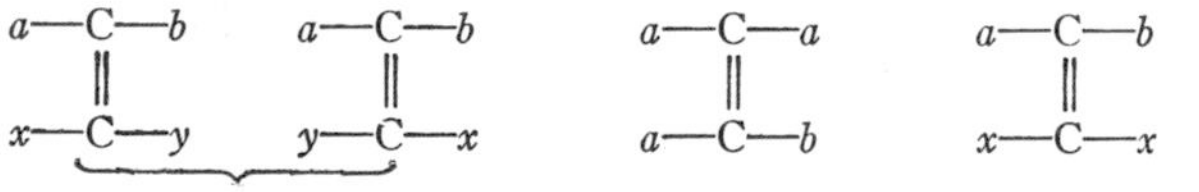

is exactly the same as that above, and a decision upon which form is appropriately termed *cis* and which *trans* is dependent on the specific nature of the groups concerned. The only requirement for geometrical isomerism is that the substituents on each carbon are different. If either unsaturated atom carries two identical groups, then isomerism vanishes.

Configuration of Maleic and Fumaric Acid. — Differentiation between a pair of geometrical isomers can be achieved chemically by relating one of the isomers to a ring compound into which it can be converted or from which it can be derived. Maleic and fumaric acid have the same skeletal structure as succinic acid, and they both yield this substance on catalytic hydrogenation. Since succinic acid readily forms a cyclic anhydride, similar

$$\begin{array}{c} \text{CHCOOH} \\ \| \\ \text{CHCOOH} \end{array} \xrightarrow{\text{Na(Hg)}} \begin{array}{c} \text{CH}_2\text{COOH} \\ | \\ \text{CH}_2\text{COOH} \end{array} \xrightarrow{-\text{H}_2\text{O}} \begin{array}{c} \text{CH}_2\text{CO} \\ | \quad \rangle\text{O} \\ \text{CH}_2\text{CO} \end{array}$$

$$\left\{ \begin{array}{l} \text{Maleic acid} \\ \text{Fumaric acid} \end{array} \right. \qquad\qquad \text{Succinic acid} \qquad\qquad \text{Succinic anhydride}$$

cyclization to an anhydride would appear possible in the case of the *cis* isomer, where the carboxyl groups are on the same side of the molecule but

$$\begin{array}{c} \text{H—C—CO}\lfloor\text{OH}\rceil \\ \| \\ \text{H—C—COO}\lfloor\text{H}\rceil \end{array} \qquad\qquad\qquad \begin{array}{c} \text{H—C—COOH} \\ \| \\ \text{HOOC—C—H} \end{array}$$

$$\qquad\quad cis \qquad\qquad\qquad\qquad\qquad\qquad trans$$

not in the *trans* form. Experiment shows that maleic acid readily affords a crystalline anhydride (m.p. 57°), for example, when warmed on the steam bath with acetyl chloride. However, fumaric acid also can be converted into the identical anhydride. One or the other acid therefore must undergo molecular rearrangement in the course of its transformation to the derivative. The acids, to be sure, differ considerably in the ease with which they are converted into the common anhydride. Thus fumaric acid remains largely unchanged when heated with pure acetyl chloride in a sealed tube at 100°, although it affords the anhydride if the temperature is raised to 140°. When maleic acid is heated alone at 160°, it is converted in part into the anhydride and in part into fumaric acid; the latter substance evidently arises as the result of rearrangement, and indeed when maleic acid is heated at 200° in a sealed tube to prevent escape of water, it yields fumaric acid as the chief product, along with some *dl*-malic acid. On the other hand, if pyrolysis is conducted in vacuum to promote elimination of water, the anhydride can be prepared at temperatures as low as 100°. Fumaric acid affords the anhydride only at much higher temperatures. This isomer melts at 287° when heated in a sealed capillary tube, but when heated in an open flask it begins to sublime at about 200°, and at 250–300° is in part carbonized and in part converted into the anhydride.

The greater ease of anhydride formation suggests but does not prove that maleic acid is the *cis* isomer. However the matter is settled unambiguously by the observation that the anhydride can be hydrolyzed with cold water, that is, under conditions where rearrangement is excluded, and yields maleic acid as the sole product. Therefore maleic acid has the *cis* configuration, and the product of dehydration is maleic anhydride. Fumaric acid is the *trans* isomer, and when heated strongly or treated with chemical dehydrating agents under special conditions, rearranges into maleic

TABLE 11.5. PYSICAL PROPERTIES OF MALEIC AND FUMARIC ACID

	MALEIC ACID cis	FUMARIC ACID trans
Melting point	130°	287°
Solubility in water, g. per 100 cc. at 25°	78.8	0.7
Density	1.590	1.635
Heat of combustion, kg.-cal. per mole	327	320
pK_{a_1}	1.9	3.0
pK_{a_2}	6.5	4.5

acid, which then yields the anhydride. That the more symmetrical *trans* structure is more stable than the *cis* is shown by the higher melting point

$$
\begin{array}{c}
\text{H—C—COOH} \\
\| \\
\text{HOOC—C—H} \\
\text{Fumaric acid}
\end{array}
\xrightarrow{\text{Rearrangement}}
\begin{array}{c}
\text{H—C—COOH} \\
\| \\
\text{H—C—COOH} \\
\text{Maleic acid}
\end{array}
\underset{\text{+H}_2\text{O}}{\overset{-\text{H}_2\text{O}}{\rightleftarrows}}
\begin{array}{c}
\text{H—C—CO} \\
\| \qquad \diagdown \text{O} \\
\text{H—C—CO} \\
\text{Maleic anhydride}
\end{array}
$$

of fumaric acid, the greater density and lesser solubility (Table 11.5), and by the maleic → fumaric rearrangement. The heats of combustion show that maleic acid has an energy content 7 kg.-cal. higher than fumaric acid and therefore has a greater tendency to undergo change. That the *cis* isomer is the more strongly acidic, as judged by comparison of the constants for the first dissociation, pK_{a_1}, means that the ionizing tendency of one carboxyl group is enhanced by the second unsaturated group in a near-by position. The greater spread between the first and second dissociation constants observed with maleic acid is also understandable. Once a proton has separated from the *cis* dibasic acid, the negatively charged group exerts an attractive force on the second hydrogen atom in the neighboring position and opposes its liberation as a proton.

The energy-richer *cis* isomer is convertible into fumaric acid at room temperature under the catalytic influence of hydrochloric or hydrobromic acid. The halogens as well as the halogen acids are effective catalysts for the rearrangement; for example, diethyl maleate is transformed rapidly into the ester of fumaric acid by a trace of iodine. The transformations represent the reversion of a labile isomer to a more stable form under the driving force of higher energy content. The reverse change is brought about by irradiation of an aqueous solution of fumaric acid with ultraviolet light at 45–50°; within a few hours, a condition of equilibrium is reached corresponding to isomerization of 75% of the material. Here the *trans* isomer acquires radiant energy by absorption, and the energy level is built up to that of the *cis* isomer. A more practicable preparation of maleic acid consists in warming malic acid with acetyl chloride, distilling the mixture, and hydrolyzing the resulting maleic anhydride. An industrial process for the preparation of maleic anhydride consists in catalytic vapor-phase oxidation of benzene with atmospheric oxygen.

$$\begin{array}{c} \underset{\text{HC}}{\overset{\text{CH}_2}{\diagdown}} \text{CH} \\ \| \quad | \\ \underset{\text{HC}}{\diagdown} \underset{\text{CH}}{\diagup} \text{CH} \\ \text{CH} \end{array} \xrightarrow{\text{[O]}} \begin{array}{c} \underset{\text{CH}}{\overset{\text{CO}}{\diagdown}} \\ \| \quad \diagdown \text{O} \\ \underset{\text{CH}}{\diagup} \underset{\text{CO}}{\diagup} \end{array} + \text{CO}_2, \text{H}_2\text{O}$$

Other *Cis-Trans* Isomers. — Citraconic acid and mesaconic acid, the methyl derivatives of maleic and fumaric acid, show the same relationships in physical properties; the configurations are similarly known from correlation of the lower-melting isomer and the cyclic anhydride.

$$\begin{array}{c} \text{CH}_3\text{—C—COOH} \\ \| \\ \text{H—C—COOH} \end{array} \qquad\qquad \begin{array}{c} \text{HOOC—C—CH}_3 \\ \| \\ \text{H—C—COOH} \end{array}$$

Citraconic acid   Mesaconic acid
(m.p. 91°, pK_{a_1} 2.42,   (m.p. 202°, pK_{a_1} 3.10,
kg.-cal./mole 482)   kg.-cal./mole 478)

Crotonic and isocrotonic acid, geometrical isomers of the structure $CH_3CH=CHCOOH$, represent a typical case where the method of determining configuration by correlation with a ring compound is not applicable. The problem, however, was solved by von Auwers (1923) by relating one of the isomers to fumaric acid by the preparation of each substance from a common intermediate under conditions shown not to permit rearrangements.

$$\begin{array}{c} \text{CCl}_3\text{—C—H} \\ \| \\ \text{H—C—COOH} \end{array} \xrightarrow[60\%]{\text{Zn, HOAc}} \begin{array}{c} \text{CHCl}_2\text{—C—H} \\ \| \\ \text{H—C—COOH} \end{array} \xrightarrow[74\%]{\text{Na(Hg)}} \begin{array}{c} \text{CH}_3\text{—C—H} \\ \| \\ \text{H—C—COOH} \end{array}$$

γ,γ,γ-Trichlorocrotonic acid   Crotonic acid

$$\xrightarrow[66\%]{\text{concd. H}_2\text{SO}_4 \text{ at } 30°} \begin{array}{c} \text{HOOC—C—H} \\ \| \\ \text{H—C—COOH} \end{array}$$

Fumaric acid

The product of stepwise reduction of the trichloro compound proved to be the higher-melting (solid) crotonic acid, and therefore this has the *trans* configuration. From the properties of the two unsaturated acids, listed under the formulas, it is seen that the relationships are the same as those

$$\begin{array}{c} \text{H—C—CH}_3 \\ \| \\ \text{H—C—COOH} \end{array} \qquad\qquad \begin{array}{c} \text{CH}_3\text{—C—H} \\ \| \\ \text{H—C—COOH} \end{array}$$

Isocrotonic acid (*cis*)   Crotonic acid (*trans*)
(m.p. 15.5°, pK_a 4.44, kg.-cal./mole 486,   (m.p. 72°, pK_a 4.70, kg.-cal./mole 478,
g./100 ml. $H_2O^{25°}$ 40.0)   g./100 ml. $H_2O^{25°}$ 8.3)

of the dibasic acids. The *trans* isomer, with the relatively large methyl and carboxyl groups balanced on the two sides of the molecule, has the more symmetrical structure, and it has the higher melting point, is less soluble, and has a lower energy content; this form also is produced readily by catalyzed rearrangement of the liquid *cis* isomer. That the *cis* form is slightly more acidic than the isomer must mean that the methyl group in the proximity of the ionizing function exerts a weak accentuating influence in the same sense as a second carboxyl group; possibly the methyl group hinders recombination of the anion with a proton.

Those instances in which physical properties have been correlated with chemically established configurations provide a rational, but not infallible, basis on which to deduce the probable configurations of other pairs of isomers. Thus the unsaturated fatty acids oleic and elaidic are regarded as having the *cis* and *trans* configurations, respectively, because the former has the lower melting point and the higher heat of combustion and is convertible into the more stable isomer under the catalytic influence of nitric or nitrous acid. In the case of the isomeric cinnamic acids, assignment of configuration on the basis of physical properties has been verified by a series

$$H-C-(CH_2)_7CH_3$$
$$\|$$
$$H-C-(CH_2)_7COOH$$
Oleic acid
(m.p. 13°, 16°; kg.-cal./mole 2682)

$$CH_3(CH_2)_7C-H$$
$$\|$$
$$H-C-(CH_2)_7COOH$$
Elaidic acid
(m.p. 44°, kg.-cal./mole 2664)

of reactions by which the *cis* isomer is obtained from a cyclic derivative where a ring extends from the carboxyl group to the benzene nucleus. Allocinnamic acid is the most stable of three polymorphic forms of *cis*-

$$C_6H_5-C-H$$
$$\|$$
$$HOOC-C-H$$
Allocinnamic acid
(m.p. 68°, pK$_a$ 3.96, kg.-cal./mole 1047,
g./100 ml. $H_2O^{25°}$ 14.4)

$$C_6H_5-C-H$$
$$\|$$
$$H-C-COOH$$
Cinnamic acid
(m.p. 133°, pK$_a$ 4.44, kg.-cal./mole 1040,
g./100 ml. $H_2O^{25°}$ 0.1)

cinnamic acid; the less stable forms melt at 58° and at 42°. Liebermann[11] (1889) first isolated the 58°-form as a degradation product of an alkaloid accompanying cocaine in coca leaves and found it to change to a more stable crystalline modification, m.p. 68° (*allo* form). Once the laboratory was seeded with the higher-melting material, Liebermann was unable to secure further lots of the 58°-form; eventually Biilmann[12] (1909) worked out special methods of crystallization by which the three known polymorphic forms can be interconverted. The greater energy content associated with the *cis* configuration is illustrated by the fact that when a solution of allocinnamic acid in methanol is saturated with hydrogen chloride in the cold, the substance is converted into the methyl ester of cinnamic acid. An interesting relationship is exhibited by the isomeric α,β-dibromocinnamic acids of the formula $C_6H_5CBr=CBrCOOH$. The more stable form, m.p. 138°, is colorless, whereas the lower-melting isomer, m.p. 100°, presumably *cis*, is yellow; the color apparently is an outward mark of higher energy content.

With the isomers angelic acid and tiglic acid, $CH_3CH=C(CH_3)COOH$, the designations *cis* and *trans* have only arbitrary significance, and there

---

[11] Carl Liebermann, 1842–1914; b. Berlin, Ph.D. Berlin; Berlin; *Ber.*, **48**, 4 (1915)

[12] Einar Biilmann, 1873–1946; b. Copenhagen; Ph.D. Copenhagen; Copenhagen; *J. Chem. Soc.*, 534 (1949)

is no obvious decision as to which configuration is the more symmetrical. The configurations formulated are assigned partly on the basis of the dissociation constants. Angelic acid is the more strongly acidic of the two isomers, just as isocrotonic acid is more strongly acidic than crotonic acid.

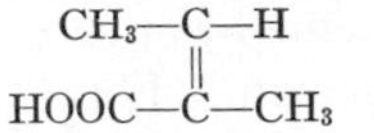

$$CH_3—C—H$$
$$HOOC—C—CH_3$$

Angelic acid
(m.p. 45°, pK_a 4.30,
kg.-cal./mole 635)

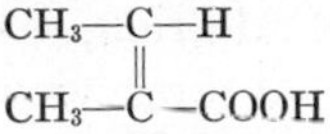

$$CH_3—C—H$$
$$CH_3—C—COOH$$

Tiglic acid
(m.p. 64.5°, pK_a 5.02
kg.-cal./mole 627)

Further evidence is that the rate of esterification of tiglic acid with methanol is greater than that of the more hindered angelic acid.

Steric Course of Additions. — Kekulé and Anschütz[13] (1880–81) established that, on controlled oxidation with alkaline permanganate at a low temperature, maleic acid yields mesotartaric acid and fumaric acid yields *dl*-tartaric acid. Both reactions correspond to an opening of one of the bonds of the ethylene linkage with affixment of a hydroxyl group to the vacated position on each carbon atom. In the hydroxylation of maleic

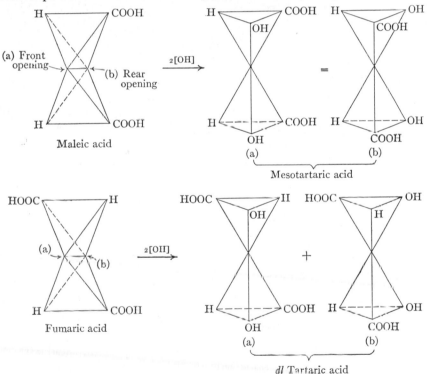

acid the same product results from severance of either of the two points of attachment between the carbon atoms, whereas in fumaric acid utilization

---

[13] Richard Anschütz, 1852–1937; b. Darmstadt, Germany; Ph.D. Heidelberg; Bonn; *Ber.*, **74 A**, 29 (1941)

of one linkage (b) affords *d*-tartaric acid and opening of the other (a) yields *l*-tartaric acid; the chances being equal, the two are formed in equal amounts. Oxidation of both isomers thus follows the same course of *cis* addition.

Since *cis* addition appeared to early chemists to represent the normal, expected course of addition, reactions that seemed to proceed in the opposite steric sense were at first viewed with suspicion. For example, addition of bromine to maleic and fumaric acid gives results just the opposite of those

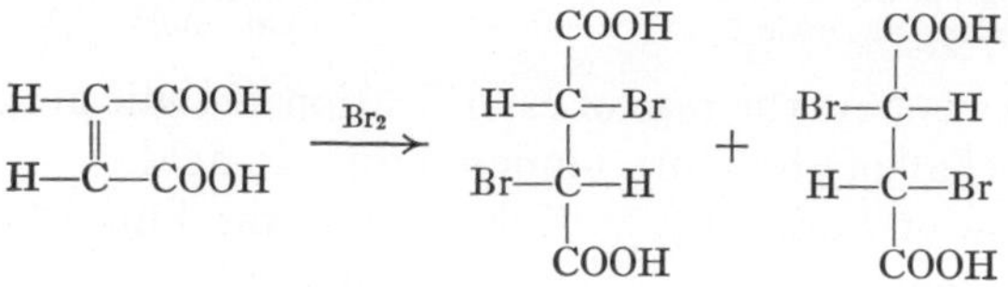

$$\begin{array}{c} H-C-COOH \\ \| \\ H-C-COOH \end{array} \xrightarrow{Br_2} \begin{array}{c} COOH \\ | \\ H-C-Br \\ | \\ Br-C-H \\ | \\ COOH \end{array} + \begin{array}{c} COOH \\ | \\ Br-C-H \\ | \\ H-C-Br \\ | \\ COOH \end{array}$$

dl-Dibromosuccinic acid
(m.p. 167°)

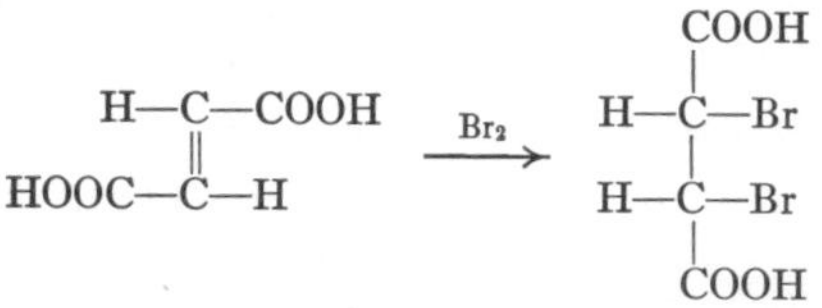

$$\begin{array}{c} H-C-COOH \\ \| \\ HOOC-C-H \end{array} \xrightarrow{Br_2} \begin{array}{c} COOH \\ | \\ H-C-Br \\ | \\ H-C-Br \\ | \\ COOH \end{array}$$

meso-Dibromosuccinic acid
(m.p. 256° dec.)

observed in the permanganate reaction, for the *cis* isomer gives a *dl*-product and the *trans* acid affords the internally compensated form.

Acetylene was found to react in both the expected and the unexpected sense. When two carbon atoms are linked by a triple bond, the configuration is symmetrical and no geometrical isomerism is possible, as shown in van 't Hoff's model for acetylenedicarboxylic acid. Opening of one of the

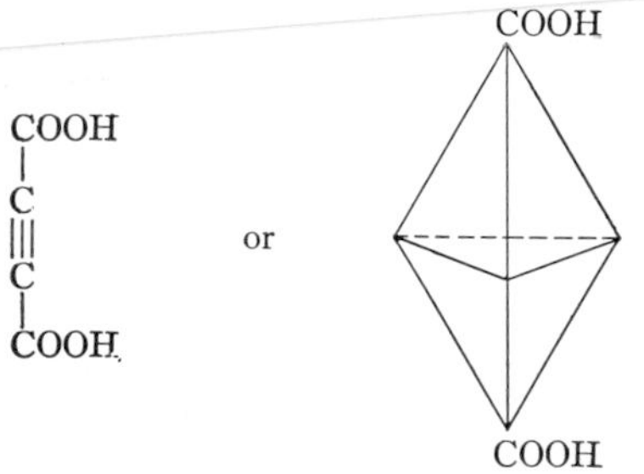

$$\begin{array}{c} COOH \\ | \\ C \\ \| \| \| \\ C \\ | \\ COOH \end{array} \quad \text{or}$$

Acetylenedicarboxylic acid

three bonds by *cis* addition of bromine would give an olefinic acid with the two bromine atoms on the same side of the molecule, namely dibromo-maleic acid, but Michael[14] showed (1892) that the reaction actually affords both this substance and the *trans* isomer in the proportions indicated.

[14] Arthur Michael, 1853–1942; b. Buffalo, N. Y.; stud. Heidelberg, Berlin, École de Médecine, Paris; Tufts, Harvard

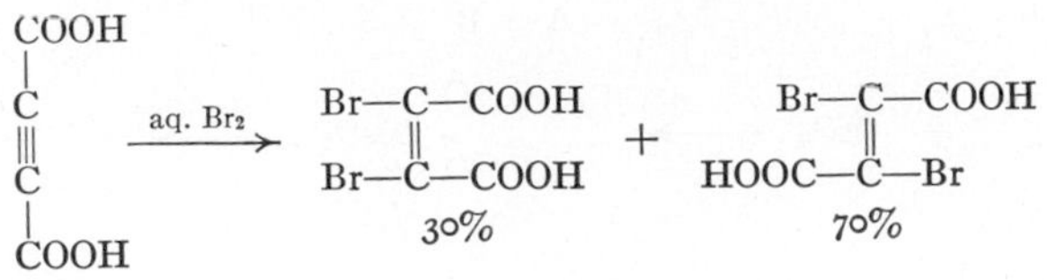

$$
\begin{array}{c}
\text{COOH} \\
| \\
\text{C} \\
||| \\
\text{C} \\
| \\
\text{COOH}
\end{array}
\xrightarrow{\text{aq. Br}_2}
\begin{array}{c}
\text{Br—C—COOH} \\
|| \\
\text{Br—C—COOH} \\
\text{30\%}
\end{array}
\quad + \quad
\begin{array}{c}
\text{Br—C—COOH} \\
|| \\
\text{HOOC—C—Br} \\
\text{70\%}
\end{array}
$$

Michael found further that addition of hydrochloric or hydrobromic acid to acetylenedicarboxylic acid leads exclusively to bromo- or chlorofumaric acid.

van't Hoff noted that halogens and halogen acids are effective catalysts for interconversion of *cis-trans* isomers, and attributed the unexpected additions to the catalyzed rearrangement of the olefinic starting material in the one case and of the olefinic reaction product in the other. Fumaric acid is actually a by-product of the addition of bromine to maleic acid. Michael (1892–95), however, demonstrated beyond question that additions in the unexpected sense can be accomplished under conditions precluding interconversion of the isomers, and his work led to eventual acceptance of the concept of *trans* addition, that is, the opening of an unsaturated linkage with attachment of the addenda to positions on opposite sides of the molecule. That reagents which favor *trans* addition are also catalysts for the conversion of labile into stable geometric forms is now regarded as an indication that the two phenomena have a common basis. *Trans* addition is recognized as the normal mode of reaction of halogens, halogen acids, and hypohalites to the ethylenic double bond. If these reactions proceed through a carbonium ion intermediate, for example (b), an attack by the second atom of bromine on the less hindered side opposite the first bromine to give (c) is understandable. If the reagent is used in only catalytic

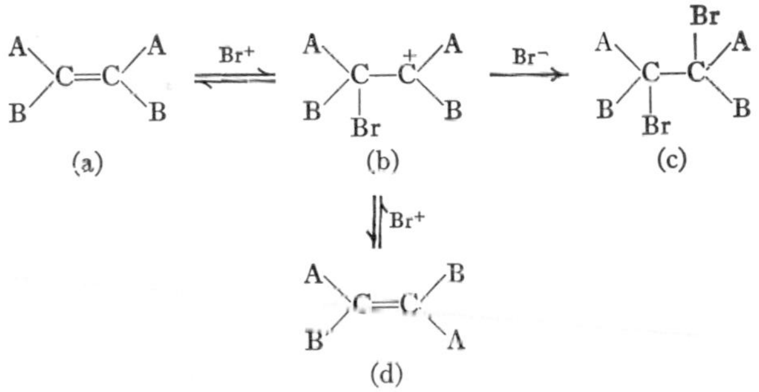

amount or if for other reasons the conditions are not favorable for rapid attachment of Br⁻ to (b), reversal of the attack of Br⁺ can afford either the original ethylene (a) or the geometrical isomer (d). Free rotation about the single bond is possible in the carbonium ion, and hence a catalyst that produces this transient species promotes equilibration of a *cis* or *trans* isomer (see Chapter 13 for fuller discussion).

A clear case of *cis* addition is hydroxylation of a double bond with osmium tetroxide. On treatment of an alkene with a solution of the reagent

$$
\begin{array}{c}
\overset{A}{\diagdown}\overset{B}{\diagup} \\
C \\
\| \\
C \\
\overset{A}{\diagup}\overset{B}{\diagdown}
\end{array}
\; + \; OsO_4 \; \longrightarrow \;
\begin{array}{c}
\overset{A}{\diagdown}\overset{B}{\diagup} \\
C-O \\
| \quad OsO_2 \\
C-O \\
\overset{A}{\diagup}\overset{B}{\diagdown}
\end{array}
\; \xrightarrow{Na_2SO_3} \;
\begin{array}{c}
\overset{A}{\diagdown}\overset{B}{\diagup} \\
C-OH \\
C-OH \\
\overset{A}{\diagup}\overset{B}{\diagdown}
\end{array}
$$

Osmic ester

in dry ether a black precipitate of the cyclic osmic ester slowly separates and is collected and reduced to the *cis*-glycol with sodium sulfite. The cyclic character of the intermediate excludes any but *cis* orientation in the addition, and cleavage of the ring proceeds without inversion. The yields are excellent, but the reagent is expensive. The permanganate oxidations of maleic and fumaric acid cited above were done in aqueous solution and under these conditions there is no evidence of the formation of a cyclic intermediate, since considerable *cis*-glycol is converted to products of overoxidation and therefore is present in free form. The yields are thus low. However, when the oxidation is conducted with a solution of permanganate in dry acetone with piperidine as catalyst a cyclic ester analogous to an osmic ester is the initial product and can be hydrolyzed to the glycol in good yield. A *cis* hydroxylation required in one step of the commercial synthesis of cortisone, done initially with osmium tetroxide, can be effected by the permanganate-acetone procedure in 98% yield.

Formation of an oxide from an alkene and perbenzoic acid in chloroform or ether solution also can proceed only by *cis* addition. An oxide can be

$$
\begin{array}{c}
\overset{A}{\diagdown}\overset{B}{\diagup} \\
C \\
\| \\
C \\
\overset{A'}{\diagup}\overset{B'}{\diagdown}
\end{array}
\; \xrightarrow{C_6H_5COOOH} \;
\begin{array}{c}
\overset{A}{\diagdown}\overset{B}{\diagup} \\
C\ (1) \\
O \\
C\ (2) \\
\overset{A'}{\diagup}\overset{B'}{\diagdown}
\end{array}
\; + \; HY
$$

Oxide

(Y = OH, Cl, Br, OCOCH$_3$)

(1)
$$
\begin{array}{c}
\overset{B}{\diagdown}\overset{A}{\diagup} \\
C-Y \\
C-OH \\
\overset{A'}{\diagup}\overset{B'}{\diagdown}
\end{array}
$$

(2)
$$
\begin{array}{c}
\overset{A}{\diagdown}\overset{B}{\diagup} \\
C-OH \\
C-Y \\
\overset{B'}{\diagup}\overset{A'}{\diagdown}
\end{array}
$$

hydrolyzed to a glycol, for example, by the action of water at 160°, but the glycol in this case corresponds to a *trans* rather than a *cis* product. Cleavage of an osmic or manganate ester can occur by fission of the O—Os or O—Mn bond without disturbance of the C—O linkage, whereas with an oxide the bond cleaved extends to carbon and its fission is always attended with Walden inversion. Thus if the bond designated (1) in the formula for the oxide suffers fission, inversion occurs at this point, and the upper carbon atom in the product has the configuration opposite to that in the oxide; if bond (2) is cleaved, inversion occurs in the lower half of the molecule. In either case the overall result of oxide formation and hydrolysis is equivalent to a *trans* addition.

Hydroxylation of an alkene is often done by adding 30% hydrogen peroxide to a solution of the material in acetic or formic acid and maintaining a temperature between 25° and 60°. The initial product is an acetyl or formyl derivative, which on hydrolysis yields a *trans* glycol. The effective reagents appear to be peracetic acid (CH_3CO_3H) and performic acid (HCO_3H), formed from the acid and hydrogen peroxide in the course of the mild heating. Of these, performic acid is considerably the more reactive. The mechanism appears to be that the peracid reacts with the alkene to form an oxide, as in the reaction with perbenzoic acid, but that in an acetic acid or formic acid solution the oxide is cleaved by the acid (acetolysis) to give an acetyl or formyl derivative of the glycol. Perbenzoic acid is used in chloroform or ether solution and the benzoic acid liberated in dilute solution does not effect acidolysis of the oxide unless the oxide has a special structure (1,2-oxide of a 1,3-diene).

Catalytic hydrogenation of an isolated double bond gives the product of *cis* addition, and selective, partial hydrogenation of an alkyne gives exclu-

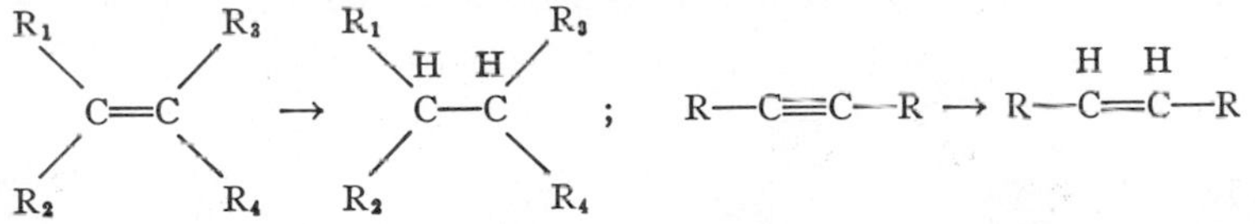

sively the *cis*-alkene. The unsaturated substance being hydrogenated is adsorbed on the catalyst surface and probably the first step is homolysis (homolytic fission), that is, separation of one electron pair to form a diradical: $R_2C{=}CR_2 \rightarrow R_2\overset{.}{C}{-}\overset{.}{C}R_2$. Possibly there is a further phase in which the catalyst surface forms part of a ring and so promotes *cis* addition.

Cis and *trans* Elimination. — The main facts regarding formation of an ethylene by elimination of HX from an alkyl halide or of HOH from an alcohol are summarized as follows. If the reaction is conducted in solution under ionic conditions *trans* elimination occurs more easily than *cis*

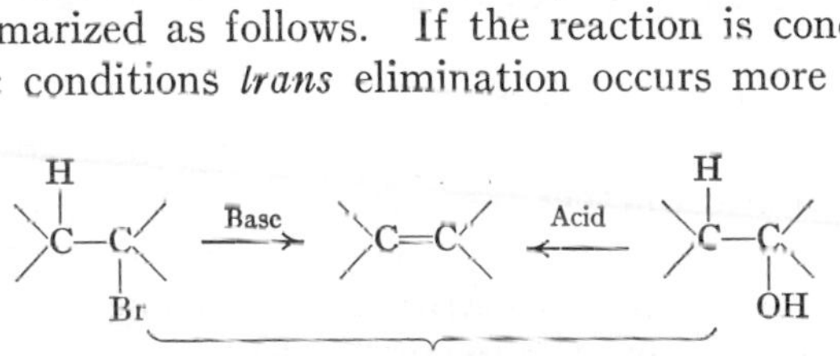

trans Eliminations (occur readily)

elimination; if only *cis* elimination is possible the substance may be resistant to dehydrohalogenation or dehydration under conditions that are practicable. In a nonionic, high-temperature dehydration of an alcohol, for example by pyrolysis of the benzoate, *cis* elimination occurs more readily than *trans* elimination (see Chapter 13 for fuller discussion).

Behavior on pyrolysis:

$$\begin{array}{c}\text{H}\\|\\\diagdown\text{C}\!-\!\text{C}\diagup\\|\quad|\\\overset{|}{\text{OCOC}_6\text{H}_5}\end{array}\qquad\begin{array}{c}\diagdown\text{C}\!-\!\text{C}\diagup\\|\quad|\\\text{H}\quad\text{OCOC}_6\text{H}_5\end{array}\xrightarrow{-\text{C}_6\text{H}_5\text{CO}_2\text{H}}\diagdown\text{C}\!=\!\text{C}\diagup$$

Resistant   Ready
elimination

Stereoisomerism of Cyclic Compounds. — In the same way that a double bond prevents free rotation of one unsymmetrically substituted carbon atom about another, a ring extending between two such centers imposes restriction and can give rise to geometrical isomerism. Thus the opportunity for a *cis* and a *trans* arrangement of groups characteristic of the structure HOOCCH=CHCOOH is encountered in the ring structure

HOOCCH—CHCOOH
   \/
    CH_2

of cyclopropane-1,2-dicarboxylic acid. The carbon atoms of the cyclopropane ring lie in a plane, and the two carboxyl groups can either project on the same side or on opposite sides of this plane. The three-membered ring, however, lacks the symmetry of a double bond, and models of all possible forms of the cyclopropanedicarboxylic acids, as shown in Fig. 11.8, show that three

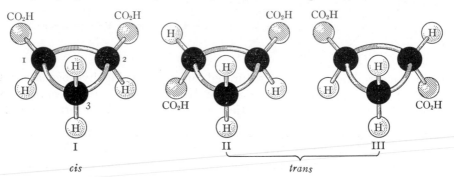

Fig. 11.8. — Cyclopropanedicarboxylic Acids

configurations are possible. One is the *cis* form I, and as long as the two carboxyl groups are represented as being on the same side of the molecule it makes no difference whether these are represented as being above or below the plane of the ring or whether they are affixed to carbon atoms 1 and 2 or 1 and 3. The molecule as written has a plane of symmetry passing through carbon atom 3 and the two attached hydrogen atoms. When the carboxyl groups are placed on opposite sides of the plane of the ring, two arrangements are possible, II and III. These possess no plane of symmetry and are asymmetric; they are not superposable and are mirror images of each other. Theory thus predicts existence of one *cis* form and of two enantiomeric *trans* forms, and the prediction has been verified by experiment. One isomeric cyclopropanedicarboxylic acid, m.p. 139°, is nonresolvable and readily forms an anhydride from which it can be regenerated on hydrolysis; it therefore has the *cis* configuration.   Another isomer, m.p. 175°, yields no anhydride and is the *dl-trans* form, resolvable into optically active components.

The relationships can be summarized with a conventional representation in which the ring system is imagined to be in a plane at right angles to the paper with the attached groups either above (full lines) or below (dotted lines) this plane.   Paralleling the relationship between maleic and fumaric acid, the *cis* form is the more labile and is converted into the *dl-trans* form

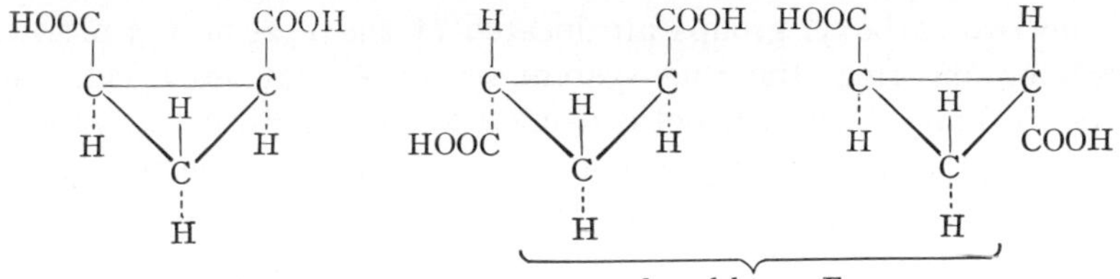

cis Form	*d*- and *l-trans* Forms
(m.p. 139°, pK$_{a_1}$ 3.40, g./100 g. H$_2$O$^{20°}$ 112)	(*dl*-acid: m.p. 175°, pK$_{a_1}$ 3.68, g./100 g. H$_2$O$^{20°}$ 19.1; *d*- and *l*-acids, m.p. 175°, [α]$_D$ ± 84.4°)

on being heated with 50% sulfuric acid at 150°. The higher melting point, lower solubility, and weaker acidic strength of the *trans* form are further marks of this configuration, and thus the relationships in both chemical and physical properties correspond to those noted in ethylenic compounds. Thus assignment of configurations on the basis of anhydride formation and physical properties is confirmed independently by the observation that one acid is resolvable whereas the other is not.

The example cited is typical only of those cyclic compounds in which the two parts of the ring extending between the unsymmetrically substituted carbon atoms are different, for, if they are the same, the situation is exactly like that of the maleic-fumaric type of isomers.   Thus cyclohexane-1,4-dicarboxylic acid presents merely the same opportunity for geometrical isomerism found in ethylenic compounds:

compare

Of the two modifications of the acid that have been isolated, neither forms an anhydride and neither is resolvable.   The configurations indicated as probable, on the basis of the more distinctive physical properties and relative stability of the isomers to isomerizing agents, are shown with simplified formulations in which the ring carbon atoms are represented as corners of the hexagon.

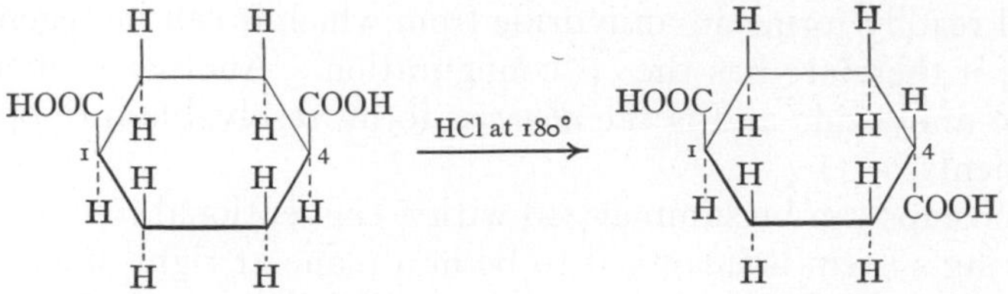

cis Form
(m.p. 161°, pK$_{a_1}$ 4.52, pK$_{a_2}$ 5.52,
kg.-cal./mole 928.6, v. sol. H$_2$O)

trans Form
(m.p. 300°, pK$_{a_1}$ 5.34, pK$_{a_2}$ 5.60,
kg.-cal./mole 929.5, g./100 g. H$_2$O$^{16.5°}$ 0.09)

If the two carboxyl groups are located at the 1,2- or 1,3-positions in the cyclohexane ring, the ring system becomes unsymmetrical, and the same opportunity exists for both geometrical and optical isomerism as in the cyclopropane series. The isomeric cyclohexane-1,2-dicarboxylic acids (hexahydrophthalic acids), for example, are represented in the following formulations:

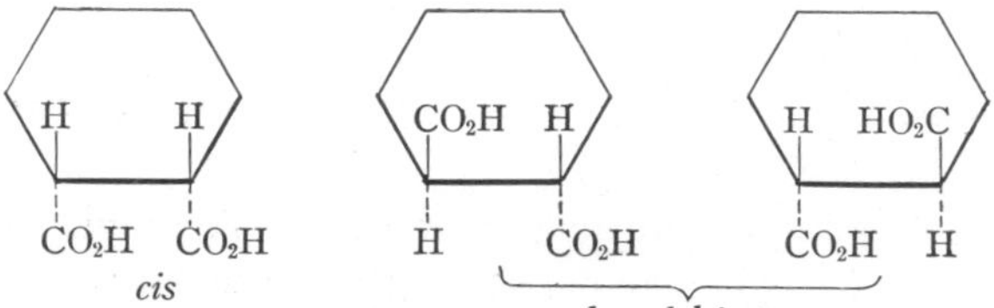

cis

d- and l-trans

DIPHENYL ISOMERISM

In 1922 Christie and Kenner reported the resolution of o,o-dinitrodiphenic acid, a diphenyl derivative which contains no asymmetric carbon atoms. Many similar and related compounds were later investigated in several laboratories and the phenomenon interpreted as due to restriction

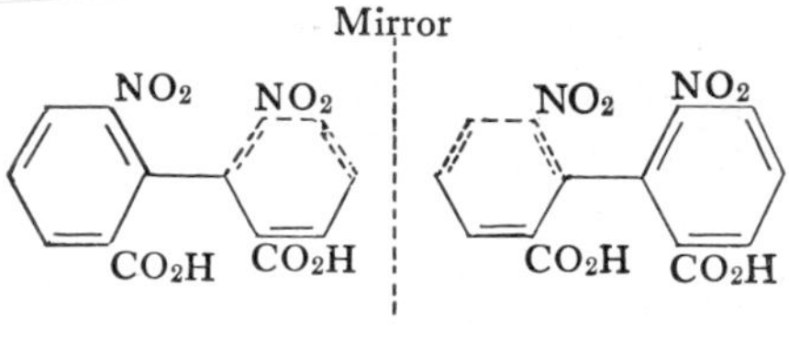

Mirror

of rotation about the single bond by bulky ortho substituents. The two rings are held in approximately perpendicular planes and hence two mirror-image forms are possible. Optical isomerism is observed principally in diphenyl derivatives having at least three ortho substituents, and the ease of racemization is correlated with the number and size of ortho groups.

PROBLEMS

Would you expect the reaction of methyl ethyl ketone with phenylmagnesium bromide to proceed in a single steric direction?

2. Write projection formulas for all the stereoisomeric forms of

$$HOOCCH(CH_3)CHBrCOOH$$

Which are enantiomers and which diastereoisomers?
3. How many optically active forms corresponding to the following formulas are possible?

(a) $CH_3CH_2CH(OH)CHClCH_3$
(b) $(CH_3)_2CHCH_2CH(CH_3)COOH$
(c) $C_6H_5CHBrCH_2CH(OH)CH_2CH(NH_2)COOH$
(d) $CH_2(OH)CH(OH)CH(OH)CH(OH)CH(OH)CHO$

4. An acid of the formula $C_5H_{10}O_2$ is optically active. What is its structure?
5. A derivative of one of the tartaric acids is optically active but gives optically inactive products when esterified with diazomethane or when hydrolyzed. What is it?
6. Give the number and nature of the possible stereoisomers, if any, corresponding to each of the following formulas:

(a) $(CH_3)_2CHCH(NH_2)CH_2CH(CH_3)_2$
(b) $CH_3CH_2C(CH_3)=C(CH_3)_2$
(c) $C_6H_5CH=CHCOC_6H_5$
(d) $CH_2=CHCH_2CH(NH_2)COOH$
(e) $C_6H_5CHBrCHBrCOC_6H_5$
(f) $(C_6H_5)_2C=CHCH_2CH_2CH=C(C_6H_5)_2$
(g) $CH_3CH(OH)CH(OH)CH_3$
(h) $HOCH_2CH(OH)CH(OH)CH(OH)CHO$

7. When a dextrorotatory isomer of the formula $HOCH_2CH(OH)CH(OH)CHO$ is boiled with dilute hydrochloric acid the rotatory power increases for a time and then becomes constant. What is the nature of the change?
8. How could you establish a rigid proof that crotonic and isocrotonic acid both have the structure $CH_3CH=CHCOOH$?
9. Formulate all possible stereoisomeric forms of cyclobutane-1,2-dicarboxylic acid and cyclobutane-1,3-dicarboxylic acid.
10. What are the possibilities for stereoisomerism in butene-2 (Table 3.1, p. 53), ricinoleic acid (p. 116), menthol and menthone (p. 193)?
11. Certain substances of the types $R_1R_2R_3R_4N^+X^-$ have been resolved into optically active components. What inference can be drawn regarding the spatial character of the nitrogen atom?
12. van't Hoff made a prediction, verified some sixty years later, concerning the stereochemistry of allenes of the following type:

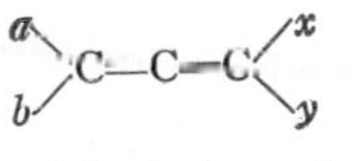

What phenomenon would you anticipate in such a structure?
13. The compound formulated below, which exhibits brilliant blue fluorescence in dilute aqueous solution and which has affinity for cotton fabric, is employed, in its most stable steric form, as a brightening agent, or colorless dye added to soap to increase whiteness of washed goods. What change would you expect to occur when the washed material is exposed to sunlight?

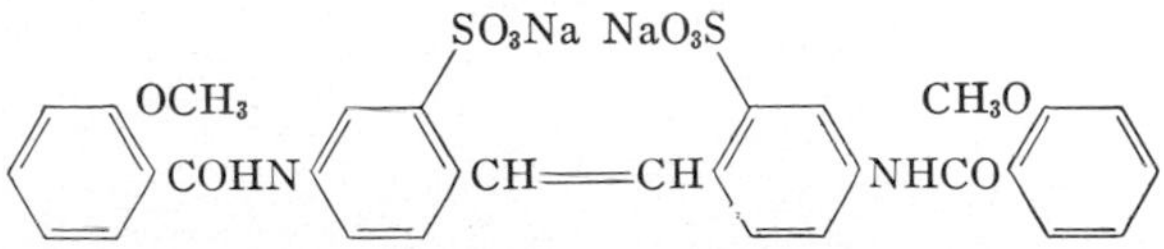

14. Account for the existence of two forms of oxalacetic acid (p. 313).

READING REFERENCES

Louis Pasteur, "Researches on Molecular Asymmetry," Alembic Club Reprints, No. 14 (1905)

P. F. Frankland, "Pasteur Memorial Lecture," *J. Chem. Soc.*, **71**, 683–711 (1897)

R. Vallery-Radot, "The Life of Pasteur," translation by R. L. Devonshire, Doubleday Page, Garden City (1926)

J. H. van't Hoff, "Chemistry in Space," translation by J. E. Marsh of "Dix Années dans l'Histoire d'une Théorie," Oxford (1891)

R. L. Shriner, R. Adams, and C. S. Marvel, "Stereoisomerism," in H. Gilman, "Organic Chemistry," 2nd Ed., I, 214–488, Wiley, New York (1943)

W. Klyne, "Progress in Stereochemistry," **1**, Academic Press (1954)

CHAPTER 12

RING FORMATION AND STABILITY

Stereochemical relationships are important not only because of the various forms of isomerism associated with spatial arrangements within molecules but also in determining ease of formation, stability, and reactivity of ring compounds. Formation and general characteristics of ring compounds other than those of the aromatic series constitute the focal point in the following discussions.

CYCLOPARAFFINS AND OTHER ALICYCLIC COMPOUNDS

Physical properties of representative cycloparaffins, which are the parent substances of the series of nonbenzenoid carbocyclic compounds designated as alicyclic (aliphatic—cyclic), are recorded in Table 2.6 (p. 47). The hydrocarbons and their derivatives exhibit considerable variation in chemical properties according to the ring size. The highest reactivity is found in compounds containing a three-membered ring, and cyclopropanes in some respects resemble olefins. Thus cyclopropane undergoes catalytic hydrogenation rather readily to n-propane; and the ring can be opened by interaction with hydrogen bromide, bromine, or sulfuric acid just as a double

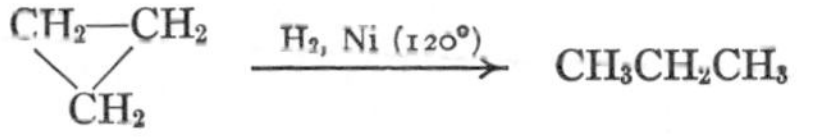

$$\underset{\displaystyle \overset{|}{CH_2}}{CH_2\!-\!CH_2} \xrightarrow{\ H_2,\ Ni\ (120°)\ } CH_3CH_2CH_3$$

bond can be saturated by addition of these reagents. Furthermore, the mode of reaction of hydrogen bromide with substituted cyclopropanes follows a course akin to the Markownikoff addition to olefins, for the ring is opened between the carbon atoms carrying the largest and the smallest number of hydrogen atoms, and the halogen becomes affixed to the latter position, as in the examples. Cyclopropane derivatives also form colored

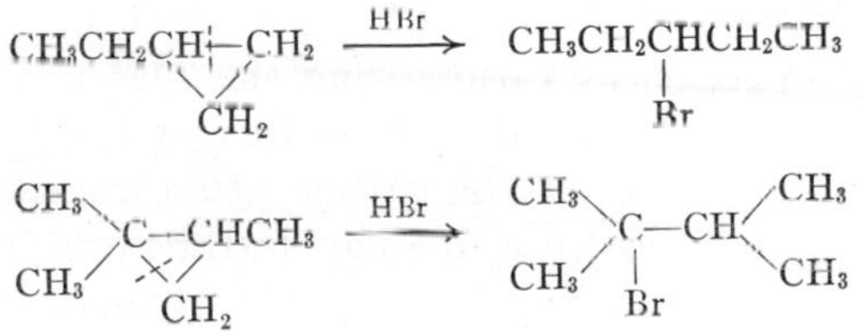

$$CH_3CH_2CH\!-\!CH_2 \xrightarrow{\ HBr\ } \underset{\displaystyle \overset{|}{Br}}{CH_3CH_2CHCH_2CH_3}$$

$$\underset{CH_3}{\overset{CH_3}{>}}C\!-\!\underset{CH_2}{\overset{|}{CHCH_3}} \xrightarrow{\ HBr\ } \underset{CH_3}{\overset{CH_3}{>}}C\!-\!\underset{Br}{\overset{|}{CH}}\!\underset{CH_3}{\overset{CH_3}{<}}$$

complexes with tetranitromethane, a property characteristic of olefins and dienes. In contrast with ethylene, however, cyclopropane is not attacked by aqueous permanganate solution or by ozone. The difference is illustrated by the permanganate oxidation of the unsaturated cyclopropane derivative shown in the formulation. Indeed compounds containing the cyclopropane ring can be distinguished from ethylenic substances by a qualitative test

$$\underset{\substack{\text{1,1-Dimethyl-2-isobutenyl-}\\\text{cyclopropane}}}{\underset{H_3C}{\overset{H_3C}{>}}C\underset{CH_2}{\overset{CHCH=C}{<}}\overset{CH_3}{\underset{CH_3}{}}} \xrightarrow{KMnO_4} \underset{\substack{\text{1,1-Dimethylcyclopropane-}\\\text{2-carboxylic acid}}}{\underset{H_3C}{\overset{H_3C}{>}}C\underset{CH_2}{\overset{CHCOOH}{<}}}$$

with permanganate, and the reagent is also used to remove traces of propylene from cyclopropane.

Natural products containing a three-carbon ring are rare. One example is lactobacillic acid, isolated from the lipids (fats) of *Lactobacillus arabinosus* and *L. casei* (K. Hofmann,[1] 1954). Another, sterculic acid, a constituent of

$$\underset{\substack{\text{Lactobacillic acid } (x+y=14)}}{CH_3(CH_2)_x CH\overset{CH_2}{\overset{/\ \backslash}{\text{——}}}CH(CH_2)_y CO_2H} \qquad \underset{\substack{\text{Sterculic acid}}}{CH_3(CH_2)_7 C\overset{CH_2}{\overset{/\ \backslash}{=\!=\!=}}C(CH_2)_7 CO_2H}$$

$$\text{M.p. } 30° \qquad\qquad\qquad\qquad \text{M.p. } 18°$$

the kernel oil of *Sterculia foetida*, contains a cyclopropene ring and can be converted by hydrogenation to the corresponding cyclopropane derivative (J. R. Nunn, 1952). Cyclopropene itself (b.p. $-36°$), prepared by Hofmann elimination from trimethylcyclopropylammonium hydroxide, is very unstable and prone to polymerize.

Cyclobutane is not so reactive as cyclopropane, for it is not only inert to permanganate and to ozone but stable at ordinary temperatures to bromine and to hydrogen iodide. The ring can be opened by hyrogenation, but under conditions more drastic than those required for opening the cyclopropane ring. Cyclopentane and cyclohexane and their derivatives

$$\underset{CH_2\text{—}CH_2}{\overset{CH_2\text{—}CH_2}{\mid\qquad\mid}} \xrightarrow{H_2,\ Ni\ (200°)} CH_3CH_2CH_2CH_3$$

are similar in chemical characteristics and are comparable to the corresponding open-chain paraffins. Five- and six-membered rings are not opened by permanganate, ozone, bromine, hydrogen bromide, or even by hydrogen in the presence of a catalyst. Cyclopentane and cyclohexane are thus chemically inert hydrocarbons, as compared with ethylene, and their resistance to hydrogenation characterizes them as less reactive than cyclobutane.

Baeyer Strain Theory. — A theoretical interpretation of the differences in reactivity of compounds of various ring size was advanced in 1885 by 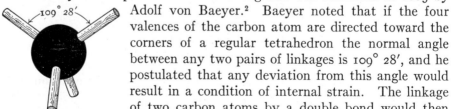 Adolf von Baeyer.[2] Baeyer noted that if the four valences of the carbon atom are directed toward the corners of a regular tetrahedron the normal angle between any two pairs of linkages is 109° 28′, and he postulated that any deviation from this angle would result in a condition of internal strain. The linkage of two carbon atoms by a double bond would then result in a very considerable distortion of the normal valence angles with

---

[1] Klaus H. Hofmann, b. 1911 Karlsruhe, Germany; Ph.D. Zurich ETH; Univ. Pittsburgh

[2] Adolf von Baeyer, 1835–1917; b. Berlin; Ph.D. Berlin; Strasbourg, Univ. Munich; Nobel Prize 1905; *J. Chem. Soc.*, **123**, 1520 (1923)

consequent strain and high energy content, and this explanation accounts for the reactivity of olefins and the tendency of the double bond (two-membered ring) to open by addition of various reagents and afford strain-free, more stable single-bond derivatives.   The extent of distortion involved in construction of a three-membered ring is less, though still considerable, and corresponds to the fact that the cyclopropane ring is opened by some reagents, but shows evidence of less strain than the ethylenic linkage. Calculations from the Baeyer theory indicate that the distortion of the normal angles is less but still appreciable in cyclobutane and practically vanishes in cyclopentane.   The representation of cyclopentane (Fig. 12.1) with wooden models cut to the normal angle of 109° 28′ scarcely reveals the deviation to an angle of 108°

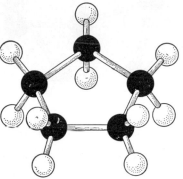

Fig. 12.1 — Cyclopentane

The strain theory agrees with facts concerning the relative chemical reactivities of ethylene, cyclopropane, cyclobutane, and cylopentane, and deviations from the normal valence angle also follow the order of energy relationships as indicated by heats of combustion (Table 12.1).   In the series of hydrocarbons from C_2 to C_5, the energy content per methylene unit falls off in the order

TABLE 12.1. HEATS OF COMBUSTION AND VALENCE ANGLES

HYDROCARBON	ETHYLENE	CYCLO-PROPANE	CYCLO-BUTANE	CYCLO-PENTANE	CYCLO-HEXANE	CYCLO-HEPTANE
Molecular heat of combustion (kg.-cal.)	340	505.5	662.5	797	939	1103
kg.-cal. per >CH_2	170	168.5	165.5	158.7	157.4	158.3
Deviation from normal angle		+54° 44′	+24° 44′	+9° 44′	+0° 44′	(−5° 16′)	(−9° 33′)

of decreasing deviations, or decreasing positive strain.   Baeyer extended to the higher cycloparaffins calculations also based on the assumption of planar molecules and, noting that from cyclohexane on the deviation becomes increasingly negative in the sense of an expansion of the normal valence angle, saw support for the theory in the fact that multimembered ring compounds had not been discovered in nature or prepared by synthesis and presumably would be under too great strain to exist.   The data in Table 12.1, however, show that, in contrast with the calculated negative deviations, cyclohexane and cycloheptane do not differ appreciably in energy content from cyclopentane; actually the three hydrocarbons are practically indistinguishable in all chemical properties.

Sachse-Mohr Concept of Strainless Rings. — An explanation of the apparent anomaly with respect to a ring larger than that of cyclopentane was advanced in 1890 by Sachse, who suggested that in cyclohexane and the higher homologs the carbon atoms do not lie in a plane, as supposed by Baeyer, but assume a strain-free, puckered configuration. Two space models of the cyclohexane ring can be constructed with preservation of the normal valence angles, as shown in Fig. 12.2. The two configurations can be

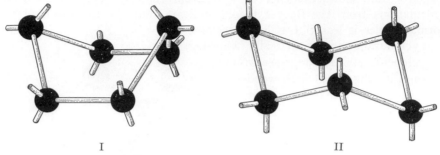

I   II

FIG. 12.2. — Steric Forms of the C$_6$-Ring

represented schematically as follows, and are designated as the boat-form and the chair-form:

Boat-Form   Chair-Form

Characteristics of the two forms are seen from the Stuart models, Fig. 12.3. Sachse's proposal was initially discounted on the ground that cyclohexane

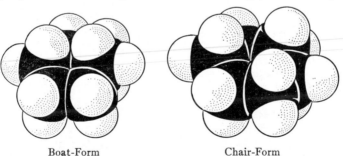

Boat-Form   Chair-Form

FIG. 12.3. — Stuart Models of the Two Strain-free Forms of Cyclohexane

had been obtained in only one form; but after the lapse of nearly thirty years, Mohr[3] (1918) revived the idea, and pointed out that interconversion of the boat- and chair-forms can be accomplished in models by rotations about single bonds with but little temporary distortion of the normal tetrahedral angles. Thus the two possible forms of cyclohexane may be so closely equivalent in energy content as to be indistinguishable. Mohr foresaw that resistance to the

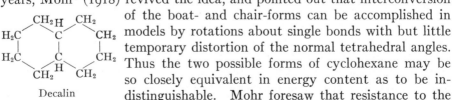

Decalin

---

[3] Ernst Mohr. 1873–1926; b. Dresden; Ph.D. Kiel (Curtius); Heidelberg; *Ber.*, **59A**, 39 (1926)

interconversion of the two steric forms would be greater in the structure of decalin (decahydronaphthalene), which is composed of two cyclohexane rings fused together and sharing two carbon atoms in common, and predicted that this substance can exist in a *cis* and a *trans* form, alternative conventional representations of which are as follows:

cis

trans

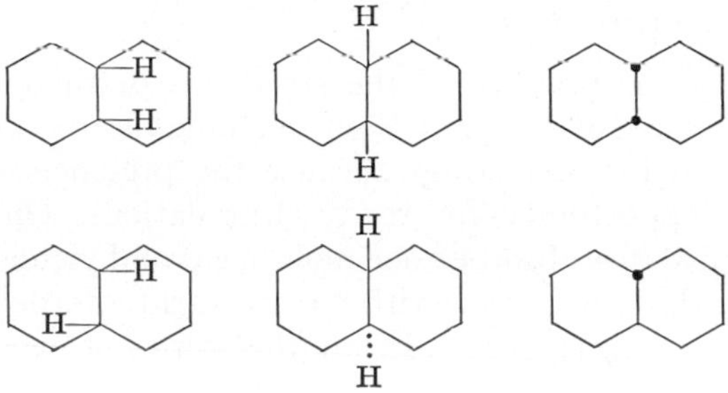

Mohr's paper was favorably received, and the concept of nonplanar, strainless rings gained support from experiments by Böeseken[4] with cyclic *vic*-diols (1921) and was unequivocally proved by W. Hückel[5] (1925), who not only isolated the two postulated steric forms of decalin, but demonstrated the existence of all the theoretically possible optical isomers of the α- and β-monohydroxy derivatives of each hydrocarbon. The hydrocarbons are both stable, and transformation of the *cis* into the *trans* form is accomplished only under rather drastic conditions (treatment with aluminum bromide); the physical constants are as follows:

	cis-Decalin	*trans*-Decalin
Melting point	$-43.3°$	$-31.5°$
Boiling point	$194°$	$185°$
Specific gravity, D_4^{20}	0.895	0.870
Molecular heat of combustion, kg.-cal.	1502.4	1500.3

Muscone and Civetone. — Baeyer's inference that multimembered ring compounds would be too unstable to exist was disproved finally in work of Ruzicka[6] at Zurich (1926) on the active principles of the rare perfume bases musk and civet. Dried musk is a dark-colored powdery substance of powerful odor obtained from an egg-sized gland situated near the abdomen of the male musk deer, a small wild animal found in mountainous regions of central Asia, particularly the Himalayas; the apparent function of musk is to attract the female animal. From about 60,000 deer killed per year, there results an average of 2000 kg. of the valuable musk, the active principle of which, muscone (Wahlbaum, 1906), is present to the extent of about 1%. Civet, valued at about one third the price of musk, occurs similarly in the African civet cat (male and female), and the active fragrant principle, which occurs along with the evil-smelling skatole, is civetone. The names

---

[4] Jacob Böeseken, 1868–1948; b. Rotterdam; Ph.D. Basel; Techn. Univ. Delft, Netherlands

[5] Walter Hückel, b. 1895 Charlottenburg; Ph.D. Göttingen (Windaus); Freiburg, Greifswald, Breslau, Tübingen

[6] Leopold Ruzicka, b. 1887 Vukova, Yugoslavia; Ph.D. Karlsruhe (Staudinger); Utrecht, Zurich ETH; Nobel Prize 1939

assigned are based on the characteristic ketonic properties; when purified through the semicarbazones the two ketones of similar musk odor have the following compositions and properties:

Muscone: $C_{15}H_{30}C{=}O$
(liquid, saturated, optically active)

Civetone: $C_{16}H_{30}C{=}O$
(m.p. 31°, unsaturated)

In attacking the problem of the structures of these substances in co-operation with the Swiss firm of Naef, manufacturer of perfumes, Ruzicka selected civetone for first study because the presence of an unsaturated center offered opportunity for ready degradation. On catalytic hydrogenation the substance absorbed one mole of gas and yielded dihydrocivetone (m.p. 63°), which on oxidation with chromic acid afforded a dibasic acid of the same carbon content (A). In another series of experiments, civetone

$$\left.\begin{array}{c}CH \\ \| \\ CH\end{array}\right\}C_{14}H_{28}CO \xrightarrow{2H} C_{15}H_{30}\left\{\begin{array}{c}{-}CO \\ | \\ {-}CH_2\end{array}\right. \xrightarrow{CrO_3} C_{15}H_{30}\begin{array}{c}\diagup COOH \\ \diagdown COOH\end{array}$$

Civetone   Dihydrocivetone A

was reduced by a method that replaces the carbonyl oxygen atom by two hydrogen atoms (Clemmensen reduction) and so converted into the unsaturated hydrocarbon civetane. On ozonization this, surprisingly, afforded the same dibasic acid A. These observations indicated that both the car-

$$\left.\begin{array}{c}CH \\ \| \\ CH\end{array}\right\}C_{14}H_{28}CO \xrightarrow{Zn(Hg){-}HCl} \left.\begin{array}{c}CH \\ \| \\ CH\end{array}\right\}C_{14}H_{28}CH_2 \xrightarrow{O_3} C_{15}H_{30}\begin{array}{c}\diagup COOH \\ \diagdown COOH\end{array}$$

Civetone   Civetane A

bonyl group and the ethylenic linkage must be present in the same ring Oxidation of civetone itself under drastic conditions led to production of a. mixture of dibasic acids, including the following substances: $HOOC(CH_2)_5$-$COOH$, $HOOC(CH_2)_6COOH$, and $HOOC(CH_2)_7COOH$ (azelaic acid). Formation of azelaic acid, the largest fragment, shows that the civetone molecule must contain one unit embracing at least seven methylene groups. Formula I is consistent with this requirement and also accounts for the production from dihydrocivetone and civetane of a common oxidation product of the composition of acid A; Ruzicka proved this inference to be

$$\begin{array}{ccc}
 & CH_2(CH_2)_7 & \\
 & | \quad\quad\diagdown CO & \\
CH(CH_2)_7\diagdown & CH_2(CH_2)_7\diagup & COOH \\
\| \quad\quad\quad CO & \text{Dihydrocivetone} & (CH_2)_{15}\diagdown \\
CH(CH_2)_7\diagup & & \diagdown COOH \\
\text{I} & CH(CH_2)_7\diagdown & \text{Acid } A \\
 & \| \quad\quad\quad CH_2 & \\
 & CH(CH_2)_7\diagup & \\
 & \text{Civetane} &
\end{array}$$

correct by synthesizing pentadecane-1,15-dicarboxylic acid, which was identical with acid A. This evidence proved the presence of a large ring and established the structure of dihydrocivetone. That civetone itself has structure I was finally proved by controlled permanganate oxidation of the unsaturated ketone to a keto dibasic acid, the structure of which was estab-

$$\underset{\text{Civetone}}{\begin{matrix} CH(CH_2)_7 \\ \| \\ CH(CH_2)_7 \end{matrix}} CO \xrightarrow{\text{KMnO}_4} \begin{matrix} HOOC(CH_2)_7 \\ \\ HOOC(CH_2)_7 \end{matrix} CO \xleftarrow[\text{hydrolysis}]{\text{Fe (290°)}} 2\,CH_3OOC(CH_2)_7COOH$$

lished by synthesis. The structure of civetone bears an interesting relationship to oleic acid, a common component of fats:

$$\underset{\text{Oleic acid}}{\begin{matrix} CH(CH_2)_7COOH \\ \| \\ CH(CH_2)_7CH_3 \end{matrix}}$$

The demonstration that nature produces a stable compound having a ring of seventeen carbon atoms completely refuted that part of Baeyer's theory pertaining to a supposed strain in large rings and encouraged Ruzicka to attempt synthesis of compounds of a type traditionally regarded as incapable of existence. The most elaborate ring compound previously synthesized was cyclooctanone, which had been obtained in minute amounts by pyrolysis of the calcium salt of azelaic acid, but Ruzicka worked out an improved technique by which cyclooctanone could be prepared in 20% yield from the thorium salt of azelaic acid. By suitable adaptations of the method, Ruzicka achieved the synthesis of the entire series of cyclic ketones from C_9 to C_{21}, and later prepared ketones having rings of as many as thirty-four carbon atoms. The correlation between ring size and odor of the synthetic ketones provided a clue to the structure of the saturated C_{16}-ketone muscone. These are described as follows: C_5, bitter almonds; C_6, mint; C_6 to C_9, transition to camphor; C_9 to C_{13}, transition to cedar; C_{14}, musky but mixed; C_{15}, pure musk; C_{16}, between muscone and civetone; C_{17}, pure civetone odor; C_{18} to C_{29}, odor decreases and practically vanishes. The double bond in civetone is without influence on the odor, for dihydrocivetone, identical with cycloheptadecanone, is indistinguishable from the unsaturated ketone. Since odor is intimately associated with ring size, the close correspondence of muscone with the synthetic C_{15}-compound suggested that the natural product has a fifteen-carbon ring with an attached methyl group. This inference was proved to be correct by reduction of the optically active muscone to an optically inactive hydrocarbon identical with a sample of methylcyclopentadecane prepared from synthetic cyclopentadecanone by

$$\underset{\text{Muscone}}{\overline{C_{15}H_{30}\ \ \ C}{=}O} \xrightarrow{\text{Clemmensen reduction}} \underset{\text{(m. p. }-19°\text{, inactive)}}{\overline{(CH_2)_{14}\ \ \ CHCH_3}}$$

$$\Bigg\downarrow {\scriptstyle 2H}$$

$$\underset{\substack{\text{Cyclopenta-}\\\text{decanone}}}{\overline{(CH_2)_{14}\ \ \ CO}} \longrightarrow \overline{(CH_2)_{14}\ \ \ C{\Big\langle}{\substack{OH\\CH_3}}} \longrightarrow \overline{(CH_2)_{13}{\Big|}{\substack{CH\\ \|\\ CCH_3}}}$$

addition of methylmagnesium iodide, dehydration, and hydrogenation. A series of degradation experiments provided strong indications that in muscone the methyl group is located in the β-position with respect to the carbonyl group, as shown in the formula [isolation of $HOOC(CH_2)_{10}COOH$

$$\begin{array}{l} CH_3 \\ | \\ *CH \cdot CH_2 \cdot CO \\ \lfloor (CH_2)_{12} \rfloor \end{array}$$

Muscone

on oxidation; failure of the active ketone to undergo racemization]. dl-Muscone was synthesized by Ziegler (1934) and by Ruzicka (1934) and found to correspond with the optically active natural product in odor and in physical constants; the semicarbazones of the dl- and (−)-forms melt at the same temperature (134°) and give no depression in melting point when mixed. Apparently the lone center of asymmetry in the large molecule has little influence on the physical properties.

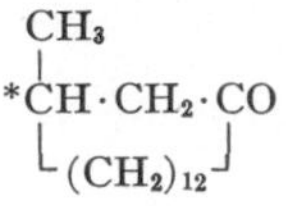

Investigations of large-ring natural compounds not only enriched the science with abundant material of considerable theoretical significance but also had the practical consequence of pointing the way to synthetic substances of a new type of value to the perfume industry. Synthetic cyclopentadecanone not only matches closely the fragrance of muscone but enhances the harmony of odors of a mixture of ingredients; it is on the market under the name Exaltone. Two natural substances of plant origin employed in perfumes and having musklike odors have been characterized as large-ring lactones (cyclic esters) of the following structures (Kerschbaum, 1927):

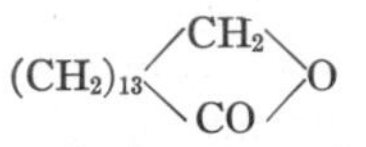

$$(CH_2)_{13} \underset{\displaystyle CO}{\overset{\displaystyle CH_2}{\big<}} \!\!\! \big> O \qquad\qquad \underset{\displaystyle CH(CH_2)_5 \cdot CO}{\overset{\displaystyle CH(CH_2)_7 CH_2}{\big\|}} \!\!\! \big> O$$

Lactone of 15-hydroxypentadecylic acid,	Ambrettolide
m.p. 31° (principle of angelica oil)	(musk ambrette)

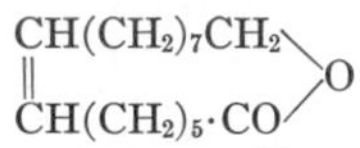

CONFORMATION

The term conformation (or, in German and Swiss usage, constellation) is used to designate a particular shape or arrangement in space of a molecule in which more than one arrangement is possible by simple rotations about single bonds. The chair and boat forms of cyclohexane are conformations that the ring can assume with maintenance of normal valence angles. With both cis- and trans-decalin various combinations of chair and boat cyclohexane rings make possible a number of conformations, each of which retains its cisoid or transoid character. Conformational analysis, that is, study of the consequences of conformational relationships, has led to interpretation of phenomena not previously understood, particularly in alicyclic compounds.

Ethane Derivatives. — In ethane or a derivative complete freedom of rotation about the carbon–carbon bond could lead to an infinite number of conformations. The evidence indicates, however, that some one conformation possesses greater stability than all the others. The conformation of greatest stability is that in which the six atoms or groups attached to the two carbon atoms are as remote as possible, and the one of least stability is that of greatest proximity. The difference in stability is slight in the case of ethane, but can be very appreciable in an ethane containing large substituent atoms or groups, for example the two stilbene dibromides, *meso* and *dl*. The large bromine atoms tend to repel each other, but the phenyl

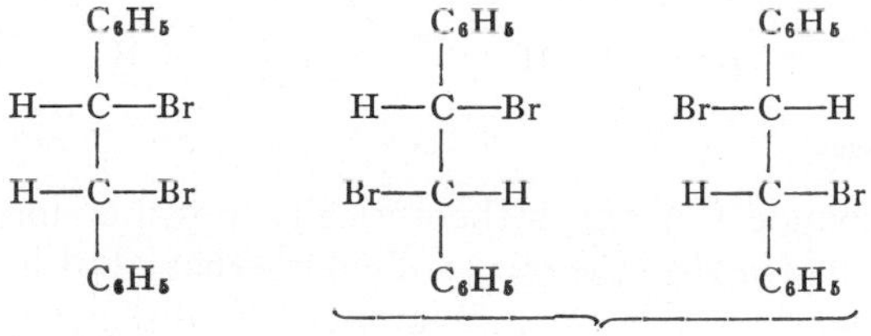

$$
\begin{array}{ccc}
\text{C}_6\text{H}_5 & \text{C}_6\text{H}_5 & \text{C}_6\text{H}_5 \\
| & | & | \\
\text{H---C---Br} & \text{H---C---Br} & \text{Br---C---H} \\
| & | & | \\
\text{H---C---Br} & \text{Br---C---H} & \text{H---C---Br} \\
| & | & | \\
\text{C}_6\text{H}_5 & \text{C}_6\text{H}_5 & \text{C}_6\text{H}_5 \\
\end{array}
$$

meso	*dl*
M.p. 237°	M.p. 114°
Sol. in 1025 parts ether (18°)	Sol. in 3.7 parts ether (18°)

Stilbene dibromides

groups exercise still greater repulsion and hence in both isomers the conformation of maximum stability is that in which the two phenyl groups are as far from each other as possible. This is represented in a projection formula in which the molecule is viewed along the axis of the bond connecting the two asymmetric carbon atoms. The carbon atom nearest to the eye is numbered 1 and its other three bonds are represented by full lines; that to the rear (2) is represented by a circle and its bonds by dotted lines. With the two phenyl groups at maximal distance, in a transoid

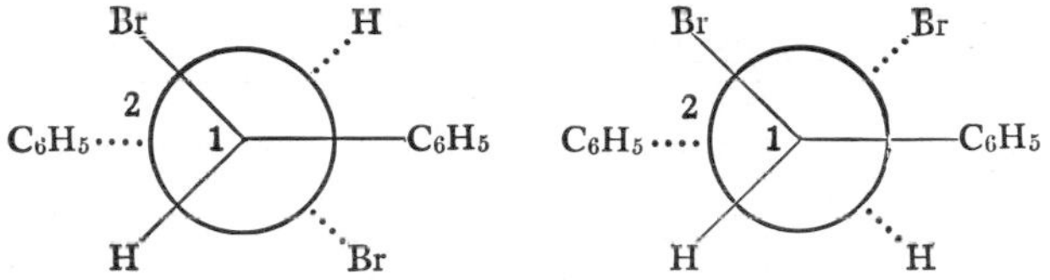

meso-Dibromide   *d*-(or *l*)-Dibromide

arrangement, the two large bromine atoms of the *meso*-form are also maximally separated but those of the *dl*-form are bunched on one side of the molecule. The *meso*-form is thus symmetrical and the *dl*-form unsymmetrical, and the difference is reflected in the marked contrast in melting point and solubility. X-ray diffraction measurements of the crystalline dibromides confirm the predominant conformations indicated, since the Br–Br distances found are: *meso*, 4.50 Å; *dl*, 3.85 Å.

Rotational isomers of 1,2-dichloroethane, although not isolable, are recognizable from two characteristic Raman and infrared spectra, one of which fades out at low temperatures ahead of the other. The more stable form is that with the chlorine atoms at maximal distance, called the staggered form (also *anti*), and the less stable form, is the skew form (also called *syn*). The staggered and skew forms correspond, respectively, to *meso-* and

Staggered   Skew   Eclipsed

dl-stilbene dibromide. A third theoretically possible form, the eclipsed form, has no reality in the case of 1,2-dichloroethane but has significance in the conformational analysis of ring compounds, discussed below. In this eclipsed form (see approximate projection formula) the three radial bonds of C_1 are coplanar with those of C_2 and the atoms attached to C_1 are as close to those of C_2 as is possible. The atoms repel one another and force the molecule to assume a more stable conformation. In the conventional terminology the instability of an eclipsed conformation is described as an eclipsed interaction (or as a nonbonded eclipsed interaction, since the effect is exerted through space between atoms that are not bonded to one another). Practically, an interaction, which makes for instability, can be understood as due to mutual repulsion of atoms or groups. The magnitude of the effect depends on the nature of the substituents, but a skew interaction is always somewhat stronger than a staggered interaction and considerably weaker than an eclipsed interaction. Thus spectrographic analysis of 1,2-dichloroethane does not reveal the presence of the eclipsed form, and dipole measurements over a range of temperature show that the staggered form is more stable than the skew form by 1.2 kg.-cal./mole. One can say either that the quantity of energy that must be supplied for transformation of the more to the less stable conformation is thus 1.2 kg.-cal., or that, with reference to the staggered interaction, the energy equivalent of the skew interaction is 1.2 kg.-cal. In the case of 1,2-dimethylethane (*n*-butane), the value is 3.6 kg.-cal./mole.

Conformation frequently influences reaction rate. Since the debromination of a *vic*-dibromide to an alkene requires a *trans* relationship of the two halogen atoms, it is not surprising that *meso*-2,3-dibromobutane reacts faster than the *dl*-isomer with sodium iodide to form butene-2. The conformations, corresponding to those of the stilbene dibromides, show that in the *meso* (staggered) form the bromine atoms are in a *trans*-relationship, ideal for elimination. The debromination of the *dl*-(skew) form is slower because the reacting molecule requires excitation to surmount the energy barrier to transformation to a conformation in which the bromine atoms are *trans*.

Cyclohexane. — In the chair conformation of cyclohexane six of the C—H bonds are parallel to the axis of symmetry of the ring and are called axial (a); the other six bonds radiate more or less in the plane of the ring

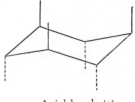

Axial bonds (a)   Equatorial bonds (e)

Cyclohexane bonds (chair)

and are called equatorial (e). This concept was introduced by Hassel[7] in 1943. Other features of the complete molecule are best considered with the aid of a model (Fig. 12.4). An idea of the stability of the chair form

FIG. 12.4. — Cyclohexane

can be gained by inspection of each of the six ethane linkages with reference to the discussion above. It will be noted that each of these linkages has the skew arrangement, as in *dl*-stilbene dibromide and the skew conformation of 1,2-dichloroethane. Hence the molecule lacks maximal stability by a factor of six skew interactions. The boat form of cyclohexane presents quite a different picture (see perspective formula). The following ethane groupings have the skew arrangement: 1,2-, 3,4-, 4,5-, and 6,1-. However,

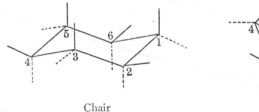

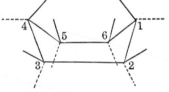

Chair   Boat

Cyclohexane

the 2,3-, and the 5,6-groupings, which form the sides of the boat, have the less stable eclipsed conformation; furthermore, the two bonds at bow (C_1) and stern (C_4) that point upwards in a near-axial orientation bring the hydrogen atoms into close proximity and so establish a strong bow-to-stern interaction. Pitzer[8] has calculated the following parameters of strain energy associated with bond conformations of three types: staggered = 0 (by definition); skew = 0.8 kg.-cal./mole; eclipsed, 3.6 kg.-cal./mole. The

[7] Odd Hassel, b. 1897 Oslo; Ph.D. Berlin; Univ. Oslo
[8] Kenneth S. Pitzer, b. 1914 Pomona, Calif.; Ph.D. Univ. Calif., Berkeley; Univ. Calif., Berkeley

energy contribution of the six skew interactions in the chair form is thus
4.8 kg.-cal./mole. On the assumption that the bow-to-stern interaction of
the boat form has a parameter comparable to that of an eclipsed interaction,
the total energy contribution is 14 kg.-cal./mole. The chair form is thus
more stable than the boat form by some 9 kg.-cal., which means that the
boat form has no reality, except as part of a cage structure formed, for example, by a methylene bridge linking C_1 and C_4. Calculations of steric
energy of bi- and tricyclic systems (Barton;[9] Turner;[10] Johnson[11]) take account of additional factors including 1,3-interactions, discussed in the next
paragraph (in the case of cyclohexane the net effect of such interactions
is probably about the same in the chair and boat forms).

Hassel, in an electron diffraction study of substituted cyclohexanes, established that the favored conformation is that in which a maximum number
of substituents occupy the relatively distant equatorial positions. A specific interpretation can be illustrated for the case of methylcyclohexane.

Methylcyclohexane

The stability is greater when the methyl group is equatorial (1) rather than
axial (2) because of interactions between this axial group and the axial
hydrogen atoms in 1,3- and 1,3'-positions (curved arrows). Such a 1,3-
interaction can be assumed to have an energy parameter comparable to
that of a skew interaction (0.8 kg.-cal.). The energy difference between (1)
and (2) of 1.6 kg.-cal. means that in equilibrated methylcyclohexane the
conformation corresponds predominantly to the equatorially substituted
form (1). Actually the conversion of (2) into (1) requires a mere flip of the
ring, to which there is little energy barrier; axial methyl at an uptilted bow
(2) becomes equatorial methyl at a downtilted bow (1) without losing its
identity as β-oriented. In the case of cis-2-methylcyclohexanol, one or the
other of the two substituents is required to assume the axial orientation,
rendered unfavorable by 1,3-interactions, and, since the methyl group
occupies a larger volume than a hydroxyl group, the more stable conformation is that (3) in which methyl is equatorial and hydroxyl axial. In

[9] Derek H. R. Barton, b. 1918 Gravesend, Kent; Ph.D. and D.Sc. London (Heilbron, E. R. H.
Jones); London, Glasgow

[10] Richard B. Turner, b. 1916 Minneapolis; Ph.D. Harvard (Fieser); Rice Institute

[11] William S. Johnson, b. 1913 New Rochelle, N. Y.; Ph.D. Harvard (Fieser); Univ. Wisconsin

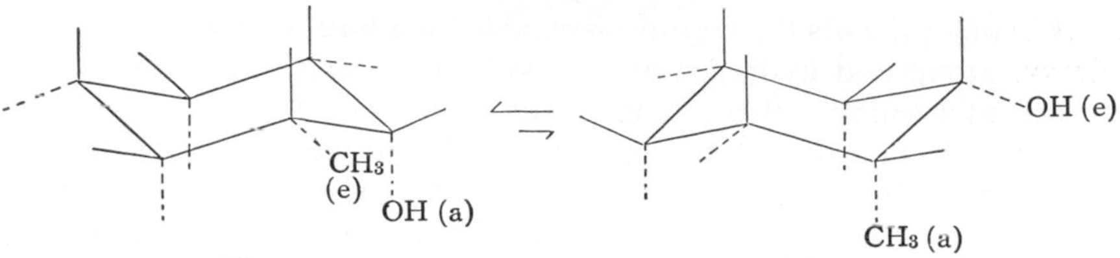

(3)   (4)

cis

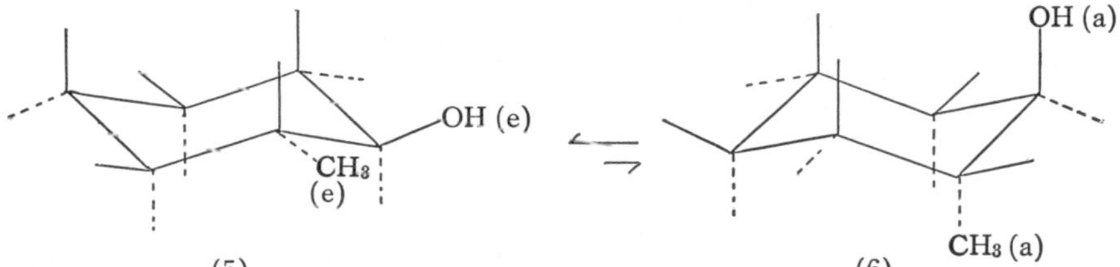

(5)   (6)

trans

2-Methylcyclohexanols

one form (5) of the *trans* alcohol both substituents are equatorial and in the
other form (6) both are axial.   Hence the former is much more stable than
the latter and also more stable than *cis*-2-methylcyclohexanol, an inference
confirmed by the observations that the *cis* alcohol is converted into the *trans*
alcohol when heated with sodium and that reduction of 2-methylcyclohexa-
none with sodium and alcohol gives the more stable *trans* alcohol.

Since an axial substituent is always close in space to two other axial substituents or hydrogen atoms, axial hydroxyl groups would be expected to be
esterified with greater difficulty than equatorial ones, and corresponding
esters should be more resistant to hydrolysis.   Such differences have been
demonstrated in many instances.   However, the reverse relationship holds
for chromic acid oxidation: an axially oriented alcoholic group is the more
sensitive to attack.   The apparent anomaly is resolved by evidence that the
rate-determining step is attack of the carbon–hydrogen bond rather than
of the oxygen–hydrogen bond.

A further difference between the 2-methylcyclohexanols is observed in
elimination reactions.   Thus the *cis* isomer (7) undergoes acid-catalyzed dehydration more readily than the *trans* isomer.   The explanation is that only

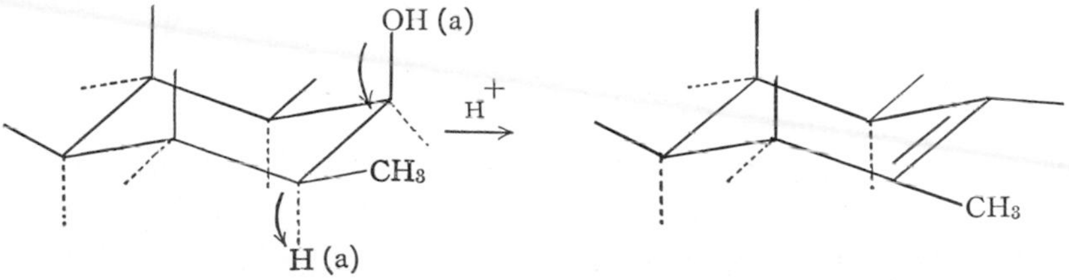

(7)   (8)

the *cis* isomer presents the feature, favorable for a *trans* elimination, that the hydroxyl group and hydrogen atom involved are axial and lie in a plane with the intervening carbon atoms.   The product is Δ^1-methylcyclohexene; the product from *trans*-2-methylcyclohexanol is Δ^2-methylcyclohexene.

Decalin. — Mohr had suggested that *cis*- and *trans*-decalin are formed of two boats and two chairs, respectively, but all conformations containing even one unstable boat form are now disregarded.   The formulas shown are

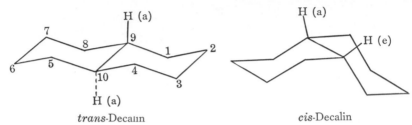

trans-Decalin   *cis*-Decalin

both chair-chair forms; that for *cis*-decalin can change freely into another equivalent one that likewise has one equatorial and one axial bridge-head hydrogen atom; in *trans*-decalin both bridge-head bonds are axial.   That the heat of combustion of *trans*-decalin is lower than that of the *cis*-isomer by 2.1 kg.-cal./mole indicates greater stability of the *trans* form.   The classical concept of strain allows of no difference in energy, since both isomers are strainless, but the strain energies can be calculated from the nonbonded interactions involved.   In *trans*-decalin there are 6 staggered and 12 skew interactions, and in *cis*-decalin 3 staggered and 15 skew interactions, and application of the Pitzer parameters gives an energy difference of 2.4 kg.-cal./mole.

Hydrindane. — This hydrocarbon, in which a six-membered ring is fused to a five-membered ring, likewise exists in a *cis*- and a *trans*-form, for which the conformations shown in the formulas have been proposed.   The cyclo-

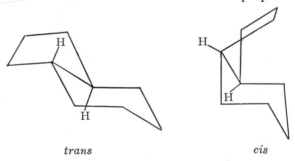

trans   *cis*

pentane ring, like the cyclohexane ring, is represented as puckered, in accordance with evidence regarding cyclopentane itself.   If the five-membered ring were planar, as in the classical concept, all five ethane bonds would be subject to eclipsed interaction.   Hence torsional forces in opposition to the unfavorable interactions tend to pucker the ring.   Entropy measurements do indeed indicate an amount of puckering small enough to escape detection by electron diffraction methods.

trans-Hydrindane is more stable than the *cis* isomer by 1.8 kg.-cal./mole, a relationship understandable by considering the hydrocarbons as 1,2-dialkylcyclohexanes: in one (*trans*) the substituents are both equatorial, and in the other (*cis*) one substituent is axial. The order of the heats of combustion of the β-hydrindones is the same (*cis*, 1347.5 kg.-cal./mole; *trans*, 1345.7 kg.-cal./mole). However, the order of stability is reversed in the case of the α-hydrindones, since on equilibration the *cis*-ketone is the preponderant isomer. A possible explanation is' that only the *cis* structure is favorable for stabilization by hydrogen bonding of the carbonyl oxygen and an axial hydrogen atom.

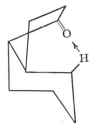

cis -α-Hydrindone

RING CLOSURE

A direct method of synthesizing cycloparaffins consists in the action of zinc or sodium on an appropriate open-chain dihalide. With the higher homologs, the reaction is akin to the Wurtz coupling of the radicals of two

$$(CH_2)_n\!\!<\!\!\begin{array}{l}CH_2Br\\CH_2Br\end{array}\quad\xrightarrow{\;Zn\ or\ 2\,Na\;}\quad (CH_2)_n\!\!<\!\!\begin{array}{l}CH_2\\|\\CH_2\end{array}$$

alkyl halides, and the closure of the cyclopropane ring resembles debromination of a *vic*-dibromide to an olefin. Cyclopropane was first prepared by the action of sodium on trimethylene bromide (Freund,[12] 1882); the yield is raised to about 70% by use of zinc dust and alcohol (Gustavson, 1888). A technical process (Hass, 1936) utilizes 1,3-dichloropropane, derived as one product of the chlorination of propane from natural gas, and the cyclization is accomplished in 80% yield by the action of zinc dust in aqueous alcohol containing sodium iodide as catalyst and sodium carbonate to react with the zinc iodide formed and release iodide ions for further catalysis. Although comparable data are not available, it appears that a cyclopropane ring is produced by the general method almost as readily as an ethylenic linkage but that larger rings are closed considerably less readily. Thus hexamethylene bromide affords cyclohexane in only 44% yield. The evident lack of direct correlation between ease of ring closure and relative stability of the ring systems can be attributed to two factors, one of which is the opportunity for ring closure. Two halogen atoms located on adjacent carbon atoms offer a target more vulnerable to attack by zinc than those in trimethylene bromide, where, because of the opportunity for free rotation about the two single carbon–carbon bonds, the molecule can assume various conformations, some of which are less favorable to ring formation than

[12] Martin Freund, 1863–1920; b. Neisse; Ph.D. Berlin (Hofmann); Frankfurt

others.   As the carbon chain is increased in length there is increasing opportunity for an unfavorable orientation of the halogen atoms at distant sites and less chance of an orientation in such a way as to invite cyclization. A second factor governing the outcome of cyclizations is the opportunity for occurrence of competing reactions; this aspect is discussed in a later section concerning cyclization of dibasic acids.

Diels-Alder Reaction. — The synthetic reaction discovered by Diels[13] and Alder[14] (1928) consists in 1,4-addition of a diene to a second component having an ethylenic linkage flanked by carbonyl or carboxyl groups, such as maleic anhydride:

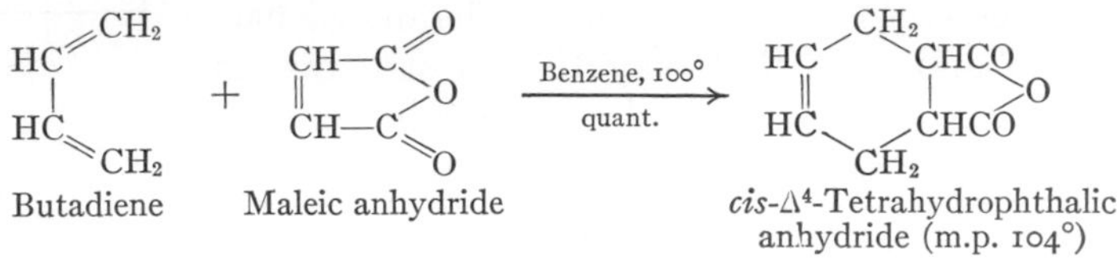

Butadiene   Maleic anhydride   *cis*-Δ^4-Tetrahydrophthalic anhydride (m.p. 104°)

The diene system opens at the 1- and 4-positions, and the terminal carbons become affixed at the double bond of the anhydride to produce a six-membered ring.   The reaction is generally applicable, and dienes and dienic compounds of a wide variety of types usually enter into the Diels-Alder reaction, or diene synthesis, though with differences in the degree of readiness of combination.   Thus 2,3-dimethylbutadiene, $CH_2=C(CH_3)-C(CH_3)=CH_2$, and piperylene, $CH_3CH=CHCH=CH_2$, react more readily than butadiene reacts, and sorbic acid, $CH_3CH=CHCH=CHCOOH$, reacts less readily.

That carbonyl groups adjacent to the double bond enhance the additive power of the dienophilic component finds an analogy in the ability of glyoxal and glyoxylic acid to form stable hydrates (p. 216).   Maleic anhydride is thus a particularly favorable reagent that finds many applications, and its methyl and dimethyl derivatives also can be employed.   A comparable structure is encountered in quinones, which add dienes with great readiness.

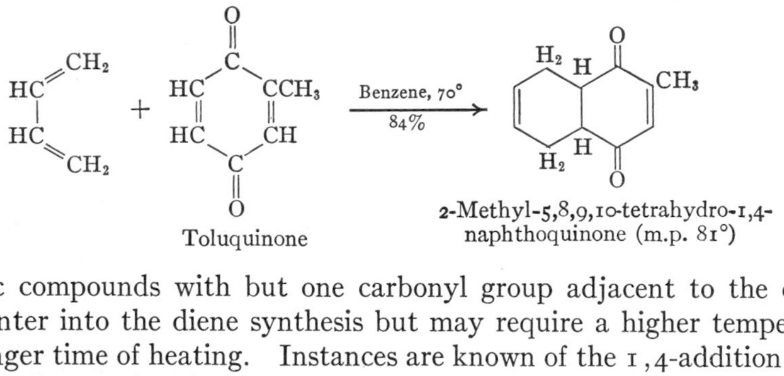

Toluquinone   2-Methyl-5,8,9,10-tetrahydro-1,4-naphthoquinone (m.p. 81°)

Olefinic compounds with but one carbonyl group adjacent to the double bond enter into the diene synthesis but may require a higher temperature or a longer time of heating.   Instances are known of the 1,4-addition of one diene to the 1,2-double bond of another.

---

[13] Otto Diels, b. 1876 Hamburg; Ph.D. Berlin (E. Fischer); Kiel; Nobel Prize 1950
[14] Kurt Alder, b. 1902 Königshütte; Ph.D. Kiel (Diels); Cologne; Nobel Prize 1950

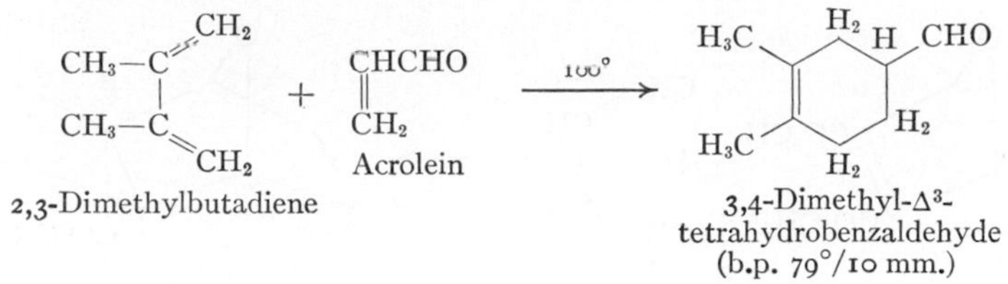

2,3-Dimethylbutadiene + Acrolein → 3,4-Dimethyl-Δ^3-tetrahydrobenzaldehyde (b.p. 79°/10 mm.)

The Diels-Alder reaction is an example of a stereospecific *cis*-addition. Thus substituents in the dienophile retain their original orientation; the adducts from maleic acid or anhydride are always *cis*-dicarboxylic acid derivatives and those from fumaric acid are *trans*. In the reaction of a dienophile with a cyclic diene two modes of addition are possible, as formulated for the reaction of cyclopentadiene with maleic anhydride. Actually one product is obtained, the endo form.

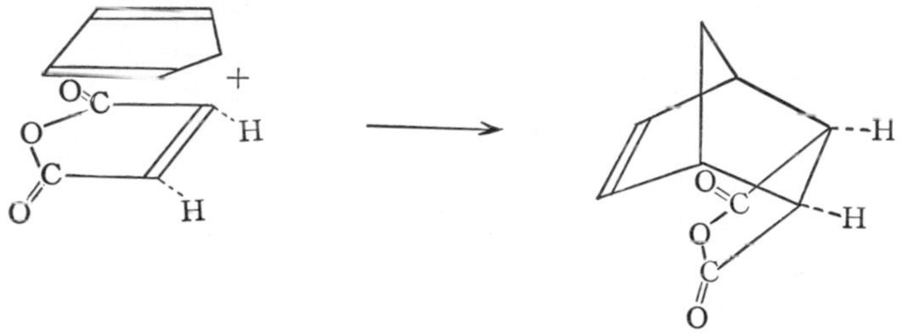

Endo

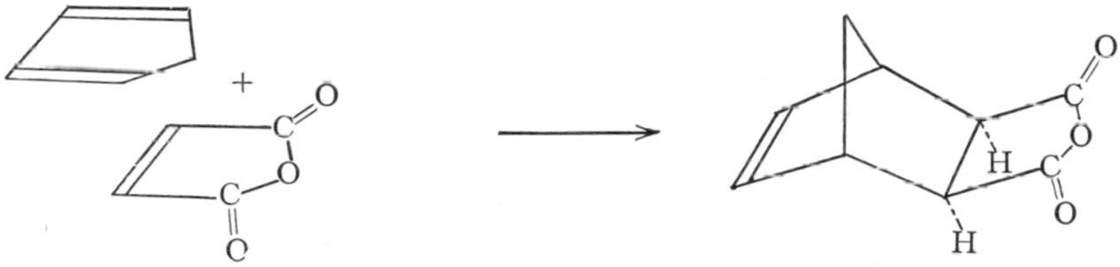

Exo

An interesting use of the Diels-Alder reaction is in a synthesis of cantharidin (Stork,[15] 1953), a vesicant principle found in cantharides beetles (Robiquet, 1810). The structure had been established (Gadamer,[16] 1914), but the stereochemistry was not known. Hence the scheme of synthesi

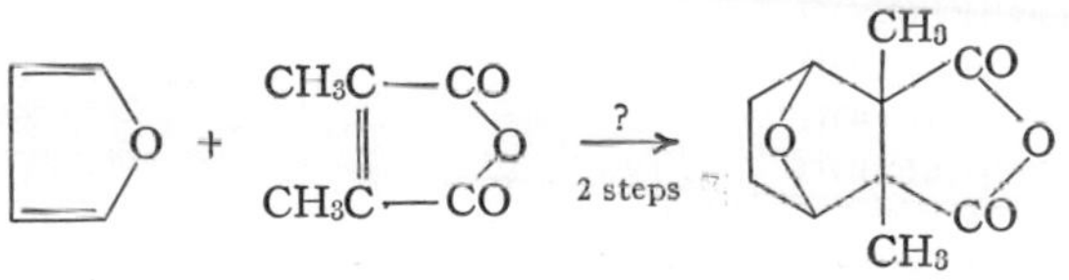

Cantharidin

by Diels-Alder reaction of furan with dimethylmaleic anhydride appeared attractive and had been tried, but with negative results. All Diels-Alder

[15] Gilbert Stork, b. 1921 Brussels, Belgium; Ph.D. Wisconsin (McElvain); Columbia Univ.
[16] Johannes Georg Gadamer, 1867–1928; Ph.D. Univ. Marburg; Marburg

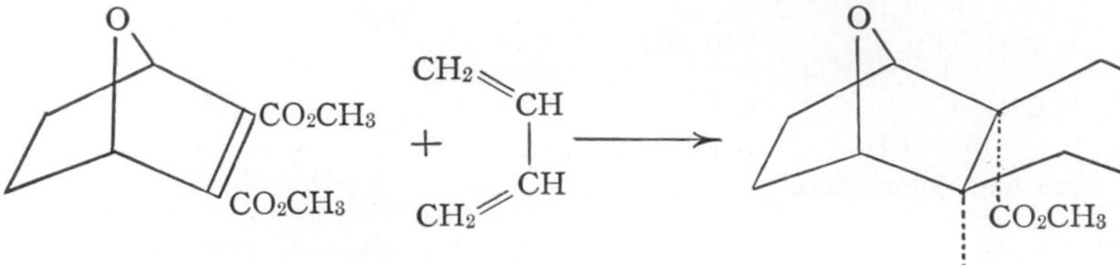

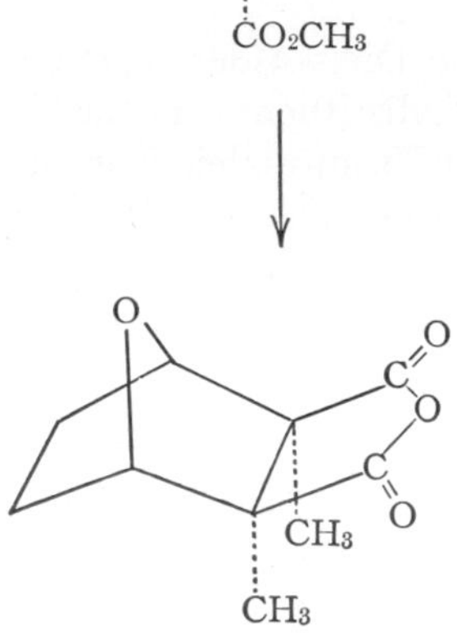

reactions are reversible, and in this case the equilibrium favors the cleavage products at the temperature required for additior to proceed. Stork, however, inferred that cantharidin is exocyclic rather than endocyclic and hence that the projected synthesis would not give the desired product. The successful synthesis involved condensation of dimethyl 3,6-epoxy-3,4,5,6-tetrahydrophthalate with butadiene, transformation of the carbomethoxy groups to methyl groups, and degradation of the unsaturated ring to a dicarboxylic acid anhydride group.

Cantharidin

DICARBOXYLIC ACIDS AND CYCLIC DERIVATIVES

The dibasic acids (Table 12.2) derived from straight-chain paraffins by attachment of carboxyl groups at the two ends of the chain are all crystalline

TABLE 12.2. DIBASIC ACIDS

ACID	FORMULA	M.P., °C.	SOLUBILITY, G./100 G. H_2O	ACIDIC DISSOCIATION	
				pK_{a_1}	pK_{a_2}
Oxalic	$HOOC \cdot COOH$	187 [1]	$10.2^{20°}$	1.46	4.40
Malonic	$HOOCCH_2COOH$	135	$138^{16°}$	2.80	5.85
Succinic	$HOOCCH_2CH_2COOH$	185	$6.8^{20°}$	4.17	5.64
Glutaric	$HOOCCH_2CH_2CH_2COOH$	97.5	$63.9^{20°}$	4.33	5.57
Adipic	$HOOC(CH_2)_4COOH$	151	$1.4^{15°}$	4.43	5.52
Pimelic	$HOOC(CH_2)_5COOH$	105	$2.5^{14°}$	4.47	5.52
Suberic	$HOOC(CH_2)_6COOH$	142	$0.14^{16°}$	4.52	5.52
Azelaic	$HOOC(CH_2)_7COOH$	106	$.2^{15°}$	4.54	5.52
Sebacic	$HOOC(CH_2)_8COOH$	134	$.1^{17°}$	4.55	5.52

[1] The dihydrate melts with loss of water at 100°.

solids of much higher melting point than the monocarboxylic acids of comparable molecular weight. Melting points fall off somewhat as the paraffinic part of the molecule becomes larger, and an alternation is apparent in both the melting points and solubilities. Acids having an even number of carbon atoms invariably are higher melting and less soluble than their immediate higher or lower homologs having an odd number of carbon atoms. The relationship is encountered also in the series of higher mono-carboxylic acids (see p. 400 for discussion). From the dissociation constants for the first stage of ionization, it is seen that in oxalic acid the one un-saturated group exerts a strong inductive effect that promotes ionization of the second, which renders the substance one of the strongest of the available organic acids and hence often useful as a condensing agent less destructive and slightly more moderate than mineral acids. The influence of one carboxyl group on the other is evident to a lesser extent when the two are separated by a methylene group (malonic acid) and is still apparent in the next higher homolog (succinic acid), but when the functional groups are separated by three or more carbon atoms, the inductive effect disappears; probably the two groups repel each other and swing the flexible zigzag chain into such a position that they are as distant from each other as possible.

Occurrence and Preparation. — **Oxalic acid** occurs in the form of its potassium and calcium salts in the cell sap of many plants. An early technical method of preparation involved fusion of sawdust with alkali at 240–250°; the acid is derived from cellulose, which contains the unit —CHOHCHOH—. A modern process consists in heating sodium formate in the presence of sodium hydroxide or carbonate, which affords sodium oxalate:

$$\begin{array}{ccc} \overline{H}\,\text{COONa} & & \text{COONa} \\ & \xrightarrow{360°} & | \quad\quad + \text{ H}_2 \\ \underline{H}\,\text{COONa} & & \text{COONa} \end{array}$$

Malonic acid was discovered as an oxidation product of malic acid (L. *malum*, apple) and was named accordingly. It is usually prepared from

$$\text{HOOCCH}_2\text{CHOHCOOH} \xrightarrow{[O]} \text{HOOCCH}_2\text{COCOOH} \xrightarrow{[O]} \text{HOOCCH}_2\text{COOH} + \text{CO}_2$$

Malic acid   Oxalacetic acid   Malonic acid
(two forms, m.p. 152° and 184°)

chloroacetic acid by the cyanide synthesis; the sodium or potassium salt is treated with potassium cyanide, and the resulting nitrile hydrolyzed to the dibasic acid.

$$\begin{array}{ccccc} \text{CH}_2\text{COONa} & & \text{CH}_2\text{COONa} & & \text{CH}_2\text{COOH} \\ | & \xrightarrow{\text{KCN}} & | & \xrightarrow{\text{Hydrol.}} & | \\ \text{Cl} & & \text{CN} & & \text{COOH} \end{array}$$

Sodium chloroacetate   Sodium cyanoacetate

Succinic acid occurs widely in nature; it was first mentioned by Agricola in 1550 as a product of distillation of the fossil resin amber (L. *succinum*, amber), in which it is present in combined form. The substance can be prepared by bacterial fermentation (reductive) of either tartaric or malic

$$\begin{array}{ccccc} \text{HOCHCOOH} & & \text{CH}_2\text{COOH} & & \text{CH}_2\text{COOH} \\ | & \xrightarrow{\text{4 H}} & | & \xleftarrow{\text{2 H}} & | \\ \text{HOCHCOOH} & & \text{CH}_2\text{COOH} & & \text{HOCHCOOH} \end{array}$$

acid.   Another method of technical application is catalytic hydrogenation of maleic acid.

Glutaric acid, so named because of relationships to glutamic and tartaric acid, is less available than the lower homologs, but can be prepared by nitric acid oxidation of cyclopentanone (p. 199) or synthesized from trimethylene glycol.   **Adipic acid,** originally obtained by oxidation of various fats (L. *adipis*, of fat), is now produced in large quantities for the manufacture of nylon by oxidation of cyclohexanol (p. 199).   **Pimelic acid,** also isolated as a product of oxidation of fats (Gr. *pimelē*, fat), can be prepared by a novel reaction involving fission of an aromatic ring; the initial step is 1,4-addition of hydrogen.   In a process developed in Germany

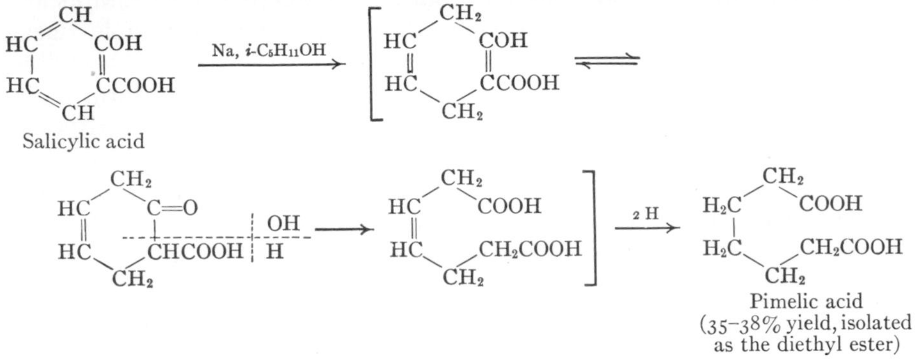

Salicylic acid

Pimelic acid
(35–38% yield, isolated
as the diethyl ester)

(1949) salicylic acid is hydrogenated (as ester, I) to *cis*-hexahydrosalicylic acid (II), and this is heated at 310° in an autoclave with strong alkali, when a mole of hydrogen is evolved and pimelic acid (V) is formed in high yield. The expected reaction was dehydrogenation of the secondary alcoholic group of II and cleavage of the β-keto acid, cyclohexanone-2-carboxylic acid; however, treatment with alkali at a lower temperature afforded

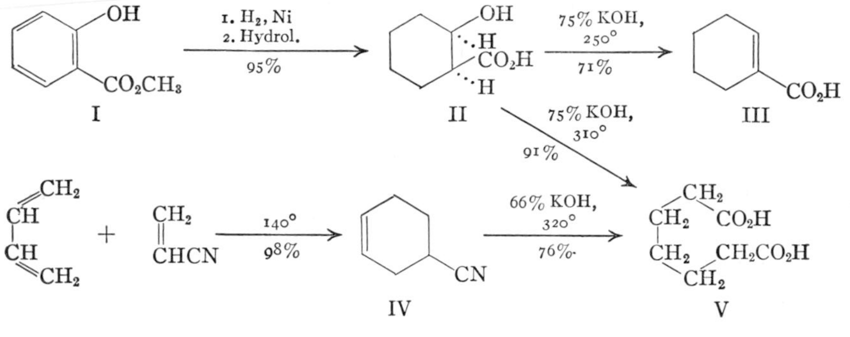

Δ^1-cyclohexene-1-carboxylic acid, III (*trans* elimination), which thus may be the intermediate in the high-temperature process.   The observation suggested a further efficient synthesis consisting in Diels-Alder condensation of butadiene with acrylonitrile to the nitrile (IV) of Δ^3-cyclohexene-1-carboxylic acid and alkaline hydrolysis and cleavage; the double bond of IV probably migrates to a position of conjugation with the carboxyl group in the course of the reaction.

Suberic acid (L. *suber*, cork) is one product of the oxidation of cork; it is not readily accessible. **Azelaic acid** also is a rather expensive chemical; the name apparently is derived from the fact that the substance is one of the products of oxidation of oleic acid with nitric acid (az, from *azote*, nitrogen, + Gr. *elaion*, olive oil):

$$CH_3(CH_2)_7CH\!\!=\!\!CH(CH_2)_7COOH \xrightarrow{HNO_3} HOOC(CH_2)_7COOH$$
$$\text{Oleic acid} \qquad\qquad\qquad \text{Azelaic acid}$$

Traumatic acid, a plant constituent which induces division and extension of certain plant cells, is 1-decene-1,10-dicarboxylic acid,

$$HOOC(CH_2)_8CH\!\!=\!\!CHCOOH$$

Special Properties of Oxalic Acid. — Oxalic acid differs from the other members of the series in being subject to ready oxidation by potassium permanganate. In analogy with the behavior of *vic*-glycols (p. 129) and α-diketones, the reaction can be interpreted as involving rupture of a weakened linkage between two highly oxidized carbon atoms. Since the

$$\begin{array}{c} COOH \\ -\!\!+\!\!- \\ COOH \end{array} + \begin{array}{c} [O] \\ KMnO_4 \end{array} \longrightarrow 2\,CO_2 + H_2O$$

reaction is quantitative and oxalic acid dihydrate is an easily purified crystalline solid, the substance is used in volumetric analysis for standardization of potassium permanganate solutions. The reducing property of oxalic acid also renders the substance useful for eradication of ink spots and as a general bleaching agent.

A second distinctive characteristic is that oxalic acid when heated rapidly decomposes to give formic acid, carbon dioxide, carbon monoxide, and water. Sulfuric acid promotes the decomposition at lower temperatures, and in this case the formic acid is converted into carbon monoxide and water. Apparently the reaction consists in initial decarboxylation to formic acid and subsequent dehydration of this substance. Thus combination

$$\begin{array}{c} COOH \\ -\!\!+\!\!- \\ COOH \end{array} \xrightarrow{-CO_2} \begin{array}{c} H \\ -\!\!+\!\!- \\ COOH \end{array} \longrightarrow CO + H_2O$$

of two carboxyl groups in direct linkage represents a structure not very stable to heat or to the action of mineral acids and has a certain analogy to the combination of two hydroxyl groups, for hydrogen peroxide is subject

$$\begin{array}{c} OH \\ | \\ OH \end{array} \longrightarrow \begin{array}{c} H \\ | \\ OH \end{array} + \tfrac{1}{2}O_2$$

to similar decomposition. Another analogous reaction is the decomposition suffered by trichloroacetic acid in boiling water:

$$CCl_3COOH \longrightarrow CHCl_3 + CO_2$$

Special Properties of Malonic Acid. — Both oxalic and malonic acid offer the possibility of loss of water with formation of cyclic anhydrides having three- and four-membered rings, respectively, but they do not yield such derivatives. Malonic acid when heated with phosphorus pentoxide affords a highly unsaturated and very reactive substance, carbon suboxide (Diels, 1908). This adds two molecules of water to regenerate

$$
\begin{array}{c}
\text{OH} \\
\text{H}_2\text{C} \overset{\displaystyle \text{C=O}}{\underset{\displaystyle \text{C=O}}{}} \quad \xrightarrow{\text{P}_2\text{O}_5} \quad \text{C} \overset{\displaystyle \text{C=O}}{\underset{\displaystyle \text{C=O}}{}} \\
\text{OH}
\end{array}
$$

Carbon suboxide
(m.p. − 108°, b.p. 7°)

malonic acid and reacts with ethanol to yield diethyl malonate. Thus the formation of this unusually reactive unsaturated system takes precedence over cyclization to an anhydride. The ready thermal or acid-catalyzed decarboxylation of malonic acid has been described (p. 221).

Cyclic Anhydrides of Dibasic Acids. — Neither oxalic nor malonic acid forms a cyclic anhydride, even though the two carboxyl groups are close to each other in space, for both acids undergo decarboxylation on being heated, and malonic acid on treatment with phosphorus pentoxide suffers dehydration to carbon suboxide. Evidently there is little tendency for formation of three- or four-membered anhydride rings. Succinic acid and glutaric acid readily afford cyclic anhydrides. The anhydrides are formed

$$
\begin{array}{c}
\text{CH}_2-\text{C} \overset{\displaystyle \text{O}}{\underset{\displaystyle \text{O}}{}} \\
\mid \\
\text{CH}_2-\text{C} \overset{}{\underset{\displaystyle \text{O}}{}}
\end{array}
\qquad
\begin{array}{c}
\text{H}_2\text{C} \overset{\displaystyle \text{CH}_2-\text{C}}{\underset{\displaystyle \text{CH}_2-\text{C}}{}} \overset{\displaystyle \text{O}}{\underset{\displaystyle \text{O}}{}} \\
\end{array}
$$

Succinic anhydride   Glutaric anhydride
(m.p. 120°)   (m.p. 57°)

when the acids are heated for some time at temperatures above the melting point, and they can be prepared conveniently in good yields by warming the acids with acetic anhydride or acetyl chloride (p. 188). Five- and six-membered ring compounds in which an oxygen atom is incorporated into a heterocyclic ring system represent stable and easily formed structures analogous to related carbocyclic compounds. Physicochemical studies (X-ray analyses, measurement of dipole moments) have established that the dimethyl ether molecule is not linear but has a triangular configuration in which the two valences of the oxygen atom extend at an angle of 111°.

$$
\text{H}_3\text{C} \underset{111°}{\overset{\displaystyle \text{O}}{\diagdown\text{-}\text{-}\diagup}} \text{CH}_3
$$

This figure is so close to the normal angle of valences of the tetrahedral carbon atom that for practical purposes an oxygen atom can be regarded as interchangeable with carbon in a ring structure. Thus the five-membered heterocyclic ring in succinic anhydride is probably planar and essentially strain-free, and that in glutaric anhydride probably has a nonplanar, puckered, and strain-free configuration.

Adipic acid, the next higher homolog in the series of dibasic acids, is converted by treatment with acetic anhydride at reflux temperature into a microcrystalline polymeric anhydride melting after recrystallization in the range 70–85°. Properties and reactions of the substance indicate that it is a mixture of chain polymers of varying chain length:

$$HOOCCH_2CH_2CH_2CH_2CO\overline{[OH}\ +\ \overline{n]H]}OOCCH_2CH_2CH_2CH_2COOH \xrightarrow{-\ nH_2O}$$

$$HOOCCH_2CH_2CH_2CH_2\overset{O}{\overset{\|}{C}}-O-\left[\overset{O}{\overset{\|}{C}}CH_2CH_2CH_2CH_2\overset{O}{\overset{\|}{C}}-O\right]_n H$$

Instead of cyclization within the individual molecules to a 7-ring structure (intramolecular condensation), the predominating reaction is condensation between different molecules (intermolecular), and the contrast in behavior to that of succinic and glutaric acid is attributable to a difference in relative opportunities for the two reactions. One carboxyl group separated from the other by a chain of four methylene groups has many opportunities to combine with functional groups of other molecules and relatively few chances of colliding and interacting with the group attached to the same chain, for the chain can assume many positions by rotations about the various single bonds, and only a few of these bring the functional groups into proximity. Thus the longer the chain the less chance there is for intramolecular cyclization and the greater the tendency to form polymers. Pimelic acid and suberic acid similarly yield chain polymers on treatment with dehydrating agents.

Although the monomeric form of adipic anhydride is not available by any known process of direct dehydration, J. W. Hill (1930) found that when the polymer is heated in high vacuum a distillate slowly accumulates consisting of the pure cyclic anhydride. Evidently the polymerization is reversible and the volatile monomer distils from the equilibrium mixture, with eventual reversion of the bulk of the nonvolatile polymer. Monomeric adipic anhydride is stable but reactive, and it is repolymerized by the catalytic action of a trace of water. The principle of converting a polymeric substance into a cyclic monomer by heating in high vacuum to a tem-

$$HOOC(CH_2)_4COO[CO(CH_2)_4COO]_n H \xrightarrow[0.1\ mm.]{98-100°} \begin{array}{c} CH_2CH_2CO \\ | \qquad\qquad \searrow \\ | \qquad\qquad\quad O \\ CH_2CH_2CO \end{array}$$

Polymer

Monomeric adipic anhydride (m.p. 20°)

perature approaching the decomposition point, in the presence of a catalyst where required, has been applied extensively to the preparation of large-ring compounds of several types by Carothers and Hill (1930–33).

Cyclic Ketones. — Pyrolysis of the barium salt of adipic acid (p. 196) affords cyclopentanone in 80% yield, and cyclohexanone is produced in high yield from pimelic acid by the same method. Five- and six-membered cyclic ketones are produced so readily that acids of the adipic and pimelic types often can be converted into the ketones by simply heating the dibasic acid with acetic anhydride and distilling the excess reagent and the product, if it is volatile, at atmospheric pressure (Blanc, 1907). Probably the acid

$$
\begin{array}{c}
\text{CH}_2\text{CH}_2\text{CO\,OH} \\
| \qquad\qquad | \\
\text{CH}_2\text{CH}_2\text{COOH}
\end{array}
\quad\xrightarrow{(\text{CH}_3\text{CO})_2\text{O, distil}}\quad
\begin{array}{c}
\text{CH}_2\!-\!\text{CH}_2 \\
| \qquad\qquad\diagdown \\
\qquad\qquad \text{CO} \;+\; \text{CO}_2 \;+\; \text{H}_2\text{O} \\
| \qquad\qquad\diagup \\
\text{CH}_2\!-\!\text{CH}_2
\end{array}
$$

Adipic acid　　　　　　　　　　　　　　　Cyclopentanone

is converted first into the polymeric anhydride, which then suffers pyrolysis rather than the depolymerization to the monomer observed when distillation is conducted in vacuum at a lower temperature, for pyrolysis of such polymers at atmospheric pressure affords ketones. Blanc observed that acids of the glutaric type, when submitted to the same process of distillation with acetic anhydride, are converted into anhydrides and not into cyclobutanone derivatives, and proposed this reaction as a diagnostic test for distinguishing between dibasic acids having a chain of five carbon atoms

$$
\text{H}_2\text{C}\!\!\begin{array}{c}\diagup \text{CH}_2\text{COOH} \\ \diagdown \text{CH}_2\text{COOH}\end{array}
\quad\xrightarrow[\text{Distil}]{(\text{CH}_3\text{CO})_2\text{O}}\quad
\text{H}_2\text{C}\!\!\begin{array}{c}\diagup \text{CH}_2\text{CO} \\ \qquad\qquad \diagdown \text{O} \\ \diagdown \text{CH}_2\text{CO}\diagup\end{array}
$$

Glutaric acid　　　　　　　　　　　　　Anhydride

$(\text{HOOC} \cdot \text{C} \cdot \text{C} \cdot \text{COOH})$ and those having six or more carbon atoms in the chains (Blanc rule). Although the generalization accurately describes the behavior of the majority of acids, exceptions have been encountered in the case of certain highly substituted compounds of the adipic acid type that yield anhydrides rather than ketones.

Synthesis of large-ring ketones by pyrolysis of metal salts of the corresponding acids is usually accomplished by heating the acid with the metal oxide. Calcium oxide appears preferable for the lower members of the series and thorium or cerium oxide better for the higher members. Ruzicka noted an interesting relationship between yield and ring size. The 5- and 6-ring ketones are obtainable in high yield, the yield of the C_7-ketone is moderate and that of the C_8-ketone fair (20%), but the ketones in the range C_9–C_{13} are obtained under optimum conditions in yields of not more than 0.5%. From C_{13} on, however, the yields improve and reach a secondary maximum of about 5% for the C_{18}-ketone, and then fall off to a level of about 2%. Ruzicka's discovery of the existence of large-ring ketones as the active principles of valuable perfumes, coupled with the observation that the pyrolytic method found applicable to the synthesis of such compounds gives at best yields of the order of 5%, presented a challenge for the development of an improved technique that was not slow in forthcoming. Ziegler in 1933 applied to the problem a principle that had appeared in the literature (Ruggli,[17] 1912) but had received little attention. The chief obstacle to formation of large-ring compounds is interference from the competing reaction of polymerization. Under ordinary conditions of experimentation a functional group B collides many more times with the group A of surrounding molecules than with that present in the same molecule, and hence polymerization predominates. Any variation in the

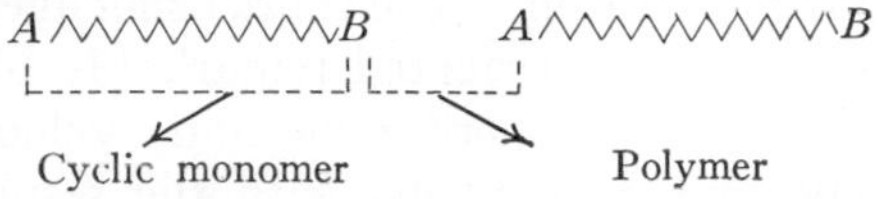

Cyclic monomer   Polymer

conditions of the reaction that will suppress polymerization must increase opportunity for intramolecular cyclization, and a means of achieving this objective consists merely in conducting the reaction at high dilution. If each molecule is surrounded largely by solvent molecules and is relatively remote from others of its kind, opportunity for intermolecular collisions is diminished and cyclization given a chance to proceed, even if slowly. As with any other monomolecular reaction, the rate of cyclization is independent of the concentration, and the reaction is just as rapid in a very dilute solution as in a concentrated one, whereas the velocity of polymerization, which is bimolecular in the initial phase, can be decreased enormously by operating at high dilution.

For utilization of the dilution principle in the preparation of large-ring ketones it was necessary to employ a cyclization reaction capable of being conducted in a homogeneous liquid phase with all the reactants in solution, and Ziegler worked out a suitable adaptation of the Dieckmann reaction meeting this requirement. A dinitrile was used in place of a diester, and a condensing agent to replace sodium or sodium ethoxide was found in the ether-soluble compound lithium ethylanilide, $LiN(C_2H_5)C_6H_5$ The full sequence of reactions is formulated:

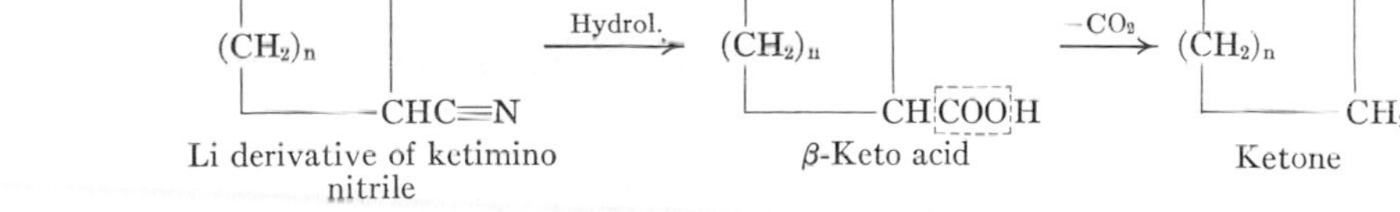

By virtue of the activated position adjacent to the unsaturated nitrile group, the dinitrile is converted into a lithium derivative, which undergoes cyclization, pictured in the formulas as addition of the C-lithium to the

[17] Paul Ruggli, 1884–1945; b. Montevideo (German parentage); Ph.D. Leipzig (Hantzsch); Basel; Helv. Chim Acta 29, 796 (1946)

second nitrile group. The resulting product suffers replacement of lithium by hydrogen on addition of water, and both the imino group (=NH) and the nitrile group are easily hydrolyzed to give a β-keto acid that readily loses carbon dioxide. The necessary high dilution at the critical stage of the cyclization step is accomplished without use of a large volume of solvent by adding a solution of the dinitrile in ether at a very slow rate to a vigorously stirred and refluxing solution of the condensing agent in ether. When the technical details were fully perfected remarkably high yields were obtained. Thus the yields of cycloheptanone and cyclooctanone were 95% and 88%, respectively, and, in contrast with the results of the pyrolytic method, cyclopentadecanone (Exaltone) and cycloheptadecanone (dihydrocivetone) were obtained in yields of 60% and 70%. Oddly enough, although all the ketones in the series C_{14} to C_{25} as well as the C_5–C_8 ketones could be obtained in yields of 60% and higher, in the series from C_9 to C_{13} the yields dropped to a practically negligible point with the C_9–C_{11} ketones and to 8% and 15% with the next two members. A yield minimum thus exists in this refined method of cyclization, as in the pyrolytic process. An interpretation based on conformational analysis has been suggested (Prelog,[18] 1950; see reading references).

An alternate cyclization process utilizing an intramolecular acetoacetic ester alkylation has been applied by Hunsdiecker (1943) to the synthesis of civetone. The starting material was aleuritic acid, a C_{16}-acid available from shellac. The substance contains a terminal primary alcohol group, and two vicinal hydroxyl groups near the middle of the chain provide a means of introducing the necessary double bond. The ω-bromo unsaturated acid is prepared as shown and condensed as the acid chloride with acetoacetic ester; the product of acid hydrolysis contains an activated methylene group adjacent to one end of the chain, and intramolecular condensation is carried out in very dilute solution. The resulting β-keto ester on hydrolysis and decarboxylation yields civetone.

$$HOCH_2(CH_2)_5CHOHCHOH(CH_2)_7COOH \xrightarrow[96\%]{HBr} Br(CH_2)_6CHBrCHBr(CH_2)_7COOH \xrightarrow[61\%]{Zn}$$

Aleuritic acid

$$Br(CH_2)_6CH{=}CH(CH_2)_7COOH \xrightarrow{\substack{1.\ SOCl_2 \\ 2.\ CH_3COCH_2COOC_2H_5}}$$

Δ^9-16-Bromohexadecenoic acid

$$\left[Br(CH_2)_6CH{=}CH(CH_2)_7CO\underset{\diagdown COOC_2H_5}{\overset{\diagup COCH_3}{CH}} \right] \xrightarrow[60-70\%]{Na,CH_3OH}$$

$$Br(CH_2)_6CH{=}CH(CH_2)_7COCH_2COOCH_3 \xrightarrow[86\%]{\substack{1.\ NaI \\ 2.\ K_2CO_3}}$$

$$\underset{\overset{\|}{CH(CH_2)_6}CHCOOCH_3}{CH(CH_2)_7CO} \xrightarrow[80\%]{KOH} \underset{\overset{\|}{CH(CH_2)_7}\diagup}{CH(CH_2)_7\diagdown}C{=}O$$

Civetone

――――――――――――――――
[18] Vladimir Prelog, b. 1906 Sarajevo, Yugoslavia; Dr. Ing. Prague (Votoček); ETH Zurich

Still another method utilizes intramolecular condensation of a bi-functional ketene (Blomquist, 1948). Ketene itself readily dimerizes when liquid condensed in a dry ice-acetone bath is allowed to come to room temperature. Diketene is an unsaturated lactone reducible to β-butyro-lactone, and it is hydrolyzed by water to acetoacetic acid. When the

$$\begin{array}{c} CH_2{=}C{=}O \\ + \\ CH_2{=}C{=}O \end{array} \rightarrow \begin{array}{c} CH_2{=}C{-}O \\ |\quad\quad| \\ CH_2{-}C{=}O \end{array} \xrightarrow{H_2O} \left[\begin{array}{c} CH_2{=}C{-}OH \\ | \\ CH_2CO_2H \end{array} \right] \rightarrow$$

Diketene
(b.p. 68°/92 mm.)

$$\begin{array}{c} CH_3C{=}O \\ | \\ CH_2CO_2H \end{array}$$

acid chloride of a higher dibasic acid is treated with triethylamine in ether solution, the bifunctional ketene resulting on dehydrohalogenation under-goes similar intramolecular condensation to a product that on hydrolysis and decarboxylation gives a cyclic ketone. Civetone and dl-muscone were

$$\begin{array}{c} CH_2COCl \\ | \\ (CH_2)_{12}CH_2COCl \end{array} \xrightarrow[\text{ether}]{(C_2H_5)_3N,} \left[\begin{array}{c} CH{=}C{=}O \\ | \\ (CH_2)_{12}CH{=}C{=}O \end{array} \right] \rightarrow \left[\begin{array}{c} CH{=}C{-}O \\ |\quad|\quad| \\ (CH_2)_{12}CH{-}C{=}O \end{array} \right] \xrightarrow{KOH}$$

Thapsic acid chloride

$$\left[\begin{array}{c} CH_2{-}C{=}O \\ |\quad\quad| \\ (CH_2)_{12}CHCOOH \end{array} \right] \xrightarrow[14\text{-}20\%]{(-CO_2)} \begin{array}{c} CH_2{-}C{=}O \\ |\quad\quad| \\ (CH_2)_{12}CH_2 \end{array}$$

Exaltone

prepared by this synthesis. The yields are lower than in the Ziegler or Hunsdiecker processes, owing to considerable linear polymerization, but the starting materials are more readily available.

For most preparative purposes all the above methods for the synthesis of macrocyclic compounds are superceded by the acyloin synthesis (Prelog; M. Stoll, 1947), in which a solution of the ester of an α,ω-dicarboxylic acid in hot xylene is stirred vigorously with molten sodium. The acyloin can

$$\begin{array}{c} {-}COOCH_3 \\ (CH_2)_n \\ {-}COOCH_3 \end{array} \xrightarrow{4\,Na} (CH_2)_n \left\| \begin{array}{c} {-}C{-}ONa \\ \\ {-}C{-}ONa \end{array} \right. + 2\,CH_3ONa$$

$$\downarrow H_2O$$

$$\left[(CH_2)_n \left\| \begin{array}{c} {-}C{-}OH \\ \\ {-}C{-}OH \end{array} \right. \right] \rightarrow (CH_2)_n \begin{array}{c} {-}C{=}O \\ | \\ {-}CHOH \end{array}$$

Acyloin

be reduced to the ketone with zinc and hydrochloric acid or by dehydration and hydrogenation of the α,β-unsaturated ketone. The procedure is convenient, particularly since high dilution is not required, and the yields are spectacular (C_{21}-acyloin, 96%).   Even in the region (C_9–C_{13}) of low yield by the Ruzicka and Ziegler procedures, yields of 40% are realized.

Cyclic Ethers. — Macrocyclic compounds of another type have been synthesized, for example, by reaction of hydroquinone with a polymethylene dihalide and cyclization of the half-ether with sodium ethoxide at high dilution (Lüttringhaus,[19] 1937).   The products are called ansa compounds

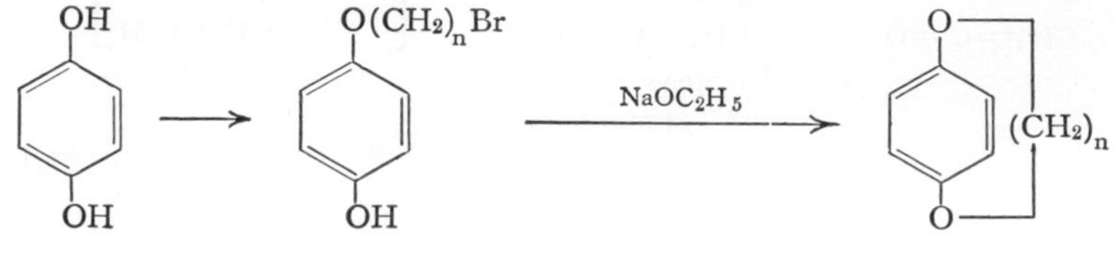

Hydroquinone   Ansa-compound

(L. *ansa*, a handle).   Optical isomerism is possible if the benzene ring in unsymmetrically substituted and the ring not too large.   In the case illustrated ring closure succeeds only if the chain contains eight or more methylene groups.

HYDROXY ACIDS AND LACTONES

Carboxylic acids containing alcoholic hydroxyl groups respond differently to the action of heat or of dehydrating agents depending upon the relative positions of the two functional groups.   The α-hydroxy acid $HOCH_2COOH$, glycolic acid, contains both types of groups required for esterification, and opportunity therefore exists either for formation of an internal ester linkage or for production of a polyester under the influence of an acidic esterification catalyst or of heat.   Actually the substance is convertible into either a polyester formed by condensation polymerization or a cyclic ester formed by esterification occurring between two molecules of the acid.   The cyclic anhydro compound glycolide has a heterocyclic

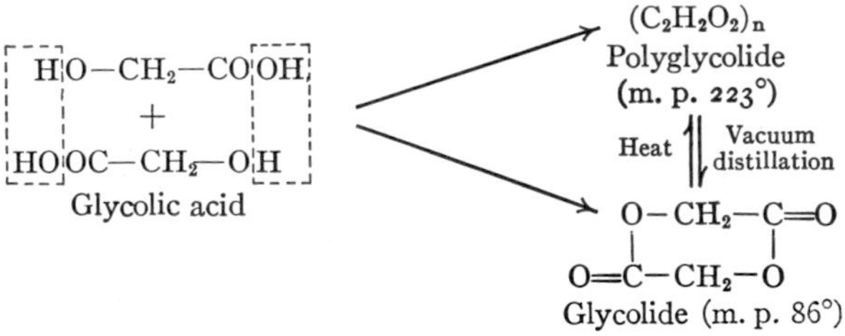

ring of six atoms, which is evidently more easily formed or more stable than the three-membered ring that would result from a monomeric cyclization.

[19] Arthur Lüttringhaus, b. 1906 Cologne-Mülheim; Ph.D. Göttingen (Windaus, Ziegler) Berlin, Greifswald, Halle, Freiburg Br.

Lactic acid yields an analogous ring compound, lactide:

$$\overline{CH_3CHCO \cdot OCH(CH_3)CO \cdot O}$$
dl-Lactide (m.p. 125°)

The behavior is characteristic of α-hydroxy acids in general.

β-Hydroxy acids on similar treatment undergo dehydration to α,β-unsaturated acids. Combination of an activated hydrogen atom in the α-po-

$$\underset{\underset{OH}{|}}{R\overset{\beta}{C}H\overset{\alpha}{C}H_2COOH} \xrightarrow{-H_2O} RCH{=}CHCOOH$$

sition and a hydroxyl group at the adjacent β-position affords so favorable an opportunity for elimination of water with establishment of a double bond that this reaction takes precedence over either polymerization or formation of a four-ring structure by monomeric cyclization or of an eight-ring structure by dimeric cyclization.

Although β-lactones are not formed on dehydration of β-hydroxy acids, they arise in certain condensation reactions of ketene. Thus ketene dimer (p. 321) is a β-lactone. Another example is the analogous condensation of ketene with formaldehyde in the presence of zinc or aluminum chloride.

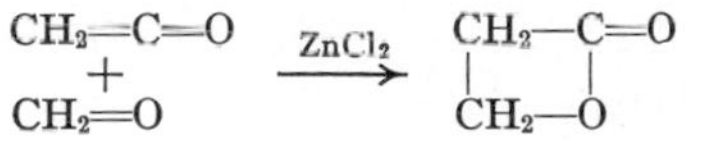

$$\begin{array}{c} CH_2{=}C{=}O \\ + \\ CH_2{=}O \end{array} \xrightarrow{ZnCl_2} \begin{array}{c} CH_2{-}C{=}O \\ | \qquad | \\ CH_2{-}O \end{array}$$

β Propiolactone
(m.p. $-33.4°$, b.p. 51°/10 mm.)

The reaction, which can be conducted on a technical scale, affords β-propiolactone, a highly reactive substance of promise for many syntheses (Gresham, Jansen, 1948). The lactone can be polymerized by acid catalysis to a solid polyester-acid (molecular weight about 1000); this affords ethyl hydracrylate on alcoholysis and acrylic acid on pyrolysis. β-Propiolactone

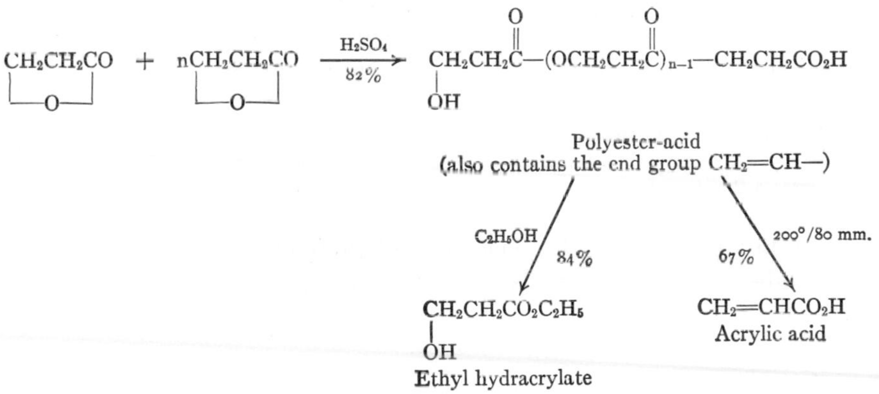

$$\underset{\underset{O}{\rule{0pt}{0pt}}}{CH_2CH_2CO} + n\underset{\underset{O}{\rule{0pt}{0pt}}}{CH_2CH_2CO} \xrightarrow[82\%]{H_2SO_4} \underset{OH}{CH_2CH_2\overset{\overset{O}{\|}}{C}{-}(OCH_2CH_2\overset{\overset{O}{\|}}{C})_{n-1}{-}CH_2CH_2CO_2H}$$

Polyester-acid
(also contains the end group $CH_2{=}CH{-}$)

C_2H_5OH 84%   67%   200°/80 mm.

$$\underset{OH}{CH_2CH_2CO_2C_2H_5} \qquad\qquad \underset{\text{Acrylic acid}}{CH_2{=}CHCO_2H}$$

Ethyl hydracrylate

reacts with aqueous sodium chloride, sodium hydrogen sulfide, and ammonia in acetonitrile solution to give β-substituted propionic acids in high yield. Curiously, the base-catalyzed reaction with methanol opens the lactone ring to form the ester, whereas the product of reaction with methanol without catalyst and the primary product of the acid-catalyzed reaction is

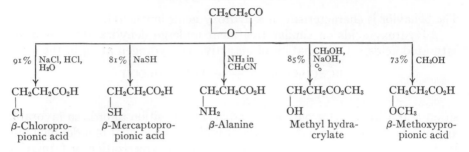

the ether acid, formed by cleavage of the ether rather than of the ester linkage of the lactone.

γ-Hydroxy acids present the possibility for formation of lactones having a favored five-membered ring, and this reaction proceeds with great readiness and predominates over other processes, for example:

$$
\begin{array}{c}
\text{CH}_2\text{CH}_2\text{CH}_2\text{COOH} \\
|\\
\text{OH} \\
\gamma\text{-Hydroxybutyric acid}
\end{array}
\xrightarrow{-\text{H}_2\text{O}}
\begin{array}{c}
\text{CH}_2\text{CH}_2\text{CH}_2\text{CO} \\
\underline{\qquad\text{O}\qquad} \\
\gamma\text{-Butyrolactone} \\
(\text{b.p. } 206°)
\end{array}
$$

Cyclic esters derived from γ-hydroxy acids are γ-lactones. The five-membered ring system is formed with such ease that γ-hydroxy acids are often difficult to isolate in the free state and tend to revert to the γ-lactones on acidification of an alkaline solution of the hydroxy acid unless the temperature is kept low and excess mineral acid is avoided. γ-Lactones are stable, neutral substances, but the lactone ring usually can be opened by the action of warm alkali. Substances of this type are often formed by isomerization of unsaturated acids by heat or by treatment with hydrobromic or sulfuric acid. In the example shown a δ-lactone would also be

$$
\begin{array}{c}
\overset{\delta}{\text{CH}_2}=\overset{\gamma}{\text{CH}}\overset{\beta}{\text{CH}_2}\overset{\alpha}{\text{CH}_2}\text{COOH} \\
\text{Allylacetic acid} \\
(\text{b.p. } 188°)
\end{array}
\xrightarrow{\text{dil. H}_2\text{SO}_4}
\begin{array}{c}
\text{CH}_3\text{CHCH}_2\text{CH}_2\text{CO} \\
\underline{\qquad\text{O}\qquad} \\
\gamma\text{-Valerolactone} \\
(\text{b.p. } 207°)
\end{array}
$$

possible but is not formed. The marked preference for formation of the five-membered γ-lactone ring is further illustrated by the behavior of acids of the sugar series that have hydroxyl groups in the α-, β-, γ-, δ-, and ϵ-positions; these regularly form γ-lactones:

$$
\begin{array}{c}
\overset{\epsilon}{\text{CH}_2}-\overset{\delta}{\text{CH}}-\overset{\gamma}{\text{CH}}-\overset{\beta}{\text{CH}}-\overset{\alpha}{\text{CH}}-\text{CO}\,\text{OH} \\
|\qquad|\qquad|\qquad|\qquad| \\
\text{OH}\quad\text{OH}\quad\text{O}\,\text{H}\quad\text{OH}\quad\text{OH}
\end{array}
\xrightarrow{-\text{H}_2\text{O}}
\begin{array}{c}
\text{CH}_2-\text{CH}-\overset{\gamma}{\text{CH}}-\text{CH}-\text{CH}-\text{CO} \\
|\qquad|\qquad\qquad|\qquad| \\
\text{OH}\quad\text{OH}\qquad\text{OH}\quad\text{OH} \\
\underline{\qquad\text{O}\qquad}
\end{array}
$$

δ-Hydroxy acids sometimes can be converted into the corresponding δ-lactones when no other course of reaction is open, and large-ring lactones are found in nature and can be prepared by persulfuric acid oxidation of the corresponding ketones (p. 302). Both inorganic peracids (Baeyer, 1899) and organic peracids ($C_6H_5CO_3H$; Karrer, 1946) oxidize acyclic ketones to esters, RCOR' → RCOOR', and cyclic ketones to lactones, as illustrated

for oxidation of β-hydrindone to the lactone of o-(hydroxymethyl)-phenyl-acetic acid.

PROBLEMS

1. Cite experimental tests that would distinguish between the following isomers of the formula C_5H_{10}: pentene-2, 1,2-dimethylcyclopropane, and cyclopentane.
2. Explain why optically active muscone yields an optically inactive hydrocarbon on reduction of the carbonyl group to a methylene group.
3. Formulate a synthesis of cis-cyclohexane-1,2-dicarboxylic acid.
4. Addition products are formed in good yield from each of the following pairs of reactants. Write equations for the reactions.

    (a) Piperylene (CH_3CH=CHCH=CH_2) and maleic anhydride.
    (b) 2,3-Dimethylbutadiene-1,3 (p. 54) and crotonic acid (p. 283).
    (c) Butadiene and diethyl acetylenedicarboxylate.

5. Glutaric acid can be prepared in 48% overall yield by a series of reactions starting with the condensation of formaldehyde with diethyl malonate in the presence of diethylamine to $CH_2[CH(COOC_2H_5)_2]_2$. Formulate the process.
6. (a) Explain the formation of malonic acid by the action of water on carbon suboxide.
    (b) What product would you expect to result from treatment of carbon suboxide with ammonia?
7. With the aid of a model, first verify the calculation of the difference in strain energy in cis- and trans-decalin. Then determine whether or not replacement of one bridge-head hydrogen at C_9 in both structures by a methyl group (angular methyl) increases or decreases the energy difference.

READING REFERENCES

W. H. Perkin, "The Early History of the Synthesis of Closed Carbon Chains," *J. Chem. Soc.*, 1347 (1929)

R. C. Fuson, "Alicyclic Compounds and the Theory of Strain," in H. Gilman, "Organic Chemistry," 2nd Ed., I, 65–116, Wiley, New York (1943)

M. C. Kloetzel, "The Diels-Alder Reaction with Maleic Anhydride," *Organic Reactions*, IV, 1 (1948)

L. Ruzicka, "The Many-Membered Carbon Rings," *Chemistry and Industry*, **54**, 2 (1935)

G. M. Bennett, "The Mechanism and Kinetics of Ring-Closure," *Trans. Faraday Soc.*, **37**, 794 (1941)

E. H. Rodd, "The Chemistry of Carbon Compounds," Vol. 2, Chapters I–VIII, by R. A. Raphael, Elsevier (1953)

W. Klyne, "Progress in Stereochemistry," Vol. 1, 36–81, Academic Press (1954)

V. Prelog, "Newer Developments of the Chemistry of Many-membered Ring Compounds," *J. Chem. Soc.*, 420 (1950)

L. E. Craig, "The Chemistry of the Eight-membered Carbocycles," *Chem. Rev.*, **49**, 103 (1951)

CHAPTER 13

REACTION MECHANISMS

Electronic interpretations of reaction mechanisms have been introduced already in this book, but sometimes in necessarily limited form and without presentation of the evidence on which they are based or the history of their development. The present chapter aims to present a unified and more complete survey of the subject as a whole, and it incidentally reviews the concepts already introduced.

In the early days of organic chemistry when this branch was scarcely differentiated from inorganic chemistry the view was frequently expressed that reactions of the carbon compounds differ from those of inorganic molecules in degree rather than kind. However, the slowness and non-quantitative character of organic reactions as compared with those of inorganic electrolytes obscured this point of view and led to the development of empirical rules specifically applicable to reactions that were regarded as essentially nonionic. The conception that the covalent linkage typical of organic compounds has some dipolar character was revived in the beginning of the present century partly as the result of the development of new physical methods for study of atomic and molecular structure. Many organic molecules when placed in an electric field show definite orientation, which must be the result of positive and negative electrical charges in the molecule. If the center of the positive charge is at a position different from that of the negative charge, the molecule possesses a dipole moment, the magnitude of which can be measured with precision (and expressed in Debye units). Methane and carbon tetrachloride, being symmetrical, have no dipole moment, but alkyl halides and alcohols, for example, have dipole moments indicative of a certain degree of polarity. The direction of the moment can be ascertained by an indirect method (p. 566), and in methyl chloride the negative pole lies toward the chlorine atom ($H_3C \overset{+\longrightarrow}{} Cl$), which means that the chlorine atom is more electron-attracting than carbon. The value and direction of the moments associated with groups commonly encountered are shown in Table 13.1. The permanent electron displacement revealed by the dipole moment corresponds to the inductive effect postulated somewhat earlier by G. N. Lewis as responsible for the effect of various substituents on the strength of organic aliphatic acids and bases (p. 164).

In the period 1925–30, Lapworth,[1] Robinson,[2] Ingold,[3] and other chem-

[1] Arthur Lapworth, 1872–1941; b. Galoshiels, Scotland; Ph.D. Birmingham; Manchester; *J. Chem. Soc.*, 989 (1947)

[2] Sir Robert Robinson, b. 1886 Rufford/Chesterfield, England; Ph.D. Manchester (Perkin); Liverpool, Manchester, Oxford; Nobel Prize 1947

TABLE 13.1. DIPOLE MOMENTS OF COVALENT LINKAGES IN SATURATED COMPOUNDS

LINKAGE $\longleftarrow\rightarrow$	MOMENT (DEBYE UNITS)	LINKAGE $\longleftarrow\rightarrow$	MOMENT (DEBYE UNITS)
C—H*	0.4	H—N	1.31
C—N	1.25	H—O	1.51
C—O	1.6	H—S	0.68
C—Cl	2.3	H—Cl	1.08
C—Br	2.2	H—Br	0.78
C—I	2.0	H—I	0.38

* C. A. Coulson, *Trans. Faraday Soc.*, **38**, 433 (1942); in acetylene the direction of the moment is reversed.

ists of the English school applied the idea of inductive effects with some success to interpretation of an array of perplexing facts about aromatic substitutions. Seeing, however, that inductive effects alone did not provide a complete explanation of the facts, Ingold introduced an intuitively conceived second factor termed mesomerism (between the parts). In an unsaturated system such as that of an α,β-unsaturated ketone the relative electronegativity of the oxygen atom induces a partial displacement ($\frown$) of an electron pair from the 3,4-position in the direction of the 2,3-position, as in (a); complete displacement would result in separation of charges to

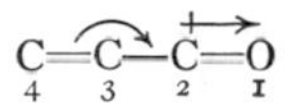

$$\underset{4\quad3\quad2\quad1}{C=C-C=O} \qquad \overset{+}{C}-C=C-\overset{-}{O}$$

(a) 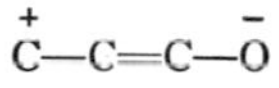   (b)

give the excited form (b). Electronic displacements can originate in a pair of unshared electrons of a hydroxyl group ($-\ddot{O}H$), an amino group ($-\ddot{N}H_2$), or a halogen atom ($-\ddot{C}l:$). Thus the molecule of vinyl chloride is not represented accurately by either the completely covalent formula (c) or the completely ionic structure (e), but rather by the intermediate

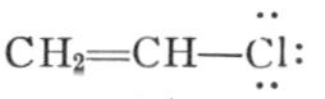

$$CH_2=CH-\ddot{C}l: \qquad \overset{\delta-}{CH_2}=CH-\overset{\delta+}{Cl} \qquad \overset{-}{CH_2}-CH=\overset{+}{Cl}$$

(c) 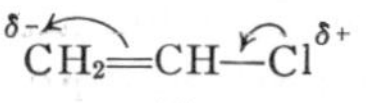   (d) 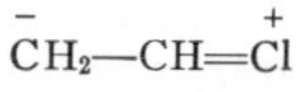   (e)

mesomeric state (d), in which, in consequence of displacement of an electron pair from the chlorine atom, chlorine bears a fractional positive charge ($\delta+$) and the terminal carbon atom a fractional negative charge ($\delta-$).

The idea of an intermediate mesomeric state arrived at intuitively by the English school represented an initial expression of the concept of resonance derived in mathematical form by Pauling[4] (1930–35) by application

[3] Christopher Kelk Ingold, b. 1893 Ilford, England; D.Sc. London (Thorpe); Univ. Coll., London

[4] Linus Pauling, b. 1901 Portland, Oregon; Ph.D. Calif. Inst. Techn.; Calif. Inst. Techn.; Nobel Prize 1954

of the principles of quantum mechanics. The particular contribution of
the resonance concept was in accounting for striking stabilization effects
associated with resonating systems and attributable in exact terms to
resonance energy. Vinyl chloride is described as a resonance hybrid partaking of the character of both form (c) and form (e); it is not a mixture of
the two forms, but a separate entity that combines the properties of the two
forms and possesses resonance stabilization that decreases the reactivity of
the system. That the hybrid partakes in part of the form (e), in which
chlorine is doubly bonded to carbon, is shown by the fact that the C–Cl
bond distance is 0.08 Å shorter in vinyl chloride (1.69 Å) than in ethyl chloride
(1.77 Å). By comparison with dimensions of reference molecules, this bond
shortening is found to correspond to about 14% double-bond character,
and consequently the chlorine is more firmly bound than when attached to a
saturated carbon atom. Although the earlier concept of mesomerism is
less definitive than that of resonance, a formulation such as (d), which
indicates the direction of electronic displacements, affords a convenient
expression of the idea of an intermediate state in a single formulation.

Reaction Types. — Organic reactions can be classified in two types. In
one type (1) the covalent bond is broken in such a way that each of the
resulting fragments contains an odd electron; a reaction proceeding by this
mechanism of homolytic fission is a free-radical reaction. In general, trans-

1.   (Free-radical reaction) $A:B \longrightarrow A\cdot + B\cdot$
2.   (Ionic reaction) $A:B \longrightarrow A:^- + B^+$ or $A^+ + :B^-$

formations induced by radiant energy or by peroxides and pyrolytic decompositions belong to this type.

Reactions of a second type (2) are ionic or electron-sharing reactions
and involve a heterolytic fission of the covalent bond in either of the two
possible directions. Such reactions proceed because an attacking ion or
fragment of the reagent has an inherent affinity for either an electron pair
or an atomic nucleus. A reactant capable of accepting electrons was defined by Ingold as electrophilic, and it may be a cation; one that donates
electrons, for example an anion, is defined as nucleophilic (attracted by a
positive center). Substitutions proceeding by electrophilic (E) and by
nucleophilic (N) attack are defined as S_E and S_N reactions, respectively,
and examples are given in equations 3 and 4. In the S_E chlorination of
benzene (3a) the chlorine atom that becomes chloride ion retains the covalent pair of electrons of the Cl:Cl bond, and the other chlorine atom
functions as an electrophilic fragment and combines with the benzene ring;
the alternate formulation 3b represents the reaction as an attack by a
cation. Hydrolysis of an alkyl halide (4) is a typical S_N reaction. An
electrophilic fragment or a cation attacks an organic molecule at the position of highest electron availability; a nucleophilic fragment or an anion
attacks a position of lowest electron availability.

3. S_E Reaction

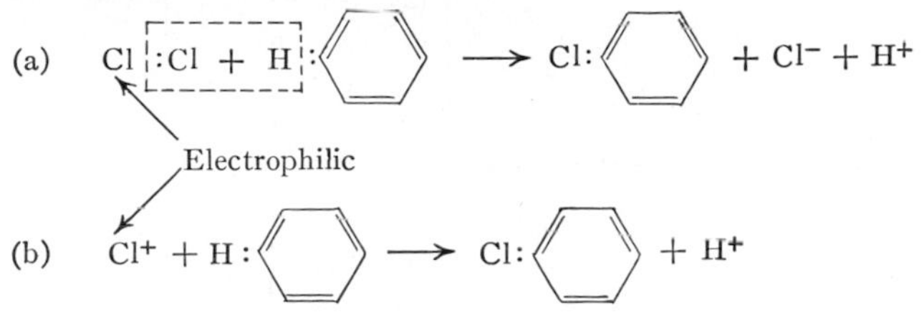

(a) Cl $\vdots$ Cl + H $\vdots$ ⟨benzene ring⟩ ⟶ Cl: ⟨benzene ring⟩ + Cl⁻ + H⁺

Electrophilic

(b) Cl⁺ + H: ⟨benzene ring⟩ ⟶ Cl: ⟨benzene ring⟩ + H⁺

4. S_N Reaction

(a) Na $\vdots$ OH + R $\vdots$ Cl ⟶ R:OH + Na⁺ + Cl⁻

Nucleophilic

(b) OH⁻ + R:Cl ⟶ R:OH + Cl⁻

Application of the newer concepts to the interpretation of organic reactions has led to greater understanding of the empirical rules of classical organic chemistry and in some instances has accounted for previously inexplicable deviations from these rules. On the other hand, the electronic theory of reaction mechanisms is still in a formative stage, and some phenomena are at present explainable only with the aid of supplementary assumptions of unestablished validity. Since some interpretations involve intermediates that are purely hypothetical, opinions often differ regarding the nature of the intermediates. Thus present theory supplements and clarifies factual information but does not take its place, and one should be warned against too great reliance on predictions based upon concepts that are still in process of development.

ADDITION REACTIONS

Alkenes. — Available evidence shows that addition of halogen or of hydrogen halide to an alkene in a polar solvent involves initial attack by an electrophilic fragment or a cation, followed by combination of the resulting positively charged ion with an anion (5). The intermediate ion is probably a resonance hybrid of the carbonium ions (a) and (c) and the bromonium ion (b); form (b) was postulated by Roberts[5] and Kimball (1937). These species sometimes seem to contribute about equally, but specific structural characteristics may lead to predominant contribution by some one structure. Many additions can be interpreted equally well as proceeding through a carbonium or bromonium ion, or a hybrid, but in other instances one intermediate ionic species seems to have dominating importance. Both types of formulation are employed in the following discussion. An early observation that is explainable in terms of a two-step but not a one-step mecha-

---

[5] Irving Roberts, b. 1915, Brooklyn; Ph.D. Columbia; Consultant.

$$
5. \quad >C{=}C< \ + \ \overset{|}{\underset{|}{Br}}{:}Br \ \longrightarrow \
\begin{cases}
(a) \ >\overset{+}{C}\!-\!C<\\
\qquad \overset{|}{Br}\\
\qquad \updownarrow\\
(b) \ >C\!-\!C<\\
\qquad \overset{|}{\underset{}{Br^+}}\\
\qquad \updownarrow\\
(c) \ >C\!-\!\overset{+}{C}<\\
\qquad \overset{|}{Br}
\end{cases}
\xrightarrow{(Br^-)}
\overset{\overset{\textstyle Br}{|}}{>}\!C\!-\!C<\ \ \underset{\underset{\textstyle Br}{|}}{}
$$

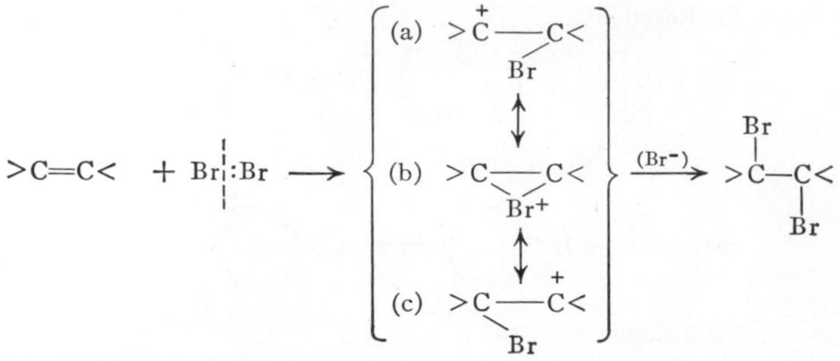

nism is that bromination of ethylene in the presence of sodium chloride or sodium nitrate leads to the formation, in addition to ethylene dibromide, of bromoethyl chloride or nitrate (Francis, 1925). The reaction evidently affords an intermediate cation, which is then capable of combination with any available anion (6).

$$
6. \quad CH_2{=}CH_2 \ + \ Br_2 \ \longrightarrow \ \underset{Br^+}{CH_2\!-\!CH_2} \ + \ Br^- \ \longrightarrow \ \underset{Br\ \ Br}{\overset{|\quad|}{CH_2CH_2}}
$$

$$
Cl^- \longleftarrow \quad \longrightarrow ONO_2^-
$$

$$
\underset{Br\ \ Cl}{\overset{|\quad|}{CH_2CH_2}} \qquad\qquad \underset{Br\ \ ONO_2}{\overset{|\quad|}{CH_2CH_2}}
$$

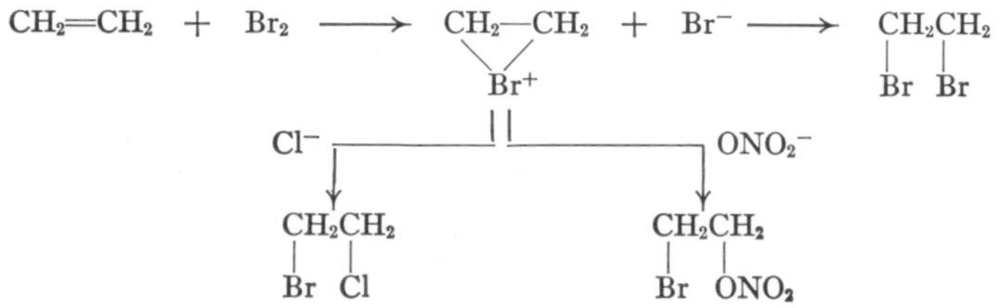

A similar interpretation can be made of the reaction of an alkene with bromine in the presence of water or of an alcohol with formation of a bromohydrin or a bromo ether. The reactions were once regarded as additions of hypobromous acid or of an alkyl hypobromite, formed in the equilibrium process 7. This interpretation has been ruled out by results of a kinetic

$$
7. \qquad\qquad Br_2 + HOH(R) \ \rightleftharpoons \ BrOH(R) + HBr
$$

study of the bromination of stilbene in methanol (Bartlett[6] and Tarbell, 1936), which results in formation of the methoxy bromide 8a in 99% yield. If the reaction involved methyl hypobromite, the rate of formation of the

$$
8. \quad \underset{Stilbene}{C_6H_5CH{=}CHC_6H_5} \ \xrightarrow{Br_2} \ \underset{Br}{\overset{}{C_6H_5CH\overset{+}{C}HC_6H_5}} \ \longrightarrow
\begin{cases}
\overset{CH_3OH}{\nearrow} \underset{Br\ \ OCH_3}{\overset{|\quad|}{C_6H_5CHCHC_6H_5}} \\
\qquad\qquad (a)\\
\\
\underset{Br^-}{\searrow} \underset{Br\ \ Br}{\overset{|\quad|}{C_6H_5CHCHC_6H_5}}\\
\qquad\qquad (b)
\end{cases}
$$

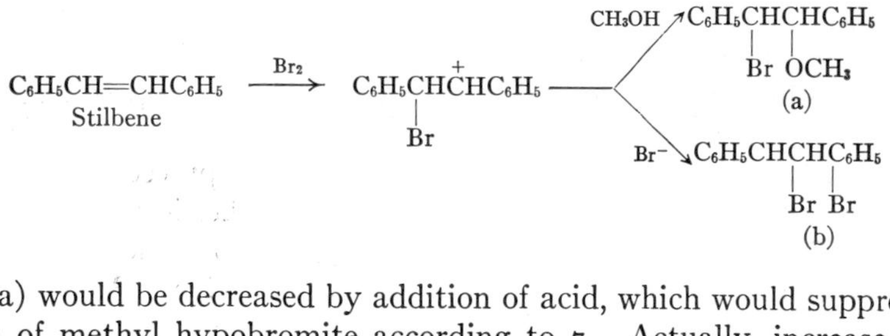

ether (a) would be decreased by addition of acid, which would suppress formation of methyl hypobromite according to 7. Actually, increase in the hydrogen-ion concentration was without effect; on the other hand, formation

[6] Paul D. Bartlett, b. 1907 Ann Arbor, Mich.; Ph.D. Harvard (Conant); Harvard Univ.

of the methoxy bromide was suppressed by added bromide ion. A rational explanation is that the initial product is a carbonium ion that can react with either methanol (a) or with bromide ion (b). From the reaction of bromine

9.

$$
\begin{array}{c}
\underset{|}{CH_3} \quad \underset{|}{CH_3} \\
C\!\!=\!\!C \\
\underset{|}{CO_2^-} \quad \underset{|}{CO_2^-}
\end{array}
\xrightarrow{Br_2}
\left[
\begin{array}{c}
\underset{|}{CH_3} \quad \underset{|}{CH_3} \\
Br\!\!-\!\!C\!\!-\!\!\underset{+}{C}\!\!-\!\!CO_2^- \\
\underset{|}{CO_2^-}
\end{array}
\right]
\longrightarrow
\begin{array}{c}
\underset{|}{CH_3} \quad \underset{|}{CH_3} \\
Br\!\!-\!\!C\!\!-\!\!C\!\!-\!\!CO_2^- \\
O\!\!=\!\!C\!\!-\!\!O
\end{array}
$$

β-Lactone

$\downarrow$ H₂O,H⁺

$$
\begin{array}{c}
\underset{|}{CH_3} \quad \underset{|}{CH_3} \\
Br\!\!-\!\!C\!\!-\!\!C\!\!-\!\!CO_2H \\
HO_2C \qquad OH
\end{array}
$$

Bromohydrin

(with H₂O arrow from the carbonium ion intermediate)

in aqueous solution with the anion of dimethylmaleic acid (9), Tarbell and Bartlett isolated a β-lactone which on hydrolysis yielded the corresponding bromohydrin. The β-lactone was found not to arise from the bromohydrin, and it evidently is formed from an intermediate carbonium ion by intra-molecular attack of the anionic carboxylate group on the electron-deficient carbon atom.

If the addition of bromine to an alkene involves initial attack by a cation, the process would be accelerated by an electron-repelling group attached to the double bond and retarded by an electron-attracting group. Propylene should add bromine more readily than ethylene in consequence of the inductive effect of the methyl group (a). Acrylic acid, on the other

$$
\begin{array}{ccc}
CH_3 \to CH\!\!=\!\!CH_2 & CH_2\!\!=\!\!CH \to CO_2H & CH_2\!\!=\!\!CH \to Br \\
(a) & (b) & (c)
\end{array}
$$

hand, should be relatively unreactive because the carboxyl group attracts electrons (b). Crotonic acid, in which the two effects oppose each other, should be intermediate. These deductions for the most part agree with the experimental data recorded in Table 13.2. The inductive effect of the bromine atom in vinyl bromide renders the double bond very inert (c). The aldehydic group of acrolein would be expected to produce similar de-

TABLE 13.2. RATES OF BROMINATION OF OLEFINIC DOUBLE BONDS

COMPOUND	FORMULA	RELATIVE RATE
Ethylene	$CH_2\!\!=\!\!CH_2$	1
Propylene	$CH_3CH\!\!=\!\!CH_2$	2.0
as-Dimethylethylene	$(CH_3)_2C\!\!=\!\!CH_2$	5.5
Tetramethylethylene	$(CH_3)_2C\!\!=\!\!C(CH_3)_2$	14.0
Styrene	$C_6H_5CH\!\!=\!\!CH_2$	3.2
Acrolein	$CH_2\!\!=\!\!CHCHO$	1.5
Acrylic acid	$CH_2\!\!=\!\!CHCO_2H$	< 0.03
Crotonic acid	$CH_3CH\!\!=\!\!CHCO_2H$	0.26
Vinyl bromide	$CH_2\!\!=\!\!CHBr$	< 0.03

activation, but actually, acrolein adds bromine more readily than ethylene does; explanations of the discrepancy have been advanced but evidence of their validity is lacking.   Judged by the effect on the dissociation of acetic acid, the phenyl group would be classified as electron-attracting, yet the reactivity of styrene toward bromine indicates that the benzene ring in this instance releases electrons (d).   Conjugation of the unsaturated ring with an olefinic linkage can lead to electron displacements in which the ring either releases or attracts electrons, as in formulas (d) and (e), respectively. Thermodynamic data provide evidence for resonance of the double bond with the benzene ring, since styrene has slightly greater resonance energy (40 kg.-cal./mole) than benzene (39.0 kg.-cal./mole); the increase is not

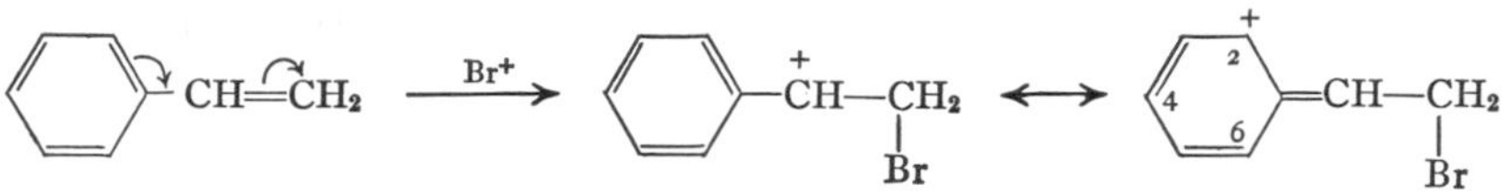

(d)   (also C_4^+ and C_6^+)

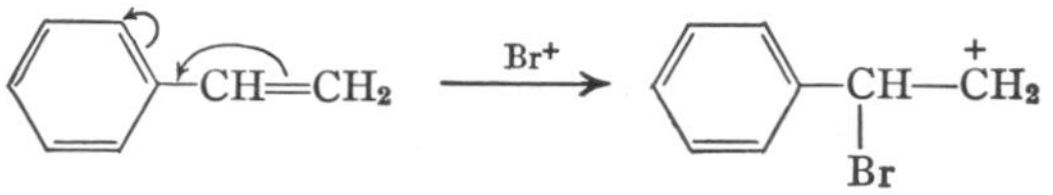

(e)

so great as the resonance energy associated with the conjugation of two aliphatic double bonds (in butadiene: 3.5 kg.-cal./mole).   Either form (d) or form (e) alone would account for the resonance stabilization.   That form (d) exerts a dominating influence on the bromination may be because the carbonium ion derived from it by attack of a bromonium ion carries a positive charge on the carbon atom adjacent to the benzene ring and is stabilized by resonance with structures carrying the positive charge at the 2-, 4-, or 6-position.   The ion from (e) lacks this stabilization.

Hydrogen Halide Addition. — The electronic theory gives a reasonable interpretation of the mode of addition of hydrogen halides to unsymmetrical olefins.   In analogy with halogenation, the initial step is assumed to involve electrophilic attack by a proton and the completing step to be combination of the resulting carbonium ion with halide ion (10).   If one carbon atom is

10. $>C{=}C< + H^+ \longrightarrow >CH{-}\overset{+}{C}< \xrightarrow{X^-} >CH{-}CX<$

negatively polarized with respect to the other it offers a preferential point of attack for the proton.   Thus the mode of addition of hydrogen bromide to propylene (11) can be ascribed to the inductive effect of the methyl group; the electronic displacement initiated by this group is transferred

11. $CH_3{\rightarrow}CH{=}CH_2 \xrightarrow{H^+} CH_3\overset{+}{C}HCH_3 \xrightarrow{Br^-} CH_3CHBrCH_3$

through the double bond to the terminal carbon atom.   The reaction of acrylic acid with hydrogen bromide to give β-bromopropionic acid (12)

12. $CH_2\!\!=\!\!CHC\!\!\underset{O}{\overset{OH}{<}}$ $\xrightarrow{H^+}$ $CH_2\!\!=\!\!CHC\!\!\underset{OH}{\overset{OH}{<}}{}^-$ $\longleftrightarrow$

$\overset{+}{C}H_2\!\!-\!\!CH\!\!=\!\!C\!\!\underset{OH}{\overset{OH}{<}}$ $\xrightarrow{Br^-}$ $BrCH_2CH_2COOH$

can be explained as involving initial attack by a proton. In the addition of iodine chloride to crotonic acid (13) the more positive iodine atom (less electron-attracting, see Table 13.1) becomes attached to the more negatively polarized α-carbon atom.

13. $CH_3\!\!\rightarrow\!\!CH\!\!\overset{\frown}{=}\!\!CH\!\!\rightarrow\!\!CO_2H + \overset{+\ -}{ICl} \xrightarrow[92\%]{} CH_3CHClCHICO_2H$

The addition of hydrogen bromide to vinyl bromide (14) takes a course opposite to that expected on the basis of the strong electron-attracting effect of the bromine atom, to which the slowness of bromine-addition was attributed in the discussion above. In this instance addition seems to be

14. $\overset{\frown}{CH_2}\!\!\overset{\frown}{=}\!\!CH\!\!\overset{\frown}{\rightarrow}\!\!Br \xrightarrow{H^+} CH_3\overset{+}{C}HBr \xrightarrow{Br^-} CH_3CHBr_2$

controlled by a shift of an electron pair from bromine in the direction opposite to that of the inductive effect. Neither inductive nor resonance polarization effects are necessarily permanent, and there is some variation with the polarity of the reagent or of the solvent; in view of such complications predictions are particularly difficult where two effects operate in opposite directions. In allyl bromide (15) an electron displacement, simi-

15. $CH_2\!\!\overset{\frown}{=}\!\!CH\!\!\overset{\frown}{-}CH_2\!\!\rightarrow\!\!Br \xrightarrow{HBr} CH_3CHBrCH_2Br$
(not $BrCH_2CH_2CH_2Br$)

lar to (14), initiated by the unshared electrons of bromine is not possible because of the absence of a double bond capable of transmitting the effect, and the inductive effect would be expected to control the mode of addition. The product, however, is not the expected 1,3-dibromopropane but 1,2-dibromopropane. The phenomenon may be due to a rather special type of electron displacement (16) originally postulated by Baker[7] and Nathan

16. $\underset{\alpha}{\overset{\frown}{CH_2}}\!\!\overset{\frown}{=}\!\!\underset{\beta}{CH}\!\!\overset{\overset{H}{|}}{\underset{\underset{H}{|}}{\overset{\gamma}{C}}}\!\!\rightarrow\!\!Br \xrightarrow{\overset{+\ -}{HBr}} CH_3CHCH_2Br \atop \quad\quad\quad\quad\ \ \underset{Br}{|}$

(1935) and known as hyperconjugation. The postulate is that electrons of each γ-CH bond in turn participate in displacements in the same way that unshared electrons associated with oxygen, nitrogen, or halogen participate, but to a lesser extent; the displacement shown in the formulation (16) is

---

[7] John W. Baker, b. 1898 London; Ph.D. London (Ingold); D.Sc. London; Leeds

supplemented by one involving the alternate hydrogen atom. Hyperconjugation is presumed to be responsible for a slight shortening of the carbon–
carbon bond in acetaldehyde in comparison with that of ethane. According to physical measurements the C–C link in acetaldehyde has about 9%
double-bond character, possibly owing to a slight contribution of the polar
structure (b) and of the two like structures involving the other two γ-CH

$$H-\underset{\underset{\text{H \ H}}{|\gamma \quad |\beta \quad \alpha}}{C-C=O} \qquad\qquad H-\underset{\underset{\text{H \ H}}{|\quad |}}{C=C-O^-}$$

$$\text{(a)} \qquad\qquad\qquad \text{(b)}$$

links of (a). Hyperconjugation is also known as no-bond resonance. The
latter term refers to the structure represented in formulation (b); this representation is not intended to imply the complete separation of a proton, for
the charged particle must remain within bonding distance of the carbon
atom. A structure such as (b), which makes a minor contribution to the
resonance hybrid, is defined by Pauling as an excited structure of the molecule; the principal contributions to the ground state are made by the un-
excited structures.

In the addition of a hydrogen halide to a symmetrical diene the electron
displacements, shown in 17 for one of the two identical structures, cause the
initial proton uptake to occur at one of the terminal atoms. The resulting
carbonium ion is a resonance hybrid (a ↔ b), and the proportion of 1,2- and
1,4-addition products formed on combination with halide ion is dependent
upon the relative rates of reactions leading from the hybrid to the products.

17. $CH_2{=}CH-CH{=}CH_2 \xrightarrow{\ H^+\ } \overset{+}{C}H_2{=}CHCHCH_3 \longleftrightarrow \overset{+}{C}H_2CH{=}CHCH_3$

(a:1,2-addition)   (b:1,4-addition)

Thus addition of hydrogen chloride to butadiene under various experimental conditions gives mixtures of two products in which crotyl chloride,
the product of 1,4-addition, invariably predominates, even though it is

18. $CH_2{=}CHCH{=}CH_2 \xrightarrow[\text{HCl}]{}$
$\overset{\text{75-80\%}}{\nearrow} CH_3CH{=}CHCH_2Cl$ (1,4-addition)
Crotyl chloride

$\underset{\text{20-25\%}}{\searrow} CH_2{=}CHCHClCH_3$ (1,2-addition)
α-Methylallyl chloride

thermodynamically less stable than α-methylallyl chloride and can be converted by prolonged treatment with hydrogen chloride into an equlibrium
mixture containing 80% of α-methylallyl chloride. The complete absence
of the third possible product, 4-chlorobutene-1, conforms to the prediction
that neither nonterminal carbon atom can become a center of negative
polarity. In an unsymmetrical diene the point of initial attack is again one
of the terminal carbon atoms, but the choice is determined by the polarity
of substituent groups. Typical examples are shown in formulations 19 to 21;

the starred carbon atoms represent the point of attack by the proton. That reaction 21 gives exclusively the 1,2-addition product probably is because this isomer retains the double bond conjugated with the ring.

19. $\overset{\bullet}{CH_2}=CCH=CH_2 \xrightarrow{HCl} CH_3C=CHCH_2Cl$
$\qquad\quad |\qquad\qquad\qquad\qquad\quad |$
$\qquad\quad CH_3 \qquad\qquad\qquad\quad CH_3$
$\qquad\qquad\qquad\qquad\qquad\text{(1,4-addition)}$

20. $\overset{\bullet}{CH}=CHCH=\overset{\bullet}{CH} \xrightarrow{HBr} CH_2CHBrCH=CH + CH_2CH=CHCHBr$
$\quad\ |\qquad\qquad |\qquad\qquad\qquad |\qquad\qquad |\qquad\quad |\qquad\qquad |$
$\quad\ CH_3 \qquad\quad CH_3 \qquad\qquad CH_3 \qquad\quad CH_3 \quad CH_3 \qquad\quad CH_3$
$\qquad\qquad\qquad\qquad\qquad\qquad\quad 90\% \qquad\qquad\qquad\qquad\quad 10\%$
$\qquad\qquad\qquad\qquad\qquad\text{(1,2-addition)} \qquad\qquad\qquad \text{(1,4-addition)}$

21. $CH=CH-CH=CH_2 \xrightarrow{HCl} CH=CHCHClCH_3$
$\quad |\qquad\qquad\qquad\qquad\qquad\qquad\quad |$
$\quad C_6H_5 \qquad\qquad\qquad\qquad\qquad C_6H_5$
$\qquad\qquad\qquad\qquad\qquad\text{(1,2-addition)}$

Steric Course. — The ion $(CH_3)_3C^+$ is almost certainly planar, since it is identical in electronic structure with $(CH_3)_3B$, which is known from physical measurements to be planar, and the special reactivity of t-alkyl icompounds undoubtedly is associated with ability to assume coplanarity in the ionic state. Bartlett synthesized a substance (triptycene, p. 760) of three-dimensional structure such that formation of a coplanar ion is impossible, and derivatives of the substance were found to lack the reactivity of analogous t-alkyl compounds that can form coplanar ions. Hence if addition of bromine to a *cis* or *trans* ethylene is assumed to involve a carbonium ion intermediate, the invariable rule of *trans* addition (p. 287) may be because an α-bromo substituted carbonium ion is formed and presents a planar area at the site of the positive charge to which the bromide ion approaches from the side not shielded by the α-bromo atom. However, one instance can be cited where the carbonium ion postulate leads to an erroneous conclusion (p. 966), and present evidence favors the alternate concept of a bromonium ion intermediate (5b). According to this concept, bromination is essentially an attack by Br^+ at both unsaturated centers to form a transient ion of rigid three-membered ring structure comparable to that of an ethylene oxide, which then is attacked by Br^- on the only accessible side opposite to that occupied by the ring; as in an oxide fission (p. 288), inversion occurs at the point of backside attack.

Hydrogen halides add *trans*, at least to acetylenes (p. 287), and elimination of HX follows the *trans* course. A proton has no unshared electrons available for formation of a rigid ring structure comparable to a bromonium ion, and explanations of the phenomena are still speculative.

Carbonyl Additions. — Additions to the carbonyl group present fundamental differences from additions to the olefinic double bond; most reagents that add to aldehydes and ketones do not react with alkenes, and *vice versa*. Addition of hydrogen cyanide or sodium bisulfite to a carbonyl compound occurs in such a way that the proton adds to oxygen and the anionic portion to carbon. The mode of addition is that expected, since the carbonyl group has a dipole moment corresponding to partial negative polarization of oxygen; the carbon atom is deficient in electrons and therefore susceptible to nucleophilic attack. Since the electron-rich oxygen atom can accommodate a negative charge more readily than carbon can accommodate a positive charge, the initial step in the formation of a cyanohydrin must consist in nucleophilic attack (22). The reaction is markedly catalyzed by base, which increases the amount of available cyanide ion.

$$22. \quad >C{=}O + CN^- \rightleftharpoons >\underset{\underset{CN}{|}}{C}{-}O^- \overset{H^+}{\rightleftharpoons} >\underset{\underset{CN}{|}}{C}{-}OH$$

The rate of the base-catalyzed aldol condensation of acetaldehyde is dependent upon the concentrations of hydroxide ion and aldehyde (second-order reaction, or one involving two reacting species), and the rate-controlling step is therefore removal of a proton from the aldehyde (23) to yield an anion (enolate ion), which undergoes more rapid reaction with a second molecule of acetaldehyde (24). If the carbonyl component is less

$$23. \quad CH_3CHO + OH^- \rightleftharpoons H_2O + \overset{-}{C}H_2CHO \longleftrightarrow CH_2{=}CH{-}O^-$$

$$24. \quad CH_3CHO + \overset{-}{C}H_2CHO \rightleftharpoons CH_3\underset{\underset{O^-}{|}}{C}HCH_2CHO \overset{H^+}{\rightleftharpoons} CH_3\underset{\underset{OH}{|}}{C}HCH_2CHO$$

reactive to anionic attack, as in the case of acetone, the rate-controlling step is the condensation reaction (24). The condensation of carbonyl compounds with amines may involve attack by a similarly formed ion $(OH^- + RNH_2 \rightarrow H_2O + R\overset{-}{N}H)$, as formulated earlier for the reaction with hydroxylamine (p. 212), or it may involve nucleophilic attack by a reactant molecule. Thus condensation with semicarbazide is catalyzed by acids but not by bases and hence is formulated by Hammett[8] as in 25.

$$25. \quad >C{=}O \overset{H^+}{\longrightarrow} >\overset{+}{C}{-}OH \xrightarrow{H_2NNHCONH_2} >C\overset{\overset{+}{NH_2NHCONH_2}}{\underset{OH}{<}} \xrightarrow{-H^+}$$

$$>C\overset{NHNHCONH_2}{\underset{OH}{<}} \xrightarrow{-H_2O} >C{=}NNHCONH_2$$

The addition of hydrocyanic acid to ethyl crotonate (26), which takes place when the ester is treated with alcoholic potassium cyanide, is undoubtedly initiated by a nucleophilic attack on the polarized olefinic double bond.

$$26 \quad CH_3CH{=}CH{-}C\overset{O}{\underset{OR}{<}} \xrightarrow{CN^-} CH_3\underset{\underset{CN}{|}}{C}H{-}\overset{-}{C}HCOOR \xrightarrow{H^+} CH_3\underset{\underset{CN}{|}}{C}HCH_2COOR$$

[8] Louis P. Hammett, b. 1894 Wilmington, Del.; Ph.D. Columbia (Beans); Univ. Columbia

DISPLACEMENT REACTIONS (SUBSTITUTIONS)

S$_N$I and S$_N$2 Mechanisms. — The first detailed kinetic studies of substitution reactions at a saturated carbon atom were carried out by Ingold and Hughes[9] and have been presented in a series of more than thirty papers (1933–46). Either electrophilic or nucleophilic reagents can effect displacements, but the former are apparently fairly complex; hence the following discussion is limited to the nucleophilic type, exemplified by hydrolysis of alkyl halides (27) and by formation of alkylammonium salts from tertiary amines and alkyl halides (28). In a study of rates of hydrolysis in 80% aqueous ethanol at 55° of methyl bromide and of halides

27. $$HO^- + R{:}Br \longrightarrow HOR + Br^-$$

28. $$R_3N{:} + R{:}Br \longrightarrow R_3\overset{+}{N}R + Br^-$$

derived from it by α-substitution of methyl groups (Table 13.3), Ingold and Hughes observed that hydrolysis of methyl bromide is predominantly a second-order reaction, dependent upon the concentration of halide and of hydroxide ion; a concurrent reaction of first-order kinetics occurs to only a minor extent ($k_1 = 0.349 \times 10^{-5}$). The rate decreases with the α-substitution of one and two methyl groups and passes through a minimum in the case of isopropyl bromide, where both first- and second-order kinetics obtain, though the latter still predominates. The rate rises sharply with introduction of a third methyl group (t-butyl bromide) and is independent of hydroxyde ion, the kinetics being of first order.

TABLE 13.3.   RATE OF HYDROLYSIS OF ALKYL BROMIDES

ALKYL BROMIDE	FIRST-ORDER REACTION CONSTANT, $k_1 \times 10^5$ UNITS: SEC.$^{-1}$	SECOND-ORDER REACTION CONSTANT, $k_2 \times 10^5$ UNITS: SEC.$^{-1}$ (G. MOL./L.)$^{-1}$
CH_3Br	0.349	2140
CH_3CH_2Br	0.139	171
$(CH_3)_2CHBr$	0.237	4.75
$(CH_3)_3CBr$	1010	....

Two distinct reactions are involved, one unimolecular and the other bimolecular, and they are regarded as proceeding by two distinctly different mechanisms identified by the designations S$_N$I and S$_N$2 (S = substitution). The bimolecular reaction (S$_N$2) is envisioned as a one-step process involving the synchronous approach of a hydroxide ion and the dissociation of a

29.   S$_N$2 Mechanism:

$$HO^{-e} + H_3C-Br \longrightarrow \left[\begin{array}{c} H \quad\;\; H \\ {\sim}{-e/2}\backslash \;\; /{\sim}{-e/2} \\ HO\cdots C\cdots Br \\ | \\ H \end{array} \right] \longrightarrow HO-CH_3 + Br^{-e}$$

Transition state

---

[9] Edward David Hughes, b. 1906 Caernarvonshire, North Wales; Ph.D. Wales (Watson); D.Sc. London (Ingold); University Coll., London

bromide ion, with intermediate formation of a transition state in which five groups or atoms are bound to the carbon atom undergoing substitution, three by covalent bonds and two by fractionally ionic bonds. The unimolecular reaction (S_N1) is considered to involve a two-step process in which the rate-determining step is ionization of the halide to form a carbonium ion, which combines rapidly with an anionoid reagent. An early objection to this proposal was that ionization would require high activation energy; however solvation effects can play an important role in ionic dis-

30. S_N1 Mechanism:
             $(CH_3)_3C—Cl \rightleftharpoons (CH_3)_3C^+ + Cl^-$ (slow)
             $(CH_3)_3C^+ + H_2O \longrightarrow (CH_3)_3C—OH + H^+$ (fast)

sociation, and indeed unimolecular substitutions are accelerated by strongly ionizing solvents, whereas bimolecular substitutions are somewhat retarded. Furthermore, S_N1 reactions of significant reaction rate occur only when some special feature of structure, for example that in a tertiary alkyl halide, contributes to the surmounting of the energy barrier required for initial ionization.

Evidence supporting the dual mechanism is found in the effect of various groups attached to the reaction center. In the series of alkyl bromides listed in Table 13.3 the successive replacement of the hydrogen atoms of methyl bromide by electron-releasing methyl groups should inhibit approach of the nucleophilic hydroxyl group and therefore replacement by the S_N2 mechanism (31); an increased number of alkyl groups would also lead to congestion of groups in the transition state and hence to decreasing rate.

31. $CH_3{\rightarrow}Br$ $CH_3{\rightarrow}CH_2{—}Br$ $\overset{CH_3}{\underset{CH_3}{\diagup}}CH{—}Br$ $CH_3{\rightarrow}\overset{CH_3}{\underset{CH_3}{\overset{\downarrow}{\underset{\uparrow}{C}}}}{—}Br$

$\xrightarrow{\hspace{3cm}}$
Increasing inductive effect

The increased inductive effect should facilitate transfer of electrons to the bromine atom and consequently increase the rate of ionization by the S_N1 reaction. Electron-attracting groups, for example a carbomethoxyl group, inhibit the S_N1 but facilitate the S_N2 mechanism. Unimolecular substitution has not been observed in a vinyl halide; the inductive effect of the bromine atom would favor ionization but is opposed by the electron displacement mentioned above (formulation 14). Allyl halides exhibit high reactivity in nucleophilic substitutions of both S_N1 and S_N2 types, according to the conditions; the participating species may be related to those formulated above (15, 16).

The polarity of the group that is being replaced may influence unimolecular substitution more than bimolecular substitution. Displacement of the strongly electron-attracting sulfonium group by bromine (32) is a first-order reaction, in contrast with the bimolecular displacement of chlorine by bromine at a similar carbon atom (33).

32. (S_N1) $C_2H_5\overset{+}{S}(C_2H_5)_2 + Br^- \longrightarrow C_2H_5Br + S(C_2H_5)_2$
33. (S_N2) $C_2H_5Cl + Br^- \longrightarrow C_2H_5Br + Cl^-$

The effect of β-methyl substitution on the bimolecular alkaline hydrolysis of alkyl halides is shown in Table 13.4 (second column). The rate relation-

TABLE 13.4. RATE OF ALKALINE HYDROLYSIS OF ALKYL HALIDES

HALIDE (PRIMARY)	SECOND ORDER,[a] $k_2 \times 10^3$	FIRST ORDER,[b] RELATIVE CONSTANT	HALIDE (TERTIARY)	FIRST ORDER,[c] $k_1 \times 10^5$
CH_3CH_2Br	1.97	1	$(CH_3)_3CCl$	0.854
$CH_3CH_2CH_2Br$	0.547	0.69	$CH_3CH_2 \diagdown$ CCl $(CH_3)_2 \diagup$	1.50
$(CH_3)_2CHCH_2Br$	0.058			
$(CH_3)_3CCH_2Br$	No reaction [d]	0.57	$(CH_3CH_2)_2 \diagdown$ CCl $(CH_3)_3C \diagup$	11.7

[a] Reaction with sodium ethoxide in absolute ethanol (55°).
[b] Reaction in aqueous alcohol (no alkali).
[c] Reaction in 80% aqueous ethanol at 25°.
[d] A slow reaction occurs at 95° ($k_2 \times 10^7 = 5.0$).

ships for the first three members accord with expectations from the electron-releasing effect of a β-methyl group, which should decrease the S$_N$2 reaction rate but less than an α-methyl substituent does. The last member of the series of primary halides, neopentyl bromide, is singularly inert to alkali, and the effect is much greater than expected from the additional substitution of a methyl group. In aqueous alcoholic solution (third column), however, neopentyl bromide undergoes ready unimolecular hydrolysis and is only slightly less reactive than ethyl and n-propyl bromide. In the tertiary series substitition of β-methyl groups actually increases the first-order reaction constant (last column).

The only reasonable explanation of the lack of reactivity of neopentyl halides (first observed by Whitmore,[10] 1933) in bimolecular but not in uni-molecular reactions is that a steric factor prevents necessary attack by the nucleophilic reagent. The bimolecular reaction involves formation of a transition complex, the most stable state of which is known from quantum mechanical considerations to have the configuration shown in Fig. 13.1.

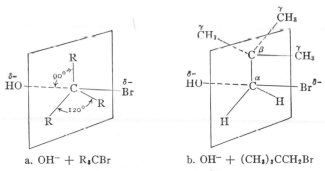

a. OH$^-$ + R$_3$CBr   b. OH$^-$ + (CH$_3$)$_3$CCH$_2$Br

FIG. 13.1. — Transition State

[10] Frank C. Whitmore, 1887–1947; b. North Attleboro, Mass.; Ph.D. Harvard (Jackson); Penn. State College; *J. Chem. Soc.*, 1090 (1948)

In the most stable state of the complex from a trialkylmethyl bromide the attacking group (OH⁻), the carbon atom at which substitution takes place, and the displaced group (Br⁻) are in linear orientation; and the covalently attached alkyl groups lie in a plane perpendicular to the line of OH⁻ and Br⁻. If the β-carbon atom of one of the alkyl groups carries a single γ-methyl substituent, this can exert practically no steric effect because of free rotation about the single bond. In the case of neopentyl bromide, however, the presence of three γ-methyl groups does not allow the stable linear arrangement of the HO····C····Br grouping.

Steric Course. — The structure of the transition state also has a bearing on the steric course of substitition at an asymmetric carbon atom. As shown in Fig. 13.1, the entering group becomes attached to carbon at the side opposite to that occupied by the expelled group, and hence in bimolecular substitition complete inversion of configuration would be expected. A unimolecular displacement (S_N1) proceeds through an intermediate carbonium ion, the most stable configuration of which is planar (see above), and hence the reaction should give racemic products. In some instances configuration is retained, possibly because the carbonium ion is short-lived or because other factors intervene to preserve the pyramidal configuration.

Racemization, retention, and inversion of configuration have all been observed experimentally and the results correlated with the mode of substitution. The results generally accord well with expectations. Among the examples listed in Table 13.5, all the S_N2 reactions result in complete

TABLE 13.5. RELATION OF MECHANISM OF SUBSTITUTION TO OPTICAL EFFECTS

HALIDE	REAGENT	MECHANISM	EFFECT ON CONFIGURATION [a]
n-C_6H_{13}CHBr │ CH_3	HO⁻ H_2O	S_N2 S_N1	I (96%) I (66%) + Ra
C_6H_5CHCl │ CH_3	H_2O CH_3O^- CH_3OH	S_N1 S_N2 S_N1	Ra + I (2–17%) I Ra + I (low)
CH_3CHBr │ CO_2H	H_2O	S_N2	I (100%)
CH_3CHBr │ CO_2CH_3	CH_3O^-	S_N2	I (100%)
CH_3CHBr │ CO_2^-	HO⁻ H_2O CH_3OH	S_N2 S_N1 S_N1	I (80–100%) Re (80–100%) Re (90–100%)
CH_3CHOH │ CH_3CHBr	HBr	S_N1	Re (80–90%)

[a] I = Inversion; Ra = Racemization; Re = Retention

or nearly complete inversion; the S_N1 reactions of the first two compounds listed proceed with racemization or incomplete inversion. In the case of

α-bromopropionic acid (or its ester) the inductive effect of the electron-at-tracting carboxyl group completely inhibits the S_N1 mechanism and facili-tates S_N2 substitution, which proceeds with quantitative inversion. Alka-line hydrolysis (HO^-) of α-bromopropionate ion also follows the S_N2 course with inversion, but both hydrolysis and alcoholysis of this ion effected under nonalkaline conditions (H_2O or CH_3OH) proceed by the S_N1 mechanism with practically complete retention of configuration. Ingold's explanation for retention in the unimolecular reaction is that the intermediate ion is a betaine (34a), in which electrostatic forces lead to retention of a pyramidal shape; the hydroxyl group then enters the position vacated by bromine. Alternately (Winstein[11]), the intermediate may be the α-lactone (b), formed directly from α-bromopropionate ion through back-side attack by the car-boxylate ion at the adjacent carbon center, with inversion and with expul-sion of bromide ion; cleavage of the oxide ring then proceeds with a second inversion that restores the original configuration. Retention of configura-tion has also been observed (Winstein) when the adjacent carbon atom bears

34.

$$
\begin{array}{c}
\bar{O}-C{=}O \\
|\ \ \ \ \ | \\
CH_3-C-Br \\
|\ \ \ \ \ \\
H
\end{array}
\xrightarrow{-Br^-}
\left[
\begin{array}{c}
\ \ \ \ C{=}O \\
\bar{O}\nearrow\ | \\
CH_3-C^+ \\
|\ \ \ \ \\
H \\
\text{(a)}
\end{array}
\quad or \quad
\begin{array}{c}
\ \ \ \ \ C{=}O \\
O\!\!<\!\!| \\
CH_3-C \\
|\ \ \ \ \\
H \\
\text{(b)}
\end{array}
\right]
\xrightarrow[-H^+]{H_2O}
\begin{array}{c}
\bar{O}-C{=}O \\
|\ \ \ \ \ | \\
CH_3-C-OH \\
|\ \ \ \ \\
H
\end{array}
$$

an atom with an unshared pair of electrons, as in the last example cited in Table 13.5. The reaction in this case (35) involves S_N1 replacement of the hydroxyl group of an alcohol by bromine at an asymmetric center vicinal to a carbon atom bearing a bromo substituent. Expulsion of the hydroxyl group proceeds by addition of a proton to oxygen and loss of water from the oxonium ion. Retention of configuration is attributed by Winstein to an intramolecular nucleophilic attack resulting in formation of an intermediate bromonium ion (35). According to this mechanism inversion at C_1 occurs

35.

$$
\begin{array}{c}
H\ \ \ \ \ CH_3 \\
\diagdown C{-}OH \\
Br{-}C \diagup \\
\diagup\ \ \diagdown \\
CH_3\ \ \ H
\end{array}
\xrightarrow{H^+}
\begin{array}{c}
H\ \ \ \ \ CH_3 \\
\diagdown \overset{+}{C}{-}OH \\
\ \ \ \ \ \ \ |\ \ H \\
Br{-}C \\
\diagup\ \ \diagdown \\
CH_3\ \ \ H
\end{array}
\xrightarrow{-H_2O}
\left[
\begin{array}{c}
H\ \ \ \ \ CH_3 \\
\diagdown C \\
Br\!\!<\!| \\
C \\
\diagup\ \ \diagdown \\
CH_3\ \ \ H
\end{array}
\right]
\xrightarrow{Br^-}
\begin{array}{c}
H\ \ \ \ \ CH_3 \\
\diagdown C{-}Br \\
Br{-}C \\
\diagup\ \ \diagdown \\
CH_3\ \ \ H
\end{array}
$$

Oxonium ion

in formation of the three-membered ring and again in its fission, with the net result that absolute configuration is retained.

In replacement of hydroxyl by chlorine, retention of configuration is often observed when thionyl chloride is used to effect substitution, whereas phosphorus halides usually cause inversion. Hughes and Ingold consider that in either case the first step consists in formation of an ester, and some esters actually have been isolated. The ester derived from thionyl chloride (36) is nonlinear and of such a structure as to permit operation of a mecha-

[11] Saul Winstein, b. 1912 Montreal; Ph.D. Calif. Inst. Techn. (Lucas); Univ. Calif. Los Angeles

nism (a), defined as internal substitution (S_Ni), in which an electron pair from the chlorine atom is received at the carbon center simultaneously with release of the electron pair to oxygen; in this way chlorine occupies the place vacated by oxygen and configuration is retained. Alternately, the

36.

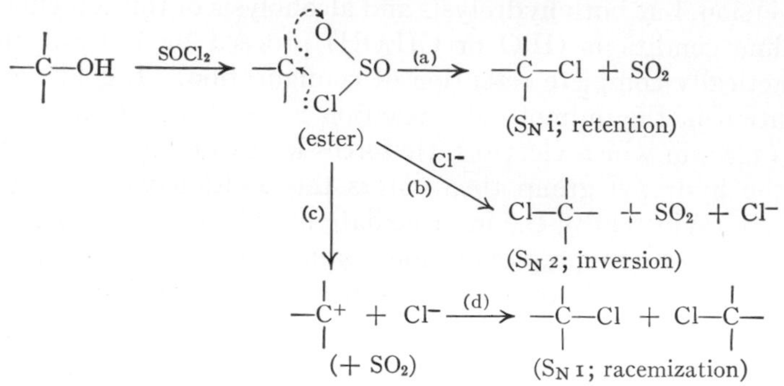

$$-\overset{|}{\underset{|}{C}}-OH \xrightarrow{SOCl_2} -\overset{|}{\underset{|}{C}} \overset{O}{\underset{:Cl}{\diagdown}} SO \xrightarrow{(a)} -\overset{|}{\underset{|}{C}}-Cl + SO_2$$

(ester)

($S_N i$; retention)

$$\xrightarrow[(b)]{Cl^-} Cl-\overset{|}{\underset{|}{C}}- + SO_2 + Cl^-$$

($S_N 2$; inversion)

(c)

$$-\overset{|}{\underset{|}{C}}{}^+ + Cl^- \xrightarrow{(d)} -\overset{|}{\underset{|}{C}}-Cl + Cl-\overset{|}{\underset{|}{C}}-$$

(+ SO$_2$)   ($S_N I$; racemization)

ester group can be displaced by chloride ion (b) in an S_N2 reaction (inversion), or ionization (c) can lead to an $S_N I$ displacement (d, racemization). The esters derived from the phosphorus halides, for example $R_3C-O-PCl_2$, undergo the ionic reactions (b) and (c) with particular facility, and inversion or racemization is commonly observed. A mechanism analogous to internal substitution has been proposed for certain special replacements of hydroxyl by halogen by means of hydrogen halides in which configuration is retained; the primary intermediate is assumed to be a hydrogen-bonded complex (37a). The more usual reactions of alcohols with halogen acids probably proceed through initial addition of a proton to oxygen (37b).

37.

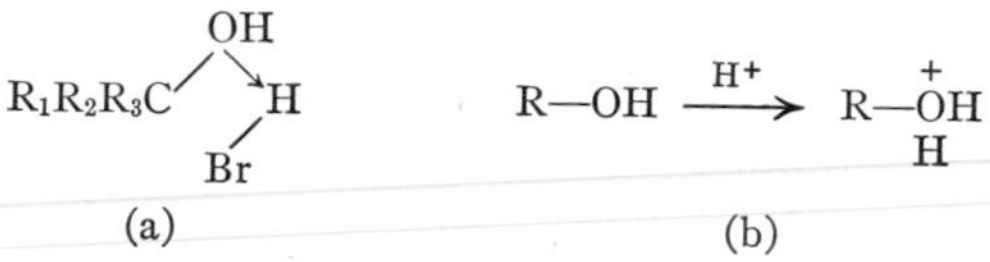

$$R_1R_2R_3C\overset{OH}{\underset{Br}{\diagup}}{}^{\diagdown}H \qquad\qquad R-OH \xrightarrow{H^+} R-\overset{+}{\underset{H}{O}}H$$

(a)   (b)

Rearrangements. — Rearrangements frequently occur during substitution reactions. Whereas the reaction of neopentyl bromide (38a) with ethoxide ion results in formation of the normal product, neopentyl ethyl ether (b, second-order kinetics), reaction with aqueous ethanol leads to

38.

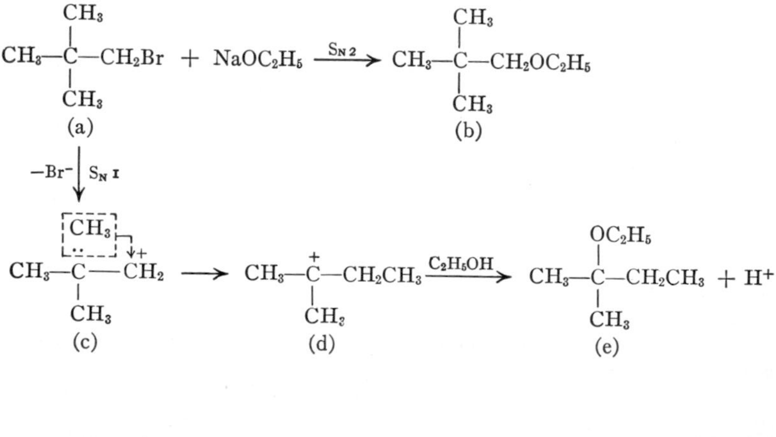

$$CH_3-\overset{CH_3}{\underset{CH_3}{\overset{|}{C}}}-CH_2Br + NaOC_2H_5 \xrightarrow{S_N2} CH_3-\overset{CH_3}{\underset{CH_3}{\overset{|}{C}}}-CH_2OC_2H_5$$

(a)   (b)

$$\downarrow{\scriptstyle -Br^-}\; S_N I$$

$$CH_3-\overset{\overline{CH_3}}{\underset{CH_3}{\overset{|}{C}}}\!\!-\!\!CH_2 \longrightarrow CH_3-\overset{+}{\underset{CH_2}{\overset{|}{C}}}-CH_2CH_3 \xrightarrow{C_2H_5OH} CH_3-\overset{OC_2H_5}{\underset{CH_3}{\overset{|}{C}}}-CH_2CH_3 + H^+$$

(c)   (d)   (e)

formation of t-amyl ethyl ether (e) and must involve rearrangement. The kinetics are first order. The first step is considered to be formation of the carbonium ion (c), followed by migration of one of the adjacent methyl groups with its pair of electrons, with transference of the charge from the α- to the β-position (d). The neopentyl-t-amyl rearrangement is analogous to the Wagner-Meerwein rearrangement (p. 126).

Rearrangements are particulary common in allylic systems, such as those shown in formulation 39. The bimolecular reactions of the methyl-allyl chlorides (a) and (b) with ethoxide ion afford the normal reaction products (c) and (d), respectively. The unimolecular reactions of the chlorides with ethanol proceed with rearrangement, for each chloride gives a mixture of the two ethers (c) and (d), and the composition of the mixture is the same regardless of the initial halide. The observations support

39.

$$
\begin{array}{c}
\overset{\displaystyle Cl}{\underset{\displaystyle \uparrow}{}} \\
CH_3-CH\ \overset{\curvearrowleft}{}\ CH{=}CH_2 \xrightarrow[S_N2]{C_2H_5O^-}\ CH_3CHCH{=}CH_2 \\
\text{α-Methylallyl chloride}\qquad\qquad (c) \\
(a)
\end{array}
$$

$$
C_2H_5OH\ \Big|\ S_N1 \longrightarrow CH_3\overset{+}{C}HCH{=}CH_2
$$

$$
CH_3CH{=}CH\overset{+}{C}H_2
$$

$$
\begin{array}{c}
C_2H_5OH\ \Big\lceil\ S_N1 \\
CH_3CH\overset{\curvearrowleft}{=}CH{-}CH_2{\to}Cl \xrightarrow[S_N2]{C_2H_5O^-}\ CH_3CH{=}CHCH_2OC_2H_5 \\
\text{γ-Methylallyl chloride}\qquad\qquad (d) \\
(b)
\end{array}
$$

the postulated ionization in unimolecular substitutions, since the hybrid carbonium ion from one allyl chloride is identical with that from the other.

ELIMINATION

Onium Salts. — Kinetic studies of $1,2$-eliminations of the type $X—C—C—Y \to X^+ + C{=}C + Y^-$ are reported by Ingold and collaborators (1927–48). Among the first reactions studied were the Hofmann decomposition of quaternary ammonium salts in a basic medium and the analogous decomposition of sulfonium salts. These eliminations exhibit second-order kinetics (E_2 reaction) and are formulated by Ingold as shown in 40 for the basic decomposition of ethyldimethylsulfonium ion. The bimolecular decomposition of onium salts containing more than one alkyl

40. $\quad CH_3CH_2\overset{+}{S}(CH_3)_2 \xrightarrow[(E_2)]{OH^-} [HO{\cdots}H{\cdots}CH_2{\vcentcolon}{=}CH_2{\cdots}S(CH_3)_2]$

Transition state

$$\to H_2O\ |\ CH_2{=}CH_2\ |\ S(CH_3)_2$$

group capable of forming an olefin conforms to the rule of Hofmann (1881) that the olefin formed preferentially is that carrying the smallest number of alkyl substituents. Thus dimethylethyl-n-propylammonium hydroxide (41) yields ethylene rather than propylene. The positively charged nitrogen

$$41. \quad CH_3 \rightarrow CH_2CH_2\overset{+}{N}\underset{\underset{CH_3 \;\; CH_3}{\diagup \;\; \backslash}}{} -CH_2 \overset{\overset{H}{r\text{-}\rceil}}{\underset{\beta}{\overset{|}{\underset{\;}{C}}}}H_2 \xrightarrow[E_2]{OH^-} CH_2{=}CH_2$$

atom produces an inductive drift of electrons from the surrounding carbon atoms sufficient to loosen and promote elimination of a β-proton. The β'-methyl substituent in the n-propyl group is electron-releasing and hence opposes the effect of the nitrogen pole, with the result that this group remains joined to nitrogen and the ethyl group suffers fission. A β'-substituent that is electron-attracting, for example halogen, augments the effect of the nitrogen pole and promotes preferential elimination, as illustrated in 42. The reaction proceeds in the same direction when the β'-

$$42. \qquad Cl{\leftarrow}\overset{\overset{H}{\overset{|}{\overset{\ulcorner\text{-}\text{-}\text{-}\urcorner}{}}}}{CH}{\overset{|}{\dashv}}CH_2{-}\overset{\overset{\frown}{+}}{\underset{CH_3}{S}}{-}CH_2CH_3 \xrightarrow[(E_2)]{OH^-} ClCH{=}CH_2$$

substituent is phenyl rather than chlorine, but in this instance the controlling factor probably is the resonance stabilization of the product, styrene.

The relative ease with which various alkyl groups form olefins, as determined by kinetic studies of the decomposition of ions of the types $\overset{+}{RS}(CH_3)_2$ and $\overset{+}{RN}(CH_3)_3$, is shown in 43. The results substantiate predictions; thus the isobutyl group, which carries two β-alkyl substituents, is eliminated with particular difficulty.

43.   ethyl $> \; n$-propyl $> \; n$-butyl $>$ n-amyl $>$ isoamyl $>$ isobutyl

$$\underset{\beta}{C{-}C} \quad \underset{\beta}{C{\rightarrow}C{-}C} \quad \underset{\beta}{C{-}C{\rightarrow}C{-}C} \quad \underset{\beta}{C{-}C{-}C{\rightarrow}C{-}C} \quad \overset{C\diagdown}{\underset{C\diagup}{}}\underset{\beta}{C{\rightarrow}C{-}C} \quad \overset{C\diagdown}{\underset{C\diagup}{}}\underset{\beta}{C{-}C}$$

Onium ions of special structural types are capable under suitable conditions of undergoing decomposition by a reaction that follows first-order kinetics (E_1). Unimolecular elimination, like unimolecular substitition, is considered to involve two stages (44): formation of a carbonium ion, followed by rapid loss of a proton. Unimolecular eliminations have been observed only when one of the alkyl groups is secondary or tertiary, as in

$$44. \qquad CH_3{\rightarrow}\overset{\overset{CH_3}{\downarrow}}{\underset{\underset{CH_3}{\uparrow}}{C}}{\overset{\frown}{\overset{+}{S}}}(CH_3)_2 \xrightarrow[(slow)]{E_1} CH_3{-}\overset{+}{\underset{\underset{CH_3}{|}}{C}}{-}CH_3 + S(CH_3)_2$$

$$H_2C{\overset{\overset{\overset{H}{\overset{\text{-}\text{-}|\text{-}\text{-}}{\underset{|\text{-}\urcorner}{}}}}{}}{{\overset{+}{\text{-}}}}}\overset{+}{\underset{\underset{CH_3}{|}}{C}}{-}CH_3 \xrightarrow[(fast)]{} H^+ + H_2C{=}\overset{}{\underset{\underset{CH_3}{|}}{C}}{-}CH_3$$

the example cited (44, dimethyl-t-butylsulfonium iodide), for the combined inductive effect of two or three alkyl substituents is required to surmount the energy barrier involved in production of the carbonium ion. In uni-molecular elimination the Hofmann rule no longer applies, and the olefin formed preferentially carries the largest number of alkyl substituents. The contrasting results are seen in the decomposition of dimethyl-t-amylsul-fonium iodide (45), which proceeds largely unimolecularly in 98% ethanol and largely bimolecularly in 80% aqueous ethanol. The E_1 reaction yields the trialkylalkene (a) and the E_2 reaction, in accordance with the Hofmann rule, yields the dialkylalkene (b). An interpretation of the E_1 reaction based upon hyperconjugation is described below as applied to the E_2 reaction of alkyl halides (47).

$$
45. \quad
\begin{array}{c}
CH_3 \\
| \quad + \\
CH_3CH_2C-S(CH_3)_2 \\
| \\
CH_3
\end{array}
\begin{cases}
\xrightarrow[E_1]{98\% \text{ EtOH}} &
\begin{array}{c}
CH_3 \\
| \\
CH_3CH=C \\
| \\
CH_3 \\
(a)
\end{array}
\begin{array}{c}
85\% \\
(+\,15\%\,\text{b})
\end{array} \\[2em]
\xrightarrow[E_2]{80\% \text{ EtOH}} &
\begin{array}{c}
CH_3 \\
| \\
CH_3CH_2C \\
\| \\
CH_2 \\
(b)
\end{array}
\begin{array}{c}
86\% \\
(+\,14\%\,\text{a})
\end{array}
\end{cases}
$$

Alkyl Halides. — The 1,2-elimination of hydrogen bromide from a saturated primary alkyl bromide requires alkaline conditions and pro-ceeds bimolecularly; Ingold's formulation of the transition state is shown in 46. The data of Table 13.6 show that elimination is greatly facilitated

$$
46. \quad OH^- + RCH_2CH_2Br \xrightarrow{E_2}
\left[
\begin{array}{c}
Br^{\delta-} \\
\vdots \\
RCH\cdots CH_2 \\
\vdots \\
{}^{\delta-}HO\cdots H
\end{array}
\right]
\longrightarrow H_2O + RCH=CH_2 + Br^-
$$

by β-alkyl substituents and that the order of their effectiveness is $CH_3 >$ $CH_3CH_2 >$ higher n-alkyls $> H$. The effect cannot be an inductive one, for then an electron-releasing β-methyl group would oppose rather than favor attack by hydroxide at the β-carbon atom; the order of decreasing electron release is $CH_3CH_2 > CH_3 > H$. The explanation suggested by Ingold is based upon hyperconjugation and is represented approximately in formu-lation 47. The incipient α,β-double bond that develops in the transition complex (a) is conjugated with the electron pair of each γ-CH link, and the

TABLE 13.6. E_2 RATE CONSTANTS

$$
\overset{\beta}{R}\overset{\;\;\alpha}{R'CHCH_2Br} \rightarrow \overset{\beta}{R}\overset{\;\;\alpha}{R'C=CH_2}
$$

HALIDE	R	R'	$k \times 10^5$
Isobutyl bromide	CH_3	CH_3	8.5
n-Propyl bromide	CH_3	H	5.3
n-Butyl bromide	CH_3CH_2	H	4.3
n-Amyl bromide	$CH_3CH_2CH_2$	H	3.5
Ethyl bromide	H	H	1.6

resulting resonance stabilization (b, no-bond resonance) promotes formation of the complex. In n-propyl bromide electrons of three γ-CH bonds are available for conjugation, in n-butyl bromide the number is two, and

47.

$$\left[\begin{array}{c} \overset{H}{\underset{HO\cdots H}{\underset{\delta-}{H_2C}}}\overset{\overset{\delta-}{Br}}{\underset{}{CH\cdots CH_2}} \quad or \quad \underset{HO\cdots H}{H_2C\cdots CH}\overset{H^+ \quad Br}{\underset{}{-CH_2}} \end{array} \right] \xrightarrow[Br^-]{-H_2O,} CH_3CH=CH_2$$

(a)   (b)

Transition state

in ethyl bromide stabilization of the intermediate by no-bond resonance is not possible; hence the order of reactivity corresponds to that found. Iso-butyl bromide, which contains six γ-CH bonds, is, as expected, more reactive than n-propyl bromide in the E_2 elimination reaction (Table 13.6).

Secondary alkyl bromides also undergo dehydrohalogenation chiefly by the bimolecular reaction and generally afford mixtures in which one of the two possible olefins predominates. Thus sec-butyl bromide (48) affords chiefly butene-2 with a lesser amount of butene-1, for the E_2 reaction constants are in ratio of about 5:1; sec-amyl bromide (49) reacts similarly. In these and other instances the olefin formed preferentially is that carrying

48.
$$\overset{\gamma}{CH_3}CH_2\overset{\alpha}{\underset{Br}{CH}}CH_3 \xrightarrow{E_2} CH_3CH=CHCH_3 + CH_3CH_2CH=CH_2$$
$$(k_2 = 2.86 \times 10^{-6}) \qquad (k_2 = 0.61 \times 10^{-6})$$

49.
$$\overset{\gamma}{CH_3}CH_2CH_2\overset{\alpha}{\underset{Br}{CH}}CH_3 \xrightarrow{E_2} CH_3CH_2CH=CHCH_3 + CH_3CH_2CH_2CH=CH_2$$
$$(k_2 = 1.96 \times 10^{-6}) \qquad (k_2 = 0.80 \times 10^{-6})$$

the maximum number of alkyl substituents, in accordance with the emprical rule due to Saytzeff (1875). The Saytzeff rule holds also for the dehydration of alcohols (p. 126). The direction of elimination is again contrary to expectations based upon the inductive forces operating at the alternate centers of proton release and may be ascribable to hyperconjugation associated with the presence of three γ-CH bonds in 48 and two in 49; the rate constants for these two halides bear the relationship expected on this basis.

Tertiary alkyl bromides can undergo dehydrobromination unimolecularly as well as bimolecularly, since the inductive effect of three alkyl groups facilitates formation of the requisite carbonium ion (50, E_1). The bimolec-

50.

$$\underset{CH_3}{\overset{CH_3}{\underset{}{}}}\overset{Br}{\underset{}{C}}-CH_3$$

$\xrightarrow[k_2 = 10 \times 10^{-6}]{E_2}$ Transition state

$\xrightarrow[k_1 = 0.29 \times 10^{-6}]{E_1, -Br^-}$ $\underset{CH_3}{\overset{CH_3}{\underset{}{}}}\overset{+}{C}-CH_3$

$\xrightarrow{(fast)}$ $\underset{CH_3}{\overset{CH_3}{\underset{}{}}}C=CH_2$

OH⁻

ular reaction involving hydroxide ion is favored by high alkalinity of the medium; in the absence of strong base the E_2 reaction is suppressed, and E_1 elimination occurs at a slower pace. The relationship is similar for t-amyl bromide (51); here the predominating product of both uni- and bimolecular elimination is that corresponding to the Saytzeff rule.

51.

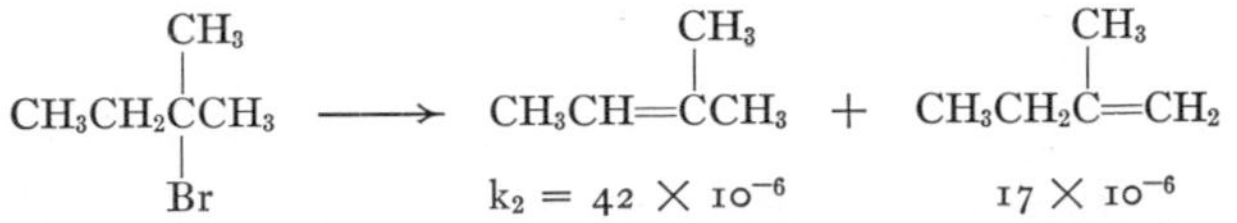

$$CH_3CH_2\overset{\overset{\displaystyle CH_3}{|}}{\underset{\underset{\displaystyle Br}{|}}{C}}CH_3 \longrightarrow CH_3CH=\overset{\overset{\displaystyle CH_3}{|}}{C}CH_3 + CH_3CH_2\overset{\overset{\displaystyle CH_3}{|}}{C}=CH_2$$

$$k_2 = 42 \times 10^{-6} \qquad 17 \times 10^{-6}$$
$$k_1 = 3.2 \times 10^{-6} \qquad 0.72 \times 10^{-6}$$

Steric Course. — In a cyclic structure the groups and atoms available for elimination of water from an alcohol or of hydrogen halide from a halo compound can have either a *cis* or *trans* orientation, and in reactions conducted under ionic conditions *trans* elimination invariably proceeds more readily than *cis* elimination. Thus in the steroid alcohol 52b the C_7-hydroxyl group projects toward the rear of the molecule (dotted line, α-orientation), and the tertiary hydrogen atom at C_8 projects toward the front (full line, β-orientation), and *trans* elimination to a 7,8-unsaturated derivative occurs readily. The reaction is very probably of the E_2 type

52.

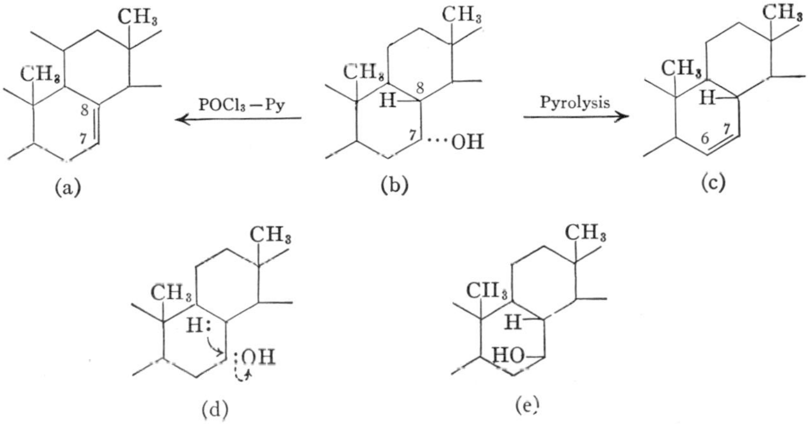

involving an ionic transition state and can be pictured as in (d): the electron pair of the C_8–H bond enters the C_7-octet from the front side as the hydroxyl group departs from the rear side with the shared pair of electrons. The epimeric *cis* alcohol (e) is very resistant to dehydration; on treatment with phosphorus oxychloride in pyridine it yields the corresponding chloride and not an ethylene. Elimination reactions that do not proceed through an ionic transition state, for example the pyrolytic dehydration of an alcohol or its benzoate, do not follow the above rule. Thus pyrolysis of 7α-hydroxysteroids of the type (b) does not follow the path of *trans* elimination involving the tertiary C_8-hydrogen atom but gives the 6,7-unsaturated derivative (c; Barton, 1949). A comparable reaction in which *cis* elimination takes precedence over the *trans* process is Tschugaeff[12] dehydration. which involves pyrolysis of a xanthogenic acid ester prepared as in 53.

53.

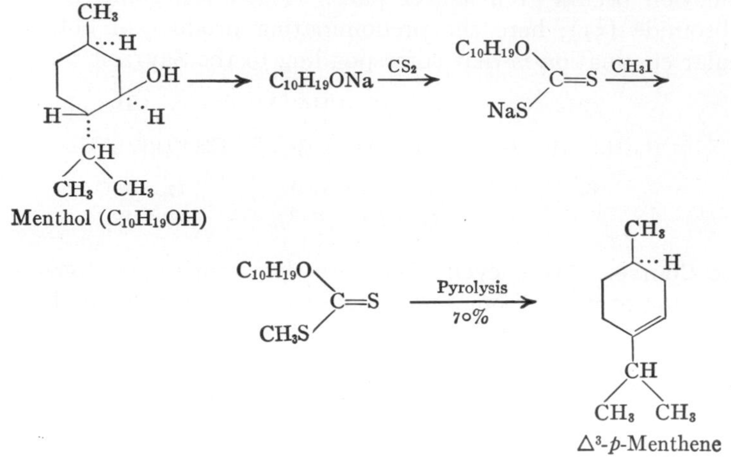

Menthol (C$_{10}$H$_{19}$OH)

Δ^3-*p*-Menthene

PROBLEMS

Suggest electronic interpretations of the following facts:

1. C$_6$H$_5$CH=CHCH$_2$Cl

→ (NaOAc, Ac$_2$O) C$_6$H$_5$CH=CHCH$_2$OAc
(a)

→ (HOAc) (a) + C$_6$H$_5$CHCH=CH$_2$
　　　　　　　　　　　|
　　　　　　　　　　　OAc

Meisenheimer and Beutter, *Ann.*, **508**, 58 (1934).

2.

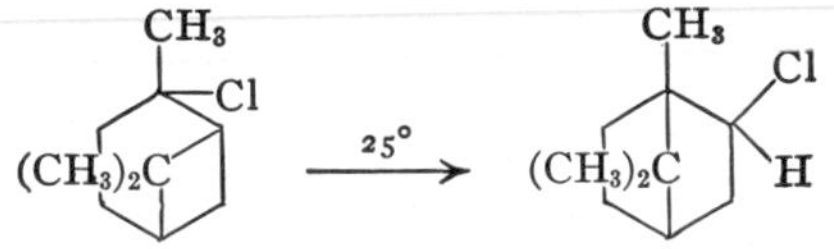

Pinene hydrochloride
(Wagner-Meerwein rearrangement)

$\xrightarrow{25°}$

Bornyl chloride

3. Malonic acid (HO$_2$CCH$_2$CO$_2$H, pK$_a$ = 2.8) is a stronger acid than acetic acid (pK$_a$ = 4.7), but the ion $^-$OOCCH$_2$CO$_2$H (pK$_a$ = 5.9) is a weaker acid.

4. CH$_3$CH$_2$CH=CHCO$_2$H $\xrightarrow{HCl}$ CH$_3$CH$_2$CHClCH$_2$CO$_2$H (ready reaction)
CH$_3$CH=CHCH$_2$CO$_2$H

$\xrightarrow{HCl}$ CH$_3$CHClCH$_2$CH$_2$CO$_2$H (slow reactions)

CH$_2$=CHCH$_2$CH$_2$CO$_2$H

5. CH$_3$C≡CH + 2 HBr ⟶ CH$_3$CBr$_2$CH$_3$

[12] Lev A. Tschugaeff, 1873–1922; b. Moscow; Ph.D. St. Petersburg; St. Petersburg

6. 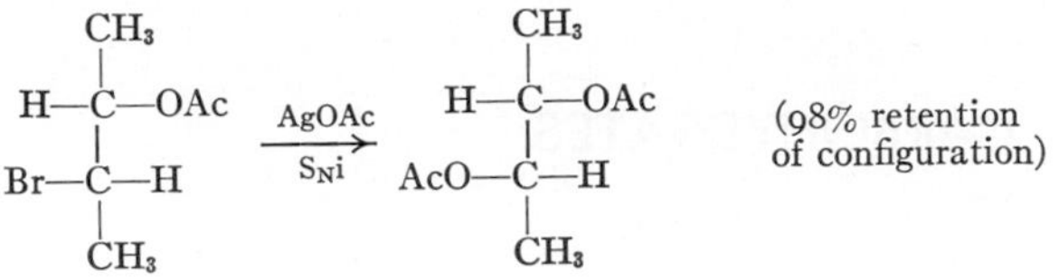
$$\underset{\substack{\text{CH}_3\\ \text{H—C—OAc}\\ \text{Br—C—H}\\ \text{CH}_3}}{} \xrightarrow[\text{S}_{\text{N}}\text{i}]{\text{AgOAc}} \underset{\substack{\text{CH}_3\\ \text{H—C—OAc}\\ \text{AcO—C—H}\\ \text{CH}_3}}{} \qquad \text{(98\% retention of configuration)}$$

Winstein and Buckles, *J. Am. Chem. Soc.*, **64**, 2780 (1942).

7. ### ORDER OF REACTIVITY OF CARBONYL COMPOUNDS WITH PHENYLMAGNESIUM BROMIDE

COMPOUND	RELATIVE REACTIVITY
Acetone	15.5
Acetaldehyde	10.8
Benzaldehyde	5.4
Pinacolone, $(CH_3)_3CCOCH_3$	4.8
Cyclohexanone	1.0

8. 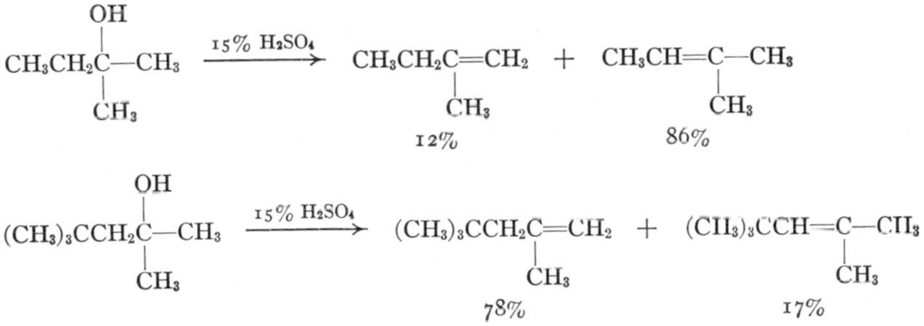
$$\underset{\substack{\text{OH}\\ |\\ \text{CH}_3\text{CH}_2\text{C—CH}_3\\ |\\ \text{CH}_3}}{} \xrightarrow{\text{15\% H}_2\text{SO}_4} \underset{\substack{\text{CH}_3\text{CH}_2\text{C=CH}_2\\ |\\ \text{CH}_3\\ 12\%}}{} + \underset{\substack{\text{CH}_3\text{CH=C—CH}_3\\ |\\ \text{CH}_3\\ 86\%}}{}$$

$$\underset{\substack{\text{OH}\\ |\\ (\text{CH}_3)_3\text{CCH}_2\text{C—CH}_3\\ |\\ \text{CH}_3}}{} \xrightarrow{\text{15\% H}_2\text{SO}_4} \underset{\substack{(\text{CH}_3)_3\text{CCH}_2\text{C=CH}_2\\ |\\ \text{CH}_3\\ 78\%}}{} + \underset{\substack{(\text{CH}_3)_3\text{CCH=C—CH}_3\\ |\\ \text{CH}_3\\ 17\%}}{}$$

9. $CHCl_2CH_2Cl \xrightarrow{E_2} CCl_2{=}CH_2$

$CH_3CBr_2CHBrCH_3 \xrightarrow{E_2} CH_3CBr{=}CBrCH_3$

READING REFERENCES

E. D. Hughes, "Substitution," *J. Chem. Soc.*, 968 (1946)

E. D. Hughes, "Aliphatic Substitution and the Walden Inversion," *Trans. Faraday Soc.*, **34**, 202 (1938)

E. D. Hughes, "Steric Hindrance," *Quart. Revs.*, **2**, 107 (1948)

E. D. Hughes and C. K. Ingold, "The Mechanism and Kinetics of Elimination Reactions," *Trans. Faraday Soc.*, **37**, 657 (1941)

Ingold and co-workers, "Constitutional Influences in Elimination. A General Discussion," *J. Chem. Soc.*, 2093 (1948)

A. E. Remick, "Electronic Interpretations of Organic Chemistry," 2nd Ed., Wiley, New York (1949)

L. P. Hammett, "Physical Organic Chemistry," McGraw-Hill, New York (1940)

C. K. Ingold, "Signs of a New Pathway in Reaction Mechanisms and Stereochemistry," *J. Chem. Soc.*, 2991 (1954)

C. K. Ingold, "Structure and Mechanism in Organic Chemistry," Cornell Univ. Press (1953)

P. D. Bartlett, "The Study of Reaction Mechanisms," in H. Gilman, "Organic Chemistry," Vol. 3, 1 (1953)

CHAPTER 14

CARBOHYDRATES

Carbohydrates, including sugars, are among the most abundant constituents of plants and animals, in which they serve many useful functions. They are a source of energy; they form supporting tissues of plants and some animals in the same way that proteins are used by the majority of animals. Two growth factors (vitamins), ascorbic acid (vitamin C) and inositol, are related to common carbohydrates, and other carbohydrates have unique biological activity. The name is derived from the fact that many sugars have the empirical formula $C_nH_{2n}O_n$, or $C_n(H_2O)_n$, and hence the French applied the name "hydrate de carbone" or carbohydrate, and the name has been retained even though it is not descriptive. They are classified systematically as monosaccharides, di-, tri-, and tetrasaccharides (oligosaccharides), and polysaccharides. Practically all natural monosaccharides contain five or six carbon atoms, and are known as pentoses and hexoses, respectively. They are colorless and most have a sweet taste. Disaccharides, which are condensation products of two hexose or pentose units, resemble monosaccharides in color and solubility. Polysaccharides are tasteless, amorphous, largely water-insoluble substances of the type formula $(C_6H_{10}O_5)_n \cdot H_2O$ or $(C_5H_8O_4)_n \cdot H_2O$, in which n is large. They are converted on hydrolysis into C_6- or C_5-sugars, as disaccharides are. Cane sugar (sucrose) yields two C_6-sugars, glucose and fructose:

$$C_{12}H_{22}O_{11} + H_2O \longrightarrow C_6H_{12}O_6 + C_6H_{12}O_6$$

Sucrose   Glucose   Fructose

Structure of Hexoses. — The greatest advances in sugar chemistry are due to the illustrious German chemist Emil Fischer,[1] who published his first paper in this field in 1884. At the time four hexoses, one pentose, and three disaccharides had been characterized. Simple sugars had been known for some time to contain an aldehydic or a ketonic group, owing to the fact that they reduce Fehling's solution (reducing sugars). Sucrose, on the other hand, was recognized as a nonreducing sugar. The function of the other five oxygen atoms in glucose ($C_6H_{12}O_6$) was demonstrated by preparation of a crystalline pentaacetate (1879). The structure of glucose as a straight-chain pentahydroxy aldehyde was established by Kiliani[2] (1886) as a result

---

[1] Emil Fischer, 1852–1919; b. Euskirchen, Germany; Ph.D. Strasbourg (Baeyer); Erlangen, Würzburg, Berlin; Nobel Prize 1902; *Ber.* **52A**, 129 (1919)

[2] Heinrich Kiliani, 1855–1945; b. Würzburg, Germany; Ph.D. Munich (Erlenmeyer); Freiburg; *Ber.*, **82A**, 1 (1949)

of his discovery that hexoses add hydrogen cyanide, another indication of the presence of a carbonyl group. Kiliani hydrolyzed glucose cyanohydrin to the corresponding acid, which he then reduced with hydrogen iodide in order to replace all hydroxyl groups by hydrogen. The reduction product was n-heptylic acid; hence the original six carbon atoms must constitute

$$
\begin{array}{ccccc}
& & \text{CN} & & \\
& & | & & \\
\text{CHO} & & \text{CHOH} & \text{COOH} & \text{COOH} \\
| & \xrightarrow{\text{HCN}} & | & \xrightarrow{\text{H}_2\text{O}} \; | \; \xrightarrow{\text{HI}} & | \\
(\text{CHOH})_4 & & (\text{CHOH})_4 & (\text{CHOH})_5 & (\text{CH}_2)_5 \\
| & & | & | & | \\
\text{CH}_2\text{OH} & & \text{CH}_2\text{OH} & \text{CH}_2\text{OH} & \text{CH}_3 \\
\text{Glucose} & & \text{Glucose cyanohydrin} & & n\text{-Heptylic acid}
\end{array}
$$

a straight chain, and since the extra carbon atom introduced in the addition of hydrogen cyanide is found at the end of this chain, the carbonyl group occupies a terminal position and is aldehydic. Since a six-carbon aldehyde having five hydroxyl groups is stable only if just one of these groups is distributed on each of the available five carbon atoms, glucose is inferred to have the formula shown. The term aldohexose describes this structure. Kiliani carried out a similar series of reactions starting with the isomeric fructose, which also forms a pentaacetate; the final acid is an isoheptylic acid, methyl-n-butylacetic acid, from which which Kiliani correctly deduced that fructose is a pentahydroxy ketone, with the carbonyl oxygen atom located at the 2-position of the chain; it is a 2-ketohexose.

$$
\begin{array}{ccccc}
1\;\text{CH}_2\text{OH} & & \text{CH}_2\text{OH} & \text{CH}_2\text{OH} & \text{CH}_3 \\
| & & | & | & | \\
2\;\text{C}{=}\text{O} & \xrightarrow{\text{HCN}} & \text{C(OH)CN} \; \xrightarrow{\text{H}_2\text{O}} & \text{C(OH)COOH} \; \xrightarrow{\text{HI}} & \text{CHCOOH} \\
| & & | & | & | \\
(\text{CHOH})_3 & & (\text{CHOH})_3 & (\text{CHOH})_3 & (\text{CH}_2)_3 \\
| & & | & | & | \\
6\;\text{CH}_2\text{OH} & & \text{CH}_2\text{OH} & \text{CH}_2\text{OH} & \text{CH}_3 \\
\text{Fructose}
\end{array}
$$

A few natural sugars are known that are not straight-chain compounds; one, apiose, which occurs in parsley, has the isoprene skeleton, established by conversion into isovaleric acid.

$$(\text{HOCH}_2)_2\text{C(OH)CH(OH)CHO} \xrightarrow{\text{HI, P}} (\text{CH}_3)_2\text{CHCH}_2\text{CO}_2\text{H}$$

Osazones. — Early progress in elucidation of sugar chemistry was handicapped by the difficulty in obtaining crystalline compounds, since sugars, especially when impure, tend to form sirups. One of the outstanding contributions of Fischer was introduction in 1884 of the use of phenylhydrazine, which reacts with many carbonyl compounds to give sparingly soluble and beautifully crystalline derivatives. Fischer's dissertation for the doctorate under Baeyer ten years earlier had described the discovery, preparation, and uses of phenylhydrazine.* The reaction with sugars proceeded in an unexpected manner, since Fischer found that the products,

---

* For twelve years following 1891, Fischer suffered from the insidious poisonous effects of phenylhydrazine, which, even so, he later described as his "first and most lasting chemical love."

which he called osazones (-ose + hydrazone), contained two phenylhydrazine residues rather than one. Moreover, glucose and fructose yielded
the same product, glucosazone ($C_{18}H_{22}O_4N_4$); the two other hexoses known
at the time, galactose and sorbose, yielded two additional osazones. Three
years later Fischer isolated the true phenylhydrazone of glucose and showed
it to be an intermediate in the formation of the osazone, and on this basis
he formulated the reaction as follows:

$$
\begin{array}{l}
\text{CHO} \\
|\\
\text{CHOH} \\
|\\
\text{(CHOH)}_3 \\
|\\
\text{CH}_2\text{OH} \\
\text{Glucose}
\end{array}
\xrightarrow{\ \text{H}_2\text{NNHC}_6\text{H}_5\ }
\begin{array}{l}
\text{CH=NNHC}_6\text{H}_5 \\
|\\
\text{CHOH} \quad + \quad \text{H}_2\text{NNHC}_6\text{H}_5 \\
|\\
\text{(CHOH)}_3 \\
|\\
\text{CH}_2\text{OH} \\
\text{Glucose phenylhydrazone}
\end{array}
\longrightarrow
$$

$$
\begin{bmatrix}
\text{CH=NNHC}_6\text{H}_5 \\
|\\
\text{C=O} \\
|\\
\text{(CHOH)}_3 \\
|\\
\text{CH}_2\text{OH}
\end{bmatrix}
\xrightarrow{\ \text{H}_2\text{NNHC}_6\text{H}_5\ }
\begin{array}{l}
\text{CH=NNHC}_6\text{H}_5 \\
|\\
\text{C=NNHC}_6\text{H}_5 \\
|\\
\text{(CHOH)}_3 \\
|\\
\text{CH}_2\text{OH} \\
\text{Glucosazone} \\
\text{(m.p. 208°)}
\end{array}
$$

(by-products: NH_3, $C_6H_5NH_2$)

In the second phase of the reaction, phenylhydrazine was assumed to act
as an oxidizing agent and to abstract two hydrogen atoms from the activated 2-position adjacent to the unsaturated center, with reductive fission
to ammonia and aniline. The newly generated carbonyl group could then
condense with a third molecule of the reagent to form the osazone. Fischer's
mechanism became questionable with recognition that phenylhydrazine does
not exhibit in other reactions the function of an oxidizing agent. Weygand[3]
(1940) has presented evidence in support of a plausible alternate mechanism,
the key step of which involves an intramolecular oxidation-reduction reac-

$$
\begin{array}{l}
\text{CHO} \\
|\\
\text{HCOH} \\
(a)
\end{array}
\longrightarrow
\begin{array}{l}
\text{CH=NNHC}_6\text{H}_5 \\
|\\
\text{HCOH} \\
(b)
\end{array}
\longrightarrow
\begin{array}{l}
\text{CH}_2\text{NHNHC}_6\text{H}_5 \\
|\\
\text{C=O} \\
|\\
(c)
\end{array}
\xrightarrow{\ \text{C}_6\text{H}_5\text{NHNH}_2\ }
$$

$$
\begin{bmatrix}
\text{CH}_2\text{NHNHC}_6\text{H}_5 \\
|\\
\text{C=NNHC}_6\text{H}_5 \\
|\\
(d)
\end{bmatrix}
\longrightarrow
\begin{bmatrix}
\text{CHNHNHC}_6\text{H}_5 \\
||\\
\text{C—NHNHC}_6\text{H}_5 \\
|\\
(e)
\end{bmatrix}
\xrightarrow{\ -\text{H}_2\text{NC}_6\text{H}_5\ }
$$

$$
\begin{bmatrix}
\text{CH=NH} \\
|\\
\text{C=NNHC}_6\text{H}_5 \\
|\\
(f)
\end{bmatrix}
\text{ or }
\begin{bmatrix}
\text{CH=NNHC}_6\text{H}_5 \\
|\\
\text{C=NH} \\
|\\
(g)
\end{bmatrix}
\xrightarrow{\ \text{C}_6\text{H}_5\text{NHNH}_2\ }
\begin{array}{l}
\text{CH=NNHC}_6\text{H}_5 \\
|\\
\text{C=NNHC}_6\text{H}_5 \quad + \text{ NH}_3 \\
|\\
\text{Osazone} \\
(h)
\end{array}
$$

tion, resulting in isomerization of the initially formed sugar phenylhydrazone (b) to a ketonic compound (c) by migration of two hydrogen atoms from the secondary alcoholic group with saturation of the carbon–nitrogen double bond. Transformations of this type have been observed under conditions such that osazone formation is not possible (Amadori reaction). Weygand assumes that the product (d) resulting from condensation of the ketonic derivative with phenylhydrazine undergoes iosmerization to (e) through an α,γ-hydrogen shift, and that (e) loses the elements of aniline in a reversal of the usual 1,4-addition reaction to give one or the other, or both, of the imino compounds (f) or (g); either intermediate can react with phenylhydrazine with formation of the osazone and liberation of ammonia.

Weygand's formulation does not explain why the reaction stops with introduction of two residues of phenylhydrazine. Why, for example, does not the osazone (h) undergo a further intramolecular oxidation-reduction reaction involving the C_3-position? In the reaction of glucose with Fehling's solution, an amount of reagent is consumed greatly beyond that calculated for oxidation of the aldehydic group, an indication that oxidation progresses down the chain through successively activated positions adjacent to a center of unsaturation. A suggestion (2nd Ed.) that the osazone is stabilized by formation of the chelate ring structure (i) or (j) has been confirmed (L. Mester).

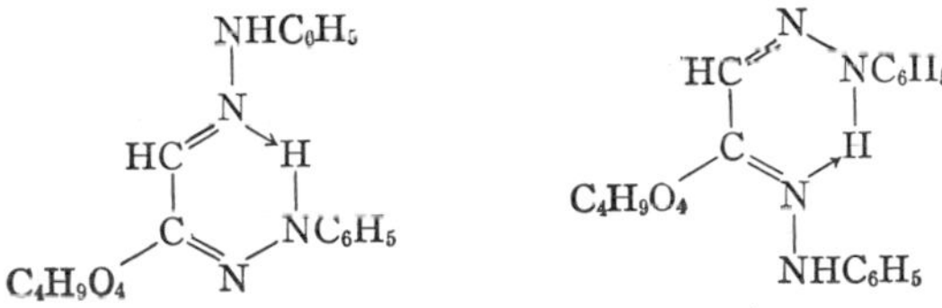

(i)   (j)

Formation of osazones is a general property of α-hydroxy ketones, for example benzoin, $C_6H_5CHOHCOC_6H_5$, and acetoin, $CH_3CHOHCOCH_3$. Fructose is attacked by the second molecule of phenylhydrazine at the primary alcoholic group at position 1 in preference to the secondary group at the alternate adjacent position 3.

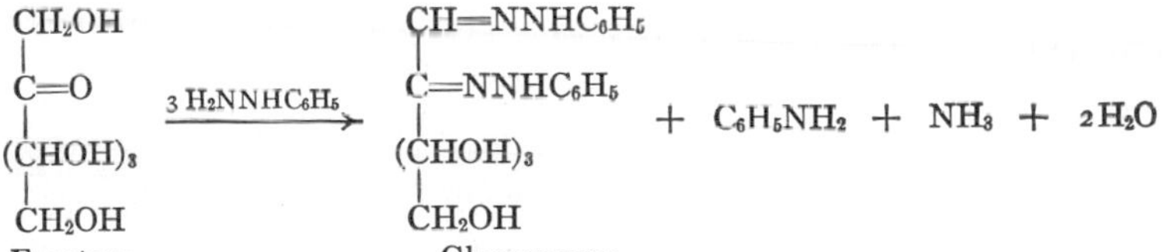

Osazones are bright yellow, crystalline compounds identifiable both from their temperatures of decomposition and from the crystalline forms. That the solubility in water is markedly less than that of the sugar is understandable, for introduction of two phenylhydrazine residues into a hexose increases the molecular weight by 64%, and the derivative contains one less hydroxyl group. Thus an osazone, which is produced easily by brief warming of a solution containing the reagent, usually will separate from a dilute solution of an impure sugar.

Configurations. — The new tool led (1888) to the discovery of mannose. Glucose is reduced by sodium amalgam in part to an alcohol, mannitol, which is oxidized not to glucose, but to a different aldohexose, mannose, which Fischer was able to isolate as the phenylhydrazone. Fischer converted

$$
\begin{array}{ccccc}
\text{CHO} & & \text{CH}_2\text{OH} & & \text{CH=NNHC}_6\text{H}_5 & & \text{CHO} \\
| & & | & \xrightarrow[\text{10\%}]{\substack{1.\ \text{dil. HNO}_3 \\ 2.\ \text{H}_2\text{NNHC}_6\text{H}_5}} & | & \xrightarrow[\text{80\%}]{\text{HCl}} & | \\
(\text{CHOH})_4 & \xrightarrow{\text{Na—Hg}} & (\text{CHOH})_4 & & (\text{CHOH})_4 & & (\text{CHOH})_4 \\
| & & | & & | & & | \\
\text{CH}_2\text{OH} & & \text{CH}_2\text{OH} & & \text{CH}_2\text{OH} & & \text{CH}_2\text{OH} \\
\text{Glucose} & & \text{Mannitol} & & \text{Mannose phenylhydrazone} & & \text{Mannose}
\end{array}
$$

mannose into n-heptylic acid, which shows that mannose, like glucose, is a straight-chain aldohexose, and in addition he found that whereas the phenylhydrazones of glucose and mannose are different, the osazones are identical. Fischer interpreted these experimental results thus:[*] "Glucose and mannose represent in the sugar series the first instance of two isomers that have the same structure and can be converted one into the other. The explanation of this isomerism is given on the basis of the Le Bel-van't Hoff theory. The

$$\text{CHOCHOHCHOHCHOHCHOHCH}_2\text{OH}$$

formula contains four asymmetric carbon atoms." These are now designated in the following order:

$$\underset{1}{\text{CHO}}\underset{2}{\overset{*}{\text{C}}\text{HOH}}\underset{3}{\overset{*}{\text{C}}\text{HOH}}\underset{4}{\overset{*}{\text{C}}\text{HOH}}\underset{5}{\overset{*}{\text{C}}\text{HOH}}\underset{6}{\text{CH}_2\text{OH}}$$

"Each of these four asymmetric carbon atoms necessitates the existence of two isomers, and therefore there are no less than sixteen foreseen by the theory." (The four centers are different; $2^4 = 16$.) "From the present experimental evidence it can be shown that the isomerism of glucose and mannose is due to the asymmetric carbon atom 2. The phenylhydrazones of the two sugars are entirely different, but these are converted with the greatest ease into the same osazone. The later has the structural formula:

$$\text{CH(N}_2\text{HC}_6\text{H}_5)\text{C(N}_2\text{HC}_6\text{H}_5)\overset{*}{\text{C}}\text{HOH}\overset{*}{\text{C}}\text{HOH}\overset{*}{\text{C}}\text{HOHCH}_2\text{OH}$$

in which the carbon atom 2 has lost its asymmetry. Since it is very unlikely that during the osazone formation, which proceeds so easily and relatively smoothly, the carbon atoms 3, 4, and 5 have changed their configuration, one must assume that the difference between mannose and glucose depends only upon the asymmetry of carbon atom 2." Fructose, with three dissimilar asymmetric carbon atoms, is one of eight possible optical isomers.

Fischer inferred that since mannitol does not correspond in configuration to glucose it is not the primary reduction product of this substance, and in the following year he showed that, under the influence of dilute alkali, glucose rearranges to mannose, which is then reduced to mannitol.

---

[*] E. Fischer and J. Hirschberger, "Ueber Mannose," *Ber.*, **22**, 365 (1889)

Catalytic hydrogenation is usually preferred to reduction with sodium amalgam for preparation of sugar alcohols, since rearrangements are avoided. By 1891 Fischer was in a position to assign relative configurations to six of the possible aldohexoses and to fructose and the enantiomeric form. His representation of natural, dextrorotatory glucose is shown in the accompanying projection formula; the Fischer convention for projection formulation is explained on page 262. Since mannose and fructose yield the same osazone as natural glucose and therefore correspond to

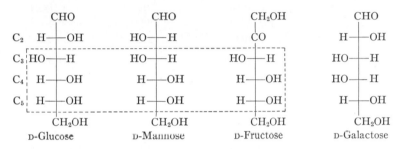

| | D-Glucose | D-Mannose | D-Fructose | D-Galactose |

glucose in configurations at C_3, C_4, and C_5, Fischer recognized the three hexoses as members of the same stereochemical series, which he defined as that of D-glucose. Fructose and mannose, being members of the D-series, are named D-fructose and D-mannose even though the former is levorotatory. The small capital letter prefix refers to the series to which a sugar belongs and not to the direction of rotation, and when desired this property can be indicated as follows: D-(−)-fructose. The natural aldohexose galactose is included in the D-series because of its correspondence to D-glucose in the center C_5. The original assigment of configurations entailed an arbitrary choice between the formulations to be attributed to D-glucose and to L-glucose. In 1896 Fischer succeeded in relating D-glucose to D-tartaric acid, which had already been shown to belong to the same steric series as the still simpler compounds D-malic acid and D-glyceraldehyde. The absolute configurations were not and are not known, but Fischer arbitrarily selected as the reference standard the configuration illustrated for D-(+)-glyceraldehyde and L-(−)-malic acid in the projection formulas, namely with hydroxyl written to the right and hydrogen to the left.

CHO	CHO		
$(CHOH)_3$	$(CHOH)_2$	CHO	CH_2COOH
HCOH	HCOH	HCOH	HCOH
CH_2OH	CH_2OH	CH_2OH	COOH
D-Aldohexose	D-Aldopentose	D-(+)-Glyceraldehyde	L (−) Malic acid

All sixteen possible aldohexoses have been isolated or synthesized and their configurations established (twelve by Fischer). Only three occur in nature: D-glucose, D-galactose, and D-mannose. The only other natural hexose is D-fructose. Strikingly enough, these are the only sugars that yeasts are able to ferment.   The eight D-aldohexoses are formulated:

CHO	CHO	CHO	CHO
HCOH	HOCH	HCOH	HCOH
HOCH	HOCH	HOCH	HCOH
HCOH	HCOH	HOCH	HCOH
HCOH	HCOH	HCOH	HCOH
CH₂OH	CH₂OH	CH₂OH	CH₂OH
D-Glucose	D-Mannose	D-Galactose	D-Allose
CHO	CHO	CHO	CHO
HOCH	HOCH	HCOH	HOCH
HCOH	HOCH	HCOH	HCOH
HCOH	HOCH	HOCH	HOCH
HCOH	HCOH	HCOH	HCOH
CH₂OH	CH₂OH	CH₂OH	CH₂OH
D-Altrose	D-Talose	D-Gulose	D-Idose

Degradation and Synthesis in the Sugar Series. — The cyanohydrin reaction discovered by Kiliani is the classical method for increasing the chain length of an aldose.   Fischer found that two isomeric nitriles are formed; for example L-arabinose, a pentose obtained on hydrolysis of various plant gums, is converted into two epimers, L-gluconic and L-mannonic acid.   A sugar acid produced in this manner can be converted into the

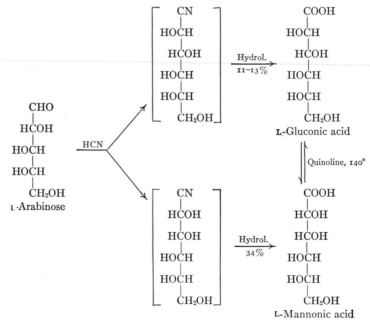

corresponding aldose by lactonization and reduction, as illustrated on p. 370. The method is limited only by the diminishing yields at each step.   Fischer prepared several nonoses (C_9) from the corresponding hexoses.

Four general methods of degradation that have been developed are illustrated below for the conversion of D-glucose into D-arabinose.   The first method (1) was developed by Wohl[4] (1893) and simplified (1a) by

1. Wohl degradation:

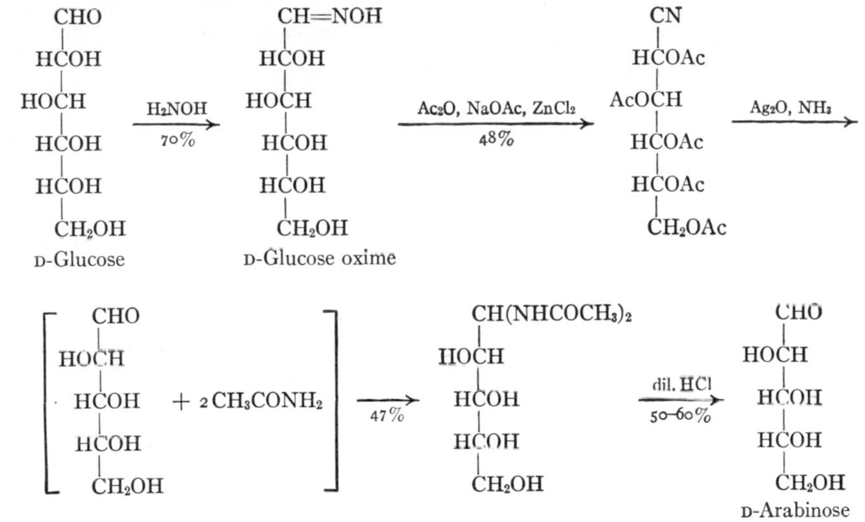

CHO		CH=NOH		CN	
HCOH		HCOH		HCOAc	
HOCH	$\xrightarrow[70\%]{H_2NOH}$	HOCH	$\xrightarrow[48\%]{Ac_2O,\ NaOAc,\ ZnCl_2}$	AcOCH	$\xrightarrow{Ag_2O,\ NH_3}$
HCOH		HCOH		HCOAc	
HCOH		HCOH		HCOAc	
CH₂OH		CH₂OH		CH₂OAc	
D-Glucose		D-Glucose oxime			

CHO		CH(NHCOCH₃)₂		CHO	
HOCH		HOCH		HOCH	
HCOH + 2 CH₃CONH₂	$\xrightarrow{47\%}$	HCOH	$\xrightarrow[50-60\%]{dil.\ HCl}$	HCOH	
HCOH		HCOH		HCOH	
CH₂OH		CH₂OH		CH₂OH	
				D-Arabinose	

1a. Zemplén simplification:

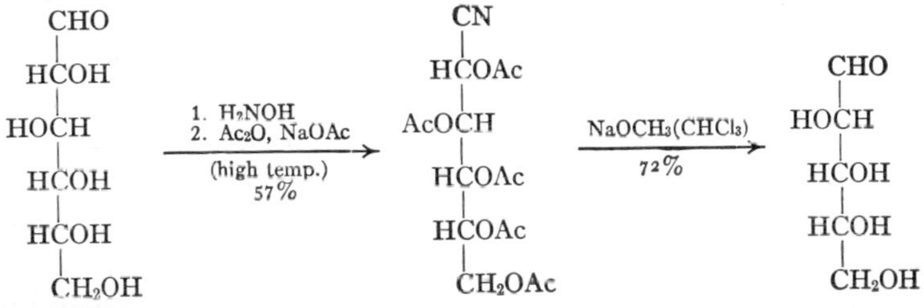

CHO		CN		CHO	
HCOH		HCOAc		HOCH	
HOCH	$\xrightarrow[\substack{(high\ temp.)\\57\%}]{\substack{1.\ H_2NOH\\2.\ Ac_2O,\ NaOAc}}$	AcOCH	$\xrightarrow[72\%]{NaOCH_3(CHCl_3)}$	HCOH	
HCOH		HCOAc		HCOH	
HCOH		HCOAc		CH₂OH	
CH₂OH		CH₂OAc			

2. Ruff degradation:

CHO		[COO		[COOH		CHO
HCOH		HCOH		C=O		HCOH
HOCH	$\xrightarrow[77\%]{Electrolytic\ oxidation}$	HOCH	$\xrightarrow{H_2O_2,\ [Fe(OAc)_2]}$	HOCH	$\xrightarrow[25\%]{-CO_2}$	HOCH
HCOH		HCOH	Ca	HCOH		HCOH
HCOH		HCOH		HCOH		HCOH
CH₂OH		CH₂OH]₂		CH₂OH]		CH₂OH
		Calcium D-gluconate				

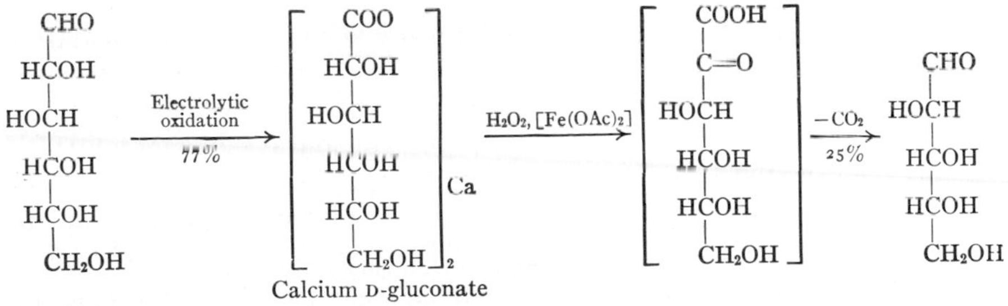

[4] Alfred Wohl, b. 1863 Graudentz; Ph.D. Berlin (Hofmann); Danzig

3. Weermann degradation:

$$
\text{Calcium} \atop \text{D-gluconate}
\xrightarrow{\text{HCl}}
\left[
\begin{array}{c}
\text{CO} \\
| \\
\text{HCOH} \\
| \quad\;\; \text{O} \\
\text{HOCH} \\
| \\
\text{HC} \\
| \\
\text{HCOH} \\
| \\
\text{CH}_2\text{OH}
\end{array}
\right]
\xrightarrow[80\%]{\text{NH}_3,\ \text{C}_2\text{H}_5\text{OH}}
\begin{array}{c}
\text{CONH}_2 \\
| \\
\text{HCOH} \\
| \\
\text{HOCH} \\
| \\
\text{HCOH} \\
| \\
\text{HCOH} \\
| \\
\text{CH}_2\text{OH}
\end{array}
\xrightarrow{\text{HOCl, Na}_2\text{CO}_3}
$$

D-Gluconolactone   D-Gluconamide

$$
\left[
\begin{array}{c}
\text{N}\!=\!\text{C}\!=\!\text{O} \\
| \\
\text{HCOH} \\
| \\
\text{HOCH} \\
| \\
\text{HCOH} \\
| \\
\text{HCOH} \\
| \\
\text{CH}_2\text{OH}
\end{array}
\right]
\xrightarrow[49\%]{-\text{HNCO}}
\begin{array}{c}
\text{CHO} \\
| \\
\text{HOCH} \\
| \\
\text{HCOH} \\
| \\
\text{HCOH} \\
| \\
\text{CH}_2\text{OH}
\end{array}
$$

Zemplén[5] (1927), the second (2) by Ruff[6] (1899), and the third (3) by Weermann (1917). The Wohl degradation represents reversal of the cyanohydrin synthesis. The nitrile group of the acetylated acid nitrile is eliminated by treatment with ammoniacal silver oxide. Acetamide is formed by ammonolysis of the acetate groups and reacts with the aldose to form the diacetamide derivative, which is readily hydrolyzed to the aldose. In the Zemplén modification the nitrile group is eliminated by treatment with sodium methoxide; the yield is more than twice that in the original procedure. The Ruff degradation consists in oxidation of an aldonic acid to a 2-ketoaldonic acid, which yields the next-lower aldose by loss of carbon dioxide. The yield is poor owing to further degradation of the aldose. The Weermann method involves degradation of the amide of a sugar acid by a variation of the Hofmann reaction with hypochlorous acid. The most recent degradation (F. Weygand, 1950) involves reaction of a sugar oxime in aqueous bicarbonate solution with 2,4-dinitrofluorobenzene; the oxime aryl ether produced decomposes to 2,4-dinitrophenol, the next lower aldose, and hydrogen cyanide (yields 50–60%): —CHOHCH=NOC$_6$H$_3$-(NO$_2$)$_2$ → —CH=O + HCN + HOC$_6$H$_3$(NO$_2$)$_2$.

Determination of Configuration. — Fischer's achievement of elucidating the configurations of all the aldohexoses was based upon use of a selection of reactions mentioned above and application of principles of geometry. One principle is that dibasic acids of types (b), (c), and (e), like mesotartaric acid (a), are all divisible into two halves that are mirror images of each other and hence are optically inactive. These planar projections can be

[5] Geza Zemplén, b. 1883 Trencsén, Hungary; Ph.D. Budapest; Budapest

[6] Otto Ruff, 1871–1939; b. Schwäbisch-Hall, Germany; Ph.D. Berlin (Piloty); Danzig, Breslau; *Ber.*, **73A**, 125 (1940)

$$
\begin{array}{ccccc}
 & & & & \text{CO}_2\text{H} \\
 & & & & | \\
 & \text{CO}_2\text{H} & \text{CO}_2\text{H} & \text{CO}_2\text{H} & \text{HCOH} \\
 & | & | & | & | \\
\text{CO}_2\text{H} & \text{HCOH} & \text{HCOH} & \text{HOCH} & \text{HOCH} \\
| & | & | & | & | \\
\text{HCOH} & \text{HCOH} & \text{HOCH} \;\;=\;\; & \text{HCOH} & \text{HOCH} \\
| & | & | & | & | \\
\text{HCOH} & \text{HCOH} & \text{HCOH} & \text{HOCH} & \text{HCOH} \\
| & | & | & | & | \\
\text{CO}_2\text{H} & \text{CO}_2\text{H} & \text{CO}_2\text{H} & \text{CO}_2\text{H} & \text{CO}_2\text{H} \\
\text{(a)} & \text{(b)} & \text{(c)} & \text{(d)} & \text{(e)}
\end{array}
$$

Optically inactive, *meso* types

turned about in the plane of the paper without change in identity; hence formula (c) is identical with formula (d).

The eight D-aldohexoses, grouped in pairs of 2-epimers by osazone formation, can be represented by the formulas I–VIII, in which a bar extending to the right or left stands for a hydroxyl group; reversal of the positions of

$$
\begin{array}{cccccccc}
\text{CHO} & \text{CHO} & \text{CHO} & \text{CHO} & \text{CHO} & \text{CHO} & \text{CHO} & \text{CHO} \\
\text{CH}_2\text{OH} & \text{CH}_2\text{OH} & \text{CH}_2\text{OH} & \text{CH}_2\text{OH} & \text{CH}_2\text{OH} & \text{CH}_2\text{OH} & \text{CH}_2\text{OH} & \text{CH}_2\text{OH} \\
\text{I} & \text{II} & \text{III} & \text{IV} & \text{V} & \text{VI} & \text{VII} & \text{VIII} \\
\text{Allose} & \text{Altrose} & \text{Glucose} & \text{Mannose} & \text{Gulose} & \text{Idose} & \text{Galactose} & \text{Talose}
\end{array}
$$

the bars gives the formulas of the eight L-enantiomers. Steps by which the formula of glucose can be inferred are as follows. (a) Nitric acid oxidation of glucose gives an optically active C_6-dibasic acid; therefore glucose cannot have formula I or VII. (b) The active C_6-dibasic acid from D-glucose results also from oxidation of L-gulose, the formula for which is derivable by inverting III and interchanging the terminal groups, —CHO and —CH$_2$OH. In formulas IV and VI, however, similar changes do not result in a new structure and hence each sugar affords an active C_6-dibasic acid not obtainable from any other aldohexose; hence IV and VI are eliminated (c) Wohl degradation of glucose followed by nitric acid oxidation gives an active C_5-dibasic acid; hence formulas II and V are eliminated. (d) Of the remaining formulas, III and VIII, III is correct because glucose gives an osazone identical with that from IV (active C_6-acid) and different from that from VII (inactive C_6-acid).*

Lower Sugars. — Since the D-hexoses as arranged above (I–VIII) are in

---

* Mnemonic for I–VIII: all altruists gladly make gum in gallon tanks. Write the names in a line and above each write CH$_2$OH. Then, for C_5 write OH to the right all the way across. For C_4 write OH to the right four times, then H; for C_3, OH, OH; then H, H, and repeat; C_2, alternate OH and H to the right.

pairs of 2-epimers, Wohl degradation of both members of each pair gives the same D-pentose. For example, allose (I) and altrose (II) give ribose;

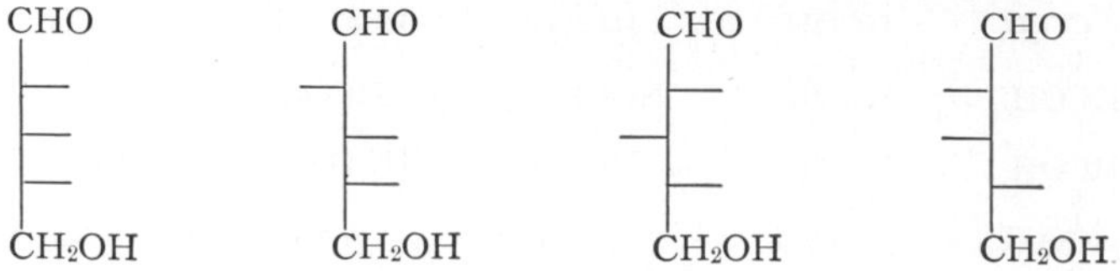

CHO	CHO	CHO	CHO
CH₂OH	CH₂OH	CH₂OH	CH₂OH
Ribose	Arabinose	Xylose	Lyxose

CHO

CH₂OH

Erythrose

CHO

CH₂OH

Threose

glucose and mannose give arabinose.   The two D-tetroses are related in the same way to pairs of D-pentoses.

Lobry de Bruyn[7]-van Ekenstein[8] Rearrangement. — Fischer's discovery that reduction of glucose in an alkaline medium affords mannitol as one of the products is a consequence of a rearrangement of α-ketols in alkaline solution named for the Dutch discoverers, which has been illustrated by the isomerization between glyceraldehyde and dihydroxyacetone (p. 124).   An aldose treated with base usually gives a mixture of the 2-epimer, the 2-ketose, and the original aldehyde.   Under usual conditions the isomerization seems to proceed through the enediol since, in the presence of heavy water, deu-

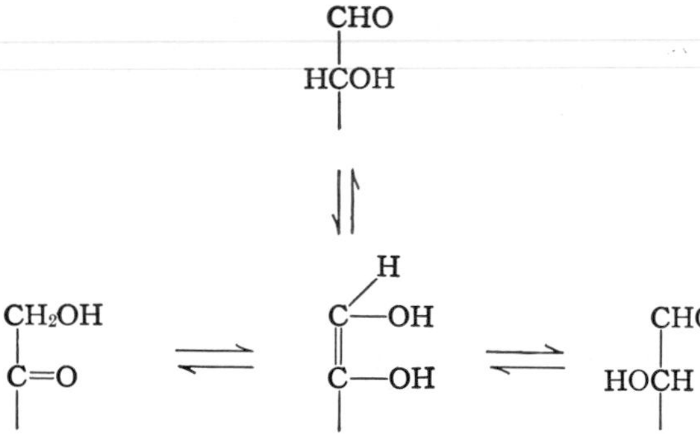

CHO
HCOH

CH₂OH   H
C=O   ⇌   C—OH   ⇌   CHO
             C—OH   HOCH

Enediol

terium appears at C_1 and C_2, evidently as the result of exchange with the acidic enediol. A sugar carrying a methoxyl group at the 2-position is

---

[7] C. A. Lobry de Bruyn, 1857–1904; b. Leedenwarden, Netherlands; Ph.D. Leiden; Amsterdam; *Ber.*, **37**, 4827 (1904); *J. Chem. Soc.*, **87**, 570 (1905)

[8] W. Alberda van Ekenstein, 1858–1937; b. Gröningen, Netherlands; Amsterdam

epimerized by alkali at C_2 with deuterium exchange at this position.   A second mechanism seems to operate in very weakly alkaline solution at low temperature, since isomerization takes place without deuterium exchange. A possible path from an aldose to a ketose is nucleophilic attack by hydroxide ion to give an ionic intermediate in which hydrogen migrates with its electron pair; reversal of the process would give opportunity for epimerization at C_2.

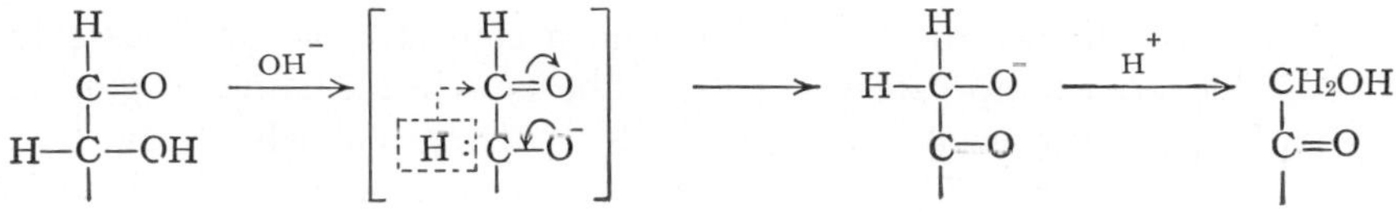

Oxide Structure. — Although glucose enters into some reactions common to aldehydes, it fails to give a color with fuchsin–sulfurous acid (Schiff test) and reacts with bisulfite to a much lesser extent than ordinary aldehydes.   Tollens[9] (1883) suggested that this behavior could be explained on the assumption of a butylene oxide (1,4) structure. Tollens's formulation, however, was not generally accepted. Ten years later, Fischer attempted to convert glucose into the methyl acetal by treatment with methanol and hydrogen chloride in accordance with the usual reaction: $-CHO + 2HOCH_3 \rightarrow -CH(OCH_3)_2$.   The reaction product, surprisingly, contained only one methyl group and was named methylglucoside (50% yield).   The substance did not reduce Fehling's solution and showed no aldehydic properties; and Fischer inferred that it must have a structure similar to that of an acetal but containing, in place of one of the usual groups, an oxidic linkage extending to one of the carbon atoms of the sugar chain.   The proposed formula indicates the presence of one additional asymmetric carbon atom, and hence the reaction should yield two isomeric glucosides. The second, β-methylglucoside, was isolated the following year by van Ekenstein.   Fischer pointed out that the oxide structure of the glucosides did not constitute evidence for a similar structure for glucose.   The structures assigned to the glucosides can be considered as derived from the cyclic form postulated by Tollens, but they were not so interpreted, and the next indication of a cyclic structure for the free sugar came from observations of another phenomenon.

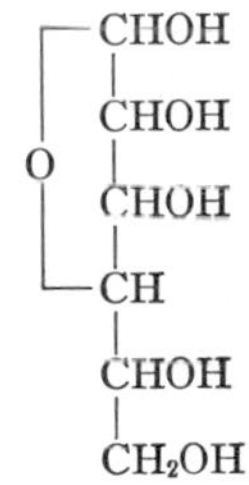

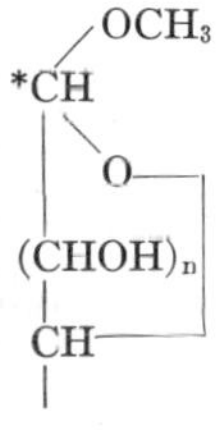

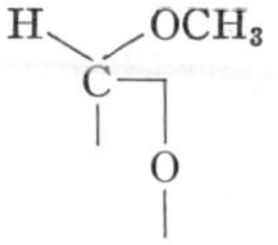

α-Methylglucoside
$[\alpha]_D + 159°$

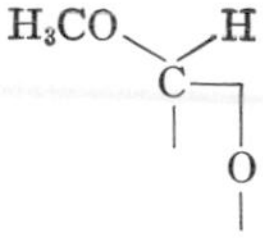

β-Methylglucoside
$[\alpha]_D - 34°$

[9] Bernhard Tollens; 1841–1918; b. Hamburg; Ph.D. Göttingen; Göttingen

A freshly prepared solution of glucose shows a rotation of $[\alpha]_D + 113°$, which gradually decreases on standing to a value of $+52°$. This change, first observed in 1846, is known as **mutarotation**. It is not the result of decomposition, for after mutarotation to a constant value, material can be recovered that has all the properties of the original D-glucose and shows a specific rotation in a fresh solution of $+113°$. Fischer attributed the change to reversible hydration, but this explanation became untenable when Tanret[10] (1895) prepared an isomeric crystalline D-glucose by crystallization of the highly rotatory form from a concentrated aqueous solution at an elevated temperature (110°). The new form, named β-glucose, shows an initial rotation of $[\alpha]_D + 19°$, which changes slowly to the equilibrium value of $+52°$. The ordinary or α-form of glucose is obtained by crystallization from alcohol–water. The obvious inference that the two forms, α- and β-glucose, are analogous to α- and β-methylglucoside was neatly confirmed by Armstrong[11] (1903). Fischer had noted that α-methylglucoside is hydrolyzed by the enzyme maltase, which has no effect on the β-modification, whereas β-methylglucoside is hydrolyzed by emulsin, which does not attack the α-form. Armstrong followed the enzymatic hydrolysis by polarimetric analysis and found that α-methylglucoside is converted into α-glucose, whereas β-methylglucoside is converted into β-glucose. Mutarotation of the sugar therefore is attributable to isomerization of one cyclic form into the other, probably by opening of the oxide ring to give the free aldehyde, and closure in the alternate steric sense by addition of the alco-

α-Form $\qquad$ Aldehydic $\qquad$ β-Form
$[\alpha]_D + 113°$ $\qquad$ form $\qquad$ $[\alpha]_D + 19°$

holic hydroxyl to the carbonyl group. An aged solution of glucose thus contains α- and β-glucose in equilibrium with the aldehydic form. Since the methylglucosides do not reduce Fehling's solution or combine with phenylhydrazine or with hydrogen cyanide, the response of glucose solutions to these reagents must be due to the aldehydic form present in the equilibrium mixture; as this form reacts and is removed from the equilibrium, more is formed from the oxides, and eventually the entire material is converted into the derivative of the aldehydic form. The equilibrium concentration of the reactive species apparently is low, and hence conditions are unfavorable for reversible addition of sodium bisulfite, and equilibrium is reached at a point of low conversion.

That the glucosidic hydroxyl group of the α-form is *cis* to the adjacent

---

[10] Charles Tanret, 1847–1917; b. Joinville s. Marne; apothecary in Paris
[11] Edward Frankland Armstrong, 1878–1945 (son of H. E. Armstrong); Dir. South Metropol. Gas Co., London; *Nature*, **157**, 154 (1946)

hydroxyl group was inferred from the observation that α-glucose, in common with *cis*-glycols, forms a complex with boric acid, as evidenced by the conductivity of α-glucose in boric acid solution, which gradually decreases as α-glucose is converted in part into β-glucose. The conductivity of β-glucose in boric acid solution gradually increases. The effect is considered to result from formation of an ionic complex:

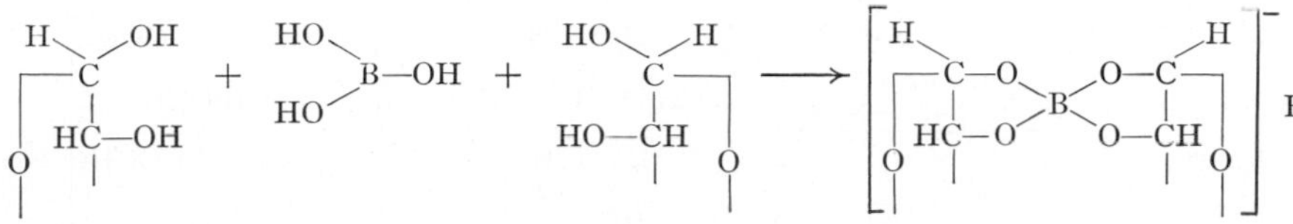

Chemical evidence is that glucose-1,2-anhydride-3,4,6-triacetate reacts rapidly with methanol at room temperature without catalyst to give β-methylglucoside-3,4,5-triacetate in nearly quantitative yield. Fission of

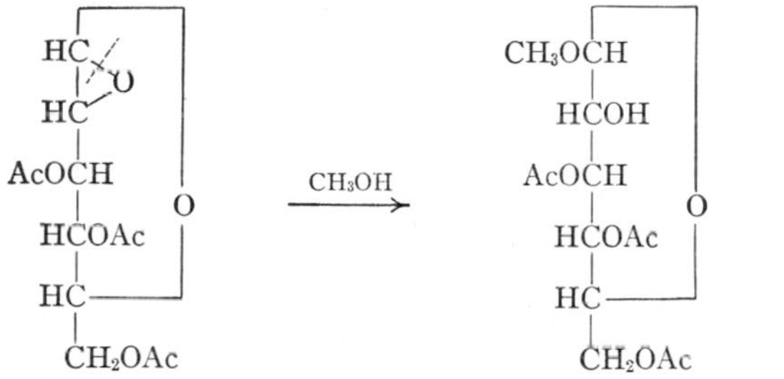

Glucose-1,2-anhydride-
3,4,6-triacetate

β-Methylglucoside-
3,4,6-triacetate

the ethylene oxide ring at the bond extending to C_1 must be attended with Walden inversion, and hence the 1-methoxyl group is *trans* to the 2-hydroxyl group, or β.

A glycoside having the six-membered pyran ring is now called a pyranoside and one corresponding to furan a furanoside. The furanoside structure was regarded as the more likely until 1926 when both Haworth[12] and Hirst[13] presented evidence that methylglucoside is a 1,5-oxide, or pyrano-

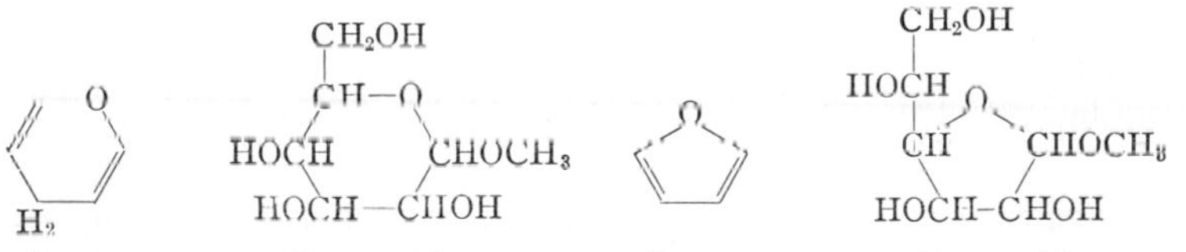

Pyran   Pyranoside   Furan   Furanoside

side. That of Hirst is based upon the oxidation products of tetramethylglucose. Methylglucoside can be methylated with methyl iodide and silver

[12] Walter Norman Haworth, 1883–1950; b. Chorley, Lancashire; Ph.D. Göttingen (Wallach); D.Sc. Manchester (Perkin, Jr.); Birmingham; Nobel Prize 1937; *J. Chem. Soc.*, 2790 (1951)

[13] Edmund Langley Hirst, b. 1898; D.Sc. Birmingham (Haworth); Birmingham; Bristol, Edinburgh

oxide (Purdie,[14] 1903) or with dimethyl sulfate in an alkaline medium (Haworth, 1915) to form a pentamethyl derivative in which four of the methyl groups are present in stable ether linkage. The glucosidic methyl group is hydrolyzed readily by dilute acids but not by alkali (cf., acetals) with formation of tetramethylglucose. Hirst oxidized tetramethylglucose

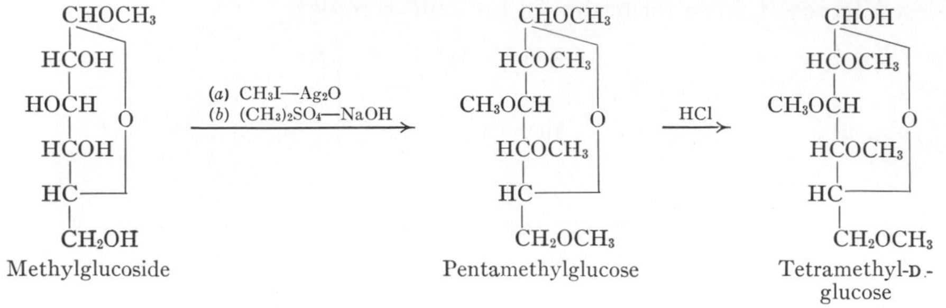

CHOCH₃
|
HCOH
|
HOCH   O
|
HCOH
|
HC————
|
CH₂OH
Methylglucoside

(a) CH₃I—Ag₂O
(b) (CH₃)₂SO₄—NaOH
→

CHOCH₃
|
HCOCH₃
|
CH₃OCH   O
|
HCOCH₃
|
HC————
|
CH₂OCH₃
Pentamethylglucose

HCl
→

CHOH
|
HCOCH₃
|
CH₃OCH   O
|
HCOCH₃
|
HC————
|
CH₂OCH₃
Tetramethyl-D-glucose

with nitric acid and obtained in good yield two acids, xylotrimethoxyglutaric acid and *d*-dimethoxysuccinic acid, both of which were isolated and identified as the diamides. Formation of these two acids can be accounted for only on the basis of a 1,5-oxide structure. Formation of xylotrimethoxyglutaric

CHOH
|
HCOCH₃
|
CH₃OCH   O
|
HCOCH₃
|
HC————
|
CH₂OCH₃
Tetramethyl-D-glucose

HNO₃
→

[
COOH
|
HCOCH₃
|
CH₃OCH
|
HCOCH₃
|
HCOH
|
CH₂OCH₃
]

→

COOH
|
HCOCH₃
|
CH₃OCH
|
HCOCH₃
|
COOH
Xylotrimethoxy-glutaric acid

+

COOH
|
HCOCH₃
|
CH₃OCH
|
COOH
d-Dimethoxy-succinic acid

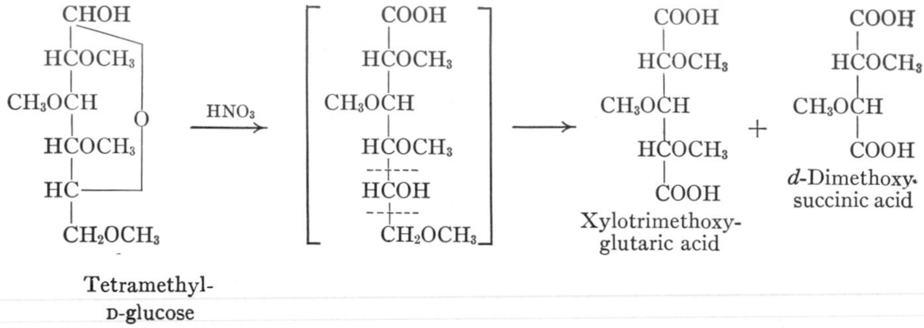

acid shows that the methoxyl groups of tetramethylglucose are located on carbon atoms 2, 3, 4, and 6, and hence these positions cannot be involved in formation of the oxide ring. Other hexoses in their normal forms also contain a six-membered, or pyranose ring.

A simple and elegant method of determining both the ring size of glycosides and the configurations at positions of glycosidic linkage developed by E. L. Jackson and C. S. Hudson (1936) involves oxidation with periodic acid in aqueous solution. The pyranoside I consumes two moles of reagent and the furanoside III consumes one mole, and both substances afford the same dialdehyde II in high yield. The oxidation eliminates three centers of asymmetry in I, and removes carbon atom 3 as formic acid; in III two centers of asymmetry are destroyed. The method has provided direct proof that glycosides assigned to the α-D-hexose series on other evidence

[14] Thomas Purdie, 1843–1916; b. Biggar, Scotland; Ph.D. Würzburg; St. Andrews Univ.

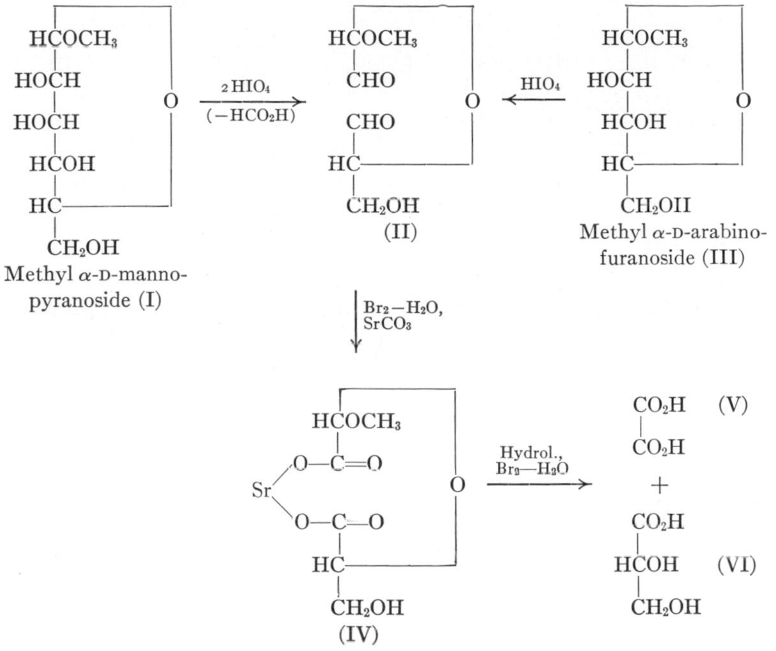

Methyl α-D-manno-pyranoside (I) $\xrightarrow[(-HCO_2H)]{2 HIO_4}$ (II) $\xleftarrow{HIO_4}$ Methyl α-D-arabino-furanoside (III)

(II) $\xrightarrow[SrCO_3]{Br_2-H_2O,}$ (IV) $\xrightarrow[Br_2-H_2O]{Hydrol.,}$ (V) + (VI)

I:

HĊOCH₃
|
HOĊH
|
HOĊH
|
HĊOH
|
HĊ——
|
ĊH₂OH

II:

HĊOCH₃
|
CHO
|
CHO
|
HĊ——
|
ĊH₂OH

III:

HĊOCH₃
|
HOĊH
|
HĊOH
|
HĊ——
|
ĊH₂OII

IV:

HĊOCH₃
|
O—C=O
Sr
O—C—O
|
HĊ——
|
ĊH₂OH

V:

CO₂H
|
CO₂H

VI:

CO₂H
|
HĊOH
|
ĊH₂OH

have the same configurations at C_1 and at C_5, for they all yield the dialdehyde II, in which these two asymmetric centers alone remain. Oxidation of the dialdehyde with bromine water in the presence of a metal carbonate affords a dibasic acid easily isolated as the crystalline salt (IV), and this on hydrolysis and oxidation yields oxalic acid and D-glyceric acid (VI). This sequence of reactions is the best method known of preparing optically pure glyceric and lactic acids.

The proper representation of α-D-glucose with a Fischer tetrahedral formula may not be obvious without reference to a mechanical model. In formula VII for D-glucose, the asymmetric carbon atoms 2, 3, 4, and 5 are aligned with the edge of each tetrahedron carrying H and OH projecting to the front. Carbon atom 1 is similarly oriented so that when the α-oxide ring is formed the C_1-OH will be to the right, adjacent to the C_2-OH. This means that the oxide link will project from the rear of C_1 and therefore will extend to the rear of C_5. Such connection to C_5 is not possible so long as the C_5-OH is oriented to the right front, and hence C_5 must be rotated about the single bond to C_5 until the hydroxyl group is oriented in the rear position, as in VIII. The oxide ring can now close by opening of the rear bond (dotted) of the carbonyl group by addition of the C_5-OH, and the result is the α-oxide IX. The most appropriate planar projection of IX is X, in which the dotted line expresses the idea that the oxide link extends to the rear of the carbon chain. Since the relationship of this projection to that ordinarily used for D-glucose is not easily apparent, alternate approximate projections, such as those shown above, are usually employed. The spatial

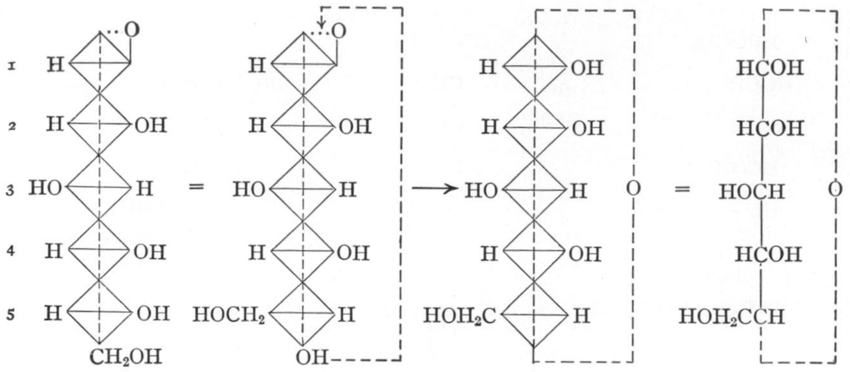

$$
\begin{array}{c|c|c|c}
\text{VII} & \text{VIII} & \text{IX} & \text{X}
\end{array}
$$

1 H—O	H—O	H——OH	HCOH
2 H——OH	H——OH	H——OH	HCOH
3 HO——H = HO——H → HO——H O = HOCH O
4 H——OH	H——OH	H——OH	HCOH
5 H——OH HOCH₂——H HOH₂C——H HOH₂CCH
CH₂OH	OH----		

  VII   VIII   IX   X

⎵_____⎵   ⎵_____⎵

  D-Glucose   α-D-Glucose

relationships of the cyclic forms of the sugars are shown with greater clarity by the formulation XI introduced by W. N. Haworth (1929); this represen-

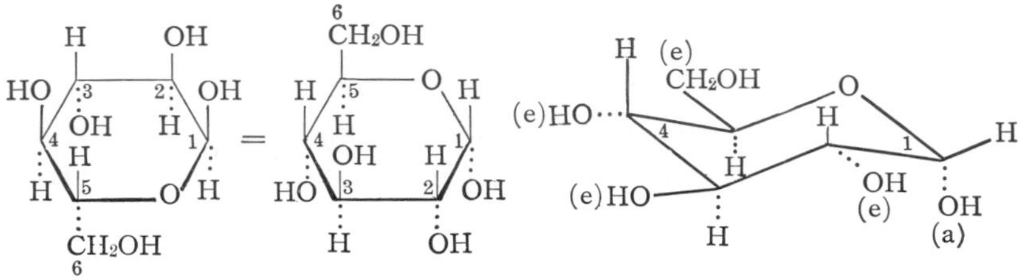

XI   XII   XIII

(Haworth)   Conformation

α-D-Glucose (pyranose)

tation is easily derivable from the tetrahedral formula IX. The formula can be inverted, and then becomes XII. The preferred conformation, as indicated by studies of cuprammonium complex formation, is shown in formula XIII (R. E. Reeves, 1949). Fructose is known in only one crystalline form, probably a pyranose; solutions probably contain the furanose as well.

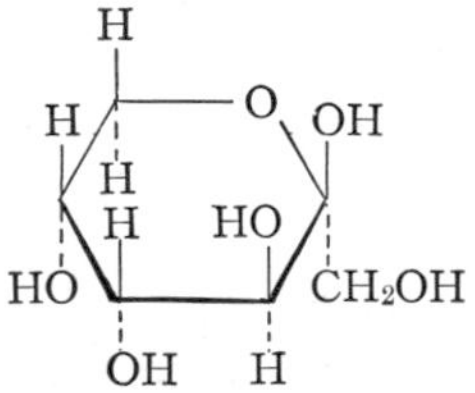

β-D-Fructopyranose 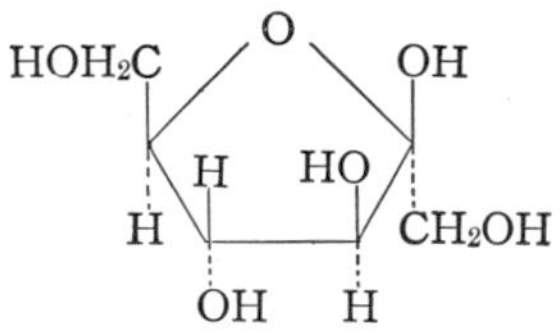   β-D-Fructofuranose

In the preparation of the methylglucosides, Fischer obtained in addition a sirup which he originally assumed to be the acetal but which he later (1914) showed contained a third isomer, γ-methylglucoside. Fischer suggested that the γ-form probably differed in the size of the oxide ring because of profound differences in properties from the α- and β-isomers: greater instability to acids, complete stability to maltase and emulsin. The substance is a mixture of α- and β-methylglucofuranosides; the structure was established in 1927 (Haworth) by the method described above. γ-Glucose

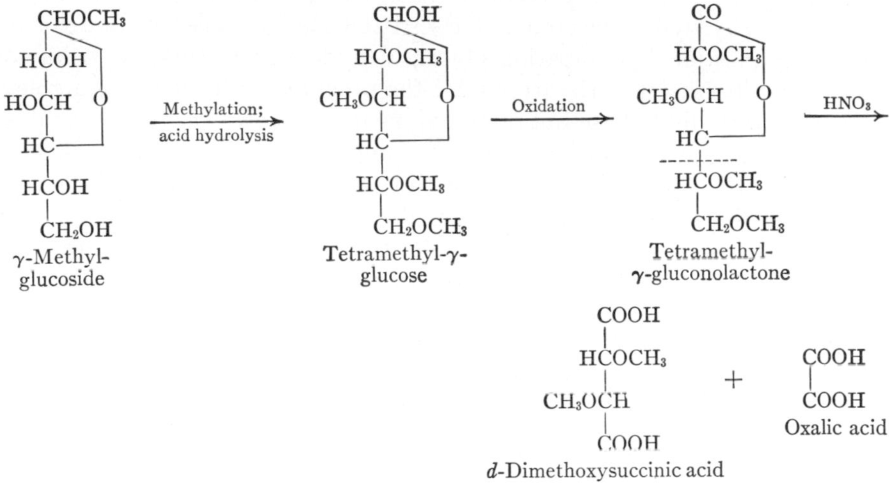

has not been isolated, but presumably is present in glucose solutions in equilibrium with the glucopyranose forms and the free aldehyde.

Synthesis of Glucose and Fructose. — Carbohydrates arise in plants from fixation of carbon dioxide and absorption of water. Photosynthesis can be expressed by a simple equation established in 1804 by de Saussure, who found that the amount of carbon dioxide absorbed by green plants is

$$6\,CO_2 \;+\; 6\,H_2O \xrightarrow{\text{Sunlight}} \underset{\text{Hexose}}{C_6H_{12}O_6} \;+\; 6\,O_2$$

$$\downarrow$$

$$\text{Polysaccharide}$$

the molecular equivalent of the oxygen expired. The combination of carbon dioxide and water to form carbohydrate and oxygen is endothermic, and the necessary energy is derived from sunlight; burning of a carbohydrate or derived product is a reversal of photosynthesis, and liberation of heat represents a tapping of stored radiant energy. Formaldehyde, CH_2O, since it has the composition of hexoses, was considered a likely intermediate in photosynthesis of sugars, and in 1861 Butleroff[15] converted the polymer, paraformaldehyde, by treatment with dilute alkali into a sweet sirup that

---

[15] Alexander M. Butleroff, 1828–86; b. Tschistopol, Gouv. Kasan, Russia; St. Petersburg

resembled glucose in chemical properties, but that was a complex mixture nonfermentable by yeast. O. Loew repeated the experiment twenty-five years later using formaldehyde, which had since become available, and obtained a similar sirup, formose. In the course of studying the osazone

CH=NNHC₆H₅ reaction with polyvalent alcohols, Fischer (1887) treated glycerol with nitric acid (or bromine) and, on adding phenylhydrazine to the solution, obtained glycerosazone. Reasoning that the nitric acid initially must have oxidized glycerol either to glyceraldehyde, $CH_2OHCHOHCHO$, or to dihydroxyacetone, $CH_2OHCOCH_2OH$, Fischer sought to settle the question by preparing glyceraldehyde and testing the behavior with phenylhydrazine. He attempted the preparation by treating acrolein dibromide with dilute base but obtained, instead of the expected glyceraldehyde, a sirup acrose, which showed the properties of an aldehyde-alcohol. "One of us (F.) has tried for a long time to isolate from the product an analyzable preparation because it seemed possible to realize in this way the synthesis of a sugar.   But only the application of phenylhydrazine furnished us a sure result. From the degradation products of dibromoacrolein we

$$
\begin{array}{c}
CH_2Br \\
| \\
CHBr \\
| \\
CHO
\end{array}
\xrightarrow{Ba(OH)_2}
\left[
\begin{array}{c}
CH_2OH \\
| \\
CHOH \\
| \\
CHO
\end{array}
\right]
\longrightarrow \text{Acrose}
$$

Acrolein dibromide

obtained an osazone of the hexane series, $C_{18}H_{22}O_4N_4$." * Shortly afterward a second osazone was isolated, and the two substances were named α-acrosazone (m.p. 205°) and β-acrosazone (m.p. 148°). At the time, Fischer suggested that the properties corresponded closely to thos of the osazones of glucose and sorbose, respectively, with the exception that the acrosazones were optically inactive. A more convenient synthesis was then developed from glycerol. The hexose chain is formed as the result of aldol addition of dihydroxyacetone, through the activated α-hydrogen atom, to the carbonyl group of glyceraldehyde. The resulting ketohexose has

$$
\begin{array}{c}
CH_2OH \\
| \\
2\ CHOH \\
| \\
CH_2OH
\end{array}
\xrightarrow{Br_2,\ Na_2CO_3}
\left\{
\begin{array}{c}
CH_2OH \\
| \\
CO \\
| \\
CH_2OH \\
| \\
+ \\
CH=O \\
| \\
*CHOH \\
| \\
CH_2OH
\end{array}
\right.
\xrightarrow[48\ hrs.]{NaOH,\ 0°,}
\begin{array}{c}
CH_2OH \\
| \\
CO \\
| \\
*CHOH \\
| \\
*CHOH \\
| \\
*CHOH \\
| \\
CH_2OH
\end{array}
$$

"Glycerose"   α- and β-Acrose

* E. Fischer and J. Tafel, "Oxydation der mehrwertigen Alkohole," *Ber.*, **20**, 1088 (1887)

three asymmetric carbon atoms, and hence eight optically active forms are possible. However, the aldehydic reaction component has an asymmetric carbon atom, and this exercises a control over the mode of addition to the carbonyl group. The glyceraldehyde involved in the synthesis is the *dl*-form, but by virtue of the principle of asymmetric synthesis (p. 276) each enantiomer directs the aldol addition in a specific steric sense, with the result that only half of the theoretically possible isomers are produced. The synthesis thus affords two substances of different physical properties, α- and β-acrose, each of which consists of a *dl*-mixture of enantiomers. The overall yield of α-acrosazone is about 1.5%. α-Acrosazone was also isolated from a sirup made from formaldehyde according to Loew's method. In 1890 Fischer showed that α-acrose is DL-fructose by the following series of reactions:

$$
\begin{array}{ccccccc}
\text{CH}{=}\text{NNHC}_6\text{H}_5 & & \text{CHO} & & \text{CH}_2\text{OH} & & \text{CH}_2\text{OH} \\
| & & | & & | & & | \\
\text{C}{=}\text{NNHC}_6\text{H}_5 & \xrightarrow{\ 2\,\text{H}_2\text{O}\ } & \text{C}{=}\text{O} & \xrightarrow{\ \text{Zn}-\text{HCl}\ } & \text{C}{=}\text{O} & \xrightarrow{\ \text{Na(Hg)}\ } & \text{CHOH} \\
| & & | & & | & & | \\
(\text{CHOH})_3 & & (\text{CHOH})_3 & & (\text{CHOH})_3 & & (\text{CHOH})_3 \\
| & & | & & | & & | \\
\text{CH}_2\text{OH} & & \text{CH}_2\text{OH} & & \text{CH}_2\text{OH} & & \text{CH}_2\text{OH} \\
\text{α-Acrosazone} & & \text{α-Acrosone} & & \text{α-Acrose} & & \text{α-Acritol}
\end{array}
$$

α-Acritol (0.2 g. from 1 kg. of glycerol) is identical with DL-mannitol, the reduction product of either DL-fructose or DL-mannose, and hence α-acrose could be either of these DL-hexoses, but the second possibility is eliminated by the fact that DL-mannose forms a characteristic insoluble phenylhydrazone, a property that is not shown by α-acrose. Fischer first attempted to separate α-acrose by preferential fermentation with yeast, but the substance isolated from the unfermented residue proved to be the dextrorotatory enantiomer of natural fructose, namely L-fructose. Consequently, he resorted

$$
\begin{array}{ccccccc}
\text{CH}_2\text{OH} & & \text{CH}_2\text{OH} & & \text{CHO} & & \text{COOH} \\
| & & | & & | & & | \\
\text{C}{=}\text{O} & \xrightarrow{\ \text{Na}-\text{Hg}\ } & \text{CHOH} & \xrightarrow{\ \text{HNO}_3\ } & (\text{CHOH})_4 & \xrightarrow{\ \text{Br}_2\ \ \text{H}_2\text{O}\ } & (\text{CHOH})_4 & \xrightarrow{\ \text{Morphine}\ } \\
| & & | & & | & & | \\
(\text{CHOH})_3 & & (\text{CHOH})_3 & & \text{CH}_2\text{OH} & & \text{CH}_2\text{OH} \\
| & & | & & \text{DL Mannose} & & \text{DL-Mannonic} \\
\text{CH}_2\text{OH} & & \text{CH}_2\text{OH} & & & & \text{acid} \\
\text{DL-Fructose} & & \text{DL-Mannitol} \\
\text{(α-acrose)}
\end{array}
$$

$$
\left.\begin{array}{l}
d\text{-Morphine salt} \\
l\text{-Morphine salt}
\end{array}\right\} \ \text{Fractional crystallization, NaOH} \ \begin{array}{l} \nearrow\ \text{D-Mannonic acid} \\ \searrow\ \text{L-Mannonic acid} \end{array}
$$

to more tedious chemical methods in order to obtain the natural form. The ketohexose was reduced to an alcohol and this was oxidized in two steps to DL-mannonic acid, which was resolved by fractional crystallization of the morphine salt to the optically active components. D-Mannonic acid was converted into the epimeric acid, D-gluconic acid, which has the stereo-

```
   COOH                      COOH                    CO─┐                   CHO
    |                         |                       |  |                    |
  HOCH                      HCOH                     HCOH |                  HCOH
    |         Pyridine, 140°   |          HCl         |   O       Na—Hg      |
  HOCH      ────────────→    HOCH      ──────→      HOCH |      ────────→   HOCH
    |                         |                       |  |                    |
  HCOH                      HCOH                     HC─┘                   HCOH
    |                         |                       |                      |
  HCOH                      HCOH                     HCOH                   HCOH
    |                         |                       |                      |
  CH₂OH                     CH₂OH                    CH₂OH                  CH₂OH
 D-Mannonic               D-Gluconic               γ-Lactone              D-Glucose
   acid                     acid
```

chemical configuration of D-glucose, by a reaction discovered by Fischer in 1890. Epimerization is a general reaction induced by heating in quinoline or pyridine, and results in inversion of the carbon atom adjacent to the carboxylic acid group (through the enol, p. 274). Conversion of D-gluconic acid into D-glucose is accomplished by reduction of the readily formed γ-lactone. The first synthesis of a natural sugar was announced in the statement:* "One is now able to prepare grape sugar (D-glucose) from glycerol and even from formaldehyde. To be sure, the way is very long, and it appears desirable to shorten it by simpler methods."

Synthesis of D-fructose was accomplished in the same year by the re-

```
   COOH                   CO─┐                     CHO
    |                      |  |                      |
  HOCH                   HOCH |                    HOCH
    |        HCl          |   O      Na—Hg          |            3 NH₂NHC₆H₅
  HOCH     ──────→      HOCH |     ───────→       HOCH        ──────────────→
    |                    |  |                       |
  HCOH                  HC─┘                      HCOH
    |                      |                        |
  HCOH                   HCOH                     HCOH
    |                      |                        |
  CH₂OH                  CH₂OH                    CH₂OH
D-Mannonic acid        γ-Lactone                D-Mannose
```

```
  CH=NNHC₆H₅                  CHO                    CH₂OH
    |                          |                       |
  C=NNHC₆H₅                   C=O                     C=O
    |                          |                       |
  HOCH           H₂O         HOCH       Zn—HOAc      HOCH
    |         ──────→         |        ────────→      |
  HCOH                       HCOH                    HCOH
    |                          |                       |
  HCOH                       HCOH                    HCOH
    |                          |                       |
  CH₂OH                      CH₂OH                    CH₂OH
D-Glucosazone              Glucosone               D-Fructose
```

actions shown. The process includes a series of reactions whereby an aldose is transformed into a ketose; the reverse transformation is illustrated by the conversion of DL-fructose into DL-mannose.

---

* E. Fischer, "Synthese des Traubenzuckers," *Ber.*, **23**, 799 (1890)

MOLECULAR ROTATION RELATIONSHIPS

When an alcohol R_1R_2CHOH is to be compared in optical properties with its derivatives, for example the acetate, benzoate, or methyl ether, compensation for incidental variations in molecular weight is made by comparisons based on molecular rotation, M_D, calculated as follows:*

$$M_D = \frac{[\alpha]_D \times \text{Mol. Wt.}}{100}$$

Thus for α-D-glucose: $[\alpha]_D^{20} = +112.2°$ W (W = water solution; extrapolated to zero time) and $M_D = (+112.2 \times 180.16)/100 = +202.1$. Whereas octaacetylsucrose, $[\alpha]_D + 59.6°$ Chf (chloroform), differs considerably from octastearylsucrose, $[\alpha]_D + 16.6°$ Chf, in specific rotation, the molecular rotations, $M_D +404$ and $+411$, are the same within the limits of error of polarimetry (c.$5°$ difference in $[\alpha]_D$ of the octastearate changes M_D by 12 units).

van't Hoff Principle of Additivity. — van't Hoff in 1898 deduced the principle that the molecular rotation of a compound containing several centers of asymmetry is the algebraic sum of the individual rotatory contributions of the component rotatory centers, or rotophores. Since experimental data were not available for calculation of individual rotatory effects, the idea was illustrated by supposing the superposition of a molecule composed of $+A +B +C$ centers with one made up of $-A +B +C$ rotophores; since the fragment $+B +C$ is common to both molecules, the difference in M_D between them is $+2A$. The van't Hoff principle of additivity thus is often described by the rather misleading designation "principle of optical superposition." Where the molecular rotations of a pair of epimers are known (M_D^{α} and M_D^{β}), the rotophoric effects at the center of epimerization can be calculated as follows:

Contribution of $C_{1\alpha} = + A = (M_D^{\alpha} - M_D^{\beta})/2$

Contribution of $C_{1\beta} - - A - - (M_D^{\alpha} - M_D^{\beta})/2$

Configurations. — When the Haworth perspective formula for α-D-glucose is oriented with the oxidic oxygen to the top or rear and C_1 to the right (I), the C_1-hydrogen projects to the front (or up, full line) and the C_1-hydroxyl projects to the rear (or down, dotted line). In β-D-glucose (II) the substituents on the carbon atom of the potential carbonyl groups have the inverted orientation; epimers of this particular type are defined as anomers.

Configurations relative to that of α-D-glucose of the other members of the series of eight α-D-pyranoses are recorded in Chart I, which gives both

---

* van't Hoff (1898) introduced the concept of molecular rotation as the product of the specific rotation and the molecular weight "for shortness divided by 100."

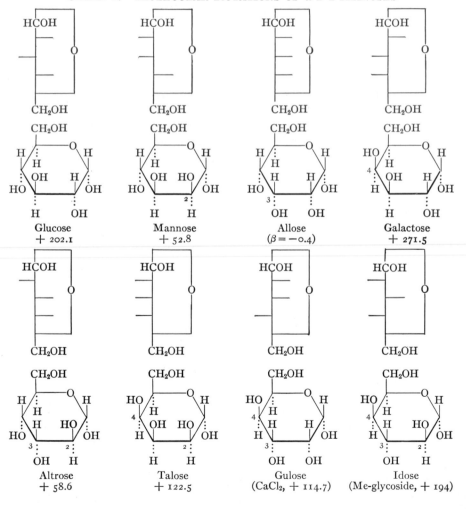

α-D-Glucose   β-D-Glucose

the Haworth formulas and the corresponding formulas written in a conventional abbreviated form; the orientation of a hydroxyl group is indicated by a bar extending to either the right or the left. Molecular rotations in water (W) at 20° are given where known; these are based upon specific

CHART I. MOLECULAR ROTATIONS OF α-D-PYRANOSES

Glucose + 202.1

Mannose + 52.8

Allose (β = −0.4)

Galactose + 271.5

Altrose + 58.6

Talose + 122.5

Gulose (CaCl₂, + 114.7)

Idose (Me-glycoside, + 194)

rotations extrapolated to zero time, for sugars exhibit mutarotation (possible exception: D-altrose). In the formula for mannose, carbon atom 2 is numbered to indicate that this sugar differs from glucose only at C_2. Allose and galactose are inverted at C_3 and C_4, respectively, and the sugars in the second line are inverted at the multiple points indicated.

Individual Rotatory Contributions. — The rotatory contribution of C_1 in α-D-glucose can be estimated by the van't Hoff principle as formulated above from rotations of the 1-epimers (mol. wt. = 180.16):

	$[\alpha]_D$	M_D	
α-D-Glucose	$+112.2$	$+202.1$	$\dfrac{M_D^\alpha - M_D^\beta}{2} = +84.2$
β-D-Glucose	$+18.7$	$+33.7$	

Thus in α-D-glucose C_1 makes a dextrorotatory contribution of $+84$ units and in β-D-glucose the contribution of C_1 is -84 units. Similar calculations from comparison of α-D-glucose with α-D-mannose and with α-D-galactose indicate that in α-D-glucose the contribution of C_2 is $+75$ and the contribution of C_4 is -35. The contributions of C_3 and C_5 cannot yet be estimated in comparable fashion because α-D-allose and α-D-idose have not been characterized.

Hudson's Rules. — Comparison of isomers that differ in configuration at each of two contiguous asymmetric centers is vitiated by an as yet undeterminable vicinal effect of each center on the rotatory contribution of the other. This vicinal action is illustrated by the comparison given in Table 14.1 of the molecular rotations of pairs of pyranoses that differ only

TABLE 14.1. COMPARISON OF Cα- AND Cβ-SUGARS

SUGAR	M_D		$M_D^\alpha - M_D^\beta$
	α	β	
Glucopyranose type			
Glucose	$+202.1$	$+33.7$	$+168.4$
Galactose	$+271.5$	-95.1	$+176.4$
Lactose (disaccharide)	$+306.3$	$+119.5$	186.8
Mannopyranose type			
Mannose	$+52.8$	-30.6	$+83.4$
Talose	$+122.5$	$+23.8$	$+98.7$
4-Glucomannose	$+53.0$	-22.0	$+75.0$

in the configuration at C_1. The isomer of the α-configuration is invariably more dextrorotatory than the 1β-epimer, but the difference amounts to an average of $+177$ units in the case of glucose, galactose, and lactose, and to an average of only $+86$ units in the case of mannose, talose, and 4-glucomannose. The difference in the averages ($+177$ and $+86$) affords an indication of the magnitude of the vicinal effect concerned. Hudson[16] (1909) expressed the relationships illustrated in Table 14.1 by a **first rule** stating that the rotatory contribution of C_1 is affected in only a minor degree by changes in the structure of the remainder of the molecule and that in the D series the more dextrorotatory anomer (C_1-epimer) is always the α-form.

Hudson's **second rule** states that changes at the glucosidic carbon atom (C_1), for example the change from C_1-OH to C_1-OR, affect in only a minor degree rotation of the remainder of the molecule. That methyl α-D-glu-

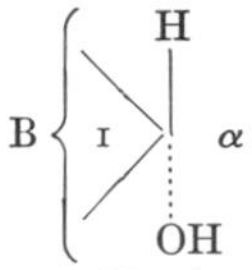

α-D-Glucose
$M_D + 202.1$

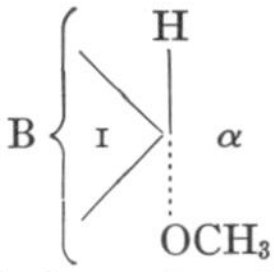

Methyl α-D-glucoside
$M_D + 308.6$

coside is distinctly more dextrorotatory than α-D-glucose can be interpreted as meaning that the bulkier OCH_3 increases dissymmetry of C_1 and hence accentuates the dextrorotatory contribution of C_1. Methyl β-D-glucoside is correspondingly more levorotatory than the parent β-D-glucose (Table 14.2). Increase in size of the alkyl group from methyl to benzyl results in progressive, smaller changes in the same direction. If the rotatory contribution of C_1 is $+A$ in the α-form and $-A$ in the β-form and the contribu-

TABLE 14.2. D-GLUCOPYRANOSIDES

C_1-SUBSTITUENT	M_D		
	1α	1β	SUM
OH (D-Glucose)	$+202.1$	$+33.7$	$+235.8$
OCH_3	$+308.6$	-66.4	$+242.2$
OC_2H_5	$+313.6$	-69.5	$+244.1$
$OC_3H_7\text{-}n$	$+312.9$	-77.6	$+235.3$
$OCH_2C_6H_5$	$+354.1$	-150.2	$+203.9$
OC_6H_5	$+463.3$	-181.9	$+281.4$

tion of the rest of the molecule is B, then the sum of the rotations of any pair of 1-epimers should be a constant quantity, 2B. The data of Table 14.2 show that ($M_D^\alpha + M_D^\beta$) is indeed substantially a constant; whereas M_D^α varies from $+202$ to $+463$, the sum of the molecular rotations deviates from the average of $+240$ to the extent of only ±15 (average).

The data of Tables 14.1 and 14.2 include several illustrations of the gen-

[16] Claude S. Hudson, 1881–1952; b. Atlanta; Ph.D. Princeton; U. S. Public Health Service; *J. Chem. Soc.*, 4042 (1954)

eral relationship that in a pair of glycosidic anomers of the D-series, the isomer with the glycosidic hydroxyl or alkoxyl group in the α-orientation is invariably more dextrorotatory than the β-epimer. The rule holds for the pentoses, D-lyxose and D-xylose, for the molecular rotation differences $(\alpha - \beta)$ are again positive:

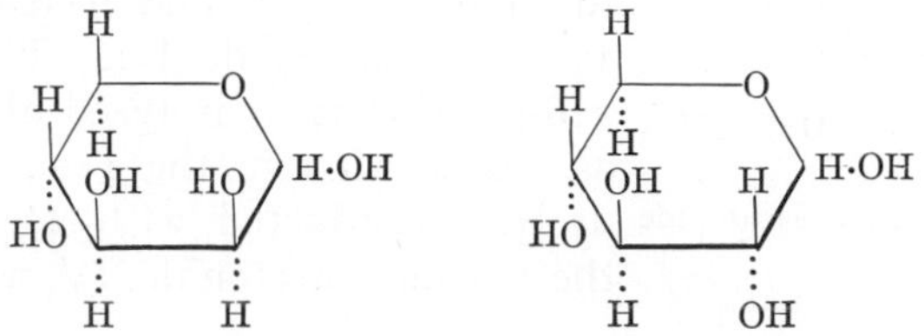

D-Lyxose
+ 117.4

D-Xylose
+ 170.5

$M_D^\alpha - M_D^\beta$

The example of L-rhamnose, a natural methylpentose, shows that in the L-series, the situation is reversed and the α-anomer is the more levorotatory form. The data of Table 14.3 show that the same relationship holds for L-

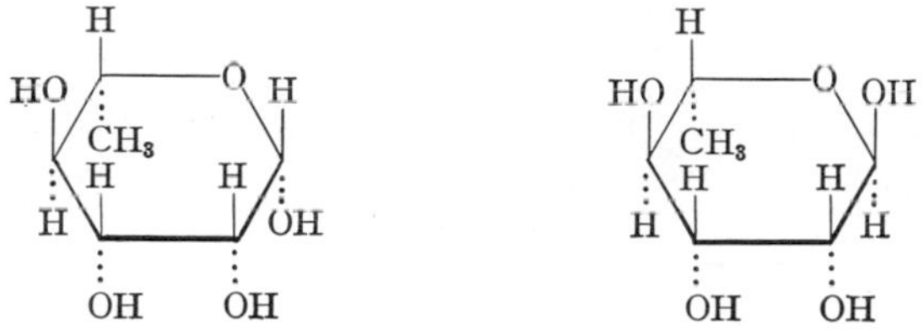

α-L-Rhamnose
$M_D - 15.7$

β-L-Rhamnose
$M_D + 63$

arabinose. D-Fructose forms a pair of methylpyranosides epimeric at C_2; the one defined as the α-isomer is the more dextrorotatory member of the pair.

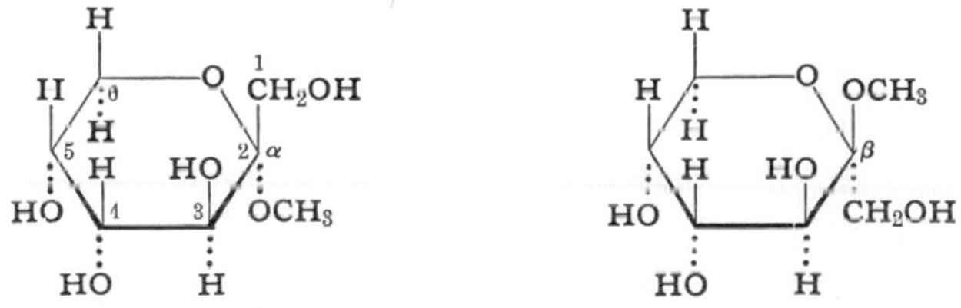

Methyl α-D-fructopyranoside
$M_D + 85$

Methyl β-D-fructopyranoside
$M_D - 334$

The rule also applies to epimeric furanosides, for example to the first pair of 5-ring epimers isolated in a crystalline condition by W. N. Haworth as follows (1929). Acetone, in the presence of an acid catalyst or dehydrating agent (HCl, H_2SO_4, $ZnCl_2$, $CuSO_4$, P_2O_5), reacts with *cis* glycols with elimination of a molecule of water to form acetonides containing

5-membered rings. α-D-Galactose has one pair of *cis* hydroxyls at C_1 and C_2 and another at C_3 and C_4; hence it readily forms a diacetonide of pyranose structure. α-D-Glucose has only one *cis vic*-glycol grouping in the pyranose form I, but has two in the furanose form II, and it reacts to give the 1,2;5,6-diacetonide III. The group in the 5,6-position is hydrolyzed about forty times as fast as that in the 1,2-position, and hydrolysis conducted with acetic acid affords the 1,2-monoacetonide, IV, which in turn can

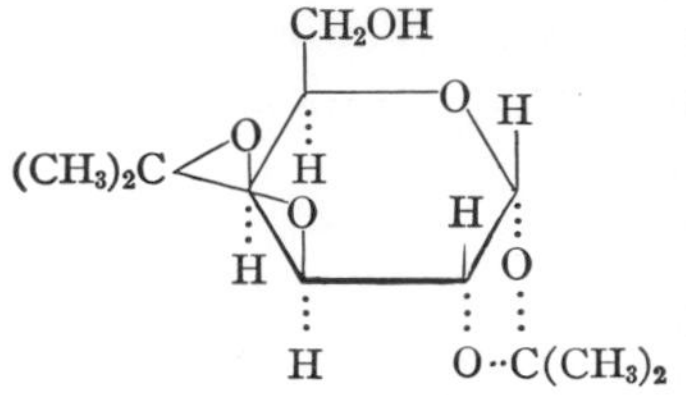

CH$_2$OH ... (CH$_3$)$_2$C< structure

α-D-Galactose 1,2;3,4-diacetonide

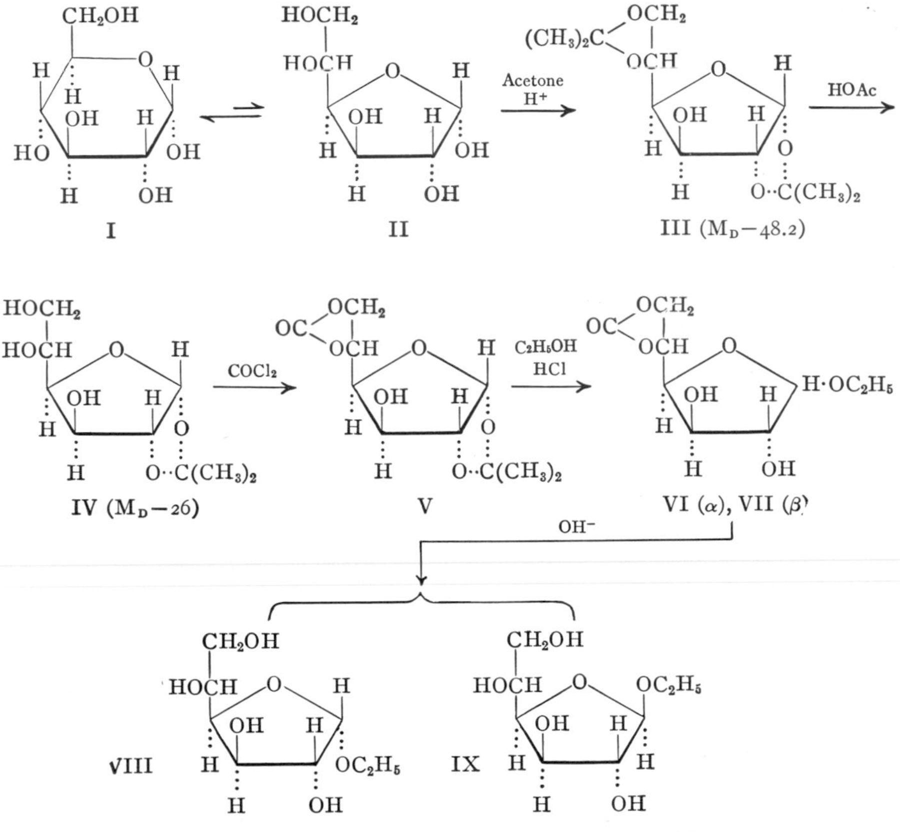

I ⇌ II →(Acetone, H$^+$) III (M$_D$ −48.2) →(HOAc)

IV (M$_D$ −26) →(COCl$_2$) V →(C$_2$H$_5$OH, HCl) VI (α), VII (β)

OH$^-$

VIII Ethyl α-D-glucofuranoside M$_D$ + 204

IX Ethyl β-D-glucofuranoside M$_D$ − 179

be converted by the action of phosgene in pyridine solution into the crystalline 1,2-acetonide-5,6-carbonate V. A carbonate ordinarily is more stable than an acetonide to acid hydrolysis, and hydrolysis of V with dilute acid gives glucose-5,6-carbonate. Treatment of the acetonide-carbonate V with ethanol and hydrogen chloride removes acetone and simultaneously effects etherification to give a mixture of the α- and β-ethylfuranoside-carbonates,

VI and VII, which can be separated by crystallization as such and as the diacetates. The acid-stable carbonate group, as well as the acetyl groups, is readily removed by basic hydrolysis to give the 1-epimeric ethyl-D-gluco-furanosides, VIII and IX. The α-anomer, with the OC_2H_5 group below the plane of the 5-ring, is more dextrorotatory than the β-epimer. In formula VIII the two-carbon side chain projects above the plane of the ring, *trans* to the C_1-OC_2H_5. Carbon atom 5 in the furanose structure (VIII) retains the original configuration of the pyranose form (I) or aldehydic form, and since C_5 is written below C_6, or in the reverse order of the usual projection formula, OH appears to the left and H to the right.

A useful relationship in molecular rotations between cyclic forms of sugars and the corresponding glycosides follows from Hudson's second rule and is illustrated by the data of Table 14.3: the sum of the molecular rotations of a pair of anomers is very nearly the same as the sum of the molecular rotations of the corresponding glycosides.

TABLE 14.3. COMPARISON OF SUGARS AND THEIR GLYCOSIDES

COMPOUND	SUGAR			METHYLPYRANOSIDE		
	M_D^α	M_D^β	SUM	M_D^α	M_D^β	SUM
D-Glucose	+202.1	+33.7	+235.8	+308.6	−66.4	+242.2
D-Mannose	+52.8	−30.6	+22.2	+153.8	−135.5	+18.3
D-Galactose	+271.5	+95.1	+366.6	+380.5	0	+380.5
D-Lyxose	+8.4	−109	−100.6	+97.5	−210.3	−112.8
D-Xylose	+140.5	−30.0	+110.5	+252.6	−107.5	+145.1
L-Arabinose	+115.6	+286.1	+401.7	+28.4	+403.0	+431.4
L-Rhamnose	−15.7	+63.0	+47.3	−111.4	+170.0	+58.6

Lactones. — The relationship between an aldonic acid and its γ-lactone is described in the following rule formulated by Hudson (1910): a γ-lactone in which the oxide ring, as represented in the conventional projection formula, lies to the right is more dextrorotatory than the parent acid, and if the ring lies to the left the lactone is more levorotatory. An illustration of the rule is the contrasting relationships of D-gluconic acid and of D-talonic acid to their γ-lactones. With but few exceptions, lactones of the γ-D-

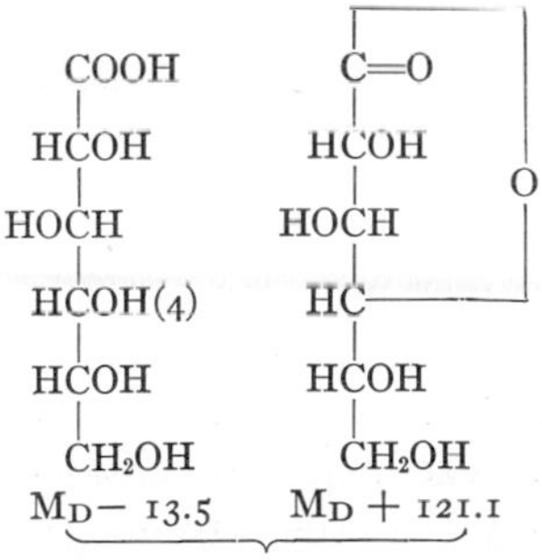

d-Gluconic acid and γ-lactone 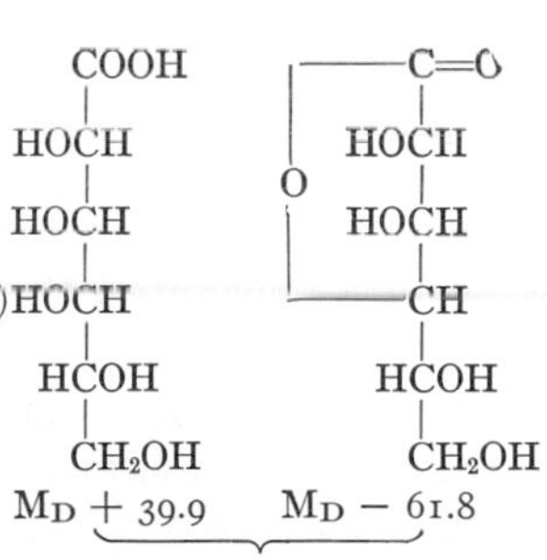   d-Talonic acid and γ-lactone

gluconic type are levorotatory. The contrast between the two types is understandable from consideration of the Haworth formulas; in γ-D-gluco-lactone the two-carbon side chain attached to C_4 is oriented up and in γ-D-

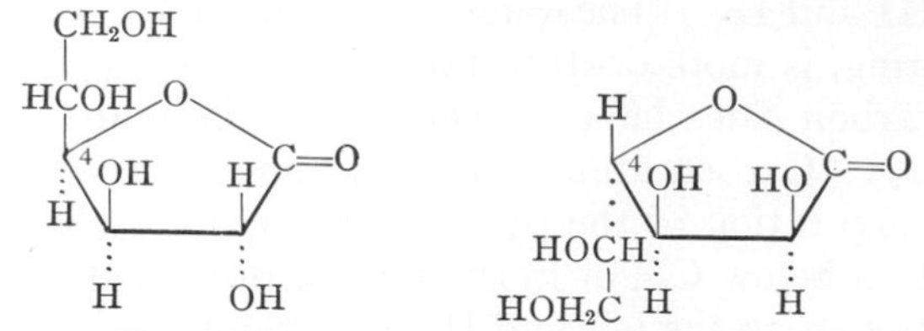

$$CH_2OH$$

$$HCOH$$

γ-D-Glucolactone   γ-D-Talolactone

talolactone it is oriented down. D-Gluconic acid forms a less stable δ-lactone $(M_D + 117.9)$, which has the same sign of rotation as the γ-lactone. This correspondence can be attributed to the fact that in uncyclized D-gluconic acid the hydroxyl at C_5 involved in δ-lactone formation lies on the same side as the hydroxyl at C_4. The same situation exists in the following instances:

D-Mannonic acid: γ-lactone $(M_D + 91.7)$; δ-lactone $(M_D + 204.5)$
L-Rhamnonic acid: γ-lactone $(M_D - 63.6)$; δ-lactone $(M_D - 162.0)$

GLYCOSIDES

The synthetic methylglucosides resulting from acid-catalyzed action of methanol on glucose exemplify a type of compound of abundant occurrence in plants. These are acetals, comparable to methylglucosides, and are derived from combination of various hydroxy compounds with various sugars. They are designated specifically as glucosides, mannosides, galactosides, etc., and the group as a whole is described by the generic name glycoside. When a sugar is combined with a nonsugar, the latter is described as an aglycone. When the second group is also a sugar unit, the combination is a di-, tri-, or polysaccharide. Glycosides are hydrolyzed by mineral acids to the sugar and the aglycone; for instance arbutin, a glycoside obtained from the bearberry (*Arctostaphylos uva-ursi*), yields glucose and

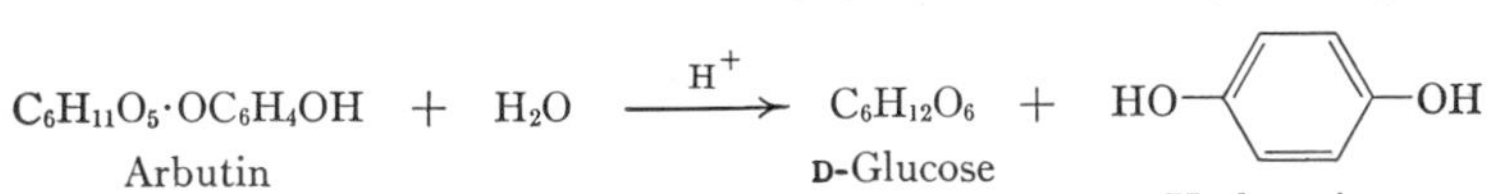

$$C_6H_{11}O_5 \cdot OC_6H_4OH + H_2O \xrightarrow{H^+} C_6H_{12}O_6 + HO-\!\!\!\bigcirc\!\!\!-OH$$

Arbutin   D-Glucose   Hydroquinone

hydroquinone on hydrolysis. Usually an enzyme that can accomplish the hydrolysis occurs in the same plant, though in different cells. When the plant tissues are macerated the enzyme comes into contact with the glycoside and hydrolysis results. Some enzymes can act on only one substance (substrate); others are not entirely specific in activity. The widely distributed emulsin and maltase both hydrolyze many glycosides, but the differentiation first noted by Fischer, namely that the former acts on β-glucosides and the latter on α-glucosides, is true for α- and β-glycosides generally, and is frequently used as a proof of the type of glycoside linkage. Most natural glycosides possess the β-configuration.

Glucose is the most common sugar component, but several interesting sugars occur only as glycosides. The rare pentose D-ribose and its 2-desoxy derivative were first isolated by Levene from nucleic acids. Both sugars occur in the furanoside form shown in the formulas. L-Rhamnose, a methyl-pentose, is encountered in glycosides; its origin is puzzling since the con-

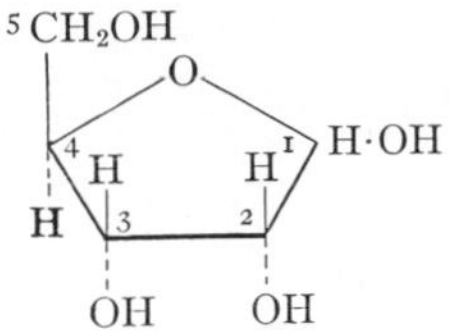

D-Ribose 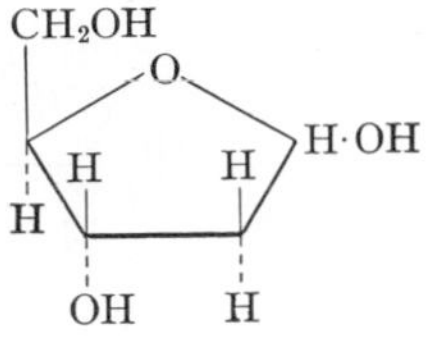   2-Desoxy-D-ribose 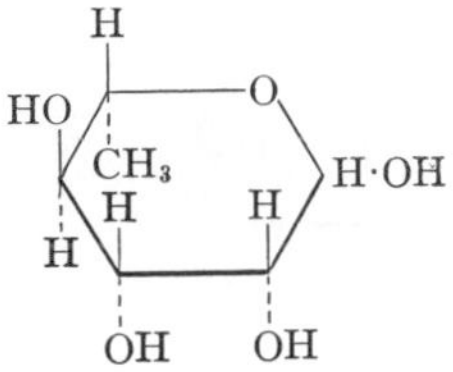   L-Rhamnose

figuration is that of L-mannose, which is unknown in nature, and hence it probably is not formed by simple reduction of the primary alcohol group of a hexose. Rhamnosides are hydrolyzed by a type-specific enzyme, rhamnase.

Arbutin and Methylarbutin. — These glucosides are hydrolyzed by emulsin to glucose and to hydroquinone and hydroquinone monomethyl ether, respectively, and hence are considered to be β-glucosides. Methylarbutin was synthesized by Michael (1881), who developed the standard

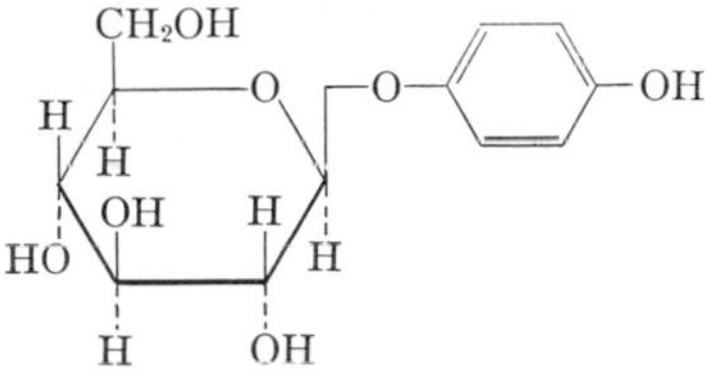

Arbutin 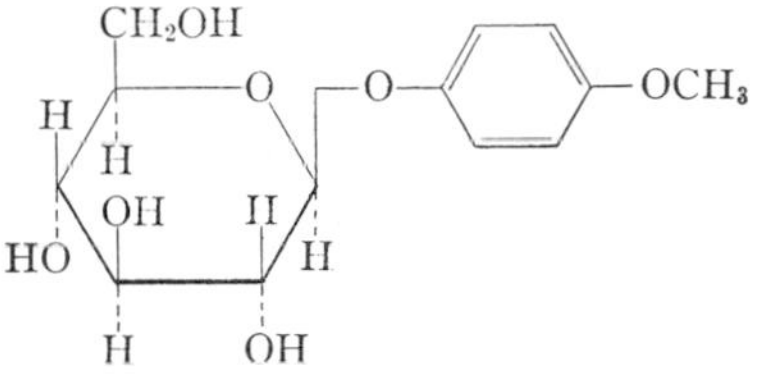   Methylarbutin

method for synthesis of glycosides. The glycosidic linkage is effected by condensing the aglycone with acetobromoglucose. Acetobromoglucose is

$$C_6H_7O(OAc)_4Br \quad + \quad KOR \quad \xrightarrow{Ag_2CO_3} \quad C_6H_7O(OAc)_4OR \quad \longrightarrow \quad C_6H_{11}O_5 \cdot OR$$

Acetobromoglucose   Aglycone salt   β-Glycoside

now considered to be an α-derivative and is usually prepared by treating the pentaacetate with hydrogen bromide in glacial acetic acid solution. In the condensation reaction a Walden inversion generally ocurs, and the

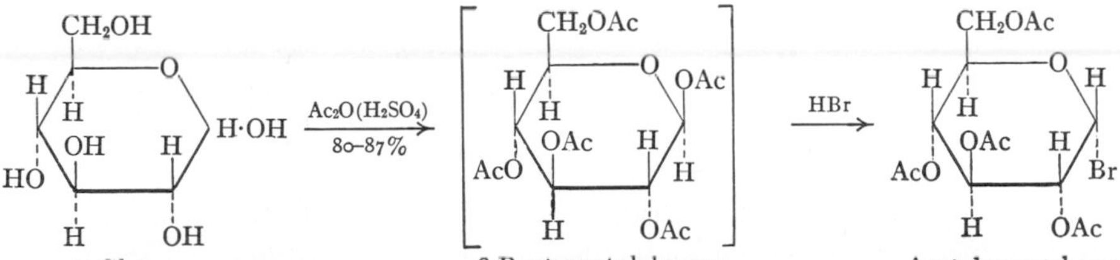

D-Glucose   β-Pentaacetylglucose   α-Acetobromoglucose

product is a β-glycoside. Both glycosides can be obtained if the condensation is carried out in the presence of quinoline.

Two glycosides closely related to arbutin are salicin (*Salix*) and picein (pine needles, willow bark). They both are hydrolyzed by emulsin, an indication that the linkage is β.

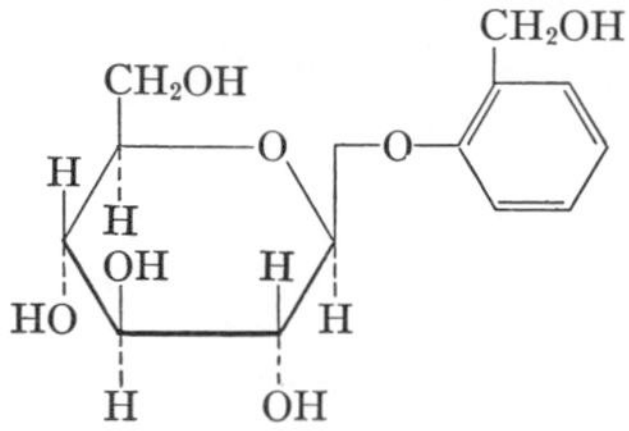

Salicin 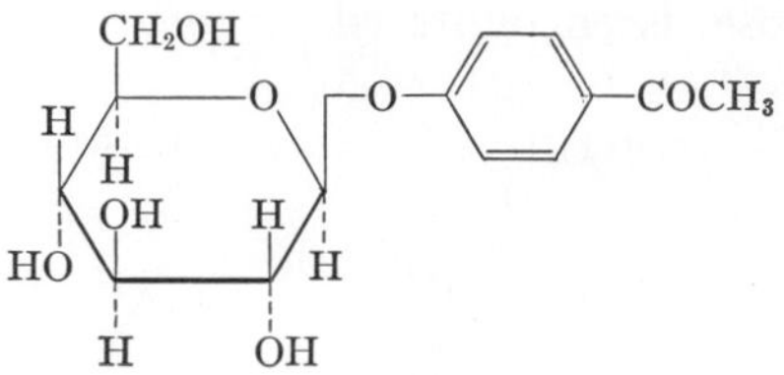   Picein

Amygdalin. — Amygdalin is the best known of the group of cyanophoric glycosides, so named because hydrogen cyanide is liberated on hydrolysis. Amygdalin was isolated in 1830 from seeds of the bitter almond (*Prunus amygdalus*) and soon attracted the attention of Liebig and Wöhler, who found that a proteinaceous substance emulsin, which could be extracted by water from the seeds, hydrolyzed the glycoside in the following way:

$$C_{20}H_{27}O_{11}N + 2 H_2O \longrightarrow C_7H_6O + HCN + 2 C_6H_{12}O_6$$

Amygdalin   Benzaldehyde   D-Glucose

If a yeast extract is employed instead of emulsin, glucose and a glucoside of *d*-mandelonitrile that is identical with prunasin (*Prunus* species) are obtained, which shows that hydrogen cyanide is part of the aglycone, and

$$C_{20}H_{27}O_{11}N + H_2O \longrightarrow C_6H_{12}O_6 + C_6H_{11}O_5 \cdot OCH(CN)C_6H_5$$

d-Mandelonitrile glucoside
(prunasin)

that the sugar unit is a disaccharide, identified in 1923 as the rare gentiobiose, a component of a trisaccharide present in the root of the *Gentiana*

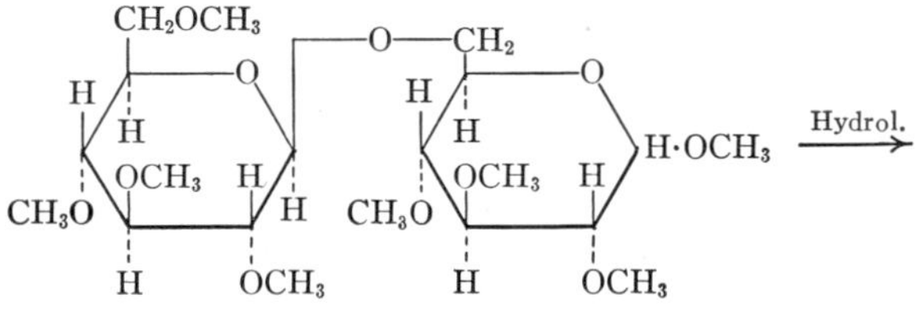

Methylgentiobiose

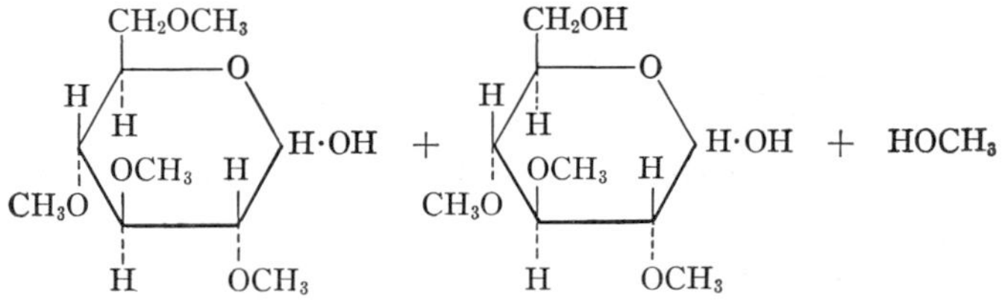

2,3,4,6–Tetramethylglucose   2,3,4–Trimethylglucose

and of the saffron pigment, crocin (p. 959). Gentiobiose is a reducing disaccharide composed of two glucose units; the structure was established (Haworth) by identification of the hydrolysis products of methylgentiobiose. The glucosidic linkage is considered to be β, since the sugar is hydrolyzable by emulsin and not by maltase. Three independent labora-

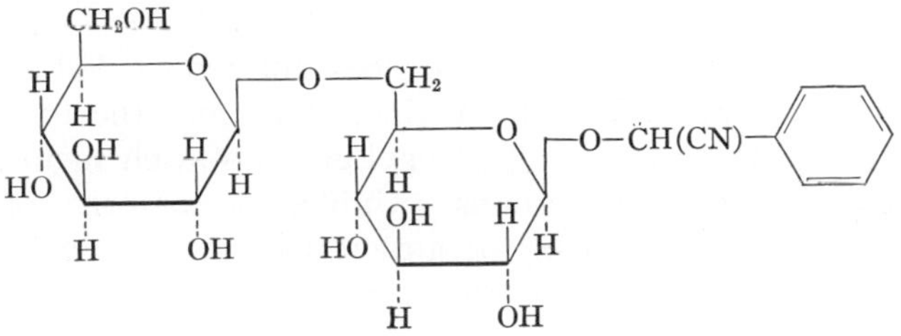

Amygdalin

tories announced the synthesis of amygdalin in 1924 (using acetobromo-gentiobiose).

Sinigrin. — Sinigrin is the simplest member of another glycoside type in which the aglycone contains the isothiocyanate grouping, $-N{=}C{=}S$. Sinigrin occurs in the seed of black mustard and the root of horseradish; it is hydrolyzed by an enzyme myosin, specific for this class of glycosides, which are not attacked by the other general enzymes: emulsin, rhamnase, maltase. The aglycone is allyl isothiocyanate, or mustard oil, and hence these sugar derivatives are referred to as mustard-oil glycosides. Since a thioglucose ($C_6H_{11}O_5 \cdot SH$) can be obtained by the action of sodium meth-

$$\overset{\displaystyle OSO_3K}{\underset{}{C_6H_{11}O_5 \cdot S - \overset{|}{C} {=} NCH_2CH{=}CH_2}} \quad \xrightarrow{H_2O}$$

Sinigrin (Gadamer, 1896)

$$C_6H_{12}O_6 \;+\; KHSO_4 \;+\; CH_2{=}CHCH_2N{=}C{=}S$$

D-Glucose   Allyl isothiocyanate

oxide, the sugar residue is attached to one sulfur atom; it is not known whether the linkage is α or β.

DISACCHARIDES

Disaccharides can be regarded as glycosides in which the aglycone is a second monosaccharide unit. They resemble monosaccharides in that they are very soluble in water. Only three occur as such in nature, sucrose (cane sugar), lactose (milk sugar), and maltose, and the latter is found free only occasionally; these are the only disaccharides that have a sweet taste. Disaccharides are encountered frequently as glycosides: gentiobiose from amygdalin is one example. Two disaccharides, maltose and cellobiose, are important because they are hydrolysis products of starch and cellulose, respectively.

Sucrose. — Sucrose on hydrolysis with acids or the enzyme invertase (plants, yeast, animals) yields D-glucose and D-fructose in equal amounts.

The mixture of two hexoses is known as invert sugar because it is levorotatory whereas sucrose is dextrorotatory. Honey is largely invert sugar,

$$\text{Sucrose} \xrightarrow{\ H_2O\ } \underbrace{\underset{[\alpha]_D + 52°}{\text{D-Glucose}} + \underset{[\alpha]_D - 92°}{\text{D-Fructose}}}_{[\alpha]_D - 20°}$$
$$[\alpha]_D + 66.5$$

since bees contain invertase. Sucrose does not reduce Fehling's solution or form derivatives with phenylhydrazine, and hence the two sugar units are linked through the glycosidic hydroxyl group of each sugar and contain no free or potential carbonyl groups. Unlike the majority of sugars, sucrose crystallizes readily, probably because it does not undergo mutarotation in solution. The ring structure of the two component units was established (Haworth, 1916) by hydrolyzing completely methylated sucrose (octamethyl). One product was the usual tetramethyl-D-glucose, but the other was a tetramethylfructose derivative unknown at the time. Its structure was not established until ten years later, when it was found to contain a furanose, or 2,5-oxide ring. No combined fructose has ever been found to have the normal or pyranose structure. The glucose unit probably has the α-configuration, since sucrose is hydrolyzed by maltase (an α-glucosidase); the configuration of the fructose unit is not established, but is considered to be β. Recombination of the two units was first effected through the action of an enzyme on a mixture of glucose 1-phosphate and fructose (Hassid[17]).

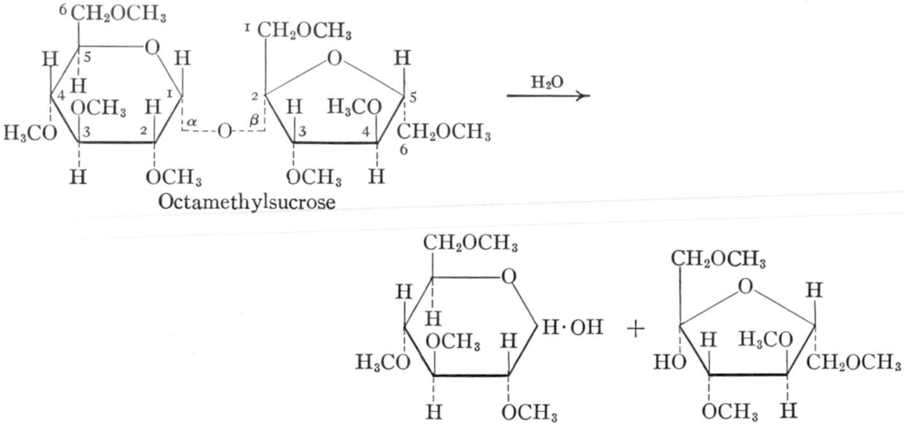

Octamethylsucrose

2,3,4,6-Tetramethyl-glucose   1,3,4,6-Tetramethyl-fructose

Chemical synthesis has been achieved (Lemieux[18] and G. Huber, 1953) by heating a mixture of triacetylglucosan (I), a derivative of 1,2-anhydroglucose, and tetraacetylfructofuranose (III) at 100° for several days. Deacetylation, chromatography, and reacetylation afforded sucrose octaacetate

[17] William Zev Hassid, b. 1897 Jaffa, Palestine; Ph.D. California; Univ. California

[18] Raymond U. Lemieux, b. 1920 Lac la Biche, Alberta, Canada; Ph.D. McGill (Purves); Univ. Ottawa

in overall yield of 5.5%. The condensation is believed to involve the ionic intermediate II The CH$_2$OAc group in I being axial shields the approach of an external reagent but is available for cyclization to II on diaxial opening of the epoxide ring.

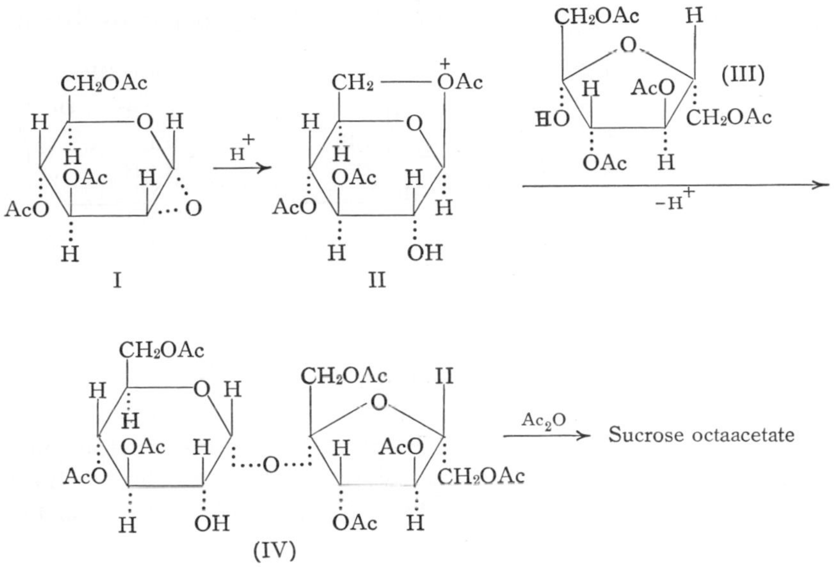

Sucrose has been an important foodstuff for centuries. Originally the only commercial source was the juice of sugar cane, a tropical plant native to India, which is now grown on plantations mainly in Cuba, Java, the Philippines, and South America. The juice as obtained by pressing the crushed canes contains about 14% sucrose; the spent cane, bagasse, is used as fuel or as a source of cellulose. Lime is added to the extract to precipitate proteinic substances (defecation), and the clear juice drawn off after settling is evaporated in vacuum to a semisolid mass. The crystalline raw sugar is freed from mother liquor (blackstrap molasses) in centrifugal baskets. Raw sugar (95% sucrose) is colored and has a slight odor; it is purchased in this form by refineries. The usual purification consists in removal of odoriferous contaminants with steam, followed by filtration through columns of charcoal to remove colored contaminants. White crystalline sucrose of high purity is obtained by concentration in vacuum.

Approximately half of the sucrose produced throughout the world now comes from the sugar beet, which can be grown in temperate climates. Although the beet was shown to contain sucrose as early as 1747, commercial production from this source commenced some time later in France, when the industry was subsidized by the state as a result of the British blockade during the Napoleonic Wars. The sugar content of the beet has been steadily improved by cultivation and is about the same as that of sugar cane (16–20%), but the yield per acre is not so high as that from cane.

Lactose. — Lactose occurs in the milk of mammals; human milk contains 5–8%, cow's milk, 4–6%. It is produced commercially from the latter source as a by-product in the manufacture of cheese. Lactose is a reducing sugar, forms an osazone, and can be obtained in crystalline α- and β-forms, $[\alpha]_D + 90°$ and $[\alpha]_D + 35°$. It is hydrolyzed by dilute mineral acid to glucose and galactose. Since the acid obtained on bromine oxidation of

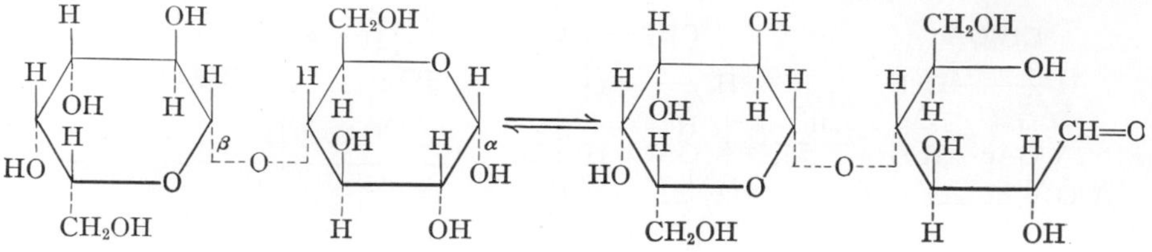

Cyclic form (α)   Aldehydic form

Lactose

lactose is hydrolyzed to galactose and gluconic acid, the reducing group must be in the glucose unit, and hence lactose is a galactoside and not a glucoside. The ring structures and point of attachment to the glucose molecule are shown by the three hydrolytic products of the octamethyl derivative. Since lactose is cleaved by a β-galactoside enzyme (lactase), it is a β- rather than an α-glycoside.

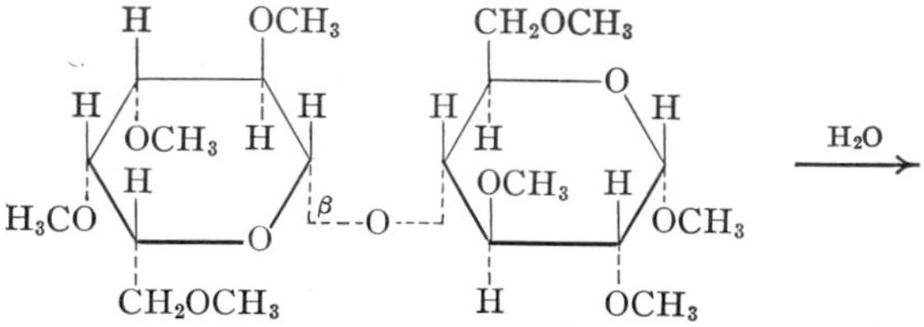

Octamethyl-α-lactose

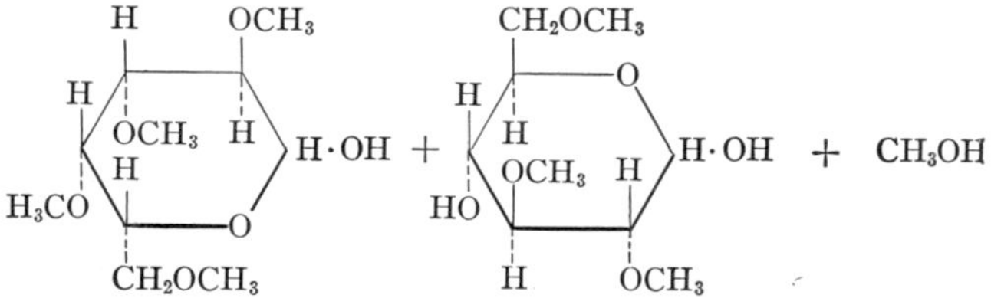

2,3,4,6-Tetramethyl-   2,3,6-Trimethyl-
galactose   glucose

Maltose. — Maltose is obtained in about 80% yield by enzymatic (amylase) degradation of starch. Since the disaccharide yields only D-glucose on hydrolysis with acids or maltase, an α-glucosidase, it is evidently a glucose-α-glucoside. It is a reducing sugar, and hence contains one potential aldehydic group. Methylation studies established the structure as that of glucose-4-α-glucoside.

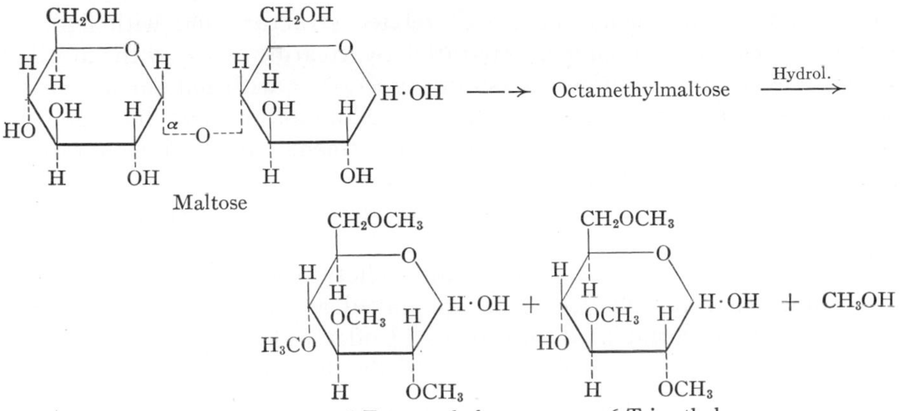

Maltose

2,3,4,6-Tetramethyl-
glucose

2,3,6-Trimethyl-
glucose

Cellobiose. — Cellobiose can be obtained by careful hydrolysis of cellulose. It is a reducing sugar consisting of two glucose units, and since it is
hydrolyzed by emulsin, a β-glucosidase, the substance is a glucose-β-
glucoside. Methylation studies have shown that cellobiose is related to
maltose in the same way that β-methylglucoside is related to the α-isomer.

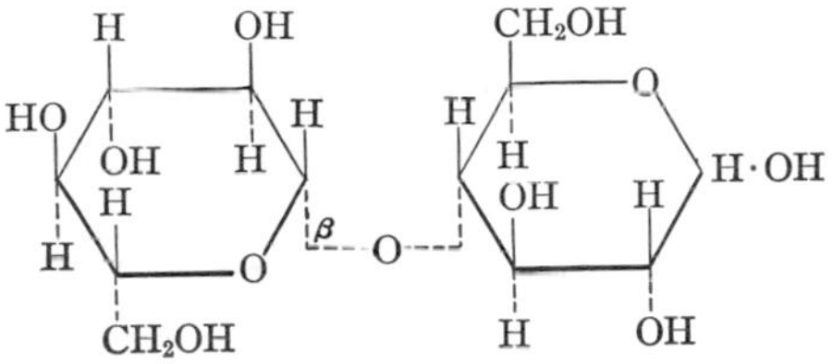

Cellobiose

POLYSACCHARIDES

Polysaccharides belong to two general groups: those that are insoluble
and form the skeletal structure of plants and of some animals; and those
that constitute reserve sources of simple sugars, which are liberated as required by the action of enzymes present in the organism. Both types are
high molecular weight polymers, often built up from a single pentose or
hexose unit. In this respect they differ from proteins, which are high
molecular weight substances containing several different units.

Cellulose. — Cellulose is the most widely distributed skeletal polysaccharide. It constitutes approximately half of the cell-wall material of
wood and other plant products. Cotton is almost pure cellulose, and together with bast from flax, is the preferred source of cellulose for use as
fiber. Cotton (or α-) cellulose can be purified by treatment with solvents
to extract fats and with dilute alkali to remove other contaminants. Wood
cellulose, the raw material for the pulp and paper industry, always occurs

in association with hemicelluloses of related structure and with lignin, a nonpolysaccharide. Lignin is separated by treating wood with an alkali bisulfite to form lignosulfonates (sulfite process) or with sodium hydroxide-sodium sulfide (kraft process). Plant celluloses are not homogeneous and can be separated into fractions by treatment with sodium hydroxide (17.5%), in which only part of the cellulose is soluble. The individual components are built from glucose units, and the difference probably lies in the degree and type of association.

Isolation of cellobiose, cellotriose, and cellotetrose on hydrolysis of cellulose shows that the glucose units are linked as in cellobiose, and hence cellulose can be formulated as shown. Under more vigorous conditions, cellulose is hydrolyzed to glucose. Actually the highest yields of glucose

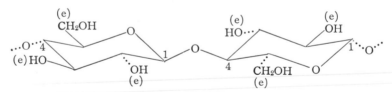

Cellulose

are only 95% of the theoretical, which may be due to further degradation of glucose or to the presence of small amounts of other units built into the chain. Even carefully purified cellulose contains a small number of carboxyl groups, which in the plant are probably esterified. These may be

Cellulose, conformation

formed by oxidation of the potential aldehydic group at one end of the chain or of primary alcohol groups at C_6 to form a glucuronic acid derivative. Polyglucuronic acids have been isolated from straw and wood.

Although cellulose is resistant to methylation, trimethylcellulose (three methyl groups per glucose unit) can be prepared by treating cellulose acetate (soluble in acetone) with dimethyl sulfate and alkali. Since one end unit in methylated cellulose must contain one more methyl group than the units constituting the chain, a small amount of tetramethylglucose should be formed on hydrolysis in addition to trimethylglucose. By careful fractionation Haworth (1932) isolated an amount of tetramethylglucose corresponding to one end group in a chain of 100–200 glucose units. The molecular weight as estimated by end-group assay is 20,000–40,000. Assuming that no degradation has occurred during the preparation of trimethylcellulose and that isolation of tetramethylglucose is fairly complete, the method is dependent upon the homogeneity of the sample hydrolyzed. The value found by Haworth is considerably lower than that found by physical methods, and evidently the methylation procedure in this case is accompanied by considerable degradation. A newer method of end-group assay depends upon cleavage of *cis*-glycols by periodic acid (Jackson and Hudson, p. 364). If three or more contiguous hydroxyl groups are present, formic acid is liberated and can be measured by titration. A polysaccharide built up of chains of hexopyranose residues linked in the 1,4-positions, such as cellulose, would give one mole of formic acid from one end and two moles from the reducing end. This method of end-group assay indicates that the cellulose chain is composed of at least 1000 glucose units; the minimum molecular weight is then at least 200,000.

Determination of the molecular weight of highly polymerized substances by physical methods is not easy. The usual cryoscopic and ebullioscopic methods are not applicable, since excessively high concentrations are required in order to obtain measurable effects. Three more sensitive methods are based upon osmotic pressure, viscosity (Staudinger), and the equilibrium or rate of sedimentation in a centrifugal field (Svedberg, p. 452). The determinations required in the first method are by no means easy, and several measurements are necessary in order to extrapolate to infinite dilution, where molecular weight can be assumed to be inversely proportional to osmotic pressure. The method is limited because low molecular weight fractions exert a greater influence than high molecular weight fractions and accurate measurements can be obtained only with substances of molecular weight less than 500,000. The viscosity method, as applied to linear macromolecules, is based upon a relationship, developed experimentally by Staudinger[19] (1930) and later theoretically interpreted by W. Kuhn,[20] according to which viscosity is proportional to molecular weight. On theoretical grounds determinations by the ultracentrifuge method are probably the soundest. All three methods are uncertain in that some degradation may attend solution of cellulose. Although cellulose is insoluble in the usual solvents, it can be dissolved in ammoniacal cupric hydroxide (Schweitzer's solution). Various nitro and acetyl derivatives are more soluble and are often used for check determinations. Values obtained by the three methods indicate an average molecular weight of 300,000–500,000.

The formula for cellulose derived from chemical evidence has been confirmed by X-ray examination, which reveals the fine structure of the cellulose molecule. The length of the unit cell along the chain axis (frequency period) is 10.3 Å, whereas the value calculated for one cellobiose unit is 10.25 Å; consequently the chains must be nearly straight with respect to the fiber axis. The fibers show crystalline regions that are explained on the basis of the micellar theory; this postulates that the crystalline supermolecular

---

[19] Hermann Staudinger, b. 1881 Worms; Ph.D. Halle (Vorländer); Strasbourg, Karlsruhe, Zurich ETH, Freiburg; Nobel Prize 1953

[20] Werner Kuhn, b. 1899 Zurich; Ph.D. Zurich (Henri); Karlsruhe, Basle

unit is made up of bundles of parallel orientated chains (micelles). The width of a micellar unit is about 60 Å, corresponding to 100–200 cellulose chains; the length is at least 600 Å, corresponding to a minimal chain length of 200 glucose units. The remarkable mechanical strength and chemical stability are considered to be a result of micellar structure. Cellulose swells to some extent in water or dilute alkali, but since the crystal lattice is not destroyed, the reaction is said to be intermicellar. The lattice is destroyed whenever solution is effected.

Man and other carnivorous animals are unable to utilize cellulose as food, since they lack enzymes required for hydrolysis. Many microorganisms, some protozoa, and the snail can decompose cellulose. Digestion of cellulose by ruminants (cud-chewing animals) is due to the presence of microorganisms within the specially constructed alimentary system.

Hemicelluloses. — Of several polysaccharides that occur in association with cellulose, two are pentosans; that is, they yield pentoses on hydrolysis. The more common one, xylan, is built from D-xylose units linked in the 1- and 4-positions. It is closely related to polyglucuronic acid with which it

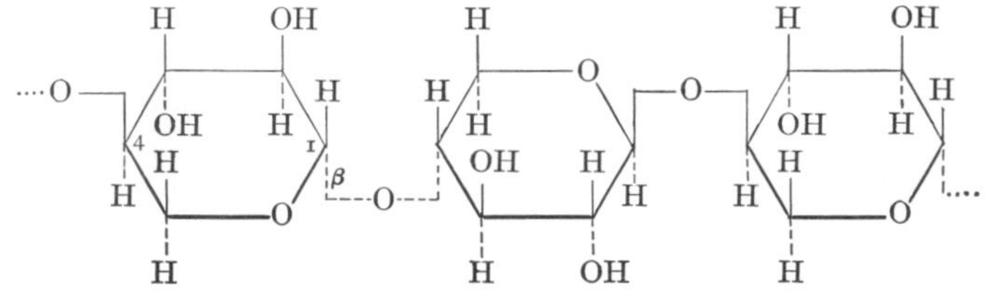

Xylan

is associated in nature, and from which it may be produced by decarboxylation. The pentosans occur in large amounts (20–40%) in cereal straws and

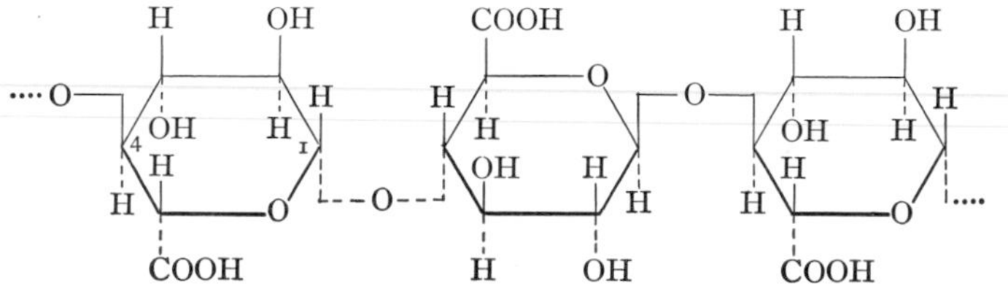

Polyglucuronic acid

brans, and are used for the large-scale industrial preparation of furfural. The pentosans are hydrolyzed by sulfuric acid, which then dehydrates the liberated pentoses.

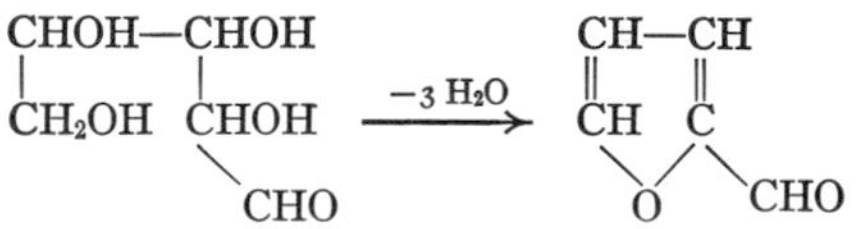

Pentose   Furfural

Chitin. — Chitin is a polysaccharide that forms the hard shell of crustaceans and insects. The 2-amino derivative of glucose, glucosamine, is obtained on chemical hydrolysis, and N-acetylglucosamine results on hydrolysis with an enzyme present in the intestine of the snail. Chitin is analogous to cellulose; for example, the identity period along the fiber axis is 10.4 Å, and hence the units probably are linked as in cellulose.

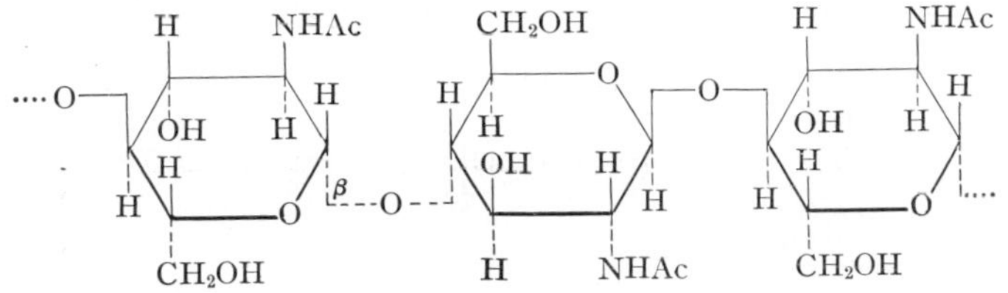

Chitin

Starch. — Starch is the reserve carbohydrate in the majority of plants. It is hydrolyzed partially by the enzyme amylase to maltose, or completely by mineral acids to glucose, and evidently starch consists of chains composed of maltose units. Starch can be separated into two fractions by treatment with hot water: a soluble component known as amylose (10–20%)

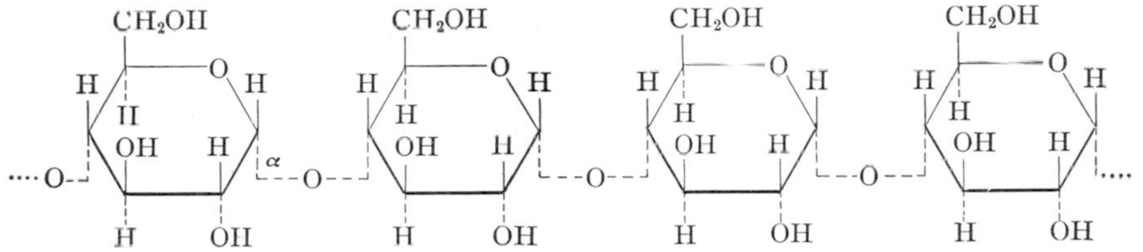

Starch chains

and an insoluble residue, amylopectin (80–90%). Both substances yield glucose or maltose on hydrolysis, but differ in several respects. Amylose gives a blue color on treatment with iodine, amylopectin a violet to red-violet color.

The molecular weight of amylose ranges from 10,000–50,000 (osmotic pressure). The value derived by end-group assay is in the same range; therefore amylose contains only one end group per molecule and is a long-chain molecule structurally related to cellulose.

Molecular weights of amylopectin samples are in the range 50,000 - 1,000,000 (osmotic pressure). Since end-group assay (periodate procedure) indicates one end group for each 25–27 units, the structure must consist of branched chains. Hydrolysis of exhaustively methylated amylopectin furnishes 2,3,6-trimethylglucose, and in addition small amounts of 2,3,4,6-tetramethylglucose derived from end groups and of 2,3-dimethylglucose corresponding to branching points. Therefore the main chains are composed of glucose units joined by 1,4-links and the branches are linked to it by 1,6-links (see formula).

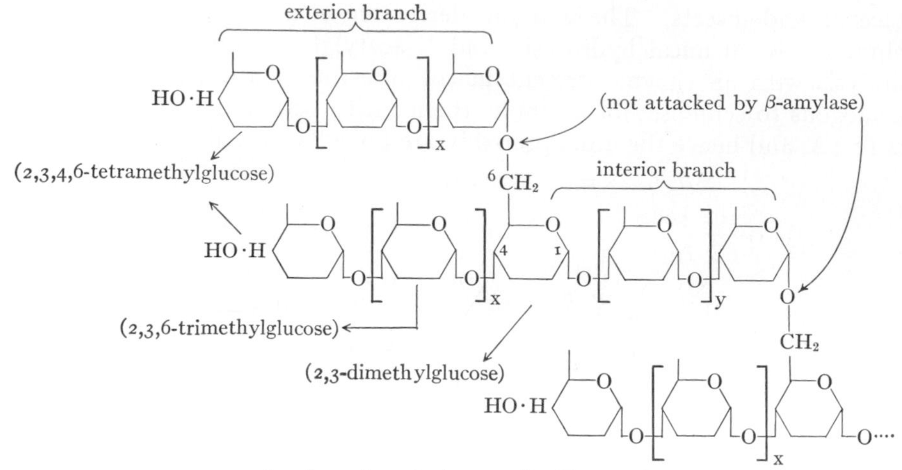

Amylopectin and glycogen (K. H. Meyer)

Further information was obtained from study of enzymatic hydrolysis by amylase, which hydrolyzes amylose completely to maltose but degrades amylopectin to maltose only to the extent of 62%. The linkage between the 1α-position of one unit and the 6-position of another offers a point of obstruction to enzymatic hydrolysis and a resistant residue known as grenzdextrin is left, which corresponds to the interior of the molecule. It is estimated that exterior branches account for more than two-thirds of the molecule.

Glycogen. — Glycogen is the reserve carbohydrate of animals; it occurs particularly in liver and muscle. It gives a brown to violet color with iodine, resembling that of grenzdextrin. It is composed entirely of glucose units joined as in maltose, a product of enzymatic hydrolysis; and the end-group method indicates one end group for every 12–18 glucose units. Glycogen is very similar to amylopectin, since methylated glycogen yields the same three methylated glucose derivatives as methylated amylopectin. One difference, indicated by an end-group content of 9% as compared with 5% for amylopectin, in that the degree of branching is about twice as great. Another is that the proportion of the molecule hydrolyzed by amylase is slightly smaller (55–60%).

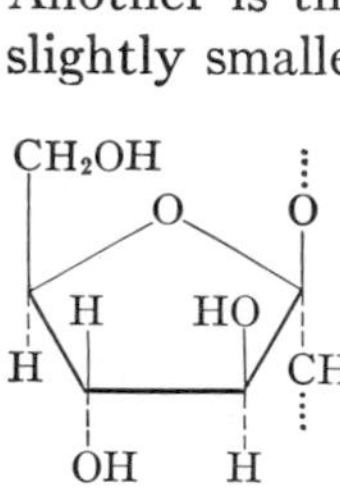

Inulin. — A number of reserve carbohydrates of plants are composed almost entirely of fructose units and are known as fructans. An example is inulin, the polysaccharide of the *Compositae* (dahlia, dandelion) and of the Jerusalem artichoke. It was originally believed to consist entirely of fructose units but more recent results (Hirst, 1950) have shown that glucose is a terminal unit of the chain as well as a minor constituent within the chain.

Inulin

PHYSIOLOGICALLY ACTIVE CARBOHYDRATES

Ascorbic Acid (Vitamin C). — Scurvy, an ancient disease of mankind, is characterized particularly by a marked tendency to hemorrhage and by structural changes in the cartilage, bone, and teeth. Although the administration of fresh fruits was known since 1752 to decrease the high incidence associated with long sea voyages and abnormal living conditions, the disease was recognized as due to a deficiency of a specific dietary factor, vitamin C, only in 1917. The majority of mammals are not subject to the disease, but the guinea pig when restricted to a cereal diet develops a hemorrhagic condition very similar to scurvy and curable by administration of the same foods that have proved of value in treating scurvy. Isolation of a pure crystalline antiscorbutic substance from lemon juice was finally achieved in 1932 (King[21]), and the material was shortly identified as hexuronic acid, $C_6H_8O_6$, isolated four years earlier from fruits and vegetables by Szent-Györgyi. The substance was renamed ascorbic acid after its striking biological activity was demonstrated.

The most distinctive chemical property of ascorbic acid is its reducing action, manifested in reversible oxidation to a dehydro compound, $C_6H_6O_6$. The majority of chemical methods for determination of C are based on the ability of the substance to reduce colored dyes to the colorless, or leuco form. Dehydroascorbic acid is a neutral lactone, and the acidity of ascorbic acid is recognized as due not to a carboxyl group but to an enediol grouping.

The structure was established in 1933. Observation that ozonization of the dimethyl ether II is attended with the uptake of two atoms of oxygen without producing two fragments established the presence in the molecule of

L-Ascorbic acid (I)

II

III

Dehydroascorbic acid (IV)

V

(VI)

(VII)

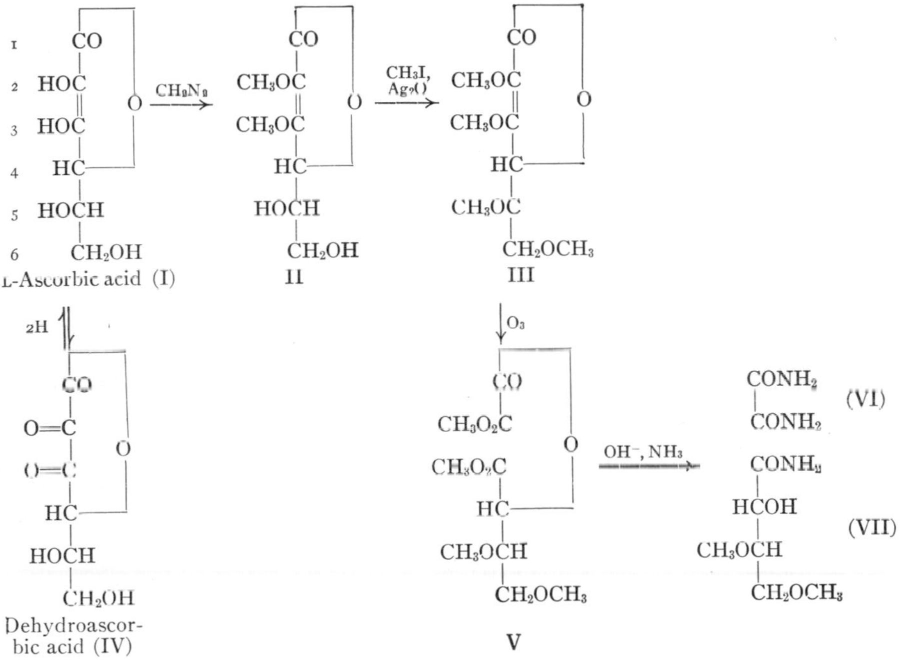

[21] Charles G. King, b. 1896 Entiat, Wash.; Ph.D. Pittsburgh; Nutrition Foundation, New York

a double bond and a ring (Micheel[22]). Similar oxidative fission of the tetramethyl ether III (Haworth, Hirst) gave 3,4-dimethyl-L-threonamide (VII), whose configuration is established by conversion to L-(+)-tartaric acid. The first synthesis of L-ascorbic acid was announced almost simultaneously by Haworth and by Reichstein in 1933. The method has only

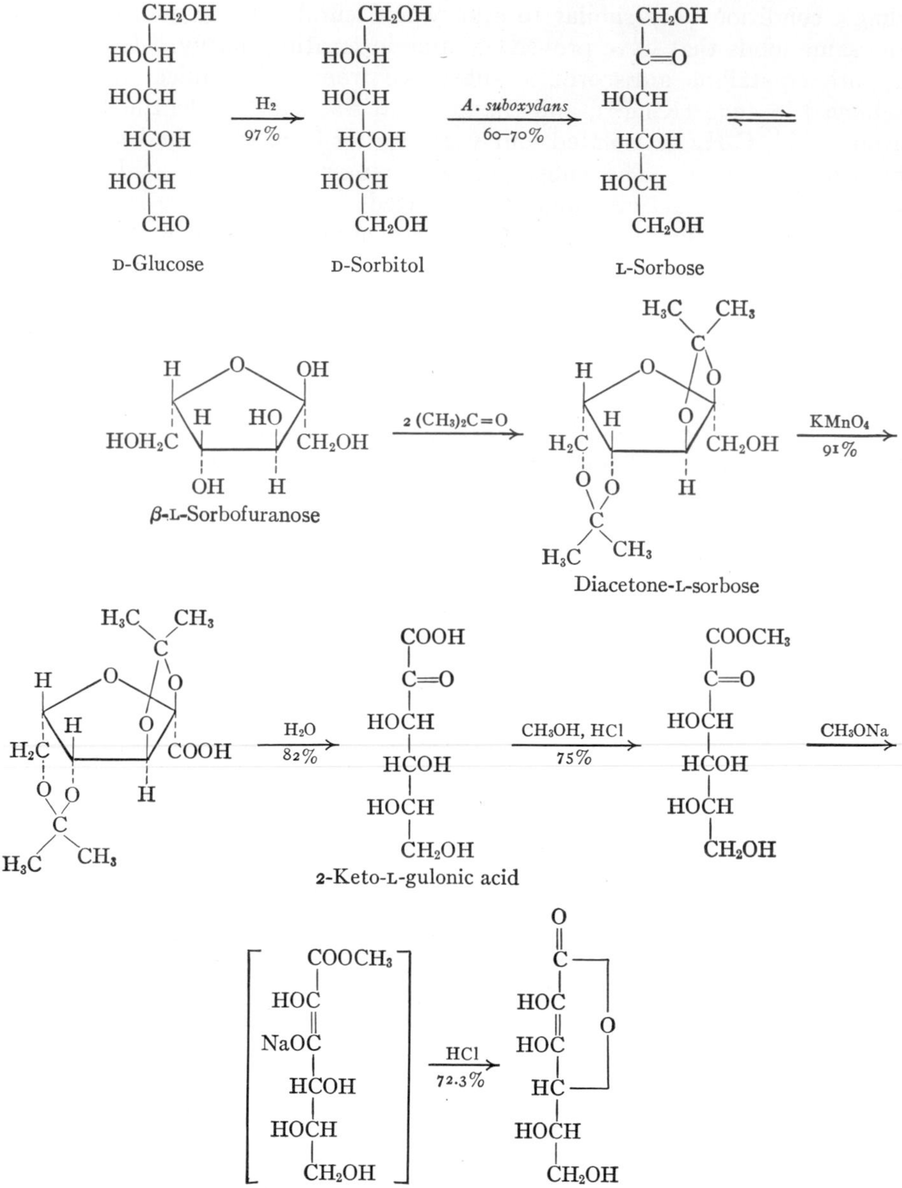

$$
\begin{array}{ccc}
\text{CH}_2\text{OH} & \text{CH}_2\text{OH} & \text{CH}_2\text{OH} \\
\text{HOCH} & \text{HOCH} & \text{C}=\text{O} \\
\text{HOCH} & \text{HOCH} & \text{HOCH} \\
\text{HCOH} & \text{HCOH} & \text{HCOH} \\
\text{HOCH} & \text{HOCH} & \text{HOCH} \\
\text{CHO} & \text{CH}_2\text{OH} & \text{CH}_2\text{OH} \\
\text{D-Glucose} & \text{D-Sorbitol} & \text{L-Sorbose}
\end{array}
$$

$\xrightarrow[97\%]{\text{H}_2}$ ， $\xrightarrow[60\text{-}70\%]{A.\ suboxydans}$ ， $\Longrightarrow$

β-L-Sorbofuranose

$\xrightarrow{2\ (\text{CH}_3)_2\text{C}=\text{O}}$

Diacetone-L-sorbose

$\xrightarrow[91\%]{\text{KMnO}_4}$

$\xrightarrow[82\%]{\text{H}_2\text{O}}$

$$
\begin{array}{c}
\text{COOH} \\
\text{C}=\text{O} \\
\text{HOCH} \\
\text{HCOH} \\
\text{HOCH} \\
\text{CH}_2\text{OH}
\end{array}
$$
2-Keto-L-gulonic acid

$\xrightarrow[75\%]{\text{CH}_3\text{OH, HCl}}$

$$
\begin{array}{c}
\text{COOCH}_3 \\
\text{C}=\text{O} \\
\text{HOCH} \\
\text{HCOH} \\
\text{HOCH} \\
\text{CH}_2\text{OH}
\end{array}
$$

$\xrightarrow{\text{CH}_3\text{ONa}}$

$$
\left[
\begin{array}{c}
\text{COOCH}_3 \\
\text{HOC} \\
\text{NaOC} \\
\text{HCOH} \\
\text{HOCH} \\
\text{CH}_2\text{OH}
\end{array}
\right]
$$

$\xrightarrow[72.3\%]{\text{HCl}}$

L-Ascorbic acid (λ_{max} 2450 hr. Å)

---

[22] Fritz Micheel, b. 1900 Strasbourg/Uckermark; Ph.D. Berlin; Münster

historical interest because the starting material is the rare L-xylose.   Present processes are modifications of a later synthesis of Reichstein, which starts with D-glucose.   The sugar is converted into the alcohol, D-sorbitol, by catalytic (Cu–Cr) hydrogenation, and this on bacterial oxidation (*Aceto-bacter suboxydans*) yields the 2-ketohexose, L-sorbose, in which the configuration at C_5 (C_2 of glucose) is that of ascorbic acid.   The next step is introduction of a carboxyl group at C_1 by oxidation of the primary alcohol group at that position in L-sorbose.   In order to protect the primary alcohol group at C_6, L-sorbose is converted into its diacetone derivative in which the other groups are covered.   Formation of acetone derivatives is a general reaction; it consists in condensation of acetone with two *cis*-hydroxyl groups. In this case, acetone reacts with the furanose, rather than the pyranose form of L-sorbose.   After the desired oxidation is carried out, the acetone derivative is readily hydrolyzed to the free acid, 2-keto-L-gulonic acid.   The final steps consist in enolization and formation of the lactone ring.   Synthetic ascorbic acid has been available since 1937 at a fraction of the cost of the natural product, which was marketed in 1934 at approximately $200 an ounce.   Although acute scurvy is very rare, many humans suffer from a partial lack of the vitamin, resulting in abnormal tooth structure, anorexia, anemia, and predisposition to some infectious diseases.   The healing of wounds and fractures has been shown to be hastened by administration of ascorbic acid.   The minimal daily requirement for an adult is 30 mg., considerably higher than that of the majority of other factors, some of which are required in daily doses as low as 1–2 mg. (thiamine hydrochloride, riboflavin) or even 5–10 γ (vitamins D and B_{12}).   Although ascorbic acid occurs abundantly in fruits and vegetables, the content may be only slight in cooked, canned, or dried foods, since the vitamin is readily oxidized.

Ascorbic acid can be regarded as a derivative of tetronic acid (synthetic), the enolic form of a β-ketolactone.   The related tetronic acid derivatives

$$HOC\!=\!\!=\!\!CH$$
$$H_2C \quad\quad C\!=\!O$$
$$O$$

Tetronic acid

$$HOC\!=\!\!=\!\!COH$$
$$HOCH_2CH(OH)CH \quad C\!=\!O$$
$$O$$

Ascorbic acid

carolic, carolosic, carolinic, and carlic acid have been isolated from the mold *P. Charlesii* (Raistrick[23]).

$$HOC\!=\!\!=\!\!CCO(CH_2)_2CH_2OH$$
$$CH_3CH \quad\quad C\!=\!O$$
$$O$$

Carolic acid

$$HOC\!=\!\!=\!\!CCO(CH_2)_2CH_3$$
$$HOOCCH_2CH \quad\quad C\!=\!O$$
$$O$$

Carlosic acid

$$HOC\!=\!\!=\!\!CCO(CH_2)_2COOH$$
$$CH_3CH \quad\quad C\!=\!O$$
$$O$$

Carolinic acid

$$HOC\!=\!\!=\!\!CCO(CH_2)_2CH_2OH$$
$$HOOCCH_2CH \quad\quad C\!=\!O$$
$$O$$

Carlic acid

[23] Harold Raistrick, b. 1890 Pudsey, Yorkshire; School Hyg. and Trop. Med., London

Further related, strongly reducing substances are methylreductinic acid, a component of the active principle of a North African arrow poison (G. Hesse, 1948), and enol-tartronaldehyde, known also as reductone. The latter substance is formed on oxidation of glucose in alkaline solution with a solution prepared by dissolving lead acetate in alkali; it evidently is derived from the C_3-products of reverse aldolization, since it can be made by oxidation of dihydroxyacetone

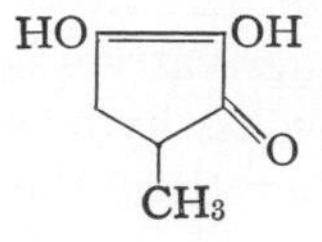

Methylreductinic acid 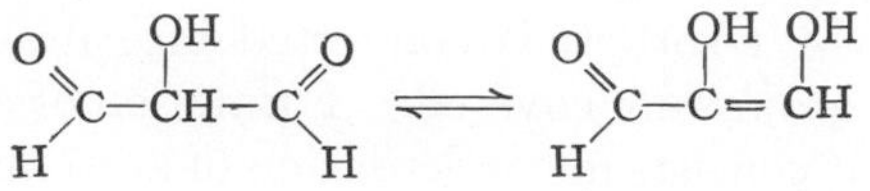   Reductone

Inositol. — The requirement of microorganisms for growth-accessory factors was postulated by Liebig in 1871, before it was recognized (1901–12) that similar substances (vitamins) are required by animals. Pasteur had been led from his experiments to assert (1860) that yeast can grow in media containing only sugar and nutrient salts, but Liebig found otherwise, and maintained that yeast requires some essential biological factor, supplied, for example, by addition of blood serum or juice of muscle. An active controversy raged for a time, and Pasteur was considered to have won the argument until 1901, when Wildiers obtained results that substantiated Liebig's position, and introduced the term "bios" for the alcohol–water extracts of boiled yeast cells, beer wort, or commercial peptone that promoted normal functioning of yeast. Bios was separated in 1923 into bios I and bios II by precipitation of the former fraction with barium sulfate, and five years later the first pure crystalline substance from bios was obtained from the precipitated material and identified as *meso*-inositol, which had been known for some time as a common constituent of plants and animals.

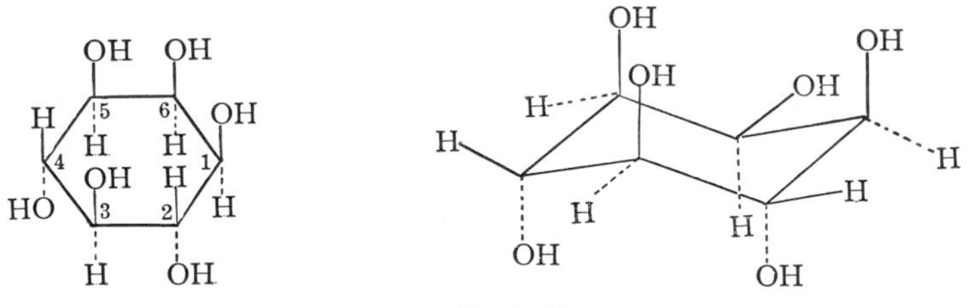

meso-Inositol*

Inositol alone added to yeast media exerts a rather slight influence, but it greatly augments the growth effect of bios II. This second bios fraction

* Eight *cis-trans* isomers are possible for the inositol structure, one of which is racemic. The two optically active forms, *d*- and *l*-cyclitol, the racemic form, and several *cis-trans* isomers occur naturally. The configuration of *meso*-inositol was established by various oxidations (Posternak, H. O. L. Fischer, 1942).

is a complicated mixture, containing at least three active constituents: pantothenic acid (p. 1009), biotin (p. 1011), and thiamine (p. 1001). Some strains of yeast do not respond to inositol or even to the total bios fraction.

In 1940 Woolley reported a disease, alopecia (Gr. *alopekia*, baldness), in mice fed on a basal diet supplemented only with factors known at the time to be required by mice, and noted the existence of an antialopecia factor in aqueous extracts of liver. Crystalline material was isolated shortly afterward from active preparations and identified as *meso*-inositol, the first instance of the requirement of inositol by organisms other than yeast.

Heparin. — Heparin is a polysaccharide present in various animal tissues and is characterized by the specific property of prolonging the clotting time of blood. It is used clinically in preventing formation of blood clots (thrombosis) after certain types of surgery. It is composed of equimolecular amounts of D-glucuronic acid and D-glucosamine (2-amino-D-glucose). The amino group is sulfated and one hydroxyl group per C_{12} unit is sul-

Heparin (?)

Chondroitin sulfate (?)

fated. A possible repeating unit suggested by Wolfrom[24] (1950) is shown in the formula.

Closely related complex polysaccharides known as chondroitin sulfate and mucoitin sulfate occur linked to protein in skeletal tissues, particularly cartilage. Gentle hydrolysis of chondroitin sulfate with oxalic acid splits off sulfuric acid and acetic acid and cleaves the polysaccharide chain to units of the disaccharide chondrosine, isolated as the crystalline ethyl ester hydrochloride. Chondrosine on further hydrolysis affords 2-amino-D-galactose (chondrosamine) and D-glucuronic acid. The formula shown for the polysaccharide is based upon the structure established for chondrosine by Meyer[25] (1954). Mucoitin sulfate is present in the gastric mucosa; it differs from chondroitin sulfate in the nature of the hexosamine unit, which is D-glucosamine.

Hyaluronic Acid. — This related complex polysaccharide was isolated first from vitreous humor (K. Meyer, 1934) and later from synovial fluid

[24] Melville L. Wolfrom, b. 1900 Bellevue, Ohio; Ph.D. Northwestern (W. L. Lewis); Ohio State Univ.

[25] Karl Meyer, b. 1899 Kerpen, Germany; M.D. Cologne, Ph.D. Berlin; Dept. Biochem., Coll. of Phys. and Surg., Columbia

(of joints), skin, and various microorganisms.   It is composed of N-acetyl-glucosamine and D-glucuronic acid and is believed to be similar to heparin except for the absence of sulfate ester groups.   Solutions are highly viscous, and this property is the basis for the biological function as a lubricant. An enzyme known as hyaluronidase causes hydrolysis; it occurs in many bacteria (but only in those that do not contain hyaluronic acid), in snake venoms, bee stings, and in various animal tissues, particularly the testes. It is the so-called spreading factor of testis extract described some time ago; the name is based on the ability to increase diffusion of dyes, toxins, and other substances on intradermal injection.   The enzyme, which occurs in spermatozoa and is involved in the fertilization process, is available commercially and has several uses.   When used in conjunction with intradermal administration of large amounts of fluid, it increases the rate of absorption of fluid by the tissue and thus prevents distention at the site of injection. When injected with a therapeutic agent, it enhances the effect.

Immunologically Active Polysaccharides. — A foreign protein (antigen) introduced into an animal stimulates production in the blood of substances (antibodies) that can combine with the antigen.   The interaction may result in formation of a precipitate (precipitin reaction).   Since the toxins, or poisonous secretions of several pathogenic organisms, have been identified as proteins, this antigen–antibody reaction is evidently the basis for immunity to specific diseases that an animal may acquire as a result of infection.   The reaction is highly specific; for instance, the pneumococci belong to some forty serological types, and an animal that has acquired immunity to one type will usually not be immune to any other type.   Landsteiner introduced the term hapten for the nonproteinoid portion of an antigen that determines the specificity of antigen to antibody.   The antibodies (or antitoxins) are modified serum globulin.

In 1917 Dochez and Avery found that filtrates of cultures of pathogenic pneumococci contain a substance that precipitates with antiserum of the same serological type.   Investigations of Heidelberger[26] have shown that these substances are polysaccharides and that the type specificity and virulence of the pneumococci are associated with the presence of the polysaccharide which is the main component of the capsule surrounding the organism.   Avirulent pneumococci are not encapsulated.   Proteins of the pathogenic pneumococci are serologically related throughout the entire group.   The polysaccharide of type III pneumococcus (molecular weight about 150,000) consists of glucose and glucuronic acid in equimolecular amounts.   It can be hydrolyzed to an aldobiuronic acid of which the probable structure is that of cellobiuronic acid.   The serum of rabbits that have been immunized to type III pneumococcus will agglutinate (L. *agglutinare*. to glue) not only type III but also type VIII pneumococcus.   This effect, which is known as an immunological cross reaction, is due to the fact that

---

[26] Michael Heidelberger, b. 1888 New York; Ph.D. Columbia (Bogert); Coll. Phys. and Surg., Columbia

the capsular polysaccharides of the two types are related chemically. Type VIII polysaccharide is also composed of glucose and glucuronic acid,

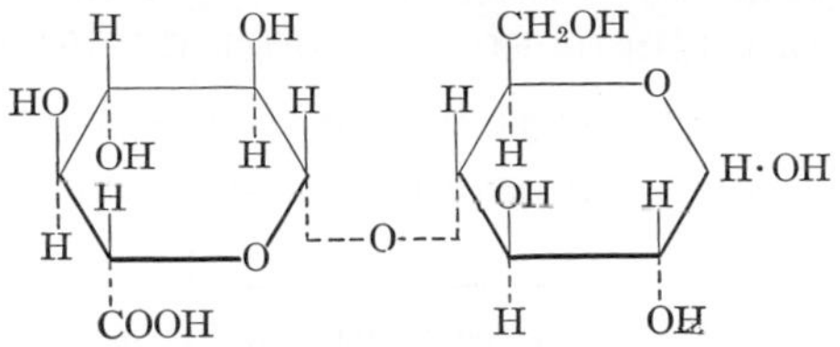

Cellobiuronic acid

but the molar ratio is 7:2, whereas it is 1:1 in type III polysaccharide. The polysaccharide of type XIV pneumococcus contains N-acetylglucosamine and galactose in the molar ratio of 1:3. Fundamental work of Avery has shown that the type specificity of the pneumococcus is controlled by the particular nucleic acid of each type. Thus the nucleic acid of type III pneumococcus can induce type II pneumococcus to change into type III pneumococcus; that is, it controls production of the polysaccharide responsible for the type specificity. When the change is once induced, the nucleic acid is also reproduced in the course of cell division. Similar specifically active polysaccharides have been obtained from other pathogenic bacteria. The hapten of group A hemolytic streptococcus is composed of N-acetylglucosamine and glucuronic acid in equimolecular amounts. Two active polysaccharides of human tubercle bacillus are highly branched, high-molecular weight substances composed of four sugar units (Haworth, 1948). The antigens of several bacteria have been identified as complexes containing a polysaccharide and a protein, and carbohydrate-protein antigens have been synthesized whose specificity is determined by the pattern of the carbohydrate constituent.

Chemical substances other than polysaccharides can act as haptens. Haptenic activity has been claimed for certain lipid fractions obtained from bacteria, but may be due to impurities. Immunological activity has been observed in the case of a unique polypeptide obtained from the capsules of *B. anthracis* and *B. mesentericus*. The substance yields only one amino acid on hydrolysis, D-glutamic acid. The virulence of these bacilli may be due to the fact that digestive enzymes are unable to hydrolyze the polypeptide owing to the unnatural configuration of the constituent amino acid.

PROBLEMS

1. A certain pentose, which forms a tetraacetate, is condensed with hydrogen cyanide and the product is hydrolyzed and reduced with HI-P. The resulting acid is identical with one synthesized from $CH_3CH_2CH_2I$ and $CH_3CH(CO_2C_2H_5)_2$. What is the structure of the pentose?
2. Rhamnose (p. 375) is a methylpentose of structure

   (a) $CH_3CHOHCHOHCHOHCHOHCHO$

Suggest an oxidation test that would distinguish between structure (a) and the following structure (b) $HOCH_2CH_2CHOHCHOHCHOHCHO$.

3. What test would distinguish between a 2-desoxyhexose (a) and a 3-desoxyhexose (b)?

    (a) $HOCH_2CHOHCHOHCHOHCH_2CHO$ (b) $HOCH_2CHOHCHOHCH_2CHOHCHO$

4. What tests would distinguish between the isomers (a), (b), and (c)?

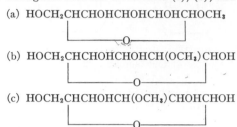

    (a) $HOCH_2CHCHOHCHOHCHOHCHOCH_3$

    (b) $HOCH_2CHCHOHCHOHCH(OCH_3)CHOH$

    (c) $HOCH_2CHCHOHCH(OCH_3)CHOHCHOH$

5. A hexose on catalytic hydrogenation in neutral solution gives a mixture of two products identified as sorbitol (p. 392) and the alcohol derived from galactose. What is the hexose?

6. Two optically active D-aldotetroses, A and B, give the same osazone, but on oxidation with nitric acid A gives an optically active C_4-dibasic acid and B gives an optically inactive C_4-dibasic acid. Identify A and B.

7. Devise a brief series of experiments by which D-ribose could be distinguished from the other three D-aldopentoses.

8. Which cyclic form of glucose, α or β, would you expect to be the more stable (see conformation, p. 366)? Does your prediction correspond with the relative abundance of the two forms at equilibrium, as judged by the rotation?

9. Which position in inositol would you expect to be most susceptible to acetylation and least susceptible to oxidation?

READING REFERENCES

C. S. Hudson, "Emil Fischer's Discovery of the Configuration of Glucose," *J. Chem. Ed.*, **18**, 353 (1941)

M. L. Wolfrom, A. L. Raymond, and E. Heuser, "The Carbohydrates," in H. Gilman, "Organic Chemistry," II, 2nd Ed., 1532–1719, Wiley, New York (1943)

K. H. Meyer, "The Chemistry of Glycogen," *Advances in Enzymology*, **3**, 109 (1943)

W. N. Haworth, "Starch," *J. Chem. Soc.*, 543 (1946)

E. L. Hirst, "The Occurrence and Significance of the Pentose Sugars in Nature, and Their Relationship to the Hexoses," *J. Chem. Soc.*, 522 (1949)

F. Micheel, "Chemie der Zucker und Polysaccharide," Akademische Verlagsgesellschaft, Leipzig (1939)

J. Honeyman, "An Introduction to the Chemistry of Carbohydrates," Oxford Univ. Press (1948)

W. W. Pigman and R. M. Goepp, Jr., "Chemistry of the Carbohydrates," Academic Press (1948)

"Advances in Carbohydrates," Academic Press, 1945–

R. L. Whistler and C. L. Smart, "Polysaccharide Chemistry," Academic Press, 1953

CHAPTER 15

FATS

Lipid is a general name for plant and animal products typified by esters of higher fatty acids but including certain other oil-soluble, water-insoluble substances. The term fat (or vegetable or animal oil, if liquid) is usually confined to esters of fatty acids with glycerol, and the term wax to esters with other alcohols. Complex lipids containing additional components also occur and are considered later. Glycerides can be hydrolyzed readily, usually by aqueous sodium hydroxide, in which case the component fatty acids are obtained as sodium salts (soap). The glyceride formulated has

$$
\begin{array}{llll}
CH_2OCOR & & CH_2OH & \\
| & & | & \\
CHOCOR & + \ 3 \ NaOH \ \rightarrow & CHOH & + \ 3 \ RCO_2Na \\
| & & | & \\
CH_2OCOR & & CH_2OH & \\
\text{Glyceride} & & \text{Glycerol} & \text{Soap}
\end{array}
$$

three identical fatty acid residues; actually fats invariably consist of mixed glycerides in which two or three fatty acids are present. The simple glycerides of palmitic and stearic acid are called tripalmitin and tristearin. Among some fifty fatty acids found in nature, almost all are straight-chain acids containing an even number of carbon atoms. One odd-numbered fatty acid isolated from fats is isovaleric acid, $(CH_3)_2CHCH_2COOH$, which occurs in relatively large amounts in dolphin and porpoise (blubber acids, 3.2% and 13.6%, respectively). The carbon skeleton of isovaleric acid is that of isoprene.

Isolation of pure, individual acids is exceedingly difficult. A traditional method of separation of acids of appreciably different molecular weights is by fractional vacuum distillation of the methyl esters. Separation of saturated and unsaturated acids is generally achieved by crystallization of the lead or lithium salts from alcohol or acetone; the saturated salts are less soluble and crystallize first. Polyunsaturated acids have been isolated as the polybromides, although changes in structure or configuration may occur in bromination or debromination. Low-temperature crystallization (to −60°) is particularly useful for isolation of unsaturated acids subject to autoxidation at room temperature (J. B. Brown, 1941). Particular success has been achieved by chromatography of methyl esters on a silica column under nitrogen. A further method depends upon the fact that long-chain esters, like normal paraffins, form solid complexes with urea (p. 46).

Saturated Fatty Acids. — Saturated fatty acids ranging from C_4 to C_{26} have been identified as constituents of fats (Table 15.1). Of these palmitic

TABLE 15.1. SATURATED FATTY ACIDS

ACID	No. OF C ATOMS	FORMULA	M.P., °C.	B.P., °C.
Butyric	4	$CH_3(CH_2)_2COOH$	-4.7	163
Isovaleric	5	$(CH_3)_2CHCH_2COOH$	-51	174
Caproic	6	$CH_3(CH_2)_4COOH$	-1.5	205
Caprylic	8	$CH_3(CH_2)_6COOH$	16.5	237
Capric	10	$CH_3(CH_2)_8COOH$	31.3	269
Lauric	12	$CH_3(CH_2)_{10}COOH$	43.6	102/1 mm.
Myristic	14	$CH_3(CH_2)_{12}COOH$	58.0	122/1 mm.
Palmitic	16	$CH_3(CH_2)_{14}COOH$	62.9	139/1 mm.
Stearic	18	$CH_3(CH_2)_{16}COOH$	69.9	160/1 mm.
Arachidic	20	$CH_3(CH_2)_{18}COOH$	75.2	205/1 mm.
Behenic	22	$CH_3(CH_2)_{20}COOH$	80.2	
Lignoceric	24	$CH_3(CH_2)_{22}COOH$	84.2	
Cerotic	26	$CH_3(CH_2)_{24}COOH$	87.7	

acid is of widest occurrence; it is a component of almost all fats. It is the major constituent (35–45%) of the fatty acids of palm oil, the fruit fat of *Elaeis guineensis*, the West African oil palm. The other most frequently encountered saturated acids are lauric, myristic, and stearic. Lauric acid is named after the laurel family, from which it was first isolated (1842). It is the most abundant fatty acid of palm-kernel oil (52%), coconut oil, and babassu oil. Myristic acid can be isolated readily from the seed fat of nutmeg. Stearic acid occurs in large amounts (10–30%) in animal fats, but is usually found only in traces in vegetable fats. The saturated fatty acids lower than C_{12} occur in the milk fat of mammals, which is the only natural source of butyric acid. Caproic, caprylic, and capric acids occur in small amounts in other fats. Fatty acids with more than eighteen carbon atoms are widely distributed but usually are present only in traces, except in waxes. Cerotic acid (L. *cera*, wax), a characteristic component of many waxes, actually is a mixture, as other wax acids are, and consists of C_{24}-, C_{26}-, and C_{28}-acids.

Fatty acids do not show a regular increase in melting point with increasing chain length; the melting point of an odd-numbered acid is slightly lower than that of the next lower even-numbered acid. X-ray studies of

No. of C atoms*	8	9	10	11	12	13	14	15	16	17	18
M.P., °C.	16.5	12.5	31	28	44	40.5	58	51	63	60	70
d_1-Crystal spacing, Å					27.4	30.4	31.5	34.2	35.6	38.6	39.9

crystalline acids show three spacings, two of which are small and nearly constant and evidently refer to the thickness and width; the third (d_1) varies with the number of carbon atoms and corresponds to twice the chain length, which means that the acids form double molecules (—COOH· HOOC—). The increment in the d_1-value for each methylene group shows

* Names of the odd-numbered acids are: C_9, pelargonic acid; C_{11}, undecylic acid; C_{13}, tridecylic acid; C_{15}, pentadecylic acid; C_{17}, margaric acid; C_{19}, nondecylic acid.

TABLE 15.2.* UNSATURATED FATTY ACIDS

ACID	CARBON ATOMS	FORMULA	M.P., °C.
Δ^9-Decylenic	10	CH_2=$CH(CH_2)_7COOH$	
Stillingic	10	$CH_3(CH_2)_4CH$=$CHCH$=$CHCO_2H$ (cis, trans)	
Δ^9-Dodecylenic	12	CH_3CH_2CH=$CH(CH_2)_7COOH$	
Palmitoleic	16	$CH_3(CH_2)_5CH$=$CH(CH_2)_7COOH$ (cis)	
Oleic	18	$CH_3(CH_2)_7CH$=$CH(CH_2)_7COOH$ (cis)	13, 16
Ricinoleic	18	$CH_3(CH_2)_5CH(OH)CH_2CH$=$CH(CH_2)_7COOH$ (cis)	50
Petroselinic	18	$CH_3(CH_2)_{10}CH$=$CH(CH_2)_4COOH$ (cis)	30
Vaccenic	18	$CH_3(CH_2)_5CH$=$CH(CH_2)_9COOH$ (cis and trans)	
Linoleic	18	$CH_3(CH_2)_4CH$=$CHCH_2CH$=$CH(CH_2)_7COOH$	−5
Linolenic	18	CH_3CH_2CH=$CHCH_2CH$=$CHCH_2CH$=$CH(CH_2)_7COOH$	−11
Eleostearic	18	$CH_3(CH_2)_3(CH$=$CH)_3(CH_2)_7COOH$ (cis, trans, trans)	49
Licanic	18	$CH_3(CH_2)_3(CH$=$CH)_3(CH_2)_4CO(CH_2)_2COOH$	75
Parinaric	18	$CH_3CH_2(CH$=$CH)_4(CH_2)_7COOH$	86
Gadoleic	20	$CH_3(CH_2)_9CH$=$CH(CH_2)_7COOH$	
Arachidonic	20	$CH_3(CH_2)_4(CH$=$CHCH_2)_4(CH_2)_2COOH$	
Cetoleic	22	$CH_3(CH_2)_9CH$=$CH(CH_2)_9COOH$	
Erucic	22	$CH_3(CH_2)_7CH$=$CH(CH_2)_{11}COOH$ (cis)	33.5
Selacholeic or nervonic	24	$CH_3(CH_2)_7CH$=$CH(CH_2)_{13}COOH$ (cis)	39

* The symbol Δ is used as an abbreviation for a double bond; the superscript gives the position of the first carbon of the double bond.

an alternation between the odd and even series. Interpretation of X-ray data leads to the conclusion that molecules of an even-numbered acid are packed more closely in the crystal lattice than those of the next higher odd-numbered acid, which is reflected in the higher melting point.

A nonconventional synthetic route to higher fatty acids is an adaptation of the Kolbe anodic hydrocarbon synthesis (Linstead,[1] 1950). Electrolysis of a monocarboxylic acid with the half-ester of an α,ω-dicarboxylic acid gives three easily separable products: a hydrocarbon, a diester formed by

$$RCO_2H + HO_2C(CH_2)_nCO_2CH_3 \xrightarrow{\text{Electrol.}}$$

$$R \cdot R + CH_3O_2C(CH_2)_{2n}CO_2CH_3 + R(CH_2)_nCO_2CH_3$$

symmetrical coupling, and a monoester formed by unsymmetrical coupling. Yields of the mono ester are in the order of 20–50%.

Olefinic Fatty Acids. — Unsaturated fatty acids with less than ten carbon atoms have not been observed in nature, and the C_{10}-, C_{12}-, and C_{14}-acids occur only in traces in a few fats. Olefinic acids of established structure are listed in Table 15.2. Three methods have proved of value in determining the position of the double bond. (1) The methyl ester is oxidized in acetone solution with permanganate, illustrated by the oxidation

[1] R. Patrick Linstead, b. 1902 London; Ph.D. and D.Sc. London (Thorpe); London (Imperial Coll.)

of methyl palmitoleate (Hilditch,[2] 1925):

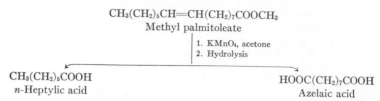

$$CH_3(CH_2)_5CH{=}CH(CH_2)_7COOCH_3$$
Methyl palmitoleate

1. $KMnO_4$, acetone
2. Hydrolysis

$CH_3(CH_2)_5COOH$
n-Heptylic acid

$HOOC(CH_2)_7COOH$
Azelaic acid

The oxidation gives a monobasic and a dibasic acid that can be separated by extracting the monobasic acid with petroleum ether, in which the dibasic acid is sparingly soluble. The dibasic acid is always obtained in better yield (80–85%) than the monobasic acid (50–60%). (2) The double bond of the acid or ester is hydroxylated, and the resulting dihydroxy compound is oxidized with a reagent specific for *vic*-glycols (lead tetraacetate or periodic acid). Oleic acid (*cis*) can be converted by oxidation with very dilute permanganate in the cold into a *vic*-diol in nearly quantitative yield; the product is the *erythro* diol resulting from *cis* addition, and the same substance is formed by hydroxylation with osmium tetroxide. Hydroxylation by reaction with hydrogen peroxide in formic acid solution and hydrolysis proceeds by *trans* addition and gives the *threo* diol in high yield (79%, pure). Cleavage of either diol with periodic acid or with red lead and acetic acid (active agent: lead tetraacetate) gives the C_9-aldehyde and the C_9-aldehyde acid in excellent yields. (3) The acid is cleaved by ozonization and the

$$CH_3(CH_2)_7\overset{H}{\underset{}{C}}{=}\overset{H}{\underset{}{C}}(CH_2)_7COOH$$
Oleic acid (*cis*)

$KMnO_4$ or OsO_4 | | $H_2O_2{-}HCO_2H$; hydrol.

$$CH_3(CH_2)_7\overset{H}{\underset{OH}{C}}{-}\overset{H}{\underset{OH}{C}}(CH_2)_7COOH$$
erythro-9,10-Dihydroxystearic acid
(m.p. 132°)

$$CH_3(CH_2)_7\overset{H}{\underset{OH}{C}}{-}\overset{OH}{\underset{H}{C}}(CH_2)_7COOH$$
threo-9,10-Dihydroxystearic acid
(m.p. 95°)

HIO_4 or $Pb(OAc)_4$

$CH_3(CH_2)_7CH{=}O$ + $O{=}CH(CH_2)_7COOH$
Pelargonic aldehyde
(89%)

Azelaic half-aldehyde
(76%)

structure deduced from the fragments. Oleic acid yields, as in (2), pelargonic aldehyde and azelaic half-aldehyde, together with the corresponding acids, pelargonic and azelaic, resulting probably from oxidation during hydrolysis or recovery.

[2] Thomas Percy Hilditch, b. 1886 London; D.Sc. London (Collie, Smith, E. F. Armstrong); Liverpool

Palmitoleic acid (C_{16}) occurs in nearly all fats but is most abundant in those of marine origin. The majority of unsaturated fatty acids of known structure contain eighteen carbon atoms. The simplest is oleic acid, which is the most widely distributed of all fatty acids. It is the major acid of olive oil (76–86%) and of almond-kernel oil (77%). It is also the chief acid of depot fats of herbivorous animals: mutton and beef tallows (50%), neat's-foot oil from ox hoof (80%). Only the *cis* form is observed in natural fat. Oleic acid can be transformed into the *trans* isomer, elaidic acid, by heating at 180–200° with a small amount of selenium. The conversion is an equilibrium process, and the same mixture, containing 66% of the *trans*

$$CH_3(CH_2)_7CH \rightleftharpoons CH_3(CH_2)_7CH$$
$$\| \qquad\qquad\qquad \|$$
$$HOOC(CH_2)_7CH \qquad\qquad HC(CH_2)_7COOH$$

Oleic acid (liq.)   Elaidic acid (m.p. 44°)

form, is attained from either acid. Linoleic acid (*cis, cis*), which contains two nonconjugated double bonds, is encountered only in traces in animal fats, but is observed as frequently as oleic acid in vegetable fats. It accounts for 25–40% of the fatty acids of linseed oil and 40–45% of those of cottonseed oil. Linoleic acid is a liquid, and is usually identified and purified as the bromine-addition compound, tetrabromostearic acid, m.p. 114°. The *trans, trans* isomer is known as linelaidic acid. Linolenic acid (*cis, cis, cis*) is the most common triethylenic acid; it is the major acid of linseed oil and of perilla-seed oil, and occurs in most seed fats, often in appreciable amounts. In these three acids and in several others the first double bond, counted from the carboxyl end of the chain, occurs in the same position (9, 10). Eleostearic acid is an isomer of linolenic acid in which the double bonds are conjugated. Its occurrence is limited almost entirely to tung oil, in which it is the main fatty acid (80%). The natural acid (*cis, trans, trans*) can be isomerized to the all *trans* β-eleostearic acid. The rare tetraethylenic C_{18}-acid, parinaric acid, has been isolated only from one species, *Parinarium laurinum*. Fatty acids of the C_{20}- and C_{22}-series with four or more double bonds occur mainly in marine fats; in these highly unsaturated acids, the grouping $=CH(CH_2)_2CH=$, rare in vegetable fats, is commonly encountered. Gadoleic and cetoleic acid have been isolated only from fish oils. Erucic acid (*cis*) occurs in large amounts in the seed oils of rape, mustard, wallflower, and nasturtium. It can be isolated readily from the last material (80% of total acids) by crystallization from alcohol–water. The constitution is established by oxidation to pelargonic acid (C_9) and brassylic acid, $HOOC(CH_2)_{11}COOH$. The *trans* isomer is brassidic acid. Nervonic acid (*cis*) occurs in fish oils and in brain tissue.

The acids of human depot fat are shown in Table 15.3; the composition is close to that of beef tallow and of lard. Unsaturated acids predominate over saturated acids in the ratio 3:2, and the most abundant single component is oleic acid. Considerable linoleic acid is also present. The tetra-unsaturated C_{20}-component present in human fat in amounts of 0.3–1.0%

TABLE 15.3. PERCENT FATTY ACIDS IN HUMAN DEPOT FAT*

SATURATED				1 C=C			2 C=C	4 C=C
C_{12}	C_{14}	C_{16}	C_{18}	C_{14}	C_{16}	C_{18}	C_{18}	C_{20}
0.5	3.3	25.0	8.4	0.4	6.2	45.9	9.6	0.6

* Average analyses of five normal specimens reported by D. L. Cramer and J. B. Brown, 1943.

is arachidonic acid, which deviates from the prevailing types both in carbon content and number of double bonds. The adrenal gland is the richest

$$CH_3CH_2CH_2CH_2CH_2CH_2CH_2CH_2CH\overset{9}{=}CHCH_2CH_2CH_2CH_2CH_2CH_2CH_2\overset{1}{CO_2H}$$
Oleic acid (Δ^9)

$$CH_3CH_2CH_2CH_2CH_2CH\overset{12}{=}CHCH_2CH\overset{9}{=}CHCH_2CH_2CH_2CH_2CH_2CH_2CH_2CO_2H$$
Linoleic acid ($\Delta^{9,12}$)

$$CH_3CH_2CH\overset{15}{=}CHCH_2CH\overset{12}{=}CHCH_2CH\overset{9}{=}CHCH_2CH_2CH_2CH_2CH_2CH_2CH_2CO_2H$$
Linolenic acid ($\Delta^{9,12,15}$)

$$CH_3CH_2CH_2CH_2CH_2CH\overset{14}{=}CHCH_2CH\overset{11}{=}CHCH_2CH\overset{8}{=}CHCH_2CH\overset{5}{=}CHCH_2CH_2CH_2CO_2H$$
Arachidonic acid ($\Delta^{5,8,11,14}$)

known source of arachidonic acid, which accounts for 22% of the fatty acids of the phosphatide fraction of beef adrenal glands. Arachidonic acid can be hydrogenated easily to the tetrahydro stage and affords 80–90% of the $\Delta^{5,14}$-dienic acid and 5–10% of the $\Delta^{8,14}$-dienic acid; the two double bonds in the central part of the molecule are thus the most susceptible to hydrogenation.

Degradative evidence that vaccenic acid is Δ^{11}-octadecenoic acid was confirmed by two syntheses. One (Strong, 1948) involves in the first step condensation of the sodio derivative of an alkyne with an α-iodo-ω-chloroal-

$$CH_3(CH_2)_5C{\equiv}CNa + I(CH_2)_9Cl \xrightarrow[95\%]{NH_3} CH_3(CH_2)_5C{\equiv}C(CH_2)_9Cl \xrightarrow[85\%]{NaCN;\ KOH}$$

$$CH_3(CH_2)_5C{\equiv}C(CH_2)_9CO_2H \xrightarrow{Pd,\ H_2} CH_3(CH_2)_5\overset{H}{C}{=}\overset{H}{C}(CH_2)_9CO_2H$$

Vaccenic acid

$$CH_3(CH_2)_5\overset{H}{C}{=}\overset{H}{C}(CH_2)_7CO_2H + HO_2C(CH_2)_2CO_2CH_3 \underset{\text{Electrol. (12%)}}{\longrightarrow}$$

kane. The product is converted through the nitrile to the acetylenic acid, which is selectively hydrogenated to the *cis*-ethylenic acid. The second synthesis (Linstead, 1954) is by electrolysis of a mixture of palmitoleic acid with a large excess of methyl hydrogen succinate (followed by hydrolysis).

Ricinoleic acid, 12-hydroxyoleic acid, constitutes 80% of the fatty acids of castor oil, the yearly production of which is about 75,000 tons. The oil is used as a medicinal (purgative), for production of Turkey-red oil, and as a lubricant (high viscosity, because the protruding hydroxyl hinders free flow of molecules past one another). Licanic acid, of structure established by oxidation experiments and by hydrogenation to 4-ketostearic acid, constitutes 75–80% of the fatty acids of Brazilian oiticica oil. Vernolic acid, another oxygenated acid not included in Table 15.2, has been characterized as 12,13-epoxyoleic acid (F. D. Gunstone, 1954).

Amides. — Neoherculin (m. p. 70°) is one of a number of natural insecticides shown to be amides of olefinic acids (L. Crombie, 1955). It is the

Neoherculin: $CH_3(CH=CH)_3CH_2CH_2CH=CHCONHCH_2CH(CH_3)_2$

Affinin: $CH_3(CH=CH)_2CH_2CH_2CH=CHCONHCH_2CH(CH_3)_2$

isobutylamide of a C_{12}-acid containing four double bonds, three of which are conjugated; the double bond conjugated with the amide linkage is *trans*. The substance is structurally related to affinin, an insecticidal principle of *Heliopsis longipes*. The active principle of red pepper (*Capsicum* species), capsaicin, is the 3-methoxy-4-hydroxybenzylamide of *trans*-8-methyl-Δ^6-nonenic acid.

Capsaicin: $(CH_3)_2CHCH=CH(CH_2)_4CONHCH_2C_6H_3$-3-$OCH_3$-4-OH

Autoxidation. — Unsaturated acids are subject to air oxidation, the *cis* isomers being more susceptible than the *trans*. The reaction is believed to involve attack by peroxide radicals to form unstable hydroperoxides, which decompose to keto and hydroxyketo acids. It appears that below 50° the attack is at a methylene group adjacent to a double bond, whereas at higher temperatures the double bond is attacked and undergoes migration:

$$—CH_2CH=CH— \xrightarrow{\cdot OOH} —CH_2\overset{\cdot}{C}HCH—\underset{|}{\overset{}{}}_{OOH} \xrightarrow{O_2} —CH=CHCH-\underset{|}{}_{OOH} - + \cdot OOH$$

Acetylenic Acids. — Tariric acid, long known to contain an acetylenic linkage (Arnaud, 1892), has been shown to be Δ^6-octadecynoic acid by syn-

Tariric acid: $CH_3(CH_2)_{10}C\equiv C(CH_2)_4CO_2H$ (m.p. 52°)

thesis, partial hydrogenation to petroselinic acid (Table 15.2), and ozonolysis to adipic and lauric acids (J. C. Smith, 1952). Ricinstearoleic acid, the acetylenic counterpart of ricinoleic acid, has been synthesized (Crombie,

Ricinstearoleic acid: $CH_3(CH_2)_5CH(OH)CH_2C\equiv C(CH_2)_7CO_2H$ (m.p. 12°)

Ximenynic acid: $CH_3(CH_2)_5CH=CHC\equiv C(CH_2)_7CO_2H$ (m.p. 40°)

1955) and partially hydrogenated to ricinoleic acid. It can be dehydrated to another natural acid, ximenynic (λ_{max} 2290Å), an enynic acid which is readily isomerized to a conjugated trienic acid (λ_{max} 2680Å).

Several naturally occurring acids have two adjacent triple bonds, and a method has been developed for oxidative coupling of two acetylenic components to produce this grouping (H. K. Black and B. C. L. Weedon, 1953). Thus erythrogenic acid, isolated from the seeds of an African tree, was synthesized by shaking a mixture of octene-1-yne-7 and Δ^9-decynoic acid with oxygen in the presence of cuprous ammonium chloride. The oxidative

$$CH_2\!\!=\!\!CH(CH_2)_4C\!\!\equiv\!\!CH + HC\!\!\equiv\!\!C(CH_2)_7CO_2H \xrightarrow{[O]}$$

$$CH_2\!\!=\!\!CH(CH_2)_4C\!\!\equiv\!\!CC\!\!\equiv\!\!C(CH_2)_7CO_2H$$

Erythrogenic acid

M.p. 39°, λ_{max} 2270, 2370, 2540Å

crossed coupling gives the expected mixture of three products, but these differ considerably in molecular weight and are readily separated. Spectrographic studies have aided investigation of these and more highly unsaturated acids and esters, such as matricaria methyl ester (Sörensen, 1940–).

$$\overset{H\ \ H}{}\qquad\overset{H\ \ H}{}$$

Matricaria methyl ester: $CH_3C\!\!=\!\!CC\!\!\equiv\!\!CC\!\!\equiv\!\!CC\!\!=\!\!CCO_2CH_3$

This substance has the *cis, cis* configuration; the Δ^2-*trans* isomer and the 2,3-dihydro ester have also been isolated.

The most unusual unsaturated acid is mycomycin, an optically active antibiotic elaborated by the fungus *Norcardia acidophilus* (structure: W. D. Celmer and I. A. Solomons, 1952–53). Even pure material ($[\alpha]_D - 130°$, λ_{max} 2670, 2810Å) is extremely unstable; the half-life at 27° in the absence of air is only three hours. The substance ($C_{13}H_{10}O_2$) is hydrogenated quantitatively to *n*-tridecanoic acid. The structure was deduced largely from infrared absorption characteristics and confirmed in various ways. Thus

$$\overset{\qquad H\ \ H\quad H}{HC\!\!\equiv\!\!CC\!\!\equiv\!\!CCH\!\!=\!\!C\!\!=\!\!CHC\!\!=\!\!CC\!\!=\!\!CCH_2CO_2H} \xrightarrow{OH^-}$$
$$\underset{\qquad\qquad\ \ H}{}$$

Mycomycin

$$\overset{\qquad\qquad\qquad H\ \ H}{CH_3C\!\!\equiv\!\!CC\!\!\equiv\!\!CC\!\!=\!\!CC\!\!=\!\!CC\!\!=\!\!CCH_2CO_2H}$$
$$\underset{\qquad\qquad\qquad H\ \ H}{}$$

Isomycomycin

the presence of an allenic group accounts for the optical activity, which is lost on isomerization of mycomycin by alkali to isomycomycin. This remarkable reaction involves an allene → acetylene isomerization, an acetylenic migration, and a *trans, cis* to *trans, trans* isomerization.

Branched-Chain Acids. — A few natural fatty acids containing a branched chain exhibit physiological activity. Three contain the cyclopentenyl ring system: hydnocarpic, chaulmoorgic, and gorlic acid. These acids occur as major components of seed fats of the family *Flacourtiaceae*, and apparently nowhere else. Chaulmoogra oil is the native (East Indian) name for the fat of *Hydnocarpus kurzii*. The acids contain an asymmetric

$$\begin{array}{c} CH=CH \\ | \qquad \overset{*}{\diagdown}CH(CH_2)_{10}COOH \\ CH_2-CH_2 \end{array}$$

Hydnocarpic acid ($C_{16}H_{28}O_2$)
$[\alpha]_D + 68°$; m.p. 59–60°

$$\begin{array}{c} CH=CH \\ | \qquad \overset{*}{\diagdown}CH(CH_2)_{12}COOH \\ CH_2-CH_2 \end{array}$$

Chaulmoogric acid ($C_{18}H_{32}O_2$)
$[\alpha]_D + 56°$; m.p. 71°

$$\begin{array}{c} CH=CH \\ | \qquad \overset{*}{\diagdown}CH(CH_2)_6CH=CH(CH_2)_4COOH \\ CH_2-CH_2 \end{array}$$

Gorlic acid ($C_{18}H_{30}O_2$)
$[\alpha]_D + 61°$; m.p. 6°

carbon atom and are dextrorotatory. Hydnocarpus oils have been used for centuries by Hindus and Chinese for treatment of leprosy, a disease produced by an acid-fast bacillus; such a bacillus is characterized by a fatty envelope and, after being stained with a specific dye for histological examination, is not easily decolorized by acids. The oils usually are administered orally and, since they are irritating in large amounts, treatment must be extended over years. The glycerides are probably converted in the body to free fatty acids, which are the active agents; the acids themselves are effective when administered in a suitably dispersed form (in stearic acid). R. Adams observed that the leprocidal activity *in vitro* of a number of branched-chain acids parallels ability of the acids to depress surface tension, and probably the physiological effect is a result of impairment of the fatty envelope of the bacilli.

Anderson[3] (1929–36) isolated from several strains of tubercle bacilli and from *B. leprae* an optically active, odd-numbered fatty acid, tuberculostearic acid, shown by oxidation and synthesis to be 10-methylstearic acid.

$$CH_3(CH_2)_7\overset{*}{C}H(CH_2)_8COOH \xrightarrow{[O]} CH_3(CH_2)_7COCH_3 + HOOC(CH_2)_7COOH$$

$$\underset{\substack{\text{Tuberculostearic acid} \\ (C_{19}H_{28}O_2,\ \text{m.p. 10–11°})}}{|\atop CH_3} \qquad \text{Methyl } n\text{-octyl ketone} \qquad \text{Azelaic acid}$$

Anderson isolated from the same source a substance named phthioic acid, which forms typical tubercular lesions on injection in animals. The material was later found to be a mixture and one component, mycolipenic acid ($[\alpha]_D +8°$, λ_{max} 2200Å), shown to have the structure formulated (N. Polgar,

$$\begin{array}{ccc} CH_3 & CH_3 & CH_3 \\ | & | & | \\ CH_3(CH_2)_{17}CHCH_2CHCH=CCO_2H \end{array}$$

Mycolipenic acid

$$\begin{array}{ccc} CH_3 & CH_3 & CH_3 \\ | & | & | \\ CH_3(CH_2)_nCHCH_2CHCH_2CHCO_2H \end{array}$$

Mycoceranic acid

1954). Mycoceranic acid is a levorotatory component (n is probably 21).

Analysis of Fats. — The saponification value, expressed as the number

[3] Rudolph J. Anderson, b. 1879 Harna, Sweden; Ph.D. Cornell; Yale Univ.

TABLE 15.4.[1] ACID COMPOSITION OF FATS AND NONDRYING OILS

FAT OR OIL	IODINE VALUE	TITER OF ACIDS, °C.	FATTY ACIDS, %							
			Caprylic	Capric	Lauric	Myristic	Palmitic	Stearic	Oleic	Linoleic
Coconut	8–10	20–23	8.0	7.0	48.0	17.5	8.2	2.0	6.0	2.5
Babassu	12–16	23–24	6.5	2.7	45.8	19.9	6.9	....	18.1	....
Palm kernel	15–18	20–25	3.0	3.0	52.0	15.0	7.5	2.5	16.0	1.0
Palm	51–58	38–47	...	...	....	1.0	42.5	4.0	43.0	9.5
Olive	80–85	17–21	...	...	....	....	6.0	4.0	83.0	7.0
Castor [2]	81–89	3	...	...	....	....	....	0.3	8.0	3.6
Peanut [3]	85–90	28–32	...	...	....	....	7.0	5.0	60.0	21.0
Rape [4]	94–106	12–18	...	...	....	1.0	1.0	1.0	29.0	15.0
Beef tallow	32–47	37–47	...	...	....	2.0	32.5	14.5	48.3	2.7
Lard (leaf)	46–66	36–43	...	...	....	1.1	30.4	17.9	41.2	5.7
Whale blubber[5]	110–150	22–24	...	...	....	8.0	12.1	2.3	33.4	9.0

[1] Data of Werner G. Smith Company.
[2] Contains 87.8% ricinoleic acid.
[3] Contains 4.0% arachidic acid and 3.0% lignoceric acid.
[4] Contains 1.0% lignoceric acid and 50.0% erucic acid.
[5] Contains 1.5% of a C_{14}-monounsaturated acid, 15% palmitoleic acid, and 18.7% C_{20}- and C_{22}- highly unsaturated acids.

of milligrams of potassium hydroxide required to hydrolyze one gram of fat, indicates the average molecular weight. Unsaturation is measured by the iodine value, the number of grams of iodine that combine with one hundred grams of fat. Test solutions employ iodine monochloride (ICl), iodine monobromide (IBr), or iodomercuric chloride (I_2HgCl_2), all of which are more reactive than iodine alone. The amount of fatty acid volatile with steam (C_{12} and less) is expressed as the Reichert-Meissl value. Mixtures of glycerides do not exhibit the usual depression in melting point, and hence the melting point, or rather range, of a fat is intermediate between those of the components. The melting range is described by citing the titer, defined as the temperature of initial solidification of a melt.

The degree of unsaturation in some cases is markedly influenced by the temperature at which biosynthesis of the glyceride occurs. Many solid animal fats are products of warm-blooded animals, which is probably due to a tendency to store fats fluid at body temperature. A variation has been noted also in the fats from different portions of the organism. Neat's-foot oil (from the hoofs of cattle) has a higher iodine value than fats derived from other locations. A gradation is noted in the subcutaneous fat of the pig, the outer layers of which are progressively more unsaturated. The striking influence of climate on the composition of linseed oil is shown by the following comparison: an iodine value of 190 has been reported for linseed oil from seed grown in the cold climate of Switzerland, and a value of 93 for oil from seed of the same stock grown in a Berlin greenhouse at a temperature of 25–30°. The degree of unsaturation is also dependent on

TABLE 15.5. ALCOHOLIC COMPONENTS OF WAXES

NAME	SOURCE	STRUCTURE	M.P., °C.
Cetyl alcohol	Sperm whale, porpoise	$CH_3(CH_2)_{14}CH_2OH$	49.3
n-Hexacosanol	Cocksfoot grass	$CH_3(CH_2)_{24}CH_2OH$	79.5
n-Octacosanol	Wheat	$CH_3(CH_2)_{26}CH_2OH$	83.4
n-Triacontanol	Lucerne leaf	$CH_3(CH_2)_{28}CH_2OH$	86.5
Cocceryl alcohol	Cochineal	$CH_3(CH_2)_{18}CO(CH_2)_{13}CH_2OH$	100.5
Oleyl alcohol	Sperm whale, porpoise	$CH_3(CH_2)_7CH=CH(CH_2)_7CH_2OH$	2

the type of fat in the diet. The iodine value of lard of corn-fed hogs is 69–72, of peanut-fed hogs, 90–100.

Fatty Acid Analysis. — Analyses reported for some fats and less unsaturated oils are listed in Table 15.4. The values usually represent averages, since fats from different localities vary somewhat in composition. No fat is known that contains no unsaturation. Some fats contain only three or four acids; butter is one of the most complex since it contains fourteen.* Highly unsaturated (drying) oils are considered in a later section.

Waxes. — Waxes differ from fats in that glycerol is replaced by complex alcohols of the sterol series or by higher even-numbered aliphatic alcohols from C_{16} to C_{36}. These often occur in excess of the acids, which are also even-numbered and range from C_{24} to C_{36}. Plant waxes also contain paraffin hydrocarbons. Several ketonic primary alcohols and some ketones have been isolated; e.g., palmitone, $CH_3(CH_2)_{14}CO(CH_2)_{14}CH_3$, and 10-hydroxypalmitone, $CH_3(CH_2)_{14}CO(CH_2)_5CHOH(CH_2)_8CH_3$, are found in sandalwood. It is extremely difficult to separate the individual alcohols, and Chibnall has shown that some of the alcohols claimed in the literature are in reality mixtures of even-numbered homologs. Occasionally only one alcohol is present, and its isolation in pure form is possible. Some of the identified alcohols are listed in Table 15.5.

Hydrogenation of Fats. — For manufacture of soap and for use as certain foods solid fats are preferable to liquid ones, which predominate in nature. Since the melting point depends on the extent of unsaturation, natural fats can be hardened by hydrogenation. Triolein, trilinolein, and trilinolenin are all liquids; tristearin is a solid melting at 71°. Simple glycerides containing C_{10}-saturated acids and higher are all solids: tricaprin melts at 31°, trilaurin at 46°, trimyristin at 59°, and tripalmitin at 60°. Vegetable oils such as cottonseed, soybean, and peanut are often either partially hardened to the consistency of lard or completely hardened and then mixed with low-melting oils. Lard is often partially hydrogenated to improve keeping qualities, since development of rancidity is associated with unsaturation.

Nickel is used as the catalyst; it can be prepared by reduction of nickel

---

* Butyric (3%), caproic (1.4%), caprylic (1.5%), capric (2.7%), lauric (3.7%), myristic (12.1%), palmitic (25.3%), stearic (9.2%), arachidic (1.3%), lauroleic (0.4%), myristoleic (1.6%), palmitoleic (4.0%), oleic (29.6%), and linoleic (3.6%).

chromate or formate in a portion of the oil that is to be hydrogenated. More generally it is prepared by precipitation of nickel carbonate on a carrier (kieselguhr), followed by reduction in a furnace by hydrogen. It

$$Ni(OOCH)_2 \cdot 2H_2O \longrightarrow Ni + 2CO_2 + H_2 + 2H_2O$$

is desirable in partial hydrogenation of a fat to add hydrogen preferentially to the more unsaturated glycerides, since the highly unsaturated compounds are undesirable owing to instability to oxygen. A natural tendency toward selective hydrogenation can be enhanced by operating at low pressures of 20–40 lbs./sq. in. and at temperatures of 175–190°.

Long-chain alcohols are made by hydrogenating glycerides at high pressures at about 250° (reduced copper chromite as catalyst). Ordinary nickel catalysts promote reduction completely to the hydrocarbon. Separation of the products is achieved readily by fractional distillation at reduced pressure. Lauryl alcohol is made from the nut oils (coconut, babassu, palm kernel), which yield mixtures containing nearly 50% of the alcohol. Unsaturated alcohols are prepared by hydrogenation of unsaturated glycerides in the presence of zinc chromite; for example, triolein yields oleyl alcohol, $CH_3(CH_2)_7CH{=}CH(CH_2)_7CH_2OH$.

Soaps. — Sodium salts are the most widely used soaps, but potassium soaps, which are softer and more soluble, serve special purposes (shaving cream, liquid soap). Natural or hardened fats are generally saponified with caustic soda, in slight excess of the theoretical amount, in an open kettle having at the bottom closed coils for indirect heating and perforated coils for direct heating through which steam can be passed at a rate to maintain agitation and ebullition. When the reaction is complete, salt is added to precipitate thick curds of the soap. The aqueous layer containing glycerol (sweet waters) is drawn off and concentrated to glycerol, which is refined by distillation in vacuum. In a process known as countercurrent hydrolysis (Ittner), advantage is taken of the fact that under pressure and at elevated temperatures water is soluble in fats to a considerable degree. Hot water is fed in near the top of the vessel and fat near the bottom. Split acids rise to the surface and are drawn off at the top, while glycerol is removed continuously in the water stream at the bottom. Hydrolysis proceeds substantially to completion and at a rapid rate even in the absence of a catalyst. Acids are obtained and are then saponified with soda ash, which costs about half as much as caustic soda. The crude curds contain glycerol, alkali. and salt; impurities are removed by boiling with sufficient water to form a homogeneous liquid, followed by reprecipitation of the soap with salt. In this way the soap is given several washings for recovery of glycerol and removal of impurities; then it is boiled with sufficient water to give a smooth mixture, which on standing separates into a homogeneous upper layer of kettle soap, and a diluted lye phase that contains nearly all the salt and excess alkali. Kettle soap contains 69–70% soap, 0.2–0.5% salt, and about 30% water; some is sold as such or after addition of perfume or dye for household purposes. Sand, sodium carbonate, and inert fillers are added for scouring soaps; cresol or other antiseptic for medicated soaps. Toilet soaps are made from kettle soap dried to a content of 85–90% and milled with perfume to thin shavings, which are then compacted in bars which are cut and pressed into cakes; transparent soaps are made by dissolving partly dried soap in alcohol. The specific gravity of ordinary soap is about 1.05, but by blowing air into hot molten kettle soap the specific gravity can be lowered to 0.8–0.9 (floating soap). In a newer process air is blown into dried soap chips at an elevated temperature, and the mass is then extruded.

Tallow (depot fat of cattle and sheep) is the most important soap stock. Soap made from tallow alone has excellent detergent and water-softening properties but must be used in hot water (tallow yields mainly C_{16}- and C_{18}-acids, whose soaps are only slightly soluble in water). The nut oils, coconut, babassu, and palm-kernel oil, are widely used in conjunction with tallow; their value lies in the high content of C_{12}- and C_{14}-acids, the soaps of which are firm and also readily soluble. Very unsaturated components cannot be used for soap since they are subject to oxidation.

Detergency is a complicated phenomenon that is not entirely understood. One important factor undoubtedly is the orientation of the molecules. Langmuir (1916–17) showed that a drop of fatty oil when placed on a clean surface of water spreads rapidly until it covers a definite area, when it spreads no farther. The area occupied by equivalent weights of homologous fatty acids from palmitic to cerotic is identical, though the depth of the film increases with increasing chain length. These films consist of monomolecular layers, in which the —COONa group is dipped in water and the hydrocarbon part directed away from water. This behavior is a property of substances that contain both a hydrophilic and a hydrophobic group, but the effect of each must be properly balanced or the molecule will be in one phase more than the other. Langmuir found that ricinoleic acid lies almost flat on the surface, an effect ascribable to the presence of a second hydrophilic group in the center of the molecule. Sodium ricinoleate is an inferior detergent. It is possible to build films in which monomolecular layers are superimposed, with the like groups adjacent to each other (Langmuir and Blodgett). If the carboxyl groups are directed outward in the last layer, the surface can be wetted by water but cannot if the hydrocarbon residues are outermost. The most striking characteristic of soap solutions is the reduction of surface tension (gas–liquid system) or of interfacial tension (liquid–liquid system). The surface tension of pure water is 73 dynes/cm.; that of solutions of sodium oleate or linoleate is about 25 dynes/cm.; of sodium laurate, myristate, and palmitate from 25 to 30 dynes/cm. Substances that lower surface or interfacial tension are known as surface-active compounds. These all contain a hydrophilic and a hydrophobic group, preferably at opposite ends of the molecule, which may be a long chain as in soap or a complicated ring system.

Satisfactory detergency is first noted with the laurates and myristates, which are often employed in soaps intended for use in sea water, since they are more soluble in salt solution than the higher soaps. Soaps of fatty acids above C_{22} are unsuitable, since they are practically insoluble in water at room temperature. Detergency generally consists in removal of oil or grease or of solid particles dispersed in oil, and photographic studies have shown that, in the initial stages, the oil is displaced from fiber by soap solution (wetting action) to form large globules that can be detached by jarring and finally dispersed (emulsified) in the aqueous solution. Emulsions consist of fine droplets of one liquid dispersed in an immiscible liquid. The particles are kept from coalescing by a protective film of an emulsifier. This stabilizing action can be correlated with surface activity and is shown by soaps and other polar-nonpolar compounds. Emulsifiers are almost always soluble in the external phase but insoluble in the dispersed liquid, and hence soaps show a detergent effect only when in solution. Foams are similar to emulsions except that gas is dispersed in a liquid, and these are also stabilized by surface-active compounds that lower surface tension at the gas–liquid interface.

Synthetic Surface-Active Compounds. — Soap is still the most widely used detergent, but it has definite limitations: it is unstable in acid solutions, and many of its salts are insoluble. In hard water, which contains calcium and magnesium ions, insoluble soaps are formed by metathesis. This reaction can be prevented by large amounts of tetrasodium pyrophosphate, sodium hexametaphosphate, or similar substances which are considered to function by forming water-soluble complexes with the objectionable metallic ions. The first synthetic compounds to compete with soap were developed about 1860, and are sulfonated (actually sulfated) oils made by treating unsaturated oils, mainly castor oil, with concentrated sulfuric acid. Sulfonated castor oil is known as Turkey-red oil (I), since it is most widely used as an assistant (wetting agent) in Turkey-red dyeing with ground madder root, which contains alizarin as the active principle Turkey-red oil soaps are not particularly good detergents.

$$CH_3(CH_2)_5CHCH_2CH{=}CH(CH_2)_7COOH$$
$$\underset{\textstyle OSO_3H}{|}$$

Turkey-red oil (I)

A group of detergents introduced in Germany about 1930 are sulfates of long-chain alcohols prepared by hydrogenation of fats. Compounds containing 10 to 14 carbon atoms are most useful and are prepared from nut

$$RCOOH \longrightarrow RCH_2OH \xrightarrow{\ O(SO_2ONa)_2\ } RCH_2OSO_2ONa$$

oils. They are more resistant to hard water, and since, unlike soap, they are salts of strong acids, they are more stable in solutions of low pH. The sodium salt of the monosulfate of a monoglyceride is an excellent nonsoapy detergent. Syntex M is a typical member of this class:

$$CH_2OCO(CH_2)_{10}CH_3$$
$$|$$
$$CHOH$$
$$|$$
$$CH_2OSO_2ONa$$

Sodium glyceryl monolaurate sulfate (Syntex M)

Sulfonates of succinic esters show pronounced wetting characteristics. In this case the solubilizing group is located near the center of the chain, as shown by formula II for a typical member of this class. The preparation involves reaction between the appropriate alcohol and maleic anhydride, followed by addition of sodium bisulfite. Alkylaryl sodium sulfonates of

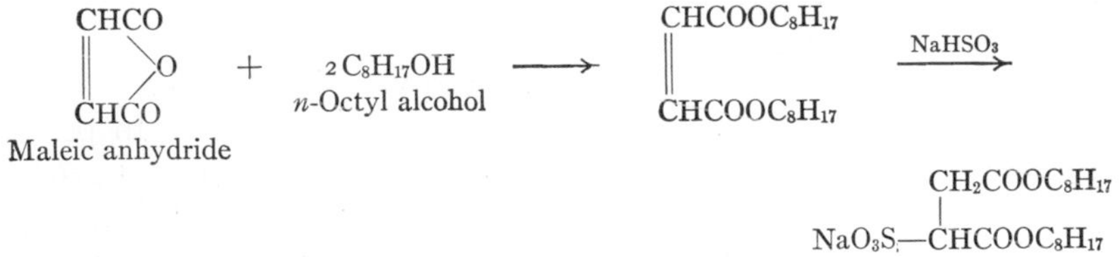

$$\begin{array}{l} CHCO \\ \big\| \big\rangle O \\ CHCO \end{array} \; + \; \underset{n\text{-Octyl alcohol}}{2\,C_8H_{17}OH} \longrightarrow \begin{array}{l} CHCOOC_8H_{17} \\ \big\| \\ CHCOOC_8H_{17} \end{array} \xrightarrow{NaHSO_3}$$

Maleic anhydride

$$CH_2COOC_8H_{17}$$
$$|$$
$$NaO_3S—CHCOOC_8H_{17}$$

Dioctyl sodium sulfosuccinate (Aerosol OT)

II

the type $R \cdot Ar \cdot SO_3Na$ have been introduced in the United States. They can be produced in quantity and at a price that competes with soap, since the long-chain alkyl group is derived from petroleum. The manufacturing process involves chlorination of a kerosene fraction, condensation with an aromatic hydrocarbon, and sulfonation of the aromatic nucleus. Alkyl sulfonates, RSO_3Na, are made by alkaline hydrolysis of sulfonyl chlorides resulting from the action of sulfur dioxide and chlorine on petroleum hydrocarbons under illumination; optimum detergency is attained in the range C_{13}–C_{18}, and higher members are used in textile finishing.

Resistance to hard water is attained in another type of detergent by blocking the carboxyl group so that it is unable to react with metals. The earliest, the German product Igepon A, is sodium β-oleylethanesulfonate (III) and is made by esterification of oleic acid with isethionic acid, with subsequent saponification (neutralization). Igepon A is not stable in an

$$\underset{\text{Oleic acid}}{CH_3(CH_2)_7CH=CH(CH_2)_7COOH} \; + \; \underset{\text{Isethionic acid}}{HOCH_2CH_2SO_3H} \longrightarrow$$

$$CH_3(CH_2)_7CH=CH(CH_2)_7COOCH_2CH_2SO_3Na$$

Igepon A (III)

alkaline medium owing to hydrolysis at the ester grouping; the defect is corrected by use of an amide linkage, —CONH—, as in Igepon T (IV):

$$\underset{\text{Oleic acid}}{CH_3(CH_2)_7CH=CH(CH_2)_7COOH} \; + \; \underset{\text{Taurine}}{NH_2CH_2CH_2SO_3H} \longrightarrow$$

$$CH_3(CH_2)_7CH=CH(CH_2)_7CO—NHCH_2CH_2SO_3Na$$

Igepon T (IV)

In a third type of surface-active agent, the problem of precipitation of insoluble soaps in hard water is solved by use of nonionizing hydrophilic groups. One group is made by partially esterifying polyglycerol or pentaerythritol, $C(CH_2OH)_4$, with one molecule of a fatty acid. Polyglycerol is a condensation product of glycerol in which several molecules have been condensed to both open-chain and cyclic ethers of the types V and VI.

$$CH_2OHCHOHCH_2\text{—}O\text{—}CH_2CHOHCH_2OH$$

$$V$$

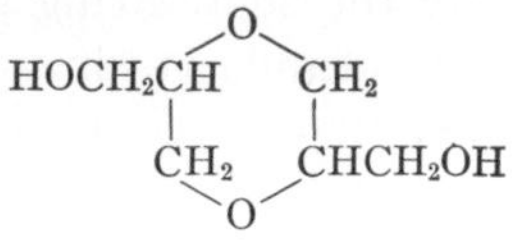

$$\begin{array}{c} O \\ HOCH_2CH\quad CH_2 \\ |\qquad\quad | \\ CH_2\quad CHCH_2OH \\ O \end{array}$$

$$VI$$

Satisfactory detergents can be prepared by esterifying a polyglycerol corresponding to a pentaglycerol with one molecule of a fatty acid. In pentaerythritol monostearate and monolaurate the unesterified hydroxyl groups serve as the water-attracting groups; several are required because the hydroxyl group is less hydrophilic than sulfate, carboxyl, or sulfonate groups (listed in the approximate order of decreasing effectiveness). Similar surface-active agents are glycol esters of fatty acids, prepared by treating the acid with ethylene oxide. A third group is made by the following reactions:

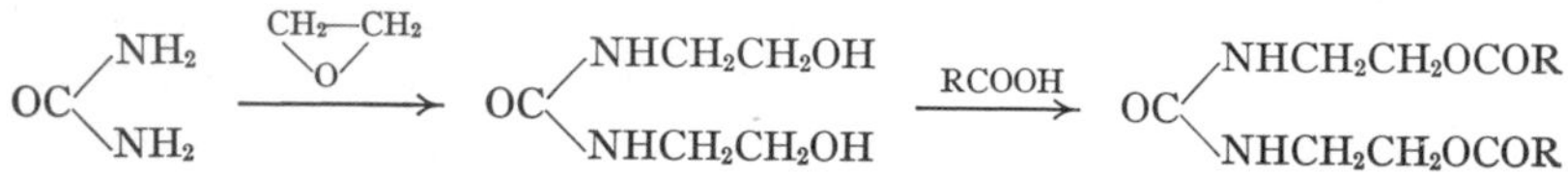

$$OC\begin{array}{l}NH_2\\NH_2\end{array}\xrightarrow{\;CH_2\text{—}CH_2\;O\;}OC\begin{array}{l}NHCH_2CH_2OH\\NHCH_2CH_2OH\end{array}\xrightarrow{\;RCOOH\;}OC\begin{array}{l}NHCH_2CH_2OCOR\\NHCH_2CH_2OCOR\end{array}$$

Substances of the ester type are not particularly good detergents but are useful wetting agents.

The triethanolamine salts of fatty acids are purely organic soaps. These are excellent emulsifiers and good dry-cleaning soaps, since they are soluble in organic solvents. Another interesting type is known as an invert soap or a cation-active compound (VII) since the organic part is positively

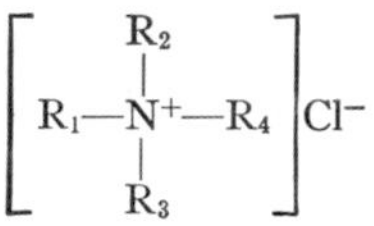

$$\left[\begin{array}{c}R_2\\|\\R_1\text{—}N^+\text{—}R_4\\|\\R_3\end{array}\right]Cl^-$$

$$VII$$

$$[C_{17}H_{33}CONHCH_2CH_2\overset{+}{N}(CH_3)_3]_2SO_4^=$$

$$VIII$$

charged, whereas in ordinary soaps the organic part is negatively charged. Invert soaps cannot react with heavy-metal ions, which are similarly charged; they are used in neutral or acid solution. One alkyl group must be a long chain; the others can be methyl or ethyl. The Sapamines are prepared from a fatty acid and an unsymmetrical dialkyldiamine, followed by alkylation. A typical Sapamine derived from oleic acid is shown in formula VIII. Invert soaps exhibit marked bactericidal activity (Zephiran), although their use is

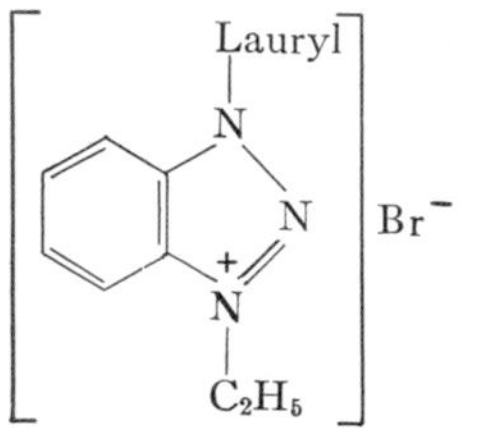

$$\left[\begin{array}{c}Lauryl\\|\\N\\ \\N\\\overset{+}{N}\\|\\C_2H_5\end{array}\right]Br^-$$

$$IX$$

TABLE 15.6.[1] DRYING OILS

OIL	IODINE VALUE	TITER, °C.	FATTY ACIDS, %						
			Palmitic	Stearic	Oleic	Linoleic	Linolenic	Licanic	Eleostearic
Cottonseed	103–111	32–38	21.0	2.0	33.0	43.5	....	....	....
Corn [2]	117–130	18–20	7.5	3.5	46.3	42.0	....	....	....
Soybean [2]	124–133	20–21	6.5	4.2	33.6	52.6	2.3	....	....
Oiticica	139–155	44–47	5.0	5.0	5.9	10.0	....	74.1	....
Tung	160–180	37–38	4.0	1.5	15.0	....	....	....	79.5
Linseed	170–185	19–21	5.0	3.5	5.0	61.5	25.0	....	....
Perilla	180–206	12–17	7.5	...	8.0	38.0	46.5	....	....

[1] Data of Werner G. Smith Company.
[2] Contains traces of arachidic and lignoceric acid.

limited due to high toxicity. 1-Lauryl-3-ethylbenzotriazolium bromide (IX) is particularly active; it kills Staphylococcus of several strains at a dilution of 1:600,000 (Kuhn).

Drying Oils. — Certain fatty oils possess the ability, when exposed on a surface to air, to form dry, tough, and durable films; 700–800 million pounds of drying oils are used each year in the United States, mainly in paints, which are drying oils with added pigments, and in varnishes, which differ from paints in containing resins. Oilcloth is made by applying several coats of linseed-oil paint to a woven canvas; linoleum is made by cementing cork particles with thickened linseed oil and rosin. The common drying oils are listed in Table 15.6; the first three are more properly known as semidrying oils, and are used only slightly in protective coatings. The main characteristic of drying oils is a high content of unsaturated fatty acids. Although linseed and perilla oils have particularly high iodine values, they do not dry so rapidly as oiticica and tung oils, and this difference is undoubtedly associated with the presence in the latter oils of conjugated double bonds, rather than isolated double bonds, characteristic of the former oils. Linseed oil is the most widely used drying oil. Fresh or raw linseed oil dries only slowly, and use is recorded as early as A.D 200 of the faster-drying boiled oil, made by heating linseed oil with lead oxide. Such an oil, however, is muddy owing to suspended insoluble lead salts; the driers in modern boiled oil are the soluble cobalt, manganese, and lead salts of linoleic, resin, or naphthenic acids. The metal is the effective portion of the molecule; one part of cobalt is equivalent to eight parts of manganese or forty parts of lead. The drier can be incorporated at temperatures that do not induce decomposition of the oil. Application of heat promotes a chemical change; boiled oils are more viscous than raw oils, and eventually set to a gel if heating is prolonged. Bodying is also attained by blowing air at 120° through an oil in which the drier has been incorporated (blown oil). Stand oils are heat-bodied oils that do not contain driers.

Drying oils are not produced in the required quantity in the United

States.   Tung oil (China-wood oil) is imported from China, oiticica from Brazil, perilla from Japan, and linseed mainly from Argentina.   Consequently attention has been turned to development of additional drying oils or to improvement of available oils.   One line of attack is to rearrange the double bonds from nonconjugated to conjugated positions by refluxing with alcoholic alkali.   For instance, linolenic acid is readily converted into pseudoeleostearic acid ($10,12,14$-octadecatrienoic acid).   Another development is use of higher polyhydric alcohols such as pentaerythritol or sorbitol instead of glycerol.

A second line of attack is preparation of drying oils from nondrying oils, an example of which is dehydrated castor oil, which has an iodine value of approximately 140.   Ricinoleic acid, the main constituent of castor oil, contains only one double bond, but an additional one is readily introduced by dehydration with sulfuric or phosphoric acid or with sodium acid sulfate. The drying ability is less than that of tung and oiticica oils, the most generally satisfactory of the natural drying oils, but equals or surpasses that of linseed oil.   An additional double bond can be introduced by the

$$CH_3(CH_2)_4CH_2CHCH_2CH=CH(CH_2)_7COOH$$
$$|$$
$$OH$$

Ricinoleic acid

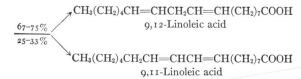

$$CH_3(CH_2)_4CH=CHCH_2CH=CH(CH_2)_7COOH$$
$9,12$-Linoleic acid

67–75%
25–33%

$$CH_3(CH_2)_4CH_2CH=CHCH=CH(CH_2)_7COOH$$
$9,11$-Linoleic acid

Münzel process, which involves treatment with hypochlorous acid to yield a chlorohydrin that is then treated with triethanolamine.   The product is said to consist of $8,10,12$- and $9,11,13$-octadecatrienoic acid.

Drying oils are prepared (1940) from various nondrying fish oils (sardine, whale, herring) that contain 5–25% of highly unsaturated C_{20}- and C_{22}-acids corresponding to four to six double bonds.   The split acids are separated by fractional vacuum distillation into drying and nondrying types, and the former are reesterified with glycerol or pentaerythritol to give drying oils claimed to rival tung oil.

READING REFERENCES

T. P. Hilditch, "The Industrial Chemistry of the Fats and Waxes," Van Nostrand, New York (1941)

T. P. Hilditch, "The Chemical Constitution of Natural Fats," Chapman and Hall, London (1947)

A. W. Ralston, "Fatty Acids and Their Derivatives," Wiley, New York (1948)

K. S. Markley, "Fatty Acids, Their Chemistry and Physical Properties," Interscience, New York (1944)

F. D. Snell, "Surface-Active Agents," *Ind. Eng. Chem.*, **35**, 107 (1943)

F. D. Gunstone, "Recent Developments in the Preparation of Natural and Synthetic Straight-chain Fatty Acids," *Quart. Rev.*, **VII**, 175 (1953)

PROTEINS

Proteins (Gr. *proteios*, primary) derive their name from their great importance in all forms of living matter. They differ from carbohydrates and fats in elementary composition, for in addition to carbon, hydrogen, and oxygen, they invariably contain nitrogen (16–18%) and usually sulfur. Proteins of one type, the fibrous proteins, are insoluble in water and serve as structural materials for animals much as cellulose serves for plants. Fibroin, the protein of silk, is a fibrous protein. Others are collagen, the protein of connective tissue, which yields gelatin when boiled with water; keratin, the protein of epithelial tissue, of hair, wool, horn, feathers, nails; elastin, the protein of elastic connective tissue. A second broad group is that of the globular proteins, characterized by solubility in water or in water solutions of acids, bases, or salts. Examples are egg albumin (white of egg), casein (from milk), and the plasma proteins. Centrifugation of blood that has been treated with citrate solution or with heparin to prevent clotting causes settling of the heavier red blood corpuscles and separation of a yellowish, opalescent supernatant liquid that constitutes blood plasma and is an approximately 7% solution of plasma proteins in water at a pH close to 7.0. If the plasma is siphoned off and the sludge of corpuscles stirred with a little ether, the ether reduces the surface tension of the liquid external to the cells but does not penetrate the cell membranes and hence does not alter the pressure within the cells, and the result is that the cells burst. A further centrifugation causes the ruptured cell membranes to settle and gives a rich red solution of the globular protein hemoglobin. This is the protein responsible for transportation of oxygen from the lungs to body tissues. The mechanism of animal respiration can be demonstrated with the solution of hemoglobin prepared as described: when the solution is shaken with oxygen it becomes bright red (arterial blood), and when it is evacuated at the suction pump it becomes bluish red (venous blood). Hemoglobin is an example of a conjugated protein, and it contrasts with the above-mentioned substances, which are simple proteins. Hemoglobin is a conjugate of a protein proper, globin, and a much smaller nonproteinic C_{34}-component, heme The component heme that is attached to the protein is known as a prosthetic group (Gr. *prosthetos*, put on). Actually heme is responsible for the red color of blood and is essential for the function as oxygen carrier.

Blood plasma, prepared by the procedure described, is a liquid slightly pigmented with carotinoids which contains the following proteins: albumins (soluble in 5% salt solution), lipoproteins (containing up to 75% lipids), fibrinogen, prothrombin.   Whole blood that is not protected with citrate or heparin as it is drawn clots on standing for a few minutes as the result of conversion of the soluble, globular fibrinogen, under the influence of prothrombin, into an insoluble, fibrous protein fibrin, strands of which form the enmeshing structure of the clot.   Centrifugation of clotted blood gives a residual mixture of fibrin and red blood corpuscles and a supernatant solution known as blood serum.   Serum differs from plasma in that it contains no fibrinogen.   Other globular proteins are: glutelins of cereal seeds (soluble in water only in presence of dilute acid or alkali); prolamines, for example zein from corn (insoluble in water or absolute ethanol but soluble in 80% ethanol); histones (strongly basic, soluble in dilute acid); protamines (even more strongly basic, soluble in water).

Proteins consist of giant molecules of molecular weights ranging from about 12,000 to several million.   Those that are soluble in water form colloidal solutions.   Chemical characterization is limited by the extreme sensitivity of the substances; treatment with an acid, a base, or an organic solvent is liable to produce a fundamental change described as denaturation, which is attended with loss of originally characteristic properties, such as water solubility or specific biological activity.   Mild heating usually results in denaturation with loss in solubility, as illustrated by the familiar phenomenon of the change induced by the action of hot water on egg white.   As in most instances, denaturation of egg albumin is irreversible.

All proteins can be hydrolyzed by aqueous solutions of mineral acids at the boiling point, and they all afford mixtures of α-amino acids of the type $RCH(NH_2)CO_2H$.   Analytical evidence shows that the carboxyl and α-amino groups are largely not present as such in the protein but are liberated in equal amounts on hydrolysis.   Thus the building units are joined together through the peptide link, $-CO \cdot NH-$, between the carboxyl group of one amino acid and the amino group of another, and the process of protein hydrolysis can be represented in part as cleavage of a polypeptide chain.

$$\begin{array}{ccc} R & R' & R'' \\ | & | & | \end{array}$$

$$-(NHCHCO)_n-(NHCHCO)_{n'}-(NHCHCO)_{n''}- \xrightarrow{\text{Hydrol.}}$$

$$nH_2NCH(R)CO_2H \ + \ n'H_2NCH(R')CO_2H \ + \ n''H_2NCH(R'')CO_2H$$

Present concepts of the structures of proteins are thus based upon evidence of the structures and proportions of the amino acids produced on hydrolysis.

Plants, under the influence of soil microorganisms, can synthesize amino acids from inorganic nitrate and carbohydrate and convert them into proteins.   The animal organism lacks the power to synthesize some amino acids from simple components but reforms plant proteins with utilization of such component acids as are required.

AMINO ACIDS

Component Acids of Proteins. — Glycine, $H_2NCH_2CO_2H$, the simplest amino acid derived from proteins, was the first member of the series to be discovered.   Braconnot (1820), investigating the hydrolysis of gelatin to see if this material, like cellusose, would yield a sugar, isolated a substance that he called glycine because it had a sweet taste (Gr. *glykys*, sweet), and eighteen years elapsed before the supposed "sugar of gelatin" was shown to con-

TABLE 16.1. COMMON AMINO ACIDS FROM PROTEINS

NEUTRAL AMINO ACIDS			
Name	Symbol	Formula	Iso-electric point
Glycine	Gly	$CH_2(NH_2)COOH$	5.97
Alanine	Ala	$CH_3CH(NH_2)COOH$	6.00
Valine	Val	$(CH_3)_2CHCH(NH_2)COOH$	5.96
Leucine	Leu	$(CH_3)_2CHCH_2CH(NH_2)COOH$	6.02
Isoleucine	Ileu	$CH_3CH_2CH(CH_3)CH(NH_2)COOH$	5.98
Phenylalanine	Phe	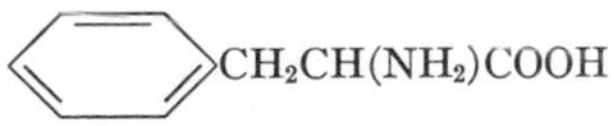 $CH_2CH(NH_2)COOH$	5.48
Tyrosine	Tyr	 HO $CH_2CH(NH_2)COOH$	5.66
Proline	Pro	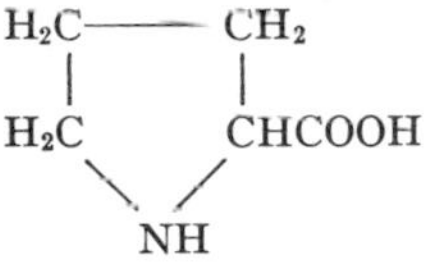	6.30
Hydroxyproline	Hypro	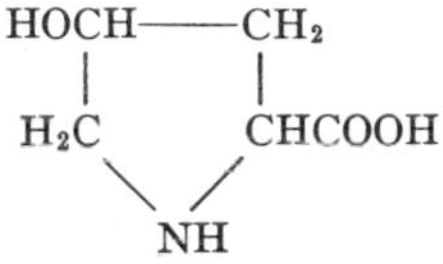	5.83
Serine	Ser	$HOCH_2CH(NH_2)COOH$	5.68
Threonine	Thr	$CH_3CH(OH)CH(NH_2)COOH$	
Cysteine	CySH	$HSCH_2CH(NH_2)COOH$	5.05
Cystine	CyS·SCy	$[-SCH_2CH(NH_2)COOH]_2$	4.8
Methionine	Met	$CH_3SCH_2CH_2CH(NH_2)COOH$	5.74
Tryptophan	Try	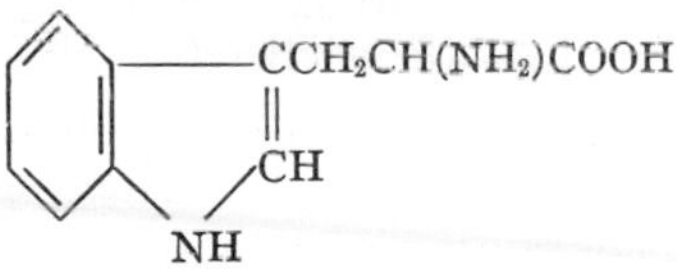 $-CCH_2CH(NH_2)COOH$	5.89
ACIDIC AMINO ACIDS			
Aspartic acid	Asp	$HOOCCH_2CH(NH_2)COOH$	2.77
Glutamic acid	Glu	$HOOCCH_2CH_2CH(NH_2)COOH$	3.22

TABLE 16.1—*Continued*

BASIC AMINO ACIDS			
Name	Symbol	Formula	Iso-electric point
Arginine	Arg	$H_2NC(=NH)NHCH_2CH_2CH_2CH(NH_2)COOH$	10.76
Lysine	Lys	$H_2NCH_2CH_2CH_2CH_2CH(NH_2)COOH$	9.74
Histidine	His	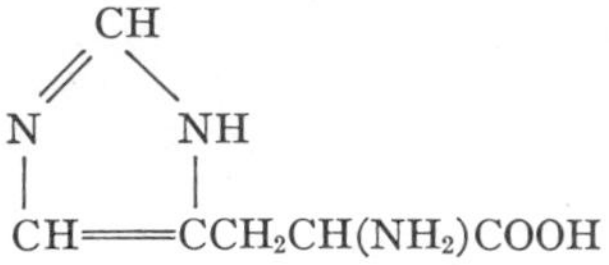 (see structure below)	7.59

$$\begin{array}{c} CH \\ \diagup\diagdown \\ N \qquad NH \\ | \qquad\quad | \\ CH=\!=\!=\!CCH_2CH(NH_2)COOH \end{array}$$

tain nitrogen. Subsequent early investigation of protein hydrolyzates was largely a matter of chance observation. The isolation of leucine (Gr. *leukos*, white) from muscle fiber and of tyrosine (Gr. *tyros*, cheese) from casein was accomplished at an early period (1820–49) since both substances are sparingly soluble in aqueous solutions of low acidity. Cystine (Gr. *kystis*, bladder), also sparingly soluble, was isolated from urinary calculi in 1810 but only recognized as a constituent of proteins in 1899 (Mörner); it can be prepared readily by acid hydrolysis of hair. The structures of these and other amino acids commonly encountered are shown in Table 16.1; all these acids were isolated in the period 1820–1922, before introduction of efficient modern methods for separation of protein hydrolyzates. In view of the fact that a large number of proteins exist and that they vary widely in properties, it is striking that they are derived from only about twenty building units.

All twenty common components of proteins (Table 16.1) are α-amino acids, and with the exception of glycine the α-carbon atom is asymmetric. The first fifteen acids listed in the table are neutral, since the basic property of the amino group is balanced by an acidic carboxyl group. All but glycine can be regarded as derivatives of alanine, and many conform to the type $RCH_2CH(NH_2)CO_2H$, where, for example, R is H (alanine), isopropyl (leucine), phenyl (C_6H_5), hydroxyl (serine), sulfhydryl (SH, cysteine). Proline and hydroxyproline are cyclized N-alkyl-α-amino acids; the parent 5-membered heterocycle is called pyrrolidine. Tryptophan contains the bicyclic indole system and can be described as β-(3-indolyl)-alanine; the five-membered ring containing nitrogen is a pyrrole ring. Although the neutral acids are structurally similar in the respect noted, their physical properties vary markedly with molecular weight and with details of structure. Leucine (mol. wt. 131) can be extracted with hot butanol, in which the lower homolog glycine (mol. wt. 75) is insoluble. Proline and leucine have about the same molecular weight, but the cyclic acid is readily soluble in cold ethanol whereas leucine is insoluble. Such properties undoubtedly are important determinants of properties of specific proteins. An alcoholic hydroxyl group (serine, threonine) enhances hydrophilic character, and a sulfhydryl (or thiol) group provides reducing properties. Cysteine, the β-sulfhydryl or thiol derivative of alanine, on oxidation affords cystine, from which it is regenerated on reduction. Some proteins have been found to be

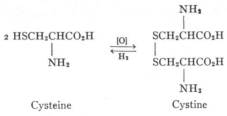

built up of two or more polypeptide chains linked through the —S·S— bond of cystine. Other proteins are known to contain free sulfhydryl units, although oxidation to cystine invariably occurs during the course of hydrolysis and isolation. If a protein containing cysteine or cystine (lactalbumin, insulin, keratin) is treated before hydrolysis with dilute sodium carbonate, the new amino acid lanthionine (Table 16.2) is formed. Lanthionine was isolated and also prepared by synthesis in 1941.

Serine is the oxygen analog of cysteine, and threonine is the β-methyl homolog of serine; threonine contains two asymmetric carbon atoms.

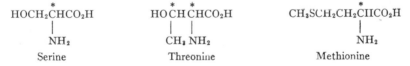

Methionine contains the thiomethyl group; it is the S-methyl ether not of cysteine but of the next higher homolog, homocysteine, which itself is not a protein component.

Aspartic acid and glutamic acid have two carboxyl groups and only one amino group and hence show acidic properties. Thus glutamic acid forms

monosodium glutamate, which is manufactured on a large scale by hydrolysis of wheat gluten and beet sugar residues for use in enhancement of food flavors. These amino derivatives of succinic and glutaric acid occur in proteins to some extent as the monoamides, asparagine and glutamine:

$H_2NCOCH_2CH(NH_2)CO_2H$ $H_2NCOCH_2CH_2CH(NH_2)CO_2H$

Asparagine = Asp(NH₂)   Glutamine = Glu(NH₂)

Acids of a third type, illustrated by lysine (α,ϵ-diaminocaproic acid), con-

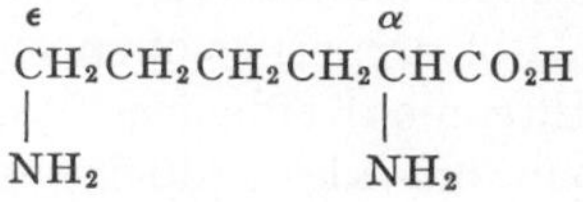

$$\overset{\epsilon}{CH_2}CH_2CH_2CH_2\overset{\alpha}{CH}CO_2H$$

with NH₂ groups below:

$$\underset{NH_2}{\quad} \qquad\qquad \underset{NH_2}{\quad}$$

Lysine

tain two basic groups and only one carboxyl group and are basic. Arginine contains the strongly basic guanidyl group, derived from guanidine, the imide of urea:

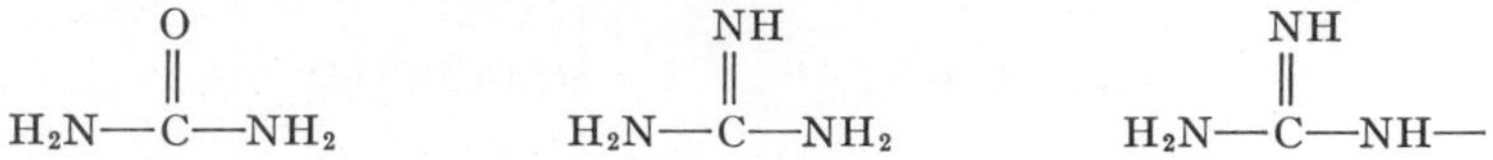

$$\underset{Urea}{H_2N\overset{O}{\overset{\|}{-}}C-NH_2} \qquad \underset{Guanidine}{H_2N\overset{NH}{\overset{\|}{-}}C-NH_2} \qquad \underset{Guanidyl}{H_2N\overset{NH}{\overset{\|}{-}}C-NH-}$$

It is α-amino-δ-guanidylvaleric acid. Histidine contains a basic imidazole ring; it is α-amino-β-(2-imidazolyl)-propionic acid. The three basic amino

TABLE 16.2.　UNUSUAL AMINO ACIDS

NAME	FORMULA	SOURCE
β-Alanine	$H_2NCH_2CH_2COOH$	Pantothenic acid
α-Aminobutyric acid	$CH_3CH_2CH(NH_2)COOH$	*Corynebacterium diphtheriae*
γ-Aminobutyric acid	$H_2NCH_2CH_2CH_2COOH$	Bacteria, plants, yeast
α,ϵ-Diaminopimelic acid	$HOOCCH(NH_2)CH_2CH_2CH_2CH(NH_2)COOH$	*Coryn. dipth.*
Thyroxine	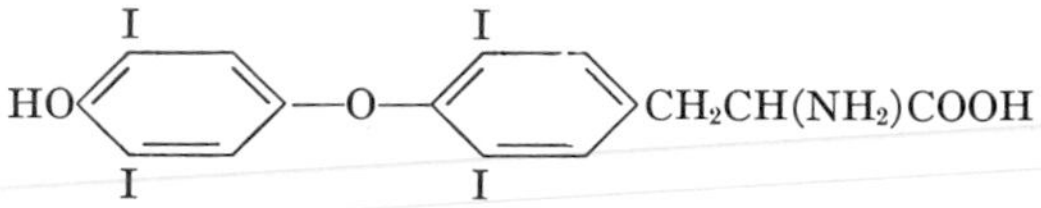	Thyroglobin
Diiodotyrosine	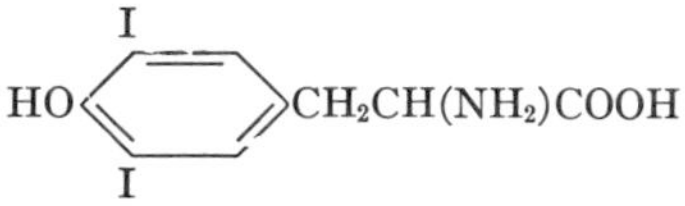	Thyroglobin
β-Thiolvaline	$(CH_3)_2C(SH)CH(NH_2)COOH$	Penicillins
Lanthionine	$S[CH_2CH(NH_2)COOH]_2$	Subtilin
Djenkolic acid	$CH_2[SCH_2CH(NH_2)COOH]_2$	Djenkel nuts
γ-Methyleneglutamic acid	$HOOCC(=CH_2)CH_2CH(NH_2)COOH$	Ground nut
α,γ-Diaminobutyric acid	$H_2NCH_2CH_2CH(NH_2)COOH$	Polymixins
Ornithine	$H_2NCH_2CH_2CH_2CH(NH_2)COOH$	Polypeptides
Hydroxylysine	$H_2NCH_2CH(OH)CH_2CH_2CH(NH_2)COOH$	Collagen
Citrulline	$H_2NCONHCH_2CH_2CH_2CH(NH_2)COOH$	Watermellon, casein
Canavanine	$H_2NC(=NH)NHOCH_2CH_2CH(NH_2)COOH$	Soybean

acids are precipitated by phosphotungstic acid, a property useful for identification of type and for separation.

Amino acids encountered as constituents of only one or two proteins or of polypeptides are listed in Table 16.2, along with some of the unusual acids that have been encountered in nonproteinoid natural products. Iodine-containing thyroxine and diiodotyrosine have been found only as constituents of thyroglobulin, a protein hormone of the thyroid gland. Hydroxylysine is obtained only from gelatin and wool.

Configuration. — All the natural acids, with two exceptions, contain a primary amino group that is situated on the carbon atom adjacent to the carboxyl group; in proline and hydroxyproline, the α-imino group can be regarded as an amino group that is involved in ring formation. The α-carbon atom of all the amino acids except glycine is asymmetric, and it is noteworthy that all the natural acids derived from proteins have the same configuration at this center, regardless of the sign of rotation. Natural alanine has been related to L-(+)-lactic acid, and hence all the acids from proteins belong to the L-series (K. Freudenberg,[1] 1924); since natural

$$
\begin{array}{cc}
\text{CO}_2\text{H} & \text{CO}_2\text{H} \\
| & | \\
\text{HOCH} \quad (\text{L}) & \text{H}_2\text{NCH} \quad (\text{L}) \\
| & | \\
\text{CH}_3 & \text{CH}_3 \\
\text{L-(+)-Lactic acid} & \text{L-(+)-Alanine}
\end{array}
$$

alanine is dextrorotatory, it is fully described as L-(+)-alanine. A natural amino acid that contains a second center of asymmetry is designated L to indicate the correspondence in the configuration of the α-carbon atom with that of L-alanine, and the enantiomer is designated D. The diastereoisomers of these substances are designated by the prefixes L-allo and D-allo, the letter denoting the configuration of the α-carbon atom; for example natural threonine was so named because of its relationship to D-threose;

$$
\begin{array}{ccc}
\text{CO}_2\text{H} & \text{CHO} & \text{CO}_2\text{H} \\
| & | & | \\
\text{H}_2\text{NCH} \quad (\text{L}) & \text{HOCH} & \text{H}_2\text{NCH} \quad (\text{L}) \\
| & | & | \\
\text{HCOH} & \text{HCOH} \quad (\text{D}) & \text{HOCH} \\
| & | & | \\
\text{CH}_3 & \text{CH}_2\text{OH} & \text{CH}_3 \\
\text{L-(−) Threonine} & \text{D-Threose} & \text{L-Allothreonine} \\
\text{(natural)} & &
\end{array}
$$

in the amino acid the prefix L- refers to the configuration of the α-carbon atom, whereas in the carbohydrate the prefix D- refers to the carbon atom β to the aldehyde function.

In water solutions where they exist largely as dipolar ions, the majority of amino acids are weakly dextrorotatory, but some are weakly levorotatory and cystine is strongly so, $[\alpha]_D$ $-214°$. Some relationships are apparent from the molecular rotations. Thus one group includes acids in which the

---

[1] Karl Freudenberg, b. 1886 Weinheim/Baden; Ph.D. Berlin (E. Fischer); Heidelberg.

side chain R is an alkyl group or an alkyl group containing oxygen or nitrogen usually two or more carbon atoms removed from the center of asym-

$$
\begin{array}{c}
CO_2H \\
| \\
H_2NCH \\
| \\
R
\end{array}
$$

ACID	R	M_D
Alanine	—CH₃	+2
α-Aminobutyric acid	—CH₂CH₃	+8
Valine	—CH(CH₃)₂	+7
Leucine	—CH₂CH(CH₃)₂	−14
Isoleucine	—CH(CH₃)CH₂CH₃	+15
Alloisoleucine	—CH(CH₃)CH₂CH₃	+18
Aspartic acid	—CH₂CO₂H	+6
Glutamic acid	—CH₂CH₂CO₂H	+17
Ornithine	—CH₂CH₂CH₂NH₂	+15
Lysine	—CH₂CH₂CH₂CH₂NH₂	+21
Arginine	—CH₂CH₂CH₂NHC(=NH)NH₂	+22

metry. The eleven acids of this group are only weakly rotatory, and under the conditions specified all but leucine are dextrorotatory. Cysteine, methionine, and serine comprise a small group of weakly levorotatory acids

$$
\begin{array}{ccc}
CO_2H & CO_2H & CO_2H \\
| & | & | \\
H_2NCH & H_2NCH & H_2NCH \\
| & | & | \\
CH_2SH & CH_2CH_2SCH_3 & CH_2OH \\
\text{Cysteine} & \text{Methionine} & \text{Serine} \\
M_D-13 & M_D-12 & M_D-7
\end{array}
$$

having sulfur or oxygen substituents at the first or second carbon atom of the alkyl group. A third group includes phenylalanine, histidine, and tryptophan, all of which have very nearly the same, rather pronounced

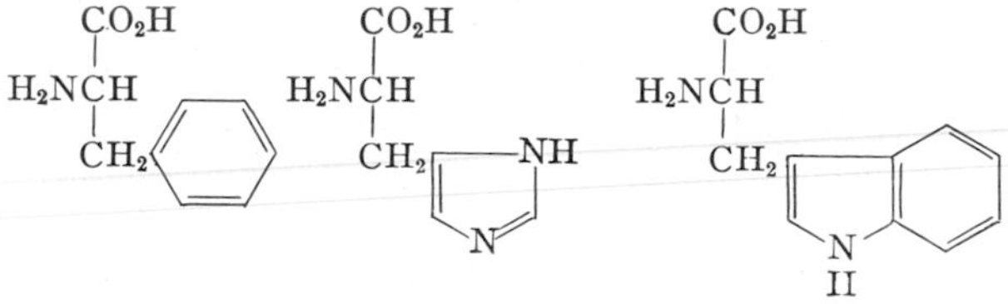

$$
\begin{array}{ccc}
CO_2H & CO_2H & CO_2H \\
| & | & | \\
H_2NCH & H_2NCH & H_2NCH \\
| & | & | \\
CH_2 & CH_2 & CH_2
\end{array}
$$

Phenylalanine	Histidine	Tryptophan
M_D-58	M_D-61	M_D-62

levorotation. The aromatic rings in these substances, derived, respectively, from benzene, imidazole, and indole, are only one carbon atom removed from

$$
\begin{array}{c}
CO_2H \\
| \\
HN\text{——}CH \\
| \quad | \\
CH_2 \quad CH_2 \\
\diagdown CH_2
\end{array}
$$

Proline
M_D-98

the center of asymmetry and exert an effect because they contain conjugated unsaturated systems that absorb light. Proline is more strongly rotatory than any of the natural acids of the above three groups. In this substance the asymmetric carbon atom is incorporated into a five-membered ring, and the case exemplifies a general rule that ring formation produces a marked change in optical rotation.

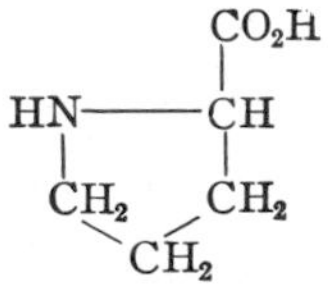

Acid-Base Equilibria. — Since amino acids contain both carboxyl and amino groups, they behave like amphoteric compounds and ionize both as acids and bases. In an electric field, the amino acid migrates to the cathode in acid solutions, to the anode in basic solutions. For each amino acid, there is a definite hydrogen-ion concentration at which the acidic and basic ionization is equal, and this particular pH is known as the isoelectric point. Considerable evidence has accumulated which indicates that the electrically neutral form, at least for aliphatic amino acids, is a dipolar ion carrying both a positive and a negative charge. The ionic structure explains the relative

$$R-\underset{\underset{NH_2}{|}}{\overset{\overset{H}{|}}{C}}-C\overset{\diagup O}{\diagdown O^-} \underset{H^+}{\overset{OH^-}{\rightleftarrows}} R-\underset{\underset{NH_3^+}{|}}{\overset{\overset{H}{|}}{C}}-C\overset{\diagup O}{\diagdown O^-} \underset{OH^-}{\overset{H^+}{\rightleftarrows}} R-\underset{\underset{NH_3^+}{|}}{\overset{\overset{H}{|}}{C}}-C\overset{\diagup O}{\diagdown OH}$$

Dipolar ion

infusibility, the low volatility, and the comparative insolubility in absolute alcohol and other organic solvents.

In protein chemistry equilibrium constants of both acidic and basic dissociation are conveniently expressed in terms of the negative logarithm of a common acidity constant K. With acids, pK corresponds numerically with pK_a. Thus for acetic acid ($k_a^{25°}$ 1.75×10^{-5}), $pK = pK_a = -\log 1.75 \times 10^{-5} = 4.76$. In the case of a basic substance such as methylamine, the ionic species $CH_3NH_3^+$ can dissociate to give a proton, and is analogous in this respect to a carboxylic acid. The acidity constant (K) is therefore defined by the expression (1). The classical basic dissociation constant,

$$(1) \quad K = \frac{[CH_3NH_2][H^+]}{[CH_3NH_3^+]}$$

k_b, is defined by equation (2), and the two constants can be correlated through application of the ionization constant of water (3), as shown in equation (4). The classical dissociation constant of methylamine, k_b, is

$$(2) \quad k_b = \frac{[CH_3NH_3^+][OH^-]}{[CH_3NH_2]}$$

$$(3) \quad [H^+][OH^-] = 10^{-14}$$

$$(4) \quad K = \frac{[CH_3NH_2] \times 10^{-14}}{[CH_3NH_3^+][OH^-]} = \frac{10^{-14}}{k_b}$$

$$(5) \quad pK = 14 - pK_b$$

4.3×10^{-4}, and hence $pK_b = -(-4 + 0.63) = 3.37$ and $pK = 14 - 3.37 = 10.63$. Aniline, a much weaker base ($k_b = 5.00 \times 10^{-10}$, $pK_b = 9.30$), has a pK value of 4.70. The logarithmic acidity constants offer a convenient basis for comparing ionizations of all types. If a strongly acidified solution containing acetic acid, methylamine, and aniline is titrated with alkali, the anilinium ion $C_6H_5NH_3^+$ liberates a proton first and is half converted into aniline at pH 4.7; the acetic acid molecule is the next to ionize (pK 4.76), and the methylammonium ion does so only in the strongly alkaline region (mid-point, pH 10.6). The titration curves are similar, and the identity of the different acidity constants, that is, whether they refer to acids or to amines, must be established by investigation of the individual compounds.

Glycine has two acidity constants, $pK_1 = 2.4$ and $pK_2 = 9.8$; contrary to early inferences, the first value refers to ionization of the carboxyl group and the second to the amino group. In a strongly acidic solution the substance is present as the positively charged ion (a). The positive charge tends to repel a proton from the carboxyl group and renders the species (a)

$$\overset{+}{H_3}NCH_2COOH \xrightarrow[pK\ 2.4]{-H^+} \overset{+}{H_3}NCH_2COO^- \xrightarrow[pK\ 9.8]{-H^+} H_2NCH_2COO^-$$
$$(a) \qquad\qquad\qquad (b) \qquad\qquad\qquad (c)$$

much more strongly acidic than acetic acid (pK 4.76). The neutral dipolar ion (b) is thus formed at a lower pH than required to convert acetic acid into the acetate ion. The electrostatic effect musτ operate against loss of a second proton by ionization of the dipolar species to give (c). The fact that the value for pK_2 is less than that of methylamine (10.6) can be, attributed to the modifying effect of the adjacent carboxylate group for glycine ethyl ester ($H_2NCH_2COOC_2H_5$), with which there is no electrostatic effect, is a still weaker base (pK 7.7).

The acidity constants of alanine, leucine, valine, and other monoamino monocarboxylic acids are very close to those of glycine. The dipeptide of glycine, glycylglycine, is weaker both as an acid and as a base, as seen from

$$\underset{(pK_2\ 9.8)\qquad (pK_1\ 2.4)}{\overset{+}{H_3}NCH_2COOH}$$
Glycine

$$\underset{(pK_2\ 8.2)\qquad\qquad (pK_1\ 3.1)}{\overset{+}{H_3}NCH_2CONHCH_2COOH}$$
Glycylglycine

the constants written under the groups to which they refer; the change in each case can be ascribed to increased distance between functional groups and consequently weaker electrostatic effects. Typical pK values for acidic and basic amino acids are illustrated for aspartic acid and for lysine.

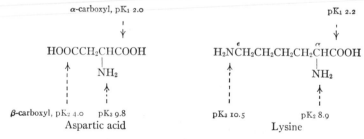

α-carboxyl, pK_1 2.0

pK_1 2.2

$$HOOCCH_2CHCOOH$$
$$NH_2$$

$$H_2N\overset{\epsilon}{C}H_2CH_2CH_2CH_2\overset{\alpha}{C}HCOOH$$
$$NH_2$$

β-carboxyl, pK_2 4.0 pK_3 9.8
Aspartic acid

pK_3 10.5 pK_2 8.9
Lysine

Specific Techniques of Isolation and Analysis. — Because they are dipolar and salt-like, amino acids are not distillable. However, Emil Fischer in 1901 introduced the technique of esterification of a protein hydrolyzate and fractional distillation of mixtures of esters of the type $RCH(NH_2)$-CO_2CH_3 derived from the neutral amino acids present. Since the component acids are of rather low molecular weight, the relatively large difference in molecular weight between homologs results in a fair spread of boiling point adequate for separation by fractional distillation. The technique of ester distillation led to the discovery in protein hydrolyzates of valine, proline, and hydroxyproline, but it did not prove to be adequate for the quantitative determination of the amino acid content of protein hydrolyzates. Selective precipitation reactions have comparable advantages and limitations. Reinecke's salt, $NH_4[Cr(SCN)_4(NH_3)_2]$, forms insoluble complexes with proline and hydroxyproline and precipitates these acids selectively; ammonium rhodanilate, $NH_4[Cr(SCN)_4(C_6H_5NH_2)_2]$, precipitates only proline. Histidine is precipitated by mercuric sulfate or, even better, by 3,4-dichlorobenzenesulfonic acid; tryptophan was first isolated from a protein hydrolyzate by precipitation with the former reagent.

Hydrolysis of a protein is usually done by refluxing it with hydrochloric (20%) or sulfuric acid (35%). Alkaline hydrolysis is attended with extensive racemization and is employed only for estimation of tryptophan and tyrosine, which are sensitive to mineral acids. If aspartic or glutamic acid is present in a protein in part in the form of the monoamide, acid hydrolysis converts the amide nitrogen to ammonia, which is bound as an ammonium salt. Kjehldahl determination gives the total nitrogen in the hydrolyzate, and the proportion present in amide linkage can be determined by alkalinization of an aliquot portion and distillation of the ammonia into standard acid. The quantity of ammonia parallels the amount of dicarboxylic acids. For instance, gliadin, which contains 46.9% of acidic amino acids, yields 5.2% of ammonia; gelatin, which contains only 9.2% of dicarboxylic acids, yields only 0.4% of ammonia. That the amide nitrogen is bound to the γ-carboxyl group of aspartic acid and the δ-carboxyl group of glutamic acid was established by isolation of asparagine and glutamine after enzymatic hydrolysis of proteins. Enzymatic hydrolysis is slow and probably never complete, but is nondestructive to sensitive primary products.

The amount of nitrogen present in a hydrolyzate or a protein in the form of primary amino groups is accurately determinable by the microgasometric method of Van Slyke (1911). An acid containing a primary amino group

$$\underset{\underset{NH_2}{|}}{RCHCOOH} \xrightarrow{HNO_2} \underset{\underset{OH}{|}}{RCHCOOH} + N_2$$

reacts with nitrous acid with quantitative evolution of nitrogen, which is determined manometrically. Both the α- and ϵ-amino groups of lysine are determinable as Van Slyke nitrogen; in arginine gas is evolved from the α-amino group but not from the guanidyl group. The —NH— groups of proline, tryptophan, and histidine liberate no nitrogen. Use of the method is illustrated by a procedure for analysis of the portion of hydrolyzate that is precipitated by phosphotungstic acid. The precipitate contains the three basic amino acids, together with cystine, the amount of which can be calculated from the total nitrogen content of the precipitate (Kjeldahl) and the result of a sulfur determination. The arginine in the precipitate is determined by boiling a sample with sodium hydroxide, which splits off two of the four nitrogens as ammonia (from the guanidyl group). The histidine content can then be calculated from the above results and from the Van Slyke nitrogen content of the precipitate, since the amount of total nitrogen not accounted for in the nitrous acid reaction corresponds to the summation of three quarters of the arginine nitrogen, which is already known, and two thirds of the histidine nitrogen.

The β-hydroxy-α-amino acids serine and threonine can be determined by cleavage with periodic acid. The amount of ammonia liberated is a measure

$$RCHCHCO_2H \xrightarrow{HIO_4} RCHO + NH_3 + OCHCO_2H$$
$$\quad\;|\quad\;|$$
$$\quad OH\;\;NH_2$$

of the total amount of the two acids, and the amounts of the individual acids can be established by determination of the specific aldehydes formed, form- aldehyde from serine and acetaldehyde from threonine. The cystine con- tent can be determined from the depth of color developed on addition of sodium 1,2-naphthoquinone-4-sulfonate and sodium hydrosulfite (Sullivan reaction); p-dimethylaminobenzaldehyde (Ehrlich's reagent) is a specific color reagent for the indole nucleus of tryptophan.

Amino Acid Analysis. — Certain of the modern methods of analysis that have proved useful are based upon chromatography. In paper-strip chro- matography (Martin[2] and Synge,[3] 1944) the components of a hydrolyzate are partitioned between water, adsorbed on cellulose and so held in a sta tionary phase, and an only partially water-soluble organic solvent such as butanol or phenol, which is caused to travel the length of the strip by either ascending or descending flow, and so constitutes a moving phase. The more lipophilic the component acid, the more it tends to travel with the organic solvent; the more hydrophilic, the greater is the tendency to be re- tained in the stationary water phase. The rate of flow (Rf) of acids of the same type increases with increasing molecular weight, and even homologs differing by a single methylene group travel at sufficiently different rates to be easily differentiated. At the end of the chromatogram the paper is dried and sprayed with ninhydrin to bring out spots revealing the positions of the component acids, since this reagent, indane-1,2,3-trione-2-hydrate, oxidizes amino acids to RCHO, NH_3, and CO_2 and affords a dihydride that

$$2\;\;\text{Ninhydrin} \xrightarrow[OH^-]{RCH(NH_2)CO_2H} \text{Pigment} + RCHO + CO_2$$

combines with the ammonia to produce a pigment. The ratio of the dis- tance travelled by the amino acid to the distance of solvent travel is the Rf

[2] Arthur John Porter Martin, b. 1910; Nat. Inst. Med. Res., Mill Hill, London; Nobel Prize 1952

[3] Richard Lawrence Millington Synge, b. 1914, Liverpool; Ph.D. Cambridge (Pirie); Rowett Res. Inst., Bucksburn, Scotland; Nobel Prize 1952

value, a constant characteristic of the specific acid. In an elaboration of the method the hydrolyzate is placed at the corner of a sheet of paper, a chromatogram is developed by allowing solvent to flow in the direction of the x-axis and then allowing another solvent to flow in the direction of the y-axis; a greater spread is thus achieved. Chromatographic fractionation on starch columns (Moore[4] and Stein, 1948) or on ion-exchange resins (Moore and Stein, 1951) has become the method of choice. It can be applied to 2–3 g. of protein, and with use of different solvents the constituents can be separated with quantitative recoveries. The rate of solvent flow must be very slow, and successful separation may require operation for more than a week.

Another method of quantitative analysis is microbiological assay (Snell,[5] 1946). A given microorganism requires certain amino acids for growth, and the rate of growth in a medium containing all but one of the essential acids provides an index of the amount of that component present in a test sample. Thus arginine in a hydrolyzate can be determined by the effect on growth of *Lactobacillus casei*; the concentration is determined by comparison with the effect of a standard sample at various concentrations.

The isotope dilution method (Rittenberg,[6] 1940) is theoretically applicable to any amino acid. A labeled acid of known isotopic content, for example isotopic glutamic acid, is added in known amount to the mixture to be analyzed, and glutamic acid is then isolated by the usual procedure. Since the chemical properties of the natural acid and the labeled acid are the same, the isolated material is a representative sample of added acid and acid originally present; the per cent recovery is thus unimportant. The amount of acid in the hydrolyzate is calculated from the isotopic analysis of the isolated acid. If the added isotopic synthetic acid is racemic, the hydrolyzate acid is racemized before isolation, or the pure L-form is separated from the isolated racemic acid. The degree of accuracy is independent of the method of isolation, the yield, and the concentration in the hydrolyzate.

Analyses of representative proteins are given in Table 16.3, inspection of which will show that protein type is not characterized by any particular amino acid pattern. The first three proteins listed, fibroin (silk), keratin (wool), and collagen (connective tissue), are of the fibrous, water-insoluble type, but they vary considerably in amino acid content. Thus the acidic acid constituents range from 5 to 21 g., the basic acids from 2 to 14 g., sulfur-containing acids from 0 to 13 g., hydroxy acids from 21 to 31 g., other neutral amino acids from 42 to 83 g. The amino acid pattern of water-soluble ovalbumin is comparable: basic 14.4 g., acidic 25.8 g., S-acids 7.1 g., hydroxy acids, 31.0 g., other neutral acids, 45.5 g. The last four proteins in the table are hormones, and again no particular amino acid pattern is

[4] Stanford Moore, b. 1913, Chicago; Ph.D. Wisconsin; Rockefeller Inst.

[5] Esmond E. Snell, b. 1914, Salt Lake City; Ph.D. Wisconsin (Peterson): Univ. Wisconsin and Univ. Texas

[6] David Rittenberg, b. 1906, New York; Ph.D. Columbia (Urey); Dept. Biochem., Coll. of Phys. and Surg., Columbia

TABLE 16.3. AMINO ACID CONTENT OF PROTEINS
Amino Acids, g./100 g. Protein

PROTEIN	Gly	Ala	Val	Leu	Ileu	CyS (CyS)$_2$	Met	Phe	Pro	Ser	Thr	Tyr	Try	Asp	Glu	Arg	Lys	His	Total,[a] g.
Fibroin (silk)	43.6	29.7	3.6	0.91	1.1	—	—	3.36	0.74	16.2	1.6	12.8	0	2.76	2.16	1.1	0.68	0.36	120.6
Keratin (wool)	6.53	4.14	4.64	11.3	—	11.9	0.7	3.65	9.5	10.01	6.42	4.65	1.8	7.2	14.1	10.4	2.76	1.1	110.8
Collagen	27.2	9.5	3.4	3.4	1.8	—	0.8	2.5	15.1	3.37	2.28	1.0	—	6.3	11.3	8.50	4.47	0.74	101.7[b]
Salmin (protamine)	2.95	1.12	3.14	0	1.64	—	—	—	5.80	9.1	—	—	—	—	—	85.2	—	—	108.9
Calf liver histone	5.07	6.94	3.22	5.21	20.5	—	—	4.08	4.04	4.71	4.80	3.30	—	5.71	4.30	17.4	10.23	2.69	102.2
Ribonuclease	1.3	—	7.3	—	3.1	7.11	4.43	3.6	3.6	12.0	9.0	7.93	—	14.2	13.0	5.16	10.4	4.22	106.3
Ovalbumin (hen)	3.05	6.72	7.05	9.2	7.0	1.86	5.2	7.66	3.6	8.15	4.03	3.68	1.20	9.30	16.50	5.72	6.30	2.35	108.6
β-Lactoglobulin	1.50	7.07	5.67	15.48	5.88	3.39	3.21	3.86	5.27	4.07	5.15	3.69	1.92	11.46	19.10	2.88	11.30	1.60	112.5
α-Casein	2.26	3.81	6.3	7.9	6.4	0.43	2.5	4.6	7.57	6.3	4.9	8.1	1.6	8.4	22.5	4.3	8.9	2.9	109.7
Hemoglobin (horse)	5.60	7.40	9.10	15.40	—	1.01	1.0	7.70	3.90	5.80	4.36	3.03	1.70	10.60	8.50	3.65	8.51	8.71	106.0
Serum albumin (human)	1.60	—	7.70	11.00	1.70	6.30	1.30	7.80	5.10	3.34	4.60	4.70	0.2	8.95	17.0	6.20	12.30	3.50	103.3
Fibrinogen	5.60	3.70	4.10	7.10	4.80	2.70	2.60	4.60	5.70	7.0	6.10	5.50	3.30	13.10	14.50	7.80	9.20	2.50	110.0
γ-Globulin	4.2	—	9.7	9.3	2.7	3.1	1.1	4.6	8.1	11.4	8.4	6.8	2.9	8.8	11.8	4.8	8.1	2.5	108.3
Edestin	—	4.31	6.5	7.5	4.7	1.43	2.4	5.45	4.25	6.30	3.85	4.34	1.48	12.0	20.7	16.7	2.4	2.5	106.8
Insulin (ox)	4.3	4.5	7.8	13.2	2.8	12.5	—	8.1	2.5	5.2	2.1	13.0	—	6.8	18.6	3.1	2.5	4.9	113.6
ACTH	8.0	4.5	3.4	7.8	3.1	7.2	1.9	4.0	8.2	6.0	3.2	2.4	—	6.7	15.6	8.7	5.0	1.3	92.5
Thyroglobulin[c] (ox)	3.7	7.4	1.45	12.80	—	3.60	1.30	6.68	3.4	10.80	—	3.12	2.08	—	—	12.72	3.42	2.23	71.3
Growth hormone (ox)	3.8	—	3.9	12.1	4.0	2.5	—	7.9	3.4	5.7	6.1	5.2	0.84	9.0	13.0	9.1	7.1	2.65	99.2

[a] Since water is incorporated into the molecules of the component acids, the theoretical totals vary from protein to protein and are all well over 100 g.

[b] Includes 14.0 g. of hydroxyproline and 1.1 g. of hydroxylysine.

[c] Contains also 0.21% thyroxine and 0.54% diiodotyrosine.

discernible, except that thyroglobulin is the only protein containing iodi-nated amino acids. Insulin has a high content of cysteine-cystine, but so does keratin. It is known that the amino acid composition of a protein of highly specialized properties varies from species to species (e.g. insulin, Harfenist, 1953).

SYNTHESIS OF AMINO ACIDS

Methods of synthesis, apart from initial interest for completion of evi-dence of structure, have been investigated extensively with the object of making acids available where required as dietary supplements; poultry feed, for example, is enriched in lysine. Although the initial product of a synthesis is racemic, resolution usually can be accomplished without difficulty. A general method consists in selective enzymatic hydrolysis of the L-form of a DL-acetylamino acid (Greenstein,[7] 1948). Currently, some amino acids are still more readily available by isolation than by synthesis.

α-**Halogen Acid Synthesis.** — This was the first method used for syn-thesis of an amino acid (glycine, Perkin and Duppa, 1858). It is based on the reaction of ammonia with α-bromo or α-chloro acids to form α amino acids and is illustrated by the classical synthesis of glycine. The yield is

$$CH_3COOH \xrightarrow{Br_2,\ 150°} CH_2BrCOOH \xrightarrow{2\ NH_3} CH_2(NH_2)COOH + NH_4Br$$

low (20%) and the product difficult to purify. With use of a large excess of ammonia (molar ratio 60:1) yields of 60–64% of pure glycine are ob-tained. Alanine and valine are conveniently prepared by this method.

Gabriel (1889) adapted his general synthetic method to a procedure for the preparation of glycine, which, although it is no longer used for this purpose, is useful in the case of other amino acids, since the yields are usually high and the products readily purified.

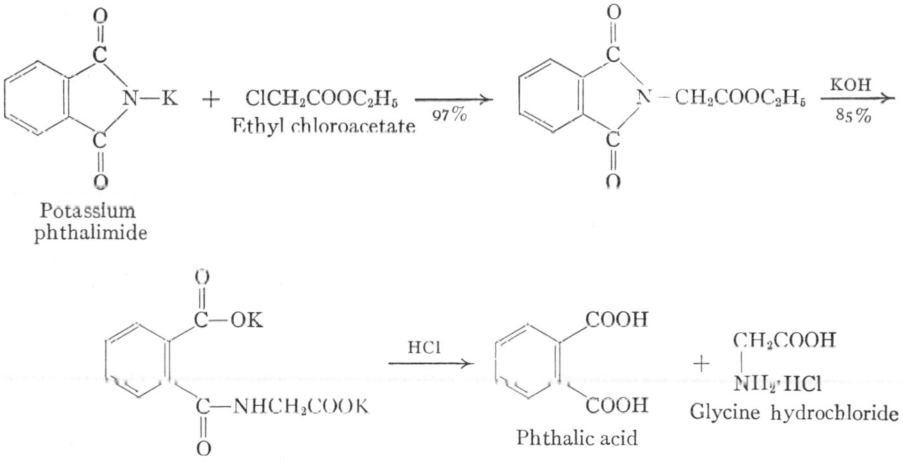

Potassium phthalimide

Phthalic acid

Glycine hydrochloride

[7] Jesse P. Greenstein, b. 1902, New York; Ph.D. Brown (Mitchell); Nat. Cancer Inst.

Cyanohydrin Synthesis (Strecker[8]). — The cyanohydrin synthesis was used for the first synthesis of alanine (1850) and has been employed mainly for the preparation of alanine, glycine (31–37% yield), and serine. When hydrogen cyanide is added to the carbonyl group of an aldehyde in the presence of ammonia, the latter reagent acts on the initially formed cyanohydrin with replacement of the hydroxyl by an amino group and subsequent formation of an aminonitrile, which affords an amino acid on hydrolysis.

$$CH_3CHO \xrightarrow{NH_3,\ HCN} \underset{\underset{NH_2}{|}}{CH_3CHC\equiv N} \xrightarrow{2\,H_2O} \underset{\underset{NH_2}{|}}{CH_3CHCOOH}$$

Acetaldehyde   Aminonitrile   Alanine

Fischer (1902) prepared serine by this method from glycolaldehyde ($HOCH_2CHO$), but this aldehyde can be prepared conveniently only in dilute solution, and polymerizes readily. Consequently the ethyl ether of glycolaldehyde, which can be prepared by dehydrogenation of ethylene glycol monoethyl ether (Cellosolve), is used instead in more recent work.

$$\underset{\substack{\text{Ethylene glycol}\\ \text{monoethyl ether}}}{C_2H_5OCH_2CH_2OH} \xrightarrow[43\%]{Cu,\ 250-275°} \underset{\text{Ethoxyacetaldehyde}}{C_2H_5OCH_2CHO} \xrightarrow{NH_3,\ HCN} C_2H_5OCH_2CH(NH_2)CN \xrightarrow{HBr}$$

$$HOCH_2CH(NH_2\cdot HBr)COOH \longrightarrow \underset{\text{Serine}}{HOCH_2CH(NH_2)COOH}$$

The overall yield of pure serine from the ethoxyacetaldehyde is 40%. A modification of the Strecker synthesis, introduced by Bucherer, consists in treatment of the aminonitrile with ammonium carbonate; the product is a hydantoin, which readily undergoes hydrolysis to the amino acid:

$$\underset{\underset{C\equiv N}{|}}{RCHNH_2} \xrightarrow{(NH_4)_2CO_3} \left[\underset{\underset{CONH_2}{|}}{RCHNHCOONH_4}\right] \longrightarrow \underset{\underset{CO-NH}{|}}{\overset{RCH-NH}{\underset{\text{Hydantoin}}{}}}\!\!\!>C=O$$

The overall yield of methionine obtained from acrolein by the Strecker reaction is only 25%, but the yield can be doubled by use of the modified Bucherer procedure (Tishler, 1948).

$$CH_3SH + CH_2=CHCHO \xrightarrow[84\%]{} CH_3SCH_2CH_2CHO \xrightarrow[79\%]{\substack{NaCN,\\ (NH_4)_2CO_3}}$$

$$\underset{\underset{NH-CO}{|}}{CH_3SCH_2CH_2CH-CO}\!\!\!>NH \xrightarrow[73.5\%]{NaOH} \underset{\underset{NH_2}{|}}{CH_3SCH_2CH_2CHCOOH}$$

Methionine

Malonic Ester Synthesis. — The malonic ester method is now the usual method for the synthesis of many amino acids and is limited only by the unavailability of certain of the alkyl halides required. The method is illustrated by Fischer's synthesis of leucine in approximately 37% yield (1906)

---

[8] Adolph Strecker, 1822–1871; assistant to Liebig at Tübingen

$$(CH_3)_2CHCH_2Br \ + \ Na^+ \begin{bmatrix} COOC_2H_5 \\ | \\ CH \\ | \\ COOC_2H_5 \end{bmatrix}^- \longrightarrow (CH_3)_2CHCH_2CH \begin{matrix} COOC_2H_5 \\ | \\ \\ | \\ COOC_2H_5 \end{matrix} \longrightarrow$$

Isobutyl bromide   Sodiomalonic ester

$$(CH_3)_2CHCH_2CH \begin{matrix} COOH \\ | \\ \\ | \\ COOH \end{matrix} \xrightarrow{Br_2} (CH_3)_2CHCH_2CBr \begin{matrix} COOH \\ | \\ \\ | \\ COOH \end{matrix} \xrightarrow{Heat}$$

$$(CH_3)_2CHCH_2CHBrCOOH \xrightarrow{NH_3} (CH_3)_2CHCH_2CH(NH_2)COOH$$
α-Bromoisocaproic acid   Leucine

A combination of the phthalimide and malonic ester syntheses has been developed for the preparation of several amino acids: phenylalanine, serine, aspartic acid, proline, tyrosine, methionine, and cystine. The following synthesis of methionine (Barger, 1931) is a typical illustration.

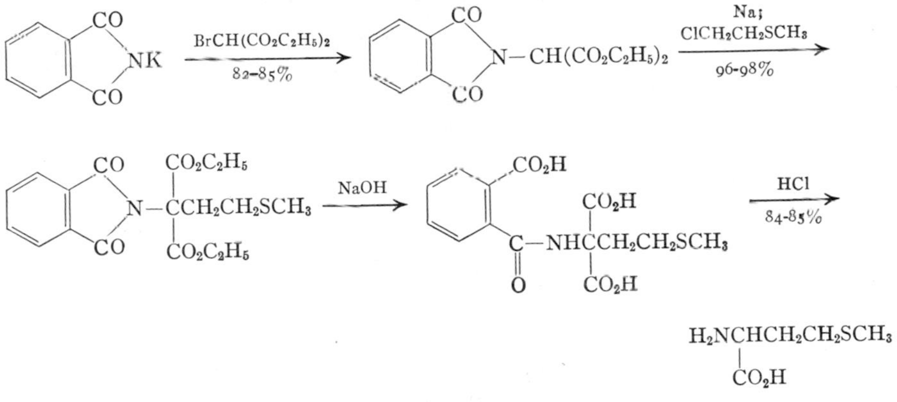

$$H_2NCHCH_2CH_2SCH_3$$
$$| $$
$$CO_2H$$

Methionine

Aminomalonic ester has been used for the preparation of a few amino acids. The steps involved are shown in the following synthesis of glutamic acid (Dunn[9] et al., 1931):

This method is generally unsatisfactory since aminomalonic ester is not stable; the hydrochloride is stable, but hygroscopic. Yields are low because

[9] Max S. Dunn, b. 1895 Milo, Iowa; Ph.D. Illinois; U. Calif. Los Angeles

secondary amine derivatives are formed as well by alkylation of nitrogen: $(H_5C_2OOC)_2CHNHR$. Most of these disadvantages are eliminated by a modification (Dunn *et al.*, 1931, 1939) that makes use of benzoylaminomalonic ester or of acetaminomalonic ester. The modified synthesis of glu-

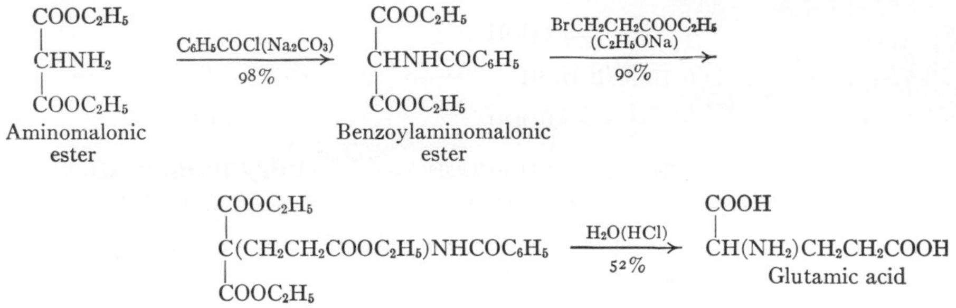

$$
\begin{array}{c}
\underset{|}{COOC_2H_5} \\
\underset{|}{CHNH_2} \\
COOC_2H_5
\end{array}
\xrightarrow[98\%]{C_6H_5COCl(Na_2CO_3)}
\begin{array}{c}
\underset{|}{COOC_2H_5} \\
\underset{|}{CHNHCOC_6H_5} \\
COOC_2H_5
\end{array}
\xrightarrow[90\%]{\underset{(C_2H_5ONa)}{BrCH_2CH_2COOC_2H_5}}
$$

Aminomalonic ester   Benzoylaminomalonic ester

$$
\begin{array}{c}
\underset{|}{COOC_2H_5} \\
\underset{|}{C(CH_2CH_2COOC_2H_5)NHCOC_6H_5} \\
COOC_2H_5
\end{array}
\xrightarrow[52\%]{H_2O(HCl)}
\begin{array}{c}
\underset{|}{COOH} \\
CH(NH_2)CH_2CH_2COOH
\end{array}
$$

Glutamic acid

tamic acid is illustrated in the formulas. The modified malonic ester synthesis is used in a recent synthesis of tryptophan from indole (66% overall

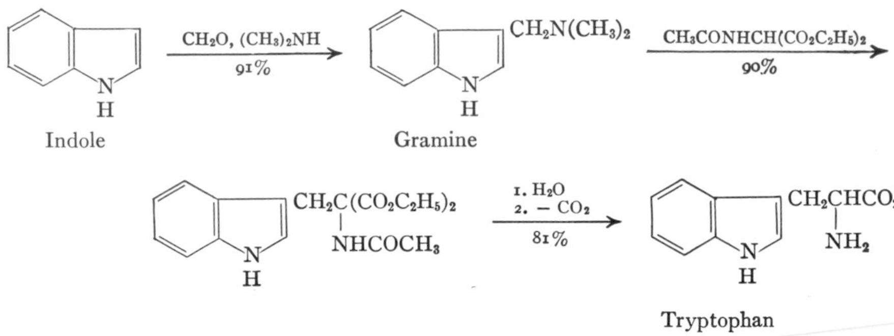

Indole $\xrightarrow[91\%]{CH_2O,\ (CH_3)_2NH}$ Gramine [$CH_2N(CH_3)_2$] $\xrightarrow[90\%]{CH_3CONHCH(CO_2C_2H_5)_2}$

[indole with $CH_2C(CO_2C_2H_5)_2$, $NHCOCH_3$] $\xrightarrow[81\%]{\substack{1.\ H_2O \\ 2.\ -CO_2}}$ [indole with CH_2CHCO_2H, NH_2]

Tryptophan

yield). The reaction involves alkylation not with a halide as in the other examples but with a tertiary amine containing a benzyl-type group.

In a method developed by Curtius, α-amino acids are obtained from derivatives of malonic ester through the intermediate azides. Curtius prepared glycine, alanine, valine, and phenylalanine by this method.

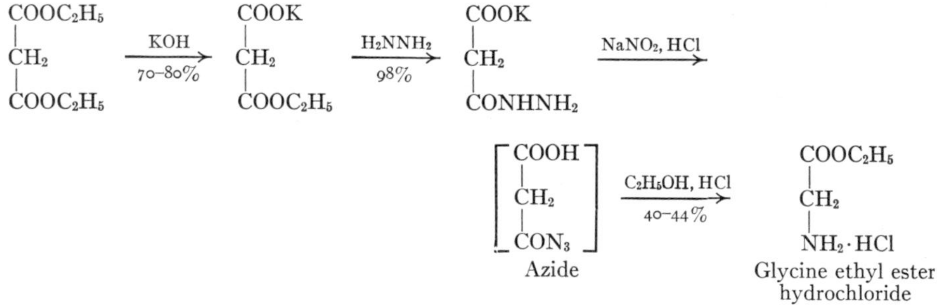

$$
\begin{array}{c}
\underset{|}{COOC_2H_5} \\
\underset{|}{CH_2} \\
COOC_2H_5
\end{array}
\xrightarrow[70-80\%]{KOH}
\begin{array}{c}
\underset{|}{COOK} \\
\underset{|}{CH_2} \\
COOC_2H_5
\end{array}
\xrightarrow[98\%]{H_2NNH_2}
\begin{array}{c}
\underset{|}{COOK} \\
\underset{|}{CH_2} \\
CONHNH_2
\end{array}
\xrightarrow{NaNO_2,\ HCl}
$$

$$
\begin{bmatrix}
\underset{|}{COOH} \\
\underset{|}{CH_2} \\
CON_3
\end{bmatrix}
\xrightarrow[40-44\%]{C_2H_5OH,\ HCl}
\begin{array}{c}
\underset{|}{COOC_2H_5} \\
\underset{|}{CH_2} \\
NH_2 \cdot HCl
\end{array}
$$

Azide   Glycine ethyl ester hydrochloride

Aldehyde Condensations. — The condensation of aromatic aldehydes with hydantoin has been useful for the synthesis of phenylalanine, tyrosine, and tryptophan. The method, including the preparation of the starting material, is illustrated by the synthesis of tyrosine (1911).

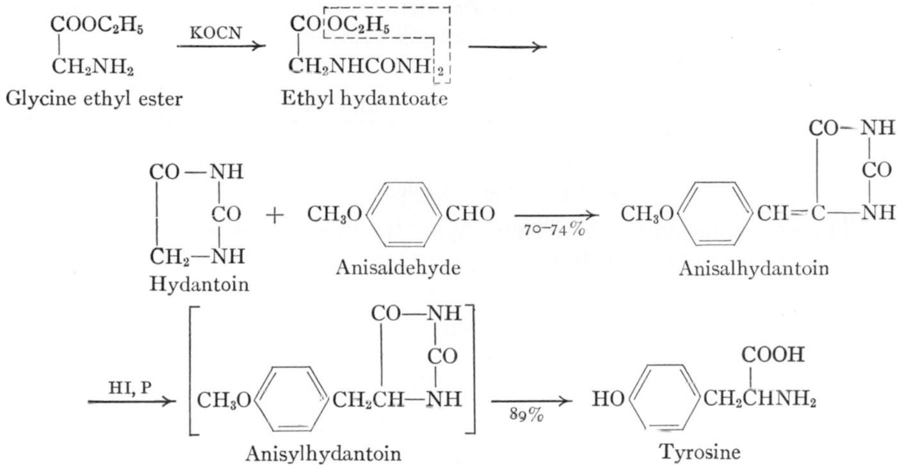

$$\begin{array}{c} \text{COOC}_2\text{H}_5 \\ | \\ \text{CH}_2\text{NH}_2 \end{array} \xrightarrow{\text{KOCN}} \begin{array}{c} \text{CO}\;\text{OC}_2\text{H}_5 \\ | \\ \text{CH}_2\text{NHCONH}_2 \end{array} \longrightarrow$$

Glycine ethyl ester   Ethyl hydantoate

Hydantoin + Anisaldehyde $\xrightarrow{70-74\%}$ Anisalhydantoin

$\xrightarrow{\text{HI, P}}$ Anisylhydantoin $\xrightarrow{89\%}$ Tyrosine

Onc improvement consists in use of thiohydantoin, which is cheaper and which usually gives higher yields in the condensation. Another is reduction of the condensation product with sodium amalgam or ammonium sulfide, instead of hydrogen iodide and red phosphorus, which is unsatisfactory for the preparation of tryptophan. These modifications have been used in a synthesis of tyrosine (1935):

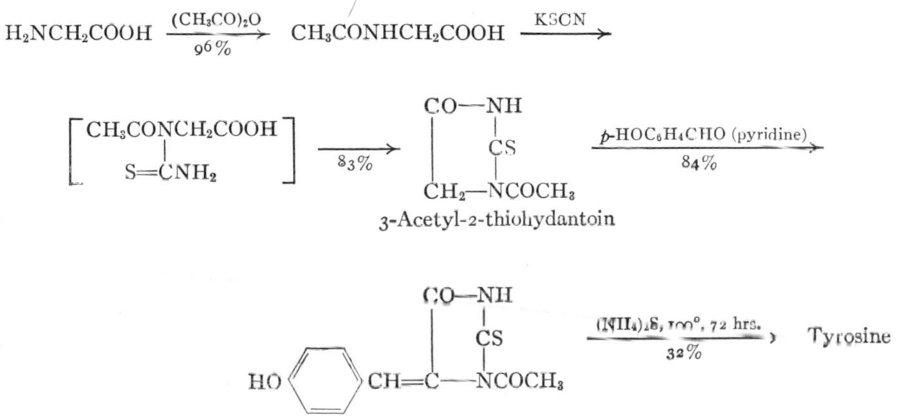

$$\text{H}_2\text{NCH}_2\text{COOH} \xrightarrow[96\%]{(\text{CH}_3\text{CO})_2\text{O}} \text{CH}_3\text{CONHCH}_2\text{COOH} \xrightarrow{\text{KSCN}}$$

$$\left[\begin{array}{c} \text{CH}_3\text{CONCH}_2\text{COOH} \\ | \\ \text{S}=\text{CNH}_2 \end{array} \right] \xrightarrow{83\%} \text{3-Acetyl-2-thiohydantoin} \xrightarrow[84\%]{p\text{-HOC}_6\text{H}_4\text{CHO (pyridine)}}$$

3-Acetyl-2-thiohydantoin

$\xrightarrow[32\%]{(\text{NH}_4)_2\text{S, 100°, 72 hrs.}}$ Tyrosine

A similar method that starts with diketopiperazine instead of hydantoin has been used for the synthesis of phenylalanine and tyrosine (Dunn). Diketopiperazine (glycine anhydride) is conveniently prepared from glycine ethyl ester (Fischer method). The anhydride can be prepared in higher yield (50–60%) by heating glycine in the minimum quantity of water and glycerol at 170° for four hours (Balbiano).

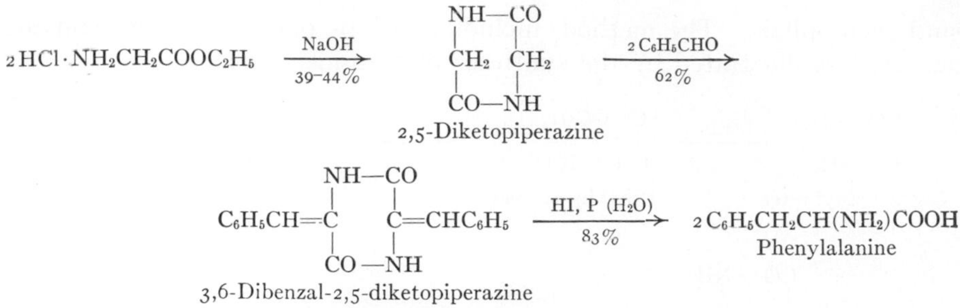

$$2\,HCl\cdot NH_2CH_2COOC_2H_5 \xrightarrow[\text{39-44\%}]{NaOH}$$

$$
\begin{array}{cc}
NH\!-\!CO & \\
| & | \\
CH_2 & CH_2 \\
| & | \\
CO\!-\!NH &
\end{array}
\xrightarrow[\text{62\%}]{2\,C_6H_5CHO}
$$

2,5-Diketopiperazine

$$
C_6H_5CH\!=\!\!\!\begin{array}{cc} NH\!-\!CO & \\ C & C \end{array}\!\!\!=\!CHC_6H_5
\xrightarrow[\text{83\%}]{HI,\ P\ (H_2O)} 2\,C_6H_5CH_2CH(NH_2)COOH
$$
Phenylalanine

$$
\begin{array}{c}
| \qquad | \\
CO\!-\!NH
\end{array}
$$

3,6-Dibenzal-2,5-diketopiperazine

The azlactone synthesis (Erlenmeyer, Jr.,[10] 1883), consisting in condensation of an aldehyde with hippuric acid to form an azlactone, which on reduction and hydrolysis yields an α-amino acid, was originally considered to be a modification of the Perkin synthesis (p. 689) and was formulated as in (a). However, convincing evidence now indicates that hippuric acid is first converted into its azlactone (b), which contains a reactive methylene group, and that the condensation involves the aldehyde and this intermedi-

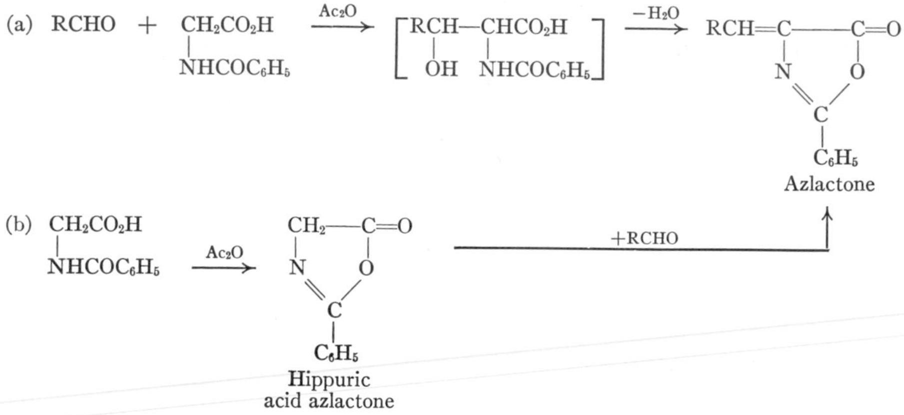

(a) $RCHO + \underset{NHCOC_6H_5}{CH_2CO_2H} \xrightarrow{Ac_2O} \left[\underset{\underset{OH\ \ NHCOC_6H_5}{\ }}{RCH\!-\!CHCO_2H}\right] \xrightarrow{-H_2O} RCH\!=\!C\!-\!-\!-\!C\!=\!O$

with azlactone ring structure

Azlactone

(b) $\underset{NHCOC_6H_5}{CH_2CO_2H} \xrightarrow{Ac_2O}$ (hippuric acid azlactone ring structure) $\xrightarrow{+RCHO}$

Hippuric
acid azlactone

ate. The synthesis of histidine (1911) is shown in the following formulation (11% overall yield). This useful method has been employed for the syn-

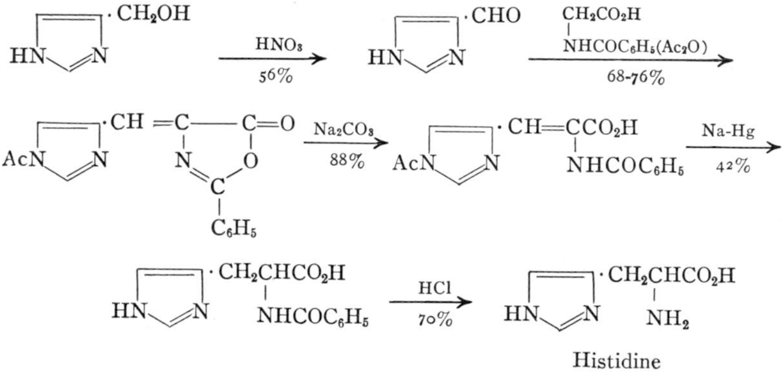

(histidine synthesis scheme with structures)

$$\xrightarrow[\text{56\%}]{HNO_3}$$

$$\xrightarrow[\text{68-76\%}]{\underset{NHCOC_6H_5(Ac_2O)}{CH_2CO_2H}}$$

$$\xrightarrow[\text{88\%}]{Na_2CO_3}$$

$$\xrightarrow[\text{42\%}]{Na\text{-}Hg}$$

$$\xrightarrow[\text{70\%}]{HCl}$$

Histidine

[10] Emil Erlenmeyer, Jr., 1864-1921, b. Heidelberg; Ph.D. Göttingen; Strasbourg, Berlin, *Ber.*, **54A**, 107 (1921)

thesis of several amino acids, including the following: phenylalanine from benzaldehyde, 39–43% yield; leucine from isobutyraldehyde; tryptophan from indole-β-aldehyde, 10–17%; thyroxine from 3,5-diiodo-4-(4'-methoxyphenoxy)-benzaldehyde.

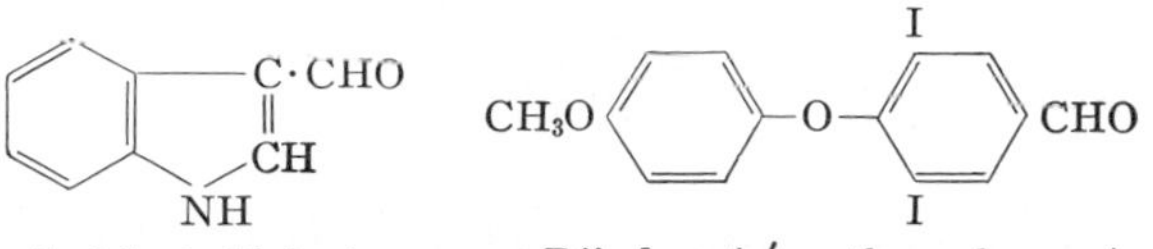

Indole-β-aldehyde   3,5-Diiodo-4-(4'-methoxyphenoxy)-benzaldehyde

An interesting variation, used for the synthesis of phenylalanine and several derivatives, involves condensation of aromatic aldehydes with rhodanine. The preparation of phenylalanine involves the following steps:

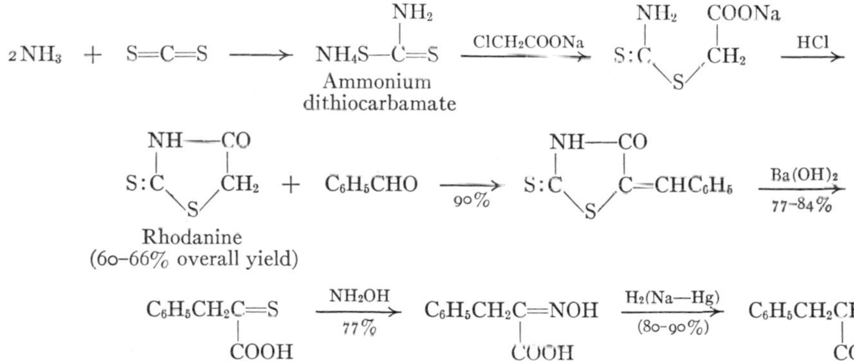

$$2\,NH_3 + S{=}C{=}S \longrightarrow NH_4S{-}\overset{\overset{\displaystyle NH_2}{|}}{C}{=}S \xrightarrow{ClCH_2COONa} \cdots \xrightarrow{HCl}$$

Ammonium dithiocarbamate

Rhodanine
(60–66% overall yield)

$$\cdots + C_6H_5CHO \xrightarrow{90\%} \cdots \xrightarrow[77-84\%]{Ba(OH)_2}$$

$$\underset{\underset{\displaystyle COOH}{|}}{C_6H_5CH_2C}{=}S \xrightarrow[77\%]{NH_2OH} \underset{\underset{\displaystyle COOH}{|}}{C_6H_5CH_2C}{=}NOH \xrightarrow[(80-90\%)]{H_2(Na-Hg)} \underset{\underset{\displaystyle COOH}{|}}{C_6H_5CH_2CHNH_2}$$

The yield in the reduction (final step) is not reported in this particular instance, but 80–90% yields are obtained with closely related compounds.

Special Methods. — The α-amino-β-hydroxy acid serine is prepared most satisfactorily through the α-halo-β-hydroxy acids (Carter, 1936); the overall yield is 30–40%:

$$CH_2{=}CHCOOCH_3 \xrightarrow[CH_3OH]{Hg(OAc)_2} CH_3OCH_2CH(HgOAc)COOCH_3 \xrightarrow{KBr}$$

Methyl acrylate   81–86% overall

$$CH_3OCH_2CH(HgBr)COOCH_3 \xrightarrow{Br_2} CH_3OCH_2CHBrCOOCH_3 \xrightarrow{NaOH(H_2SO_4)}$$

Methyl α-bromo-β-methoxypropionate

$$CH_3OCH_2CHBrCOOH \xrightarrow{NH_3} CH_3OCH_2CH(NH_2)COOH \xrightarrow{HBr}$$

$$CH_2(OH)CH(NH_3Br)COOH \xrightarrow{NH_3} CH_2(OH)CH(NH_2)COOH$$

Serine

The classical threonine synthesis utilized similar reactions applied to crotonic acid. Most methods of making the intermediate α-bromo-β-methoxy-n-butyric acid give material that on amination affords chiefly allothreonine and at most 35% of threonine, as determined by microbio-

$$\begin{matrix} \text{HCCO}_2\text{H} \\ \parallel \\ \text{CH}_3\text{CH} \end{matrix} \xrightarrow[\text{(trans)}]{\text{Br}_2,\text{CH}_3\text{OH}} \begin{matrix} \text{CO}_2\text{H} \\ | \\ \text{BrCH} \\ | \\ \text{CH}_3\text{OCH} \\ | \\ \text{CH}_3 \end{matrix} + \begin{matrix} \text{CO}_2\text{H} \\ | \\ \text{HCBr} \\ | \\ \text{HCOCH}_3 \\ | \\ \text{CH}_3 \end{matrix} \xrightarrow[\text{(no inversion)}]{\substack{\text{NH}_3; \\ \text{hydrol.}}} \begin{matrix} \text{DL-Allothreonine} \\ \text{(chiefly)} \end{matrix}$$

Crotonic acid

DL-Allo (chiefly)

$$\begin{matrix} \text{CONR}_2 \\ | \\ \text{BrCH} \\ | \\ \text{CH}_3\text{OCH} \\ | \\ \text{CH}_3 \end{matrix} + \begin{matrix} \text{CONR}_2 \\ | \\ \text{HCBr} \\ | \\ \text{HCOCH}_3 \\ | \\ \text{CH}_3 \end{matrix} \xrightarrow[\text{(inversion)}]{\substack{\text{NH}_3; \\ \text{hydrol.}}} \begin{matrix} \text{DL-Threonine} \\ \text{(chiefly)} \end{matrix}$$

logical assay of the natural L-threonine in the mixture. Tishler and co-workers (1949) found that amination of the bromomethoxy acid proceeds without inversion and that under most conditions the addition of hypobromite follows predominantely the *trans* course to give an intermediate of

$$\text{CH}_3\text{COCH}_2\text{CO}_2\text{C}_2\text{H}_5 \xrightarrow{\text{C}_6\text{H}_5\text{N}_2\text{Cl}} \begin{matrix} \text{CH}_3\text{COCHCO}_2\text{C}_2\text{H}_5 \\ | \\ \text{N}{=}\text{NC}_6\text{N}_5 \end{matrix} \xrightarrow[\text{88\% from I}]{\text{Ac}_2\text{O, Zn}}$$

$$\quad\quad\quad\text{I} \quad\quad\quad\quad\quad\quad\quad\quad\quad\quad\quad\quad \text{II}$$

$$\begin{matrix} \text{CO}_2\text{C}_2\text{H}_5 \\ | \\ \text{CHNHCOCH}_3 \\ | \\ \text{C}{=}\text{O} \\ | \\ \text{CH}_3 \end{matrix} \xrightarrow[\text{(quant.)}]{\text{H}_2,\ \text{Pt}} \begin{matrix} | \\ \text{CH}_3\text{CONHCH} \\ | \\ \text{HOCH} \\ | \end{matrix} + \begin{matrix} | \\ \text{CH}_3\text{CONHCH} \\ | \\ \text{HCOH} \\ | \end{matrix}$$

$$\quad\quad\text{III} \quad\quad\quad\quad\quad \begin{matrix}\text{DL-Acetyl allo ester} \\ \text{IV (85\%)}\end{matrix} \quad\quad \begin{matrix}\text{DL-Acetyl threo ester} \\ \text{V (15\%)}\end{matrix}$$

(inversion) | Mixture + SOCl$_2$, C$_6$H$_6$

$$\begin{matrix} \text{CH}_3\text{C}{=}\text{NCH} \\ | \quad\quad | \\ \text{HC}{-}\text{O} \\ | \quad\quad | \end{matrix} + \begin{matrix} \text{CH}_3\text{C}{=}\text{NCH} \\ | \quad\quad | \\ \text{O}{-}{-}\text{CH} \\ | \quad\quad | \end{matrix}$$

Threo-oxazoline   Allothreo-oxazoline

Hydrol., separation

$$\begin{matrix} \text{CO}_2\text{H} \\ | \\ \text{H}_2\text{NCH} \\ | \\ \text{HCOH} \\ | \\ \text{CH}_3 \end{matrix} \begin{matrix} \text{CO}_2\text{H} \\ | \\ \text{HCNH}_2 \\ | \\ \text{HOCH} \\ | \\ \text{CH}_3 \end{matrix} \quad\quad \begin{matrix} \text{CO}_2\text{H} \\ | \\ \text{H}_2\text{NCH} \\ | \\ \text{HOCH} \\ | \\ \text{CH}_3 \end{matrix} \begin{matrix} \text{CO}_2\text{H} \\ | \\ \text{HCNH}_2 \\ | \\ \text{HCOH} \\ | \\ \text{CH}_3 \end{matrix}$$

(L)   (L)

DL-Threonine   DL-Allothreonine
(57% yield from I)

allothreo configuration. They then found that when the acid is converted into an amide (preferably tertiary), and this is aminated, inversion occurs to a large extent; this sequence of reactions constitutes one practicable synthesis. Another, also developed by the Merck group, proceeds from acetoacetic ester (I) through its acetylamino derivative (III), which is hydrogenated quantitatively in water solution to a mixture containing 85% of DL-acctylallothreonine (IV). The mixture, without being separated, is cyclized to a mixture of oxazolines; since both IV and V react with inversion, the oxazoline hydrolyzate is a mixture in which DL-threonine predominates in the ratio 85:15. On conversion into the sodium salt in alcohol the salt of the small amount of DL-allothreonine remains in solution, and the much less soluble salt of DL-threonine separates and affords the pure DL-acid in high yield. The oxazoline of allothreonine ester can be isomerized with a trace of alkali to the oxazoline of threonine (Elliot, 1948) and when this step is applied no separation is required and the yield is raised.

All early syntheses of cystine or cysteine utilized serine as starting material. Fischer (1908) prepared L-cystine in approximately 25% yield from L-serine. DL-Cystine has been prepared by the phthalimidomalonic

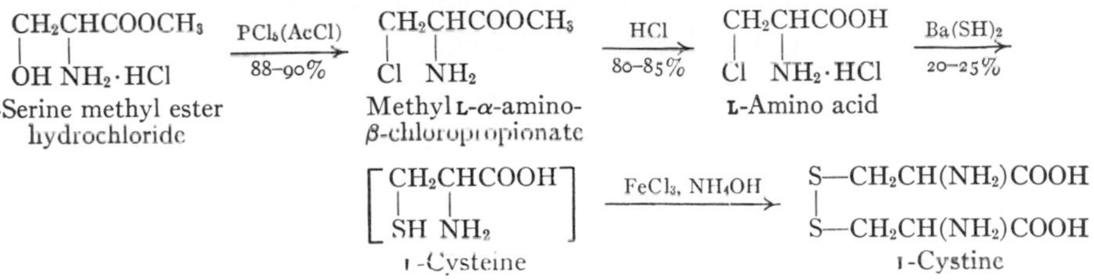

ester method (du Vigneaud, 1939). Cystine can be prepared readily by hydrolysis of keratin (hair); 100–106 g. of cystine is obtained from 2 kg. of human hair, about half that amount from 2 kg. of sheep's wool.

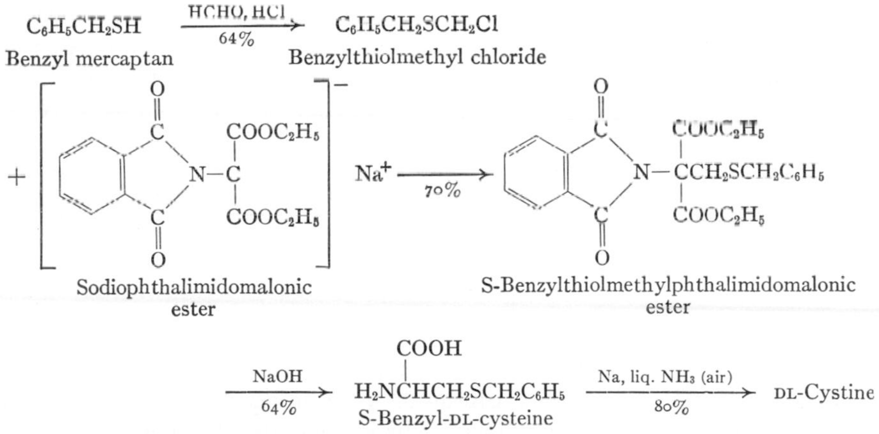

Reduction of α-oximino acids was first employed in 1887 for the synthesis of aspartic acid; some years later (1906), Bouveault prepared isoleucine in 60–70% yield from the oxime of methylethylpyruvic ester (II). The oxime is prepared by treating the substituted acetoacetic ester (I) with

$$
\underset{I}{\underset{\displaystyle |}{CH_3COCHCOOC_2H_5}} \quad \xrightarrow[75\%]{SO_2(OH)ONO} \quad \left[\begin{array}{c} CH(CH_3)CH_2CH_3 \\ | \\ CH_3CO{-}CCOOC_2H_5 \\ | \\ N{=}O \\ \cdots + \cdots \\ HO{\mid}H \end{array} \right] \longrightarrow
$$

with CH(CH₃)CH₂CH₃ group on top of I.

$$
\underset{\underset{\displaystyle Oxime\ (II)}{\underset{\displaystyle NOH}{\parallel}}}{\overset{\overset{\displaystyle CH_3}{|}}{CH_3CH_2CHCCOOC_2H_5}} \quad \xrightarrow[60–70\%]{Zn—HCl} \quad \underset{\underset{\displaystyle Isoleucine}{}}{\overset{\overset{\displaystyle CH_3}{|}}{CH_3CH_2CHCH(NH_2)COOH}}
$$

nitrosylsulfuric acid, a latent source of nitrous acid; acid cleavage occurs during the reaction. The method has been modified slightly (1941–42) in preparations of alanine, α-aminobutyric acid, norvaline, norleucine, isoleucine, aspartic acid, phenylalanine, glutamic acid, and tyrosine. The oximino esters are prepared by treating the appropriately substituted aceto-acetic ester with an alkyl nitrite. Reduction is accomplished by hydrogenation in the presence of palladinized charcoal. Overall yields are 60–70%.

$$
\underset{\displaystyle CH_3COCHCOOC_2H_5}{\overset{\overset{\displaystyle R}{|}}{}} \quad \xrightarrow{R'ONO(H_2SO_4)} \quad \left[\begin{array}{c} R \\ | \\ CH_3CO{-}CCOOC_2H_5 \\ | \\ HONOR' \end{array} \right] \longrightarrow
$$

$$
\left[\begin{array}{c} R \\ | \\ HCCOOC_2H_5 \\ | \\ N{=}O \end{array} \right] \longrightarrow \underset{\underset{\displaystyle NOH}{\parallel}}{RCCOOC_2H_5} \quad \xrightarrow{H_2(Pd)} \quad \underset{\underset{\displaystyle NH_2}{|}}{RCHCOOH}
$$

In a new method developed by Feofilaktov, amino acids are prepared by reduction of the corresponding phenylhydrazones, which are made by condensation of a suitably substituted acetoacetic acid ester with benzene-diazonium chloride (p. 610). Leucine, isoleucine, valine, alanine, phenyl-alanine, and hydroxyproline have been synthesized by this general procedure.

$$
\underset{\underset{\displaystyle COCH_3}{|}}{\overset{\overset{\displaystyle CH_3}{\diagdown}}{\underset{CH_3\diagup}{}}CHCHCOOC_2H_5} \xrightarrow{\underset{55\%}{C_6H_5N_2Cl}} \underset{\underset{\displaystyle NNHC_6H_5}{\parallel}}{\overset{\overset{\displaystyle CH_3}{\diagdown}}{\underset{CH_3\diagup}{}}CHCCOOH} \xrightarrow{\underset{98\%}{Zn—C_2H_5OH}} \underset{\underset{\underset{\displaystyle DL\text{-}Valine}{}}{\underset{\displaystyle NH_2}{|}}}{\overset{\overset{\displaystyle CH_3}{\diagdown}}{\underset{CH_3\diagup}{}}CHCHCOOH}
$$

SYNTHESIS OF POLYPEPTIDES

In 1901 Fischer initiated work on the synthesis of polypeptides to see if substances could be produced having properties characteristic of proteins. Eventually a polypeptide was produced containing eighteen amino acid residues: leucyltriglycylleucyltriglycylleucyloctaglycylglycine.   Although such substances lack some of the important properties of proteins, they have proved useful as models for studying enzymatic degradation and chemical reactions of proteins. Although the synthesis of actual proteins is still a distant goal, the field of research has been greatly stimulated by the discovery of natural polypeptides of interesting and unusual properties of relatively simple structures amenable to synthesis. Furthermore synthetic di- and tripeptides have greatly facilitated determination of amino acid sequences in proteins (p. 446).

Ester Condensation. — This early procedure used by Fischer (1901) is based on the observation that methyl esters of amino acids when gently heated tend to form linear condensation products. Fischer achieved the

$$2\,NH_2CH_2CH(NH_2)COOCH_3 \xrightarrow{100°} NH_2CH_2CH(NH_2)CO\text{—}NHCH_2CH(NH_2)COOCH_3$$
Methyl α,β-diamino-
propionate

synthesis of pentaglycylglycine by this method, but the yields became discouragingly poor when the chain was lengthened still further.

$$2\,NH_2CH_2CO\text{—}NHCH_2CO\text{—}NHCH_2COOCH_3 \xrightarrow[76\%]{100°}$$
Diglycylglycine methyl ester

$$NH_2CH_2CO\text{—}NHCH_2CO\text{—}NHCH_2CO\text{—}NHCH_2CO\text{—}NHCH_2CO\text{—}NHCH_2COOCH_3$$
Pentaglycylglycine methyl ester

Chloroacid Chloride Synthesis. — In this method, described by Fischer in 1903, the peptide link is formed by condensation of an acid chloride of one amino acid with the amino group of another one. The problem of preventing self-condensation with the amino group of the acid chloride fragment was solved by using the acid chloride of an α-halo acid and replacing the α-halo atom by an amino group after the peptide bond is formed (1, 2). This method was used for synthesis of the octadecapeptide mentioned earlier

1. $ClCH_2COCl + H_2NCH_2CO\text{—}NHCH_2COOC_2H_5 \xrightarrow[27\%]{}$
Chloroacetyl chloride   Glycylglycine ester

$$ClCH_2CO\text{—}NHCH_2CO\text{—}NHCH_2COOC_2H_5 \xrightarrow[100\%]{NaOH}$$
Chloroacetylglycylglycine ester

$$ClCH_2CO\text{—}NHCH_2CO\text{—}NHCH_2COOH \xrightarrow{25\% NH_4OH} NH_2CH_2CO\text{—}NHCH_2CO\text{—}NHCH_2COOH$$
Chloroacetylglycylglycine   Diglycylglycine

2. $(CH_3)_2CHCH_2CHBrCOCl + H_2NCH_2CO\text{—}NHCH_2COOC_2H_5 \xrightarrow[76\%]{}$
  α-Bromoisocaproyl   Glycylglycine ester
  chloride

$$C_4H_9CHBrCO\text{—}NHCH_2CO\text{—}NHCH_2COOC_2H_5 \xrightarrow[100\%]{NaOH}$$
α-Bromoisocaproylglycylglycine ester

$$C_4H_9CHBrCO\text{—}NHCH_2CO\text{—}NHCH_2COOH \xrightarrow[63\%]{NH_3}$$

$$\begin{array}{c} CH_3 \\ \\ CH_3 \end{array}\!\!\!\!> CHCH_2CH(NH_2)CO\text{—}NHCH_2CO\text{—}NHCH_2COOH$$
Leucylglycylglycine

and the principle of using an acid chloride is the basis of several modern procedures. The original scheme is not so well adapted to synthesis of optically active polypeptides as later methods that utilize natural or synthetic L-amino acids as building units.

Azide Synthesis. — In this method, introduced by Curtius[11] (1902), the peptide bond is formed by interaction of an acid azide with an amino group. The acid azide is prepared by the action of nitrous acid on the corresponding acid hydrazide. For the necessary protection of the amino group of the

$$C_6H_5CONHCHRCO_2CH_3 \xrightarrow{H_2NNH_2} C_6H_5CONHCHRCONHNH_2 \xrightarrow{HNO_2}$$

Acid hydrazide

$$C_6H_5CONHCHRCON_3 \xrightarrow{H_2NCHR'CO_2CH_3} C_6H_5CONHCHRCONHCHR'CO_2CH_3$$

Acid azide   N-Benzoyldipeptide ester

initial amino acid component both during transformation of the ester to the acid azide and during the peptide synthesis, Curtius chose the benzoyl group and so synthesized benzoylated polypeptides. A shortcoming is that the benzoyl group cannot be removed by hydrolysis without cleavage of the peptide bond as well. Fischer tried to circumvent the difficulty by use of the carbethoxyl (cathyl) derivative, $-NHCO_2C_2H_5$, but Wessely[12] later (1928) found that hydrolysis of carbethoxypeptides is attended with rearrangement.

Carbobenzoxy Synthesis. — Although the azlactone synthesis and other methods were introduced with some success after Fischer's pioneering work, the greatest advance in synthesis was made in 1932 by Bergmann,[13] who used carbobenzoxy chloride, prepared from benzyl alcohol and phosgene (a), as a reagent for conversion of an amine by Schotten-Baumann reaction to a protected derivative (b) from which the amino group can be regenerated when desired by catalytic hydrogenation (c) without disturbance of peptide linkages. The phenyl group promotes reductive fission by activating the

(a) $C_6H_5CH_2OH + ClCOCl \longrightarrow C_6H_5CH_2OCOCl + HCl$

(b) $C_6H_5CH_2OCOCl + H_2NR \xrightarrow{NaOH} C_6H_5CH_2OCONHR + NaCl + H_2O$

(c) [benzene ring]$-CH_2|OCONHR \xrightarrow{H_2, Pt}$ [benzene ring]$-CH_3 + CO_2 + H_2NR$

carbon–oxygen bond. The toluene formed is easily removed by evaporation in vacuum. L-Glutamyl-L-glutamic acid was the first dipeptide synthesized by this method.

---

[11] Theodor Curtius, 1857–1928; Ph.D. Leipzig (Kolbe); successor (1902) to Victor Meyer at Heidelberg

[12] Friederich Wessely, b. 1897, Kirchberg, Austria; Ph.D. Vienna (Franke); Univ. Vienna

[13] Max Bergmann, 1886–1944; Ph.D. Berlin, asst. to E. Fischer; from 1933, Rockefeller Inst. *J. Chem. Soc.*, 716 (1945).

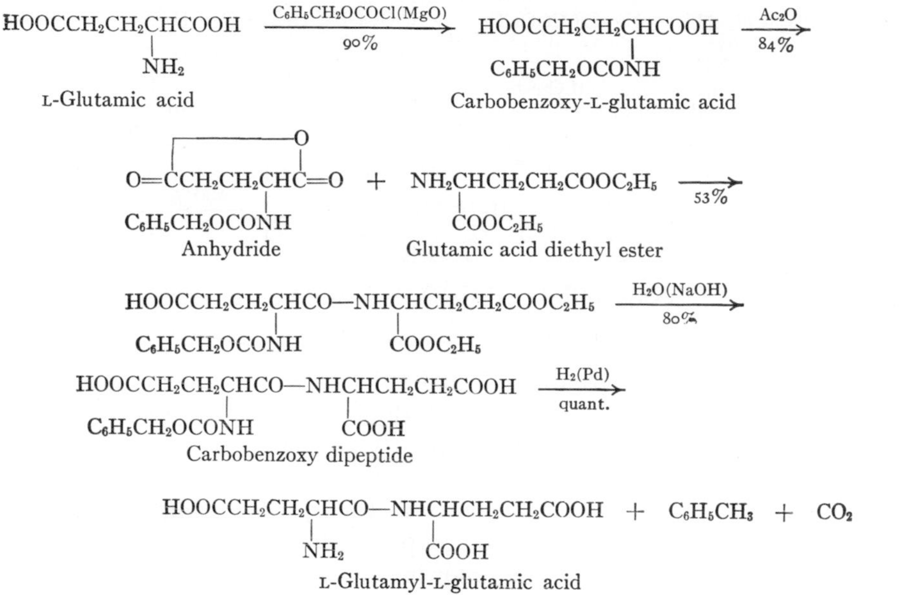

$$HOOCCH_2CH_2CHCOOH \xrightarrow[90\%]{C_6H_5CH_2OCOCl(MgO)} HOOCCH_2CH_2CHCOOH \xrightarrow[84\%]{Ac_2O}$$
$$\underset{NH_2}{|} \qquad\qquad \underset{C_6H_5CH_2OCONH}{|}$$

L-Glutamic acid Carbobenzoxy-L-glutamic acid

$$\overset{\overbrace{\hspace{3cm}}O}{O=CCH_2CH_2CHC}=O \;+\; NH_2CHCH_2CH_2COOC_2H_5 \xrightarrow{53\%}$$
$$\underset{C_6H_5CH_2OCONH}{|} \qquad\qquad \underset{COOC_2H_5}{|}$$

Anhydride Glutamic acid diethyl ester

$$HOOCCH_2CH_2CHCO—NHCHCH_2CH_2COOC_2H_5 \xrightarrow[80\%]{H_2O(NaOH)}$$
$$\underset{C_6H_5CH_2OCONH}{|} \qquad \underset{COOC_2H_5}{|}$$

$$HOOCCH_2CH_2CHCO—NHCHCH_2CH_2COOH \xrightarrow[quant.]{H_2(Pd)}$$
$$\underset{C_6H_5CH_2OCONH}{|} \qquad \underset{COOH}{|}$$

Carbobenzoxy dipeptide

$$HOOCCH_2CH_2CHCO—NHCHCH_2CH_2COOH \;+\; C_6H_5CH_3 \;+\; CO_2$$
$$\underset{NH_2}{|} \qquad \underset{COOH}{|}$$

L-Glutamyl-L-glutamic acid

Hydrogenative cleavage of the carbobenzoxy derivative is not applicable to peptides containing sulfur, since even combined sulfur poisons the cata-

$$\begin{array}{l} NH_2 \\ | \\ 1. \; SCH_2CHCOOH \\ \;\; | \\ \;\; SCH_2CHCOOH \\ \qquad\quad | \\ \qquad\quad NH_2 \end{array} \xrightarrow{2\,C_6H_5CH_2OCOCl(NaOH)} \begin{array}{l} NHCOOCH_2C_6H_5 \\ | \\ SCH_2CHCOOH \\ | \\ SCH_2CHCOOH \\ \qquad\quad | \\ \qquad\quad NHCOOCH_2C_6H_5 \end{array} \xrightarrow{PCl_5}$$

Cystine

$$[acid\ chloride] \xrightarrow[75\%]{CH_2(NH_2)COOC_2H_5} \begin{array}{l} NHCOOCH_2C_6H_5 \\ | \\ SCH_2CHCO—NHCH_2COOC_2H_5 \\ | \\ SCH_2CHCO—NHCH_2COOC_2H_5 \\ \qquad\quad | \\ \qquad\quad NHCOOCH_2C_6H_5 \end{array} \xrightarrow[95\%]{PH_4I}$$

$$\begin{array}{l} NH_2 \cdot HI \\ | \\ HSCH_2CHCO—NHCH_2COOC_2H_5 \; (+2\,C_6H_5CH_2I) \;+\; ClOCCH_2CH_2CHCOOCH_3 \end{array} \xrightarrow{58\%}$$
Cysteinylglycine ethyl ester $\underset{NHCOOCH_2C_6H_5}{\qquad\qquad\qquad\qquad\qquad |}$
hydroiodide Acid chloride of α-methyl
carbobenzoxyglutamate

$$\begin{array}{l} NHCOOCH_2C_6H_5 \\ | \\ NH—COCH_2CH_2CHCOOCH_3 \\ | \\ HSCH_2CHCO—NHCH_2COOC_2H_5 \end{array} \xrightarrow{90\%}$$

$$HOOCCHCH_2CH_2CO—NHCHCO—NHCH_2COOH \xrightarrow[11\%]{PH_4I}$$
$$\underset{NHCOOCH_2C_6H_5}{|} \qquad \underset{CH_2SH}{|}$$

$$HOOCCHCH_2CH_2CO—NHCHCO—NHCH_2COOH$$
$$\underset{NH_2}{|} \qquad\qquad \underset{CH_2SH}{|}$$

Glutathione

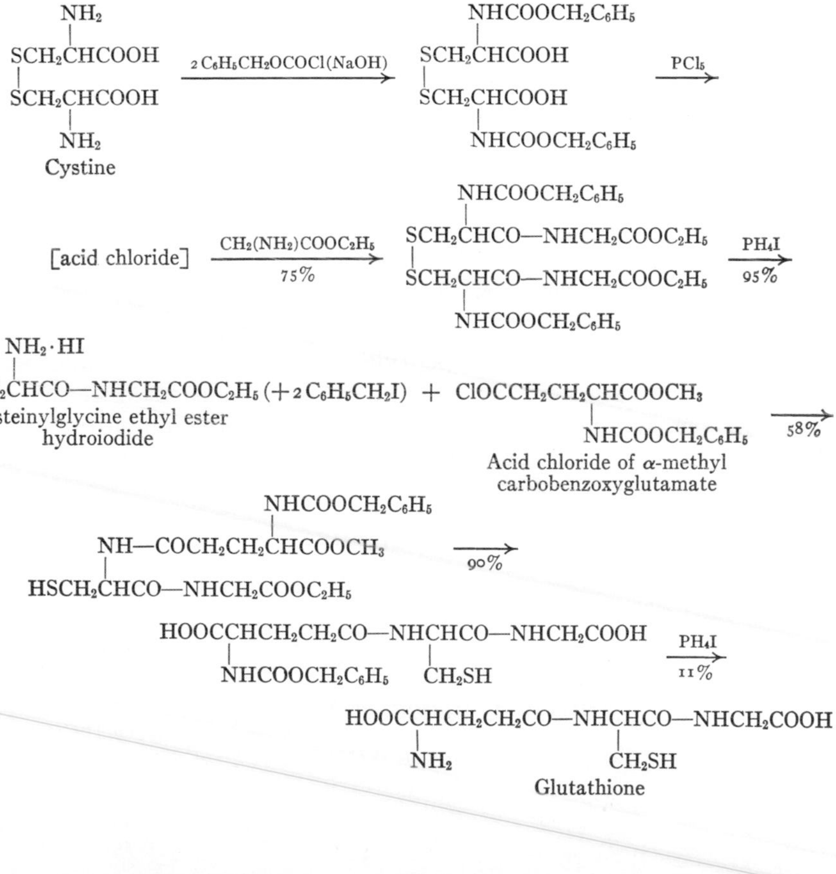

2. 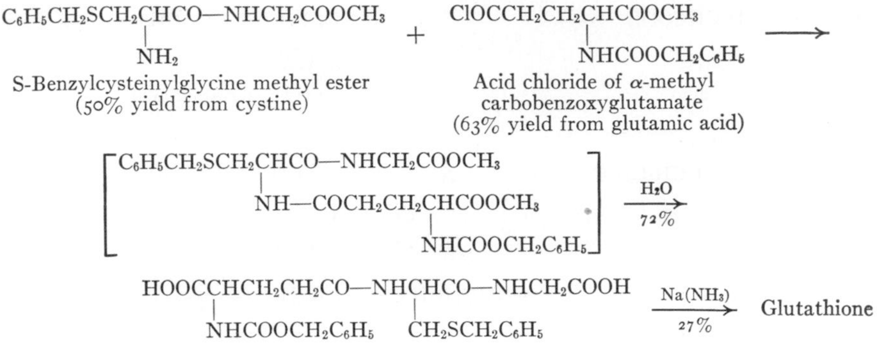 $C_6H_5CH_2SCH_2CHCO—NHCH_2COOCH_3$ + $ClOCCH_2CH_2CHCOOCH_3$ $\longrightarrow$

      | |

    NH_2 $NHCOOCH_2C_6H_5$

S-Benzylcysteinylglycine methyl ester   Acid chloride of α-methyl
(50% yield from cystine)   carbobenzoxyglutamate
                                                                (63% yield from glutamic acid)

$$\begin{bmatrix} C_6H_5CH_2SCH_2CHCO—NHCH_2COOCH_3 \\ \quad\quad | \\ \quad NH—COCH_2CH_2CHCOOCH_3 \\ \quad\quad\quad\quad\quad\quad\quad | \\ \quad\quad\quad\quad\quad\quad NHCOOCH_2C_6H_5 \end{bmatrix} \xrightarrow[72\%]{H_2O}$$

$HOOCCHCH_2CH_2CO—NHCHCO—NHCH_2COOH$ $\xrightarrow[27\%]{Na(NH_3)}$ Glutathione

    | |

$NHCOOCH_2C_6H_5$ $CH_2SCH_2C_6H_5$

lyst. In this case reduction is effected either with phosphonium iodide or metallic sodium in liquid ammonia. Both procedures were used in the synthesis (1935–36) of glutathione, a naturally occurring tripeptide identified as glutamylcysteinylglycine.

By a variation of the carbobenzoxy method peptides can be made containing lysine in which the ε-amino group is free, as it is in natural proteins. The method is illustrated in the following reactions:

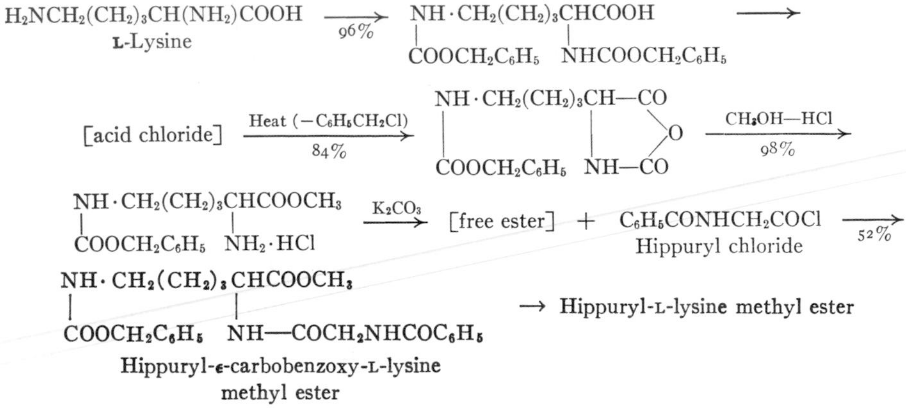

$H_2NCH_2(CH_2)_3CH(NH_2)COOH$ $\xrightarrow{96\%}$ $NH·CH_2(CH_2)_3CHCOOH$ $\longrightarrow$

L-Lysine | |

                                          $COOCH_2C_6H_5$ $NHCOOCH_2C_6H_5$

                                                    $NH·CH_2(CH_2)_3CH—CO$

[acid chloride] $\xrightarrow[84\%]{Heat\,(-C_6H_5CH_2Cl)}$ | | $\rangle O$ $\xrightarrow[98\%]{CH_3OH—HCl}$

                                          $COOCH_2C_6H_5$ $NH—CO$

$NH·CH_2(CH_2)_3CHCOOCH_3$ $\xrightarrow{K_2CO_3}$ [free ester] + $C_6H_5CONHCH_2COCl$ $\xrightarrow{52\%}$

| |

$COOCH_2C_6H_5$ $NH_2·HCl$ Hippuryl chloride

$NH·CH_2(CH_2)_3CHCOOCH_3$

| | $\longrightarrow$ Hippuryl-L-lysine methyl ester

$COOCH_2C_6H_5$ $NH—COCH_2NHCOC_6H_5$

Hippuryl-ε-carbobenzoxy-L-lysine
methyl ester

β-Aspartyl and γ-glutamyl peptides can be prepared by another modification of the carbobenzoxy method, which is illustrated in the simplest form in the synthesis of L-asparagine. From the anhydride of carbobenzoxy-L-aspartic acid or of carbobenzoxy-L-glutamic acid on treatment

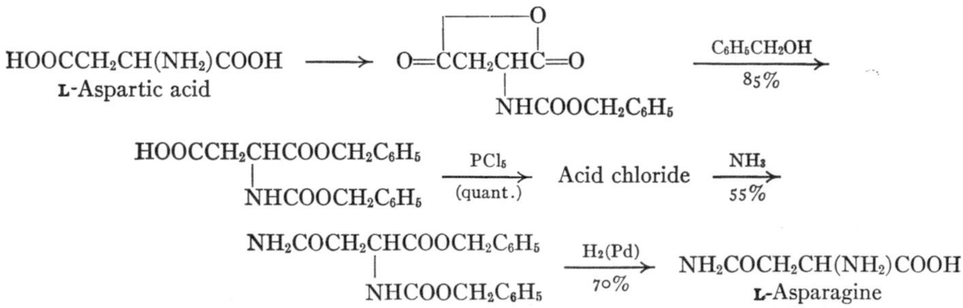

$HOOCCH_2CH(NH_2)COOH$ $\longrightarrow$ $O=CCH_2CHC=O$ $\xrightarrow[85\%]{C_6H_5CH_2OH}$

L-Aspartic acid |

                                          $NHCOOCH_2C_6H_5$

$HOOCCH_2CHCOOCH_2C_6H_5$ $\xrightarrow[(quant.)]{PCl_5}$ Acid chloride $\xrightarrow[55\%]{NH_3}$

            |

$NHCOOCH_2C_6H_5$

$NH_2COCH_2CHCOOCH_2C_6H_5$ $\xrightarrow[70\%]{H_2(Pd)}$ $NH_2COCH_2CH(NH_2)COOH$

            |

$NHCOOCH_2C_6H_5$ L-Asparagine

with benzyl alcohol, only the α-ester is formed; the other carboxyl group is free and available for condensation.

Another method for removal of the carbobenzoxy group involves brief treatment with hydrogen bromide in acetic acid; the hydrobromide of the peptide is formed and can be isolated by precipitation with ether:

$$C_6H_5CH_2OCONHR + HBr + H_2O \rightarrow C_6H_5CH_2OH + CO_2 + BrNH_3R$$

Phthalyl Synthesis. — Of a number of other blocking groups proposed, the phthalyl group has proved particularly useful (Sheehan,[14] 1949; King and Kidd, 1949). The phthalyl derivative is prepared by heating the amino acid with phthalic anhydride, and after the peptide bond is formed treatment with alcoholic hydrazine followed by hydrochloric acid effects cleavage of the protective group as phthalhydrazide and liberates the free amino group (Ing and Manske, 1926). Cleavage of the phthalyl derivative proceeds more readily than the hydrogenolysis of the carbobenzoxy group, which sometimes requires several days. The dipeptide is obtained as the hydrochloride; the free amine can be liberated by passage over a basic ion-exchange resin (p. 870). Glycyl-DL-phenylalanine and glycyl-L-cysteine have been prepared by this method in overall yields of 60–61%. Sheehan has also reported preparation from phthalylglycyl chloride (I) and silver dibenzyl

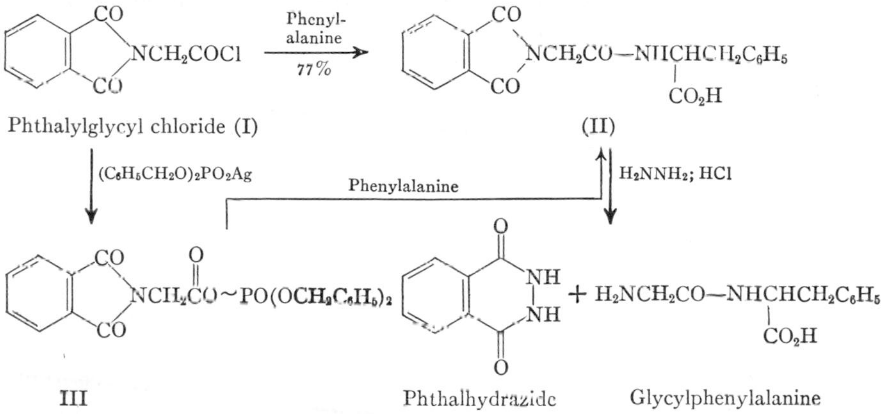

Phthalylglycyl chloride (I) (II)

III Phthalhydrazide Glycylphenylalanine

phosphate of the derivative III (91% yield), which contains an energy-rich phosphate bond (curved line, see p. 478) and in aqueous solution at pH 7.4 acylates phenylalanine to give II in good yield.

Mixed Anhydride Synthesis. — This method was developed in 1950–51 by three independent groups: T. Wieland in Germany, R. A. Boissonnas in Switzerland, and J. R. Vaughan in the United States. The fundamental principle is that the mixed anhydride of a carboxylic acid with an alkyl acid carbonate ($HOCO_2R$) is an efficient reagent for acylation of amines. In the standard procedure the amino group of the amino acid is protected as the carbobenzoxy (Cb) or phthalyl (Ph) derivative, which is treated in an inert

[14] John C. Sheehan, b. 1915, Battle Creek, Mich.; Ph.D. Michigan (Bachmann); Mass. Inst. Techn.

solvent (tetrahydrofuran) with enough base (triethylamine) to form the salt and then with an alkylchlorocarbonate. The mixed anhydride produced need not be isolated, and on addition of an amino acid (usually as ester) carbon dioxide is formed and the N-substituted peptide ester is obtained, usually in excellent yield and optical purity. The ester group is eliminated

$$\underset{\substack{|\\ \text{NHCb}}}{\text{RCHCO}_2\text{H}} \xrightarrow{\text{N(C}_2\text{H}_5)_3} \underset{\substack{|\\ \text{NHCb}}}{\overset{- \quad +}{\text{RCHCO}_2\text{NH(C}_2\text{H}_5)_3}} \xrightarrow[\text{--(C}_2\text{H}_5)_3\overset{+}{\text{NH}}\overset{-}{\text{Cl}}]{\text{ClCO}_2\text{C}_2\text{H}_5}$$

$$\underset{\substack{|\\ \text{NHCb}}}{\text{RCHC}\overset{\text{O}}{\overset{\|}{-}}\text{O}\overset{\text{O}}{\overset{\|}{-}}\text{COC}_2\text{H}_5} \xrightarrow{\text{H}_2\text{NCHR}'\text{CO}_2\text{CH}_3} \underset{\substack{|\\ \text{NHCb}}}{\text{RCHCONHCHR}'\text{CO}_2\text{CH}_3} + \text{CO}_2 + \text{C}_2\text{H}_5\text{OH}$$

by hydrolysis with dilute acid and the blocking group by an appropriate standard procedure. The simplicity and versatility of the method is demonstrated by a synthesis of an octapeptide in which each unit is different.

Pyrophosphite Synthesis. — In the procedures discussed so far the peptide bond is formed by condensation of a reactive derivative of a carboxylic acid with an amino group. In a new method (G. W. Anderson, 1952) direct condensation of the free carboxylic acid itself with an amino group is effected by use of tetraethylpyrophosphite.

$$\underset{\substack{|\\ \text{NHCO}_2\text{CH}_2\text{C}_6\text{H}_5}}{\text{RCHCO}_2\text{H}} + \underset{\substack{|\\ \text{R}'}}{\text{H}_2\text{NCHCO}_2\text{C}_2\text{H}_5} + (\text{C}_2\text{H}_5\text{O})_2\text{P}\cdot\text{O}\cdot\text{P}(\text{OC}_2\text{H}_5)_2 \rightarrow$$

$$\underset{\substack{|\\ \text{C}_6\text{H}_5\text{CH}_2\text{OCONH}}}{\text{RCHCONHCHCO}_2\text{C}_2\text{H}_5}\underset{\substack{|\\ \text{R}'}}{} + 2(\text{C}_2\text{H}_5\text{O})_2\text{POH}$$

PEPTIDES

End-Group Analysis. — An important advance is protein chemistry was the development of methods for determination of the amino acid sequence in a polypeptide chain. The methods involve reactions of the free amino group in one terminal unit or of the carboxyl group at the other end of the chain. Sanger[15] (1945) introduced use of 2,4-dinitrofluorobenzene as a reagent for labeling a terminal amino group (as well as the ϵ-amino groups of lysine residues). Condensation occurs under mild conditions to form a 2,4-dinitrophenyl protein; on acid hydrolysis the terminal amino acid is

$$2,4\text{-(NO}_2)_2\text{C}_6\text{H}_3\text{F} + \text{H}_2\text{NCHRCO—protein} \rightarrow 2,4\text{-(NO}_2)_2\text{C}_6\text{H}_3\text{NHCHRCO—protein}$$

$$\xrightarrow{\text{HCl}} 2,4\text{-(NO}_2)_2\text{C}_6\text{H}_3\text{NHCHRCO}_2\text{H} + \text{Amino acids}$$

liberated as the bright yellow 2,4-dinitrophenyl derivative, which is easily separated from the accompanying amino acid mixture and which can be identified by paper chromatography. The phenolic group of tyrosine and

---

[15] Frederick Sanger, b. 1918, Gloucestershire, England; Ph.D. Cambridge; Cambridge Univ.

the imino group of histidine also react with the reagent, but the derivatives Known acid constituents of cerebrosides are: lignoceric acid, α-hydroxy-labeled terminal peptide fragment whose structure can then be deduced by further degradation to the component amino acids. For determination of the sequence within the chain, the protein is subjected to partial hydrolysis to give a mixture of di and tripeptides, whose structures can be investigated by end group analysis. If all possible dipeptides in the hydrolyzate can be characterized, a unique solution can be established for the sequence in the protein. Sanger applied the method to insulin, one of the smallest protein molecules (mol. wt. 12,000) and deduced a complete structure, which conforms reasonably well with the gross requirements of the amino acid analysis of the protein (Table 16.3).

A second method of end-group analysis introduced by P. Edman (Sweden) in 1950 involves selective elimination of the terminal unit containing a free amino group. Reaction of this group with phenylisothiocyanate (a) gives the phenylthiocarbamyl derivative (b), which is cleaved by hydrogen chloride to a phenylthiohydantoin (c). Finally, alkaline hydrolysis of (c) affords the free amino acid (d). In the few cases in which peptides have

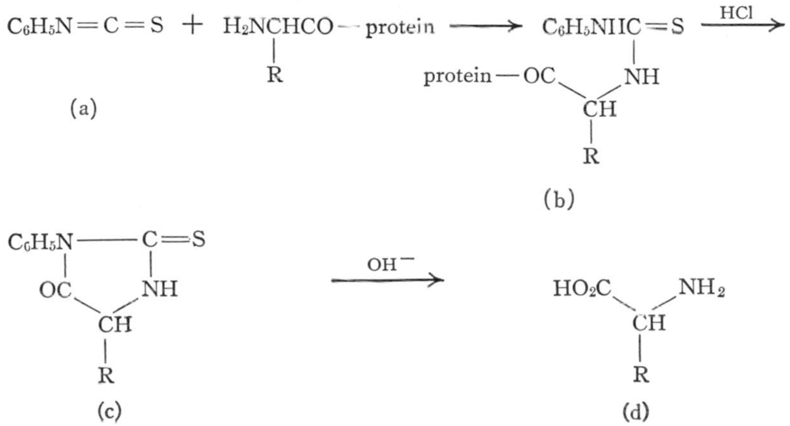

$$C_6H_5N{=}C{=}S \;+\; H_2NCHCO{-}protein \longrightarrow C_6H_5NHC{=}S \xrightarrow{HCl}$$

(a)

(b)

(c)

(d)

been analyzed by both the Sanger and the Edman method, the same sequence has been deduced.

Procedures for labeling the terminal carboxyl group by reduction to the amino alcohol have been reported but not extensively applied.

Peptide Hormones. — Peptides, arbitrarily defined as protein-like substances of molecular weight less than 10,000, are considerably more stable than proteins and are not subject to denaturation. A few have been known for some time, for example, glutathione, which occurs in nearly all living cells. This tripeptide is γ-L-glutamyl-L-cysteinylglycine (synthesis, p. 443), a structure that can be represented with the conventional abbrevations as γ-L-Glu-L-CySH-Gly. With improvement in techniques of isolation, many new natural peptides have been discovered. The hormones oxytocin and vasopressin isolated from the posterior pituitary gland have been charac-

terized as relatively simple peptides.   The former is involved in contraction
of the uterus, the latter is the pressor principle of the gland.   Oxytocin was
recognized as a chemical entity in 1906, and in 1952 it was obtained in
relatively pure form by counter-current distribution.   Analysis of the
hydrolyzate indicated the presence of eight amino acids in equimolecular
ratio, and the amount of ammonia liberated on hydrolysis showed that three
of the units are present as acid amides.   Cystine was one of the acids isolated from the hydrolyzate, and the manner in which it is bound in the peptide was established by the observation that oxidation of oxytocin with
performic acid cleaves an —S·S— group to form two sulfonic acid groups
without significant change in molecular weight.   The peptide molecule,
therefore, contains a cyclic system that includes the disulfide link of cystine.
This component is represented in the hydrolyzate of oxidized oxytocin as
two molecules of cysteic acid, $HO_3SCH_2CH(NH_2)CO_2H$ (symbol, Cysteic).

From the mixtures formed on partial hydrolysis of oxytocin and its oxidation product nine smaller peptides were isolated and characterized as to
the component units.   Where the amino acid sequence is known, as in the
case of glutathione, the symbols for the components are conventionally
separated by a hyphen or a period; use of a comma signifies that the order is
not known, which was the case for all but one (II) of the fragments from
oxytocin and oxidized oxytocin, which were as follows:

I	Cysteic, Asp, Glu	IV	Cysteic, Pro, Leu	VII	Tyr, CyS·SCy, Asp, Glu
II	Asp-Cysteic	V	Cysteic, Pro, Leu, Gly	VIII	CyS·SCy, Asp, Glu
III	Cysteic, Pro	VI	Leu, Gly, Pro	IX	Tyr, CyS·SCy, Asp, Glu, Leu, Ileu

From the overlapping constituents of peptides I to V a probable sequence
for a part of the molecule can be deduced to be: Glu-Asp-Cysteic-Pro-Leu-
Gly.   Fragment VI fits into the terminal part of this sequence.   Peptide
VII shows that this sequence is linked through cystine to tyrosine, thus:

$$
\begin{array}{c}
\text{Tyr-CyS} \\
| \\
\text{Glu-Asp-CyS-Pro-Leu-Gly}
\end{array}
$$

Finally, the position of isoleucine, the eighth amino acid unit, was established
by an Edman degradation of oxidized oxytocin, which indicated the sequence
Cysteic-Tyr-Ileu-Glu.   Hence the complete amino acid sequence is:

$$
\begin{array}{c}
\text{Ileu-Tyr-CyS} \\
| \qquad | \\
\text{Glu-Asp-CyS-Pro-Leu-Gly}
\end{array}
$$

Since the only places available for the three amide groups are in the aspartic
acid, glutamic acid, and terminal glycine units, the complete structure is
that shown in the formula (du Vigneaud;[16] Tuppy, 1953).

---

[16] Vincent du Vigneaud, b. 1901, Chicago; Ph.D. Rochester (Murlin); Cornell Med. Coll.;
Nobel Prize 1955

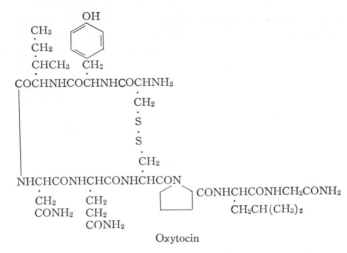

CH₃
CH₂
CHCH₃ CH₂
COCHNHCOCHNHCOCHNH₂
CH₂
S
S
CH₂
NHCHCONHCHCONHCHCON
CH₂ CH₂ CONHCHCONHCH₂CONH₂
CONH₂ CH₂ CH₂CH(CH₃)₂
CONH₂

Oxytocin

The structure was confirmed by a synthesis (du Vigneaud, 1954) involving coupling the N-carbobenzoxy-S-benzyl dipeptide I with the heptapeptide triamide II by means of tetraethylpyrophosphite. On removal of the car-

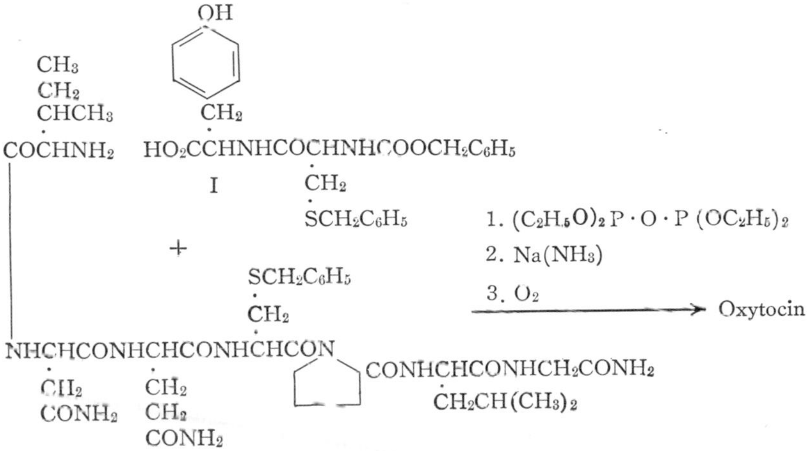

bobenzoxy and benzyl groups protecting respectively the α-amino group of one cysteine unit and the sulfhydryl groups of both units, the dithiol derivative was produced and this on air oxidation was cyclized to oxytocin.

The pressor principle vasopressin differs from oxytocin only in that phenylalanine replaces isoleucine and lysine replaces leucine.

┌────────Phe-Tyr-CyS
│   │
Glu(NH₂)-Asp(NH₂)-CyS-Pro-Lys-Gly(NH₂)

Vasopressin

Peptides of Unusual Acid Components. — A variety of polypeptides isolated from bacteria and lower plants are characterized by the presence of an unusual amino acid as one or more of the constituents (Table 16.2), the D-isomer of one of the common amino acids, or a component which is not an amino acid. A peptide found in the capsules of *Bacillus anthracis* and *B. subtilis* appears to be composed solely of D-glutamic acid. Unlike other peptides containing this acid, the peptide bonds are formed mainly through the γ-amino groups (Kovǎcs, 1953).

Several closely related peptides possessing antibiotic properties have been isolated from a strain of soil microorganism, *Bacillus brevis* (Dubos, 1940). They fall into two groups, the tyrocidines and the gramicidins, individual members of which have been isolated in relatively pure form by countercurrent distribution. The most extensively investigated member is gramicidin-S (S = Soviet; the substance was first described by Russian scientists), a cyclic decapeptide of the structure; cyclo-(L-Val-L-Orn-L-Leu-D-Phe-L-Pro)$_2$.

Bacitracin-A, isolated from *B. subtilis*, appears to be a cyclic hexapeptide with two side chains, and the probable structure is that shown in the formulation (Craig,[17] 1954). Ornithine is the only uncommon amino acid. Sub-

Ileu-CySH-Leu-Glu-Ileu-Lys-Orn-Ileu
| |
Asp-Asp-His-Phe

Bacitracin-A

tilin, another polypeptide from the same organism, is unusual in that it contains lanthionine (Table 16.2) and another sulfur-containing diamino-dicarboxylic acid of unknown structure. Polymixins A–E have been isolated from various strains of *Bacillus polymyxa*. They all contain two unusual acids, L-α,γ-diaminobutyric acid and 6-methyloctanoic acid, and differ in the nature of the common amino acid residues.

PROTEINS

Denaturation. — A serious difficulty in the investigation of proteins is that most of them are extremely prone to undergo some form of alteration, described as denaturation. Almost all proteins (gelatin is an exception) are sensitive to heat, and the temperature coefficient of the reaction is remarkably high. Similar changes occur on treatment with acid or alkali, alcohol, acetone, urea, potassium iodide, trichloroacetic acid, tungstic acid, sulfosalicylic acid, ultraviolet light or X-rays, or even as the result of shaking or application of high pressure. The resultant changes are at least qualitatively if not entirely similar.

A denatured protein is always less soluble than the native form; any physiological activity originally associated with the substance is lost. Probably the ability to exist in crystalline form is lost, since no denatured

---

[17] Lyman C. Craig, b. 1906, Palmyra, Iowa; Ph.D. Iowa State Coll. (Hixon); Rockefeller Inst.

protein has been crystallized. In many cases an increase in sulfhydryl groups accompanies the change. The molecular weight is sometimes but not always affected. The hemocyanin of *Helix pomatia* shows a molecular weight at the isoelectric point of 6,740,000, but dissociates with change in pH into fragments that are progressively one half, one eighth, and one sixteenth the size of the original protein. The same effect has been observed on treatment with urea; for instance, hemoglobin is split into halves that are apparently identical, edestin into fourths. There are some indications that the number of acidic or basic groups is reduced upon denaturation, probably owing to intramolecular reaction.

Denaturation is a property unique to proteins and is not shown by polypeptides or any other known macromolecules. Proteins vary widely in sensitivity; insulin, for example, is notable in its resistance to denaturation. Some proteins can revert more or less to the native form after removal of the denaturing agent.

Isolation and Purification. — Since most proteins are highly sensitive and occur as mixtures of closely related substances, isolation of homogeneous individual components in native form presents considerable difficulty. Since the solubility is usually at a minimum at the isoelectric point, adjustment of the pH to a particular value may favor separation of one component of the mixture and retention of the others when either a salt or a water-miscible organic solvent such as ethanol is added in controlled amount. A method favored for slow addition of ammonium sulfate for isoelectric salting out of a protein is to rotate a cellophane bag of solid ammonium sulfate in the buffered protein solution; the electrolyte diffuses through the membrane and eventually causes precipitation of protein. If the precipitate, consisting of protein contaminated with the salt, is put in a bag and dialyzed against distilled water the ammonium sulfate is eliminated and the protein dissolves and can then be reprecipitated as before. Crystallization of proteins has been effected by suitable repetition of the process. An alternate method of effecting precipitation, and sometimes crystallization, is adjustment to the isoelectric point, addition of ethanol, and refrigeration.

Proteins purified by repeated precipitation or crystallization have been found to be not fully homogeneous when examined by the ultracentrifuge technique described below (p. 452) or by the method of electrophoresis (Tiselius,[18] 1937). In an electric field, proteins move at a rate determined by the size and shape of the molecule and by the number and kind of ionized groups. Material that appears homogeneous by the criterion of solubility may contain components that differ in rate of electrophoretic travel. The techniques of ultracentrifugation and electrophoresis unfortunately are not applicable on a preparative scale. Methods of countercurrent distribution and chromatography seem to offer particular promise in selectivity for at least small-scale purification.

Molecular Weights. — The osmotic pressure method for determination

---

[18] Arne Tiselius, b. 1902, Stockholm; Uppsala; Nobel Prize 1948

of the mean molecular weights of proteins has been largely supplanted by
the ultracentrifuge method of Svedberg. When a protein solution contained in a small cell is spun at very high speeds, the protein moves to the
outer edge because of the centrifugal force, to an extent dependent upon
its molecular weight. Observations and photographs are made while the
centrifuge is in operation through use of special optical systems. The
molecular weight can be determined either from the sedimentation equilibrium or from the rate of sedimentation; although theoretically the first
method is sounder, an excessive amount of time is required to establish
equilibrium, and values obtained from the velocity determinations are considered more reliable. The error is probably 3–5% for medium-sized
proteins, but is likely to be more for smaller molecules. By use of the
ultracentrifuge it is also possible to tell whether the molecules are all the
same size and shape. In a few special cases, accurate minimal molecular
weights have been established by analytical determination of one constituent; the most outstanding example is the case of the iron content of the
various hemoglobins (p. 455).

TABLE 16.4. MOLECULAR WEIGHTS OF CERTAIN PROTEINS

PROTEIN	EQUILIBRIUM CENTRIFUGE	SEDIMENTATION DIFFUSION	OSMOTIC PRESSURE
Pepsin	39,000	35,500	36,000
Lactoglobulin	38,000	41,500	
Insulin		46,000	
Egg albumin	40,500	44,000	43,000–46,000
Serum albumin (horse)	68,000	70,000	73,000
Hemoglobin	68,000	63,000	67,000
Edestin		310,000	
Bushy stunt virus	7,600,000		
Tobacco mosaic virus		40,000,000	

Reactive Groups. — Proteins react with both acids and bases and are
characteristic amphoteric substances. In neutral solution both the basic
and carboxyl groups are generally charged, corresponding to the dipolar
ions of amino acids. At the isoelectric point dissociation as an acid is equal
to that as a base, solubility is at a minimum, and rate of migration in an

TABLE 16.5. ISOELECTRIC POINTS OF VARIOUS PROTEINS (pH UNITS)

Casein	4.6
Egg albumin	4.84–4.90
Silk fibroin	2.0–2.4
Serum globulin	5.4–5.5
Gelatin	4.80–4.85
Insulin	5.30–5.35
Lactoglobulin	4.5–5.5
Hemoglobin	6.79–6.83
Serum albumin	4.88

electric field is at a minimum. Table 16.5 shows that proteins vary considerably in the pH of isoelectricity.

The amount of acid bound has been correlated satisfactorily with the basic amino acid content. With the exception of the few terminal α-amino groups, the ϵ-amino (lysine), imidazole (histidine), and guanidyl (arginine) groups are responsible for the acid-combining capacity. The guanidyl group is more basic than the ϵ-amino group, which in turn is more basic than the imidazole group, as shown by comparison of the negative loga-

$$
\begin{array}{cc}
\underset{\substack{| \quad | \\ CH\!=\!CH}}{\overset{\displaystyle CH}{\underset{\displaystyle N \diagup \diagdown NH}{}}} & \underset{\displaystyle H_2NCNH_2}{\overset{\displaystyle NH}{\overset{\displaystyle \|}{}}} \\
\text{Imidazole} & \text{Guanidine}
\end{array}
$$

rithms of the acidity constants, pK, in Table 16.6. The amount of base bound depends on the content of dicarboxylic acids and of tyrosine, which is

TABLE 16.6. IONIZING GROUPS OF PROTEINS

GROUP	AMINO ACID	pK
α-Carboxyl	(terminal group of molecule)	3
Carboxyl	{ Aspartic acid / Glutamic acid	4
Imidazole	Histidine	6–7 :
α-Amino	(terminal group of molecule)	7.5–8.5
Phenolic hydroxyl	Tyrosine	10
Sulfhydryl	Cysteine	9–11
ϵ-Amino	Lysine	9–11
Guanidine	Arginine	12–13

a weak acid. Values of the amino acid content derived from titration curves of proteins are reasonably close to values derived from ordinary analysis.

Fibrous Proteins (Insoluble). — This group includes fibroin (silk), collagen (connective tissue), and keratin (skin, hair, wool, horn, feathers, nails) They are all insoluble in water, but collagen on being boiled with water is converted into water-soluble gelatin. Fibroin and keratin are resistant to hydrolysis by water or by enzymes.

X-ray diffraction analysis (Meyer and Mark,[10] 1928) of fibroin reveals an identity period along the fiber axis apparently corresponding to recurring pairs of amino acids of analogous type. The protein is made up largely of four neutral amino acids, two with hydroxyl groups and two without, and an identity period of 7 Å may be due to a pair such as that formulated. The length of one amino acid unit is then half this amount, or 3.5 Å. The keratins of hair and wool possess elastic properties, believed from X-ray evidence to be because in the unstretched protein the polypeptide chain is folded over onto itself. Stretching unfolds the loops and gives a chain of amino acid units of identity period 3.3 Å, comparable to fibroin. Keratin

[10] Herman Mark, b. 1895, Vienna; Ph.D. Vienna; Polytechn. Inst. Brooklyn

is rich in cystine, which probably provides disulfide cross links between peptide chains. Wool can be modified and hair curled by reduction with

$$
\begin{array}{ccccccc}
H & O & CH_2OH & H & O \\
| & \| & | & | & \| \\
N & C & CH & N & C \\
& CH & N & C & CH \\
& | & | & \| & | \\
& CH_3 & H & O & CH_3 \\
\end{array}
$$

$\longleftarrow$ 7Å $\longrightarrow$

Fibroin (?)

a mercaptan to break some of the cross links, and reoxidation to produce different cross links. Collagen has an unusually high content of proline and hydroxyproline. The identity period of only 2.9 Å suggests that the chain is distorted in some way. The structure is believed to be maintained by hydrogen bonding between NH and CO groups in adjacent chains, which are disrupted on conversion to water-soluble gelatin.

Globular Proteins (Soluble). — Proteins of this general classification are much more numerous than fibrous proteins; subclassification according to solubility has already been mentioned. They are spherical in shape and seem to contain cross links formed by interactions between side chains. Some globular proteins containing an active prosthetic group are enzymes. Some, known as glucoproteins, contain a carbohydrate component. Hemoglobin is a protein conjugated with a ferroporphyrin. Lipoproteins are particularly complex. Those of the blood are comprised of protein, phospholipid, cholesterol, and varying amounts of neutral fat (glycerides) and may serve for transport of fat. Myelin, a structural unit of nervous tissue, is a combination of protein, phospholipid, and cholesterol.

Plasma Proteins. — Blood plasma, drawn with prevention of clotting as already described, is a transparent yellow (carotenoids) fluid containing about 7% of protein. Early methods of separation of the components depended mainly upon fractional precipitation with ammonium or sodium sulfate and with alcohol at a low temperature. Thus fibrinogen, the protein involved in clotting by virtue of its transformation into insoluble threads of fibrin that entangle the red cells, is obtained fairly readily by salting-out techniques. Later Tiselius (1937) introduced electrophoretic analysis, which afforded four main protein fractions designated as albumin and as α-, β-, and γ-globulin. When the technique was refined further it became clear that these fractions are not individual proteins but groups of proteins having similar rates of migration. Electrophoretic separation suffers from the disadvantage that it is not suitable for large-scale work. Further advances made during World War II by Cohn and Edsall (Harvard Medical School) were prompted by the demand for large quantities of plasma preparations suitable for treatment of shock. Since the effect is due to maintenance of osmotic pressure by the serum proteins and since whole plasma contains proteolytic enzymes that eventually cause extensive degradation, the preparation of stable, solid protein fractions offers many advantages. The method developed at Harvard involves fractional precipitation with alcohol at low temperature and with suitable variation of the pH, and takes advantage of the marked influence of extremely low concentrations of salts on the solubility of proteins.   In this manner five principal fractions are obtained, which are by no means homogeneous but which are suitable for clinical purposes and for further fractionation into individual components. One fraction consists mainly of albumin and is particularly effective against shock.   Another fraction contains the γ-globulins, which include a large number of antibodies.   These are proteins formed in the animal organism in response to the introduction of foreign proteins (antigens), for example those of various pathogenic organisms.   This fraction has clinical use in providing temporary passive immunization to various diseases.   About ten globulins, belonging to all three types, have been obtained as individual components.   Two are lipoproteins, one containing 75% lipid.

Hemoglobin. — The solid content of the red blood corpuscles of mammals contains on the average 32% of the chromoprotein hemoglobin, the first protein to be obtained crystalline.   The red corpuscles are separated from the lighter plasma by centrifugation; the plasma is siphoned, and on addition of ether to the residual corpuscular cream the cells burst (hemolysis).   After another centrifugation to remove the ruptured cell envelopes, a clear red solution of the protein is obtained.   Crystallization of the protein in the oxygenated form (oxyhemoglobin) is accomplished by adding alcohol and cooling to $-20°$, by treating a cold solution with carbon dioxide and oxygen, or by electrodialysis.   Values for the percentage composition vary slightly for different animal species; a typical empirical formula is as follows: $(C_{738}H_{1166}O_{208}N_{203}S_2Fe)_n$.   Minimal molecular weights of 16,500–17,000 are indicated on this basis.   Since the ultracentrifuge values are four times this value, n evidently has a value of four.

On careful hydrolysis with hydrochloric acid the protein is cleaved in two fragments: hemin (4%) and globin (96%).   Hemoglobin is then a conjugated protein; it is made up of the protein globin linked to a prosthetic group, which contains the iron.   The chlorine atom of hemin is derived from

Hemin

the acid used to effect hydrolysis; hemin has the formula $C_{34}H_{32}O_4N_4FeCl$, and is a chloride derived from the parent compound heme, $C_{34}H_{32}O_4N_4FeOH$. Although far simpler than the original protein, the hemin molecule presents a structure that is both unusual and elaborate, as can be seen from the formula, and the problem of elucidating the structure was solved eventually only as the result of exhaustive researches extending over a period of forty years (Nencki, Piloty, Küster, Willstätter,[20] H. Fischer[21]).

The four heterocyclic five-membered rings of hemin are pyrrole nuclei; they are substituted with methyl, vinyl, and propionic acid groups and are bridged by unsaturated carbons constituting methene groups. The iron is considered to be bound to all four nitrogens, by either primary valences or coordinated links. Hemin (hemin chloride) on hydrolysis with dilute alkali affords the halogen-free hydroxide heme (hemin hydroxide). Methods are available for removal and re-introduction of the iron; iron-free substances having the characteristic system of four linked pyrrole rings are known as porphyrins and iron-containing derivatives as hemes. A key substance is etioporphyrin ($C_{32}H_{38}N_4$), obtained by degradation of hemin involving

Etioporphyrin

elimination of iron, decarboxylation, and reduction of the vinyl groups; it is a tetramethyltetraethylporphyrin. Isolation of the same etioporphyrin as a degradation product of the green plant pigment chlorophyll establishes a close structural relationship between the leaf and blood pigments.

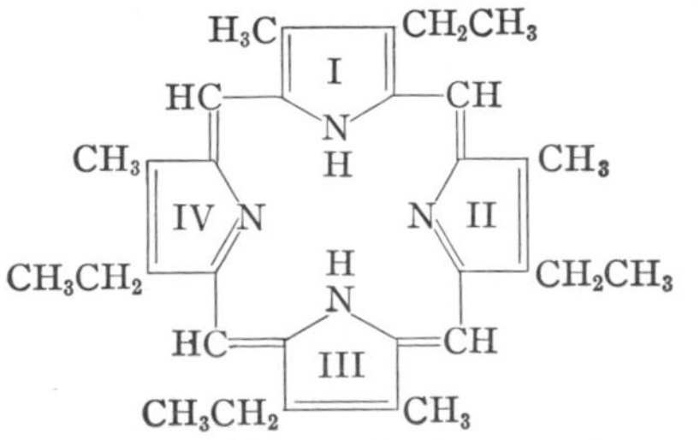

The first insight into the porphyrin structure resulted from development of degradative methods by which hemin could be broken into mixtures of smaller fragments that could be isolated and characterized. Thus drastic

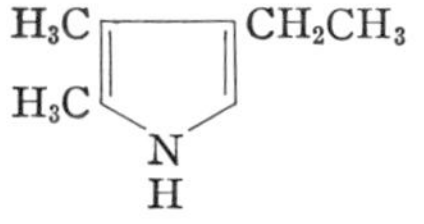

Hemopyrrole
(2,3-dimethyl-4-ethylpyrrole)

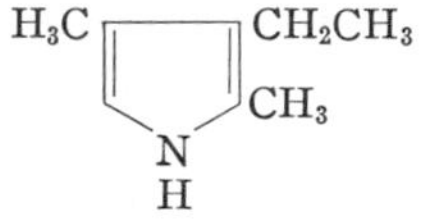

Cryptopyrrole
(2,4-dimethyl-3-ethylpyrrole)

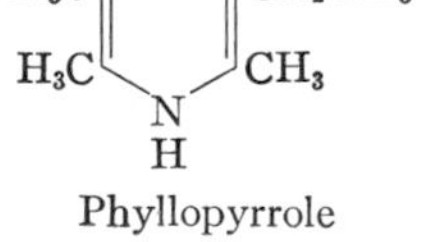

Phyllopyrrole

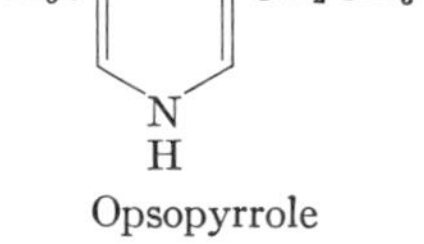

Opsopyrrole

[20] Richard Willstätter, 1872–1942; Ph.D. Munich (Einhorn); Zurich, Berlin, Munich; Nobel Prize 1930; J. Chem. Soc., 999 (1953)

[21] Hans Fischer, 1881–1945; b. Höchst/Main; Ph.D. Marburg (Zincke), M. D. Munich; Techn. Hochsch. Munich; Nobel Prize 1930

reduction with hydrogen iodide and red phosphorus gives a mixture of four pyrroles variously substituted with methyl and ethyl groups as shown in

$$H_3CC = CCH_2CH_2COOH$$

the formulas. Oxidative degradation also proved of value in providing the further fragment hematinic acid, a maleic imide derivative carrying a methyl and a propionic acid group as substituents, which corresponds to the arrangement in two of the four original rings. Structures of the various fragments not only provided information concerning the substituents but gave a basis for the formulation of a working hypothesis concerning the character of the porphyrin system, and eventually it became feasible to approach the problem from the synthetic route. Attempts to link pyrrole nuclei together by synthesis derived assistance from the fact that porphyrins exhibit very characteristic line spectra observable with a simple visual instrument, and synthetic experiments initiated by Hans Fischer were rewarded with the discovery that the combination of four pyrrole rings, condensed with bridging methine groups to form a system of conjugated double bonds of no less than eighteen atoms, possesses such remarkable stability that it is formed, if in low yield, in unusual reactions consisting in

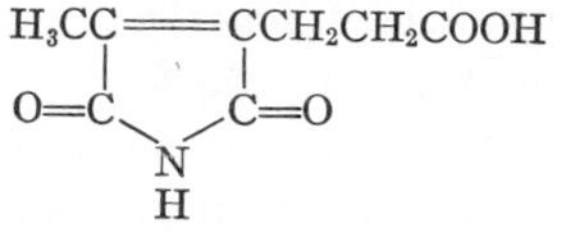

4,5,3',5'-Tetramethyl-
pyrro-2,2'-methene
hydrobromide

Fusion in
succinic acid,
180–190°
1.5%

Deuteroporphyrin

5,5'-Dibromo-3,3'-di β-carboxyethyl-
4,4'-dimethylpyrro-2,2'-methene
hydrobromide

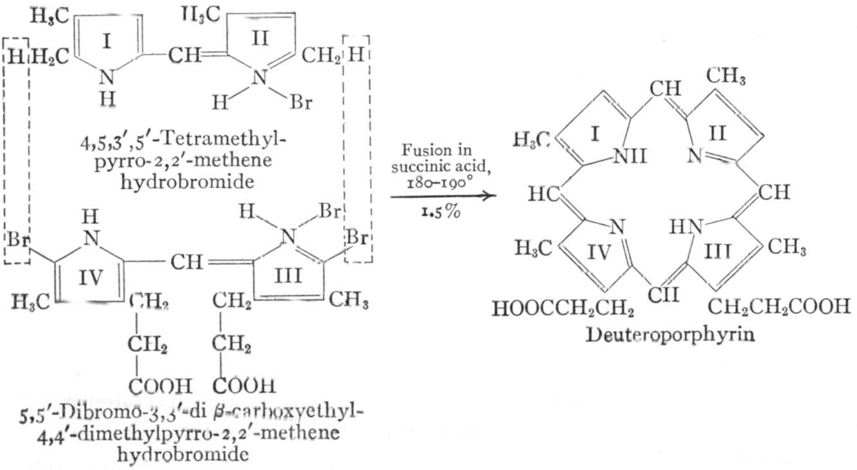

condensation of even approximate moieties of the final molecule. Fischer achieved the synthesis of deuteroporphyrin in 1928 by the fusion of the two pyrromethene bases shown in the formulas. Elimination of two molecules of hydrogen bromide links the two parts by methylene bridges and must produce initially a dihydroporphyrin structure, but the tendency to form the unsaturated porphyrin structure evidently is so great that two hydrogen atoms are eliminated during the condensation.

Fischer's further researches were eminently successful and culminated in 1930 in synthesis of hemin itself. The two free nuclear positions in deuteroporphyrin were substituted with acetyl groups by the action of acetic anhydride and stannic chloride, and the new substituents were transformed into vinyl groups by the sequence of reactions: $—COCH_3 \rightarrow —CH(OH)CH_3 \rightarrow —CH{=}CH_2$. Introduction of iron afforded hemin.

Hemoglobin plays an important role in the organism, since it transports oxygen from the lungs to the tissues, and this function is associated with the iron-containing part of the conjugate. One gram of hemoglobin combines with 1.35 ml. of oxygen (0°, 760 mm.), which corresponds to a ratio of one atom of iron to one molecule of oxygen. The position of equilibrium is

$$\text{Hemoglobin} + 4O_2 \rightleftharpoons \text{Oxyhemoglobin}$$

affected by the partial pressure of oxygen, and in the tissues serviced by arterial blood, where the partial pressure is lower, oxyhemoglobin dissociates into hemoglobin and oxygen. Carbon monoxide is a poison because it combines readily with hemoglobin to form an addition compound more stable than oxyhemoglobin and prevents the protein from exerting its normal function of transporting oxygen. Chemical oxidizing agents convert hemoglobin (ferrohemoglobin) into the brownish-red substance methemoglobin (ferrihemoglobin), which cannot act as an oxygen carrier.

Globin, the protein to which the functional heme group is attached, belongs to the histone group of proteins, for it is soluble in dilute acid solutions (isoelectric point, pH 7.5). About one fifth of the molecule consists of basic amino acids, of which lysine predominates; in most histones the preponderant constituent is arginine. The amino acid analysis of horse globin is shown in Table 16.3 (p. 430). The sulfur content (cystine) of the globins varies widely: horse hemoglobin, 0.39%; cat hemoglobin, 0.62%; fowl hemoglobin, 0.86%.

PROTEIN HORMONES

Insulin. — This hormone secreted by the pancreas is required for normal metabolism of carbohydrates; deficiency of the substance leads to the disease diabetes mellitus, characterized by increased blood glucose, excretion of sugar and acetone bodies in the urine, and depletion of glycogen normally stored in liver and muscle. A procedure for preparation of concentrated active extracts suitable for treatment of diabetic patients was developed in 1921 by Banting[22] and Macleod[23] by use of special techniques to protect the hormone from destruction by enzymes present in the gland. Crystalline insulin was isolated in 1926 by Abel by isoelectric precipitation and found to contain 0.52% zinc.

In very dilute solution at pH 2–3, insulin has the relatively low molecular weight of 12,000. Aggregation occurs at higher concentration (0.9%) and higher pH (7), and the maximal molecular weight is 48,000. The hormone has a high content of sulfur-containing amino acids (Table 16.3), but

---

[22] Sir Frederick G. Banting, 1891–1941; Univ. Toronto; Nobel Prize 1923
[23] John J. R. Macleod, 1877–1935; Univ. Toronto, Aberdeen; Nobel Prize 1923

is nearly matched in this respect by the entirely different fibrous protein keratin. The sulfur is present as cystine units, and when the disulfide linkages are broken by oxidation with performic acid the molecule is cleaved to four peptide chains, two (A) having glycyl end groups and two (B) having phenylalanyl end groups. By the procedure already described (p. 446), Sanger worked out the amino acid sequence of both chains.

Insulin is denatured, and consequently inactivated, by treatment with alkali. The physiological activity is largely lost on acetylation and is partially restored on hydrolysis. If only the amino groups are acetylated (ketene), no appreciable decrease in activity is observed; thus the phenolic hydroxyl groups are an important factor. Insulin loses its activity on reduction of the disulfide linkages by hydrogen sulfide, cysteine, thioglycolic acid; approximately half of the activity is lost when only one or two disulfide groups have been reduced, and the only detectable chemical difference is the appearance of a few sulfhydryl groups. The activity is not restored on oxidation by the usual methods, and this observation is explained on the following basis:

$$RS \cdot SR' \xrightarrow{\text{H}_2} RSH + HSR' \xrightarrow{\text{O}_2} RS \cdot SR + R'S \cdot SR'$$

Thyroglobulin. — The hormone of the thyroid gland, thyroglobulin, is a protein whose primary function is to increase the rate of metabolism (calorigenic action) The syndrome resulting from thyroglobulin deficiency is known as myxedema and is characterized by dry skin and swollen connective tissues. Dramatic cures are obtained on administration of the hormone. Congenital hypofunction results in cretinism (a specific mental deficiency), which can also be cured by the hormone if treatment is started early in life. The presence of iodine was detected in the thyroid gland in 1896, and at about this time an almost inactive iodine-containing amino acid, diiodotyrosine, was isolated from the coral *Gorgonia cavolini*. The successful isolation from the thyroid gland of the active substance thyroxine, which contains iodine, was accomplished in 1915 by Kendall. The synthesis was achieved in 1927 by Harington, who had proposed the correct formula the previous year. This amino acid accounts for about half the iodine content of the gland; the remainder is present as diiodotyrosine. Thyroxine is about 10,000 times as potent as diiodotyrosine, and on the basis of the iodine content, is as active as thyroglobulin. Probably the organism is able to effect conjugation of thyroxine with a specific protein. In certain instances the gland enlarges (goiter), evidently in order to elaborate sufficient hormone, since the basal metabolism rate is normal. Administration of iodides for prevention of simple goiter is effective, and this fact, coupled with the close relationship among thyroxine and diiodotyrosine and tyrosine, indicates that the body probably synthesizes thyroxine from these latter substances.

Substances known as goitrogens interfere with the synthesis of thyroid hormone. Thiouracil and some of its derivatives are particularly effective,

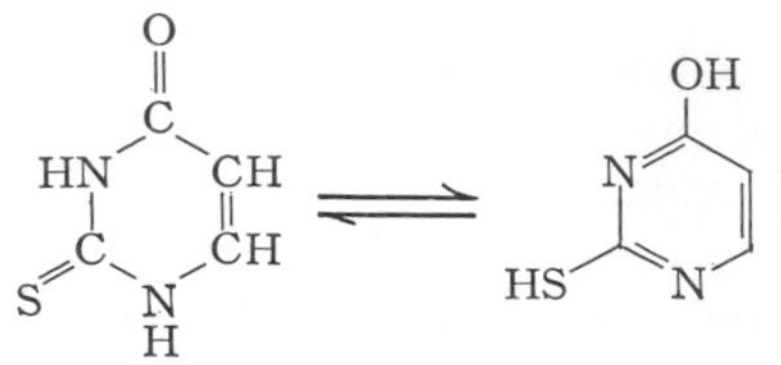

Thiouracil

but other compounds containing the grouping —NHC(=S)NH— are active. The substances have clinical use in the treatment of hyperthyroidism.

Hormones of the Anterior Pituitary Lobe. — Purified hormones of the posterior lobe apparently are polypeptides (p. 447) and act directly at the site of origin. Those of the anterior lobe are proteins that act indirectly at a distant site by stimulating other hormones in various endocrine glands. One is a hormone essential to growth; molecular weight, 49,000; isoelectric point, 6.85; amino acid content, Table 16.3 (last entry); properties of a globulin.

Particular interest attaches to the adrenocorticotropic hormone (ACTH) because of its remarkable therapeutic action in rheumatoid arthritis and other diseases associated with hypofunction of the adrenal cortex. The hormone consists of a mixture of closely related proteins of molecular weight about 20,000; the amino acids present are known (Table 16.3). The complete amino acid sequence of one of the physiologically active components (pork adrenal), β-corticotropin, has been worked out (P. H. Bell, American Cyanamid, 1954). In the symbolized formula the unit containing the free amino group (Ser) is at the left and that carrying the free α-carboxyl group (Phe) is at the right. A random distribution is not observed; the basic

```
 Ser-Tyr-Ser-Met-Glu-His-Phe-Arg-Try-Gly-Lys-Pro-Val-Gly┐
└Lys-Lys-Arg-Arg-Pro-Val-Lys-Val-Tyr-Pro-Asp-Gly-Ala-Glu-Asp┐
 └Glu-Leu-Ala-Glu(NH₂)-Ala-Phe-Pro-Leu-Glu-Phe
```

amino acid units are largely clustered in the center of the chain, and the acidic amino acid units are close together near the free carboxyl end.

Other hormones of the anterior lobe include two which are necessary for proper functioning of the gonads, FSH (follicle-stimulating hormone) and ICSH (interstitial-cell stimulating hormone). Both are glucoproteins.

ENZYMES

Enzymes are catalysts elaborated by living organisms that control the many processes associated with life. Many have high specificity with respect to the substances (substrates) whose reactions they catalyze; hence they are usually named by addition of the suffix -ase to the root of the name of the substrate. Sumner[24] isolated a pure enzyme for the first time in 1926 and named it urease because it is specific to the substrate urea and catalyzes hydrolysis to carbon dioxide and ammonia. Since Sumner's pioneering work many more enzymes have been isolated in substantially pure form.

They are all proteins, although some contain a nonproteinoid prosthetic group essential for activity.

Enzymes fall into two broad divisions: hydrolases, which control hydrolysis (and resynthesis) of esters, carbohydrates, proteins, amides; and enzymes that control various oxidation-reduction reactions. The former appear to be simple proteins and the latter to contain prosthetic groups essential for the oxidation-reduction process controlled by the enzyme. Table 16.7 lists enzymes of both types that have been isolated in substantially pure

TABLE 16.7. ENZYMES

1. HYDROLYTIC ENZYMES		
Name	Substrate	Products
A. Esterases:		
Acetylesterase	Esters of acetic acid	CH_3CO_2H + alcohol
Cholinesterase	Acetylcholine	CH_3CO_2H + choline
Lipase	Glycerides	Fatty acids + glycerol
Phosphatases	Phosphate esters	H_3PO_4 + alcohols
B. Carbohydrases:		
Maltase	Maltose	Glucose
Amylase	Starch	Maltose
Lactase	Lactose	Galactose + glucose
C. Proteases and Peptidases:		
Rennin	Casein	Paracasein
Pepsin	Proteins	Proteoses, peptones
Trypsin	Proteins	Polypeptides, amino acids
Carboxypeptidase	Carboxypolypeptides	Amino acids
D. Phosphorylases	Polysaccharides	Hexose phosphate
E. Amidases:		
Urease	Urea	CO_2 + NH_3
Arginase	Arginine	Urea + ornithine
2. OXIDATIVE ENZYMES		
F. Dehydrogenases:		
Lactic dehydrogenase	Lactic acid	Pyruvic acid
Alcohol dehydrogenase	Ethanol	Acetaldehyde
Succinic dehydrogenase	Succinic acid	Fumaric acid
G. Oxidases:		
Tyrosinase	Tyrosine	Melanin
Ascorbic acid oxidase	Ascorbic acid	Dehydroascorbic acid
H. Catalase	$2H_2O_2$	$2H_2O$ + O_2

form; it does not include instances where the prosthetic group is known but the enzyme has not been characterized as a complete conjugated protein. Almost all enzymes show stereochemical specificity; thus lactic acid dehydrogenase catalyzes oxidation of L- but not of D-lactic acid. A few have

[24] James B. Sumner, 1887–1955 b. Canton, Mass.; Ph.D. Harvard; N. Y. State Agr. Coll., Cornell: Nobel Prize 1946

absolute specificity in that they control reaction of only one substrate. Urease is such an enzyme.   Certain enzymes show only linkage specificity; for example, there are esterases capable of promoting hydrolysis of any ester regardless of the structures of the acid and alcohol components.   The more usual requirements fall in between the absolute and the linkage type, that is, the enzyme requires a specific linkage and also that certain functional groups be in the vicinity of this linkage.   Pioneering work on group specificity was carried out with synthetic peptides by Bergmann (1937), who found that various proteinases have definite requirements in order to catalyze hydrolysis of peptide bonds.   Some, exopeptidases, affect only terminal peptide bonds.   Carboxypeptidase, for example, requires a free carboxyl adjacent to the peptide linkage: $-CO:NHCHRCO_2H$.   The majority of proteolytic enzymes are endopeptidases, that is, they attack centrally located peptide bonds.   Pepsin and trypsin are of this type, and each has been shown to require specific amino acid residues in the vicinity of a peptide bond in order to effect cleavage.   An important group of enzymes effect phosphorolysis rather than hydrolysis.   Thus phosphorylase catalyzes degradation of glycogen to glucose-1-phosphate (p. 474).

Structural Units of Prosthetic Groups. — The pyrimidine ring occurs as such in the prosthetic group of some enzymes, but more often it is fused to a second heterocyclic ring. If this second ring is imidazole, the structural unit is purine.   In isoalloxazine, the basic unit of riboflavin, a reduced

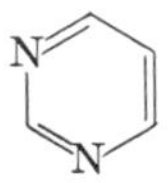

Pyrimidine 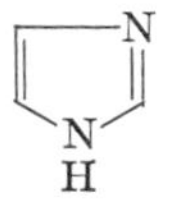 Imidazole 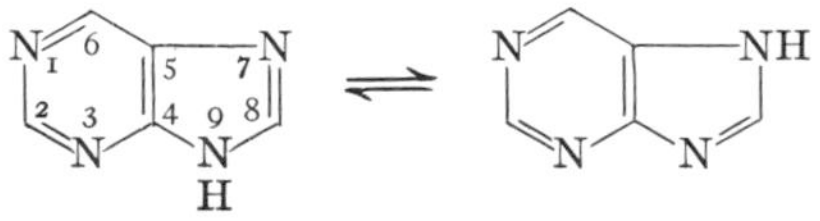   Purine 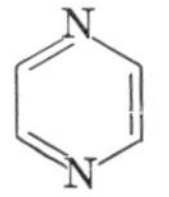   Pyrazine

pyrimidine ring is fused to a pyrazine ring and this is fused to a benzene ring. The isoalloxazine structure is less aromatic and hence less stable than the alloxazine structure, and exists as such only when the central nitrogen at position 9 carries a carbon substituent in place of hydrogen.   The chief base constituent is adenine, or 6-aminopurine.

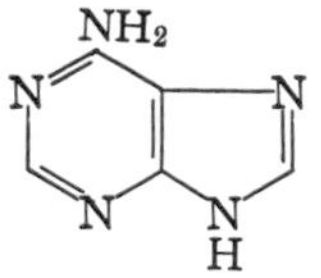

Adenine 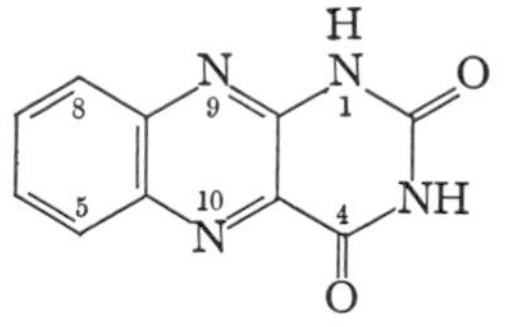   Alloxazine 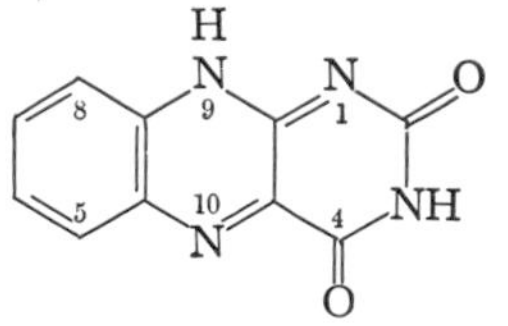   Isoalloxazine

A further component is the pentose D-ribose, which is combined with purines as β-D-ribofuranose.   In riboflavin the reduction product ribitol is combined at position 1 with an isoalloxazine derivative.

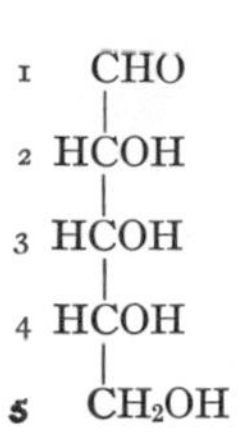

1	CHO	HOCH		CH₂OH
2	HCOH	HCOH		HCOH
3	HCOH	HCOH		HCOH
4	HCOH	HC—		HCOH
5	CH₂OH	CH₂OH		CH₂OH

$$\text{1 CHO — 2 HCOH — 3 HCOH — 4 HCOH — 5 CH}_2\text{OH}$$

D-Ribose 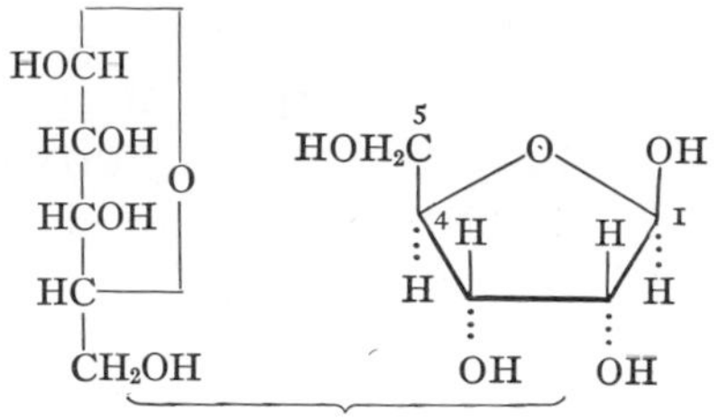   β-D-Ribofuranose 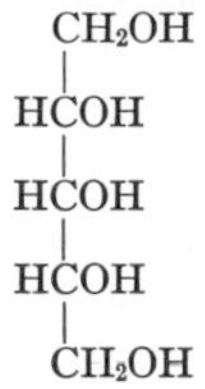   D-Ribitol

The formula of adenosine is derived by elimination of the elements of water between the 1-hydroxyl group of β-D-ribofuranose and the 9-NH group

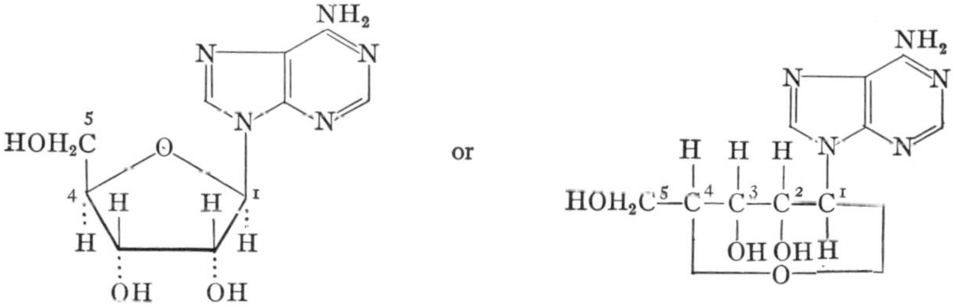

Adenosine

of adenine. An adenylic acid contains one molecule of phosphoric acid esterified with adenosine and is an adenosine monophosphate (AMP). If a second molecule of phosphoric acid is condensed with the first in a pyrophosphate grouping, —OPO(OH)—OPO(OH)₂, the substance is an adenosine diphosphate (ADP). If a third molecule of the acid is condensed to give the grouping —OPO(OH)—OPO(OH)—OPO(OH)₂, the substance is an adenosine triphosphate (ATP). Adenosine is called a nucleoside; its phosphoric esters are called mono-, di-, and trinucleotides.

Oxidative Enzymes. — Enzymes that effect oxidation by transfer of hydrogen from the substrate directly to oxygen are known as oxidases. Tyrosinase is an enzyme of this type, which catalyzes air oxidation of tyrosine to the pigment melanin (p. 511). Others, dehydrogenases, transfer hydrogen not to oxygen but to an acceptor enzyme or coenzyme. The term coenzyme is sometimes applied to a proteinoid enzyme necessary for activation of another proteinoid enzyme, but a prosthetic group without which a protein is inactive also is often described as a coenzyme. The donor enzyme requires an acceptor enzyme of specific oxidation-reduction potential and cannot function with another acceptor, even one with a closely related prosthetic group. A specific unit in the prosthetic group of each acceptor enzyme is responsible for the uptake of two hydrogen atoms. In some instances this unit is a nicotinamide group, and nicotinamide is an essential dietary constituent for many animals. This residue contributes a reversible oxidoreduc-

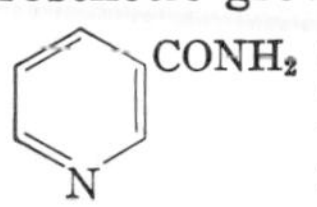

Nicotinamide

tion function:

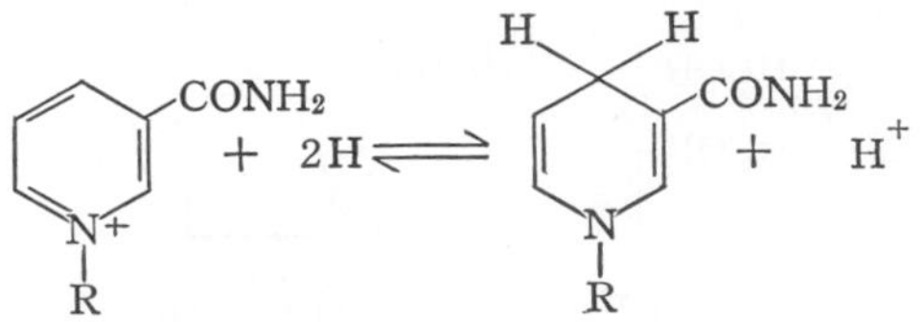

$$\text{(pyridine-CONH}_2, N^+R) + 2H \rightleftharpoons \text{(dihydropyridine-CONH}_2, NR) + H^+$$

Two acceptor **pyridinoprotein enzymes** containing the nicotinamide unit are called coenzyme I and coenzyme II. The structures of the prosthetic groups are now known and these groups are known as **diphosphopyridine nucleotide (DPN)** and **triphosphopyridine nucleotide (TPN)**. The former is characteristic of the acceptor enzyme of yeast (coenzyme I) discovered by Harden[25] and Young in 1904 in their classical investigation of alcoholic fermentation. They separated yeast juice by dialysis into a protein and a nonprotein fraction (prosthetic group) and found that neither alone promotes fermentation but that ability to promote fermentation is restored by mixing the two solutions. The linkage between the protein and the prosthetic group is thus loose, and separation into the two fragments or recombination to the enzyme occurs readily. The structure of DPN was finally settled in 1942 through work of von Euler, Karrer, Schlenk, and Warburg. The complicated substance is composed of one molecule each of nicotinamide and of adenine, and two molecules each of D-ribose and of phosphoric acid, joined as shown in the formula. TPN contains one more molecule of phosphoric acid, which was shown in 1953 to be esterified with the hydroxyl group at position 3 in the ribose unit linked to adenine. Each of the two enzymes can accept two hydrogen atoms to form a dihydro derivative, which then can serve as hydrogen donor enzyme.

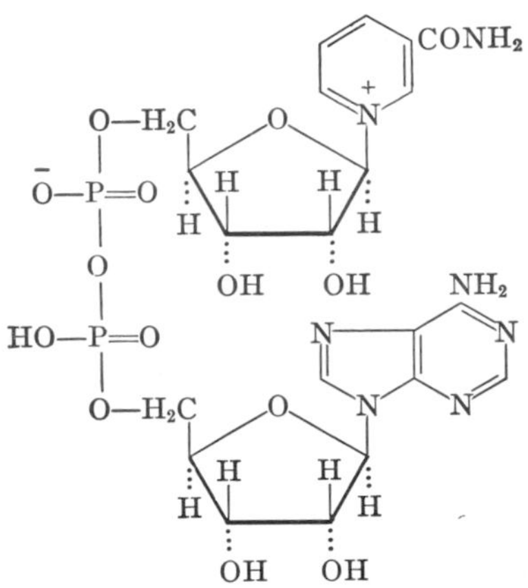

Diphosphopyridine nucleotide (DPN)

A representative of another important group of dehydrogenases known as flavoproteins is the yellow enzyme of yeast (Warburg[26] and Theorell,[27] 1934). The chromophoric group is riboflavin, and the prosthetic group is the 5'-phosphate ester, named flavin mononucleotide. Combination of the synthetic 5'-phosphate ester with the specific protein of yellow enzyme affords active flavoprotein (Kuhn,[28] Karrer[29]).

[25] Arthur Harden, 1865–1940; Univ. Manchester, Lister Inst., London; Nobel Prize 1929

[26] Otto Warburg, b. 1883 Freiburg; Ph.D. Berlin and Heidelberg; Kaiser Wilhelm Inst., Berlin; Nobel Prize 1931

[27] Hugo Theorell, b. 1903 Linköping, Sweden; M.D. Stockholm; Stockholm; Nobel Prize 1955

[28] Richard Kuhn, b. 1900 Vienna; Ph.D. Munich (Willstätter); Zurich, Heidelberg, KWI Med. Res.; Nobel Prize 1938

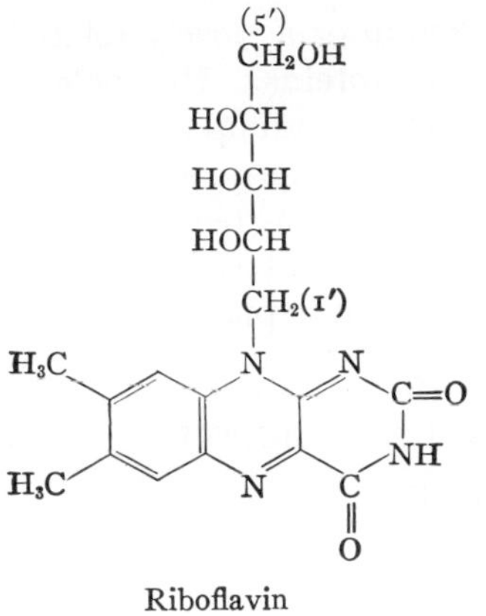

Riboflavin
(6,7-dimethyl-9-D-ribitylisoalloxazine)

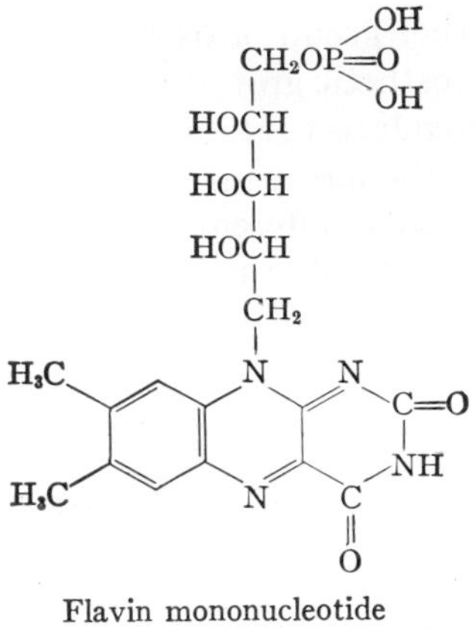

Flavin mononucleotide
(riboflavin-5'-phosphoric acid)

Riboflavin contains the isoalloxazine nucleus, and this grouping is responsible for the oxidation-reduction function; reduction involves 1,4-addition of hydrogen to the conjugated system:

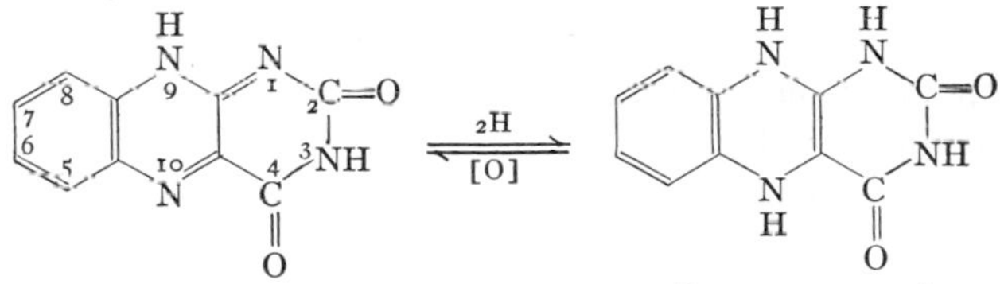

Isoalloxazine
(flavin, yellow)

Leuco compound
(colorless)

Several other flavoproteins are similarly constituted.   In one the prosthetic group is riboflavin adenine dinucleotide, in which riboflavin is linked at the 5'-position to a pyrophosphate group which, in turn, is linked at the 5-position in the riboside residue to adenosine.

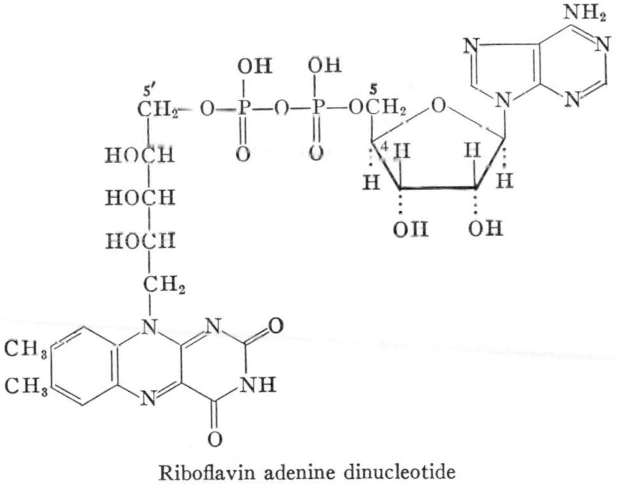

Riboflavin adenine dinucleotide

[29] Paul Karrer, b. 1889 Moscow; Ph.D. Zurich (Werner); Univ. Zurich; Nobel Prize 1937

Another group of oxidases contain hemin or a closely related substance as the prosthetic group and are called **hemoproteins**. **Hemoglobin, catalase,** and **peroxidase** contain heme as the prosthetic group. In hemoglobin the iron is in the ferrous state, in catalase it is in the ferric state. **Cytochrome c** has a slightly different prosthetic group, the iron-free porphyrin of which, designated porphyrin c (Theorell) has been found to contain two residues of cysteine linked to two-carbon side chains that replace the vinyl groups in

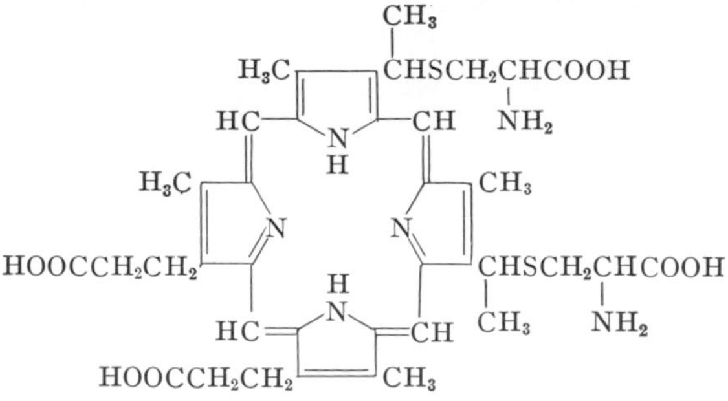

$$
\begin{array}{c}
CH_3 \\
H_3C \qquad CHSCH_2CHCOOH \\
HC \qquad N \qquad CH \qquad NH_2 \\
H \\
H_3C \qquad CH_3 \\
N \qquad N \\
HOOCCH_2CH_2 \qquad CHSCH_2CHCOOH \\
H \qquad CH_3 \qquad NH_2 \\
HC \qquad N \qquad CH \\
HOOCCH_2CH_2 \qquad CH_3
\end{array}
$$

Porphyrin c

the porphyrin of heme. Cytochrome c functions as an electron transfer system by change of valency of the iron: $Fe^{+++} + e \rightleftharpoons Fe^{++}$.

In the living cell the transfer of hydrogen from a substrate to molecular oxygen proceeds through a series of coupled oxidation-reduction reactions involving enzymes of different types and of graded potential, such that the oxidation energy of oxygen is released in a series of graded steps. The coupled steps may be as follows:

Substrate–H_2 + DPN–protein → Substrate + H_2–DPN–protein

H_2–DPN–protein + Yellow enzyme → DPN–protein + Leuco yellow enzyme

Leuco yellow enzyme + Cytochrome → Yellow enzyme + H_2–Cytochrome

H_2–Cytochrome + ½ O_2 → Cytochrome + H_2O

A generalized representation of the energy relationships given in the chart includes approximate values of E_0, the oxidation-reduction potential in a solution of equimolecular amounts of oxidant and reductant. In spite of

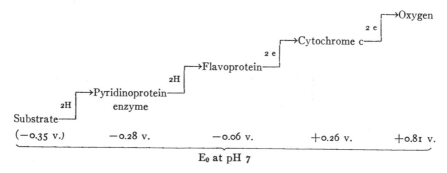

E_0 at pH 7

the large difference in potential between systems at the two ends of the respiratory chain, these systems are unable to interact with each other directly. The chart suggests the hypothesis that the initial changes occur by hydrogen transfer and the terminal changes by electron transfer.

Other Enzymes. — A more limited number of enzymes control processes other than hydrolysis and oxidation-reduction. One is **carboxylase,** which catalyzes decomposition of α-keto acids such as pyruvic acid: $CH_3COCO_2H \rightarrow CH_3CHO + CO_2$. The prosthetic group, cocarboxylase, was isolated as the crystalline hydrochloride and identified as the diphosphate ester (pyrophosphate) of thiamine (vitamin B_1). The enzyme also requires the presence of magnesium salts for activity. Inorganic salts are often required in enzymatic reactions.

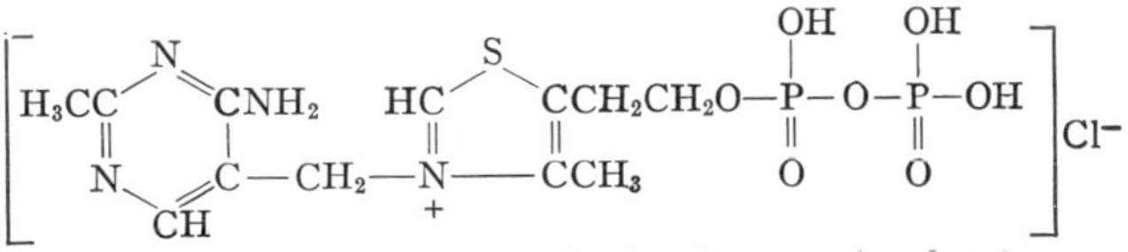

Cocarboxylase (thiamine hydrochloride pyrophosphate)

Catalase, a hemoprotein containing four atoms of iron (ferric) per molecule, catalyzes decomposition of hydrogen peroxide but of no other peroxide: $2 H_2O_2 \rightarrow 2 H_2O + O_2$. It occurs almost universally and has the function of protecting the organism from hydrogen peroxide, formed on oxidation of various oxidases. The hemoprotein **peroxidase** catalyzes the oxidation of many phenols and aromatic amines.

Coenzyme A. — This substance is the prosthetic group of an enzyme first recognized as a catalyst required for biological acetylation (Lipmann,[30] 1947), and it was named accordingly (A = Acetylation). Investigations of structure (Lipmann, Lynen,[31] Baddiley[32]) established that coenzyme A is composed of an adenylic acid residue (1) linked through a pyrophosphate

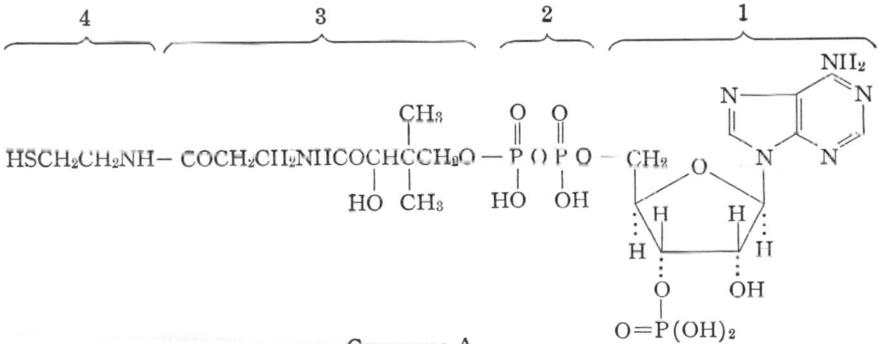

Coenzyme A

---

[30] Fritz Lipmann, b. 1899, Königsberg; Ph.D. Berlin; Rockefeller Inst., Mass. Gen. Hospital and Harvard; Nobel Prize 1953

[31] Fedor Lynen, b. 1911 Munich; Ph.D. Munich (Wieland); Munich

[32] James Baddiley; b. 1918 Manchester; Ph.D. and D.Sc. Manchester (Todd); Durham

group (2) to pantothenic acid (3; p. 1010), which is joined by a peptide bond to β-mercaptoethanolamine (4). The terminal sulfhydryl group is important for the biological functions of the coenzyme (symbol, CoASH) because the S-acetyl derivative (CoAS-COCH$_3$) serves as acetyl donor in various biological acetylations. Actually the role of the coenzyme is much wider than was first realized, for CoA apparently is involved in all biological syntheses and degradations proceeding through C$_2$-units (metabolism of carbohydrates, p. 482; of fats, p. 494).

NUCLEOPROTEINS

Nucleoproteins, so called because those first recognized are invariable constituents of cell nuclei, are proteins conjugated with complex organic acids of high molecular weight, the nucleic acids. Nucleic acids are made up of three components, liberated on acid hydrolysis: an organic base or bases, phosphoric acid, and a sugar (Levene,[33] 1934). As far as is known, the sugar unit is either ribose or 2-desoxyribose, and a given nucleic acid contains only one or the other, not both. The principal bases isolated from nucleic acids are the purines adenine and guanine, and the pyrimidines cytosine, uracil, and thymine, of the structures shown.

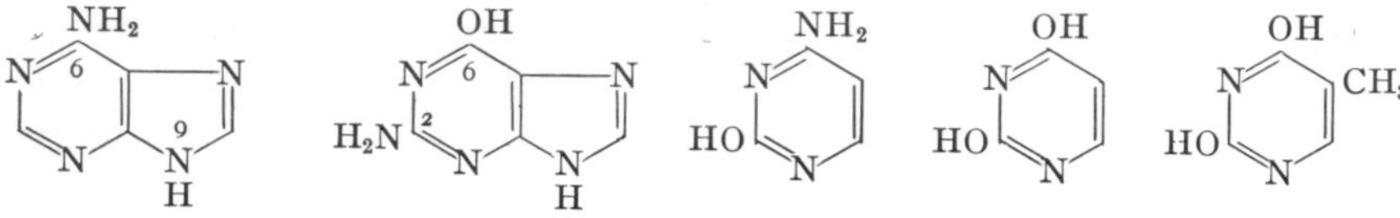

Adenine   Guanine   Cytosine   Uracil   Thymine

Levene found that enzymatic hydrolysis of yeast nucleic acid yields approximately equal amounts of four nucleotides, which are phosphate esters of a combination of ribose with a purine or pyrimidine base. Yeast adenylic acid, one of the four nucleotides, is hydrolyzed by alkali with cleavage of the

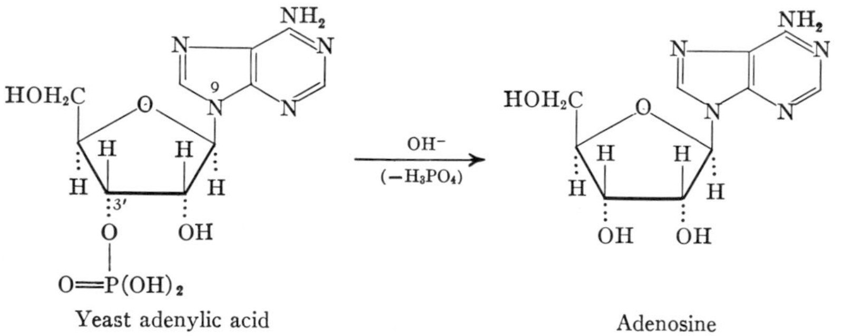

Yeast adenylic acid   Adenosine

phosphate ester and production of adenosine, which shows that the arrangement is base–sugar–phosphoric acid. Adenosine is a β-riboside. That the

---

[33] Phoebus A. Levene, 1869–1940; b. Russia; Ph.D. St. Petersburg; Rockefeller Inst.; *Science*, **92**, 392 (1940)

phosphate ester group in adenylic acid is at the 3'-position of the sugar component was suggested by observation that acid hydrolysis of a derivative of adenylic acid yielded an optically active phosphoribose which on hydro-

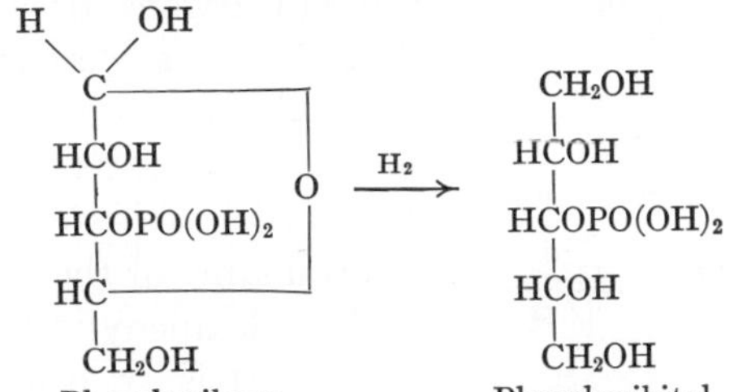

Phosphoribose → Phosphoribitol

genation gave an optically inactive phosphoribitol. If the ester group were at any position other than 3' the ribitol would be optically active.

The other three nucleotides of yeast nucleic acid differ from adenylic acid in having as basic unit in place of adenine a unit of guanine, cytosine, or uracil; they are guanylic acid, cytidylic acid, and uridylic acid. Evidence

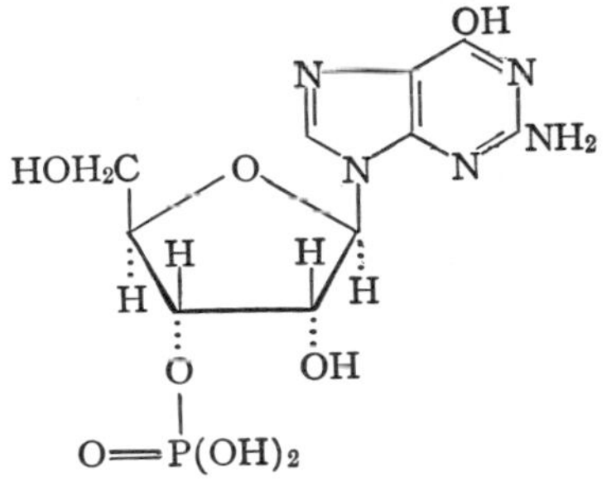

Guanylic acid

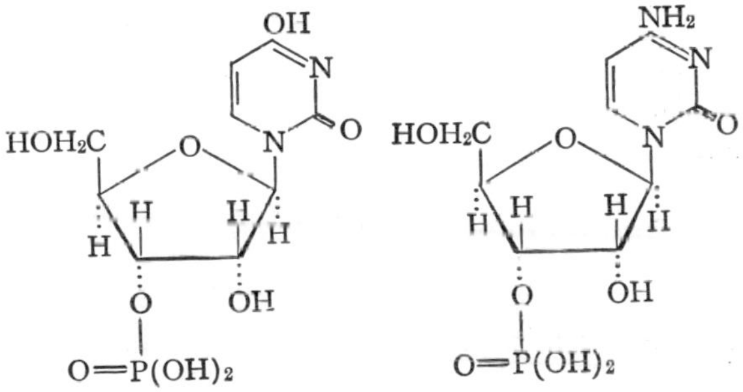

Uridylic acid   Cytidylic acid

has accumulated that yeast nucleic acid is a polynucleotide of molecular weight about 20,000 in which the nucleoside units are linked by phosphodiester groups extending between the 3'- and 5'-positions of riboside units (Todd,[34] 1954).

[34] Sir Alexander R. Todd, b. 1907 Glasgow; Ph.D. Oxford (Robinson); Univ. Cambridge

The relative composition of the nucleotides vary widely depending upon the source. Many different kinds of nucleic acids exist, but preparations from different organs or different strains exhibit the same relative proportions of individual purines and pyrimidines. This finding is consistent with the hypothesis that nucleic acids control the hereditary determinants of the species (p. 397).

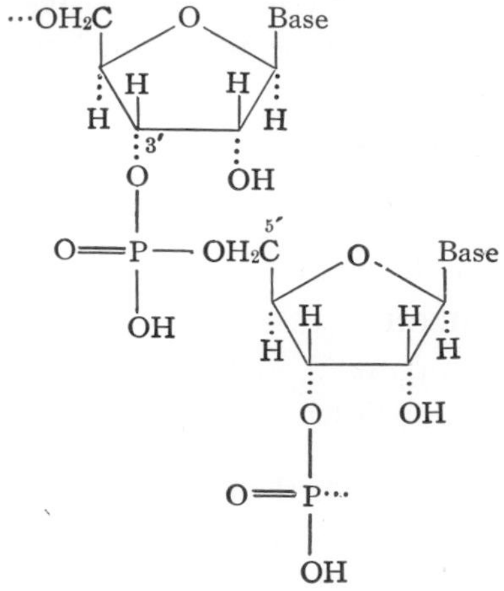

Muscle adenylic acid (isolation, Embden, 1927) is an isomer of yeast nucleic acid which yields adenosine on alkaline hydrolysis and therefore differs only in the position of the phosphoric acid residue. Since muscle adenylic acid, unlike yeast adenylic acid, is capable of forming a complex with boric acid, a property characteristic of *cis* glycols, the 2'- and 3'-hydroxyl groups must be free and the ester group is therefore at the

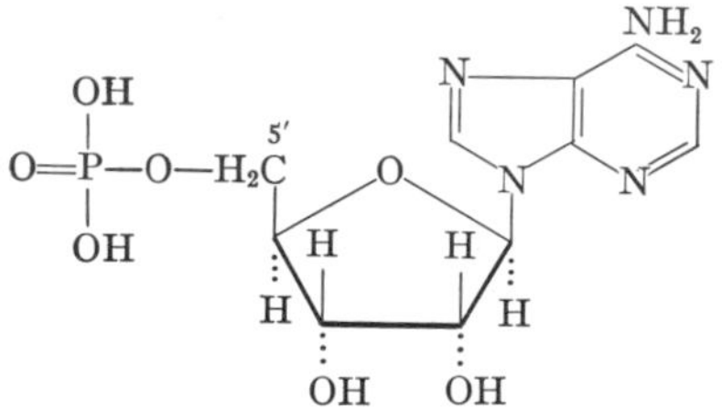

Nucleic acid

Muscle adenylic acid

5'-position. This inference is supported by the synthesis of muscle adenylic acid (Baddiley and Todd, 1947).

The protein portion of a nucleoprotein is generally one of basic type, a protamine or a histone. It is believed to be linked to the nucleic acid portion by covalent bonds.

VIRUS PROTEINS AND TOXINS

A virus is a submicroscopic infective agent that will pass through a filter (Berkefeld) capable of removing all known living cells. Viruses are capable of autocatalytic growth and multiplication in living tissues, and were once regarded as living organisms smaller than any known ones. One, tobacco mosaic virus, present in filtered juice of plants infected with a disease known as tobacco mosaic, was isolated by Stanley[35] (1935) in crystalline form and found to be a nucleoprotein. The molecular weight is unusually high (40

[35] Wendell M. Stanley, b. 1904 Ridgeville, Ind.; Ph.D. Illinois (R. Adams); Rockefeller Inst., Virus Lab., U. Calif.; Nobel Prize 1946

million); the nucleic acid portion amounts to about 6% of the total weight. The crystalline protein is highly infectious and its virus activity exactly parallels the range of pH stability. The substance is able to reproduce itself in the tobacco leaf, and amounts of 2–3 g. of virus protein have been isolated from plants inoculated with as little as 1 microgram of the protein. Since this pioneering work a number of other plant viruses have been isolated and shown to be nucleoproteins (examples: cucumber mosaic, tomato bushy stunt, potato x virus, tobacco ringspot).

Some of the substances secreted by pathogenic organisms and responsible for the lethal effect have been obtained in pure form and characterized as proteins. These include diphtheria toxin and *Clostridium botulinum* type A and type B toxin. The substances are extremely toxic; 1 mg. of the botulinus A toxin is sufficient to kill 30 million mice. The molecular weight of this toxin is 900,000. The amino acid content reveals no clue to the physiological effect.

READING REFERENCES

C. L. A. Schmidt, "The Chemistry of the Amino Acids and Proteins," C. C. Thomas, Baltimore (1938)

E. J. Cohn and J. T. Edsall, "Proteins, Amino Acids and Peptides," Rheinhold, New York (1943)

H. B. Vickery and C. L. A. Schmidt, "The History of the Discovery of the Amino Acids," *Chem. Rev.*, **9**, 169 (1931)

R. J. Block, "The Isolation and Synthesis of the Naturally Occurring α-Amino Acids," *Chem. Revs.*, **38**, 501 (1946)

M. Bergmann and J. S. Fruton, "The Specificity of Proteinases," *Advances in Enzymology*, **1**, 63 (1941)

W. M. Stanley, "The Isolation and Properties of Tobacco Mosaic and Other Virus Proteins," *The Harvey Lectures*, 170 (1937–1938)

M. L. Anson and J. T. Edsall, "Advances in Protein Chemistry," Academic Press (1944–)

H. Neurath and K. Bailey, "The Proteins," Vol. 1, Academic Press (1953)

F. Haurowitz, "Chemistry and Biology of Proteins," Academic Press (1950)

A. Tiselius, "Some Applications of the Separation of Large Molecules and Colloidal Particles," *J. Chem. Soc.*, 2650 (1954).

CHAPTER 17

CARBOHYDRATE METABOLISM

One important metabolic process involving carbohydrates is glycolysis, exemplified by the hydrolysis of dietary polysaccharides and of liver glycogen to monoses; the reverse change is typified by the synthesis of glycogen in the liver from glucose. These processes involve cleavage and formation of glycosidic links and occur anaerobically. The overall metabolic conversion of hexose to carbon dioxide and water, as a source of muscular energy, requires oxygen, but comprises two sets of reactions, one of which occurs anaerobically in muscle tissue and converts hexose into three-carbon fragments, while the other completes the degradation to carbon dioxide aerobically. An important instance of carbohydrate metabolism not involving animal tissues is the fermentation of hexoses to ethanol in the presence of yeast, an anaerobic reaction. Pasteur was the first to recognize that oxygen is not required, since the overall change is $C_6H_{12}O_6 \rightarrow 2\ C_2H_5OH + 2\ CO_2$. The term fermentation (L. *fermentare*, to boil), introduced by Pasteur to describe a microbiological reaction in which evolution of carbon dioxide causes the appearance of boiling, has come to mean an enzymatic reaction other than one involving oxygen.

Present knowledge of the mechanism of these and other paths of carbohydrate metabolism is based in large part upon characterization of the enzymes that control each step in the often elaborate sequences of reversible reactions that form parts of cycles. Historically, the study of alcoholic fermentation preceded that of carbohydrate degradation in muscle, and the systematic investigation of enzymes commenced in 1897 when Buchner[1] prepared a cell-free extract of yeast that converted glucose into ethanol, and the active principles came to be known as enzymes (Gr. *en*, in; *zyme*, yeast). In subsequent years contributions to the knowledge of the enzyme systems and the intermediate steps involved were made by many distinguished biochemists, but only a few can be cited specifically in this brief review. Harden and Young (1905) recognized that intermediates in the fermentation of glucose are phosphorylated substances, one of which was isolated and characterized as fructose-1,6-diphosphate ("the Harden-Young ester"). Another intermediate, acetaldehyde, was demonstrated by Neuberg[2] (1911) by use of a trapping technique: added sodium bisulfite forms a non-fermentable addition product and allows the aldehyde to accumulate. Perhaps the

---

[1] Eduard Buchner, 1860–1917; b. Munich; Ph.D. Munich (Curtius); Breslau, Würzburg; Nobel Prize 1907

[2] Carl Neuberg, b. 1887 Hannover; Ph.D. Berlin (Wohl); Kaiser Wilhelm Inst., New York Med. Coll.

greatest advance is that made by Meyerhof[3] (1917–18) when he discovered that some of the coenzymes involved in alcoholic fermentation are also present in animal cells and surmised that metabolic processes follow essentially the same paths in all organisms. Subsequent studies of fermentation and of carbohydrate metabolism in muscle tissue and in a variety of microorganisms proved Meyerhof's surmise to be correct. Thus, the steps leading to formation of C_3-metabolites in muscle are involved also in alcoholic fermentation. Hence, information gained from study of one system has often aided interpretation of phenomena associated with a different system. Metabolic cycles in microorganisms are sometimes parts of more elaborate cycles in animal tissues and, therefore, are more easily elucidated.

Glycolysis. — Carbohydrates in the diet consist of sugars and polysaccharides that can be utilized by the animal organism only after enzymatic glycolysis to hexoses, which are absorbed from the intestine and carried to various tissues where they are either oxidized or stored as glycogen, mainly in the liver. The sugar content of the blood is practically constant, since when sugar absorption is high, storage of liver glycogen is increased; and when the sugar content falls below the normal level, glycogen is converted into glucose. Removal of the liver causes rapid drop in blood sugar, and death results unless glucose is injected in quantity sufficient to maintain the normal blood level.

Glycolysis occurs under the influence of enzymes of the digestive tract. Intestinal enzymes of one type, described as glucogenic amylases, effect hydrolysis of starchs and glycogens to glucose; amylases of another type effect hydrolysis of the same substrates to the disaccharide maltose. Specific intestinal enzymes catalyze hydrolysis of maltose (maltase), sucrose (sucrase), and lactose (lactase). Little is known about the mode of action of these glycolytic enzymes of the gastrointestinal tract, since metabolic intermediates have not been isolated.

Glycogenolysis. — Contrary to early belief, the synthesis and degradation of glycogen in the liver is controlled by enzymes which are different from the digestive enzymes and which operate by producing a succession of phosphorylated intermediates, some identical with intermediates of alcoholic fermentation. One group of dialyzable coenzymes concerned includes adenosine mono , di , and triphosphate (p. 463), which can be represented by abbreviated formulas or by initials:

A–OPO(OH)$_2$ A–OPO(OH)–OPO(OH)$_2$ A–OPO(OH)–OPO(OH)–OPO(OH)$_2$
　　AMP　　　　　　　　　　　ADP　　　　　　　　　　　　　　　　ATP

These esters, components of the adenylic acid system, function as carriers of phosphoric acid: AMP is a phosphoric acid acceptor, ATP is a phosphoric acid donor, and ADP can function as donor or acceptor. The steps in the

---

[3] Otto Meyerhof, 1884–1951; b. Hannover; Ph.D. Heidelberg; Heidelberg, Paris, Philadelphia; Nobel Prize 1922; *Nature*, **168**, 895 (1951); *Science*, **115**, 365 (1952)

degradation and synthesis of glycogen as elucidated by Cori[4] and Cori[5] (1937–41) are shown in Chart 1. The first step is phosphorolysis of the

CHART 1. GLYCOGENESIS AND GLYCOGENOLYSIS

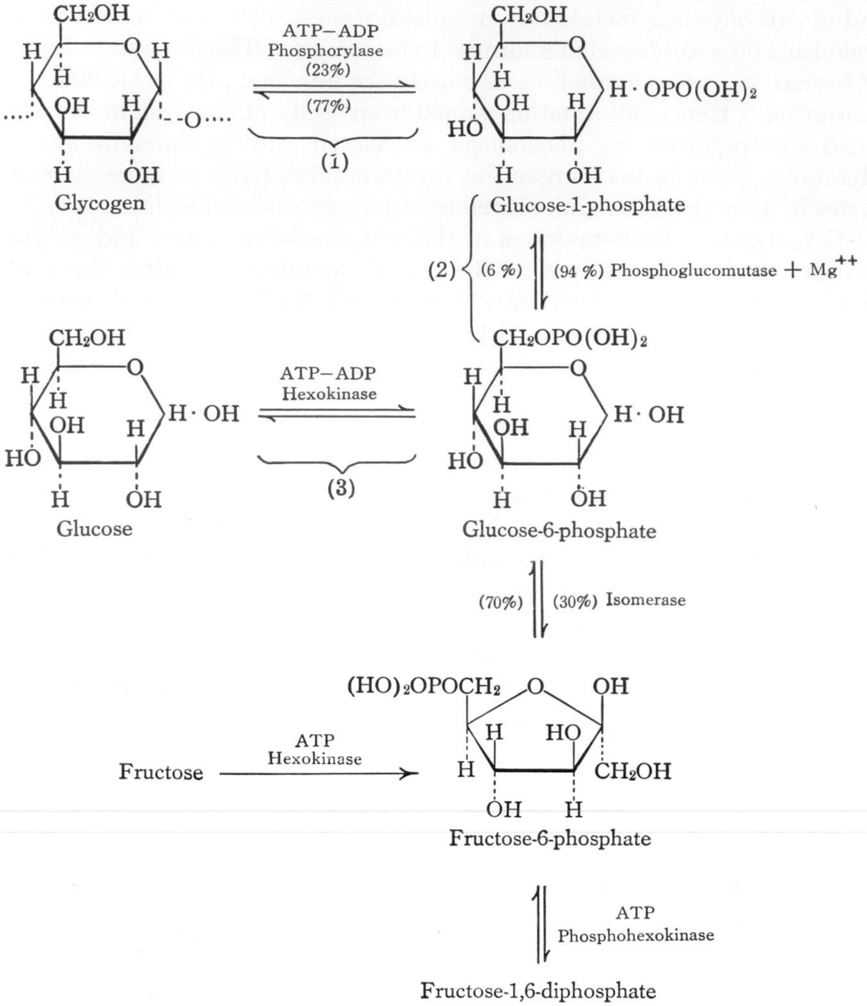

Glycogen

(1) ATP—ADP Phosphorylase (23%) / (77%)

Glucose-1-phosphate

(2) (6 %) / (94 %) Phosphoglucomutase + Mg^{++}

Glucose

(3) ATP—ADP Hexokinase

Glucose-6-phosphate

(70%) / (30%) Isomerase

Fructose → ATP Hexokinase →

Fructose-6-phosphate

ATP Phosphohexokinase

Fructose-1,6-diphosphate

polysaccharide with production of glucose-1-phosphate; the second is transposition of the phosphate group from the 1- to the 6-position; the third is hydrolysis to glucose. Each step is reversible and each requires a specific enzyme, but steps (1) and (3) require in addition an adenylic acid coenzyme for donation or acceptance of phosphoric acid. Thus, Cori and Cori syn-

[4] Carl Cori, b. 1896 Prague; M.D. Prague; Washington Univ. School Med.; Nobel Prize 1947

[5] Gerty Cori, b. 1896 Prague; M.D. Prague; Washington Univ. School Med.; Nobel Prize 1947

thesized glycogen *in vitro* from glucose in the presence of hexokinase, phosphoglucomutase ($+$ Mg^{++}), phosphorylase, and ATP. The initial product of glycogenolysis, glucose-1-phosphate, can be isolated after incubation of glycogen with a tissue extract that has been dialyzed to remove magnesium salts, which otherwise activate the enzyme required for the next step. The enzyme of reaction (1), phosphorylase, can be freed from the enzyme of reaction (2), phosphoglucomutase, which accompanies it in all animal tissues, by specific precipitation methods.

In the resting state of the organism glucose is the chief sugar metabolite of glycogen, but in periods of muscular activity fructose-6-phosphate and 1,6-diphosphate appear in predominance (Chart 1) and function in a further metabolic sequence described below (Chart 2). Free fructose does not arise as a product of metabolism but when present in the diet can participate in the system under the influence of hexokinase and ATP.

Various organisms utilize galactose as readily as glucose or fructose. The transformations involved have been elucidated by Leloir.[6] The initial step is phosphorylation of galactose (in the presence of galactokinase and ATP) to galactose-1-phosphate, which is then epimerized at C_4 to glucose-1-phosphate by an enzyme known as galactowaldenase. The equilibrium concentration of the two 1-phosphates is: 75% glucose $\rightleftharpoons$ 25% galactose; the reaction is to be considered a part of the changes formulated in Chart 1. The coenzyme (prosthetic group) of galactowaldenase has been identified as 5-uridylribosidodiphosphatoglucoside (UDPG), of the structure shown. It is not known how the epimerization at C_4 is effected.

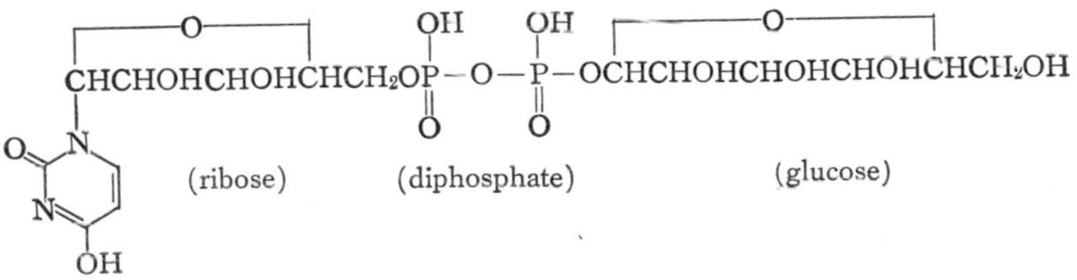

Cogalactowaldenase

Haure (1940) found that the terminal step in synthesis of starch in plants follows the path of the glycogen synthesis. The phosphorylase enzyme, readily extracted from potato juice and purified by precipitation with ammonium sulfate, does not require a coenzyme to catalyze the reversible reaction:

$$\text{Amylose} + \text{Phosphate} \underset{\text{H}^+}{\overset{\text{Phosphorylase}}{\rightleftharpoons}} \text{Glucose-1-phosphate}$$

The enzymatically synthesized polysaccharide is similar to the amylose fraction of starch. The potato also contains a branching factor, or Q-enzyme, analogous to that of animal tissue. It is unstable in aqueous solution, but has been obtained free from other enzymes (Peat, 1949). In asso-

[6] Luis F. Leloir, b. 1906 Paris (Argentine citizen); M.D. Buenos Aires; Buenos Aires

ciation with phosphorylase it catalyzes the synthesis of amylopectin from glucose-1-phosphate. In addition, it can convert amylose into amylopectin; that is, it effects scission of the chains and formation of branching 1,6-linkages.

Glycogen is synthesized in the animal organism from substances other than sugars. These include the three-carbon compounds: lactic acid, propionic acid, dihydroxyacetone, glycerol, propylene glycol, glyceraldehyde, pyruvic acid; at least one six-carbon compound: citric acid; and the amino acids: glycine, alanine, arginine, tyrosine, threonine, cysteine, aspartic acid, glutamic acid, phenylalanine, histidine, valine (through intermediate C_3-compounds). Reactions leading to a phosphorylated sugar are in the main the exact reverse of those of degradation of phosphorylated sugars in muscle and other tissues, and are discussed later.

Metabolism of Carbohydrate in Muscle. — During muscular activity glycogen is degraded through glucose-6-phosphate and fructose-6-phosphate to fructose-1,6-diphosphate, as formulated in Chart 1. Under the influence of enzymes present in muscle tissue the 1,6-diphosphate is cleaved anaerobically to two C_3-units through the series of phosphorylated intermediates shown in Chart 2. The first step is a reversal of aldol condensation. The aldol condensation of unphosphorylated dihydroxyacetone and glyceraldehyde is the key step in E. Fischer's classical synthesis of fructose (p. 368). The next step, conversion of 3-glyceraldehyde phosphate into 1,3-diphosphoglyceric acid, is postulated as involving addition of phosphoric acid to the carbonyl group and dehydrogenation by diphosphopyridine nucleotide (DPN), which is converted into its dihydride (DPNH₂); the significance of the specially designated (reactive) phosphorus linkage is discussed in the next section. 1,3-Diphosphoglyceric acid transfers the anhydride phosphate group to ADP and the remaining ester group migrates to the 2-position. Elimination of water gives the anhydro-ester of enolpyruvic acid, from which ADP removes the phosphate group to give pyruvic acid. Reduction to lactic acid, the terminal step, is achieved by reaction with DPNH₂, and since an equivalent amount of this coenzyme was generated in an earlier step of the cycle, the oxidation-reduction steps are balanced and the overall reaction is anaerobic.

Chart 2 also indicates the pathway of alcoholic fermentation. The steps proceeding to pyruvic acid are identical, but yeast contains carboxylase, an enzyme absent from muscle tissue, and this decarboxylates pyruvic acid irreversibly to acetaldehyde. Acetaldehyde is reduced to alcohol by transfer of hydrogen from DPNH₂ derived from the dehydrogenation leading to 1,3-diphosphoglyceric acid, and hence fermentation is anaerobic.

Energy Transfer. — Pasteur expressed the close relationship between fermentation and metabolism in the statement "la fermentation est la vie sans air," by which he meant that fermentation is the source of energy for the life processes of microorganisms. In the case of muscle, the energy

CHART 2. METABOLISM OF HEXOSE DIPHOSPHATE

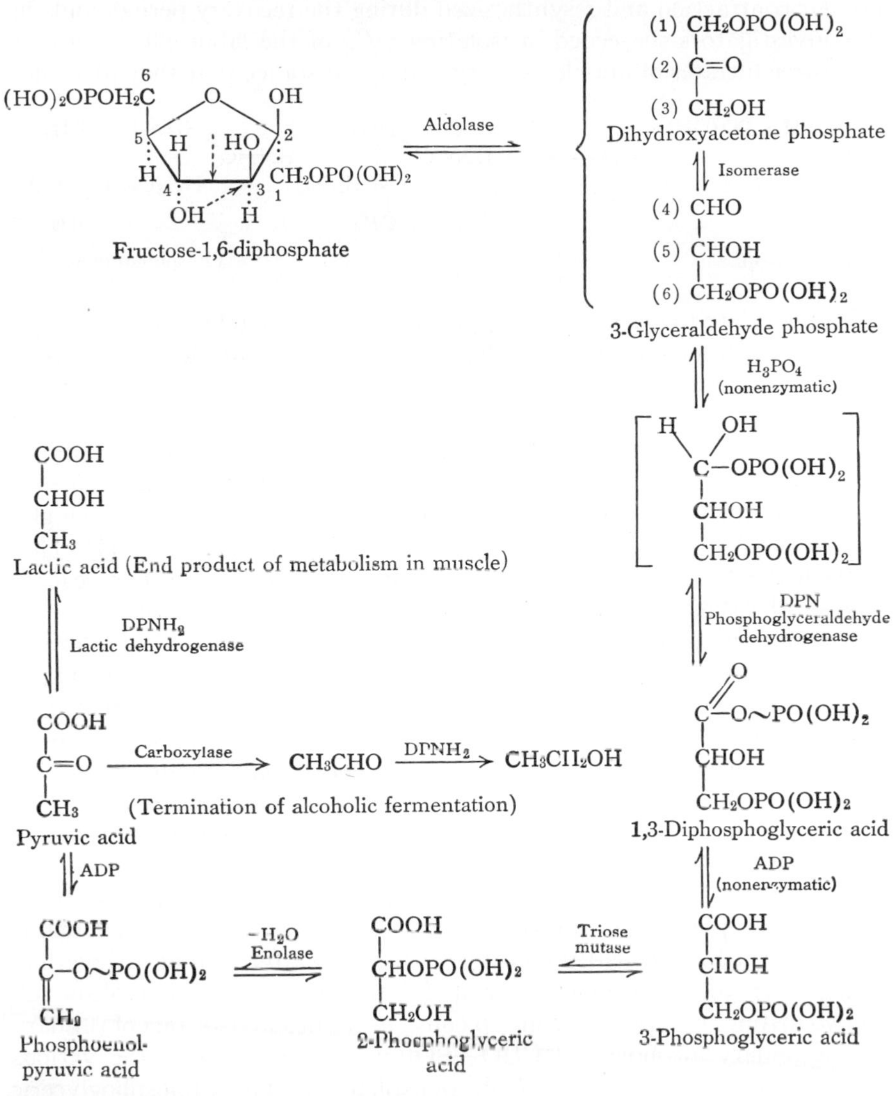

$$
\begin{aligned}
&(1)\ CH_2OPO(OH)_2 \\
&(2)\ C{=}O \\
&(3)\ CH_2OH
\end{aligned}
$$

Dihydroxyacetone phosphate

↕ Isomerase

$$
\begin{aligned}
&(4)\ CHO \\
&(5)\ CHOH \\
&(6)\ CH_2OPO(OH)_2
\end{aligned}
$$

3-Glyceraldehyde phosphate

$$
(HO)_2OPOH_2\overset{6}{C}
$$

5 H : HO 2
H
4 : : 3 1 CH₂OPO(OH)₂
OH H

Aldolase ⇌

Fructose-1,6-diphosphate

↕ H_3PO_4 (nonenzymatic)

$$
\begin{bmatrix}
H\ \ \ OH \\
C{-}OPO(OH)_2 \\
CHOH \\
CH_2OPO(OH)_2
\end{bmatrix}
$$

COOH
CHOH
CH₃
Lactic acid (End product of metabolism in muscle)

↕ DPN
Phosphoglyceraldehyde dehydrogenase

↕ DPNH₂
Lactic dehydrogenase

$$
\begin{aligned}
&C{-}O{\sim}PO(OH)_2 \\
&CHOH \\
&CH_2OPO(OH)_2
\end{aligned}
$$
1,3-Diphosphoglyceric acid

COOH
C=O —Carboxylase→ CH₃CHO —DPNH₂→ CH₃CH₂OH
CH₃ (Termination of alcoholic fermentation)
Pyruvic acid

↕ ADP
(nonenzymatic)

↕ ADP

COOH
C—O∼PO(OH)₂
CH₂
Phosphoenol-
pyruvic acid

—H₂O
Enolase ⇌

COOH
CHOPO(OH)₂
CH₂OH
2-Phosphoglyceric
acid

Triose
mutase ⇌

COOH
CHOH
CH₂OPO(OH)₂
3-Phosphoglyceric acid

released by metabolism of glucose to lactic acid is translated into mechanical work. Lactic acid accumulates during muscular activity, and it was originally considered that the conversion of glycogen into lactic acid furnishes energy utilized for muscular contraction. It is now known however that muscle can contract for a time when the formation of lactic acid is blocked by addition of iodoacetic acid, which poisons the enzyme system involved in lactic acid formation (Lundsgaard, 1930). Shortly before this observation was made, Eggleston, and Fiske and Subbarow, noted that a labile organic compound containing phosphorus (phosphogen) is hydrolyzed during muscular contraction and resynthesized during the recovery period, and the latter investigators succeeded in isolating 70% of the labile phosphorus in protein-free filtrates of muscle as a crystalline substance that they identified

$$HN{=}C\underset{\displaystyle\underset{CH_3}{|}}{\overset{\displaystyle NH{\sim}PO(OH)_2}{\big\langle}}\quad\overset{\angle\ ADP{-}ATP}{\Longrightarrow}\quad HN{=}C\underset{\displaystyle\underset{CH_3}{|}}{\overset{\displaystyle NH_3^{+}}{\big\langle}}\qquad HN{=}C\underset{\displaystyle\underset{NH_2}{|}}{\overset{\displaystyle NH{\sim}PO(OH)_2}{\big\langle}}$$

Phosphocreatine   Phosphoarginine

as phosphorylated creatine. The phosphogen of invertebrates is phospho-arginine. Additional experiments have led to the present view that muscular energy is derived from hydrolysis of phosphocreatine and that energy obtained from the breakdown of glycogen to lactic acid is used for resynthesis of phosphocreatine by transfer of a phosphate group from adenosine triphosphate to creatine. Quantitative measurements show that four molecules of phosphocreatine are synthesized as the result of the degradation of one glucose unit of glycogen to two moles of lactic acid (Lundsgaard, 1931). Glucose itself is not so efficient a substrate, since degradation of this hexose leads to the synthesis of only two to three molecules of phosphocreatine.

A more exact picture of the mechanism of the transfer of energy derived from glucolysis into mechanical work has been presented by Lipmann (1941). The essential change involved in muscle metabolism is degradation of a glucose unit into two C_3-units with concomitant conversion of the relatively unreactive inorganic phosphate ion into the very labile organic phosphate groups of adenosine triphosphate and eventually of phosphocreatine. This conversion has been established experimentally by feeding animals radioactive sodium phosphate ($Na_2HP^{32}O_4$) and isolating, from the muscles of sacrificed animals, adenosine triphosphate containing radioactive phosphorus. The phosphate transfer is rapid, for the radioactive organic phosphate can be detected within thirty minutes after feeding (Meyerhof, Parnas, 1937–39). The phosphorylated intermediates of metabolism fall into two distinct groups. One group consists of phosphate esters of primary or of secondary alcohols [—RCHO—PO(OH)$_2$]; these esters (the various hexose phosphates, 3-glyceraldehyde phosphate, 2- and 3-phosphoglyceric acid) are all relatively stable and readily isolable, and on hydrolysis they liberate rather small amounts of energy, approximately 3000 cal. The second group consists of difficultly isolable phosphorus compounds containing four different types of reactive linkage (indicated by $\sim$): —PO(OH)O$\sim$ PO(OH)$_2$ (adenosine triphosphate contains two of these anhydride linkages and one ester linkage); —C(=O)O$\sim$PO(OH)$_2$(1,3-diphosphoglyceric acid contains one reactive phosphate group and one ester group); —C(=CH$_2$)O$\sim$ PO(OH)$_2$ (phosphoenolpyruvic acid); and —HN$\sim$PO(OH)$_2$ (phosphocreatine). Three of the groups can be considered to contain an anhydride-like bond, formed by loss of water between two phosphate groups or between a phosphate group and either a carboxyl group or an acidic enol group. Just as acetyl chloride and acetic anhydride are more active acetylating agents than acetic acid or ethyl acetate, the anhydride-like phosphates are much more active phosphorylating agents than phosphoric acid or phosphate esters. The fourth type, exemplified by phosphocreatine and phospho-arginine, contains a phosphorus atom linked directly to a nitrogen atom. The energy obtained by hydrolysis of any one of these labile phosphate groups is in the order of 9000 to 12,000 cal. Lipmann deduced that the energy derived from glucolysis is used to convert phosphate ion or energy-poor phosphate esters into energy-rich phosphorus compounds, which represent, according to this picture, a reservoir of energy that can be utilized for muscular contraction or other functions. Inorganic phosphate is introduced into the metabolic process by means of reactions requiring little energy: (a) phosphorolysis of glycogen, and (b) addition of phosphoric acid to a carbonyl group (3-glyceraldehyde phosphate $+ H_3PO_4 \rightarrow 1,3$-diphospho-glyceraldehyde), a reaction comparable to the addition reactions of aldehydes encountered in the laboratory. The primary, energy-poor phosphate esters are converted into energy-rich phosphate anhydrides by dehydrogenation ($1,3$-diphosphoglyceraldehyde $- 2 H \rightarrow 1,3$-diphosphoglyceric acid) and by dehydration (2-phosphoglyceric acid $- H_2O \rightarrow$ phosphoenolpyruvic acid). This mechanism agrees with the experimental observation cited above that one glucose unit of glycogen furnishes enough energy for resynthesis of four molecules of phosphocreatine, for by degradation of one glucose unit (Charts 1 and 2) four energy-rich phosphate groups are transferred to the adenylic acid system. Glucose is not so efficient a substrate as glycogen, because the initial phosphorylation of glucose (reaction 3, Chart 1), unlike that of glycogen (reaction 1, Chart 1), requires transformation of an energy-rich phosphate anhydride group from adenosine triphosphate into the energy-poor phosphate ester group of glucose 6-phosphate; and the net gain in energy-rich phosphate groups is thereby reduced. In the case of other cells, which utilize energy derived from metabolism for a variety of elaborate syntheses rather than for the specific function of mechanical work, it is not possible to correlate the transfer of energy so precisely, but even so, it is believed that energy is conveyed through phosphate bonds.

In the recovery period, in the presence of oxygen, about two thirds of the lactic acid formed during contraction is retransformed into glycogen and one third is oxidized to carbon dioxide and water. All the reactions leading from glycogen to lactic acid are reversible except the phosphorylation of pyruvic acid (Chart 2).

Alcoholic Fermentation (Chart 2). — The course of fermentation and metabolism in muscle indicated in Charts 1 and 2 is a very brief summary of a vast amount of experimental work contributed by many of the investigators already mentioned, as well as by Embden, Kluyver, Lohmann, v. Euler, Nilsson, Parnas, Warburg, and others. The technique of employing cell-free extracts played an important role, since it is practically impossible to isolate intermediates from living cells in which fermentation ordinarily occurs. Separation of nonprotein constituents by dialysis facilitated characterization of the coenzymes of the system. Some intermediates were isolated by fixation methods. Acetaldehyde can be fixed as the bisulfite addition product, as already stated, or as the dimedone derivative, which is sparingly soluble and nonfermentable. Glycerol, rather than eth-

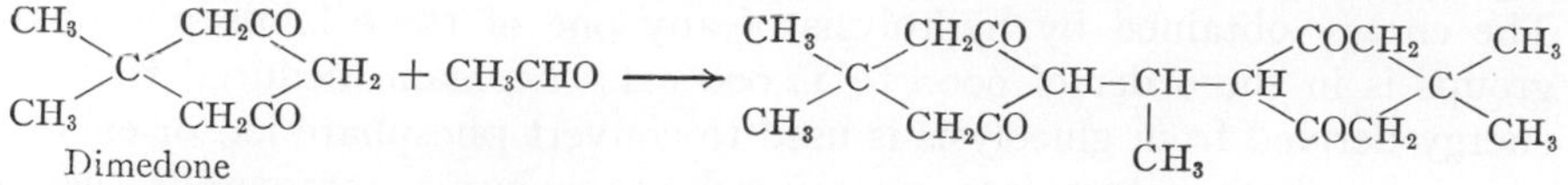

Dimedone
(5,5-dimethylcyclo-
hexanedione-1,3)

Aldomedone

anol, is then the main product and is produced commercially by this principle. Pyruvic acid has been isolated by fixation with β-naphthylamine, with which it forms a derivative which is fermentable but isolable because of its sparing solubility. A further method of investigation is based upon

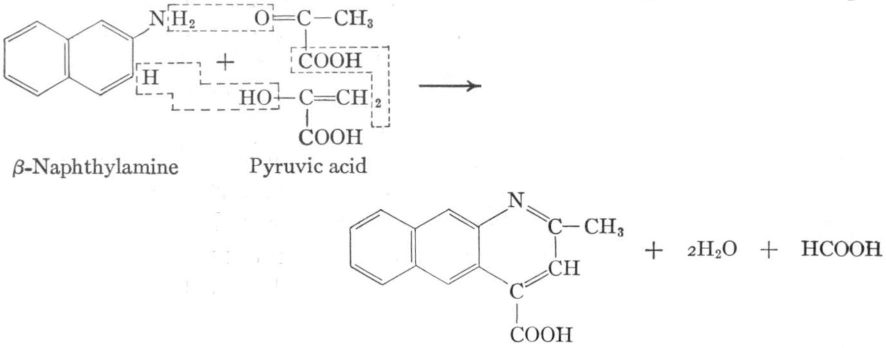

β-Naphthylamine   Pyruvic acid

$+ \quad 2H_2O \quad + \quad HCOOH$

α-Methyl-β-naphthocinchonic acid

the ability of certain chemicals to poison specific enzyme systems. When sodium fluoride is added to the fermentation, the enzyme enolase is poisoned, with the result that the phosphoglyceric acids accumulate and are not converted into phosphopyruvic acid. The addition of monoiodoacetic acid poisons coenzyme I, and thus inhibits reduction of acetaldehyde to alcohol by hydrogen transfer from $DPNH_2$. If other hydrogen acceptors are introduced, they compete with acetaldehyde and themselves become reduced. Nitrobenzene added to the fermentation is reduced to aniline, benzaldehyde to benzyl alcohol, sulfur to hydrogen sulfide.

Yeasts and molds are varieties of fungi, a group of parasitic plants that are unable to synthesize organic material from carbon dioxide and are dependent upon preformed nutrients. The industrial yeasts belong to the genus *Saccharomyces*, so named because they live in media containing sugar. *S. cerevisiae*, the variety usually employed for brewing and baking, is a cultivated yeast of uncertain origin that has been known for centuries but is not found growing wild. Coenzyme I is present to the extent of about 0.5 g. per kg. of fresh yeast. The presence in yeast dialyzate of the acidic coenzyme cocarboxylase was indicated (1932) by the observation that alkali-washed yeast is incapable of fermenting sugar; the coenzyme was isolated in crystalline form in 1937. Glycolytic enzymes of yeast hydrolyze di-saccharides but not polysaccharides. About 90% of the U. S. industrial alcohol production of some hundreds of millions of gallons starts with black-strap molasses, a syrupy mixture containing 45–55% of sugars, mainly sucrose.

Only four hexoses are fermented by yeast: D-glucose, D-fructose, D-mannose, and D-galactose; the last is fermented only with difficulty and not by all species of yeasts. The first three sugars have corresponding configurations at C_3 and C_4, the positions involved in fission of the carbon chain (Chart 2). Galactose differs in the configuration at C_4 and requires epimerization at this position under the influence of a special enzyme before it can be utilized.

Minor by-products of alcoholic fermentation are fusel oil, a mixture of isoamyl and d-amyl alcohol, succinic acid, and tyrosol. They appear to arise from leucine, isoleucine, glutamic acid, and tyrosine by transamination, decarboxylation, and reduction. On addition of one of these acids to a

$$(CH_3)_2CHCH_2CH(NH_2)CO_2H \rightarrow (CH_3)_2CHCH_2COCO_2H \rightarrow$$

$$(CH_3)_2CHCH_2CHO \rightarrow (CH_3)_2CHCH_2CH_2OH$$

sugar fermentation the corresponding alcohol is produced in 80–85% yield (F. Ehrlich, 1905–07). Tyrosol, a bitter-tasting substance, has been found in beer (1917) and probably contributes to the flavor.

Tyrosine → Tyrosol

Aerobic Metabolism. — Pyruvic acid formed by anaerobic metabolism is subject to rapid oxidation by oxygen to carbon dioxide and water. Oxygen uptake, measurable manometrically in the Warburg apparatus, proceeds at a particularly high rate in suspensions of muscle tissue. The net result is expressed by the equation: $CH_3COCO_2H + 5[O] \rightarrow 3 CO_2 + 2 H_2O$, but various observations suggested participation of several other metabolites. Szent-Györgyi[7] (1936) noted that addition of a small amount of either fumaric, succinic, malic, or oxalacetic acid greatly increases the rate of oxygen consumption by muscle tissue, and shortly afterward Krebs[8] noted the similar catalytic effect of α-ketoglutaric and citric acid. The suggestion that all these substances are participating metabolites eventually was firmly established. Utilization of pyruvate by liver tissue is accelerated by carboxyl-

---

[7] Albert Szent-Györgyi, b. 1893 Budapest; M.D. Budapest, Ph.D. Cambridge; Marine Biol. Lab., Woods Hole, Mass.; Nobel Prize 1937

[8] Hans Adolf Krebs, b. 1900 Hildesheim, Germany; Ph.D. Hamburg; Oxford; Nobel Prize 1953

ase, an indication that one reaction is carboxylation or decarboxylation. Pyruvate oxidation in dialyzed brain dispersions requires the following substances: one of the above C_4-dicarboxylic acids, the adenylic acid system, carboxylase, cocarboxylase, coenzyme I (DPN), coenzyme A, inorganic phosphate, and magnesium ion.

Krebs (1940) interpreted the oxidation in terms of an elaborate cycle of changes in which various catalytic acids are involved as intermediates that are continuously synthesized and destroyed. Originally the first step was described as conversion of pyruvic acid into an "active acetate" unit, but this was later identified as acetyl coenzyme A. The reaction requires CoA itself and the cofactors cocarboxylase (decarboxylation), thioctic acid (activation, p. 139), and DPN (hydrogen acceptor):

$$CH_3COCO_2H + CoASH + DPN \rightarrow CoASCOCH_3 + DPNH_2 + CO_2$$

The Krebs cycle (citric acid cycle) as presently conceived is represented in Chart 3. After the first step of oxidative decarboxylation just discussed, acetyl coenzyme A under the influence of the "condensing enzyme" undergoes "tail" condensation with oxalacetic acid, one of the C_4-catalytic acids, to form the citryl derivative of CoA, which is hydrolyzed to citric acid with regeneration of CoA. Citric acid, in the presence of the enzyme aconitase, is in equilibrium with *cis*-aconitic acid and isocitric acid (the reactions involved are loss of water and addition of water in the opposite direction). Isocitric acid undergoes dehydrogenation to oxalosuccinic acid, which, being a β-keto acid, readily loses carbon dioxide to form α-ketoglutaric acid. Oxidative decarboxylation then gives the C_4-dicarboxylic acid, succinic acid; the cycle is then completed by dehydrogenation to fumaric acid, addition of water (malic acid), and dehydrogenation to oxalacetic acid. The carbon dioxide (3 moles) formed by metabolic oxidation of pyruvate results from decarboxylation of three intermediates in the Krebs cycle (pyruvic acid, oxalosuccinic acid, α-ketoglutaric acid); and the two and one-half moles of oxygen required for oxidation of one mole of pyruvic acid are actually used for combustion of the five moles of hydrogen (with formation of water) obtained by five dehydrogenation steps in the Krebs cycle. The process is particularly efficient because of the high heat of combustion of hydrogen.

Many lines of evidence support the Krebs cycle. One is that malonic acid is a respiratory poison (Quastel); it resembles succinic acid closely enough to deactivate succinic dehydrogenase, the enzyme that dehydrogenates succinic acid to fumaric acid. Addition of malonic acid therefore can block one step in the cycle and thus prevent normal oxidation of pyruvate. Sodium arsenite interferes with a different enzyme system, and in the presence of this poison α-ketoglutaric acid accumulates and can be readily isolated. The Krebs cycle accounts for the fact that glutamic acid, aspartic acid, and alanine, and only these amino acids, are oxidized rapidly in

CHART 3. KREBS CYCLE

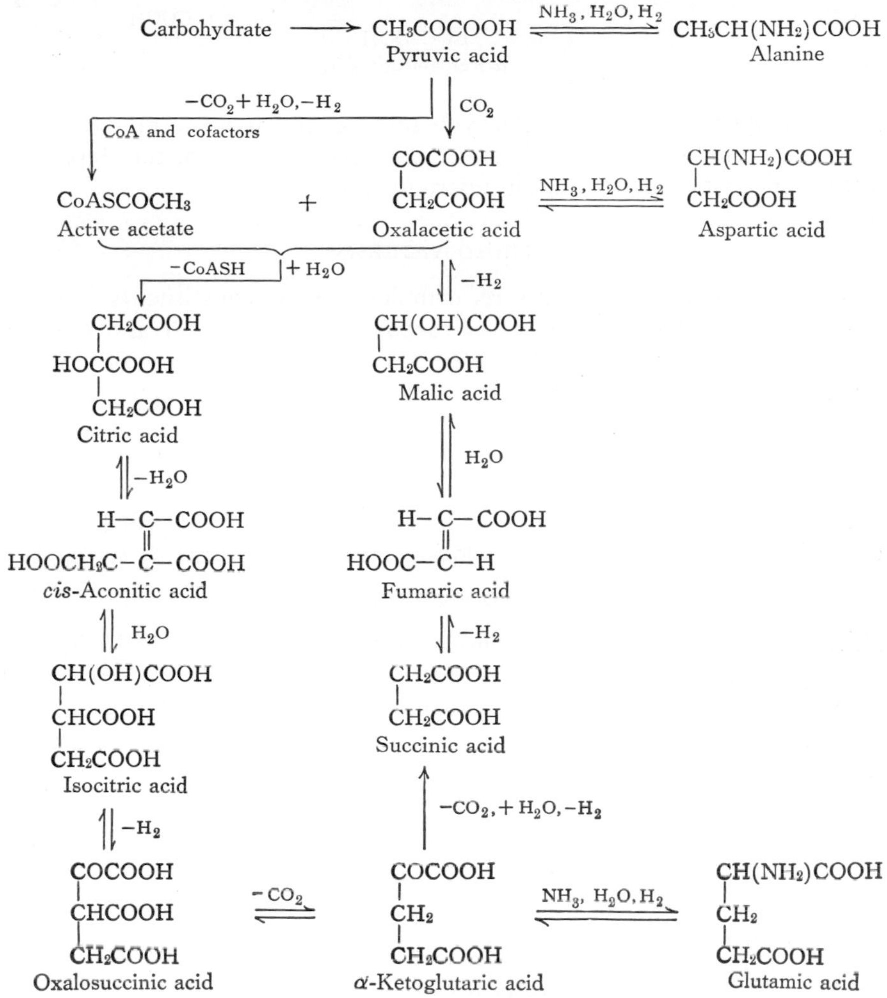

Carbohydrate $\longrightarrow$ CH₃COCOOH $\underset{}{\overset{NH_3, H_2O, H_2}{\rightleftharpoons}}$ CH₃CH(NH₂)COOH
Pyruvic acid $\qquad$ Alanine

−CO₂ + H₂O, −H₂ | CO₂

CoA and cofactors

CoASCOCH₃ $\qquad$ + $\qquad$ COCOOH | CH₂COOH $\underset{}{\overset{NH_3, H_2O, H_2}{\rightleftharpoons}}$ CH(NH₂)COOH | CH₂COOH
Active acetate $\qquad$ Oxalacetic acid $\qquad$ Aspartic acid

−CoASH | + H₂O $\qquad$ −H₂

CH₂COOH | HOCCOOH | CH₂COOH
Citric acid

CH(OH)COOH | CH₂COOH
Malic acid

−H₂O $\qquad$ H₂O

H−C−COOH ‖ HOOCH₂C−C−COOH
cis-Aconitic acid

H−C−COOH ‖ HOOC−C−H
Fumaric acid

H₂O $\qquad$ −H₂

CH(OH)COOH | CHCOOH | CH₂COOH
Isocitric acid

CH₂COOH | CH₂COOH
Succinic acid

−H₂ $\qquad$ −CO₂, + H₂O, −H₂

COCOOH | CHCOOH | CH₂COOH
Oxalosuccinic acid

−CO₂

COCOOH | CH₂ | CH₂COOH
α-Ketoglutaric acid

$\underset{}{\overset{NH_3, H_2O, H_2}{\rightleftharpoons}}$

CH(NH₂)COOH | CH₂ | CH₂COOH
Glutamic acid

muscle, since they are convertible by transamination into keto acids that are intermediates in the cycle. In certain tissues, though not in muscle, cocarboxylase shows the same catalytic effect as the C₄-dicarboxylic acids. This effect is due to the fixation of carbon dioxide by pyruvic acid to form oxalacetic acid, required for initiation of the cycle. Evans (1940) found that pyruvic acid incubated with minced pigeon liver in a buffer containing radioactive bicarbonate ($HC^{11}O_3^-$) was converted into radioactive α-ketoglutaric acid and that the radioactivity was located in the carboxyl group adjacent to the carbonyl group, the position at which radioactivity would be expected if α-ketoglutaric acid were formed by the reactions postulated in the Krebs cycle.

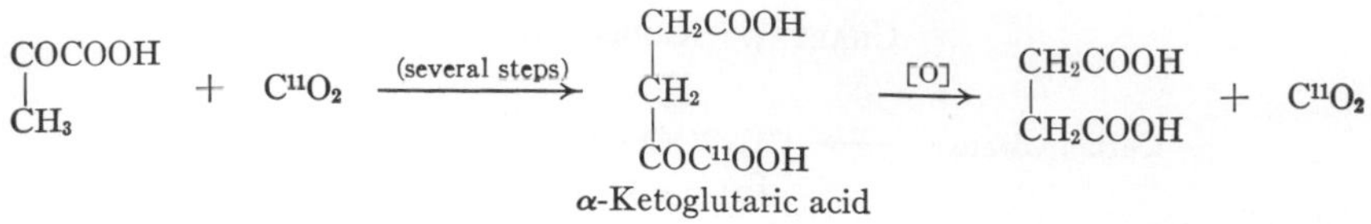

$$\begin{array}{c} \text{COCOOH} \\ | \\ \text{CH}_3 \end{array} + \text{C}^{11}\text{O}_2 \xrightarrow{\text{(several steps)}} \begin{array}{c} \text{CH}_2\text{COOH} \\ | \\ \text{CH}_2 \\ | \\ \text{COC}^{11}\text{OOH} \end{array} \xrightarrow{[O]} \begin{array}{c} \text{CH}_2\text{COOH} \\ | \\ \text{CH}_2\text{COOH} \end{array} + \text{C}^{11}\text{O}_2$$

α-Ketoglutaric acid

It now appears that the Krebs cycle presents the major terminal pathway of oxidation in animal, bacterial, and plant cells. Many of the steps in the cycle were first demonstrated in microorganisms.

PHOTOSYNTHESIS

The green plant synthesizes its complex organic constituents from carbon dioxide, as the only source of carbon, and from water and inorganic salts derived from the soil. The animal organism lacks the power of initiating syntheses from such simple entities, and is dependent upon preformed organic materials supplied in the diet. Since fats and proteins of plants are apparently derived from carbohydrate precursors rather than the reverse, carbohydrates are the probable primary products of photosynthesis.

Energy required for reduction of carbon dioxide is supplied by solar energy absorbed by the green coloring matter of the plant, which Will-

$$n\text{CO}_2 + n\text{H}_2\text{O} \xrightarrow{h\nu} (\text{CH}_2\text{O})_n + n\text{O}_2$$

stätter showed (1906–14) to consist of two chemically allied pigments, chlorophyll-a and chlorophyll-b, both of which are related in structure to hemin, the red pigment of blood. Minor details of the structures are still

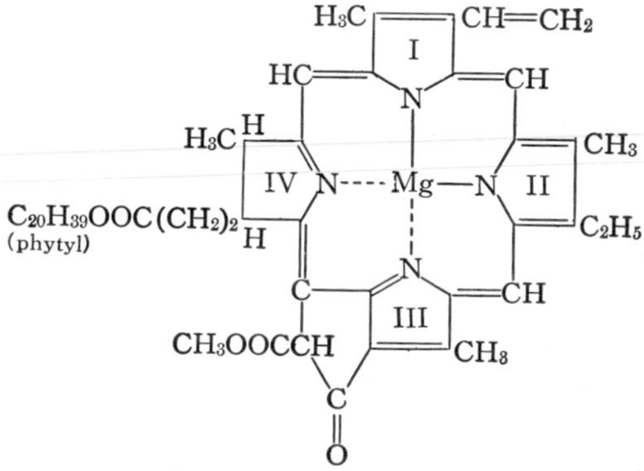

Chlorophyll-a (H. Fischer)

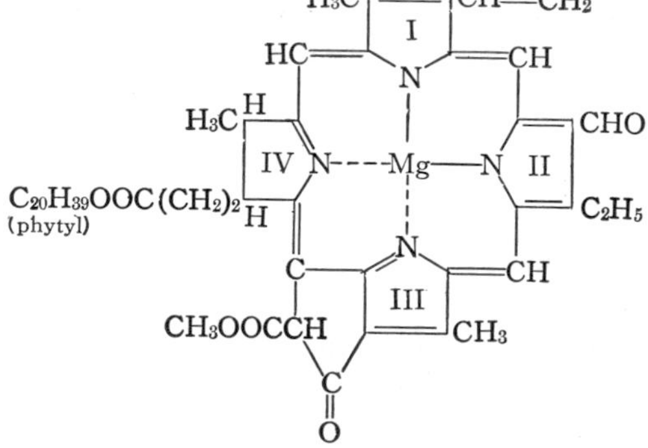

Chlorophyll-b (H. Fischer)

uncertain. In the plant the pigments are bound to protein. Maximum rate of photosynthesis is observed at wave lengths corresponding to maximum absorption by chlorophyll.

If photosynthesis were a simple photochemical reaction, the rate would be determined by the intensity of illumination and be practically insensitive to changes of temperature. This relationship is observed only at low light intensities; under strong irradiation the rate is approximately doubled by a $10°$ rise in temperature and therefore must be determined by a chemical reaction. Blackman (1905) postulated that at least two reactions are involved and that the rate of photosynthesis is determined by the rate of the slower reaction. At low intensities the rate of the light reaction is less and determines the rate of photosynthesis, whereas at high intensities the rate of the dark or "Blackman" reaction becomes the limiting factor. Later additional evidence has confirmed the concept of a light and dark reaction. Warburg (1919) found that the yield of carbon dioxide reduced per unit time of illumination of high intensity is much higher if the light is applied intermittently rather than continuously.

Many theories have been advanced for the mechanism of photosynthesis. Baeyer (1870) suggested that the initial product of the photochemical reaction is formaldehyde, which then undergoes condensation to sugars. Although the condensation can be realized in the laboratory under certain conditions, there is no evidence that the reaction can occur under conditions encountered in the living cell. Formaldehyde has never been isolated from plant tissue, and is poisonous to plants if added in more than traces. Some recent theories are modifications of Villstätter's concept (1918) that the dark reaction involves formation of a chlorophyll-carbon dioxide complex, which undergoes photochemical rearrangement with liberation of transient formaldehyde and regeneration of chlorophyll.

Investigation of photosynthesis is difficult since the process is dependent upon living cells and even slight injury causes complete loss of photosynthetic activity. Addition of postulated intermediates, which has proved so useful in the study of fermentation, has been of no value in determining the course of photosynthesis, perhaps because the added chemicals cannot penetrate the intact cell. More fruitful results have been obtained by studying the fixation of radioactive carbon dioxide, which can be detected in minute amounts. Thus Ruben (1939–43) found that carbon dioxide is fixed by green plants in the dark and that none of the radioactivity is associated with the chlorophyll fraction. Evidently fixation of carbon dioxide precedes the photochemical reaction involving reduction and is independent of chlorophyll. Large amounts of the radioactivity are found in the phosphoglyceric acid and the triose phosphate, and hence the synthesis of hexose undoubtedly proceeds by reversal of the metabolic cleavage of fructose diphosphate (Calvin,[9] 1947–49). The distribution of radioactivity in glucose synthesized in the presence of $C^{14}O_2$ is as follows: 61% in the

[9] Melvin Calvin, b. 1911 St. Paul; Ph.D. Minnesota (Glockler); Univ. of California, Berkeley

3,4-positions, 24% in the 2,5-positions, and 15% in the 1,6-positions; the result supports the supposition that glucose is formed by condensation of two molecules of a triose. A further experimental observation is that even after very brief periods of photosynthesis (ninety seconds) as many as fifteen identified compounds contain labeled carbon. These include, in addition to glucose and fructose, the triose phosphates, pyruvic acid, malic acid, succinic acid, glycolic acid, glyoxylic acid, the amino acids glycine, serine, alanine, aspartic acid, and glutamic acid. When the time of photosynthesis is reduced to five seconds, radioactivity is fixed in only four or five compounds, particularly in the carboxyl group of 2-phosphoglyceric acid.

A different approach to the problem of photosynthesis has been followed by van Niel,[10] who has studied the metabolism of bacteria, particularly the purple bacteria, which resemble green plants in several respects. They contain, in addition to a typical red pigment, a green pigment that was shown by Schneider and further by H. Fischer to be closely related to chlorophyll, as reflected in the name, bacteriochlorophyll. It differs from chlorophyll-b only in that the vinyl group (ring I) is replaced by $-COCH_3$. In common with algae, bacteria show a phototactic response to irradiation (movement toward the light source); however they do not evolve oxygen. Although it was suspected as early as 1883 that purple bacteria might be photosynthetic, this inference was not established until 1930 when van Niel showed that certain species, the purple sulfur bacteria (*Thiorhodaceae*) and the related green sulfur bacteria, can develop on media containing any one of a number of inorganic sulfur compounds and bicarbonate as the only source of carbon, but only when irradiated. In these cases, the following equations have been verified for the photosynthetic process:

Green bacteria: $$CO_2 + 2H_2S \xrightarrow{h\nu} (CH_2O) + H_2O + 2S$$

Purple bacteria:
$$2CO_2 + 4H_2O + H_2S \xrightarrow{h\nu} 2(CH_2O) + 2H_2O + H_2SO_4$$
$$3CO_2 + 8H_2O + 2S \xrightarrow{h\nu} 3(CH_2O) + 3H_2O + 2H_2SO_4$$
$$CO_2 + 2H_2O + 2H_2SO_3 \xrightarrow{h\nu} (CH_2O) + H_2O + 2H_2SO_4$$

These processes follow the general equation:

$$CO_2 + 2H_2A \xrightarrow{h\nu} (CH_2O) + H_2O + 2A$$

According to this concept carbon dioxide is reduced by a hydrogen donor, which, in the case of the green and purple sulfur bacteria, is an oxidizable sulfur compound. The general equation was shown to be applicable to the purple bacteria that require an organic substance as substrate (*Athiorhodaceae*), when a strain was found that reduced one mole of carbon dioxide by oxidation of two moles of isopropyl alcohol:

$$CO_2 + 2(CH_3)_2CHOH \xrightarrow{h\nu} (CH_2O) + 2(CH_3)_2CO + H_2O$$

On the basis of present evidence, it appears that one manifestation of the

---

[10] Cornelius B. van Niel, b. 1897 Haarlem, Netherlands; D.Sc. Delft; Hopkins Marine Station, Stanford

general phenomenon of photosynthesis consists in reduction of carbon dioxide in plants with utilization of water as the hydrogen donor, and that another, operative in microorganisms, embodies photochemical reduction of the same carbon source in a process in which water is replaced as the hydrogen donor by hydrogen sulfide or comparable inorganic compound or even by an organic substance.

READING REFERENCES

O. Meyerhof, "Oxidoreductions in Carbohydrate Breakdown," *Biol. Symposia*, 5, 141 (1941)

C. F. Cori, "Phosphorylation of Glycogen and Glucose," *ibid.*, 5, 131 (1941)

H. A. Krebs, "The Intermediary Stages in the Biological Oxidation of Carbohydrate," *Advances in Enzymology*, 3, 191 (1943)

W. N. Haworth, "Carbohydrate Components of Biologically Active Materials,'' *J. Chem. Soc.*, 582 (1947)

D. J. Bell, "An Introduction to Carbohydrate Biochemistry," University Tutorial Press, London (1948)

A. W. D. Avison and J. D. Hawkins, "The Role of Phosphoric Esters in Biological Reactions," *Quart. Rev.*, 5, 171 (1951)

S. Ochoa, "Enzymatic Mechanisms in the Citric Acid Cycle," *Advances in Enzymology*, 15, 183 (1954)

CHAPTER 18

FAT METABOLISM

Complex Lipids. — Fats are stored in plants mainly in the seed, fruit, and spore, and in animals mainly in subcutaneous and intermuscular tissue and in the abdominal cavity. Fats are present in almost all cells, but in the more active tissues (brain, liver, kidney, etc.) they usually occur in a form more complex than depot fats, which are mainly glycerides. The physiological function of complex lipids is largely a matter of speculation. Most complex fats are phosphatides (or phospholipids), which differ from simple fats in that they contain a phosphoric acid grouping and usually also a nitrogenous base in addition to fatty acid components. The lecithins (Gr. *lekithos*, yolk; first isolated from egg yolk) all have the same general structure (I) and differ only in the fatty acid component. The base of the

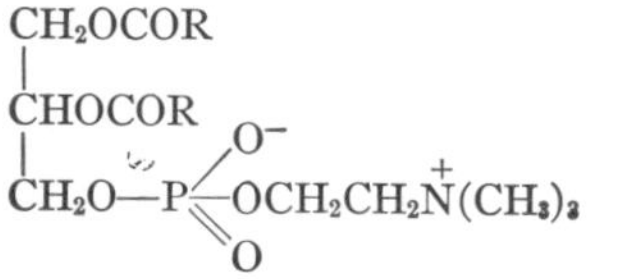

CH$_2$OCOR
|
CHOCOR
|
CH$_2$O—P$\diagdown$O$^-$—OCH$_2$CH$_2$N$^+$(CH$_3$)$_3$
  $\diagdown$O

I. α-Lecithin

CH$_2$OCOR
|
CHOCOR
|
CH$_2$O—P$\diagdown$OH—OCH$_2$CH$_2$NH$_2$
  $\diagdown$O

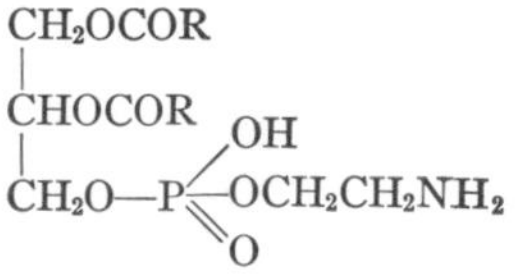

II. α-Cephalin

CH$_2$OCOR
|
CHOCOR
|
CH$_2$O—P$\diagdown$OH—OCH$_2$CHCO$_2$H
  $\diagdown$O |
        NH$_2$

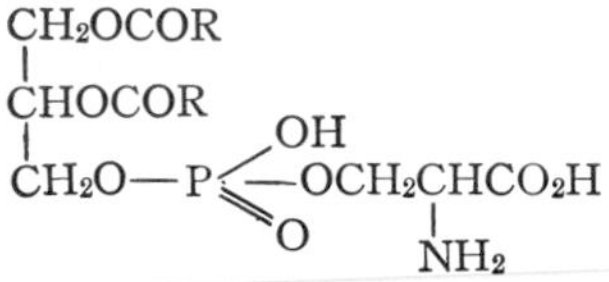

III. Phosphatidylserine

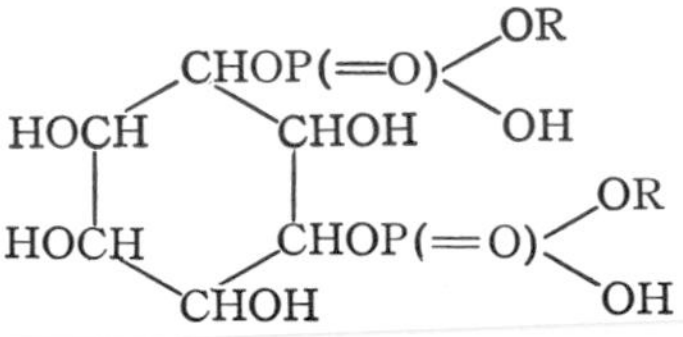

           OR
CHOP(=O)$\diagdown$
HOCH   CHOH   OH
| |
HOCH   CHOP(=O)$\diagdown$OR
  CHOH   OH

IV. Diphosphoinositide

lecithins is choline HOCH$_2$CH$_2$N$^+$(CH$_3$)$_3$OH$^-$, and these substances are glycerides in which a fatty acid in one of the α-positions is replaced by a phosphorylcholine residue. The lecithin mixture extracted from egg yolk or soybean oil, a waxy, hygroscopic material which rapidly darkens owing to air oxidation, is a powerful emulsifying agent. The cephalins (Gr. *kephale*, head; first isolated from brain tissue) were formerly believed to differ from lecithins only in that the basic component is ethanolamine instead of choline (II), but they are now known to be mixtures of phosphatides of three types, only one of which corresponds to the classical formula II. Another (III) is similar but the nitrogen-containing component is the amino acid serine. A third type (IV), unusual in that it contains no basic component, is comprised of fatty acid esters of *meso*-inositol diphosphate (Folch,[1] 1949).

---

[1] Jordi Folch (Folch-Pi), b. 1911 Barcelona, Spain; M.D. Barcelona; McLean Hospital, Belmont, Mass., and Harvard Univ.

Acids isolated from phosphatide hydrolyzates include stearic, oleic, linoleic, linolenic, and arachidonic acid.

A method for synthesis of lecithins of the natural L-configuration (one asymmetric carbon atom) developed by Baer[2] (1950) involves phosphorylation of the free hydroxyl group of an L-α,β-diglyceride (V) with phenylphosphoryl dichloride to give a diacyl α-glycerylphenylphosphoryl chloride (VI), which can react with the alcoholic group of choline chloride to form a phosphate diester (VII). The protective phenyl group is removed by cata-

$$
\begin{array}{c}
\text{CH}_2\text{OCOR} \\
| \\
\text{CHOCOR} \quad + \quad \text{Cl}_2\text{P}\!\!\begin{array}{c}\diagup\text{OC}_6\text{H}_5\\[2pt]\diagdown\!\!\!=\!\!\text{O}\end{array} \\
| \\
\text{CH}_2\text{OH}
\end{array}
\quad\longrightarrow\quad
\begin{array}{c}
\text{CH}_2\text{OCOR} \\
| \\
\text{CHOCOR} \\
| \quad\quad\quad \diagup\text{OC}_6\text{H}_5 \\
\text{CH}_2\text{O}\!-\!\text{P}\!\!\begin{array}{c}-\,\text{Cl}\\[2pt]\diagdown\!\!\!=\!\!\text{O}\end{array}
\end{array}
\xrightarrow[\text{Pyridine}]{\overset{+}{\text{HOCH}_2\text{CH}_2\text{N(CH}_3)_3}\overset{-}{\text{Cl}}}
$$

V   VI

$$
\begin{array}{c}
\text{CH}_2\text{OCOR} \\
| \\
\text{CHOCOR} \\
| \quad\quad \diagup\text{OC}_6\text{H}_5 \\
\text{CH}_2\text{O}\!-\!\text{P}\!\!\begin{array}{c}-\,\text{CH}_2\text{CH}_2\overset{+}{\text{N(CH}_3)_3}\overset{-}{\text{Cl}}\\[2pt]\diagdown\!\!\!=\!\!\text{O}\end{array}
\end{array}
\xrightarrow[\text{2. BaCO}_3]{\text{1. H}_2.\text{Pt}}
\begin{array}{c}
\text{CH}_2\text{OCOR} \\
| \\
\text{CHOCOR} \\
| \quad\quad \overset{-}{\text{O}} \\
\text{CH}_2\text{O}\!-\!\text{P}\!\!\begin{array}{c}-\,\text{OCH}_2\text{CH}_2\overset{+}{\text{N(CH}_3)_3}\\[2pt]\diagdown\!\!\!=\!\!\text{O}\end{array}
\end{array}
$$

VII   VIII

lytic hydrogenation and the salt is hydrolyzed to the free lecithin. Synthetic L-α-(distearoyl)-lecithin proved to be identical with hydrogenated egg yolk lecithin, the acids of which are stearic and oleic acid; L-α-(dipalmitoyl)-lecithin is identical with a natural phosphatide of brain, lung, and spleen.

Hydrolysis of an α-lecithin gives rise to both α- and β-glycerophosphoric acids; the migration of the phosphoric acid residue probably occurs through an intermediate cyclic ortho ester. Isolation of β-glycerophosphoric acid in

$$
\text{VIII} \longrightarrow
\begin{array}{c}
\text{CH}_2\text{OH} \\
| \\
\text{CHOH} \\
| \quad\quad \diagup\text{OH} \\
\text{CH}_2\text{O}\!-\!\text{P}\!\!\begin{array}{c}\\[2pt]\diagdown\!\!\!=\!\!\text{O}\end{array}\!\!\text{Chol.}
\end{array}
\underset{}{\overset{\text{H}_2\text{O}}{\rightleftharpoons}}
\begin{array}{c}
\text{CH}_2\text{OH} \\
| \\
\text{CHO}\!\!\diagdown \\
| \quad\quad\quad \text{P}\,\text{Chol.} \\
\text{CH}_2\text{O}\!\!\diagup\;\;\diagdown\text{O}
\end{array}
\underset{}{\overset{\text{H}_2\text{O}}{\rightleftharpoons}}
\begin{array}{c}
\text{CH}_2\text{OH} \quad\;\; \diagup\text{OH}\\
| \quad\quad\quad\quad \\
\text{CHO}\!-\!\text{P}\!\!\begin{array}{c}-\,\text{Chol.}\\[2pt]\diagdown\!\!\!=\!\!\text{O}\end{array} \\
| \\
\text{CH}_2\text{OH}
\end{array}
$$

$$
\downarrow \quad\quad\quad\quad\quad\quad\quad\quad\quad\quad\quad\quad\quad\quad\quad\quad \downarrow
$$

$$
\begin{array}{c}
\text{CH}_2\text{OH} \\
| \\
\text{CHOH} \\
| \\
\alpha\ \text{CH}_2\text{OPO(OH)}_2
\end{array}
\quad\quad\quad\quad\quad
\begin{array}{c}
\text{CH}_2\text{OH} \\
| \\
\beta\ \text{CHOPO(OH)}_2 \\
| \\
\text{CH}_2\text{OH}
\end{array}
$$

early structural studies was taken as evidence of the existence of natural β-lecithins, but the facts just cited show this evidence to be invalid.

The lecithin synthesis was modified by Baer (1951) for the synthesis of cephalins. In this case the diacylphenylphosphoryl chloride VI is condensed with N-carbobenzoxyethanolamine and then the protective carbo-

[2] Erich Baer, b. 1901 Berlin; Ph.D. Berlin; Univ. Toronto

benzoxy and phenyl groups are removed simultaneously to give the α-cephalin (overall yield 48–51%).

A number of phosphatides contain the base sphingosine (structure, Klenk,[3] 1931; Carter,[4] 1942). The fats containing this basic component are known as sphingolipids and are particularly prevalent in nerve tissue. The phosphosphingosides, or sphingomyelins (Gr. *sphingein*, to bind tight + Gr.

$$CH_3(CH_2)_{12}CH{=}CHCHOHCH(NH_2)CH_2OH$$
Sphingosine

myelos, marrow), are composed of a fatty acid, phosphoric acid, and both choline and sphingosine. Choline is linked as usual to phosphoric acid

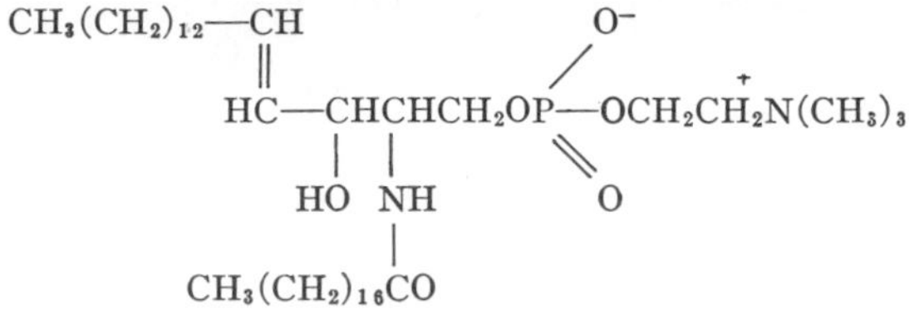

$$
\begin{array}{c}
CH_3(CH_2)_{12}{-}CH \\
\parallel \\
HC{-}CHCHCH_2OP{-}OCH_2CH_2N(CH_3)_3 \\
\mid \quad \mid \\
HO \quad NH \\
\mid \\
CH_3(CH_2)_{16}CO
\end{array}
$$
Sphingomyelin

which, in turn, is esterified with the primary alcoholic group of sphingosine; the double bond has the *trans* configuration (Stotz,[5] 1953–54). Only four acids have been isolated from hydrolyzates of sphingomyelins: lignoceric acid, palmitic acid, stearic acid, and nervonic (selacholeic) acid.

$$CH_3(CH_2)_{22}COOH \qquad\qquad CH_3(CH_2)_7CH{=}CH(CH_2)_{13}COOH$$
Lignoceric acid   Nervonic acid

The cerebrosides, or glycosphingosides, are complex lipids containing sphingosine, a fatty acid, and a sugar (either glucose or galactose); they differ from most complex lipids in containing no phosphoric acid. The probable arrangement of the component units is shown in the formula.

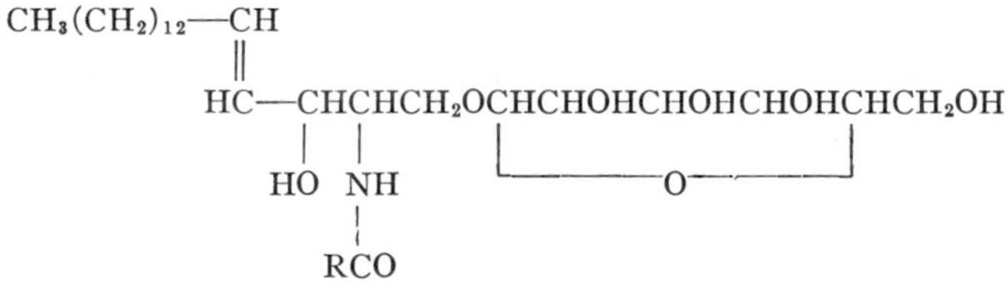

$$
\begin{array}{c}
CH_3(CH_2)_{12}{-}CH \\
\parallel \\
HC{-}CHCHCH_2OCHCHOHCHOHCHOHCHCH_2OH \\
\mid \quad \mid \qquad\qquad\qquad\qquad \\
HO \quad NH \qquad\mid\!\!-\!\!-\!\!-O\!\!-\!\!-\!\!-\!\mid \\
\mid \\
RCO
\end{array}
$$
Cerebroside

Known acid constituents of cerebrosides are: lignoceric acid, α-hydroxylignoceric (cerebronic) acid, nervonic acid, and α-hydroxynervonic acid. The lipids of ganglia (gangliosides) are even more complex (Klenk, 1942).

---

[3] Ernst Klenk, b. 1896 Pfalzgrafenweiler, Germany; Ph.D. Tübingen; Univ. Cologne

[4] Herbert E. Carter, b. 1910 Mooresville, Ind.; Ph.D. Illinois (Marvel); Dept. Chem., Illinois

[5] Elmer H. Stotz, b. 1911, Boston; Ph.D. Harvard (Hastings); Dept. Biochem., Rochester School of Med. Dent.

They contain a fatty acid, sphingosine, neuraminic acid ($C_{10}H_{19}NO_9$, structure unknown), and hexose (both galactose and glucose).

Digestion and Absorption of Fats. — Fats pass unchanged through the stomach and are hydrolyzed to glycerol and acids in the intestine by lipases of pancreatic and intestinal juices. Since the medium is essentially aqueous, fats are emulsified by the salts of the bile acids, glycocholic and taurocholic acid (I), and thus brought into contact with the enzymes. If the bile duct

Glycocholic acid, $R = -CH_2COOH$
Taurocholic acid, $R = -CH_2CH_2SO_3H$

is occluded, a large quantity of undigested fat is excreted in the feces. The bile acids resemble nonbiological surface-active compounds in that an ionizing hydrophilic group ($-CO_2^-$, $-SO_3^-$) is balanced by a lipophilic hydrocarbon moiety (lecithin is similar). Clear dispersions of fatty acids can be prepared in the presence of sodium glycocholate or taurocholate. This emulsifying action of the bile enables the split acids to be absorbed into the intestinal mucosa, where resynthesis to fat occurs. About 60% of the resynthesized fat passes into the lymph, and finally into the venous circulation. The remainder apparently passes directly into the portal system and is transported to the liver, the chief site of fat metabolism. Fat is transported in blood as minute particles that are stabilized by a protective film of serum protein (α- and β-globulin) at the oil–water interface.

Metabolism of Fats. — Use of isotopic tracers in biochemical studies was introduced by Schoenheimer[6] at Columbia University in 1935 in a classical study of fat metabolism. Deuterium, discovered by Urey at Columbia in 1932, was the only tracer available at the time. A compound labeled with the heavy isotope of hydrogen has properties so similar to those of the corresponding hydrogen compound that the body does not distinguish between the two. However, a sample to be analyzed can be burned to carbon dioxide and water (H_2O, D_2O) and the deuterium content measured in a mass spectrograph or from determination of density and refractive index. Other heavy isotopes of biologically important elements are now available, for example N^{15}, useful in studies of proteins and amino acids. Development of the nuclear reactor for uranium fission made possible the production of radioactive isotopes in quantity. Particularly useful is radioactive C^{14}, made by exposing N^{14} to neutron bombardment. This long-lived isotope

---

[6] Rudolf Schoenheimer, 1898–1941; b. Berlin; Ph.D. Berlin; Dept. Biochem., Coll. Phys and Surg., Columbia

has a half-life of about 5700 years. Its decay is attended with weakly penetrating β-radiation, which is accurately measurable with a Geiger counter even with small samples containing minute amounts of C^{14}. Radioactive tritium has now largely supplanted deuterium.

Schoenheimer's orienting experiment was done to test a long held hypothesis that that part of ingested fat which is not burned to satisfy energy requirements is stored in adipose tissue, from which it can be mobilized in time of need. Combustion of fat is the richest source of energy; the energy liberated per gram of substance burned is: fat, 9.5 kg.-cal.; protein, 4.4 kg.-cal.; glycogen, 4.2 kg.-cal. If depot fat is immobile, as supposed, mice fed deuterio fat, prepared by deuteration of linseed oil, and maintained at constant body weight should burn the labeled fat completely and not store it. However, at the end of four days the depot fat contained at least 44% of the ingested fat, which shows that depot fat is actually in a dynamic state. Comparable experiments with carbohydrates and proteins have given similar results.

In later experiments the fate of individual fatty acids was investigated. Labeled acids are prepared by heating a given saturated acid with heavy water in the presence of platinum catalyst until a certain percentage of the hydrogen atoms are replaced by deuterium. In a typical experiment deuteriopalmitic acid containing 22% of randomly distributed deuterium was fed to rats that were supplied liberally with butter. After eight days the body fats were found to contain 44% of the deuterium ingested. Analysis of individual acids revealed the presence of considerable deuterium in acids other than palmitic (Table 18.1). Almost 10% of the stearic acid and slightly less of the myristic and lauric acid had evidently been derived from palmitic acid, which shows that synthesis and degradation occur even on a diet that contains considerable amounts of these particular acids. At the same time some fatty acids are dehydrogenated to the oleic stage, and in a separate experiment Schoenheimer showed that the reverse reaction (saturation) also occurs.

TABLE 18.1. CONVERSION OF PALMITIC ACID (RATS)

FATTY ACID ISOLATED	DEUTERIUM, ATOM % ± 0.3
Palmitic (C_{16})	24.2
Stearic (C_{18})	9.3
Myristic and lauric ($C_{14} + C_{12}$)	5.6
Palmitoleic (C_{16}, 1Δ)	6.3
Oleic (C_{18}, 1Δ)	1.0
Linoleic (C_{18}, 2Δ)	0.3

These experiments indicated that fatty acids are rapidly destroyed and resynthesized but did not reveal the intermediates. As a means of characterizing intermediates, Knoop[7] (1904) had introduced an experimental

[7] Franz Knoop, 1875-1946; b. Shanghai; Ph.D. Freiburg; Tübingen

method that was a forerunner of modern tracer techniques: he used the phenyl group as a label, since it is not readily destroyed in the body. Ingested benzoic acid and phenylacetic acid are excreted in the urine as hippuric acid (II) and phenylaceturic acid (IV), respectively. Knoop found

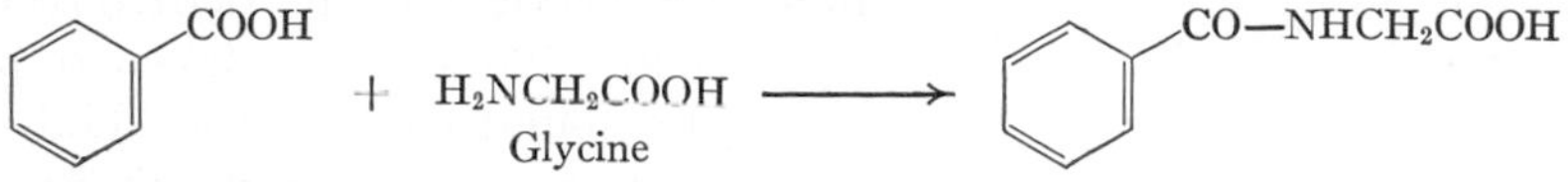

Benzoic acid
I

+ H₂NCH₂COOH
Glycine

Hippuric acid
II

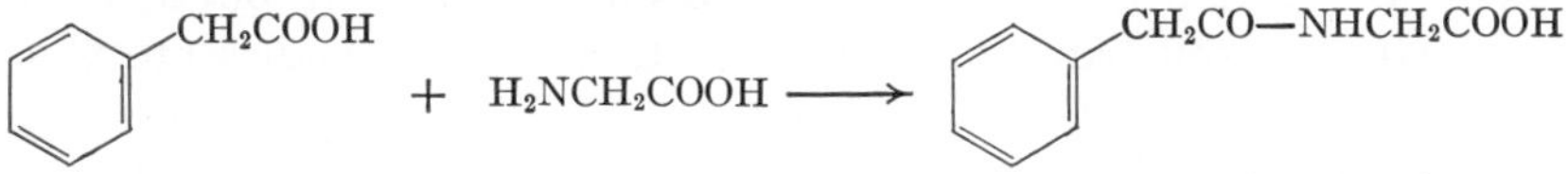

Phenylacetic acid
III

+ H₂NCH₂COOH ⟶

Phenylaceturic acid
IV

that a synthetic acid of the type $C_6H_5(CH_2)_nCO_2H$ fed to dogs is excreted either as the benzoic acid or as the phenylacetic acid conjugate with glycine, and that if n is an even number the product of the initial degradation is benzoic acid, but that if n is odd the product is phenylacetic acid. The results showed that degradation proceeds from the carboxyl end of the chain and eliminates carbon atoms in pairs of two. Use of the phenyl group as a label was validated by later experiments with isotopically labeled acids (Weinhouse,[8] 1944).

Knoop postulated an initial hydroxylation at the β-position, with subsequent oxidation to a β-keto acid and cleavage, and the phenomenon became known as **β-oxidation.** β Oxidation may account for the natural occurrence

$$RCH_2CH_2COOH \longrightarrow RCHOHCH_2COOH \longrightarrow RCOCH_2COOH \longrightarrow RCOOH$$

of pyolipic acid, or β-hydroxydecanoic acid, $CH_3(CH_2)_6CH(OH)CH_2COOH$ isolated from *Pseudomonas pyocyanea* (Theorell, 1946). Chibnall (1934) suggested that methyl heptyl ketone, methyl nonyl ketone, and methyl undecyl ketone, found in essential oils, arise by β-oxidation of fatty acids, followed by decarboxylation. Reduction of the ketonic group would then lead to the saturated paraffins of plant waxes. The hypothesis accounts for the fact that the natural methyl ketones and paraffin hydrocarbons of plant origin have an odd number of carbon atoms. β-Oxidation of a fatty acid side chain by chromic anhydride has been demonstrated (K. Nakanishi, 1952). Biological ω-oxidation, that is, oxidation of the terminal methyl group of an acid to carboxyl, has been observed, but only with C_8–C_{12} acids, which are not normally stored in depot fat. Verkade[9] showed that man excretes ingested triundecylin (C_{11}-glyceride) as undecanedioic acid, $HOOC(CH_2)_9COOH$; azelaic acid, $HOOC(CH_2)_7COOH$; and pimelic

---

[8] Sidney Weinhouse, b. 1909 Chicago; Ph.D. Chicago; Lankenau Hospital, Philadelphia

[9] Pieter E. Verkade, b. 1891 Zaandam, Netherlands· Ph.D. Delft (Böeseken); Rotterdam, Delft

acid, $HOOC(CH_2)_5COOH$. The two latter acids evidently arise by combined β- and ω-oxidation.

In certain diseases, such as diabetes, metabolism is abnormal and products of incomplete oxidation known as **ketone bodies** accumulate in the blood and urine (ketonuria). They include acetoacetic acid, its decarboxylation product acetone, and β-hydroxybutyric acid. These were shown to be derived from fatty acids by Embden,[10] who found that acetone bodies are formed on perfusion of liver with even-numbered straight-chain acids. Whether phenomena associated with abnormal metabolism and perfusions afford a valid insight into normal metabolism is a question, but at least the two primary intermediates that accumulate as ketone bodies are C_4-compounds of the type postulated by Knoop.

The first definitive evidence concerning the intermediates of fat metabolism resulted from study of synthesis, rather than degradation, of fats. Rittenberg and Bloch[11] (1944–45) showed that doubly labeled $CD_3C^{13}OONa$ fed to animals is converted into fatty acids of high content of both labeled atoms, and thereby demonstrated fat synthesis from C_2-units. The self-condensation of acetate units, however, requires such a large energy release (16 kg.-cal. per mole) that some active form of acetate seemed indicated. It is now known from the work of many investigators, particularly Lipmann (1951) and Ochoa[12] (1951) that this active C_2-unit is the acetylated form of coenzyme A, first isolated by Lynen (1951). The acetyl group is bound to the β-mercaptoethanol portion of the coenzyme (CoASH) to form a thiol ester (CoASCOCH$_3$). The C—S linkage in such a compound is highly reactive; thus thiolacetic acid, CH_3COSH, is an active acetylating agent for sulfhydryl compounds. Studies of fatty acid synthesis in both bacteria and animal tissues have shown that synthesis from C_2-units involves four steps (Chart 1). The first is a condensation of two molecules of acetyl CoA

CHART 1. FATTY ACID CYCLE

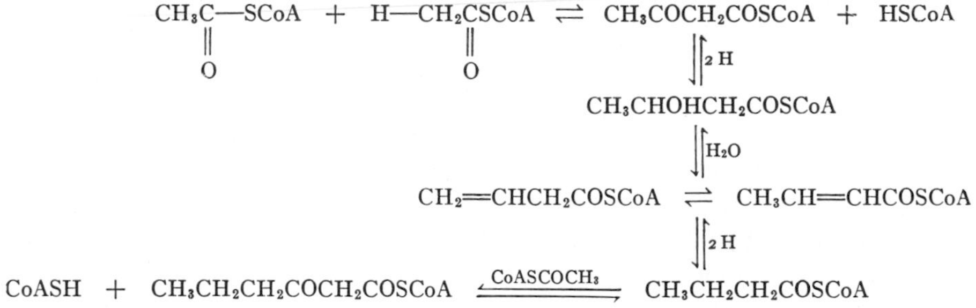

$$CH_3C\!\!-\!\!SCoA \;+\; H\!\!-\!\!CH_2CSCoA \;\rightleftharpoons\; CH_3COCH_2COSCoA \;+\; HSCoA$$

(with $\underset{O}{\parallel}$ on first two terms)

$$\Big\downarrow 2H$$

$$CH_3CHOHCH_2COSCoA$$

$$\Big\downarrow H_2O$$

$$CH_2\!=\!CHCH_2COSCoA \;\rightleftharpoons\; CH_3CH\!=\!CHCOSCoA$$

$$\Big\downarrow 2H$$

$$CoASH \;+\; CH_3CH_2CH_2COCH_2COSCoA \;\xrightarrow{\;CoASCOCH_3\;}\; CH_3CH_2CH_2COSCoA$$

to form acetoacetyl CoA and CoASH. This is described as a "head" reaction (head of the C_2-unit) and differs from the "tail" reaction involving the

---

[10] Gustav Embden, 1874–1933; b. Hamburg; Ph.D. Strasbourg; Frankfort

[11] Konrad E. Bloch, b. 1912 Neisse, Germany; Ph.D. Columbia (Schoenheimer); Harvard Univ.

[12] Severo Ochoa, b. 1905 Luarca, Spain; M.D. Madrid; Dept. Biochem., New York Univ.

methyl group in the citric acid cycle (p. 482). The next step is reduction to β-hydroxybutyryl CoA, followed by dehydration to α,β- and β,γ-unsaturated derivatives, and finally hydrogenation to butyryl CoA. The cycle is repeated by reaction of butyryl CoA with another molecule of acetyl CoA to form CoASH and β-ketocaproyl CoA, which undergoes reduction, dehydration and hydrogenation. In animals the cycle is repeated until full chain length is reached; bacteria that carry the cycle only to the butyric acid stage were of use in isolation of enzymes involved in the simpler steps. All the reactions are reversible, and degradation of fat occurs by reversal of the above sequence. Initiation of a degradation requires fixation of coenzyme A to the fatty acid to produce the active form. In most tissues this is achieved by reaction of the acid with CoA and adenosine triphosphate (ATP, derived from oxidation of carbohydrates). Since CoASH is regenerated in the succeeding step of condensation of two molecules of

$$RCOOH + CoASH + A\text{—}OPO(OH)\text{—}OPO(OH)\text{—}OPO(OH)_2 \rightleftharpoons$$
$$ATP$$

$$RCOSCoA + A\text{—}OPO(OH)_2 + (HO)_2PO\text{—}OPO(OH)_2$$
$$AMP \qquad\qquad PP$$

CoASCOCH$_3$, CoASH functions as a catalyst. Oxidation of the final C$_2$-unit, acetyl CoA, to carbon dioxide and water proceeds through the citric acid cycle. It is now clear why previous searches in the lipid fraction for intermediary metabolites were unsuccessful: the intermediates are all bound through coenzyme A to proteins.

Lipmann (1954) postulates that polyisoprenoid compounds arise by a path that is somewhat similar but involves "tail" condensation. Acetyl coenzyme A first adds to the carbonyl group of acetoacetic acid to form the CoA-derivative of dicrotalic acid, a naturally occurring acid (R. Adams, 1953). This derivative by decarboxylation and dehydration could form β-methylcrotonyl CoA, which by self-condensation could give long-chain compounds of the polyterpene type.

$$
\underset{\underset{O}{\overset{\overset{CH_3}{|}}{\|}}{HO_2CCH_2C} + HCH_2COSCoA \rightarrow \underset{\underset{OH}{\overset{\overset{CH_3}{|}}{|}}{HO_2CCH_2CCH_2COSCoA} \xrightarrow{-CO_2,\ H_2O}
$$

$$
\underset{\overset{CH_3}{|}}{CH_3C}\text{=}CHCO\text{—}SCoA \xrightarrow{H\text{—}CH_2\overset{\overset{CH_3}{|}}{C}\text{=}CHCOSCoA}
$$

$$
\underset{\overset{CH_3}{|}}{CH_3C}\text{=}CHCOCH_2\underset{\overset{CH_3}{|}}{C}\text{=}CHCOSCoA \xrightarrow[-H_2O,\ +2\ H]{+2\ H;} \underset{\overset{CH_3}{|}}{CH_3C}\text{=}CHCH_2CH_2\underset{\overset{CH_3}{|}}{C}\text{=}CHCOSCoA
$$
$$(+HSCoA)$$

Essential Fatty Acids. — Inability to synthesize highly unsaturated fatty acids was first demonstrated by Burr and Burr (1929), who found that rats maintained on a fat-free diet developed a typical dermatitis. The

Burr and Burr syndrome was found to be cured by administration of linoleic, linolenic, and arachidonic acid, the latter acid being particularly effective (Turpeinen, 1938). The essential nature of these and related unsaturated acids or alcohols has been demonstrated in other animals, but the evidence in man is indirect.

READING REFERENCES

R. Schoenheimer, "The Dynamic State of Body Constituents," pages 1–24, Harvard University Press (1942)

F. Lynen and S. Ochoa, "Enzymes of Fatty Acid Metabolism," *Biochimica et Biophysica Acta*, **12**, 299 (1953)

F. Lipmann, "Development of the Acetylation Problem, a Personal Account," *Science*, **120**, 855 (1954)

E. Klenk, "Lipoide im chemischen Aufbau des Nervensystems," *Naturwissenschaften*, **40**, 449 (1953)

J. A. Lovern, "The Chemistry of Lipids of Biochemical Significance," Methuen, London (1955)

CHAPTER 19

PROTEIN METABOLISM

Protein Metabolism. — Proteins are not utilized by the animal organism in their native form, but are broken down by enzymatic action in the digestive tract into amino acids, a certain proportion of which are required for construction or maintenance of tissue and of special proteins. The remainder is oxidized or converted into carbohydrate or fat for storage. In normal adult animals, the total amount of body proteins remains fairly constant, and the amount of nitrogen-containing products excreted corresponds closely to the nitrogen ingested in food (exogenous origin), and hence such animals are said to be in nitrogen equilibrium. This fact was originally interpreted to mean that body proteins exist in a more or less static condition. Schoenheimer, in a brilliant series of researches utilizing amino acids tagged with isotopic nitrogen, showed that body proteins are steadily broken down and resynthesized from amino acids of exogenous origin. On feeding animals of constant weight various amino acids containing heavy nitrogen (N^{15}), Schoenheimer observed that only a small proportion of the isotopic nitrogen appeared in the excreta and large amounts of the marked amino acids were recovered from various proteins. The rate at which an amino acid is incorporated into proteins varies in different tissues, being rapid in serum and liver proteins and particularly slow in skin proteins. It is still uncertain whether the process involves partial replacement of amino acids or complete hydrolysis and resynthesis. That the former can take place is indicated by model experiments by Bergmann (1937) later extended by Fruton[1] (1950). For example, when hippuryl-amide is hydrolyzed by the proteolytic enzyme papain in the presence of

1. $C_6H_5CONHCH_2CONH_2 + C_6H_5NH_2 \xrightarrow{\text{Papain}} C_6H_5CONHCH_2CONHC_6H_5 + NH_3$

2. $C_6H_5CO-NHCHCOOH + H_2NCH_2CO-NHC_6H_5 \xrightarrow{\text{Papain}}$
   $\underset{\displaystyle C_4H_9}{|}$
   Benzoyl-L-leucine   Glycine anilide

$$C_6H_5CO-NHCHCO-NHC_6H_5 + H_2NCH_2COOH$$
$$\underset{\displaystyle C_4H_9}{|} \qquad\qquad\qquad \text{Glycine}$$
Benzoyl-L-leucine anilide

aniline, hippuric acid anilide is formed (1). Another example is the reaction of benzoyl-L-leucine and glycine anilide to form benzoyl-L-leucine

[1] Joseph E. Fruton, b. 1912 Czestochowa, Poland; Ph.D. Columbia (H. T. Clarke, M. Bergmann); Dept. Biochem., Yale

anilide (2). Replacements have been demonstrated with more nearly natural substrates.

Since the amount of amino acids in plasma (the amino acid pool) remains relatively constant, the processes of breakdown and synthesis are carefully balanced. Many of the enzymes involved in hydrolysis have been isolated in pure form, and their mode of action is fairly well understood. Knowledge of the biosynthesis of proteins, however, is scanty. Synthesis apparently is not controlled by the same enzymes that hydrolyze proteins. It is not even certain whether proteins are formed by stepwise addition of individual amino acid units to a peptide or by more or less simultaneous combination of many units. Nucleic acids and ATP are known to be involved.

Essential Amino Acids. — In 1906, young mice fed on a diet containing zein (protein of corn) as the source of protein were found incapable of maintaining body weight. Zein lacks lysine and tryptophan, and the addition of these amino acids to the diet was shown later to permit normal growth in young rats. Isolation of the amino acid threonine (Rose,[2] 1935) was a direct result of nutritional studies. After the observation that the butyl alcohol fraction of hydrolyzed casein maintained growth of young rats, Rose succeeded in isolating 4.5 g. of the new amino acid from 12 kg. of fibrin (the protein of blood clot). Omission of threonine from a mixture of twenty pure amino acids capable of supporting growth causes a loss in body weight; therefore the animal organism cannot synthesize this essential amino acid. Rose defined an essential amino acid as one that is not synthesized by animals from materials ordinarily available at a rate necessary for normal growth. The amino acids are classified in this respect for growing rats in Table 19.1 (Rose, 1948). Man requires eight amino acids, those required

TABLE 19.1. GROWTH EFFECTS OF AMINO ACIDS (RAT)

INDISPENSABLE	DISPENSABLE
Lysine	Glycine
Tryptophan	Alanine
Histidine	Serine
Phenylalanine	Norleucine
Leucine	Glutamic acid
Isoleucine	Proline
Threonine	Hydroxyproline
Methionine	Tyrosine
Valine	Cystine
Arginine	Aspartic acid
	Citrulline

by the rat with the exception of arginine and of histidine (Rose, 1949).

Transamination, Deamination, Decarboxylation. — The α-keto acid analogs of most amino acids are equivalent to the amino acids themselves in

[2] William C. Rose, b. 1887 Greenville, S. C.; Ph.D. Yale; Univ. Illinois

animal organisms, evidently because of conversion to amino acids. That the interconversion of α-amino and α-keto acids involves utilization by one acid of the amino group of another was indicated by experiments of Schoenheimer, who found that isotopic nitrogen of dietary glycine or leucine is incorporated into almost all amino acids, particularly into the dicarboxylic acids, and thus demonstrated the process of transamination:

$$H_2N\overset{R}{C}HCO_2H + O{=}\overset{R'}{C}CO_2H \xrightleftharpoons{\text{Enzyme}} O{=}\overset{R}{C}CO_2H + H_2N\overset{R'}{C}HCO_2H$$

Although aspartic and glutamic acid undergo transamination particularly readily, all amino acids probably enter into the reaction to some extent. Thus one route of amino acid biosynthesis is by transamination of keto acids derived from carbohydrate metabolism, for example, alanine from pyruvic acid, aspartic acid from oxalacetic acid, glutamic acid from α-ketoglutaric acid.

Transaminases, that is, enzymes that catalyze transaminations involving specific amino acids, have been isolated. Those specific to aspartic and glutamic acid contain pyridoxal phosphate or pyridoxamine phosphate as the prosthetic group. Pyridoxal and pyridoxamine are derivatives of pyridoxine (vitamin B_6, p. 1004). Transamination has been achieved nonenzy-

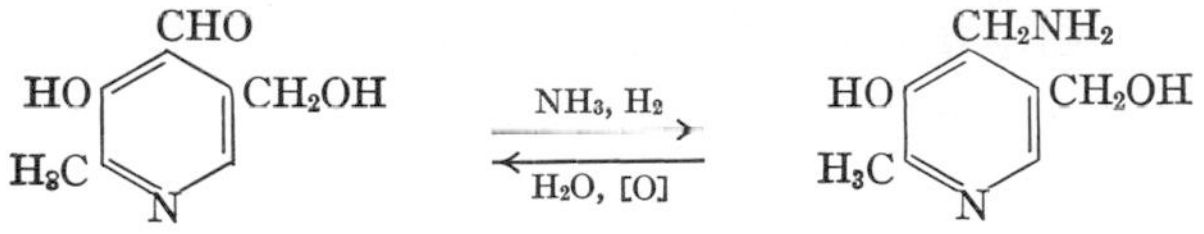

Pyridoxal   Pyridoxamine

matically (in absence of protein) under the influence of pyridoxal phosphate and suitable metal salts (Snell). The aldehyde and amine derivatives are interconvertible and are believed to function in the overall reaction as shown in the formulation (X = ring system of pyridoxine):

$$\underset{R}{\overset{COOH}{C}}{=}O + H_2NCH_2X \xrightleftharpoons{-H_2O} \underset{R}{\overset{COOH}{C}}{=}NCH_2X \rightleftharpoons \underset{R}{\overset{COOH}{C}}HN{=}CH\cdot X \xrightleftharpoons{H_2O} \underset{R}{\overset{COOH}{C}}HNH_2 + OHCX$$

Deamination, first observed by Krebs (1933) was once believed to be of general significance, but L-amino acid oxidases are found mostly in snake venoms and certain molds and are not present in appreciable amounts in

$$\underset{CO_2H}{RCHNH_2} \xrightleftharpoons{-2H} \underset{CO_2H}{RC{=}NH} \xrightleftharpoons[NH_3]{H_2O} \underset{CO_2H}{RC{=}O}$$

animal tissues. D-Oxidases occur rather widely and may serve for destruction or utilization of unnatural amino acids.

Another transformation is the enzymatic decarboxylation of an amino acid to the corresponding amine. Only about six amino acids are known to

$$RCH(NH_2)CO_2H \xrightarrow{\text{Decarboxylase}} RCH_2NH_2 + CO_2$$

undergo this reaction in mammalian tissues, but decarboxylases occur widely in microorganisms. Pyridoxal phosphate (but not pyridoxamine phosphate) is the coenzyme and is considered to function by condensation of the aldehyde group with the α-amino group of the acid; decarboxylation of the imino acid followed by hydrolysis regenerates the enzyme and affords the amine (X = ring system of pyridoxine, attached to a protein):

$$XCHO + H_2NCHRCO_2H \xrightarrow[-H_2O]{} XCH=NCHRCO_2H \xrightarrow[-CO_2]{} XCH=NCH_2R \xrightarrow{H_2O}$$

$$XCHO + H_2NCH_2R$$

Many of the amines resulting from this reaction have physiological activity. Thus the simple amines derived from alanine, valine, leucine, phenylalanine, namely $CH_3CH_2NH_2$, $(CH_3)_2CHCH_2NH_2$, $(CH_3)_2CHCH_2CH_2NH_2$, $C_6H_5CH_2CH_2NH_2$, stimulate the central nervous system (sympathomimetic bases). The pressor hormone of the adrenal glands, adrenaline, is believed to be formed from tyrosine via tyramine, as formulated. Adrenaline causes a marked rise in blood pressure on intravenous

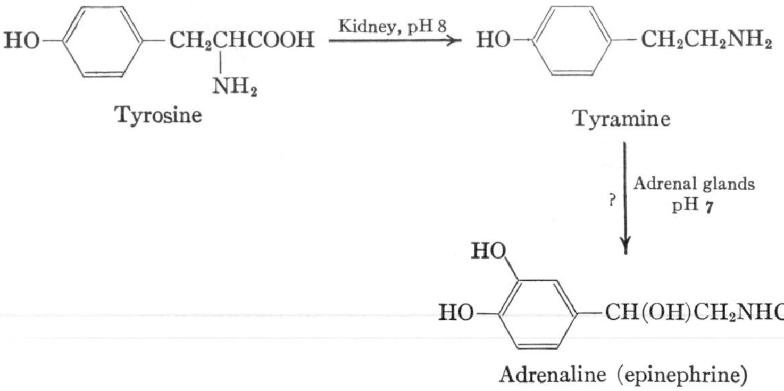

Tyrosine   Tyramine

Adrenaline (epinephrine)

injection. Ephedrine (*Ephedra vulgaris*) exerts a similar, but less intensive action, and is believed to arise in the plant from phenylalanine:

$$C_6H_5CH_2CH(NH_2)COOH \xrightarrow{?} C_6H_5CH(OH)CH(CH_3)NHCH_3$$

Phenylalanine   Ephedrine

Benzedrine, β-phenylisopropylamine[$C_6H_5CH_2CH(CH_3)NH_2$], was found (1930) to possess the pressor activity of adrenaline and ephedrine. The amine is a volatile liquid, and can be administered orally in the form of the sulfate. Although the activity is markedly less than that of the hormone, the response is of much longer duration, owing to the fact that benzedrine, unlike adrenaline, is not deaminated in the body. Benzedrine is used also as a vasoconstriction agent for local application in rhinology.

It can be prepared by several methods, all of which utilize phenylacetone as an intermediate.   Two schemes are illustrated.

1. $C_6H_5CH_2CN$ + $CH_3COOC_2H_5$ $\xrightarrow[86\%]{NaOC_2H_5}$ $C_6H_5CHCOCH_3$ $\xrightarrow[77-86\%]{H_2SO_4}$
   Benzyl cyanide

$\overset{|}{CN}$

$C_6H_5CH_2COCH_3$ $\xrightarrow[50-55\%]{\underset{180-195°}{HCONH_2,}}$ $C_6H_5CH_2CHNH_2$
Phenylacetone

$\overset{|}{CH_3}$
Benzedrine

2. $C_6H_5CH_2COOH$ + $(CH_3CO)_2O$ $\xrightarrow[77\%]{NaOAc, 145-150°}$ $C_6H_5CH_2COCH_3$ $\xrightarrow{H_2NOH}$
Phenylacetic acid

Phenylacetone

$C_6H_5CH_2C{=}NOH$ $\xrightarrow{Reduction}$ $C_6H_5CH_2CHNH_2$

$\overset{|}{CH_3}$

$\overset{|}{CH_3}$

Oxime

Benzedrine

The vasoconstrictor principle in blood, serotonin, has been identified as 5-hydroxytryptamine.   The precursor is tryptophan, and the biosynthesis

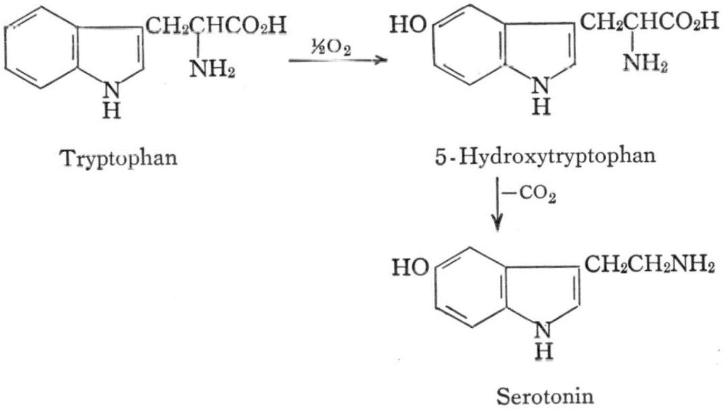

Tryptophan

5-Hydroxytryptophan

$|-CO_2$

Serotonin

has been shown to involve hydroxylation of the benzene ring followed by decarboxylation; the animal organism cannot decarboxylate tryptophan directly.   Serotonin and the N,N-dimethyl derivative, butotenin, have both been isolated from toad venom.

Histamine, the product of decarboxylation of histidine, is a powerful vasodilator.   In the animal organism it is normally bound in an inactive form, but certain allergies lead to excessive release of histamine and are

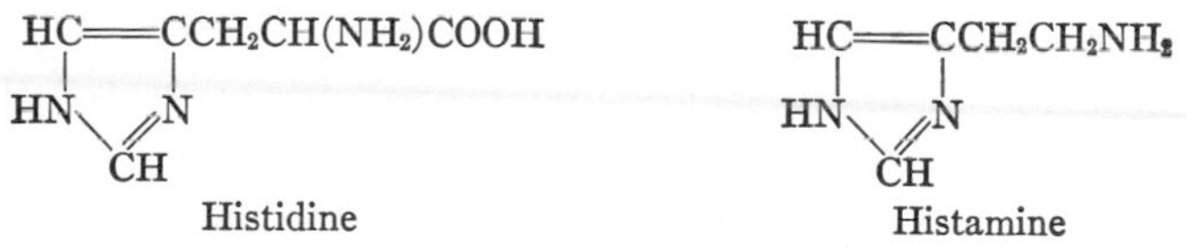

Histidine

Histamine

treated by administration of agents that inhibit histamine release (anti-histaminics).

Other natural products that may arise by decarboxylation of amino acids are as follows: taurine, $H_2NCH_2CH_2SO_3H$, from cystine via cysteic acid; β-alanine from aspartic acid; β-ethanolamine from serine; putrescine, $H_2N(CH_2)_4$-NH_2, from ornithine; cadaverine, $H_2N(CH_2)_5NH_2$, from lysine. Skatole (3-methylindole), partially responsible for the disagreeable odor of feces, is probably a degradation product of tryptophan.

The Urea-Ornithine Cycle. — Urea, the principal excretory product of amino acids in animals, is not formed, as once supposed, by direct combination of ammonia with carbon dioxide. Krebs (1932) observed that ornithine and citrulline greatly enhance the formation of urea (liver slices) and considered that urea is formed indirectly in a cycle in which ornithine plays a continuous role. Subsequent studies show that the intermediates

CHART 1. ORNITHINE CYCLE (KREBS)

$$NH_2(CH_2)_3CH(NH_2)COOH \xrightarrow{CO_2,\ NH_3} NH_2CONH(CH_2)_3CH(NH_2)COOH \xrightarrow{NH_3}$$

Ornithine · Citrulline

$$NH_2C(=NH)NH(CH_2)_3CH(NH_2)COOH \xrightarrow{H_2O,\ Arginase}$$

Arginine

$$NH_2CONH_2 \quad + \quad NH_2(CH_2)_3CH(NH_2)COOH$$

Urea · Ornithine

pictured are correct but that, because of energy requirements, the steps are more elaborate than initially conceived. Thus ornithine does not react directly with ammonia and carbon dioxide but with the phosphate ester of carbamic acid, $H_2NCO_2PO(OH)_2$. The citrulline → arginine step is also indirect and involves reaction of citrulline with aspartic acid to form arginosuccinic acid (Sarah Ratner), which is then split to arginine and fumaric acid.

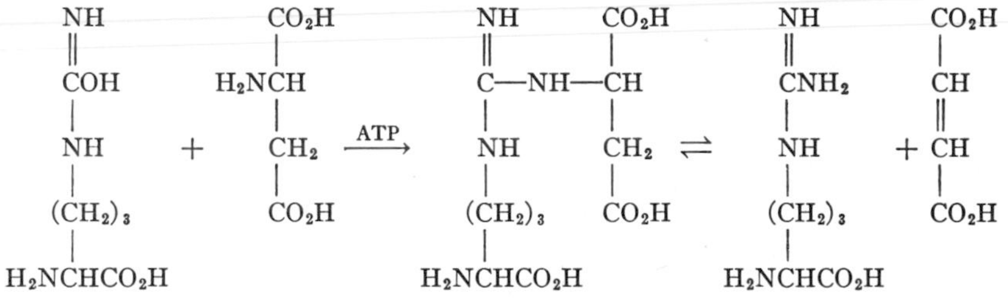

Citrulline (enol)	Aspartic acid		Arginosuccinic acid	Arginine	Fumaric acid
NH ‖ COH │ NH │ (CH₂)₃ │ H₂NCHCO₂H	CO₂H │ H₂NCH │ CH₂ │ CO₂H	$\xrightarrow{ATP}$	NH CO₂H ‖ │ C—NH—CH │ │ NH CH₂ │ │ (CH₂)₃ CO₂H │ H₂NCHCO₂H	NH CO₂H ‖ │ CNH₂ CH │ ‖ NH CH │ │ (CH₂)₃ CO₂H │ H₂NCHCO₂H	

$$+ \qquad\qquad \rightleftharpoons \qquad +$$

Arginine can also transfer the amidine group, $-C(=NH)NH_2$, to another amino acid. Thus Schoenheimer (1939) demonstrated that creatine and creatinine are formed in a sequence of reactions in which guanidylacetic acid is an intermediate. Glycine can be replaced by its N-methyl derivative sarcosine, $CH_3NHCH_2CO_2H$.

$$
\begin{array}{c}
\underset{\text{Glycine}}{\overset{\displaystyle NH_2}{\underset{CH_2CO_2H}{|}}}
\quad + \quad
\underset{\text{Arginine}}{\overset{\displaystyle NH_2}{\underset{\displaystyle \underset{H_2NCHCO_2H}{\overset{(CH_2)_3}{\underset{|}{\overset{|}{NH}}}}}{\overset{|}{\underset{|}{C=NH}}}}}
\quad \longrightarrow \quad
\underset{\substack{\text{Guanidylacetic}\\\text{acid}}}{\overset{\displaystyle NH_2}{\underset{CH_2CO_2H}{\overset{|}{\underset{|}{\overset{C=NH}{\underset{NH}{|}}}}}}}
\quad + \quad
\underset{\text{Ornithine}}{\overset{\displaystyle NH_2}{\underset{H_2NCHCO_2H}{\overset{|}{\underset{|}{(CH_2)_3}}}}}
\end{array}
$$

Methylation | Choline

$$
\underset{\text{Creatine}}{\overset{\displaystyle NH_2}{\underset{CH_2CO_2H}{\overset{|}{\underset{|}{\overset{C=NH}{\underset{NCH_3}{|}}}}}}}
\quad \longrightarrow \quad
\underset{\text{Creatinine}}{\text{(ring structure: } HN{-}C({=}NH){\cdots}NH{-}C({=}O){-}CH_2{-}N(H_3C)\text{)}}
$$

Transmethylation. — The first indication that a methyl group can be transferred from one amino acid to another was provided by dietary experiments. du Vigneaud (1939) observed that choline becomes indispensable if methionine is replaced by its desmethyl derivative, homocysteine. The

$$[HO(CH_2)_2N(CH_3)_3]^+OH^- \qquad CH_3S(CH_2)_2CH(NH_2)COOH \qquad HS(CH_2)_2CH(NH_2)COOH$$

Choline (ethanoltrimethylammonium hydroxide)   Methionine   Homocysteine

postulated transfer of a methyl group from choline to homocysteine (and to guanidylacetic acid, above) has since been demonstrated by use of isotopically labeled acids. Also, a number of natural ammonium and sulfonium compounds have been found capable of donating methyl groups. Thus betaine, $(CH_3)_3\overset{+}{N}CH_2CO_2^-$, and the sulfur analog dimethylthetin, $(CH_3)_2\overset{+}{S}CH_2CO_2^-$, can replace methionine in the diet. Betaine is specifically the betaine of glycine. The betaines of proline, histidine, and ornithine are natural products; the betaine of 5 thiolhistidine, ergothioneine, occurs in

$$
\underset{\text{Histidine betaine}}{\overset{\displaystyle CH}{\underset{HC{=}CCH_2CH\overset{+}{N}(CH_3)_3}{\overset{/\!\!\!\backslash}{\underset{|}{\overset{N\quad NH}{\underset{COO^-}{}}}}}}}
\qquad
\underset{\text{Ergothioneine}}{\overset{\displaystyle CSH}{\underset{HC{=}CCH_2CH\overset{+}{N}(CH_3)_3}{\overset{/\!\!\!\backslash}{\underset{|}{\overset{N\quad NH}{\underset{COO^-}{}}}}}}}
$$

ergot and in blood. Only a few other ammonium or sulfonium compounds are known to be natural products. Dimethylpropiothetin, $(CH_3)_2\overset{+}{S}CH_2$-

$CH_2CO_2^-$, is a constituent of a marine algae, and the sulfonium derivative of methionine, $(CH_3)_2\overset{+}{S}CH_2CH_2CH(NH_2)CO_2^-$, has been isolated from cabbage juice. Since ATP is required for activation of methionine, G. L. Cantoni (1953) suggested that methionine is active in transmethylation in the form of the sulfonium derivative, S-adenosylmethionine. Baddiley (1954) found support for the hypothesis in the observation that synthetic

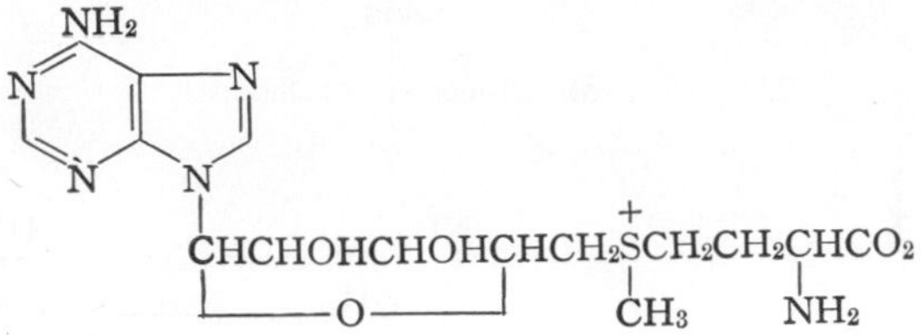

S-Adenosylmethionine

dl-material reacts readily with amines to form the corresponding N-methyl derivatives and S-adenosylhomocysteine.

Until recently, the animal organism was believed incapable of synthesizing methyl groups, but it is now known that the methyl group of methionine, for example, can arise from one-carbon units derived from various metabolites. The actual donor, citrovorum factor, is described on the next page. Thus homocysteine can replace methionine in the diet if vitamin B_{12} and folic acid are included.

Transthiolation. — Nutritional and isotopic investigations of the biogenesis of cysteine have shown that the carbon chain arises from serine and the sulfur atom from methionine. The process probably involves demethylation of methionine to homocysteine and condensation of this with serine to form cystathionine, which is cleaved by phosphorolysis to cysteine and the ester of homoserine.

$$HOOCCH(NH_2)CH_2OH \ + \ HSCH_2CH_2CH(NH_2)COOH \xrightarrow{-H_2O}$$
Serine · Homocysteine

$$HOOCCH(NH_2)CH_2-S-CH_2CH_2CH(NH_2)COOH \xrightarrow{H_3PO_4}$$
Cystathionine

$$HOOCCH(NH_2)CH_2SH \ + \ (HO)_2OPOCH_2CH_2CH(NH_2)COOH$$
Cysteine · Phosphohomoserine

The net effect, replacement of —OH by —SH, is described as a transthiolation.

Glycine–Serine Interconversion. — One experimental observation indicating that glycine and serine are interconvertible is that administered

$$CH_2(NH_2)CO_2H + C_1\text{-unit} \rightleftharpoons HOCH_2CH(NH_2)CO_2H$$

labeled serine can be recovered as labeled hippuric acid; the reverse process has also been demonstrated. The interconversion is further suggested by the observation that certain mutants of *E. coli* require either glycine or serine. Carbon dioxide cannot supply the C_1-unit required, and although both formate and formaldehyde are utilized under appropriate conditions, they are utilized in the form of derivatives and not as such. Pteroylglutamic acid (folic acid, p. 1007) derivatives have been implicated in other reactions involving C_1-units, and that involved in the glycine–serine change has been identified as the growth factor known as citrovorum factor; it is 5-formyltetrahydropteroylglutamic acid. This substance does promote

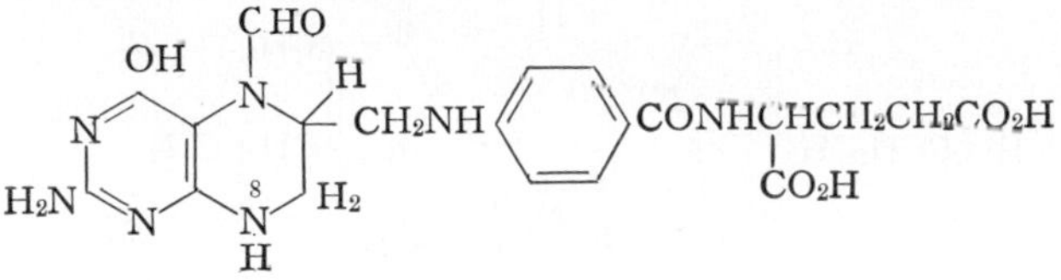

Citrovorum factor

formation of serine from glycine and formic acid. It functions as a donor of C_1-units (formate, formaldehyde) and is thus analogous to coenzyme A, a donor of C_2-units.

Biosyntheses Involving Glutamic Acid. — Metabolic interconversion of glutamic acid, proline, and ornithine has been demonstrated both by isotope experiments and by use of mutant strains of microorganisms. Since glutamic acid is coupled to carbohydrate metabolism through α-ketoglutaric acid, proline and ornithine are linked indirectly. Glutamic acid has been

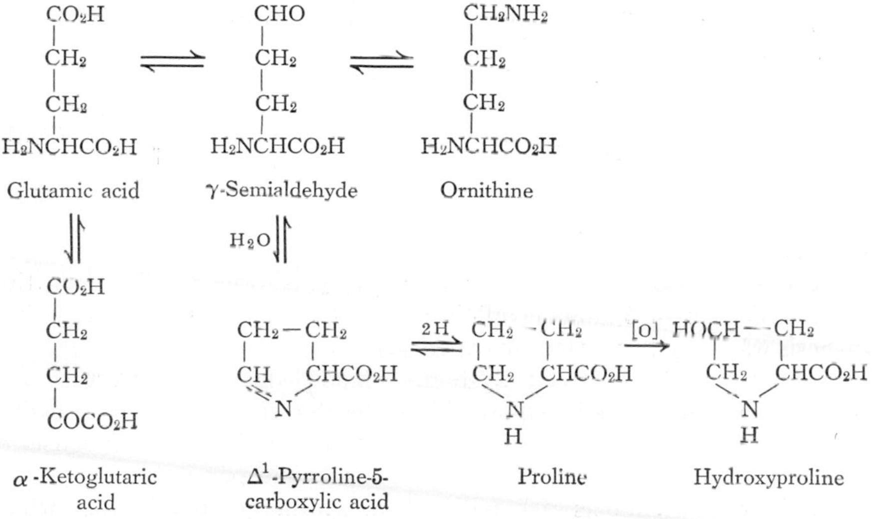

shown to undergo conversion to the two other amino acids through the γ-semialdehyde, which yields ornithine by transamination and yields a pyrroline acid on cyclodehydration. The latter on hydrogenation yields proline (pyrrolidine-5-carboxylic acid). Hydroxyproline has been shown to be formed from proline, but the reverse reaction probably does not occur.

Biosynthesis of Porphyrins. — The biosynthesis of the porphyrin system was elucidated by Shemin[3] through isotope studies. The four nitrogen atoms are derived from glycine, as are the four methine bridge carbon atoms. In addition, the α-carbon atom of glycine is the source of one carbon atom in each pyrrole ring, in each case that adjacent to a nitrogen atom (see form-

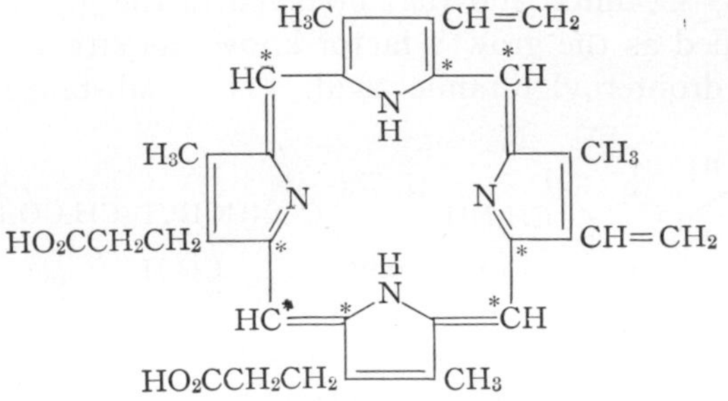

$$H_3C \quad CH=CH_2$$
$$\overset{*}{H}C \quad \overset{*}{CH}$$
$$N$$
$$H$$
$$H_3C \qquad CH_3$$
$$N \qquad N$$
$$HO_2CCH_2CH_2 \qquad CH=CH_2$$
$$H$$
$$N$$
$$\overset{*}{H}C \quad \overset{*}{=}CH$$
$$HO_2CCH_2CH_2 \qquad CH_3$$

Protoporphyrin

Carbon atoms derived from $\overset{*}{C}H_2(NH_2)CO_2H$

ula). The carboxyl group is not utilized, and the remainder of the carbon atoms are supplied by succinic acid. Shemin reasoned that the unusual distribution of the α-carbon atoms of glycine can be accounted for on the assumption that glycine condenses with succinic acid (1), in the form of succinyl coenzyme A, to form α-amino-β-ketoadipic acid, which, being a β-keto acid readily loses carbon dioxide to form δ-aminolevulinic acid. In

1. $HO_2C\overset{*}{C}H_2NH_2 + HO_2CCH_2CH_2CO_2H \longrightarrow HO_2C\overset{*}{C}H(NH_2)COCH_2CH_2CO_2H$

$\longrightarrow H_2N\overset{*}{C}H_2COCH_2CH_2CO_2H$

2. $HO_2CCH_2CH_2 \qquad COCH_2CH_2CO_2H \qquad\qquad HO_2CCH_2 \qquad CH_2CH_2CO_2H$

$H_2N\overset{*}{C}H_2CO \quad + \quad \overset{*}{C}H_2 \qquad \longrightarrow \qquad H_2N\overset{*}{C}H_2 \qquad \overset{*}{}$

$H_2N \qquad\qquad\qquad\qquad\qquad\qquad\qquad\qquad\qquad N$
$\qquad\qquad\qquad\qquad\qquad\qquad\qquad\qquad\qquad\qquad H$

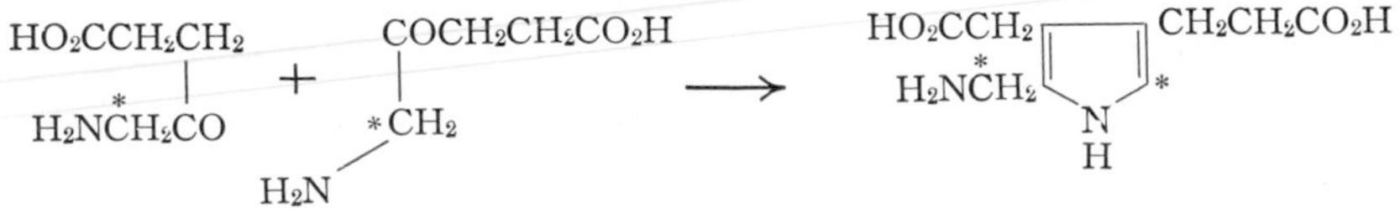

the next step postulated (2) a precursor pyrrole is formed by condensation of two molecules of δ-aminolevulinic acid. The postulated path of biosynthesis was fully supported by experiment.

Biosynthesis of the Purine System. — Knowledge of the precursors of the purine ring system is based largely on the stepwise degradation possible with uric acid (2,6,8-trihydroxypurine), the end product of metabolism of purines in many animals. Oxidation with alkaline permanganate results in loss of carbon atom 6 as carbon dioxide and formation of allantoin, which on acid hydrolysis yields urea and glyoxylic acid. Degradation of uric acid produced by biosynthesis from isotopically labeled suspected precursors

[3] David Shemin, b. 1911, New York; Ph.D. Columbia (Herbst); Dept. Biochem., Coll. Phys. and Surg., Columbia

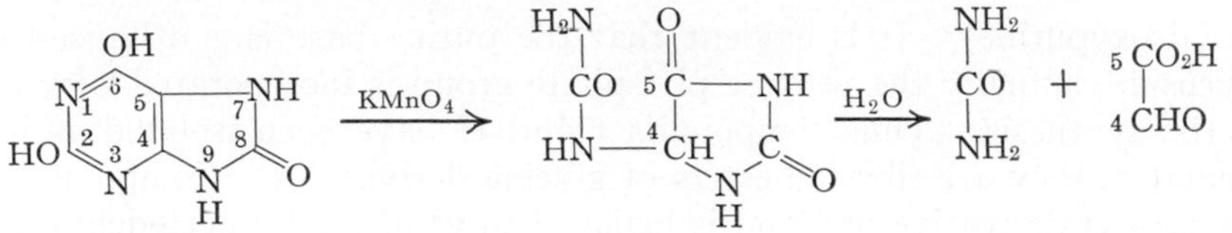

Uric acid   Allantoin

showed that glycine supplies C_4, C_5, and N_7, carbon dioxide is the source of C_6, formic acid is the precursor of C_2 and C_8, and ammonia is the source of N_1, N_3, and N_9. That these small fragments are not the immediate precursors is indicated by the observation that aspartic and glutamic acid are utilized in the biosynthesis more efficiently than ammonia.

Although not all the steps in purine synthesis are known, various lines of evidence support a scheme summarized by Buchanan[4] (1955) and shown in Chart 2. One important clue was isolation from *E. coli* of an imidazole derivative that lacks only one carbon atom (C_2) of the purine ring system.

CHART 2.   PURINE BIOSYNTHESIS

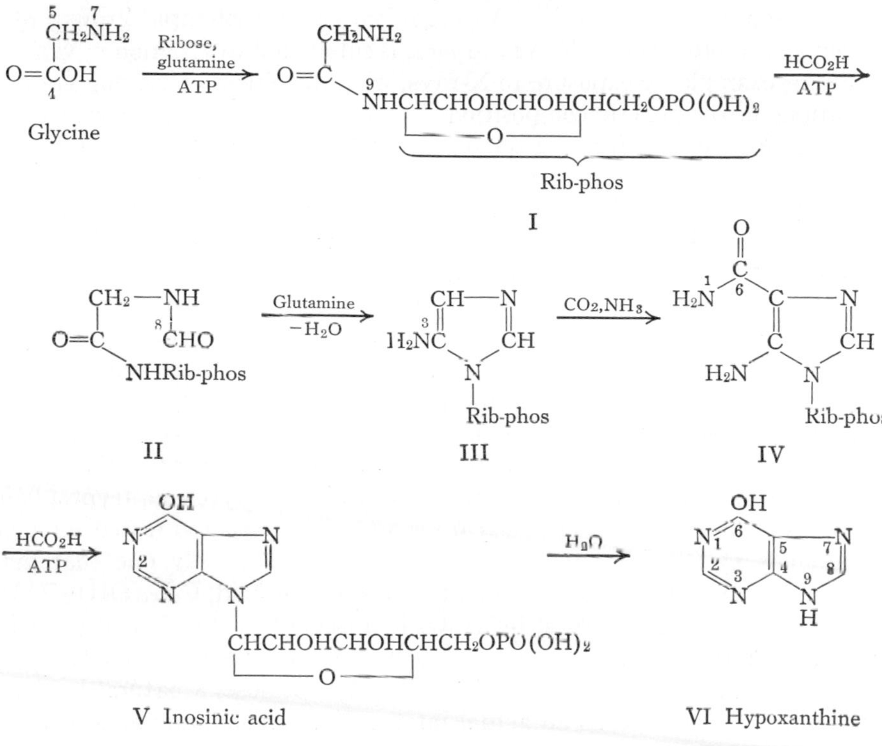

V Inosinic acid   VI Hypoxanthine

This substance, 5-amino-4-imidazole carboxamide, is itself ineffective as a precursor, but its riboside-5-phosphoric acid derivative IV is readily converted into inosinic acid, V, shown to be a precursor of hypoxanthine (VI,

---

[4] John M. Buchanan, b. 1917 Winamac, Ind.; Ph.D. Harvard; Mass. Inst. Techn.

6-hydroxypurine). It is evident that the purine base is synthesized as a glycoside; actually the pentose phosphate group is incorporated very early in the synthesis. Thus compounds I and II have been isolated as intermediates; they are riboside esters of glycine derivatives. Compound II is the formyl derivative of I and is believed to yield III by cyclodehydration followed by replacement of the oxygen function by an amino group (glutamine serving as donor); III, like IV, has definitely been characterized as an intermediate by isolation. The manner in which C_6 and N_1 are added in conversion of III into IV is not clear. Inosinic acid (V) is formed by reaction of IV with an active derivative of formic acid, 8-formyltetrahydropteroylglutamic acid.

Biosynthesis of Aromatic Amino Acids. — The prime source of the benzene ring present in some of the amino acids has been identified in experiments with isotopically labeled derivatives as glucose; inositol is not a precursor. Some of the biogenetic intermediates between glucose and the amino acids have been identified as substances that specialized organisms require but are unable to synthesize. The technique was introduced by Beadle[5] and Tatum[6] in 1941. An organism capable of rapid growth and reproduction, often the mold *Neurospora*, is submitted to attrition in various ways, for example by exposure to X-rays, with the object of causing various mutations in the genetic composition. New mutant strains are sorted out and examined for ability to grow on a diet lacking a metabolite under investigation. Mutant strains may thus be found which can carry out some of the steps in the synthesis of the metabolite but which lack the genes required for completion of the synthesis. Strains that grow normally in the presence of the metabolite but not in its absence will also grow normally if the medium is enriched with any intermediate that comes after the genetic block in the sequence of biosynthetic reactions. The intermediate coming immediately before the genetic block tends to accumulate and may be isolable. A series of mutant strains blocked at different stages of a synthesis provides a powerful tool for elucidation of steps in the process.

Davis[7] developed a set of mutant strains of *Neurospora* and *E. coli* blocked at various steps and requiring phenylalanine, tyrosine, tryptophan, *p*-hydroxy-, and *p*-aminobenzoic acid for normal growth and tested some 55 compounds as possible synthetic intermediates. The only one that permitted normal growth was a rare plant acid, shikimic acid, $C_6H_6(OH)_3CO_2H$, which had been characterized by H. O. L. Fischer.[8] This C_7-acid must be capable of formation from glucose, and hence a C_7-sugar is a likely intermediate. Indeed the 1,7-diphosphate of sedoheptulose, a natural heptose, although not identified as an actual intermediate to shikimic acid, is a far

[5] George W. Beadle, b. 1903 Wahoo, Nebraska; Ph.D. Cornell; Stanford Univ.

[6] Edward L. Tatum, b. 1909 Boulder, Colorado; Ph.D. Wisconsin; Stanford Univ.

[7] Bernard D. Davis; b. 1916 Franklin, Mass.; M.D. Harvard; Dept. Pharmacol., New York Univ.

[8] Hermann O. L. Fischer, b. 1888 Würzburg, Germany; Ph.D. Jena (Knorr, E. Fischer): Berlin, Basel, Toronto, U. Calif. (Berkeley)

better substrate for amino acid synthesis than glucose. Chart 3 shows the structures of shikimic acid and of two immediate precursors that have been identified, 5-dehydroquinic acid and 5-dehydroshikimic acid. An intermediate between shikimic acid and phenylalanine is a labile C_{10}-acid named prephenic acid. At pH of 7 or below it undergoes decarboxylation and dehydration and affords phenylpyruvic acid, which presumably is trans-

CHART 3. BIOSYNTHESIS OF AROMATIC AMINO ACIDS

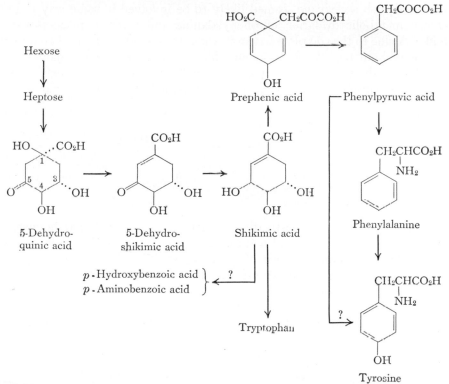

formed into phenylalanine by transamination. Tyrosine possibly is also formed from prephenic acid, or it may be synthesized by hydroxylation of phenylalanine, a reaction which has been demonstrated in both microorganisms and animals.

Less information is available concerning the conversion of shikimic acid to tryptophan. Two terminal steps in the biosynthesis of this acid, demonstrated with *Neurospora* mutant strains (Tatum, Bonner, and Beadle 1943–44) involve formation of indole from anthranilic acid and glycine and condensation with serine.

Metabolism of Aromatic Amino Acids. — It has long been known that benzene itself can be oxidized in the animal organism to *cis,cis*-muconic

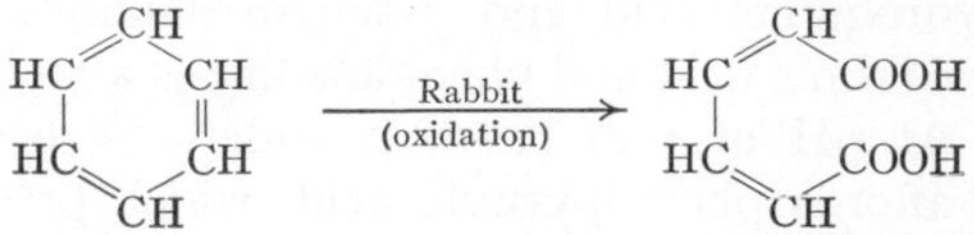

Benzene   Rabbit (oxidation)   Muconic acid

acid, and such a cleavage seemed likely to be involved in some way in the known metabolic oxidation of phenylalanine and tyrosine to acetoacetic acid. A clue to the complete pathway came from study of a rare hereditary disease of humans, alkaptonuria, in which tyrosine and phenylalanine are excreted in the urine as homogentisic acid to the extent of 80–85%. Although the curious reaction was initially regarded as merely an example of

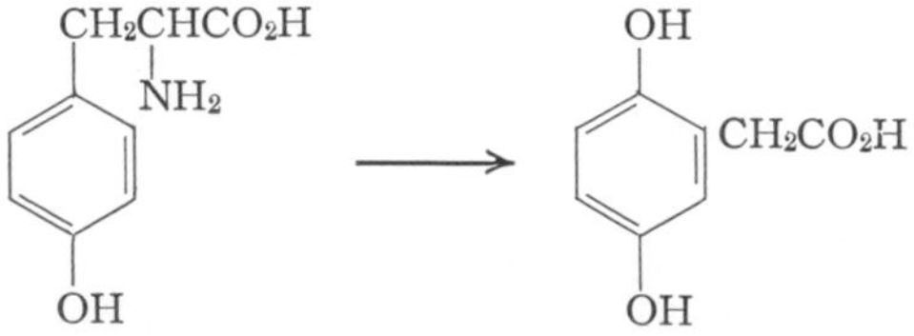

Tyrosine   Homogentisic acid

abnormal metabolism, investigation eventually established that homogentisic acid is actually a normal metabolic intermediate (W. E. Knox, 1951). Alkaptonuria therefore is a case of a genetic block in which the gene necessary for the next enzymatic transformation of the intermediate is lacking. The rearrangement of the side chain of tyrosine in the conversion to homogentisic acid is analogous to the methyl migration involved in the oxidation of *p*-cresol with Caro's acid to methylhydroquinone (Bamberger, 1903).

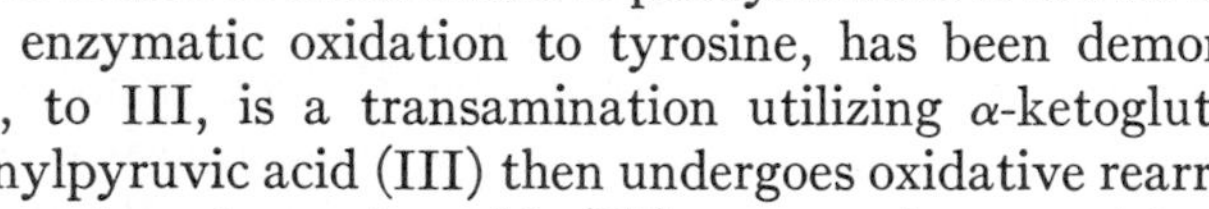

The complete course of metabolism of phenylalanine is shown in Chart 4. The first step, enzymatic oxidation to tyrosine, has been demonstrated.* The next step, to III, is a transamination utilizing α-ketoglutaric acid. *p*-Hydroxyphenylpyruvic acid (III) then undergoes oxidative rearrangement to 2,5-dihydroxyphenylpyruvic acid (IV), a reaction requiring ascorbic acid as coenzyme. The keto acid IV is the precursor of homogentisic acid

---

* A pathological condition known as phenylpyruvic oligophrenia is characterized by mental deficiency and increased excretion of phenylpyruvic acid, shown to be proportional to the phenylalanine in the diet. The inference that phenylketonurics are unable to carry out the normal oxidation of phenylalanine to tyrosine is supported by the finding that livers of such patients lack the enzyme responsible for this transformation (hydroxylase).

CHART 4. METABOLISM OF PHENYLALANINE AND TYROSINE

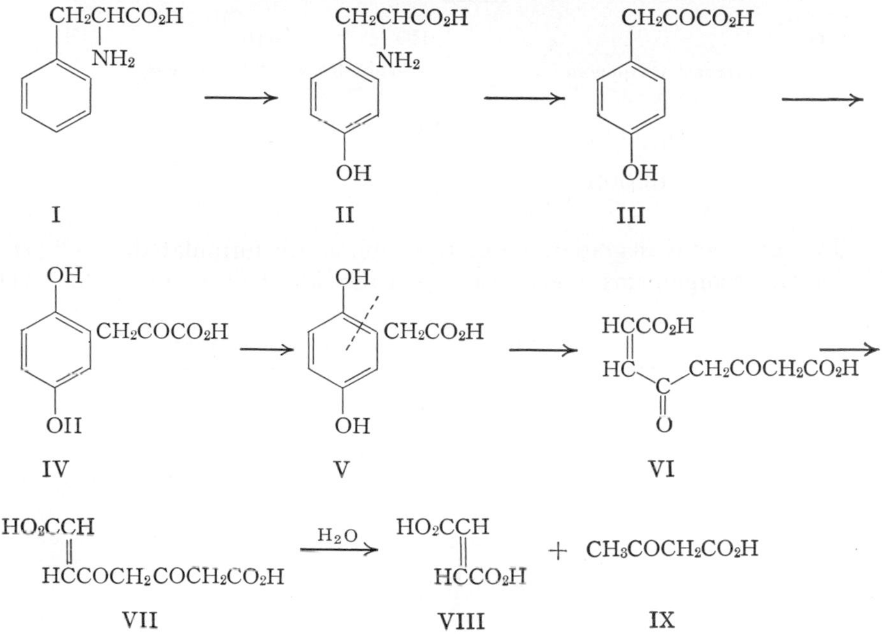

$$CH_2CHCO_2H \quad\quad CH_2CHCO_2H \quad\quad CH_2COCO_2H$$

(structures with benzene rings)

$$NH_2 \quad\quad\quad NH_2$$

$$OH \quad\quad\quad\quad OH$$

I   II   III

$$OH \quad\quad\quad\quad OH$$

$$CH_2COCO_2H \quad\quad CH_2CO_2H \quad\quad HCCO_2H$$

$$HC \quad C \quad CH_2COCH_2CO_2H$$

$$OH \quad\quad\quad\quad OH \quad\quad\quad\quad O$$

IV   V   VI

$$HO_2CCH \quad\quad\quad\quad\quad\quad HO_2CCH$$
$$\|\quad\quad\quad\quad\quad\quad\quad\xrightarrow{H_2O}\quad \|\quad\quad + CH_3COCH_2CO_2H$$
$$HCCOCH_2COCH_2CO_2H \quad\quad HCCO_2H$$

VII   VIII   IX

(V). Oxidative cleavage under the influence of an oxidase then cleaves the benzene ring to give maleylacetoacetic acid (VI), analogous to the *cis,cis* acid from benzene. The maleyl derivative is isomerized to the fumaryl derivative VII in an enzymatic reaction in which glutathione (GSH) functions as coenzyme. The final step involves enzymatic hydrolysis to fumaric acid (VIII) and acetoacetic acid (IX).

Tyrosine is also the precursor of thyroxin, but nothing is known about the steps. The transformation of tyrosine into adrenaline has been mentioned (p. 500). Tyrosine is the postulated precursor of melanin, a brownish black pigment that occurs normally in the retina, skin, and hair of higher animals with the exception of albinos. The excessive deposition of melanin associated with melanotic tumors is sometimes accompanied by melanuria (excretion of melanin in urine). The composition of melanin is not known, but the pigment is formed readily from tyrosine on oxidation with tyrosinase, an enzyme that can be prepared from the potato, many plants, and the meal worm. 3,4-Dihydroxyphenylalanine and the 5,6-quinone of dihydroindole α-carboxylic acid have been isolated from the reaction leading to melanin. The following mechanism is postulated (Raper, 1937):

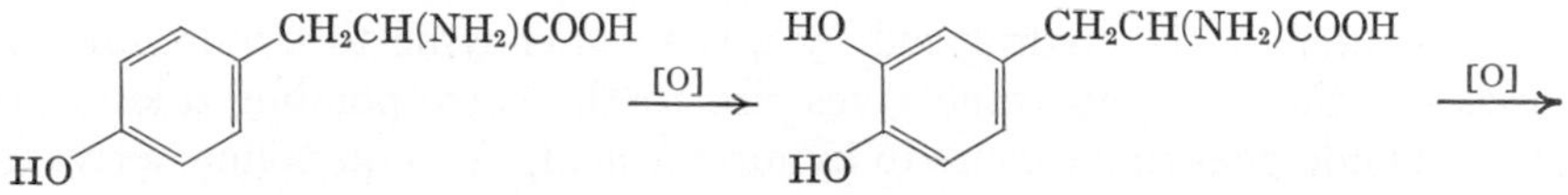

$$CH_2CH(NH_2)COOH \quad\quad\quad\quad HO \quad\quad CH_2CH(NH_2)COOH$$

$$HO \quad\quad\quad\xrightarrow{[O]}\quad\quad\quad HO \quad\quad\quad\xrightarrow{[O]}$$

Tyrosine   3,4-Dihydroxyphenylalanine

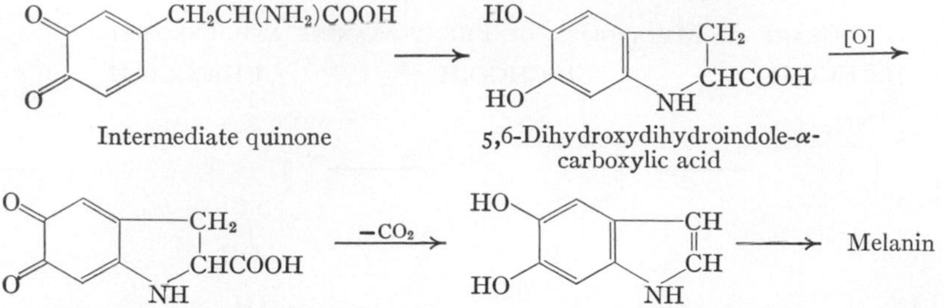

Intermediate quinone → 5,6-Dihydroxydihydroindole-α-carboxylic acid $\xrightarrow{[O]}$

$\xrightarrow{-CO_2}$ → Melanin

Two of several degradations of tryptophan are formulated in Chart 5 Various microorganisms effect cleavage of the side chain to give indole (III)

CHART 5. TRYPTOPHAN-KYNURENINE METABOLISM

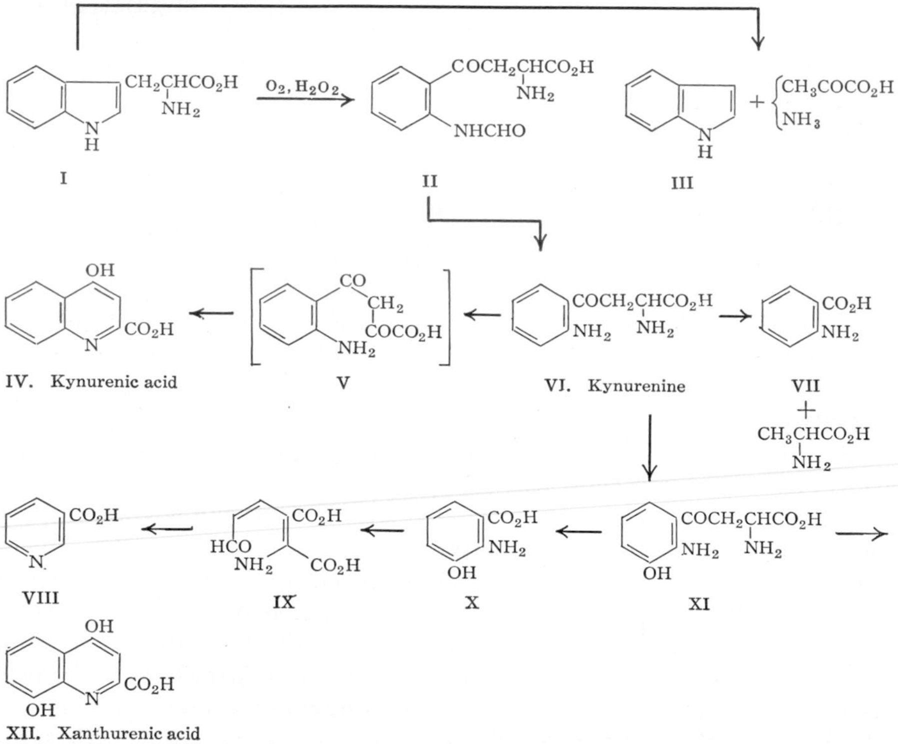

I   II   III

IV. Kynurenic acid   V   VI. Kynurenine   VII

+

CH_3CHCO_2H
$\quad$ NH_2

VIII   IX   X   XI

XII. Xanthurenic acid

pyruvic acid, and ammonia. Another degradation, effected by mammalian and bacterial enzymes, involves enlargement of the pyrrole ring to a pyridine ring. The first step, for which both oxygen and hydrogen peroxide are required, involves cleavage of the heterocyclic ring to give formylkynurenine, II, hydrolyzed by a specific enzyme to kynurenine, VI. Transamination of kynurenine gives rise to the corresponding α-keto acid V, which undergoes ring closure to kynurenic acid, IV, a quinoline derivative excreted in the urine. Kynurenine also undergoes oxidation to the 3-hydroxy derivative XI, which, like the parent compound, can afford a quinoline derivative, xanthurenic acid (XII). In microorganisms that utilize tryptophan as a major source of energy, kynurenine is hydrolyzed to alanine and anthranilic acid (VII). The latter acid is metabolized via catechol and cis,cis-muconic acid to β-ketoadipic acid. Another metabolic end product is the vitamin nicotinic acid, VIII. It is formed from 3-hydroxykynurenine, XI, through 3-hydroxyanthranilic acid, X. Formation of the pyridine ring is believed to involve oxidative cleavage of the aromatic ring (IX) and cyclization to quinolinic acid, which undergoes ready decarboxylation to nicotinic acid. 3-Hydroxykynurenine is also the precursor of various insect pigments of unknown structure, the ommochromes.

The transformation of tryptophan into the animal hormone serotonin has been mentioned above. Tryptophan is also the precursor of the plant growth hormone indole-3-acetic acid and the transformation has been demonstrated in both plants and humans. Indoleacetaldehyde is the immediate precursor, but it is not known whether the aldehyde arises through indolepyruvic acid or through tryptamine, both of which have activity. Another possible intermediate is indoleacetonitrile, for this has been isolated from cabbage and is even more active than indoleacetic acid. The standard assay method (Went, 1928) utilizes oat seedlings (*Avena*), in which native hormone is present largely in the tip, since decapitation prevents normal cell elongation. Unilateral application of active material to a decapitated seedling results in unequal distribution and hence in unequal growth of the two sides, manifested by curvature of the stem away from the side of application. Indole-3-acetic acid is considerably more active than the 3-propionic or the 3-butyric acid or than α-naphthylacetic acid. In high concentrations the growth hormones are toxic to plants, and this observation was the basis of the development of synthetic acids suitable for use as weed killers. Halogenated phenoxyacetic acids are particularly lethal to broad-leaved plants but relatively innocuous to cereals and grasses. One of the most active of these herbicides is 2,4-dichlorophenoxyacetic acid, commonly called 2,4-D.

READING REFERENCES

R. Schoenheimer, "The Dynamic State of Body Constituents," Harvard University Press (1942)

R. Schoenheimer and S. Ratner, "The Metabolism of Proteins and Amino Acids," *Ann. Rev. Biochem.*, 10, 197 (1941)

M. Bergmann, "The Structure of Proteins in Relation to Biological Problems," *Chem. Rev.*, 22, 423 (1938)

W. C. Rose, "The Nutritive Significance of the Amino Acids," *Physiol. Rev.*, 18, 109 (1938)

W. D. McElroy and N. B. Glass, "Amino Acid Metabolism," Johns Hopkins University Press (1955)

CHAPTER 20

STRUCTURE OF BENZENE

In the period when the Kekulé theory of valence was being applied to compounds of the methane series, which were called aliphatic because of inclusion of the initially prominent fatty acids, a certain number of substances failed to fit into the general classification and seemed differentiated by a low hydrogen content coupled with an apparently saturated character. Some were fragrant substances derived from balsams, resins, and essential oils, and consequently these compounds of deviating nature acquired the name aromatic. Kekulé first recognized that such aromatic compounds as oil of bitter almonds, or benzaldehyde (C_7H_6O), toluene (C_7H_8) from tolu balsam, benzoic acid $(C_7H_6O_2)$ and benzyl alcohol (C_7H_8O) from gum benzoin benzene (C_6H_6), phenol (C_6H_6O), aniline (C_6H_7N), salicylic acid $(C_7H_6O_3)$, and cymene $(C_{10}H_{14})$ all contain at least six carbon atoms and retain a six-carbon unit throughout ordinary chemical transformations and degradations. The simplest six-carbon compound of the group, benzene, eventually was recognized as the parent hydrocarbon, and aromatic compounds are now defined as substances derived from or related to benzene.

Benzene was discovered in 1825 by Michael Faraday, who isolated the substance from an oily condensate deposited from compressed illuminating gas. He established that it is composed of equal numbers of carbon and hydrogen atoms and named it carbureted hydrogen. Mitscherlich (1834) found that benzoic acid can be converted by dry distillation with lime into an identical hydrocarbon, which he further characterized by vapor density measurements as having the formula C_6H_6. As a convenient name indicating the relationship to derivatives designated as benzoic, benzoyl, and benzyl because they had been obtained from gum benzoin, Mitscherlich coined the German word benzin, but Liebig, influential editor of the leading chemical journal of the day, criticized the name as implying a relationship to strychnine and quinine and recommended a change to benzol, based on oleum, or the German öl, oil. Laurent[1] (1837) proposed the alternate name pheno from the Greek "I bear light," in recognition of the discovery of the hydrocarbon in illuminating gas, and this gained usage in the form of the name phenyl for the C_6H_5 radical though not for the hydrocarbon itself. The name benzol soon became established in the German literature, but in England and France the ending eventually was changed to -ene to avoid confusion with the systematic designation of alcohols. The German literature still employs the names benzol, toluol, xylol, whereas benzene, toluene, and xylene are employed in English and French literature.

---

[1] Auguste Laurent, 1807–53; b. Langres, France; Bordeaux, Paris

In 1845 Hofmann found that benzene can be isolated by redistillation of the tar resulting as a by-product of the conversion of coal into coke for use in metallurgy. In the next decade some progress was made on the technological production from coal tar of benzene and other aromatic compounds, which were destined to constitute key starting materials for a variety of syntheses. The first synthetic dye, one derived from coal tar, was discovered in 1856 by Perkin,[2] a young English student of Hofmann. The discovery was the result of fortunate circumstance coupled with rare vision on the part of the experimenter reminiscent of the early work of Pasteur. Perkin's dye mauveine initiated the development of what has now become a dominant factor in world economics: the synthetic organic chemical industry. The initial spectacular advances were based on empirical findings, but the young industry could hardly have enjoyed normal growth for long without guidance in the form of an elucidation of the chemical nature of benzene. The Kekulé theory of valence announced in 1859 accounted for most known compounds of the methane series but did not at first appear applicable to benzene and derivatives.

Kekulé Formula (1865). — A perplexing aspect of the problem is that the formula of benzene, C_6H_6, indicates a degree of unsaturation comparable to that of acetylene (C_2H_2), and yet the hydrocarbon does not display the reactivity so characteristic of unsaturated aliphatic compounds. Whereas alkenes are oxidized rapidly by cold alkaline permanganate, add bromine or sulfuric acid at $0°$, and are oxidized by nitric acid, benzene is resistant to boiling alkaline permanganate and is not attacked by the other reagents mentioned to any appreciable extent at low temperatures in the absence of special catalysts. Under forcing conditions bromine, sulfuric acid, and nitric acid react with benzene, but the typical reaction products do not result from additions, as in the alkenes, but from substitutions.

$$C_6H_6 \ + \ Br_2 \ \xrightarrow{\text{FeBr}_3 \text{ catalyst, heat}} \ \underset{\text{Bromobenzene}}{C_6H_5Br} \ + \ HBr$$

$$C_6H_6 \ + \ H_2SO_4 \ \xrightarrow{\text{Heat}} \ \underset{\substack{\text{Benzenesulfonic} \\ \text{acid}}}{C_6H_5SO_3H} \ + \ H_2O$$

$$C_6H_6 \ + \ HNO_3 \ \xrightarrow{\text{Heat}} \ \underset{\text{Nitrobenzene}}{C_6H_5NO_2} \ + \ H_2O$$

Since the chemical behavior evidently does not resemble that of other unsaturated compounds, the structure of the parent substance of the aromatic series could hardly be inferred from analogy.

Another approach occurred to Kekulé, after his realization that the six-carbon unit of benzene constitutes a fundamental durable structure recurring in all aromatic compounds. The structure of a hydrocarbon can be inferred from the number of substitution products. There is but one monochloroethane; hence the six hydrogen atoms are all equivalent, and the fact that

[2] Sir William Henry Perkin, 1838–1907; b. London; Sudbury/London; *J. Chem. Soc.*, **93**, 2214 (1908)

propane affords two mono-, four di-, and five trichloro derivatives is evidence supporting the accepted structure.   From an evaluation of the still fragmentary and partly erroneous data on hand, Kekulé concluded that benzene must have a structure allowing for only a single product of monosubstitution and for three disubstitution products, and saw that these relationships can be accounted for only by a cyclic formula.   A ring of six carbon atoms, each carrying a hydrogen atom, would explain the equivalence of all six possible positions for monosubstitution and account for the existence of three di derivatives.   The possibilities for di- and tri-substitution are shown with outline formulas.   As new compounds were prepared and char-

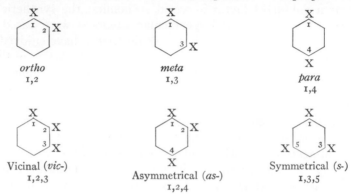

ortho
1,2

meta
1,3

para
1,4

Vicinal (vic-)
1,2,3

Asymmetrical (as-)
1,2,4

Symmetrical (s-)
1,3,5

acterized and old ones reinvestigated, abundant evidence soon accumulated that left no doubt of the correctness of this part of Kekulé's theory, for the number of isomers in different series invariably corresponded with the predicted number.

Confirmation of another nature came from correlation of benzene derivatives with compounds of the cyclohexane series.   Baeyer, in a classical investigation of the reduction of benzenedicarboxylic acids (1887–92), isolated hexahydro derivatives that could be identified by synthesis.   The para isomer, for example, afforded both the cis and trans forms of the reduced acid, and these were synthesized by Perkin, Jr.[3] (1892) by an adaptation of the malonic ester synthesis, as formulated.   Cyclohexane itself was later obtained by hydrogenation of benzene (Sabatier and Senderens, 1901).   Independent evidence came from the field of physics.   The interesting substance mellitic acid of the formula $C_6(COOH)_6$, occurring in a mineral found in brown coal, can be converted into and obtained from known derivatives of benzene, and it also can be produced by oxidation of graphite or amorphous carbon with nitric acid.   X-ray crystallographic analysis (Debye and Scherrer, 1917) established that graphite is made up of a series of interconnected honeycombs of six-membered carbon rings (in graphite the rings appear to be planar, whereas the diamond molecule, characterized by the

[3] William Henry Perkin, Jr., 1860–1929; b. Sudbury/London; Edinburgh, Manchester, Oxford: Nature. 124, 263 (1929)

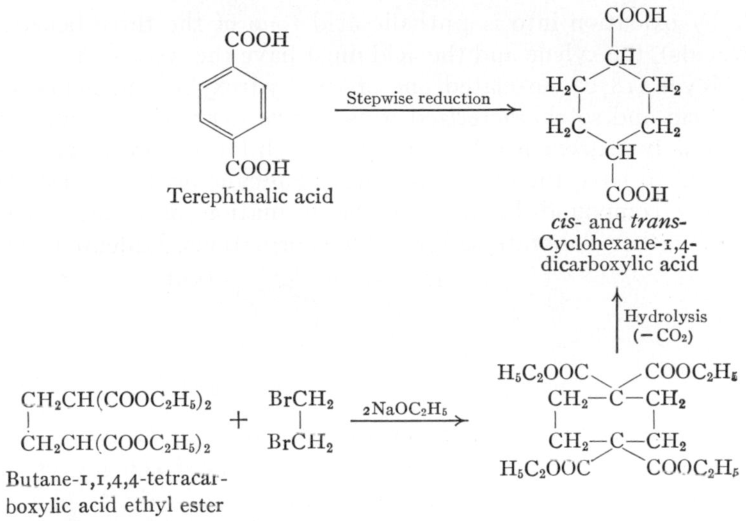

COOH

Stepwise reduction →

Terephthalic acid

$$\underset{\text{COOH}}{\overset{\text{COOH}}{\Big|}}$$

cis- and trans-
Cyclohexane-1,4-
dicarboxylic acid

↑ Hydrolysis
(− CO₂)

CH₂CH(COOC₂H₅)₂
|
CH₂CH(COOC₂H₅)₂

Butane-1,1,4,4-tetracar-
boxylic acid ethyl ester

+

BrCH₂
|
BrCH₂

2NaOC₂H₅ →

H₅C₂OOC   COOC₂H₅
    CH₂—C—CH₂
    | |
    CH₂—C—CH₂
H₅C₂OOC   COOC₂H₅

X-ray studies of W. H. and W. L. Bragg, contains puckered rings corresponding to the chair-form of cyclohexane). Since graphite is correlated with
benzene, benzene must have a six-membered ring structure. Later direct
X-ray analysis of hexamethylbenzene (Bragg, Lonsdale, 1922–29) not only
confirmed the presence of a ring but established the interatomic distances
in the molecule.

Orientation of Substituents. — The early work of testing the postulated
ring structure by chemical methods included development of proof of the
symmetry of benzene through establishment of the equivalence of the six
positions. For example, Ladenburg[4] (1876) succeeded in interconverting
benzoic acid (C_6H_5COOH) and phenol (C_6H_5OH), and in transforming all
three hydroxybenzoic acids into benzoic acid on the one hand and into
phenol on the other; since all samples of each substance were identical in
every case, four positions in the molecule are equivalent.

Some early inferences regarding the structures were speculative but
nevertheless correct. Thus mesitylene, a trimethyl derivative of benzene
resulting from condensation of three molecules of acetone under the influence of concentrated sulfuric acid, was regarded by Baeyer as the symmetrical, or 1,3,5-derivative because of the manner of its formation, and
Ladenburg (1874) proved this structure by demonstrating,
through interconversions of nitro and amino derivatives of
the hydrocarbon, that any two of the positions not occupied
by methyl groups are equivalent; this relationship is consistent with the 1,3,5-structure but not with the alternate

Mesitylene

1,2,3- or 1,2,4-formulation. In mesitylene each of the three methyl groups
occupies a position *meta* to the other two groups, and since the hydrocarbon
can be degraded to one of the xylenes (or dimethylbenzenes) that is con-

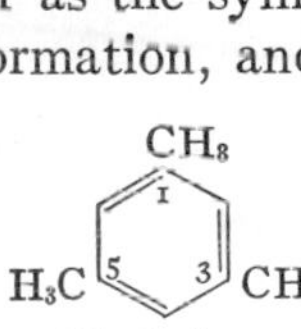

[4] Albert Ladenburg, 1842–1911; b. Mannheim, Germany; Ph.D. Heidelberg; Kiel

vertible by oxidation into isophthalic acid (one of the three benzenedicar boxylic acids), the xylene and the acid must have the *meta*, or 1,3-structure Victor Meyer (1870) correlated one of the hydroxybenzoic acids with iso-phthalic acid and so characterized it as a *meta* derivative. Since phthalic acid is the only benzenedicarboxylic acid which forms a cyclic anhydride, it was inferred to have the *ortho* structure. Salicylic acid was also classified as an *ortho* compound because of the formation of cyclic derivatives. Through a rather elaborate series of transformations, Ladenburg was able

COOH   COOH

COOH   OH
Phthalic acid   Salicylic acid

to characterize as *para* isomers certain key compounds of the dimethyl, dicarboxy, and hydroxycarboxy series, and these served as points of reference for elucidation of the structures of other compounds.

Other early inferences were less secure, and in some instances proved to be erroneous. In 1874 Körner[5] pointed out that any method of orientation involving a sequence of transformations must be subject to some uncer-tainty because it is based on the assumption that the reactions proceed normally, with one group directly replacing another. A new principle was proposed and experimentally exploited that is free from any such uncer-tainty. Körner's absolute method consists in establishment of the number of isomeric substitution products of a given kind derivable from a substance under investigation. The three xylenes, for example, offer different oppor-tunities for monosubstitution. The *ortho* isomer can give rise to two deriva-tives containing the radical A, for this can be placed at either the 3- or 4-position, as shown in the outline formulas I and II. If A is introduced at position 5, the structure is identical with II, and substitution at position 6 is equivalent to that at 3; the formula stands for a symmetrical ring, and the identity of the pairs of structures can be seen by rotating or inverting

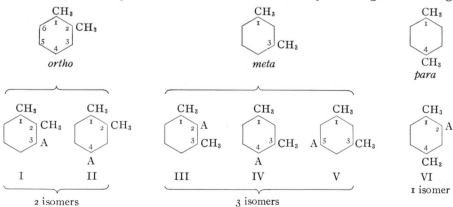

[5] Wilhelm Körner, 1839–1925; b. Kassel, Germany; Giessen, Milan; *J. Chem. Soc.*, **127**, 2975 (1925)

one ring. The rule for numbering is the obvious one of starting with a substituted position and counting in a direction that gives the simplest set of numbers, and hence if a bromine atom were located at either position 3 or 6, as formula I is written, the substance would be named 1,2-dimethyl-3-bromobenzene. The structure of the *meta* compound permits three different orientations of the A-substituted derivative, III-V, whereas in the *para* isomer, all available nuclear positions are identical, and only one monosubstitution product (VI) is possible. Thus the *ortho*, *meta*, and *para* compounds can be differentiated by establishing which one leads to two mononitro, monobromo, or other derivatives, which gives three isomers, and which but one.

Application of the principle is not easy, for the derivatives are not all obtainable by direct substitution, and even when the direct method can be employed, mixtures often result and care is required to secure pure substances. In experiments characterized by scrupulous attention to purity of the products, Körner established the structures of the dibromobenzenes by determining the number of mononitro derivatives and of the tribromobenzenes derivable from each isomer; this research also fixed the structures of the tribromo compounds. Griess (1874) characterized the isomeric diaminobenzenes (phenylenediamines) by eliminating the carboxyl group from each member of the series of six diaminobenzoic acids by distillation with lime. Two of these gave the same diamine, m.p. 103°, three gave an isomer, m.p. 63°, and the sixth afforded a third diamine, m.p. 140°.

Bond Structure of Benzene. — If benzene consists of a symmetrical ring of six equivalent CH groups, the question of the disposition of the fourth valence of each carbon atom remains. Kekulé suggested that these valences are utilized in formation of three double bonds and that benzene is cyclohexatriene. Although the hydrocarbon does not exhibit the reactivity characteristic of open-chain dienes and trienes and reacts, if at all, chiefly by substitution rather than addition, instances of addition do exist and seem to indicate the presence of three double bonds. Thus though benzene is resistant to catalytic hydrogenation as compared with olefins, it does absorb three moles of hydrogen under the influence of nickel catalyst at high temperatures or of an active platinum catalyst in an acidic medium at room temperature, and affords cyclohexane. The characteristic action of bromine on benzene is substitution of hydrogen by bromine, catalyzed by a trace of an iron salt, but when the catalyst is excluded and the pure reagents are brought together in sunlight and in the absence of oxygen, the hydrocarbon forms a hexabromide.

α-Benzene hexabromide
(m.p. 212°)

Chlorine also adds under these special conditions and gives a hexachloride (α-form, m.p. 157°). Ozone, a reagent that affords one of the most reliable means of probing for double bonds, also adds to benzene. The reaction proceeds with difficulty, but a triozonide has been isolated and characterized by decomposition to three molecules of glyoxal (Harries, 1904), as shown.

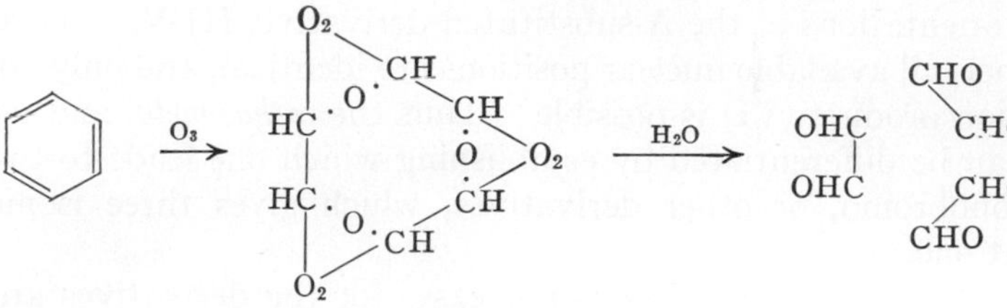

Triozonide   Glyoxal

Although these additions tend to indicate the presence of three double bonds, Ladenburg noted (1879) that the Kekulé cyclohexatriene formula predicts the existence of more disubstitution products than actually exist. The theory would allow the existence of an *ortho* derivative in two forms, VIIa and VIIb, and of an unsymmetrically substituted *meta* derivative in the forms VIIIa and VIIIb, differing in the location of the double bonds with

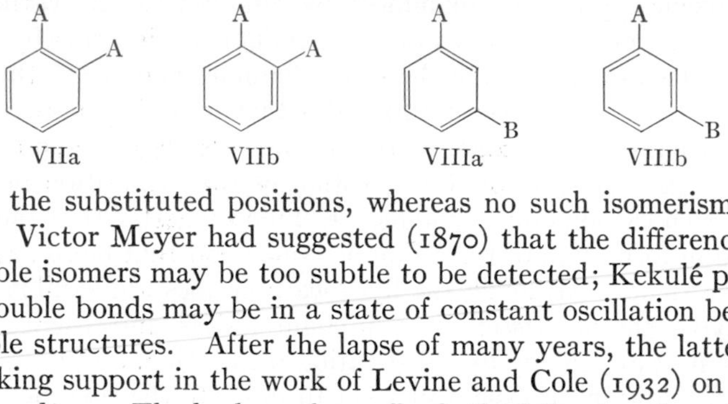

VIIa   VIIb   VIIIa   VIIIb

respect to the substituted positions, whereas no such isomerism has been observed. Victor Meyer had suggested (1870) that the difference between such possible isomers may be too subtle to be detected; Kekulé pointed out that the double bonds may be in a state of constant oscillation between the two possible structures. After the lapse of many years, the latter view received striking support in the work of Levine and Cole (1932) on the ozonization of o-xylene. The hydrocarbon affords the following three fragments: glyoxal (OHC·CHO = A), diacetyl ($CH_3COCOCH_3$ = B), and methyl-

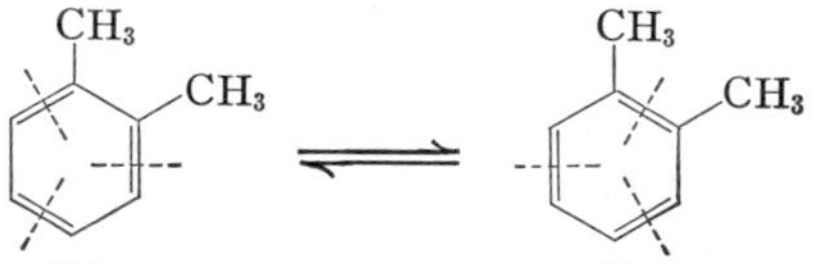

IX   X

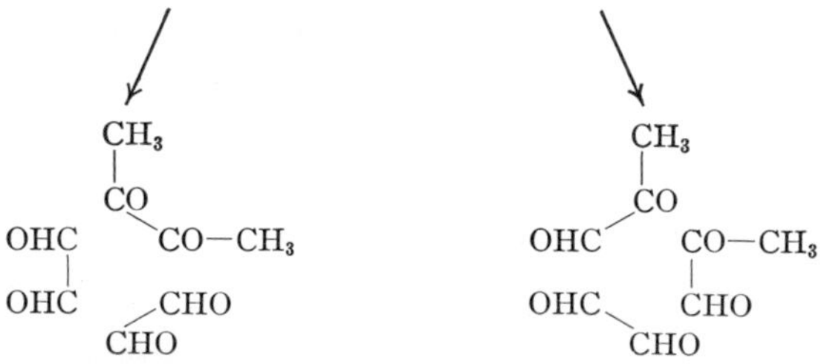

glyoxal ($CH_3COCHO = C$). The fragments A and B can come from one Kekulé structure (IX) in the ratio of two to one, and A and C from the other structure (X), but neither structure alone can give rise to all three substances; therefore o-xylene must exist in both forms. In a quantitative reinvestigation of the reaction Wibaut[6] observed (1941) that the three dicarbonyl compounds are produced in the relative amounts calculated for a mixture of equal parts of the two Kekulé forms. Ozonization of 1,2,4-trimethylbenzene also indicated a 50:50 ratio between the two structures. The hydrocarbons can hardly consist of equilibrium mixtures, for some preferential stability would be manifested in a predominance of one form.

The possibility was also considered that benzene has a symmetrical structure containing some unique linkage different from a double bond but responsive to some double-bond reagents. The marked difference in reactivity seemed to many of Kekulé's contemporaries to indicate that a unique linkage must be present, and the relatively inert character of benzene constituted an objection to the cyclohexatriene formula that could not be answered as plausibly as Ladenburg's criticism. One of the alternate benzene formulas devised in an attempt to avoid this objection is Ladenburg's prismatic formula (1869), which is symmetrical but contains no double bonds. Formulas utilizing diagonal, or *para* bonds were suggested by Claus (1867) and by Dewar (1867). Another concept, advanced in 1887 by Armstrong[7] in England and by Baeyer in Germany, was that of a centric formula

Ladenburg	Claus	Dewar	Armstrong-Baeyer	Thiele

in which the fourth valence of each carbon is directed toward the center Thiele[8] (1899) introduced a useful concept based on the observation that conjugated systems of double and single bonds function as a unit and are more stable than unconjugated systems of the same degree of unsaturation. He considered each carbon atom of a double bond to possess a certain partial valence, represented by a dotted line, and postulated that in a diene the partial valences on the pair of central carbon atoms neutralize each other with resulting accumulation of residual energy at the ends of the conjugated

$$>C=C<$$

Isolated double bond   Conjugated system

system. The Kekulé formula, Thiele noted, represents a closed conjugated system without terminal positions, which permits neutralization of all six partial valences in pairs to form three inactive double bonds alternating

[6] Johan Pieter Wibaut, b. 1886 Middleburg, Netherlands; D.Sc. Amsterdam; Amsterdam
[7] Henry E. Armstrong, 1848–1937; b. England; Ph.D. Leipzig (Kolbe); South Kensington
[8] Johannes Thiele, 1865–1918; b. Ratibon, Germany; Ph.D. Halle; Munich, Strasbourg; *Ber.*, **60A**, 75 (1927)

with the original deactivated double bonds, or a system of six nearly equivalent inert linkages.

Baeyer's researches on the hydrophthalic acids refuted the Ladenburg formula, for the positions in the prism, numbered in accordance with the requirements for o $(1,2)$-, m $(1,3)$-, and p $(1,4)$-substitution in accordance with the Körner principle, do not correspond to the location of substituents in the cyclohexane derivatives resulting on reduction. X-ray analyses of crystalline hexaalkyl derivatives of benzene prove that the six carbon atoms of the ring all lie in a plane and that attached alkyl groups radiate from the ring in this plane, and thus exclude the Ladenburg formula. Interatomic distances determined by the X-ray method also are incompatible with a *para*-bond formula, for the distances are such that a linkage extending between *para* carbon atoms would have a length (2.80 Å) considerably greater than in any known compound. Thus the distance between carbon centers in saturated paraffinic hydrocarbons is 1.54 Å, and the normal distance for the olefinic C=C bond is 1.34 Å. Since a bond of abnormal length would correspond to a weak attachment and a consequently reactive system, a formulation utilizing such a linkage is inconsistent with the properties of benzene.

The distance between adjacent carbon centers in the benzene ring, as determined by the X-ray method and confirmed by electron-diffraction studies, is 1.40 Å, a value intermediate between the paraffinic C—C and C=C distances, whereas the $C_{aliphatic}$—$C_{aromatic}$ bond between an alkyl substituent and a nuclear carbon atom corresponds in length (1.50 Å) to a paraffinic C—C bond. Furthermore all six connecting bonds in the ring are identical. In terms of the classical concept of organic structures, the equivalence of the six bonds could be regarded as consistent with the Armstrong-Baeyer or the Thiele formula or with the idea of two oscillating Kekulé structures. The electronic theory of valence, however, provided a clear decision between these alternatives. The well-established concept of the covalent bond as a pair of shared electrons (G. N. Lewis, 1916) describes in exact terms the nature of the single and double bonds pictured in the Kekulé formula, but does not provide any modern counterpart for neutralized or centrally directed bonds or for partial valences. Thus neither the Armstrong-Baeyer formula nor the Thiele formula can be said to have any recognized physical reality. The Kekulé formulation can be translated directly into an electronic equivalent in which the carbon atoms are joined

alternately by one and by two pairs of shared electrons, and on inspection of the two forms, which Kekulé described as being in a state of dynamic oscillation, it is seen that the phenomenon is that now defined as **resonance**. The two forms are equivalent, and their interconversion requires only re-distribution of electrons in the planar system, without movement of atomic centers. Results of the ozonization experiments cited above accord with the concept of two resonant Kekulé forms contributing in an equal extent to the structure. Since each bond has the same hybrid character and is intermediate between a single and a double bond, the six bonds in the benzene ring have the same length. That there is a shortening of the bond distance to 1.40 Å, as compared with the average value 1.46 Å for three double and three single bonds, finds a parallel in noncyclic resonant systems.

Resonance also provides a concrete expression of Thiele's idea that a closed conjugated system would possess special stability. The stable character of the aromatic ring is shown by the production of aromatic hydrocarbons during the coking of coal at high temperatures. A measure of the energy content of benzene as compared with nonbenzenoid hydro-derivatives of benzene is available from determination of the heats of hy-drogenation (Kistiakowsky, 1936). Whereas establishment of a double bond by removal of two hydrogen atoms is ordinarily an endothermic reac-tion requiring an energy input of some 28–30 kg.-cal./mole, the conversion of 1,2-dihydrobenzene (cyclohexadiene-1,3) into benzene and hydrogen is weakly exothermic and tends to proceed spontaneously, with liberation of energy. The thermodynamic stability, or low energy content, of benzene

$$\text{(cyclohexadiene)} \longrightarrow \text{(benzene)} \quad + \quad H_2 \quad + \quad 5.6 \text{ kg.-cal.}$$

and the consequent low order of reactivity are distinguishing attributes of aromaticity. Calculations from thermochemical data indicate that benzene is more stable than hypothetical nonresonant cyclohexatriene by 39 kg.-cal/ mole in consequence of resonance energy (Pauling, 1933).

1,6-Diphenylhexatriene-1,3,5 (XI) contains an open-chain conjugated system that approaches the inert triene system of the benzene ring in stabil-ity, for the substance is unusually resistant to oxidation by alkaline perman-

—CH=CHCH=CHCH=CH—
XI (stable)

ganate and does not add hydrogen bromide (Kuhn, 1928). Here the open-chain system is conjugated at the ends of the chain with benzene rings that contribute to the resonance of the system as a whole. The hydrocarbon

—CH₂CH=CHCH=CHCH₂—
XII (reactive)

undergoes 1,6-reduction to the dihydride XII, in which the terminal rings are no longer conjugated with the chain, and which does not possess comparable stability but resembles the usual reactive polyenes. The formula of cyclooctatetraene on first inspection would also seem to represent a symmetrical closed conjugated system capable of resonance, and a knowledge

Cyclooctatetraene

of this hydrocarbon is obviously important to the theory of benzenoid compounds. By a long and difficult synthesis, Willstätter, Waser, and Heidelberger (1913) achieved the preparation of a hydrocarbon that they regarded as cyclooctatetraene on the basis of composition, degree of unsaturation, and conversion into cyclooctane on hydrogenation. The hydrocarbon proved to be too unstable for any but brief study, but it was characterized as wholly unlike benzene and comparable in reactivity in addition and polymerization processes to ordinary open-chain dienes. Willstätter's original synthesis has been confirmed (Cope,[9] 1948); in the meantime Reppe at the I. G. Farbenindustrie found that by operating at a suitably high pressure (in tetrahydrofuran in the presence of a nickel catalyst) acetylene can be polymerized to cyclooctatetraene. The method is suitable for large-scale production. A third method of preparation (Cope, 1948) utilizes as the initial step the dimerization of chloroprene to an octadiene.

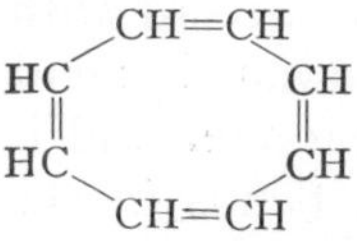

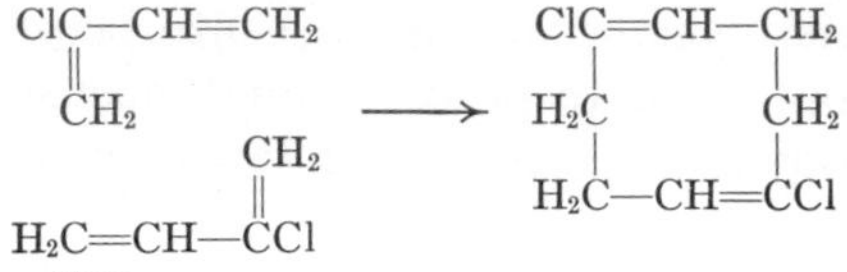

Chloroprene

Samples prepared by both processes are identical with Willstätter's material, and hence his observation of the high reactivity of cyclooctatetraene is confirmed. Cyclooctatetraene is particularly prone to undergo reactions

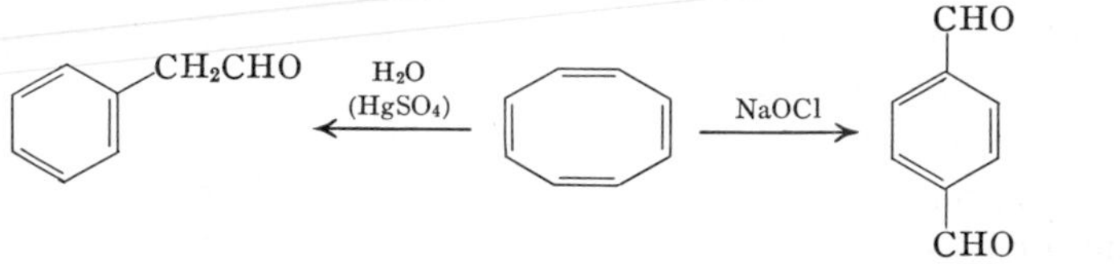

Phenylacetaldehyde   Terephthalaldehyde

leading to aromatic compounds, two examples of which are shown in the formulas. All four bonds are reducible by hydrogen (cyclooctane, m.p. 13°), in a neutral medium the reaction proceeds very slowly after addition of three moles of hydrogen. Thus cyclooctene, b.p. 142°, can be prepared in about 90% yield by hydrogenation with palladium catalyst in methanol. Oxidation of cyclooctene with chromic acid leads to suberic acid (64% yield).

Thus the eight-membered conjugated system does not possess the aro-

---

[9] Arthur C. Cope, b. 1909 Dunreith, Indiana; Ph.D. Wisconsin (McElvain); Mass. Inst. Tech.

matic characteristics of the six-membered system. This relationship would appear anomalous on the basis of classical concepts; however it is understandable in terms of the resonance theory. Whereas the planar cyclohexatriene ring is practically strain-free, the cyclooctatetraene ring would be under significant strain if all eight carbon atoms were in a plane, and physical evidence indicates that, in analogy with saturated large-ring hydrocarbons and ketones, the ring assumes a puckered and largely strain-free conformation. Alternate nonplanar, or puckered structures can be visualized, comparable to the two Kekulé forms of benzene, but the transformation of one form into the other would require movement of certain carbon atoms from one side of the median plane of the molecule to the other. Since resonance can occur only when interconversion of the contributing structures entails no migration or movement of atomic centers but merely electron shifts, cyclooctatetraene is incapable of achieving stabilization through resonance.

The interpretation of the properties of benzene afforded by the **orbital theory** is as follows. Each carbon atom can provide three bonds lying in a plane by sp^2, or trigonal, hybridization (p. 77, Fig. 3.11), which prepares the atoms for formation of σ bonds of maximal strength if the valence angle of $120°$ is preserved. This condition is uniquely fulfilled in a six-carbon ring, and hence benzene has a strongly σ-bonded, coplanar ring (Fig. 20.1 a)

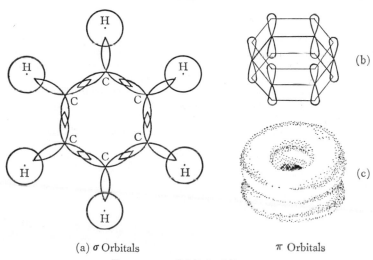

(a) σ Orbitals π Orbitals

Fig. 20.1. — Orbitals of Benzene

The conditions are also ideal for multiple overlapping of p orbitals, as shown schematically in the loop-diagram of Fig. 20.1 b. Because the system is cyclic, each p orbital overlaps an orbital on either side of it, with particularly extensive delocalization and consequently high resonance energy. The cloud charge of the π orbital takes on the shape of a pair of doughnuts (Fig. 20.1 c), and all six bonds of benzene are identical and of a unique character.

The orbital shown accommodates only two electrons (Pauli exclusion principle); the other four are assumed to occupy two additional π orbitals that encompass all six nuclei, each with a nodal plane perpendicular to the plane of the ring in addition to the primary node coplanar with the ring. The orbital theory provides a simple explanation of the fact that cyclooctatetraene lacks aromaticity: overlapping of atomic orbitals requires coplanarity of the atoms concerned.

PROBLEMS

1. Suggest a synthesis of cyclohexane-1,3-dicarboxylic acid similar to that of the 1,4-isomer by Perkin (p. 517). How can the tetracarboxylic acid esters required for these two syntheses be obtained?
2. Could Körner's absolute method of determining structures be applied to the three isomeric trimethylbenzenes?
3. Explain why the Körner principle requires numbering the positions in the Ladenburg formula in the manner indicated on page 521.
4. Write formulas for the six diaminobenzoic acids, and explain the significance of the results obtained by Griess on decarboxylation of these substances (p. 519).
5. What type of isomerism would be expected in benzene hexabromide (p. 519)?
6. Calculate the molecular ratio of the reaction products expected to result from ozonization of 1,2,4-trimethylbenzene on the theory of a resonance system of the two possible Kekulé forms.

READING REFERENCES

F. R. Japp, "Kekulé Memorial Lecture," *J. Chem. Soc.*, **73**, 97 (1898)

W. H. Perkin, "Baeyer Memorial Lecture," *J. Chem. Soc.*, **123**, 1520 (1923)

L. F. Fieser, "Theory of the Structure and Reactions of Aromatic Compounds," in H. Gilman, "Organic Chemistry," I, 2nd Ed., 117–213, Wiley, New York (1943)

L. Pauling, "The Significance of Resonance to the Nature of the Chemical Bond and the Structure of Molecules," in H. Gilman, "Organic Chemistry," II, 2nd Ed., 1970–1979 (1943)

G. M. Badger, "The Aromatic Bond," *Quart. Rev.*, **5**, 147 (1951)

G. M. Badger, "The Structures and Reactions of Aromatic Compounds," Cambridge Univ. Press (1954)

AROMATIC HYDROCARBONS

PRODUCTION

From Coal. — The heating of bituminous coal at temperatures in the range 1000–1300° in a retort without access of air converts the bulk of the material into coke, a hard porous residuum consisting largely of carbon admixed with ash, and affords a quantity of gas (coal gas) and a mixture of less volatile products separating as a condensate consisting of black viscous coal tar and a water layer containing ammonia. The coking process can be conducted somewhat differently and with utilization of different types of coals according as coal gas or metallurgical coke is the chief objective, which varies with localities and economic conditions. The optimum conditions and type of coal for production of coal gas of high calorific value afford a soft inferior coke, and if conditions are chosen to give a coke hard enough for use in the reduction of iron oxide, the gas is not of the highest quality. It is most economical to manufacture high-grade coke in by-product ovens so constructed as to permit recovery of coal tar, ammonia, and coal gas, and to use a part of the gas as fuel for the ovens and the rest in admixture with either natural gas or water gas for distribution through city gas mains. Refined **coke-oven gas**, amounting to some 11,200 cu. ft./ ton of coal, consists largely of hydrogen (52% by volume) and methane (32%), with smaller amounts of carbon monoxide (4–9%), carbon dioxide (2%), nitrogen (4–5%), and ethylene and other olefins (3–4%). The average calorific value is 570 B.T.U./cu. ft. In the refining process, the gas passes through tar and ammonia scrubbers and through oil-absorption tanks for recovery of **light oil**, a crude oil amounting to 3.2 gal./ton of coal and containing benzene (60%), toluene (15%), xylenes, and naphthalene. A small additional amount of comparable light oil results from distillation of coal tar, but in the modern process over 90% of the benzene and toluene obtainable from coal is derived from the scrubbing of coke-oven gas. Introduction of the recovery process made available vast amounts of previously unutilized benzene of value as a motor fuel.

The yield of **coal tar** is about 3% of the weight of the coal. Initial refining is done by batch distillation; each fraction is further refined by extraction with alkali to separate the weakly acidic aromatic hydroxy compounds (phenols), by extraction of nitrogen bases with dilute mineral acid, and by refractionation. The principal hydrocarbons available commercially from coal tar are listed in Chart 1 in the order of increasing boiling points;

CHART 1.   HYDROCARBONS AVAILABLE FROM COAL TAR

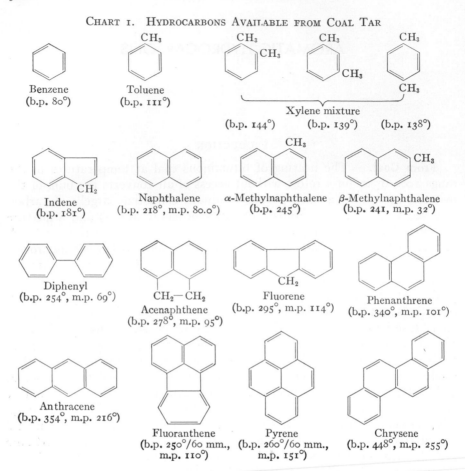

Benzene
(b.p. 80°)

Toluene
(b.p. 111°)

Xylene mixture
(b.p. 144°)   (b.p. 139°)   (b.p. 138°)

Indene
(b.p. 181°)

Naphthalene
(b.p. 218°, m.p. 80.0°)

α-Methylnaphthalene
(b.p. 245°)

β-Methylnaphthalene
(b.p. 241, m.p. 32°)

Diphenyl
(b.p. 254°, m.p. 69°)

Acenaphthene
(b.p. 278°, m.p. 95°)

Fluorene
(b.p. 295°, m.p. 114°)

Phenanthrene
(b.p. 340°, m.p. 101°)

Anthracene
(b.p. 354°, m.p. 216°)

Fluoranthene
(b.p. 250°/60 mm.,
m.p. 110°)

Pyrene
(b.p. 260°/60 mm.,
m.p. 151°)

Chrysene
(b.p. 448°, m.p. 255°)

melting points are included for substances that are solids at ordinary temperature. In addition to aromatic hydrocarbons, coal tar is a practical source of cyclopentadiene (b.p. 41°), which can be stored as the more stable dimer and regenerated when required by slow distillation. Cyclopentadiene is found in light oil, which also contains small amounts of a number of paraffinic and olefinic hydrocarbons. The benzene and toluene found in light oil can be separated effectively by fractional distillation, but each is accompanied by a small amount of a heterocyclic analog of nearly the same boiling point. Thus coal-tar benzene, unless specially processed, contains a trace of thiophene. This unsaturated substance displays aromatic characteristics, for it undergoes sulfonation and nitration and is more stable and chemically inert than olefins. The resemblance to benzene is so marked that the presence of the substance in coal-tar benzene remained unsuspected till an incident in one of Victor Meyer's lectures provided a clue leading to the discovery of the sulfur compound (1882). Meyer periodically demonstrated a supposedly characteristic color test for benzene,

HC——CH
HC   CH
   S

Thiophene (b.p. 84°)

which consists in shaking a sample with concentrated sulfuric acid and a crystal of isatin (Baeyer's indophenine reaction), but on one occasion he applied the test in expectation of proving that benzoic acid on decarboxylation gives benzene. The beautiful blue color failed to appear, since the color reaction is specific for the previously unknown thiophene and not for benzene.

The three xylenes boil at too nearly the same temperature to be separable by distillation, but the xylene mixture is obtained to the extent of about 1% of the weight of dry coal tar. Naphthalene is the most abundant single constituent (average yield about 11%); it also is accompanied by a sulfur analog, thionaphthene (b.p. 220°). In addition to α- and β-methylnaphthalene and acenaphthene, coal tar affords a considerable fraction containing dimethylnaphthalenes (2,3-, 2,6-, 2,7-, and 1,6-; b.p. 261–262°), which are separable by elaborate processing and have appeared on the market only briefly. Anthracene was valued in the early days of coal-tar technology as the starting material for production of alizarin, the first natural dye that was prepared synthetically (1868), and it gained new importance with discovery of the indanthrone vat dyes (1901), also obtainable from this hydrocarbon. Thus the higher-boiling fractions of the coal-tar distillate have long been worked for anthracene. Some of the other hydrocarbons shown in the chart, though currently available, are rare and expensive. The processing often includes such chemical methods as sulfonation and desulfonation and treatment with alkali or sodium. Thus technical anthracene has a yellowish tinge due to a trace of naphthacene, and gives a positive test for nitrogen, owing to the presence of the heterocyclic analog carbazole (see Chart 2). Naphthacene can be eliminated on a small scale by chromatographic adsorption and on a large scale by selective distillation of the anthracene with

Naphthacene
(orange, m.p. 335°)

ethylene glycol. Pure anthracene (m.p. 216°) exhibits a spectacularly beautiful blue fluorescence in either the crystalline or dissolved state; the fluorescence disappears on fusion of the solid and reappears on solidification of the melt. Although naphthacene does not inhibit the fluorescence of anthracene in solution, as little as 0.1% of this persistent contaminant present in solid solution in anthracene gives rise to a distinctly altered fluorescence spectrum (Miller and Baumann, 1943). Naphthacene also persists in repeatedly crystallized samples of chrysene, to which it imparts a beautiful golden color that was the basis for the name (Gr. *chrysos*, gold), though by special techniques completely colorless and fluorescent chrysene can be obtained. Carbazole is comparable in structure to succinimide, and is not extracted by washing with dilute acid; since it is sufficiently acidic to form a sodium salt, it can be eliminated by fusion of technical anthracene with alkali.

The chief nitrogen components produced commercially are listed in Chart 2. These are all basic except indole and carbazole, which are weakly

CHART 2. PRINCIPAL NITROGEN COMPOUNDS FROM COAL TAR

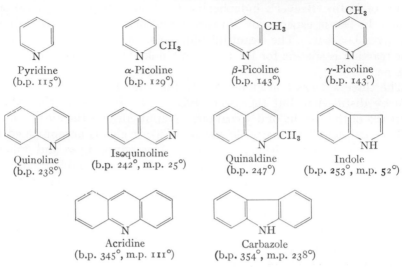

Pyridine
(b.p. 115°)

α-Picoline
(b.p. 129°)

β-Picoline
(b.p. 143°)

γ-Picoline
(b.p. 143°)

Quinoline
(b.p. 238°)

Isoquinoline
(b.p. 242°, m.p. 25°)

Quinaldine
(b.p. 247°)

Indole
(b.p. 253°, m.p. 52°)

Acridine
(b.p. 345°, m.p. 111°)

Carbazole
(b.p. 354°, m.p. 238°)

acidic. The oxygen-containing substances produced from coal tar are listed in Chart 3. The phenolic constituents can be separated from the

CHART 3. PRINCIPAL OXYGEN-CONTAINING COMPOUNDS FROM COAL TAR

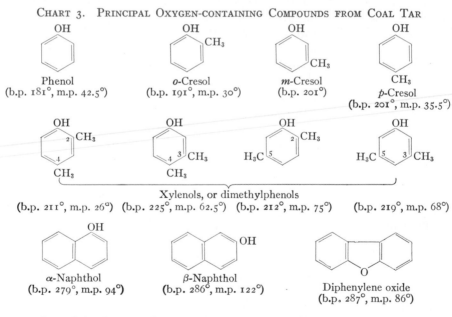

Phenol
(b.p. 181°, m.p. 42.5°)

o-Cresol
(b.p. 191°, m.p. 30°)

m-Cresol
(b.p. 201°)

p-Cresol
(b.p. 201°, m.p. 35.5°)

Xylenols, or dimethylphenols
(b.p. 211°, m.p. 26°)   (b.p. 225°, m.p. 62.5°)   (b.p. 212°, m.p. 75°)   (b.p. 219°, m.p. 68°)

α-Naphthol
(b.p. 279°, m.p. 94°)

β-Naphthol
(b.p. 286°, m.p. 122°)

Diphenylene oxide
(b.p. 287°, m.p. 86°)

neutral and basic constituents of coal-tar distillates by extraction with alkali, and efficient fractionation on a technical scale affords cuts consisting preponderantly of phenol, o-cresol, and a mixture of m- and p-cresol. Isolation of pure components of the cresol and xylenol fractions is accomplished by selective precipitation and by sulfonation.

Some forty compounds have been mentioned as derived from the coking process, but the total number of identified substances from this source is one hundred twenty-two. Only those substances listed in the charts are normally available for synthetic uses. The benzenoid compounds are not present as such in coal, but arise in the course of pyrolysis. Coal is a product of gradual decomposition of vegetable material containing cellulose, $(C_6H_{10}O_5)_n$, without free access of air, often under the influence of moisture and increased pressure and temperature, and is formed through the successive stages of peat, lignite or brown coal, bituminous or soft coal, and anthracite or hard coal, characterized by increasing carbon content. The bituminous coal ordinarily employed in by-product coking contains about 80-82% carbon, 5-6% hydrogen, 1-2% each of nitrogen and sulfur, 3-5% oxygen, and 5-7% ash. The carbon is combined with the other elements present in the form of large polymeric molecules. The coking process conducted at 1000-1300° must involve cracking of the large molecules, probably followed by an elaborate sequence of reforming steps. The low-temperature carbonization of coal has been investigated on an experimental scale with results indicating that at temperatures of 500-700° the tar is richer in paraffinic and hydroaromatic compounds, which suggests that in the usual process a terminal step consists in thermal dehydrogenation. Thus far, low-temperature methods have not been commercially successful, largely because the carbonaceous residue is a soft semicoke.

From Petroleum. — The aromatization of *n*-heptane from petroleum has been mentioned as a source of toluene (p. 107). A method for conversion of petroleum fractions into a whole series of aromatic hydrocarbon has been developed (Weizmann and co-workers, 1948). The charging stock (naphtha, kerosene, or gas oil) is passed over a copper catalyst at temperatures of 630-680°; 95% of the liquid product consists of aromatic hydrocarbons, and compounds containing nitrogen, sulfur, or oxygen are notably absent. Evidently some of the hydrocarbons are formed by cyclization and dehydrogenation; but breakdown into 2- and 4-carbon units followed by synthesis of aromatic hydrocarbons is also operative. Thus in the reaction of stocks in the boiling range 110-190°, olefins and particularly butadiene are formed in large amounts in the initial stages. Benzene and alkylbenzenes are then formed by recombination of the small units (Diels-

Alder reaction). Certain hydrocarbons, particularly styrene and phenanthrene, are formed in higher proportion in this process than in the pyrolysis of coal.

HYDROCARBONS OF THE BENZENE SERIES

The most frequently encountered benzenoid hydrocarbons are included in Table 21.1. Some are obtainable on a practical scale directly from coal

TABLE 21.1. BENZENOID HYDROCARBONS[1]

NAME	FORMULA	M.P., °C.	B.P., °C.
Benzene	C_6H_6	5.4	80.1
Toluene	$C_6H_5CH_3$	−93	110.6
o-Xylene	$1,2\text{-}(CH_3)_2C_6H_4$	−28	144
m-Xylene	$1,3\text{-}(CH_3)_2C_6H_4$	−54	139
p-Xylene	$1,4\text{-}(CH_3)_2C_6H_4$	13	138
Hemimellitene	$1,2,3\text{-}(CH_3)_3C_6H_3$	liq.	176
Pseudocumene	$1,2,4\text{-}(CH_3)_3C_6H_3$	liq.	169
Mesitylene	$1,3,5\text{-}(CH_3)_3C_6H_3$	−57	165
Prehnitene	$1,2,3,4\text{-}(CH_3)_4C_6H_2$	−4	205
Isodurene	$1,2,3,5\text{-}(CH_3)_4C_6H_2$	liq.	196
Durene	$1,2,4,5\text{-}(CH_3)_4C_6H_2$	80	195
Pentamethylbenzene	$C_6H(CH_3)_5$	53	231
Hexamethylbenzene	$C_6(CH_3)_6$	166	265
Ethylbenzene	$C_6H_5CH_2CH_3$	−93	136
n-Propylbenzene	$C_6H_5CH_2CH_2CH_3$	liq.	159.5
Cumene	$C_6H_5CH(CH_3)_2$	liq.	152
n-Butylbenzene	$C_6H_5CH_2CH_2CH_2CH_3$	liq.	180
t-Butylbenzene	$C_6H_5C(CH_3)_3$	liq.	168
p-Cymene	$p\text{-}CH_3C_6H_4CH(CH_3)_2$	−73.5	177
1,3,5-Triethylbenzene	$1,3,5\text{-}(CH_3CH_2)_3C_6H_3$	liq.	215
Hexaethylbenzene	$C_6(CH_2CH_3)_6$	129	305
Styrene	$C_6H_5CH{=}CH_2$	liq.	146
Allylbenzene	$C_6H_5CH_2CH{=}CH_2$	liq.	156
Stilbene (trans)	$C_6H_5CH{=}CHC_6H_5$	124	307
Diphenylmethane	$(C_6H_5)_2CH_2$	27	262
Triphenylmethane	$(C_6H_5)_3CH$	92.5	359
Tetraphenylmethane	$(C_6H_4)_4C$	285	431
Diphenyl	$C_6H_5 \cdot C_6H_5$	70.5	254
p-Terphenyl	$C_6H_5 \cdot C_6H_4 \cdot C_6H_5$	171	
p-Quaterphenyl	$C_6H_5 \cdot C_6H_4 \cdot C_6H_4 \cdot C_6H_5$	320	$428^{18\,mm.}$
1,3,5-Triphenylbenzene	$1,3,5\text{-}(C_6H_5)_3C_6H_3$	174.5	

[1] The hydrocarbons listed that contain only one benzene ring have specific gravities in the range 0.86–.90.

tar, but the majority are synthesized from starting materials derived from coal tar. Benzene and its more volatile homologs are characterized by a strong and rather pleasant aromatic odor. The liquids are highly refractive, lighter than water, and very sparingly soluble in water. They possess marked toxicity, and continued breathing of the vapors is dangerous. Benzene vapor is also heavy and highly flammable. Like other members of the series, the hydrocarbon burns with a luminous sooty flame and has a high calorific value. The heat of combustion is 781 kg.-cal./mole, or 8.79

kg.-cal. (34.87 B.T.U.)/ml.   The values for toluene (8.79 kg.-cal./ml.) and for the xylenes and ethylbenzene (8.86 kg.-cal./ml.) are similar; the available aromatic hydrocarbons are distinctly more efficient fuels, on a volume basis, than hexane (7.58 kg.-cal./ml.) and are slightly superior to cyclohexane (8.68 kg.-cal./ml.).

In the series of alkylbenzenes, the boiling points show a regular relationship to the molecular weight and are almost independent of the positions of substituents in the ring.   Thus the xylenes all boil at nearly the same temperatures, an average of 29° higher than the temperature at which toluene boils, and the tri- and tetramethylbenzenes fall into groups of boiling points about 30° apart.   A similar progressive decrease in volatility with increasing molecular weight attends lengthening of the chain of the alkyl substituent.   The most noteworthy feature of the melting point data is that substances of symmetrical structure usually melt at higher temperatures than unsymmetrical isomers.   Thus *p*-xylene freezes at 13°, whereas the *ortho* and *meta* isomers remain liquid at temperatures well below zero. The symmetrical 1,2,4,5-tetramethyl derivative durene melts at 80°, whereas its isomers are liquids; hexamethylbenzene is a high-melting solid (166°).

PREPARATION AND SYNTHESIS

From Aliphatic and Alicyclic Compounds. — Berthelot (1886) demonstrated the partial trimerization of acetylene to benzene at 500°; the reaction has no practical application but is a demonstration of the stability and ease of formation of an aromatic hydrocarbon, as is the production of *p*-cymene by the action of dehydrating agents on camphor.   The bridge linkage carrying the *gem*-dimethyl group is severed in the process of molecular rearrange-

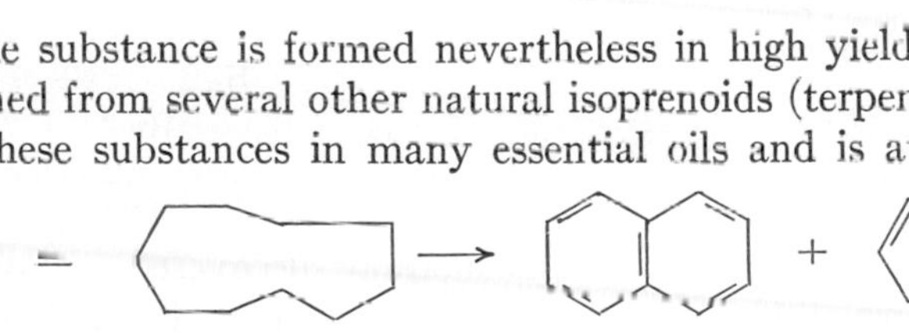

ment, but the substance is formed nevertheless in high yield.   *p*-Cymene can be obtained from several other natural isoprenoids (terpenes); it occurs along with these substances in many essential oils and is available from

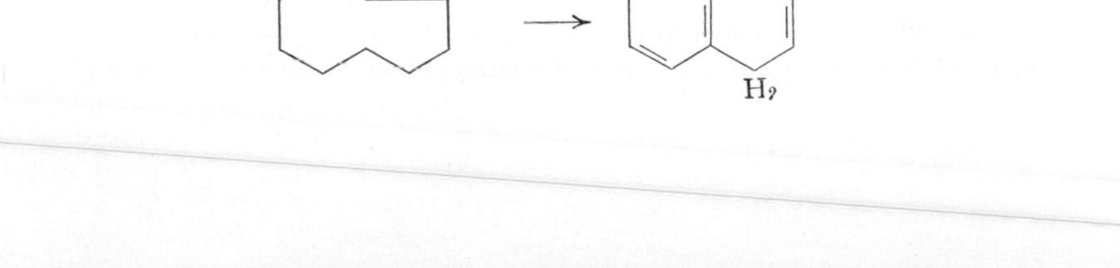

4.5 %   20 %

H?

spruce turpentine. When macrocyclic paraffins are heated in the gas phase in the presence of a palladium-charcoal catalyst cyclodehydrogenation occurs to give aromatic hydrocarbons (Plattner, 1953). Thus cyclodecane gives a mixture of naphthalene and azulene in which the latter predominates, and cyclononane gives indene as the main aromatic product. Intramolecular condensations are also possible, as in a synthesis of acenaphthene from naphthalic anhydride by reduction to the di alcohol, conversion to the

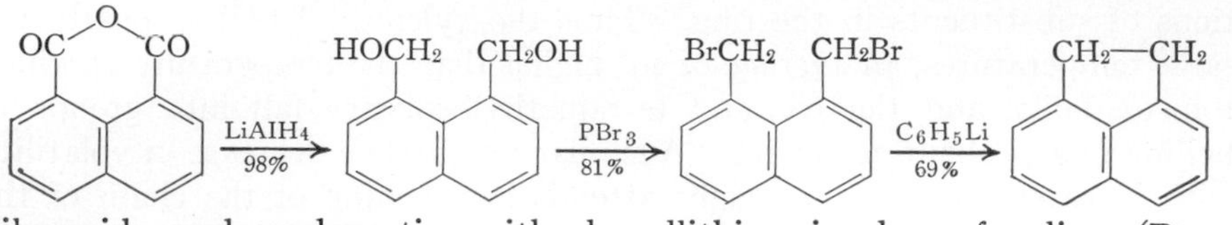

dibromide, and condensation with phenyllithium in place of sodium (Bergmann[1] and Szmuszkovicz, 1953).

A synthetic method applicable on a preparative scale is the production of mesitylene by the action of concentrated sulfuric acid on acetone. Mesityl oxide, phorone (p. 209), and other condensation products are formed, and the yield of mesitylene is low. 1,3,5-Triphenylbenzene is formed

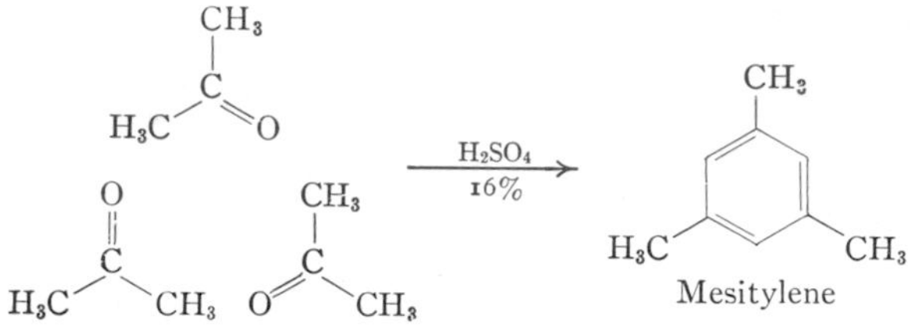

Mesitylene

similarly from acetophenone, $C_6H_5COCH_3$. The reaction has been applied to synthesis of the interesting tetracyclic hydrocarbon dodecahydrotriphenylene from cyclohexanone; the product crystallizes from the reaction mixture in large, sparlike needles.

Dodecahydrotriphenylene
(m.p. 233°)

Wurtz-Fittig Synthesis. — The method discovered by Wurtz in 1855 for coupling two alkyl residues by interaction of an alkyl halide with sodium was applied by Fittig[2] in 1864 to synthesis of hydrocarbons containing an

[1] Ernst David Bergmann, b. 1903 Karlsruhe, Germany; Ph.D. Berlin (Schlenk); Hebrew University, Jerusalem, and Scientific Department, Israel Ministry of Defence

[2] Rudolph Fittig, 1835–1910; b. Hamburg, Germany; Ph.D. Göttingen; Strasbourg

alkyl group linked to an aromatic residue, or aryl group (Ar). The synthetic method, the Wurtz-Fittig reaction, is represented as follows:

$$ArX + RX + 2Na \longrightarrow Ar \cdot R + 2NaX$$

Although in the Wurtz synthesis condensation of two different alkyl halides by interaction with sodium gives difficultly separable mixtures of paraffinic hydrocarbons, Fittig's adaptation of the reaction to the preparation of compounds of mixed types can be applied successfully because the reaction products are easily separable. In the production of hydrocarbons of the type Ar·R, the by-products are the paraffinic hydrocarbon R·R and the aromatic hydrocarbon Ar·Ar, and the difference in the boiling points is so profound that separation usually can be accomplished. For example, if methyl bromide is condensed with bromobenzene in the presence of two equivalents of sodium with the object of preparing toluene (b.p. $111°$), the by-products are ethane and diphenyl (b.p. $254°$). The reaction is illustrated (1) by the synthesis of p-xylene from either p-dibromobenzene or p-bromotoluene, and (2) by a particularly favorable synthesis of a mixed alkyl-aryl hydrocarbon requiring little excess alkyl halide. As in the re-

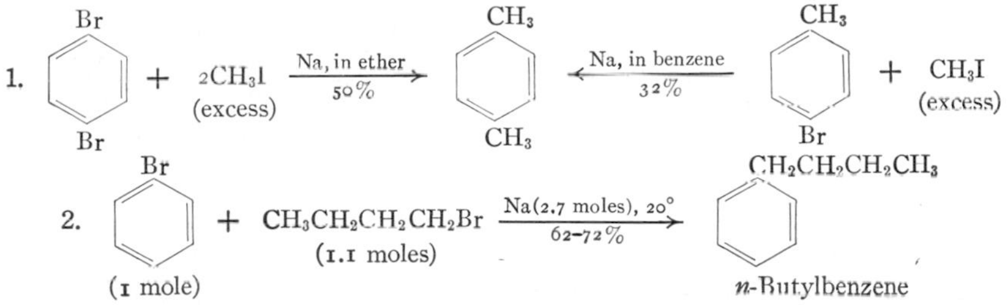

action of Wurtz, the condensation probably proceeds through formation or a sodium alkyl (RNa) or sodium aryl (ArNa), which interacts with the coresponding halogen compound.

Friedel-Crafts Hydrocarbon Synthesis. — In 1877 the French chemist Friedel[3] and his American collaborator Crafts[4] investigated the action of metallic aluminum on alkyl halides, possibly with a view to varying the Wurtz reaction. Little change occurred at first, even on heating, but after an induction period a reaction set in, with evolution of hydrogen chloride, and became particularly brisk whenever a considerable amount of aluminum chloride was formed. The inference that aluminum chloride is the effective catalytic agent was confirmed by experiments on the action of this substance on amyl chloride. A reaction was easily initiated, with evolution of hydrogen chloride and production of amylene and a mixture of other hydrocarbons. Investigation showed that this mixture could hardly consist merely of polymerized amylene and suggested that, under the influence

[3] Charles Friedel, 1832–99; b. Strasbourg, France; Paris; *Ber.*, **32**, 3721 (1899); *Bull. Soc. Chem.*, [4], **51**, 1493 (1932); *J. Chem. Ed.*, **26**, 3 (1949)

[4] James M. Crafts, 1839–1917; b. Boston; Ph.D. Harvard; Mass. Inst. Techn.

of aluminum chloride, amyl chloride may have condensed with amylene or other hydrocarbon. This inference led to trial condensation with a preformed hydrocarbon, and it was found that amyl chloride reacts smoothly with benzene in the presence of aluminum chloride as catalyst to yield amylbenzene. A general synthetic reaction of broad application was thereby discovered, for Friedel and Crafts and later workers found that almost any alkyl chloride or bromide can be condensed catalytically with an aromatic hydrocarbon to produce a hydrocarbon of mixed type, as indicated for the general case as follows:

$$Ar \cdot H + RX \longrightarrow Ar \cdot R + HX$$

Ordinarily the hydrocarbon must be aromatic and the halogen compound aliphatic. Thus benzene reacts with ethyl chloride or ethyl bromide in the presence of anhydrous aluminum chloride to form ethylbenzene, but the hydrocarbon cannot be synthesized in a comparable manner from ethane and chlorobenzene. Useful applications of the Friedel-Crafts reaction are the syntheses of the di- and triphenyl derivatives of methane:

$$C_6H_5CH_2Cl + H \cdot C_6H_5 \xrightarrow[59\%]{AlCl_3 \; (0.4 \; equiv.), \; 0-20°} C_6H_5CH_2C_6H_5$$
Diphenylmethane

$$3\,C_6H_5 \cdot H + \underset{Cl}{ClCHCl} \xrightarrow[21\%]{AlCl_3 \; (0.2 \; equiv.), \; 80°} \underset{C_6H_5}{C_6H_5CHC_6H_5}$$
(excess)

Triphenylmethane

A disadvantage of the Friedel-Crafts hydrocarbon synthesis is that the reaction does not stop at the stage of monosubstitution but proceeds to the formation of polysubstitution products, for the alkylbenzenes initially formed undergo alkylation more readily than the starting materials. Mixtures result, and a given product requires extensive purification.

The reaction provides a practicable synthesis of durene, $1,2,4,5$-tetramethylbenzene, because this symmetrically substituted hydrocarbon has a higher melting point and lower solubility than any of its isomers or than the tri- and pentamethylbenzenes that invariably accompany it in the reaction of benzene with four equivalents of methyl chloride, and hence can be separated from the reaction mixture by freezing and purified by recrystallization. The preparation is modified to advantage by treatment of

$$\text{(benzene)} + 4CH_3Cl \xrightarrow{AlCl_3(0.4 \; equiv.), \; 95°} \text{Mixture} \xrightarrow{Cryst.} \text{(durene structure)}$$
Durene

the xylene mixture from coal tar with two equivalents of methyl chloride in the presence of aluminum chloride, for each of the three isomers can afford durene on dimethylation, though a mixture of tri-, tetra-, and pentamethylbenzenes also results. A practicable procedure (L. I. Smith,[5] 1926)

---

[5] Lee Irvin Smith, b. 1891 Indianapolis; Ph.D. Harvard (Kohler); Minnesota

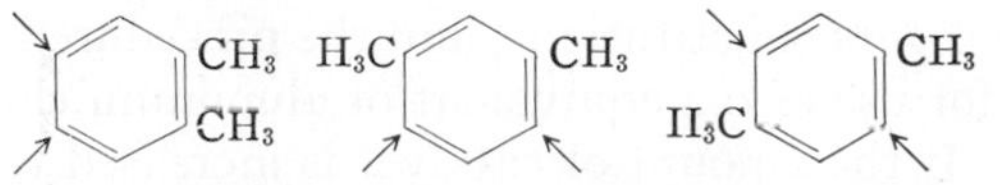

consists in passing methyl chloride (2.3 moles) under slight pressure into technical xylene (1 mole) and aluminum chloride (0.4 mole) at 95°, separating the crude tri-, tetra-, and pentamethylbenzene fractions by distillation, freezing the durene from the middle fraction, and crystallizing it three times from alcohol. The yield of pure durene is 10–11%, but can be raised to 18–25% by submitting the trimethylbenzene fraction to methylation and by heating the liquid portion of the tetramethylbenzene fraction with aluminum chloride. Pure pentamethylbenzene can be isolated from the highest-boiling fraction in 8% yield by redistillation and crystallization. Hexamethylbenzene is prepared by methylation of pentamethylbenzene with methyl chloride and aluminum chloride; the yield of the high-melting, easily purified hydrocarbon is 24–30%.

Although aluminum chloride has been the most frequently used catalyst, several other catalysts are now available, of varying activity below that of aluminum chloride, and hence condensation can be moderated by use of these milder agents. Suitable anhydrous inorganic halides, listed in the order of decreasing potency, are as follows:

$$AlCl_3 > FeCl_3 > SnCl_4 > BF_3 > ZnCl_2$$

The reagents are all electron-acceptors, or Lewis acids. In some variations of the general reaction the following catalysts are used:

$$HF > H_2SO_4 (96\%) > P_2O_5 > H_3PO_4$$

Hydrogen fluoride, employed as the anhydrous liquid (b.p. 19.4°), is a particularly valuable reagent introduced in 1938–39 (Simons, Calcott). The control that is possible through the choice and amount of catalyst and regulation of the temperature is important in polysubstitutions, for under mild conditions the entering groups tend to become oriented in *ortho* and *para* positions, whereas under forcing conditions *meta* orientation obtains. Thus trisubstitution can be directed to afford chiefly either the 1,2,4- or the 1,3,5-derivative. Substitution in the *meta* position is favored by use of a considerable amount (usually 2 equivalents) of aluminum chloride, the most active catalyst, or of a high reaction temperature. The effect

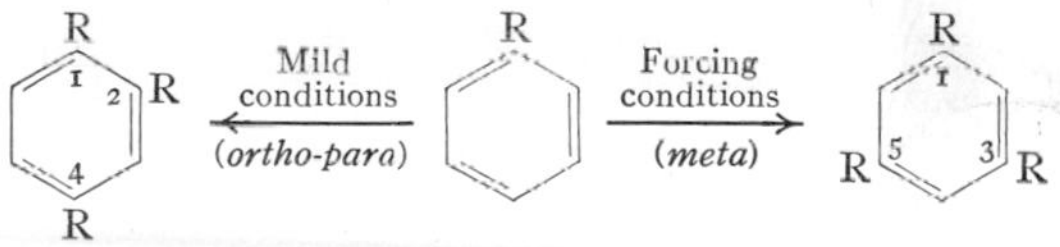

of temperature is seen in the fact that the reaction of benzene with three moles of methyl chloride gives chiefly 1,2,4-trimethylbenzene when conducted at 0°, but yields chiefly the 1,3,5-isomer when carried out at 100°. The proportion of catalyst is even more important. Durene is formed in a series of *ortho* and *para* substitutions, and the procedure for its preparation cited above calls for use of 0.4 equivalent of aluminum chloride (calculated as $AlCl_3$) at 95°. If the amount of catalyst is increased to 2 equivalents of $AlCl_3$ (or 1 of the actual double molecule Al_2Cl_6), the *meta* derivative mesitylene can be obtained in yields up to 63% in a reaction conducted at 100° (J. F. Norris,[6] 1938–39). *Meta* ethylation can be realized even at a low temperature by employing sufficient catalyst and allowing an extended period for reaction, as shown in the example. Aluminum chloride has such

$$\text{(1 mole)} \quad + \quad \underset{\text{(3.3 moles)}}{3CH_3CH_2Br} \quad \xrightarrow[85\%]{AlCl_3 \text{ (2 moles), } 0-25°, 24 \text{ hrs.}} \quad \text{C}_2\text{H}_5\text{—C}_6\text{H}_3\text{—(C}_2\text{H}_5)_2$$

a tendency to give *meta* derivatives that milder catalysts are preferred where the alternate course of reaction is desired. Boron fluoride, introduced in the reaction mixture as a gas, is particularly satisfactory for the preparation of *p*-dialkylbenzenes, for example:

$$+ \quad n\text{- or } i\text{-C}_3\text{H}_7\text{OH} \quad \xrightarrow{BF_3 (0.7 \text{ equiv.}), 60°} \quad \underset{(24\%)}{CH(CH_3)_2} \quad + \quad \underset{\substack{CH(CH_3)_2 \\ (13-14\%)}}{CH(CH_3)_2}$$

The example illustrates use of an alcohol in place of an alkyl halide as the alkylating agent, and this variation is generally applicable also when aluminum chloride is employed as catalyst.

A likely explanation of the remarkable variation in the course of the reaction with conditions is found in the fact that the Friedel-Crafts reaction is reversible. If an alkylbenzene is treated with aluminum chloride in the absence of an alkylating agent, it is converted in part into a mixture of higher and lower substitution products; alkyl groups evidently are severed from one molecule and transposed to another. Furthermore, 1,2,4-trimethylbenzene rearranges to mesitylene in the presence of aluminum chloride. Therefore production of 1,3,5-derivatives under forcing conditions may be the result of initial *ortho-para* substitution followed by elimination of one group and affixture in a more secure position.

$$\longrightarrow \quad \underset{CH_3}{\overset{CH_3}{C_6H_3\text{(CH}_3)}} \quad \longrightarrow \quad \underset{CH_3}{C_6H_4\text{(CH}_3)} \quad \longrightarrow \quad H_3C\text{—C}_6H_3\text{—CH}_3$$

1,2,3-Trialkylbenzenes are available by introduction into a *m*-dialkylbenzene such as *m*-xylene (I) of a blocking *t*-butyl group; this bulky group avoids positions *ortho* to the methyl substituents and gives II in good yield. This derivative undergoes alkylation in the position *para* to the *t*-butyl

[6] James F. Norris, 1871–1940; b. Baltimore; Ph.D. Johns Hopkins Univ.; Mass. Inst. Techn.

$$H_3C \overset{CH_3}{\bigcirc} \xrightarrow[\text{AlCl}_3]{\text{t-BuCl}} H_3C \overset{CH_3}{\underset{C(CH_3)_3}{\bigcirc}} \xrightarrow[\text{AlCl}_3]{\text{RX}} H_3C \overset{R}{\underset{C(CH_3)_3}{\overset{CH_3}{\bigcirc}}} \xrightarrow[\text{HF}]{} H_3C \overset{R}{\overset{CH_3}{\bigcirc}} + II$$

$$\quad\quad\quad I \quad\quad\quad\quad\quad II \quad\quad\quad\quad\quad III \quad\quad\quad\quad\quad IV$$

group; the blocking group is then removed by transfer to *m*-xylene to re-generate II and yield the 1,2,3-trisubstituted benzene IV (M. J. Schlatter, 1954).

A peculiarity of the Friedel-Crafts reaction is that the hydrocarbon radical of the alkyl halide frequently suffers rearrangement. Thus *n*-propyl bromide and isopropyl bromide on reaction with benzene in the presence of aluminum chloride both yield isopropylbenzene, or cumene (Gustavson, 1878); normal halides invariably give rise in whole or in part to hydrocarbons having secondary groups regardless of the catalyst, and *n*-alkyl deriva-

$$C_6H_6 + CH_3CH_2CH_2Br \xrightarrow{\text{AlCl}_3} \overset{H_3C\diagdown_{\displaystyle CH}\diagup CH_3}{\bigcirc} \xleftarrow{\text{AlCl}_3} C_6H_6 + CH_3\underset{Br}{CHCH_3}$$

Cumene

tives cannot be synthesized by the Friedel-Crafts method. An example cited above shows that isomerization occurs in the condensation of *n*-propyl alcohol with benzene in the presence of boron fluoride. The apparent abnormality was clarified by Kekulé's observation (1879) that *n*-propyl bromide is isomerized to isopropyl bromide by aluminum chloride, probably because the reagent catalyzes formation of a carbonium ion capable of isomerizing to an ion stabilized by electron-release from two alkyl groups:

$$CH_3CH_2CH_2Br \xrightarrow{-Br^-} [CH_3CH_2\overset{+}{C}H_2 \longrightarrow CH_3\overset{+}{C}HCH_3] \xrightarrow{Br^-} CH_3CHBrCH_3$$

The structure of the Friedel-Crafts reaction product is predictable from the Markownikoff rule of addition. Isobutyl chloride, for example affords *t*-butylbenzene as the result of isomerization:

$$(CH_3)_2CHCH_2Cl \xrightarrow{-Cl^-} [(CH_3)_2CH\overset{+}{C}H_2 \longrightarrow (CH_3)_2\overset{+}{C}CH_3] \xrightarrow{C_6H_6} (CH_3)_3CC_6H_5$$

Both olefins and alcohols can be employed in the Friedel-Crafts reaction in place of alkyl halides. Examples of these variations in the general method are shown in reactions 1 to 4. Alkylation of benzene by propylene

1. $C_6H_6 + CH_3CH=CH_2 \xrightarrow[84\%]{\text{HF, o}^\circ} C_6H_5CH(CH_3)_2$

Cumene

2. $\bigcirc + \bigcirc \xrightarrow[62\%]{\text{HF, o}^\circ} \bigcirc\!\!-\!\!\bigcirc$

Cyclohexene $\quad\quad\quad\quad\quad\quad$ Cyclohexylbenzene
$\quad\quad\quad\quad\quad\quad\quad\quad\quad\quad$ (m.p. 8°)

3. [cyclohexane] + HO[cyclohexyl] $\xrightarrow{\text{BF}_3(\text{0.7 equiv.}), 60°}$ { 56% Cyclohexylbenzene
27% *p*-Dicyclohexylbenzene

Cyclohexanol

4. [phenol with OH] + 3(CH₃)₂CHOH $\xrightarrow[94.5\%]{\text{HF, 25°}}$ (CH₃)₂CH[ring]CH(CH₃)₂
CH(CH₃)₂
2,4,6-Triisopropylphenol
(b.p. 125° at 7 mm.)

with production of cumene has been accomplished also with use of ferric chloride, sulfuric acid, or phosphoric acid in place of hydrogen fluoride. Condensation between the two hydrocarbons when formulated as a simple addition resembles the acid-catalyzed condensations of olefinic and paraffinic

$$\begin{array}{c} \diagdown \text{C—H} \\ | \\ \diagup \text{CH} \end{array} + \begin{array}{c} \text{CHCH}_3 \\ \| \\ \text{CH}_2 \end{array} \longrightarrow \begin{array}{c} \diagdown \text{C—CHCH}_3 \\ | \quad | \\ \diagup \text{CH} \; \text{CH}_3 \end{array}$$

hydrocarbons used in production of alkylate and polymer gasoline (pp. 104–106).

Synthesis of Ketones.—A widely useful variation of the catalyzed substitution reaction that is free from complications associated with alkylation is the **Friedel-Crafts ketone synthesis**. In the usual case this involves condensation of an acid chloride of either the aliphatic or the aromatic series with an aromatic hydrocarbon in the presence of a molecular equivalent of anhydrous aluminum chloride:

$$\text{RCO}\lceil\text{Cl} \; + \; \text{H}\rceil\text{Ar} \xrightarrow{\text{AlCl}_3} \text{RCOAr} \; + \; \text{HCl}$$
Acyl halide

$$\text{ArCO}\lceil\text{Cl} \; + \; \text{H}\rceil\text{Ar}' \xrightarrow{\text{AlCl}_3} \text{ArCOAr}' \; + \; \text{HCl}$$
Aroyl halide

The reaction proceeds readily and affords pure products in high yield, as in the synthesis of the diaryl ketone benzophenone. Excess benzene or

[benzoyl chloride]—COCl + [benzene] $\xrightarrow[82\%]{\text{AlCl}_3 \text{ (1.1 equiv.)}}$ [benzophenone structure with C=O]

Benzoyl chloride   Benzophenone

carbon disulfide can be used as solvent; in either case the reaction proceeds exothermally for a time and can be completed by brief refluxing. The mixture is then cooled and treated cautiously with ice and hydrochloric acid to decompose an aluminum chloride complex and bring aluminum salts into the aqueous phase; the ketonic reaction product is then recovered from the washed and dried organic layer by distillation of the solvent. Acid anhydrides generally enter into the same reactions as acid chlorides and can replace these substances in the Friedel-Crafts reaction, as illustrated for the preparation of acetophenone.

$$\begin{array}{c} CH_3CO \\ \diagdown \\ CH_3CO \end{array}\!O \;+\; \bigcirc \xrightarrow[\text{82--85\%}]{\text{AlCl}_3\,(2.4\ \text{equiv.})} \bigcirc^{COCH_3} \;+\; CH_3COOH$$

Acetophenone

More aluminum chloride is required in the synthesis of ketones than in the alkylation reaction because this reagent combines with oxygen-containing compounds to form oxonium-salt complexes. Thus when benzoyl chloride and aluminum chloride in equivalent amounts are heated together or refluxed in carbon disulfide solution, they unite to form a crystalline complex that, like aluminum chloride, is bimolecular in solution (Kohler, 1900). In the following formulation of the probable mechanism for formation and reaction of the complex, the aluminum salts are written as single molecules, but they actually have twice the molecular weights indicated. In the first step (a) aluminum chloride functions as a Lewis acid and accepts

(a) $C_6H_5\overset{\overset{\displaystyle Cl}{|}}{C}=\overset{..}{\underset{..}{O}}: \;+\; \overset{\overset{\displaystyle Cl}{|}}{\underset{\underset{\displaystyle Cl}{|}}{\overset{..}{Al}}}\!:\!Cl \;\rightleftharpoons\; C_6H_5\overset{\overset{\displaystyle Cl}{|}}{C}=\overset{+}{\underset{..}{O}}\!:\!\overset{..}{\underset{\underset{\displaystyle Cl}{|}}{Al}}\!:\!\overset{-}{Cl}$

(b) $C_6H_5\overset{\overset{\displaystyle Cl}{|}}{C}=\overset{+}{\underset{..}{O}}\!:\!\overset{\overset{\displaystyle Cl}{..}}{\underset{\underset{\displaystyle Cl}{..}}{Al}}\!:\!\overset{-}{Cl} \;\rightleftharpoons\; C_6H_5\overset{+}{C}=O \;+\; Cl\!:\!\overset{\overset{\displaystyle Cl}{..}}{\underset{\underset{\displaystyle Cl}{..}}{Al}}\!:\!Cl$

(c) $C_6H_5\overset{+}{C}=O \;+\; C_6H_6 \;\longrightarrow\; C_6H_5\overset{\overset{\displaystyle C_6H_5}{|}}{C}=O \;+\; H^+$

(d) $(C_6H_5)_2C=O \;+\; AlCl_4^- \;\rightleftharpoons\; (C_6H_5)_2C=\overset{+}{\underset{..}{O}}\!:\!\overset{\overset{\displaystyle Cl}{..}}{\underset{\underset{\displaystyle Cl}{..}}{Al}}\!:\!\overset{-}{Cl} \;+\; Cl^-$

(e) $(C_6H_5)_2C=\overset{+}{\underset{..}{O}}\!:\!Al\overset{-}{Cl}_3 \;+\; H_2O \;\longrightarrow\; (C_6H_5)_2C=O \;+\; Al(OH)Cl_2 \;+\; HCl$

a pair of electrons from the ketonic oxygen atom to form a coordinate covalent complex. This complex dissociates (b) to a certain extent to give the benzoyl cation, which is the effective agent in electrophilic attack of benzene (c), with expulsion of a proton. The reaction product, benzophenone, combines with the ion $AlCl_4^-$ to form a second coordinate covalent complex (d) that, at the end of the reaction, is decomposed by water (e). Complex formation thus binds an equivalent quantity of the metal halide. When an anhydride is the acylating agent, sufficient aluminum chloride must be used to allow for oxonium-salt formation at both carbonyl groups.

A useful application of the synthetic method is the preparation of keto acids by interaction of an aromatic hydrocarbon with one of the readily available cyclic anhydrides, as illustrated in the examples. The γ-keto acids of the aromatic and mixed aliphatic-aromatic types that are obtainable in this way are important intermediates for further syntheses. If toluene is employed in place of benzene, the orientation of the substituent is almost exclusively in the position *para* to the methyl group.

1. Phthalic anhydride + (excess) benzene $\xrightarrow[88\%]{\text{AlCl}_3 \text{ (2.6 equiv.)}}$ o-Benzoylbenzoic acid (m.p. 128°)

2. CH₂CO / CH₂CO >O (Succinic anhydride) + (excess) $\xrightarrow[92-95\%]{\text{AlCl}_3 \text{ (2.2 equiv.)}}$ COCH₂CH₂COOH β-Benzoylpropionic acid (m.p. 116°)

The reactions proceed smoothly and stop abruptly with introduction of a single acyl group, and the primary condensation product is not contaminated with polysubstituted products. In analogy to other phenomena to be described in the next chapter, the difference from the Friedel-Crafts alkylation reaction can be attributed to the fact that the group introduced is unsaturated rather than saturated, for benzene derivatives containing groups of the former type are less subject to further attack. Thus preformed acetophenone is indifferent to acetic anhydride or acetyl chloride in the presence of aluminum chloride. This behavior is both an advantage and a limitation, for the reaction usually is inapplicable to benzene derivatives having an unsaturated group in combination with the aromatic nucleus, for example: $C_6H_5CH{=}O$, $C_6H_5COOCH_3$, C_6H_5CN, $C_6H_5NO_2$. The last compound listed, nitrobenzene, is so inert to acylation and has such a marked and specific solvent power for aluminum chloride (with which it forms an oxonium-salt complex) that it is frequently employed as a solvent for Friedel-Crafts condensations with other aromatic compounds. The rearrangement of the substituting group observed in alkylations does not apply to the ketone synthesis, and the reactions of acyl halides and anhydrides are generally more satisfactory than those of alkyl halides. Although a larger proportion of catalyst is required, the same relationships hold with respect to the applicability and effectiveness of the various catalytic agents. Thus aluminum chloride is the most potent of the common catalysts; stannic chloride and boron fluoride are mild but effective catalysts; and fused zinc chloride is a weakly active agent. These substances are useful where a moderation of the reaction is desirable. For example, thiophene is so much more reactive than benzene that it is polymerized to a considerable extent in a reaction mixture containing aluminum chloride, and its acylation is accomplished best by use of the less potent catalyst stannic chloride. Liquid hydrogen fluoride has some advantage as catalyst

Thiophene + CH_3COCl $\xrightarrow[79-83\%]{\text{SnCl}_4 \text{ (1 equiv.)}}$ Methyl 2-thienyl ketone (b.p. 89–91°/9 mm.) COCH₃

for the ketone synthesis in that the free acid, rather than the acid chloride or anhydride, can be employed as the acylating agent; with polynuclear hydrocarbons, the reagent is also useful in leading to an orientation different from that encountered with the metal halide catalysts.

A useful application of the reaction is the synthesis of cyclic ketones by intramolecular Friedel-Crafts cyclization between an aromatic ring and an acid chloride group in an attached side chain, as illustrated by the preparation of α-tetralone. Five- and six-membered ring ketones are generally

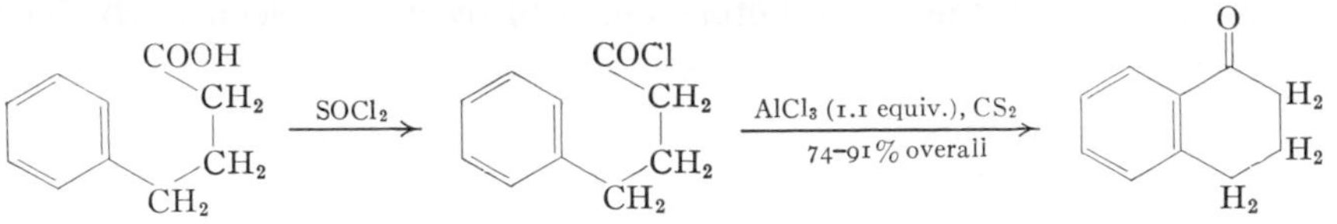

γ-Phenylbutyric acid

α-Tetralone
(b.p. 105–107°/2 mm.)

obtainable in good yield by this method. An alternate procedure that is often effective consists in treatment of the free acid with liquid hydrogen fluoride. γ-Phenylbutyric acid can be cyclized directly to α-tetralone by

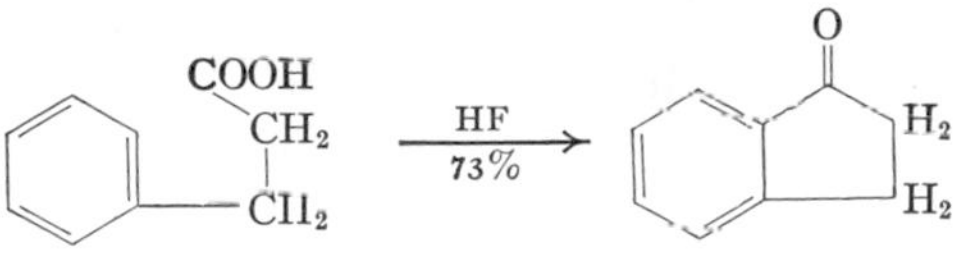

Hydrocinnamic acid
(m.p. 48.5°)

α-Hydrindone
(m.p. 42°)

this method in 92% yield. Polyphosphoric acid (a mixture of phosphorous acid and phosphorus pentoxide) is now commonly employed for these cyclodehydrations.

Reduction of Ketones. — Several efficient methods are available for reduction of carbonyl compounds, including the ketones produced by the Friedel-Crafts synthesis. One, the **Clemmensen method of reduction** (1913), consists in refluxing a ketone with amalgamated zinc and hydrochloric acid. Acetophenone, for example, is reduced to ethylbenzene. The

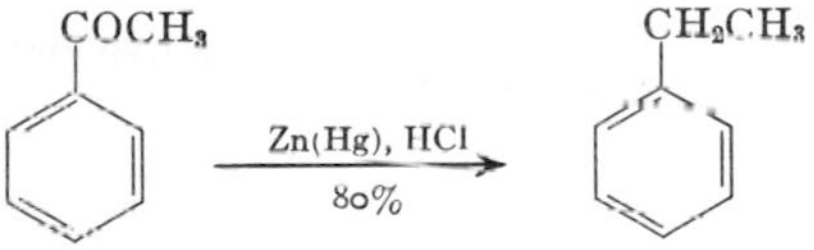

Acetophenone

Ethylbenzene

method is applicable to the reduction of most aromatic-aliphatic ketones and to at least some aliphatic and alicyclic ketones. The reaction apparently does not proceed through initial reduction to a carbinol, for carbinols that might constitute intermediates are stable under the conditions used. With substances sparingly soluble in aqueous hydrochloric acid, improved results sometimes are obtained by addition of a water-miscible organic solvent such as ethanol, acetic acid, or dioxan. Particularly favorable results are obtained by addition of the water-insoluble solvent toluene (Martin, 1936), stirring the mixture vigorously, and using for amalgamation zinc that has been freshly melted and poured into water (Sherman, 1948). The ketone is retained largely in the upper toluene layer and is distributed into the aqueous solution of hydrochloric acid in contact with the zinc at so high a dilution that the side reaction of bimolecular reduction is suppressed.

The Clemmensen method of reduction is applicable to the γ-keto acids obtainable by Friedel-Crafts condensations with succinic anhydride (succinoylation) and to the cyclic ketones formed by intramolecular condensation.

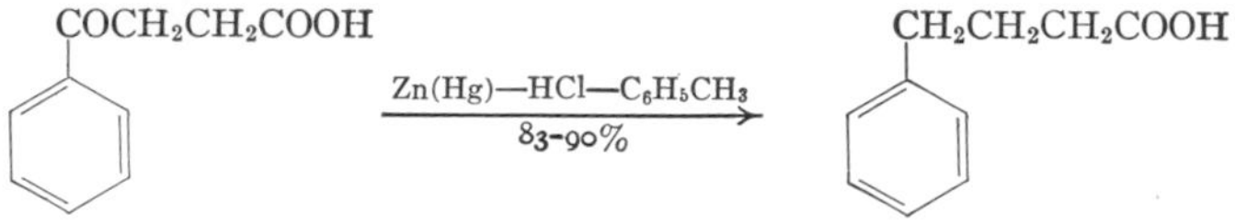

COCH$_2$CH$_2$COOH $\xrightarrow[\text{83-90\%}]{\text{Zn(Hg)—HCl—C}_6\text{H}_5\text{CH}_3}$ CH$_2$CH$_2$CH$_2$COOH

β-Benzoylpropionic acid γ-Phenylbutyric acid

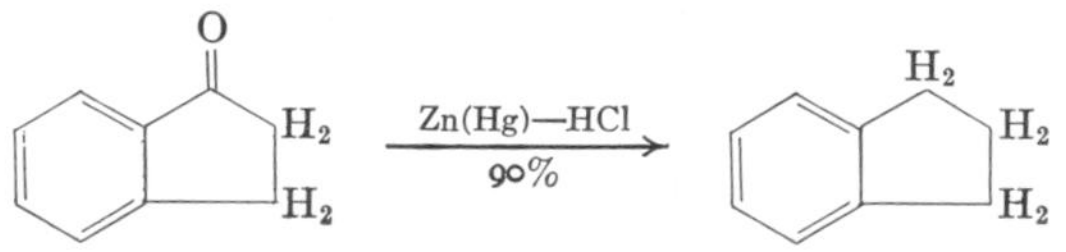

α-Hydrindone $\xrightarrow[\text{90\%}]{\text{Zn(Hg)—HCl}}$ Hydrindene or indane (b.p. 177°)

This and the Wolff-Kishner method of reduction supplement each other; the Clemmensen method is inapplicable to acid-sensitive compounds and the Wolff-Kishner method cannot be used with compounds sensitive to alkali or containing other functional groups that react with hydrazine.

Ketones of the type of acetophenone and α-tetralone can also be reduced to hydrocarbons by **catalytic hydrogenation** (Pd catalyst); β-aroylpropionic acids are reduced to γ-arylbutyric acids. A fourth method consists in hydrogenolysis of a dialkyl thioacetal derivative with Raney nickel (Bougault, 1938; Mozingo, 1943; Wolfrom, 1944):

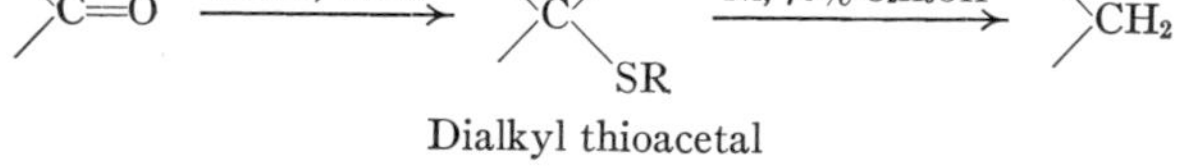

$$\text{>C=O} \xrightarrow{\text{2 RSH, ZnCl}_2} \text{>C(SR)(SR)} \xrightarrow{\text{Ni, 70\% C}_2\text{H}_5\text{OH}} \text{>CH}_2$$

Dialkyl thioacetal

Dehydrogenation of Hydroaromatic Hydrocarbons. — Hydro derivatives of aromatic compounds are called hydroaromatic: cyclohexane, cyclohexanol, 1,2,3,4-tetrahydronaphthalene (tetralin), perhydronaphthalene (decalin). Alicyclic substances containing six-membered rings but having carbon substituents that block conversion to the aromatic state unless they are eliminated (e.g., camphor and 1,1-dimethylcyclohexane) are not classified as hydroaromatic. Hydroaromatic compounds can be aromatized by various methods of dehydrogenation. The chief experimental methods, illustrated for a general case, include dehydrogenation with sulfur at a rather low temperature (Vesterberg, 1903), dehydrogenation with the less active and often less destructive selenium at distinctly higher temperatures (Diels, 1927), and catalytic dehydrogenation (Zelinsky,[7] 1911). Dehydrogenation over a 10% palladium charcoal catalyst, prepared by reduction of palladium chloride in an alkaline suspension of activated carbon (Norit) with formaldehyde, often proceeds very smoothly. The reaction can be conducted in the vapor phase by distillation of the hydroaromatic compound through a tube containing the catalyst at temperatures in the

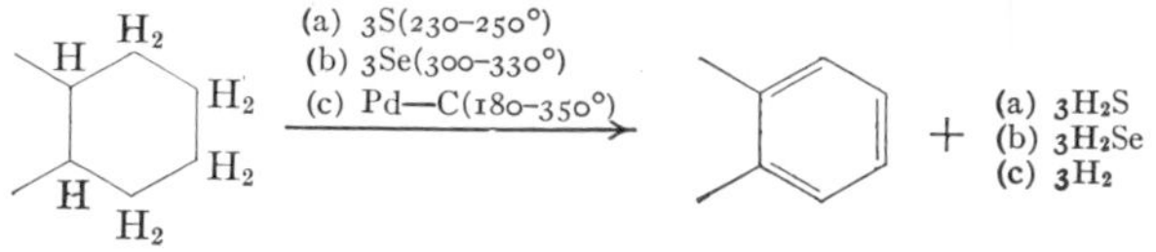

range 300–350°, but the liquid-phase method is usually more convenient. If the substance to be dehydrogenated is heated with one tenth part of palladium charcoal to about 310–320°, hydrogen is evolved steadily and the material is soon aromatized. The reaction is promoted by passing carbon dioxide into the solution to entrain and remove the evolved hydrogen from the equilibrium mixture, and also by vigorous boiling, which helps to dislodge the hydrogen from the active surface of the catalyst (Linstead, 1940). Tetralin, b.p. 207°, can be dehydrogenated to naphthalene by heating at the boiling point in a stream of carbon dioxide, and the reaction can be made to proceed at temperatures as low as 185° by addition of a diluent boiling at this temperature. A fourth method involves bromination with N-bromosuccinimide followed by dehydrobromination with acetate. Examples are the conversion of tetralin into naphthalene (74% yield) and of dibenzyl into stilbene (50% yield).

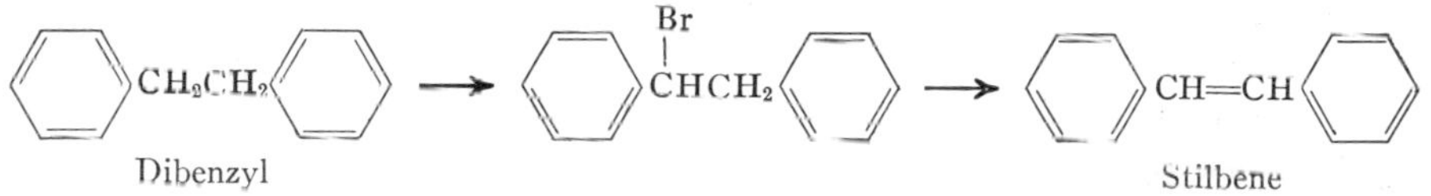

Dehydrogenation of hydroaromatic compounds can usually be effected in high yield by one or another chemical or catalytic procedure, and the reaction has particular significance owing to the generally applicable methods available for synthesis of hydroaromatic compounds. Thus α-tetralone, obtainable readily by reactions discussed in the preceding sections, can be converted into naphthalene by Clemmensen reduction to tetralin and dehydrogenation, or it can be condensed with methylmagnesium iodide and the resulting carbinol then dehydrated to a methyldihydronaphthalene that is dehydrogenated to α-methylnaphthalene. By use of appropriate Grignard reagents a variety of α-alkyl and α-aryl derivatives of naphthalene can be synthesized. Another illustration is the synthesis of triphenylene

---

[7] Nikolai D. Zelinsky, 1861–1953; b. Tiraspol, Russia; Ph.D. Odessa; Moscow

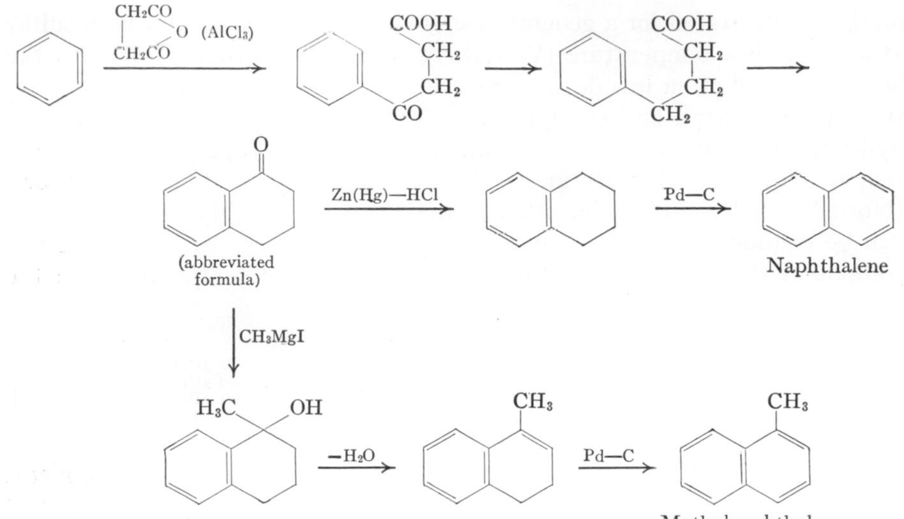

(abbreviated formula)

Naphthalene

α-Methylnaphthalene

(m.p. 199°) through the dodecahydride obtained by condensation of three cyclohexanone molecules under the influence of sulfuric acid (p. 534); the hydroaromatic compound has been dehydrogenated in nearly quantitative yield by treatment with copper at 475°.

Although aromatic hydrocarbons are end products of dehydrogenations conducted at temperatures near 500°, further dehydrogenation to a diaryl sometimes can be accomplished at still higher temperatures. Thus diphenyl is manufactured by passing benzene vapor through an iron tube packed with pumice at temperatures in the range 650–800°: $2C_6H_6 \rightarrow C_6H_5\cdot C_6H_5 + H_2$. In another process the vapor is bubbled through molten lead. Diphenyl is used as a heat-transfer fluid, particularly as a component of Dowtherm A, a eutectic mixture of 73.5% diphenyl oxide and 26.5% diphenyl. The mixture (b.p. 260°) is fluid above 12° and can be used at operating temperatures up to about 400° (150 lbs./sq. in.).

Grignard Syntheses. — The Grignard reaction can be applied in numerous other ways to synthesis of hydrocarbons of mixed aromatic-aliphatic type, containing both saturated and unsaturated side chains. One type of

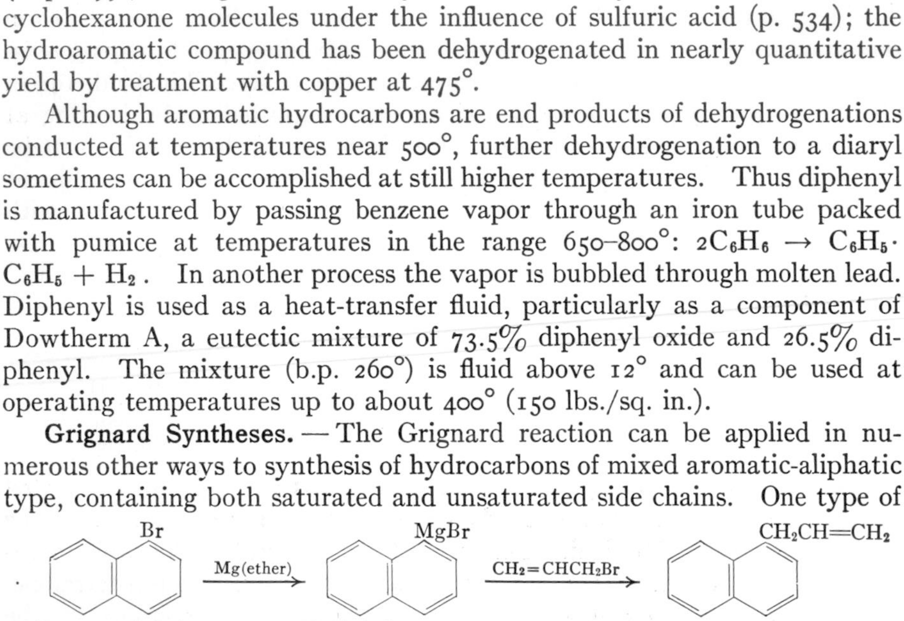

α-Bromonaphthalene

α-Naphthylmagnesium bromide

α-Allylnaphthalene (b.p. 266°)

synthesis, illustrated in examples (1), (2), and (3), utilizes the aryl Grignard reagents easily prepared by interaction of aromatic bromides or iodides with magnesium.

2. C_6H_5MgBr + $CH_3COC_6H_5$ $\longrightarrow$

Phenylmagnesium bromide   Acetophenone

α,α-Diphenylethylene (b.p. 275°)

A generally useful reaction consists in the introduction of a nuclear methyl group by interaction of an aryl Grignard reagent with dimethyl sulfate. The net result is equivalent to a Wurtz-Fittig synthesis, but methylation of a Grignard reagent often proceeds more smoothly and is applicable to more selective synthetic operations, as illustrated in example (3).

3.

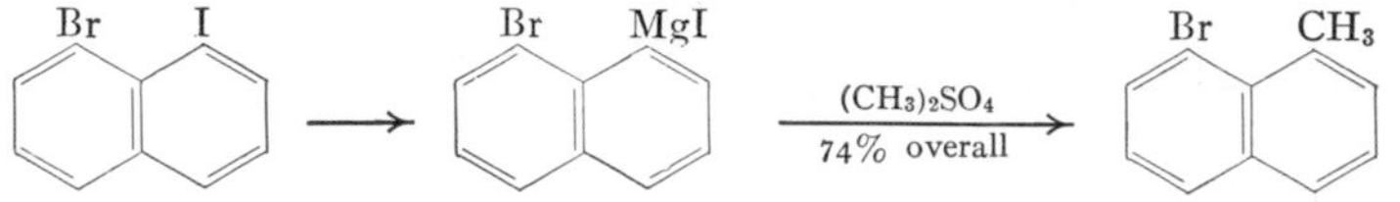

1-Bromo-8-iodonaphthalene
(m.p. 100°)

(CH₃)₂SO₄
74% overall

1-Bromo-8-methylnaphthalene
(m.p. 78°)

Other elaborations of the Grignard reaction involve addition of an alkylmagnesium halide to a carbonyl component of the aromatic series, as illustrated by the synthesis of *p*-cymene (4). The terminal step of saturation of the double bond in the side chain has been accomplished most

4.

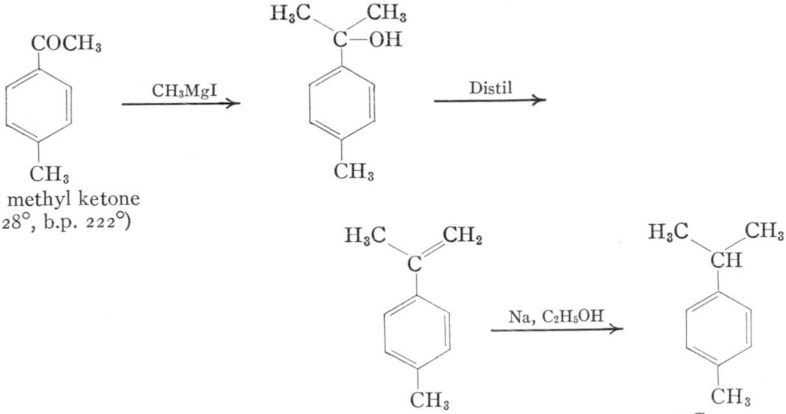

p-Tolyl methyl ketone
(m.p. 28°, b.p. 222°)

p-Cymene

satisfactorily in comparable cases by catalytic hydrogenation in the presence of platinum, for there is no difficulty in stopping short of hydrogenation of the nucleus (much slower), but it is of special interest that a double bond conjugated with the aromatic ring can be reduced with sodium and absolute ethanol. This reduction method is specific for conjugated systems and is not applicable to isolated double bonds, as shown by the behavior of 1-phenylbutadiene, conveniently synthesized by a further application of the Grignard method (5). Reduction with sodium and alcohol results in the

5. $C_6H_5CH=CHCHO$ $\xrightarrow{CH_3MgBr}$ $C_6H_5CH=CHCH(OH)CH_3$ $\xrightarrow[70\% \text{ overall}]{30\% H_2SO_4}$
Cinnamaldehyde

$C_6H_5CH=CHCH=CH_2$ $\xrightarrow{Na, C_2H_5OH}$ $C_6H_5CH_2CH=CHCH_3$ $\xrightarrow{alc. KOH}$ $C_6H_5CH=CHCH_2CH_3$
1-Phenylbutadiene-1,3   1-Phenylbutene-2   1-Phenylbutene-1
(b.p. 86°/11 mm.)   (β-butenylbenzene,   (α-butenylbenzene,
                     b.p. 176°)   b.p. 188°)

1,4-addition of hydrogen to the diene system of the side chain and affords

1-phenylbutene-2, which has an isolated double bond not conjugated with the ring and therefore is not attacked by the reagent and can be isolated in good yield. This hydrocarbon can be isomerized by boiling alcoholic potassium hydroxide to 1-phenylbutene-1, which is more stable by virtue of conjugation of the double bond with the ring and which is reducible to *n*-butylbenzene with sodium and alcohol. A Grignard synthesis of the hydrocarbon is shown in example (6).

6. $C_6H_5CHO \xrightarrow{n\text{-}C_3H_7MgI} C_6H_5CH(OH)CH_2CH_2CH_3 \xrightarrow{HCl \text{ in ether}}$

$$C_6H_5CHClCH_2CH_2CH_3 \xrightarrow{Pyridine, \ 125°} C_6H_5CH{=}CHCH_2CH_3$$
$$\text{1-Phenylbutene-1}$$

Hydrolysis of Sulfonates. — The reaction of an aromatic hydrocarbon with concentrated or fuming sulfuric acid with production of an aryl-sulfonic acid ($ArSO_3H$) is reversible, and under suitable conditions the hydrocarbon can be regenerated from the sulfonic acid or the alkali salt, or sulfonate ($ArSO_3Na$). The hydrolysis, or desulfonation, usually proceeds best in an aqueous solution of dilute sulfuric acid at temperatures of 135–200°, and can be carried out by heating the reagents in a sealed tube or by passing superheated steam into a dilute sulfuric acid solution of the sulfonic acid or sulfonate; the hydrocarbon steam distils from the reaction mixture as it is formed. Desulfonation is valuable in the isolation of pure hydro-

$$ArSO_3H(Na) \ + \ H_2O \xrightarrow{dil. \ H_2SO_4 \ (heat)} ArH \ + \ H_2SO_4(NaHSO_4)$$

carbons from the isomer mixtures derived from coal tar or petroleum that cannot be separated by fractional distillation (xylenes, dimethylnaphthalenes). The mixture can be sulfonated and the sulfonic acids converted into the solid water-soluble sodium or potassium salts, which are fractionally crystallized; hydrolysis of the isolated sulfonates then affords the liquid or solid hydrocarbons.

The xylene fraction from coal tar usually contains some 50–60% of *m*-xylene and 10–25% each of the *ortho* and *para* isomers, along with some ethylbenzene (Eastman xylene: 15.2% *ortho*, 61% *meta*, 23.8% *para*). Separations have been worked out that utilize in part differences in the ease of sulfonation and desulfonation. *m*-Xylene is the most reactive isomer and slowly dissolves in 80% sulfuric acid at room temperature as the re-sult of conversion into the derivative I; *o*- and *p*-xylene are not attacked on being shaken with 80% acid but undergo sulfonation with 84% acid to give the sulfonic acids II and III, respectively. Other experiments show that *o*-xylene is slightly more reactive than the *para* isomer. Thus in one

CH₃ ⬡ CH₃ / SO₃H	CH₃ ⬡ CH₃ SO₃H	CH₃ ⬡ SO₃H CH₃
m-Xylene-4-sulfonic acid	*o*-Xylene-4-sulfonic acid	*p*-Xylene-2-sulfonic acid
I	II	III

method of separation the mixture is partially sulfonated with concentrated sulfuric acid at 20°; the residue is rich in *p*-xylene, which is sulfonated with oleum.   The acid III is crystallized from dilute acid in which it is less soluble than the isomers.   The mixture containing I and II on crystallization of the sodium salts affords the *o*-derivative II in the least soluble fraction, whereas the *m*-derivative I concentrates in the more soluble fraction. The purified acids or their salts are hydrolyzed with hydrochloric acid at 190–195°.   In another process crude xylene is sulfonated completely, and the mixture of sulfonic acids heated with hydrochloric acid at 122°, when the particularly reactive *m*-xylene derivative I alone suffers hydrolysis.

Another use of the reversible sulfonation reaction is the introduction of blocking groups that permit special orientations, as in the example shown:

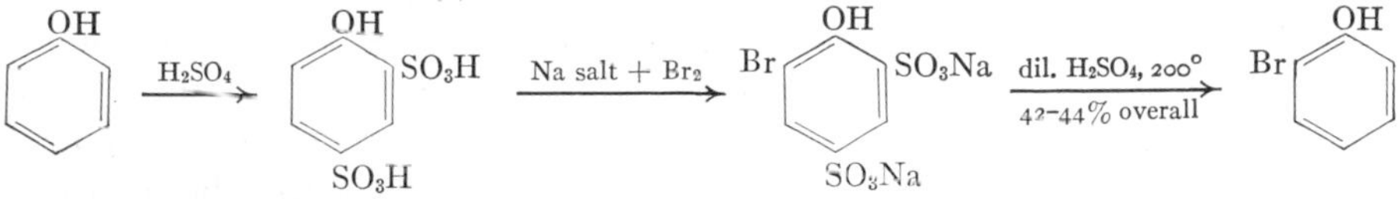

Decarboxylation. — A degradative method sometimes offering a useful route to a hydrocarbon consists in heating the sodium salt of a carboxylic acid with soda lime to effect decarboxylation.   As noted previously, thiophene-free benzene was first prepared by this method.   The carboxyl group eliminated may be located in a side chain rather than in the nucleus, as in a laboratory preparation of styrene:

$$C_6H_5CH{=}CHCOOH \xrightarrow[38-41\%]{Distil} C_6H_5CH{=}CH_2$$

Cinnamic acid · · · · · · · · · · · · · · · Styrene

A carboxyl group located on an unsaturated carbon atom is subject to ready elimination, and the reaction proceeds at a temperature close to the boiling point of styrene (146°) and requires no basic catalyst.   Elimination of a carboxyl group attached to an aromatic nucleus is accomplished only under more drastic conditions, and a usually satisfactory procedure consists in heating the acid with copper-powder catalyst in quinoline solution (J. R. Johnson, 1930).   A practicable application is the preparation of furan, a heterocyclic oxygen compound exhibiting aromatic characteristics to a moderate degree.   Furfural, available on a technical scale by the processing of oathulls, is converted in part by the Cannizzaro reaction into 2-furoic acid, which is decarboxylated.

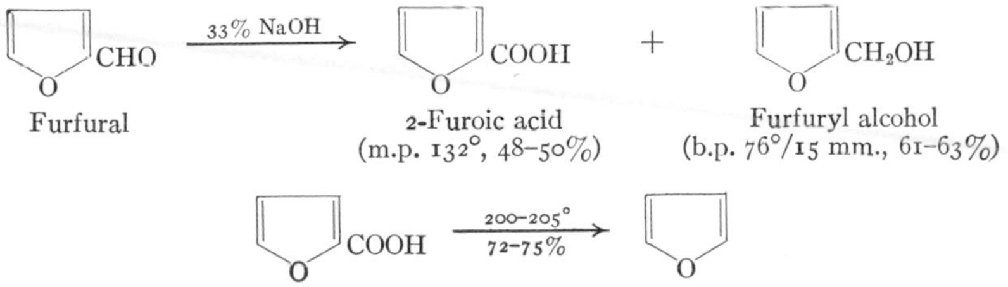

Furfural   2-Furoic acid   +   Furfuryl alcohol
                       (m.p. 132°, 48–50%)   (b.p. 76°/15 mm., 61–63%)

Furan
(b.p. 31.5°)

Zinc-Dust Distillation of Phenols. — Phenolic substances are often convertible into the parent hydrocarbons by interaction with zinc dust at a red heat; presumably the oxygen is eliminated as zinc oxide. The reaction

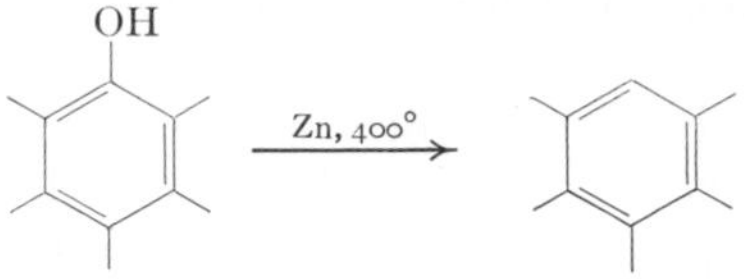

is carried out either by distilling the phenol through a hard-glass tube of zinc dust heated to a dull glow in a furnace or by heating a gram or two of the phenol with 25–50 g. of zinc dust in a sealed-off Pyrex distilling flask until the glass begins to soften. The degradative reaction has little preparative value, but is useful in investigation of substances of unknown structure because it affords a means of establishing the nature of the parent hydrocarbon. Thus the alkaloid morphine was first recognized as a phenanthrene derivative by degradation to phenanthrene, and the method provided the first clue that the natural dye alizarin is a member of the anthracene series.

PROPERTIES

Oxidation of Alkylbenzenes. — A characteristic reaction of toluene is oxidation to benzoic acid, accomplished by heating with dilute nitric acid

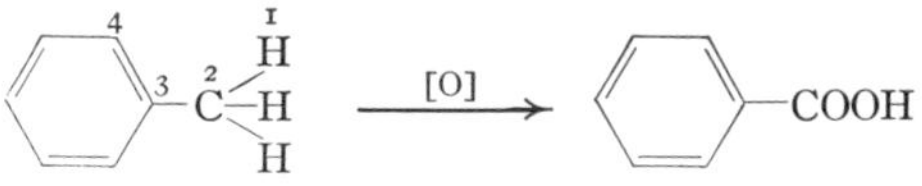

in a sealed tube, by refluxing with potassium dichromate and sulfuric acid, or by the action of alkaline potassium permanganate at 95° (nearly quantitative yield). The reaction not only illustrates the stability of the benzene ring, which survives the oxidation unscathed, but points to vulnerability of a methyl group attached to the aromatic nucleus not found in methane. The difference is attributable to activation of the hydrogen atoms of the methyl group by the adjacent unsaturated aromatic nucleus, and the reactivity, as compared with that of methane, is seen also in the ready chlorination of toluene in sunlight to benzyl chloride, $C_6H_5CH_2Cl$, and in the oxidation with lead tetraacetate to benzyl acetate, $C_6H_5CH_2OCOCH_3$ (in low yield). Xylenes are convertible into the corresponding phthalic acids, and mesitylene affords 1,3,5-benzenetricarboxylic acid. Ethyl, *n*-butyl, and still larger side chains are also easily degraded to carboxyl groups by oxidation, as the result of initial attack at the activated position adjacent to the benzene ring. The *t*-butyl group, which has no hydrogen atom in the activated position, is stable to oxidation.

Diphenylmethane can be converted by oxidation into the ketone benzophenone, but data for comparison with toluene are lacking. In triphenyl-

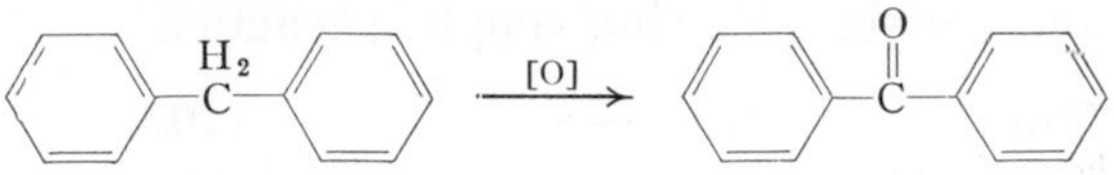

Diphenylmethane   Benzophenone

methane the lone methane hydrogen atom is subject to the combined activating influence of three phenyl groups, and its lability is manifested in the ready oxidation of the hydrocarbon to triphenylcarbinol. Thus the

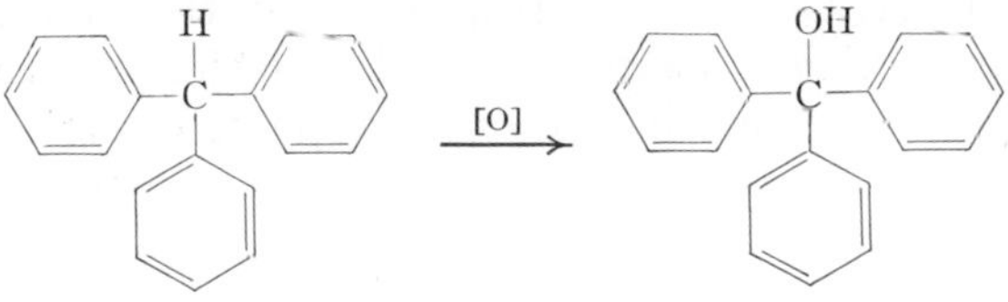

Triphenylmethane   Triphenylcarbinol (m.p. 162°)

reaction has been effected by passing air into a solution of the hydrocarbon in carbon disulfide in the presence of a trace of aluminum chloride.

Free Radicals. — In the early part of the nineteenth century many attempts were made to prepare methyl, ethyl, and comparable radicals in a free state, in analogy with the isolation of sodium from sodium chloride. A likely approach appeared to consist in abstraction of the halogen of a halogen compound by interaction with a metal, and prior to 1864, when Cannizzaro demonstrated the applicability of the Avogadro principle for the establishment of true molecular weights (1811), several substances were prepared that were thought to be radicals: Gay-Lussac's[8] "CN" (1815) proved to be cyanogen, $(CN)_2$; Bunsen's[9] supposed radical cacodyl, resulting from the action of zinc on cacodyl chloride, $(CH_3)_2AsCl$, became recognized as $(CH_3)_2As—As(CH_3)_2$; Frankland's[10] "ethyl" (1850), obtained from ethyl iodide and zinc, as well as the hydrocarbons produced by the Kolbe electrolysis of acid salts (1849), proved to have twice the expected molecular weight.

An authentic free radical was prepared for the first time by Gomberg[11] in 1900. Gomberg had synthesized tetraphenylmethane (m.p. 285°) and was interested to observe that the tetranitro derivative of this hydrocarbon, which has no hydrogen on the methane carbon atom, gave no color reaction with alcoholic potassium hydroxide and thereby contrasted with trinitro-triphenylmethane. In order to determine whether the difference was general, Gomberg sought to synthesize the completely phenylated ethane,

---

[8] Louis Joseph Gay-Lussac; 1778–1850; b. St. Léonard; Paris (Sorbonne)

[9] Robert W. Bunsen, 1811–99; b. Göttingen, Germany; Ph.D. Marburg; Marburg, Breslau, Heidelberg

[10] Sir Edward Frankland, 1825–99; b. Churchtown, Lancaster, England; Ph.D. Marburg; London; *Ber.*, **33**, 3847 (1900); *J. Chem. Soc.*, **87**, 574 (1905)

[11] Moses Gomberg, 1866–1947; b. Elisabetgrad, Russia; Ph.D. Michigan (Prescott); Michigan; *J. Am. Chem. Soc.*, **69**, 2921 (1947)

hexaphenylethane, by the following coupling reaction:

$$2(C_6H_5)_3CCl \ + \ 2Ag \ \longrightarrow \ (C_6H_5)_3C—C(C_6H_5)_3 \ + \ 2AgCl$$

Triphenylchloro-　　　　　　　　　　Hexaphenylethane
methane (m.p. 113°)

The product was a high-melting, sparingly soluble, white solid resembling tetraphenylmethane in physical properties and in its inert character. Analysis, however, showed that it was no hydrocarbon but an oxygen-containing compound $(C_{38}H_{30}O_2)$. The experiment was then repeated with exclusion of air by shaking a solution of triphenylchloromethane in benzene with finely divided silver or zinc in an atmosphere of carbon dioxide. A yellow solution resulted that, on evaporation in the absence of air, deposited colorless crystals of a hydrocarbon having the composition expected for hexaphenylethane but exhibiting remarkable reactivity. Solutions in benzene or carbon disulfide absorbed oxygen with avidity, with separation of the white oxygen compound, and in the absence of oxygen, they absorbed chlorine, bromine, and iodine. When the colorless hydrocarbon was first dissolved in a solvent, the solution was momentarily colorless, but within a few seconds became tinged with yellow, and the color soon deepened to a point of maximum intensity. The change was reversible, for by evaporation of the solution, the colorless hydrocarbon could be recovered. Gomberg interpreted the results as follows: "The experimental evidence . . . forces me to the conclusion that we have to deal here with a free radical triphenylmethyl $(C_6H_5)_3C—$. The action of zinc results, as it seems to me, in a mere abstraction of the halogen:

$$2(C_6H_5)_3C—Cl \ + \ Zn \ \longrightarrow \ 2(C_6H_5)_3C— \ + \ ZnCl_2$$

Now, as a result of the removal of the halogen atom from triphenylchloromethane, the fourth valence of the methane is bound either to take up the complicated group $(C_6H_5)_3C—$ or remain as such, with carbon as trivalent. Apparently the latter is what happens."

Molecular weight determinations established that the colorless solid is hexaphenylethane and that in solution it undergoes dissociation to colored triphenylmethyl radicals to a point of equilibrium. The free radical com-

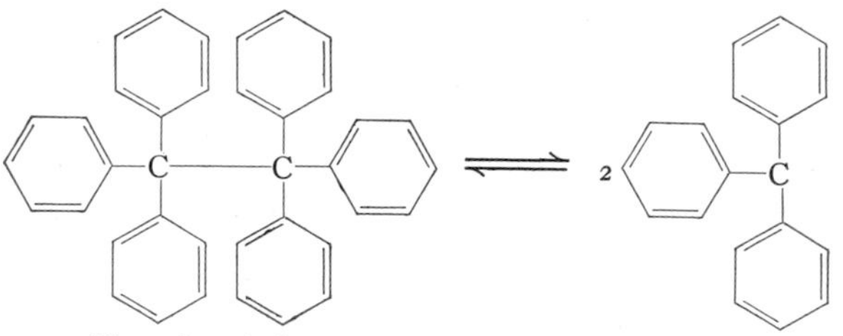

Hexaphenylethane　　　　　　　　Triphenylmethyl
(colorless, m.p. 147° dec.)　　　　　　　(yellow)

bines with halogens to produce triphenylmethyl halides, and with molecular oxygen to form the colorless peroxide, $(C_6H_5)_3C—O\cdot O—C(C_6H_5)_3$ m.p.

186°, with disturbance of the equilibrium and eventual dissociation of the whole of the hexaphenylethane. Many other hexaarylethanes and related compounds subsequently have been examined, and the degree of dissociation determined from the molecular weights observed at the boiling points and freezing points of various solvents. The point of equilibrium between the ethane and the radical at any temperature can be determined by measurement of either the molecular extinction coefficients of the colored solutions or of the paramagnetic susceptibilities of solutions containing the paramagnetic free radical (attracted by a magnet) and the diamagnetic ethane (not attracted). The extent of dissociation is dependent on the specific compound, concentration, solvent, and temperature. Values found for dissociation of hexaphenylethane in benzene at 20° are: 3.6% in a 4% solution, 9.6% in a 0.5% solution, 25.8% in a 0.055% solution. The dissociation constant for this substance is slightly less in acetone (1.7×10^{-4}) or in dioxan (2.5×10^{-4}) than in benzene (4.1×10^{-4}), but considerably greater in carbon disulfide (19.2×10^{-4}). An increase in temperature favors dissociation; for example, a 0.07% solution in benzene contains 18% of the free radical at 13° and 42% at 43°. Some of the more striking variations in the extent of dissociation with changes in the nature of the aryl groups are illustrated in the formulas, which include the per cent of the radical present at equilibrium in benzene at 5° in approximately 0.08 molar solution; such a solution contains about 3% of triphenylmethyl. In gen-

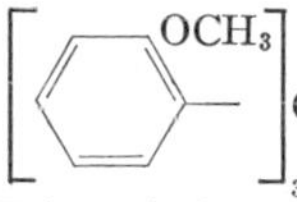

Tri-o-anisylmethyl
95–100% (orange)

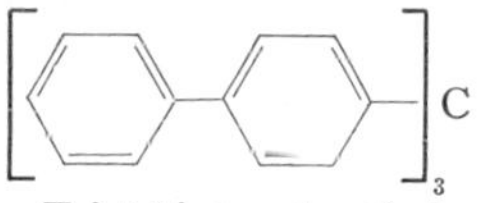

Tri-p-biphenylmethyl
74% (deep violet)

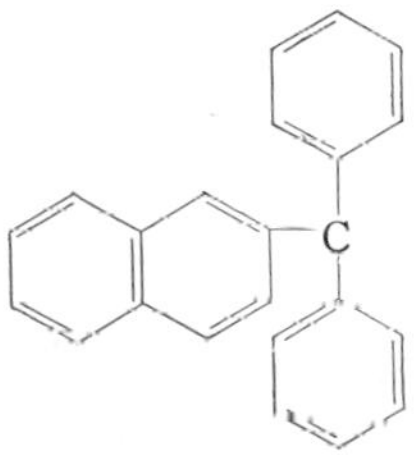

Diphenyl-β-naphthylmethyl
7–9% (wine red)

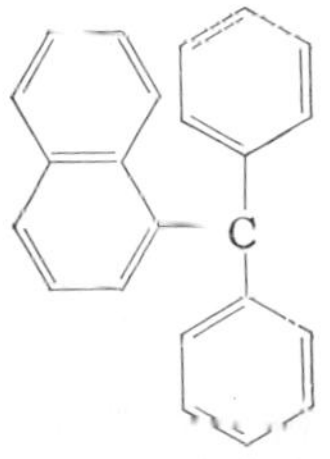

Diphenyl-α-naphthylmethyl
28–31% (deep red-brown)

eral, the order of effectiveness of aryl groups in promoting dissociation is: α-naphthyl > o-anisyl > p-anisyl > p-biphenyl > β-naphthyl > p-alkylphenyl > phenyl > p-chlorophenyl.

An empirical correlation of the dissociation of hexaphenylethane with other phenomena, such as the susceptibility of triphenylmethane to oxidation, is that the bond connecting the two ethane carbon atoms is subject to the activating influence of all six unsaturated phenyl groups, and indeed thermochemical studies have shown that this bond is weaker than that in ethane by about 30 kg.-cal. (Bent, 1936). Steric hindrance between the two clusters of benzene rings may contribute to weakening the linkage. However the dissociation to radicals is determined less by weakening of the ethane linkage than by stabilization of the free radical through resonance. The triphenylmethyl radical contains an unpaired electron, and the paramagnetic property of the substance is due to the presence of an odd electron

$$(C_6H_5)_3C:C(C_6H_5)_3 \rightleftharpoons 2(C_6H_5)_3C\cdot$$

that is not compensated magnetically. Pauling (1933) and Hückel[12] (1933) developed by quantum-mechanical calculations a concept, stated qualitatively by Ingold (1929), that the odd electron is distributed between the methane carbon atom and all *ortho* and *para* positions in the three phenyl groups, as shown in the formulas for one of the rings. In all, there are ten electron structures that can contribute to the resonance state, and resonance results in marked stabilization of the radical.

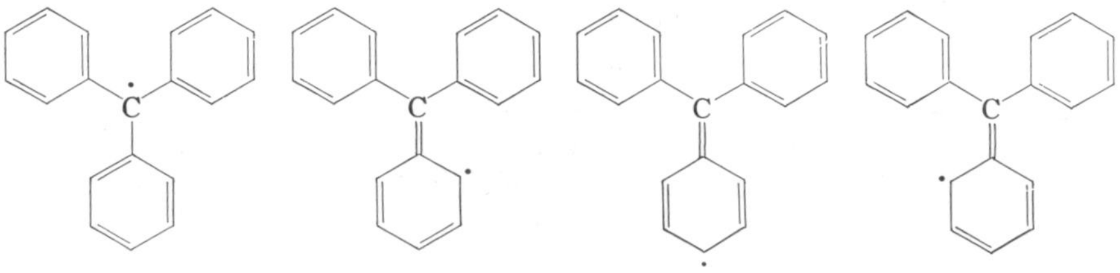

The triphenylmethyl group can form both positive and negative ions. Colorless solutions of triphenylcarbinol in alcohol or acetic acid become intensely colored on addition of mineral acids owing to formation of ionized halochromic salts:

$$(C_6H_5)_3OH \; + \; HX \; \longrightarrow \; [(C_6H_5)_3C]^+ \; + \; X^- \; + \; H_2O$$

On the other hand, addition of finely powdered sodium to a solution of the triphenylmethyl radical in ether—benzene or in liquid ammonia produces intensely red solutions of the ionic but nevertheless ether-soluble triphenylmethylsodium:

$$(C_6H_5)_3C \; + \; Na \; \longrightarrow \; [(C_6H_5)_3C]^- \; + \; Na^+$$

The relationship of the two ions to the radical is shown in the following electronic formulas:

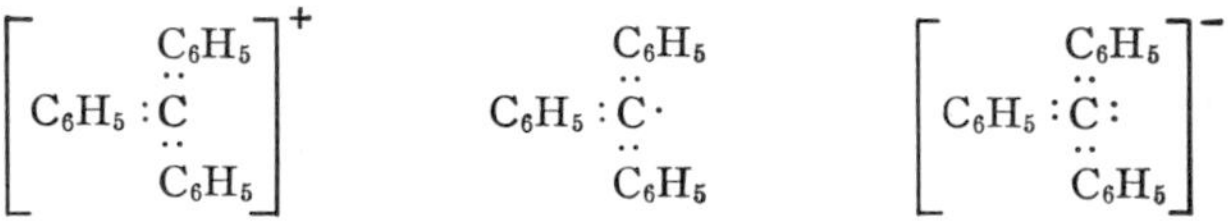

Triphenylmethyl
carbonium ion

Triphenylmethyl
radical

Triphenylmethyl
carbanion

---

[12] Ernst Hückel, b. 1896 Charlottenburg, Germany; Ph.D. Göttingen (Debye); Stuttgart, Marburg

PROBLEMS

1. Suggest methods for the Friedel-Crafts synthesis of (a) t-butylbenzene, (b) p-di-t-butylbenzene.
2. How could p-$(CH_3)_3CC_6H_4CO_2H$ be synthesized starting with toluene?
3. Devise a synthesis of p-$(CH_3)_2CHC_6H_4CO_2H$ starting with benzene.
4. What products would you expect to result from the following reactions?

   (a) C_6H_6 + $(CH_3)_2C{=}CH_2$ + HF
   (b) $C_6H_5CH_2CH_3$ + $(CH_3)_2CHCl$ + BF_3
   (c) $C_6H_5CH_2CH_3$ + $2CH_3CH_2Cl$ + $AlCl_3$ (2 equivalents, no cooling)
   (d) $C_6H_5CH_3$ + CH_3COCl + $AlCl_3$ (1 equivalent)

5. Indicate syntheses of n-butylbenzene utilizing any aliphatic components desired and starting with: (a) benzene, (b) bromobenzene, (c) benzaldehyde.
6. Work out a synthesis of α-phenylnaphthalene starting with benzene and succinic anhydride.
7. Devise a synthesis of β-methylnaphthalene from toluene and succinic anhydride.
8. Give two ways of preparing α-methylnaphthalene from α-bromonaphthalene.
9. Suggest a synthesis of $C_6H_5(CH_2)_5COOH$, starting with bromobenzene and cyclohexanone.

READING REFERENCES

E. L. Martin, "The Clemmensen Reduction," in R. Adams, *Organic Reactions*, I, 155–209, Wiley, New York (1942)

M. Gomberg, "The Existence of Free Radicals," *J. Am. Chem. Soc.*, **36**, 1144–1170 (1914)

W. E. Bachmann, "Free Radicals," in H. Gilman, *Organic Chemistry*, I, 2nd Ed., 581–630, Wiley, New York (1943)

W. A. Waters, "Some Recent Developments in the Chemistry of Free Radicals," *J. Chem. Soc.*, 409 (1946)

M. E. Cameron, "Victor Meyer and the Thiophene Compounds," *J. Chem. Ed.*, **26**, 521 (1949)

CHAPTER 22

AROMATIC SUBSTITUTIONS

Relatively few reactions are available for direct introduction of substituent groups into the aromatic nucleus that are sufficiently general to be applicable to benzene, alkylbenzenes, naphthalene, and higher polynuclear hydrocarbons. Although each of these reactions has specific characteristics, they can be classified in two somewhat differentiated types:

Type I $\left\{ \begin{array}{l} \text{Nitration} \\ \text{Halogenation (Br}_2, \text{Cl}_2) \end{array} \right.$ (normal)

Type II $\left\{ \begin{array}{l} \text{Sulfonation} \\ \text{Friedel-Crafts acylation} \\ \text{Friedel-Crafts alkylation} \end{array} \right.$ (abnormal)

The Friedel-Crafts alkylation reaction is reversible and markedly subject to the effect of temperature; the same is true of sulfonation and, at least with regard to the temperature factor, of Friedel-Crafts acylation. Examples already cited indicate a further dependence on the steric factor, in that substitution *ortho* to a group already present in the ring occurs, if at all, only at low reaction temperatures. Nitration and halogenation, being irreversible processes not subject to the influences noted, are described as normal substitutions, and the type II reactions are described as abnormal.

Control of the severity of conditions for nitration is possible by regulation of the temperature and of the concentration of the reagent. Some nitrations can be accomplished with dilute nitric acid, others with concentrated acid (sp. gr. 1.42) or with fuming nitric acid (sp. gr. to 1.52). Water is formed in the reaction, $ArH + HONO_2 \rightarrow ArNO_2 + H_2O$, with consequent dilution of the nitric acid, and a useful expedient to compensate for the resulting loss of efficiency as the reaction progresses is to mix the nitric acid with concentrated or fuming sulfuric acid to absorb the water. Nitration with mixed acid is a standard procedure. Some nitrations are conducted to advantage in acetic acid solution, and the reaction can be intensified by use of acetic anhydride as solvent, in which case the effective nitrating agent is acetyl nitrate, CH_3COONO_2. From the reaction temperature, strength of acid, and requirement for an accessory dehydrating agent, a given nitration is said to proceed very easily, readily, or with difficulty. The same is true of halogenations and of Friedel-Crafts substitutions, where the controlling factors are the nature and amount of catalyst and the reaction temperature. The intensity of sulfonation is controllable over a rather wide range by regulation of the temperature (0° to about 360°) and of the concentration of acid (dilute acid to oleum).

Directive Influence of Substituent Groups. — Different substitution reactions are influenced in the same way by substituent groups already present in the benzene ring, which exert a profound control over both the orientation and the ease of introduction of the entering substituent. Phenol can be nitrated so easily that dilute nitric acid suffices at room temperature (mixture of *ortho* and *para* isomers), whereas in order to nitrate nitrobenzene

$$OH \xrightarrow{20\% \ HNO_3, \ 25°} OH\text{-}NO_2 + OH\text{-}NO_2$$

ortho (30–40%)
para (14%)

efficiently the substance must be warmed with a mixture of fuming nitric acid and concentrated sulfuric acid; in this case the orientation is exclusively in the *meta* position. Control over the direction of substitution is described

$$NO_2 \xrightarrow[88\% \ yield]{Fuming \ HNO_3 + concd. \ H_2SO_4, \ 95°} NO_2\text{-}NO_2$$

meta

as a directive influence, though promotion or retardation of substitution is no less important than the orientation of the entering group. The *meta* directing nitro group, which renders substitution more difficult or exerts a deactivating effect on the aromatic nucleus, is strongly unsaturated, whereas the *ortho-para* directing hydroxyl group, which facilitates substitution, is saturated. An important feature of the nitro group is a polar character, owing to the ionic character of the fifth valence of nitrogen. Nitrobenzene has one double and one semipolar bond, and is a resonance hybrid of two equivalent structures. The nitro group thus not only is unsaturated but

$$C_6H_5-N\underset{O}{\overset{O}{\diagup}} \longleftrightarrow C_6H_5-\overset{+}{N}\underset{O}{\overset{\bar{O}}{\diagup}}$$

possesses a positively charged atom in the key position adjacent to the benzene ring. Most other groups conform sufficiently closely either to the type exemplified by the nitro group or to that of the hydroxyl group to warrant the empirical classification into *meta* or *ortho-para* directing groups.

Meta directing groups: Groups in which the atom directly joined to the aromatic nucleus is either strongly unsaturated or positively charged deactivate the whole ring but permit substitution, though with difficulty, in the *meta* position. In the list shown they are arranged roughly in the order of decreasing effectiveness. The strongly ionic trimethylammonium group heads the list, for the highly polar phenyltrimethylammonium

$$-\overset{+}{N}(CH_3)_3 \qquad -\overset{+}{N}\underset{O}{\overset{\bar{O}}{\diagup}} \qquad -C\equiv N \qquad -\overset{+}{S}\underset{OH}{\overset{\bar{O}}{\diagup}}\!\!=\!\!O \qquad -C\underset{O}{\overset{H}{\diagup}}$$
(powerful)

$$-C\underset{O}{\overset{CH_3}{\diagup}} \qquad -C\underset{O}{\overset{OH}{\diagup}} \qquad -C\underset{O}{\overset{OCH_3}{\diagup}} \qquad -C\underset{O}{\overset{NH_2}{\diagup}} \qquad -\overset{+}{N}H_3$$
(weak)

nitrate, $[C_6H_5N(CH_3)_3]^+NO_3^-$, is substituted with great difficulty and exclusively in the *meta* position. A primary amino group attached to the benzene ring gives a much less powerful positive pole, for the ammonium group ($-NH_3^+$) functions only weakly as a *meta* directing substituent. Nitro and sulfonic acid groups contain positively polarized key atoms by virtue of their semipolar bonds, and in a carbonyl group displacement of a pair of electrons of the double bond toward oxygen (a) results in a fractional positive polarization of the carbon atom (b).

$$-\overset{\curvearrowright}{\underset{\underset{R}{|}}{C}}\!\!=\!\!O \qquad \overset{\delta+\ \delta-}{-\underset{\underset{R}{|}}{C}\!\!=\!\!O}$$

$$(a) \qquad\qquad (b)$$

Ortho-para directing groups: Groups that are saturated or only weakly unsaturated at the point of attachment to the ring direct entering substituents to the *ortho* and *para* positions, and with the exception of halogen atoms, facilitate substitution. The chief groups of this type are shown in the following list; the order is significant only with respect to the position of the amino group (nonionized) and hydroxyl group at the head of the list, for these substituents far surpass all others, and the other groups differ only in minor degree. The very powerful *ortho-para* directing dimethylamino,

$$-N(CH_3)_2 \qquad -NH_2 \qquad -OH \qquad -OCH_3 \qquad -NHCOCH_3 \qquad -OCOCH_3$$

$$\underbrace{}$$

(very powerful)

$$-CH_3 \qquad -Cl,\ Br,\ I \qquad -C_6H_5 \qquad -CH_2COOH \qquad -CH=CHCOOH$$

amino, and hydroxyl groups have a marked activating influence, and the same effect is displayed to a lesser degree by all the others except the halogen substituents, which direct the entering group to the *ortho* and *para* positions but nevertheless render substitution more difficult, as the *meta* type groups do.

Meta Substitutions. — The rules of orientation are useful in predictions of the chief products of substitution reactions, but they indicate the predominant, rather than the exclusive products. Careful quantitative studies have been made by the Netherlands school of Holleman,[1] Wibaut, and others to determine, often by physical methods of analysis, the exact proportion of the isomers present, even in small amounts, in reaction mixtures resulting from various substitutions, usually nitration. The results are conveniently summarized by affixing to the formula of a substance undergoing a given substitution figures representing the proportions of the different isomers found in the total substitution product; the percentages established by analysis should not be confused with the percentage yields that can be secured in practice. Thus in actual preparative work *m*-dinitrobenzene can be obtained in 88% yield by nitration of nitrobenzene, but analysis of the total nitrated material has shown that the *meta* isomer constitutes 93% of the whole and that the *ortho* and *para* isomers are present to the extent of 6% and 1%, respectively, as indicated in the abbreviated summary. The *ortho* and *para* isomers are produced in such small amounts that they

NO₂ 6% 93% 1% Nitration

---

[1] Arnold Frederick Holleman, 1859–1953; b. Oisterwyk, Netherlands; Ph.D. Leiden (Franchimont); Amsterdam

are easily eliminated during crystallization. The trimethylammonium group is even more potent than the nitro group because it affords exclusive *meta* substitution, and carboxyl is weaker than nitro because it allows *ortho-para* substitution to proceed to a considerable extent. That positively charged or highly unsaturated groups direct an entering group to the *meta* position by deactivating all the positions, with particular suppression of attack at the *ortho* and *para* carbon atoms, is illustrated by results of nitration of *p*-nitrobenzoic acid. The only positions available are *ortho* to either a carboxyl or a nitro group, and

Nitration

it is understandable that the reaction proceeds with difficulty; the suppression of *ortho* substitution is greater for the nitro substituent, and the group introduced takes a place *ortho* to the weaker carboxyl.

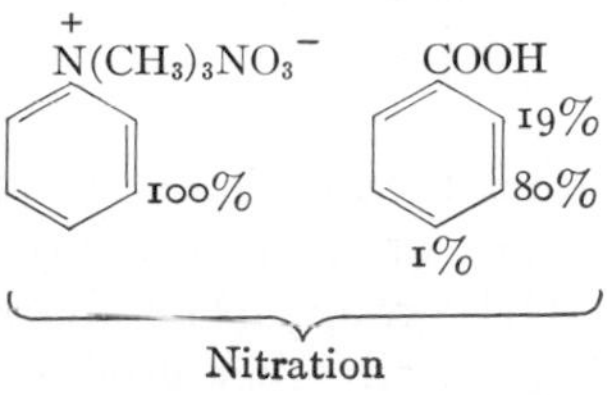

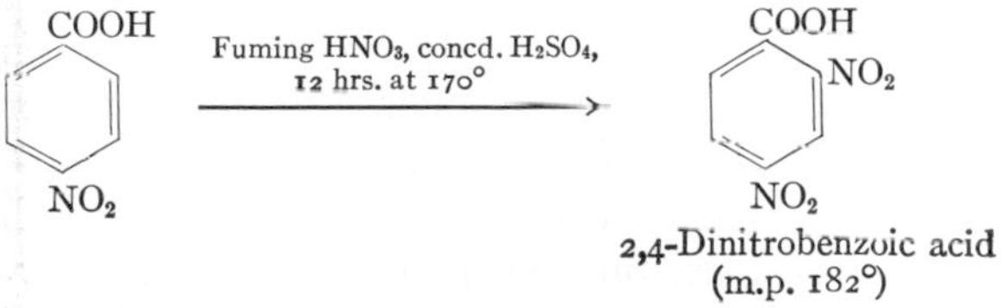

Fuming HNO_3, concd. H_2SO_4, 12 hrs. at 170°

2,4-Dinitrobenzoic acid
(m.p. 182°)

The deactivating influence of *meta* directing groups controls the course of substitution of polynuclear compounds. In 4-nitrodiphenyl, for example,

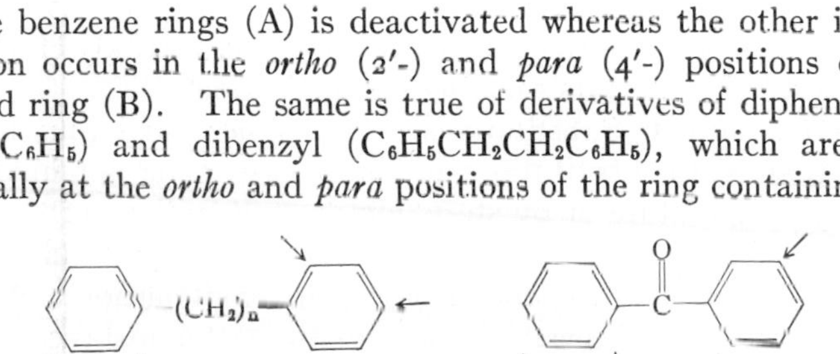

one of the benzene rings (A) is deactivated whereas the other is not, and substitution occurs in the *ortho* (2'-) and *para* (4'-) positions of the unsubstituted ring (B). The same is true of derivatives of diphenylmethane ($C_6H_5CH_2C_6H_5$) and dibenzyl ($C_6H_5CH_2CH_2C_6H_5$), which are attacked preferentially at the *ortho* and *para* positions of the ring containing no nitro

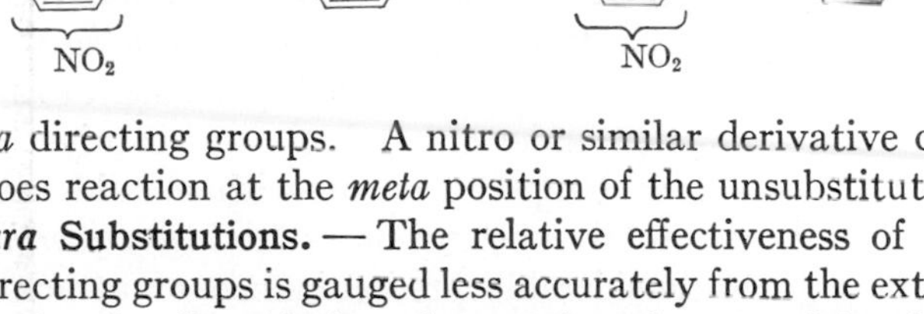

or other *meta* directing groups. A nitro or similar derivative of benzophenone undergoes reaction at the *meta* position of the unsubstituted ring.

Ortho-Para Substitutions. — The relative effectiveness of the various *ortho-para* directing groups is gauged less accurately from the extent to which *meta* substitution is allowed than by results of competition between two groups in the same molecule, preferably in the *para* positions. In *p*-aminophenol substitution occurs preferentially in the position *ortho* to the amino group, which therefore is more powerful in its influence than hydroxyl. If

OH   OH   NH₂   CH₃   CH₃

NH₂   CH₃   Cl   NH₂   Cl

either the amino or hydroxyl group is pitted against methyl or other alkyl group, or against halogen, substitution is dominated by the —NH₂ or —OH group. The dimethylamino, amino, and hydroxyl groups so far surpass all other groups of the *ortho-para* type that amines and phenols undergo special substitutions not applicable to other aromatic compounds. The other *ortho-para* directing groups included in the list given above are arranged in the approximate order of effectiveness, as judged by competition reactions, but in this category of second-order effectiveness the differences are relatively slight. There is so little difference between methyl and halogen, for example, that the *p*-halotoluenes ordinarily afford mixtures of the two possible monosubstitution products.

Groups of the saturated type transmit an activating influence to both the *ortho* and *para* positions, but the ratio of *ortho* and *para* substitution varies over a rather wide range, as illustrated by the following summary:

NHCOCH₃ 5%   OH 40%   Cl 30%   CH₃ 59%
                                                  4%

95%   60%   70%   37%

Nitration

Para substitution generally predominates over substitution in the *ortho* position. Toluene is an exception, but in this case the *ortho-para* ratio is sensitive to conditions and varies from 3:2 to 2:3 according to the nitrating agent; it will be noted also that the methyl group is a weakly effective member of the series and permits some *meta* substitution.

Type II (Abnormal) Substitutions. — Examples cited thus far refer to nitrations, that is, to substitutions of the normal type not influenced appreciably by temperature or by steric factors. Reactions of the abnormal type show considerable dependence on these factors, particularly with respect to the ratio of *ortho* to *para* substitution. Sulfonation and alkylation

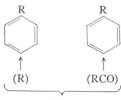

R   R

(R)   (RCO)

Friedel-Crafts reaction

are reversible, and in the latter instance a group initially introduced at a position *ortho* to a second alkyl group may undergo displacement to a more remote position under the influence of catalyst or heat. At a low temperature or with a mild catalyst, where the total substitution is exclusively *ortho-para*, there is considerable predominance of attack in the *para* position, rather than in the more hindered site adjacent to the directing group. Thus the boron fluoride catalyzed dialkylation of benzene gives exclusively *p*-dialkyl derivatives, and acylation of toluene with acetyl or benzoyl chloride or with succinic or phthalic anhydride yields solely *para* derivatives. A similar tendency is observable in sulfonations, as is evident from the comparative data on nitration and sulfonation of chlorobenzene and of toluene. In each

Cl   30%   Cl   CH$_3$ 59%   4%   CH$_3$ 32%   6%

70%   100%   37%   62%
Nitration   Sulfonation   Nitration   Sulfonation

case the reversible sulfonation gives a lower proportion of the *ortho* isomer than nitration (or halogenation). Avoidance of the *ortho* position in reversible reactions appears attributable to steric hindrance, or a spatial blocking of the adjacent *ortho* sites. A further indication of steric effects is that *ortho* substitution is particularly suppressed when the directing group is bulky; thus *t*-butylbenzene is sulfonated exclusively in the *para* position, whereas under comparable conditions toluene affords a significant amount of the *ortho* isomer. Conditions of sulfonation are important, and a comparison of the results obtained with toluene at

CH$_3$ 43%   4%   53%   0°   CH$_3$ 13%   8%   79%   100°

Sulfonation

0° and at 100° shows that the proportion of *ortho* substitution decreases with increasing temperature.

Mono- and Polysubstitutions. — The contrast between the effect of *meta* directing groups in deactivating the benzene ring for substitutions and the substitution-promoting influence of *ortho-para* directors has important consequences. When benzene is nitrated, the reaction comes to a sharp stopping point with introduction of one nitro group, for the resistance of the nucleus to substitution is so increased that a second group can be introduced only under much more drastic conditions. The mononitro derivative is thus obtainable in high yield and without contamination by polynitro compounds. Since the group introduced on sulfonation is of the same type, hydrocarbons can be converted easily into their monosulfonic acids, and forcing conditions are required for introduction of a second group *meta* to the first. In the Friedel-Crafts ketone synthesis, the maximum intensity obtainable is such that the reaction is limited, in all but exceptional cases, to monosubstitution. Thus even with considerable excess of acetyl chloride and aluminum chloride, benzene is converted into acetophenone and no further. The *meta* directing group introduced inhibits further reaction, and this suppression accounts for the generally satisfactory character of the synthesis. Other *meta* directing groups also have an inhibitory influence, and the Friedel-Crafts acylation and alkylation reactions are inapplicable to such compounds as nitrobenzene, benzaldehyde, or benzonitrile. Halo-

gen atoms in the benzene ring possess the unique character of directing substituents into the *ortho* and *para* positions but of exerting a weak deactivating
influence.   Thus dibromination of benzene requires greater severity of
treatment than monobromination, and the successive stages of polysubstitution are attainable in discrete steps.   Friedel-Crafts alkylation is the one
instance in which the group introduced facilitates further substitution.
Toluene is distinctly more susceptible than benzene to nitration and sulfonation; also it undergoes methylation more readily than the parent hydrocarbon, and hence when benzene is condensed with methyl chloride in the
presence of aluminum chloride, the product initially formed inevitably consumes some of the reagent before the starting material is exhausted, with
formation of polysubstitution products.

Reactions of Polysubstituted Compounds. — When more than one group
is present in a substance undergoing substitution, the location and nature of
the groups may exert either an antagonistic or a reinforcing influence on
the course of the reaction.   In mesitylene each of the three equivalent
positions is under the substitution-facilitating influence of one *para*-methyl
and two *ortho*-methyl groups, and consequently the hydro-
carbon undergoes ready substitution even though the only
position attacked is subject to the steric hindrance of two
adjacent methyl groups.   Among the xylenes, the order of
reactivity as indicated by sulfonation and desulfonation reactions employed in the separation (p. 548) is: $m > o > p$.   The superior
reactivity of *m*-xylene can be attributed to the reinforcing influence of the
strong *para* and moderate *ortho* direction to the 4-position, the site of the
sulfonation; both methyl groups exert a moderate activating influence at

position 2, but this position is well blocked, particularly to a reaction notably
subject to steric hindrance.   Of the two positions available in *o*-xylene, one
(4) is under the strong *para* influence of a methyl group, and the other (3) is
ortho activated and moderately hindred; hence sulfonation occurs at the
former position.   In *p*-xylene the only position available corresponds to
the less reactive 3-position of *o*-xylene, and consequently the hydrocarbon
is the least readily sulfonated of the three isomers.

p-Nitrophenol contains groups of different types, but these are not antagonistic.   The nitro group deactivates position 3 strongly but influences
the *meta* position 2 only moderately in an adverse sense, and since the latter

position is under the powerful *ortho* influence of the hydroxyl group, it is the exclusive site of monosubstitution, for example, on nitration or bromination. In *o*-nitrophenol the expected sites of substitution are positions 4 and 6, which are *para* and *ortho*, respectively, to the hydroxyl and *meta* to the nitro group. Since *para* orientation ordinarily is stronger than *ortho*, predominance of attack at position 4 would be anticipated. Actually sulfonation gives the 4-sulfonic acid exclusively; bromination affords the 4-monobromo compound along with the 4,6-dibromo derivative; and nitration gives chiefly 2,4-dinitrophenol, along with a small amount of the isomeric 2,6-dinitrophenol.

THEORY OF AROMATIC SUBSTITUTIONS

Many theories have been advanced in the attempt to account for processes of substitution in the benzene ring. A long-favored general interpretation, which had attractive features and considerable plausibility but which eventually was shown to be untenable, postulated that substitutions occur by an addition-elimination mechanism. In the ferric bromide catalyzed bromination of benzene, for example, it was supposed that bromine adds to a double bond to give an intermediate addition product which loses hydrogen bromide under catalysis by the metal halide in a reaction comparable to that apparently involved in the isomerization of *n*-propyl bromide (p. 539). Other substitutions can be formulated similarly by

assuming the addition of CH_3—Cl, HO—NO_2, HO—SO_3H. Arguments and analogies have been adduced both for and against the theory, but a decision was difficult. In the benzene series, the supposed addition products are hypothetical; the more reactive hydrocarbon phenanthrene, however, combines with one mole of bromine to form a crystalline addition product corresponding to the postulated intermediate in bromination of benzene and constituting a suitable test material. The dibromide is formed by interaction of the pure components in nonaqueous solvents. If the hydrocarbon is treated with bromine in the presence of a catalyst such as ferric bromide, a substitution product is obtained, 9-bromophenanthrene. Formation of the dibromide shows that addition in the postulated sense is possible, and there remains the question whether or not this addition product is a necessary intermediate required for formation of the aromatic substitution product. Price[2] (1936) investigated this point by measuring the velocities of the addition and substitution reactions and found that the dibromide is formed in a reversible reaction and that, when treated with a bromination

[2] Charles C. Price, b. 1913 Passaic, N. J.; Ph.D. Harvard (Fieser); Univ. Pennsylvania

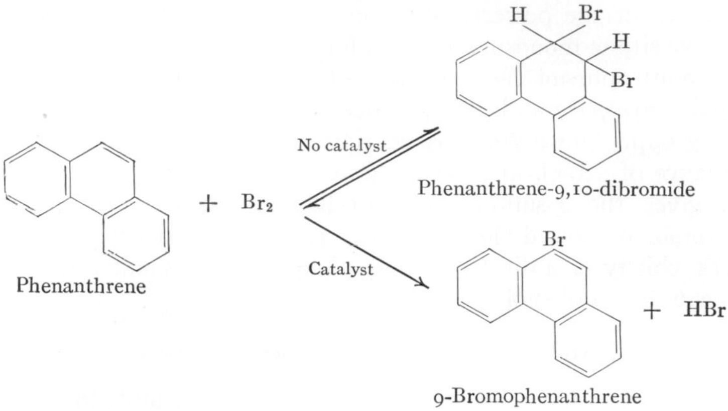

Phenanthrene   +   Br$_2$

No catalyst

Phenanthrene-9,10-dibromide

Catalyst

9-Bromophenanthrene   +   HBr

catalyst, it does not lose hydrogen bromide and afford 9-bromophenanthrene but is converted into this substance by virtue of reversion to phenanthrene and bromine, which then enter into an independent, catalyzed substitution reaction. Thus an addition product, even though capable of existence, is not a necessary intermediate for substitution.

Substitution is now regarded as replacement of a hydrogen atom of the intact unsaturated nucleus as the result of attack by a positive ion, or equivalent electrophilic fragment. The reactions occur in ionizing media, such as a solution in concentrated sulfuric acid, or under the influence of catalysts that favor formation of ionic species. Thus substitution by bromine, in preference to addition, is promoted by a trace of ferric bromide, iodine, antimony pentachloride, or aluminum chloride. These catalysts are all capable of incorporating one atom of the bromine molecule into an anion, which can act as acceptor for the hydrogen atom to be displaced from the benzene ring; the other atom is left as a positively charged ion, for example: $Br^+[FeBr_4]^-$ and $Br^+[IBr_4]^-$. Kinetic studies show that ferric bromide catalyzed bromination of benzene is a two-step bimolecular reaction. The first, a slow, rate-controlling step, is attack of one of the double bonds by the bromonium ion to give a carbonium ion in which the charge is distributed

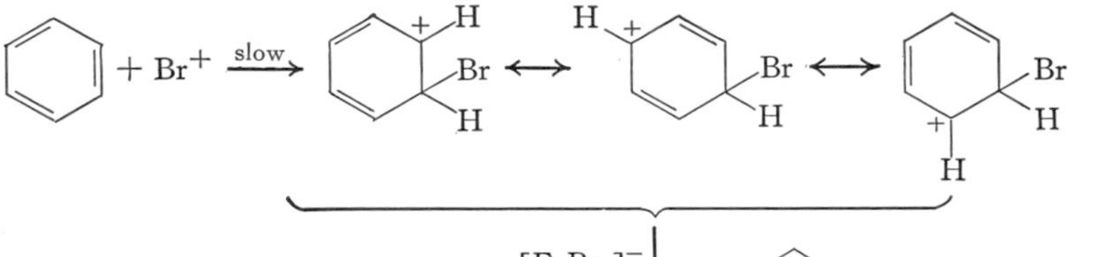

among three principal valency structures. The second step involves elimination of a proton with restoration of the aromatic ring. The first step is the same as that in addition of bromine to an olefin. That this is not followed by reaction of the carbonium ion with bromide ion to give a dibromide if a proton acceptor is available is because the dibromide lacks the resonance stabilization of the aromatic ring.

The mechanism of nitration has been studied particularly extensively (Ingold and Hughes). When the reaction is conducted in nitric-sulfuric acid solution the active nitrating agent is the nitronium ion, NO_2^+, the existence of which is established by the extent of the depression of the freezing point of sulfuric acid by added nitric acid. The depression is exactly four times that of an ideal solute, which means that four ions are produced quantitatively, corresponding to the reaction:

$$HNO_3 + 2H_2SO_4 \rightarrow NO_2^+ + H_3O^+ + 2HSO_4^-$$

Kinetic studies have shown that the rate-determining step in nitration is bimolecular (S_E2) and are consistent with formulation of the reaction as a two-step bimolecular process:

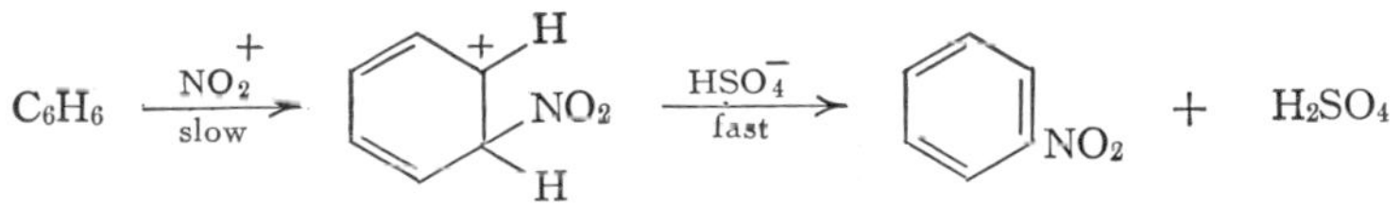

Nitration in acetic acid solution involves two steps, the slower of which is formation of the nitronium ion.

$$HNO_3 + HNO_3 \rightleftharpoons H_2NO_3^+ + NO_3^-; \qquad H_2NO_3^+ \xrightarrow{slow} NO_2^+ + H_2O$$

Studies of sulfonation are less extensive but indicate that monomeric sulfur trioxide is the active species and that the reaction is analogous to nitration. Friedel-Crafts catalysts are similar to halogenation catalysts

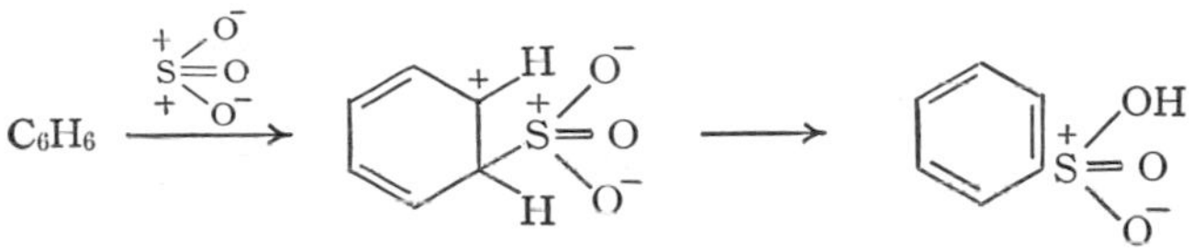

and would be expected to function by forming ionic complexes: $CH_3^+[AlCl_4]^-$ $CH_3CO^+[AlCl_4]^-$. However, the reaction rate is first order with respect to three components: rate = $k[ArH][RCl][AlCl_3]$. The rate-determining step therefore appears to be termolecular.

The consistently electrophilic character of the attacking agent provides one indication that polarity plays a dominant role in substitutions; another indication is that the nonionized amino group facilitates substitution in the ortho and para positions, whereas the positively charged ammonium group —NH_3^+ has a deactivating, meta directing influence. Deactivation in this instance can be attributed to repulsion of the electrophilic attacking agent by the electrophilic directing group, and the effect is even stronger with the more positive trimethylammonium group, —$NH(CH_3)_3^+$. The nitro and sulfonic acid groups, since they contain key atoms in a positively polarized condition, also deactivate substitutions by electrophilic reagents.

The **inductive effect** associated with an ammonium group results in decreased electron density throughout the ring and hence in decreased susceptibility to attack at any position by an electron-seeking agent. Conversely, a directing group of an electron-repelling character displaces electrons toward the ring and promotes attack by an electron-acceptor agent. The direction and magnitude of the displacement of the electric centers of different directing groups are known from measurements of dipole moments (p. 327). Benzene has no dipole moment and neither has p-xylene, but a small dipole moment is observed for toluene (0.41) and a large one for nitrobenzene (3.97). The experimental observations do not indicate whether the methyl group displaces the electric center in the same sense as the nitro group or in the opposite sense, but a decision can be reached from the observation that p-nitrotoluene has a dipole moment of 4.40, which corresponds closely to the sum of the values noted and not to the difference; hence the substituents attached to opposite positions in the ring cooperate in producing a drift of electrons in the same direction. If the nitro group at one terminal position attracts electrons, then the methyl group at the other extremity

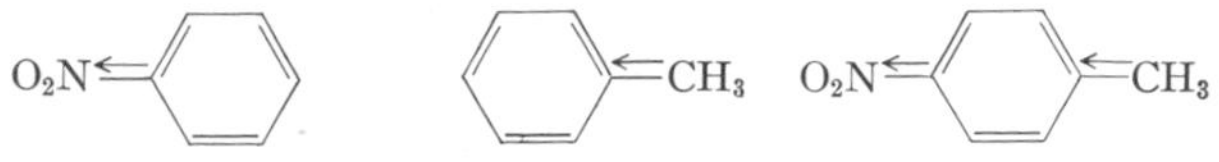

Dipole moments (benzene solution)

must repel electrons. By this method of comparison the direction of the inductive effect of a given group is established, and the magnitude is revealed by the dipole moment of the monosubstituted benzene derivative, as recorded in Table 22.1. Strongly ionized groups unfortunately fall outside the scope of the experimental method, but the other groups can be classified as electron-attracting, if they operate in the same sense as the nitro group, and electron-releasing, if they operate in the opposite sense. The first series, headed by the powerful nitro group, includes other unsaturated substituents recognized as deactivating and *meta* directing groups, whereas the second includes amino, hydroxyl, and alkyl groups in an order conforming

TABLE 22.1. DIPOLE MOMENTS OF BENZENE DERIVATIVES
(IN BENZENE SOLUTION AT 22–25°)

ELECTRON-ATTRACTING		ELECTRON-RELEASING	
Substituent	Dipole moment	Substituent	Dipole moment
—NO_2	3.97	—$N(CH_3)_2$	1.58
—CN	3.90	—NH_2	1.52
—$COCH_3$	2.93	—OH	1.61
—CHO	2.75	—$OCOCH_3$	1.52
—$COOC_2H_5$	1.91	—OCH_3	1.16
—Cl	1.56	—CH_3	0.41
—Br	1.53		
—I	1.30		
—COOH	1.0		

to that of their substitution-facilitating, or activating influence. Halogen atoms are seen from the dipole moment data to attract electrons from the benzene ring and to induce in the nucleus a condition of low electron density, and hence of lowered vulnerability to attack by electrophilic agents. That the chlorine atom is electron-attracting is shown also by the effect of α-chloro substitution on the ionization of carboxylic acids. However, the amino, hydroxyl, and derived groups, seen to be electron-releasing when attached to a benzene ring, are electron-attracting in aliphatic compounds; for example, an α-hydroxyl group increases the acidic strength of acetic acid. This reversal is attributed to operation of the resonance effect, as described below.

The electric displacement effects inferred from dipole moments account for the activating or deactivating influence of different groups, but do not explain the orientation; although the majority of electron-attracting groups orient an entering group to the *meta* position, halogen substituents, like the electron-releasing amino and hydroxyl groups, are *ortho-para* directing. A clue to this apparent anomaly is found in the interatomic distances, determined by the electron-diffraction method, in which electrons impinging at right angles on a stream of molecules of a vaporized substance are scattered and produce an interference pattern on a photographic plate. The C—Cl distance in chlorobenzene (1.70Å) is found to be notably shortened as compared with that in methyl chloride (1.76Å), which indicates a partial double-bond character due to a **resonance effect**. Chlorobenzene is

regarded as a resonance hybrid of four structures. In the composite structure the halogen is joined to the ring by a linkage that partakes of the character of both a single and a double bond and that is therefore intermediate in both length and strength of binding. A further consequence of resonance in the chlorobenzene molecule is a decreased dipole moment, as compared with that of methyl chloride.

The *ortho-para* directing influence of the halogen atom can be interpreted as a consequence of the resonance effect. If the substituting agent is electrophilic, it must react preferentially at positions of highest electron density, and in chlorobenzene such centers are set up through resonance at the *ortho* and *para* positions. The halogen atom, by induction, tends to withdraw electrons from the ring and render substitution more difficult than in benzene, but the relatively anionic centers in the *ortho* and *para* positions of the resonance structures represent sites at least more vulnerable to substitution than the *meta* carbon atoms.

In aromatic derivatives substituted with powerful electron-repelling groups containing nitrogen or oxygen as the key atom, such as amines and phenols as well as their alkyl and acyl derivatives, resonance is possible by virtue of the unshared electrons associated with the key atom. A marked reduction even involving reversal of the direction of the dipole moments, as compared with values for corresponding aliphatic compounds, provides evidence of this effect. Resonance structures can be written for both phenol and the phenoxide ion as follows:

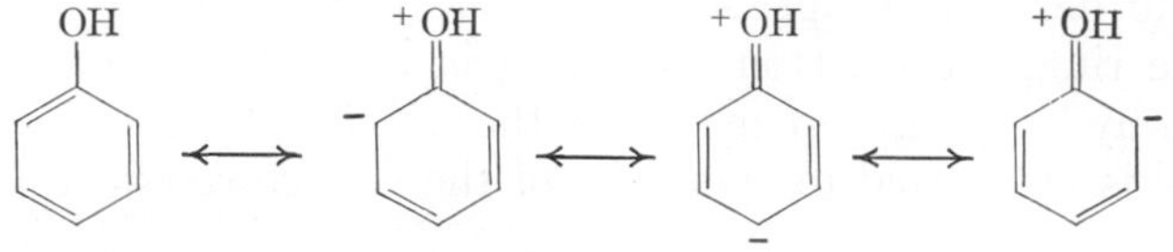

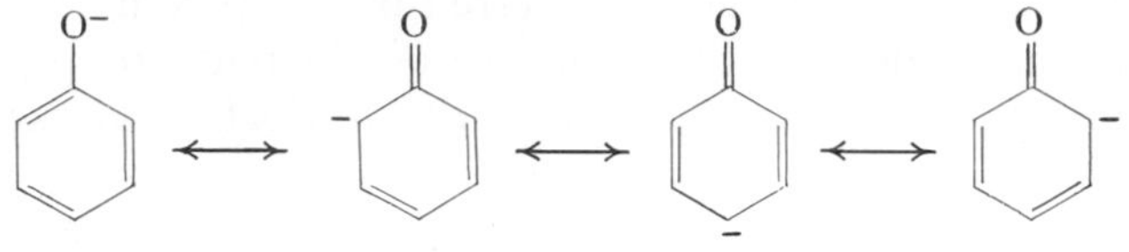

The first formulation typifies that applicable to phenol ethers and acyl derivatives and to the nonionized amines and the acylamines. Centers of high electron density are established through resonance at the *ortho* and *para* positions, which consequently are attractive sites for attack by electrophilic agents. In these instances resonance appears to control the direction of substitution and operates in opposition to and with substantial obliteration of the inductive effect in activating the *ortho* and *para* positions for the entrance of electrophilic agents. Indeed there are many instances of special substitutions applicable almost exclusively to amines and phenols, as described in later chapters, indicative of the powerful activation by amino and hydroxyl groups. Interpretation of the directive influence of the methyl group is less clear, for the C—C bond distance for the linkage connecting the substituent to the nucleus is the same as that of an aliphatic single-carbon link, and hence there is no experimental evidence of resonance (hyperconjugation, see p. 333). The *o-p* directive influence, to be sure, is feeble in comparison with that of amino and hydroxyl groups. The weak *o-p* directing influence of the methyl group undergoes a gradual transition to the *meta* type with introduction of halogens in the side chain. Thus while toluene gives only 4% of the *meta* isomer on nitration, the following chloro derivatives afford larger amounts of the *m*-nitro compounds: $C_6H_5CH_2Cl$, 12%; $C_6H_5CHCl_2$, 34%; $C_6H_5CCl_3$, 64%. A sufficient number of electron-attracting halogen atoms on the key carbon atom evidently induces enough displacement of electrons to give the key atom a positive character with respect to the ring. Another instance of transmission of an inductive effect in a side chain is the decreasing influence of an electron-attracting group when moved to positions progressively remote from the nucleus, as shown by the following figures for the percentage of *meta* substitution: $C_6H_5NO_2$ 93%; $C_6H_5CH_2NO_2$, 50%; $C_6H_5CH_2CH_2NO_2$, 13%.

Among typical *meta* directing substituents the only one for which a resonance structure is definitely indicated is the nitro group.   Nitrobenzene is regarded as a resonance hybrid involving four structures; since resonance is possible only when a transition from one form to another involves no movement of atoms, the atoms in each structure must lie in a single plane. The effect of resonance in nitrobenzene must be to set up positive centers at

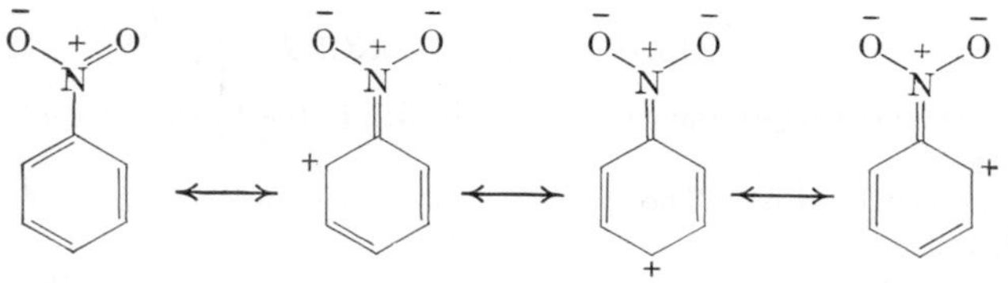

the *ortho* and *para* positions, and hence to render these sites particularly inaccessible to electrophilic agents; the *meta* carbon atoms are deactivated, along with the rest, but at least offer better points for attack than the *ortho* and *para* positions.   This interpretation of *meta* direction, however, is not applicable to the even more powerful trimethylammonium group.   The ions derived from aniline, dimethylaniline, and the quaternary ammonium salts are believed incapable of resonance comparable to that in nitrobenzene because of the requirement that one valence of pentavalent nitrogen must retain a polar character.   Thus in the ion $C_6H_5\overset{+}{N}(CH_3)_3$, the charge is held firmly by nitrogen and is not free to shift to positions in the ring; the ionic nitrogen has a completed shell of eight electrons, and is incapable of sharing another pair.   A plausible explanation is that in the trimethylanilinium ion the powerful positive pole induces a fractional negative charge on the adjacent carbon of the ring that is balanced by a fractional positive charge that can appear at positions 2, 4, and 6, which are thereby rendered inaccessible for electrophilic attack.

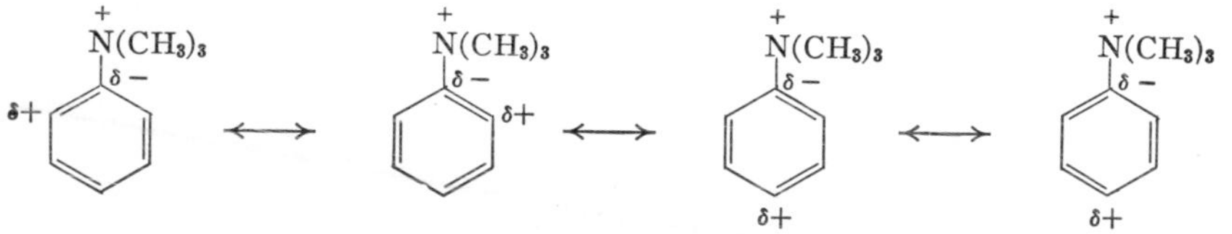

PROBLEM

Predict the chief products of the following reactions:

(a) Nitration of resorcinol dimethyl ether (1,3-dimethoxybenzene)

(b) Monobromination of p-CH$_3$CONHC$_6$H$_4$OCOCH$_3$

(c) Sulfonation of p-cymene, p-CH$_3$C$_6$H$_4$CH(CH$_3$)$_2$

(d) Sulfonation of p-methylacetophenone

(e) Nitration of phenol-p-sulfonic acid

(f) Condensation of 1,2,4-trimethylbenzene with acetyl chloride in the presence of aluminum chloride

(g) Nitration of m-dichlorobenzene

(h) Friedel-Crafts condensation of succinic anhydride with desoxybenzoin, C$_6$H$_5$COCH$_2$C$_6$H$_5$

(i) Nitration of diphenylmethane-p-carboxylic acid

(j) Friedel-Crafts methylation of p-chlorodiphenylmethane

(k) Mononitration of 4-methyl-4'-hydroxydiphenyl

(l) Nitration of $C_6H_5CH_2\overset{+}{N}(CH_3)_3NO_3^-$

(m) Chlorination of $C_6H_5CCl_3$ in the presence of $FeCl_3$

READING REFERENCES

A. F. Holleman, "Some Factors Influencing Substitution in the Benzene Ring," *Chem. Rev.*, **1**, 187–230 (1924)

P. D. Bartlett, "The Electronic Theory of Aromatic Substitutions," in H. Gilman, *Organic Chemistry*, I, 2nd Ed., 205–213, Wiley, New York (1943)

H. B. Watson, "Modern Theories of Organic Chemistry," Oxford University Press (1941)

J. F. Bunnett and R. E. Zahler, "Aromatic Nucleophilic Substitutive Reactions," *Chem. Rev.*, **49**, 273 (1951)

CHAPTER 23

NITRO COMPOUNDS

Nitration, conducted with nitric acid alone or in combination with acetic acid, acetic anhydride, or sulfuric acid, provides an efficient method for preparation of mono-, di-, and trinitro derivatives of many aromatic hydrocarbons and of hydroxy, halo, and other substitution products. The polynitro compounds accessible by the direct route have the *meta* orientation, and *ortho* and *para* dinitro compounds, though obtainable by indirect methods, are rare. Products of nitration find use as solvents, explosives, dyes, perfumes, and analytical reagents, and are important as intermediates for primary amines, into which they are convertible by reduction.

As can be seen from the properties of representative compounds listed in Table 23.1, polynitro derivatives have relatively high melting points, particularly if they are symmetrical (*para*; 1,3,5). Introduction of the

TABLE 23.1. NITRO COMPOUNDS

NAME	FORMULA	M.P., °C.	B.P., °C.
Nitrobenzene	$C_6H_5NO_2$	5.7	210
o-Dinitrobenzene	$C_6H_4(NO_2)_2(1,2)$	118	$319^{774\,mm.}$
m-Dinitrobenzene	$C_6H_4(NO_2)_2(1,3)$	89.8	$303^{770\,mm.}$
p-Dinitrobenzene	$C_6H_4(NO_2)_2(1,4)$	174	$299^{777\,mm.}$
1,3,5-Trinitrobenzene	$C_6H_3(NO_2)_3(1,3,5)$	122	
o-Nitrotoluene	$CH_3C_6H_4NO_2(1,2)$	$\begin{cases} -9.5\alpha \\ -4\beta \end{cases}$	222
m-Nitrotoluene	$CH_3C_6H_4NO_2(1,3)$	16	231
p-Nitrotoluene	$CH_3C_6H_4NO_2(1,4)$	52	238
2,4-Dinitrotoluene	$CH_3C_6H_3(NO_2)_2(1,2,4)$	70	
2,4,6-Trinitrotoluene	$CH_3C_6H_2(NO_2)_3(1,2,4,6)$	80.6	
2,4,6-Trinitro-*m*-xylene	$(CH_3)_2C_6H(NO_2)_3(1,3,2,4,6)$	182	
Picric acid	$HOC_6H_2(NO_2)_3(1,2,4,6)$	122.5	
2,4,6-Trinitroresorcinol	$(HO)_2C_6H(NO_2)_3(1,3,2,4,6)$	176	
Tetryl	$CH_3(NO_2)NC_6H_2(NO_2)_3(1,2,4,6)$	129	
o-Nitrochlorobenzene	$ClC_6H_4NO_2(1,2)$	32.5	245
m-Nitrochlorobenzene	$ClC_6H_4NO_2(1,3)$	47.9	236
p-Nitrochlorobenzene	$ClC_6H_4NO_2(1,4)$	83	239
2,4-Dinitrochlorobenzene	$ClC_6H_3(NO_2)_2(1,2,4)$	53	
Picryl chloride	$ClC_6H_2(NO_2)_3(1,2,4,6)$	83	
o-Nitrodiphenyl	$C_6H_5 \cdot C_6H_4NO_2(1,2)$	37	320
p-Nitrodiphenyl	$C_6H_5 \cdot C_6H_4NO_2(1,4)$	114	340

nitro group produces an increase in boiling point out of proportion to the increase in molecular weight, amounting to 120–130° for the nitro derivatives of benzene and toluene. Nitrobenzene has about the same molecular weight (123.11) as mesitylene (120.19), but the boiling point is higher by 46°. Nitro compounds are heavier than water, and unless they contain a solubilizing group, they are practically insoluble in water. They dissolve in cold concentrated sulfuric acid, usually without permanent change, as the result of formation of oxonium salts. Technical preparations of nitrobenzene, trinitrobenzene, and trinitrotoluene usually have a yellowish color, but purified substances are colorless.

Nitrobenzene. — Nitrobenzene can be produced on a technical scale in yields up to 98% by nitration of benzene with mixed acid at 50–55°. It is a colorless hygroscopic liquid, immiscible with water and volatile with steam, D_4^{25} 1.197. It has a characteristic sweetish odor and was once called oil of mirbane because the smell is reminiscent of that of oil of bitter almonds. Nitrobenzene has remarkable solvent power for organic compounds and is employed as a crystallizing solvent for substances that are practically insoluble in more usual solvents, though it has the disadvantage of being somewhat difficult to remove from the crystals because of its low volatility and of acting as a mild oxidizing agent at temperatures near the boiling point. It also dissolves anhydrous aluminum chloride as the result of complex formation, and is a useful solvent for the Friedel-Crafts reaction.

Nitrobenzene is toxic and is taken into the body both by inhalation of the vapor and by absorption through the skin. It produces chronic intoxication and turns the blood a chocolate brown color owing to either oxidation of hemoglobin to methemoglobin or formation of a complex, Hb—nitrobenzene. The substance is excreted in part as *p*-aminophenol. The methyl homologs do not share the poisonous quality, apparently because a mechanism is available for their elimination from the system. Thus *p*-nitrotoluene is oxidized in the body to *p*-nitrobenzoic acid, which presumably is excreted in conjugation with glycine.

Nitration of nitrobenzene under rather drastic conditions affords *m*-dinitrobenzene; reaction with fuming sulfuric acid gives *m*-nitrobenzenesulfonic acid with only traces of the *ortho* and *para* isomers; and the chief product of catalyzed chlorination is *m*-nitrochlorobenzene. When warmed with powdered potassium hydroxide, nitrobenzene undergoes a reaction that contrasts with these normal *meta* substitutions; the material is converted in part into a mixture of the oxidation products *o*- and *p*-nitrophenol, in which the former predominates, and in part into a product of reduction,

Azoxybenzene

azoxybenzene. The reaction proceeds in the absence of oxygen and is a disproportionation; it is of little practical value but of considerable theoretical significance. Unlike the characteristic *meta* substitutions, where the nucleus is attacked by an electrophilic positive ion or fragment, hydroxylation induced by hydroxide anion represents nucleophilic attack, and the fact that the hydroxyl group enters the *ortho* and *para* positions substantiates the general theory of aromatic substitutions; resonance in nitrobenzene renders these positions centers of low electron density.

Nitrotoluenes. — The mixtures of *o*- and *p*-nitrotoluene resulting in nearly theoretical yield from nitration of toluene with nitric acid or with mixed acid can be separated on a technical scale by fractional distillation in vacuum, for the isomers differ more than usual in boiling point (16° at 760 mm.). The more volatile fraction containing the *ortho* isomer can be freed from some 4–5% of *p*-nitrotoluene by prolonged heating with alcoholic alkali, when the slightly more reactive *para* compound suffers dehydrogenation to *p*,*p'*-dinitrostilbene, $NO_2C_6H_4CH{=}CHC_6H_4NO_2$. Preferential reduction of the *para* isomer with an arsenate also can be utilized for separation. *m*-Nitrotoluene is obtained in 4% yield as a by-product of nitration.

Dinitrobenzenes. — The *ortho* and *para* isomers are obtainable in two steps from the appropriate nitroaniline, which can be oxidized with Caro's

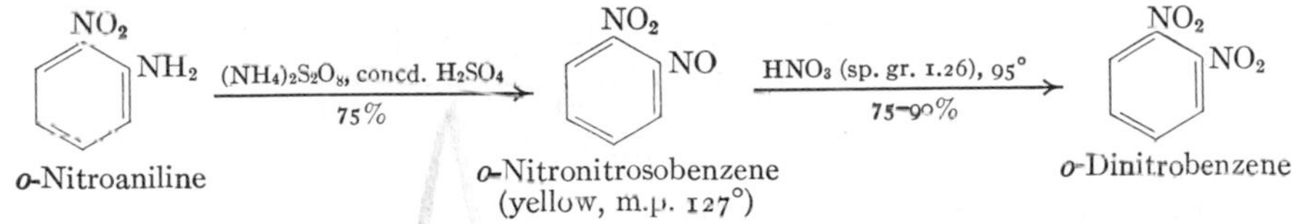

o-Nitroaniline —(NH₄)₂S₂O₈, concd. H₂SO₄, 75%)→ *o*-Nitronitrosobenzene (yellow, m.p. 127°) —(HNO₃ (sp. gr. 1.26), 95°, 75–90%)→ *o*-Dinitrobenzene

acid (H_2SO_5) to the nitroso compound, as in the example. The nitroso derivative is then oxidized with dilute nitric acid or with nitric acid containing hydrogen peroxide. An alternate route from the nitroanilines is the Sandmeyer reaction (pp. 613–615, yields: *ortho*, 35%; *para*, 75%).

The *ortho* and *para* isomers differ in chemical behavior from the product of normal nitration, *m*-dinitrobenzene, the nitro groups of which are reducible but otherwise inert. In *o*- and *p*-dinitrobenzene one nitro group has a

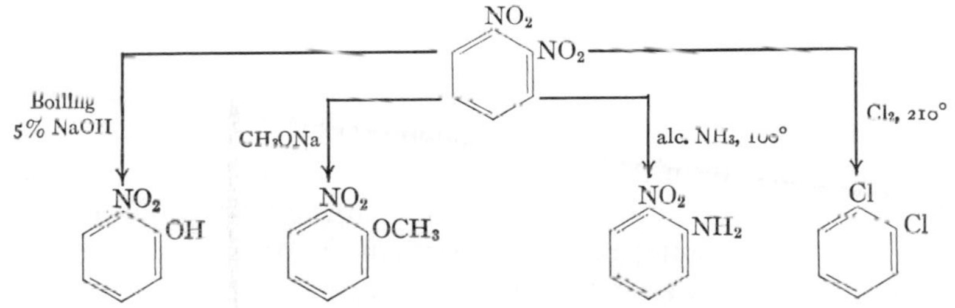

labilizing influence on the other, as indicated by the fact that at least one of the groups is easily displaced by hydroxyl, amino, or halo groups, as illustrated. This activation is another manifestation of the general phenomenon illustrated above in the *ortho-para* hydroxylation of nitro compounds by interaction with alkali. The key atom of the nitro group is positively polarized and by the resonance effect establishes positive centers at the *ortho* and *para* positions; a second positively polarized group located at such a center presents a situation of incompatibility and hence is easily displaced by a group of the opposite character.

The nucleophilic displacement induced by alkali can be pictured as an attack by an anion at a positive carbon atom in one of the resonance struc-

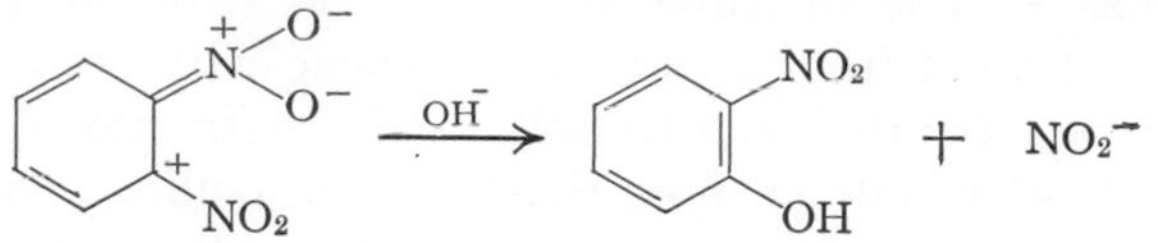

tures with expulsion of nitrite ion. *m*-Dinitrobenzene represents a state of electronic compatibility of the substituent groups and is inert to alcoholic ammonia even at 250°. On the other hand, it is susceptible to anionic attack at the relatively electron-poor centers *ortho* and *para* to the two nitro groups, and can be partially hydroxylated by the action of powdered potassium hydroxide or by oxidation with alkaline ferricyanide.

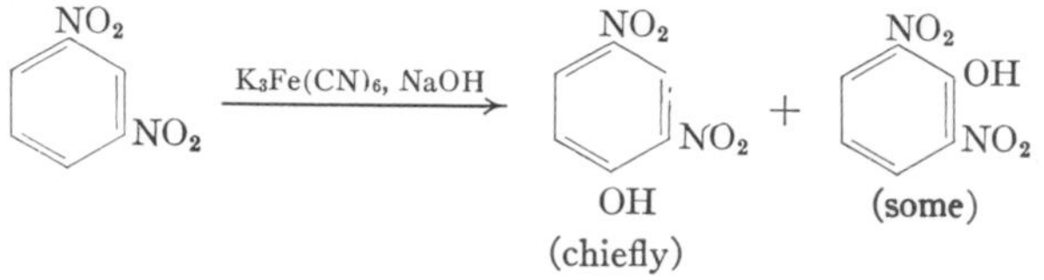

Nitrochlorobenzenes. — All three mononitrochlorobenzenes can be obtained from benzene by combination of nitration and halogenation, for

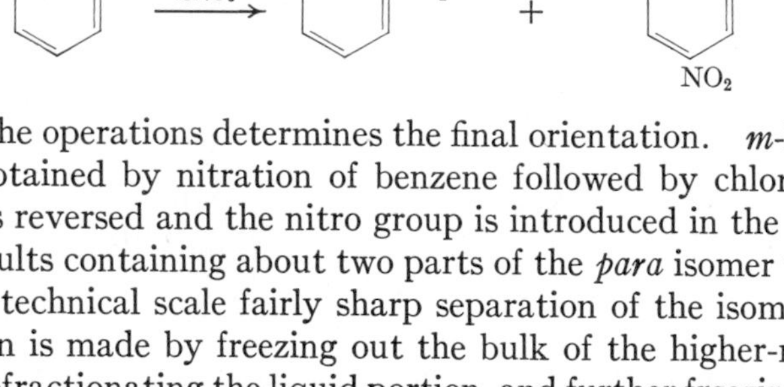

the order of the operations determines the final orientation. *m*-Nitrochlorobenzene is obtained by nitration of benzene followed by chlorination, but if the order is reversed and the nitro group is introduced in the second step, a mixture results containing about two parts of the *para* isomer to one of the *ortho*. On a technical scale fairly sharp separation of the isomers resulting from nitration is made by freezing out the bulk of the higher-melting *para* compound, refractionating the liquid portion, and further freezing. Samples free from traces of isomers are best prepared from the corresponding nitroanilines by the Sandmeyer reaction (p. 613).

2,4-Dinitrochlorobenzene is reported to be formed in 97% yield by nitration of chlorobenzene in fuming sulfuric acid. Since the halogen atom has a deactivating influence, the reaction proceeds with considerable difficulty beyond the introduction of two substituents, and 2,4,6-trinitrochlorobenzene (picryl chloride) is not obtained readily by the direct route and is usually prepared from the corresponding phenol (see below).

The halogen atom in *o*- or *p*-nitrochlorobenzene is distinctly more reactive than that in chlorobenzene, and is subject to ready nucleophilic displacement by hydroxyl, methoxyl, or amino groups; under comparably mild conditions chlorobenzene is unattacked. The reactions illustrated for *o*-ni-

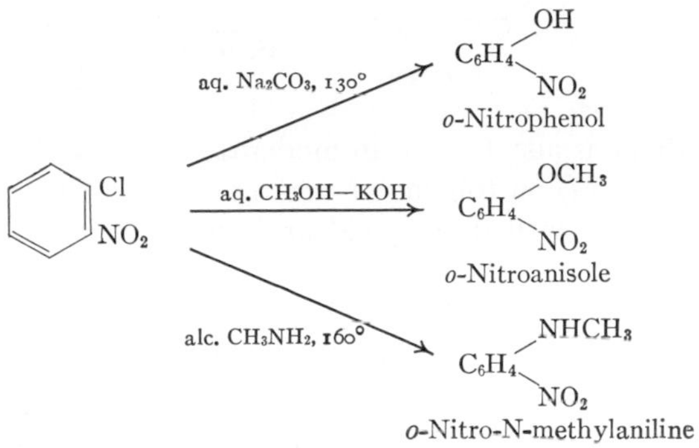

$$C_6H_4\!\!<^{OH}_{NO_2}$$

aq. Na$_2$CO$_3$, 130°

o-Nitrophenol

$$C_6H_4\!\!<^{OCH_3}_{NO_2}$$

aq. CH$_3$OH—KOH

o-Nitroanisole

$$C_6H_4\!\!<^{NHCH_3}_{NO_2}$$

alc. CH$_3$NH$_2$, 160°

o-Nitro-N-methylaniline

trochlorobenzene are paralleled in the *para* series, but no comparable reactivity of the halogen atom is discoverable in the *meta* isomer, for the chlorine atom in *m*-nitrochlorobenzene is inert to amines even in the temperature range 180–190°. The labilizing influence of the nitro group on a halogen atom in the *ortho* or *para* position, but not in the *meta* position, parallels that noted with *o*- and *p*-dinitrobenzene and is explicable in the same way. The chlorine atom of 2,4-dinitrochlorobenzene is even more labile in the same sense, as illustrated by the smooth reaction with aniline to give a diphenylamine derivative. A comparable reaction with alcoholic ammonia occurs even at room temperature.

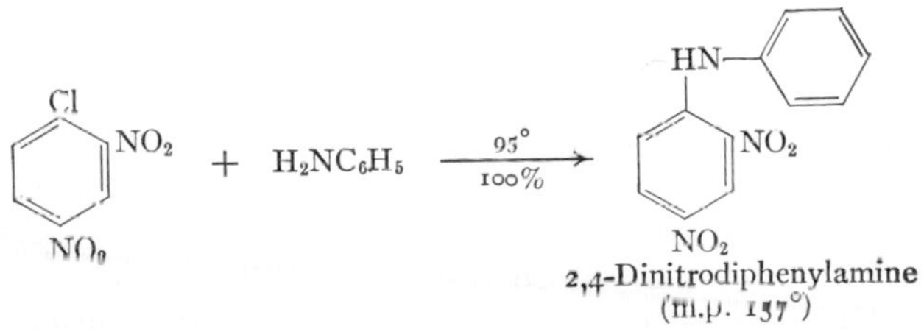

$$+ \ H_2NC_6H_5 \xrightarrow[100\%]{95°}$$

2,4-Dinitrodiphenylamine
(m.p. 157°)

Phenylnitromethane.—In this substance, a yellow liquid of the formula $C_6H_5CH_2NO_2$, the hydrogen atoms of the methylene group are activated by the flanking unsaturated nitro and phenyl groups, and though the sub-

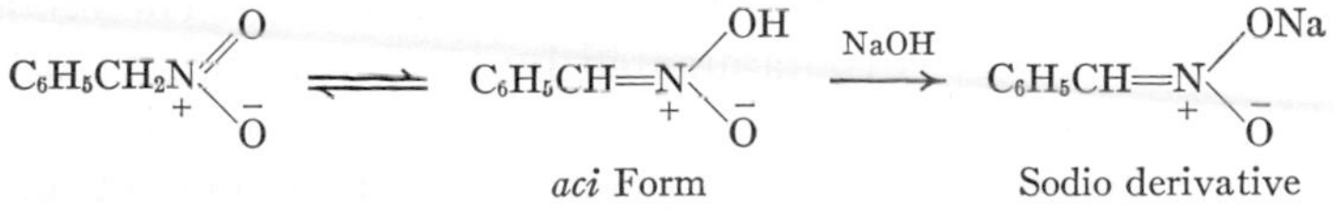

$$C_6H_5CH_2N\!\!<^O_O \rightleftharpoons C_6H_5CH\!\!=\!\!N\!\!<^{OH}_O \xrightarrow{NaOH} C_6H_5CH\!\!=\!\!N\!\!<^{ONa}_O$$

aci Form   Sodio derivative

stance is neutral, it dissolves in alkali as the result of enolization to an *aci* form. Careful acidification of the sodium salt gives a solid substance, m.p. 84°, regarded as the *aci* form, and this on standing reverts to liquid phenylnitromethane. The nitro compound can be prepared as follows:

$$C_6H_5CH \cdot \overline{H} + \overline{CH_3O}NO_2 \xrightarrow{NaOC_2H_5} C_6H_5CHNO_2 \xrightarrow{NaOH}$$

$$\underset{\text{Benzyl cyanide}}{\overset{|}{CN}} \quad \underset{\text{nitrate}}{\overset{\text{Methyl}}{}} \quad \underset{\substack{\text{(as sodio} \\ \text{derivative)}}}{\overset{|}{CN}}$$

$$C_6H_5CHNO_2 \xrightarrow[\text{50--55\% overall}]{-CO_2} C_6H_5CH_2NO_2$$

$$\underset{\text{COOH}}{\overset{|}{}} \qquad \underset{\substack{\text{Phenylnitromethane} \\ \text{(yellow liquid, b.p. 91°/3 mm.)}}}{}$$

Phenylnitromethane is also formed in moderate yield by the action of dilute nitric acid (sp. gr. 1.12) on toluene at 100° in a sealed tube; the nitro group enters the side chain with dilute acid and the nucleus with concentrated acid.

2,4,6-Trinitrotoluene (TNT). — The preparation of this important high explosive is accomplished by nitration of toluene with mixed acid, usually in three steps, with utilization of the spent acid from trinitration for the dinitration, and of the spent acid from dinitration for mononitration. The main end product, the 2,4,6-trinitro derivative (VI), is formed through the intermediates JI–V. Monosubstitution gives the *ortho* and *para* isomers

I   II   III

IV (chief product)   V (minor product)   VI

in a ratio varying somewhat with temperature, and the mixture contains a small amount (4%) of *m*-nitrotoluene. In the next step the *p*-nitro compound III yields exclusively 2,4-dinitrotoluene (IV) by substitution *ortho* to the methyl and *meta* to the nitro group; in the *o*-nitro isomer II, comparable positions are available at 4 and 6 but substitution occurs preponderantly at the point of the stronger *para* direction by the methyl group and gives the same 2,4-isomer; 2,6-dinitrotoluene (V, m.p. 65°) is produced in only minor amounts. Both dinitro compounds are converted on further nitration into the same trinitro derivative VI, or TNT. The crude 2,4,6-trinitrotoluene (α-TNT) is contaminated by small amounts of the isomers VII and VIII (β- and γ-TNT), which arise from nitration of *m*-nitrotoluene. These by-products depress the melting point of the main product (m.p. 80.6°) and impart a greasy character; they are objectionable also because they contain labile *o*- and *p*-nitro groups which render the material subject to hydrolysis with liberation of free nitric acid. The reactive character of the

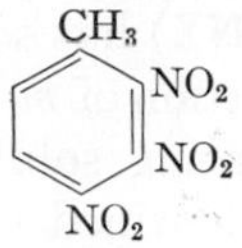

CH$_3$ [ring] NO$_2$, NO$_2$, NO$_2$

2,3,4-Trinitrotoluene
(m.p. 112°)
VII

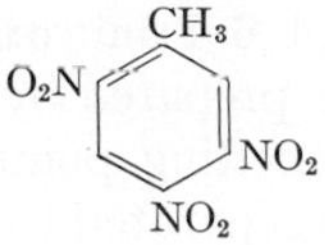

CH$_3$ [ring] O$_2$N, NO$_2$, NO$_2$

2,4,5-Trinitrotoluene
(m.p. 104°)
VIII

contaminants provides the basis of efficient methods for their elimination. When crude TNT is warmed in a 5% aqueous solution of sodium sulfite, a labile nitro group in VII and VIII is replaced by a sodium sulfonate group to give the water-soluble derivatives IX and X (reddish sulfite extract). A process for utilization of these otherwise wasted by-products consists in con-

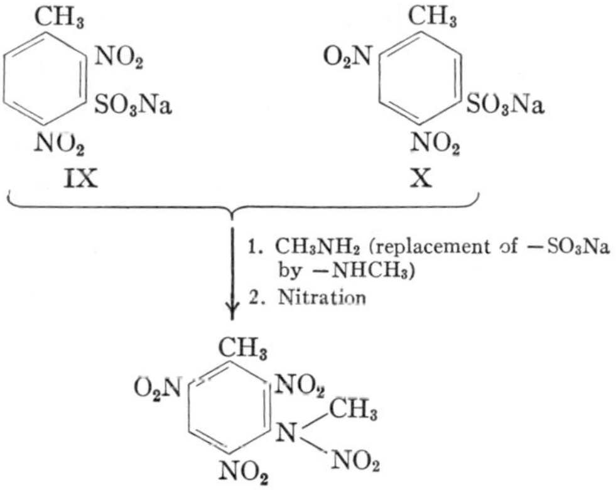

CH$_3$ [ring] NO$_2$, SO$_3$Na, NO$_2$
IX

CH$_3$ [ring] O$_2$N, SO$_3$Na, NO$_2$
X

1. CH$_3$NH$_2$ (replacement of —SO$_3$Na
   by —NHCH$_3$)
2. Nitration

CH$_3$ [ring] O$_2$N, NO$_2$, N(CH$_3$)(NO$_2$), NO$_2$

3-Methyltetryl (m.p. 102°)
XI

version into the nitramine XI, a useful explosive. The isomeric trinitro compounds also can be eliminated by alkaline hydrolysis to the dinitro-*m*-cresols, which can be converted into explosives by nitration. On a technical scale, overall yields of purified TNT up to 85% are realized.

In addition to the explosive character and ability to form complexes, discussed below, trinitrotoluene is distinguished by the fact that its methyl group possesses reactivity to aldehydic reagents comparable to that of the methyl group of acetaldehyde or of nitromethane. Thus in the presence of the basic catalyst piperidine (perhydropyridine), the nitro compound reacts

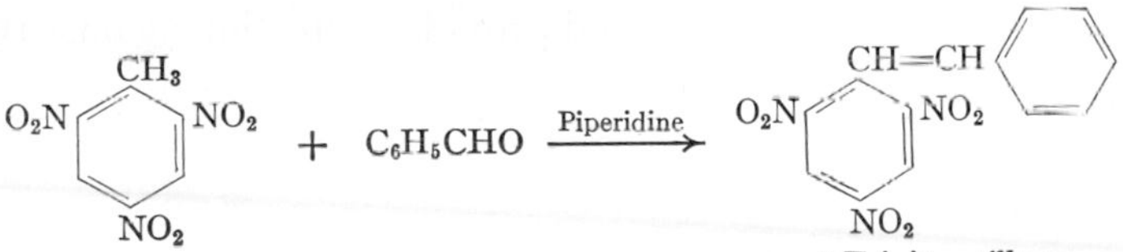

CH$_3$ [ring] O$_2$N, NO$_2$, NO$_2$ $+$ C$_6$H$_5$CHO $\xrightarrow{\text{Piperidine}}$ CH=CH[ring] [ring] O$_2$N, NO$_2$, NO$_2$

2,4,6-Trinitrostilbene
(yellow, m.p. 158°)

with benzaldehyde in a manner analogous to an aldol condensation. 2,4-Dinitrotoluene condenses similarly under the influence of piperidine or sodium ethoxide at 170°, and affords 2,4-dinitrostilbene, m.p. 140°.

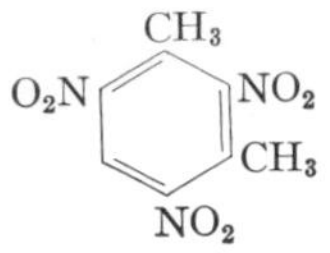

CH₃ — O₂N, NO₂, CH₃, NO₂ (structure)

2,4,6-Trinitroxylene (TNX) has some use as an explosive and is prepared by the nitration of *m*-xylene. Because of its high melting point and sparing solubility, the substance is easily separated from and identified in a mixture containing TNT.

1,3,5-Trinitrobenzene (TNB). — The marked influence of nitro groups in deactivating the benzene ring is illustrated by the difficulty of preparing trinitrobenzene by direct nitration. One procedure calls for heating 60 g. of *m*-dinitrobenzene with 1 kg. of fuming sulfuric acid and ½ kg. of fuming nitric acid (sp. gr. 1.52) at 100–110° for five days; the yield is 45%. No practical procedure has been found for preparing trinitrobenzene from benzene, though the substance has greater explosive power than trinitrotoluene. Trinitrotoluene is the commonly used high explosive because it can be prepared readily by direct nitration of the hydrocarbon, thanks to the activating influence of the methyl group in counteracting, to a sufficient extent, the influence of the nitro groups. The methyl group in TNT thus is required for the production, and not for the functioning, of the substance. The usual

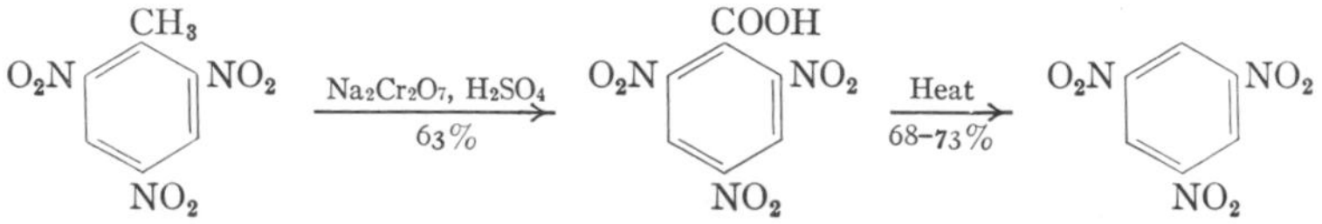

laboratory preparation of trinitrobenzene is indirect and consists in degradation of trinitrotoluene by oxidation in concentrated sulfuric acid solution with solid sodium dichromate. The product, 2,4,6-trinitrobenzoic acid, loses carbon dioxide with such readiness that decarboxylation is accomplished by heating a suspension of the substance in water to the boiling point.

The solubility of trinitrobenzene in 100 g. of water at 16° is 0.04 g., in benzene 6.2 g., and in alcohol 1.9 g. Trinitrobenzene yields picric acid on oxidation with alkaline ferricyanide and reacts with hydroxylamine to form picramide (formula below).

Picric Acid. — Picric acid, 2,4,6-trinitrophenol, cannot be prepared satisfactorily by the action of nitric acid because phenol is so sensitive to oxidation that it is mainly destroyed rather than nitrated. A satisfactory procedure consists in first sulfonating phenol to the 2,4-disulfonic acid and then adding nitric acid to the reaction mixture. The unsaturated sulfonic acid groups stabilize the molecule and provide protection against the oxidiz-

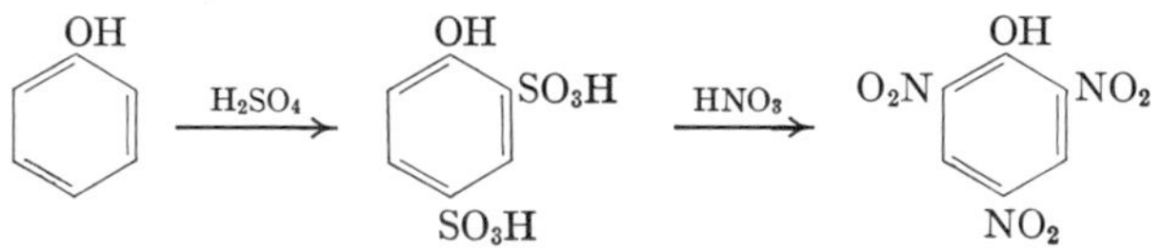

Picric acid

ing action of nitric acid, and since sulfonation is reversible, the acid groups are smoothly replaced by nitro groups. The process is simple and a yield of 70% is obtainable. A still more economical method utilizes chlorobenzene as starting material; this can be converted efficiently into the 2,4-dinitro derivative, which, by virtue of its highly labile halogen, is readily hydrolyzed to the dinitrophenol; the latter is ther nitrated.   Chlorobenzene

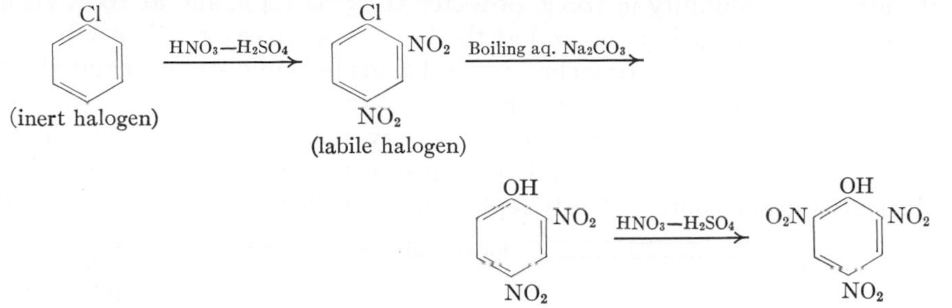

(inert halogen) NO_2
(labile halogen)

is a cheaper starting material than phenol, and in a modern process phenol is made from chlorobenzene in a reaction requiring a high temperature and pressure because of the inert character of the halogen (p. 625).   In the picric acid process, replacement of halogen by hydroxyl is accomplished at a stage where it proceeds under mild conditions.

Picric acid is formed by the action of nitric acid on a number of organic substances containing a benzene ring, often as a result of extensive oxidative degradation, displacement of attached groups by nitro substituents, and hydrolysis of a nitrogen substituent with formation of a hydroxyl group. Thus the substance arises from the action of nitric acid on salicylic acid or on indigo, and was first obtained from the latter source (1771).   Picric acid is characterized by a bitter taste and strongly acidic nature as well as by the

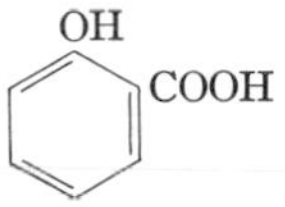

Salicylic acid $CH_2CH(NH_2)COOH$
Tyrosine

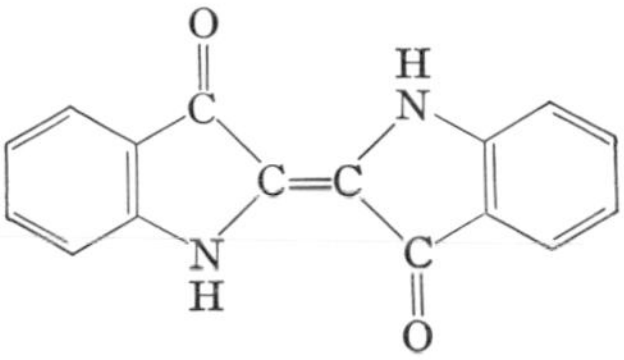

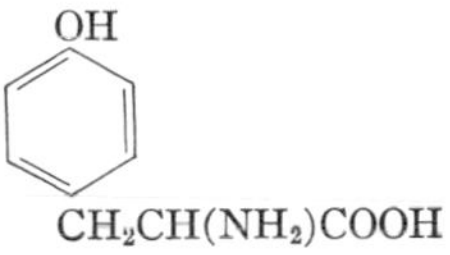

Indigo

yellow color.   It was observed to be formed by the action of nitric acid on silk (1799), the specific source probably being the tyrosine units in the protein.   Dumas (1836) established the composition by analysis and introduced the present name (Gr. *pikros*, bitter), and Laurent (1841) recognized the substance as a trinitro derivative of phenol and prepared it from the parent compound.   Picric acid was found to stain proteins yellow and was introduced as a dye for silk in 1849, the first instance of use of an artificial dye. Application as an explosive was announced in an English patent (Sprengel, 1871).   The versatile nitro compound also has bactericidal activity and formerly found use in treatment of burns, and it is employed in the laboratory for characterization of organic bases (amine picrates) and of polynuclear hydrocarbons.

Picric acid crystallizes from water in bright yellow plates, but separates from solutions in ligroin or in strong hydrochloric acid as nearly colorless crystals, which become yellow on the surface in contact with moisture of the air. The solubility in 100 g. of water at 25° is 1.4 g. and at 100°, 7.2 g.; in benzene, at 20° it is 5.3 g. and at the boiling point 123 g. The substance has a pK_a of 0.80 and approaches mineral acids in acidic strength and ability to corrode metals. Since phenol is but weakly acidic (pK_a 10.01), the nitro groups evidently are responsible for a very marked enhancement in the tendency to ionize. Characteristic transformations of the compound are illustrated in the chart. Ready replacement of the phenolic hydroxyl group

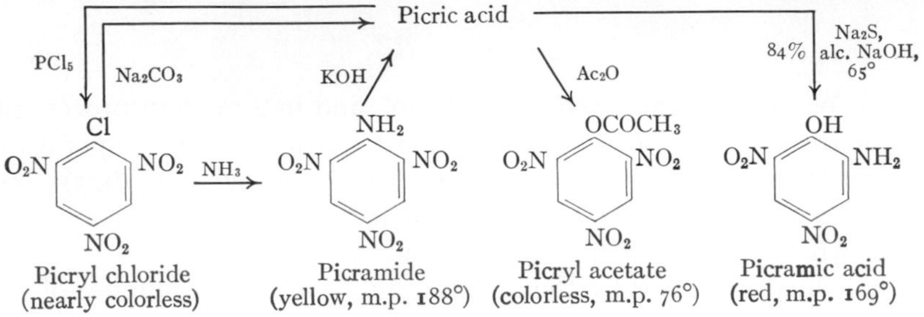

Picryl chloride   Picramide   Picryl acetate   Picramic acid
(nearly colorless) (yellow, m.p. 188°) (colorless, m.p. 76°) (red, m.p. 169°)

by halogen is a reaction specific to polynitro compounds and is not realizable with ordinary phenols. An improved method of converting picric acid into picryl chloride is the action of p-toluenesulfonyl chloride ($CH_3C_6H_4SO_2Cl$) in the presence of dimethylaniline in nitrobenzene solution (70% yield); the method is applicable also to 2,4-dinitrophenol (Ullmann,[1] 1908).

2,4,6-Trinitroresorcinol (Styphnic Acid). — In analogy with picric acid, this substance is best prepared by sulfonation followed by nitration. It is

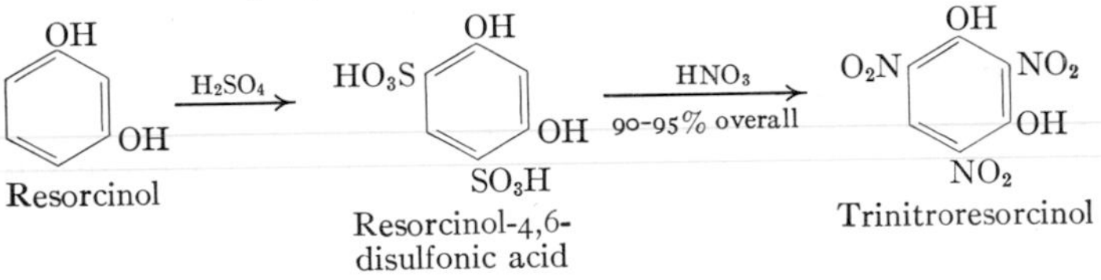

Resorcinol   Resorcinol-4,6-   Trinitroresorcinol
                    disulfonic acid

also obtained from m-nitrophenol, which on nitration yields a tetranitro compound having one labile o-p substituent that is hydrolyzed by boiling water (nucleophilic attack). Because of an astringent action, trinitroresor-

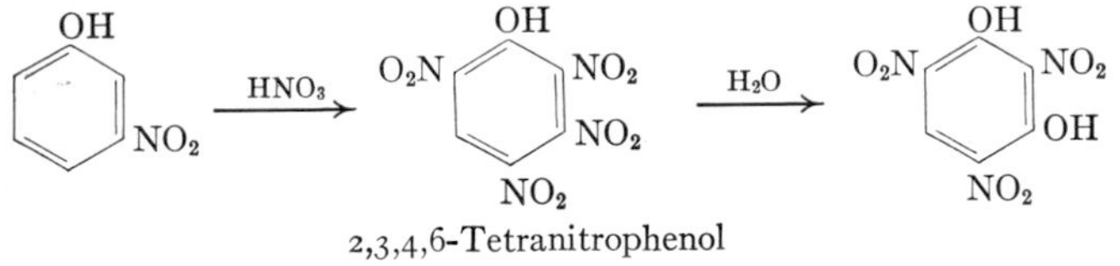

2,3,4,6-Tetranitrophenol

cinol is known as styphnic acid (Gr. *styphein*, to contract). Like picric acid, it is yellow, strongly acidic, and forms hydrocarbon complexes.

---

[1] Fritz Ullmann, 1875–1939; b. Fürth, Germany; Ph.D. Lausanne; Berlin, Geneva; *Helv. Chim. Acta*, **23**, 93 (1940)

Tetryl. — The common name of this useful explosive is an abbreviation of N,2,4,6-tetranitro-N-methylaniline, and the compound can be described also as methyl-2,4,6-trinitrophenylnitramine.   One nitro group is affixed to nitrogen by displacement of hydrogen in the methylamino group: —NHCH$_3$ + HONO$_2$→ —N(NO$_2$)CH$_3$ + H$_2$O; this reaction can be reversed by the action of concentrated sulfuric acid, for a nitro group attached to nitrogen is less firmly held than one in the nucleus (tetryl → methylpicramide, m.p. 112°).   Tetryl can be obtained from N-methylaniline, but it is prepared more economically from the less expensive N,N-dimethylaniline, which suffers loss of one methyl group by oxidation:

$$—N(CH_3)_2 \longrightarrow —N(CH_3)COOH \longrightarrow —NHCH_3 + CO_2$$

The steps indicated in the accompanying formulation have been established by isolation of the intermediates.   The initial reaction is an *ortho-para* substitution of the amine in sulfuric acid solution, that is, under conditions such that ionization might occur with resulting *meta* direction.   *Meta* substitution does indeed occur if a large excess of sulfuric acid is employed, but with limited reagent substitution can be controlled to the direction desired

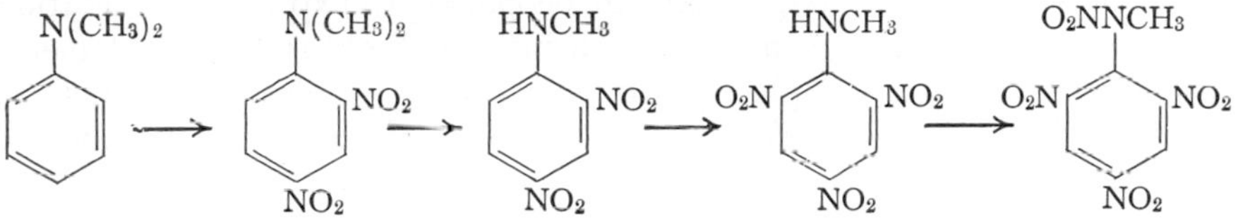

Tetryl

An alternate preparation that avoids the loss of nitric acid expended in oxidation of the methyl group consists in condensation of 2,4-dinitrochlorobenzene with methylamine and nitration of the product.

Explosives. — In the series of compounds with adequate explosive power, the most important factor in determining the specific applications of the substances is the sensitivity to the shock of impact.   Although the impact sensitivity, as measured by the height from which a weight must fall for its impact to cause a small sample of the substance to explode, is dependent somewhat on the physical state of the sample and varies with the size, shape, and extent of confinement of the metal cup used as container for the charge, the common explosives falling outside the group of propellants can be arranged in the following order of sensitivity:

Increasing impact sensitivity	Trinitrobenzene Ammonium picrate TNT	} High explosives
	Compressed picric acid Tetryl	} Boosters
	Lead azide Mercury fulminate	} Detonators

A 5-kg. weight must fall 150 cm. to explode trinitrobenzene but only 110 cm.

to explode TNT, whereas mercury fulminate detonates when struck by a 2-kg. weight falling only 5 cm. The relatively impact-resistant nitro compounds are classified as high explosives; they are not exploded easily by heat or by shock, and in practice are detonated by the shock of a primary explosive. Mercury fulminate is highly sensitive to either impact or heat and is the primary explosive used in small percussion caps and electric squibs to initiate explosion of less sensitive material. Lead azide is a preferred detonator for military uses because it is slightly less sensitive than fulminate and is less subject to accidental or premature detonation and because much less material is required to detonate a given charge ($\frac{1}{10}$ to $\frac{1}{8}$ the weight of fulminate). Tetryl occupies an intermediate place in the scale, and is not sensitive enough to serve as a detonator but is too easily exploded to be employed as the main charge in a shell or bomb; the intermediate character renders the substance ideally suited to the function of a booster, as illustrated in an example cited below.

TNT is the most widely used filling for shells and air-borne demolition bombs. It is sufficiently insensitive to withstand the shock entailed in the ejection of a shell from a gun barrel under the pressure developed from ignition of a propellant charge, and can be caused to explode on operation of an impact- or time-fuse mechanism firing a detonator-booster element. It is the only one of the explosive nitro compounds of aromatic or heterocyclic type (cyclonite, p. 214) that melts below 100°, and it is conveniently melted with steam and poured into shells and bombs. Cast TNT is less sensitive than crystalline or pelleted material and is not exploded by a fulminate blasting cap or a lead azide detonator, but satisfactory operation is obtained with either type of detonator in combination with a charge of tetryl representing only a fraction of the charge of TNT; the booster is exploded by the detonator and produces a wave sufficient to set off the TNT. The more sensitive crystalline form of the explosive has been employed in the form of Cordeau detonating fuse, made by casting molten TNT into a 1-inch lead pipe and drawing this down repeatedly, with crushing of the filling, until the tube is about $\frac{3}{8}$ inch in diameter and the explosive is in the form of a fine crystalline powder. Cordeau tubing, which is sensitive enough to be detonated by a fulminate blasting cap, is used to set off multiple charges, but has been largely displaced by PETN-Primacord (p. 132).

Picric acid as such was used extensively for a time as a military explosive, but has been abandoned because of the serious disadvantage that the strongly acidic substance corrodes metal surfaces of shells with formation of highly sensitive heavy-metal picrates. The iron (ferric), nickel, and chromium salts of picric acid are more sensitive to impact than tetryl and fall in the range of the detonators; lead picrate is particularly dangerous owing to its sensitivity to heat or shock. Cast picric acid requires a booster of the tetryl type, and it is interesting that the more sensitive compressed picric acid serves this function. Ammonium picrate is less sensitive to shock than the phenol and is free from the disadvantage of tending to form dangerous metal salts. It is at least equal to TNT in power and brisance and is less sensitive than this substance, but can be used satisfactorily with a tetryl booster. Ammonium picrate might be preferred to TNT as a general shell filling if it were not a high-melting solid (m.p. about 270°, dec.) that cannot be loaded by casting. It finds specific use as a charge for armor-piercing shells because it withstands the severe shock of impact better than TNT and is conserved for explosion under detonation after the shell has penetrated. The ammonium salt can be crystallized from water in a bright red metastable form or in a stable yellow one; the two forms do not differ in explosive properties.

Tetryl is employed as a booster for TNT, trinitrobenzene, cyclonite, ammonium picrate, and is the usual component, in combination with lead azide, of reinforced detonators. It is used also to increase the sensitivity of TNT; a mixture of 65% TNT and 35% tetryl melts below the boiling point of water and is fired by an ordinary fulminate blasting cap. For use as a booster, tetryl is compressed into pellets, either alone or mixed with 1–2% of graphite.

Artificial Nitro Musks. — The polynitro derivatives of certain benzenoid hydrocarbons containing the tertiary butyl group have an odor roughly approximating that of natural musk (Baur, 1891), and they are employed in perfuming cheap soaps. One of these derivatives is prepared from toluene; a t-butyl group is introduced in the *meta* position by Friedel-Crafts alkylation conducted at high temperature, and the product is then nitrated.

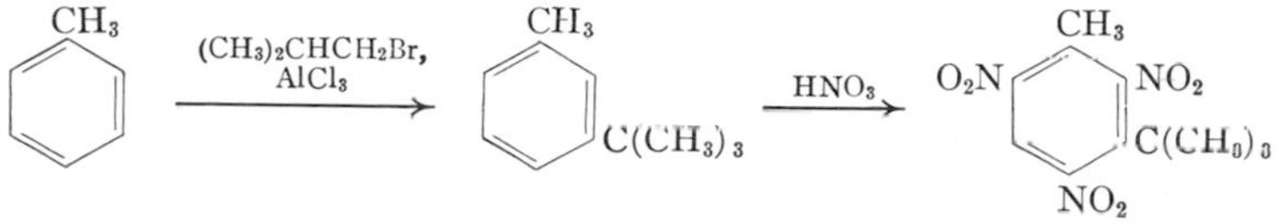

"Baur musk"
(m.p. 97°)

The musklike odor is retained on introduction of an additional methyl group or of an acetyl group.

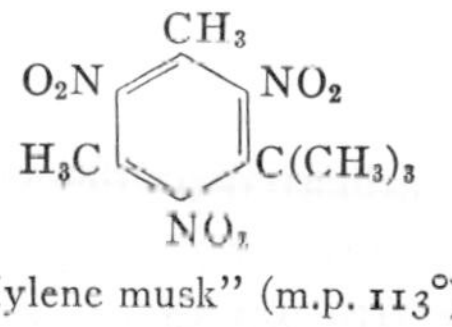

"Xylene musk" (m.p. 113°) 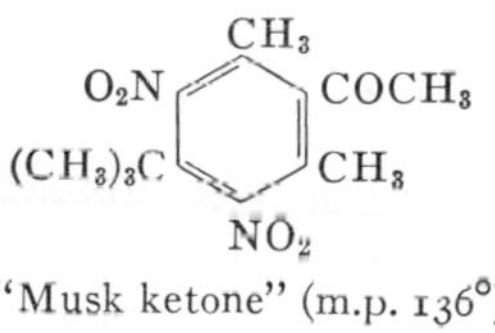   "Musk ketone" (m.p. 136°)

REDUCTION OF NITRO COMPOUNDS

By reduction with a sufficiently powerful reagent (e.g., stannous chloride) nitrobenzene can be converted in high yield into aniline. By use of milder reagents and by control of the acidity or alkalinity of the reaction mixture, it is possible to produce a number of substances of various intermediate stages of reduction, some of which are products of direct reduction, whereas others arise through secondary changes. Particularly comprehensive studies have been made of electrolytic reduction (Haber, 1900), where exact control is possible through adjustment of the imposed potential, current density, and hydrogen-ion concentration, and the results indicate that the sequence of primary reduction steps is as follows:

$$C_6H_5NO_2 \xrightarrow{2H} C_6H_5NO \xrightarrow{2H} C_6H_5NHOH \xrightarrow{2H} C_6H_5NH_2$$

Nitrobenzene   Nitrosobenzene   Phenylhydroxyl-   Aniline
                                amine

Nitrosobenzene is reduced to phenylhydroxylamine too readily to be isolable as such, but its formation as the initial product of reduction has been demonstrated by special tests. Both nitrosobenzene and phenylhydroxylamine are reactive, and under the catalytic influence of alkali they condense with elimination of a molecule of water in a manner reminiscent of aldol condensation, and afford azoxybenzene. Azoxybenzene is made up of two

$$C_6H_5N{=}O \quad + \quad HN{-}C_6H_5 \xrightarrow{OH^-(-H_2O)} C_6H_5{-}N{=}\overset{+}{N}{-}C_6H_5$$

Nitrosobenzene   OH   O^-

                        Phenylhydroxylamine   Azoxybenzene

units derived from nitrobenzene molecules linked through the nitrogen atoms, one of which carries an oxygen atom joined by a semipolar bond. This oxygen is readily removed during electrolytic reduction or by treatment with iron powder and water, with formation of azobenzene, which, in turn, can add two hydrogen atoms and form hydrazobenzene. A terminal

$$C_6H_5{-}N{=}\overset{+}{N}{-}C_6H_5 \xrightarrow{2H} C_6H_5N{=}NC_6H_5 \xrightarrow{2H} C_6H_5N{-}NC_6H_5$$

           O^-   Azobenzene   H H

    Azoxybenzene   Hydrazobenzene

reaction stage is reached with reductive fission of the N–N bond in hydrazobenzene, with formation of two molecules of aniline. Both the intermediate

$$C_6H_5N{+}NC_6H_5 \xrightarrow{2H} C_6H_5NH_2 \quad + \quad H_2NC_6H_5$$

          H H   Aniline

    Hydrazobenzene

reduction products and the substances indicated as derived from them by secondary transformations are thus convertible into aniline. Procedures have been devised for the efficient preparation of all these intermediate compounds by chemical methods, as recorded in the following summary.

Phenylhydroxylamine.

$$C_6H_5NO_2 \xrightarrow[\text{62–68\%}]{\text{Zn, aq. NH}_4\text{Cl, 65°}} C_6H_5NHOH$$

                                              (m.p. 81°)

Nitrosobenzene. — This sensitive primary reduction product of nitrobenzene is best prepared by oxidation of its successor in the reduction process (Bamberger,[2] 1894). Nitrosobenzene forms colorless crystals melting at 67.5–68° to a green liquid, which solidifies again to the colorless form;

$$C_6H_5NHOH \xrightarrow[77\%]{K_2Cr_2O_7,\ H_2SO_4,\ 0°} C_6H_5NO$$

the substance also gives green solutions. The colorless solid is bimolecular and dissociates to a green monomer in solution or on melting.

Azoxybenzene. — When nitrobenzene is reduced with a mild reagent in an alkaline medium, opportunity arises for condensation between the first two products of reduction, nitrosobenzene and phenylhydroxylamine.

$$2\ C_6H_5NO_2 \xrightarrow[71-74\%]{Glucose,\ NaOH,\ 100°} C_6H_5-N\overset{+}{=}N-C_6H_5$$
$$\overset{|}{O^-}$$

(yellow, m.p. 36°)

Azobenzene. — This compound containing two doubly bound nitrogen atoms can be prepared by reduction of nitrobenzene in boiling methanolic sodium hydroxide solution with the calculated amount of zinc dust.

$$C_6H_5NO_2 \xrightarrow[84-86\%]{Zn,\ NaOH,\ CH_3OH} C_6H_5N=NC_6H_5$$

(orange-red, m.p. 68°)

Hydrazobenzene is obtained by reduction of nitrobenzene with zinc dust and alcoholic alkali in the manner just described, but with sufficient zinc to carry the reaction to the desired stage, as indicated by the discharge of the red color; yield 88%. The pure substance forms colorless crystals, m.p. 126°. It is sensitive to air oxidation, and is cleaved to aniline by powerful reducing agents (stannous chloride).

Rearrangement Products. — Two other useful products result from nitrobenzene through processes of rearrangement to the *para* position, namely *p*-aminophenol from phenylhydroxylamine and benzidine, or *p,p'*-diaminodiphenyl, from hydrazobenzene:

$$C_6H_5NHOH \xrightarrow{H^+} HOC_6H_4NH_2(p)$$

$$C_6H_5NHNHC_6H_5 \xrightarrow{H^+} (p)H_2NC_6H_4 \cdot C_6H_4NH_2(p')$$

HYDROCARBON–POLYNITRO COMPOUND COMPLEXES

When concentrated solutions of picric acid and napththalene in benzene or alcohol are mixed at room temperature, crystallization soon occurs with separation of a golden yellow substance having a higher melting point (150°) than either component and having a more pronounced yellow color than picric acid. The substance is a molecular complex containing equivalent amounts of the hydrocarbon and the polynitro compound, and in solution it dissociates to the components till equilibrium is established. Benzene forms only a very labile complex that reverts to picric acid on brief

[2] Eugen Bamberger, 1857–1932; b. Berlin; Ph.D. Berlin (Liebermann); Zurich ETH; *Helv. Chim. Acta*, **16**, 644 (1933)

exposure to air, but naphthalene, anthracene, phenanthrene, and other higher hydrocarbons form stable complexes. The behavior finds some parallel in chemical reactivities, for the condensed-ring hydrocarbons are all more reactive than benzene; however, a high degree of alkyl substitution also results in increased stability of the picric acid derivatives, as shown by the formation of complexes with penta- and hexamethylbenzene (m.p. 131° and 170°) The complexes are commonly called picrates, but should not be confused with salts of the acid with amines or inorganic bases. The condensed-ring polynuclear hydrocarbons form similar molecular complexes with trinitrobenzene, trinitrotoluene, trinitroresorcinol, 2,4,7-trinotrofluorenone (M. Orchin, 1946–47), picryl chloride, and picramide; some examples are listed in Table 23.2. The picric acid, trinitrobenzene, and trinitrofluorenone

TABLE 23.2. MELTING POINTS OF COMPLEXES, °C.

HYDROCARBON	NITRO COMPONENT		
	Picric acid	Trinitrobenzene	Trinitrofluorenone
Naphthalene	150 (yellow)	153 (yellow)	154 (yellow)
Acenaphthene	162 (orange)		176 (red)
Anthracene	142 (red)	164 (red)	194 (red)
Phenanthrene	145 (yellow)		197 (yellow)
Methylcholanthrene (light yellow, m.p. 180°)	182.5 (purplish black)	204.5 (dark red)	254 (green)
3,4-Benzpyrene (light yellow, m.p. 179°)	198 (purple-brown)	227 (bright red)	

derivatives have considerable value in identification and purification of hydrocarbons and in isolation of hydrocarbons from reaction mixtures, by virtue of the superior crystallizing tendency, sparing solubility, and relatively high melting points. The derivatives often have identifying colors, and the phenomenon of color intensification is particularly marked with the two hydrocarbons listed at the end of the table, which are carcinogenic agents of exceptional chemical reactivity. The complexes are easily purified by crystallization, sometimes in the presence of a slight excess of the nitro component to suppress dissociation and decrease solubility. A hydrocarbon can be regenerated from its purified picrate by extraction of the acidic component from a benzene or ether solution with aqueous ammonia. Complexes can be split by passing a benzene solution through a tower packed with activated (heat-treated) alumina; the nitro component is adsorbed more strongly than the hydrocarbon and the latter appears first in the filtrate (chromatographic adsorption). A hydrocarbon–trinitrobenzene derivative also can be reduced with stannous chloride and hydrochloric acid to convert the nitro compound into an acid-soluble amine incapable of complex formation.

PROBLEMS

1. Suggest a method of preparing 2,4-diamino-N-methylaniline, starting with chloro-benzene.
2. Summarize examples cited of nucleophilic substitutions of nitro compounds and account for the phenomena.
3. Summarize examples cited of nucleophilic displacements.
4. Predict the products of the reactions:

   (a) Mononitration of $\alpha(1)$-tetralone.
   (b) Dinitration of diphenyl ether.
   (c) Reaction of 3,4-dichloronitrobenzene with $NaOCH_3$.
   (d) Phenylnitromethane and benzaldehyde, trace of piperidine.

5. Lead tetraacetate when heated in acetic acid decomposes to carbon dioxide and methyl radicals. When TNT is present it is converted into $C_8H_7(NO_2)_3$. Predict the structure.

READING REFERENCE

W. C. Lothrop and G. R. Handrick, "The Relationship between Performance and Constitution of Pure Organic Explosive Compounds," *Chem. Rev.*, **44**, 419 (1949)

CHAPTER 24

SULFONIC ACIDS

Arylsulfonic acids are derivatives of sulfuric acid in which one hydroxyl is replaced by an aryl group, $ArSO_2OH$, and they resemble the parent compound in chemical and physical properties.   They are comparable in acidic strength to sulfuric acid, very hygroscopic, liberally soluble in water, and share to some extent the destructive action on organic materials.   They are thus not easily manipulated and stored, but the metallic salts serve adequately for most purposes.   The free sulfonic acids are used chiefly as catalytic agents, for they sometimes promote reactions of esterification, dehydration, polymerization, or depolymerization as readily as sulfuric acid does without as much damage to the reactants.   Isolation usually is accomplished by diluting the sulfonation mixture with a moderate amount of water and adding concentrated hydrochloric acid; the solubility is decreased by the common-ion effect and the sulfonic acid crystallizes on cooling, usually as a hydrate.   Benzenesulfonic acid when dried over concentrated sulfuric acid melts at $43-44°$ and varies in composition, $C_6H_5SO_3H \cdot 1\frac{1}{2}-2H_2O$; anhydrous material, obtained by drying at $100°$, melts at $50-51°$. p-Toluenesulfonic acid monohydrate melts at $104°$.   Benzene-m-disulfonic acid, formed along with the *para* isomer in the ratio of $3:1$ by sulfonation of benzene with fuming sulfuric acid at $245°$, has the composition of a hemihydrate after being dried at $135°$.   A minor by-product in sulfonations is the diaryl sulfone, $ArSO_2Ar$, but this is insoluble in water and is easily eliminated.

Usually the free sulfonic acids are not isolated but are converted directly into the sodium or potassium salts.   One procedure is to pour the sulfonation mixture into water and add excess sodium chloride.   Since the arylsulfonic acid has the same acidic strength as hydrochloric acid, an equilibrium is set up, and the solubility of the sodium sulfonate is so decreased by

$$C_6H_5SO_3H \ + \ NaCl \ \rightleftharpoons \ C_6H_5SO_3Na \ + \ HCl$$

excess sodium ion that the substance readily crystallizes.   This process of salting out with common salt can be employed also in recrystallization of the product, but sodium benzenesulfonate, as well as salts of other acids of comparable molecular weight, is so very soluble in water that a large amount of sodium chloride is required and the product is liable to be contaminated with inorganic material.   A pure product is sometimes obtainable by crystallization from absolute ethanol; sodium benzenesulfonate dissolves in this solvent, though sparingly, whereas sodium chloride is insoluble.   Sulfonates of higher molecular weight derived from polynuclear aromatic compounds are insoluble in methanol or ethanol, but can be prepared in salt-free condition by an alternate process that depends on the solubility of sodium acetate in methanol. The sulfonate is repeatedly salted out from aqueous solution with sodium acetate in order to replace sodium chloride as a contaminant by sodium acetate, which is then removed by repeated extraction of the dried and powdered product with boiling methanol. Another method of obtaining a sodium salt from a sulfonation reaction mixture containing excess sulfuric acid is to neutralize the diluted mixture with calcium hydroxide or with barium or lead carbonate. The calcium, barium, or lead sulfonate can be extracted with hot water and thus separted from a residue of inorganic sulfate, and the aqueous extract is then treated with sodium carbonate to precipitate an insoluble carbonate and give a solution that on evaporation affords the sodium salt of the sulfonic acid. A lead sulfonate also can be decomposed with hydrogen sulfide to give a solution of the free acid.

Usually sodium and ammonium sulfonates are more soluble in water than other salts; potassium salts are slightly less soluble and often crystallize better, and barium and calcium salts are distinctly less soluble. The metal salts are infusible and completely insoluble in ether. Amine salts, such as those formed with p-toluidine, are composed of two organic parts, and they are less soluble in water than the alkali-metal salts and often crystallizable from alcohol or alcohol–water mixtures; also they have characteristic

$$ArSO_3H \;+\; CH_3C_6H_4NH_2 \longrightarrow Ar\overset{-}{S}O_3\overset{+}{N}H_3C_6H_4CH_3$$
p-Toluidine salt

melting points. The p-toluidine salts thus are useful derivatives for characterization, and they are easily prepared by addition of the amine and hydrochloric acid to a solution of a sodium salt.

$$ArSO_3Na \;+\; NH_2C_6H_4CH_3 \;+\; HCl \longrightarrow Ar\overset{-}{S}O_3\overset{+}{N}H_3C_6H_4CH_3 \;+\; NaCl$$

The sulfonate group often is introduced to provide water solubility, particularly in the case of dyes. Use for separation of hydrocarbon mixtures is illustrated for the xylenes (p. 548). Chemical transformations of aromatic sulfonates are not numerous but are useful.

Acid Chlorides. — Arylsulfonic acids, either free or as salts, are convertible into acid chlorides of the formula $ArSO_2Cl$ by the methods applicable to preparation of chlorides of carboxylic acids, namely by interaction with phosphorus halides. Alternate procedures for the preparation of benzenesulfonyl chloride are indicated (1, 2). The reaction mixture is cooled and

$$1. \; 3C_6H_5SO_2ONa \;+\; PCl_5 \;\xrightarrow[\text{75–80\%}]{170-180°}\; 3C_6H_5SO_2Cl \;+\; 2NaCl \;+\; NaPO_3$$

$$2. \; 2C_6H_5SO_2ONa \;+\; POCl_3 \;\xrightarrow[\text{74–87\%}]{170-180°}\; 2C_6H_5SO_2Cl \;+\; NaCl \;+\; NaPO_3$$

treated with water and ice, and the acid chloride separating as an oil is collected, dried, and distilled. Another method is the action of at least two equivalents of chlorosulfonic acid on benzene (3). If chlorosulfonic acid

$$3. \ C_6H_6 \ + \ \underset{\text{(3 equiv.)}}{2\,ClSO_2OH} \ \xrightarrow[75-77\%]{20-25°} \ C_6H_5SO_2Cl \ + \ H_2SO_4 \ + \ HCl$$

is not used in considerable excess, a significant amount of diphenyl sulfone is formed as a by-product, and when an aromatic hydrocarbon is treated in carbon tetrachloride solution with just one equivalent of chlorosulfonic acid, the reaction product is the free sulfonic acid. Production of the acid chlo-

$$C_6H_6 \ + \ ClSO_2OH \ \rightarrow \ C_6H_5SO_2OH \ + \ HCl$$

ride with the use of excess reagent probably proceeds through formation of the free acid and replacement of hydroxyl by the chlorine of chlorosulfonic acid.

Benzenesulfonyl chloride is an easily solidified liquid, m.p. 14.4°, b.p. 251.5°. It can be digested with cold water with little hydrolysis, but reacts readily with alcohols and with ammonia, as described below, and it is useful as a reagent in the Hinsberg test for characterization of amines of different types (p. 236). A reagent often preferred because it is a solid is p-toluene-sulfonyl chloride (tosyl chloride), m.p. 69°.

Esters. — Ester derivatives of sulfonic acids are sometimes prepared for purposes of identification, but they are lower melting and much less easily prepared than the p-toluidine salts. The preparation is accomplished

$$1. \ ArSO_3Na \ + \ (CH_3)_2SO_4 \ \xrightarrow{150-160°} \ ArSO_3CH_3 \ + \ CH_3NaSO_4$$

$$2. \ ArSO_2Cl \ + \ HOCH_3 \ \longrightarrow \ ArSO_2OCH_3 \ + \ HCl$$

either (1) by heating the solid sodium salt of the acid with dimethyl or diethyl sulfate or (2) by the action of an alcohol or of a sodium alkoxide (in ether) on the acid chloride. The methyl ester of benzenesulfonic acid is a liquid that is slowly hydrolyzed by water at room temperatue. Methyl p-toluenesulfonate, $CH_3C_6H_4SO_3CH_3$, melts at 28°.

Sulfonamides. — The acid chlorides react readily with ammonia or with amines to form sulfonamides. Thus benzenesulfonyl chloride affords ben-zenesulfonamide when shaken with aqueous ammonia or on interaction with ammonium carbonate. This easily prepared neutral derivative crystallizes

$$C_6H_5SO_2Cl \ + \ NH_3 \ \longrightarrow \ C_6H_5SO_2NH_2 \ + \ HCl$$
Benzenesulfonamide
(m.p. 156°)

well from alcohol, and in general sulfonamides are satisfactory derivatives for characterization of aromatic sulfonic acids.

Chloroamides. — The action of sodium hypochlorite on a sulfonamide results in substitution of halogen for an amide hydrogen atom. p-Toluene-sulfonamide is converted initially into the N-monochloro derivative, known as chloramine-T. This substance slowly liberates hypochlorous acid on

$$p\text{-}CH_3C_6H_4SO_2NH_2 \ + \ NaOCl \ \longrightarrow \ p\text{-}CH_3C_6H_4SO_2NHCl \ + \ NaOH$$

contact with water and is an effective antiseptic agent used for treatment of wounds. The active chlorine atom is described as positive. Chloramine-T is employed for external application in the form of a dilute (0.2%) aqueous solution of the sodium salt, $[p\text{-}CH_3C_6H_4SO_2NCl]^-Na^+$. The second amide hydrogen can be replaced by further treatment with hypochlorite to give dichloramine-T, $p\text{-}CH_3C_6H_4SO_2NCl_2$; this is insoluble in water and is employed as an antiseptic spray in the form of a solution in chlorinated paraffin. A related chloroamide halozone, $p\text{-}HOOCC_6H_4SO_2NCl_2$, is pelleted with sodium carbonate into tablets suitable for sterilization of drinking water; addition to water produces a solution of the sodium carboxylate.

Chloroamides are the only practical agents for decontamination of mustard gas, $S(CH_2CH_2Cl)_2$, which is converted by the active-halogen compounds into the sulfoxide, $O{=}S(CH_2CH_2Cl)_2$, and the chlorosulfoxide, $ClCH_2CHClS({=}O)CH_2CH_2Cl$. Haloamides useful as antiseptic and decontaminating agents are derived from the amides of carboxylic as well as sulfonic acids. Thus the substance $2,4\text{-}Cl_2C_6H_3N(Cl)COC_6H_5$ is employed for impregnation of clothing to provide protection against mustard gas (British Impregnite).

Saccharin (o-Sulfobenzoic Acid Imide). — The cyclic imide of o-sulfobenzoic acid was first prepared by Remsen[1] (1879) and found to have extraordinary sweetness of taste. The substance is about 550 times as sweet as cane sugar, and the aqueous solution retains a detectable sweet taste at a dilution of 1:100,000. It is employed as a sweetening agent, particularly by diabetics incapable of tolerating sugar, and is excreted unchanged in the urine. The technical preparation is essentially that introduced by Remsen, namely oxidation of o-toluenesulfonamide with aqueous permanganate solution at 35°. The o-sulfonamidobenzoic acid initially formed undergoes spontaneous loss of water in a neutral or weakly alkaline solution with closure of the heterocyclic ring. The starting material is obtained from the mixture of *ortho* and *para* acids resulting from sulfonation of tol-

o-Toluenesulfonamide   Saccharin
(m.p. 155°)   (m.p. 229°)

uene; the acids are converted into the acid chlorides by the action of phosphorus pentachloride, the solid p-toluenesulfonyl chloride is largely removed by freezing, and the liquid residue containing the *ortho* compound treated with ammonia. Saccharin is sparingly soluble in cold water, but the doubly activated imino hydrogen atom is acidic, and saccharin forms a water-soluble sodium salt.

A substance of still greater sweetening power has been described by

[1] Ira Remsen, 1846–1927; b. New York; Ph.D. Göttingen; Williams Coll., Johns Hopkins Univ.; *J. Chem. Soc.*, **3182** (1927)

Verkade (1946); 2-amino-1-n-propoxy-4-nitrobenzene is 4000 times as sweet as cane sugar.

Alkali Fusion of Sulfonates. — An important use of the products of sulfonation is the preparation of phenols, accomplished by fusion with molten sodium or potassium hydroxide in the temperature range 290–340°. The

$$ArSO_3Na \; + \; NaOH \; \longrightarrow \; ArONa \; + \; NaHSO_3$$

$$ArONa \; + \; HCl \; \longrightarrow \; ArOH \; + \; NaCl$$

sulfonate group is replaced by the —ONa(K) group, and the phenol is obtained by treating the cooled melt with ice and hydrochloric acid. A typical laboratory procedure is illustrated for the preparation of β-naphthol. A charge of potassium hydroxide is placed in a nickel, copper, or iron crucible, along with a small amount of water to render the material more easily

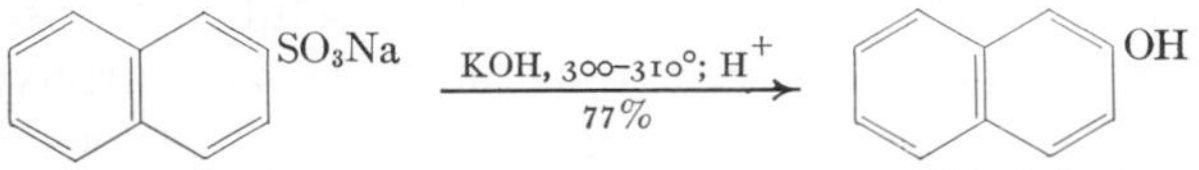

Sodium naphthalene- β-Naphthol
β-sulfonate

KOH, 300–310°; H$^+$
77%

fusible, and heated over a free flame to a temperature of about 250°. The melt is stirred with a thermometer enclosed in a protective metal case while the fully dried and powdered sodium naphthalene-β-sulfonate is added. The solid only partly dissolves and there is no initial reaction, but as the temperature is gradually raised a critical point is reached at which the mass rapidly changes, with separation of a mobile yellow-brown layer of potassium β-naphtholate floating on an almost clear layer of alkali. The fusion is soon over, and the cooled melt is added in portions to ice and hydrochloric acid and the precipitated β-naphthol collected. The cheaper sodium hydroxide is employed where possible in technical operations, but it has less solvent action than potassium hydroxide, gives a less mobile melt, and may prove unsatisfactory. A successful compromise in some instances consists in use of mixtures of the two alkalis, as in the second example, where sodium hydroxide alone gives none of the desired product. A further variation, used

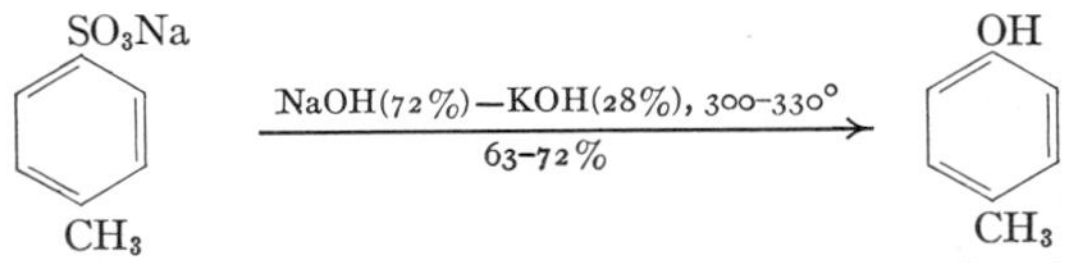

Sodium p-toluene- p-Cresol
sulfonate

NaOH(72%)–KOH(28%), 300–330°
63–72%

widely in the industry, is to conduct the fusion in pressure vessels with aqueous solutions of alkali. Alkali fusion is not applicable to sulfonated compounds containing nitro or halo substituents, which may undergo nucleophilic displacement.

Conversion to Nitriles. — A reaction that would appear analogous to alkali fusion is conversion of a sulfonate into a nitrile by heating with potassium cyanide or potassium ferricyanide. The nitrile reaction, however,

$$C_6H_5SO_3K + KCN \xrightarrow{\text{Pyrolysis}} C_6H_5CN + K_2SO_3$$

Benzonitrile

differs in that the mixture of the dry salts remains unfused even at very high temperatures. The conditions thus are unfavorable for both chemical interaction and heat interchange. Only a small quantity of the mixture can be processed in one charge in a glass flask or retort, or else the material in the interior will not reach the pyrolysis temperature; even so the vessel usually is damaged at the temperature required to obtain the maximum amount of nitrile, which distils from the salt mixture. The yields often are poor and at best seldom exceed 50%.

RELATED SULFUR COMPOUNDS

An arylsulfonate ion offers opportunity for three resonance structures within the substituent group, and is very stable and resistant to reduction.

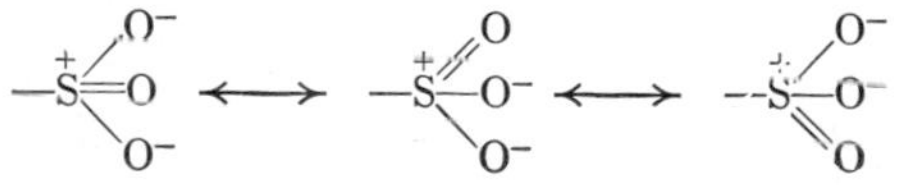

The situation is changed on conversion into the sulfonyl chloride, which is reducible by chemical means. The case is analogous to that of the unreactive carboxylic acids and corresponding chlorides, which are convertible to aldehydes by catalytic hydrogenation. The initial reduction product of a sulfonyl chloride is a sulfinic acid, $ArSO_2H$, obtained by reduction with zinc dust and water. Sulfinic acids differ markedly from the more highly

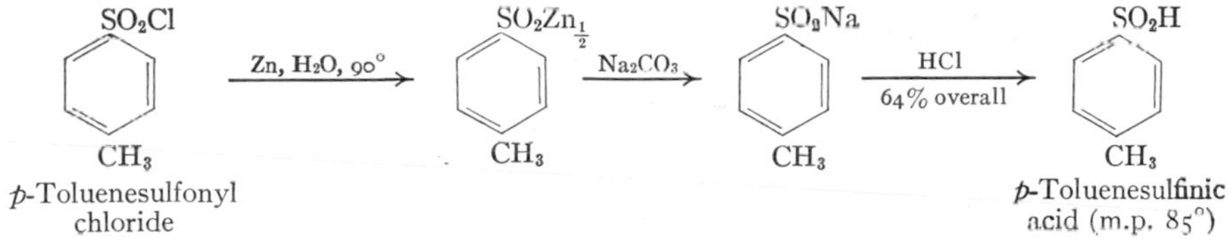

oxidized and more stable sulfonic acids. Benzenesulfinic acid, m.p. 84°, is subject to air oxidation and can be converted into the sulfonic acid with chlorine water; it decomposes when heated above 100°, and samples cannot be stored for long without deterioration. It is soluble in benzene, ether, or hot water, but, unlike the sulfonic acid, is sparingly soluble in cold water. The substance is distinctly less acidic (pK_a 1.80) than benzenesulfonic acid and is liberated from its metal salts by mineral acids, as illustrated in the preparation cited. An alternate method of preparation is the Grignard

$$C_6H_5MgBr + SO_2 \rightarrow C_6H_5SO_2MgBr \xrightarrow{H_2O} C_6H_5SO_2H$$

reaction. Arylsulfinic acids are comparable to sodium bisulfite in ability to add to carbonyl and related unsaturated nitrogen compounds (azomethines).

Sulfinic acids are reducible in turn to **thiophenols** or **aryl mercaptans**, which are obtained on reduction of sulfonyl chlorides with the more powerful combination of zinc dust and hydrochloric or sulfuric acid. Thiophenol, a very feebly acidic liquid of repulsive odor, is readily oxidized by air, par-

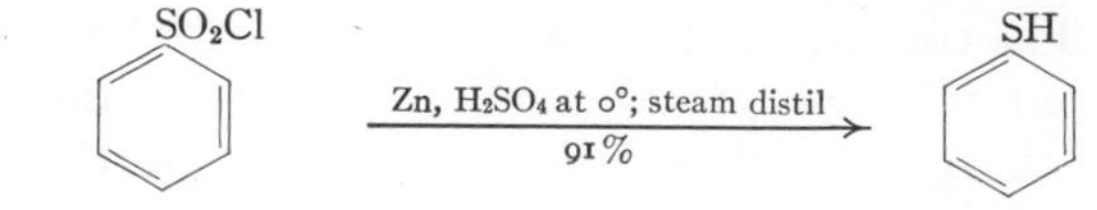

$$\text{Benzenesulfonyl chloride (SO}_2\text{Cl)} \xrightarrow[\substack{\text{Zn, H}_2\text{SO}_4 \text{ at } 0°; \text{ steam distil} \\ 91\%}]{} \text{Thiophenol (SH) (b.p. 169.5°)}$$

Benzenesulfonyl chloride   Thiophenol
    chloride   (b.p. 169.5°)

ticularly when dissolved in alcoholic ammonia, to diphenyl disulfide, $C_6H_5S\text{—}SC_6H_5$ (m.p. 61°). It is oxidized by nitric acid to benzenesulfonic acid. Thiophenols have about the same physical properties as the corresponding hydroxy compounds: thio-o-cresol, m.p. 15°; thio-p-cresol, m.p. 43°; thio-β-naphthol, m. p. 81°. They also result from interaction of arylmagnesium halides with sulfur.

Benzenesulfonyl chloride enters into Friedel-Crafts condensations in the same manner as benzoyl chloride. The aluminum chloride catalyzed reaction with benzene affords **diphenyl sulfone**, encountered as a by-product in the sulfonation of benzene with fuming sulfuric acid. Diphenyl sulfone

Diphenyl sulfone
(m.p. 129°)

is stable to oxidation and reduction, and is the end product of the oxidation of **diphenyl sulfide**, which can be prepared by a process akin to a Friedel-Crafts condensation. Diphenyl sulfide is oxidized to **diphenyl sulfoxide**

$$2 C_6H_6 \; + \; S_2Cl_2 \xrightarrow[81-83\%]{\text{AlCl}_3, \, 10-30°} C_6H_5SC_6H_5 \; + \; S \; + \; 2 HCl$$

Sulfur   Diphenyl sulfide
chloride   (b.p. 296°)

by one equivalent of hydrogen peroxide in acetic acid solution, and to diphenyl sulfone by more than one equivalent.

$$C_6H_5\text{—}S\text{—}C_6H_5 \xrightarrow{\text{H}_2\text{O}_2, \, \text{HOAc}, \, 25°} C_6H_5\text{—}S\text{—}C_6H_5 \xrightarrow{\text{H}_2\text{O}_2, \, \text{HOAc}} C_6H_5\text{—}S\text{—}C_6H_5$$

Diphenyl sulfoxide   Diphenyl sulfone
(m.p. 70.5°)

CHAPTER 25

ARYL AMINES

Aniline was first obtained by destructive distillation of indigo (Unver-dorben, 1826) and later was isolated from a coal-tar distillate (Runge, 1834). Fritzsche (1840) introduced an improved method of preparation consisting in heating indigo with concentrated alkali, established the formula, and pro-posed the subsequently accepted name (Spanish *añil*, Sanskrit *nēlē*, indigo); for a time this method was the most practicable route to the then rare chemi-cal. A base subsequently recognized as identical with aniline was obtained (Zinin, 1842) by reduction of nitrobenzene; and with development of the coal-tar industry this reaction eventually became the standard method for the technical production of a key chemical on a scale mounting to several million pounds per year. Aniline is convertible into various nuclear sub-stitution products or, by alkylation on the nitrogen atom, into N-methyl-and N,N-dimethylaniline.

Primary aromatic amines are obtained almost entirely by combination of nitration and reduction. A number of methods of reduction are available. Small-scale reductions are often carried out with tin and hydrochloric acid ($C_6H_5NO_2 \rightarrow C_6H_5NH_2$, 80%), or somewhat more cleanly with a solution of stannous chloride in concentrated hydrochloric acid; the basic product usually is isolated from the diluted reaction mixture either by addition of enough alkali to neutralize the acid and dissolve the tin in the form of sodium stannite and sodium stannate or by precipitation of the metal as sulfide. In technical practice it is more economical to reduce the nitro compound with iron powder and water, with addition of either hydrochloric or acetic acid as catalyst. Where proper reaction conditions have been worked out, this procedure also serves for laboratory preparations, as in the reduction of

1.

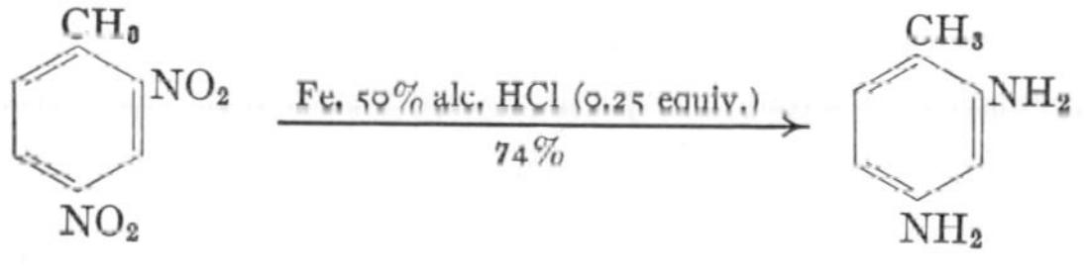

$$
\begin{array}{ccc}
& CH_3 & \\
& | & \\
\text{(ring)} & NO_2 & \xrightarrow[74\%]{\text{Fe, 50\% alc. HCl (0.25 equiv.)}} & \text{(ring)} \quad NH_2 \\
& NO_2 & & NH_2
\end{array}
$$

2,4-dinitrotoluene (1). Reduction with zinc dust and alkali is less widely employed but sometimes gives excellent results (2).

2.

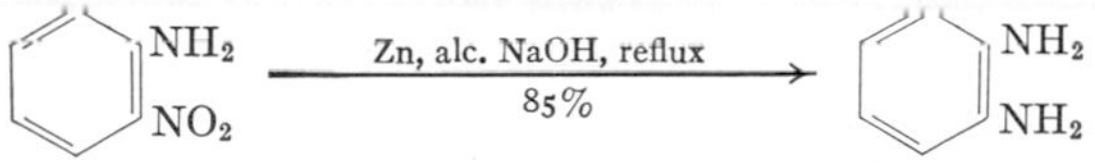

$$
\text{(ring)} \begin{array}{c} NH_2 \\ NO_2 \end{array} \xrightarrow[85\%]{\text{Zn, alc. NaOH, reflux}} \text{(ring)} \begin{array}{c} NH_2 \\ NH_2 \end{array}
$$

If the nitro compound contains an acetylamino or acetoxy group reduction in either an acidic or a basic medium results in hydrolysis of the acetyl groups. In example 3 hydrolysis is not objectionable because the

3.

CH₃CONH⟨benzene⟩SO₂⟨benzene⟩NO₂ $\xrightarrow[74-77\%]{\text{Sn, HCl}}$ H₂N⟨benzene⟩SO₂⟨benzene⟩NH₂

p-Acetylamino-*p′*-nitrodiphenyl   *p*,*p′*-Diaminodiphenyl
sulfone (m.p. 228°)   sulfone (m.p. 178°)

desired product was the deacetylated diamine. If retention of an acetyl group is required, as in the preparation of the monoacetyl derivative of *o*-phenylenediamine (4), the most satisfactory method of reduction is cata-

4.   NH₂   NHCOCH₃   NHCOCH₃

⟨benzene⟩NO₂ $\xrightarrow[93\%]{\substack{\text{(CH₃CO)₂O in C₆H₆,}\\ \text{trace H₂SO₄}}}$ ⟨benzene⟩NO₂ $\xrightarrow[90\%]{\text{Pt, H₂, in alcohol}}$ ⟨benzene⟩NH₂

                                                                     o-Aminoacetanilide
                                                                        (m.p. 133°)

lytic hydrogenation in a neutral medium.   Ethyl *p*-nitrobenzoate (m.p. 57°) can be reduced by the same method in nearly quantitative yield to ethyl *p*-aminobenzoate, *p*-H₂NC₆H₄COOC₂H₅ (m.p. 92°).   Another catalytic process is illustrated by hydrogenation of 2-nitro-*p*-cymene in alcoholic solution over Raney nickel catalyst at 100–200° and 1000–1500 lbs. pressure; the yield of 2-amino-*p*-cymene (b.p. 242°) is 87–90%.

Selective reduction of one group in a polynitro compound often can be accomplished with use of the calculated amount of sodium or ammonium sulfide or hydrosulfide.   One example is reduction of picric acid to picramic acid (p. 580); another is shown in example 5.   The reactions can be con-

5.   NO₂   NH₂

⟨benzene⟩NO₂ $\xrightarrow[70-80\%]{\text{H₂S, alc. NH₃}}$ ⟨benzene⟩NO₂

ducted with a weighed quantity of crystalline sodium sulfide or by dissolving the nitro compound in alcoholic ammonia and passing in hydrogen sulfide to a given gain in weight.   The reagent reduces one nitro group before attacking another, but the reaction will proceed beyond this stage unless the amount of reagent is controlled.

PHYSICAL PROPERTIES; BASIC CHARACTER

The more commonly encountered amines of the benzene and diphenyl series are listed in Table 25.1.   Among the isomeric toluidines, nitroanilines, and phenylenediamines, the symmetrical *para* isomer invariably has the highest melting point.   It is noteworthy that the boiling point of methyl- and of dimethylaniline is practically the same and only slightly higher than that of aniline, and also that in the series of the toluidines, phenylenedia-

TABLE 25.1. AMINES

NAME	FORMULA	M.P., °C.	B.P., °C.	pK$_b$
Aniline	$C_6H_5NH_2$	− 6	184	9.30
Methylaniline	$C_6H_5NHCH_3$	liq.	194	9.60
Dimethylaniline	$C_6H_5N(CH_3)_2$	2	193	9.62
Diethylaniline	$C_6H_5N(C_2H_5)_2$	− 39	215	
o-Toluidine	$CH_3C_6H_4NH_2(1,2)$	− 15.5	197	9.47
m-Toluidine	$CH_3C_6H_4NH_2(1,3)$	liq.	203	9.30
p-Toluidine	$CH_3C_6H_4NH_2(1,4)$	44	200	9.70
o-Nitroaniline	$H_2NC_6H_4NO_2(1,2)$	71.5		13.82
m-Nitroaniline	$H_2NC_6H_4NO_2(1,3)$	114		11.40
p-Nitroaniline	$H_2NC_6H_4NO_2(1,4)$	146		12.0
2,4-Dinitroaniline	$H_2NC_6H_3(NO_2)_2(1,2,4)$	187		
o-Phenylenediamine	$C_6H_4(NH_2)_2(1,2)$	103	257	9.48
m-Phenylenediamine	$C_6H_4(NH_2)_2(1,3)$	63	284	
p-Phenylenediamine	$C_6H_4(NH_2)_2(1,4)$	140	267	
o-Anisidine	$H_2NC_6H_4OCH_3(1,2)$	5.2	225	9.7
p-Anisidine	$H_2NC_6H_4OCH_3(1,4)$	57	244	8.82
p-Phenetidine	$H_2NC_6H_4OC_2H_5(1,4)$	2	254	8.70
o-Chloroaniline	$H_2NC_6H_4Cl(1,2)$	liq.	209	12.05
m-Chloroaniline	$H_2NC_6H_4Cl(1,3)$	liq.	236	10.40
p-Chloroaniline	$H_2NC_6H_4Cl(1,4)$	70	231	12.0
p-Bromoaniline	$H_2NC_6H_4Br(1,4)$	66		10.0
2,4,6-Trichloroaniline	$H_2NC_6H_2Cl_3(1,2,4,6)$	78	262	
2,4,6-Tribromoaniline	$H_2NC_6H_2Br_3(1,2,4,6)$	118	300	
Diphenylamine	$C_6H_5NHC_6H_5$	54	302	
Triphenylamine	$(C_6H_5)_3N$	126	348	
Benzidine	$(4)H_2NC_6H_4—C_6H_4NH_2(4')$	127	401$^{740mm.}$	12.13
o-Tolidine	$[—C_6H_3(CH_3)NH_2]_2(3,3',4,4')$	129		
o-Dianisidine	$[—C_6H_3(OCH_3)NH_2]_2(3,3',4,4')$	131		

mines, and chloroanilines, the *ortho* isomer has a lower boiling point than the *meta* and *para* compounds.

Aniline has only weak basic properties (pK$_b$ 9.3) as compared with methylamine (pK$_b$ 3.4). The diminished basicity of aromatic amines can be attributed empirically to the unsaturated aromatic nucleus, in analogy with the relationship of acetamide to ammonia. The explanation provided by the resonance theory is that the anilinium ion is incapable of resonance involving the nitrogen, for a reason already stated (p. 569), whereas resonance stabilization is possible in the free aniline molecule; there is thus little driving force to promote ionization. The N-methyl derivatives of aniline and the three toluidines all have dissociation constants in the same range as the parent amine, and hence alkyl substitution in either the amino group or the nucleus has little influence on the basic strength. Introduction of a nitro substituent, however, results in a marked decrease in basicity, particularly prominent in the case of o-nitroaniline. The feebly basic character of nitroanilines is evidenced by the fact that the colorless salts formed by these substances with concentrated sulfuric or hydrochloric acid are hydrolyzed on dilution with moderate amounts of water to yellow, water-insoluble bases; the *ortho* isomer is precipitated most readily, the *para* compound separates next, and *m*-nitroaniline separates only on more extensive dilution. Decrease in basicity attending introduction of the nitro group at any position in the ring can be attributed to the inductive effect; the positively polarized nitro group induces a drift of electrons in the sense of withdrawal from the ring and from the amino nitrogen atom, and hence affinity of the nitrogen for protons is decreased. The effect is magnified in the polynitro compounds 2,4-dinitroaniline and picramide (2,4,6-trinitroaniline); the latter compound forms with concentrated sulfuric acid a salt scarcely more stable than oxonium salts of ethers. The three chloroanilines are distinctly weaker bases than aniline, but show an alternation owing to substitution in the three positions that conforms to the order in the series of nitro compounds but is less profound. Since the chlorine atom is known from dipole moment data to be electron-attracting, a comparable inductive effect evidently is responsible for the relationship. A slight effect in the opposite direction is observed in the *para* methoxyl and ethoxyl derivatives, *p*-anisidine and *p*-phenetidine, which are stronger bases than aniline. As would be anticipated, diphenylamine is feebly basic and salts formed with concentrated acids are readily hydrolyzed.

Acid Salts. — Aniline, as well as the toluidines and other amines of comparable basic strength and molecular weight, dissolves readily in dilute solutions of mineral acids with formation of salts which are so soluble in water that they are not easily precipitated by excess acid. Hydrochloride salts of this type are isolated most easily by passing dry hydrogen chloride gas into an ethereal solution of the amine, for the salts are insoluble in ether and separate quantitatively. Salts of higher amines, for example those of the naphthalene series, are less soluble in water and can be crystallized from an aqueous medium, with use of excess acid where required to decrease solubility. Salts of moderate molecular weight often have sharp melting points and are even distillable; for example: aniline hydrochloride, m.p. 198°, b.p. 245°; methylaniline hydrochloride, m.p. 122°; dimethylaniline hydrochloride, m.p. 85°; *m*-toluidine hydrochloride, m.p. 228°, b.p. 250°. The picrate of aniline melts at 181° dec., that of dimethylaniline at 142°. Dimethylaniline also forms a complex molecular compound with trinitrobenzene, m.p. 108° (dark violet).

Inner Salts. — Sulfanilic acid (p-$H_2NC_6H_4SO_3H$), a typical amine sulfonic acid, has properties indicative of a dipolar ion, or inner salt struc-

Sulfanilic acid
(sparingly soluble in water)

Sodium sulfanilate
(readily soluble in water)

ture, as shown in the formula. It is insoluble in ether and soluble in water at room temperature only to the extent of about 1%, and when heated in a capillary tube it begins to decompose at 280°. Sulfanilic acid dissolves readily when warmed with aqueous sodium carbonate solution with formation of the sodium salt, but it has so little tendency to combine with mineral acids that the original substance crystallizes from the solution in concentrated hydrochloric acid (anhydrous form; the commercial preparation is the monohydrate). Sulfanilic acid has a logarithmic acidity constant pK = 3.22, attributable to separation of a proton from the —NH$_3^+$ group.

Acetyl Derivatives. — As in the aliphatic series, acetylation obliterates basic characteristics of aromatic amines. Acetanilide is neutral and no more soluble in dilute hydrochloric acid than in water. An acetyl derivative is prepared easily either by the action of acetic anhydride on the an-

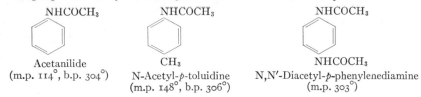

Acetanilide
(m.p. 114°, b.p. 304°)

N-Acetyl-p-toluidine
(m.p. 148°, b.p. 306°)

N,N'-Diacetyl-p-phenylenediamine
(m.p. 303°)

hydrous amine or by dissolving the amine with an equivalent quantity of hydrochloric acid in water and adding acetic anhydride, followed by enough sodium acetate to react with the hydrochloride salt and liberate the free amine. The acetyl derivatives melt at higher temperatures than the free amines and are useful for characterization. They are also useful by virtue of stability to oxidation, in contrast with free amines, and because of moderation in the substitution-facilitating influence of the amino group.

PREPARATION OF SPECIFIC AMINES

Aniline. — The standard industrial preparation of aniline involves reduction of nitrobenzene with iron chips and 30% hydrochloric acid. After the reaction is complete the mixture is neutralized with soda, and the aniline removed by distillation with steam saturated with aniline. Since aniline is slightly soluble in water (3 g. in 100 g. H$_2$O), sodium chloride is added to the distillate to make a 20% solution of sodium chloride, in which aniline is insoluble. After separation of the two layers, aniline is obtained pure by distillation in practically quantitative yield. Reduction with hydrogen or water gas in the presence of a catalyst is also used. In one process aniline is made by treating chlorobenzene with ammonia at 340° and 340 atmospheres.

Methyl- and Dimethylaniline. — Methylation of aniline by any standard method of alkylation is liable to afford mixtures of the mono- and dimethyl derivatives, along with unchanged starting material, but by control of the conditions one or the other derivative can be obtained as the chief product. A technical process for production of dimethylaniline consists in heating a mixture of aniline, methanol, and concentrated sulfuric acid at 230–235° and a pressure of 25–30 atmospheres (97% yield). Small amounts of aniline and methylaniline present in technical preparations can be eliminated by adding enough acetic anhydride to react with these contaminants and distilling the unattacked tertiary amine from a residue containing the much less volatile acetyl derivatives. Technical methylaniline is produced by heating aniline with methanol and hydrochloric acid at 180° in an autoclave. A generally applicable laboratory method consists in alkylation of the arylsulfonyl, or Hinsberg, derivative of a primary amine in the form of the sodium salt (Ullmann):

$$C_6H_5NH_2 \xrightarrow{C_6H_5SO_2Cl} \underset{\underset{H}{|}}{C_6H_5N}-SO_2C_6H_5 \xrightarrow{NaOH}$$

$$\underset{\underset{Na}{|}}{C_6H_5NSO_2C_6H_5} \xrightarrow{(CH_3)_2SO_4} \underset{\underset{CH_3}{|}}{C_6H_5NSO_2C_6H_5} \xrightarrow{Hydrol.} \underset{\underset{CH_3}{|}}{C_6H_5NH}$$

A method of preparing N-alkylarylamines is catalytic hydrogenation of a mixture of a primary amine and an aldehyde; the reaction possibly proceeds through formation and reduction of the anil derivative (Schiff base) of the aldehyde. A simplification is to generate the primary amine in the

$$ArNH_2 + O{=}CHR \longrightarrow ArN{=}CHR \xrightarrow{2\,H} ArNHCH_2R$$

reaction mixture by hydrogenation of the corresponding nitro compound in the presence of sodium acetate as condensing agent.

$$C_6H_5NO_2 + n\text{-}C_4H_9CHO \xrightarrow[84\%]{Raney\ Ni,\ H_2,\ NaOAc} \underset{N\text{-}n\text{-Amylaniline}}{C_6H_5NHC_5H_{11}(n)}$$

A process of reductive alkylation related to those cited is the **Leuckart reaction** (1885), in which an aldehyde or ketone is heated with either an amine and formic acid or ammonium formate, as the reducing agent. The product is often a formyl derivative, which on hydrolysis affords an amine, as in the reaction of benzophenone with ammonium formate:

$$(C_6H_5)_2CO \xrightarrow{HCO_2NH_4} (C_6H_5)_2CHNHCHO \xrightarrow{H_2O} (C_6H_5)_2CHNH_2$$

Toluidines. — The *ortho* and *para* methyl derivatives of aniline are obtained technically by reduction of the corresponding nitrotoluenes with iron powder and a catalytic amount of hydrochloric acid. Prior to the development of distillation technique for separation of the nitro compounds by fractionation, the o-p mixture was reduced and the toluidines separated through the oxalate salts. The oxalate of o-toluidine is much more soluble in either water or ether than that of p-toluidine, and separation can be accomplished by preferential precipitation of the *para* isomer by the measured addition of oxalic acid to a solution of the mixture of amines in ether. In technical practice m-toluidine is made from m-nitrotoluene, available in small yield in production of the o- and p-isomers.

Nitroanilines. — Nitration of aniline with nitric acid alone is not satisfactory because the amine is sensitive to oxidation and is subject to considerable destruction as a result of the oxidizing action of the reagent. The amine is stabilized against oxidation by dissolving it in sulfuric acid, and nitration in such a solution proceeds somewhat more smoothly and affords *m*-nitroaniline as the chief product, though in only moderate yield, for the amine is present largely as the ionic salt and substitution occurs under the influence of the rather weakly *meta* directing ammonium group, —NH$_3^+$. The reaction has no practical use since *m*-nitroaniline can be prepared more efficiently by partial reduction of *m*-dinitrobenzene with ammonium hydrosulfide.

Acetylation of aniline provides stabilization to oxidation and does not lead to a *meta* directing ionic group. Acetanilide on nitration with mixed

NHCOCH$_3$ $\xrightarrow{\text{HNO}_3-\text{H}_2\text{SO}_4}$ NHCOCH$_3$ / NO$_2$ (90% yield)   +   NHCOCH$_3$ / NO$_2$ (trace)

acid reacts smoothly with almost exclusive production of *p*-nitroacetanilide (m.p. 215°); a small amount of *o*-nitroacetanilide (m.p. 94°) is formed but is easily eliminated by crystallization of the much higher-melting and less soluble *para* isomer. Acid hydrolysis of the recrystallized product affords *p*-nitroaniline in good overall yield. In a large-scale operation, a certain amount of *o*-nitroaniline can be recovered from the mother liquors of crystallization of the nitration product by hydrolysis and steam distillation (volatility ascribable to chelation, see p. 622). A more efficient process is

NHCOCH$_3$ $\xrightarrow{\text{H}_2\text{SO}_4}$ NHCOCH$_3$ / SO$_3$H $\xrightarrow{\text{HNO}_3}$ NH$_2$ / NO$_2$ / SO$_3$H (*o*-Nitroaniline-*p*-sulfonic acid) $\xrightarrow[56\%]{57\% \text{ H}_2\text{SO}_4,\text{ reflux}}$ NH$_2$ / NO$_2$

indicated. Sulfonation of acetanilide blocks the *para* position, and on reaction with nitric acid in sulfuric acid solution a nitro group is introduced at the 2-position and the acetyl group is eliminated. Hydrolysis of the sulfonic acid substituent then affords *o*-nitroaniline.

The diminished basicity of nitroanilines has been noted. Another deviation from the behavior of aniline, shown by *o*- and *p*-nitroaniline but not by the *meta* isomer, is the ready reaction with alkalis with displacement of the amino group by hydroxyl. This reaction is another manifestation

NH$_2$ / NO$_2$ $\xrightarrow{\text{NaOH}}$ OH / NO$_2$

of the sensitivity of nitro compounds to nucleophilic attack in the *ortho* and *para* positions.

Phenylenediamines. — The *ortho* and *para* diamino derivatives of benzene are obtainable by reduction of the corresponding nitroanilines; a specific procedure for preparation of *o*-phenylenediamine is indicated in example 2, p. 595. *m*-Phenylenediamine is prepared by reduction of the readily available *m*-dinitro compound.

Halogen Derivatives. — Aniline combines with bromine with such avidity that interaction of the amine with a dilute aqueous solution of bromine

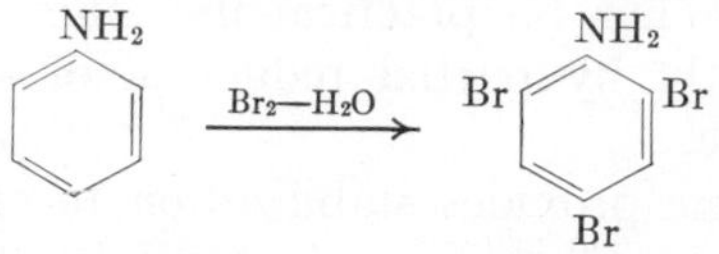

affords a precipitate of the sparingly soluble 2,4,6-tribromoaniline. The reaction demonstrates the powerful substitution-facilitating influence of the amino group, for this directing group causes the three bromine atoms, which ordinarily are *o-p* directing, to assume positions *meta* to one another. Bromination in aqueous solution is useful for obtaining solid derivatives for identification, since most aromatic amines respond with affixture of bromine at all available positions *ortho* and *para* to the amino group; thus the toluidines react to give the following products: dibromo-*o*-toluidine, m.p. 50°; tribromo-*m*-toluidine, m.p. 97°; dibromo-*p*-toluidine, m.p. 73°. Bromination of aniline proceeds so rapidly even at high dilution that an early process for extraction of bromine from sea water consisted in the addition of chlorine to liberate bromine from the sodium bromide, followed by aniline to combine with the free halogen and give a filterable precipitate.

The effect of the amino group in promoting halogenation is so powerful that the acetyl derivative is used to control the reaction to the stage of monosubstitution. Acetanilide reacts to give almost exclusively the *p*-bromo derivative, which is hydrolyzed easily to the amine. *p*-Chloro-

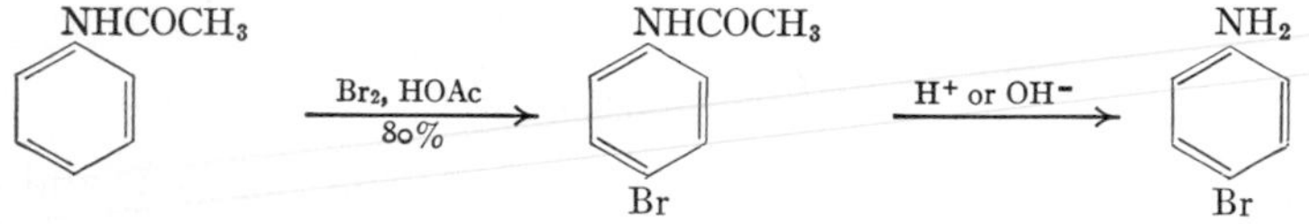

p-Bromoacetanilide
(m.p. 166°)

p-Bromoaniline

aniline is obtainable similarly; a small amount of the *ortho* compound is formed, and in technical practice the mixture is separated, after hydrolysis, by steam distillation of the *o*-chloroaniline. The *meta* isomer is prepared by reduction of *m*-nitrochlorobenzene.

Sulfanilic Acid and Isomers. — Sulfanilic acid, used extensively as a dye intermediate, is prepared by mixing equal moles of aniline and concentrated sulfuric acid and baking the resulting acid sulfate at 180° until a test portion when neutralized with sodium hydroxide no longer liberates

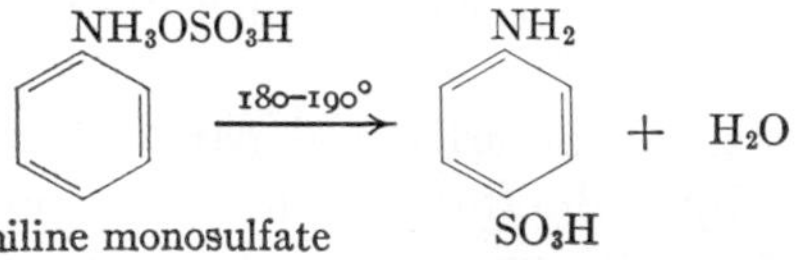

Aniline monosulfate

Sulfanilic acid

aniline. Sulfanilic acid monohydrate crystallizes on pouring the cooled mixture into water. The reaction involves migration of the sulfonic acid group from the side chain to the nucleus and dehydration; experiments of Bamberger (1897) established that the initial reaction is loss of water from the sulfate with formation of phenylsulfamic acid, a dehydration comparable to the pyrolytic conversion of an ammonium salt into an amide. When phenylsulfamic acid is heated cautiously, the sulfonic acid group first migrates to the *ortho* position, giving orthanilic acid, which rearranges at 180° to sulfanilic acid. The progressive migrations to the *ortho* and then the

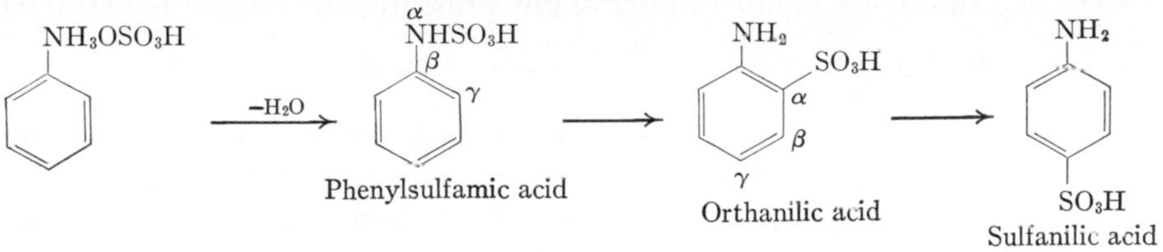

para position can be correlated empirically with other phenomena; for example, the shift of a hydrogen atom in an enol to give the corresponding keto form, and the reverse process. Lapworth (1898) described each process as a shift of hydrogen from the α- to the γ-position in a system having a double

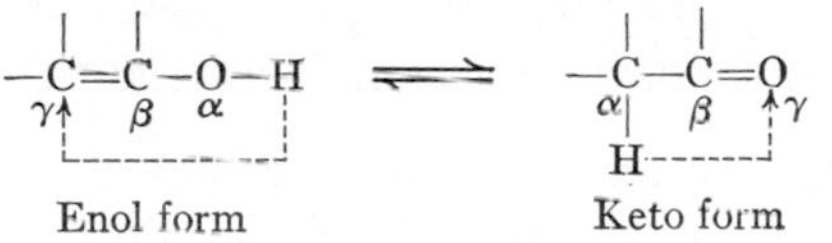

bond between the β- and γ-atoms in the chain. Phenylsulfamic acid affords orthanilic acid by an α,γ-shift of the sulfonic acid group to the *ortho* position, with a similar shift of hydrogen in the reverse direction. Another α,γ-shift brings the acid group into the evidently more stable *para* position, and this interpretation accounts for the absence of the *meta* derivative from the reaction. Several comparable rearrangements involve migration of a group from an initial position of attachment to nitrogen or to oxygen into *ortho* or *para* positions in the ring; for example, the acid-catalyzed rearrangement of phenylhydroxylamine to *p*-aminophenol (p. 585).

Orthanilic acid is also employed technically and is prepared by the procedure shown.

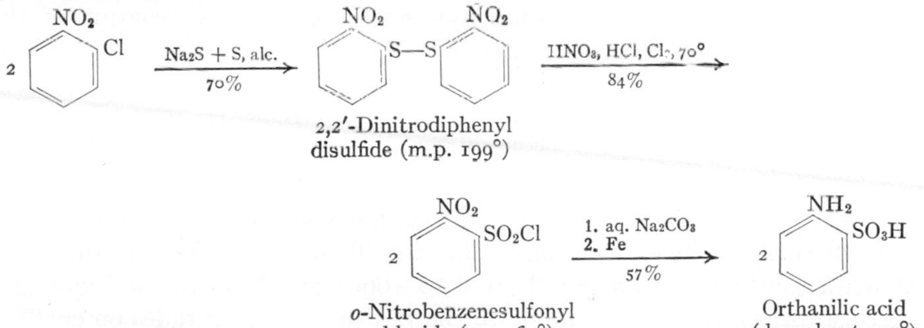

Metanilic acid, used to some extent in production of dyes, is prepared by sulfonating nitrobenzene with fuming sulfuric acid (25% SO_3) at $60-70°$ and reducing the resulting *m*-nitrobenzenesulfonic acid.

Anisidines. — The *o*- and *p*-methoxy derivatives of aniline are prepared by reduction of the corresponding nitroanisoles (m.p. $9°$ and $54°$), which in turn are obtainable by nitration of anisole, by the action of methyl alcoholic potassium hydroxide on the nitrochlorobenzenes, or by methylation of the nitrophenols (sodium salts) with dimethyl sulfate in boiling toluene.

Diphenylamine is prepared by heating aniline hydrochloride with a small excess of aniline (1.1 equiv.) under slight pressure; the aniline is extracted

$$C_6H_5NH_3Cl + C_6H_5NH_2 \xrightarrow[82\%]{210-240°,\, 6\,atm.} C_6H_5NHC_6H_5 + NH_4Cl$$

from the resulting melt with warm dilute hydrochloric acid, and an oily layer of the feebly basic diarylamine is collected and distilled.

Triphenylamine. — Introduction of a third phenyl group can be accomplished by dissolving potassium (two moles) in hot aniline and adding bromobenzene to the resulting melt of the potassium derivative, $C_6H_5NK_2$; a more convenient procedure is as follows:

$$2(C_6H_5)_2NH + 2C_6H_5I + K_2CO_3 \xrightarrow[82-85\%]{\text{Boiling } C_6H_5NO_2} 2(C_6H_5)_3N + 2KI + H_2O + CO_2$$

SPECIAL CHEMICAL PROPERTIES

Oxidation. — Primary and secondary aromatic amines are so sensitive to oxidation that they often deteriorate in storage owing to attack by atmospheric oxygen. Pure aniline is a colorless oil, but on exposure to air it eventually acquires a deep reddish brown color. Pure samples deteriorate less rapidly than technical preparations, which initially are somewhat colored. The extent of oxidation, however, is not great, and practically colorless aniline can be recovered in good yield from very dark material by distillation from a trace of zinc dust. Solid amines (e.g., *p*-toluidine) are less vulnerable to air oxidation than liquid amines. An inference regarding the initial phase of oxidation can be made on the basis of the established course of oxidation of diphenylamine. Wieland (1911) discovered that diphenylamine on careful oxidation with potassium permanganate in acetone solution is converted into tetraphenylhydrazine, apparently through formation and association of diphenylamino radicals. Association of the

$$2 \begin{array}{c} C_6H_5 \\ C_6H_5 \end{array}\!\!\!\diagdown NH \xrightarrow{[O]} 2 \begin{array}{c} C_6H_5 \\ C_6H_5 \end{array}\!\!\!\diagdown N\cdot \rightleftharpoons \begin{array}{c} C_6H_5 \\ C_6H_5 \end{array}\!\!\!\diagdown N-N\!\!\!\diagup \begin{array}{c} C_6H_5 \\ C_6H_5 \end{array}$$

Diphenylnitrogen   Tetraphenylhydrazine
                        (m.p. $147°$ dec.)

radicals is practically complete at room temperature, for the colorless tetraphenylhydrazine gives solutions that are likewise colorless in the cold. When a solution in toluene is heated to about $70°$, however, it acquires a greenish brown color attributable to the radical; the color fades on cooling, and the original hydrazine derivative is recoverable from the solution. The behavior is similar to that of hexaphenylethane, except that the diphenylamino radical does not combine with oxygen (or with iodine) and is present in equilibrium with the diarylhydrazine in amounts too small to be determined. Evidence of dissociation to free radicals, apart from the color phenomena, is provided by interaction of the substance with triphenylmethyl to form the compound $(C_6H_5)_3C—N(C_6H_5)_2$ and with sodium to give $(C_6H_5)_2NNa$.

With the use of different oxidizing agents under varying conditions, aniline is convertible into a host of products, including azobenzene, azoxybenzene, nitrobenzene, quinone, the dye Aniline Black and intermediates, and many products resulting from secondary processes of condensation. Most of the products appear derivable through an initial abstraction of one amino hydrogen atom with formation of a transient free radical sensitive to further attack, either at the nitrogen atom or at the *para* position of the nucleus.

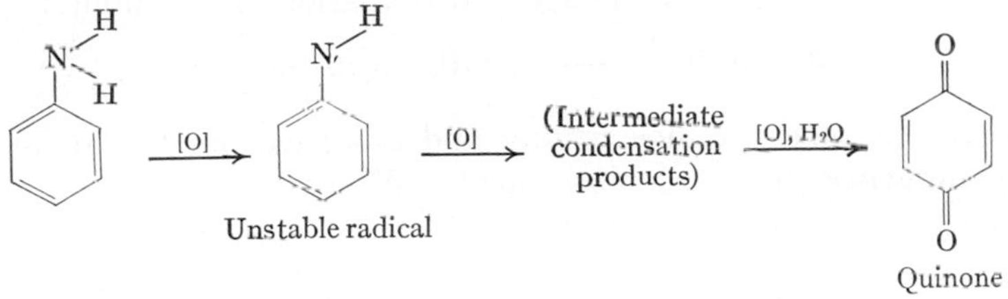

Unstable radical   (Intermediate condensation products)   Quinone

Action of Nitrous Acid on Primary Amines. — The response of aromatic amines of the three classes to nitrous acid parallels only in part the behavior of aliphatic amines (p. 236). Whereas a primary alkylamine on treatment with nitrous acid in hydrochloric acid solution affords an alcohol and nitrogen, aniline hydrochloride is convertible under controlled conditions (low temperature, excess acid) into a crystalline salt of the formula $C_6H_5N_2^+Cl^-$, benzenediazonium chloride. The product undergoes hydrolytic decomposition when boiled with dilute acid, and hence the overall reaction resembles

$$C_6H_5NH_2Cl \ + \ HONO \ \xrightarrow{\ o^o\ } \ C_6H_5N_2^+Cl^- \ + \ 2\,H_2O$$

$$C_6H_5N_2Cl \ + \ H_2O \ \xrightarrow{\text{dil. } H_2CO_4,\ heat} \ C_6H_5OH \ + \ N_2 \ + \ HCl$$

that in the aliphatic series. The diversified reactions of aryldiazonium salts are described later.

N-Nitroso Compounds. — Secondary aromatic amines, like dialkylamines, combine with nitrous acid to form N-nitroso derivatives, or nitroso-

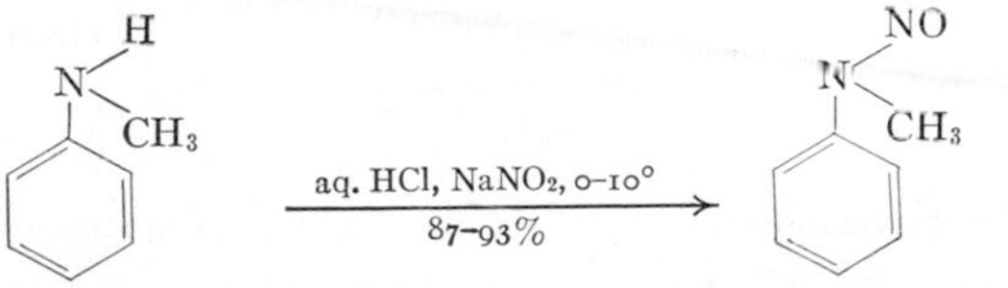

aq. HCl, NaNO2, o-10°
87-93%

N-Nitroso-N-methylaniline
(yellow, m.p. 15°)

amines. The product from methylaniline is known as either N-nitroso-N-methylaniline or methylphenylnitrosoamine; it is a bright yellow oil that crystallizes on cooling and can be distilled in vacuum but not at atmospheric pressure. The N-nitroso derivative of N-methyl-p-toluidine is a yellow solid which melts at 54°; that of diphenylamine melts at 67°. N-Nitrosodiphenylamine undergoes nitration in acetic acid solution to a mixture of the 2- and 4-nitro derivatives. A reaction of preparative value consists in reduction of nitroso compounds to the substituted hydrazines with zinc dust and dilute acetic acid or with sodium amalgam (see example). Reduc-

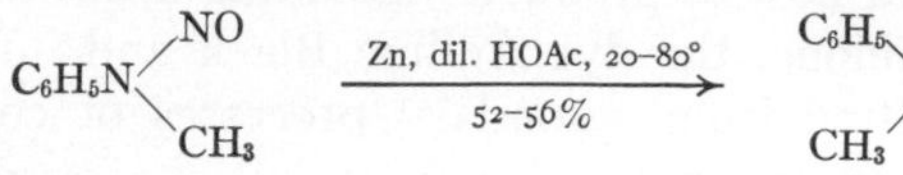

$$C_6H_5N \overset{NO}{\underset{CH_3}{<}} \quad \xrightarrow[52-56\%]{\text{Zn, dil. HOAc, 20–80°}} \quad \overset{C_6H_5}{\underset{CH_3}{>}} N—NH_2$$

α-Methylphenylhydrazine
(b.p. 107°/13 mm.)

tion with a more powerful reagent such as tin or zinc and a mineral acid results in fission of the N–N linkage and formation of the amine:

$$C_6H_5N(NO)CH_3 \longrightarrow C_6H_5NHCH_3 + NH_3$$

N-Nitroso-N-methylaniline readily undergoes rearrangement under the catalytic influence of hydrochloric acid. When a solution in alcohol is

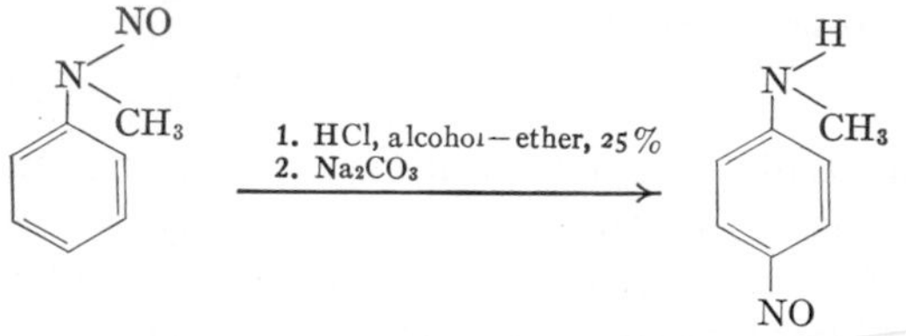

p-Nitroso-N-methylaniline
(blue-green, m.p. 118°)

treated with concentrated hydrochloric acid and allowed to stand for a time at room temperature, the substance rearranges to p-nitroso-N-methylaniline, which separates as the crystalline hydrochloride (yellow).

The N-nitroso derivative of phenylhydroxylamine is employed as the colorless ammonium salt, cupferron, in quantitative analysis as a reagent for the precipitation of copper and iron. The salt is prepared by passing ammonia gas into an ethereal solution of phenylhydroxylamine and n-butyl nitrite. The marked acidic character of free N-nitrosophenylhy-

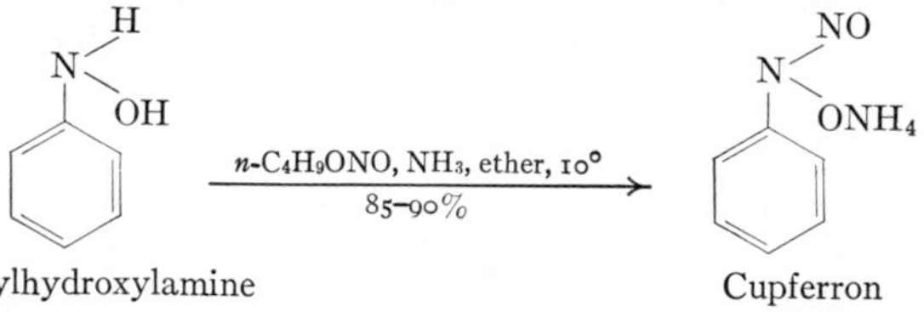

Phenylhydroxylamine   Cupferron

droxylamine (colorless, m.p. 51°, pK$_a$ 5.3) suggests that the substance exists largely not in the nitroso hydroxy form (a) but in the tautomeric amine oxide form (*b*), which has a hydroxyl group joined to an unsaturated nitrogen atom. The sparingly soluble copper and iron salts are formulated as

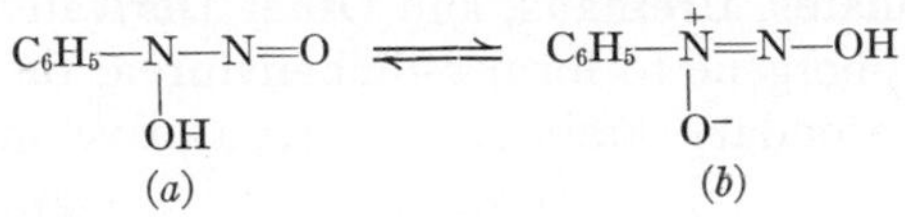

$$C_6H_5-\underset{\underset{OH}{|}}{N}-N=O \;\rightleftarrows\; C_6H_5-\underset{\underset{O^-}{|}}{\overset{+}{N}}=N-OH$$

$$(a) \qquad\qquad\qquad (b)$$

derivatives of the amine oxide form (*b*), which permits formation of stabilizing chelate rings:

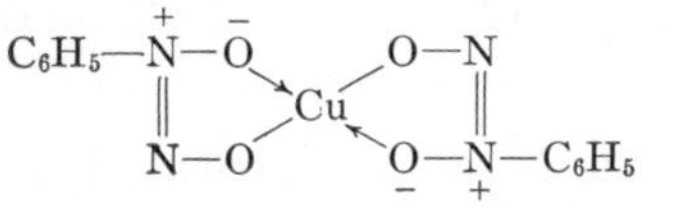

$$
\begin{array}{ccc}
C_6H_5-\overset{+}{N}-\overset{-}{O} & & O-N \\
\overset{\|}{} & \diagdown\text{Cu}\diagup & \overset{\|}{} \\
N-O & & O-\underset{-}{\overset{+}{N}}-C_6H_5
\end{array}
$$

C-Nitroso Compounds. — Whereas tertiary aliphatic amines are inert to nitrous acid, those of the aromatic series undergo nitrosation in the nucleus

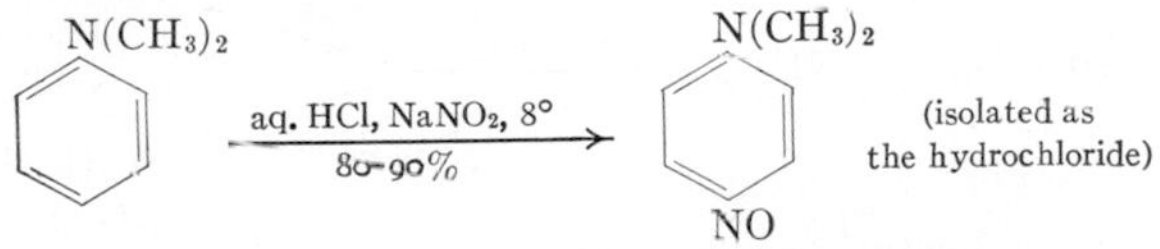

aq. HCl, NaNO₂, 8°
80–90%

(isolated as the hydrochloride)

p-Nitrosodimethylaniline
(green, m.p. 86°)

with formation of C-nitroso compounds. Nitrosation proceeds rapidly at 0°, usually with exclusive substitution in the *para* position, if available, or otherwise in the *ortho* position. Phenols also yield C-nitroso derivatives, in transformations characterized by the low temperature of reaction and by exclusive attack at the *para* position, whereas neither aromatic hydrocarbons nor any derivatives other than the free amines and phenols react with nitrous acid. C-Nitrosation is applicable only to compounds containing the powerful substitution-facilitating dialkylamino or hydroxyl group.

p-Nitrosodimethylaniline crystallizes in green plates and forms a yellow hydrochloride (dec. 177°). It is hydrolyzed quantitatively by hot alkali to *p* nitrosophenol and dimethylamine, and this hydrolysis has found some

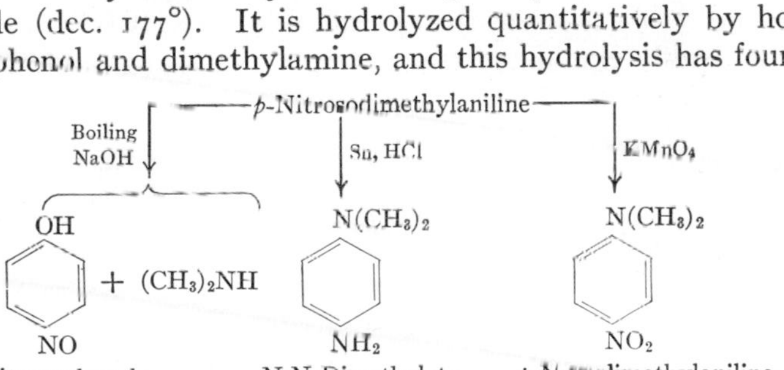

Boiling NaOH

p-Nitrosodimethylaniline

Sn, HCl

KMnO₄

OH

+ (CH₃)₂NH

p-Nitrosophenol

N(CH₃)₂

NH₂

N,N-Dimethyl-*p*-phenylenediamine
(m.p. 41°)

N(CH₃)₂

NO₂

p-Nitrodimethylaniline
(m.p. 164°)

use in preparation of secondary aliphatic amines. Reduction of the nitroso derivative affords the N,N-dimethyl derivative of *p*-phenylenediamine, and oxidation with permanganate yields the corresponding nitro compound. *p*-Nitrosodimethylaniline is employed as a dye intermediate.

Ureides, Isocyanates, Urethans, and Other Derivatives. — Aniline combines readily with phosgene to form **s-diphenylurea**; the reaction is general for primary and secondary amines. A preparative method that affords

$$O=C\begin{smallmatrix}Cl\\Cl\end{smallmatrix} \quad + \quad 2\,H_2NC_6H_5 \quad \longrightarrow \quad O=C\begin{smallmatrix}NHC_6H_5\\NHC_6H_5\end{smallmatrix}$$

s-Diphenylurea
or carbanilide
(m.p. 239°)

phenylurea along with the N,N′-disubstituted urea consists in boiling an aqueous solution of aniline hydrochloride and urea, when ammonium chloride is eliminated between the reactants; the diphenyl derivative sepa-

$$C_6H_5NH_2\cdot HCl \quad + \quad CO(NH_2)_2 \quad \xrightarrow{\text{Boiling water}} \quad$$

$$\xrightarrow{52\text{–}55\%} \quad \begin{matrix}C_6H_5NHCONH_2\\ \text{Phenylurea}\\ (\text{m.p. } 147°)\end{matrix}$$

$$\xrightarrow{38\text{–}40\%} \quad (C_6H_5NH)_2CO\\ \text{s-Diphenylurea}$$

rates from the hot solution and phenylurea is deposited on cooling. Another route to these ureides starts from **phenyl isocyanate**, $C_6H_5N{=}C{=}O$, an offensive smelling, lachrymatory liquid, b.p. 164°; this reactive compound with twinned double bonds combines with ammonia to yield phenylurea and with aniline to give *s*-diphenylurea, probably by addition to the carbonyl group and ketonization. Aryl isocyanates usually are prepared by

$$C_6H_5N{=}C{=}O \quad + \quad H_2NC_6H_5 \quad \longrightarrow \quad \left[\begin{matrix}C_6H_5N{=}C{-}OH\\ |\\ C_6H_5NH\end{matrix}\right] \quad \longrightarrow \quad \begin{matrix}C_6H_5NHC{=}O\\ |\\ C_6H_5NH\end{matrix}$$

Phenyl isocyanate   s-Diphenylurea

condensation of an amine with one equivalent of phosgene and heating or distilling the resulting arylcarbamyl chloride, ArNHCOCl, when hydrogen chloride is readily eliminated (see example). Ethanol adds to phenyl iso-

NH₂   NHCOCl   N=C=O

$$\xrightarrow{\text{COCl}_2 \text{ in C}_2\text{H}_5\text{OAc}} \qquad \xrightarrow[85\text{–}95\% \text{ overall}]{\text{Mild heat}}$$

NO₂   NO₂   NO₂

p-Nitroaniline   *p*-Nitrophenyl-
carbamyl chloride   *p*-Nitrophenyl
isocyanate
(m.p. 57°)

cyanate in the same manner as ammonia or aniline to form **phenylurethan**. This method of preparing solid derivatives of alcohols is useful for identifica-

$$C_6H_5N{=}C{=}O \quad + \quad HOC_2H_5 \quad \longrightarrow \quad \left[\,C_6H_5N{=}C\begin{smallmatrix}OC_2H_5\\ OH\end{smallmatrix}\,\right] \quad \longrightarrow \quad C_6H_5NHCOOC_2H_5$$

Phenylurethan (ethyl
N-phenylcarbamate,
m.p. 53°)

tion and has the advantage of being applicable to tertiary, as well as to primary and secondary, alcohols. Urethans also are used for characterization of amines, for they are obtainable by acylation with ethyl chlorocarbonate:

$$C_6H_5NH_2 \ + \ ClCOOC_2H_5 \ \xrightarrow{\text{aq. Na}_2\text{CO}_3,\ 0°} \ C_6H_5NHCOOC_2H_5$$

s-Diphenylthiourea, employed as an accelerator for vulcanization of rubber, can be prepared by heating aniline and carbon disulfide in alcohol with powdered potassium hydroxide as catalyst. The reaction probably proceeds through addition of aniline to carbon disulfide, elimination of hydro-

$$2 C_6H_5NH_2 \ + \ CS_2 \ \xrightarrow[78\%]{\text{Boiling alcohol, KOH}} \ \begin{array}{c} C_6H_5NH \\ \diagdown \\ \diagup \\ C_6H_5NH \end{array} C{=}S \ + \ H_2S$$

s-Diphenylthiourea
(thiocarbanilide, m.p. 153°)

gen sulfide, and addition of aniline to the unsaturated intermediate, phenyl isothiocyanate. The terminal addition reaction can be reversed by acids,

$$C_6H_5NH_2 \ \xrightarrow{CS_2} \ C_6H_5NHC\diagdown_{SH}^{\diagup S} \ \xrightarrow{\ -H_2S\ } \ C_6H_5N{=}C{=}S \ \xrightarrow{C_6H_5NH_2} \ (C_6H_5NH)_2CS$$

Phenyldithiocarbamic acid · · · · · Phenyl isothiocyanate

and this reaction is the standard method of preparing **phenyl isothiocyanate** (b.p. 221°), also called **phenyl mustard oil** because of the mustardlike odor and the relationship to the active component of mustard, allyl isothiocyanate ($CH_2{=}CHCH_2N{=}C{=}S$). Another property of *s*-diphenylthiourea is ready replacement of sulfur by the imino group ($=NH$) through an unsaturated intermediate that can be isolated in the absence of ammonia:

$$\begin{array}{c} C_6H_5NH \\ \diagdown \\ \diagup \\ C_6H_5NH \end{array} C{=}S \ \xrightarrow{\text{Alcohol, PbO, NH}_3} \ \left[\begin{array}{c} C_6H_5N \\ \diagdown \\ \diagup \\ C_6H_5N \end{array} C \right] \ \longrightarrow \ \begin{array}{c} C_6H_5NH \\ \diagdown \\ \diagup \\ C_6H_5NH \end{array} C{=}NH$$

Carbodiphenylimide
(liq., b.p. 331°) · · · Diphenylguanidine
(m.p. 147°)

Another type of amine derivative obtainable through the hydrazine is illustrated by **phenyl azide**, $C_6H_5N_3$, a pale yellow, pungent smelling oil that explodes when heated. The usual preparation involves the action of nitrous acid on phenylhydrazine, when the nitroso compound initially formed loses water, with rearrangement to the azide structure. The sub-

$$C_6H_5NHNH_2 \ \xrightarrow{\text{aq. HCl, NaNO}_2,\ 0°} \ C_6H_5N{-}N\!\underset{\underset{N}{|}}{H_2} \ \xrightarrow[65\text{-}68\%]{-H_2O} \ C_6H_5N_3$$

Phenyl azide
(b.p. 50°/5 mm.)

stance does not have a cyclic structure expected from the mode of formation and probably is a hybrid of resonance forms:

$$C_6H_5N{=}\overset{+}{N}{=}\overset{-}{N} \ \longleftrightarrow \ C_6H_5\overset{-}{N}{-}\overset{+}{N}{\equiv}N$$

Phenyl isocyanide, $C_6H_5N{=}C$, is formed on heating aniline with chloro-form and alcoholic potassium hydroxide (Hofmann, 1867). The isocyanide

$$C_6H_5N\overline{H_2} \;+\; \overline{H}\overline{|C|Cl_3} \xrightarrow{\text{KOH}} C_6H_5N{=}C$$
Phenyl isocyanide
(b.p. 166°)

(or isonitrile) is toxic, and has a penetrating, characteristic odor resembling that of hydrogen cyanide, and since the substance can be recognized by smell, its formation from a drop of aniline is used as a test (general for pri-mary amines). It is colorless when freshly distilled, but is unstable in the presence of air and becomes discolored on brief exposure and soon resinifies. Phenyl isocyanide is formulated conventionally as containing bivalent car-bon, but dipole moment data indicate the presence of one polar link $C_6H_5\overset{+}{N}{\equiv}\overset{-}{C}$; the substance has a marked tendency to enter into reactions by which the carbon atom acquires its normal condition.

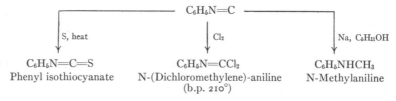

$C_6H_5N{=}C$

S, heat	Cl_2	Na, $C_5H_{11}OH$
$C_6H_5N{=}C{=}S$	$C_6H_5N{=}CCl_2$	$C_6H_5NHCH_3$
Phenyl isothiocyanate	N-(Dichloromethylene)-aniline (b.p. 210°)	N-Methylaniline

DIAZONIUM SALTS

Benzenediazonium chloride, $C_6H_5N_2{}^+Cl^-$, the product of the reaction be-tween aniline hydrochloride and nitrous acid in the presence of excess hy-drochloric acid at ice-bath temperature, is an ionic salt very soluble in water and completely insoluble in ether and other organic solvents, and in aqueous solutions it is completely dissociated. The crystalline solid is very sensitive to shock when fully dried and detonates violently on mild heating. Prepa-ration of the solid can be accomplished by employing the combination of an organic nitrite and an organic acid as the source of nitrous acid, for the diazonium salt is then the only ether-insoluble product and is precipitated from this solvent. The reaction product is sensitive and requires careful

$$C_6H_5NH_3Cl \;+\; n\text{-}C_4H_9ONO \;+\; CH_3COOH \xrightarrow{\text{Ether}} C_6H_5N_2Cl \;+\; CH_3COOC_4H_9$$

handling. Fortunately, for nearly all reactions, isolation of the dry solid is not required, for the reactions can be carried out satisfactorily with use of the readily prepared aqueous solutions. Preparation of such a solution, or diazotization of an amine, is conducted as follows. The amine is dis-solved in water containing three equivalents of hydrochloric acid, by heating if required, and the solution is cooled well in ice, when the amine hydrochlo-ride usually crystallizes. With control of the temperature to 0–5°, an aque-ous solution of sodium nitrite is added in portions until, after allowing a few minutes for reaction, the solution gives a positive test for excess nitrous acid with starch–iodide paper. The amine hydrochloride dissolves in the process to give a clear solution of the much more soluble diazonium salt. One equivalent of hydrochloric acid is bound by the amine and provides the anion of the reaction product, a second reacts with sodium nitrite to liberate nitrous acid, and the third maintains proper acidity required to stabilize the diazonium salt by inhibition of secondary changes. The process can be summarized as follows:

$$\text{ArNH}_2 + 3\,\text{HCl} + \text{NaNO}_2 \xrightarrow{\text{In water at 0°}} \text{ArN}_2\text{Cl} + \text{NaCl} + \text{HCl} + 2\,\text{H}_2\text{O}$$

Diazonium salts were discovered by Griess[1]. The name is based on the presence of two nitrogen atoms (Fr. *azote*, nitrogen) and on analogy to ammonium compounds. The structure and a possible mechanism of formation through the N-nitroso derivative are shown in the formulation.

$$\left[\underset{\text{H} \quad \text{H}}{\overset{+}{\text{C}_6\text{H}_5\text{N}}-\text{H}}\right]\text{Cl}^- \xrightarrow{\text{HONO}} \left[\underset{\text{H} \quad \text{H}----}{\overset{+}{\text{C}_6\text{H}_5\text{N}}-\text{N}=\text{O}}\right]\text{Cl}^- \longrightarrow$$

$$\left[\underset{\text{H}}{\overset{+}{\text{C}_6\text{H}_5\text{N}}=\text{N}-\text{OH}}\right]\text{Cl}^- \xrightarrow{-\text{H}_2\text{O}} \left[\overset{+}{\text{C}_6\text{H}_5\text{N}}\equiv\text{N}\right]\text{Cl}^-$$
Benzenediazonium
chloride

Addition of alkali to a well-cooled solution of benzenediazonium chloride may result in initial conversion to the quaternary ammonium hydroxide, $[\text{C}_6\text{H}_5\overset{+}{\text{N}}\equiv\text{N}]\text{OH}^-$, which isomerizes at once to a weakly acidic substance, benzenediazoic acid, characterized as metal salts, or diazotates. The aryldiazoic acids, referred to also as diazo hydroxides or diazo hydrates, are

$$[\text{C}_6\text{H}_5\overset{+}{\text{N}}\equiv\text{N}] + \text{OH}^- \rightleftharpoons \underset{\substack{\text{Benzenediazoic}\\\text{acid}}}{\text{C}_6\text{H}_5\text{N}=\text{NOH}} \overset{\text{KOH}}{\rightleftharpoons} \underset{\substack{\text{Potassium benzene-}\\\text{diazotate}}}{\text{C}_6\text{H}_5\text{N}=\text{NOK}}$$

comparable in structure and degree of acidity to nitrous acid; they have not been isolated in crystalline form, for acidification of the alkaline solution, even with acetic acid, results largely in reversal of the equilibrium and reconversion to the diazonium salt. Potassium salts have been isolated as crystallizates from concentrated alkaline solutions and purified by precipitation from alcoholic solution with ether. Two forms have been isolated and

$$\begin{array}{ccc} \underset{\substack{\text{KO}-\text{N}}}{\overset{\text{C}_6\text{H}_5-\text{N}}{\|}} & \longrightarrow & \underset{\substack{\text{N}-\text{OK}}}{\overset{\text{C}_6\text{H}_5-\text{N}}{\|}} \\ \textit{cis} \text{ Form} & & \textit{trans} \text{ Form} \\ \text{(normal diazotate)} & & \text{(isodiazotate)} \end{array}$$

characterized by Hantzsch[2] as geometrical isomers. The initially produced form (normal, or *cis*) of potassium benzenediazotate is labile, and is more

[1] Peter Griess, 1829–88; b. Kirchhosbach, Germany; asst. to Hofmann in London; chemist in an English brewery

[2] Arthur Hantzsch, 1857–1935; b. Dresden; Ph.D. Würzburg (R. Schmitt): Leipzig; *J Chem. Soc.*, 1051 (1936)

reactive and has a higher energy content than the *iso* form (*trans*) to which it changes rather rapidly in either the solid or the dissolved state. A freshly alkalized solution of benzenediazonium chloride thus consists principally of the alkali salt of the *cis* form of benzenediazoic acid; the *trans* form predominates in an aged solution. A further, structural isomerization has been demonstrated most clearly for acyl derivatives (Huisgen,[3] 1951–). Thus nitrosoacetanilide (a) undergoes reversible acyl migration to the benzenediazoacetate (b). The *trans* configuration of these esters was established

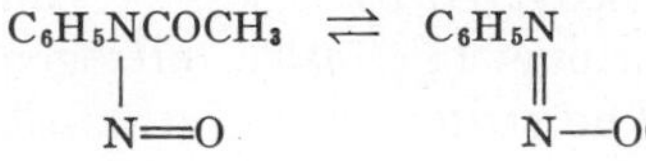

$$C_6H_5NCOCH_3 \quad \rightleftharpoons \quad C_6H_5N$$

$$\begin{matrix} | & & \| \\ N=O & & N-OCOCH_3 \end{matrix}$$

$$\text{(a)} \qquad\qquad \text{(b)}$$

by demonstration that the nitrosolactam (c) can be isomerized to the cyclic diazo ester (d).

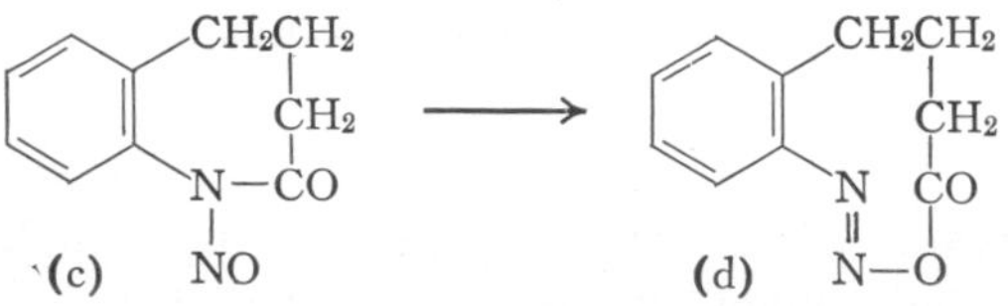

Most aromatic primary amines can be diazotized by the procedure indicated. Usually a clear colorless solution of the diazonium salt results, even though the amine salt used is only sparingly soluble, but in some instances the diazonium salt crystallizes. This is the case with sulfanilic acid because of the formation of an inner salt. The substance is diazotized by bringing it into solution as the sodium salt, adding the requisite amount of sodium nitrite, and pouring the solution on a mixture of ice and hydrochloric acid; nitrous acid and the dipolar sulfanilic acid are liberated together and after a few seconds the dipolar diazonium salt separates. Difficulty in effecting

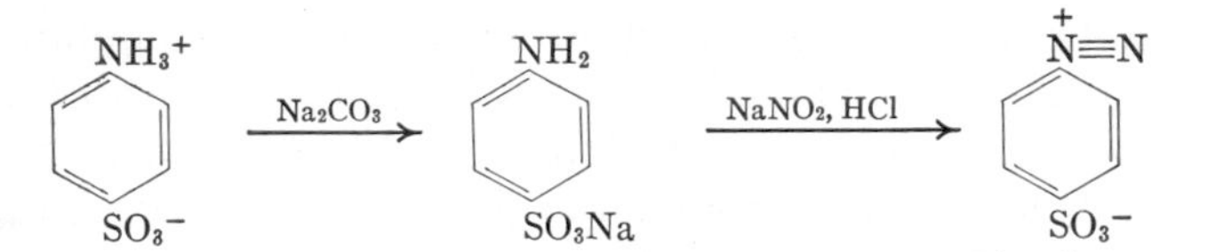

diazotization is experienced with very weakly basic amines, particularly polynitro compounds such as picramide, but satisfactory procedures have been developed for conducting such diazotizations in a mixture of concentrated sulfuric acid and acetic acid or in concentrated sulfuric acid alone. Another limiting factor is that nitrous acid has oxidizing properties and is liable to attack sensitive compounds (*o*- and *p*-aminophenols), but oxidation often can be inhibited by a zinc or copper salt.

---

[3] Rolf Huisgen, b. 1920 Gerolstein, Germany; Ph.D. Univ. Munich (Wieland); Munich

Hydrolysis to Phenols. — When an aqueous solution of a diazonium salt is strongly acidified with sulfuric acid and heated at the boiling point, nitrogen is evolved and the amine derivative is converted into the corresponding phenol. Usually 40–50% sulfuric acid is used in order to attain a

$$[Ar\overset{+}{N}{\equiv}N]\overset{-}{Cl} + HOH \longrightarrow ArOH + N_2 + HCl$$

reflux temperature sufficiently high to promote reasonably rapid hydrolysis, and the strong acid may have a destructive action on the sensitive hydroxy compound. Hydrochloric acid is less satisfactory as an acidifying agent because adequate temperatures are not obtainable and also because the diazonium salt group may be replaced in part by halogen. Diazotization is carried out in sulfuric acid solution in order to avoid this side reaction. The crude reaction product also may be deeply colored owing to contamination with azo compounds almost invariably formed as by-products, but purification can be accomplished by extraction with alkali or by steam distillation, and the pure phenol obtained in moderate yields. Since the diazonium salt need not be isolated, introduction of a hydroxyl group can be accomplished in essentially three steps: nitration, reduction to the amine, and diazotization in aqueous medium followed by hydrolysis in the same solution. The overall process is more elaborate than that of sulfonation and alkali fusion, and ordinarily the yields are not so satisfactory. The chief preparative application of the route through the diazonium derivative is in instances where the alternate method is inapplicable. Thus *m*-nitrophenol cannot be prepared through the sulfonate because of the sensitivity of nitro compounds to alkali, but is obtainable through the diazo reaction. Nuclear

halogen substituents also are liable to be attacked by alkali at the elevated temperatures required for alkali fusion of a sulfonate, but *o*- and *p*-chlorophenol, for example, can be prepared satisfactorily from the corresponding amines by diazotization and hydrolysis.

Sandmeyer Reaction. — When an aqueous solution of benzenediazonium chloride is treated with one equivalent of potassium iodide and warmed, the benzenediazonium iodide present in the equilibrium mixture decomposes with evolution of nitrogen and formation of iodobenzene in good yield. Neither chloro- nor bromobenzene can be prepared satisfactorily

$$C_6H_5NH_2 \xrightarrow{\text{aq. HCl, NaNO}_2,\ 5°} [C_6H_5\overset{+}{N}{\equiv}N]\overset{-}{Cl} \xrightarrow[\substack{74-76\% \\ \text{overall}}]{\text{KI, 95°}} C_6H_5I + N_2 + KCl$$

by this procedure, but Sandmeyer[4] (1884) discovered that replacement of the diazonium salt group by halogen is catalyzed markedly by cuprous

---

[4] Traugott Sandmeyer, 1854–1922; b. Wettingen, Switzerland; asst. to V. Meyer and Hantzsch; Geigy Co., Basel

salts and thereby contributed a practicable preparative method capable of wide application and of certain elaborations that can be described as Sandmeyer-type replacements. For the preparation of aryl chlorides by the Sandmeyer procedure, the amine is diazotized in ice-cold solution in hydrochloric acid with sodium nitrite, and a solution of one equivalent of cuprous chloride in hydrochloric acid is added; a brown, sparingly soluble complex separates consisting of a double molecule of the diazonium salt and cuprous chloride, and when the suspension of this substance is warmed, decomposition sets in with evolution of nitrogen, disappearance of the solid, and separation of an oily layer containing the organic halide. Although the crude reaction mixture usually is dark colored, separation of the halide from contaminants and inorganic salts can be accomplished by steam distillation. Both *o*- and *p*-chlorotoluene can be prepared in good yield; this method also

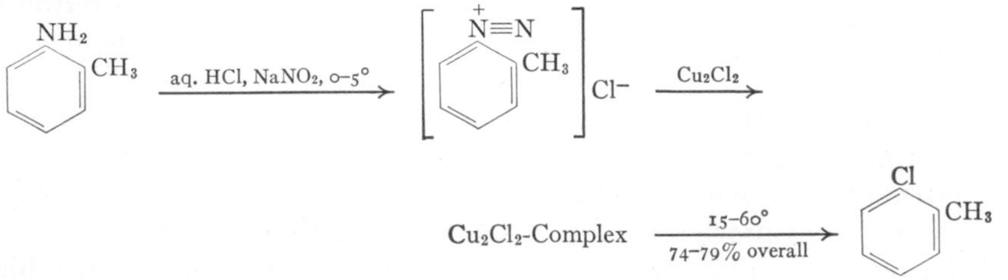

o-Chlorotoluene

is convenient for obtaining *m*-nitrochlorobenzene free from isomers, since pure *m*-nitroaniline is available (yield 68–71%). For preparation of a bromide by the Sandmeyer reaction, the amine is diazotized in sulfuric acid solution and the resulting aryldiazonium sulfate treated with a solution of cuprous bromide in excess hydrobromic acid; the complex is then decomposed by heating. *p*-Bromotoluene can be prepared from *p*-toluidine in 70–73% yield, and *o*-chlorobromobenzene is obtainable from *o*-chloroaniline with equal success. The reaction can be applied to preparation of nitriles, which result from the action of a solution of cuprous cyanide in excess potassium cyanide on a diazonium salt, as shown in the example (the yield is the same for the conversion of *p*-toluidine into *p*-tolunitrile, m.p. 29°, b.p. 218°).

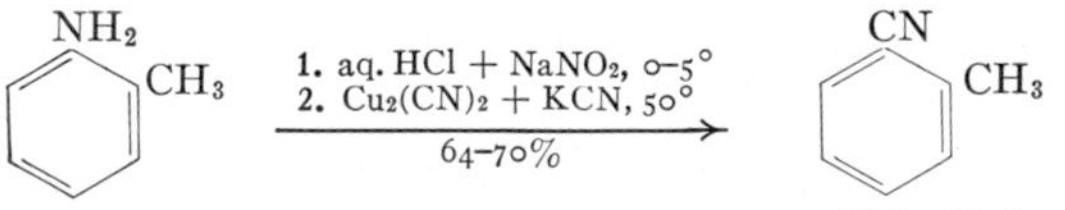

o-Tolunitrile
(b.p. 205°)

In the examples cited a molecular equivalent of the cuprous salt component is required, apparently because of formation of the intermediate molecular complex. Gattermann (1890) discovered that freshly precipitated copper powder (zinc dust and copper sulfate solution) can replace the cuprous salt as promoter for the replacement and is effective in catalytic amounts and at temperatures lower than required in the Sandmeyer procedure. Gattermann's procedure is the simpler of the two, but the yields, though high in some instances, never surpass those of the Sandmeyer procedure and are sometimes lower. If a cuprous salt is not available, the

$$p\text{-}CH_3C_6H_4NH_2 \xrightarrow[43-47\%]{\substack{1.\ \text{aq. HBr, NaNO}_2,\ 10° \\ 2.\ \text{Cu powder, gentle heat}}} p\text{-}CH_3C_6H_4Br$$

copper-catalyzed reaction of Gattermann is applicable. Thus benzene-diazonium sulfate is converted in good yield into benzenesulfinic acid (p. 593) by the action of sulfur dioxide and copper powder, and when treated with potassium cyanate and copper affords phenyl isocyanate, C_6H_5NCO, though in low yield (20%). The most useful application of the Gattermann procedure is for joining two aromatic nuclei by interaction of a diazonium salt and a hydrocarbon under the catalytic influence of metallic copper or zinc, for example:

$$C_6H_5N_2Cl \ + \ C_6H_6 \xrightarrow[13\%]{\text{Cu (or Zn), alcohol, }30\text{--}40°} \underset{\text{Diphenyl}}{C_6H_5{\cdot}C_6H_5} \ + \ N_2 \ + \ HCl$$

The yield in this instance is low, and the product is accompanied by higher hydrocarbons of the same type (terphenyl, quaterphenyl, quinquiphenyl) formed by interaction of the diazonium salt with diphenyl.

A further variation of the Sandmeyer reaction is the preparation of aryl thiocyanates, or rhodanates, ArSCN, from diazonium salts and cuprous thiocyanate. Another is replacement of the diazonium salt group by the nitro group by interaction with sodium nitrite in the presence of precipitated cuprous oxide. In other instances the replacement reaction can be brought about with a catalyst other than copper or a copper salt, or even proceeds without a catalyst (compare $C_6H_5N_2I \rightarrow C_6H_5I$). Fluoro-benzene can be prepared (50–56% yield) by the action of fluoroboric acid (HBF_4, made by dissolving solid boric acid in 60% hydrofluoric acid) on a solution of benzenediazonium chloride at 10° (Schiemann reaction). Benzenediazonium chloride reacts with sodium arsenite in the presence of a trace of copper sulfate to give phenylarsonic acid, $C_6H_5AsO(OH)_2$, in 39–45% yield (Bart reaction). Replacement by the sulfhydryl group (—SH), the thioglycolyl residue (—SCH$_2$COOH), and the azide group (—N$_3$) in the absence of a catalyst is brought about by the reagents KSH, HSCH$_2$COOH, and NaN$_3$, respectively.

Deamination. — Methods of reduction are available for replacement of the diazonium salt group by hydrogen, and hence for elimination of a primary amino substituent; the reaction is described as a deamination. The first known experimental procedure, discovered by Griess in 1864, consists in treatment of the diazonium salt with ethanol, which serves as a hydrogen donor and becomes oxidized to acetaldehyde. An appreciable amount of

$$ArN_2Cl \ + \ CH_3CH_2OH \longrightarrow ArH \ + \ N_2 \ + \ HCl \ + \ CH_3CHO$$

water must be avoided or else hydrolysis will occur, but the isolation of the dry diazonium salt is not always required. The utility of deamination is illustrated by the preparation of s-tribromobenzene, which is not accessible by direct bromination, for it contains o-p directing groups *meta* to one another. The desired orientation is achieved in the bromination of aniline by virtue of the dominating directive influence of the amino group. Thus 2,4,6-tribromoaniline is obtainable from aniline in nearly quantitative yield, and can be converted into s-tribromobenzene by reduction of the diazotized amine with ethanol. The moist precipitate of tribromoaniline is

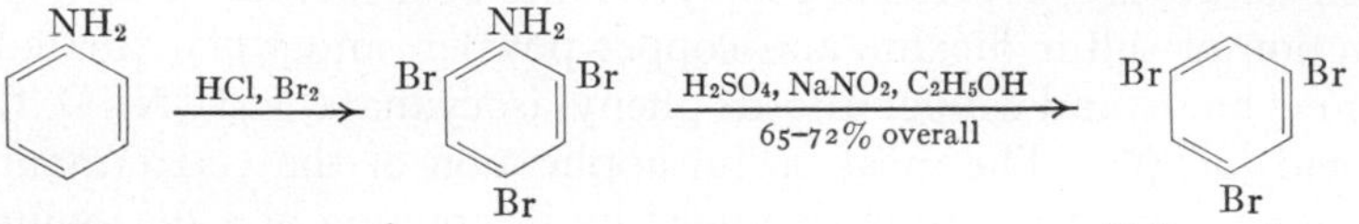

dissolved in ethanol containing some benzene as diluent and treated with concentrated sulfuric acid followed by solid sodium nitrite; the diazonium salt is reduced as formed, with evolution of nitrogen and production of the deaminated product and acetaldehyde.

Deamination with ethanol gives good results with the diazonium salts of several polyhalo- and polynitroamines, but with simpler compounds a considerable amount of material is converted into the corresponding ethyl ether by the side reaction:

$$ArN_2Cl + HOC_2H_5 \rightarrow ArOC_2H_5 + N_2 + HCl$$

A superior and more convenient procedure is reduction of the diazonium salt in aqueous solution with a large excess of hypophosphorous acid, H_3PO_2 (Mai, 1902). The reaction proceeds in the cold, and the reagent can be added to the aqueous solution of the diazotized amine. The example cited illustrates the preparation through an amine derivative of a hydro-

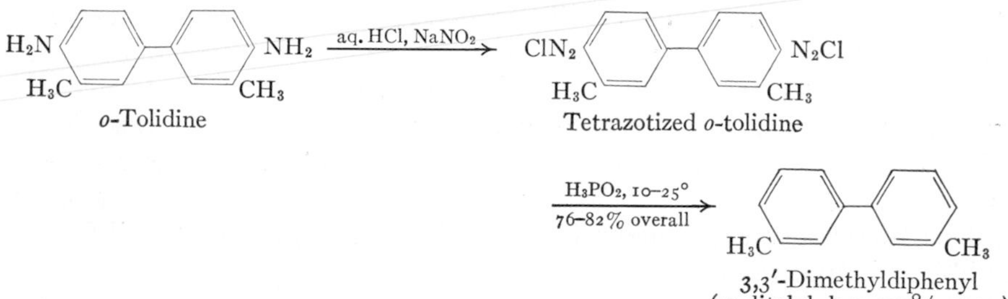

o-Tolidine   Tetratozized o-tolidine

3,3'-Dimethyldiphenyl
(m-ditolyl, b.p. 115°/3 mm.)

carbon difficulty accessible by other methods. Diazonium salts can also be reduced in aqueous solution with sodium stannite (Friedländer,[5] 1889) or with alkaline formaldehyde solution (Brewster, 1939). A further example of the value of deamination is the method for preparation of m-toluidine from p-toluidine. The amine is acetylated both to prevent oxidation and to permit *ortho* orientation, a nitro group is introduced, and after deacetyla-

[5] Paul Friedländer, 1857–1923; b. Königsberg, Germany; asst. to Baeyer in Munich; Darmstadt; *Ber.*, **57A**, 13 (1924)

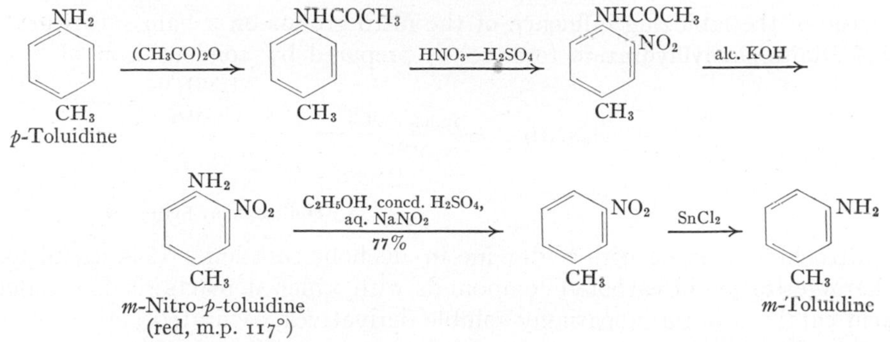

NH2
CH3
p-Toluidine
(CH3CO)2O
NHCOCH3
CH3
HNO3—H2SO4
NHCOCH3
NO2
CH3
alc. KOH
NH2
NO2
CH3
m-Nitro-p-toluidine
(red, m.p. 117°)
C2H5OH, concd. H2SO4,
aq. NaNO2
77%
NO2
CH3
SnCl2
NH2
CH3
m-Toluidine

tion the amino substituent is eliminated. The diazonium salt is not isolated but is produced under conditions suitable for the replacement reaction; thus *m*-nitro-*p*-toluidine is suspended in alcohol, treated with concentrated sulfuric acid, and, after cooling, a concentrated aqueous solution of sodium nitrite is added in portions.

Reduction to Arylhydrazines. — Reduction of a diazonium salt with the calculated amount of stannous chloride at a low temperature, or better with excess sodium sulfite in a warm solution, results in formation of the corresponding arylhydrazine. The reaction probably proceeds through the diazo chloride ($C_6H_5N{=}NCl$) or diazo sulfonate ($C_6H_5N{=}NSO_3Na$) present in equilibrium with the diazonium salt. The product can be isolated as

$$[Ar\overset{+}{N}{\equiv}N]\overset{-}{X} \rightleftharpoons ArN{=}N{-}X \xrightarrow{4\,H} ArNHNH_3X \xrightarrow{NaOH} ArNHNH_2$$

either the hydrochloride or the free base. An efficient procedure for the preparation of **phenylhydrazine** consists in diazotization of aniline in hydrochloric acid solution, reduction with sodium sulfite, treatment with hydro-

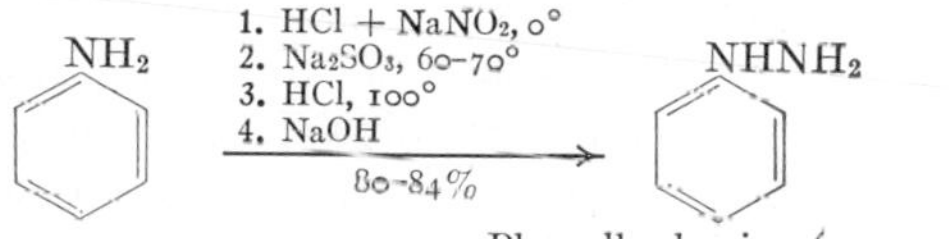

NH2
1. HCl + NaNO2, 0°
2. Na2SO3, 60–70°
3. HCl, 100°
4. NaOH
80–84%
NHNH2

Phenylhydrazine (m.p. 24°, b.p. 243°, pK_b 8.80)

chloric acid to destroy excess sulfite and decompose the sulfamic acid sodium salt ($C_6H_5NHNHSO_3Na$), and liberation of the base with alkali. Phenylhydrazine when freshly distilled is a nearly colorless liquid, but it darkens rather rapidly on exposure to air as the result of oxidation. The hydrochloride, m.p. 243° dec., is more stable. Phenylhydrazine is rather toxic and must be kept off the skin; it is a valuable reagent for carbonyl compounds and is a reducing agent.

Although mononitroamines can be converted into hydrazines by reduction of the diazonium salts with sodium sulfite (e.g., *p*-nitrophenylhydrazine, orange, m.p. 157°), the reaction is not applicable to polynitroamines, which are so weakly basic that diazotization is accomplished only in strongly acidic solutions. In such a case, however, an alternate method is available by

virtue of the labilizing influence of the nitro groups on a halo substituent.
2,4-Dinitrophenylhydrazine (orange) is prepared by condensation of 2,4-

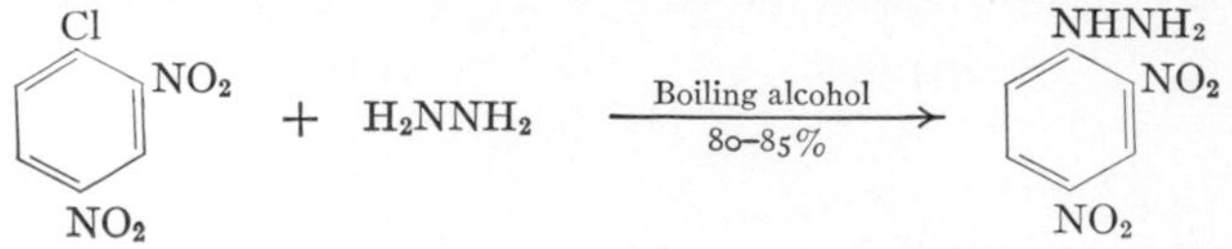

2,4-Dinitrophenylhydrazine

dinitrochlorobenzene with hydrazine in alcoholic solution. It is useful for
characterization of carbonyl compounds with which it reacts readily under
acid catalysis to form sparingly soluble derivatives; saturated ketones give
yellow derivatives, α,β-unsaturated ketones give red ones. The reagent is
also useful for dehydrohalogenation of α-bromo ketones, with which it reacts to give bromine-free, red hydrazones, which can be cleaved to the unsaturated ketone.

Coupling Reaction. — Diazonium salts react readily with phenols and
aromatic amines to form bright-colored azo compounds in which the two
aromatic nuclei are linked through the azo grouping, —N=N—. The
smoothly proceeding union of the diazo component with the phenol or
amine is described as coupling. Benzenediazonium chloride couples with
phenol in alkaline solution very rapidly at ice-bath temperature to form
p-hydroxyazobenzene (or p-benzeneazophenol). Since a diazonium salt

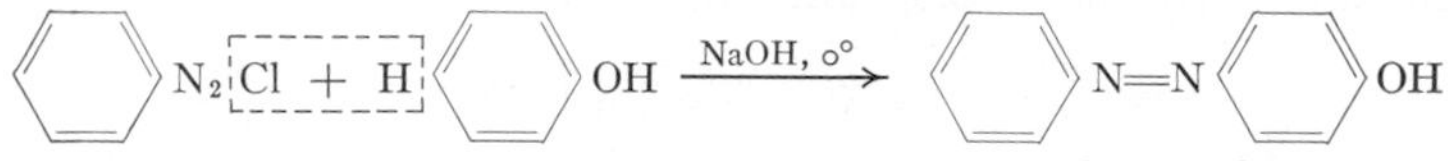

p-Hydroxyazobenzene
(orange, m.p. 152°)

undergoes change in alkaline solution with eventual formation of the *trans*
diazotate, which fails to couple, the proper procedure is to stir the solution
of benzenediazonium chloride slowly into a chilled solution of phenol containing sufficient alkali to neutralize the organic and inorganic acids in the
resulting mixture and maintain suitable alkalinity. Coupling occurs so
rapidly as to preclude destruction of the diazo component. Dimethylaniline couples in an analogous manner in an aqueous medium that is either
neutral or weakly acidified with acetic acid, and gives a yellow p-benzeneazo

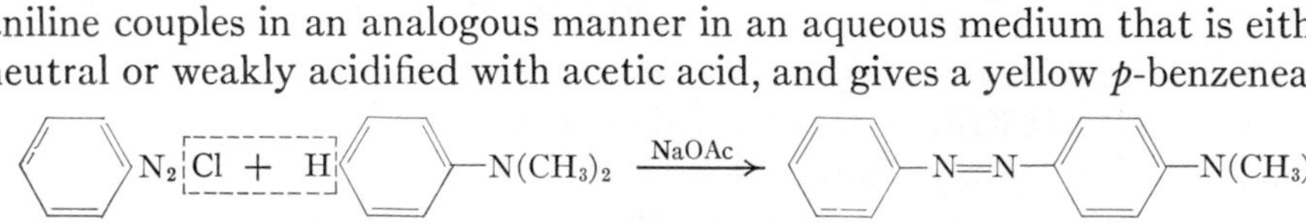

p-Dimethylaminoazobenzene
(yellow, m.p. 117°)

compound. These examples illustrate a reaction that is general to phenols
and to tertiary amines having available a free position *ortho* or *para* to the
hydroxyl or amino group. Where a choice is open, coupling occurs practically exclusively in the *para* position. The product of coupling of benzenediazonium chloride with phenol contains at most 1% of o-hydroxyazo-
benzene (orange, m.p. 83°); the small amount of *ortho* isomer can be

separated from the nonvolatile *para* compound by steam distillation.   Although there is a marked preference for *para* substitution, coupling occurs readily enough in the *ortho* position if this alone is available, for example:

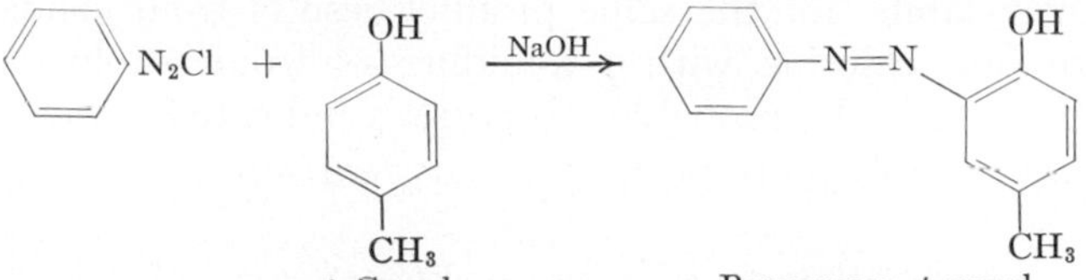

p-Cresol

Benzeneazo-*p*-cresol
(yellow, m.p. 108°)

The coupling reaction is spectacular because of the rapid formation of brightly colored products from colorless components.   The reaction is comparable to that of C-nitrosation with nitrous acid (p. 607) with respect to exclusive *para* orientation and rapidity of combination in aqueous solution even at 0°.   Both reactions are specific to amines and phenols and depend on the powerful directive influence of the hydroxyl and amino group. Studies of the rate of coupling in solutions of varying acidity indicate that one reacting species is always the diazonium ion and that the other, in an amine coupling (1), is the nonionized amine, and in a phenol coupling (2), is the phenoxide ion (Bartlett, 1941).   In the pH range 2–6 the velocity of

1. ArN_2^+ + $C_6H_5N(CH_3)_2$
2. ArN_2^+ + $C_6H_5O^-$

an amine coupling increases with decreasing acidity till the concentration of free amine reaches a maximum, and in a phenol coupling in the region pH 5–8 the rate of reaction increases with increasing pH because a greater proportion of the reactive phenoxide component becomes available.   This interpretation not only accords with the general concept of other aromatic substitutions but extends the evidence.   Here the entering group is an actual cation, and that it is attracted to the nucleus of the phenoxide ion more strongly than to that of the phenol is a consequence of the inductive and resonance effect of the negatively charged oxygen, which results in increased electron density at the nuclear positions, particularly *ortho* and *para*.   A positive charge on the nitrogen atom of an amine would have the opposite effect, and hence it is the free amine that couples.

Just as primary and secondary amines are attacked by nitrous acid in the amino group rather than in the nucleus, such amines ordinarily react with diazonium salts to give N-substitution products known as diazoamino derivatives.   Thus benzenediazonium chloride and aniline combine to form diazoaminobenzene.   A convenient procedure consists in dissolving

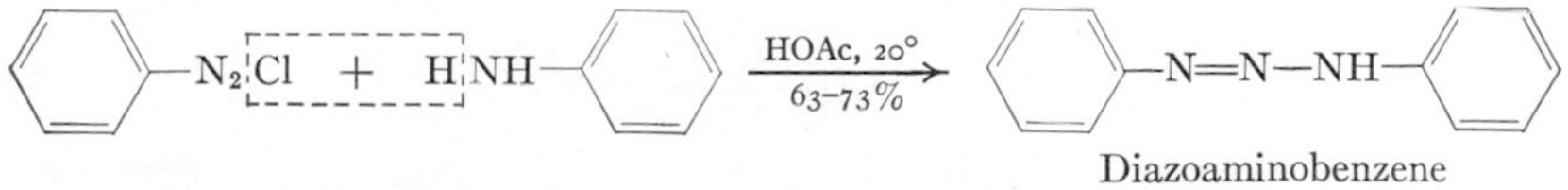

Diazoaminobenzene
(yellow, m.p. 98°)

two equivalents of aniline in three equivalents of hydrochloric acid and adding one equivalent of sodium nitrite, followed by two equivalents of sodium acetate. The hydrogen in the system —N=N—NH— is activated and apparently labile, for the same product results from condensation of benzenediazonium chloride with p-toluidine as from p-toluenediazonium chloride with aniline; the probable structure is indicated. Like N-nitroso-

$$C_6H_5N_2Cl \;+\; p\text{-}H_2NC_6H_4CH_3 \qquad\qquad\qquad C_6H_5NH_2 \;+\; p\text{-}CH_3C_6H_4N_2Cl$$

$$C_6H_5N{=}NNHC_6H_4CH_3(p)$$
4-Methyldiazoamino-
benzene (yellow, m.p. 91°)

amines, diazoamino compounds rearrange under the influence of acid catalysts with transposition of the arylazo group to the *para* position in the nucleus. Thus diazoaminobenzene rearranges to p-aminoazobenzene, the

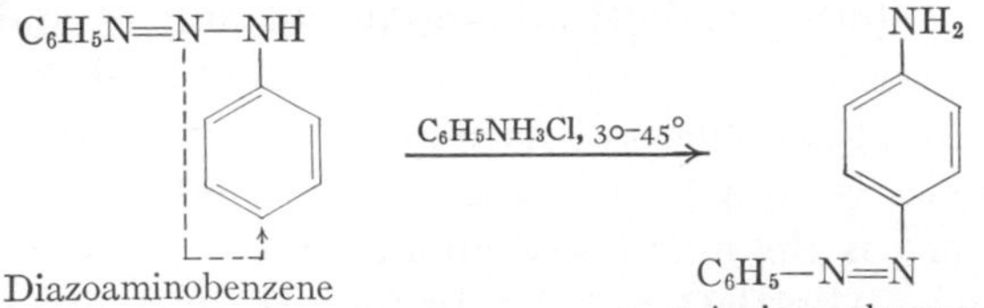

$$C_6H_5N{=}N{-}NH$$

$$\xrightarrow{\;C_6H_5NH_3Cl,\ 30\text{-}45°\;}$$

Diazoaminobenzene

$$C_6H_5{-}N{=}N$$
p-Aminoazobenzene
(yellow, m.p. 126°)

product that would have resulted from direct nuclear coupling. Such rearrangements proceed slowly under the influence of mineral acids at room temperature and can be brought about more readily by gentle heating in the presence of the amine hydrochloride, often with use of an excess of the free amine as diluent. Test experiments indicate that the rearrangement actually involves fission of the diazoamino compound under the influence of the acidic catalyst to the diazonium salt and the amine and recombination of the components with nuclear substitution. Secondary amines, N-methyl-aniline for example, react similarly, and yield as the initial product the N-substituted aryldiazoamino compound, which can be rearranged to the azo compound. An initial attachment of the diazo residue to nitrogen is the usual but not the invariable mode of reaction of primary and secondary amines. Direct coupling to an aminoazo compound occurs under the following conditions: (1) with a particularly reactive amino component (m-phenylenediamine, m-toluidine, naphthylamines), (2) with a highly reactive diazo component (p-nitrobenzenediazonium chloride), or (3) in aqueous formic acid solution, which is acidic enough to cause the N-azo compound to be unstable but not to inhibit combination of the diazonium salt with the amine.

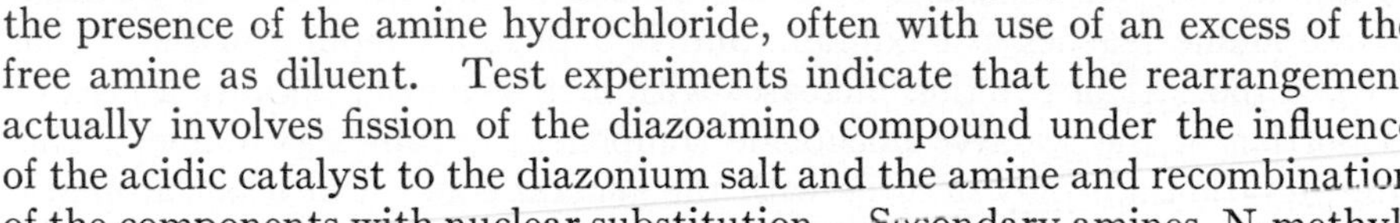

2,4,6-Trinitrobenzeneazomesitylene
(dark red, m p. 189° dec.)

The diazo coupling reaction is exhibited by aromatic compounds other than phenols and amines having free *ortho* or *para* positions only in rare instances. One is the coupling of mesitylene with diazotized picramide. This hydrocarbon coupling can be attributed in part to the special reactivity of the nuclear position in mesitylene, for this site is activated by one *para* and two *ortho* methyl groups, and in part to the enhanced reactivity of diazonium salts containing nitro substituents. Thus *p*-nitrobenzenediazonium chloride is distinctly more reactive than benzenediazonium chloride, and progressive activations are noted with the 2,4-dinitro and 2,4,6-trinitro derivatives. Mesitylene couples only with the most reactive member of the series. The activation can be attributed to an inductive effect of the positively polarized nitrogen atoms of the nitro groups, which results in withdrawal of electrons from the ring and consequent enhancement of the positive character of the functional diazonium ion. Nuclear halogen atoms also have some influence in increasing the coupling potency of the diazo component; they produce an inductive effect in the same sense as nitro substituents. Phenol ethers are distinctly less reactive than free phenols in nitrations and brominations, and they do not couple with benzenediazonium chloride. With suitable activation by nitro substituents in the diazo component, however, coupling can be accomplished in acetic acid solution; for example anisole couples with 2,4-dinitrobenzenediazonium chloride.

The outstanding property of the azo compounds is the color, and a considerable number of the products obtainable by coupling possess other attributes required in dyes (Chapter 36). A preparative use is the synthesis of *ortho* and *para* aminophenols and diamines, obtainable by reductive fission of the azo linkage. Thus *p*-hydroxyazobenzene is cleaved by reduction with stannous chloride or sodium hydrosulfite to *p*-aminophenol and aniline. An amino group can be introduced into the *para* position of phenol by coupling with diazotized aniline and reduction of the azo compound.

p-Hydroxyazobenzene   *p*-Aminophenol

Separation of the two amines resulting on reduction is facilitated by employing *p*-diazobenzenesulfonic acid, for the sulfanilic acid subsequently formed on reduction is easily removed as the water-soluble sodium salt:

$$p\text{-HOC}_6\text{H}_4\text{N}=\text{NC}_6\text{H}_4\text{SO}_3\text{Na} \xrightarrow{\text{Na}_2\text{S}_2\text{O}_4} p\text{-HOC}_6\text{H}_4\text{NH}_2 + \text{H}_2\text{NC}_6\text{H}_4\text{SO}_3\text{Na}$$

An interesting difference is observable in the properties of azo compounds having a hydroxyl group in the positions *ortho* and *para* to the azo linkage. The *para* hydroxy compounds dissolve freely in aqueous alkali, whereas the *ortho* compounds are either insoluble in dilute alkali in the cold or at most moderately soluble in hot alkali. The difference is illustrated in the properties of two isomeric hydroxyazo compounds of the naphthalene series; the first is soluble in alkali and the second insoluble.

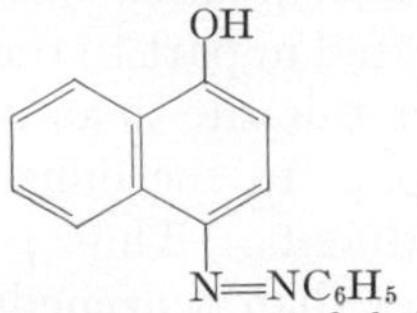

4-Benzeneazo-1-naphthol

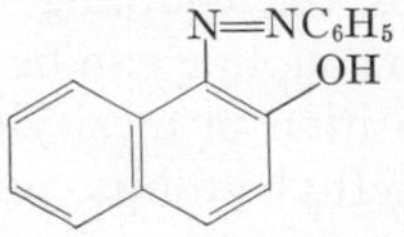

1-Benzeneazo-2-naphthol

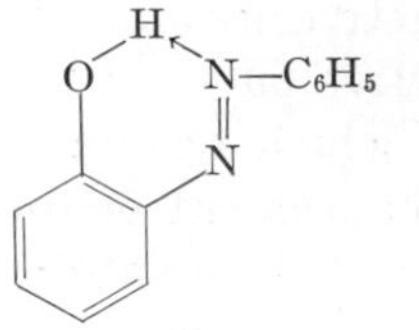

A likely explanation of the striking difference is that the *ortho* compounds exist in a chelated condition, as represented in the formulation. The presence of a chelate ring would account also for the fact, noted above, that *o*-hydroxyazobenzene is volatile with steam, whereas the *para* isomer is not, since hydrogen bonding would moderate the hydroxylic characteristics of the *ortho* compound.

PROBLEMS

1. Write equations for the alternate methods of preparing *o*- and *p*-anisidine mentioned on page 604.
2. In what respects are amines subject to oxidation? Indicate two methods by which stabilization can be achieved, and explain how each modification influences substitutions.
3. Describe three instances of initial attack by a reagent on the nitrogen atom of an amine, with subsequent rearrangement into the nucleus.
4. How can *p*-bromophenol be prepared from acetanilide?
5. Indicate reactions by which *o*-toluidine can be converted into phthalic acid.
6. Utilizing *p*-toluidine as the starting material, devise methods for the preparation of:

   (a) *p*-Bromobenzoic acid
   (b) *p*-Tolylhydrazine
   (c) 3,5-Dibromotoluene

   (d) 4,4′-Dimethyldiphenyl
   (e) 4-Methyl-2-aminophenol
   (f) N-Methyl-*p*-toluidine

7. How could N-methylaniline be converted into 4-amino-N-methylaniline?
8. Suggest methods for the preparation of the following compounds:

   (a) *m*-Chloroaniline   (b) *m*-Cresol   (c) *m*-Bromochlorobenzene

9. Starting with hydrocarbons available from coal tar or by ready synthesis, suggest methods for the preparation of the following compounds:

   (a) 2,4,6-Trimethylphenol
   (b) 2-Cyano-1,4-dimethylbenzene
   (c) 4-Chlorobenzene-1,3-dicarboxylic acid

   (d) 2,5-Dimethyl-4-aminophenol
   (e) 3-Amino-4-methylacetophenone

READING REFERENCE

K. H. Saunders, "The Aromatic Diazo-Compounds and Their Technical Application," E. Arnold, London (1949)

PHENOLS

Phenols usually are crystalline solids, but certain alkylphenols are liquids (*m*-cresol). Phenol itself is a solid at room temperature, but the melting point (43°) is greatly depressed by small amounts of water, and liquid preparations containing 2–10% of water find some use in medicine (cauterization) and in extraction operations. Introduction of the phenolic hydroxyl group produces a marked increase in boiling point and also raises the melting point, particularly when in the *para* position to a methyl, halogen, or nitro substituent, as shown by the data in Table 26.1.

The most distinctive property of phenols is the weakly acidic character, attributable to combination of a hydroxyl group with an unsaturated nucleus, or to the presence of an enolic grouping: $-CH=C(OH)-$. Phenol is a weak acid, pK_a 10.0, and it forms salts (phenolates) with sodium hydroxide but not with the carbonate. This behavior is typical and distinguishes phenols from carboxylic acids, which react with bicarbonate. An aromatic substance found to be more soluble in sodium hydroxide solution than in water but showing no increased solubility in the presence of sodium carbonate is likely to be a phenol. Dissociation constants of substituted phenols show little regularity, except in the series of nitro compounds. The three mononitrophenols are more acidic (pK_a 7.2–8) than the parent substance, and the effect is greatly magnified in 2,4-dinitrophenol (pK_a 4.0) and in picric acid, which is nearly as strongly acidic as a mineral acid. Stabilization of the anionic form by nitro groups is the counterpart of suppression of the basic dissociation of the amines, and likewise can be attributed to inductive and resonance effects.

Properties of representative polyhydric phenols are listed in Table 26.2. Among dihydroxy compounds the symmetrical *para* derivative, hydroquinone, has the highest melting point, and the symmetrically trisubstituted 1,3,5-compound, phloroglucinol, melts higher than its isomers. Solubility data indicate that multiple hydroxyl groups increase the solubility in water, but that the effect is counteracted by symmetry of structure.

PREPARATION

Generally applicable methods for preparation of phenols are **alkali fusion of a sulfonate** (p. 592) and **hydrolysis of a diazonium salt** (p. 613), and these two reactions render phenols available from hydrocarbons through initial sulfonation or nitration. A third method, alkaline **hydrolysis of an aryl halide**, is applied industrially to the preparation of phenol from chloro-

TABLE 26.1. MONOHYDRIC PHENOLS

NAME	FORMULA	M.P., °C.	B.P., °C.	$pK_a^{25°}$
Phenol	C_6H_5OH	43	181	10.0
o-Cresol	$CH_3C_6H_4OH(1,2)$	30	191	10.20
m-Cresol	$CH_3C_6H_4OH(1,3)$	11	201	10.01
p-Cresol	$CH_3C_6H_4OH(1,4)$	35.5	201	10.17
o-Chlorophenol	$ClC_6H_4OH(1,2)$	8	176	9.11
m-Chlorophenol	$ClC_6H_4OH(1,3)$	29	214	
p-Chlorophenol	$ClC_6H_4OH(1,4)$	37	217	9.39
p-Bromophenol	$BrC_6H_4OH(1,4)$	64	236	
2,4,6-Trichlorophenol	$HOC_6H_2Cl_3(1,2,4,6)$	69	244	7.59
2,4,6-Tribromophenol	$HOC_6H_2Br_3(1,2,4,6)$	95		
o-Nitrophenol	$HOC_6H_4NO_2(1,2)$	44.5	214	7.21
m-Nitrophenol	$HOC_6H_4NO_2(1,3)$	96		8.0
p-Nitrophenol	$HOC_6H_4NO_2(1,4)$	114		7.16
2,4-Dinitrophenol	$HOC_6H_3(NO_2)_2(1,2,4)$	113		4.0
Guaiacol	$HOC_6H_4OCH_3(1,2)$	32	205	7.0
Anol	$HOC_6H_4CH{=}CHCH_3(1,4)$	93		
Eugenol	$HOC_6H_3(OCH_3)CH_2CH{=}CH_2(1,2,4)$		248	
Isoeugenol	$HOC_6H_3(OCH_3)CH{=}CHCH_3(1,2,4)$	33	267	
Saligenin	$HOC_6H_4CH_2OH(1,2)$	87		
Carvacrol	$HOC_6H_3(CH_3)\cdot CH(CH_3)_2(1,2,5)$	1	237	8.4
Thymol	$HOC_6H_3(CH_3)\cdot CH(CH_3)_2(1,5,2)$	51	233	
o-Hydroxyacetophenone	$HOC_6H_4COCH_3(1,2)$	liq.	97 [10 mm.]	
p-Hydroxyacetophenone	$HOC_6H_4COCH_3(1,4)$	110	148 [3 mm.]	
o-Hydroxydiphenyl	$C_6H_5C_6H_4OH(1,2)$	56	275	
p-Hydroxydiphenyl	$C_6H_5C_6H_4OH(1,4)$	165	308	
o-Cyclohexylphenol	$C_6H_{11}C_6H_4OH(1,2)$	57		
p-Cyclohexylphenol	$C_6H_{11}C_6H_4OH(1,4)$	133		

TABLE 26.2. POLYHYDRIC PHENOLS AND AMINOPHENOLS

NAME	FORMULA	M.P., °C.	B.P., °C.	$pK_a^{20-25°}$	SOLUBILITY, g./100 cc. $H_2O^{20°}$
Catechol	$C_6H_4(OH)_2(1,2)$	105	245	9.4	45
Resorcinol	$C_6H_4(OH)_2(1,3)$	110	281	9.4	123
Hydroquinone	$C_6H_4(OH)_2(1,4)$	170		10.0	8
Pyrogallol	$C_6H_3(OH)_3(1,2,3)$	133	309	7.0	62
Hydroxyhydroquinone	$C_6H_3(OH)_3(1,2,4)$	140			
Phloroglucinol	$C_6H_3(OH)_3(1,3,5)$	219		7.0	1
o-Aminophenol	$HOC_6H_4NH_2(1,2)$	174		9.7	
m-Aminophenol	$HOC_6H_4NH_2(1,3)$	123			
p-Aminophenol	$HOC_6H_4NH_2(1,4)$	186		8.16	

benzene at a high temperature and pressure, and is applicable under ordinary conditions to the highly reactive polynitro halogen compounds. A fourth method, effective in special instances but employed to only a limited extent, consists in **dehydrogenation of a hydroaromatic ketone** conducted

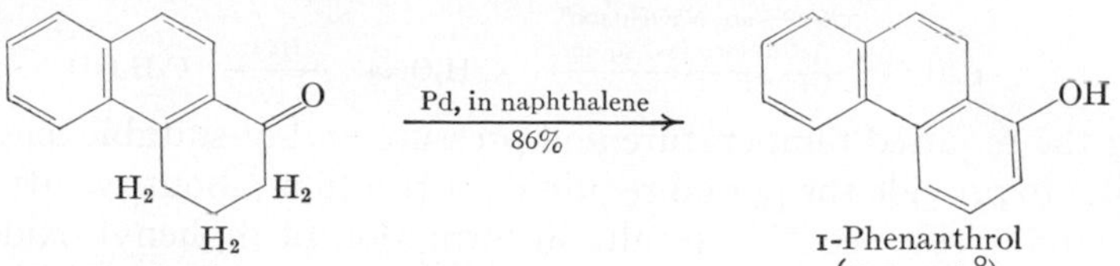

1-Ketotetrahydrophenanthrene
(m.p. 96°)

1-Phenanthrol
(m.p. 157°)

either with a palladium or platinum catalyst or with sulfur or selenium. The reaction probably proceeds by removal of two hydrogen atoms with formation of an unstable keto form of dihydrobenzenoid structure, which isomerizes to the phenol. Temperature control is essential, for under too

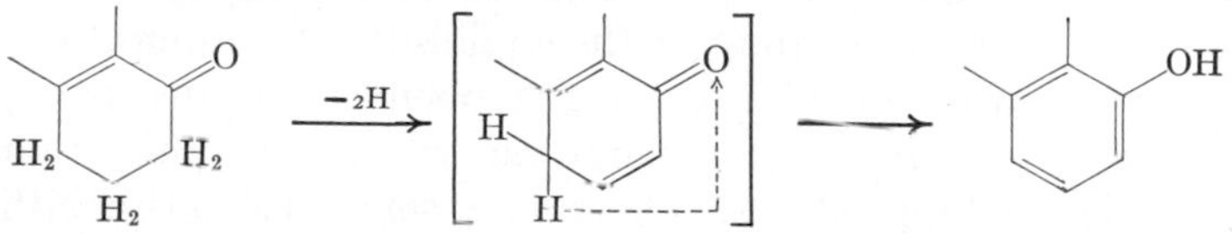

drastic conditions the hydroxyl group is lost. An alternate procedure involving the same intermediate is α-bromination of the ketone and elimination of hydrogen bromide by treatment with a basic reagent, as in the following example:

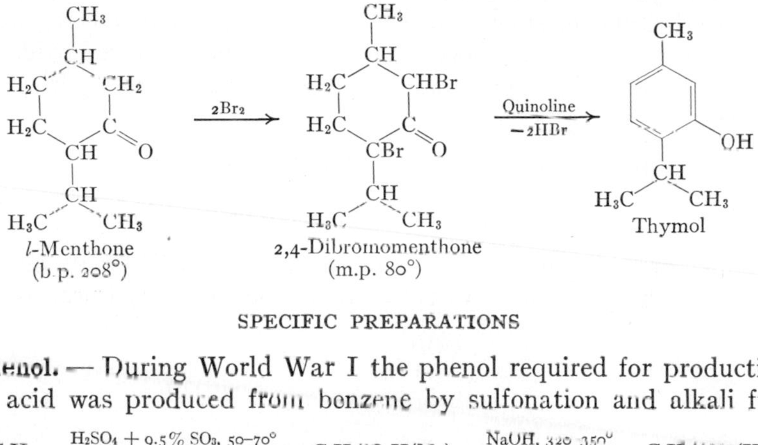

l-Menthone
(b.p. 208°)

2,4-Dibromomenthone
(m.p. 80°)

Thymol

SPECIFIC PREPARATIONS

Phenol. — During World War I the phenol required for production of picric acid was produced from benzene by sulfonation and alkali fusion.

$$C_6H_6 \xrightarrow[50-70°]{H_2SO_4 + 9.5\% \ SO_3,} C_6H_5SO_3H(Na) \xrightarrow[\text{NaOH, } 320-350°]{} C_6H_5ONa(H)$$

The overall yield was only 60–75%, and a considerable loss was entailed in the sulfonation process, which reaches equilibrium with the accumulation of water from the reaction. In a vapor-phase process introduced in 1923 with resumption of production of synthetic phenol to meet increasing requirements of material for production of phenol-formaldehyde plastics, sulfonation is accomplished at 170–180° with concentrated sulfuric acid.

An innovation, announced by the Dow Chemical Company in 1928, consists in hydrolysis of chlorobenzene by a dilute aqueous solution of alkali at high temperature and pressure. Hydrolysis is conducted as a continuous process by flowing the reactants through a pipe line system capable of main-

$$C_6H_5Cl \xrightarrow[\text{2000–3000 lbs./sq. in.}]{\text{6–8\% aq. NaOH, 300°,}} C_6H_5ONa \xrightarrow{\text{HCl}} C_6H_5OH$$

taining the required temperature and pressure and of suitable length (about one mile) to provide the period required for reaction (about twenty minutes). An inevitable side reaction results in formation of diphenyl oxide, and accumulation of this material, for which no large-scale use has arisen, would detract from the efficiency of the process. A solution of this apparent

$$C_6H_5ONa + C_6H_5OH \rightleftharpoons \underset{\text{Diphenyl oxide}}{C_6H_5OC_6H_5} + NaOH$$

difficulty followed from the observation that the by-product is formed in a reversible reaction and can be kept from accumulating by simply recirculating the amount necessary to meet the equilibrium requirement. The tar waste remaining from distillation of the phenol contains 20–25% of a mixture of o- and p-hydroxydiphenyl, in which the *para* isomer predominates. These by-products, which find some use, arise either from condensation of chlorobenzene to the chlorodiphenyls and hydrolysis $(2C_6H_5Cl \rightarrow C_6H_5C_6H_4Cl \rightarrow C_6H_5C_6H_4OH)$ or by condensation of chlorobenzene with phenol $(C_6H_5Cl + C_6H_5OH \rightarrow C_6H_5C_6H_4OH)$.

In the German Raschig process, benzene is converted through chlorobenzene into phenol by a sequence of reactions at atmospheric pressure with utilization of atmospheric oxygen as the only reagent not regenerated. Benzene is chlorinated by halogen generated by the catalyzed oxidation of hydrogen chloride with oxygen, and on catalytic hydrolysis hydrogen chloride is regenerated (97% recovery):

$$C_6H_6 + HCl + \tfrac{1}{2}O_2 \xrightarrow{\text{Catalyst, 230°}} C_6H_5Cl + H_2O$$

$$C_6H_5Cl + H_2O \xrightarrow{\text{Catalyst, 425°}} C_6H_5OH + HCl$$

A newer process utilizes cumene, available by Friedel-Crafts alkylation of benzene with propylene. Air is blown into the liquid hydrocarbon in the

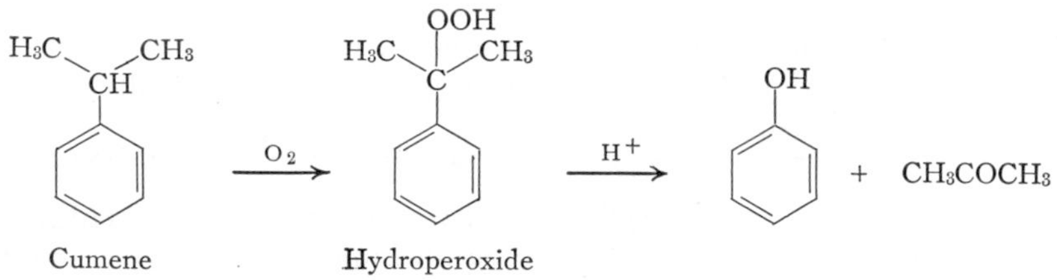

Cumene   Hydroperoxide

presence of a trace of base ($NaOH$, $CaCO_3$) to produce the hydroperoxide which, on acid catalysis decomposes to phenol and acetone.

Derivatives of Phenol. — The ether derivatives, **anisole**, $C_6H_5OCH_3$ (b.p. 154°), and **phenetole**, $C_6H_5OC_2H_5$ (b.p. 172°), are liquids with an aromatic fragrance, obtained conveniently by alkylation of phenol with dimethyl or diethyl sulfate in a weakly alkaline aqueous medium. This method is usual in preparation of phenol ethers, but in special instances alkylation is accomplished with diazomethane or diazoethane. A phenol often is converted into its ether to provide protection against oxidation or other undesired side reaction during transformations not involving the oxygen function, for the masking group subsequently can be removed and the hydroxyl group regenerated. Anisole can be demethylated by refluxing in acetic acid solution with 48% hydrobromic acid or by heating with hydriodic acid at 130°: $C_6H_5OCH_3 + HX \rightarrow C_6H_5OH + CH_3X$. Aluminum chloride is a further effective dealkylating agent; the ether can be heated with aluminum chloride alone at 120°, or more sensitive ethers are refluxed in benzene or carbon disulfide solution with an amount of the reagent equivalent to the number of alkoxyl groups present. High yields in the fission of aro-

$$C_6H_5OCH_3 \xrightarrow{AlCl_3} \left[\begin{array}{c} C_6H_5 \\ \diagdown \\ \overset{+}{O}-AlCl_2 \\ \diagup \\ CH_3 \end{array} \right] Cl^- \xrightarrow{Heat} \underset{(+CH_3Cl)}{C_6H_5OAlCl_2} \xrightarrow{H_2O} C_6H_5OH + HOAlCl_2$$

matic ethers have been obtained by heating with pyridine hydrochloride and by the action of sodium in refluxing pyridine (Prey, 1942–43).

Phenoxyacetic acid, $C_6H_5OCH_2COOH$, is a solid ether derivative useful for identification; it is prepared by slow addition of aqueous alkali to a melt of phenol and chloroacetic acid. The product separates as the sodium salt, which is collected and acidified.

Phenoxyacetic acid
(m.p. 98°, b.p. 285° dec.)

Phenyl acetate, $C_6H_5OCOCH_3$, is a liquid, b.p. 196°; acetyl derivatives in general are prepared by warming the phenol with excess acetic anhydride with addition of either a basic catalyst (fused sodium acetate, pyridine, triethylamine) or an acid catalyst (sulfuric acid, boron fluoride etherate). **Phenyl benzoate,** $C_6H_5COOC_6H_5$ (m.p. 71°), is obtained by shaking a weakly alkaline solution of phenol with benzoyl chloride (Schotten[1]-Baumann reaction) or by interaction of the components in cold pyridine solution. The Schotten-Baumann procedure is applicable to the preparation of **phenyl *p*-toluenesulfonate** (m.p. 95°):

$$C_6H_5OH + p\text{-}CH_3C_6H_4SO_2Cl \longrightarrow C_6H_5OSO_2C_6H_4CH_3(p)$$

Halophenols. — Chlorination of phenol without solvent at temperatures from 40–155° affords mixtures of *o*- and *p*-chlorophenol in which the latter predominates. Phenol present in the reaction mixture can be removed, owing to the greater acidic strength of the chlorophenols, by extraction of

---

[1] Carl Schotten, 1853-1910; b. Marburg, Germany; Ph.D. Berlin (Hofmann); Berlin; *Ber.*, **43**, 3703 (1910)

the substitution products with 10% potassium carbonate solution from an ethereal solution, which retains the less acidic phenol. The mixture of chlorophenols is easily separated by fractionation, for the o- and p-isomers differ in boiling point by 41°. When chlorination is conducted in carbon tetrachloride solution at a low temperature, the more volatile *ortho* isomer can be obtained in 26% yield. Pure o- and p-chlorophenol, like the *meta* isomer, are best prepared from the corresponding chloroanilines by diazotization and hydrolysis. Monobromination of phenol at low temperatures

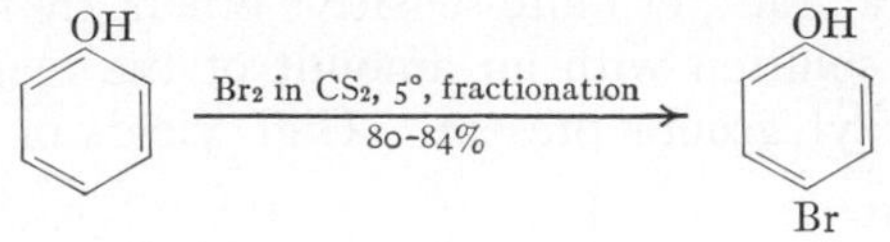

results in almost exclusive *para* substitution; the *ortho* isomer is produced in appreciable amounts only at higher temperatures. Thus in contrast with chlorination, bromination is satisfactory for preparation of the p-halo derivative. An indirect preparation of pure o-bromophenol is given on page 549. On treatment with a sufficient amount of chlorine or bromine, with or without solvent, phenol is converted into the 2,4,6-trihalo derivative. In analogy to the behavior of aniline, phenol is converted rapidly by bromine water into the sparingly soluble tribromo derivative. The reaction is employed for detection of phenol, since turbidity is discernible at dilutions as high as 1:100,000.

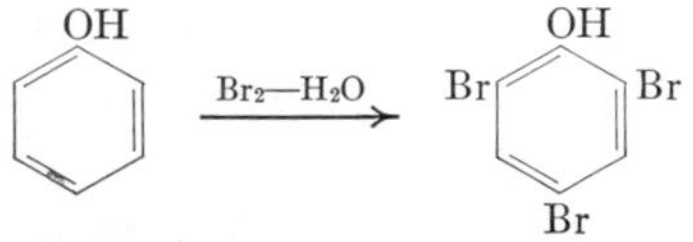

Nitrophenols. — Nitration of phenol with dilute aqueous nitric acid gives a mixture of the o- and p-isomers, with some predominance of the former substance (p. 557), and since a sharp separation can be made by steam distillation, both isomers are obtainable satisfactorily from the reaction mixture. o-Nitrophenol is readily volatile with steam and is obtained from the distillate in substantially pure form, whereas the nonvolatile p-isomer is retained in the distillation flask along with any dinitrophenols and other contaminants and requires more extensive purification. The steam volatility of o-nitrophenol, as that of o-nitroaniline, is attributed to the presence of a chelate ring. A method of preparing p-nitrophenol in better yield and subject to no contamination with the *ortho* isomer consists in oxidation of p-nitrosophenol with nitric acid. A satisfactory preparation of m-nitrophenol proceeds from

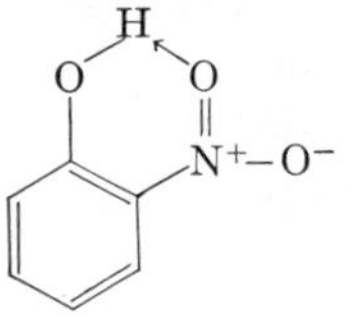

o-Nitrophenol

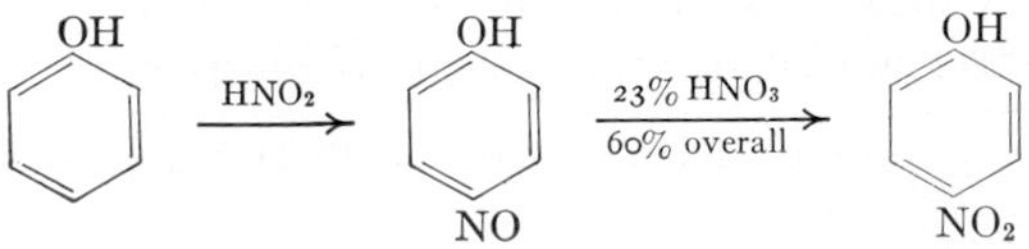

m-nitroaniline by the diazo reaction. 2,4-Dinitrophenol is produced as an intermediate in the preparation of picric acid by nitration of chlorobenzene.

Catechol. — Catechol, or 1,2-dihydroxybenzene, occurs in many plants and is excreted in horse urine both as such and as a sulfate ester. Several methods are available for the preparation of this technically important compound. One is demethylation of the monomethyl ether guaiacol, obtainable from natural sources, accomplished either by heating the ether with aluminum chloride at 210° or by refluxing with 48% hydrobromic acid (85–87% yield). A technical process involves hydrolysis of either o-chlorophenol or o-dichlorobenzene with aqueous alkali in the presence of a catalyst under forcing conditions. In another technical process, sodium phenol-2,4-

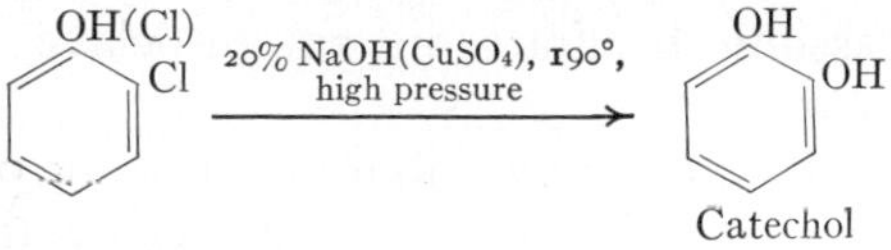

Catechol

disulfonate is fused with alkali under conditions so controlled that only the *ortho* sulfonate group is replaced by hydroxyl; the *para* sulfonate group is then removed by hydrolysis. A further method by which catechol can be

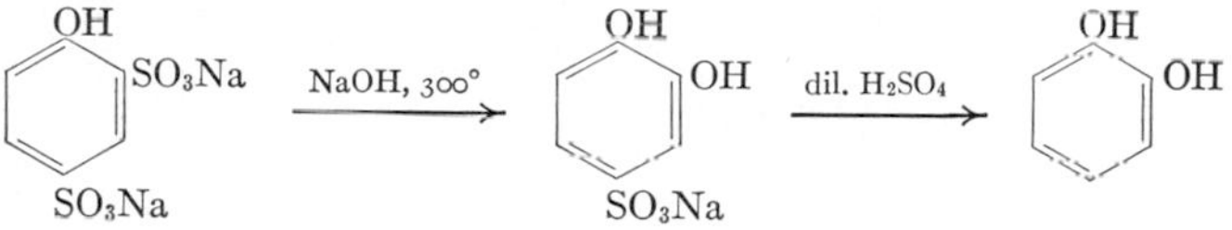

obtained in moderate yield illustrates a reaction generally applicable to the o- and p-hydroxy derivatives of aromatic aldehydes and aceto compounds; this consists in oxidation with hydrogen peroxide in alkaline solution and results in replacement of the aldehydic or acetyl group by hydroxyl (Dakin reaction). Evidence supports the reaction mechanism shown in the following formulation:

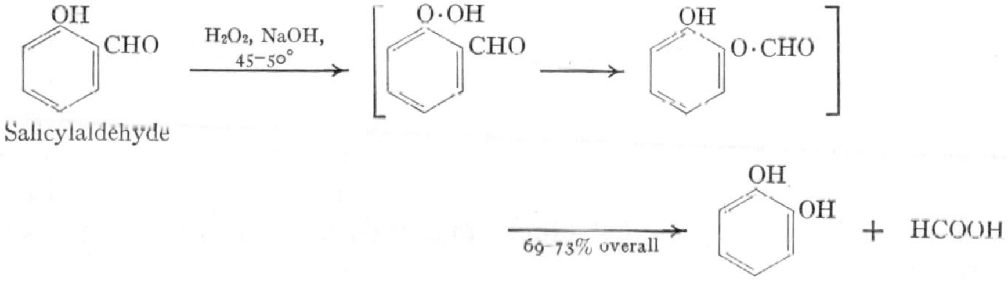

Catechol Ethers. — The monomethyl ether guaiacol, o-C_6H_4(OH)OCH_3 (Table 26.1), first obtained by distillation of the resin guaiacum, is prepared synthetically from o-anisidine by the diazo reaction. The dimethyl ether veratrole. o-C_6H_4(OCH$_3$)$_2$ (m.p. 22.5°, b.p. 207°), is obtainable from catechol in 95% yield by methylation with dimethyl sulfate and alkali.

Resorcinol. — The m-dihydroxy derivative of benzene, not found in nature, is prepared by alkali fusion of sodium m-benzenedisulfonate. Re-

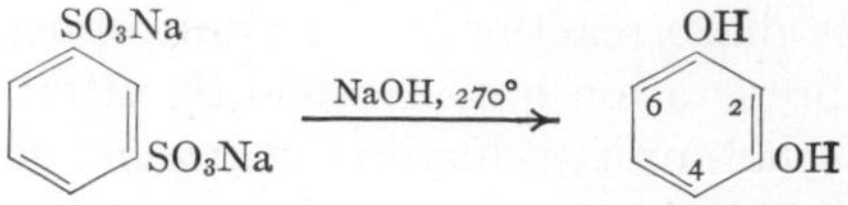

Resorcinol

sorcinol is highly reactive because of the reinforcing action of the two hydroxyl groups, and is substituted initially at the 4-position, *para* to one hydroxyl and *ortho* to the other. The course of disubstitution is dependent on the reagent and on the conditions; specific procedures afford the 4,6-dichloro and the 2,4-dinitro derivatives. Partial alkylation of a polyhydric phenol presents inevitable difficulties, and **resorcinol monomethyl ether** (liq., b.p. 244°) is obtained at best in 31% yield by heating resorcinol with methanol and potassium bisulfate in an autoclave at 165–170°. The **dimethyl ether** boils at 217°.

Hydroquinone. — Hydroquinone occurs in certain plants as the glycoside arbutin, from which it is liberated on hydrolysis with emulsin or sulfuric acid. A special method of preparation is oxidation of aniline, through a succession of intermediates leading to the yellow substance quinone, from which hydroquinone (colorless) is obtained on reduction. The reduction is

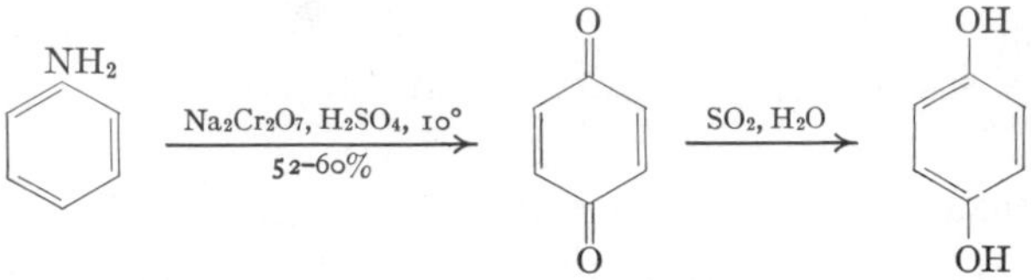

Quinone   Hydroquinone

reversible, and hydroquinone has reducing properties. It is employed as a photographic developer because of its ability to reduce to metallic silver the silver subhalide resulting from exposure of silver halide emulsion to light.

Hydroquinone is the only compound of the benzene series known to

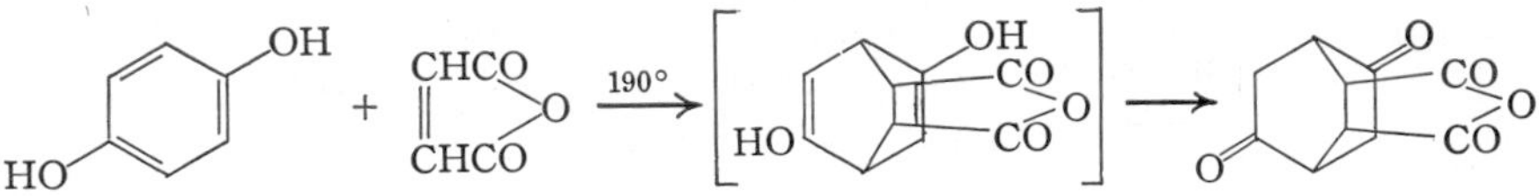

enter into Diels-Alder addition with maleic anhydride (R. C. Cookson, 1955). The transient adduct ketonizes to a bridge-ring diketo anhydride.

Hydroquinone monomethyl ether, m.p. 53°, b.p. 243°; **dimethyl ether,** m.p. 56°, b.p. 213°.

Pyrogallol is produced technically from the natural product gallic acid

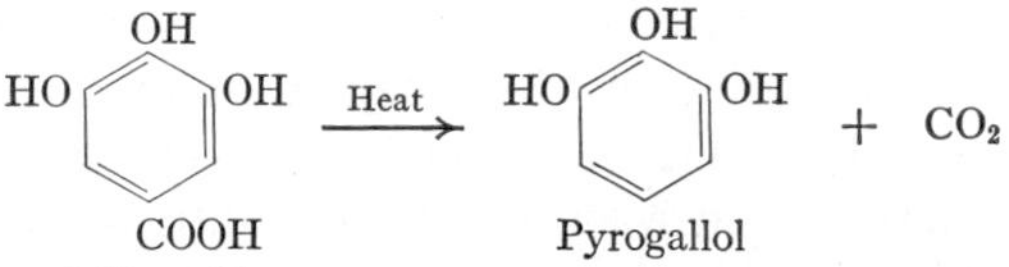

Gallic acid   Pyrogallol

by distillation from a mixture with pumice in an atmosphere of carbon dioxide. Like other polyhydroxy acids, gallic acid undergoes decarboxylation more readily than ordinary aromatic carboxylic acids. Pyrogallol has strong reducing properties and is used as a photographic developer. It is also employed in a strongly alkaline solution as an absorbent for oxygen in gas analysis. **Pyrogallol 1,3-dimethyl ether** is obtained by methylation with methyl iodide in methanol solution in the presence of potassium hydroxide at 150–160°.

Phloroglucinol, or *s*-trihydroxybenzene, is an expensive chemical obtainable from *s*-triaminobenzene. The amine is available as a reduction product of the corresponding trinitro compound, which in turn is prepared from TNT, and the intermediate 2,4,6-trinitrobenzoic acid is a point of departure for the preparation of phloroglucinol. The reduction product of the trinitro compound when refluxed in a nearly neutral solution for a pro-

COOH   COOH

O_2N ⟨ ⟩ NO_2 Sn, HCl → H_2N ⟨ ⟩ NH_2 H_2O, 100° → HO ⟨ ⟩ OH

      NO_2 NH_2 46–53% overall   OH

2,4,6-Trinitro-benzoic acid   Phloroglucinol

longed period undergoes hydrolysis of the amino groups to hydroxyl groups, and decarboxylation. The ready replacement of amino groups by hydroxyl and the low-temperature decarboxylation are both reactions specific to the structures in question and are probably associated with the tendency of the symmetrical triol system to react in the triketo form. Thus phloroglucinol reacts with hydroxylamine to form the trioxime of cyclohexane-1,3,5-trione.

Aminophenols. — *o*-Aminophenol is prepared by reduction of *o*-nitrophenol, for example with sodium hydrosulfite ($Na_2S_2O_4$) in alkaline solution or with zinc dust and aqueous calcium chloride solution. The *m*-isomer, a dye intermediate, is produced technically by the following method·

OH   OH

⟨ ⟩   10% aq. NH_3, NH_4Cl, autoclave, 200° → ⟨ ⟩

     OH NH_2

Resorcinol   *m*-Aminophenol

p-Aminophenol is employed in production of dyes and as a photographic developer; it has strong reducing properties and is rapidly discolored in neutral or alkaline solution. Technical processes of preparation are reduction of *p*-nitrophenol with iron powder and dilute hydrochloric acid, and electrolytic reduction of nitrobenzene in sulfuric acid solution; the latter reaction proceeds through formation and rearrangement of phenylhydroxylamine. Convenient laboratory procedures for preparation of *p*-aminophenols from phenols are based on the reduction of the *p*-nitroso or *p*-sulfobenzeneazo derivatives resulting from nitrosation or coupling with diazotized sulfanilic acid. Typical N-substituted derivatives of *p*-amino-phenol are obtainable by methods summarized as follows:

1. *p*-HOC$_6$H$_4$NH$_2$·HCl + (CH$_3$CO)$_2$O + CH$_3$COONa $\xrightarrow{\text{aq. solution, 25°}}$ *p*-HOC$_6$H$_4$NHCOCH$_3$
   p-Acetylaminophenol
   (m.p. 169°)

2. *p*-HOC$_6$H$_4$NH$_2$ $\xrightarrow{\text{C}_6\text{H}_5\text{CHO}}$ *p*-HOC$_6$H$_4$N=CHC$_6$H$_5$ $\xrightarrow{\text{Zn, NaOH}}$ *p*-HOC$_6$H$_4$NHCH$_2$C$_6$H$_5$
   p-Benzalaminophenol p-Benzylaminophenol
   (m.p. 183°)   (m.p. 90°)

3. *p*-HOC$_6$H$_4$OH + C$_6$H$_5$NH$_2$ $\xrightarrow{\text{aq. CaCl}_2,\ 260°}$ *p*-HOC$_6$H$_4$NHC$_6$H$_5$
   p-Hydroxydiphenylamine
   (m.p. 70°)

Selective acetylation of the amino group (1) is easily accomplished in aqueous solution. A solution of *p*-aminophenol hydrochloride in water is treated with one equivalent of acetic anhydride, followed at once by one equivalent of sodium acetate; the free amine is acetylated as it is liberated.

Carvacrol and **thymol** occur in several essential oils and probably are transformation products of terpenoid constituents. The preparation of thymol from a typical terpene ketone by dehydrogenation with bromine has

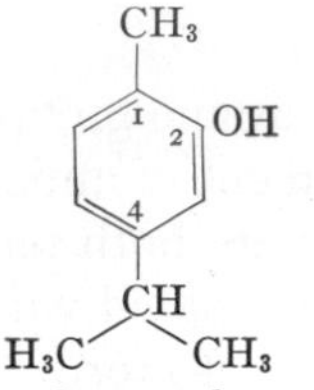

Carvacrol 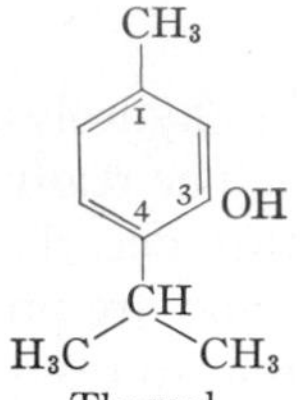   Thymol

been recorded (p. 625). A practicable synthesis of carvacrol consists in sulfonation of *p*-cymene (1-methyl-4-isopropylbenzene) and alkali fusion of the resulting 2-sulfonic acid. No route is open for introduction of a hy-droxyl group at position 3, *ortho* to the more bulky isopropyl group, but the isomer thymol can be produced satisfactorily from natural sources. When either carvacrol or thymol is heated with phosphorus pentoxide, the iso-propyl group is split off as propylene, and the nonvolatile residue is a phos-phoric acid ester that on alkaline hydrolysis affords *o*-cresol in the first instance and *m*-cresol in the second. In various substitution reactions carvacrol and thymol are attacked almost exclusively in the position *para* to the hydroxyl group.

Anol is the *p*-α-propenyl derivative of phenol. It can be obtained from

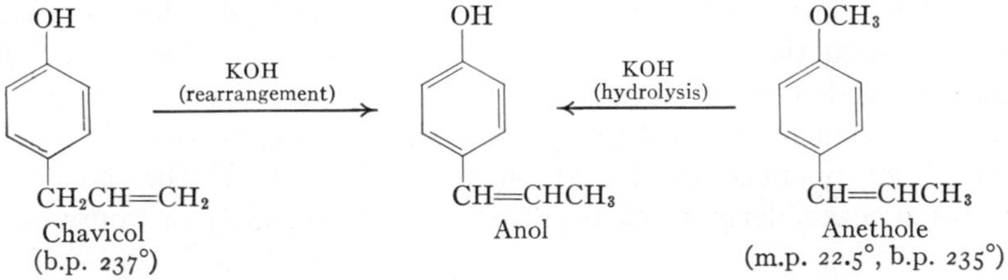

Chavicol   Anol   Anethole
(b.p. 237°)   (m.p. 22.5°, b.p. 235°)

the naturally occurring allyl isomer chavicol by boiling with alkali, which causes the double bond to rearrange to a position conjugated with the ring. A more abundant source is alkali fusion of the methyl ether, **anethole,** one of the chief constituents of oil of aniseed.

Eugenol, or 2-methoxy-4-allylphenol, is a colorless liquid widely distributed among plants and obtainable in practical amounts from oil of cloves. It is isomerized by alkali to the α-propenyl isomer, **isoeugenol.**

Saligenin, o-$HOC_6H_4CH_2OH$, results from hydrolysis of salicin $(C_{13}H_{18}O_7)$, a bitter glucoside found in the bark of willow and poplar trees and used to some extent in medicine as an antipyretic and a tonic.

4-n-Hexylresorcinol, a synthetic disinfectant, is prepared by condensation of resorcinol with caproic acid in the presence of anhydrous zinc chloride.

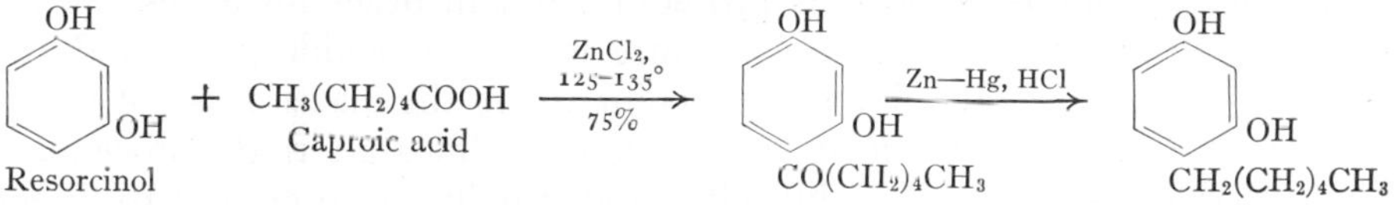

The condensation is a Friedel-Crafts type, but resorcinol is substituted with such ease that an acid, rather than an acid chloride, can be employed and the moderately active zinc chloride provides adequate catalysis. The completing step is reduction of the ketone by the Clemmensen method.

REACTIONS

Typical phenols are differentiated from the majority of other organic compounds by their characteristic weakly acidic nature, recognizable by ready solubility in alkali but not in sodium carbonate solution (exception: the more strongly acidic nitrophenols). Many phenols, like aliphatic enols, give rise to characteristic colors when treated with ferric chloride in very dilute aqueous or alcoholic solution as the result of complex formation (phenol, violet; cresols, blue; catechol, green; resorcinol, dark violet).

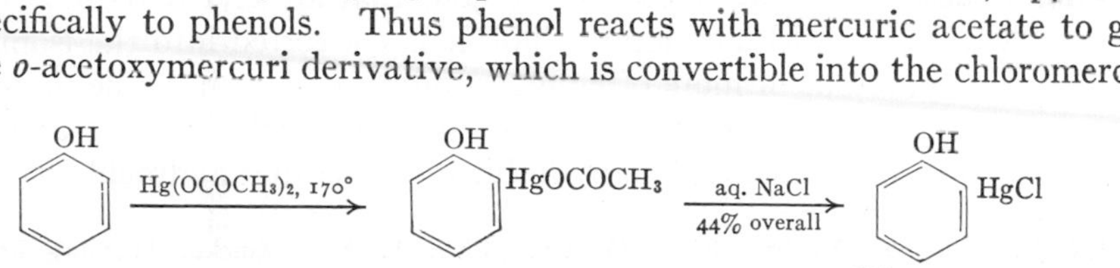

Substitutions. — The facility with which phenols undergo substitution is illustrated by the ready formation of the 2,4,6-tribromo derivative (p. 628), by the diazo coupling reaction (p. 603), and by nitrosation (p. 607), preferentially in the *para* position, on interaction with nitrous acid at ice-bath temperature. A further instance of the substitution-facilitating influence of the hydroxyl group is the mercuration reaction, applicable specifically to phenols. Thus phenol reacts with mercuric acetate to give the o-acetoxymercuri derivative, which is convertible into the chloromercuri derivative by interaction with sodium chloride. The chloromercuri group is replaceable by iodine; for example o-chloromercuriphenol is converted by iodine in chloroform solution into o-iodophenol (m.p. 43°) in 63% yield.

Friedel-Crafts Reaction. — The presence of a phenolic hydroxyl group alters the behavior in the Friedel-Crafts reaction, for phenol initially reacts with aluminum chloride with evolution of hydrogen chloride and production of a salt:

$$C_6H_5OH \ + \ AlCl_3 \ \longrightarrow \ C_6H_5OAlCl_2 \ + \ HCl$$

One equivalent of the reagent is thus consumed, and in order to promote condensation with an acid chloride or anhydride a suitable additional quantity of aluminum chloride must be used. Satisfactory acylations are sometimes accomplished by this procedure, but in other instances the results are unfavorable, sometimes because the metal halide group reduces the solubility in organic solvents to a point where the material is not easily brought into a state conducive to interaction. Two alternate procedures are available that avoid this difficulty, and usually are preferred to direct condensation. One is use of the methyl ether derivative, and the other is a modification of the general method known as the Fries reaction.

A phenol methyl ether enters into Friedel-Crafts reactions normally if the mixture is kept at a temperature low enough to avoid cleavage of the ether group by aluminum chloride. In large-scale preparations, where uniform cooling may be difficult, some cleavage of the ether group may occur and the crude reaction product is remethylated prior to purification. If

OCH$_3$ OCH$_3$

Anisole $+$ $\begin{array}{c} CH_2CO \\ | \quad\quad >O \\ CH_2CO \end{array}$ $\xrightarrow[\text{85%}]{\substack{AlCl_3 \text{ (2 equiv.),} \\ C_6H_5NO_2—CHCl_2CHCl_2, \, o°}}$

COCH$_2$CH$_2$COOH
β-4-Methoxybenzoylpropionic
acid (m.p. 147°)

the free phenol is ultimately required, the crude material can be treated with more aluminum chloride in a warm solution (80°) to complete demethylation. The ether group forms a labile complex with aluminum chloride, and the reagent so bound is not restrained from exerting a catalytic function. Thus in the example shown, the amount of catalyst used is that required for condensation of an anhydride with a hydrocarbon, and the same amount suffices for succinoylation of the diether veratrole (67% yield).

Fries Reaction. — Fries[2] discovered (1908) that an acyl derivative of a phenol when heated with aluminum chloride is converted into the isomeric o- or p-hydroxy ketone or more often into a mixture of both. The material is present in the reaction mixture as the aluminum chloride salt, and the hydroxy compound is liberated on hydrolysis with ice and hydrochloric acid.

---

[2] Karl Fries, b. 1875 Kiedrich/Rhine, Germany; Ph.D. Marburg (Zincke); Marburg, Braunschweig

$$C_6H_5OCOCH_3 \xrightarrow{\text{AlCl}_3(-\text{HCl})} CH_3COC_6H_4OAlCl_2 \longrightarrow CH_3COC_6H_4OH$$

Phenyl acetate   o- and p-Hydroxyacetophenone

m-Hydroxy ketones have been observed very rarely as products of the Fries reaction, and the chief variation is in the ratio of the *ortho* and *para* isomers. This ratio varies with the solvent and the amount of catalyst, and is influenced particularly by the temperature at which the reaction is conducted, as illustrated strikingly by the behavior of *m*-cresyl acetate, which can be converted into either of two products in good yield by adjustment of the temperature. Although the temperature effect usually is not so

2-Methyl-4-hydroxy-
acetophenone
(m.p. 128°, b.p. 313°)

m-Cresyl acetate

4-Methyl-2-hydroxy-
acetophenone
(m.p. 21°, b.p. 245°)

pronounced as in this instance, a similar effect is general, for a low temperature favors *para* substitution and a high temperature *ortho* substitution. This orientation is just the opposite of the relationship encountered in Friedel-Crafts condensations with substituted hydrocarbons, where the extent of attack in a hindered *ortho* position decreases with rise in temperature, and hence the Fries reaction is not adequately interpreted on the hypothesis that the ester is merely cleaved to the phenoxyaluminum chloride and acetyl chloride, with interaction of the components as in a usual Friedel-Crafts reaction. That the *o*-hydroxy ketone, in the form of the aluminum chloride complex, accumulates at a high temperature in preference to the *p*-isomer contrasts with the rearrangement of the heat-labile orthanilic acid into the more stable *p*-isomer, sulfanilic acid (p. 603). It is unlikely that the Fries reaction proceeds by intramolecular migration of the acyl group, for the primary low-temperature product is not the *o*-isomer expected by analogy. A more plausible mechanism is that of an intermolecular acylation; that is, substitution in one molecule of an acyl group derived from another, with formation of the *p*-hydroxy ketone as the normal product because of the greater accessibility of the *p*-position:

(+ phenol)

In analogy with the known reversibility of other reactions of the Friedel-Crafts type, it would be inferred that formation of the *o*-hydroxy ketone at high temperatures may result from reversion of the normal *p*-compound to the original ester and reintroduction of the acyl group in the *o*-position; indeed it is known that the Fries reaction can be reversed by acids and that *p*-hydroxy ketones can be isomerized to the *o*-isomers by aluminum chloride at high temperatures. Thus 2-methyl-4-hydroxyacetophenone, formulated above, is converted into *m*-cresyl acetate when heated with sulfuric or phosphoric acid, and it affords 4-methyl-2-hydroxyacetophenone when heated with aluminum chloride. The *o*-isomer thus may predominate at elevated temperatures because it has superior stability, and stabilization of this structure and not of that of the *p*-isomer can be attributed to the presence of a chelate ring in the aluminum chloride complex produced in the reaction. This interpretation is supported by the fact that the free *o*-hy-

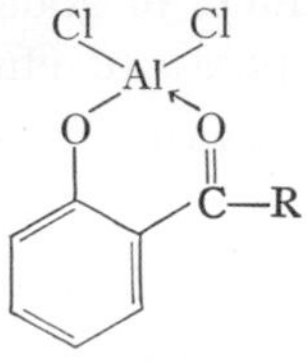

o-Acylphenoxy-
aluminum chloride

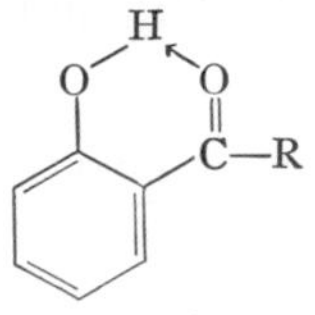

o-Hydroxy ketone

droxy ketones are chelated, since ordinarily chelation is stronger in a metal derivative than in the corresponding hydroxy compound. Thus the isomeric methylhydroxyacetophenones formulated in the first example cited in this section differ considerably in boiling point (68°); the (chelated) *o*-hydroxy ketone is distinctly more volatile than the fully hydroxylic *p*-isomer. Another example is that *o*-heptanoylphenol boils at 135–140°/3 mm., whereas the *p*-isomer boils at 200–207°/4 mm. *o*-Hydroxy ketones except those of particularly high molecular weight are also volatile with steam, whereas the *p*-isomers are not; a further indication of the chelated nature of the former compounds is that they are more soluble in ligroin than the hydroxylic isomers.

The distinct differences in properties associated with the presence or absence of chelation facilitate separation of the mixtures ordinarily obtained in Fries reactions. The *o*-isomer often can be removed selectively by steam distillation, or the isomers can be separated adequately by fractional distillation; if the substances are slightly volatile the *p*-isomer usually can be separated by crystallization. Thus, unlike many substitutions that afford mixtures, the Fries reaction has practical preparative value and offers a convenient route to both the *o*- and *p*-acyl derivatives of phenols. An example is the production of *o*- and *p*-hydroxypropiophenone from phenyl propionate, which can be obtained in a condition suitable for the reaction by heating equivalent quantities of phenol and propionyl chloride until the evolution of hydrogen chloride ceases. Aluminum chloride is then added,

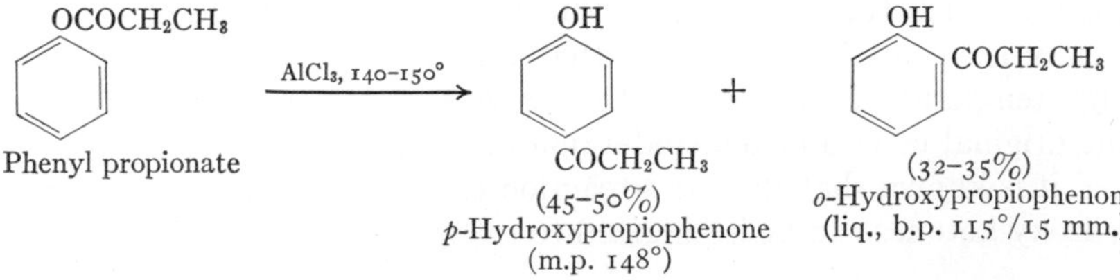

Phenyl propionate

p-Hydroxypropiophenone
(m.p. 148°)
(45–50%)
COCH$_2$CH$_3$

o-Hydroxypropiophenone
(liq., b.p. 115°/15 mm.)
(32–35%)

along with carbon disulfide, in which solvent the reaction is begun; after an initial evolution of hydrogen chloride has ceased, the solvent is removed by distillation and the mixture is heated to the required temperature. After hydrolysis of the cooled mixture, the *p*-hydroxy ketone largely crystallizes and is purified by recrystallization, whereas the *o*-isomer is recovered from the oily residue by distillation.

Oxidation. — Phenols, like amines, are susceptible to attack by oxidizing agents, and the initial step consists in abstraction of the hydroxylic hydrogen atom with formation of a free radical containing univalent oxygen. Such radicals usually are so unstable and reactive that they undergo rapid transformation into secondary products, but certain hydroxy derivatives of phenanthrene afford radicals of stability comparable to triphenylmethyl (Goldschmidt,[3] 1922). Thus 9-chloro-10-phenanthrol, on oxidation with potassium ferricyanide in alkaline solution or with lead dioxide in organic solvents, gives a colored phenanthroxyl radical that slowly associates to a colorless dimeric form till equilibrium is reached; the monomer and dimer are present in about equal amounts at equilibrium in pyridine solution at room temperature. Reducing agents regenerate chlorophenanthrol. The

9-Chloro-10-phenanthrol   9-Chloro-10-phenanthroxyl   Dimer (peroxide)
(m.p. 121°)   (deep blue-red)   (colorless, m.p. 125° dec.)

9-methoxyl, 9-ethoxyl, and 9-bromo derivatives of 10-phenanthrol on oxidation also afford equilibrium mixtures containing radical forms, but the 9-acetoxy derivative is oxidized to a dimeric peroxide that is colorless in solution, as in the solid state, and shows no indication of dissociation.

Even where neither a phenoxyl radical nor a peroxide has been isolated, the structure of a secondary product of oxidation sometimes is indicative of a radical intermediate, and apparently the phenoxyl radical can isomerize to a radical containing trivalent carbon in a position *ortho* or *para* to the oxygen atom. Thus β-naphthol is oxidized by ferric chloride in dilute aqueous solution to a substance, 2,2'-dihydroxydinaphthyl or di-β-naphthol, that corresponds in empirical formula to the dimeric form of a radical but with a linkage between carbon rather than oxygen atoms. The formation is attributed to resonance between the initial naphthoxyl radical (*a*) and a carbon radical (*b*), dimerization of the latter radical, and enolization. An isomeric oxidation product, dehydro-β-naphthol, resulting in low yield from oxidation of β-naphthol in weakly alkaline solution with potassium ferricyanide evidently arises by union of the naphthoxyl radical and the carbon

---

[3] Stefan Goldschmidt, b. 1889 Nürnberg, Germany; Ph.D. Munich (Dimroth); Karlsruhe, Munich

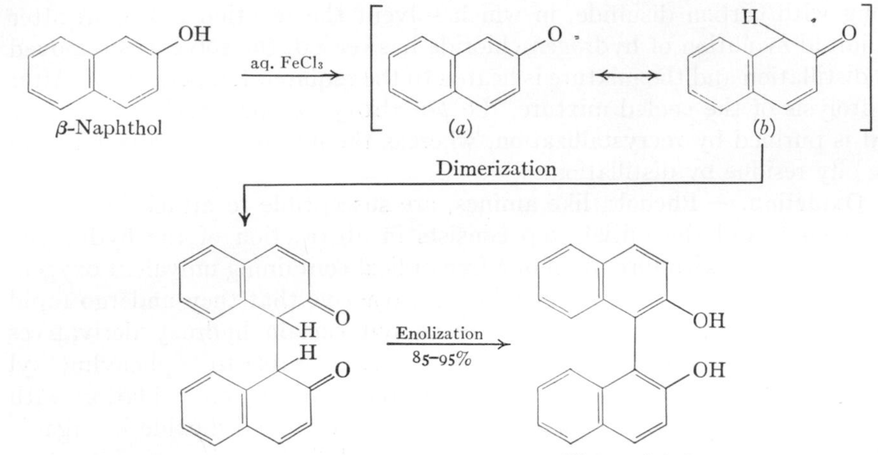

β-Naphthol   aq. FeCl₃ →   (a) ↔ (b)

Dimerization

Di-β-naphthol
(colorless, m.p. 219°)

Enolization
85–95%

radical, and enolization (Pummerer, 1914). A reaction that probably proceeds through a radical with trivalent carbon in the *para* position is the

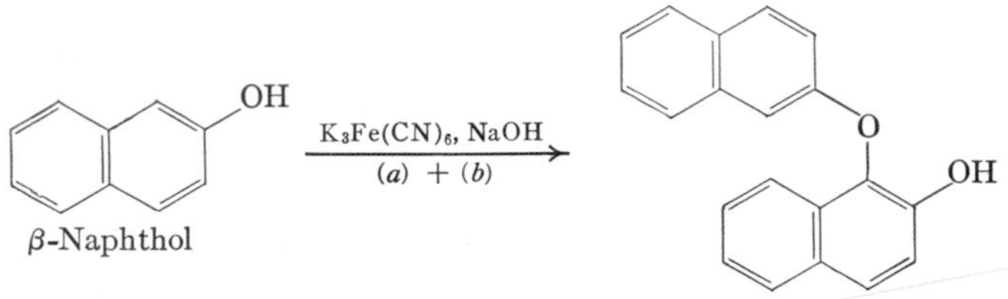

β-Naphthol   K₃Fe(CN)₆, NaOH / (a) + (b) →

Dehydro-β-naphthol
(colorless, m.p. 196°)

oxidation of pyrogallol 1,3-dimethyl ether (Hofmann, 1878). The reaction product was first isolated as a blue pigment arising in the purification of

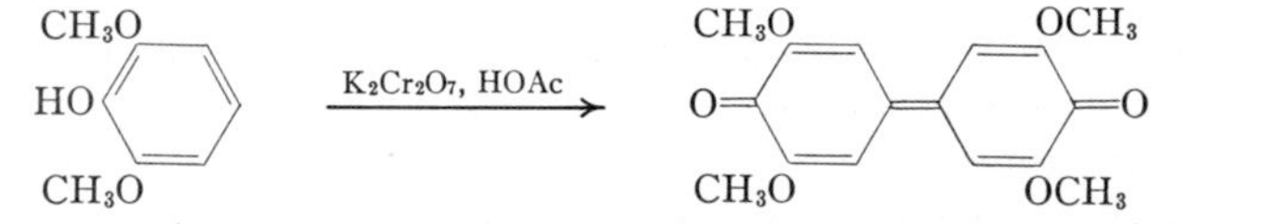

Pyrogallol 1,3-
dimethyl ether   K₂Cr₂O₇, HOAc →

Cerulignone (cedriret, 3,5,3',5'-
tetramethoxy-4,4'-diphenoquinone, blue)

acetic acid derived from beechwood by treatment with potassium dichromate, and accordingly was named cerulignone (L. *caeruleus*, sky blue, + *lignum*, wood, + qui*none*). The isolation of pyrogallol 1,3-dimethyl ether from beechwood tar suggested the oxidative reaction found applicable to the synthesis of the pigment. The deeply colored cerulignone is sparingly soluble in ordinary organic solvents and is best crystallized from phenol.

Condensation with Aldehydes. — Phenols condense readily with aliphatic and aromatic aldehydes to give initial products that arise from an aldol-like addition of the phenol molecule, at a reactive *o*- or *p*-position, to the carbonyl group of the aldehyde.   With adjustment of the proportion of

$$R—C\begin{smallmatrix}H\\\\O\end{smallmatrix} \quad + \quad H·C_6H_4OH \quad \longrightarrow \quad R—CHC_6H_4OH \ (o \text{ and } p)$$
$$\quad\quad\quad\quad\quad\quad\quad\quad\quad\quad\quad\quad\quad\quad\quad\quad | \atop OH$$

the reactants and the conditions, two molecules of phenol react with one of
the aldehyde.   The type of condensation lends itself to continuation, with

$$HOC_6H_4·H \quad + \quad RCH{=}O \quad + \quad H·C_6H_4OH \quad \longrightarrow \quad HOC_6H_4—CH—C_6H_4OH$$
$$\quad\quad\quad\quad\quad\quad\quad\quad\quad\quad\quad\quad\quad\quad\quad\quad\quad\quad\quad\quad\quad\quad\quad | \atop R$$

the resulting production of polymeric products, and forms the basis for the
preparation of phenol-formaldehyde plastics.

Claisen Allylation. — Claisen[4] discovered (1923) that phenol allyl ether
when heated undergoes rearrangement to o-allylphenol (nearly quantitative
yield); the allyl group migrates from oxygen exclusively to the o-position in
the ring.   Allyl ethers usually are obtained in excellent yield by reaction of

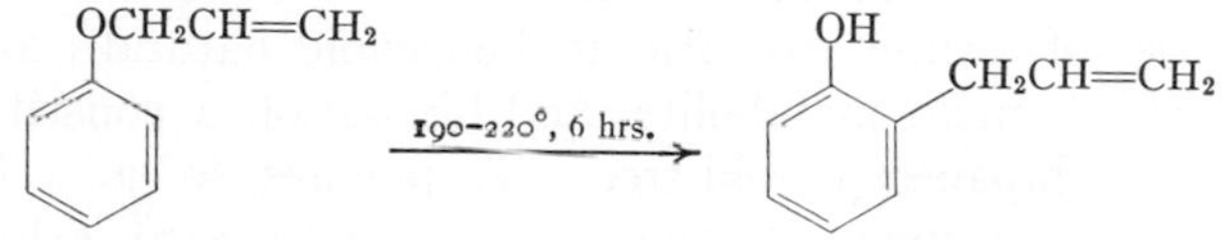

Phenol allyl ether o-Allylphenol
(b.p. 192°)   (b.p. 220°)

allyl bromide with a solution of the phenol in acetone containing suspended
potassium carbonate to neutralize the hydrogen bromide liberated (phenol
allyl ether, 86–97% yield).   When the procedure is altered by use of anhydrous potassium phenolate in suspension in benzene, the chief product is
the C-allyl derivative, o-allylphenol.   Acetone, a polar solvent, favors
O-allylation, and the nonpolar benzene favors allylation of the ring.   The
product of C-allylation is identical with that produced by rearrangement in
this instance, but not in the general case of substituted β-alkenyl compounds.
Thus the ether I is formed by alkylation in acetone and rearranges on being

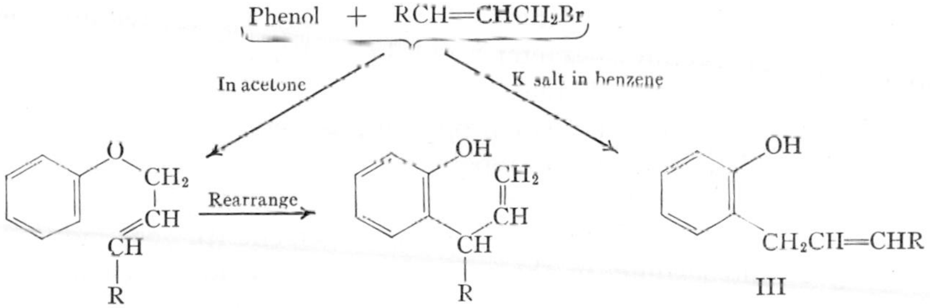

heated to II, an isomer of the substance III resulting as the chief product of

[4] Ludwig Claisen, 1851–1930; b. Cologne, Germany; Ph.D. Bonn (Kekulé); Aachen, Kiel, Berlin; *Ber.*, **69A**, 97 (1936)

direct C-alkylation. An allylic rearrangement, or α,γ-shift, thus occurs in the allyl group in the course of the migration.

TROPOLONES

Some members of this group that occur in nature have been investigated extensively since early times, but the basic structure was not known until 1945, when M. J. S. Dewar in England and the Japanese chemist Nozoe in Formosa independently noted that the heptatrienolone structure (1) should have aromatic properties, since two equivalent Kekulé-like structures are

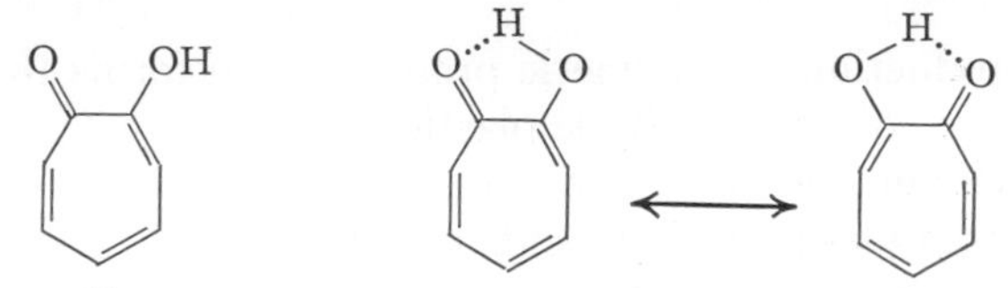

(1)   (2)

possible (2), and suggested structures that accounted satisfactorily for known properties of certain aromatic nonbenzenoid natural products, such as stipitatic acid, a mold metabolite, and hinokitiol, a constituent of the essential oil of the Japanese hinoki tree. Tropolones, so called because the seven-carbon ring corresponds to that of tropane (p. 837), exhibit marked

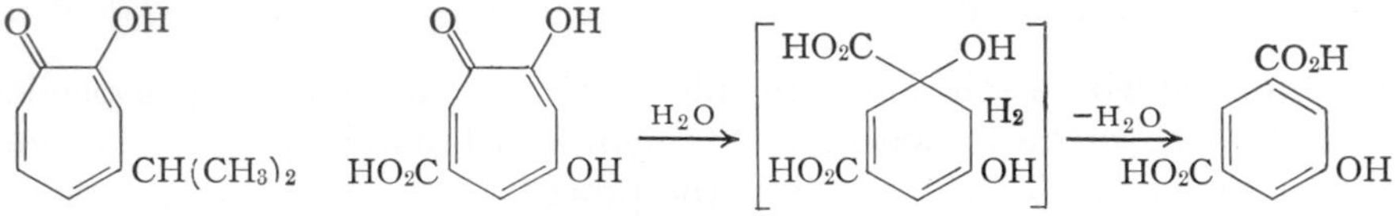

Hinokitiol   Stipitatic acid

phenolic properties (positive ferric chloride test) and have pK values close to 7, intermediate between those for phenol and for acetic acid. They undergo substitution reactions with bromine and with nitric acid and couple with diazotized amines. The enolic hydroxyl group can be alkylated with ease (diazomethane), but acylation occurs with some difficulty. Tropolones are resistant to permanganate oxidation, they are not readily hydrogenated, and the ketonic character is masked, although after complete or partial hydrogenation the ketone group reacts normally. The probable explanation for the lack of ketonic properties, as well as for the acidity and resistance to acylation, is that a tropolone is a vinylog of a carboxyl group, the components being separated by a conjugated system. Another characteristic reaction is a benzilic acid type rearrangement (p. 707) induced by alkali at 300° and leading, in the case of stipitatic acid, to 5-hydroxyisophthalic acid.

In addition to a number of other natural monocyclic tropolones, this system is present in more complicated structures such as that of purpurogallin, a red pigment which occurs as glucosides in various galls. It was first prepared synthetically in 1869 by oxidation of pyrogallol; sodium iodate is the reagent of choice. The pigment was investigated prior to 1945 by many chemists, notably by A. G. Perkin and by Willstätter, but no satisfactory formula was advanced, although Perkin correctly deduced the structure of the naphthalene derivative produced by alkaline rearrangement. The benzotropolone formula was advanced in 1948 by Barltrop and Nichol-

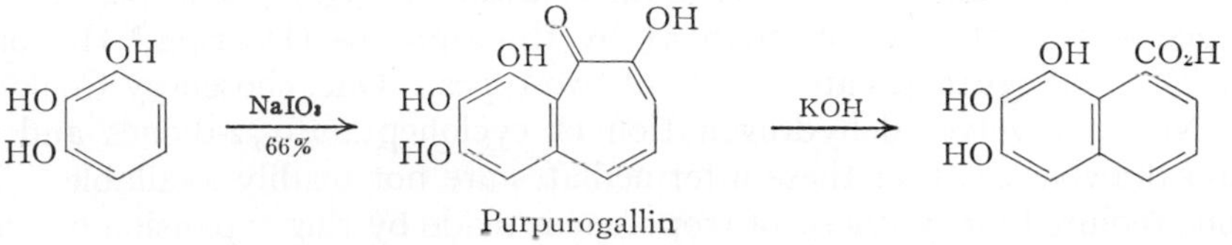

OH
HO
HO
$\xrightarrow[66\%]{\text{NaIO}_4}$
O OH
OH
HO
HO
$\xrightarrow{\text{KOH}}$
OH CO$_2$H
HO
HO

Purpurogallin

son and by R. D. Haworth[5] and confirmed by synthesis. However, the mode of formation from pyrogallol remains obscure.

The most complicated known tropolone is the tricyclic alkaloid colchicine, which occurs in the autumn crocus and which has intrigued many investigators because of its biological activity. It is invaluable for treatment of gout and it arrests cell division in both plant and animal cells. Early fundamental work by Windaus (1911–24) led to suggestion of a formula containing a partially reduced phenanthrene ring system. Dewar (1945) suggested that one of the end rings is a tropolone methyl ether, and this feature is incorporated in the structure now considered correct although not

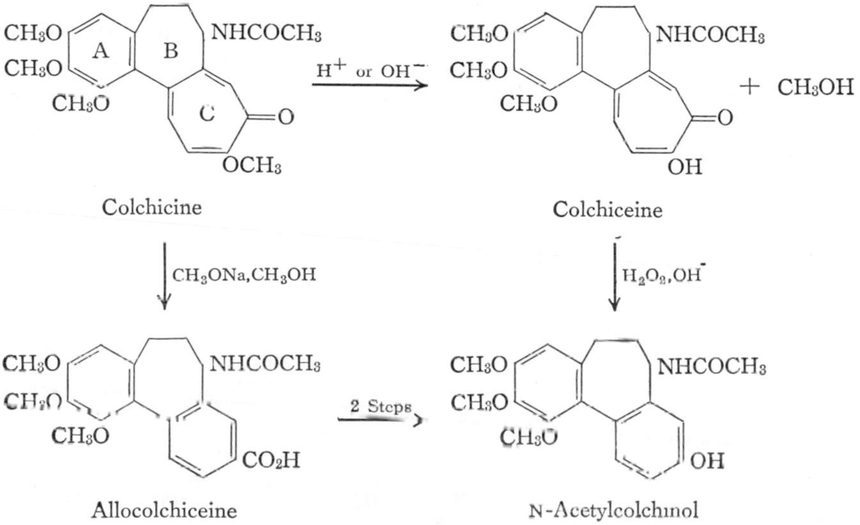

CH$_3$O
CH$_3$O
A B
CH$_3$O
NHCOCH$_3$
C =O
OCH$_3$
$\xrightarrow{\text{H}^+ \text{ or OH}^-}$
CH$_3$O
CH$_3$O
CH$_3$O
NHCOCH$_3$
=O
OH
+ CH$_3$OH

Colchicine   Colchiceine

↓ CH$_3$ONa, CH$_3$OH   ↓ H$_2$O$_2$, OH$^-$

CH$_3$O
CH$_3$O
CH$_3$O
NHCOCH$_3$
CO$_2$H
$\xrightarrow{\text{2 Steps}}$
CH$_3$O
CH$_3$O
CH$_3$O
NHCOCH$_3$
OH

Allocolchiceine   N-Acetylcolchinol

entirely established. In this the partly saturated central ring B is also seven-membered. The enol methyl ether group is readily split by acid or alkaline hydrolysis with formation of colchiceine. In 1886 Zeisel submitted 32.9 g. of the alkaloid to acid hydrolysis and determined the volatile fragment (1.5 g.) by conversion to methyl iodide (6.6 g.); the experience led to development of a method for methoxyl determination now applicable to a sample of a few milligrams. The tropolone ring (C) readily rearranges to

[5] Robert Downes Haworth, b. 1898 Cheadle (Cheshire); Ph.D. and D.Sc. Manchester (Lapworth, Perkin, Jr.); Sheffield

an aromatic ring. Colchicine undergoes benzilic acid rearrangement to allocolchiceine, but colchiceine rearranges only in the presence of an oxidizing agent; alkaline hydrogen peroxide leads to N-acetylcolchinol.

Synthesis. — The first syntheses were of benzotropolones (Cook,[6] 1949; Tarbell,[7] 1950) and of purpurogallin (Haworth, 1950). The parent substance was synthesized in 1950–51 by three groups (Doering;[8] Haworth; Cook). The syntheses are mainly of two types. One, chosen by Cook and by Nozoe, involves dehydrogenation of cycloheptane-1,2-diones and the main drawback is that these intermediates are not readily available. The dione required for synthesis of tropolone is made by ring expansion of cyclo-

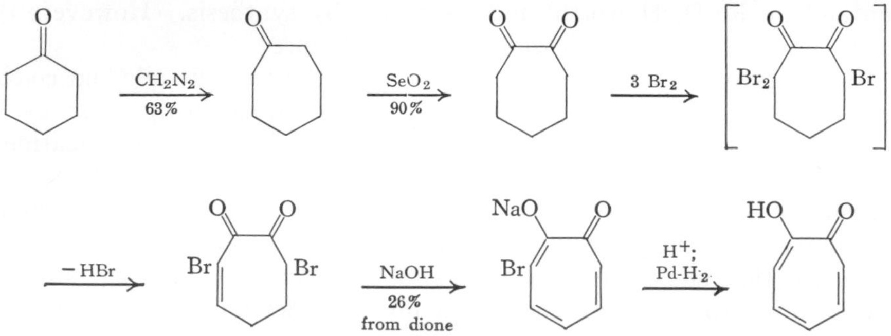

hexanone with diazomethane and selenium dioxide oxidation of an activated methylene group. In the introduction of double bonds by bromination and dehydrobromination it is experimentally advantageous to introduce an extra atom of bromine, which is eliminated in a terminal step of hydrogenation.

A second general synthesis, developed principally by A. W. Johnson,[9] is exemplified by the synthesis of stipitatic acid from 1,2,4-trimethoxyben-

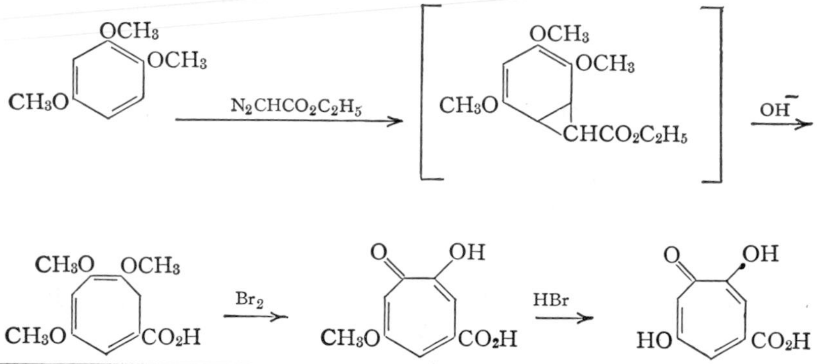

---

[6] James Wilfred Cook, b. 1900 London; Ph.D. and D.Sc. London (Barnett); London, Glasgow, Univ. Coll. of the South West (Exeter, Devon)

[7] D. Stanley Tarbell, b. 1919 Hancock, N. H.; Ph.D. Harvard (Bartlett); Univ. Rochester

[8] William von E. Doering, b. 1917 Ft. Worth, Texas; Ph.D. Harvard (Linstead); Yale Univ.

[9] Alan Woodworth Johnson, b. 1917 South Shields, Co. Durham; M.A. Cambridge (Todd); Ph.D. London (Heilbron); Univ. Cambridge

zene. The ring is expanded by reaction with ethyl diazoacetate, which also provides the carboxyl function required. Treatment with alkali gives the trimethoxycycloheptatrienecarboxylic acid, which requires oxidation and demethylation to give the tropolone structure. Oxidation with bromine proved most satisfactory, and finally cleavage of the remaining enol ether group gave stipitatic acid (overall yield 4.5%).

PROBLEMS

1. Compare the effect of o-, m-, and p-nitro groups on the dissociation of phenol and of aniline (see Tables, pp. 597, 624).
2. Summarize instances of the modification of physical properties attributable to chelation.
3. Outline a series of experiments by which saligenin (p. 633) could be shown to contain one phenolic hydroxyl group and one alcoholic group.
4. Suggest a method for the synthesis of 4-ethylcatechol.
5. Outline the steps involved in the synthetic production from benzene of:

    (a) Anisole   (d) p-Aminophenol
    (b) Catechol   (e) 4-n-Hexylresorcinol
    (c) o-Aminophenol

6. Cite qualitative tests that would distinguish between the following compounds: $C_6H_5OCH_2COOH$, p-$CH_3COC_6H_4OH$, $C_6H_5OCOCH_3$, $C_6H_5COCH_2OH$.
7. Formulate syntheses of α- and of β-naphthol starting with benzene or anisole and succinic anhydride.
8. By what sequence of reactions could p-aminophenol be converted into 2-bromo-4-aminophenol?

READING REFERENCES

A. H. Blatt, "The Fries Reaction," *Organic Reactions*, **1**, 342, Wiley, New York (1942)
S. D. Tarbell, "The Claisen Rearrangement," *Organic Reactions*, **2**, 1 (1944)
J. W. Cook and J. D. Loudon, "The Tropolones," *Quart. Rev.*, **5**, 99 (1951)
A. W. Johnson, "Aromaticity in Seven-Membered Rings," *J. Chem. Soc.*, 1331 (1954)

CHAPTER 27

ARYL HALIDES

The more common aryl halides available for synthetic uses or as solvents are listed in Table 27.1. Methods of preparation are summarized in the following section.

TABLE 27.1. ARYL HALIDES

NAME	FORMULA	M.P., °C.	B.P., °C.
Fluorobenzene	C_6H_5F	−45	85
Chlorobenzene	C_6H_5Cl	−45	132
Bromobenzene	C_6H_5Br	−30.6	155.5
Iodobenzene	C_6H_5I	−29	188.5
o-Chlorotoluene	$o\text{-}CH_3C_6H_4Cl$	−36	159
m-Chlorotoluene	$m\text{-}CH_3C_6H_4Cl$	−48	162
p-Chlorotoluene	$p\text{-}CH_3C_6H_4Cl$	7	162
o-Bromotoluene	$o\text{-}CH_3C_6H_4Br$	−26	182
m-Bromotoluene	$m\text{-}CH_3C_6H_4Br$	−40	184
p-Bromotoluene	$p\text{-}CH_3C_6H_4Br$	28	184
o-Bromoanisole	$o\text{-}CH_3OC_6H_4Br$	liq.	222
p-Bromoanisole	$p\text{-}CH_3OC_6H_4Br$	11	223
p-Bromodimethylaniline	$p\text{-}(CH_3)_2NC_6H_4Br$	55	264
o-Dichlorobenzene	$C_6H_4Cl_2(1,2)$	liq.	179
p-Dichlorobenzene	$C_6H_4Cl_2(1,4)$	53	173
1,2,4-Trichlorobenzene	$C_6H_3Cl_3(1,2,4)$	17	213
1,2,3,4-Tetrachlorobenzene	$C_6H_2Cl_4(1,2,3,4)$	46	254
1,2,4,5-Tetrachlorobenzene	$C_6H_2Cl_4(1,2,4,5)$	138	245
Hexachlorobenzene	C_6Cl_6	228	332
p-Dibromobenzene	$p\text{-}C_6H_4Br_2$	89	218
o-Bromochlorobenzene	$C_6H_4ClBr(1,2)$	liq.	199
p-Bromochlorobenzene	$C_6H_4ClBr(1,4)$	67	196
o-Bromoiodobenzene	$C_6H_4BrI(1,2)$	liq.	257
p-Bromoiodobenzene	$C_6H_4BrI(1,4)$	92	252
o-Chloroiodobenzene	$C_6H_4ClI(1,2)$	liq.	235
p-Chloroiodobenzene	$C_6H_4ClI(1,4)$	57	227

Preparation. — The benzene nucleus is readily substituted by chlorine or bromine atoms on interaction with the halogens in the presence of ferric chloride or bromide, aluminum chloride, or iodine. The less reactive iodine does not give comparable substitutions because a condition of equilibrium is reached. The equilibrium can be displaced by conducting the reaction in

$$ArH + I_2 \rightleftharpoons ArI + HI$$

the presence of an oxidizing agent to destroy the hydrogen iodide. Iodic acid and mercuric oxide have been used, but nitric acid usually is preferred, as in the example. Aryl iodides can also be prepared by reaction of an aryl

$$\text{(benzene)} + I_2 \xrightarrow[86\text{--}87\%]{\substack{\text{HNO}_3 \text{ (sp. gr. 1.50),} \\ \text{reflux}}} \text{(iodobenzene, I)}$$

(excess)

Grignard reagent with diiodoacetylene (Franzen, 1954). At the end of the

$$2C_6H_5MgBr + IC\equiv CI \rightarrow 2C_6H_5I + BrMgC\equiv CMgBr$$

reaction the acetylenedimagnesium bromide is hydrolyzed with dilute acid to acetylene; the iodide is isolated easily in yields up to 95%. Iodobenzene is also made from aniline by the Sandmeyer reaction, which is the standard preparative route to fluorobenzene, to the chloro- and bromotoluenes, and to most of the mixed halides. The total process for preparation of m-bromotoluene either requires the preparation of m-toluidine from p-toluidine, or the alternate route from the same starting material as formulated. The

$$\underset{\text{CH}_3}{\overset{\text{NH}_2}{\bigcirc}} \xrightarrow[60\text{--}67\%]{\substack{\text{1. Acetylate} \\ \text{2. Brominate} \\ \text{3. Hydrolyze}}} \underset{\text{CH}_3}{\overset{\text{NH}_2}{\bigcirc}}\text{Br} \xrightarrow[54\text{--}57\%]{\substack{\text{1. Diazotize} \\ \text{2. Deaminate (C}_2\text{H}_5\text{OH)}}} \underset{\text{CH}_3}{\overset{}{\bigcirc}}\text{Br}$$

Sandmeyer reaction affords the best route to o-bromochlorobenzene, to o- and p-bromoiodobenzene, and to the chloroiodobenzenes. Several p-dihalobenzenes can be obtained satisfactorily by direct halogenation; the p-isomers are formed as the chief products, along with smaller amounts of the o-dihalides, and since the symmetrically substituted p-isomers are all solids, in contrast with the companion substances, they can be purified by crystallization. p-Dibromobenzene has been obtained in yields of 61–71% and 85% by bromination of benzene with use of aluminum chloride or ferric bromide, respectively, and by similar processes chlorobenzene affords p-bromochlorobenzene in yields of 77% and 88%. The p-bromo derivatives of anisole and of dimethylaniline also can be made satisfactorily by direct bromination without catalyst. Dichlorination of benzene in the presence of aluminum chloride gives a preponderant amount of solid p-dichlorobenzene, employed as a moth repellant, and the liquid o-isomer, formed to the extent of about 30%, is useful as a special solvent, for which purpose the presence of small amounts of the m- and p-isomers is not objectionable. A higher proportion of o-dichlorobenzene results from the use of ferric chloride as catalyst. Further chlorination gives chiefly 1,2,4-trichlorobenzene, which is also formed on treatment of the stereoisomeric benzene hexachlorides with alkali. The symmetrical 1,2,4,5-derivative is the principal product of tetrachlorination, and a fifth and sixth halogen can be introduced, though with increased difficulty.

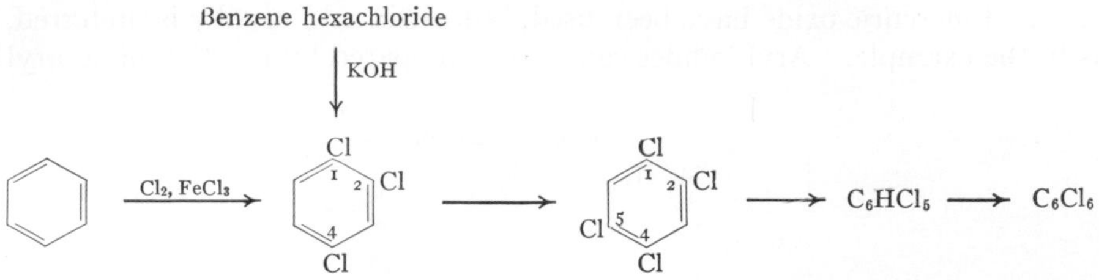

Benzene hexachloride

$$\downarrow \text{KOH}$$

Side-Chain Halogenation. — Toluene undergoes catalyzed chlorination or bromination in the nucleus in the same manner as benzene, with orientation to about the same extent in the *ortho* and *para* positions. When, however, the catalyst is omitted and the hydrocarbon is treated with either halogen at the reflux temperature, preferably with exposure to light, the chlorine or bromine atoms enter the methyl side chain rather than the nucleus, with formation in succession of the mono-, di-, and trihalo derivatives. The conversion of toluene into benzyl chloride proceeds more readily

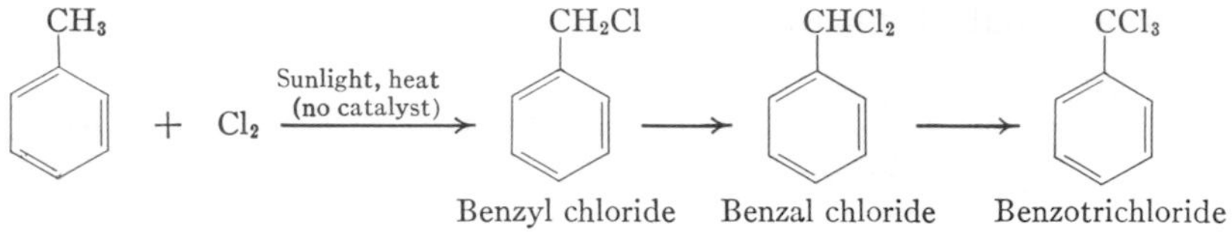

Benzyl chloride   Benzal chloride   Benzotrichloride

than the chlorination of methane, for the unsaturated phenyl group activates the hydrogens of the methyl group for substitution. This influence is particularly apparent in the behavior of hydrocarbons with longer side chains, for halogenation is effected in the α-positions of the chain but not at more remote sites. The differentiation between nuclear and side-chain

$$ArCH_2CH_2CH_3 \longrightarrow ArCHClCH_2CH_3 \longrightarrow ArCCl_2CH_2CH_3$$

halogenation is sharply defined. In the absence of a catalyst, attack of methyl or other alkyl groups is favored by light and heat, but if a potent catalyst such as an aluminum or iron halide is present nuclear substitution occurs exclusively. Kharasch discovered (1939) that side-chain chlorination can be accomplished with sulfuryl chloride (SO_2Cl_2) in the presence of a peroxide. The peroxide-catalyzed reaction proceeds rapidly in the

$$C_6H_5CH_3 + SO_2Cl_2 \xrightarrow[\text{80\%}]{\text{Dibenzoyl peroxide, 15 min.}} C_6H_5CH_2Cl + SO_2 + HCl$$

dark, whereas in the absence of peroxide the light-promoted reaction with sulfuryl chloride is complete only in seven hours. Side-chain chlorination is also favored by reaction in the vapor phase at 400–600°. Bromination of toluene with N-bromosuccinimide is likewise influenced by peroxides. In the absence of peroxide the predominant reaction is nuclear substitution in the *p*-position; in the presence of peroxide benzyl bromide is formed in 64% yield.

The benzyl and benzal halides and benzotrihalides are all liquids (Table 27.2) with the exception of benzyl iodide, a low-melting solid that can be

TABLE 27.2. SIDE-CHAIN HALOGENATED DERIVATIVES OF TOLUENE

NAME	FORMULA	M.P., °C.	B.P., °C.
Benzyl chloride	$C_6H_5CH_2Cl$	liq.	179
Benzal chloride	$C_6H_5CHCl_2$	liq.	206
Benzotrichloride	$C_6H_5CCl_3$	−5	221
Benzyl bromide	$C_6H_5CH_2Br$	liq.	199
Benzyl iodide	$C_6H_5CH_2I$	24	98/11 mm.

prepared from a mixture of benzyl chloride and potassium iodide in refluxing alcohol. The halides listed all undergo rapid hydrolysis in moist air, and they are potent lachrymators. Benzyl bromide and benzyl iodide cause a flow of tears, with painful swelling of the eyes, at concentrations of 0.004 mg. and 0.002 mg. per liter, respectively. ω-Chloroacetophenone (phenacyl chloride), $C_6H_5COCH_2Cl$ (m.p. 54°, b.p. 245°) is a still more powerful lachrymator, effective at a concentration of only 0.0003 mg. per liter, and has been used as a chemical warfare agent and in police work; it is dispersed by explosion in grenades, either in the solid form or in solution, and also by burning a mixture of the substance with black powder. The substance is made by chlorination of acetophenone in acetic acid solution.

Chloromethylation. — The chloromethyl group, —CH_2Cl, characteristic of benzyl chloride can be introduced directly by a process akin to the Friedel-Crafts reaction. This consists in interaction with formaldehyde and hydrogen chloride in the presence of a catalyst such as zinc chloride or aluminum chloride (Blanc reaction). Benzyl chloride, for example, can be prepared in good yield by passing hydrogen chloride gas into a suspension of paraformaldehyde and anhydrous zinc chloride in benzene. Paraformaldehyde undergoes depolymerization under the influence of hydrogen chloride, and

$$3 \, \bigcirc + (CH_2O)_3 + 3HCl \xrightarrow[70\%]{ZnCl_2,\ 60°} 3 \, \bigcirc^{CH_2Cl} + 3H_2O$$

(with some p-xylylene
dichloride, $ClCH_2C_6H_4CH_2Cl$,
m.p. 100°)

in the presence of the catalyst benzene condenses with formaldehyde or the addition product with hydrogen chloride, $HOCH_2Cl$, with ultimate production of benzyl chloride. The procedure can be varied by replacing formaldehyde by methylal, $CH_2(OCH_3)_2$, or by chloromethyl ether, produced as follows:

$$(CH_2O)_3 + 3CH_3OH + 3HCl \longrightarrow 3CH_3OCH_2Cl + 3H_2O$$

Zinc chloride is sometimes fused with a small quantity of aluminum chloride

to increase the activity, or even replaced entirely by the more reactive reagent, and in other instances sufficient catalysis is obtained with a mineral
acid alone, as in the preparation of 2-hydroxy-5-nitrobenzyl chloride.

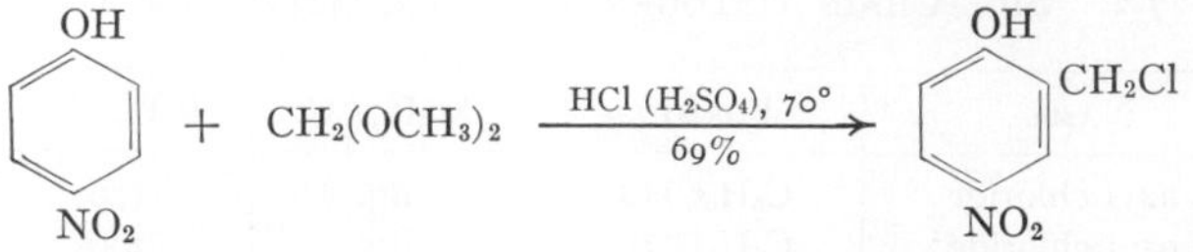

2-Hydroxy-5-nitrobenzyl
chloride (m.p. 130°)

Chloromethylation is subject to most of the limitations and specific
characteristics of the Friedel-Crafts alkylation reaction. The orientation
is comparable, and some polysubstitution usually occurs; thus in the first
example cited benzyl chloride is accompanied by the p-disubstitution
product. Introduction of the chloromethyl group perhaps proceeds under
milder conditions and more selectively than Friedel-Crafts alkylations, and
the reaction, followed by reduction, has occasionally been employed in synthesis of the methyl derivatives: $ArH \rightarrow ArCH_2Cl \rightarrow ArCH_3$; the reduction
can be accomplished with zinc and acetic acid or with stannous chloride.
The great value of the chloromethylation reaction, however, is that the
products are reactive halides capable of being transformed into products of
a variety of types: $ArCH_2OH$, $ArCH_2OCH_3$, $ArCH_2CN$, $ArCH_2COOH$,
$ArCH_2N(CH_3)_2$. One synthetic use is the introduction of an acid side
chain required for formation of a new ring:

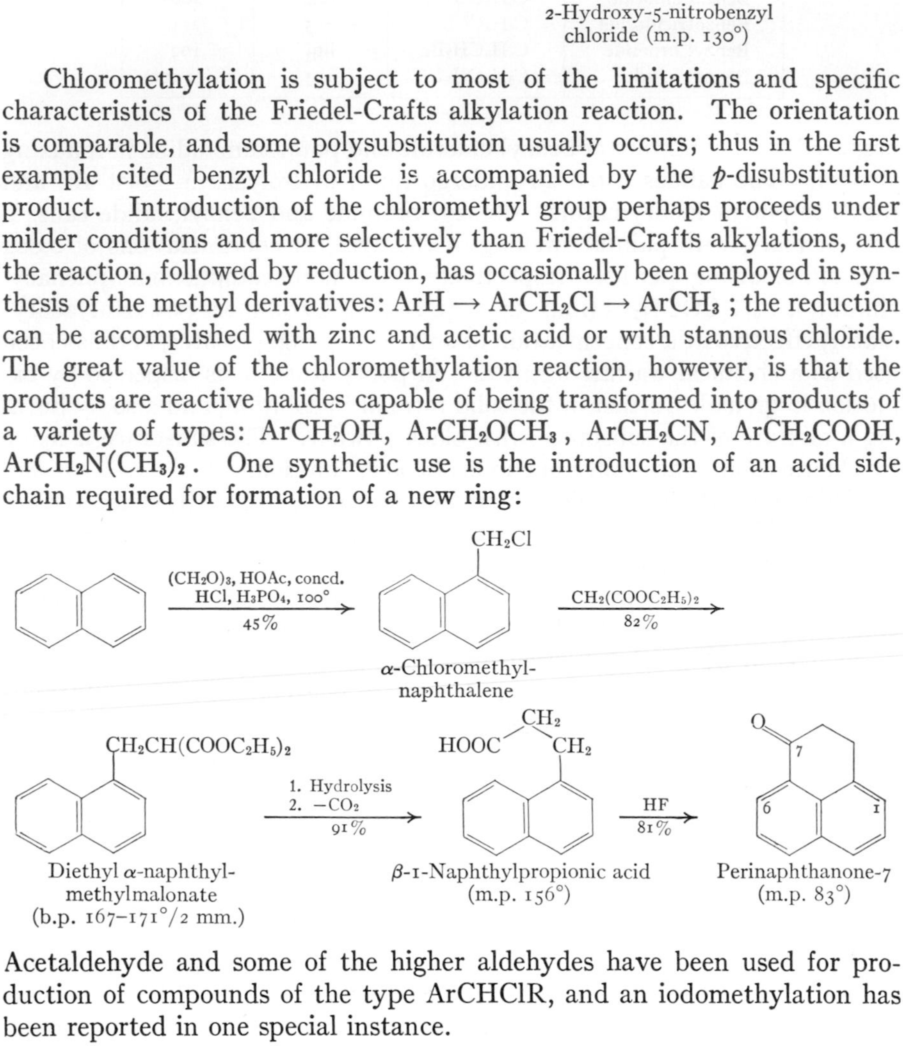

α-Chloromethyl-
naphthalene

Diethyl α-naphthyl-
methylmalonate
(b.p. 167–171°/2 mm.)

β-1-Naphthylpropionic acid
(m.p. 156°)

Perinaphthanone-7
(m.p. 83°)

Acetaldehyde and some of the higher aldehydes have been used for production of compounds of the type ArCHClR, and an iodomethylation has
been reported in one special instance.

Reactivity. — Compounds of the benzyl halide type show greatly enhanced reactivity as compared with alkyl halides, and are similar to allyl
halides. Activation in benzyl halides, as in allyl halides, is attributed to a
tendency to form an intermediate carbonium ion stabilized by resonance.
In the present instance resonance involves establishment of positive centers

at the *ortho* and *para* positions in the nucleus, as well as in the side chain, as shown in the formulas. Whereas substituted allyl halides in-

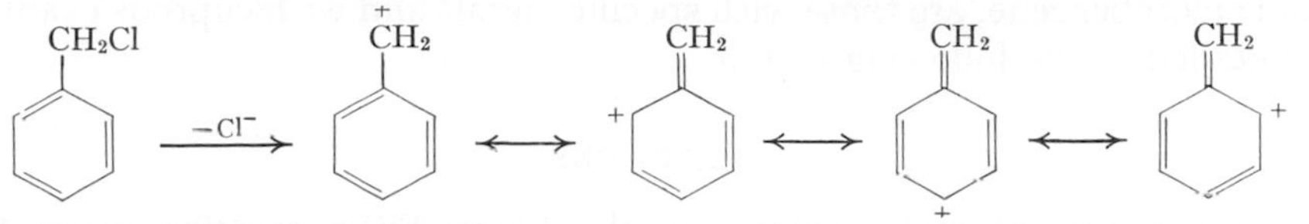

variably undergo some allylic rearrangement in replacement reactions [C_6H_5CH=$CHCH_2Br \rightarrow C_6H_5CH(OAc)CH$=$CH_2$ + normal product], the resonance structures of the benzyl ion that carry a charge in the nucleus do not play so prominent a role in determining the point of attack by reagents, for the usual products are those of the benzyl type: $C_6H_5CH_2A$. However allylic rearrangements occur in some condensations of benzylmagnesium halides (Tiffeneau[1]). Thus the reaction of the chloride with formaldehyde gives none of the normal product, $C_6H_5CH_2CH_2OH$, but affords *o*-tolylcar-binol. *o*-Tolyl derivatives resulting from allylic rearrangements are formed

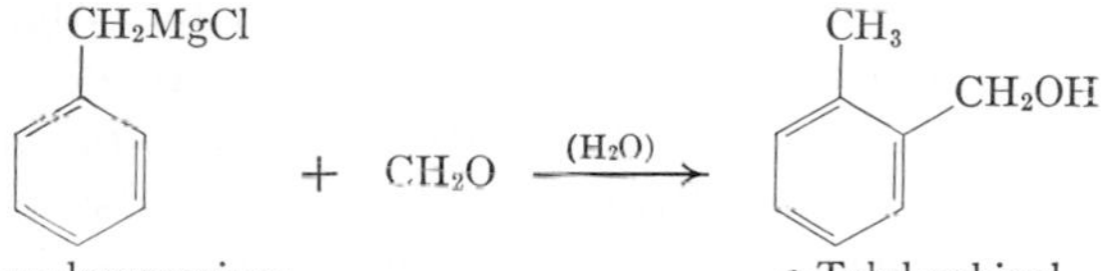

Benzylmagnesium
chloride

o-Tolylcarbinol

similarly in condensations of the same Grignard reagent with acid chlorides and anhydrides, but the normal benzyl derivatives are produced in reactions with ketones, carbon dioxide, and typical esters. The greater disposition of comparable aliphatic systems to react in the abnormal sense is indicated by the observation that the Grignard reagent of cinnamyl chloride reacts chiefly to give products of the type $C_6H_5CH(A)CH$=CH_2, even with carbon dioxide (Gilman).

In contrast with benzyl halides, the nuclear-substituted halogen de-rivatives of benzene are markedly less reactive than the corresponding alkyl halides and are comparable to the similarly constituted vinyl halides. The inert character of the aryl and vinyl compounds is attributed to the oppor-tunity for resonance in the halide molecules, rather than in a derived ion, with resulting shortening of the carbon–halogen bond distance and in-creased firmness of binding. Labilization of ordinarily inert chlorine or bromine atoms by nitro groups in *ortho* or *para* positions has been noted and interpreted as due to resonance. In the absence of labilizing groups, aryl halides are inert to alkalis except at high temperatures and pressures (chlorobenzene → phenol, 300°), and often can be freed from persistent impurities by steam distillation from a mixture with aqueous alkali. Chloro- and bromobenzene depart from the behavior of alkyl halides in being unattacked by silver hydroxide, alcoholic ammonia, or sodium ethoxide

---

[1] Marc Tiffeneau, 1873–1945; b. France; Paris (Sorbonne); *J. Chem. Soc.*, 1668 (1949)

even at temperatures of 100–150°. The chief practicable reactions involving the halogen atoms, other than the technical production of phenol from chlorobenzene, are those with specific metals and with cuprous cyanide, as detailed in the following section.

REACTIONS

Aryl halides generally enter into the **Wurtz-Fittig reaction** under the influence of metallic sodium. Bromides and iodides also combine with magnesium in the presence of ether to give **Grignard reagents**; the reaction usually is initiated somewhat less readily than when an alkyl halide is used, but arylmagnesium bromides and iodides nevertheless are obtainable without difficulty and in good yield, and are of inestimable value in syntheses. There are few limitations beyond those encountered as well in the aliphatic series (incompatible groups), though the factor of steric hindrance sometimes is important. Thus a bromine atom flanked in both *ortho* positions by substituents, one of which is a chlorine atom, may react abnormally. However, *o*- and *p*-bromochlorobenzene afford mono-Grignard derivatives satisfactorily; the *p*-compound, p-ClC_6H_4MgBr, is characterized by a beautiful chemiluminescence of its solutions, observable in the dark and due to slow air oxidation. *p*-Bromodimethylaniline also yields a Grignard reagent, p-$(CH_3)_2NC_6H_4MgBr$. In chlorobenzene the reactivity of the halogen atom is so slight that there is no interaction with magnesium under usual conditions.

Aryllithium Compounds. — Either chloro- or bromobenzene, when treated in ethereal solution with two equivalents of freshly cut metallic lithium by the technique employed in preparing a Grignard reagent, reacts with the separation of lithium halide and production of phenyllithium.

$$C_6H_5Br(Cl) \quad + \quad 2\,Li \quad \xrightarrow{\text{Ether}} \quad C_6H_5Li \quad + \quad LiBr(Cl)$$
$$\text{Phenyllithium}$$

The organometallic compound is soluble in ether and is decomposed by water, alcohol, acids, or bases, for example:

$$C_6H_5Li \quad + \quad H_2O \quad \longrightarrow \quad C_6H_6 \quad + \quad LiOH$$

Aryllithiums are also available (1) by halogen–metal exchange and, in certain cases, (2) by metalation with phenyllithium (Gilman; Wittig;[2] 1938). The latter reaction, an electrophilic substitution ($C_6H_5^-Li^+$), is facilitated by o,p-directing groups. Benzene itself is not attacked, but

1. $\qquad\qquad ArBr + C_6H_5Li \rightarrow ArLi + C_6H_5Br$
2. $\qquad\qquad ArH + C_6H_5Li \rightarrow ArLi + C_6H_6$

anisole gives the 2-lithium derivative and resorcinol dimethyl ether gives 2,4-dimethoxyphenyllithium; substitution is generally *ortho* rather than *para* to an ether linkage. Phenyllithium affords benzoic acid on carbona-

---

[2] Georg Wittig, b. 1897 Berlin; Ph.D. Marburg (v. Auwers); Freiburg, Tübingen

tion, and adds to the carbonyl group of aldehydes, ketones, and esters.

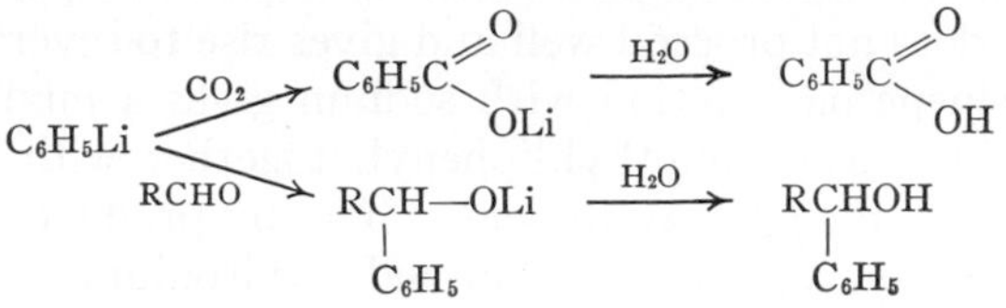

There are some differences in the behavior of aryllithium and arylmagnesium halide derivatives in the selective attack on polyfunctional carbonyl components, but in general the two are comparable, with slight advantages with respect to yields in favor of selection of the Grignard derivative where a choice is open. Thus if a bromide can be secured as a synthetic intermediate, it is usually treated with magnesium rather than with lithium, whereas if only the chloride is available, it can be utilized through conversion into the aryllithium. Occasions arise where advantage can be taken of the gradation in reactivity. Thus in 1-chloro-8-bromonaphthalene the more reactive halogen can be replaced by methyl through the Grignard derivative, and the other one utilized in production of a lithium derivative that will link the aryl residue to another component:

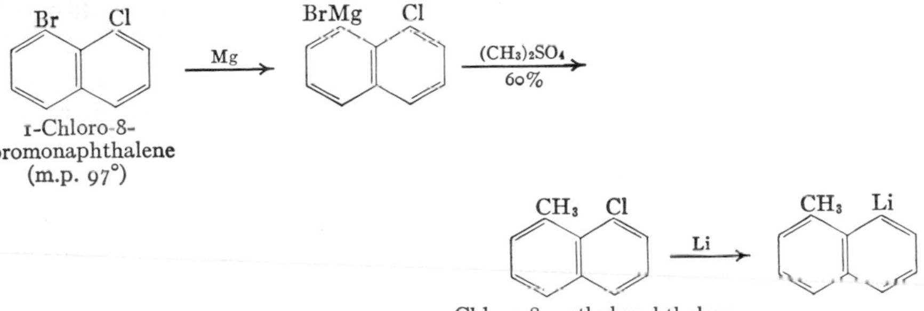

1-Chloro-8-
bromonaphthalene
(m.p. 97°)

1-Chloro-8-methylnaphthalene
(m.p. 69°)

Reactions of phenyllithium with onium salts are of interest. The product of the reaction with tetramethylammonium bromide (3) is tri

3. $(CH_3)_3N^+CH_3Br^- + C_6H_5Li \rightarrow (CH_3)_3N^+{-}CH_2^- + C_6H_6 + LiBr$

4. $(C_6H_5)_3P^+CH_3Br^- + C_6H_5Li \rightarrow (C_6H_5)_3P{=}CH_2 + LiBr + C_6H_6$

5. $(C_6H_5)_3P{=}CH_2 + R_2C{=}O \rightarrow (C_6H_5)_3PO + R_2C{=}CH_2$

6. $(C_6H_5)_4P^+I^- + C_6H_5Li \rightarrow (C_6H_5)_5P + LiI$

methylammonium methylide (Wittig, 1947), and that formed on reaction with methyltriphosphonium bromide (4) is triphenylphosphinemethylene, which reacts with carbonyl compounds (5) with replacement of oxygen by methylene (Wittig, 1954). Cinnamaldehyde reacts with the reagent to give *trans*-1-phenylbutadiene. Tetraphenylphosphonium iodide, which is typically ionic (m.p. about 340°), reacts (6) to give nonionic pentaphenylphosphorus (m.p. 124°, crystallizes from cyclohexane).

Ullmann Reaction. — The action of metallic sodium on an aryl halide results in formation of a certain amount of the expected diphenyl derivative, but the reaction does not proceed well and gives rise to several by-products. Thus *p*-bromotoluene on reaction with sodium gives a mixture containing the normal product, 4,4'-dimethyldiphenyl, together with 3,4'-dimethyldiphenyl, dibenzyl, and *p*-benzyltoluene. The by-products probably arise through isomerization of initially formed arylsodium (*p*-CH₃C₆H₄Na), with migration of the sodium to other positions in the nucleus and also into the side chain. Ullmann discovered that diphenyl derivatives can be prepared more satisfactorily by use of copper powder or copper bronze at an elevated temperature. The high-boiling iodobenzene affords diphenyl when refluxed with copper, but this parent hydrocarbon is made more easily by a method described earlier (p. 546). The Ullmann reaction, however, is valuable for the synthesis of substituted diphenyls. The reaction

NO₂

2 ⟨⟩—Cl →(Copper bronze, 215–225° / 52–61%)→ 2,2'-Dinitrodiphenyl (m.p. 125°)

(mixed with sand)

is sometimes conducted in nitrobenzene solution, with suspended copper.

Conversion to Nitriles. — Although alkyl halides react readily with potassium cyanide in aqueous alcohol, the aryl halides are indifferent to this reagent. They do, however, afford nitriles on interaction with anhydrous cuprous cyanide in pyridine solution at somewhat elevated temperatures. Pyridine is required to promote reaction, perhaps because it not only dissolves the halide but forms a molecular complex with cuprous cyanide which separates as a crystalline solid on mixing the reagents and dissolves on heating. The reagents are employed in a strictly anhydrous condition to obviate hydrolysis of the nitrile at the high temperature required. If the halide has a sufficiently high boiling point, a suitable reaction temperature can be obtained in an open flask, as in the following example:

Br   CN

⟨⟩ + Cu₂(CN)₂ →(Pyridine, 215–225° / 82–90%)→ ⟨⟩

α-Bromonaphthalene   α-Naphthonitrile

When applied to a more volatile halide the reaction is conducted in a sealed tube or autoclave. Chlorides serve as satisfactorily as bromides, and the yield and purity of the products leave little to be desired.

POLYVALENT IODINE COMPOUNDS

Aromatic iodides can form a variety of derived compounds containing polyvalent iodine, the first of which was discovered by Willgerodt[3] (1886).

---

[3] Conrad Willgerodt, 1841–1930; b. Braunschweig, Germany; Ph.D. Freiburg; Freiburg; *Ber.*, **64A**, 5 (1931)

Iodobenzene reacts with chlorine to form **iodobenzene dichloride** (phenyl iodochloride), $C_6H_5ICl_2$, a yellow substance which is moderately soluble in chloroform or benzene and sparingly soluble in ether, and which when heated to $110-120°$ decomposes abruptly, chiefly as follows: $C_6H_5ICl_2 \rightarrow$ p-$ClC_6H_4I + HCl$. The dichloride can be prepared in $87-94\%$ yield by chlorination of iodobenzene in cold chloroform solution, from which it separates in a crystalline condition. The dichloride is converted into **iodosobenzene** by alkali. The reaction is conducted by grinding the dichloride

$$C_6H_5ICl_2 \xrightarrow[60-62\%]{NaOH} C_6H_5IO$$

Iodobenzene dichloride Iodosobenzene

in a mortar with sodium carbonate and ice and stirring in the required amount of alkali. Iodosobenzene is an amorphous yellow solid, somewhat soluble in hot water or alcohol and sparingly soluble in ether; it decomposes explosively when heated to about $210°$. The substance is basic and is reconverted into iodobenzene dichloride by hydrochloric acid. Properties of these trivalent iodine compounds suggest a saltlike character, and consideration of the possible disposition of the electrons shows that one of the three linkages of the iodine atom must be polar. Iodosobenzene is structurally comparable to amine oxides (p. 239), and the union between iodine and oxygen must involve transfer of an electron from iodine to oxygen, with development of ionic charges and establishment of a pair of shared electrons. Iodobenzene dichloride can be considered as formed from the components by transfer of an electron from iodine to one of the chlorine atoms and sharing of electrons with the second atom. The salt of iodosobenzene

and acetic acid, **iodosobenzene diacetate** (phenyliodoso acetate), $[C_6H_5IOCOCH_3]^+CH_3COO^-$ (m.p. $157°$), is soluble in acetic acid or benzene, but insoluble in ether; it is obtained from iodosobenzene and acetic acid, and can be purified by crystallization from benzene petroleum ether. The substance is an oxidizing agent comparable to lead tetraacetate; for example, it cleaves vic-glycols in the same manner, though less rapidly.

The compounds mentioned above are not distinctive to the aromatic series, for aliphatic iodides also form iodoso and dichloride derivatives, but the products are much less stable. Iodosobenzene can be obtained as a solid, but is not stable and undergoes slow change on storage. The change, which can be brought about rapidly by heat, consists in disproportionation to iodobenzene and **iodoxybenzene**, a pentavalent iodine compound. Iodobenzene is removed as formed from the mixture by steam distillation. Iodoxybenzene is a colorless solid that melts with explosive

$$2 C_6H_5\overset{+}{I}-\overset{-}{O} \xrightarrow[92-95\%]{\text{Steam distil}} C_6H_5\overset{+}{I}\underset{O}{\overset{\overset{-}{O}}{\diagdown}} + C_6H_5I$$

Iodosobenzene   Iodoxybenzene   Iodobenzene

decomposition at $237°$; it is practically insoluble in benzene or acetone, and soluble in water to the extent of 12 g. per liter at $100°$. An alternate method of preparation is oxidation of iodobenzene dichloride with sodium hypochlorite solution (87–92% yield).

A further compound containing trivalent iodine is **diphenyliodonium hydroxide**, a strongly basic substance resembling quaternary ammonium hydroxides; it is not stable in the solid state but can be prepared in aqueous solution by the action of silver hydroxide on a mixture of iodosobenzene and iodoxybenzene (Victor Meyer, 1894). The same substance results

$$C_6H_5\overset{+}{I}-\overset{-}{O} + C_6H_5\overset{+}{I}\underset{O}{\overset{\overset{-}{O}}{\diagdown}} + AgOH \longrightarrow [(C_6H_5)_2I]^+OH^- + AgIO_3$$

Iodosobenzene   Iodoxybenzene   Diphenyliodonium hydroxide

from interaction of iodosobenzene with phenylmagnesium bromide and

$$C_6H_5\overset{+}{I}-\overset{-}{O} + C_6H_5MgBr \xrightarrow{\text{(H}_2\text{O)}} [(C_6H_5)_2I]^+OH^-$$

hydrolysis. The iodide salt, diphenyliodonium iodide, $[(C_6H_5)_2I]^+I^-$, is a stable solid, m.p. $176°$, dec.

Insecticides Containing Halogen. — The remarkably active contact insecticide known as DDT (dichlorodiphenyltrichloroethane) was introduced in 1942 by the Swiss firm J. R. Geigy. The substance is prepared by condensation of chlorobenzene with chloral hydrate in the presence of sulfuric acid, based upon the original synthesis by Zeidler (1874). Various isomers

$$Cl\text{—}\langle\bigcirc\rangle + \underset{CCl_3}{CH(OH)_2} + \langle\bigcirc\rangle\text{—}Cl \xrightarrow{H_2SO_4} Cl\text{—}\langle\bigcirc\rangle\text{—}\underset{CCl_3}{CH}\text{—}\langle\bigcirc\rangle\text{—}Cl$$

DDT(p,p', m.p. $109°$)

are also formed, particularly o,p'-DDT, and technical preparations contain only about 70% of the p,p'-form, which is the most active isomer. The toxic effect may be due to combination of the action of the chlorobenzene unit (respiratory poison) with that of chloroform (lipid-soluble narcotic). DDT has shown spectacular success in control of diseases (typhus, malaria) that are transmitted by insect carriers. It is also used effectively in protecting agricultural crops against a variety of pests.

An insecticide of even simpler constitution was announced in 1945 by the Imperial Chemical Industries. It is one of six isomeric benzene hexachlorides produced by chlorination of benzene under illumination. The isomers are distinguished by the prefixes α, β, γ, etc. Only the γ-isomer (m.p. 111°) has insecticidal properties and it is a minor constituent of the mixture (10–12%).   It is known as gammexane or as 666.   Nine isomeric

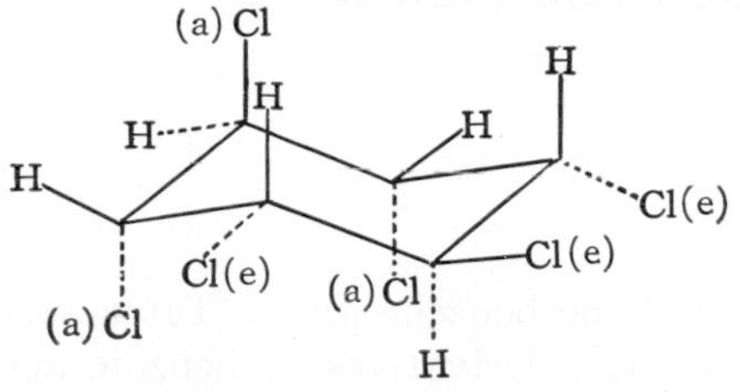

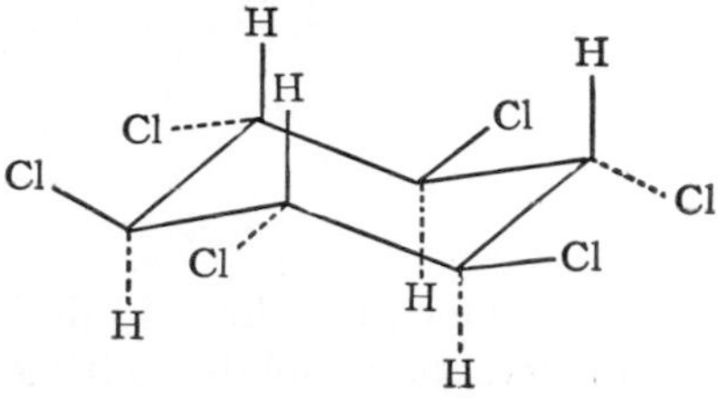

forms are possible (compare inositol, p. 394).   The conformation established for the substance is shown in the formula.   Contrary to early inferences based on the ability of gammexane to interfere with utilization of inositol (yeast), the insecticide differs from the growth factor in stereochemistry. The β-form (m.p. 200°) is known from X-ray studies to have the centro-symmetric configuration.   This isomer is capable of undergoing only *cis*-elimination of hydrogen chloride, and it is dehydrohalogenated by sodium ethoxide at a rate 1/7000 to 1/24000 that of the other isomers, all of which can undergo *trans* elimination.

PROBLEMS

1. Indicate all the steps required for preparation of *p*-bromoiodobenzene from aniline.
2. What products would be expected to result from the action of alkali on the three products of the side-chain chlorination of toluene?
3. (*a*) How could *p*-$CH_3C_6H_4CH_2OH$ be made in two steps from toluene?   Would you anticipate difficulty in securing a pure product?
   (*b*) Suggest a synthesis of pure *p*-methylbenzyl alcohol from *p*-bromochlorobenzene.
4. Suggest a method for the preparation of 2,5-dimethylbenzyl chloride.
5. How could you convert anisole into 2 amino-4-bromoanisole?
6. Suggest a method for the removal of an aromatic bromine atom (replacement by hydrogen).
7. What alternate procedures are available for the conversion of *m*-xylene, through a monohalo derivative, into 2,4-dimethylbenzoic acid?

READING REFERENCE

R. C. Fuson and C. H. McKeever, "Chloromethylation of Aromatic Compounds," in R. Adams, "Organic Reactions," I, 63–90, Wiley, New York (1942)

CHAPTER 28

AROMATIC CARBOXYLIC ACIDS

The monocarboxylic acid derivatives of the benzene series (Table 28.1) are all crystalline solids melting above 100°; derivatives of benzoic acid substituted in the p-position by methyl, halo, nitro, hydroxyl, methoxyl, or amino groups melt at a temperature in the neighborhood of 200°. As com-

TABLE 28.1. MONOBASIC ACIDS

ACID	FORMULA	M.P., °C.	B.P., °C.	$pK_a^{25°}$
Benzoic	$C_6H_5CO_2H$	121.7	249	4.17
o-Toluic	o-$CH_3C_6H_4CO_2H$	104	259 $^{751\,mm.}$	3.89
m-Toluic	m-$CH_3C_6H_4CO_2H$	111	263	4.28
p-Toluic	p-$CH_3C_6H_4CO_2H$	180		4.35
o-Chlorobenzoic	o-$ClC_6H_4CO_2H$	141		2.89
m-Chlorobenzoic	m-$ClC_6H_4CO_2H$	158		3.82
p-Chlorobenzoic	p-$ClC_6H_4CO_2H$	243		4.03
o-Bromobenzoic	o-$BrC_6H_4CO_2H$	149		2.82
m-Bromobenzoic	m-$BrC_6H_4CO_2H$	155		3.85
p-Bromobenzoic	p-$BrC_6H_4CO_2H$	252		4.18
o-Nitrobenzoic	o-$NO_2 \cdot C_6H_4CO_2H$	148		2.21
m-Nitrobenzoic	m-$NO_2 \cdot C_6H_4CO_2H$	142		3.46
p-Nitrobenzoic	p-$NO_2 \cdot C_6H_4CO_2H$	240		3.40
3,5-Dinitrobenzoic	$3,5$-$(NO_2)_2 \cdot C_6H_3CO_2H$	205		2.80
Salicylic	o-$HOC_6H_4CO_2H$	159		3.00
m-Hydroxybenzoic	m-$HOC_6H_4CO_2H$	200		4.12
p-Hydroxybenzoic	p-$HOC_6H_4CO_2H$	215		4.54
Anisic	p-$CH_3OC_6H_4CO_2H$	184	277	4.49
Gallic	$3,4,5$-$(HO)_3C_6H_2CO_2H$	253 dec.		4.40
Syringic	4-(HO)-$3,5(CH_3O)_2C_6H_2CO_2H$	205		
Anthranilic	o-$NH_2 \cdot C_6H_4CO_2H$	145		5.00
m-Aminobenzoic	m-$NH_2 \cdot C_6H_4CO_2H$	174		4.82
p-Aminobenzoic	p-$NH_2 \cdot C_6H_4CO_2H$	187		4.92

pared with aliphatic acids of similar molecular weight, the boiling points are slightly higher and the melting points very much higher. Benzoic acid is somewhat more acidic (pK_a 4.17) than acetic acid (pK_a 4.74), and nearly all the common substituents, other than the amino group, increase the acidic strength, particularly when in the o-position. A hydrophilic carboxyl group joined to the benzene nucleus tends to decrease solubility in hydrocarbons or ether and to produce some solubility in water; the monocarboxylic acids are only slightly soluble in cold water, and on the addition of sodium carbonate or bicarbonate characteristically pass into solution with liberation of carbon dioxide.

GENERAL METHODS OF PREPARATION

One route to carboxylic acids is **oxidation of carbon side chains or rings.** Thus toluene yields benzoic acid, *m*- and *p*-xylene afford isophthalic and terephthalic acid, respectively, and mesitylene and durene are convertible into the corresponding polybasic acids. On a laboratory scale the poly-alkyl compounds usually are oxidized most satisfactorily either with a dilute aqueous solution of potassium permanganate at the reflux temperature or with dilute nitric acid at an elevated temperature, attained in a sealed tube or autoclave. In technical operations the most economical process usually is chlorination and hydrolysis: $ArCH_3 \rightarrow ArCCl_3 \rightarrow ArCO_2H$ (see benzoic acid, below). Another degradative method of preparation is **hypohalite oxidation of aceto compounds**: $ArCOCH_3 \xrightarrow{HOCl} ArCOCCl_3 \xrightarrow{NaOH} ArCO_2H +$ $CHCl_3$. The required methyl ketones are readily available by the Friedel-Crafts reaction, and the combination of this efficient condensation with the haloform reaction often offers an excellent method of introducing a carboxyl group. An advantage over the method of oxidation of alkyl derivatives is that the hypohalite reaction is more generally applicable because the reagent is not destructive to ring systems less resistant to oxidative attack than the isolated benzene nucleus. Thus β-methylnaphthalene is oxidized in the nucleus in preference to the methyl group, but the aceto derivative made by the Friedel-Crafts method undergoes hypochlorite oxidation readily:

Methyl β-naphthyl ketone   β-Naphthoic acid

Carboxylic acids are also prepared by **hydrolysis of nitriles**, available from aryl halides by reaction with cuprous cyanide and pyridine, from amines by diazotization and the Sandmeyer reaction (or from the less efficient fusion of sulfonates with potassium cyanide). A further general method is **carbonation of Grignard reagents or aryllithiums.** For example 2-bromomesitylene forms a Grignard reagent which on reaction with carbon dioxide yields mesitylenecarboxylic acid, $2,4,6\text{-}(CH_3)_3C_6H_2COOH$ (yield 45%, m.p. 152°, pK_a 4.43); carbonation of an ethereal solution of α-naphthylmagnesium bromide with carbon dioxide gas or with dry ice affords α-naphthoic acid in 70–85% yield from the bromide.

SPECIFIC ACIDS

Benzoic Acid. — The simplest acid of the series occurs in both the free and esterified condition in various plants, particularly resins and balsams, and early supplies were derived from hippuric acid of horse urine by acid or alkaline hydrolysis or by bacterial decomposition. The acid inhibits fermentation and decay of foodstuffs and has been used as a food preservative in the form of the sodium salt. Values for the solubility in various solvents at 17° are as follows (g. per 100 g.): water, 0.21; hexane, 0.94; benzene, 0.82;

chloroform, 14.6; acetone, 28.6; ethanol, 29.4; methanol, 36.4. The acid is volatile with steam and easily sublimed. One method of technical production is hydrolysis of benzotrichloride with lime in the presence of iron powder as catalyst at 50°, followed by acidification. The reaction may

$$C_6H_5CCl_3 \xrightarrow{\text{Ca(OH)}_2} [C_6H_5C(OH)_3] \xrightarrow{-H_2O} C_6H_5COOH$$

proceed through a triol stage or by elimination of hydrogen chloride from a mono- or diol $[C_6H_5C(OH)Cl_2, C_6H_5C(OH)_2Cl]$. An alternate process that obviates contamination with chlorobenzoic acids is oxidation of toluene with manganese dioxide and sulfuric acid.

The methyl and ethyl esters of benzoic acid (Table 28.2) are prepared

TABLE 28.2. DERIVATIVES OF BENZOIC ACID

NAME	FORMULA	M.P., °C.	B.P., °C.
Methyl benzoate	$C_6H_5COOCH_3$	liq.	199
Ethyl benzoate	$C_6H_5COOC_2H_5$	liq.	213
Phenyl benzoate	$C_6H_5COOC_6H_5$	71	314
Benzyl benzoate	$C_6H_5COOCH_2C_6H_5$	21	324
Benzoic anhydride	$(C_6H_5CO)_2O$	42	360
Benzoyl chloride	C_6H_5COCl	−1	197
Perbenzoic acid	C_6H_5COOOH	43	dec.
Benzoyl peroxide	$(C_6H_5COO)_2$	105 dec.	
Benzamide	$C_6H_5CONH_2$	130	
Benzanilide	$C_6H_5CONHC_6H_5$	163	$119^{10\,mm.}$
Benzhydrazide	$C_6H_5CONHNH_2$	112	

conveniently by the Fischer method (excess alcohol, mineral acid catalyst); they can be prepared also by heating potassium benzoate with the dialkyl sulfate at 205–210°. Phenyl benzoate is made by heating a mixture of benzoic acid and phenol with phosphorus oxychloride. The benzyl ester, which occurs in tuberose oil, can be prepared from benzoyl chloride and benzyl alcohol. Benzoic anhydride is prepared in 72–74% yield by fractional distillation of a mixture of benzoic acid and acetic anhydride containing a small amount of sirupy phosphoric acid. Benzoyl peroxide is made by stirring benzoyl chloride at 0° with a 5–7% solution of sodium peroxide, and the peroxide can be converted into perbenzoic acid in 83–86% yield by treatment with a solution of sodium methoxide in methanol at 0° in the presence of chloroform to extract the methyl benzoate formed, careful acidification of the aqueous layer, and extraction with chloroform (phosgene-free). The dried chloroform solution is used for conversion of ethylenic

$$(C_6H_5COO)_2 + CH_3ONa \xrightarrow{\text{CHCl}_3,\, 0°} C_6H_5COOONa + C_6H_5COOCH_3$$

$$C_6H_5COOONa + H_2SO_4 \xrightarrow{0°} C_6H_5COOOH + NaHSO_4$$

compounds into oxides; in the following formulation perbenzoic acid is assumed to react as $C_6H_5CO_2\overset{-+}{OH}$:

$$\text{\Large$\rangle$}C=C\text{\Large$\langle$} \xrightarrow{\overset{+}{O}H} \text{\Large$\rangle$}C\text{---}C\text{\Large$\langle$} \xrightarrow{C_6H_5CO_2^{-}} \text{\Large$\rangle$}C\text{---}C\text{\Large$\langle$} + C_6H_5CO_2H$$
$$\underset{HO^+}{} \qquad \underset{O}{}$$

Perphthalic acid is used similarly but in ether solution. Quantitative titration with perbenzoic acid, by which the number of double bonds in a given compound can be established, is conducted by allowing a solution of the substance and excess perbenzoic acid in chloroform to stand for several hours at a low temperature and determining the amount of perbenzoic acid remaining in the solution, in comparison with a blank. The amido derivatives listed in Table 28.2 can be prepared by the action of benzoyl chloride on the appropriate amine.

Phthalic Acid. — Phthalic acid is the normal oxidation product of *o*-xylene and other *o*-dialkylbenzenes. Naphthalene, abundantly available from coal tar, can be regarded as a benzene derivative with a carbon side ring fused to adjacent positions; it is readily oxidized and provides the chief source of the acid or of the anhydride, formed on heating. The bicyclic hydrocarbon is attacked easily by oxidizing agents under conditions

Naphthalene   Phthalic acid   Phthalic anhydride

to which benzene is resistant, and since the benzenoid reaction product is stabilized still further by two *meta* directing groups, there is no danger of overoxidation. The modern method is vapor-phase catalytic oxidation (H. D. Gibbs). Naphthalene vapor is passed with air over a catalyst at an elevated temperature at which the acid is cyclized to the anhydride, which sublimes into a condenser and is obtained very pure. Results of experiments approximating commercial conditions (Shreve, 1943) indicate that phthalic anhydride can be obtained in 76% yield from commercial naphthalene with vanadium pentoxide catalyst on silica gel at 460–480°. α-Naphthoquinone (p. 712) is a by-product.

Phthalic acid (pK_a 3.0) melts with decomposition to the anhydride at temperatures ranging from 200° to 230°, depending on the rate of heating and the condition of the glass capillary surfaces. It is sparingly soluble in ether or chloroform and readily soluble in alcohol or water; 100 parts of water dissolve 0.77 part at 11.5° and 18 parts at 99°. The anhydride is very soluble in ether, melts sharply at 132°, and sublimes easily in long sparlike needles. A convenient qualitative test for phthalic anhydride consists in the formation of the dye fluorescein by fusion with resorcinol in the presence of sulfuric acid.

Derivatives of Phthalic Acid and Phthalic Anhydride. — The mono-methyl ester of phthalic acid can be prepared in good yield by refluxing phthalic anhydride with methanol; the half-ester melts at 85°, and is slightly less acidic (pK$_a$ 3.18) than the dibasic acid. The **dimethyl ester** is a liquid, b.p. 282°. The normal acid chloride derivative, **phthaloyl chloride,** is made by heating phthalic anhydride with phosphorus pentachloride and distilling the product; when heated with aluminum chloride at 95° for a

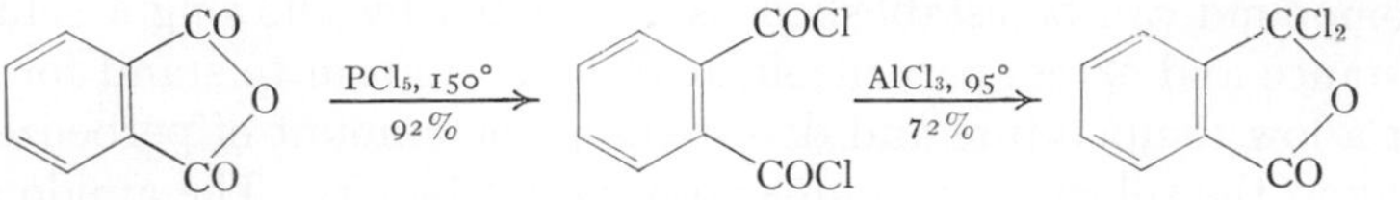

Phthaloyl chloride
(m.p. 16°, b.p. 277°)

as-Phthalyl chloride
(m.p. 89°)

prolonged period, the normal chloride rearranges into the isomeric **as-phthalyl chloride**, a derivative of phthalic anhydride in which one of the carbonyl oxygen atoms is replaced by two chlorine atoms. The equilibrium between the isomers is shifted in favor of the noncyclic acid chloride at high temperatures, and hence as-phthalyl chloride reverts to phthaloyl chloride on slow distillation in the absence of a catalyst.

Phthalimide, an important member of the series, is produced in industry by saturating molten phthalic anhydride with dry ammonia and heating the mixture to 170–240° under pressure. The cyclic imide can be prepared

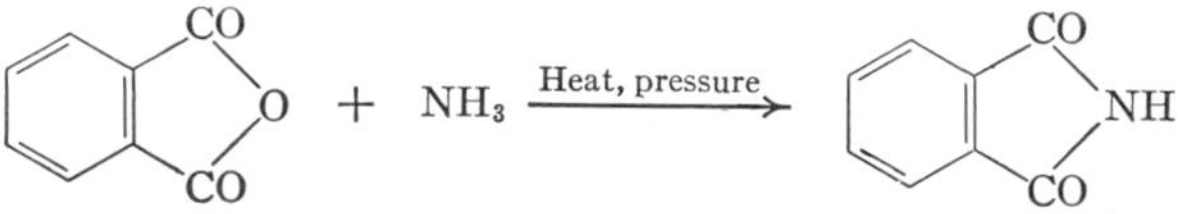

Phthalimide
(m.p. 234°)

on a laboratory scale in 95–97% yield by heating the anhydride with concentrated aqueous ammonia solution and eventually raising the temperature to 300°. The acidic character of phthalimide (pK$_a$ 8.30) and the use of the potassium salt in the Gabriel synthesis of primary amines have been mentioned. By careful saponification the heterocyclic ring can be opened without elimination of nitrogen; thus when a solution of phthalimide in 25% aqueous potassium hydroxide is allowed to stand in the cold for one to two hours and acidified, the acid-amide, **phthalamidic acid,** is produced.

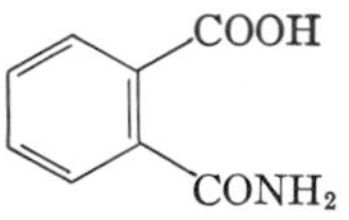

Phthalamidic acid

Phthalide, a γ-lactone, has been obtained by reduction of phthalic anhydride by various methods. A convenient laboratory procedure is reduction of phthalimide in aqueous sodium hydroxide solution with zinc dust activated with a small amount of copper (deposited from copper sulfate solution) at 8°; yield 67–71%. **Perphthalic acid,** which is comparable in

Phthalide
(m.p. 74°, b.p. 228°/730 mm.)

Perphthalic acid
(m.p. 110° dec.)

properties and uses to perbenzoic acid but more available and more stable, is prepared by stirring a suspension of phthalic anhydride in an aqueous solution of sodium perborate at 0° followed by acidification.

Anthranilic Acid. — This *o*-amino derivative of benzoic acid is prepared in high yield by the action of sodium hypochlorite on phthalimide in alkaline solution at 80°; the ring is opened by hydrolysis and the phthalamidic acid formed undergoes the Hofmann reaction. The amino acid is largely precipitated on neutralization of the alkaline solution, and an additional amount can be recovered as the copper salt. **Methyl anthranilate,** found

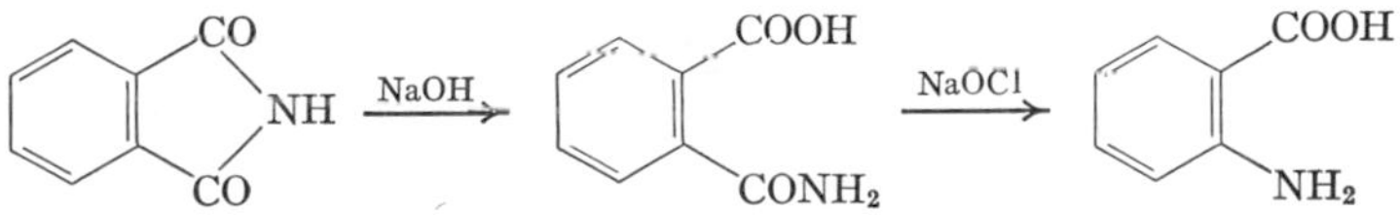

Phthalimide

Anthranilic acid

in oils extracted from jasmine and orange leaves, is obtained by esterification with methanol and sulfuric acid as a crystalline solid of characteristic fragrance (m.p. 25°, b.p. 135°/15 mm.).

Salicylic Acid. — The *o*-hydroxy derivative of benzoic acid was obtained for the first time in 1838 by the action of alkali on the corresponding aldehyde, probably as the result of disproportionation (Cannizzaro reaction). In 1859 Kolbe discovered a method of preparation that, in slightly modified form (Schmitt,[1] 1885), has made the substance available in quantity at a low price. In the technical process a solution of phenol in aqueous alkali is evaporated to a dry powder, and the sodium phenolate is saturated with carbon dioxide at 4–7 atmospheres pressure and heated to 125°; free salicylic acid is liberated on acidification of an aqueous solution of the cooled melt and is obtained in close to the theoretical amount. The Kolbe reaction may proceed by addition of the aromatic component to a carbonyl group of carbon dioxide. The reaction is applicable to other phenols and usually

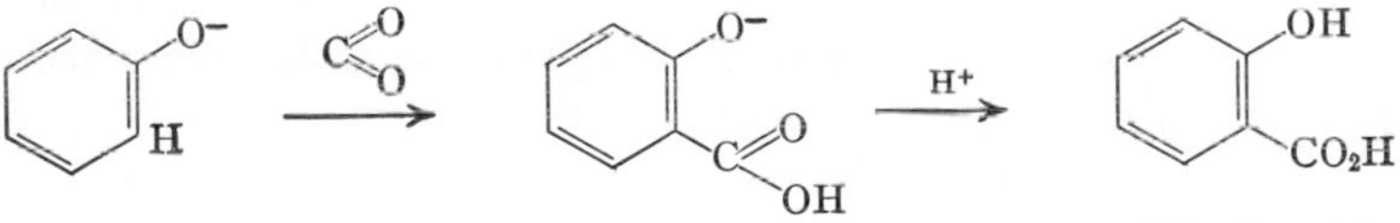

Salicylic acid

proceeds in good yield. Carboxylation *ortho* to the phenolic hydroxyl group is the rule, but *p*-derivatives are sometimes produced as well.

---

[1] Rudolf Schmitt, 1830–98; b. Wippershain, Germany; Ph.D. Marburg; Dresden

Methyl salicylate occurs in many plants and was known first as the fragrant principle of wintergreen and called oil of wintergreen. It is one of three ester derivatives used in medicine, the others being **acetylsalicylic acid**, or **aspirin**, and the phenyl ester, **salol**. The methyl ester is prepared synthetically by Fischer esterification of salicylic acid. The acetyl derivative can be prepared efficiently by acetylation with acetic anhydride with sulfuric acid as catalyst. Salol is made by condensation of salicylic acid with phenol under the influence of phosphorus oxychloride. The application of these substances in medicine is based on the fact that salicylic acid itself produces a beneficial physiological response when absorbed through the intestinal membrane, but, being rather strongly acidic, is disagreeably

Methyl salicylate (oil of wintergreen, m.p. −8°, b.p. 223°)   Acetylsalicylic acid (aspirin, m.p. 137°, pK_a 3.48)   Salol (phenyl salicylate, m.p. 43°)

irritating when taken by mouth. The irritating action is eliminated by esterification of the carboxyl group with either methanol or phenol and also by acetylation, for the acetyl derivative is less acidic than the phenolic carboxylic acid. The three ester derivatives, methyl salicylate, aspirin, and salol, are not hydrolyzed to an appreciable extent on contact with the weakly acidic digestive fluids of the stomach, and pass through without harmful action; on discharge to the alkaline intestinal tract, however, the esters undergo hydrolysis, and salicylic acid is liberated.

Toluic Acids. — The three isomers can be prepared by hydrolysis of the corresponding nitriles with 75% sulfuric acid; the nitrile intermediates are available from the amines (Sandmeyer reaction). *m*-Toluic acid is prepared also by partial oxidation of *m*-xylene with dilute nitric acid.

Halobenzoic Acids. — The readily available anthranilic acid provides a convenient starting material for preparation of the *o*-chloro, bromo, and iodo derivatives of benzoic acid (diazotization and Sandmeyer reaction). Another method, applicable to the *o*- and *p*-chloro and bromo acids, is permanganate oxidation of the appropriate halogen derivative of toluene. Chlorination of benzoic acid at room temperature in the presence of ferric chloride gives *m*-chlorobenzoic acid as the chief product, along with the 2,5-and 3,4-dichloro derivatives. A technical process for production of 2,4-dichlorobenzoic acid is side-chain chlorination of 2,4-dichlorotoluene and hydrolysis.

Nitrobenzoic Acids. — The *ortho* and *para* isomers are made by oxidation of the nitrotoluenes with potassium permanganate or potassium dichromate. *m*-Nitrobenzoic acid is the chief product of nitration of benzoic acid and can be prepared also from benzotrichloride by virtue of the *meta* directing effect of the trichloromethyl group and the susceptibility of the side-chain substituents to hydrolysis. Methyl m-nitrobenzoate (m.p. 78°) can be prepared in 81–85% yield by nitration of methyl benzoate with mixed acid, and alkaline hydrolysis affords the acid in 85–90% yield. 3,5-Dinitrobenzoic acid is prepared by nitration with mixed acid; 3,5-dinitrobenzoyl chloride (m.p. 74°) is useful as a reagent for conversion of alcohols into often sparingly soluble and high-melting esters.

Hydroxy and Methoxy Acids. — The ready preparation of salicylic acid by the Kolbe reaction has been described above. A route to m-hydroxybenzoic acid is fusion of sodium benzoic acid 3-sulfonate with sodium and potassium hydroxide at 220°. The p-methoxy derivative, anisic acid, is

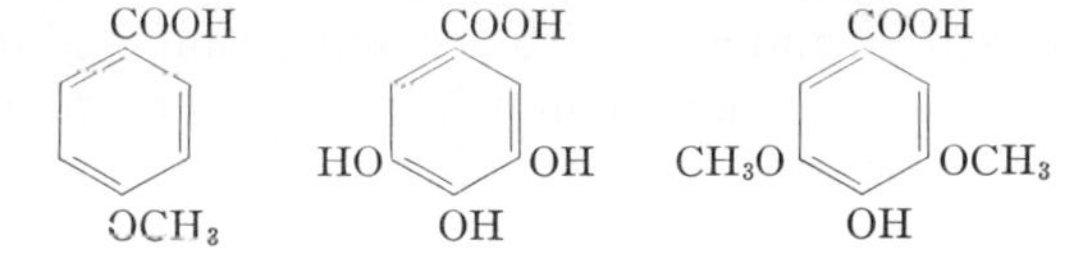

COOH
OCH₂
Anisic acid

COOH
HO   OH
OH
Gallic acid

COOH
CH₃O   OCH₃
OH
Syringic acid

found in extracts of natural oils containing anethole (p. 632), from which it probably arises by oxidation. Gallic acid, or 3,4,5-trihydroxybenzoic acid, results from fermentative cleavage of tannins, and is extracted by a process based on a method used by Scheele in 1786. The dimethyl ether, syringic acid, is also derived from natural sources. Gallic acid is soluble in three parts of boiling water, it has reducing properties, and it readily loses carbon dioxide on heating (pyrogallol). Decarboxylation at relatively low temperatures is a property characteristic of phenolic acids of *ortho* or *para* orientation of the two functional groups, but not of m-hydroxy acids. A possible interpretation is that a hydroxyl group in the o- or p-position, by virtue of resonance, increases the electron density at the carboxylated

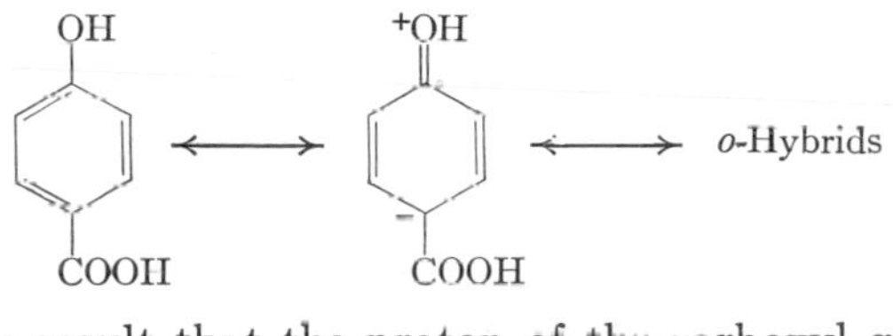

OH
COOH
$\longleftrightarrow$
⁺OH
COOH
$\longleftrightarrow$ o-Hybrids

position with the result that the proton of the carboxyl group is attracted to the nucleus with expulsion of carbon dioxide.

POLYBASIC ACIDS

Isophthalic acid, m-$C_6H_4(COOH)_2$ (m.p. 348°), and **terephthalic acid** (*para*, sublimes at about 300°) are obtained from the xylenes by permanganate oxidation or by partial bromination in the side chains, hydrolysis, and oxidation. The difficulty fusible terephthalic acid is but sparingly soluble in water, whereas the isomers of unsymmetrical structure are soluble in hot water.

Characteristic properties of the three benzenetricarboxylic acids are indicated in the notations under the formulas. The first two acids of unsymmetrical structure are very soluble in water and are extracted from aqueous solution by ether or ethyl acetate only after several applications of fresh

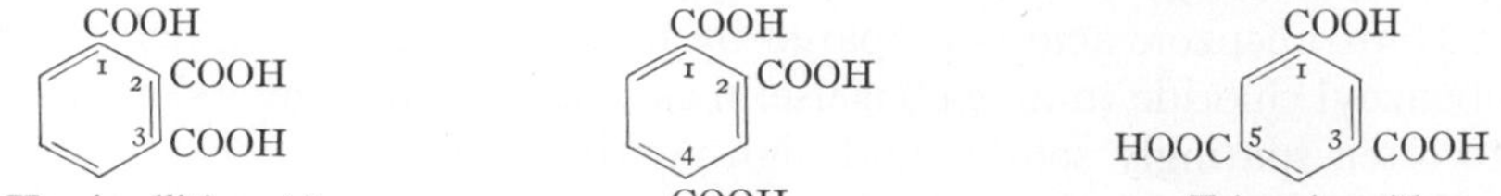

Hemimellitic acid
(m.p. 190–197° dec.; anhydride, m.p. 196°; trimethyl ester, m.p. 102°)

Trimellitic acid
(m.p. 225–235° dec.; anhydride, m.p. 166°; trimethyl ester, liq.)

Trimesic acid
(m.p. 380°; trimethyl ester, m.p. 144°)

solvent or with a continuous extractor. The 1,2,3- and 1,2,4-acids yield anhydrides when heated, and melt with decomposition in ill-defined temperature ranges. The 1,2,3-isomer, hemimellitic acid, is prepared most conveniently by stepwise oxidation of acenaphthene from coal tar. Trimellitic

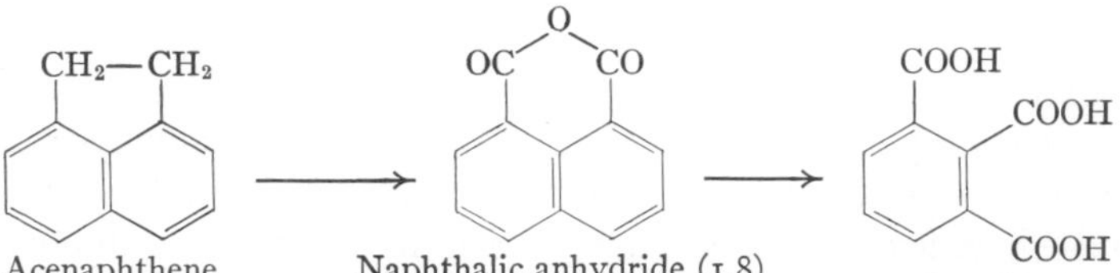

Acenaphthene · Naphthalic anhydride (1,8) · Hemimellitic acid

acid (1,2,4) and trimesic acid (1,3,5) result from permanganate oxidation of the corresponding trimethylbenzenes, pseudocumene and mesitylene.

Prehnitic Acid (Benzene-1,2,3,4-tetracarboxylic Acid). — This acid results from oxidation of a tetramethylbenzene named prehnitene. Although this hydrocarbon is not available as a starting material by direct synthesis, it can be prepared from pentamethylbenzene by the Jacobsen

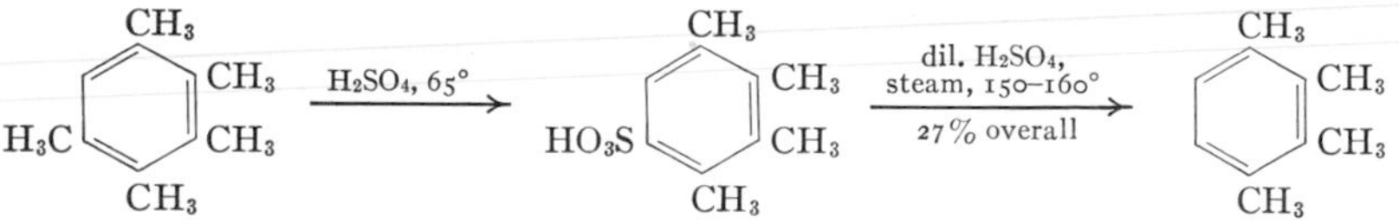

Pentamethylbenzene

Prehnitenesulfonic acid
(+ hexamethylbenzene)

Prehnitene

reaction (1886). This reaction, characteristic of polyalkylbenzenes and of halogenated polyalkylbenzenes, involves a rearrangement induced by concentrated sulfuric acid. In this instance, treatment of pentamethylbenzene with sulfuric acid results in displacement of one of the methyls by a sulfonic acid group, with transfer of the methyl substituent to a second molecule to produce hexamethylbenzene. Hydrolysis of the water-soluble reaction product affords prehnitene, which can be converted by oxidation into prehnitic acid (L. I. Smith). The acid is very soluble in water and is extracted

---

[2] Oskar Jacobsen, 1840–89; b. Ahrensburg/Holstein, Germany; Ph.D. Kiel; Rostock

with ether only slowly. It is best characterized as the crystalline tetramethyl ester,
prepared with diazomethane; a remarkable
property of this ester is that on exposure to
light a purple color is acquired that disappears
when the sample is either melted or recrystal-

Prehnitic acid

lized. On esterification with methanol and (m.p. 241° dec.; dianhydride, m.p.
hydrogen chloride, the less hindered carboxyl 196°; tetramethyl ester, m.p. 133°;
groups in the 1- and 4-positions react prefer- 1,4-dimethyl ester, m.p. 177°)
entially to form the 1,4-dimethyl ester. An alternate path to prehnitic
acid is permanganate oxidation of naphthalene-1,4-dicarboxylic acid (33%
yield); the starting material is obtained through a process involving 1,2-
and 1,4-addition of sodium to naphthalene. A more readily available starting material is obtained by succinoylation of acenaphthene. The 3-acid

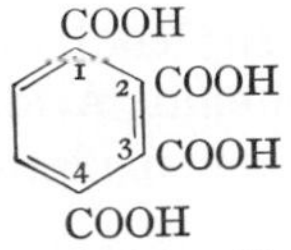

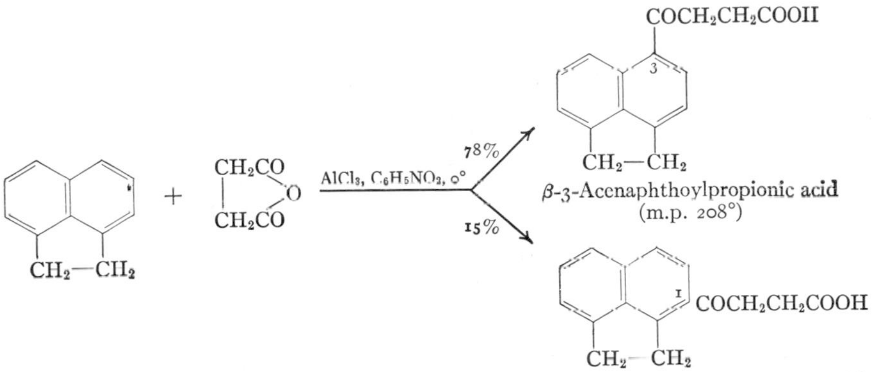

β-3-Acenaphthoylpropionic acid
(m.p. 208°)

β-1-Acenaphthoylpropionic acid
(m.p. 181°)

is the chief product and can be isolated as the less soluble sodium salt;
the solubility relationship is reversed in the methyl esters, and hence the
1-acid can be isolated easily by esterification of the material recovered from
the mother liquor. Separation is not required, however, for both isomers
are converted on permanganate oxidation into prehnitic acid (yield, 25%).

Mellophanic Acid (Benzene-1,2,3,5-tetracarboxylic Acid). — This substance has been isolated as a product of oxidation of a number of derivatives

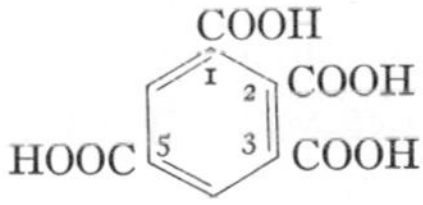

Mellophanic acid
(m.p. 260–265° dec.; tetramethyl ester, m.p. 111°)

of benzene and of polynuclear compounds, and identification of such degradation products, usually as the sharply melting esters, often constitutes
evidence of structure. A comparison sample of mellophanic acid can be

prepared conveniently by oxidation of mesitylenecarboxylic acid (from bromomesitylene) with nitric acid at 170–180°.

Pyromellitic Acid. — This symmetrically substituted tetrabasic acid can be made by oxidation of durene with nitric acid or by condensation of pseudocumene with acetyl chloride in the presence of aluminum chloride and oxidation of the resulting acetopseudocumene (2,4,5-trimethylaceto-phenone) with sodium hypobromite and then permanganate. The name is

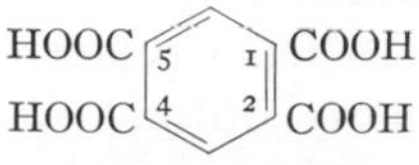

$$
\begin{array}{c}
\text{HOOC} \underset{\substack{4 \quad 2}}{\overset{\substack{5 \quad 1}}{\bigcirc}} \text{COOH} \\
\text{HOOC} \qquad \text{COOH}
\end{array}
$$

Pyromellitic acid
(m.p. 276° dec.; tetramethyl ester,
m.p. 141°; dianhydride, m.p. 286°)

derived from the fact that the substance is produced as the stable dian-hydride when the hexabasic mellitic acid is strongly heated.

Benzenepentacarboxylic acid, obtained by the action of potassium per-manganate on pentamethylbenzene, when heated above the melting point

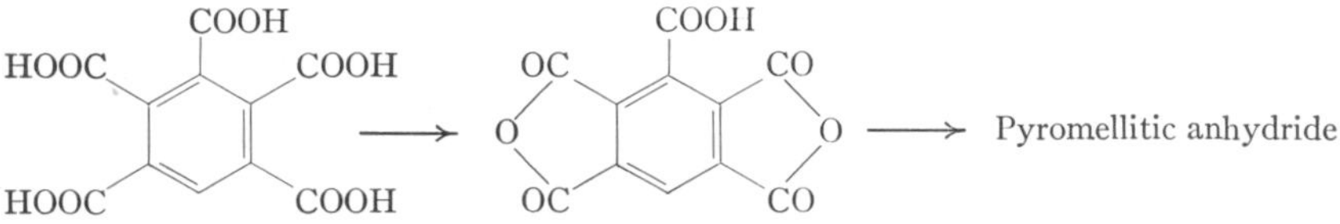

Benzenepentacarboxylic acid
(m.p. 238° dec.)   Dianhydride
(amorphous)   ⟶ Pyromellitic anhydride

at reduced pressure gives a glassy dianhydride, which undergoes decar-boxylation when heated at 270–300° and affords pyromellitic anhydride.

Mellitic Acid. — The hexabasic acid derives its name from the occur-rence of the aluminum salt ($Al_2C_{12}O_{12} \cdot 18H_2O$) as the mineral mellite (honey-stone), found in brown coal. It results from oxidation of graphite or of hexamethylbenzene with permanganate or of wood charcoal with nitric acid (sp. gr. 1.5). A dianhydride melting with de-composition at about 300° has been produced by treatment with thionyl chloride, and probably has the free carboxyl groups in the 1,4-positions. When heated with acetyl chloride at 160° in a sealed tube, mellitic acid yields a stable trianhydride that sublimes when heated at 200° at 3–4 mm. pressure.

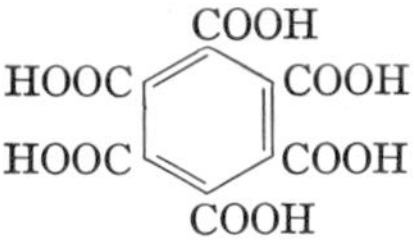

Mellitic acid
(m.p. in sealed tube 288°;
hexamethyl ester, m.p. 188°)

Diphenic Acid. — Diphenic acid, the 2,2'- or o,o'-dicarboxy derivative of diphenyl, can be prepared by a synthesis applicable to more highly substi-tuted members of the series. This consists in diazotization of anthranilic acid and reduction of the diazonium salt with freshly prepared cuprous ammonium hydroxide solution. Diphenic acid can be prepared also by oxidation of phenanthrenequinone with hydrogen peroxide (p. 757).

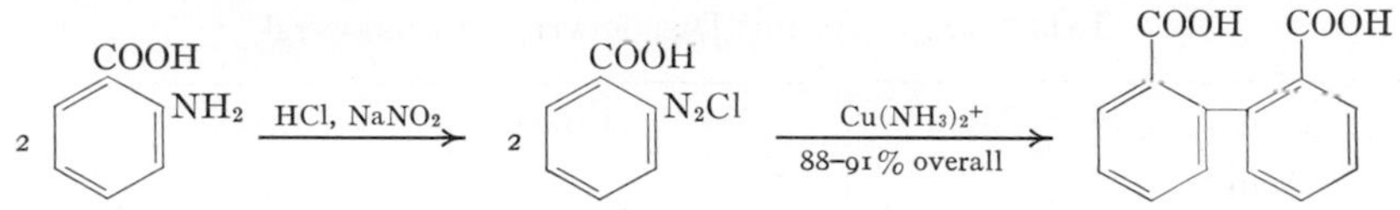

Anthranilic acid → Diphenic acid (m.p. 229; dimethyl ester, m.p. 74°; pK$_{a_1}$ ca. 3.3)

Diphenic acid can be converted into the anhydride by treatment with acetyl chloride or acetic anhydride, but it does not suffer dehydration on

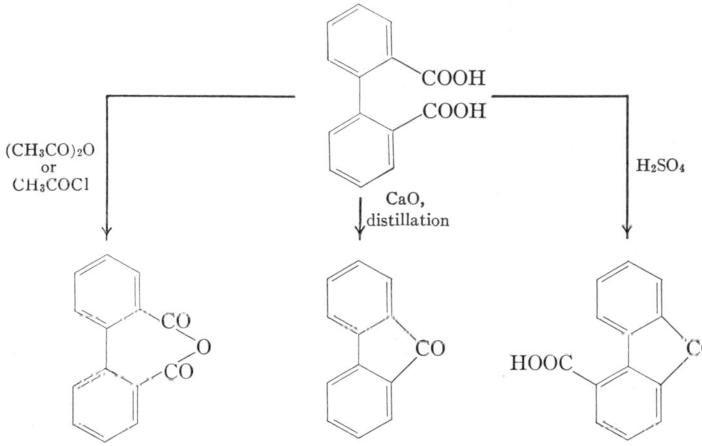

Diphenic anhydride (m.p. 217°)   Fluorenone (m.p. 84°, b.p. 341.5°)   Fluorenone-4-carboxylic acid (m.p. 227°)

heating with the readiness characteristic of polybasic acids containing carboxyl groups in adjacent positions in the same ring, where cyclization gives a five-membered rather than a seven-membered ring structure. Thus by careful heating diphenic acid can be sublimed (needles) without dehydration. Another transformation (see chart), accomplished by distillation with lime, results in closure of a five-membered ketonic ring by loss of carbon dioxide and production of fluorenone. A ring closure involving elimination of water between one of the carboxyl groups and an *ortho* position in the adjoining ring is brought about by treatment of diphenic acid with concentrated sulfuric acid (fluorenone-4-carboxylic acid).

Dissociation Constants of Polybasic Acids. — The constants of successive stages of dissociation of the polybasic carboxylic acids have been determined (Maxwell and Partington, 1937, Table 28.3). The acidic strength, as measured by pK$_{a_1}$, increases progressively with introduction of additional carboxyl groups, particularly into *ortho* or *vicinal* positions, and the relationship roughly parallels that in dibasic aliphatic acids, where enhanced acidic strength is associated with proximity of the functional groups. With increase in the number of nuclear carboxyl groups, separation of the last proton from the multiple-charged ion becomes increasingly difficult.

TABLE 28.3. ACIDIC DISSOCIATION CONSTANTS[1]

ACID	POSITION OF CARBOXYL GROUPS	DISSOCIATION CONSTANTS					
		pK_{a_1}	pK_{a_2}	pK_{a_3}	pK_{a_4}	pK_{a_5}	pK_{a_6}
Benzoic	1	4.17					
Phthalic	1,2	3.00	5.28				
Isophthalic	1,3	3.28	4.46				
Terephthalic	1,4	(3.82)					
Hemimellitic	1,2,3	2.80	4.20	5.89			
Trimellitic	1,2,4	2.52	3.85	5.20			
Trimesic	1,3,5	3.12	3.89	4.70			
Prehnitic	1,2,3,4	2.06	3.25	4.72	6.21		
Mellophanic	1,2,3,5	2.38	3.51	4.44	5.82		
Pyromellitic	1,2,4,5	1.92	2.89	4.49	5.64		
Benzenepentacarboxylic	1,2,3,4,5	1.80	2.74	3.96	5.25	6.46	
Mellitic	1,2,3,4,5,6	1.40	2.19	3.31	4.80	5.89	6.96

[1] With the exception of the value given in parentheses, the constants are based on determinations at an ionic strength of 0.03.

ARYL-SUBSTITUTED PARAFFINIC ACIDS

Acids having a phenyl group at the terminal position of an aliphatic chain, or ω-phenyl fatty acids, are useful synthetic intermediates; representatives are listed in Table 28.4 along with two frequently encountered unsaturated acids. **Phenylacetic acid** can be prepared from toluene through benzyl chloride, which reacts with sodium cyanide in aqueous alcohol to give benzyl cyanide in 80–90% yield; hydrolysis of the nitrile with dilute sulfuric acid then affords phenylacetic acid (80% yield). The acid is also produced in 90% yield by reduction of mandelic acid with potassium iodide, red phosphorus, and phosphoric acid. The next member of the series, β-phenylpropionic acid, is known as **hydrocinnamic acid** because it is made most

TABLE 28.4. BENZENE DERIVATIVES WITH ACIDIC SIDE CHAINS

ACID	FORMULA	M.P., °C.	B.P., °C.	$pK_a^{25°}$
Phenylacetic	$C_6H_5CH_2CO_2H$	78	265	4.31
Hydrocinnamic	$C_6H_5CH_2CH_2CO_2H$	49	280	4.64
γ-Phenylbutyric	$C_6H_5CH_2CH_2CH_2CO_2H$	51	171[15 mm.]	
δ-Phenyl-n-valeric	$C_6H_5CH_2CH_2CH_2CH_2CO_2H$	61	178[13 mm.]	
ε-Phenyl-n-caproic	$C_6H_5CH_2CH_2CH_2CH_2CH_2CO_2H$		208[30 mm.]	
Cinnamic (trans)	$C_6H_5CH{=}CHCO_2H$	136		4.43
Phenylpropiolic	$C_6H_5C{\equiv}CCO_2H$	137		2.23
Homophthalic	$o\text{-}C_6H_4(COOH)CH_2CO_2H$	183		
o-Phenylenediacetic	$o\text{-}C_6H_4(CH_2CO_2H)_2$	150		3.96
m-Phenylenediacetic	$m\text{-}C_6H_4(CH_2CO_2H)_2$	170		
p-Phenylenediacetic	$p\text{-}C_6H_4(CH_2CO_2H)_2$	244		
o-Phenyleneacetic-β-propionic	$o\text{-}HOOCCH_2C_6H_4CH_2CH_2CO_2H$	139		

readily by reduction of its unsaturated derivative, cinnamic acid ($C_6H_5CH=CHCO_2H$), with sodium amalgam, by catalytic hydrogenation, or by electrolytic reduction. **Cinnamic acid** can be synthesized readily from benzaldehyde (p. 690), and it is the chief constituent of the fragrant balsamic resin storax, formerly used as an expectorant and as incense; oriental and American storaxes contain 47–51% of free cinnamic acid and small amounts of styrene, $C_6H_5CH=CH_2$, the product of decarboxylation. The acetylenic derivative **phenylpropiolic acid**, $C_6H_5C≡CCOOH$, is made by addition of bromine to the double bond of cinnamic acid and treatment of the dibromide with alcoholic potassium hydroxide, which eliminates two molecules of hydrogen bromide. Nuclear substituted derivatives of hydrocinnamic acid that are not obtainable in the manner described for the parent substance, because of unavailability of the aldehydic starting materials, sometimes can be prepared from benzyl halides by the malonic ester synthesis (p. 648).

γ-**Phenylbutyric acid,** $C_6H_5CH_2CH_2CH_2COOH$, is prepared conveniently by the Friedel-Crafts succinoylation of benzene and Clemmensen reduction of the keto acid. The method is applicable to the preparation of many other γ-arylbutyric acids, but where a particular orientation is not achievable by substitution, the intermediate keto acid required may be obtainable by a Grignard synthesis. The Stobbe reaction (p. 699) affords γ-alkyl-γ-

$$C_{14}H_9MgBr \quad + \quad \begin{array}{c} CH_2CO \\ | \quad \rangle O \\ CH_2CO \end{array} \quad \xrightarrow{45\%} \quad C_{14}H_9COCH_2CH_2COOH$$

9-Phenanthrylmagnesium bromide   β-9-Phenanthroylpropionic acid (m.p. 181°)

phenylbutyric acids. The next homolog, **δ-phenyl-*n*-valeric acid,** has been made from cinnamaldehyde in three steps (the yields in the last two reactions are reported as practically quantitative). Another synthesis involves

$$C_6H_5CH=CHCHO \; + \; CH_2(COOH)_2 \xrightarrow[70-80\%]{HOAc,\,95°} C_6H_5CH=CHCH=C(COOH)_2 \xrightarrow{H_2,\,Pd}$$

Cinnamaldehyde   Cinnamalmalonic acid (m.p. 208° dec.)

$$C_6H_5CH_2CH_2CH_2CH(COOH)_2 \xrightarrow{Heat\,(-CO_2)} C_6H_5CH_2CH_2CH_2CH_2COOH$$

ω-Phenyl-*n*-propylmalonic acid (m.p. 98°)   δ-Phenyl-*n*-valeric acid

condensation of phenylmagnesium bromide with a cyclic ketone and oxidation of the tertiary carbinol with chromic anhydride in anhydrous acetic acid and reduction of the keto acid (Fieser and Szmuszkovicz, 1948). The carbinols from cyclopentanone, cyclohexanone, and cyclooctanone are oxi-

$$O= \!\!\bigcirc \xrightarrow{C_6H_5MgBr} C_6H_5- \!\!\bigcirc\!\!-OH \xrightarrow[81\%]{\substack{CrO_3 \\ HOAc}} \begin{array}{c} H_2C-CH_2 \\ C_6H_5-CO \quad CH_2 \\ HO_2C-CH_2 \end{array}$$

$$\downarrow$$

$$C_6H_5CH_2CH_2CH_2CH_2CH_2CO_2H$$

ε-Phenyl-*n*-caproic acid

dized rapidly at room temperature in yields of 75–85% and afford the homologs $C_6H_5(CH_2)_nCO_2H$, when n = 4, 5, and 7. Arachidic acid (C_{20}) is available by the same synthesis from tetradecyl bromide and cyclohexanone (58% overall yield). The anhydrous procedure is faster than the classical procedure of dissolving the organic substance in acetic acid and the chromic anhydride in a little water (1 part to 10 parts of acetic acid). The initial product is a dialkyl chromate, $(RO)_2CrO_2$; some chromate esters can be isolated as orange, crystalline substances that are soluble in ether or benzene, insoluble in water, nonionic, and devoid of oxidizing power at room temperature.

ε-**Phenyl-*n*-caproic acid** (see above) has been synthesized by Friedel-Crafts condensation of the acid chloride of adipic acid with benzene and Clemmensen reduction of the keto acid; it has been made also by stepwise elaboration of the side chain:

$$Ar(CH_2)_nCOOR \longrightarrow Ar(CH_2)_nCH_2OH \longrightarrow Ar(CH_2)_nCH_2Br \longrightarrow$$

$$Ar(CH_2)_nCH_2CN \longrightarrow Ar(CH_2)_nCH_2COOH \longrightarrow Ar(CH_2)_nCH_2COOR, \text{etc.}$$

Homophthalic Acid. — This *o*-carboxy derivative of phenylacetic acid can be prepared from an intermediate nitrile available by a special reaction discovered by Wislicenus (1886). The nitrile is obtained by heating molten phthalide with potassium cyanide, followed by solution of the cooled melt in water and acidification, and it is then hydrolyzed with sulfuric acid. Homophthalic acid forms an anhydride (six-membered ring) on being heated

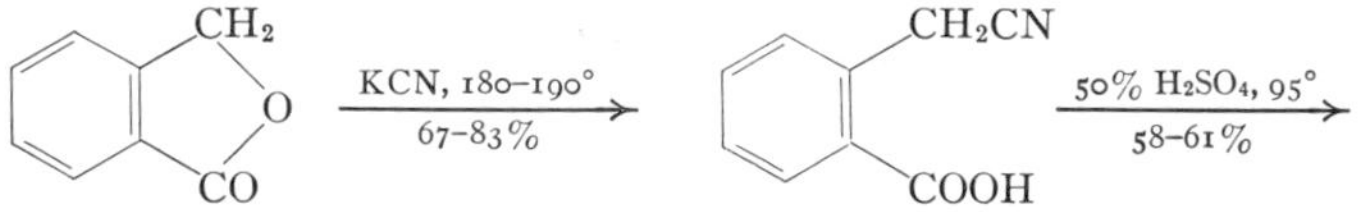

Phthalide   KCN, 180–190° / 67–83%   *o*-Carboxyphenylacetonitrile (m.p. 116° dec.)   50% H_2SO_4, 95° / 58–61%

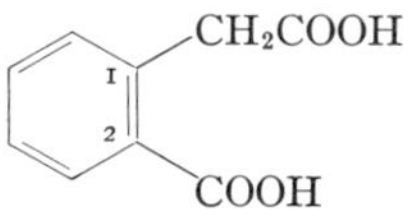

Homophthalic acid
(m.p. 183° dec., pK_{a1} 3.72, pK_{a2} 6.05;
dimethyl ester, m.p. 42°; anhydride, m.p. 141°).

or on treatment with acetyl chloride. The carboxyl group located in the side chain is more easily esterified than that joined to the nucleus, for partial esterification with methanol and hydrogen chloride in the cold gives the ester $HOOCC_6H_4CH_2COOCH_3$ (homophthalic acid 1-methyl ester, m.p. 98°, pK_a 4.12); the anhydride reacts with benzene in the presence of aluminum chloride to give desoxybenzoin-2'-carboxylic acid, $C_6H_5COCH_2C_6H_4$-COOH (m.p. 170°).

o-**Phenylenediacetic acid** can be prepared from *o*-xylene by side-chain bromination and application of the nitrile synthesis (isolated as the ester).

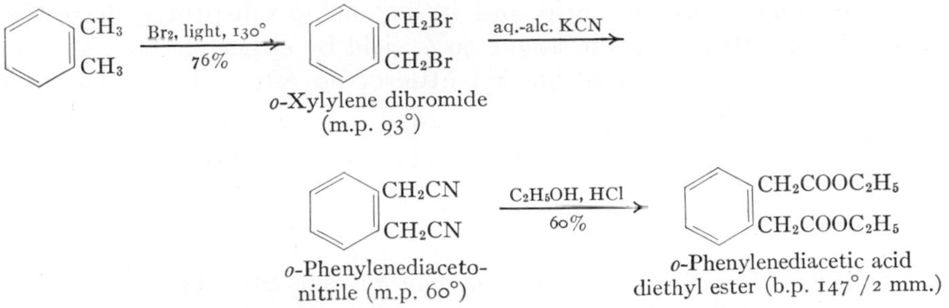

o-Xylylene dibromide
(m.p. 93°)

o-Phenylenediaceto-
nitrile (m.p. 60°)

o-Phenylenediacetic acid
diethyl ester (b.p. 147°/2 mm.)

The next higher homolog of the o-series, **o-phenyleneacetic-β-propionic acid,** is readily available by a special reduction reaction similar to the

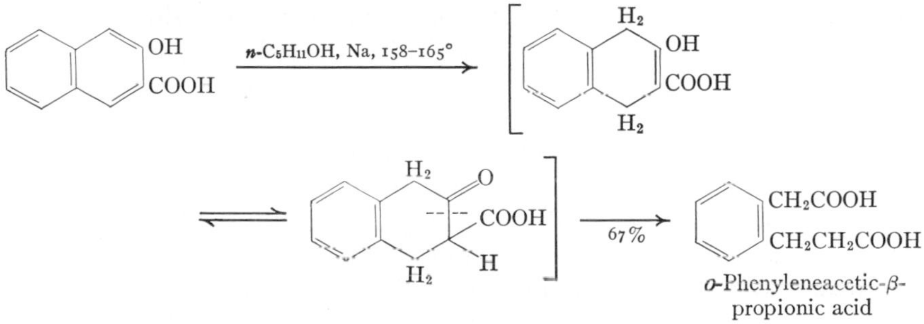

o-Phenyleneacetic-β-
propionic acid

conversion of salicylic acid into pimelic acid (p. 314); a 1,4-addition of hydrogen yields an intermediate enol, the tautomeric form of which is a β-keto acid susceptible to hydrolytic cleavage (reversal of the Dieckmann reaction, p. 220).

ESTERIFICATION OF AROMATIC ACIDS

Among aliphatic carboxylic acids, those of primary structure (RCH_2-CO_2H) are esterified readily with an alcohol and a mineral acid catalyst, whereas those in which the carboxyl group is joined to a quaternary carbon atom (R_3CCOOH) react sluggishly, probably because the alkyl groups dominate so much space in the neighborhood of the carboxyl group that they tend to block formation of an intermediate ionic addition complex (p. 175). Still more striking instances of the suppression of catalyzed esterification are encountered in benzoic acid derivatives having substituents in the two *ortho* positions. The phenomenon was discovered and extensively investigated by Victor Meyer (1894), but isolated instances of a comparable blocking effect had been encountered earlier by Hofmann (1872), who observed that certain dialkylaniline derivatives having substituents *ortho* to the functional group are very resistant to the action of alkyl halides. Meyer investigated the response of aromatic acids to attempted esterification either by refluxing (3–5 hrs.) a solution in methanol containing 3% of hydrogen chloride (Fischer method) or by saturating a methanol solution of the acid with hydrogen chloride in the cold and allowing the solution to stand overnight. Benzoic acid and its *m*- and *p*-substituted derivatives afforded the methyl esters in about 90% yield by either method, but di-*o*-substituted acids formulated yielded little or no ester. If the two *ortho*

positions are blocked by nitro, chloro, or bromo substituents, no appreciable esterification results, even under forcing conditions, and if methyl, hydroxyl, or fluoro substituents occupy both positions flanking the carboxyl group, esterification proceeds to only a slight extent. A single *ortho* substituent exerts a significant blocking effect; for example, the *o*-hydroxyl group of salicylic acid has a retarding action such that the refluxing period adequate for esterification of benzoic acid must be extended about fivefold to produce methyl salicylate in practical quantity.

Esterification of *o*-disubstituted acids does not fail as the result of any instability of the reaction products, for the esters of mesitylenecarboxylic acid, 2,6-dibromobenzoic acid, and comparable acids can be prepared by the action of methyl iodide on the silver salt of the acids, by esterification with diazomethane, or by interaction of the acid chloride with the alcohol, and are very resistant to hydrolysis by acids or alkalis. Thus *ortho* substituents block hydrolysis of the esters just as they inhibit catalyzed esterification. Meyer introduced the term steric hindrance to describe the blocking effect, and suggested an association of the effectiveness of a given group in blocking esterification or hydrolysis with the relative size, as judged by the atomic weight. Thus an *o*-fluoro substituent exerts less hindrance than a chloro or bromo substituent, and hence the chemical nature of the substituent is not the controlling factor; groups of both the *ortho-para* and the *meta* directing type exert a hindering effect when adjacent to the carboxyl group. The resistance to esterification noted in mesitylenecarboxylic acid, $2,4,6\text{-}(CH_3)_3C_6H_2CO_2H$, disappears on separation of the carboxyl group from the nucleus, for mesityleneacetic acid, $2,4,6\text{-}(CH_3)_3C_6H_2CH_2COOH$, is esterified easily by the Fischer method. The influence of an *ortho* substituent, however, probably is the result of several factors, including the effective volume of the group, the effect of the substituent on the acidic dissociation constant, and the extent of coordination or chelation with the acidic group.

Newman[3] (1941) discovered that 2,4,6-trimethylbenzoic acid can be esterified by dissolving it in 100% sulfuric acid and pouring the solution into an alcohol; the reaction takes only a few minutes and the yields are excellent. Conversely, the ester is efficiently hydrolyzed by pouring a sulfuric acid solution into water. When treated in the same way, benzoic acid is not esterified and methyl benzoate is not hydrolyzed. According to Newman's

[3] Melvin S. Newman, b. 1908 New York; Ph.D. Yale (R. J. Anderson); Ohio State Univ.

interpretation, both the hindered and unhindered acid combine with a proton from sulfuric acid to form a conjugate acid (I), stabilized by resonance

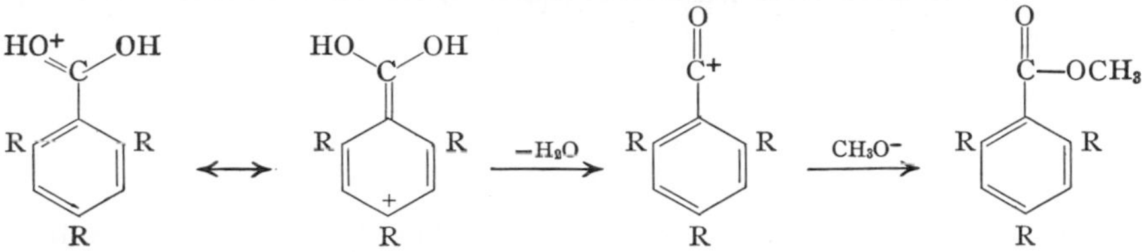

HO$^+$ C OH

R ⟮benzene ring⟯ R

R

I

⟷

HO C OH

R ⟮benzene ring⟯ R

R

(With *o*-forms)

II

$-H_2O$ →

O ‖ C$^+$

R ⟮benzene ring⟯ R

R

III

CH_3O^- →

O ‖ C—OCH$_3$

R ⟮benzene ring⟯ R

R

IV

(II). The resonance structures, however, require coplanarity of all the carbon and oxygen atoms, and if R = methyl, interference between methyl and hydroxyl groups enhances the tendency for expulsion of water with formation of the positive acyl ion III, which can reac with methanol to form the ester IV. In the absence of this steric factor (R = H), structures I and II are stable and have no tendency to lose water. The method of esterification is not successful with some esters, for example 2,4,6-tribromobenzoic acid.

PROBLEMS

1. Suggest methods for the preparation of 2,4- and 2,5-dimethylbenzoic acid, starting with coal-tar hydrocarbons.
2. Indicate all the steps in the preparation of anthranilic acid from naphthalene.
3. Outline the steps in the preparation of *m*-toluic acid, starting with toluene.
4. Explain why polycarboxy derivatives of benzene are identified in the form of certain derivatives and not in the free form.
5. Suggest a scheme for the synthesis of 4,4'-dibromodiphenic acid (4,4'-dibromodiphenyl 2,2'-dicarboxylic acid).
6. How could the following substances be synthesized:

(*a*) γ-*p*-Tolylbutyric acid
(*b*) 1,5-Diphenylpentane

(*c*) β-Tetralone (from one of the acids of Table 28.4):

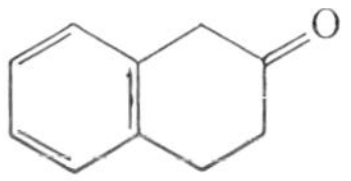

CHAPTER 29

AROMATIC ALDEHYDES AND KETONES

Aldehydes and ketones in which the carbonyl group is linked to an aromatic nucleus differ from aliphatic carbonyl compounds in relatively minor respects. The main interest in the chemistry of the aromatic derivatives are synthetic uses and methods employed for preparation. Ketones of the types ArCOR and ArCOAr' are available by the Friedel-Crafts reaction, but several specific reactions are employed for production of aldehydes. In the following sections these methods are classified with respect to types of starting materials. Properties of the better known members are indicated in the tables and formula charts.

ALDEHYDES FROM ARYLMETHANES

$$(ArCH_3 \longrightarrow ArCHO)$$

Benzaldehyde. — Benzaldehyde occurs as the glycoside amygdalin, found in seed of bitter almonds. As noted previously (p. 380), amygdalin is a β-gentiobioside of mandelonitrile, $C_6H_5CH(CN)O-C_{12}H_{21}O_{10}$, and undergoes enzymatic hydrolysis with liberation of benzaldehyde, hydrogen cyanide, and the sugar component. Because of this formerly utilized source of the liquid hydrolysis product of characteristic aromatic fragrance, benzaldehyde was known as oil of bitter almonds. Benzaldehyde is also the chief constituent of essential oils expressed from kernels of the peach, cherry, laurel, and other fruits.

The chief technical processes for production of benzaldehyde, required as an intermediate for dyes and other synthetic chemicals and in flavors and soap perfumes, utilize toluene as starting material. One efficient method of conversion into the aldehyde is side-chain chlorination in Pyrex glass or porcelain reactors (preferably with illumination), fractionation, and hydrolysis of the benzal chloride cut. The hydrolysis is accomplished with water at 95–100° in the presence of iron powder or ferric benzoate as cata-

$$C_6H_5CH_3 \longrightarrow C_6H_5CHCl_2 \xrightarrow[76\%]{} C_6H_5CHO$$

lyst; lime is then added for neutralization and the benzaldehyde is steam distilled. Benzoic acid usually appears as a by-product. Phosphorus pentachloride is sometimes used as catalyst for the side-chain chlorination; traces of iron (factory dust) or antimony (rubber stoppers and tubing) promote substitution in the nucleus, and commercial preparations of benzaldehyde from the chlorination process usually contain small amounts of

TABLE 29.1. MONOSUBSTITUTED DERIVATIVES OF BENZALDEHYDE

NAME	FORMULA	M.P., °C.	B.P., °C.
Benzaldehyde	C_6H_5CHO	liq.	179
m-Tolualdehyde	m-$CH_3C_6H_4CHO$	liq.	199
p-Tolualdehyde	p-$CH_3C_6H_4CHO$	liq.	204
o-Chlorobenzaldehyde	o-ClC_6H_4CHO	11	208[748 mm.]
p-Chlorobenzaldehyde	p-ClC_6H_4CHO	49	213[748 mm.]
o-Nitrobenzaldehyde	o-$NO_2 \cdot C_6H_4CHO$	44	
m-Nitrobenzaldehyde	m-$NO_2 \cdot C_6H_4CHO$	58	
p-Nitrobenzaldehyde	p-$NO_2 \cdot C_6H_4CHO$	106	
o-Aminobenzaldehyde	o-$NH_2 \cdot C_6H_4CHO$	40	
p-Aminobenzaldehyde	p-$NH_2 \cdot C_6H_4CHO$	71	
Salicylaldehyde	o-HOC_6H_4CHO	-7	197
m-Hydroxybenzaldehyde	m-HOC_6H_4CHO	108	
p-Hydroxybenzaldehyde	p-HOC_6H_4CHO	116	
o-Methoxybenzaldehyde	o-$CH_3OC_6H_4CHO$	3, 35	244
Anisaldehyde	p-$CH_3OC_6H_4CHO$	0	248
p-Dimethylaminobenzaldehyde	p-$(CH_3)_2NC_6H_4CHO$	75	

chlorobenzaldehyde. Such contamination is undesirable in material to be used in perfumery, and a premium is placed on alternate processes that afford chlorine-free benzaldehyde. One method consists in partial oxidation of toluene with manganese dioxide in 65% sulfuric acid at 40° followed by steam distillation; the process can be operated to yield either benzaldehyde or benzoic acid as the chief product. Another is vapor-phase air oxidation of toluene with vanadium pentoxide catalyst.

2,6-Dichlorobenzaldehyde. — This aldehyde is produced technically for use in the synthesis of triphenylmethane dyes. The process starting with o-nitrotoluene is interesting because it involves introduction of chlorine by three methods: catalytic nuclear halogenation, side-chain chlorination, and the Sandmeyer reaction. Initial chlorination gives the 6- and 4-chloro derivatives in the ratio of about 2:1, and the former isomer can be isolated

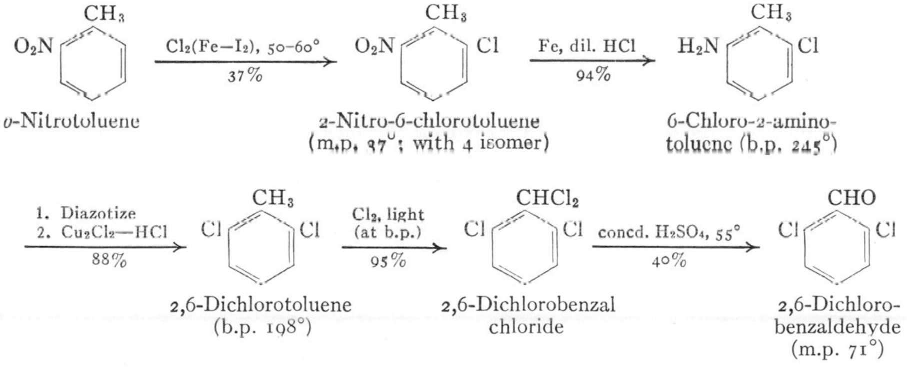

by fractional distillation in vacuum. A noteworthy feature of the subsequent steps is that the di-o-substituted dichlorobenzal chloride is resistant to hydrolysis with water and iron, even under pressure or with potassium hydroxide, but can be hydrolyzed in moderate yield when warmed in sulfuric acid for twelve hours.

The chlorination and oxidation processes employed for preparation of benzaldehyde from toluene are used in isolated instances for laboratory-scale preparation of other aldehydes; o-nitro- and o-chlorotoluene have been converted into the corresponding aldehydes with 65% sulfuric acid and manganese dioxide; partial oxidation of m-xylene by this method gives m-tolualdehyde.

Other Procedures. — The transformation $ArCH_3 \rightarrow ArCHO$ can be accomplished also by the Étard reaction (1881). A solution of two equivalents of chromyl chloride (CrO_2Cl_2) in carbon disulfide is added cautiously to the hydrocarbon with control of the temperature to 25–45°. The red color of the reagent is discharged slowly and a chocolate-brown crystallizate separates consisting of a molecular complex containing two equivalents of the inorganic component. The dry solid on treatment with water decomposes to give the aldehyde and an aqueous solution containing chromic acid and chromic chloride, and the aldehyde must be removed rapidly by

$$ ArCH_3 \ + \ 2 \, CrO_2Cl_2 \ \longrightarrow \ ArCH_3 \cdot (CrO_2Cl_2)_2 \ \xrightarrow{H_2O} \ ArCHO $$

distillation or solvent extraction to avoid destruction. Instances are reported where yields are as high as 70–80% when the reaction is conducted under closely defined conditions (m-tolualdehyde from m-xylene), but the results may be much poorer. The method has limited use.

Another method, which probably is more reliable and has given good service in several instances, is oxidation of the methyl derivative with anhydrous **chromic acid in acetic anhydride** solution; the aldehyde as it is formed is converted into its *gem*-diacetate, which is stable to oxidation

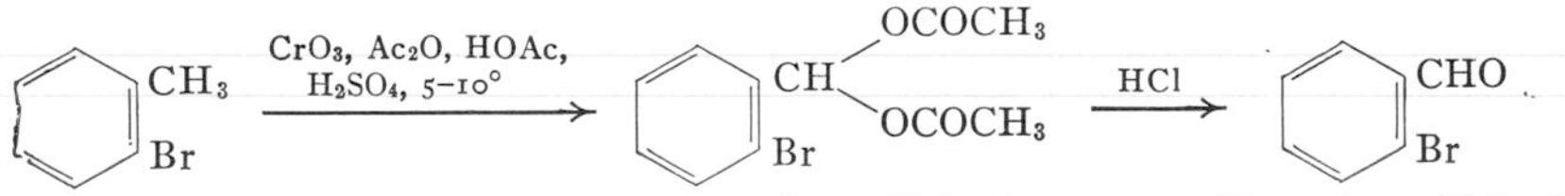

o-Bromotoluene   o-Bromobenzaldehyde diacetate (m.p. 72°)   o-Bromobenzaldehyde (m.p. 22°, b.p. 230°)

The diacetate is collected and purified and can be converted into the free aldehyde by acid hydrolysis. The overall yield of o-bromobenzaldehyde is about 45%.

ALDEHYDES FROM ARYLMETHYL HALIDES

$$ (ArCH_2Cl \ \longrightarrow \ ArCHO) $$

An early technical process for preparation of benzaldehyde consisted in heating **benzyl chloride with aqueous lead nitrate or copper nitrate**. Hydrolysis and oxidation are involved, but the mechanism has not been clarified. The method has been employed somewhat for preparation of substituted benzaldehydes, for example the p-nitro compound; the starting material is produced along with the *o*-nitro isomer on nitration of benzyl chloride, and, being a solid, can be purified by crystallization. Another

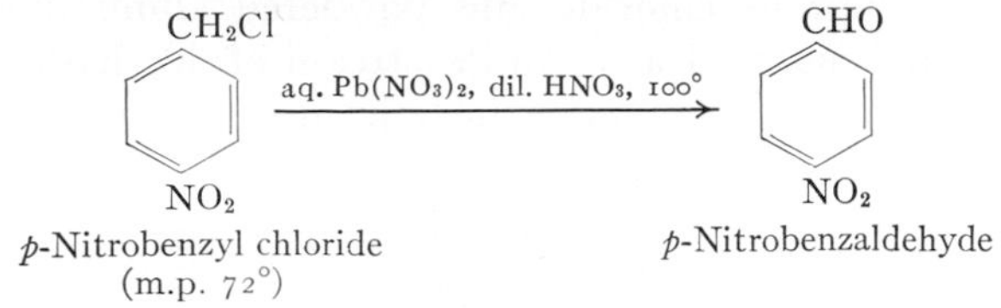

$$CH_2Cl \quad \xrightarrow{\text{aq. } Pb(NO_3)_2,\ \text{dil. } HNO_3,\ 100°} \quad CHO$$

NO₂	NO₂
p-Nitrobenzyl chloride (m.p. 72°)	*p*-Nitrobenzaldehyde

favorable factor is that *p*-nitrobenzaldehyde is more resistant to oxidation than ordinary aldehydes, and withstands the prolonged heating required for complete reaction.

An alternate process, **the Sommelet reaction** (1913), consists in refluxing a solution of a component of the benzyl halide type with hexamethylene-tetramine (p. 213) in 60% aqueous alcohol, when the aldehyde is produced directly. If the components are mixed in a nonaqueous solvent, they com-

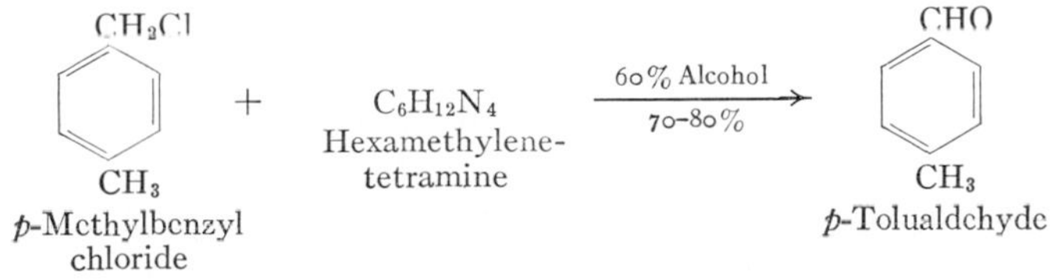

$$CH_2Cl \quad + \quad C_6H_{12}N_4 \quad \xrightarrow[70-80\%]{60\% \text{ Alcohol}} \quad CHO$$

CH₃		Hexamethylene-tetramine	CH₃
p-Methylbenzyl chloride			*p*-Tolualdehyde

bine to form a quaternary ammonium salt, $[C_6H_{12}N_4CH_2Ar]^+Cl^-$, which is decomposed by water as indicated. The mechanism of the Sommelet reaction is not known, and the method has been but little explored. High yields are reported in a few instances, low ones in others; the reaction fails where the chloromethyl group is flanked by methyl groups in both *ortho* positions.

DIRECT FORMYLATION

$$(ArH \longrightarrow ArCHO)$$

Gattermann-Koch Synthesis (1897). — Gattermann[1] and Koch devised a method for direct introduction of the formyl group (—CHO) by a process analogous to the Friedel-Crafts ketone synthesis utilizing a mixture of gaseous carbon monoxide and hydrogen chloride in the presence of a metal halide catalyst, usually a mixture of aluminum chloride and cuprous chloride. Formyl chloride may be a transient intermediate, but has not been isolated as such; formyl fluoride however is known. Cuprous chlo-

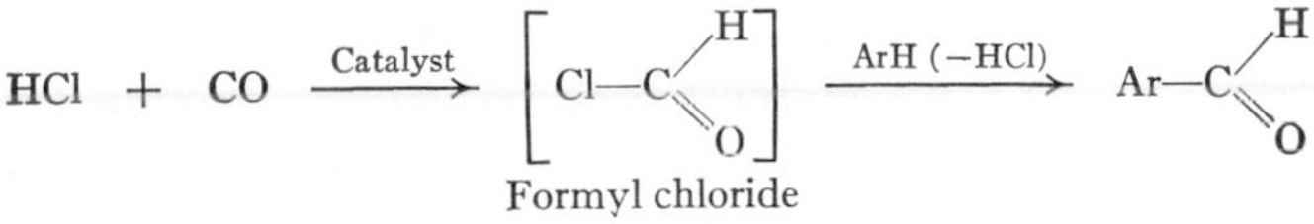

$$HCl + CO \xrightarrow{\text{Catalyst}} \left[Cl-C{\overset{H}{\underset{O}{\diagdown}}} \right] \xrightarrow{ArH\ (-HCl)} Ar-C{\overset{H}{\underset{O}{\diagdown}}}$$

Formyl chloride

---

[1] Ludwig Gattermann, 1860–1920; b. Goslar, Germany; Ph.D. Göttingen (Hübner); Freiburg; *Ber.*, **54A**, 115 (1921)

ride probably functions as a catalyst because it can bind carbon monoxide in the form of a labile molecular complex. In a typical example a suspension of anhydrous cuprous chloride and powdered aluminum chloride in dry toluene is stirred mechanically, and a stream of dry hydrogen chloride and carbon monoxide is passed into the mixture for several hours. The

$$\text{Toluene} \quad + \quad CO \quad + \quad HCl \quad \xrightarrow[\text{50-55\%}]{\text{Cu}_2\text{Cl}_2\text{—AlCl}_3,\ 20°} \quad p\text{-Tolualdehyde}$$

reaction mixture is decomposed with ice and steam distilled; the p-tolualdehyde formed is separated from unchanged toluene by distillation. The orientation and the limits of the reaction are much the same as in the Friedel-Crafts ketone synthesis, but yields are lower. Benzene does not react under ordinary conditions unless aluminum chloride is replaced by aluminum bromide, and has been used as a solvent for the reaction of other hydrocarbons. Although high-pressure adaptations of the synthesis are claimed in patents, the reaction is limited by low yields.

Gattermann Synthesis (1907). — This variation consists in use of liquid anhydrous hydrogen cyanide in place of carbon monoxide as a source of the formyl substituent; hydrogen chloride is required, usually in combination with aluminum chloride or zinc chloride, but cuprous chloride is omitted. The reaction formerly was regarded as proceeding through a transient addition product of hydrogen cyanide and hydrogen chloride (formimino chloride, $ClCH{=}NH$), but now appears to follow a more complicated course. In the absence of the hydrocarbon component the other reagents combine to form a molecular complex, $AlCl_3 \cdot 2HCN \cdot HCl$, possibly by addition of the intermediate formimino chloride to hydrogen cyanide. The com-

1. $HC{\equiv}N + HCl \longrightarrow [ClCH{=}NH] + HC{\equiv}N \xrightarrow{AlCl_3} ClCH{=}NCH{=}NH \cdot AlCl_3$

2. $ArH + ClCH{=}NCH{=}NH \cdot AlCl_3 \xrightarrow{-HCl} ArCH{=}NCH{=}NH \cdot AlCl_3$

3. $ArCH{=}NCH{=}NH \cdot AlCl_3 \xrightarrow{H_2O} ArCHO + 2NH_3 + HCOOH$

plex condenses with the hydrocarbon component (2) with elimination of hydrogen chloride and formation of an arylmethyleneformamidine complex, which subsequently is hydrolyzed to the aldehyde (3). The Gattermann synthesis has been improved by use of special solvents, chlorobenzene, o-dichlorobenzene, and tetrachloroethane, and by conducting the reaction at temperatures of 60–100° instead of at 40°; a distinct simplification is use of sodium cyanide in place of the hazardous hydrogen cyanide. Thus a simple procedure consists in passing hydrogen chloride into a suspension of sodium cyanide and aluminum chloride in an excess of the hydrocarbon component. Yields of aldehydic derivatives of hydrocarbons by the best procedures are generally low, however (benzaldehyde, 11–39%; *p*-ethylbenzaldehyde, 22-27%; 9-anthraldehyde, 60%; mesitylaldehyde, 83%).

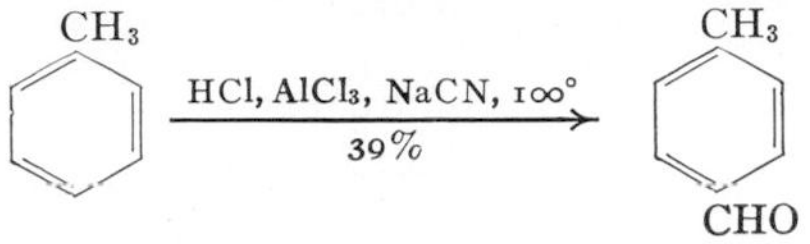

CH3
HCl, AlCl3, NaCN, 100°
39%
CH3
CHO

Condensation with hydrogen cyanide or a metal nitrile, unlike that with carbon monoxide, is applicable to phenols and phenol ethers, often with considerable success. Thus anisaldehyde is reported to be formed in nearly quantitative yield by the Gattermann synthesis. Aluminum chloride is required as catalyst in the case of phenol ethers and some phenols; the less potent zinc chloride is generally adequate for phenols. The procedure has

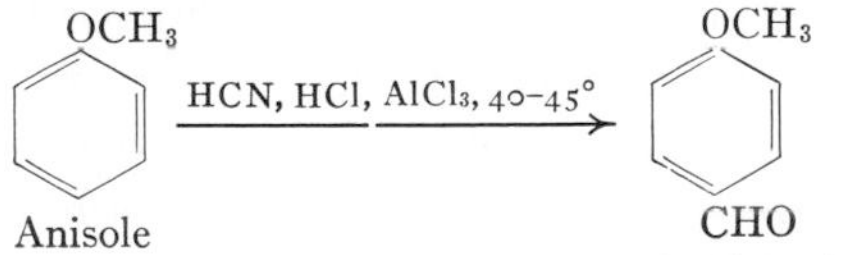

OCH3
HCN, HCl, AlCl3, 40–45°
OCH3
CHO

Anisole

Anisaldehyde

been modified to advantage (R. Adams, 1923) by substitution of zinc cyanide for hydrogen cyanide and a metal halide. When hydrogen chloride is passed into a mixture of the phenol or phenol ether and zinc cyanide in absolute ether or benzene, it liberates the hydrogen cyanide required for condensation and produces zinc chloride as catalyst. The method is illustrated for the reaction of thymol.

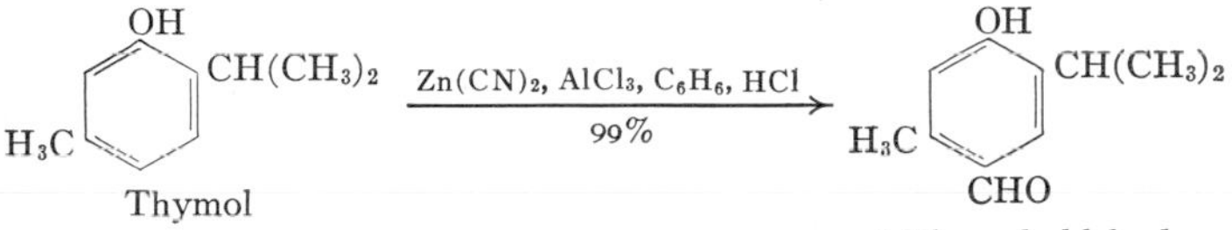

OH
CH(CH3)2
H3C
Zn(CN)2, AlCl3, C6H6, HCl
99%
OH
CH(CH3)2
H3C
CHO

Thymol

p-Thymol-aldehyde (m.p. 133°)

Formylation with N-Methylformanilide. — By heating N-methylaniline with formic acid in toluene solution and displacing the equilibrium by slow

$$C_6H_5N(H)(CH_3) + HCOOH \xrightarrow[93\text{–}97\%]{\text{Boiling toluene}} C_6H_5N(CHO)(CH_3) + H_2O$$

N-Methylformanilide (b.p. 131°/22 mm.)

$$C_6H_5N(CHO)(CH_3) + ArH \xrightarrow{POCl_3} ArCHO + C_6H_5N(H)(CH_3)$$

distillation of the water formed, the amine can be converted into N-methylformanilide. In the presence of phosphorus oxychloride, this substance acts as a formylating agent for aromatic compounds that possess a particularly

reactive nuclear position. Anthracene is converted smoothly into an aldehyde, preferably in solution in o-dichlorobenzene, an effective inert solvent.
If the hydrocarbon or other component is liquid at the required temperature,

$$\text{Anthracene} \xrightarrow[\text{in } o\text{-}C_6H_4Cl_2,\ 90\text{--}95°]{C_6H_5N(CH_3)CHO,\ POCl_3,} \text{9-Anthraldehyde}$$

Anthracene — 9-Anthraldehyde (m.p. 105°) — CHO

no solvent is needed. Although anthracene, pyrene, acenaphthene, and a
few other highly reactive polynuclear hydrocarbons can be formylated by
this method, the reaction is not applicable to benzene or naphthalene or to
any but exceptional hydrocarbon derivatives of these two series (e.g., acenaphthene). The reaction is applicable, usually with distinct success, to
phenol ethers and to dialkylamines, which are formylated in an activated
nuclear position *ortho* or *para* to the directing group. Thus 2-ethoxynaph-
thalene reacts with N-methylformanilide and phosphorus oxychloride without solvent to give 2-ethoxy-1-naphthaldehyde (m.p. 112°), and dimethylaniline yields p-dimethylaminobenzaldehyde.

Dimethylformamide, $(CH_3)_2NCHO$, can be used in the same way; the
yields are somewhat lower, but the reagent is inexpensive. Another route
to aldehydes utilizes methylphenylcarbamyl chloride, prepared from N-
methylaniline and phosgene (Weygand, 1955). This reacts with aromatic
hydrocarbons under Friedel-Crafts conditions to give the N-methylanilide
of a carboxylic acid; this derivative is reducible to the aldehyde with lithium
aluminum hydride.

$$C_6H_5N(CH_3)COCl + C_6H_5CH_3 \xrightarrow[53\%]{AlCl_3} C_6H_5N(CH_3)COC_6H_4CH_3\text{-}p \xrightarrow[60\%]{LiAlH_4}$$

$$CH_3C_6H_4CHO\text{-}p$$

REIMER-TIEMANN REACTION

(Phenol $\longrightarrow$ Phenol-Aldehyde)

The Reimer[2]-Tiemann[3] reaction (1876) was discovered in Hofmann's
laboratory as the result of an experiment carried out to determine how a
phenol would respond when substituted for an amine in the Hofmann isonitrile reaction, involving treatment with chloroform and alkali. A reaction
occurs, and results in introduction of an aldehydic group *ortho* or *para* to the
hydroxyl group. The reaction succeeds with most phenols containing an
available activated position, and provides a useful path to phenolic aldehydes, but it does not appear applicable to hydrocarbons, phenol ethers, or

---

[2] Carl Reimer, 1856–1921; b. Berlin; Ph.D. Berlin; indust. chem.
[3] Ferdinand Tiemann, 1848–99; b. Rübeland, Germany: Berlin; *Ber.*, **32**, 3239 (1899); **34**,
4403 (1901)

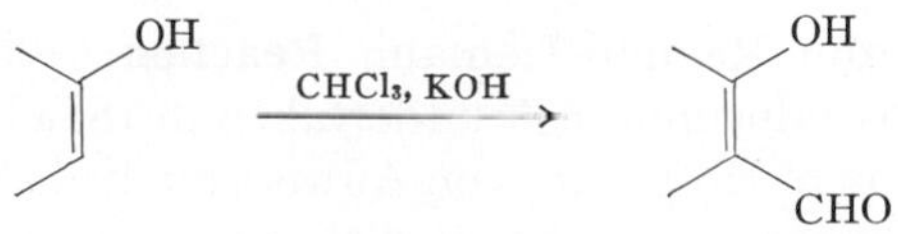

even tertiary amines. The specific requirement of a free hydroxyl group, coupled with the fact that the reaction is conducted in alkaline solution, indicates that the reactive species undergoing the special substitution is the phenoxide ion. The superior reactivity of the phenoxide ion, noted also in diazo coupling, is explained by the opportunity for distribution of the negative charge on oxygen to *ortho* and *para* positions in the ring. In a free phenol or an ether, contribution by resonance structures of comparable *o*-, *p*-electron density requires separation of charge in the nonionized molecule.

Salicylaldehyde. — This substance, the *o*-hydroxy derivative of benzaldehyde, is a fragrant oil found in meadowsweet and other plants. The Reimer-Tiemann reaction is used in one of the technical processes for its production, and details of the laboratory procedure are indicated in the formulation. At the end of the reaction the mixture is acidified and steam distilled; salicylaldehyde passes into the distillate along with a considerable amount of phenol, from which it can be separated through the bisulfite-

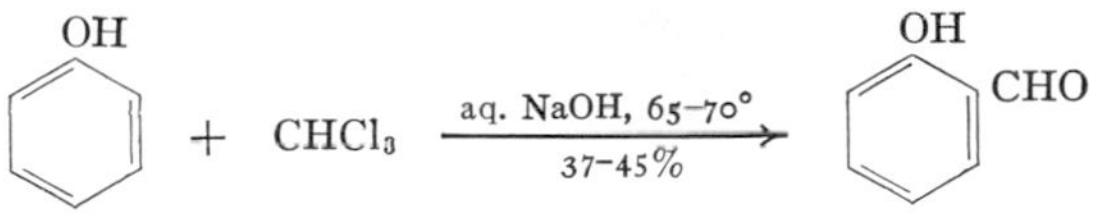

Phenol

Salicylaldehyde
($+$ 8-11% of *p*-isomer)

addition product. From the residue not volatile with steam the solid isomer, *p*-hydroxybenzaldehyde, can be isolated by crystallization in quantity amounting to about one fifth the weight of the salicylaldehyde. Although the yields are low, the processes of separation are efficient, and the recovered phenol can be recycled. The methyl ether is prepared with use of dimethyl sulfate. The methyl ether of *p*-hydroxybenzaldehyde, anisaldehyde, is made by gentle oxidation of aniseed oil, which is rich in anethole, p-CH_3O-$C_6H_4CH=CHCH_3$, with potassium dichromate and 50% sulfuric acid.

Salicylaldehyde forms colored chelate ring complexes with metal ions; the sodium salt is deep yellow. The complex cobaltous bis-salicyaldehyde-ethylenediimine (Salcomine), prepared by Pfeiffer in 1933, was investigated by Calvin (1946) for use in production of pure oxygen from air. The substance is capable of selectively absorbing 4.9% of its weight of oxygen from the air and then of evolving the pure gas when heated to 50-60°.

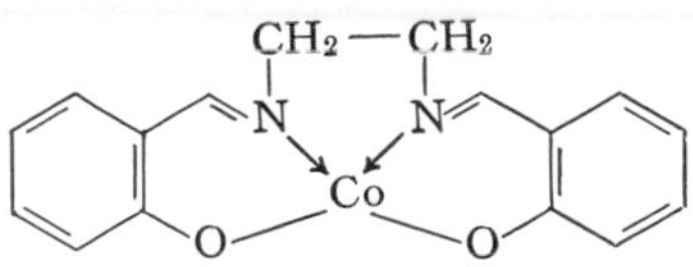

Salcomine

By-Product of the Reimer-Tiemann Reaction. — In the course of a research on "solid pseudocumidine" undertaken in 1884 in the Berlin laboratory at the suggestion of Hofmann, von Auwers applied the Reimer-Tiemann reaction to pseudocumenol and observed that the reaction proceeded poorly and gave at most only about 5% of the theoretical amount of the expected aldehyde, accompanied by some unchanged starting material. He noticed that a considerable amount of alkali-insoluble material is produced, from which he isolated a chlorine-containing by-product characterized by a striking tendency to form large crystals. The structure, established only several years later (1902), is that of a cyclic ketone with a dichloromethyl group linked to the *para* carbon atom along with the original methyl substituent, as shown in the formulation. Evidently chloroform reacts as $Cl \cdot CHCl_2$, and the carbon-containing part enters the *para* position of the phenol and the chlorine atom abstracts hydrogen from the hydroxyl group.

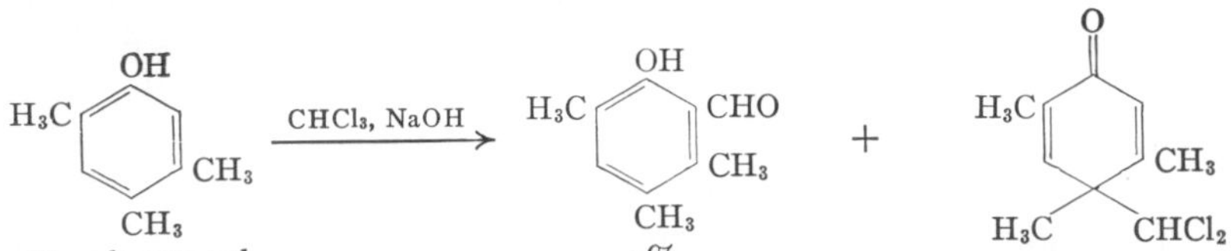

Pseudocumenol (m.p. 73°, b.p. 232°) → [CHCl₃, NaOH] → 2-Hydroxy-3,5,6-trimethylbenzaldehyde (m.p. 106°) 5% + 2,4,5-Trimethyl-4-dichloromethyl-$\Delta^{2,5}$-cyclohexadienone-1 (colorless, m.p. 96.5°) 42%

The chlorine atoms in the ketonic by-product are not activated by adjacent unsaturation, as those of a compound of the benzal halide type are, and survival of the substance in the alkaline medium is understandable.

von Auwers found that comparable ketonic by-products are formed rather generally from phenols having alkyl groups in the *ortho* or *para* positions, but not from *m*-cresol, picric acid, or 2,4,6-tribomophenol. The isolation is accomplished by acidifying the reaction mixture, steam distilling the monomolecular products to effect separation from a certain amount of resinous material, extracting the phenolic aldehyde and starting material with alkali, and recovering the dichloro ketone from the neutral portion by crystallization. Both *o*- and *p*-cresol afford alkali-insoluble by-products, even though free positions *ortho* or *para* to the hydroxyl group are available for normal substitution. Yields and properties of the products resulting from *p*-cresol are indicated in the formulas. *o*-Cresol gives only about half

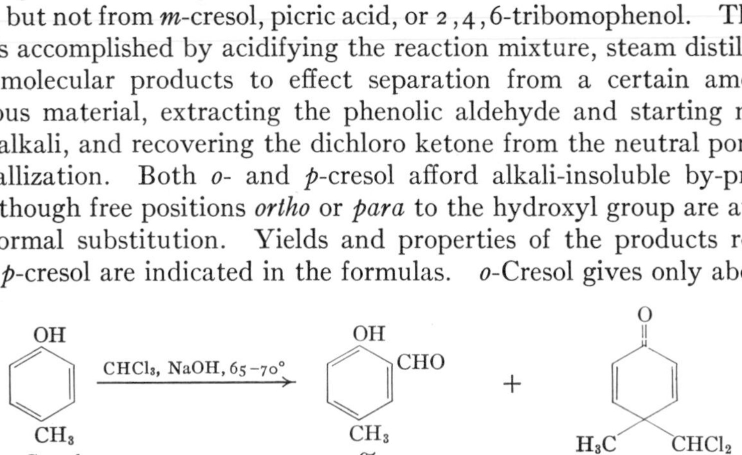

p-Cresol → [CHCl₃, NaOH, 65–70°] → Homosalicylaldehyde (m.p. 56°) 35% + 4-Methyl-4-dichloromethyl-$\Delta^{2,5}$-cyclohexadienone-1 (m.p. 55°) 12%

as much of the ketonic by-product under optimum conditions.   The yield of ketone is somewhat fortuitous and does not give an accurate index of the initial ratio of normal to abnormal substitution, for the dichloromethyl compounds differ considerably in their resistance to hydrolytic destruction in the alkaline medium.   Test experiments have shown, for example, that the dichloro ketone from o-cresol is hydrolyzed by alkali more rapidly than the product from p-cresol.   The ketone derived from pseudocumenol is particularly resistant to alkaline hydrolysis, probably because of the blocking effect of the methyl group *ortho* to the halogenated group.

The fact that in p-cresol the chloroform residue enters the *para* position to a significant extent, even though it is blocked, indicates that the methyl group tends to promote attack at the carbon atom to which it is joined. This activation can be attributed to the electron-repelling character of the methyl substituent, which induces at the 4-position in one of the resonance

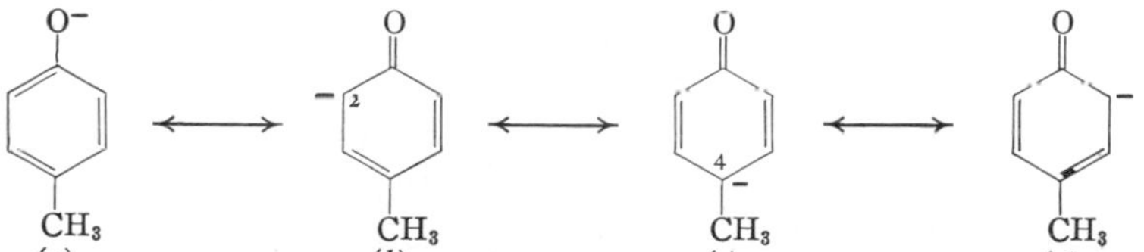

structures of the ion (c) an electron density greater than that established at the 2-position in any of the other resonance structures.

The vulnerability of alkylated phenols to abnormal attack has been utilized in the preparation of compounds difficulty accessible by other syntheses.   Thus Woodward (1940) employed the abnormal reaction for synthesis of a model compound containing an angular methyl group.   The phenolic starting material ar-tetralol (ar- indicates that the substituent is

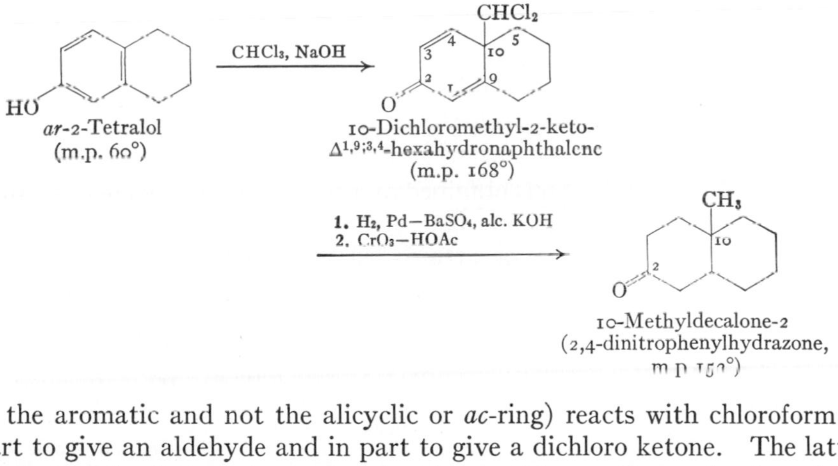

in the aromatic and not the alicyclic or ac-ring) reacts with chloroform in part to give an aldehyde and in part to give a dichloro ketone.   The latter product on hydrogenation under drastic conditions suffers reduction of the three unsaturated centers and replacement of halogen by hydrogen, and the crude alcoholic product on oxidation gives a liquid ketone that has been isolated as the crystalline dinitrophenylhydrazone.

Mechanism of the Normal Reaction. — If the abnormal reaction consists in introduction of a dichloromethyl group, it is reasonable to infer that such a substitution is the first step in the normal Reimer-Tiemann aldehyde synthesis. The postulated intermediate benzal halide, II, may be converted by alkali directly into the aldehyde. Another possibility is indicated by work of Armstrong and Richardson (1933), who sought the reason for the

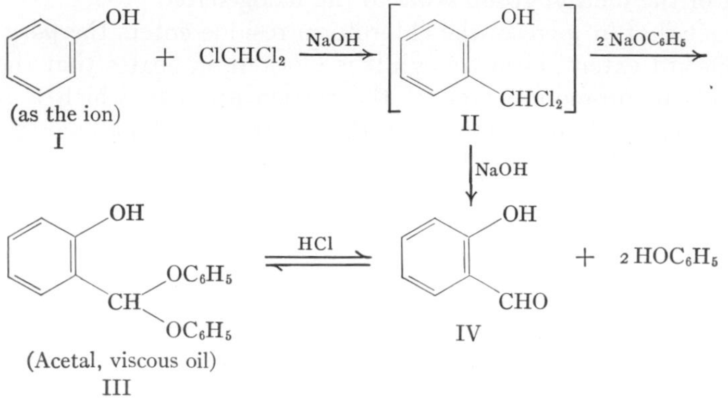

inevitable apperance in the reaction mixture of considerable starting material. Evidence was obtained that the alkaline solution contains the diphenylacetal (III) of the ultimate reaction product, and that this is reasonably stable to alkali but is hydrolyzed readily when the mixture is acidified. The acetal may be produced by condensation of the benzal halide with two molecules of sodium phenoxide or as a by-product by combination of salicyl aldehyde with phenol. The phenol present in acetal combination is unavailable for the synthesis, which accounts for the presence in the final mixture of unutilized starting material.

ALDEHYDIC DERIVATIVES OF POLYHYDRIC PHENOLS

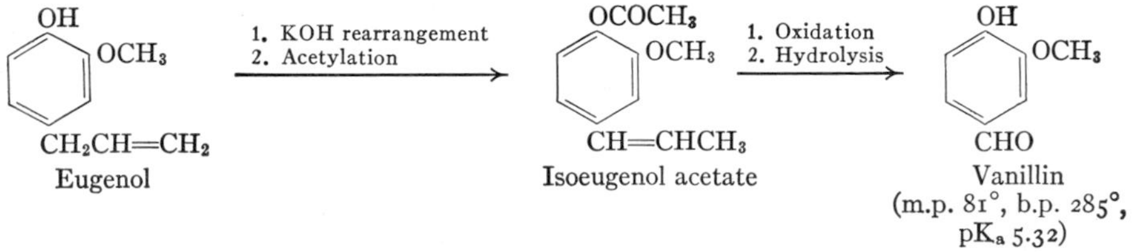

Vanillin, a partially methylated aldehyde of the catechol series, is the fragrant constituent of vanilla bean, and occurs also in the sugar beet and in balsams and resins; it also is obtained as a by-product of the manufacture of cellulose pulp by the action of alkali on basic calcium lignosulfonate. It is an important component of artificial flavors. One synthetic process utilizes eugenol, available from essential oils. Under the influence of alcoholic alkali at 140° or of concentrated aqueous potassium hydroxide at 220°, the double bond of this allyl compound migrates to a position of conjugation with the ring and gives isoeugenol. This is acetylated to protect the phenolic group and oxidized under mild conditions (dichromate, electrochemical oxidation, ozone), when the double bond of the α-propenyl group is severed and an aldehyde group produced. A second process is applica-

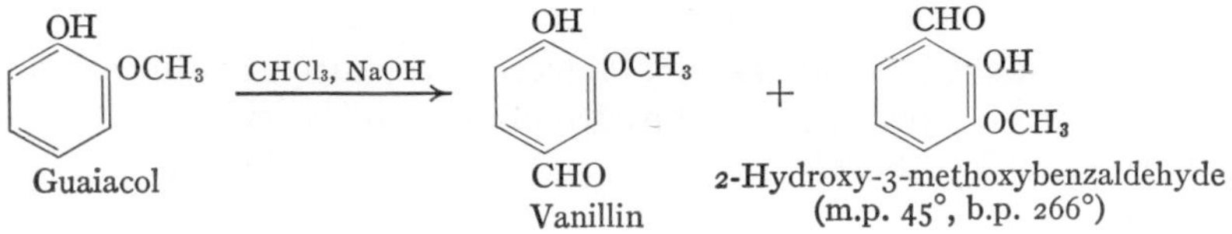

Guaiacol   Vanillin   2-Hydroxy-3-methoxybenzaldehyde
(m.p. 45°, b.p. 266°)

tion of the Reimer-Tiemann reaction to guaiacol; vanillin is the chief product but is accompanied by **2-hydroxy-3-methoxybenzaldehyde**, which can be separated by virtue of its greater volatility with steam (chelation). This by-product of the vanillin preparation and its ether, **2,3-dimethoxybenzaldehyde** (m.p. 54°), are cheap starting materials available for use in synthesis. Still more useful in synthesis is **veratraldehyde**, or 3,4-dimethoxybenzaldehyde, obtainable in 92–95% yield by methylation of vanillin with dimethyl sulfate; it can be synthesized by the Gattermann reaction from veratrole, hydrogen cyanide, and aluminum chloride.

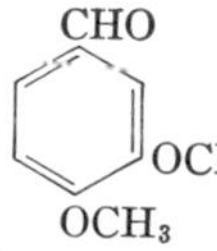

Veratraldehyde
(m.p. 44°, b.p. 285°)

The parent dihydroxy compound from which vanillin is derived is known as **protocatechualdehyde,** and its methylene ether is **piperonal,** for which a convenient source is the degradation of **safrole,** the methylene ether of 3,4-dihydroxyallylbenzene. Safrole is the chief constituent of oil of sassa-

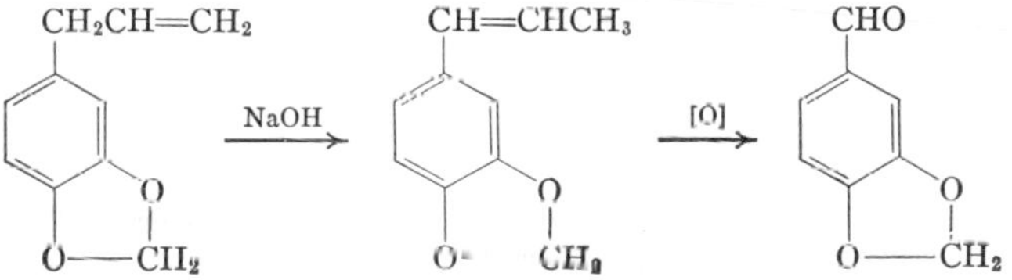

Safrole   Isosafrole   Piperonal
(m.p. 11°, b.p. 233°)   (cis, b.p. 243°;   (m.p. 37°, b.p. 263°)
     trans, b.p. 248°)

fras, and is produced commercially from camphor oil. When heated with alkali it is converted by migration of the double bond into **isosafrole**, which on oxidation yields piperonal. Piperonal has an agreeable odor like that of heliotrope and is manufactured for the perfume industry under the name heliotropine. This inexpensive aldehyde is a satisfactory starting material for preparation of protocatechualdehyde; a convenient procedure is indicated in the formulas.

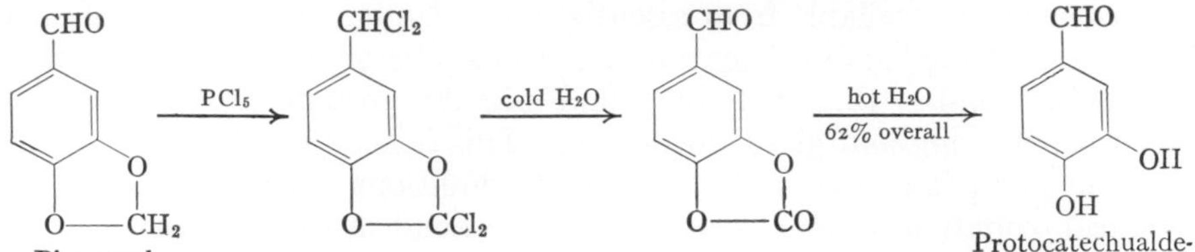

CHO   CHCl₂   CHO   CHO

$\xrightarrow{\text{PCl}_5}$ $\xrightarrow{\text{cold H}_2\text{O}}$ $\xrightarrow[\text{62\% overall}]{\text{hot H}_2\text{O}}$

O—CH₂   O—CCl₂   O—CO   OH / OH

Piperonal   Protocatechualdehyde (m.p. 154°, pKₐ 7.55)

β-**Resorcylaldehyde** and **gentisaldehyde** are fairly readily accessible formyl derivatives of resorcinol and hydroquinone, respectively. They have been synthesized by the Gattermann and the Reimer-Tiemann reactions;

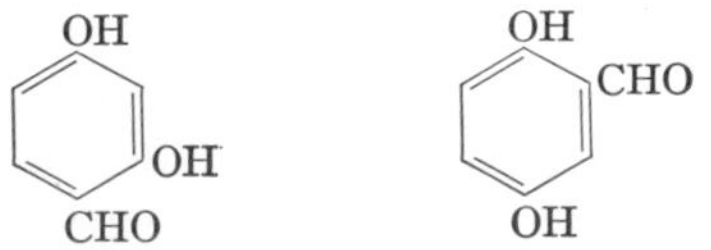

OH / OH / CHO   OH / CHO / OH

β-Resorcylaldehyde   Gentisaldehyde
(m.p. 136°)   (m.p. 99°)

gentisaldehyde can be prepared somewhat more satisfactorily by oxidation of salicylaldehyde with potassium persulfate in alkaline solution:

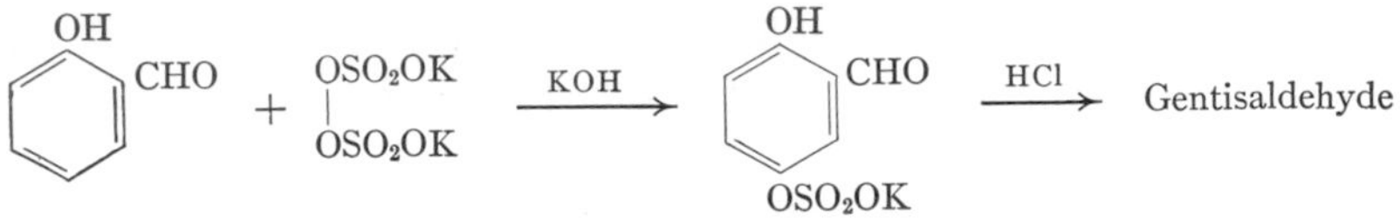

OH / CHO + OSO₂OK / OSO₂OK $\xrightarrow{\text{KOH}}$ OH / CHO / OSO₂OK $\xrightarrow{\text{HCl}}$ Gentisaldehyde

SYNTHESIS OF ALDEHYDES FROM ACIDS AND NITRILES

The **Rosenmund reaction** (1918), consisting in conversion of a carboxylic acid chloride into an aldehyde by hydrogenation in the presence of a palladium—barium sulfate catalyst, has been illustrated (p. 196) and is summarized as follows:

$$\text{ArCOCl} \xrightarrow{\text{H}_2,\ \text{Pd—BaSO}_4} \text{ArCHO} + \text{HCl}$$

In the production of mesitylaldehyde and comparable hindered substances, there is little danger of overhydrogenation, but when the desired product is more reactive it may be necessary to add to the reaction mixture a sulfur–quinoline poison, which arrests reduction at the aldehyde stage without stopping the initial replacement of halogen by hydrogen.

An alternate scheme for conversion of the chloride of an aromatic carboxylic acid into an aldehyde, introduced by **Sonn and Müller** (1919), involves condensation of the acid chloride with aniline and conversion of the anilide with phosphorus pentachloride into an imino chloride, probably by enolization and replacement of the enolic hydroxyl group by chlorine. On reaction with anhydrous stannous chloride the halogen of the imino chloride

$$\text{ArCOCl} \xrightarrow{\ C_6H_5NH_2\ } \underset{\overset{\|}{O}}{\text{ArC}}-\text{NHC}_6H_5 \xrightarrow{\ PCl_5\ }$$

Acid chloride

Anilide

$$\underset{\overset{|}{Cl}}{\text{ArC}}=\text{NC}_6H_5 \xrightarrow{\ SnCl_2\ } \underset{\overset{|}{H}}{\text{ArC}}=\text{NC}_6H_5 \xrightarrow{\ H_2O,\ -C_6H_5NH_2\ } \underset{}{\text{ArCHO}}$$

Imino chloride   Anil   Aldehyde

is replaced by hydrogen with formation of an anil derivative that is cleaved on hydrolysis to the aldehyde and aniline. Isolation of the intermediates is not necessary. The 1-, 2-, 3-, and 9-aldehydes of phenanthrene have been prepared by this method with an average yield of 62% (typical yield by the Rosenmund reaction, 90%).

The **method of McFadyen and Stevens** (1936) involves conversion of an ester into a hydrazide, preparation of the benzenesulfonyl derivative, and decomposition with alkali. The method is applicable only to aromatic

$$\text{ArCOOC}_2H_5 \xrightarrow{\ H_2NNH_2\ } \text{ArCONHNH}_2 \xrightarrow{\ C_6H_5SO_2Cl\ }$$

$$\text{ArCONHNHSO}_2C_6H_5 + \text{KOH} \longrightarrow \text{ArCHO} + N_2 + C_6H_5SO_2OK$$

aldehydes and even so gives variable results; yields, 40-85%.

The **Stephen reaction** (1925) is conducted by passing hydrogen chloride into a mixture of an aromatic nitrile and anhydrous stannous chloride in absolute ether; probably a transient imino chloride resulting from addition of hydrogen chloride to the nitrile group is the effective intermediate and gives rise to an aldimine complex that affords the aldehyde on hydrolysis.

$$\text{ArC}\equiv N \xrightarrow{\ HCl\ } \underset{\overset{|}{Cl}}{\text{ArC}}=\text{NH} \xrightarrow{\ SnCl_2,\ HCl\ } \left[\underset{\overset{|}{H}}{\text{ArC}}=\text{NH}\cdot HCl\right]_2 SnCl_4 \xrightarrow{\ H_2O\ } \text{RCHO}$$

The results are highly variable, for though benzaldehyde and β-naphthaldehyde are obtained in over 90% yield, the reaction fails in the attempted preparation of α-naphthaldehyde, and gives only negligible amounts of other aldehydes (o-tolualdehyde).

OTHER ROUTES TO SUBSTITUTED BENZALDEHYDES

The many synthetic processes described in the preceding sections, and still others, do not exhaust the opportunity for practicable preparation of aldehydes, for this functional group, though reactive, is sufficiently durable to withstand certain alterations at other positions. Thus **m-nitrobenzaldehyde** can be prepared satisfactorily by nitration of benzaldehyde, and can be converted into **m-hydroxybenzaldehyde** by reduction with stannous chloride and hydrochloric acid, diazotization without isolation of the amine or of the hydrochloride, and hydrolysis. **o-Nitrobenzaldehyde,** a substance very useful in syntheses but difficulty attainable by any method, has been prepared not only from o-nitrotoluene (p. 676) but by an interesting process starting with cinnamic acid, $C_6H_5CH\!=\!CHCOOH$. This acid on nitration affords the o- and p-nitro compounds, separable by fractional crystallization. The purified o-nitrocinnamic acid is then oxidized with permanganate at $0°$ in a dilute aqueous solution of the sodium salt covered with a layer of benzene and vigorously agitated. The o-nitrobenzaldehyde produced passes into the benzene phase and is thereby protected from overoxidation; the yield is 50–53%.

Both **o- and p-aminobenzaldehyde** can be isolated as crystalline solids by reduction of the corresponding nitro compounds, but neutral solutions of the substances darken rapidly as the result of condensations involving the two functional groups. The m-isomer is known only in the form of aqueous solutions of the hydrochloride.

REACTIONS OF ALDEHYDES

Aromatic aldehydes enter into reactions of reduction, oxidation, addition, and condensation in much the same fashion as aliphatic aldehydes, with the minor difference that the aryl residue depresses somewhat the reactivity of the carbonyl group. Absence of hydrogen atoms at the α-carbon atom adjacent to the carbonyl group prevents self-condensation of the aldol type under the influence of acids or bases, and hence certain other reactions promoted by such catalytic agents are realizable. The reactions are not specific to aromatic aldehydes, for most of them are shown also by aliphatic aldehydes of the type R_3CCHO. One is the **Cannizzaro reaction** (p. 210), a disproportionation induced by concentrated alkali, resulting in transformation of half of the aldehyde into the corresponding alcohol and of the other half into the acid.

Claisen-Schmidt Condensation. — When a mixture of benzaldehyde and acetaldehyde is agitated with aqueous alkali at room temperature, slow condensation occurs with formation of the α,β-unsaturated compound **cinnamaldehyde,** $C_6H_5CH\!=\!CHCHO$. The reaction probably in-

$$
C_6H_5CHO \ + \ CH_3CHO\,[NaOH] \underset{\textstyle\searrow}{\overset{\textstyle CH_3CHO}{\rightleftharpoons}}
\begin{array}{l}
CH_3CHCH_2CHO \\[2pt]
\quad\ \ \underset{\displaystyle OH}{|}
\end{array}
$$

$$
\left[\begin{array}{l} C_6H_5CHCH_2CHO \\[2pt] \quad\ \ \underset{\displaystyle OH}{|} \end{array}\right] \xrightarrow{-H_2O} \begin{array}{l} C_6H_5CH\!=\!CHCHO \\ \text{Cinnamaldehyde} \\ \text{(b.p. } 127°/15 \text{ mm.)} \end{array}
$$

volves a reversible aldol addition of acetaldehyde to the carbonyl group of benzaldehyde and an irreversible elimination of water from the addition product; the dehydration is favored by the circumstance that the intermediate has an activated hydrogen atom in an α-position to the carbonyl group and also, on the adjacent carbon atom, a hydroxyl group that is activated by the phenyl group. Acetaldehyde undoubtedly undergoes bimolecular condensation to form aldol, but this reaction is not followed by **irreversible dehydration,** and the other aldol intermediate thus is utilized for production of cinnamaldehyde. Cinnamaldehyde, a fragrant liquid, occurs as the chief constituent of oil of cinnamon and oil of cassia and is used in flavoring and in perfumery. It can be purified through the bisulfite-addition compound.

The Claisen-Schmidt condensation is applicable also to synthesis of α,β-unsaturated ketones, as illustrated by the following examples:

1. C_6H_5CHO + CH_3COCH_3 $\xrightarrow[\substack{65-78\%}]{\text{10\% aq. NaOH, 25-31°}}$ $C_6H_5CH=CHCOCH_3$
   (excess)   Benzalacetone
   (yellow, m.p. 42°, b.p. 262°)

2. C_6H_5CHO + $CH_3COC_6H_5$ $\xrightarrow[\substack{85\%}]{\text{aq.-alc. NaOH, 15-30°}}$ $C_6H_5CH=CHCOC_6H_5$
   Benzalacetophenone
   (yellow, m.p. 62°)

One technical process for production of cinnamic acid is oxidation of benzalacetone with sodium hypochlorite.

An extension of the Claisen-Schmidt reaction was made by Kuhn (1929), who found that crotonaldehyde can condense with an aldehydic component in a manner analogous to acetaldehyde. Hydrogen atoms in the α-position

$C_6H_5CH\underline{O + H_2}CHCH=CHCH=O$ $\xrightarrow[\substack{10\%}]{\text{alc. NaOH, 11°}}$ $C_6H_5CH=CHCH=CHCHO$
5-Phenylpentadienal
(b.p. 162°/12 mm.)

of acetaldehyde are activated for the condensation by the adjacent carbonyl group, and in crotonaldehyde the methyl group is similarly activated by the conjugated system. Piperidine acetate is a particularly effective catalyst for the condensation. With cinnamaldehyde as the aldehydic component, the synthesis of higher phenylpolyenals can be accomplished by single and multiple condensation with crotonaldehyde; simplified procedures described by J. Schmitt (1941) are summarized as follows:

1. $C_6H_5CH=CHCHO$ + $CH_3CH=CHCHO$ $\xrightarrow{\substack{\text{Piperidine acetate,} \\ \text{70\% alcohol}}}$
   Cinnamaldehyde   Crotonaldehyde

   $C_6H_5CH=CHCH=CHCH=CHCHO$ +
   7 Phenylheptatrienal
   (50%; orange-yellow, m.p. 116°)

   $C_6H_5CH=CHCH=CHCH=CHCH=CHCH=CHCHO$
   11-Phenylundecapentaenal
   (20%; orange, m.p. 183°)

2. $C_6H_5(CH=CH)_5CHO$ + $CH_3CH=CHCHO$ $\xrightarrow[\substack{80\%}]{\substack{\text{Piperidine acetate,} \\ \text{benzene}}}$ $C_6H_5(CH=CH)_7CHO$
   15-Phenylpentadecahepta-
   enal (deep red, m.p. 232°)

Perkin Reaction. — Perkin in 1868 discovered a reaction of aromatic aldehydes of value for synthesis of α,β-unsaturated acids. An aldehyde is heated with the anhydride of an aliphatic acid and the sodium or potassium salt of the same acid; for example a mixture of benzaldehyde, acetic anhydride, and potassium acetate is heated at 175–180° for five hours under reflux, the melt is poured into water, steam distilled to remove unchanged benzaldehyde, and the aqueous solution is clarified with decolorizing carbon and acidified. The reaction product is cinnamic acid. Perkin thought that

$$C_6H_5CHO \ + \ (CH_3CO)_2O \ \xrightarrow[55-60\%]{CH_3COOK, \ 175-180°} \ C_6H_5CH{=}CHCOOH$$
$$\text{Cinnamic acid}$$

the aldehyde probably condenses with acetic anhydride, rather than with the metal salt of the acid, and that the salt is a basic catalyst; extensive investigations of the mechanism have led to eventual acceptance of this early inference. The reaction is considered to proceed through the enolic form of the anhydride.

The Perkin reaction gives only fair results with benzaldehyde itself, but proceeds better when the benzene ring contains nitro or halo substituents; thus o-, m-, and p-nitrocinnamic acid are obtained from the nitrobenzaldehydes in 75–82% yield, and the yields of the corresponding chloro compounds are 71, 63, and 52%, respectively. Methyl substituents in the aldehydic component influence the reaction in an adverse manner, particularly when in the o-position (yield of o-methylcinnamic acid, 15%). When a hydroxyl group is present in the *ortho* position, cyclization with the unsaturated acid side chain can occur, and the condensation of the sodium salt of salicylaldehyde with acetic anhydride to give the cyclic product **coumarin** was the first instance of the reaction observed by Perkin; the free

Coumarin   Acetylcoumaric acid
(m.p. 67°, b.p. 291°)   (m.p. 146°)

phenol can also be used in combination with sodium acetate. Coumarin is the lactone of the *cis* form of the reaction product, **coumarinic acid**, and gives a solution of the salt of this substance when warmed with alkali; the *cis* acid is not known in the free state, for on liberation from its salts by acidification, it reverts to coumarin. The reaction mixture from salicylaldehyde affords a small amount of the acetyl derivative of the *trans* isomer, **coumaric acid** (m.p. 208°), which is incapable of lactonization. Coumarin has a fragrance resembling that of new-mown hay and is important in the perfume industry.

Perkin (1877) applied the condensation method to synthesis of the doubly unsaturated cinnamalacetic acid (1), and Michael and Gabriel (1877) discovered that phthalic anhydride can function as the carbonyl component (2). The reaction product, phthalylacetic acid, undergoes a number of interesting transformations, two of which are illustrated. Cold

1. $C_6H_5CH=CHCHO$ + $(CH_3CO)_2O$ $\xrightarrow[\text{25\%}]{\text{NaOAc, 167°}}$ $C_6H_5CH=CHCH=CHCOOH$
     Cinnamaldehyde   Cinnamalacetic acid
                                                                 (m.p. 166°)

2.

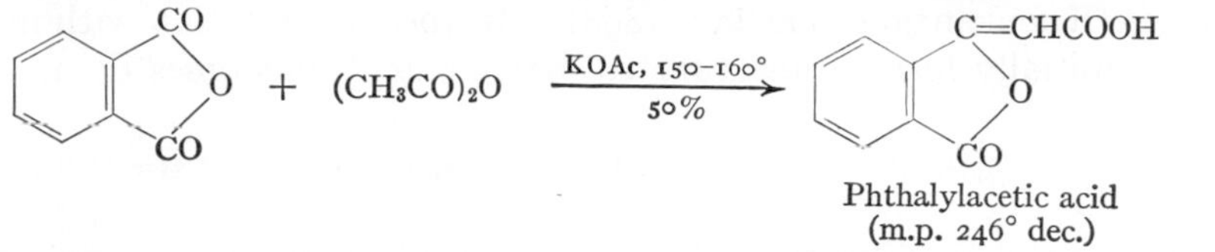

     + $(CH_3CO)_2O$ $\xrightarrow[\text{50\%}]{\text{KOAc, 150–160°}}$

     Phthalylacetic acid
     (m.p. 246° dec.)

aqueous alkali opens the lactone ring, and on careful acidification of the solution a keto dibasic acid separates; this β-keto acid readily loses carbon

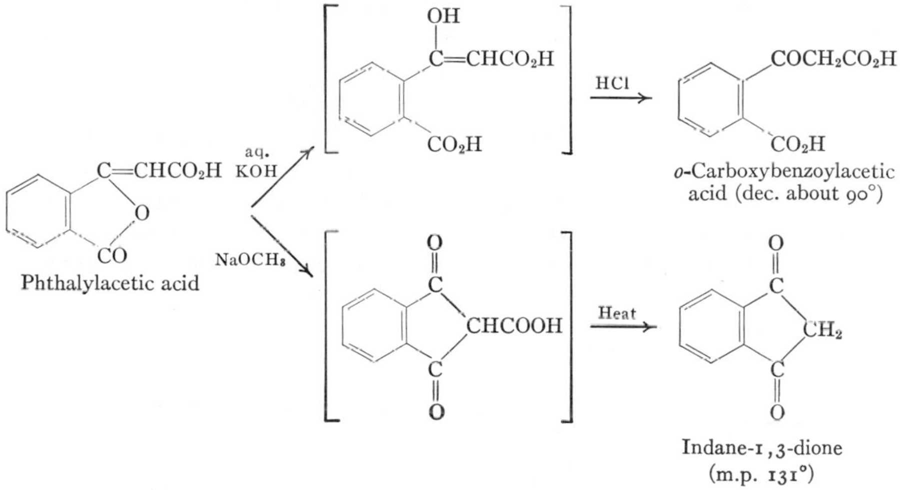

o-Carboxybenzoylacetic
acid (dec. about 90°)

Phthalylacetic acid

Indane-1,3-dione
(m.p. 131°)

dioxide when heated, and yields acetophenone-o-carboxylic acid, $o\text{-}C_6H_4\text{-}$ $(COCH_3)COOH$ (m.p. 115°). Another variation of the Perkin reaction was utilized by Kuhn (1928) for synthesis of diphenylpolyenes, as illustrated in examples 3 and 4. Lead oxide functions as the basic catalyst and also promotes decarboxylation of the intermediate unsaturated acids.

3. $C_6H_5CH=CHCHO$ + $CH_2C_6H_5$ $\xrightarrow{\text{PbO, (CH}_3\text{CO)}_2\text{O}}$ $\left[C_6H_5CH=CHCH=CC_6H_5 \right.$
                                  | $\left. COOH \right]$
                                  COOH

     $\xrightarrow[\text{23–25\%}]{\text{Heat}}$ $C_6H_5CH—CHCH=CHC_6H_5$
                           1,4-Diphenylbutadiene
                           (trans-trans form, m.p. 153°)

4. $2 C_6H_5CH=CHCHO$ + $HOOCCH_2CH_2COOH$ $\xrightarrow[\text{16\%}]{\text{PbO, (CH}_3\text{CO)}_2\text{O, reflux}}$

     $C_6H_5CH=CHCH=CHCH=CHCH=CHC_6H_5$
     1,8-Diphenyloctatetraene
     (yellow, m.p. 232°)

Condensation with Malonic Acid. — Aldehydes, both aliphatic and aromatic, condense readily with malonic acid and other compounds having a methylene group activated by carbonyl, nitrile, or nitro groups under basic catalysis (**Knoevenagel[4] reaction**, 1898). In the condensation with malonic acid the initially formed unsaturated malonic acid undergoes decarboxyla-

$$ArCHO + CH_2(CO_2H)_2 \xrightarrow{\text{Base}} [ArCH=C(CO_2H)_2] \xrightarrow{-CO_2} ArCH=CHCO_2H$$

tion during the condensation. Knoevenagel used ammonia or a primary or secondary amine to effect condensation, but pyridine, or pyridine with a trace of piperidine, is more satisfactory. With the latter combination piperonal, $C_7H_5O_2CHO$, is converted in 85–90% yield to β-piperonylacrylic acid, $C_7H_5O_2CH=CHCO_2H$; crotonaldehyde similarly affords sorbic acid (m.p. 134°), $CH_3CH=CHCH=CHCO_2H$ (30% yield). If such condensation is carried out in acetic acid solution rather than in the presence of a base the unsaturated malonic acid sometimes can be isolated.

Related Condensation Reactions. — The **Claisen reaction** consists in condensation of an aromatic aldehyde with excess ethyl acetate or comparable ester under the influence of metallic sodium and a trace of alcohol at a low temperature, as illustrated for benzaldehyde. The reaction product is the ester of an α,β-unsaturated acid. **Erlenmeyer's azlactone synthesis**

$$C_6H_5CHO + CH_3COOC_2H_5 \xrightarrow[68-74\%]{\text{Na, } 0-5°} C_6H_5CH=CHCOOC_2H_5$$
$$\text{Ethyl cinnamate}$$

(1892) utilizes a further variation of the general type of reaction; it is particularly useful in the synthesis of amino acids (p. 436).

The **Reformatsky[5] reaction** (1887) depends on interaction between a carbonyl compound, an α-halo ester, and activated zinc in the presence of anhydrous ether or ether—benzene, followed by hydrolysis. The halogen component, for example ethyl bromoacetate, combines with zinc to form an organozinc bromide that adds to the carbonyl group of the second component to give a complex readily hydrolyzed to a carbinol. The reaction

$$Zn + BrCH_2COOC_2H_5 \longrightarrow BrZnCH_2COOC_2H_5 \xrightarrow{>C=O}$$

$$\underset{CH_2COOC_2H_5}{\overset{OZnBr}{>C}} \xrightarrow{H_2O} \underset{CH_2COOC_2H_5}{\overset{OH}{>C}}$$

is conducted by the usual Grignard technique except that the carbonyl component is added at the start. Magnesium has been used in a few reactions in place of zinc but with poor results, for the more reactive organometallic reagent tends to attack the ester group; with zinc this side reaction

[4] Emil Knoevenagel, 1865–1921, b. Linden/Hannover, Germany; Ph.D. Göttingen; Heidelberg

[5] Sergius Reformatsky, 1860–1934; b. Russia; Kiev; *Ber.*, **68A**, 61 (1935)

is not appreciable, and the reactivity is sufficient for addition to the carbonyl group of aldehydes and ketones of both the aliphatic and aromatic series. The product of the reaction is a β-hydroxy ester and can be dehydrated to the α,β-unsaturated ester; thus the product from benzaldehyde and ethyl bromoacetate yields ethyl cinnamate. α-Bromo esters of the types $RCHBrCO_2C_2H_5$ and $RR'CBrCO_2C_2H_5$ react satisfactorily, but

$$\underset{\text{CHO}}{\bigcirc} + BrCH_2CO_2C_2H_5 \xrightarrow[61-64\%]{\text{Zn, benzene—ether}} \underset{\overset{OH}{|}\\ CHCH_2COOC_2H_5}{\bigcirc}$$

Ethyl β-phenyl-β-hydroxy-propionate (b.p. 130°/6 mm.)

β- and γ-bromo derivatives of saturated esters do not have adequate reactivity. Methyl γ-bromocrotonate ($BrCH_2CH=CHCO_2CH_3$), however, has a reactive, allylic bromine atom and enters into the Reformatsky reaction.

Benzoin Condensation. — Under the catalytic influence of an alkali cyanide in aqueous alcohol, benzaldehyde undergoes bimolecular condensation to the α-hydroxy ketone benzoin. Cyanide ion is an indispensable catalyst and probably participates as shown. Discovery of the benzoin

$$C_6H_5\underset{O}{\overset{||}{C}}{-}H \xrightarrow{CN^-} C_6H_5\underset{O^-}{\overset{CN}{\underset{|}{\overset{|}{C}}}}{-}H \rightleftharpoons C_6H_5\underset{OH}{\overset{CN}{\underset{|}{\overset{|}{C}}}}{^-} \xrightarrow{\overset{H}{\underset{\delta\ O}{\delta^+CC_6H_5}}}$$

$$C_6H_5\underset{OH}{\overset{CN}{\underset{|}{\overset{|}{C}}}}{-}\underset{O^-}{\overset{H}{\underset{|}{\overset{|}{C}}}}C_6H_5 \xrightarrow{-CN^-} C_6H_5{-}\underset{O}{\overset{H}{\underset{||}{\overset{|}{C}}}}{-}\underset{OH}{\overset{|}{\underset{|}{C}}}{-}C_6H_5$$

Benzoin (m.p. 134°)

condensation resulted from the fortutious circumstance that early workers purified crude "oil of bitter almonds" by washing with aqueous alkali to extract acids; the crude material from amygdalin contained hydrogen cyanide, and the sodium cyanide produced in the alkali wash catalyzed formation of benzoin (Wöhler and Liebig, 1832). Other aromatic aldehydes form benzoins (acyloins) under catalysis by cyanides. Treatment of a combination of two different aromatic aldehydes with a cyanide usually results in formation of chiefly one of the mixed acyloins, ArCHOHCOAr' and Ar'CHOHCOAr; mixed benzoins also are produced from a mixture of a benzoin, a substituted benzaldehyde, and a cyanide; the benzoin condensation is therefore reversible. The optically active l-benzoin (m.p. 132°, $[\alpha]_D^{12}$ – 117.5°) has been synthesized from l-mandelamide and phenylmagnesium bromide (low yield), and found to undergo rapid racemization in alcoholic alkaline solution through tautomerism to the enediol $C_6H_5C(OH)=$

$C(OH)C_6H_5$. The same phenomenon may be involved in the partial iso-merization of the mixed benzoin benzoyl-p-anisylcarbinol to p-anisoyl-phenylcarbinol by cold alcoholic potassium hydroxide.

Formation of acyloins by the action of an alkali cyanide on an aldehyde is not specific to aromatic aldehydes, but is seldom encountered in the ali-phatic series because the basic reagent promotes the more rapid aldol con-densation. However, enzymes can bring about the acyloin condensation of aliphatic aldehydes; for example under the influence of yeast enzymes acetaldehyde condenses to form acetoin (methylacetylcarbinol), $CH_3CH-OHCOCH_3$ (m.p. $15°$), and added benzaldehyde combines with acetaldehyde to form benzacetoin (phenylacetylcarbinol), $C_6H_5CHOHCOCH_3$ (liq., b.p. $207°$).

Like the α-hydroxy ketones of the sugar series, benzoin reduces Fehling's solution and forms an osazone (m.p. $225°$) with phenylhydrazine. A charac-teristic color reaction is observed on addition of aqueous alkali to a solution of benzoin in the presence of air (autoxidation). After a certain induction period the solution acquires a violet color, which disappears when the solution is oxygenated by shaking and reappears in the quiet state. The ultimate product is the α-diketone benzil, $C_6H_5COCOC_6H_5$, which itself is not colored by alkali but which apparently forms a colored complex with benzoin and alkali, as demonstrated by the appearance of the violet color when the three components are brought together in the absence of air. The colored substance, which is very sensitive to oxidation by air, probably is derived from the enediol form of benzoin and is regarded as a radical containing univalent oxygen (Weissberger; Michaelis, 1937).

Autoxidation of Aldehydes. — Oxidations induced by air at room tem-perature are known as autoxidations; for example the conversion of ben-zoin into benzil. Benzaldehyde readily undergoes oxidation to benzoic acid by air, particularly in the presence of minute traces of iron or on exposure to light, and the transformation is readily apparent because the aldehyde is a liquid and the acid a solid. If benzaldehyde is distilled through an air-cooled condenser and the hot liquid allowed to flow down the walls of a receiver in a thin film in contact with air, crystals of benzoic acid usually are visible in the film. Thus distillation should be conducted with exclu-sion of air and the material stored in a completely filled brown bottle.

Autoxidation of benzaldehyde has the characteristics of a free radical chain reaction, for it is photocatalytic, subject to catalysis by traces of metal derivatives and to suppression by inhibitors. H. Bächström (1934) con-cluded from results of physicochemical studies of the autoxidation that the reactive chain-propagating species is the benzoyl radical, produced photo-

1. $ArCH{=}O \xrightarrow{h\nu} ArCHO\cdot$

2. $ArCHO\cdot + ArCHO \rightarrow Ar\dot{C}{=}O + Ar\dot{C}HOH$

3. $Ar\dot{C}{=}O + O_2 \rightarrow ArC({=}O)O{-}O\cdot$

4. $ArC({=}O)O{-}O\cdot + ArCHO \rightarrow ArCO_3H + Ar\dot{C}{=}O$

5. $ArCO_3H + ArCHO \rightarrow 2ArCO_2H$

chemically (1 and 2) or otherwise, and which is assumed to combine with oxygen to form a perbenzoyl radical (3). This reacts with benzaldehyde with regeneration of the benzoyl radical and formation of perbenzoic acid (4), which converts benzaldehyde into benzoic acid (5); perbenzoic acid indeed has been detected in autoxidized benzaldehyde. The essential feature of the process is that a free-radical intermediate promotes the ultimate transformation and is regenerated in each cycle. The chain mechanism explains the efficacy of antioxidants in inhibiting autoxidation at low concentrations. Hydroquinone, which is easily oxidized, inhibits autoxidation of benzaldehyde at a concentration of only 0.001%, and it is commonly added to benzaldehyde for protection in storage; since the phenolic substance is nonvolatile, the protective action applies only to the liquid phase and not to a vapor space over the liquid. The inhibitor molecules react with and destroy free-radical intermediates, each of which otherwise would initiate a chain process resulting in the conversion of hundreds of molecules of aldehyde into the acid.

KETONES

Preparation. — Standard methods have been indicated for the preparation of ketones of types exemplified by:

Acetophenone, $C_6H_5COCH_3$ (m.p. 20°, b.p. 202°/749 mm.)

Propiophenone, $C_6H_5COCH_2CH_3$ (m.p. 21°, b.p. 218°)

Benzophenone, $C_6H_5COC_6H_5$ (stable form, m.p. 48°; labile form, m.p. 26°; b.p. 306°)

α,β-Unsaturated ketones are readily available from aldehydes by the Claisen Schmidt condensation, and the preparation of cyclic ketones by intramolecular acylation is illustrated by the synthesis of α-tetralone and α-hydrindone (p. 543). The aceto derivatives of resorcinol and pyrogallol

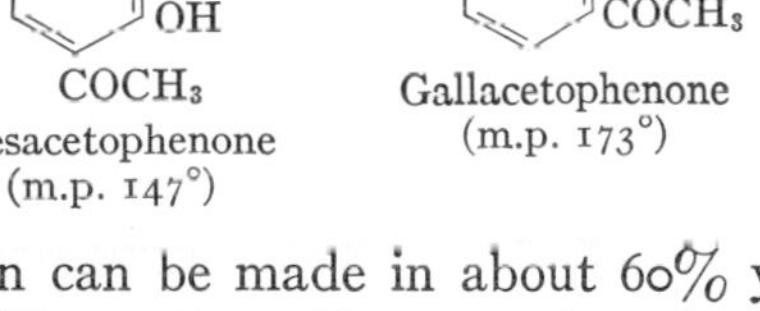

Resacetophenone
(m.p. 147°)

Gallacetophenone
(m.p. 173°)

of the structures shown can be made in about 60% yield by heating the phenolic component with acetic acid or acetic anhydride and fused zinc chloride in the temperature range 140–160°. n-Hexylresorcinol is prepared from a ketone made by a similar process. The Fries reaction (p. 634) is another practical method of preparing phenolic ketones; a further method is the **Hoesch[6] synthesis** (1915), which is essentially a modification of the Gattermann aldehyde synthesis and consists in the condensation of a phenol with acetonitrile and hydrogen chloride in the presence of zinc chloride or aluminum chloride as catalyst in solution in ether or chlorobenzene. The

---

[6] Kurt Hoesch, 1882–1932; b. Düren, Germany; Ph.D. Berlin (E. Fischer); Istanbul; *Ber.,* **66A, 16 (1933)**

reaction is illustrated for the preparation of phloroacetophenone, a useful intermediate in the synthesis of naturally occurring flavone and flavanol pigments. Saturation of the ethereal solution of the phenol, acetonitrile,

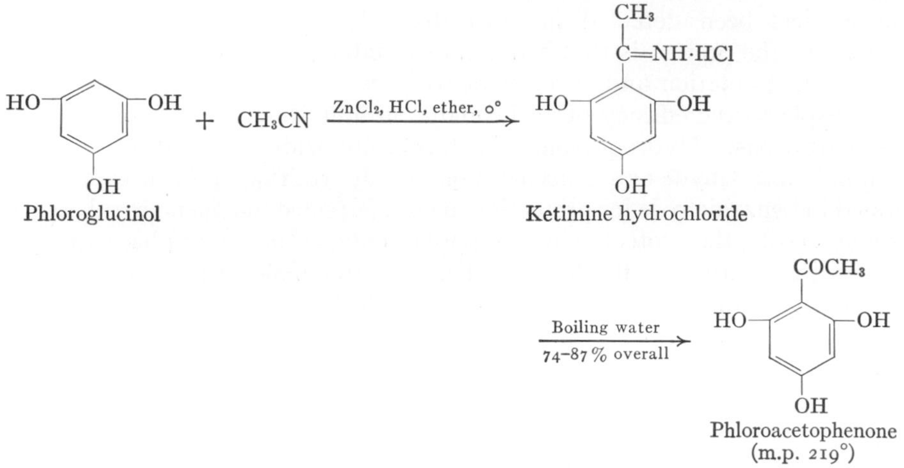

Phloroglucinol + CH₃CN $\xrightarrow{\text{ZnCl}_2,\ \text{HCl, ether, o}^\circ}$ Ketimine hydrochloride

$\xrightarrow[\text{74-87\% overall}]{\text{Boiling water}}$ Phloroacetophenone (m.p. 219°)

and zinc chloride with hydrogen chloride results in separation of a crystalline yellow precipitate of the ketimine hydrochloride, which is collected and hydrolyzed with boiling water to the aceto compound. The reaction proceeds well with many polyhydric phenols and can be varied by use of trichloroacetonitrile (CCl₃CN), but it is not applicable to phenol itself, for this substance is converted merely into an imido ester, C₆H₅OC(CH₃)=NH·HCl.

Diaryl ketones containing dialkylamino groups are useful intermediates in synthesis of triphenylmethane dyes, and are made by special condensations in the activated nuclear positions of dimethyl- and diethylaniline. The important p,p'-dimethylaminobenzophenone, or **Michler's ketone,** is prepared by interaction of dimethylaniline with phosgene in the ratio of

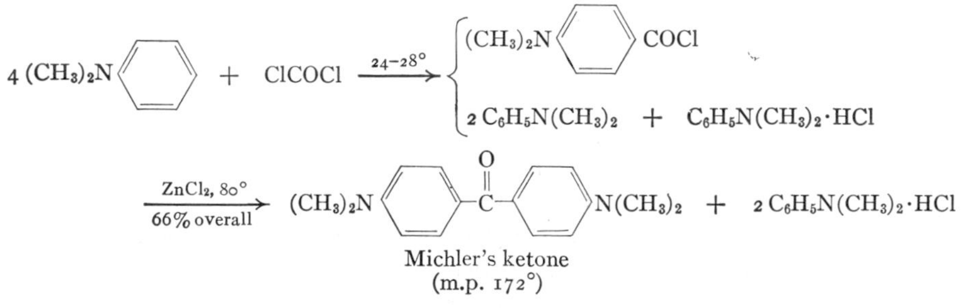

Michler's ketone (m.p. 172°)

four moles to one; the excess amine binds the hydrogen chloride liberated. The mixture is kept at a controlled temperature till the phosgene has been consumed and the —COCl radical introduced into one equivalent of the amine; fused zinc chloride is then added, and the temperature is raised to effect further condensation. The reaction mixture is poured into water, and enough hydrochloric acid is added to keep the dimethylaniline in solution;

the precipitated Michler's ketone, being less basic, remains undissolved and is collected. *p*-Dimethylaminobenzophenone can be prepared from dimethylaniline by reaction with benzanilide and phosphorus oxychloride. The effective reagent probably is the imino chloride derived from the enolic form of benzanilide (compare the Sonn-Müller reaction, p. 686):

$$C_6H_5CONHC_6H_5 \rightleftharpoons C_6H_5C(OH){=}NC_6H_5 \longrightarrow C_6H_5CCl{=}NC_6H_5$$

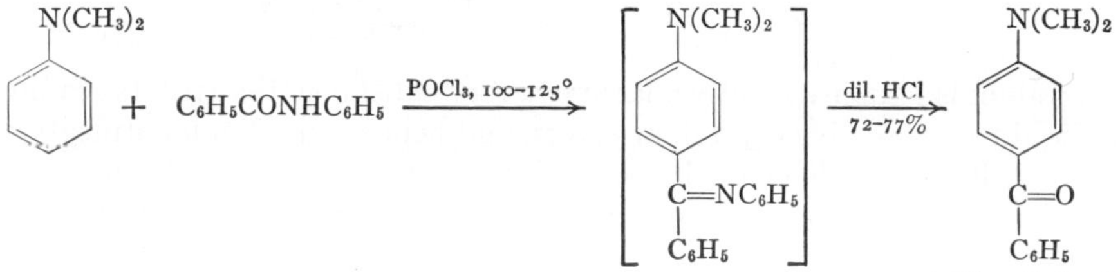

N(CH₃)₂

    + C₆H₅CONHC₆H₅   POCl₃, 100–125° →

$$\left[\begin{array}{c} N(CH_3)_2 \\ \\ C{=}NC_6H_5 \\ C_6H_5 \end{array} \right] \xrightarrow[72\text{-}77\%]{\text{dil. HCl}}$$

N(CH₃)₂

C=O

C₆H₅

p-Dimethylamino-
benzophenone
(m.p. 90°)

REACTIONS OF KETONES

Acetophenone, typical of ketones of the aromatic-aliphatic type, enters into various reactions that may involve substitution in the nucleus, attack of the activated hydrogen atoms in the methyl group, or addition to the carbonyl group. The additive power is somewhat less than that of typical aliphatic ketones, as indicated by the failure of acetophenone to form a bisulfite-addition product, but this ketone adds Grignard reagents in the normal fashion and can be reduced to the carbinol, the pinacol, or to ethylbenzene. One of the few deviations from normal behavior is that acetomesitylene, which has a highly hindered carbonyl group, does not add Grignard reagents but instead is converted into the magnesiohalide salt of the enolic form:

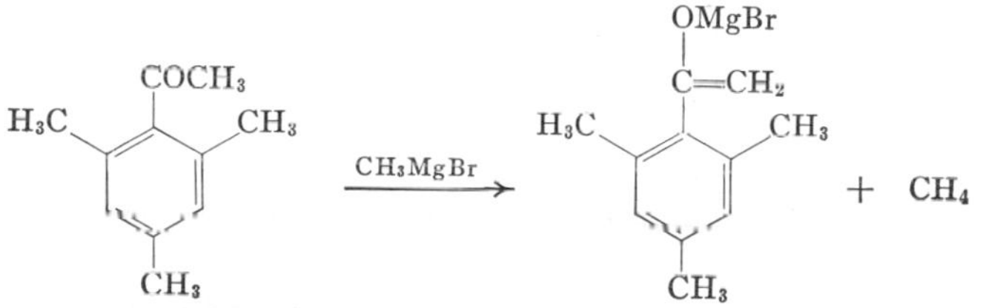

COCH₃   H₃C — CH₃   CH₃MgBr →   OMgBr   C=CH₂   H₃C — CH₃   + CH₄

CH₃
Acetomesitylene
(b.p. 236°)

CH₃

Substitution in the nucleus is illustrated by the nitration of acetophenone with mixed acid at 0°; considerable substitution occurs in the *o*-position, but *m*-nitroacetophenone (m.p. 81°) can be isolated as the chief product in 55% yield. Reactions resulting in attack of the ketonic side chain are described in the following section.

ω-Substitutions. — Introduction of halogen into the methyl group of acetophenone proceeds readily and gives products with the halogen in a position designated as ω (terminal). **Phenacyl bromide,** or ω-bromoaceto-phenone, is prepared by bromination in ether in the presence of aluminum chloride, and although this reagent is a catalyst for nuclear bromination, the alternate reaction proceeds so readily and at so low a temperature as to predominate to the practical exclusion of entrance of bromine into the ring.

$$C_6H_5COCH_3 \xrightarrow{\text{Br}_2(\text{AlCl}_3), \text{ ether, } 0°} C_6H_5COCH_2Br$$
$$\text{Phenacyl bromide}$$
$$\text{(m.p. } 51°)$$

The product is a highly reactive, lachrymatory substance that reacts readily with liquid acids to give crystalline esters, and hence is used in identification of acids. Further side-chain halogenation can be accomplished; thus two molecular equivalents of bromine convert acetophenone (carbon disulfide or acetic acid solution) into **ω,ω-dibromoacetophenone,** $C_6H_5COCHBr_2$, m.p. 37°. This substance undergoes an interesting hydrolytic rearrangement with alkali; when shaken with 10% aqueous potassium hydroxide at room temperature, it slowly dissolves, and on acidification of the solution mandelic acid is liberated in good yield. The reaction is blocked by sub-

$$C_6H_5COCHBr_2 \xrightarrow{\text{10\% aq. KOH}} C_6H_5CHCOOH$$
$$\text{ω,ω-Dibromoacetophenone} \qquad\qquad\qquad\qquad |$$
$$\text{OH}$$
$$\text{Mandelic acid}$$

stituents in both positions *ortho* to the acyl group, but otherwise is generally applicable; for example 2,4-dimethylacetophenone on dibromination and treatment of the crude product with alkali is converted in 61% yield into 2,4-dimethylmandelic acid (two polymorphic forms, m.p. 103° and 119°). Trihalo derivatives of the type $C_6H_5COCX_3$ are intermediates in the conversion of acetophenone into benzoic acid by the action of sodium hypochlorite or hypobromite.

Another instance of attack of the activated methyl group of acetophenone is oxidation with selenium dioxide to the α-keto aldehyde phenylglyoxal:

COCH₃   COCHO

$$\xrightarrow[69-72\%]{\text{SeO}_2, \text{ aq. dioxane, } 50-55°}$$

Phenylglyoxal
(b.p. 96°/25 mm.)

Condensation Reactions. — The **Claisen-Schmidt condensation** of benzaldehyde with acetophenone to give benzalacetophenone has been described

$$C_6H_5C{=}O \ + \ CH_3COC_6H_5 \xrightarrow[77-82\%]{\substack{\text{Al[OC(CH}_3)_3]_3, \\ \text{xylene, } 133-137°}} C_6H_5C{=}CHCOC_6H_5$$
$$| \qquad\qquad\qquad\qquad\qquad\qquad\qquad\qquad\qquad\qquad\qquad |$$
$$CH_3 \qquad\qquad\qquad\qquad\qquad\qquad\qquad\qquad\qquad\qquad CH_3$$
$$\text{Dypnone}$$
$$\text{(b.p. } 150-155°/1 \text{ mm.)}$$

(p. 689). Acetophenone can undergo self-condensation in the presence of various catalysts, one of the best being aluminum t-butoxide. The name of the product, dypnone, is derived from the fact that acetophenone has soporific properties and has been known as hypnone; the condensation product is thus a di-hypnone. Formation of dypnone is analogous to the condensation of acetone to mesityl oxide. Acetophenone condenses to form s-triphenylbenzene when heated with hydrochloric acid in a sealed tube:

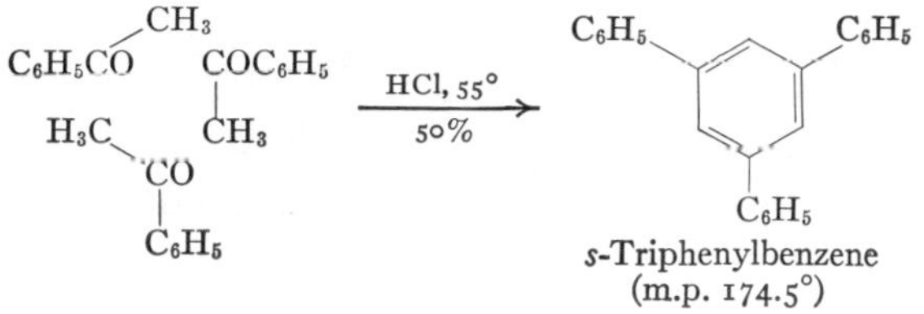

$$C_6H_5CO \quad \overset{CH_3}{\underset{H_3C}{\diagup}} \quad COC_6H_5 \quad \underset{\overset{|}{CO} \underset{C_6H_5}{|}}{CH_3} \quad \xrightarrow[50\%]{HCl,\ 55°}$$

s-Triphenylbenzene
(m.p. 174.5°)

Ester condensation is exemplified by the reaction of acetophenone with ethyl benzoate to give a 1,3-diketone:

$$C_6H_5COOC_2H_5 \ + \ CH_3COC_6H_5 \ \xrightarrow[62-71\%]{\overset{1.\ NaOC_2H_5,\ 150-160°}{2.\ H_2SO_4}} \ C_6H_5COCH_2COC_6H_5$$

Dibenzoylmethane
(m.p. 78°)

One of many types of the **Michael reaction** (1887) is illustrated by the condensation of benzalacetophenone with malonic ester in presence of a base

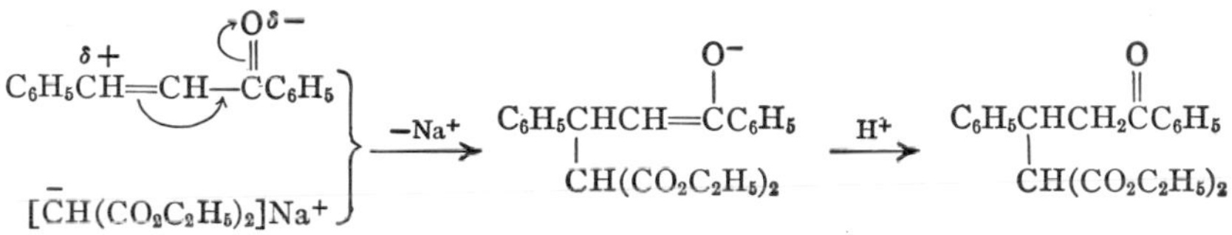

$$\left.\begin{array}{l} \overset{\delta+}{C_6H_5CH}\!=\!CH\!-\!\overset{\overset{O\,\delta-}{\|}}{C}C_6H_5 \\[4pt] [\bar{C}H(CO_2C_2H_5)_2]Na^+ \end{array}\right\} \xrightarrow{-Na^+} \underset{CH(CO_2C_2H_5)_2}{C_6H_5CHCH\!=\!\overset{O^-}{\overset{|}{C}}C_6H_5} \xrightarrow{H^+} \underset{CH(CO_2C_2H_5)_2}{C_6H_5CHCH_2\overset{\overset{O}{\|}}{C}C_6H_5}$$

The base-catalyzed aldol-type condensation of a succinic ester with an aldehyde or a ketone (**Stobbe condensation**, 1899) is useful for building up an acid side chain. Thus γ-2-naphthylvaleric acid can be prepared from 2-acetonaphthalene by Stobbe condensation, decarboxylation (with lactonization), and hydrogenation in alkaline solution (W. S. Johnson, 1945):

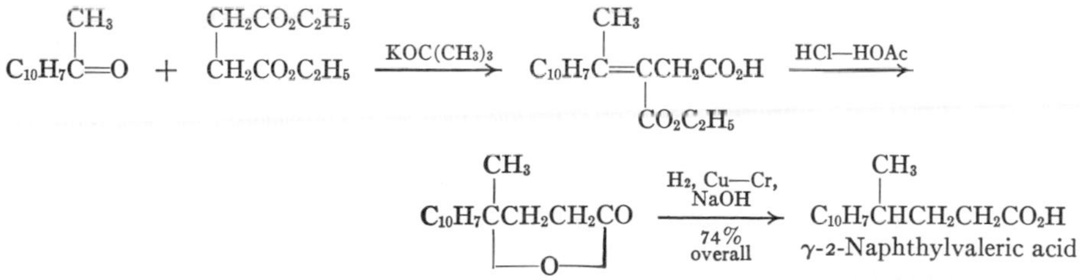

$$\underset{}{\overset{CH_3}{\overset{|}{C_{10}H_7C}}}\!=\!O \ + \ \underset{CH_2CO_2C_2H_5}{\overset{CH_2CO_2C_2H_5}{\overset{|}{}}} \ \xrightarrow{KOC(CH_3)_3} \ \underset{CO_2C_2H_5}{\overset{CH_3}{\overset{|}{C_{10}H_7C}}}\!=\!CCH_2CO_2H \ \xrightarrow{HCl-HOAc}$$

$$\underset{\underset{O}{|_____|}}{\overset{CH_3}{\overset{|}{C_{10}H_7CCH_2CH_2CO}}} \ \xrightarrow[\underset{overall}{74\%}]{\overset{H_2,\ Cu-Cr,}{NaOH}} \ \underset{}{\overset{CH_3}{\overset{|}{C_{10}H_7CHCH_2CH_2CO_2H}}}$$

γ-2-Naphthylvaleric acid

The **Darzens**[7] **condensation** (1905–12) is exemplified by the addition of ethyl chloroacetate to the carbonyl group of acetophenone under catalysis by a strong base (potassium t-butoxide is particularly effective, as it is in the Stobbe condensation). The initial chlorohydrin (1) cyclizes irreversibly

$$CH_3 \\ | \\ C_6H_5C{=}O + ClCH_2CO_2C_2H_5 \underset{}{\overset{NaNH_2}{\rightleftharpoons}} \left[\begin{array}{c} CH_3 \\ | \\ C_6H_5C{-}CHCO_2C_2H_5 \\ | \quad | \\ OH \ Cl \end{array} \right] \xrightarrow{63\%}$$

(1)

$$\begin{array}{ccc} CH_3 & CH_3 & CH_3 \\ | & | & | \\ C_6H_5C{-}{-}{-}CHCO_2C_2H_5 & C_6H_5C{-}{-}{-}CHCO_2Na & C_6H_5CHCHO \\ \searrow \quad \swarrow & \searrow \quad \swarrow & \\ O & O & \end{array}$$

$$C_6H_5C\text{---}CHCO_2C_2H_5 \xrightarrow{NaOR} C_6H_5C\text{---}CHCO_2Na \xrightarrow[67\%]{HCl} C_6H_5CHCHO$$

(2)   (3)   (4)

to the α,β-epoxy ester (2), described as a glycidic ester (ethyl β-methyl-β-phenylglycidate). The ester group is saponified and the glycidic acid (3) warmed with dilute mineral acid to effect oxide cleavage and decarboxylation to the aldehyde (4). The last step must involve fission of the oxide to the α-hydroxy-β-chloro acid, which loses hydrogen chloride to give the α-keto acid, which then suffers decarboxylation.

Formation and Rearrangement of Pinacols. — Aromatic ketones, like aliphatic ketones, are subject to bimolecular reduction by metal combinations to pinacols, that is, *vic*-glycols in which both hydroxylated carbon atoms are substituted by alkyl or aryl groups. Benzophenone affords a pinacol in high yield when exposed to light in solution in isopropyl alcohol, which functions as a hydrogen donor. Like related compounds, benzo-

$$2(C_6H_5)_2C{=}O + (CH_3)_2CHOH \xrightarrow[95\%]{Sunlight} \begin{array}{c} (C_6H_5)_2C{-}OH \\ | \\ (C_6H_5)_2C{-}OH \end{array} + \begin{array}{c} CH_3 \\ \diagdown \\ CH_3 \diagup \end{array}C{=}O$$

Benzopinacol
(m.p. 189°)

pinacol undergoes characteristic **pinacol rearrangement** under the influence of mineral acids or iodine, and is converted into benzopinacolone, in which one phenyl group has migrated to the adjacent carbon atom and water

$$\begin{array}{cc} C_6H_5\diagdown \quad \diagup C_6H_5 & C_6H_5\diagdown \\ \quad C{-}C & \quad C_6H_5{-}C{-}C{-}C_6H_5 \\ \diagup | \quad | \diagdown & \diagup \quad \| \\ C_6H_5 \ OH \ OH \ C_6H_5 & C_6H_5 \quad O \end{array}$$

$$\xrightarrow[95\%]{I_2, \ HOAc}$$

Benzopinacol   Benzopinacolone
                                  (m.p. 180°)

has been eliminated. This rearrangement is shown even by aliphatic pinacols that can undergo normal dehydration to dienes and that afford such

---

[7] Georges Darzens, b. 1867 Moscow; Paris

products on dehydration over alumina. All reagents that promote pinacol rearrangement are electrophilic, and the key step in the process is elimination of one hydroxyl group and production of an intermediate carbonium ion (Whitmore, 1932). The pair of electrons originally shared

$$
\begin{array}{c}
\underset{R}{\overset{R}{\diagdown}}C-\underset{\underset{OH}{|}}{\overset{|}{C}}\underset{OH}{\overset{R}{\diagup}}\xrightarrow{\text{H}^{+} (-\text{H}_2\text{O})}
\left[\underset{R}{\overset{R}{\diagdown}}\overset{\downarrow}{C}-\underset{\underset{OH}{|}}{\overset{+}{C}}\underset{R}{\overset{R}{\diagup}}\right]
\longrightarrow R-\underset{R}{\overset{R}{\diagdown}}C-\underset{\underset{O}{\parallel}}{C}-R \;+\; \text{H}^{+}
\end{array}
$$

between the carbon atom and the hydroxyl group is retained by hydroxyl in the separation as an ion, and the charged carbon atom is left with an incomplete shell of six electrons. A hydrocarbon group migrates from the adjacent carbon atom with its full complement of eight electrons, while the hydrogen atom of the remaining hydroxyl acquires the positive charge and is expelled as a proton.

Isomerism and Rearrangement of Oximes. — Acetophenone condenses in the usual way with aniline, phenylhydrazine, hydroxylamine, and other amine derivatives, though somewhat less readily than acetone; still more drastic conditions are required with benzophenone. The oxime derivatives are particularly interesting, for they exist in two geometrically isomeric forms analogous to diazotates (p. 611). *Cis* and *trans* oximes of aliphatic and aromatic aldehydes are known. Thus the product of the reaction of benzaldehyde with hydroxylamine in the presence of excess sodium hydroxide is the low-melting *cis* form, which is stable to alkali but rapidly rearranged by acids to the higher-melting *trans* form. The isomerization,

$$
\underset{\underset{\text{N--OH}}{\parallel}}{\text{C}_6\text{H}_5\text{--C--H}} \quad \xrightarrow[\text{2. Na}_2\text{CO}_3]{\text{1. dry HCl, ether}} \quad \underset{\underset{\text{HO--N}}{\parallel}}{\text{C}_6\text{H}_5\text{--C--H}}
$$

cis-Benzaldoxime   *trans*-Benzaldoxime
(m.p. 35°)   (m.p. 130°)

which is comparable to the acid-catalyzed conversion of maleic into fumaric acid, is accomplished by passing dry hydrogen chloride into an ethereal solution of the *cis* form; a crystalline precipitate separates consisting of the hydrochloride of the *trans* isomer, from which the free oxime is obtained on neutralization with soda solution. The reverse change occurs on irradiation of the benzene solution (compare fumaric → maleic acid). The *trans*-oxime undergoes dehydration to benzonitrile, for example under the influence of hot acetic anhydride, more readily than the *cis* form; the ready elimination of water between hydrogen and hydroxyl on opposite sides of the molecule corresponds to the normally occurring *trans* elimination observed in dehydration of alcohols.

Oximes of certain ketones also have been isolated in two geometrical forms, and in this series the configuration determines the course of a characteristic rearrangement discovered by Beckmann[8] (1886). The **Beckmann**

---

[8] Ernst Beckmann, 1853–1923; b. Solingen, Germany; Ph.D. Leipzig (Kolbe); Giessen, Erlangen, Leipzig, KWI Berlin; *Ber.*, **61A**, 87 (1928)

rearrangement, for example of benzophenone oxime, is brought about by treatment of the oxime with phosphorus pentachloride in ether solution, and results in conversion into benzanilide by exchange of place between the hydroxyl group and a phenyl group on the opposite side of the molecule, and ketonization of the enolic intermediate. The rearrangement occurs also

$$
\begin{array}{ccc}
C_6H_5\!-\!\overset{\mid}{\underset{\parallel}{C}}\!-\!C_6H_5 & \xrightarrow{\;PCl_5,\ ether\;} & C_6H_5\!-\!\overset{\parallel}{C}\!-\!OH \\
\underset{}{HO\!-\!N} & & C_6H_5\!-\!N
\end{array}
\quad\dashrightarrow\quad
\begin{array}{c}
C_6H_5C\!=\!O \\
\mid \\
NHC_6H_5
\end{array}
$$

Benzophenone oxime   Benzanilide
(m.p. 144)

under the influence of sulfuric acid, hydrogen chloride in acetic acid, benzenesulfonyl chloride in pyridine, or aluminum chloride in benzene. Evidence for a *trans* exchange of groups is derived from experiments with unsymmetrical diaryl ketoximes that have been isolated in two geometrical forms of established configuration; for example the isomeric oximes of *p*-methoxybenzophenone:

$$
\begin{array}{cc}
C_6H_5\!-\!\overset{\parallel}{C}\!-\!C_6H_4OCH_3 & \xrightarrow{\;PCl_5,\ ether,\ -10°\;} & \begin{array}{c} O\!=\!CC_6H_4OCH_3 \\ \mid \\ NHC_6H_5 \end{array} \\
N\!-\!OH & \\
(m.p.\ 147°) & \text{Anisanilide (m.p. 171°)}
\end{array}
$$

Ultraviolet light $\Updownarrow$

$$
\begin{array}{cc}
C_6H_5\!-\!\overset{\parallel}{C}\!-\!C_6H_4OCH_3 & \xrightarrow{\;PCl_5,\ ether\;} & \begin{array}{c} C_6H_5C\!=\!O \\ \mid \\ NHC_6H_4OCH_3 \end{array} \\
HO\!-\!N & \\
(m.p.\ 117°) & \text{Benz-}p\text{-anisidide} \\
& (m.p.\ 156°)
\end{array}
$$

Aliphatic ketoximes undergo the Beckmann rearrangement, and the reaction is used in degradation of ketones through the oximes to amide derivatives capable of being hydrolyzed to acid and amine components, which, when identified, provide evidence for the structure of the original ketone. The reaction has useful application to oximes of the mixed aliphatic-aromatic type obtainable by the Friedel-Crafts acylation of aromatic hydrocarbons. Acetophenone affords only one oxime, which is converted on Beckmann rearrangement with sulfuric acid at 100° into acetanilide:

$$
\begin{array}{ccc}
C_6H_5\!-\!\overset{\parallel}{C}\!-\!CH_3 & \longrightarrow & \left[\begin{array}{c} HO\!-\!\overset{\parallel}{C}\!-\!CH_3 \\ NC_6H_5 \end{array}\right] & \longrightarrow & \begin{array}{c} O\!=\!CCH_3 \\ \mid \\ NHC_6H_5 \end{array} \\
N\!-\!OH & & & & \\
\end{array}
$$

Acetophenone oxime   Acetanilide
(m.p. 59°)

This behavior is typical of aryl methyl ketoximes; because of the dissimilarity of the two groups, aryl and methyl, one geometrical isomer is more stable than the other and is the sole product of oximation, and it is this stable isomer that on Beckmann rearrangement yields the acetyl derivative of an aromatic amine. Thus where other methods of preparing aromatic amines fail, such compounds may be obtainable through the acetoximes. A case in point is methyl dehydroabietate, where the usual method for introduction of one amino group is inapplicable because nitration under very mild conditions affords the 6,8-dinitro compound. The Friedel-Crafts acylation, however, stops at monosubstitution, and gives almost exclusively the 6-aceto derivative (with 3–4% of the 8-isomer). Rearrangement of the

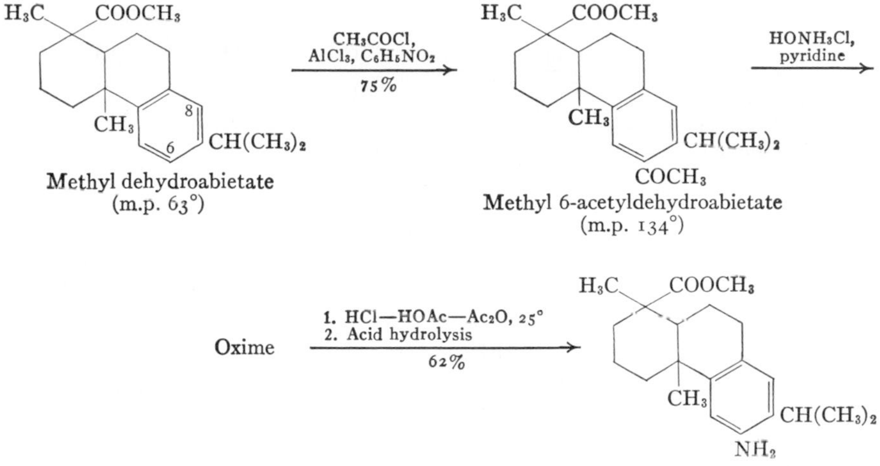

Methyl dehydroabietate
(m.p. 63°)

Methyl 6-acetyldehydroabietate
(m.p. 134°)

Methyl 6-aminodehydroabietate
(m.p. 137°)

oxime yields 88% of the desired product ArNHCOCH₃ and only 4% of the isomer ArCONHCH₃, and hence the 6-amine, obtained by hydrolysis with hydrochloric and acetic acid, can be produced in satisfactory overall yield.

Synthesis of Amines from Ketones. — Several methods are available for the synthesis of compounds having an amino group in an alkyl side chain. One is oximation of a ketone and reduction; for example α-phenylethylamine can be made by reduction of acetophenone oxime with sodium and absolute

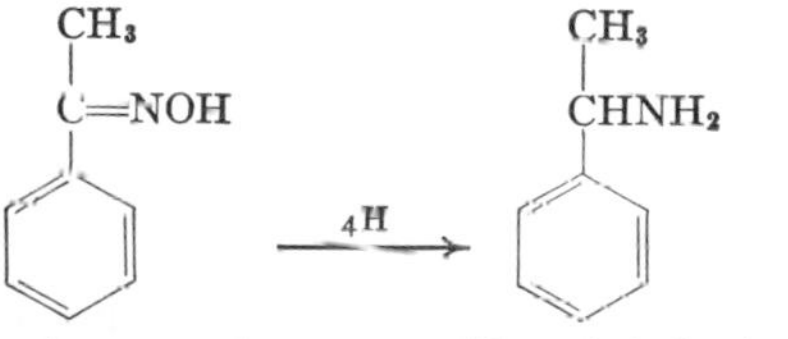

Acetophenone oxime

α-Phenylethylamine
(b.p. 186°)

alcohol or with sodium amalgam. A more convenient preparation of the same compound is by the Leuckart reaction (p. 600).

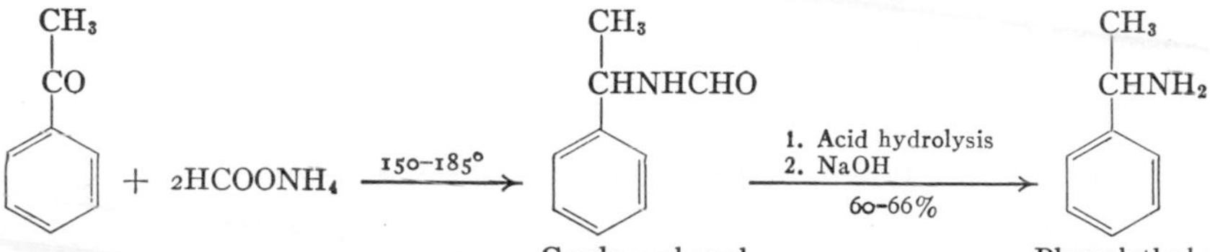

Crude α-phenylethylformamide

α-Phenylethylamine

In another method, a ketone of the type $ArCOCH_2R$, where R is alkyl or hydrogen, is condensed with a nitrous acid ester in the presence of sodium ethoxide (or hydrogen chloride) to an oximino ketone, $ArCOCR{=}NOH$ (Claisen, 1887). The reaction is comparable to a Claisen-Schmidt condensation. The oximino ketone yields a primary amino compound on reduction.

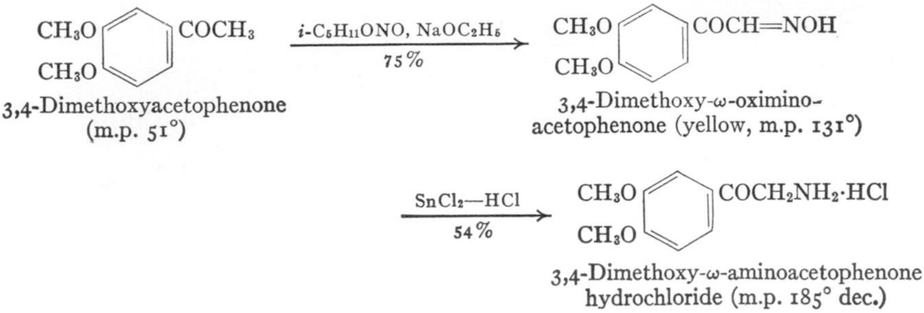

CH₃O⟨⟩COCH₃ →[i-C₅H₁₁ONO, NaOC₂H₅][75%] CH₃O⟨⟩COCH=NOH
CH₃O   CH₃O

3,4-Dimethoxyacetophenone   3,4-Dimethoxy-ω-oximino-
(m.p. 51°)   acetophenone (yellow, m.p. 131°)

→[SnCl₂—HCl][54%] CH₃O⟨⟩COCH₂NH₂·HCl
                  CH₃O

3,4-Dimethoxy-ω-aminoacetophenone
hydrochloride (m.p. 185° dec.)

The **Mannich[9] reaction** (1917) involves condensation of a carbonyl compound, for example acetophenone, with formaldehyde and ammonia or a primary or secondary amine. Certain ketonic amines of the type illustrated

$C_6H_5COCH_3 + CH_2O + (CH_3)_2NH \cdot HCl$ →[Alcohol (reflux)][60%] $C_6H_5COCH_2CH_2N(CH_3)_2 \cdot HCl$
                                                                    ω-Dimethylaminopropiophenone
                                                                    hydrochloride (m.p. 156°)

afford on reduction physiologically active amino alcohols of value in therapy. Amino alcohols of similar types are available also from oximino ketones by catalytic hydrogenation in an alcoholic solution containing hydrochloric acid (Hartung and Munch, 1929), as shown. In certain condensations a

$C_6H_5COCH_2CH_3 + C_4H_9ONO$ →[Ether, HCl][72.5%] $C_6H_5CO\overset{\underset{|}{CH_3}}{C}{=}NOH$ →[H₂, Pd—C, alc. HCl][84-98%]
Propiophenone   Oximinopropiophenone
                                           (m.p. 106°)

$C_6H_5\underset{\underset{OH}{|}}{CH}{-}\underset{\underset{NH_2 \cdot HCl}{|}}{CH}CH_3$
Phenylpropanolamine hydrochloride
(m.p. 191°; base, m.p. 103°)

Mannich base, as quaternary salt, acts as the equivalent of an α,β-unsaturated ketone. Thus in a key step in the synthesis of a natural steroid (Cornforth and Robinson, 1946), diethylaminobutanone methiodide (I) was condensed with the ketone III; ring closure between II and III involves both aldol condensation and Michael addition.

[9] Carl Mannich, 1877–1947; b. Breslau, Germany; Ph.D. Basel (Thoms); Berlin; *Ber.*, **88**, 1 (1955)

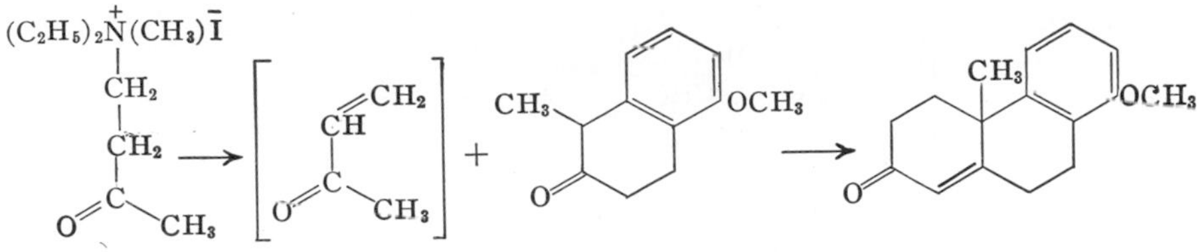

$(C_2H_5)_2\overset{+}{N}(CH_3)\bar{I}$

I   II   III   IV

Willgerodt Reaction. — This reaction, discovered in 1887, is conducted by heating a ketone, for example $ArCOCH_3$, with an aqueous solution of yellow ammonium sulfide (sulfur dissolved in ammonium sulfide), and results in formation of an amide derivative of an arylacetic acid and in some reduction of the ketone. The dark reaction mixture usually is refluxed with

$$ArCOCH_3 + (NH_4)S_x \longrightarrow ArCH_2CONH_2 + ArCH_2CH_3$$

alkali to effect hydrolysis of the amide, and the arylacetic acid is recovered from the alkaline solution. Although the yields are not high, the process sometimes offers the most satisfactory route to an arylacetic acid, as in the preparation of 1-acenaphthylacetic acid from 1-acetoacenaphthene, a starting material made in 45% yield by acylation of the hydrocarbon with acetic acid and liquid hydrogen fluoride. The product is obtained in better yield

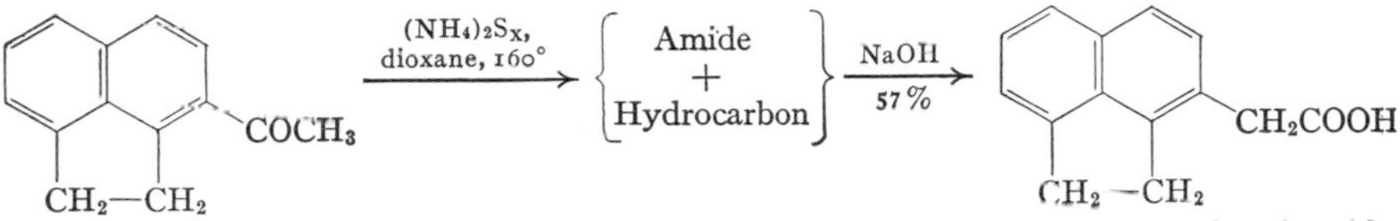

1-Acetoacenaphthene
(m.p. 105°)

1-Acenaphthylacetic acid
(m.p. 168°)

and is more easily purified than that from an alternate process consisting in hypochlorite oxidation, conversion to the acid chloride, and Arndt-Eistert reaction (p. 184).

$C_{12}H_9COCH_3$
1-Acetoacenaphthene

$C_{12}H_9COCl$

$[C_{12}H_9COCHN_2]$
Diazo ketone

$C_{12}H_9CH_2COOH$
1-Acenaphthylacetic acid

A modification of the Villgerodt reaction that simplifies the procedure by obviating the necessity of a sealed tube or autoclave consists in refluxing the ketone with a high-boiling amine and sulfur (Schwenk, 1942). Morpholine, so named because of a relationship to an early erroneous partial formula suggested for morphine, is suitable and is made technically by dehydration of diethanolamine. The reaction is conducted in the absence of water, and the reaction product is not the amide but the thioamide; this, however, undergoes hydrolysis in the same manner to the arylacetic acid.

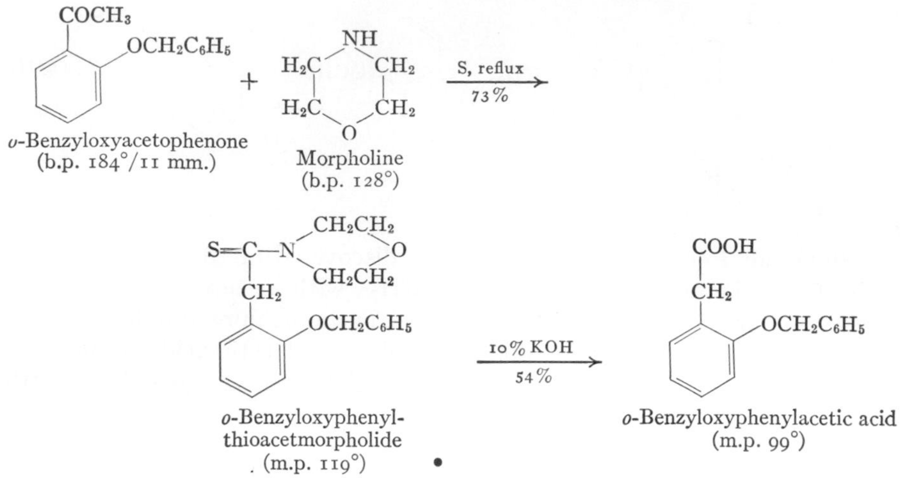

COCH₃

o-Benzyloxyacetophenone
(b.p. 184°/11 mm.)

+

NH

Morpholine
(b.p. 128°)

S, reflux
73%
→

o-Benzyloxyphenyl-
thioacetmorpholide
(m.p. 119°)

10% KOH
54%
→

COOH

o-Benzyloxyphenylacetic acid
(m.p. 99°)

BENZOIN-BENZIL SERIES

The α-diketone benzil is obtained in high yield by oxidation of benzoin with nitric acid in acetic acid solution or with copper sulfate in aqueous

$$C_6H_5CHCOC_6H_5 \xrightarrow[86\%]{CuSO_4,\ aq.\ pyridine,\ 95°} C_6H_5COCOC_6H_5$$

OH

Benzoin

Benzil
(yellow, m.p. 95°)

pyridene. The yellow color of benzil is discharged by a variety of oxidizing and reducing agents. Thus the diketone is oxidized to benzoic acid by hydrogen peroxide in warm acetic acid, and it is reduced to benzoin by stannous chloride in alcohol or by sodium hydrosulfite in aqueous alcohol. The reduction proceeds by 1,4-addition of hydrogen and ketonization of the initially formed enediol. Thiele (1899) established this mechanism by

$$C_6H_5-\overset{O}{\underset{||}{C}}-\overset{O}{\underset{||}{C}}-C_6H_5 \xrightarrow{2\ H} \left[C_6H_5-\overset{OH}{\underset{|}{C}}=\overset{OH}{\underset{|}{C}}-C_6H_5 \right] \longrightarrow C_6H_5CHOHCOC_6H_5$$

conducting the reduction in the presence of acetic anhydride and a catalyst in order that the alcoholic product would be acetylated as formed (reductive acetylation); two stereoisomeric diacetates of the enediol were isolated. Both isomers are colorless and afford benzoin on hydrolysis. Although

$$C_6H_5-\overset{O}{\underset{||}{C}}-\overset{O}{\underset{||}{C}}-C_6H_5 \xrightarrow{Zn,\ Ac_2O,\ H_2SO_4} C_6H_5-\overset{AcO}{\underset{|}{C}}=\overset{OAc}{\underset{|}{C}}-C_6H_5$$

α- and β-Stilbenediol
diacetate (m.p. 153° and 119°)

benzoin results from reduction of benzil by the methods indicated, it can be converted by further reduction into a number of products, some of which are indicated in the chart. Addition of hydrogen to the carbonyl group to

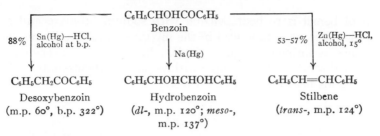

$C_6H_5CHOHCOC_6H_5$
Benzoin

88% | Sn(Hg)—HCl, alcohol at b.p.

53–57% | Zn(Hg)—HCl, alcohol, 15°

Na(Hg)

$C_6H_5CH_2COC_6H_5$
Desoxybenzoin
(m.p. 60°, b.p. 322°)

$C_6H_5CHOHCHOHC_6H_5$
Hydrobenzoin
(*dl*-, m.p. 120°; *meso*-, m.p. 137°)

$C_6H_5CH{=}CHC_6H_5$
Stilbene
(*trans*-, m.p. 124°)

give **hydrobenzoin**, in the two optically inactive forms, is accomplished with sodium amalgam. Amalgamated tin and hydrochloric acid in alcohol at the reflux temperature removes one oxygen and produces **desoxybenzoin**, whereas combination of amalgamated zinc with cold alcoholic hydrochloric acid eliminates both oxygens and gives the unsaturated hydrocarbon **stilbene**. Desoxybenzoin can be made also from phenylmagnesium bromide and benzyl cyanide or by the Friedel-Crafts reaction of phenylacetyl chloride with benzene (68–72% yield). The end product of the series, **dibenzyl** ($C_6H_5CH_2CH_2C_6H_5$, m.p. 52°), is produced by hydrogenation of benzil over nickel catalyst at 230° or by the action of sodium on benzyl chloride. A reaction of benzil generally characteristic of α-diketones is condensation with *o*-phenylenediamine with closure of an aromatic heterocyclic ring (pyrazine ring).

$$C_6H_5C{=}O$$
$$C_6H_5C{=}O$$

$+$

H_2N

$\xrightarrow{\text{quant.}}$

2,3-Diphenylquinoxaline
(colorless, m.p. 126°)

Another general reaction, benzilic acid rearrangement, is brought about by heating the α-diketone with 70% aqueous sodium hydroxide at 140° or by refluxing the diketone with alcoholic potassium hydroxide. Benzil is converted into benzilic acid, the α-hydroxy derivative of diphenylacetic acid, $(C_6H_5)_2C(OH)COOH$. The rearrangement, which involves rupture of a carbon-carbon linkage, is probably initiated through nucleophilic attack by hydroxide ion with formation of an ionic intermediate that rearranges by migration of a phenyl group. A preparative method that dispenses with

$$C_6H_5C{-}CC_6H_5 \xrightarrow{OH^-} \left[\begin{array}{c} C_6H_5C{-}C \vdots C_6H_5 \\ OH \end{array} \right. \longrightarrow \left. \begin{array}{c} C_6H_5 \\ C{-}C \\ C_6H_5 \quad OH \end{array} \right]$$

$$\xrightarrow{\overset{+}{H}} (C_6H_5)_2C(OH)CO_2H$$

Benzilic acid
M. p. 151°, pK_a 3.04

isolation of benzil is to heat benzoin with sodium bromate and alkali at
85–90°; the diketone is produced in the mixture under conditions such that
it rearranges as formed (84–90% yield). Benzilic acid is sensitive to oxidation in acid solution, for example with potassium dichromate and sulfuric
acid, and yields benzophenone and carbon dioxide.

PROBLEMS

1. Suggest methods for the synthesis of the following aldehydes:

   (a) p-Bromobenzaldehyde   (c) 2,4-Dimethoxybenzaldehyde
   (b) 2,5-Dimethylbenzaldehyde   (d) Terephthalaldehyde

2. Prepare a chart summarizing the principal methods available for introduction into
   the aromatic nucleus of each of the following groups: CH_3, NO_2, NH_2, SO_3H, OH,
   Cl, I, CN, COOH, CHO, $COCH_3$.
3. How can each of the substituents mentioned in the preceding question be eliminated
   from the nucleus (replaced by hydrogen)?
4. Would you expect condensation to occur between the following pairs of components?
   If so, indicate the type of catalyst required and write the reactions:

   (a) $C_6H_5CHO + CH_3CH_2CH_2CHO$
   (b) $C_6H_5CH=CHCHO + C_6H_5COCH_3$
   (c) $C_6H_5CHO + CH_3CH=CHCHO$

5. Suggest a synthesis of o-bromocinnamic acid from o-bromotoluene.
6. Formulate a synthesis of the acid $C_6H_5CH(CH_3)CH_2COOH$ from acetophenone by
   the Reformatsky reaction.
7. Summarize methods of preparing aromatic aldehydes and ketones that are applicable
   specifically to phenols and amines.

READING REFERENCES

R. L. Shriner, "The Reformatsky Reaction," in R. Adams, *Organic Reactions*, I, 1–37, Wiley,
New York (1942)
W. E. Bachmann and W. S. Struve, "The Arndt-Eistert Synthesis," *ibid*, 38–62 (1942)
J. R. Johnson, "The Perkin Reaction and Related Reactions," *ibid.*, 210–265 (1942)
F. F. Blicke, "The Mannich Reaction," *ibid.*, 303–341 (1942)
M. Carmack and B. J. Magerlein, "The Willgerodt Reaction," *ibid.*, **3**, 83 (1946).
W. S. Ide and J. S. Buck, "The Synthesis of Benzoins," *ibid.*, **4**, 269 (1948)
P. E. Spoerri and A. S. DuBois, "The Hoesch Synthesis," *ibid.*, **5**, 387 (1949)
M. S. Newman and M. A. Spielman, "The Darzens Glycidic Ester Condensation," *ibid.*, **5**, 413
(1949)
W. S. Johnson and G. H. Daub, "The Stobbe Condensation," *ibid.*, **6**, 1 (1951)
E. S. Wallis, "Molecular Rearrangements," in H. Gilman, *Organic Chemistry*, I, 2nd Ed., 965–
1031, Wiley, New York (1943)
J. R. Johnson, "Modern Electronic Concepts of Valence," *ibid.*, II, 2nd Ed., 1821–1942 (1943)
R. Kuhn, "Synthesis of Polyenes," Pedler Lecture, *J. Chem. Soc.*, 605 (1938)

CHAPTER 30

QUINONES

The generic name quinone is derived from the fact that the first-known and commonest member of the series was discovered in Liebig's laboratory as a product of the oxidation of quinic acid with manganese dioxide and sulfuric acid (Woskresensky, 1838). Quinic acid, a constituent of cinchona bark and of the coffee bean, is a 1,3,4,5-tetrahydroxyhexahydrobenzoic acid of the configuration shown, and its conversion into quinone involves dehy-

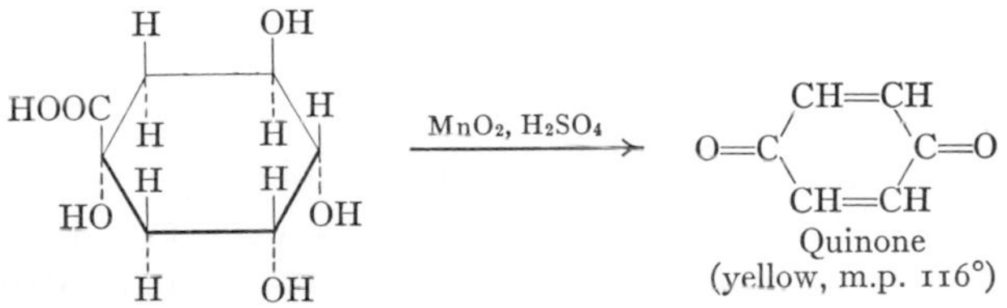

Quinic acid
(monohydrate, m.p. 162°, $[\alpha]_D^{15°} -44°$)

MnO_2, H_2SO_4

Quinone
(yellow, m.p. 116°)

dration, decarboxylation, and oxidation. The yellow reaction product is called quinone, or p-benzoquinone; the isomeric o-benzoquinone is known, but *meta* quinones do not exist.

One characteristic of quinones is color, and a usual differentiation between *para* and *ortho* quinones is that most of the former are yellow and the majority of the latter are orange or red. Particularly beautiful color phenomena often are observed on dusting a few crystals of a quinone on the surface of a dilute aqueous solution of alkali or on a drop or two of concentrated sulfuric acid. Hydroxyqui-

ortho (red)

para (yellow)

Benzoquinones

nones form intensely colored alkali salts, and quinones of all types form vividly colored oxonium salts in concentrated sulfuric acid. The quinone ring contains only two double bonds and is nonaromatic, quinones are analogous to open-chain α,β-unsaturated ketones but considerably more reactive. They are reduced by mild reagents to colorless hydroquinones.

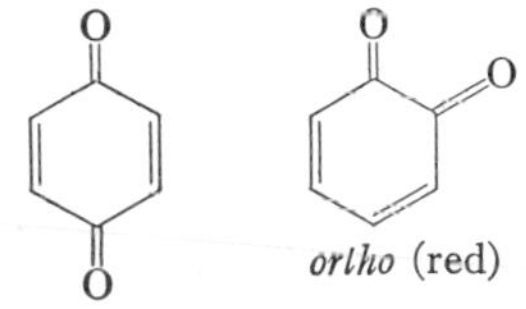

Quinone. — Quinone is the end product of oxidation of aniline in sulfuric acid solution with manganese dioxide. An initially formed free radical condenses with aniline to form a succession of intensely colored dyes, which afford quinone by oxidation and hydrolysis. The crude product is vacuum distilled and reduced with iron to hydroquinone. Quinone is then produced by reoxidation.

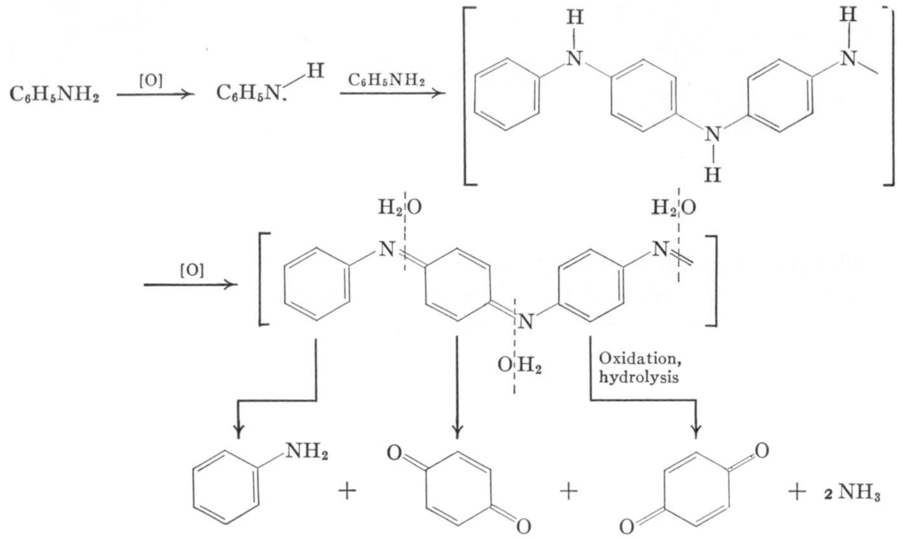

Quinone in the solid state has considerable vapor pressure, and when heated gently sublimes readily to form large yellow crystals.   The substance has a characteristic pungent odor and causes sneezing, particularly in individuals subject to hay fever.   It is attacked by aqueous alkali, with transient coloration, and is rapidly converted into a humuslike material.   Quinone readily combines with proteins, probably by addition reactions involving free amino and sulfhydryl groups; it stains the skin and can be used for tanning leather.

Quinhydrone. — When a yellow solution of quinone in alcohol is added to a colorless solution of hydroquinone in the same solvent, the color deepens to brown-red, and dark green crystals separate.   The substance, quinhydrone (m.p. $171°$), is a molecular complex composed of equimolecular amounts of quinone and hydroquinone.   It is much less soluble than either component, but dissociates to the components to a point of equilibrium.

OXIDATION-REDUCTION POTENTIALS

The reduction of quinone to hydroquinone in aqueous solution is a rapid, quantitative, and reversible process comparable to the reduction of ferric to ferrous ions, and can be formulated as an electrochemical reaction.   A

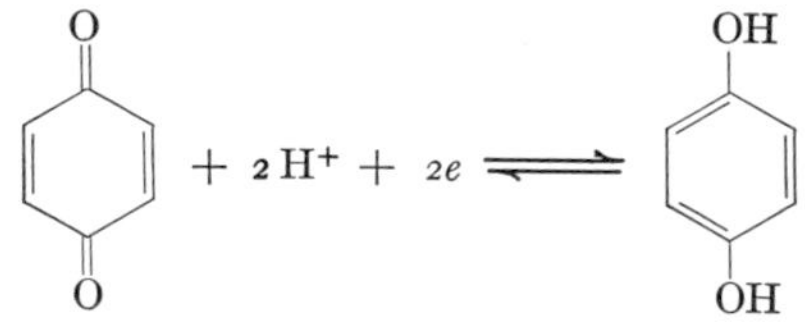

platinum electrode introduced into a solution containing quinone and hydroquinone at a fixed hydrogen-ion concentration acquires an electric potential that can be measured by making connection through a conducting liquid to a reference half-cell such as a calomel or hydrogen electrode. The electrode potential (E) of the organic half-cell is dependent on the concentrations of the species entering into equilibrium, namely quinone, hydroquinone, and hydrogen ions, in accordance with the equation:

$$E^{25°} = E_0 + 0.05912 \log [H^+] + 0.02956 \log \frac{[Quinone]}{[Hydroquinone]}$$

The quantity E_0 is a normal potential characteristic of a specific quinone-hydroquinone system, and is defined as the potential of the half-cell when the hydrogen-ion concentration is unity and the concentration of the quinone, or oxidant, is equal to that of the hydroquinone, or reductant. Thus the second term in the right-hand side of the equation is reduced to zero if $[H^+] = 1$, and the third term disappears if [Quinone] = [Hydroquinone]. A method that ensures the latter condition is to employ quinhydrone for the measurement, for the complex dissociates to give equivalent amounts of the oxidant and reductant. The only variable then remaining is the hydrogen-ion concentration, which can be determined; but since the expression $0.05912 \log[H^+]$ is the potential of a hydrogen electrode (at 25°), a technique of measuring the normal potential is to make connection between a half-cell containing a solution of quinhydrone in a given buffer and a hydrogen electrode in the same buffer. The hydrogen-ion potential on the two sides is then the same, and since the concentration of quinone is equal to that of hydroquinone, the cell potential, or the potential difference between the two half-cells, is equal to the normal potential of the quinone-hydroquinone system. The value of the normal potential for the system from p-benzoquinone is 0.699 v. With this constant accurately known, the hydrogen-ion concentration of a given solution can be determined: quinhydrone is added to the solution, connection is made to a reference electrode, the potential (E) of the organic half-cell is measured, and the hydrogen-ion concentration is calculated from the expression: $0.05912 \log[H^+] = E^{25°} - 0.699$.

In instances other than the specific one cited the normal potential can be determined by titrating potentiometrically either a solution of the quinone with a reducing agent or one of the hydroquinone with an oxidizing agent, for the mid-point of either titration curve corresponds to equivalence of oxidant and reductant. If a hydrogen electrode containing the same solution used to dissolve the organic reactants is used as the reference half-cell, normal potentials can be determined even in alcoholic solutions of unknown hydrogen-ion concentration, and hence quinones insoluble in water can be characterized. The normal potential provides a precise characterization of the oxidizing power of the quinone or, conversely, of the reducing intensity of the hydroquinone. Values for quinones derived from benzene and from some of the polynuclear hydrocarbons are shown (determinations at 25°). Diphenoquinone, with the unsaturated conjugated quinonoid system extending throughout two rings, has a very high potential

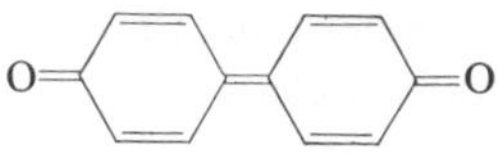

Diphenoquinone
E_0alc. 0.954 v.

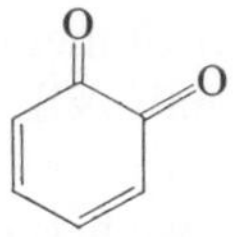

o-Benzoquinone
E_0aq., 30° 0.792 v.

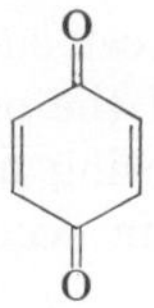

Quinone
E_0aq. 0.699 v.
E_0alc. 0.715 v.

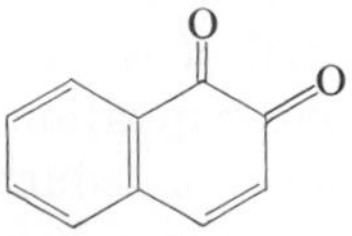

β-Naphthoquinone
E_0aq. 0.555 v.
E_0alc. 0.576 v.

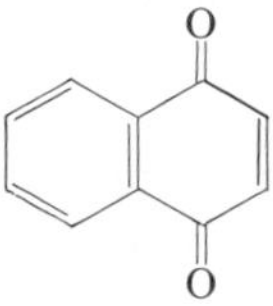

α-Naphthoquinone
E_0aq. 0.470 v.
E_0alc. 0.484 v.

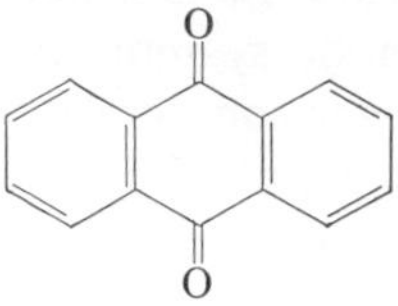

Anthraquinone
E_0alc. 0.154 v.

and is a powerful oxidizing agent. Since *ortho* quinones of the benzene and naphthalene series have potentials higher by 85–95 mv. than the isomeric *para* quinones, the former structure has a higher energy content than the latter. Comparison of benzoquinones with corresponding naphthoquinones indicates a regular difference in potential of 230–240 mv., which represents a diminished energy content of the bicyclic compounds. Stabilization attending fusion of a benzene ring to a double bond of either *o*- or *p*-benzoquinone can be attributed to the fact that the double bond is then incorporated in the aromatic nucleus and hence is relatively inert. In anthraquinone both the otherwise reactive quinonoid double bonds participate in benzenoid ring systems; hence the quinone has a low potential. Conversely, its reduction product, anthrahydroquinone, is a powerful reducing agent.

Substituent groups often exert a marked influence on the oxidation-reduction potential in either a positive or negative sense, as illustrated in

TABLE 30.1. EFFECT OF 2-SUBSTITUENTS ON THE POTENTIAL
OF 1,4 NAPHTHOQUINONE

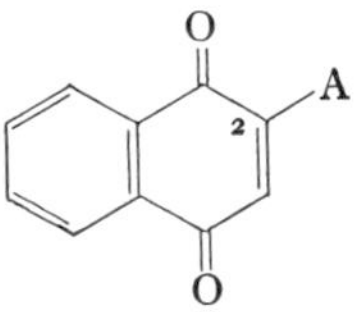

Substituent	Effect, in mv.	Substituent	Effect, in mv.
$NHCH_3$	−252	$NHCOCH_3$	−67
NH_2	−210	C_6H_5	−32
$N(CH_3)_2$	−181	$OCOCH_3$	−9
OH	−128	Cl	+24
OCH_3	−131	SO_3Na	+69
CH_3	−76	$SO_2C_6H_4CH_3$	+121

Table 30.1 for a series of α-naphthoquinone derivatives (Fieser[1] and Fieser,[2] 1935). *m*-Directing groups, such as NO_2, CN, SO_2Ar, COAr, COOH, and SO_3H, as well as halogens, raise the potential of the parent quinone, whereas a potential-lowering effect is exerted by the following groups, arranged approximately in order of decreasing effectiveness: NHR, NH_2, $N(CH_3)_2$, OH, OR, CH_3, $NHCOCH_3$, C_6H_5, $OCOCH_3$. The relationships are those expected from the course of aromatic substitutions. Strongly unsaturated groups and halogen atoms are electron-attracting and tend to increase the attractive power of the system terminating in the oxygen atoms for external electrons, the acquisition of which converts the quinone into the hydroquinone ion. Combination of this ion with protons is a secondary process occurring to an extent dependent on the acidity of the solution; if reduction is accomplished at a sufficiently high pH, no association occurs and electron transfer is the sole process involved. Amino, hydroxyl, alkyl,

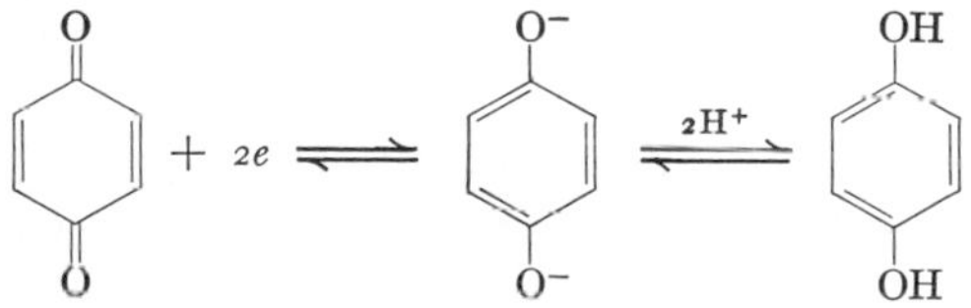

and other electron-repelling substituents decrease affinity for electrons and hence lower the potential.

Oxidation-reduction potential data are valuable in interpretation of the behavior of those hydroxy- and aminoquinones that can exist in tautomeric forms, for example 2-hydroxy-1,4-naphthoquinone. The tautomer of

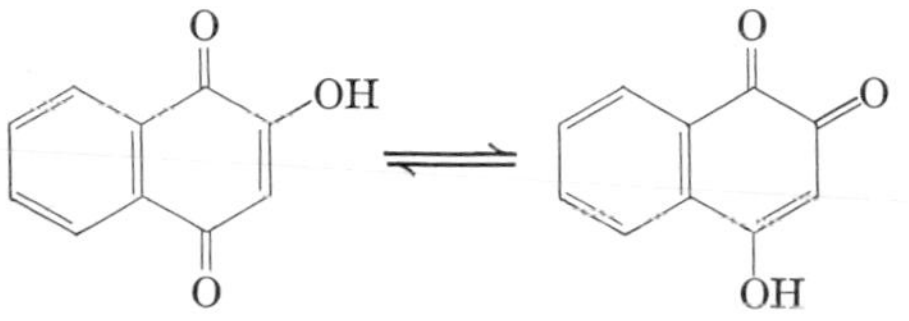

α-Form $\qquad$ β-Form

2-Hydroxy-1,4-naphthoquinone

(yellow, m.p. 192° dec., $E_0^{alc.}$ 0.356 v., pK_a 4.0)

lower potential and consequent lower energy content must predominate in solutions, and a reliable estimate of relative potentials can be made from

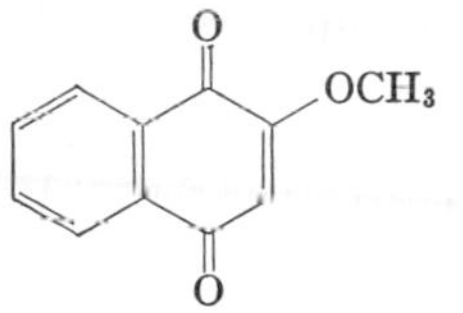

2-Methoxy-1,4-naphthoquinone $\qquad$ 4-Methoxy-1,2-naphthoquinone

(yellow, m.p. 183.5°, $E_0^{alc.}$ 0.353 v.) $\quad$ (orange-yellow, m.p. 190°, $E_0^{alc.}$ 0.433 v.)

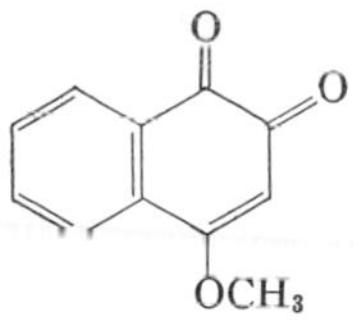

---

[1] Louis F. Fieser, b. 1899 Columbus, Ohio; Ph.D. Harvard (Conant); Harvard Univ.

[2] Mary Fieser, b. 1909 Atchison, Kansas; stud. Harvard (L. F. Fieser); Harvard Univ.

values found for the corresponding ethers, which are produced together in
the reaction of the silver salt of the hydroxy compound with methyl iodide.
The β-quinone ether has a potential higher by 80 mv. than the α-isomer,
and a difference of similar magnitude must exist between the hydroxy compounds; hence the α-form is the more stable.   The difference corresponds to
a difference of 3.7 kg.-cal. in the free energy of reduction.   The relative
abundance of the tautomers can be estimated from the following expression
correlating the equilibrium constant (K = [α-Form]/[β-Form]) with the
oxidation-reduction potentials of the two forms (Fieser, 1928):

$$\log K^{25°} = \frac{E_0\beta\text{-Form} - E_0\alpha\text{-Form}}{0.02956}$$

If the difference in potential is 80 mv., only 0.2% of the β-form is present in
the equilibrium mixture.   The conclusion is supported by chemical evidence;
for example, by the fact that esterification of the strongly acidic hydroxy
compound with diazomethane gives 2-methoxy-1,4-naphthoquinone as the
only isolated product (87% yield).

The aminoquinone 4-amino-1,2-naphthoquinone (Ia) offers the possibility of tautomerism to a hydroxyquinonimine (Ib).   One tautomer has a

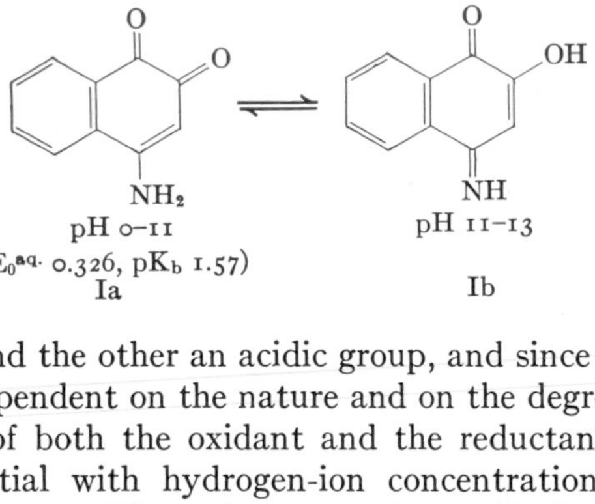

NH₂ form:
pH 0–11
($E_0^{aq.}$ 0.326, pK$_b$ 1.57)
Ia

NH form:
pH 11–13
Ib

basic substituent and the other an acidic group, and since the potential in a
given solution is dependent on the nature and on the degree of ionization of
functional groups of both the oxidant and the reductant, analysis of the
variation of potential with hydrogen-ion concentration indicates which
tautomer predominates.   The substance exists exclusively in the aminoquinone form Ia in all pH regions except those of extreme alkalinity.   Both
tautomers participate in the equilibrium in a transition region (pH 10.4 to
11.5), but beyond this point the hydroxyquinonimine form Ib becomes the
form of lower potential and hence the predominant tautomer.   This tautomerism accounts for the fact that the substance dissolves freely in sodium

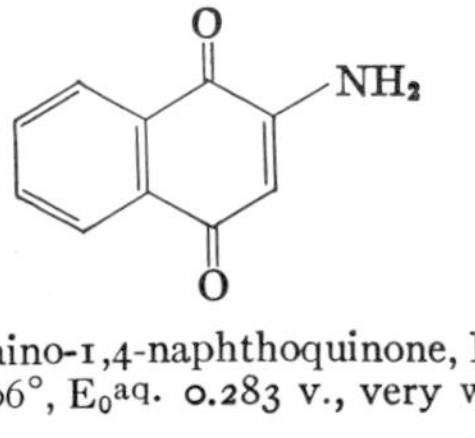

2-Amino-1,4-naphthoquinone, II
(red, m.p. 206°, $E_0^{aq.}$ 0.283 v., very weak base)

hydroxide solution but, unlike hydroxynaphthoquinone, does not dissolve in sodium carbonate solution. The amino derivative of α-naphthoquinone, II, is found by potentiometric analysis to exist exclusively in the amino quinone form throughout the entire pH range; it does not dissolve even in strong alkali.

PREPARATION

The general procedure for preparation of a quinone starts with a phenol or an amine, followed by introduction of either a hydroxyl or an amino group in an *ortho* or *para* position and oxidation of the intermediate in acid solution. The initial oxidation product of p-aminophenol, p-quinonimine, is extremely sensitive and has been isolated and characterized potentiometrically only by special techniques; even in an oxidation conducted at o° in dilute acid solution, it is transient and undergoes hydrolysis to quinone. p-Phenylenediamine similarly is converted into quinone through the easily

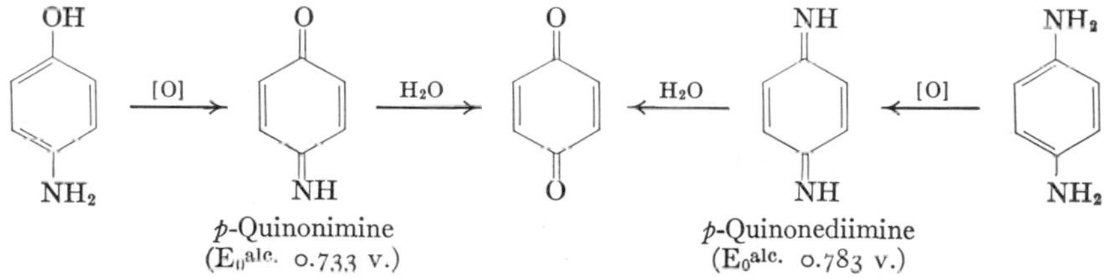

p-Quinonimine
($E_0^{alc.}$ o.733 v.)

p-Quinonediimine
($E_0^{alc.}$ o.783 v.)

hydrolyzed p-quinonediimine. The highly pigmented N-phenyl derivatives of quinonimine and quinonediimine, indophenol and indamine, are relatively stable, crystallizable substances but they also can be hydrolyzed to quinone. One route to a bifunctional compound suitable for oxidation is illustrated by the preparation of β-naphthoquinone from β-naphthol. The naphthol is coupled in alkaline solution with diazotized sulfanilic acid, and the azo dye Orange II, without being isolated, is reduced with sodium hydrosulfite and

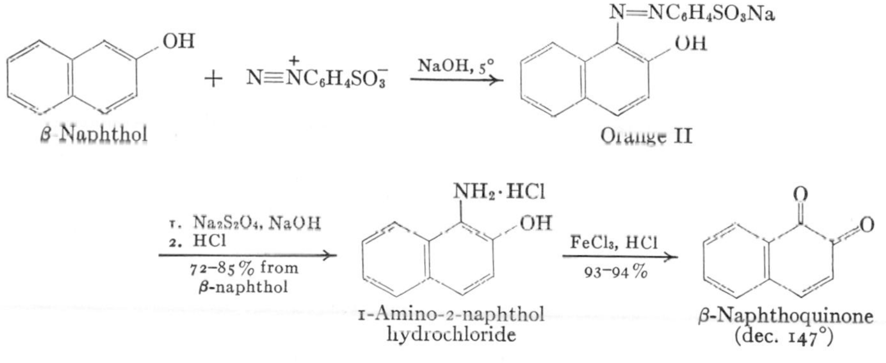

β-Naphthol

+ N≡NC₆H₄SO₃⁻

NaOH, 5°

Orange II

1. Na₂S₂O₄, NaOH
2. HCl
72-85% from
β-naphthol

1-Amino-2-naphthol
hydrochloride

FeCl₃, HCl
93-94%

β-Naphthoquinone
(dec. 147°)

the aminonaphthol is purified as the hydrochloride, which is oxidized with ferric chloride to the quinone.

Some quinones are so reactive and sensitive that oxidation must be carried out under carefully controlled conditions. Investigators attempted without success to convert catechol into a quinone till willstätter (1904), recognizing that o-benzoquinone is extremely sensitive to water, devised a preparation that consists in oxidation in absolute ether solution with carefully dehydrated silver oxide in the presence of fused sodium sulfate to absorb the water formed:

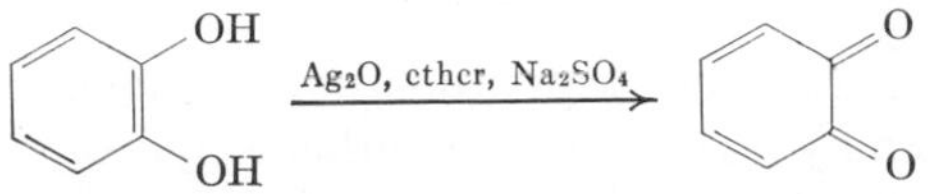

REACTIONS

1,4-Additions. — Quinones are more reactive than open-chain α,β-unsaturated ketones, and show a greater diversification in the reagents with which they combine. Reactions of one type, exemplified by the reaction of quinone with dry hydrogen chloride, can be represented as 1,4-additions, followed by enolization, but the mechanism is not known. Additions con-

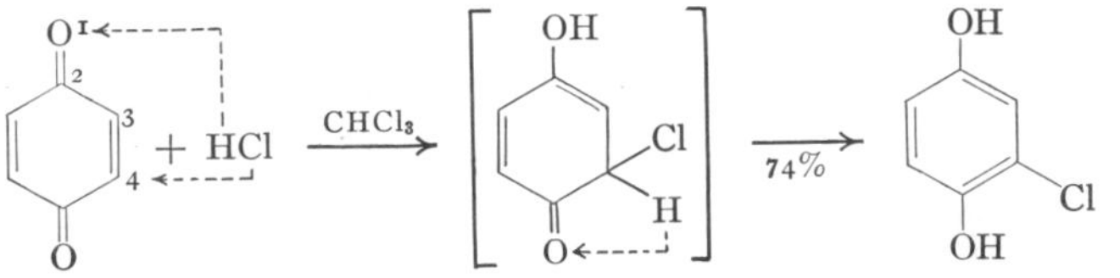

Chlorohydroquinone
(m.p. 106°)

ducted in aqueous or alcoholic solution are attended with oxidation-reduction equilibration of product with starting material. Thus aniline reacts

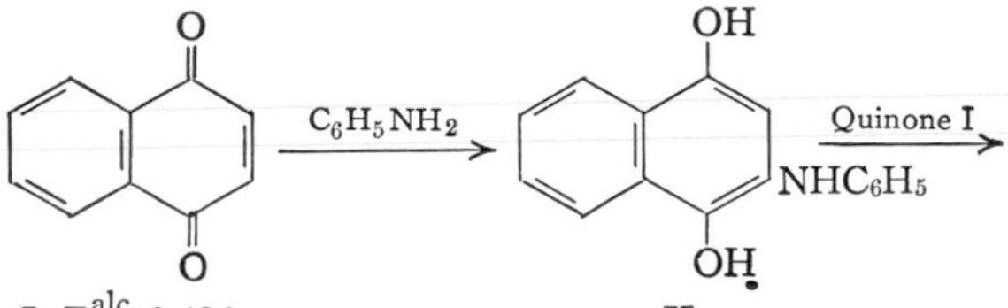

I, $E_o^{alc.}$ 0.484v.   II

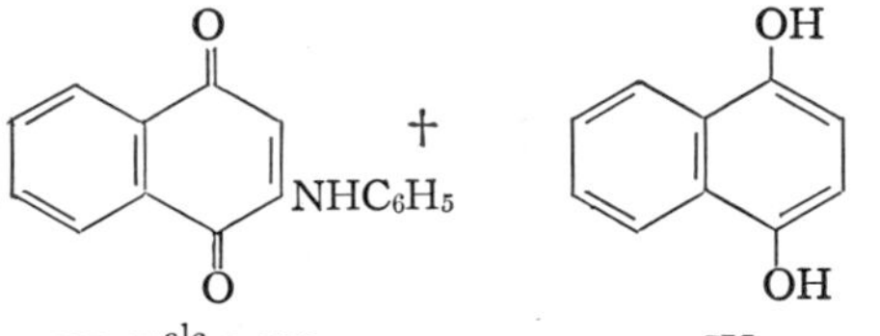

III, $E_o^{alc.}$ 0.286v.   IV

with α-naphthoquinone (I) in alcoholic solution with prompt separation of red needles of 2-anilino-1,4-naphthoquinone (III), formed by oxidation of the initial product II by I. The potential of the substituted quinone is so far below that of the starting material that the reaction is practically complete; hence two moles of I are required to produce one of III. In bisulfite addition, the group introduced raises the potential and oxidation of the substituted product does not occur. The reaction is applicable to nitroso-phenols, in equilibrium with quinone oximes, as in the standard preparation of 1,2-naphthoquinone-4-sulfonate. On oxidation of the aminonaphthol-

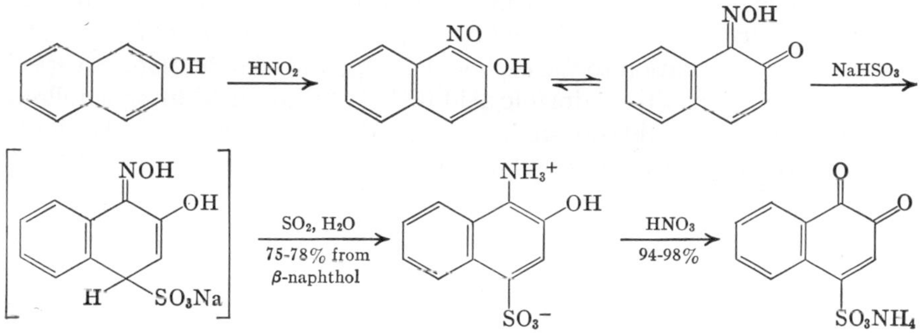

sulfonic acid with nitric acid the ammonia liberated on cleavage of the imino group forms a salt with the sulfonic acid. Reactions of the quinone-sulfonate that probably proceed by 1,4-additions and illustrate the reactivity specific to quinones are as follows:

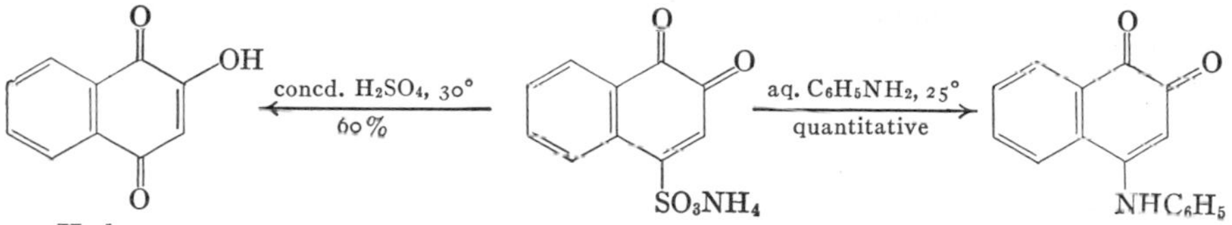

2-Hydroxy-1,4-
naphthoquinone

4-Anilino-1,2-
naphthoquinone
(red, dec. 260°)

The Thiele reaction (1898), in which acetic anhydride is added to a quinone under catalysis by sulfuric acid or boron fluoride etherate with formation of the hydroxyhydroquinone triacetate, affords a route to hy-

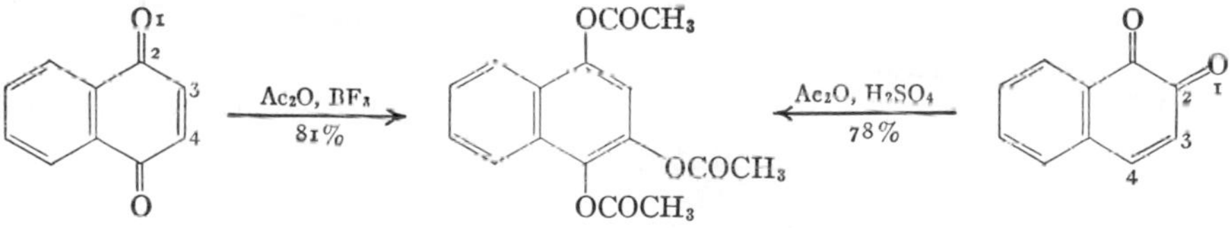

2-Hydroxy-1,4-naphthohydroquinone
triacetate (m.p. 136°)

droxyquinones. Thus the product from either α- or β-naphthoquinone on alkaline hydrolysis and air oxidation gives 2-hydroxy-1,4-naphthoquinone. The Thiele reaction is blocked by a 2-methyl group in the *para* naphthoquinone but not by a 3-methyl group in the *ortho* isomer. In the benzoquinone series a 2-methoxyl or 2-methyl group directs the entering acetoxyl group to the 5-position, and methyl substituents in the 2,6- and 2,3,5-positions, but not in the 2,5-positions, inhibit the Thiele reaction.

1,4-Additions to benzo- and naphthoquinones occur with a number of other reagents of the HA type, including hydrogen cyanide, mercaptans, benzenesulfinic acid, benzene in the presence of aluminum chloride, malonic ester, cyanoacetic ester, and acetoacetic ester. Grignard reagents react with substituted and unsubstituted quinones to give mixtures of products of 1,4-addition, of addition to the carbonyl group, and of reduction. A special case is the reaction with hydrazoic acid (HN_3); an initial addition is followed by intramolecular oxidation-reduction, with transference of the hydroquinone hydrogen atoms to the azido group, which suffers reductive cleavage:

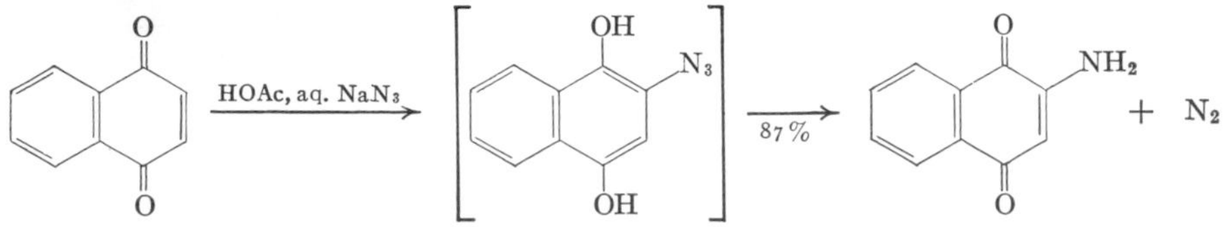

The reaction of the silver salt of 2-hydroxy-1,4-naphthoquinone with alkyl halides affords a 4-alkoxy-1,2-naphthoquinone along with the product of normal replacement. Formation of the *o*-quinonoid isomer probably proceeds by 1,4-addition. The isomers are easily separated by extraction of

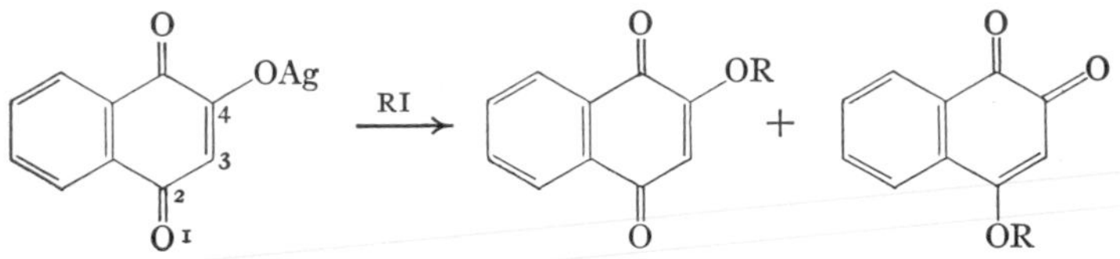

(by replacement) (by 1,4-addition)

the *ortho* quinone ether with aqueous sodium bisulfite, which dissolves the substance as a labile addition complex that subsequently can be decomposed with acid or with sodium carbonate; the *para* quinone reacts with bisulfite only to a minor extent.

Mercaptans react with quinones by addition and oxidation-reduction equilibrium to give thio-substituted quinones, and all free positions in the quinonoid ring are attacked. Thus toluquinone reacts with thioglycolic acid ($HSCH_2CO_2H$) to give the trithioacetic acid derivative. The reduced form of glutathione, GSH, adds readily in the same way. The product is a

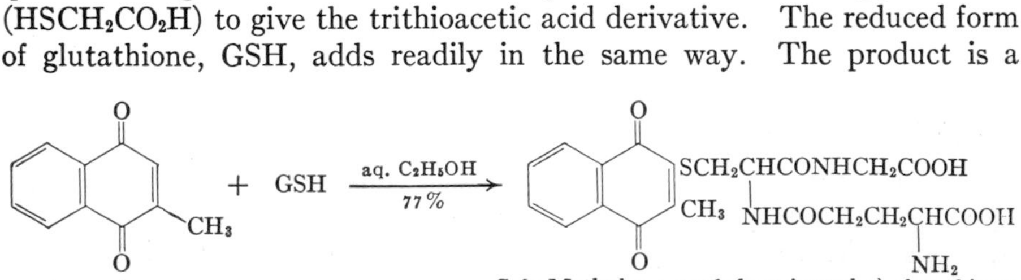

(excess) S-(2-Methyl-1,4-naphthoquinonyl-3)-glutathione

conjugated tripeptide that differs from glutathione in having in place of the sulfhydryl-disulfide system a quinonoid group capable of establishing an oxidoreduction system. Proteins containing free sulfhydryl groups likewise form conjugates with methylnaphthoquinone, as established by the appearance of characteristic ultraviolet absorption bands that persist after repeated purification by precipitation with ammonium sulfate.

Ethylenic Additions. — Methylnaphthoquinone forms a crystalline dibromide from which hydrogen bromide is easily eliminated with production of a bromoquinone, and it reacts with hydrogen peroxide under basic cataly-

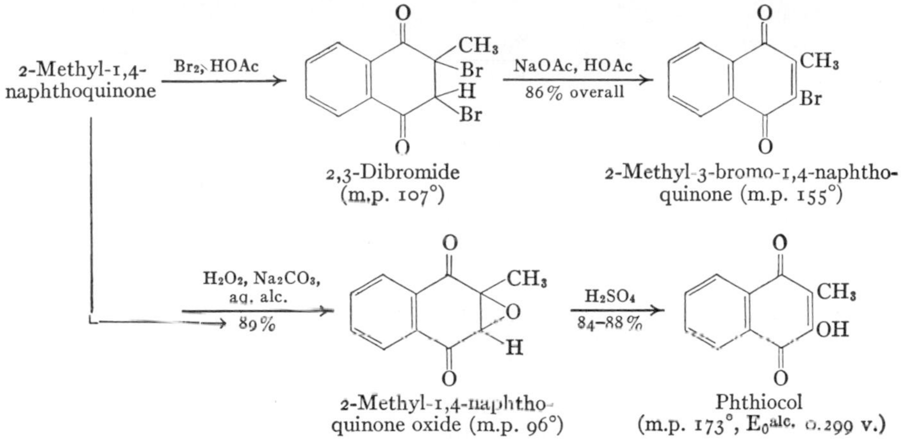

2-Methyl-1,4-naphthoquinone $\xrightarrow{\text{Br}_2,\ \text{HOAc}}$ 2,3-Dibromide (m.p. 107°) $\xrightarrow[\text{86\% overall}]{\text{NaOAc, HOAc}}$ 2-Methyl-3-bromo-1,4-naphthoquinone (m.p. 155°)

$\xrightarrow[\text{89\%}]{\substack{\text{H}_2\text{O}_2,\ \text{Na}_2\text{CO}_3, \\ \text{aq. alc.}}}$ 2-Methyl-1,4-naphthoquinone oxide (m.p. 96°) $\xrightarrow[\text{84–88\%}]{\text{H}_2\text{SO}_4}$ Phthiocol (m.p. 173°, $E_0{}^{\text{alc.}}$ 0.299 v.)

sis to give an oxide. The oxide ring is easily opened by the action of concentrated sulfuric acid in the cold, and hence combination of the two reactions constitutes an efficient synthesis of phthiocol.

One example of the Diels-Alder reaction of quinones has been cited (p. 310). p-Benzoquinone can be converted efficiently into either a mono or di adduct of butadiene; the former (1) is convertible by enolization (2) and

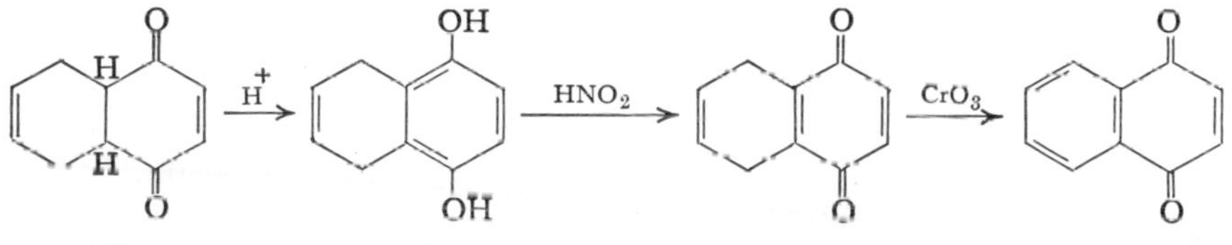

(1)   (2)   (3)   (4)

oxidation (3, 4) into α-naphthoquinone (overall yield 76%), and the di adduct affords anthraquinone on air oxidation in an alkaline medium.

Methyl groups substituted on one or both of the ethylenic carbon atoms do not stop the reaction but necessitate a slight increase in the reaction

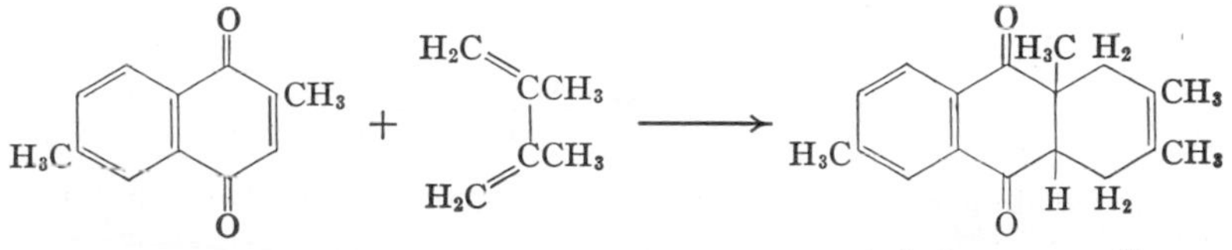

(colorless, m.p. 77°)

temperature. Halogen substituents likewise fail to interfere with addition of a diene, and in the β-naphthoquinone series such substitution stabilizes the otherwise sensitive quinone ring. Thus 3-chloro-1,2-naphthoquinone can be employed in a Diels-Alder reaction, whereas the parent quinone is destroyed.

Additions occur with unsaturated nitrogen compounds of the diazoalkane and aryl azide types. Diazomethane reacts with α-naphthoquinone to give a hydroquinone (alkali-soluble), which in the course of recrystallization is

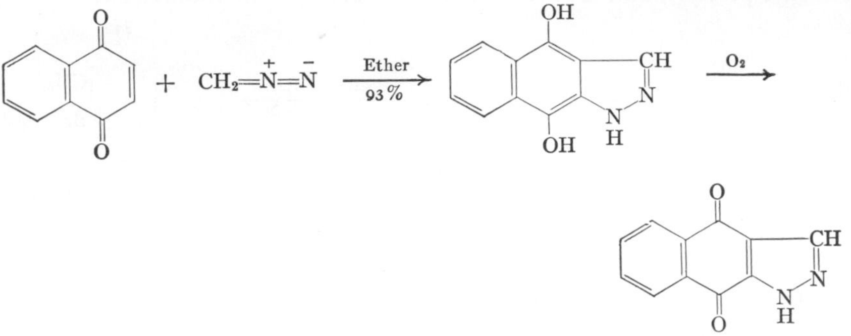

lin-Naphthindazole-4,9-quinone
(m.p. 349°, $E_0^{alc.}$ 0.154 v.)

oxidized by air to the quinone. The resulting product, *lin*-naphthindazole-4,9-quinone, has a potential practically identical with that of anthraquinone, which is evidence that the heterocyclic pyrazole ring is comparable in aromaticity to the benzene ring. Similar additions occur with phenyl azide and methyl azide to give further analogs of anthraquinone, obtained in either the oxidized or reduced form. Diphenyldiazomethane, prepared by

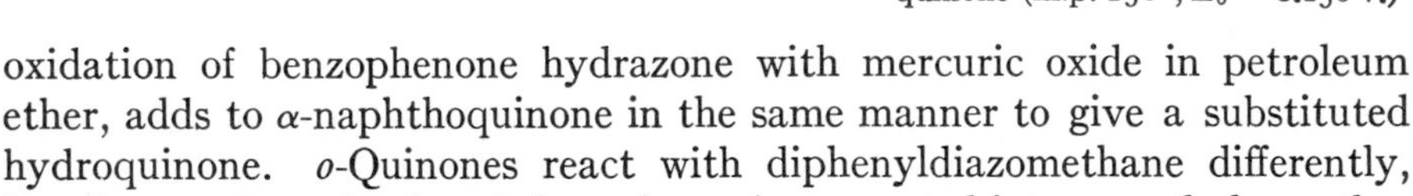

α-Naphthoquinone + CH₃N=N=N
Methylazide

1-Methyl-*lin*-naphthotriazole-4,9-quinone (m.p. 250°, $E_0^{alc.}$ 0.256 v.)

oxidation of benzophenone hydrazone with mercuric oxide in petroleum ether, adds to α-naphthoquinone in the same manner to give a substituted hydroquinone. *o*-Quinones react with diphenyldiazomethane differently, for nitrogen is evolved and the quinone is converted into a methylene ether derivative of its hydroquinone.

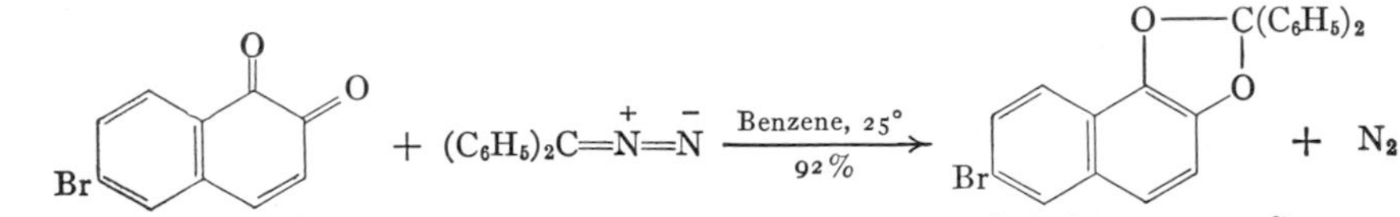

6-Bromo-1,2-naphthoquinone
(orange-red, dec. 168°)

+ (C₆H₅)₂C=N=N   Benzene, 25°   92%

(colorless, m.p. 151°)   + N₂

Substitutions. — In view of the sensitivity of quinones, it is not surprising that aromatic substitution reactions are applicable only rarely. The nitration of β-naphthoquinone is particularly remarkable because this quinone cannot be recrystallized without undergoing some decomposition

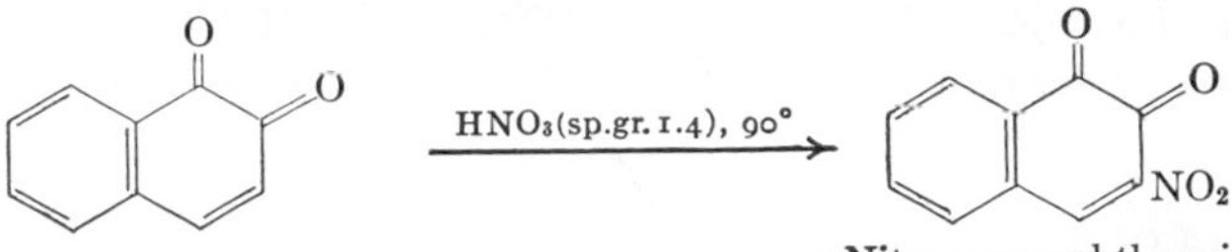

$$\xrightarrow{\text{HNO}_3(\text{sp.gr. 1.4}),\ 90°}$$

3-Nitro-1,2-naphthoquinone
(red, m.p. 158°)

and because in aqueous solutions of hydrochloric or sulfuric acid it is converted into products of dimerization and hydration, depending on the concentration. β-Naphthoquinone also can be brominated in the 3-position (67% yield). Addition rather than substitution of halogen occurs in the *para* quinone series.

Quinones are particularly prone to undergo substitutions involving free radicals. One example is the reaction with diazonium salts (Günther, 1930). In an aqueous alcoholic solution of the components, weakly acidified with acetic acid, nitrogen is evolved and the aryl group of the diazonium salt enters the quinone ring. The reaction of benzenediazonium chloride with

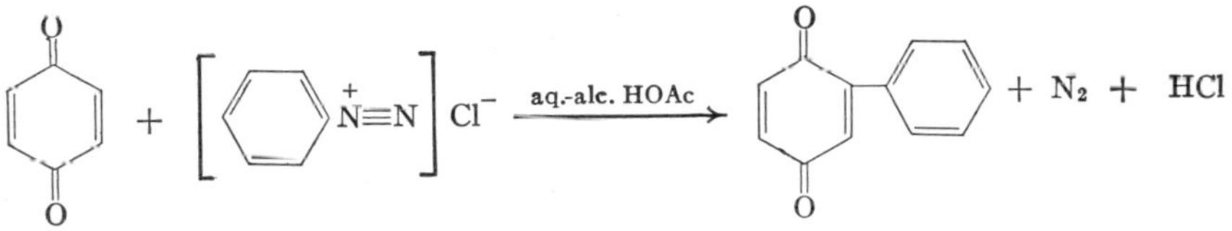

$$\xrightarrow{\text{aq.-alc. HOAc}} \quad + \ N_2 \ + \ HCl$$

2-Phenyl-1,4-benzoquinone
(m.p. 114°, $E_0^{\text{alc.}}$ 0.694 v.)

p-benzoquinone affords the monophenyl derivative, and with excess reagent the 2,5-diphenylquinone and the tetraphenylquinone are produced, though in low yield. 2-Hydroxy-1,4-naphthoquinone reacts partly by coupling and partly to give the 3-aryl derivative in 10–30% yield.

Another reaction that apparently proceeds by a free-radical mechanism is alkylation of the quinone nucleus with either an acyl peroxide or a lead tetraacylate (Fieser *et al.*, 1942). When a solution of 2 methyl-1,4-naphthoquinone in acetic acid is warmed with slightly more than one equivalent of acetyl peroxide or with 3–4 equivalents of lead tetraacetate, a brisk reaction ensues with evolution of gas, and the starting material is converted into the 2,3-dimethyl compound. In the warm solution acetyl peroxide

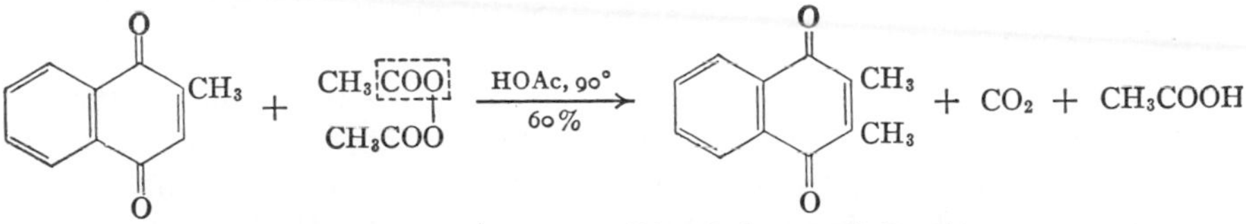

$$\xrightarrow[60\%]{\text{HOAc, }90°} \quad + \ CO_2 \ + \ CH_3COOH$$

2,3-Dimethyl-1,4-naphthoquinone
(m.p. 127°)

probably decomposes with liberation of carbon dioxide and formation of methyl and acetate radicals; the latter radical functions as acceptor for the hydrogen atom of the quinonoid nucleus, while the methyl radical substitutes at the position vacated. Identified by-products are of the types: CO_2, RCO_2H, RH, RR, $ROCOCH_3$, ROH, and $ROCOR$. Lead tetraacetate perhaps undergoes decomposition in large part to the same reactive species:

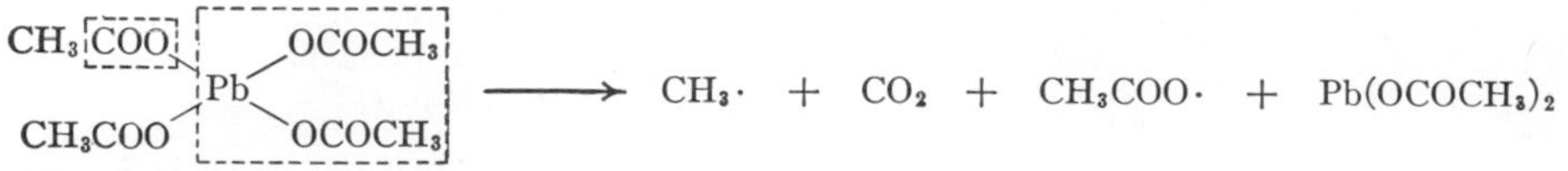

$$CH_3COO \quad OCOCH_3 \atop CH_3COO \quad Pb \quad OCOCH_3 \longrightarrow CH_3 \cdot + CO_2 + CH_3COO \cdot + Pb(OCOCH_3)_2$$

NATURALLY OCCURRING QUINONES

A considerable number of pigments characterized as quinones have been isolated from high and lower plants, and a few members of the series have been found in animal organisms. Some are dyes, some are growth factors, some are antibiotics, some catalyze respiratory processes, and some are respiration inhibitors. Although the following discussion is limited to benzo-, naphtho-, and phenanthrenequinones, many anthraquinones are produced by molds, and pigments from aphids have been characterized as perylenequinones (p. 780).

Benzoquinones. — A number of mold pigments have been characterized as benzoquinones or dibenzoquinones (Raistrick, Oxford, 1938), for example, fumigatin (*Aspergillus fumigatus* Fresenius), spinulosin (*Penicillium spinulosum* Thom), and phoenicin (*P. phoeniceum* van Beyma). Isolation of

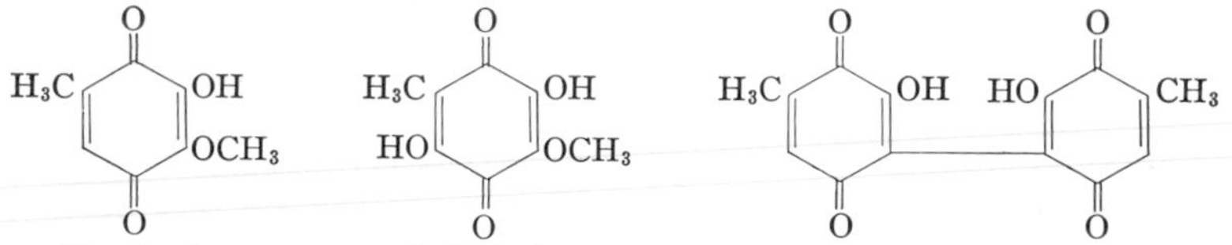

Fumigatin
(brown, m.p. 116°)

Spinulosin
(purple-bronze, m.p. 203°)

Phoenicin
(yellow-brown, m.p. 231°)

fumigatin hydroquinone along with the pigment under conditions indicative of the presence of both substances in the growing mold is regarded as an indication that the oxidation-reduction system functions in the metabolism of the organism. Spinulosin has been prepared from fumigatin by Thiele addition of acetic anhydride, hydrolysis of the resulting tetraacetate, and oxidation. Phoenicin increases the respiration of washed unpigmented cells of *Bacillus pyocyaneus* by as much as 200-300% at very low concentrations, and may function as a respiratory catalyst by virtue of the reversible oxidation-reduction system.

2,6-Dimethoxyquinone (m.p. 250°) has been isolated from *Adonis vernalis* L. (W. Karrer, 1930); it is obtainable in 80% yield by nitric acid oxidation of pyrogallol trimethyl ether. Toluquinone, ethylquinone, and methoxyquinone have been isolated from flour beetle (P. Alexander; A. R.

Todd, J. R. Loconti). The secretion of the Uruguayan arachnid *Gonyleptide* contains an antibiotic pigment (C. Estable) characterized as a mixture of 2,3-dimethylquinone, I, 2,5-dimethylquinone, II, and 2,3,5-trimethylquinone, III (Fieser and Ardao, 1955). The mixture resulting from treatment of a 115-mg. sample with butadiene was reduced with hydrosulfite and the hydroquinones of II and III extracted with alkali from an ethereal solution retaining the adduct of I; the mixture of II and III on Thiele reaction and steam distillation afforded III in the distillate and the Thiele product from II in the residue. Hydroxybenzoquinones with long-chain alkyl groups also have been encountered. **Embelin** is found in the berries of an Indian shrub (*Embelia ribes*). **Rapanone,** a higher homolog having two additional

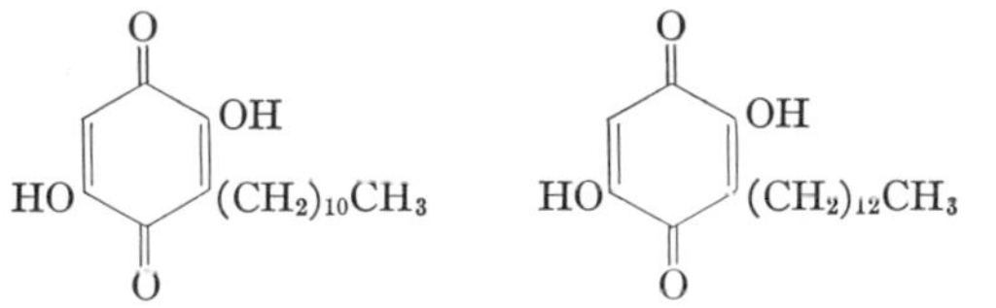

Embelin
(orange-yellow, m.p. 142°)

Rapanone
(orange-yellow, m.p. 140°)

methylene groups in the alkyl chain, occurs in *Rapanea Maximowiczii* and in *Oxalis purpurata* Jacq. Both have been synthesized by peroxide alkylation of 2,5-dihydroxyquinone.

The pigment **perezone,** isolated from the root of various Mexican species of *Perezonia* in yields up to 3.6%, is a *p*-benzoquinone having a methyl, a hydroxyl, and a branched-chain unsaturated C_8-group (Kögl,[3] 1935). The structure is divisible into isoprene units, as shown by the dotted

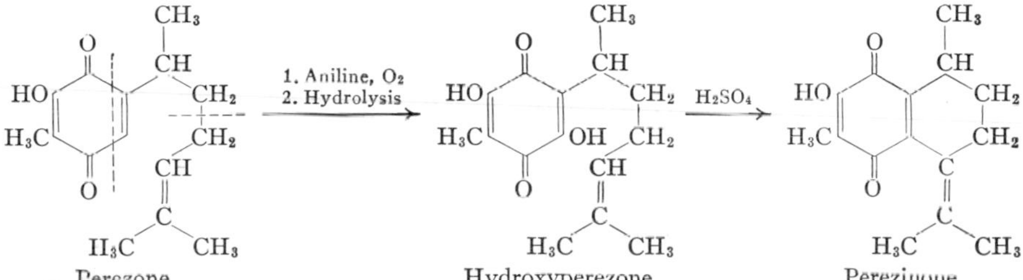

Perezone
(orange, m.p. 103°,
$[\alpha]_D^{20°} - 17°$)

Hydroxyperezone
(m.p. 130°)

Perezinone
(m.p. 145°)

lines, and it is thus a quinone of the sesquiterpene series. The free position in the quinone ring can be hydroxylated by formation and hydrolysis of the anilino derivative, and the hydroxy compound undergoes cyclodehydration under the influence of sulfuric acid to give perezinone.

Fungus Pigments. — The metabolism of parasitic fungi is fundamentally different from that of assimilating plants and the fungus pigments constitute a rather distinct chemical class. Three have been characterized by Kögl as 2,5-diphenyl-1,4-benzoquinone derivatives; the fundamental

---

[3] Fritz Kögl, b. 1897 Munich; Dr. Ing. Munich (Wieland, H. Fischer); Utrecht, Netherlands

skeletal unit is the hydrocarbon terphenyl. **Polyporic acid,** shown by degradation (Kögl) and synthesis (R. Adams) to be the 3,6-dihydroxy derivative of the diphenylquinone, has been extracted in yields as high as 18% of the dry weight of a fungus (*Polyporus nidulans* Pers.) found growing on diseased oak trees. **Atromentin**, a dihydroxy derivative of polyporic

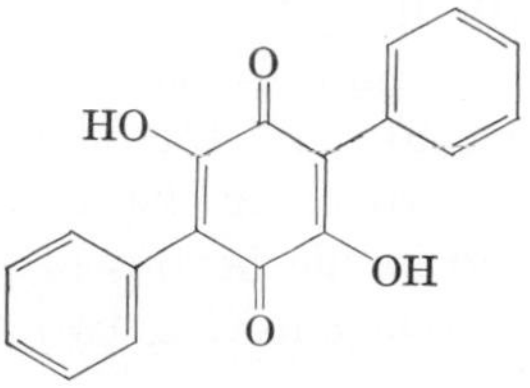

Polyporic acid
(brown-violet, m.p. 118°,
deep violet in aq. NH₃)

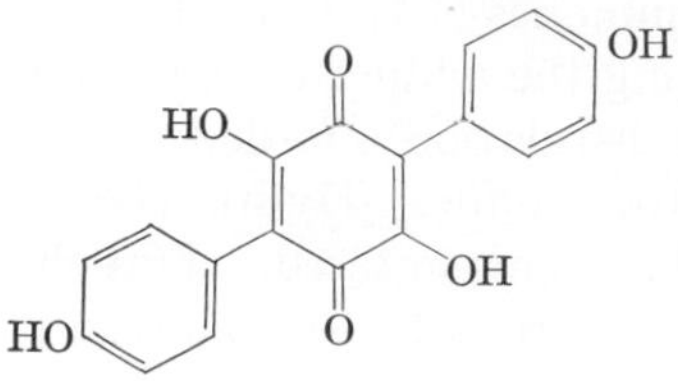

Atromentin
(bronze crystals with a
metallic luster, no m.p.)

acid, is found in a fungus growing on old oak trunks. More material is obtained by direct solvent extraction from the highly pigmented fungus collected in the autumn than from the superficially colored fresh fungus.

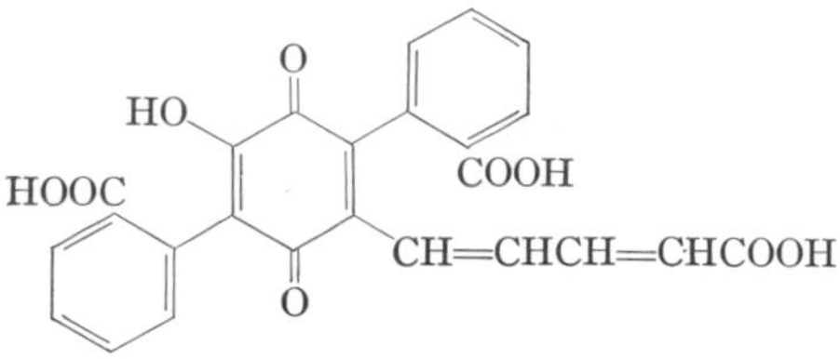

Muscarufin
(orange-red, m.p. 275.5°)

The latter contains substantially the same total amount of material (2%) but the bulk of pigment is present in the reduced, or leuco, form. The pigment **muscarufin** is present, probably as a glycoside, in the reddish skins of the common poisonous mushroom, or fly agaric, *Amanita muscaria* L. The substance has been isolated by alcohol extraction of the skins in yield amounting to 850 mg. from 500 kg. of the fresh mushrooms. It is a derivative of 2,5-diphenyl-1,4-benzoquinone with o-carboxyl groups in the aryl substituents, and a dienic acid side chain.

Thelephoric acid, found in fungi of several *Thelephora* species, is a phenanthrenequinone derivative (Kögl, 1930), but nevertheless bears some resemblance to the foregoing compounds. One ring (C) corresponds to the reduced form of a *p*-benzoquinone nucleus and bears a dienic acid side chain identical with that found in muscarufin; the attached phenyl group (A) carries a *p*-hydroxyl group (compare atromentin) and a carboxyl substituent (compare muscarufin).

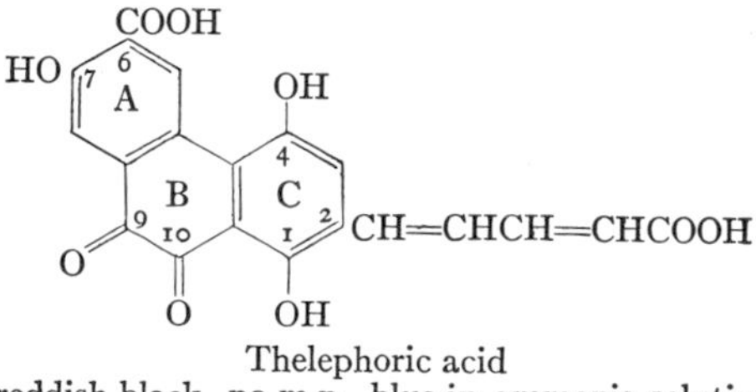

Thelephoric acid
(reddish black, no m.p., blue in ammonia solution)

α-Naphthoquinones. — A yellow pigment **lawsone** is extracted from leaves of the tropical shrub henna (*Lawsonia inermis*), which is cultivated in Egypt. The substance is identical with synthetic 2-hydroxy-1,4-naphthoquinone. It dyes wool and silk an orange shade, and a paste made from powdered henna leaves and catechu has been used for tinting the hair red.

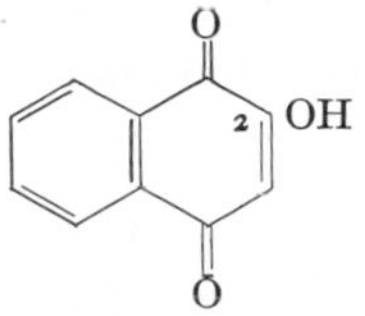

Lawsone

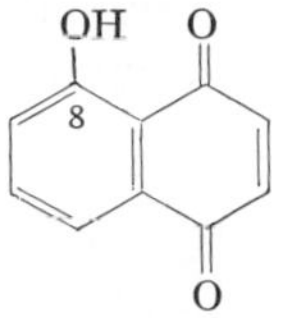

Juglone
(yellow-brown, m.p. 154°,
E_0alc. 0.447 v.)

The isomeric 8-hydroxy compound **juglone** is present in shells of unripe walnuts, largely as α-hydrojuglone, a ketonic form of the normal hydroquinone. The colorless hydro compound undergoes rapid oxidation on exposure to air and the resulting quinone stains the skin (addition of active groups of protein). Juglone can be prepared in 15% yield by oxidation of 1,5-dihydroxynaphthalene with dichromate in aqueous sulfuric acid solution.

Two monohydroxy derivatives of 2-methyl-1,4-naphthoquinone have been isolated from natural sources. **Plumbagin**, shown by synthesis to be the 5-hydroxy isomer, was known in a fairly pure form as early as 1828 and is the active principle of Chita, a drug of medicinal value obtained from Indian shrubs of various *Plumbago* species. **Phthiocol**, or 2-hydroxy-3-methyl-1,4-naphthoquinone (synthesis, p. 719), has been isolated from

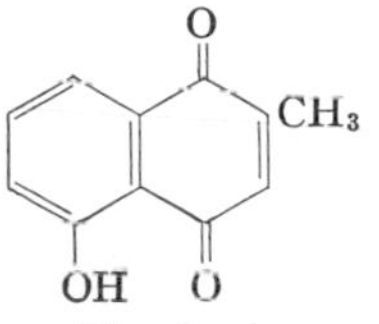

Plumbagin
(yellow, m.p. 79°)

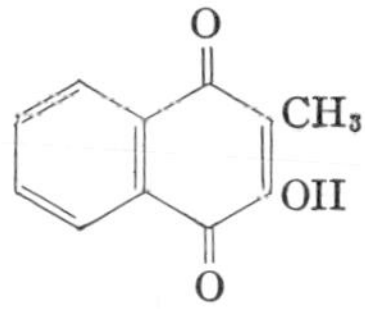

Phthiocol

human tubercle bacilli (*Mycobacterium tuberculosis*), but probably is formed during the isolation process by degradation of a vitamin K factor during saponification with alcoholic potassium hydroxide.

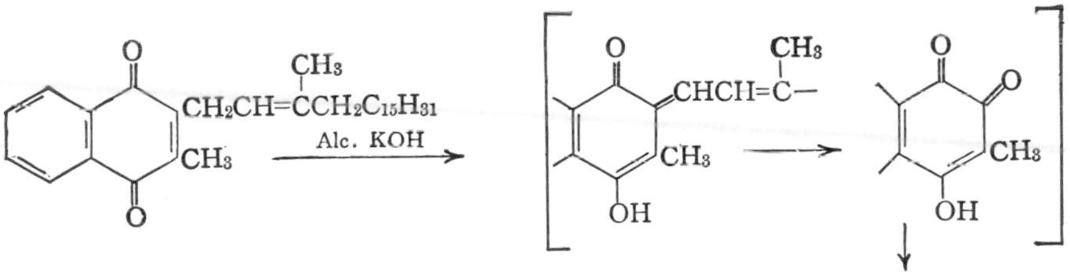

Vitamin K₁

Phthiocol

The related pigments **droserone** and **hydroxydroserone** are found under the outer covering of bulbous root growths of *Drosera Whittakeri*, a plant of Australia (Rennie, 1887). The more highly hydroxylated pigment has been characterized as 3,5,8-trihydroxy-2-methyl-1,4-naphthoquinone and synthesized by condensation of maleic anhydride with the hydroquinone component shown in the formulation (MacBeth and Winzor, 1936). The methoxyl group of the hydroquinone component is cleaved in the process.

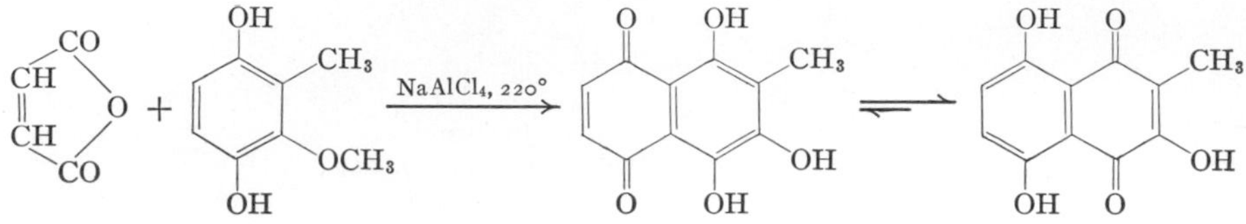

Ia   Ib

Hydroxydroserone
(red, m.p. 193°, $E_0^{alc.}$ 0.200 v.)

The initial reaction product Ia is less stable thermodynamically than the tautomeric form Ib, since methyl and hydroxyl groups have a much greater potential-lowering effect when attached to a quinonoid ring than when present in an adjacent benzenoid nucleus. Hydroxydroserone is thus assigned the structure Ib, which combines features of the structures of lawsone, juglone, plumbagin, and phthiocol. Droserone (yellow, m.p. 178°) lacks one of the two nonquinonoid hydroxyl groups of Ib and is 3,5-dihydroxy-2-methyl-1,4-naphthoquinone (R. H. Thomson, 1949).

Echinochrome A. — This pigment of sea urchin eggs (10 mg. per ovary) was characterized by Kuhn and Wallenfels (in 1939) as a pentahydroxyquinone derivative of β-ethyl- rather than β-methylnaphthalene, the parent hydrocarbon of the plant pigments cited above. Two tautomeric *para* quinone forms are possible, Ia and Ib, as well as several *ortho* quinone forms.

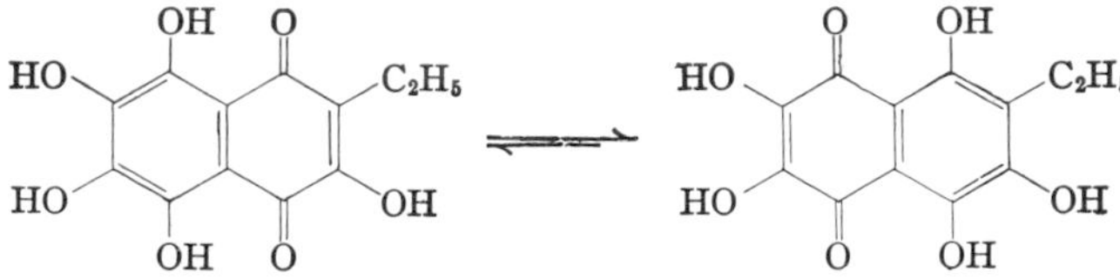

Ia   Ib

Echinochrome A
(red, m.p. 220° dec., $E_0^{aq.,30°}$ 0.080 v.)

Form Ib, with two effective potential-lowering hydroxyl groups in the quinone nucleus, probably has a potential some 25 mv. lower than that of Ia and hence predominates to the extent of 90% of the equilibrium mixture in solution. Brief treatment of the pigment with diazomethane affords a trimethyl ether in which the two free hydroxyl groups have been shown to occupy α-positions; the predominant tautomer probably has the structure shown. The reaction is interpreted as involving esterification of the two strongly acidic quinonoid hydroxyl groups of the more stable form Ib, followed by esterification of the acidic quinonoid hydroxyl group of the less abundant tautomeric form.

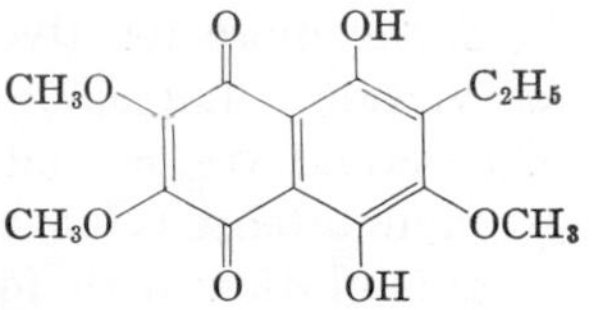

Echinochrome A trimethyl ether
(red, m.p. 130°)

Lapachol — Lapachol is a beautifully crystalline yellow coloring matter occurring in the grain of various woods, including Lapacho and Bethabarra, once imported to the United States from the west coast of Africa for the manufacture of high quality bows and fishing rods. The pigment forms a bright red, water-soluble sodium salt, and can be isolated by extraction of the ground wood with cold 1% sodium carbonate solution, precipitation, and extraction with ether. Elucidation of the structure and of a number of remarkable transformations was the theme of researches conducted by Hooker[4] in the years 1889–96 and 1915–35. Hooker characterized the pigment as a 2-hydroxy-1,4-naphthoquinone having a C_5-isoprenoid side chain at position 3 (1896), and this structure was later confirmed by synthesis

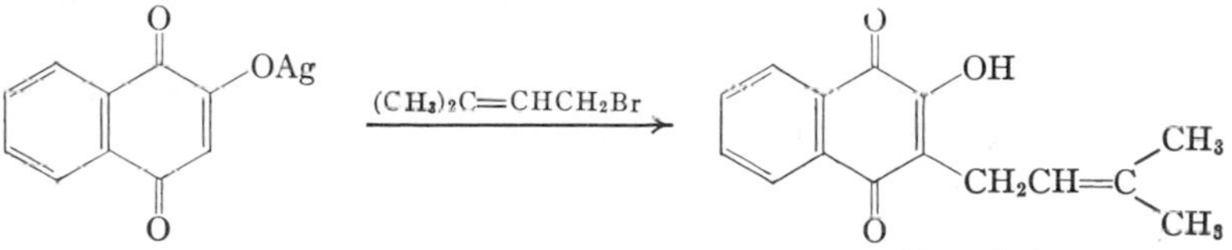

Lapachol
(yellow, m.p. 140°, $E_0^{alc.}$ 0.287 v.)

from the silver salt of 2-hydroxy-1,4-naphthoquinone (lawsone) and isoprene hydrobromide; whereas saturated alkyl halides give *ortho* and *para* quinone

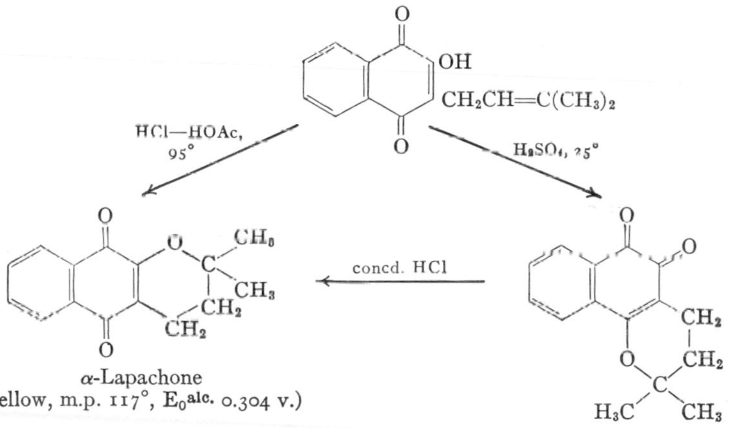

α-Lapachone
(yellow, m.p. 117°, $E_0^{alc.}$ 0.304 v.)

β-Lapachone
(orange-red, m.p. 154°, $E_0^{alc.}$ 0.403 v.)

---

[4] Samuel C. Hooker, 1864–1935; b. Brenchley (Kent), England; Ph.D. Munich (Bamberger); Franklin Sugar Refining Co.; private laboratory

ethers, the more reactive allylic halides also give some of the product of C-alkylation. Lapachol can be converted quantitatively into either of two cyclic derivatives, α- and β-lapachone. The *ortho* quinone is distinguished by a more intense color, higher oxidation potential, and solubility in sodium bisulfite solution with formation of a colorless complex, from which the quinone can be regenerated by either sodium carbonate or a mineral acid.

Hooker investigated the action of dilute permanganate on lapachol at low temperature, and discovered that the reaction leaves the double bond untouched and results in elimination of a methylene group from the side chain, as shown in the accompanying formulation. The oxidation product

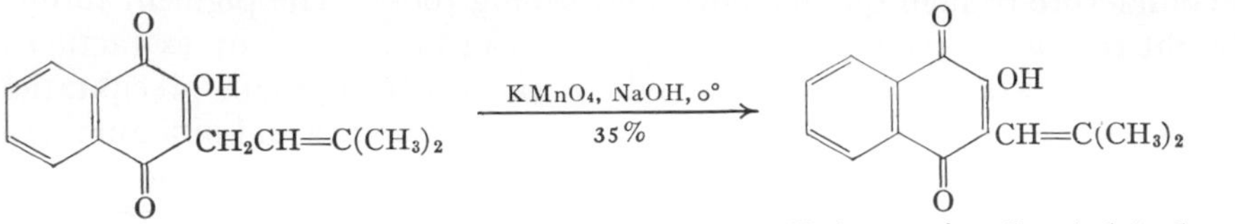

2-Hydroxy-3-(β,β-dimethylvinyl)-
1,4-naphthoquinone (red, m.p. 120°)

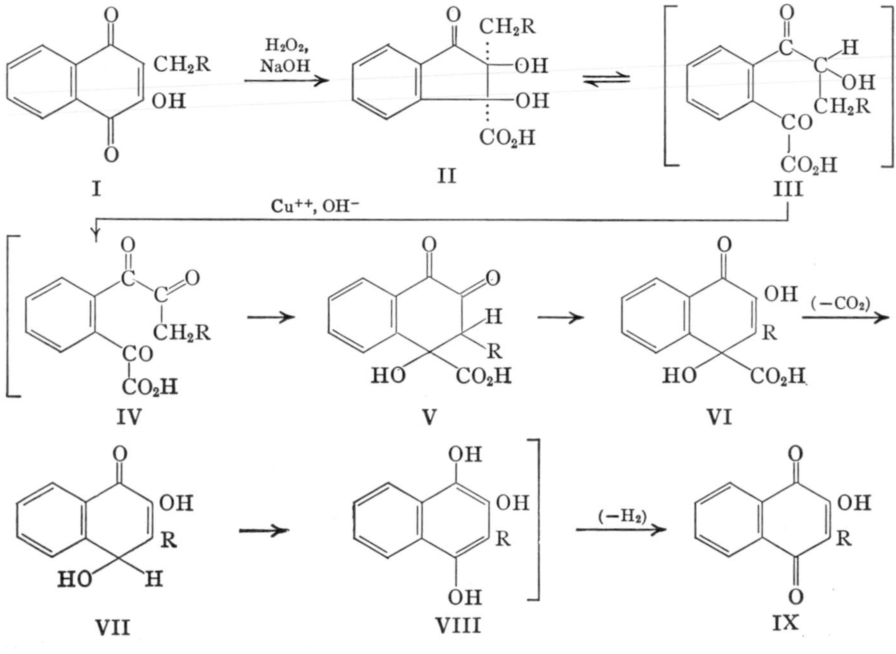

has a red color ascribable to conjugation of the double bond in the side chain with the quinone nucleus. The reaction is generally applicable to alkyl and β-alkenyl derivatives of hydroxynaphthoquinone. The observation that the initial red color of the solution disappears during the oxidation and then reappears suggested that the quinone ring opens and then closes again in a different manner, and experiments with quinones having a marking substituent in the benzenoid ring established that the hydroxyl group changes place with the alkyl or alkenyl group in the course of the oxidation. The mechanism of the Hooker oxidation was finally elucidated by isolation and characterization of a colorless intermediate (Fieser and Fieser, 1948). The intermediates from a variety of quinones of type I are obtainable in 85–95% yield by the action of hydrogen peroxide in alkaline solution. The crystalline intermediate is a dihydroxyindanone-carboxylic acid (II), but when oxidized by copper sulfate in an alkaline solution it reacts in the tautomeric ketol form III. Oxidation of the ketol group activates the adjacent methylene group (IV) and promotes aldolization to a product (V) that can enolize to a structure (VI) subject to ready decarboxylation (vinylog of a β-keto acid); the product VII then enolizes to a hydroquinone (VIII), which is easily oxidized. The two-step Hooker oxidation affords pure products in 80–90% overall yield.

Lomatiol. — This pigment, discovered by Rennie (1895) and characterized by Hooker as the ω-hydroxy derivative of lapachol, is found as a yellow powder surrounding the nuclei of seeds of the Australian plant *Lomatia ilicifolia*. The structure and some reactions of the pigment are shown in the formulas. The product of cyclization with sulfuric acid is an *ortho* quinone formed as the result of an allylic shift of hydroxyl, as is evident from the structure of the hydroxy compound obtained by hydrolysis of the cyclic product with alkali. Another consequence of the presence of an allylic alcohol grouping is that catalytic hydrogenation affords not only the product of saturation of the double bond with hydrogen but also hydrolapachol.

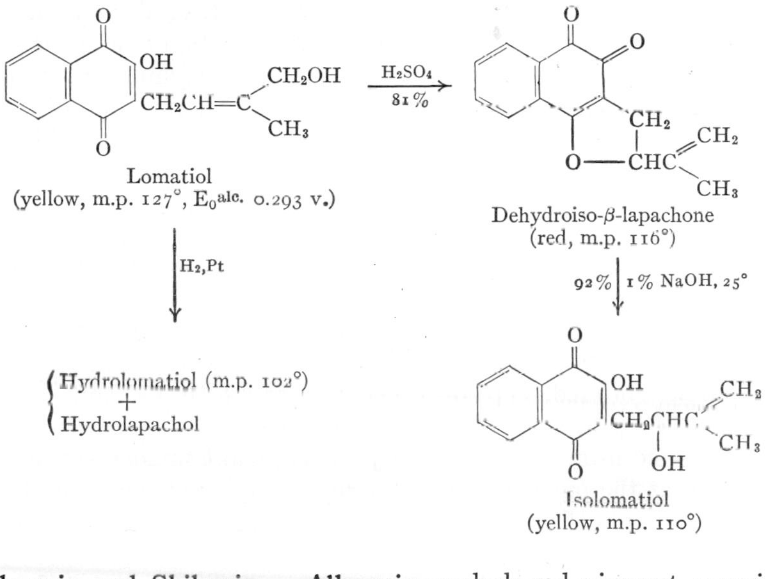

Lomatiol
(yellow, m.p. 127°, $E_0^{alc.}$ 0.293 v.)

Dehydroiso-β-lapachone
(red, m.p. 116°)

Hydrolomatiol (m.p. 102°)
+
Hydrolapachol

Isolomatiol
(yellow, m.p. 110°)

Alkannin and Shikonin. — **Alkannin,** a dark red pigment occuring as the angelic ester in the root of *Alkanna tinctoria* and employed to some extent as a mordant dye and indicator, has been characterized by Brockmann[5] (1935) as a derivative of naphthazarin (5,8-dihydroxy-1,4-naphtho-

---

[5] Hans Brockmann, b. 1903 Altkloster, Germany; D.Sc. Halle (Abderhalden, Kuhn); Göttingen

quinone) having as a substituent in the quinonoid ring an unsaturated side
chain containing a secondary alcoholic group.   The side chain contains a
terminal isoprenoid unit and resembles the side chains of perezone and

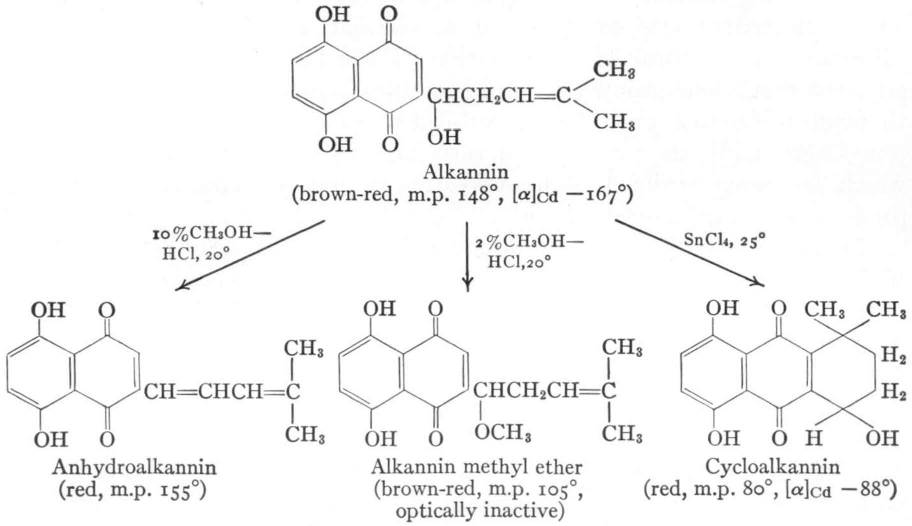

Alkannin
(brown-red, m.p. 148°, $[\alpha]_{Cd}$ −167°)

Anhydroalkannin
(red, m.p. 155°)

Alkannin methyl ether
(brown-red, m.p. 105°,
optically inactive)

Cycloalkannin
(red, m.p. 80°, $[\alpha]_{Cd}$ −88°)

lapachol.   The hydroxyl group in the α-position of the side chain is reactive
and is easily eliminated by the action of 10% methyl alcoholic hydrogen
chloride in the cold (or of hot 2 N alkali) with formation of a dienic system;
this dehydration reaction eliminates the center of asymmetry responsible
for the optical activity of the natural pigment.   Etherification of the reactive hydroxyl group by the action of 2% methyl alcoholic hydrochloric acid
in the cold is accompanied by racemization.   On cyclization of the pigment
with stannic chloride in benzene solution at room temperature the hydroxyl
group is left intact and optical activity is retained.   Dry distillation of either
cycloalkannin or the original pigment results in loss of methane and water
and formation of 1-methyl-5,8-dihydroxyanthraquinone (1-methylquiniz-
arin, m.p. 247°), synthesized for comparison from naphthazarin diacetate
and piperylene.   The product of hydrogenation of anhydroalkannin, 3-iso-
hexylnaphthazarin (red, m.p. 98°), occurs along with alkannin.   Another
red pigment of the same composition and properties, shikonin (m.p. 147°),
has been isolated from the root of the Japanese plant shikone.   Brockmann
discovered that the pigment is the dextrorotatory enantiomer of alkannin,
for it yields an optically inactive methyl ether identical with that obtained
from the levorotatory pigment.

   Dunnione is an orange-red pigment (m.p. 99°, $[\alpha]_D$ + 310°) derived
from *Streptocarpus Dunnii* Mast.; it occurs as a deposit on the 2-ft. long
leaves of the plant (0.5–2 g. per leaf).   The structure shown (III) was deduced by J. R. Price and R. Robinson (1939), and racemic dunnione has

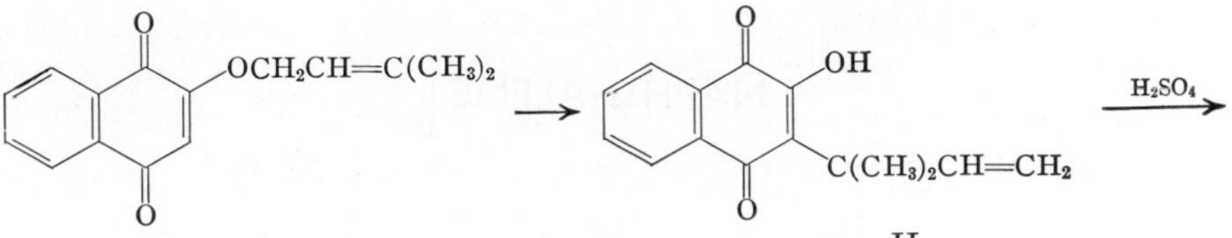

I   II

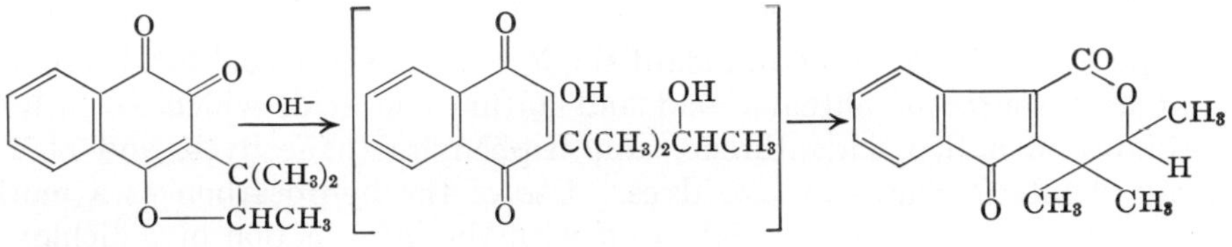

Dunnione (III)   IV   Allodunnione (V)

been synthesized (Cooke, 1948) by Claisen rearrangement of 2-γ,γ-dimethylalloxy-1,4-naphthoquinone (I) and ring closure. Dunnione (III) is isomerized by alkali to allodunnione (V); the hydroxy-p-quinone IV is formed and undergoes benzilic acid rearrangement.

READING REFERENCES

"The Constitution and Properties of Lapachol, Lomatiol, and Other Hydroxynaphthoquinone Derivatives," Memorial Volume to Samuel C. Hooker (1936)

F. Mayer. "The Chemistry of Natural Coloring Matters," 96–161, Reinhold, New York (1943)

CHAPTER 31

NAPHTHALENE

Naphthalene, the most abundant single constituent of coal tar, is important as a source of phthalic acid and anthranilic acid, which are intermediates to indigo, indanthrene, and triphenylmethane dyes, and of an array of intermediates for azo dyes. Use of the hydrocarbon as a moth repellant and insecticide has fallen off with the introduction of p-dichlorobenzene. Liquid hydro derivatives of naphthalene (m.p. 80°) utilized in motor fuels and lubricants and as solvents are the 1,2,3,4-tetrahydride, tetralin, and the decahydride, decalin.

Monosubstituted naphthalenes usually are designated by the prefix α- or β-, while the positions of groups in polysubstituted derivatives are indicated by numbers. Ten isomeric disubstitution products are possible; all ten dihydroxy derivatives are known. 1,8-Derivatives are designated *peri-* (Gr. *peri*, near) and 2,6-derivatives are designated *amphi-* (Gr. *amph-*, on both sides). Structures of simple derivatives are established by oxidation to phthalic acid or a substituted phthalic acid. A nitro group stabilizes the ring to which it is attached, and hence the unsubstituted ring (A) of α-nitronaphthalene is degraded on oxidation and the product is 3-nitrophthalic acid. If the nitro compound is reduced, the substituted ring (B) becomes the more vulnerable center, and oxidation of α-naphthylamine yields phthalic acid. This sequence of reactions proves that naphthalene contains two fused benzene rings, for each ring is identified in a degradation

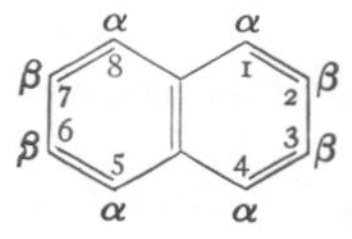

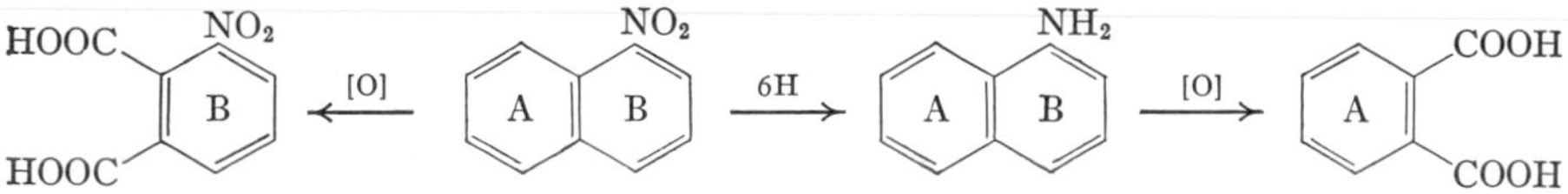

product with carbon substituents in the o-positions. This structure was postulated by Erlenmeyer[1] in 1866 and proved by Graebe[2] (1868), who applied the above principle in a more elaborate sequence involving chlorinated quinones. Structures of substances such as β-naphthol or β-ethylnaphthalene, which yield phthalic acid on drastic oxidation, are established by correlation with other derivatives that undergo degradation in the alternate direction. β-Ethylnaphthalene results from Clemmensen reduction of an aceto compound established as a β-derivative by oxidation to

---

[1] Emil Erlenmeyer, Sen., 1825–1909; b. Wehen/Wiesbaden, Germany; Ph.D. Giessen; Techn. Hochsch. Munich; *Ber.*, **43**, 3645 (1910)

[2] Carl Graebe, 1841–1927; b. Frankfurt, Germany; Ph.D. Heidelberg (Bunsen); Königsberg, Geneva; *Ber.*, **61A**, 9 (1928)

trimellitic acid (benzene-1,2,4-tricarboxylic acid). β-Naphthol can be correlated through β-naphthylamine with β-naphthoic acid, which also yields the 1,2,4-acid.

BOND STRUCTURE

When the concept of the Kekulé ring system is extended to naphthalene, three resonance bond structures are possible, the symmetrical structure I

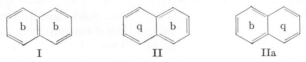

I   II   IIa

and the two unsymmetrical, equivalent structures II and IIa. In formulations of the unsymmetrical structures, one of the two rings is indicated as quinonoid (q) because the arrangement of double bonds corresponds to that of o-benzoquinone. Rings that correspond to the normal Kekulé benzene formula in containing three double bonds, in contrast with a quinonoid ring containing two, are described as normal benzenoid rings (b). Fries (1927), recognizing that quinonoid systems are more reactive, or less stable, than benzenoid systems, formulated a generalization known as the Fries rule, which states that the most stable form of a polynuclear hydrocarbon is that in which the maximum number of rings have the benzenoid arrangement of three double bonds. On this basis the symmetrical structure composed of two normal Kekulé rings would be expected to be more stable than the quinonoid structures.

Certain peculiarities in the reactions of β-naphthol and β-naphthylamine are interpretable only on the basis of the symmetrical formula. A striking difference in the two positions *ortho* to the functional group in these compounds was noted first by Marckwald (1893) and investigated extensively by Zincke,[3] Fries, and others. Whereas the 1-position exhibits functions normally associated with the *o*-position of an amine or a phenol, the 3-position does not. On reaction with a diazotized amine in alkaline solution, β-naphthol (III) couples exclusively at the 1-position in preference to the

(couples)

OH

1
2
3 (not attacked)

III

CH₃

OH

3 (not attacked)

IV

OH

1
2
4

CH₃

V

(couples)

Response to diazotized amines

alternate position 3. The lack of reactivity at the 3-position is more apparent in the behavior of 1-methyl-2-naphthol (IV), for this naphthol fails to enter into the diazo coupling reaction. The possibility that resistance to

---

[3] Theodor Zincke, 1843–1928; b. Ülsen, Germany; Ph.D. Göttingen; Marburg; *Ber.*, **62A**, 17 (1929)

attack is due to any lack of reactivity inherent in a β-position in the naphthalene nucleus can be dismissed, for 4-methyl-1-naphthol (V) couples at
the β-position 2.   The behavior of IV is therefore anomalous, and one of
the two positions adjacent to the hydroxylated carbon atom does not have
the characteristics of a normal *ortho* position.   An interpretation of this
deviating behavior can be developed from the consideration that aliphatic
enols having the grouping —CH=C(OH)— couple with diazotized amines
to give azo compounds, —C(N=NAr)=C(OH)—, whereas alcohols with the
grouping —CH₂—CH(OH)— do not.   The diazo group evidently can
attack a position connected to a hydroxylated carbon by a double bond,
but not one joined by a single linkage.   This relationship would indicate
that in β-naphthol the 1- and 2-carbon atoms are connected by a double
bond and the 2- and 3-carbon atoms by a single bond. Position 1 is
therefore described as a normal *ortho* position because it is enolic,

$\overset{1}{—}CH=C(OH)\overset{}{—}_{3}$, whereas the 3-position, with the grouping =C(OH)—

CH=, is nonenolic and hence abnormal.   *p*-Coupling, as observed with
α-naphthol, can be ascribed to attack at the end of a dienolic system:
—CH=CHCH=C(OH)—.

The facts cited suggest that the bond structure of the naphthalene
nucleus is not so mobile as that of benzene and that there is a relative
fixation of bonds in at least that part of the molecule at which substitution
occurs.   Investigations of the properties of compounds hydroxylated in both
rings have shown that the two rings have the same character (Fieser and
Lothrop, 1935).   2,7-Dihydroxynaphthalene (VI) couples at positions 1
and 8, but if these positions are blocked by alkyl groups (VII), no coupling

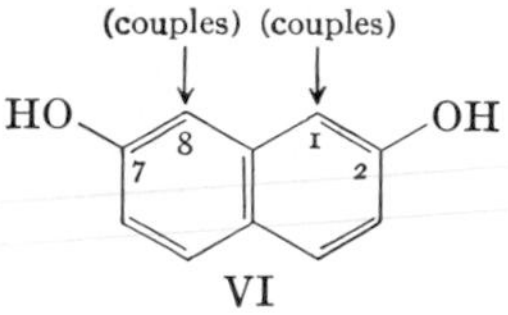

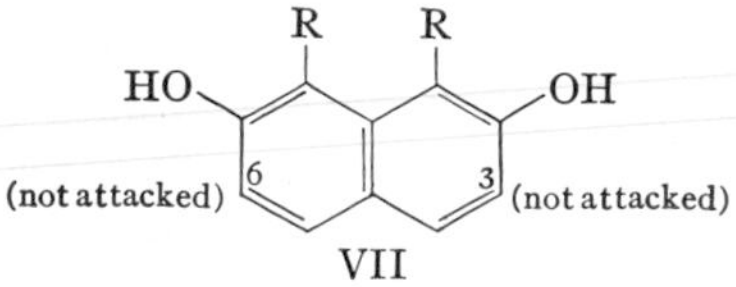

occurs.   The observation is consistent with the symmetrical, but not the
unsymmetrical formulation for naphthalene.

Analogous phenomena are encountered in other reactions.   β-Naphthol
allyl ether (VIII) undergoes the Claisen rearrangement when heated and
affords 1-allyl-2-naphthol (IX), but when the 1-position is blocked by an

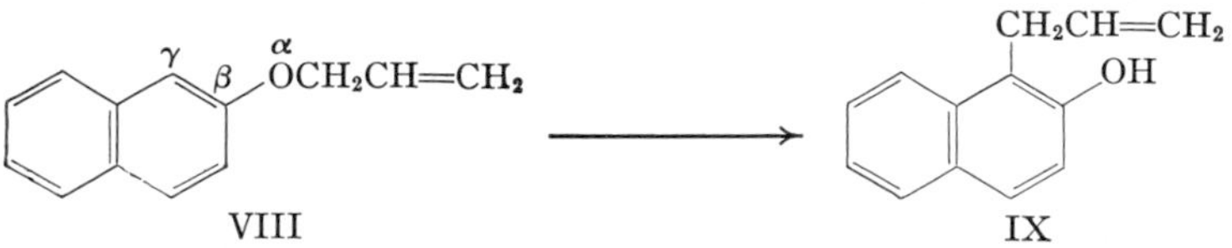

alkyl group no rearrangement occurs.   If the normal reaction is regarded
as an α,γ-migration of the allyl group, the failure of the 1-substituted compounds to rearrange is an indication that the double bond normally present

at the 1,2-position does not shift to the alternate 2,3-position to form a second α,γ-system, even at the elevated reaction temperature, in an extent sufficient to allow the allyl group to migrate.

Another manifestation of bond fixation is the course of halogenation and nitration of β-naphthol and β-naphthylamine derivatives (Zincke, Fries), as illustrated in the following typical example. p-Cresol is easily chlorinated in both free o-positions, and the reaction sequence can be visualized as proceeding by substitution at an initial enolic position, progression of the double bonds to render the alternate o-position enolic, and further substitution at this site. Chlorination of β-naphthol follows a different course, for the initially formed 1-chloro derivative (X) can be converted by interaction with a second mole of chlorine (particularly in the presence of sodium acetate) into the keto dichloride XI (1,1-dichloro-2-keto-1,2-dihydro-

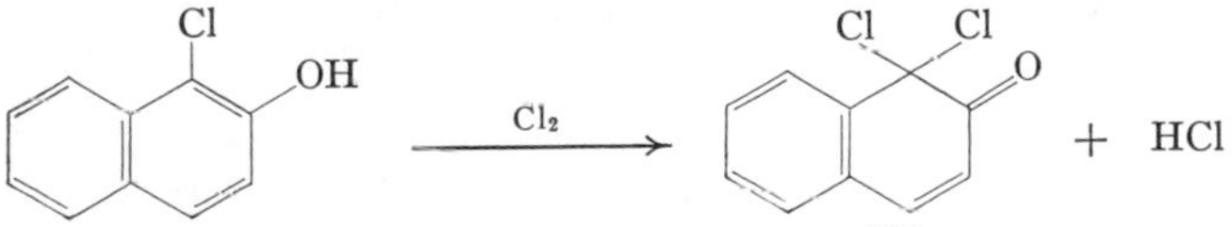

naphthalene). Apparently there is in this case no bond migration to produce an enolic center at the 3-position, $-\overset{3}{C}(OH)=\overset{1}{C}H-$, and chlorine attacks the perhaps less reactive system $-CCl=C(OH)-$ with introduction of a second halogen at the 1-position. The comparable ketonic substances

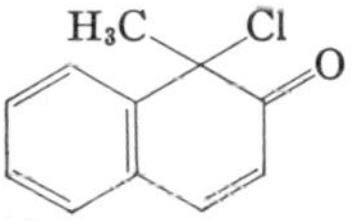

XII and XIII result from chlorination and nitration of 1-methyl-2-naphthol, and the mixed halogenide XIV has been prepared from both the 1-bromo and 1-chloro derivatives of β-naphthol.

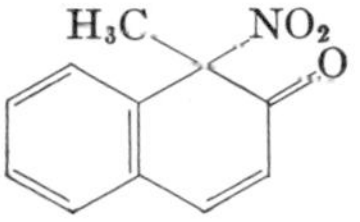

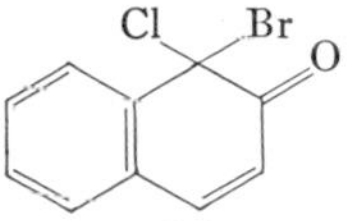

X-ray and electron-diffraction analysis (Robertson, 1951) has confirmed chemical evidence. Whereas in benzene the C—C bond distances are all 1.40 Å, intermediate between aliphatic C—C (1.54 Å) and C—C (1.34 Å) bonds, the bond distances in naphthalene are not identical. The 1,2-bond distance is 1.36 Å, shorter than any other bond, and the 2,3-distance is 1.39 Å. That these distances do not correspond exactly to aliphatic double and single bonds indicates some resonance stabilization, and the chemical evidence requires only bond fixation in the part of the molecule undergoing substitution and is not incompatible with resonance stabilization in another part. Attack of a 1,8-dialkyl-2,7-dihydroxynaphthalene (XV) by $C_6H_5N_2^+$, Cl^+, or other electrophilic agent requires a center of adequate electron density at an unsubstituted center, as in the o-quinonoid structure XVIII. However, four other resonance structures are possible in which the negative charge is located at a position at which substitution is blocked by

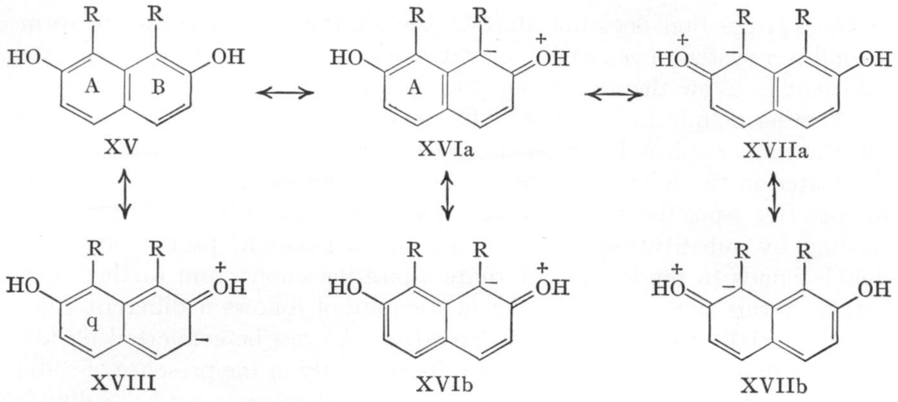

XV

XVIa

XVIIa

XVIII

XVIb

XVIIb

an alkyl group. A separation of charge associated with the 2-hydroxy group gives structure XVIa, with a negative charge at position 1 and a now isolated Kekulé ring (A) susceptible to usual resonance stabilization (structure XVIb). Charge separation at the alternate hydroxyl group gives a structure (XVIIa) that is likewise stabilized by resonance with an alternate Kekulé structure, XVIIb. That substitution does not occur at position 3 (or 6) means that structure XVIII (or its equivalent counterpart) is an excited structure that makes little contribution to the hybrid because of the high energy associated with the o-quinonoid arrangement of linkages.

SUBSTITUTION REACTIONS

In reactions of the normal type represented by nitration and halogenation the more reactive α-positions of naphthalene are attacked almost exclusively, whereas reversible reactions subject to steric hindrance result in substitution in the less hindered β-position to an extent that increases with increasing reaction temperature but varies with the reagent and perhaps with the bulkiness of specific group complexes. Nitration, bromination, or chlorination of naphthalene affords exclusively α-substituted derivatives; a possible analogy is the preferential α-bromination of an alkylbenzene.

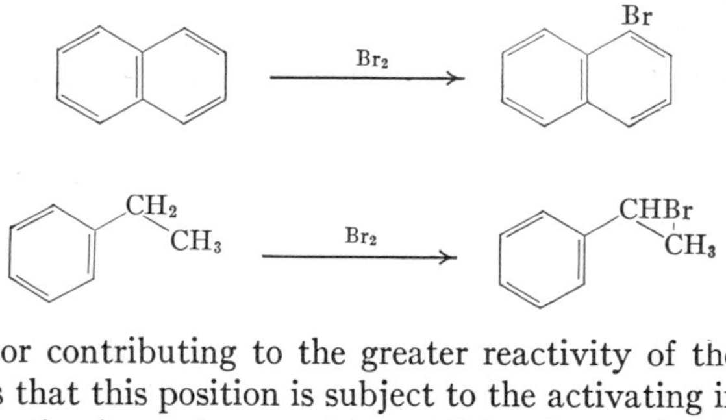

Thus one factor contributing to the greater reactivity of the α-position of naphthalene is that this position is subject to the activating influence of the adjacent aromatic ring, whereas the β-position is too far removed to be affected. A further analogy can be drawn between the reduction of naphthalene with sodium amalgam to give 1,4-dihydronaphthalene and the reduction of diphenylbutadiene with aluminum amalgam in a reaction involving addition to the ends of a 1,4-system.

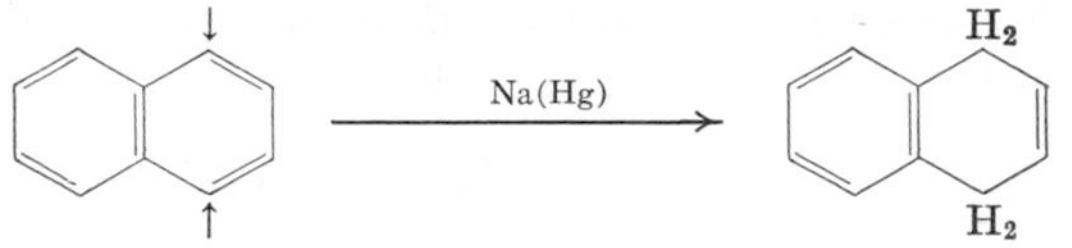

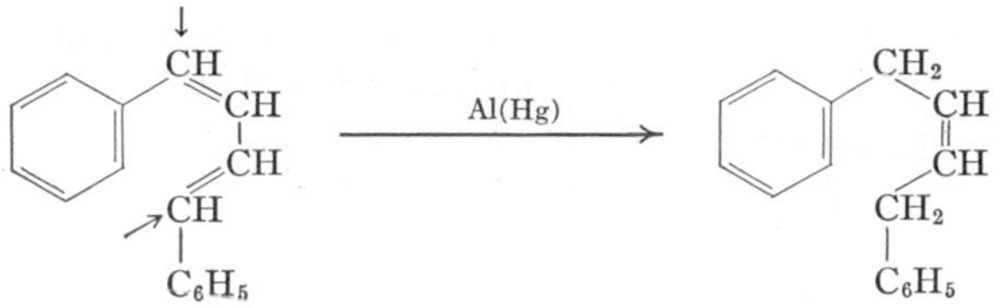

Sulfonation, notably subject to both steric and temperature effects, can be controlled to yield either the α or β-sulfonic acid derivative. With concentrated acid at a controlled low temperature, the hydrocarbon can be sulfonated largely in the α-position; the β-sulfonic acid can be produced in high yield by introducing sulfuric acid into molten naphthalene at 165°

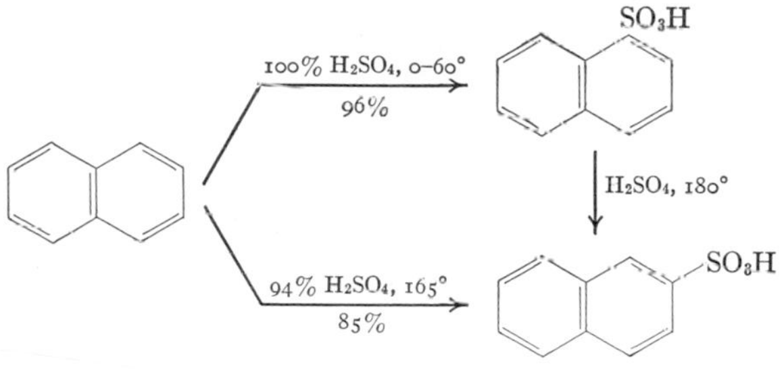

and stirring the mixture for a few minutes. Naphthalene-α-sulfonic acid when heated with sulfuric acid is transformed into the β-isomer, probably as the result of a reversal of the substitution followed by resulfonation.

The course of Friedel-Crafts acylations of naphthalene varies more with the nature of the reagent and solvent than with the temperature. The hydrocarbon is converted by acetyl chloride or acetic anhydride in carbon

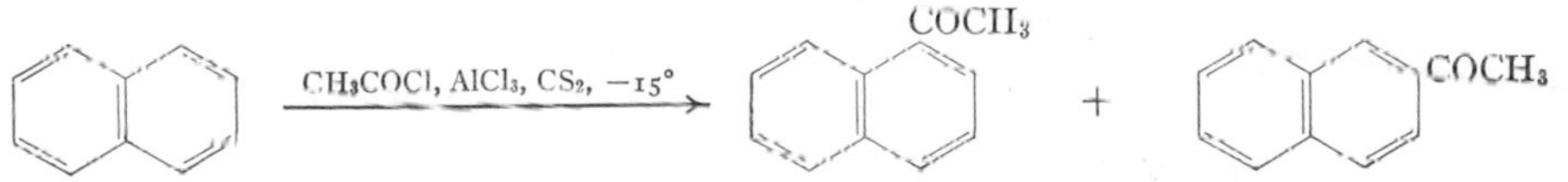

3 parts	1 part
α-Acetonaphthalene	β-Acetonaphthalene
(liq., b.p. 302°;	(m.p. 56°, b.p. 302°;
picrate, m.p. 120°)	picrate, m.p. 85°)

disulfide solution into a mixture of the α- and β-aceto derivatives in the ratio of about 3:1. The ketones boil at the same temperature and the solid β-isomer is not present in large enough amount to be separable from the liquid α-isomer by crystallization. However, the relationship in properties is reversed in the picrates, for the picrate of the liquid α-isomer is the higher melting and the less soluble; hence the more abundant liquid ketone can be isolated in pure form by one crystallization of the picrate mixture and regeneration by cleavage with ammonia. β-Acetonaphthalene is more readily available, for it is the chief product of acylation in nitrobenzene solution and,

$$\text{Naphthalene} \xrightarrow[\text{90\%}]{\text{CH}_3\text{COCl, AlCl}_3, \text{C}_6\text{H}_5\text{NO}_2} \text{β-Acetonaphthalene}$$

being a solid, can be freed easily from a small amount of the accompanying liquid isomer by crystallization. Since nitrobenzene is known to form molecular complexes with aluminum chloride and acid chlorides, the preferential β-substitution may be attributable to an avoidance of the hindered α-position by a bulky intermediate complex. Friedel-Crafts succinoylation of naphthalene proceeds most satisfactorily in nitrobenzene solution and affords a mixture of isomeric keto acids that can be separated by special procedures (crystallization of the β-isomer, esterification of the mother liquor material, distillation and hydrolysis; fractional precipitation from alkali); the optimum yields are indicated in the formulation:

36%
β-1-Naphthoylpropionic
acid (m.p. 133°)

47%
β-2-Naphthoylpropionic
acid (m.p. 173°)

Friedel-Crafts substitution of an acyl group derived from an aromatic acid gives predominantly the α-isomer, and the course of the reaction is not greatly influenced by the solvent or temperature. Benzoylation is best

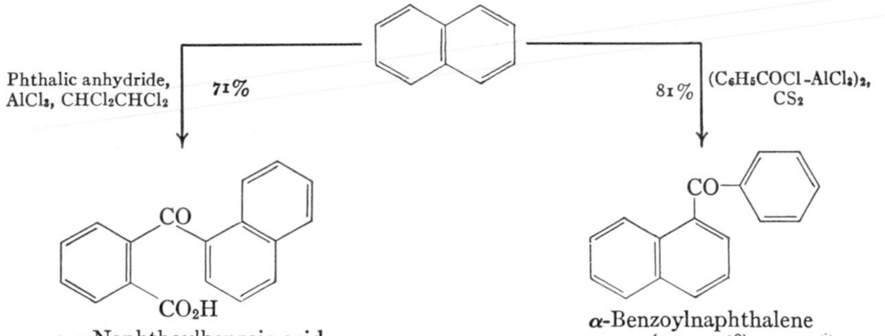

2-α-Naphthoylbenzoic acid
(m.p. 173°)

α-Benzoylnaphthalene
(m.p. 76°)

accomplished by the Perrier procedure (1904). An equimolecular mixture of benzoyl chloride and aluminum chloride is heated over a free flame until the solid has dissolved and is then cooled; the resulting crystalline molecular complex is dissolved in carbon disulfide and the hydrocarbon component added. A rapid reaction ensues, with separation of a crystalline aluminum chloride complex of α-benzoylnaphthalene, from which the pure ketone is liberated on decomposition with water. Some β-benzoylnaphthalene (m.p.

82°) is produced but remains in the carbon disulfide mother liquor as a much more soluble complex.

When a β-acyl derivative of naphthalene is required as a synthetic intermediate, advantage can be taken of the fact that the orientation of tetralin in the Friedel-Crafts reaction is exclusively at the unhindered β-position. The resulting ketonic product, for example I, can be dehydro-

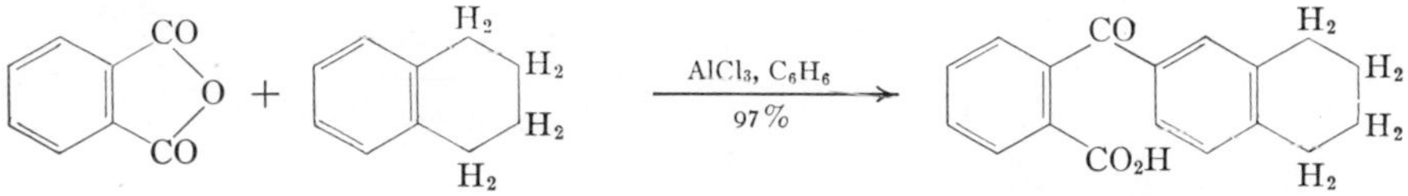

Tetralin

o-(2-Tetroyl)-benzoic acid, I
(m.p. 155°)

genated directly to the naphthalene derivative, or dehydrogenation can be accomplished at some later stage in the synthesis. The product of succinoylation, II, has been transformed into γ-2-naphthylbutyric acid (III) by heating the corresponding ester with palladium charcoal (Newman, 1943); the nucleus is dehydrogenated and the carbonyl group adjacent to the

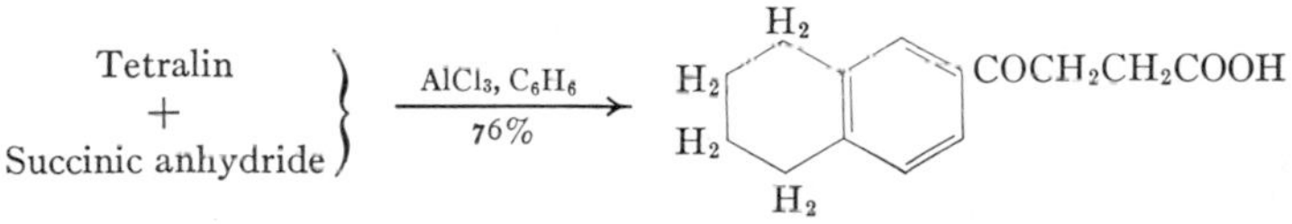

β-2-Tetroylpropionic acid, II

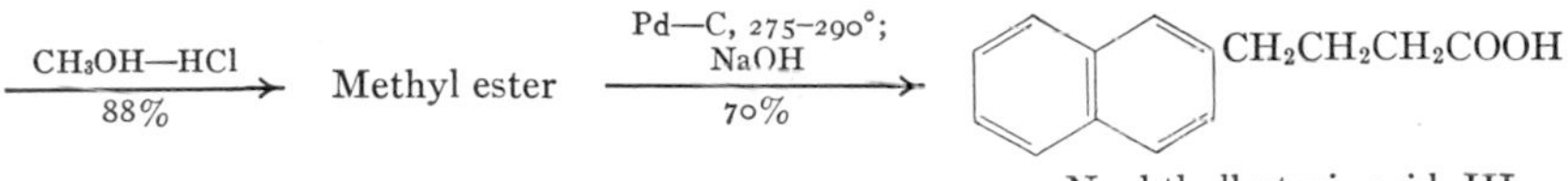

γ-2-Naphthylbutyric acid, III

aromatic ring is reduced to a methylene group. The useful intermediate III can be made by this method more efficiently than from naphthalene.

MONOSUBSTITUTION PRODUCTS

The chief substitution reactions of naphthalene of practical value are summarized in Chart I, which also shows key transformation products of the resulting substances. Properties of the substances formulated and of a few additional members of the series are listed in Table 31.1.

Nitration of naphthalene must be conducted under controlled conditions to avoid formation of dinitro compounds, for the nitro group initially introduced into one ring has only a weak deactivating influence on the other nucleus. Naphthalene reacts much more readily than benzene, and best results are obtained with diluted mixed acid. In a procedure described by Fierz-David[4] and Blangey (1938), finely pulverized naphthalene (128 g.) is stirred into a mixture of 62% nitric acid (103 g.) and 80% sulfuric acid (300 g.), and the reaction conducted at 50–60° for seven hours. The crude

---

[4] Hans Eduard Fierz-David, 1882–1953; b. Zurich; Ph.D. London (Forster) and Zurich (on recommendation of Werner); ETH Zurich

Chart 1. Naphthalene Substitutions

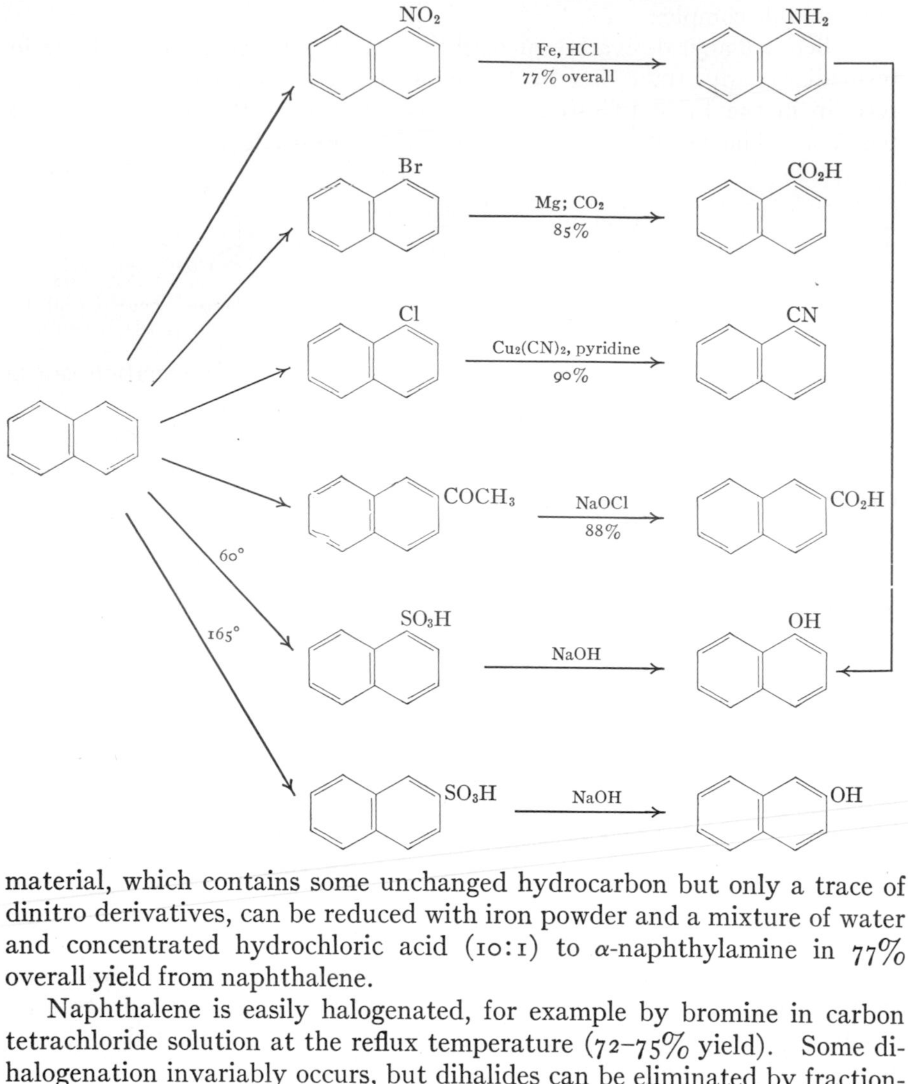

material, which contains some unchanged hydrocarbon but only a trace of dinitro derivatives, can be reduced with iron powder and a mixture of water and concentrated hydrochloric acid (10:1) to α-naphthylamine in 77% overall yield from naphthalene.

Naphthalene is easily halogenated, for example by bromine in carbon tetrachloride solution at the reflux temperature (72–75% yield). Some dihalogenation invariably occurs, but dihalides can be eliminated by fractionation after the crude product has been warmed with powdered sodium hydroxide or steam distilled from an alkaline medium to destroy labile halo compounds. α-Bromonaphthalene readily forms a Grignard reagent, and carbonation of this derivative is the preferred method for preparation of α-naphthoic acid. A convenient preparation of α-naphthonitrile by refluxing α-bromonaphthalene in pyridine with cuprous cyanide has been described (p. 652); the less expensive but higher boiling α-chloro compound can be employed with use of pressure equipment. The best route to β-naphthoic acid is hypochlorite oxidation of β-acetonaphthalene (p. 657).

β-Naphthol is produced efficiently by alkali fusion of sodiumnaphtha-

TABLE 31.1. MONOSUBSTITUTION PRODUCTS OF NAPHTHALENE

NAME	M.P., °C.	B.P., °C.	DISSOCIATION CONSTANT
Naphthalene-α-sulfonic acid (dihydrate)	90		
Naphthalene-β-sulfonic acid (monohydrate)	124		
α-Nitronaphthalene	61	304	
β-Nitronaphthalene	79		
α-Naphthylamine	49	301	pK_b 10.0
β-Naphthylamine	112	306	pK_b 9.3
α-Naphthol	94	280	pK_a 8.0
β-Naphthol	122	286	
α-Naphthoic acid	162		pK_a 3.7
β-Naphthoic acid	185		pK_a 4.15
α-Chloronaphthalene	liq.	259	
α-Bromonaphthalene	6.2	281	
β-Bromonaphthalene	59	282	
α-Naphthonitrile	37	299	
β-Naphthonitrile	66	306	

lene-β-sulfonate. The reaction can be conducted on a laboratory scale with 1 part of sodium hydroxide, mixed with 23% of water to lower the melting point, and 1.5 parts of the sulfonate; in the technical process the amount of sulfonate is increased to 2.8 parts. The sulfonate is added to the melt at 270–290°, and the temperature eventually is brought to 318°. The cooled melt is extracted with water, and the solution is acidified; the yield of β-naphthol, purified by distillation, is 84%. Economy in the technical process is achieved by adding the sodium sulfite-containing mother liquor from precipitation of the β-naphthol to the diluted sulfonation mixture in order to salt out sodium naphthalene-β-sulfonate; sulfur dioxide is liberated and is utilized to acidify the solution of the β-naphtholate melt. α-Naphthol can be prepared in a similar manner, but the product is not pure. A better process consists in hydrolysis of α-naphthylamine with 9.2% aqueous sulfuric acid at 200° and 14 atmospheres pressure; the product is pure and the yield 94–95%. The ready hydrolysis of the amine to the naphthol is a reaction seldom encountered in the benzene series but often applicable to amines of the more reactive naphthalene.

Bucherer Reaction. — β-Naphthylamine is prepared by a procedure developed by Bucherer[5] (1904), consisting in this instance in heating β-naphthol with aqueous ammonium sulfite or bisulfite. A sulfite solution is prepared by saturating concentrated ammonia solution with sulfur dioxide and adding an equal volume of concentrated ammonia solution; β-naphthol is added, and the charge is heated in an autoclave provided with a stirrer or

[5] Hans Th. Bucherer, 1869–1949; b. Cologne, Germany; Ph.D. Leipzig (Wislicenus); Techn. Hochsch. Munich

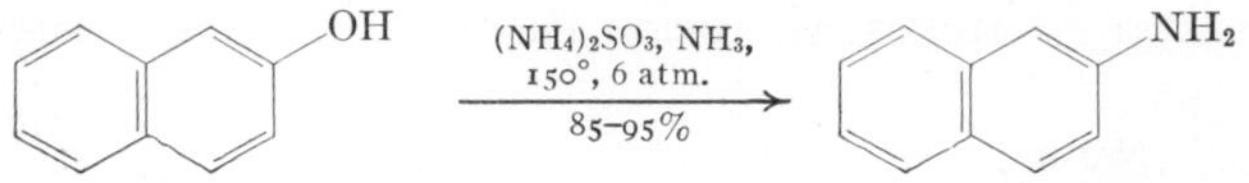

a shaking mechanism.   The corresponding amine is obtained in excellent purity and high yield.   Several comparable aminations have been realized in the naphthalene series, but the reaction requires a reactive aromatic nucleus and is not practicable for benzene derivatives other than particularly reactive polyhydroxy compounds such as resorcinol.   Amination is reversible; for example, β-naphthylamine can be reconverted into β-naphthol by heating with aqueous sodium bisulfite solution and then adding alkali and boiling the solution until the ammonia is expelled.   Both the amination and hydrolysis reactions are classified as Bucherer reactions.   Intermediate bisulfite products have been isolated and are currently regarded as resulting from tautomerization of the naphthol or naphthylamine followed by addition of bisulfite to the carbonyl or ketimine group.   The addition product is produced by heating the naphthol with sodium bisulfite; it is stable in

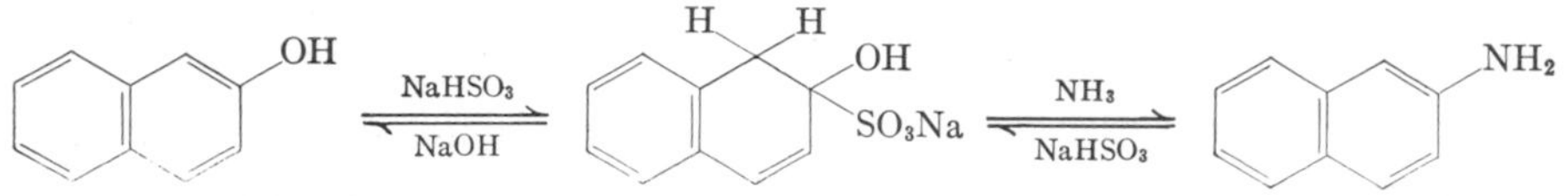

the presence of excess bisulfite or dilute mineral acid, but is hydrolyzed by alkali and is converted into the amine on reaction with ammonia.   The same intermediate is produced by the action of sodium bisulfite on the naphthylamine and can be subsequently hydrolyzed by alkali.   The amination reaction can be extended to the preparation of secondary amines; for example, a naphthol when heated with sodium bisulfite solution and either methylamine or aniline is converted into the derivative $ArNHCH_3$ or $ArNHC_6H_5$.

Other Derivatives. — The ready preparation of β-naphthylamine by the Bucherer reaction makes available substances otherwise difficulty accessible.   Thus β-bromonaphthalene can be prepared in moderate yield by the Sandmeyer reaction, which likewise is employed for the preparation of

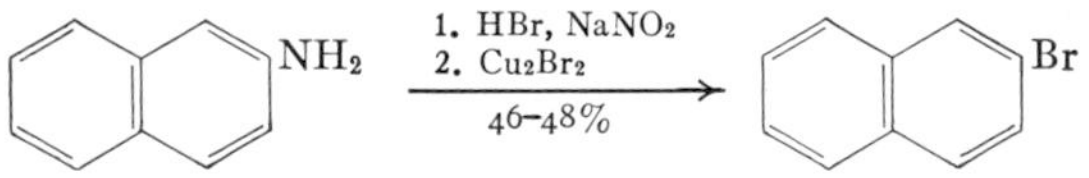

β-naphthonitrile.   β-Nitronaphthalene is produced to a certain extent by the action of sodium nitrite on diazotized β-naphthylamine in the presence of cuprous hydroxide, but the process involves a time-consuming steam distillation of the difficulty volatile product, and the yield is only 10%.

SUBSTITUTION REACTIONS OF NAPHTHALENE DERIVATIVES

The course of substitution reactions of naphthalene derivatives is determined by a combination of factors.   The group initially present exerts a directive influence, and either activates or deactivates the ring to which it is attached.   α-Positions are, *per se*, more reactive than β-positions to normal substitutions or to sulfonations and Friedel-Crafts reactions conducted at low temperatures. In α-naphthol (I), the 4-position is particularly favored because it is a reactive α-position *para* to the powerfully activating hydroxyl group, and consequently it is the first point of attack. Dinitra-

I   II   III

tion of α-naphthol is conducted, as in the preparation of picric acid, by conversion into the disulfonic acid and treatment of this derivative with nitric acid; the product is 2,4-dinitro-1-naphthol (II), or Martius Yellow, a dye. After introduction of one sulfonic acid or nitro group, the ring carrying the substituents is activated by the hydroxyl group and deactivated by the unsaturated, *meta* directing group, but the outcome of the reaction shows that the activating tendency predominates. In α-methylnaphthalene (III) the 4-position is also the preferential point of attack, for example in nitration or in low-temperature sulfonation (conducted with chlorosulfonic acid in carbon tetrachloride solution at 0°; 88% yield). Direct bromination affords chiefly 1-bromo-4-methylnaphthalene (m.p. 7°) in an impure condition and in low yield; the pure bromide is made more readily from the 4-sulfonate by the action of bromine in an aqueous solution of sodium bromide at 50° (yield 68%). α-Methylnaphthalene is substituted at the 4-position also in Friedel-Crafts acylations, even in nitrobenzene solution, which indicates that the *p*-directing effect of the methyl group overcomes the hindrance effect noted with naphthalene itself.

If one ring of the naphthalene nucleus carries a *m*-directing, deactivating group, a substituent tends to enter the other ring, preferentially at the more reactive α-position. Thus α-nitronaphthalene gives on nitration a mixture of the 1,5- and 1,8-dinitro compounds in which the latter predominates. The higher-melting 1,5-dinitronaphthalene is much less soluble than the isomer, and separation can be accomplished by crystallization from

HNO_3—H_2SO_4, 0°

(1 part, m.p. 211°)   (2 parts, m.p. 172°)

pyridine or by warming the nitration mixture till the solid is dissolved and then allowing the 1,5-compound to crystallize. Another example of heteronuclear substitution is bromination of the rare β-nitronaphthalene, which affords 5-bromo-2-nitronaphthalene (m.p. 131°) as the chief product.

In β-naphthol, β-methoxynaphthalene, and β-methylnaphthalene, the point of first attack is the activated 1-position, which is the only available normal position *ortho* to the directing group. Thus β-naphthol couples exclusively at this position, β-ethoxynaphthalene on reaction with N-methylformanilide gives the 1-formyl derivative, and β-methylnaphthalene undergoes bromination and nitration at the 1-position. This position, however, though particularly reactive by virtue of both the α- and the *o*-relationships, is flanked by a substituent on one side and by the adjacent ring on the other, and it is consequently hindered. In reactions subject to hindrance and to temperature effects, a 1-derivative is produced only as a transient phase, for under the usual operating conditions the substituent assumes a position in the second ring. Nitration of β-methylnaphthalene, which proceeds normally, may be contrasted to the sulfonation at only slightly elevated temperature, which affords the pure 6-sulfonic acid in high yield. Unhindered β-positions are available in the second ring at 6 and 7, and the fact that the 6-derivative is produced in high yield shows that the methyl group across

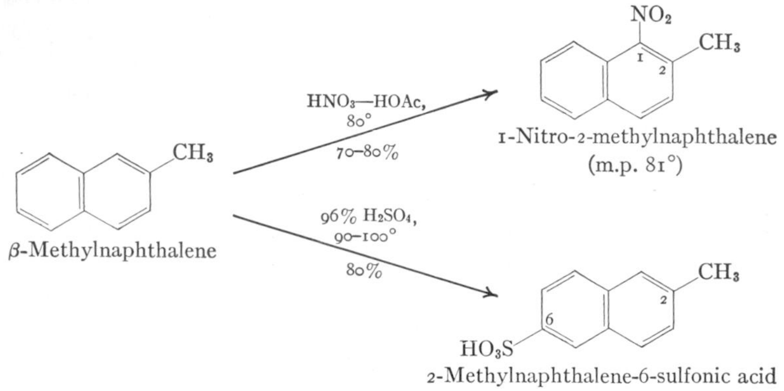
NO₂
CH₃
HNO₃—HOAc, 80°
70–80%
1-Nitro-2-methylnaphthalene (m.p. 81°)
CH₃
β-Methylnaphthalene
96% H₂SO₄, 90–100°
80%
CH₃
HO₃S
2-Methylnaphthalene-6-sulfonic acid

the molecule in the *amphi* position exercises control over the course of heteronuclear substitution. The behavior of 2,6-dimethylnaphthalene is interesting. On sulfonation in the cold the substance is attacked in an unhindered α-position to give the 8-sulfonic acid, which rearranges quantitatively when the sodium salt is heated with 78% sulfuric acid to give the β-substituted 3-sulfonate, the product of high-temperature sulfonation.

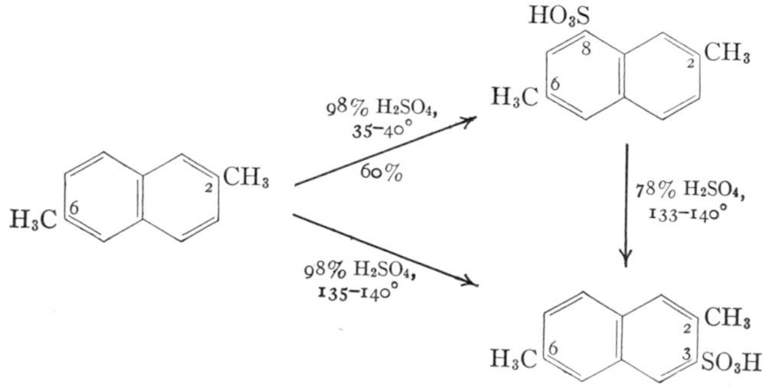
HO₃S
CH₃
H₃C
98% H₂SO₄, 35–40°
60%
CH₃
H₃C
78% H₂SO₄, 133–140°
98% H₂SO₄, 135–140°
CH₃
H₃C
SO₃H

The concentration of acid employed to effect the rearrangement is critical, for the sulfonate is hydrolyzed quantitatively to the hydrocarbon by 70% acid.

In Friedel-Crafts acylations, which also are subject to hindrance, β-methylnaphthalene is substituted in the 1-position in large part, though not exclusively, when the reaction is conducted with carbon disulfide or tetrachloroethane as solvent. In nitrobenzene solution β-methylnaphthalene is substituted principally in the 6-position (R. D. Haworth, 1932), as illustrated for the succinoylation reaction. The 6-propionyl derivative (m.p.

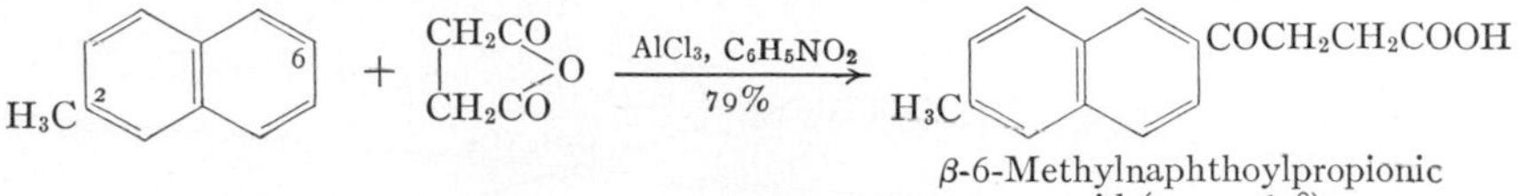

β-6-Methylnaphthoylpropionic
acid (m.p. 162°)

62°) also is easily prepared (62% yield) by acylation in nitrobenzene solution. In general, 6-acylation in this solvent is a usual reaction of β-alkylnaphthalenes.

The 6-position is the favored point of secondary attack in substitutions of β-naphthol and analogous compounds. Dibromination of β-naphthol in acetic acid solution proceeds exothermally to give the 1,6-dibromo derivative, and the more reactive bromine atom at position 1 can be eliminated by adding tin and refluxing the mixture; reduction is accomplished by reaction of the metal with hydrogen bromide derived from the bromination

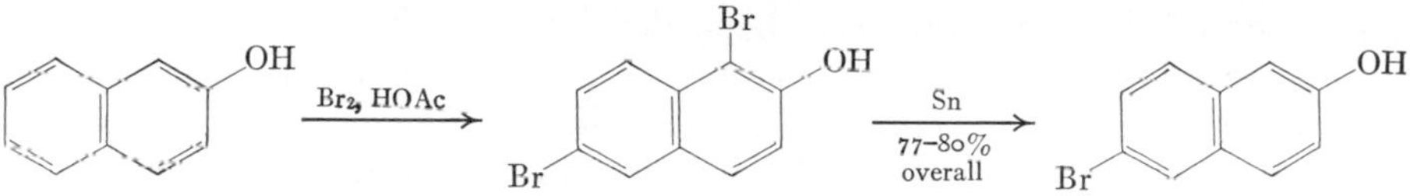

1,6-Dibromo-2-naphthol
(m.p. 106°)

6-Bromo-2-naphthol
(m.p. 129°)

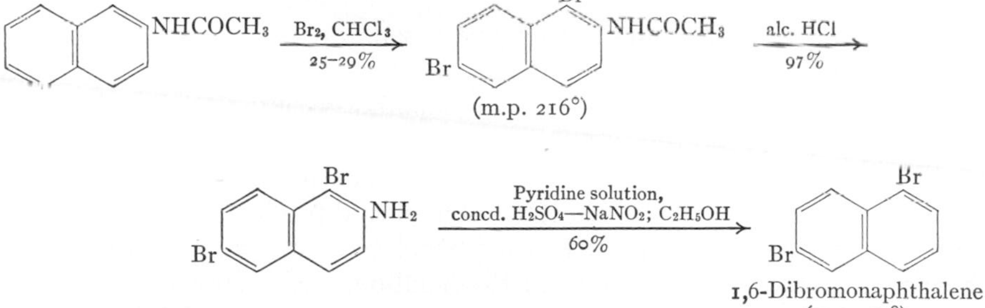

step. Investigations of the reaction by Zincke and by Fries have shown that the initially formed 1-bromo-2-naphthol reacts with bromine reversibly to from the 1,1-dibromo-2-keto compound (compare p. 735), which can be isolated if sodium acetate is added to neutralize the hydrogen bromide. If the acid is not neutralized, as in the dibromination procedure cited, the equilibrium is shifted, and the material is converted irreversibly into the 1,6-dibromo derivative. A parallel reaction is conversion of acetyl β-naphthylamine into the 1,6-dibromo derivative, a substance useful as an intermediate to 1,6-dibromonaphthalene:

(m.p. 216°)

1,6-Dibromonaphthalene
(m.p. 57°)

The effect of hindrance in the Friedel-Crafts reaction is illustrated further by results of acetylation of β-methoxynaphthalene under different conditions. In carbon disulfide (or benzene) solution the chief product is the

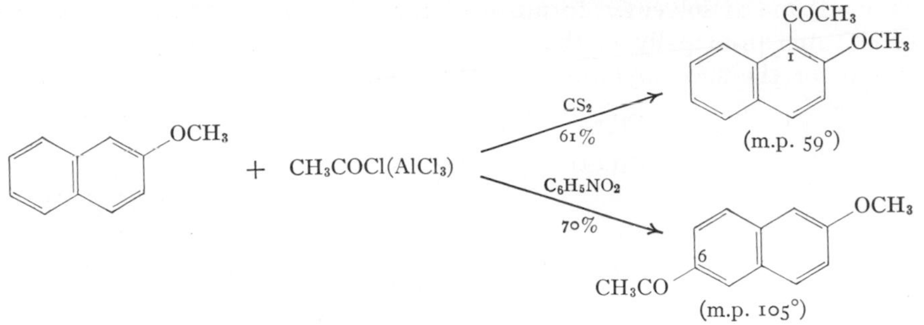

1-aceto derivative; but when the reaction is conducted in nitrobenzene solution the 6-aceto derivative is produced in good yield.

AZO DYE INTERMEDIATES

Several sulfonic acid derivatives of α- and β-naphthol and α- and β-naphthylamine are valuable coupling components for production of azo dyes, and efficient methods have been developed in the industry for preparation of important members of the series. The following summary is based largely on an account by Fierz-David and Blangey (1938).

From α-Naphthylamine. — In analogy to the formation of sulfanilic acid, the acid sulfate of α-naphthylamine, when heated at diminished pressure for several hours, undergoes rearrangement to 1-naphthylamine-4-sulfonic acid, or **naphthionic acid** (II). By a reverse Bucherer reaction,

CHART 2. REARRANGEMENT OF α-NAPHTHYLAMINE ACID SULFATE

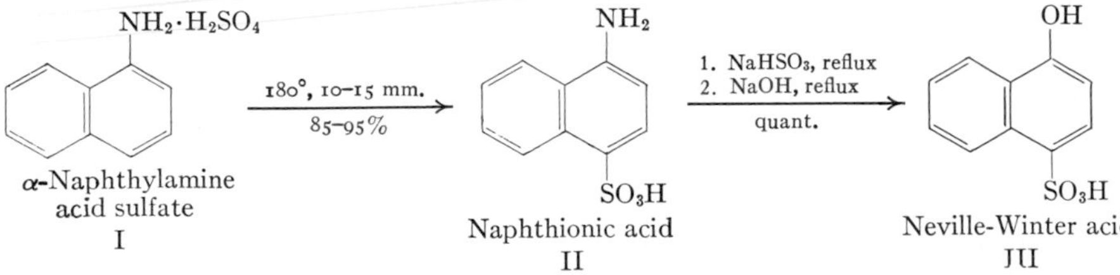

α-Naphthylamine acid sulfate
I

Naphthionic acid
II

Neville-Winter acid
III

that is, by heating the amine with aqueous sodium bisulfite and hydrolyzing the bisulfite-addition product with alkali, the substance can be converted in yield reported as quantitative into **1-naphthol-4-sulfonic acid**, or **Neville-Winter acid.**

From β-Naphthol. — The chief products obtainable by sulfonation of β-naphthol are indicated in Chart 3. The initial product, as established in low-temperature sulfonations, is 2-naphthol-1-sulfonic acid; however, this is very unstable and rearranges to the 8-sulfonic acid, **crocein acid,** which can be prepared by operating at a low temperature, but which in the more useful sulfonation conducted at steam-bath temperature rearranges to the technically important **2-naphthol-6-sulfonic acid,** or **Schaeffer acid.** Although with proper control this acid is the chief product, it is accompanied by the 6,8- and 3,6-disulfonic acids, which are used as dye intermediates and are known as **G-acid** and **R-acid,** respectively, because of the yellowish ("gelb") and reddish colors of the derived azo dyes. The sulfonation mixture also contains small amounts of 2-naphthol-1,6-disulfonic acid and

CHART 3. SULFONATION OF β-NAPHTHOL

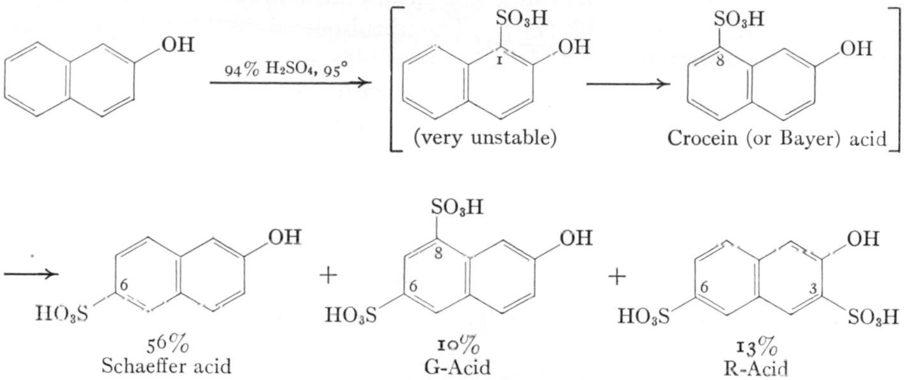

2-naphthol-1,3,6-trisulfonic acid, but since these by-products have no technical value and complicate isolation of the main products, the sulfonation mixture is diluted with water and boiled to effect hydrolysis of the 1-sulfonic acid group. The mixture is then separated by virtue of the different solubilities of the metal salts, and the three important products, Schaeffer acid, G-acid, and R-acid, are obtained in a fairly pure state in the yields indicated. The procedure can be varied to make G-acid the principal product (87–93% yield) by increasing the amount and concentration of acid and by controlling the temperature to 60° to favor retention of the α-sulfonic acid group at the 8-position. Schaeffer acid on alkali fusion affords 2,6-dihydroxynaphthalene, m.p. 218° (51% yield).

When β-naphthol is sulfonated with sulfuric acid, even at room temperature, the initially formed 2-naphthol-1-sulfonic acid rearranges rapidly under hydrogen-ion catalysis. The rearrangement can be prevented by conducting the sulfonation with chlorosulfonic acid in a suspension in nitrobenzene at ice-bath temperature (Chart 4), and the 1-sulfonic acid,

CHART 4. SULFONATION OF β-NAPHTHOL IN A NONAQUEOUS MEDIUM

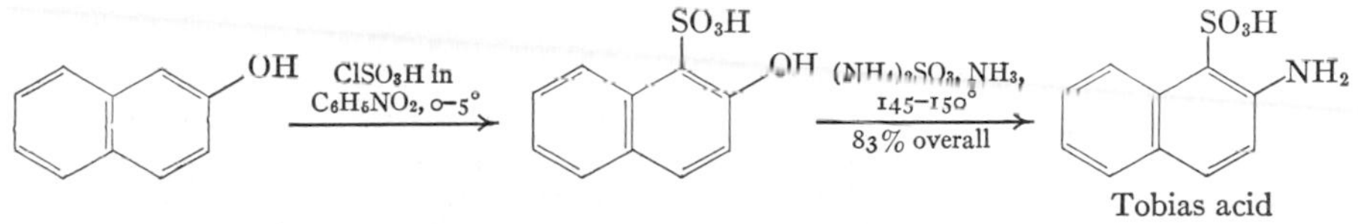

which can be isolated if desired as the pure sodium salt by extraction with water and addition of sodium chloride, is an intermediate in the production, by the Bucherer reaction, of the dye component **2-naphthylamine-1-sulfonic acid,** or **Tobias acid.**

   From β-Naphthylamine. — Two useful dye intermediates, **γ-acid** and **J-acid,** are prepared in a sequence of reactions starting with the sulfonation of β-naphthylamine sulfate (I) with strong oleum (Chart 5). The amine is present as the ion, and the positively charged ammonium group deactivates the ring to which it is attached and hence largely diverts the entering groups into the other ring. With suitable adjustment of the conditions the main products are 2-naphthylamine-6,8-disulfonic acid (II) and 2-naphthylamine-1,5,7-trisulfonic acid (IV). The disulfonic acid is distinctly less soluble than the trisulfonic acid and is precipitated in a pure condition on suitable dilution of the reaction mixture with ice. The precipitated 2-naphthylamine-6,8-disulfonic acid on fusion with alkali under appropriate conditions is converted into γ-acid (III), since the sulfonic acid group at the α-position 8 is distinctly more reactive than that situated at the β-position 6. In technological terminology, γ-acid is described as aminonaphtholsulfonic acid-2,8,6; the functional groups are numbered in the order in which they are designated in the name. The mother liquor remaining from the diluted sulfonation mixture after collection of the precipitated 2,6,8-

CHART 5. γ-ACID AND J-ACID FROM β-NAPHTHYLAMINE SULFATE (I)

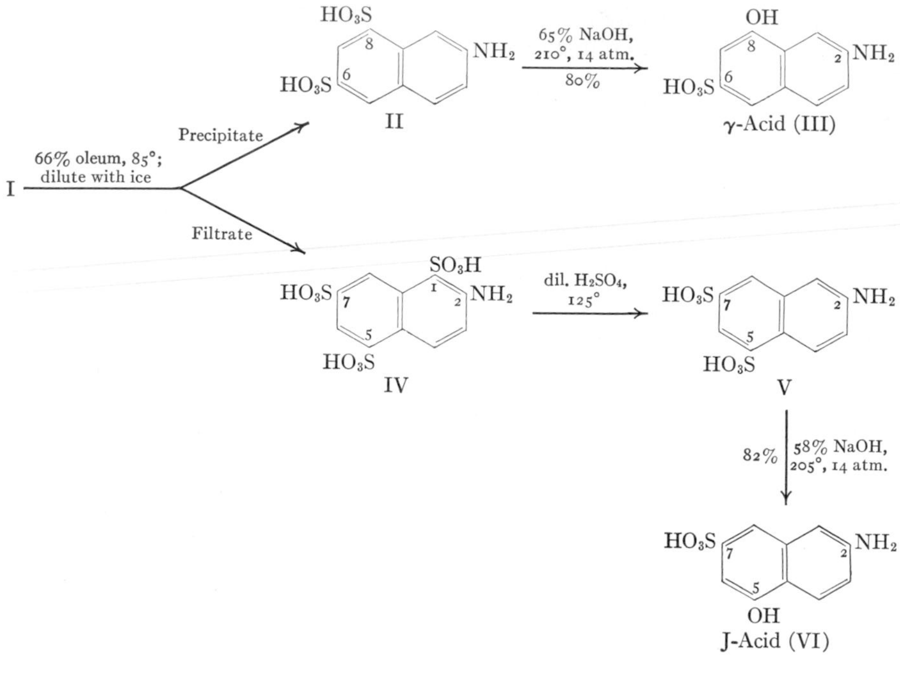

acid (II) contains 2-naphthylamine-1,5,7-trisulfonic acid (IV). When the dilute sulfuric acid solution is heated at 125°, the sulfonic acid group in the 1- or α-position is eliminated, with formation of 2-naphthylamine-5,7-disulfonic acid (V). Alkali fusion of V proceeds, as with the isomer II, by preferential attack of the α-sulfonic acid group, and 2-amino-5-naphthol-7-sulfonic acid, or J-acid, is produced in good yield.

From Naphthalene-β-Sulfonic Acid. — Mononitration of naphthalene-β-sulfonic acid (Chart 6) results in attack of the unsubstituted ring in the

CHART 6. CLEVE'S ACID-1,6 AND -1,7

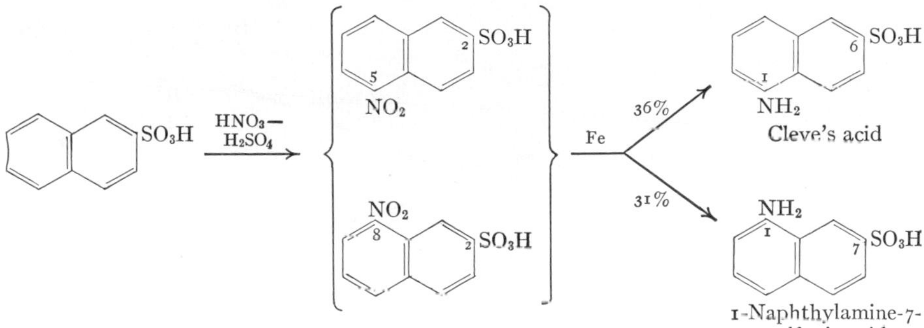

α-positions 5 and 8, and reduction of the product affords an easily separated mixture of **1-naphthylamine-6-sulfonic acid**, or **Cleve's acid**, and **1-naphthylamine-7-sulfonic acid** (or Cleve's acid-1,7). In the process starting with naphthalene, neither the β-sulfonic acid nor other intermediate is isolated. The hydrocarbon is sulfonated at 165° as described (p. 737); the mixture is cooled, diluted with 85% sulfuric acid, and nitrated with 62% nitric acid, with reduction of the temperature to 15° as soon as the initially stiff mass becomes fluid enough to permit proper stirring. The mixture of nitronaphthalenesulfonic acids is reduced as the sodium salts with iron powder and water weakly acidified with acetic and hydrochloric acid. 1-Naphthylamine-7-sulfonic acid is separated by crystallization as the sparingly soluble sodium salt, and the 1,6- or Cleve's acid precipitates on acidification of the mother liquor. The two acids are valuable dye components; since they give azo dyes of practically identical color, they are often used in the form of the mixture. The yields of the separated acids indicated in Chart 6 are the overall yields from naphthalene.

H-Acid (V) and **chromotropic acid** (VI) can be made as alternative products of a sequence of reactions involving in the key step disulfonation of naphthalene-β-sulfonic acid (Chart 7). In analogy with the sulfonation of β-naphthylamine sulfate (see Chart 5), two sulfonic acid groups enter *meta* positions in the second ring on treatment of the monosulfonic acid (not isolated) with 60% oleum. On nitration of the resulting naphthalene-1,3,6-trisulfonic acid (II), substitution occurs in the only available position not *ortho* or *para* to one of the sulfonic acid groups to give III, which on reduction yields the corresponding amine, IV, **Koch acid**. Replacement of the α-sulfonic acid group at 8 to give H-acid (V, 1-amino-8-naphthol-3,6-disulfonic acid) is accomplished by fusion with weak alkali in an autoclave

CHART 7. H-ACID AND CHROMOTROPIC ACID

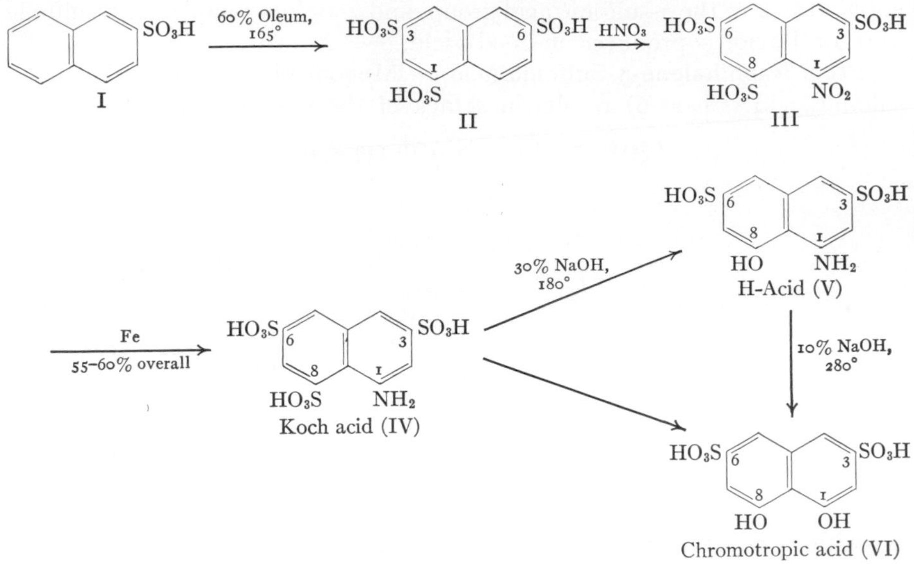

HO_3S $\xrightarrow{\text{60\% Oleum, 165°}}$ (II) $\xrightarrow{HNO_3}$ (III)

I → II → III

(V) H-Acid — 30% NaOH, 180°

$\xrightarrow{\text{Fe}}$ 55–60% overall → Koch acid (IV)

H-Acid (V) → 10% NaOH, 280°

Chromotropic acid (VI)

at a controlled temperature.   The amino group is hydrolyzed at higher temperatures, and the process thus can be varied to afford 1,8-dihydroxynaphthalene-3,6-disulfonic acid, or chromotropic acid (VI).

Nitration of Naphthalene-α-Sulfonic Acid. — By a process analogous to the preparation of Cleve's acid (Chart 6), naphthalene-α-sulfonic acid resulting from low-temperature sulfonation is converted by nitration and reduction (Chart 8) into **1-naphthylamine-8-sulfonic acid (Peri acid)** and **1-naphthylamine-5-sulfonic acid.** The 1,8-acid, resulting as the chief product in 45% yield from naphthalene, is isolated by crystallization of the sodium salt; the 1,5-acid separates as the inner salt on acidification of the mother liquor.

CHART 8.   1,8- AND 1,5-NAPHTHYLAMINESULFONIC ACIDS

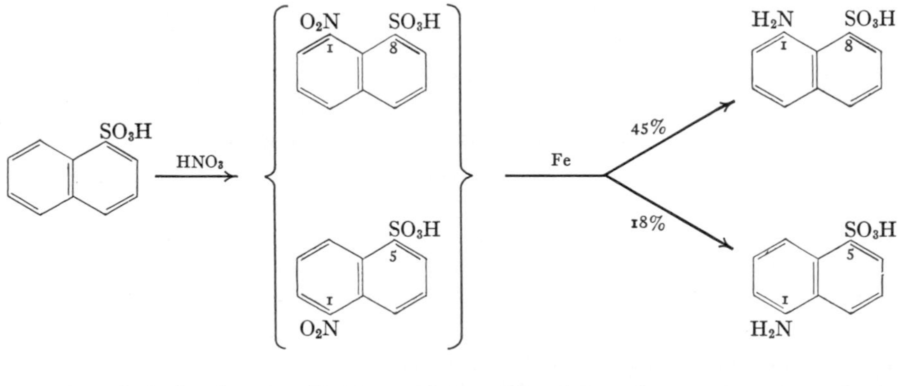

SO_3H $\xrightarrow{HNO_3}$ { (1,8-nitro) / (1,5-nitro) } $\xrightarrow{\text{Fe}}$ 45% → (1,8-amine) ; 18% → (1,5-amine)

1-Naphthylamine-8-sulfonic acid is utilized for the preparation of the further dye component **Chicago acid,** or **1-amino-8-naphthol-2,4-disulfonic acid** ("1,8,2,4-acid"), by the process outlined in Chart 9.

CHART 9. CHICAGO ACID

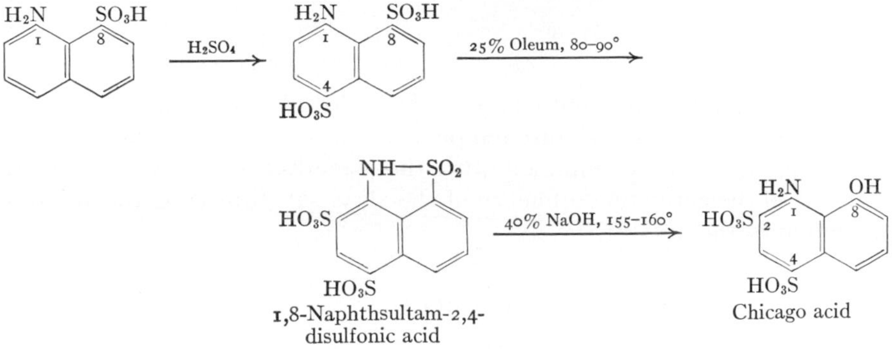

H$_2$N   SO$_3$H $\xrightarrow{\text{H}_2\text{SO}_4}$ H$_2$N   SO$_3$H $\xrightarrow{\text{25\% Oleum, 80-90°}}$

HO$_3$S

NH—SO$_2$

HO$_3$S $\xrightarrow{\text{40\% NaOH, 155-160°}}$ H$_2$N   OH   HO$_3$S

HO$_3$S   HO$_3$S
1,8-Naphthsultam-2,4-   Chicago acid
disulfonic acid

RELATIVE REACTIVITY OF NAPHTHALENE AND BENZENE

Substitutions generally proceed under milder conditions with naphthalene than with benzene, and a striking demonstration of the greater susceptibility of the bicyclic hydrocarbon to substitution is that in the Friedel-Crafts reaction of naphthalene with phthalic anhydride to form 2-α-naphthoylbenzoic acid, benzene can be used as solvent without interference with the reaction, for even though the monocyclic hydrocarbon is employed in large excess of naphthalene, very little o-benzoylbenzoic acid is formed. Naphthalene also shows greater reactivity in additions. It is reduced by sodium amalgam to the 1,4-dihydride, whereas benzene under the same conditions is unattacked. Naphthalene also is reducible to the tetrahydro stage (tetralin) with sodium and amyl alcohol, and the reaction stops abruptly at this stage because the benzenoid ring in the re-

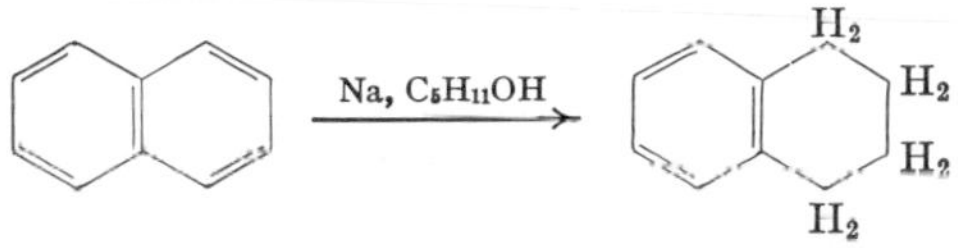

$\xrightarrow{\text{Na, C}_5\text{H}_{11}\text{OH}}$ H$_2$ H$_2$ H$_2$ H$_2$

Tetralin

action product is resistant to addition, even though the saturated side ring affixed at adjacent positions must have an activating influence. Tetralin is prepared technically by partial catalytic hydrogenation.

A similar difference in reactivity is observable in oxidation reactions. Naphthalene is oxidized more readily, but a better criterion is the course of oxidation of the methyl derivatives of the two hydrocarbons. In toluene the methyl group is more susceptible to oxidation than the aromatic nucleus, for oxidation of the hydrocarbon affords benzoic acid in high yield. In the case of β-methylnaphthalene, the reactive α-positions in the nucleus appear more susceptible to oxidation than the methyl group, for oxidation with chromic acid under mild conditions affords chiefly 2-methyl-1,4-naphtho-

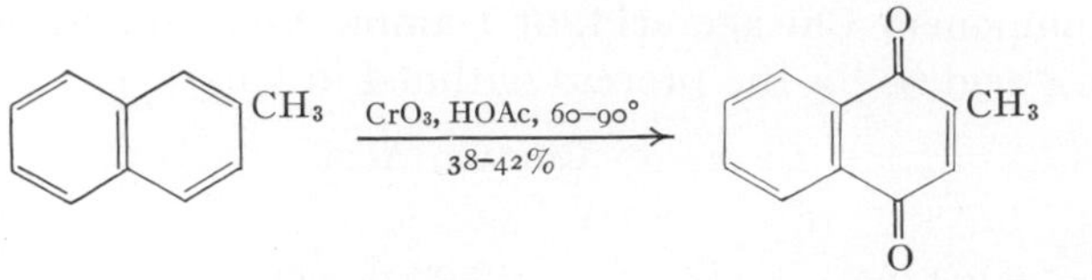

$$\text{CH}_3 \xrightarrow[\substack{38\text{-}42\%}]{\text{CrO}_3,\ \text{HOAc},\ 60\text{-}90^\circ} \text{CH}_3$$

2-Methyl-1,4-naphthoquinone

quinone. Naphthalene itself has been converted by oxidation with chromic acid in acetic acid at a moderate temperature into α-naphthoquinone in 16% yield; the higher yield obtained with the β-methyl derivative can be attributed to the activating influence of the alkyl substituent on the adjacent α-position of the nucleus.

PROBLEMS

1. Suggest methods for the preparation of each of the following compounds from an available monosubstitution product of naphthalene:

   (a) β-Benzoylnaphthalene   (c) β-Iodonaphthalene
   (b) α-Naphthaldehyde   (d) β-Isopropylnaphthalene

2. Indicate methods by which each of the following compounds can be prepared from β-naphthol:

   (a) 2,6-Dihydroxynaphthalene   (d) 6-Ethyl-2-hydroxynaphthalene
   (b) 1-Amino-2-naphthol   (e) 1-n-Propyl-2-naphthol
   (c) 1-Nitroso-2-naphthol

3. Give methods for the preparation of each of the following compounds from β-methyl-naphthalene:

   (a) 1-Amino-2-methylnaphthalene   (c) 6-Methyl-2-naphthylamine
   (b) 2-Methylnaphthalene-6-carboxylic acid

4. How could the following compounds be obtained starting with α-nitronaphthalene or its reduction product?

   (a) 1,5-Diaminonaphthalene   (c) 2,4-Diamino-1-naphthol
   (b) 1,3-Dibromonaphthalene

5. Outline a synthesis of phenanthrene from naphthalene.

READING REFERENCES

H. E. Fierz-David and L. Blangey, "Grundlegende Operationen der Farbenchemie," J. Springer. Vienna (1938)
N. L. Drake, "The Bucherer Reaction," in R. Adams, "Organic Reactions," I, 105–128, Wiley New York (1942)

POLYNUCLEAR HYDROCARBONS

PHENANTHRENE

Phenanthrene is made up of three benzene rings fused at the *o*-positions in the angular arrangement, and the name is derived from the fact that the structure includes a diphenyl unit and is isomeric with that of anthracene. On the basis of the Fries rule, the bond structure I, which contains three normal Kekulé rings, would be expected to represent the most stable state; the ring systems AB and BC correspond to normal naphthalenoid units. Evidence of the same nature as that adduced with respect to naphthalene indicates comparable bond fixation. Thus the allyl ether of 2-phenanthrol (II) undergoes Claisen rearrangement to the 1-allyl-2-hydroxy compound III, but the allyl ether of III fails to undergo further rearrangement; the normal diazo coupling of 2-phenanthrol in the 1-position is blocked by an alkyl substituent at position 1.

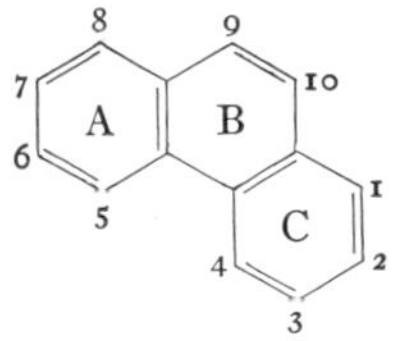

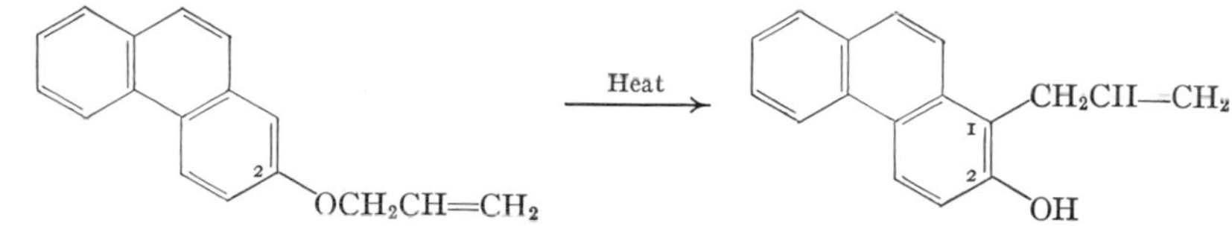

The positions 1, 2, 3, 4, and 9 are all different, and hence five monosubstitution products of phenanthrene are possible. The number of possible disubstitution products is twenty-five. All the monomethylphenanthrenes and the phenanthrols are known (Table 32.1). The succinic anhydride syn-

TABLE 32.1. METHYLPHENANTHRENES AND PHENANTHROLS; M.P., °C.

POSITION	CH$_3$			OH		
	Hydrocarbon	Picrate	Quinone	Phenanthrol	Acetate	Methyl ether
1	118	136	191	157	206	105
2	56	119	147	169	143	100
3	63	138	206	123	116	63
4	50	141	187	113	59	68
9	91	153	. . .	155	77	98

thesis, as elaborated by R. D. Haworth (1932), provides a route to the majority of the hydrocarbons. Succinoylation of naphthalene affords a separable mixture of β-1- and β-2-naphthoylpropionic acid (p. 738), with the keto-acid side chain shown in the partial formula IV, Chart 1. Such an acid can be reduced by the Clemmensen method, the γ-arylbutyric acid (V)

CHART 1. VARIATIONS OF THE SUCCINIC ANHYDRIDE SYNTHESIS

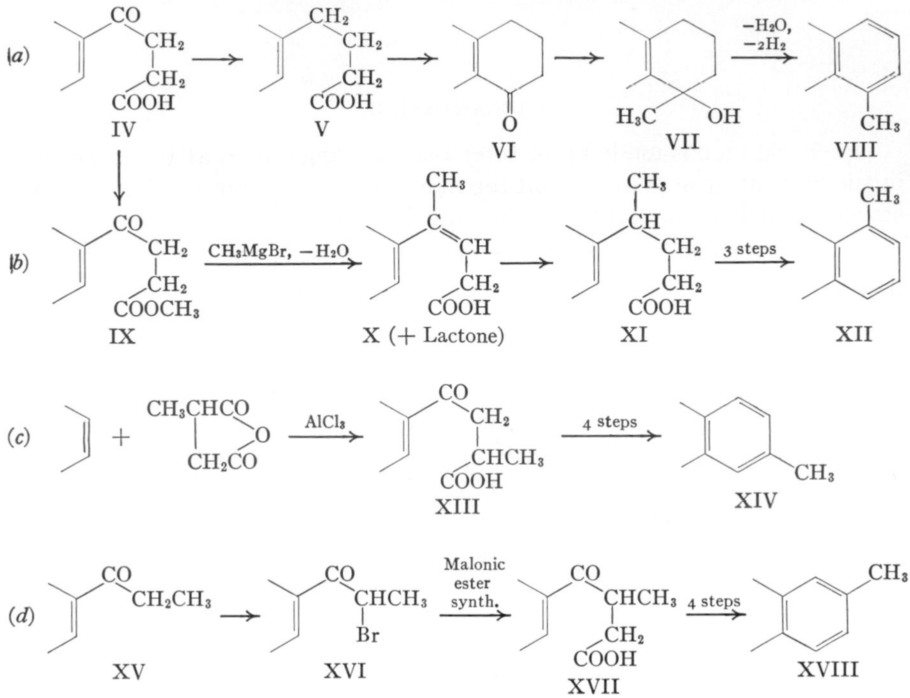

cyclized, and a methyl group introduced by the Grignard reaction, as shown in scheme (a). In the variation (b) a methyl group is introduced by a Grignard reaction on the keto ester IX, or sometimes on the free acid; the initially formed carbinol suffers loss of water and hydrolysis of the estei group in the course of the reaction to give the unsaturated acid X, along with some of the corresponding γ-lactone. The acid X is hydrogenated and the synthesis completed by ring closure, Clemmensen reduction of the ketone, and dehydrogenation. Methylsuccinic anhydride can be used, as shown in (c), and condensation occurs at the less hindered carbonyl group farther removed from the methyl substituent (XIII). Scheme (d) illustrates a method of introducing a methyl group at the remaining position in the chain by the malonic ester synthesis. Cyclic ketones of the type VI serve as intermediates for preparation of 1- and 4-phenanthrol, as already illustrated (p. 625). Both 2- and 3-phenanthrol are prepared from the sulfonates, and the 9-isomer is available by a method described below.

Most substitution reactions proceed poorly with phenanthrene, for the reaction mixture usually contains not only several monosubstitution products but appreciable amounts of di derivatives and unchanged hydrocar-

bon.   One exception is bromination, which affords 9-bromophenanthrene
in good yield (p. 564).   This compound is a useful intermediate for preparation of the 9-nitrile and 9-carboxylic acid.   9-Acetophenanthrene (m.p.

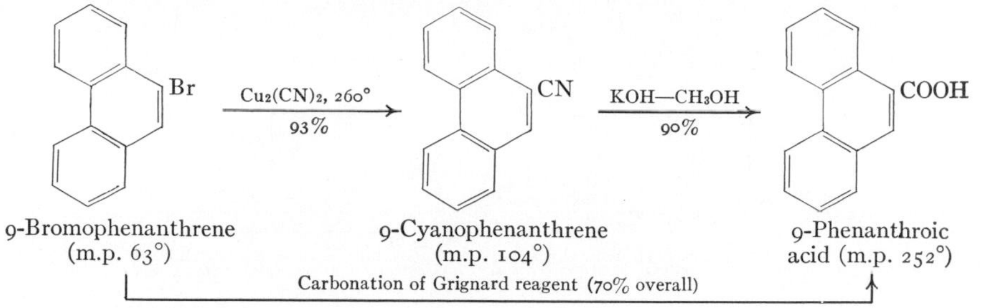

9-Bromophenanthrene   9-Cyanophenanthrene   9-Phenanthroic
(m.p. 63°)   (m.p. 104°)   acid (m.p. 252°)

Carbonation of Grignard reagent (70% overall)

74.5°) is made by the action of methyl Grignard reagent on the nitrile (57%
yield), and 9-phenanthraldehyde (m.p. 101°) from the acid by the Rosenmund reaction (90% yield).   A route to 9-phenanthrol is addition of methyl
hypobromite (mixture of bromine and methanol) to the reactive double
bond, elimination of hydrogen bromide, and hydrolysis.   Another useful

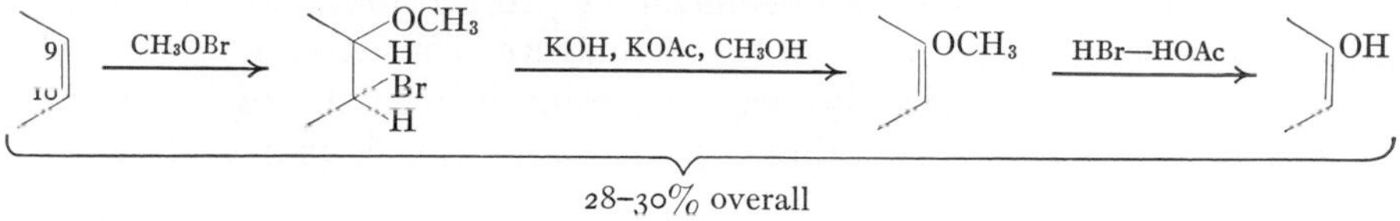

28–30% overall

addition illustrating the olefinic character of the 9,10-double bond is hydrogenation of phenanthrene to the 9,10-dihydride, accomplished in nearly
quantitative yield by the use of copper–chromium oxide at a moderate
temperature.

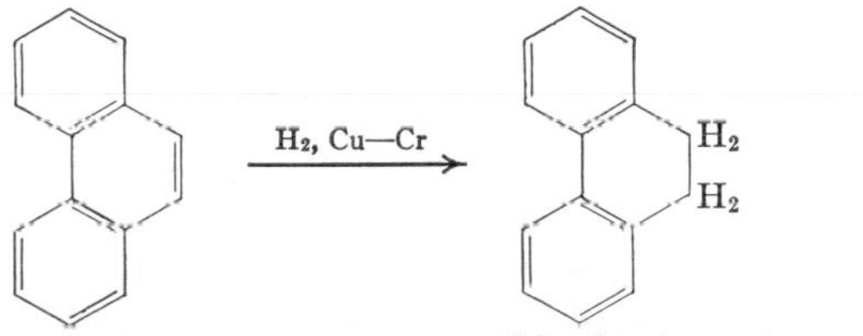

9,10-Dihydrophenanthrene
(m.p. 35°)

The course of sulfonation and of Friedel-Crafts reactions is influenced
by hindrance at positions corresponding to α-positions in the naphthalene
rings.   The β-positions 2, 3, 6, and 7 are favored sites of attack, and α-
derivatives have been isolated in small amounts only in low-temperature
reactions.   Results of sulfonations at two temperatures are indicated in the
formulas.   The reaction mixture resulting at 60° contains, in addition to
the four monosulfonic acids indicated, the 2,6-, 2,7-, 2,8-, 3,6-, and 3,8-
disulfonic acids.   When the temperature is increased to 120°, there is less
sulfonation in the hindered α-positions and an increase in the amounts of

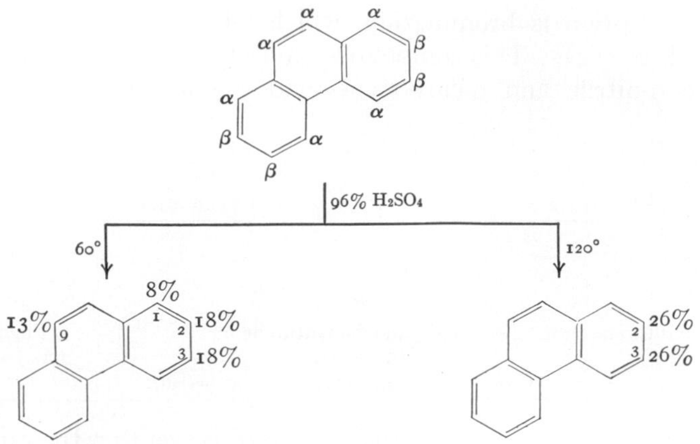

α α
α β
β
α α
β α
β

96% H_2SO_4

60°

120°

13% 8% 18% 18%

26% 26%

the β-acids 2 and 3; the 2-acid is isolated as the sparingly soluble barium salt and the 3-acid by crystallization of the potassium salt. The 2- and 3-sulfonic acids can be obtained readily enough to serve as intermediates for preparation of 2- and 3-phenanthrol.

Friedel-Crafts acylations of phenanthrene proceed most satisfactorily in nitrobenzene solution at 0–15° and give mixtures consisting largely of the 2- and 3-isomers with the 3-isomer predominating, as shown in the first two citations. 3-Acetophenanthrene (m.p. 74.5°) can be prepared in prac-

Phenanthrene, $C_{14}H_{10}$

CH_3COCl, $AlCl_3$, $C_6H_5NO_2$ → { 2-$C_{14}H_9COCH_3$ (15%)
3-$C_{14}H_9COCH_3$ (64%)

Succinic anhydride, $AlCl_3$, $C_6H_5NO_2$ → 3-$C_{14}H_9COCH_2CH_2COOH$ (50–60%)

$(C_6H_5COCl \cdot AlCl_3)_2$, CS_2 → 1-$C_{14}H_9COC_6H_5$ (8%)

tical amounts by this method and serves as the best source of 3-phenanthroic acid (m.p. 270°), which results on hypochlorite oxidation (75% yield), and of 3-phenanthrylamine (m.p. 87.5°), obtained by Beckmann rearrangement of the oxime and hydrolysis of the acetylamino compound (56–66% yield). Succinoylation of phenanthrene in nitrobenzene solution similarly affords β-3-phenanthroylpropionic acid (m.p. 149°) in fair yield. The best route to 2-acyl derivatives is Friedel-Crafts acylation of 9,10-dihydrophenanthrene and dehydrogenation, for the dihydride, which in effect is a diphenyl derivative, is substituted exclusively in position 2, *para* to the diphenyl linkage. When phenanthrene is condensed in carbon disulfide solution with the Perrier compound from benzoyl chloride and aluminum chloride,

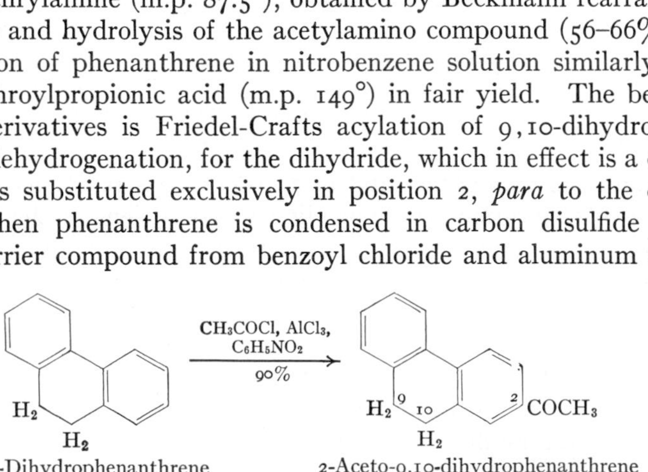

CH_3COCl, $AlCl_3$, $C_6H_5NO_2$
90%

H_2
H_2
9,10-Dihydrophenanthrene

H_2 9 10 2 $COCH_3$
H_2
2-Aceto-9,10-dihydrophenanthrene
(m.p. 52°)

1-benzoylphenanthrene (m.p. 149.5°) is deposited as a sparingly soluble, and hence easily separated complex; the 1-isomer is thus isolated readily though in low yield.

Contrary to expectations based on analogy to the behavior of naphthalene, nitration takes a course different from that of bromination and results in attack not only at the reactive position 9 but at positions 2, 3, and 4. The separation of isomers is difficult and the reaction has no preparative value. The 2- and 3-phenanthrylamines are made preferably from the aceto compounds, and the 1-, 4-, and 9-isomers from the phenanthrols by the Bucherer reaction. Oxidation takes the normal course of attack at the reactive central position and affords the 9,10-quinone; the yield is higher than that obtained in the oxidation of naphthalene. The orange o-quinone is readily purified by extraction from the reaction mixture as

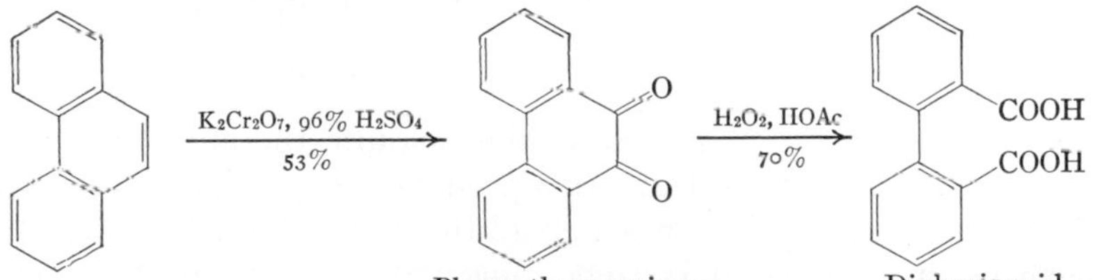

$K_2Cr_2O_7$, 96% H_2SO_4
53%

H_2O_2, HOAc
70%

COOH
COOH

Phenanthrenequinone
(orange, m.p. 206°)

Diphenic acid

the colorless water-soluble bisulfite compound, which is subsequently decomposed by neutralization with soda of the sodium bisulfite in the equilibrium mixture. The quinone ring can be opened by further oxidation, preferably with hydrogen peroxide in acetic acid solution, with the production of diphenic acid. Alkylphenanthrenes having no substituents at 9 and 10 are converted into the corresponding alkyl-9,10-phenanthrenequinones on oxidation with chromic acid, as illustrated by the example of retene, a

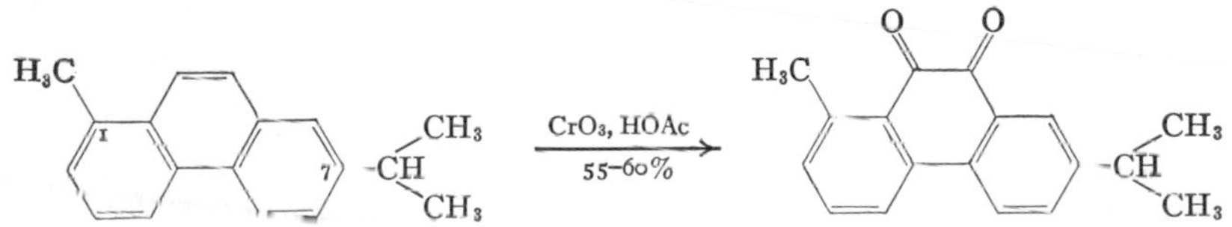

H_3C

CH_3
-CH
CH_3

CrO_3, HOAc
55–60%

H_3C
O O

CH_3
-CH
CH_3

Retene (m.p. 99°)

Retenequinone (m.p. 197.5°)

degradation product of acids derived from pine resin. When phenanthrene is oxidized with alkaline permanganate the phenanthrenequinone formed undergoes benzilic acid rearrangement (p. 707), and the final product is fluorenone:

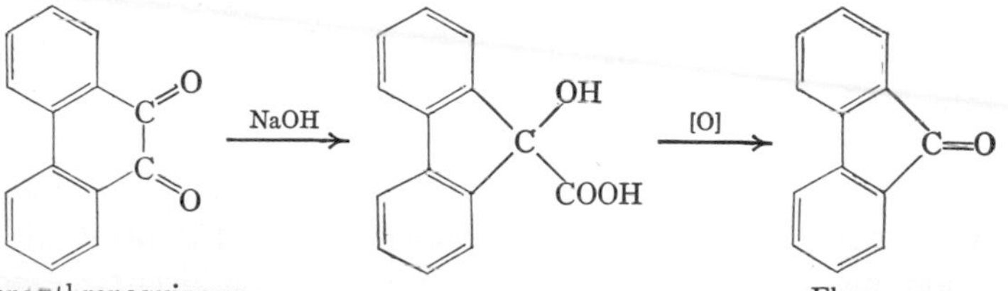

C=O
C=O

NaOH

OH
C
COOH

[O]

C=O

Phenanthrenequinone

Fluorenone
(yellow, m.p. 84°)

ANTHRACENE

The linear tricyclic hydrocarbon anthracene (Gr. *anthrax*, coal) is an important dye intermediate produced in quantity from coal tar. The physical properties (p. 528), characteristic blue fluorescence (p. 529), and nitro complexes (p. 586) have been described. X-ray measurements indicate that all fourteen carbon atoms lie in the same plane. Since the hydrocarbon is easily converted into and obtained from anthraquinone, the numbering system conforms to that obviously applicable to the quinone. The middle

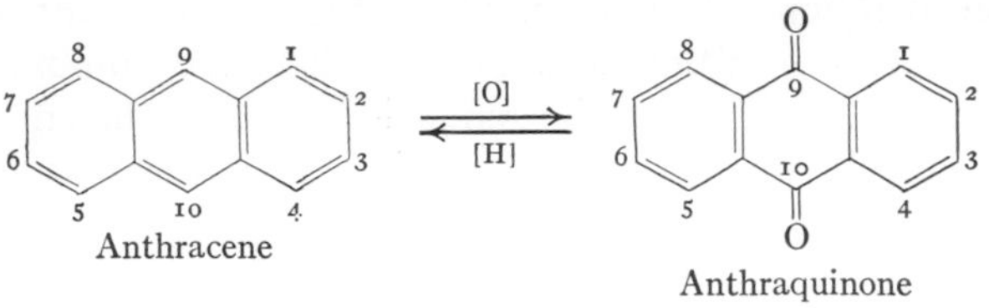

Anthracene

Anthraquinone

or *meso* positions in the hydrocarbon thus acquire the numbers 9 and 10. Three mono- and fifteen disubstitution products are possible. No formulation of anthracene is possible in which all three rings have the normal bond arrangement of an isolated benzene ring. Structure I at least contains only one *o*-quinonoid ring, whereas the alternate structure II has two, and hence on the basis of the Fries rule, I would be the more stable. Chemical

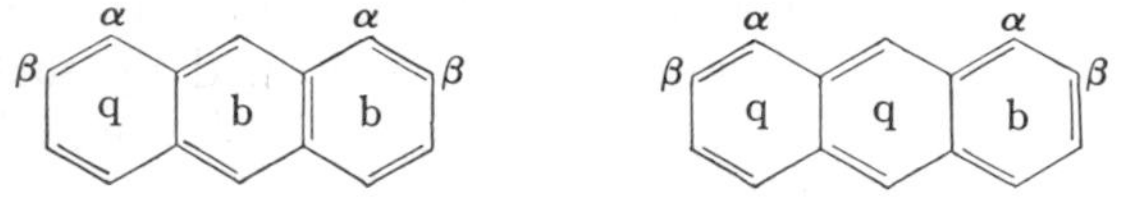

I

II

evidence indicates that the diquinonoid form II does not participate in reactions of the hydrocarbon. A differentiation can be made from the fact that in I the α- and β-positions in each terminal ring are connected by double bonds, whereas in II the connecting link is a single bond in one case. The course of bromination of 2,6-dihydroxyanthracene should provide an index of the preferred locations of the enolic *ortho* positions, and since the exclusive product of dibromination is the 1,5-isomer, the product can be formulated in accordance with form I for the hydrocarbon, as shown in III. A more rigorous test is the behavior of 1,5-dimethyl-2,6-dihydroxyanthra-

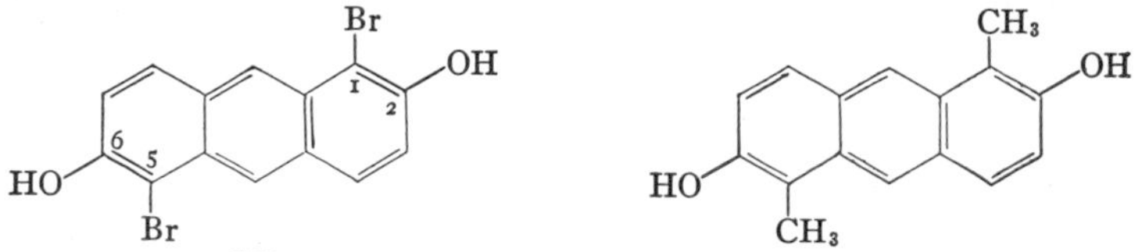

III

IV

cene (IV) toward diazo coupling components; with the positions of normal substitution blocked by alkyl groups, no coupling occurs; evidently the bond structure IV, with double bonds located at all α,β-positions, is relatively immobile.

In anthracene, or any symmetrically substituted derivatives, the structures Ia and Ib are equivalent and contribute equally to the resonance; change from one to the other requires merely a progression of the bonds in the central nucleus. In an unsymmetrical derivative such as 1,2-benzanthracene, however, the corresponding forms are not identical. Whereas form Va contains an o-benzoquinonoid ring, the nonbenzenoid nucleus in

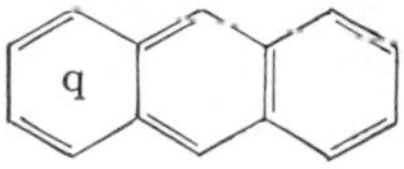

Ia 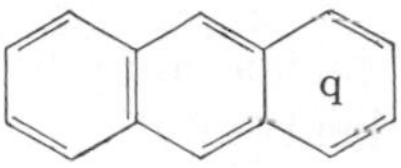   Ib

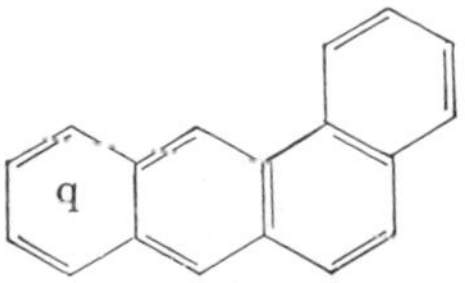

Va
(less stable)

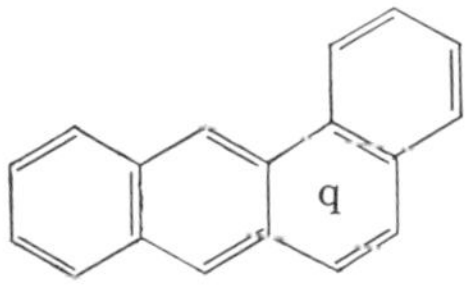

Vb
(more stable)

Vb forms a β-naphthoquinonoid system with the attached 1,2-benz ring. Since β-naphthoquinone has a much lower reduction potential than o-benzoquinone, Vb must have the lower energy content and the greater stability. Stabilization in the same sense but to a progressively decreasing extent can be anticipated for anthracenes substituted with amino, hydroxyl, and alkyl groups, whereas the reverse relationship holds for compounds with unsaturated substituents.

Reactivity of a particularly high degree is manifested at the *meso* or 9,10-positions in anthracene, a property probably attributable in part to the quinonoid system of linkages terminating at these positions and in part to the fact that the 9- and 10-positions are adjacent to and under the activating influence of both terminal rings.

Oxidation to anthraquinone can be accomplished in substantially quantitative yield with either chromic acid in acetic acid or dichromate and aqueous sulfuric acid, and the reaction proceeds more readily than oxidation of phenanthrene. Thus crude phenanthrene from coal tar can be freed from anthracene, which has the unusual effect of raising the melting point, by preferential oxidation of the latter. Another indication that anthracene surpasses the angular isomer in energy content is that the heat of combustion is higher by 7.0 kg.-cal. The special reactivity is evident further in additions. Hydrogen and bromine add to give the 9,10-dihydride and the 9,10-dibromide, respectively, but a more distinctive property is the ability of anthracene to function as a diene component in the Diels-Alder reaction. When heated with the hydrocarbon in boiling xylene solution, maleic anhydride adds to the diene system of the central nucleus or to the ends of the conjugated quinonoid system, to give a crystalline product having a carbon bridge spanning the *meso* positions and forming a part of two new six-membered rings. The reaction is reversible and the addition is favored by

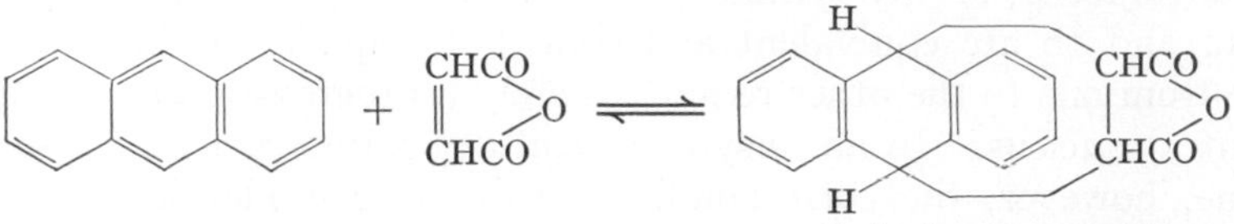

endo-Anthracene—maleic
anhydride (m.p. 263°)

an excess of maleic anhydride. The hydrocarbon can be regenerated by heating the diene-addition product in vacuum at such a temperature that

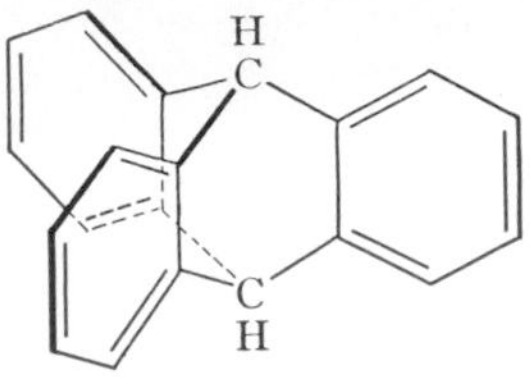

Triptycene
(colorless, m.p. 255°, unreactive)

maleic anhydride distils and displaces the equilibrium. The endocyclic derivative is stable at ordinary temperatures and withstands such transformations as hydrolysis to the corresponding dibasic acid. With the exception of certain highly alkylated hydrocarbons, naphthalene and phenanthrene derivatives do not enter into diene additions. Quinone also adds to anthracene, and the addition product has been degraded to a hydrocarbon of interesting three-dimensional configuration named triptycene (Bartlett, 1942).

Reactivity in substitutions is illustrated by the combination of anthracene with N-methylformanilide to form the 9-aldehyde (p. 680); under comparable conditions neither naphthalene nor phenanthrene is attacked. Friedel-Crafts acylations in a reactive though hindered *meso* position can sometimes be accomplished by operating at a low temperature, but the acyl group is prone to migrate to a position in a terminal ring. Mixtures result on sulfonation or nitration in the usual manner, and under certain conditions nitric acid gives a product of *meso* addition. Such substitutions are of little preparative use, for key derivatives of the series are readily available by way of anthraquinone. Anthracene reacts with lead tetraacetate in acetic acid solution to give the 9-acetoxy derivative, but when the reaction

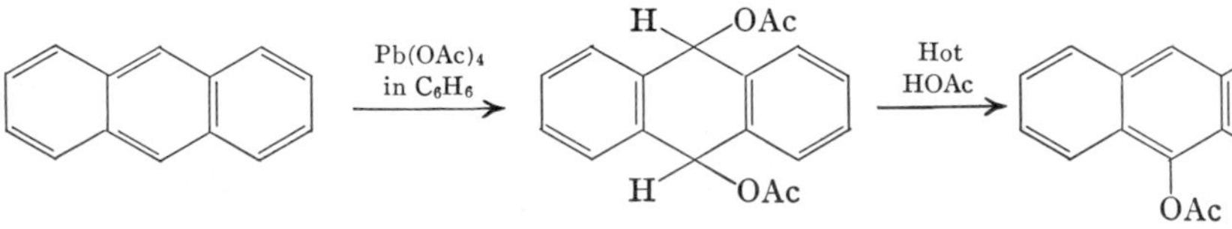

cis and *trans*

is conducted in benzene solution two isomeric products of the addition of two acetoxyl groups can be isolated; in acetic acid solution these readily lose a molecule of acetic acid and give the substitution product.

ANTHRAQUINONES

Preparation and Synthesis. — Alkyl, acetoxyl, and comparable derivatives of anthracene, like the parent hydrocarbon, are convertible into anthraquinones in high yield by direct oxidation.   In one process for the technical production of anthraquinone, coal-tar anthracene of 80–92% purity is prepared in a finely divided state by distillation with superheated steam and oxidized with sodium dichromate in suspension in dilute sulfuric acid at 80°; the anthraquinone is purified by sulfonation of any unchanged hydrocarbon and obtained in 91% yield.   The successful outcome of the reaction can be attributed to both the special reactivity of the *meso* positions and the great stability of anthraquinone.   The double bonds associated with the central ring are rendered inert by incorporation in the terminal benzene rings, and these rings are subject to the deactivating influence of the quinonoid carbonyl groups.   The system thus is resistant to oxidizing agents not only under conditions suitable for effecting oxidation at the *meso* centers but under the very drastic conditions often required for production of carboxylic acids.   Anthraquinone-β-carboxylic acid is made by oxidation of the β-methyl compound with chromic acid in boiling acetic acid solution, extraction with dilute ammonia, and reoxidation of the residue; there is

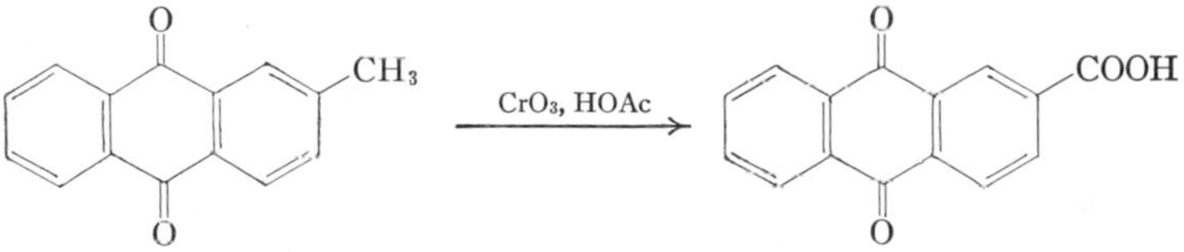

β-Methylanthraquinone

CrO₃, HOAc

Anthraquinone-β-carboxylic acid
(m.p. 291°; methyl ester, 165°)

little attack of the nucleus.   The α-carboxylic acid is made conveniently by oxidative degradation of benzanthrone (p. 915).

Benzanthrone
(m.p. 170°)

CrO₃, HOAc

Anthraquinone α-carboxylic acid
(m.p. 294°; methyl ester, 189°)

Anthraquinones of wide variety can be made in high yield by the phthalic anhydride synthesis.   Phthalic anhydride is condensed with benzene in the presence of aluminum chloride to *o*-benzoylbenzoic acid, and the keto acid is heated with concentrated sulfuric acid on the steam bath, when cyclization occurs with formation of anthraquinone.   Water is eliminated be-

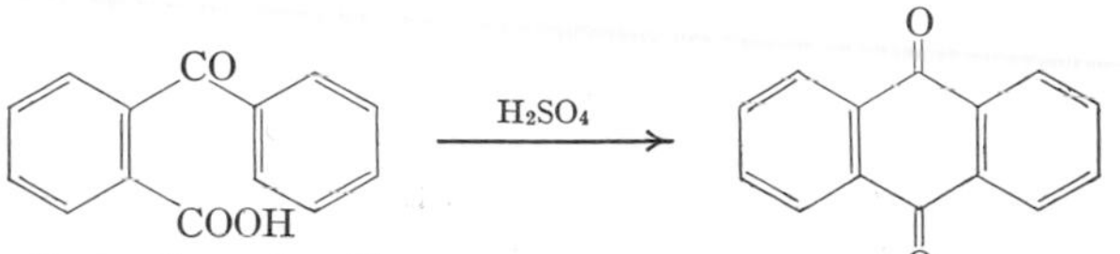

o-Benzoylbenzoic acid

H₂SO₄

Anthraquinone
(pale yellow, m.p. 286°, b.p. 377°)

tween the carboxyl group and the nuclear position of the second aryl ring *ortho* to the carbonyl group. The process rivals that of the oxidation of coal-tar anthracene as a source of the large supplies of anthraquinone required as a dye intermediate. The method of cyclization can be varied to meet specific requirements, for example by employing 80% sulfuric acid at 160°, by heating the acid with aluminum chloride, or by conducting the dehydration with benzoyl chloride at the boiling point of a solution of the keto acid in α-chloronaphthalene. The keto acids resulting from the Friedel-Crafts condensation of phthalic anhydride with toluene, *p*-xylene, and naphthalene afford the following anthraquinones:

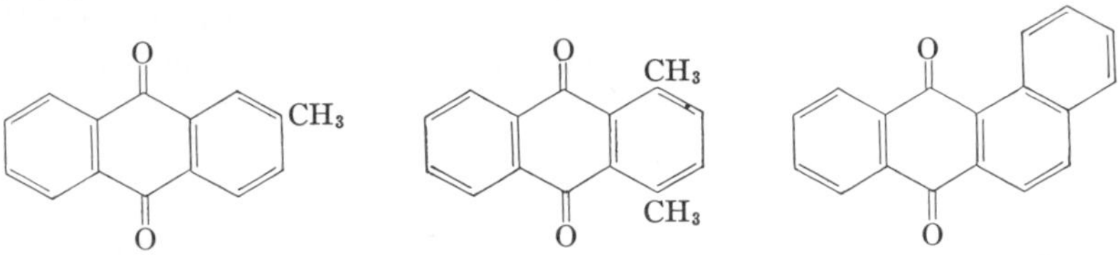

β-Methylanthraquinone   1,4-Dimethylanthraquinone   1,2-Benzanthraquinone
(m.p. 173°)   (m.p. 119°)   (m.p. 168°)

Intermediate keto acids also can be obtained by the action of the Grignard reagent of an aromatic halide on phthalic anhydride. Substituted derivatives of phthalic anhydride also can be employed, though in some instances rearrangement occurs in the course of ring closure.

The cyclization of *o*-benzoylbenzoic acid is remarkable because it involves intramolecular acylation *ortho* to a ketonic function; ordinarily ketones are not amenable to Friedel-Crafts acylation at any position. Newman (1942) suggested that the reaction proceeds through the carbonium

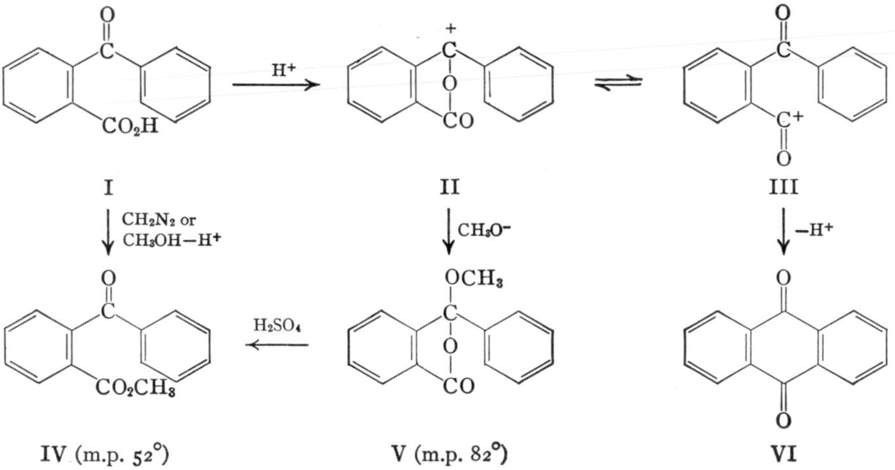

I   II   III

IV (m.p. 52°)   V (m.p. 82°)   VI

ions II and III, and showed that if a cold solution of *o*-benzoylbenzoic acid in 98% sulfuric acid is poured into methanol the chief product is the pseudo ester V; this is rearranged by sulfuric acid into the normal ester IV.

Syntheses utilizing the Diels-Alder reaction are of less practical importance. One synthesis already mentioned is from *p*-benzoquinone and two molecules of diene (p. 719). Another, involving an initial addition of a diene to a β-aroylacrylic acid, is illustrated in the following formulation:

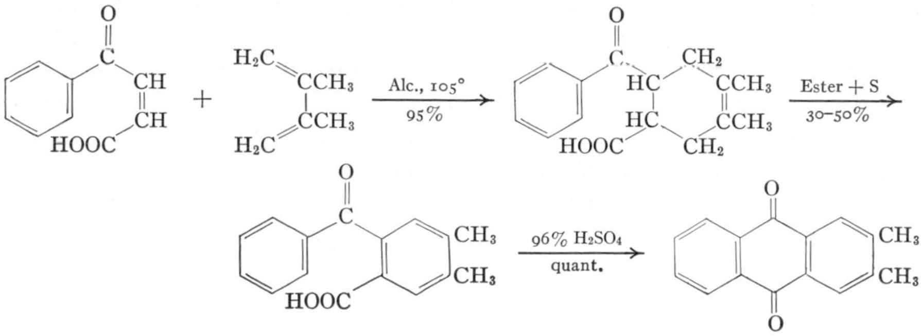

Substitution Reactions. — The resistance of anthraquinone to oxidation is paralleled by its behavior in aromatic substitutions. Halogenation is achieved with such difficulty as to be impracticable. Concentrated sulfuric acid has little action except at excessive temperatures, and oleum is required for efficient sulfonation. Anthraquinone is not subject to Friedel-Crafts acylation or alkylation under any known conditions. The resistance to substitution in a benzenoid ring can be ascribed to the deactivating influence of the two *m*-directing carbonyl groups; the α-position is *ortho* to and protected by one of these groups, and the β-position is *para* to the other. Nitration, accomplished with mixed acid under forcing conditions, affords

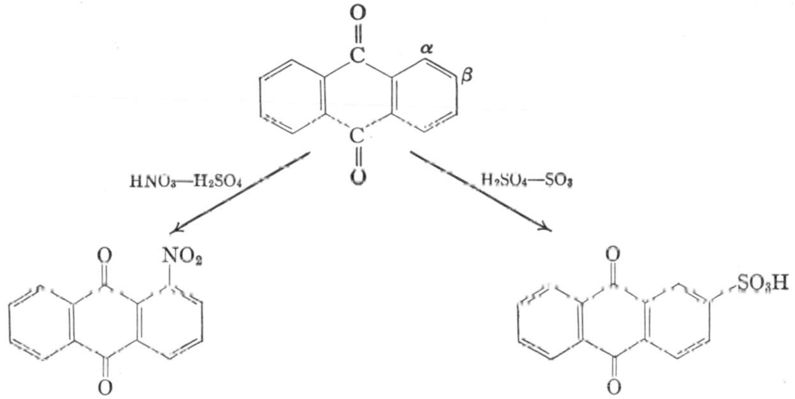

α-Nitroanthraquinone
(m.p. 230°)

Anthraquinone-β-sulfonic acid

chiefly the α-nitro derivative as the initial product, but the group first introduced has little influence on the reactivity of the other terminal ring and hence some α-substitution in this ring is inevitable, with the result that the α-nitro compound is contaminated with appreciable amounts of the 1,5- and 1,8-dinitro derivatives.

Sulfonation with fuming sulfuric acid results in attack of the less hindered β-position. Since a second sulfonic acid group enters the other terminal ring nearly as easily as the first, the most satisfactory results are obtained by conducting the reaction under such conditions that about half of the anthraquinone is sulfonated and the rest left in a recoverable condition. In one process, anthraquinone is treated with 18% oleum at 135° and then with 66% oleum at 110°; 37% of the starting material is recovered unchanged, and 78% of the material utilized is isolated as sodium anthraquinone-β-sulfonate, a substance known in the industry as silver salt because of the silvery appearance of the crystals. Disulfonation results in β-substitution in the second benzenoid ring, with formation of about equal amounts of the 2,6- and 2,7-diacids:

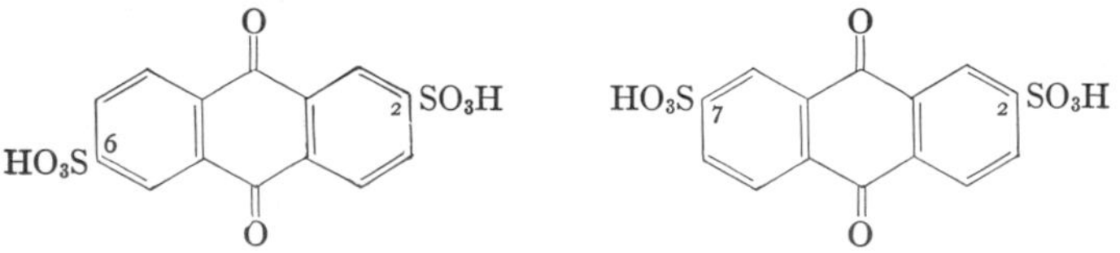

A remarkable alteration in the direction of substitution brought about by addition of a trace of a mercury salt to the sulfonation mixture was discovered independently by R. E. Schmidt[1] in Germany and by Iljinsky in Russia (1903–04); in the presence of this catalyst the sulfonic acid group enters the α-position almost exclusively. The α-sulfonic acid, isolated as the potassium salt, can be prepared in good yield (based on material utilized) by stirring an intimate mixture of anthraquinone with 2% of mercuric sulfate into 20% oleum at 135° and adding 60% oleum to the solution. On mercury-catalyzed disulfonation, the second substituent largely enters the α-positions in the other nucleus. A mixture of anthraquinone-1,6- and

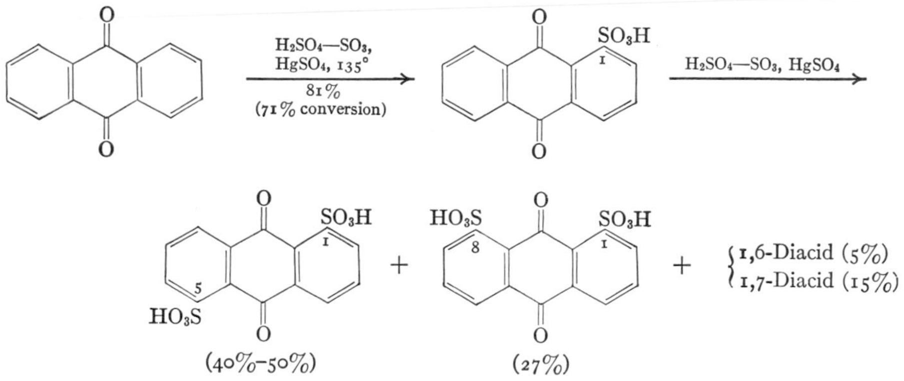

-1,7-disulfonic acid results on sulfonation of the 1-acid without catalyst and also on sulfonation of the 2-acid in the presence of a mercury salt.

---

[1] Robert E. Schmidt, 1864–1938; b. Kolmar, Germany; Ph.D. Zurich; I. G. Farbenind.

Iljinsky's discovery of the effect of mercury salts was the result of an incident in the technical production of the dye alizarin from anthraquinone by the preparation and alkali fusion of the β-sulfonate (p. 903). When production was resumed after a lapse occasioned by the Franco-Prussian war, the yield of final product was low, apparently because of the presence of a poison in the new lot of anthraquinone. Attempts to extract the poison with acids and bases gave no direct result but led to the discovery that the poisoned anthraquinone when washed with dilute hydrochloric acid reacted satisfactorily, and that the effect of the poison could be counteracted by addition of sodium chloride to the sulfonation mixture. Eventually the poisoning agent was identified as mercuric sulfate, which leads to a sulfonate that does not afford alizarin on alkali fusion; on addition of a chloride, the catalytic agent is converted into mercuric chloride (corrosive sublimate), which sublimes from the reaction mixture.

Replacement Reactions. — β-Aminoanthraquinone, an intermediate for several dyes, is made by a reaction specific to the anthraquinone series that consists in replacement of the β-sulfonic acid group by an amino group. The sulfonate group is rendered labile by the quinonoid carbonyl group in the *para* position, just as a halogen or nitro substituent in the benzene ring is activated by *ortho* or *para* unsaturated groups. When the reaction is conducted by heating the sulfonate with aqueous ammonia in an autoclave,

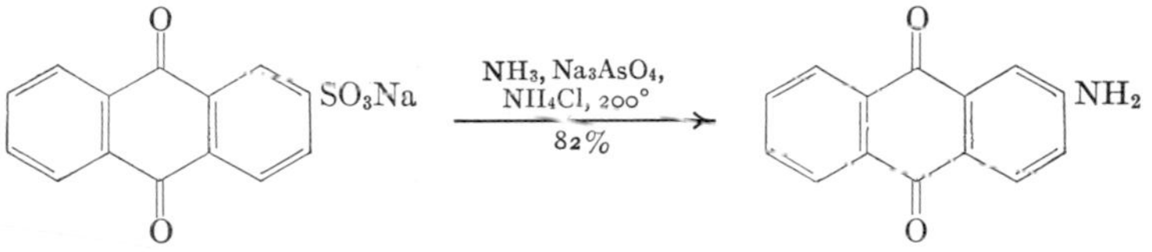

β-Aminoanthraquinone
(m.p. 302°)

the sulfite liberated has a destructive action on the end product. In a successful technical process this difficulty is obviated by use of sodium arsenate to oxidize sulfite as it is liberated to sulfate; ammonium chloride is added to check the alkalinity. Under these conditions an efficient conversion is achieved at an autoclave temperature of 200° (40 atmospheres). An even better yield of β-aminoanthraquinone is obtained by amination of β-chloroanthraquinone, prepared from phthalic anhydride and chlorobenzene. Since an α-sulfonic acid group is still more labile, α-aminoanthraquinone can be prepared by amination at a distinctly lower temperature; in this case the preferred reagent for oxidation of the liberated sulfite is

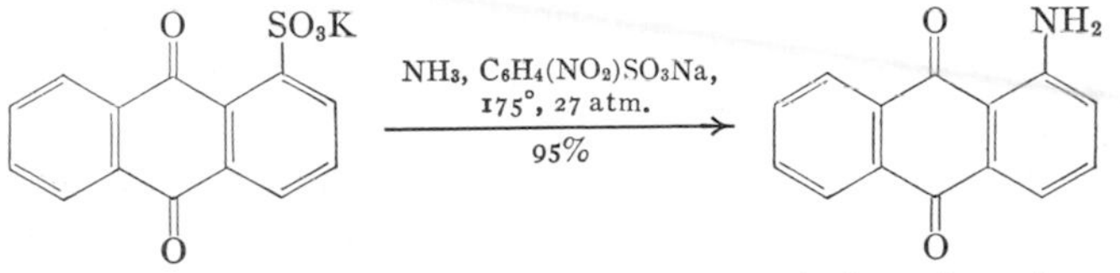

α-Aminoanthraquinone
(m.p. 246°)

sodium *m*-nitrobenzenesulfonate. Another route to α-amino compounds is reduction of α-nitroanthraquinones with sodium sulfide; thus 1-amino-2-methylanthraquinone (m.p. 202°) is prepared by nitrating the β-methyl derivative with concentrated sulfuric acid and potassium nitrate at 5° (82% yield) and reducing the 1-nitro-2-methylanthraquinone (m.p. 270°) with aqueous sodium sulfide (97% yield). The reduction potential of the anthraquinone is so low that the reagent leaves the quinonoid nucleus untouched; an intermediate alkali-soluble product is the hydroxylamine derivative.

Another special reaction is replacement of the sulfonic acid group by chlorine. The more reactive α-substituents are replaced readily as illustrated by the preparation of α-chloroanthraquinone in nearly quantitative yield by addition of sodium chlorate solution to a refluxing solution of potassium anthraquinone-α-sulfonate in dilute hydrochloric acid; nascent chlorine effects displacement of the sulfonate group and the chloro com-

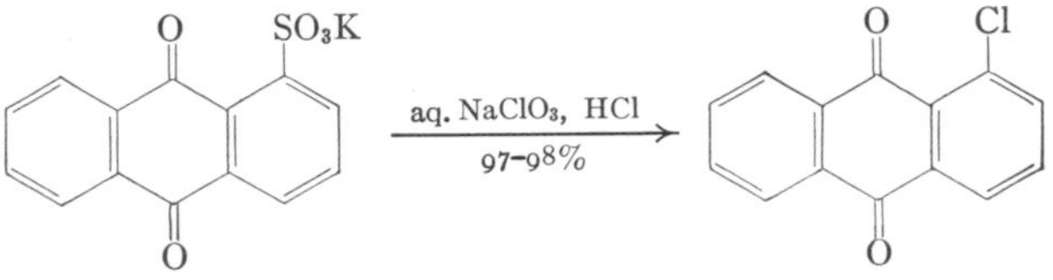

O   SO₃K

aq. NaClO₃, HCl
—————————→
97–98%

O   Cl

α-Chloroanthraquinone
(m.p. 162.5°)

pound separates as a precipitate. Sulfonic acid groups in β-positions are also replaceable by chlorine, but less rapidly and in lower yield.

Replacement of chlorine by hydroxyl is involved in the technical production of quinizarin by heating phthalic anhydride and *p*-chlorophenol with sulfuric acid containing boric acid. Hydroquinone can also be employed, but *p*-chlorophenol is cheaper. Hydrolysis probably occurs sub-

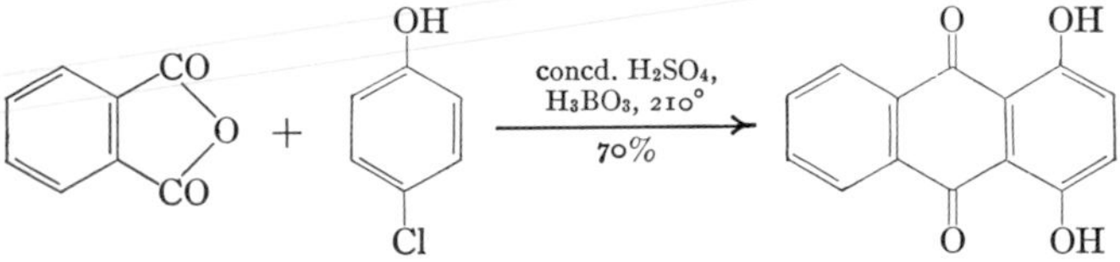

CO
      O   +
CO

OH

Cl

concd. H₂SO₄,
H₃BO₃, 210°
—————————→
70%

O   OH

O   OH

Quinizarin
(m.p. 202°)

sequently to ring closure. Boric acid combines with the quinizarin to form an ester, and hence exerts a protective action. The boric acid ester is precipitated by addition of ice and hydrolyzed by warming the diluted mixture. A related reaction is hydroxylation of anthraquinones with fuming sulfuric acid, often with the addition of boric acid (Bohn-Schmidt reaction, p. 903); the reaction is comparable to the nucleophilic hydroxylation of nitro derivatives of benzene (p. 574).

Reduction Products. — When a suspension of anthraquinone in aqueous alkali is treated with a reducing agent of suitable potential, notably sodium hydrosulfite or zinc dust, the material dissolves to give a rich blood-red solution of the sodium salt of anthrahydroquinone. On shaking with air the red color is discharged and anthraquinone is reprecipitated. The conversion of a phenolic alkali-soluble hydroquinone into a water-insoluble quinone by air oxidation of the solution is the basis of vat dyeing, and hence the red liquor resulting on the alkaline reduction of anthraquinone is known as a vat. The color is associated with salt formation, for anthrahydroquinone itself, isolated with difficulty because of its extreme sensitivity to

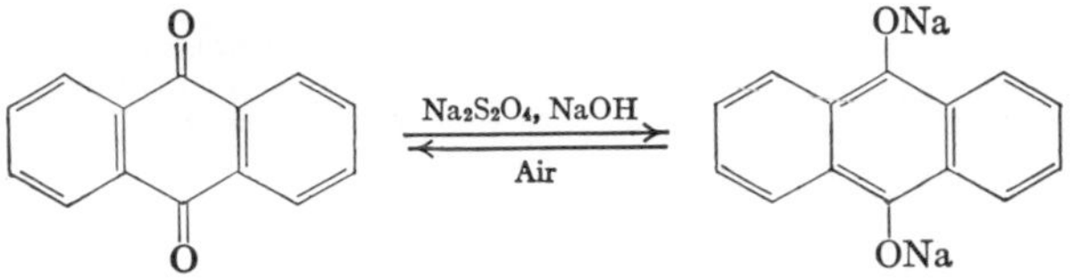

Anthrahydroquinone sodium salt

air, is yellow. All but very few anthraquinones give characteristic red vats and are hence distinguishable from quinones of other series, for example phenanthrenequinones, which give yellow vats. Purification is often accomplished by vatting a crude anthraquinone with excess hydrosulfite and alkali, filtering the red solution to remove hydrocarbon or other inert material, and blowing air through the solution. A reagent useful as an absorbent for oxygen in gas analysis or as a wash liquor for removing traces of oxygen from nitrogen or hydrogen is made by dissolving sodium hydrosulfite in alkali and adding a small amount of sodium anthraquinone-β-sulfonate. The water-soluble quinone is reduced to a blood-red vat having strong affinity for oxygen (Fieser's solution, 1924).

If the red vat from anthraquinone is heated to boiling in the presence of excess hydrosulfite or zinc dust, the color fades to yellow as the result of

Anthrone (m.p. 156°)

o-Benzylbenzoic acid (m.p. 114°)

o-Benzoylbenzoic acid

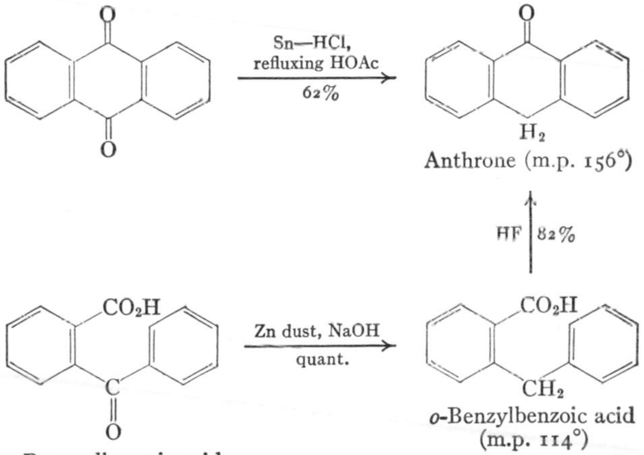

further reduction involving elimination of one of the oxygen atoms and formation of anthrone. Reduction to this stage is accomplished more satisfactorily by the action of tin and hydrochloric acid on anthraquinone, as indicated in the chart, which also shows an efficient synthesis of anthrone from the product of the Friedel-Crafts reaction of phthalic anhydride and benzene. Anthrone is the keto form of a tautomeric pair of which the enol form is anthranol. The keto compound is the more stable tautomer and is

Anthrone
(pale yellow, nonfluorescent,
insoluble in alkali)

Anthranol
(brown-yellow, fluorescent,
deep yellow in alkali)

the exclusive product of both preparative methods indicated above; the cyclization process, unlike the reduction method, is generally applicable to preparation of substituted anthrones free from the enolic form, for example 1,2-benz-10-anthrone (faintly yellow, m.p. 181°). Anthrone does not dissolve in cold alkali, but slowly tautomerizes in warm alkali to the phenolic form, and a deep yellow solution of the sodium salt of anthranol results. Free anthranol has been isolated by acidification of the alkaline solution at a low temperature. A better method consists in cleavage of anthranyl acetate with a Grignard reagent. An anthranyl acetate usually can be prepared by treatment of the anthrone with acetic anhydride in pyridine solution, for pyridine catalyzes both enolization and acetylation. The production of an intermediate ester by synthesis and its cleavage by a Grignard reagent is illustrated.

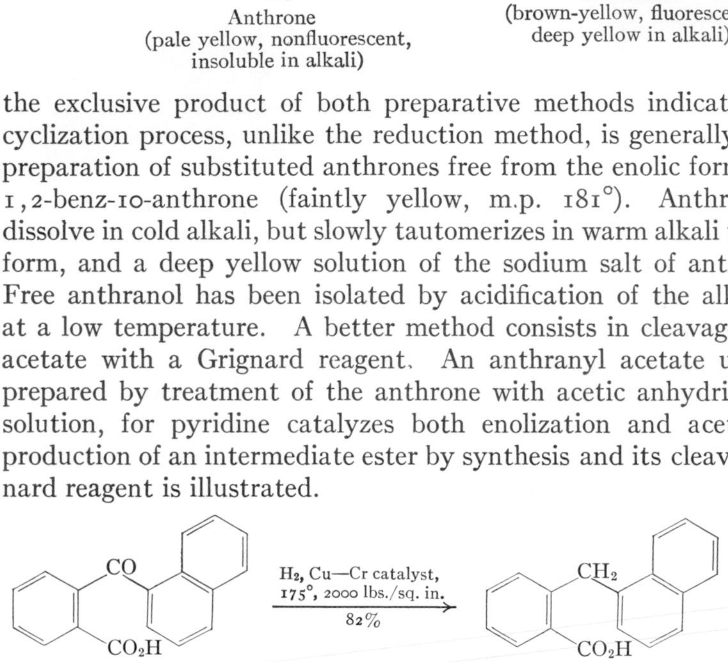

2-α-Naphthoylbenzoic acid

H_2, Cu—Cr catalyst,
175°, 2000 lbs./sq. in.
82%

2-α-Naphthylmethylbenzoic
acid (m.p. 148°)

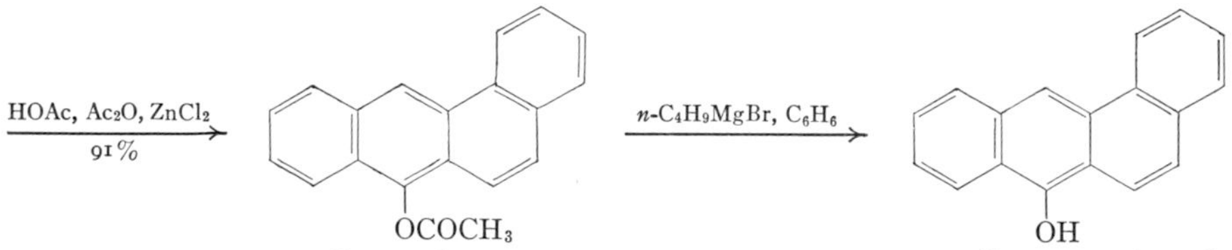

HOAc, Ac₂O, ZnCl₂
91%

1,2-Benzanthranyl-10-
acetate (m.p. 163°)

n-C₄H₉MgBr, C₆H₆

1,2-Benz-10-anthranol
(golden-yellow, m.p. 155°)

When either an anthrone or an anthranol is dissolved in an organic solvent, tautomerization occurs and the material is slowly converted into an equilibrium mixture, the point of equilibrium being dependent on the compound, the solvent, and the temperature. The ketonic, or anthrone, form adds Grignard reagents but is indifferent to most other reagents. The anthranol form on the other hand is highly reactive. It couples with diazotized amines, whereas the anthrone form does not; it is easily halogenated; it is converted by ferric chloride into a bimolecular oxidation product. That the *meso* hydroxy derivative of anthracene exists largely in a ketonized form appears to be a consequence of the *o*-quinonoid bond structure of anthracene. The migration of hydrogen from oxygen to carbon gives a more stable arrangement containing two normal Kekulé rings and a central nucleus that is not of a quinonoid, but rather of a dihydride, structure.

As noted above, the red vat from anthraquinone fades to yellow on further reduction in alkaline solution as result of conversion to the sodium salt of anthranol. Elimination of a *meso* hydroxyl group on reduction with zinc dust or hydrosulfite and alkali or ammonia is a special reaction dependent on the activated character of the *meso* position. The second *meso*

hydroxyl group can be eliminated as well, merely by continued reaction under the same conditions. Thus if anthraquinone or a substitution product is submitted to exhaustive reduction with zinc dust and sodium or ammonium hydroxide, the final product is anthracene or a corresponding derivative. Since hydroxyl groups in the terminal benzene rings are not attacked, hydroxyanthraquinones are convertible by this method into hydroxyanthracenes. The α- and β-sulfonic acid derivatives of anthraquinone can be reduced with zinc dust and ammonia to the anthracene-α- and -β-sulfonates, which on fusion with alkali afford α- and β-anthrol. The anthramines are similarly obtainable by reduction of the aminoanthraquinones. Anthraquinone itself is reduced preferably in two stages; anthrone is prepared by the method described above and is refluxed with copper sulfate-activated zinc dust, sodium hydroxide solution, and toluene. The hydrocarbon is obtained in pure and spectacularly fluorescent form in 93% yield.

INSECT DYES

Cochineal - Carminic Acid. — The natural dye cochineal consists of dried bodies of the female insect *Coccus cacti*, which lives on a species of cactus native to Mexico but cultivated elsewhere (Java). Before development of the synthetic coal tar colors, cochineal was an important mordant dye for wool and silk (red, crimson, scarlet, and violet shades). The coloring principle, carminic acid, is extracted by water and crystallizes in bright red needles (50 g. from 1 kg. of cochineal). Investigations by Liebermann, v. Miller, and notably Dimroth[2] (1909-20) established that carminic acid

---

[2] Otto Dimroth, 1872-1940; b. Munich, Germany; Ph.D. Munich (Thiele); Würzburg; *Ber.*, **74A**, 1 (1941)

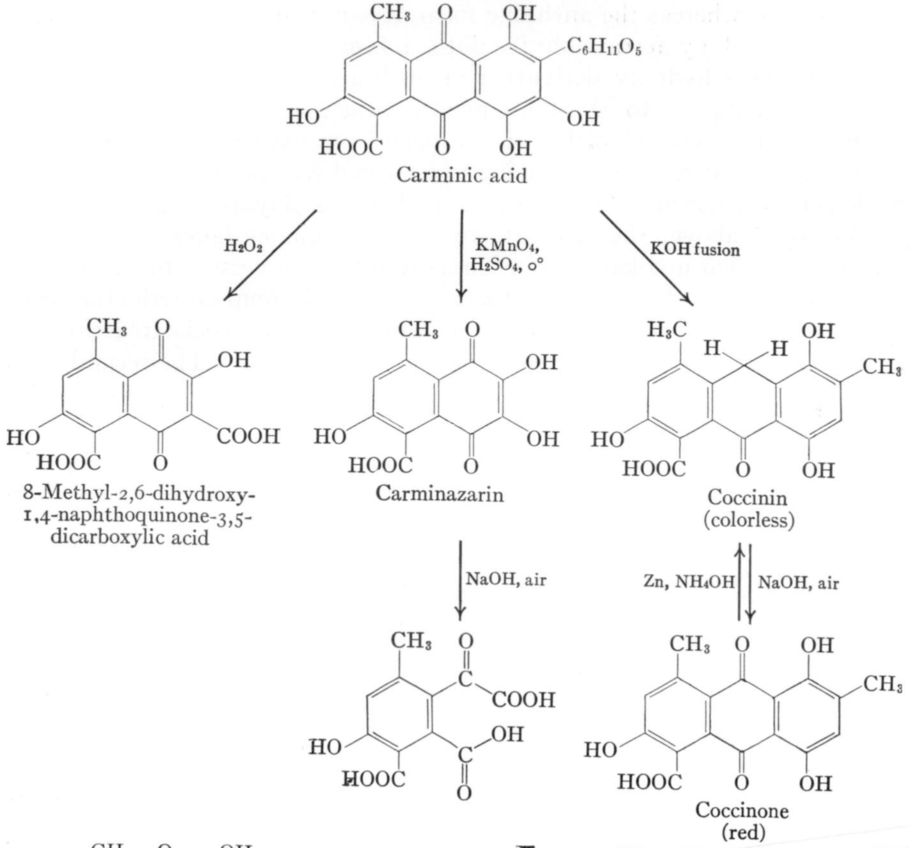

Carminic acid

H$_2$O$_2$

KMnO$_4$, H$_2$SO$_4$, 0°

KOH fusion

8-Methyl-2,6-dihydroxy-
1,4-naphthoquinone-3,5-
dicarboxylic acid

Carminazarin

Coccinin
(colorless)

NaOH, air

Zn, NH$_4$OH ‖ NaOH, air

Coccinone
(red)

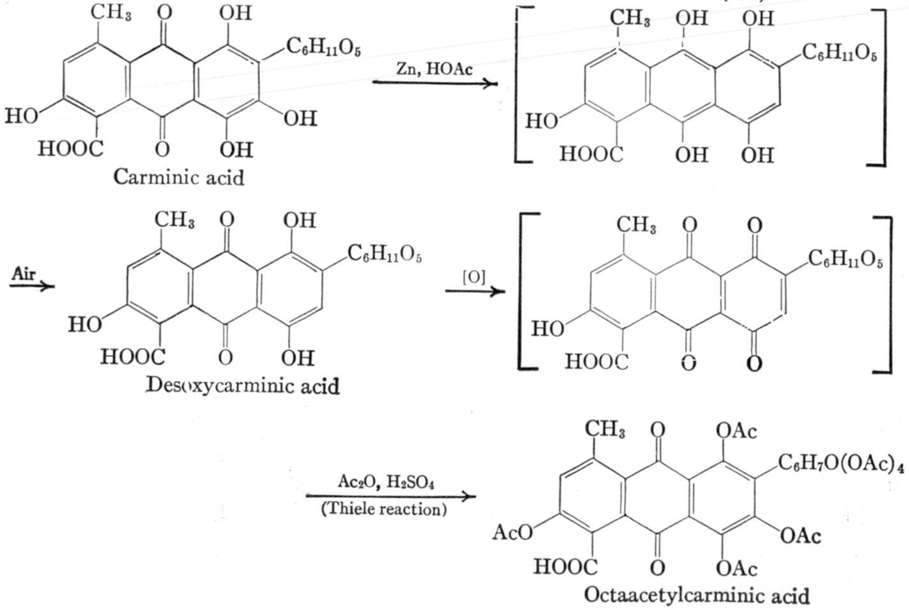

Carminic acid

Zn, HOAc

Air

Desoxycarminic acid

[O]

Ac$_2$O, H$_2$SO$_4$
(Thiele reaction)

Octaacetylcarminic acid

is a hydroxylated anthraquinonecarboxylic acid with a sugar side chain. Oxidative degradations to naphthoquinones established a part of the nuclear structure of the pigment   The product of alkali fusion, coccinin, was found to be related to its oxidation product coccinone in the same way that anthrone is related to anthraquinone, and this evidence pointed to an anthraquinonoid structure.   Reduction of carminic acid with zinc and acetic acid, like alkali fusion, eliminates the β-hydroxyl group from the more highly hydroxylated ring; the product resulting after air oxidation, desoxy-carminic acid, was shown to have hydroxyl groups in the 1,4-relationship by oxidation to a diquinone.   By application of the Thiele reaction to the diquinone, the hydroxyl group of carminic acid was restored.   The location of this group at the 3- rather than the 2-position was established from the absorption spectrum, in analogy to known polyhydroxyanthraquinones. Dimroth later (1923) found that the sensitive diquinones of high potential can be prepared by oxidation with lead tetraacetate, and in this way introduced a new and useful reagent to organic practice.

Kermes — Kermesic Acid. — Kermes consists of dried bodies of the insect *Coccus ilices* and was used in ancient times as a scarlet mordant dye (Venetian scarlet). The pigment kermesic acid is a brick-red, water-insoluble substance of the formula $C_{18}H_{12}O_9$ (Dimroth, 1910–13). The probable structure and some of the degradation products are shown in the formulation.

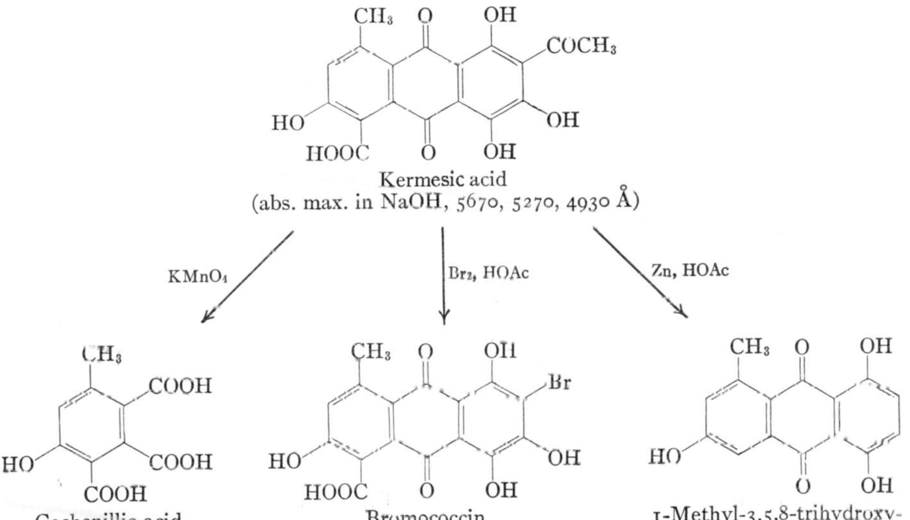

Kermesic acid
(abs. max. in NaOH, 5670, 5270, 4930 Å)

KMnO₄   Br₂, HOAc   Zn, HOAc

Cochenillic acid   Bromococcin   1-Methyl-3,5,8-trihydroxy-anthraquinone

Lac Dye — Laccaic Acid. — Lac dye is a deep red coloring matter that is extracted by dilute soda solution from stick lac, an exudate of the lac insect, *Coccus lacca*. The pale yellow residue is shellac. Lac dye has properties comparable to cochineal; the pigment, laccaic acid, $C_{20}H_{14}O_{11}$, is very similar in properties to carminic acid. The structure is not fully established.

lin-POLYNUCLEAR HYDROCARBONS

The hydrocarbon biphenylene, $C_{12}H_8$, was synthesized by W. C. Lothrop (1941) by the action of cuprous oxide on 2,2'-dibromodiphenyl. Particular interest is attached to this hydrocarbon because it is a derivative of the unknown cyclobutadiene. A substance containing a four-membered ring

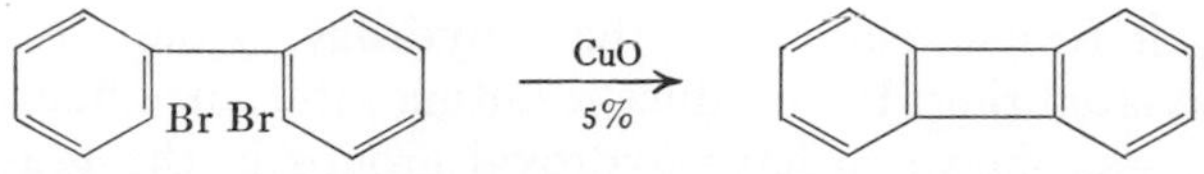

Biphenylene (m.p. 110°)

should be under considerable strain, yet biphenylene has typical aromatic properties. The substance however is coplanar, and resonance may confer stability. Evidence for the structure is that the hydrocarbon yields phthalic anhydride on oxidation and diphenyl on hydrogenation (85% yield); conclusions from chemical observations have been confirmed by X-ray analysis.

Naphthacene, an orange tetracyclic hydrocarbon of linear structure, is the 2,3- or *lin*-benz derivative of anthracene. The hydrocarbon and the quinone derived from it are both obtainable from 2,3-tetralanthraquinone (I), one of two isomers resulting from cyclization of *o*-(2-tetroyl)-benzoic acid (p. 739). Formation of the hydrocarbon results from disproportionation and reduction, while the quinone is produced by introducing two

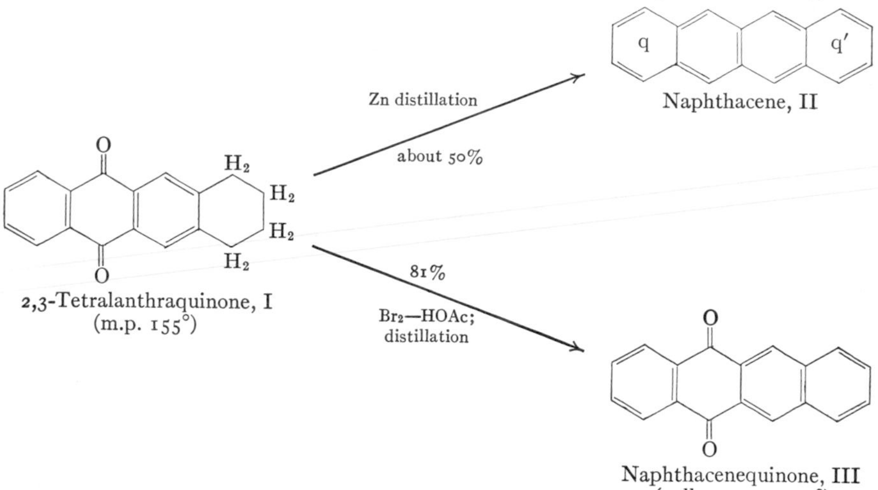

Zn distillation
about 50%

Naphthacene, II

2,3-Tetralanthraquinone, I
(m.p. 155°)

Br₂—HOAc;
distillation
81%

Naphthacenequinone, III
(yellow, m.p. 294°)

bromine atoms into the alicyclic ring and eliminating hydrogen bromide by removal of the solvent and distillation of the product in vacuum.

The bond structure shown in the formula for the hydrocarbon (II) represents the most stable arrangement predicted by the Fries rule. This contains two terminal quinonoid rings, whereas anthracene has only one; hence the tetracyclic hydrocarbon is definitely more reactive than anthracene. Thus naphthacenequinone fails to give the usual vat test with aqueous alkali and hydrosulfite, apparently because of the low potential of the system or the reactivity of naphthacenehydroquinone. This substance, IV, can be produced in solution in organic solvents, and it displays reactivity manifested by a marked tendency to undergo reduction to the anthrone V and to ketonize to the derivative VI. In both reactions the

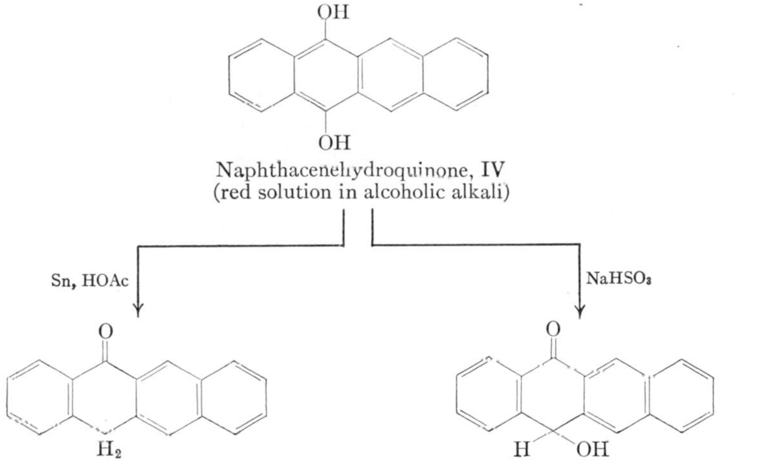

Naphthacenehydroquinone, IV
(red solution in alcoholic alkali)

Sn, HOAc

NaHSO₃

2,3-Benz-9-anthrone, V
(yellow, dec. 196°)

2,3-Benz-9-hydroxy-10-anthrone, VI
(yellow, dec. 230°)

doubly quinonoid naphthacene bond system reverts to the more stable dihydride structure. The anthrone V is indifferent to boiling aqueous alkali and is isomerized to the anthranol only with use of alcoholic alkali.

The bond structure for naphthacenequinone shown in formula II accords with predictions of the Fries rule and is substantiated by investigations of the action of Grignard reagents. Whereas phenylmagnesium bromide adds to the two carbonyl groups of anthraquinone, it reacts with naphthacenequinone by 1,4-additions to the conjugated systems comprising the carbonyl groups and the double bonds in the adjacent nucleus:

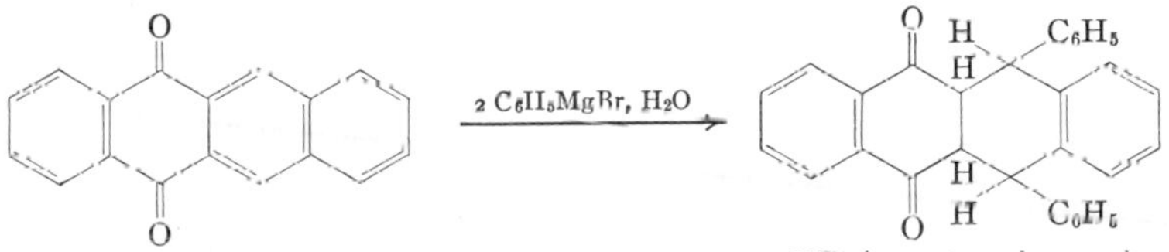

III

2 C₆H₅MgBr, H₂O

VII (two stereoisomers)

Rubrene. — This ruby-red hydrocarbon was discovered as a cyclization product of the acetylenic carbinol $(C_6H_5)_2C(OH)C \equiv CC_6H_5$ (Moureu[3] and Dufraisse,[4] 1926) and was recognized only some years later as a naphthacene derivative (Dufraisse, 1935). Various syntheses have established that

[3] Charles Moureu, 1863–1929; b. Moureux, Basse-Pyrénées, France; Ph.D. Paris; Coll. de France, Paris; *Ber.*, **62A**, 93 (1929)

[4] Charles Dufraisse, b. 1885 Excideuil/Dordogne, France: Ph.D. Paris (Moureu); Coll. de France, Paris

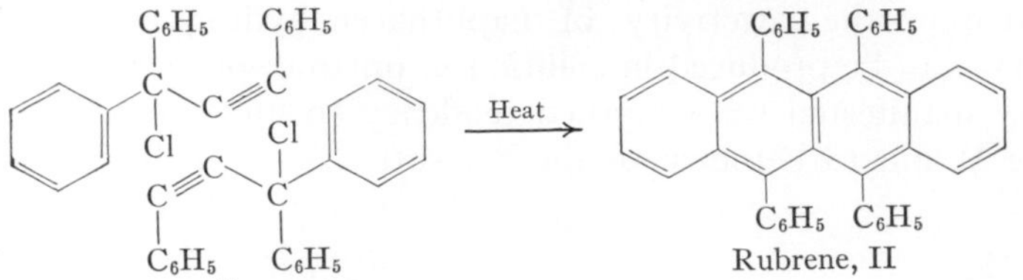

rubrene is 5,6,11,12-tetraphenylnaphthacene, II. Formation of the hydrocarbon from the chloride (I) corresponding to the above carbinol has been interpreted in various ways; for example, as an α,γ-rearrangement to an allene followed by an intramolecular Diels-Alder reaction. One synthesis utilizes as starting material the substance formulated as VII in the preceding section. This substance on treatment with alcoholic alkali in contact with air undergoes a succession of enolization and oxidation reactions with dehydrogenation to III, which adds two molecules of phenyllithium to give a

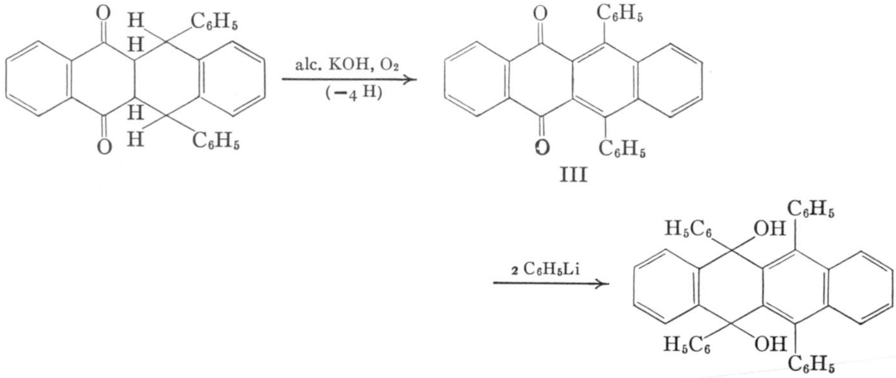

carbinol (IV) that on reduction with iron and acetic acid affords the hydrocarbon rubrene (Allen,[5] 1936).

Rubrene dissolves in benzene to give an orange or pink solution characterized by strong yellow florescence; when shaken with air in moderate sunlight, the color is slowly discharged, and evaporation affords the peroxide V as a white solid. When the photooxide is heated at about 120°, it dis-

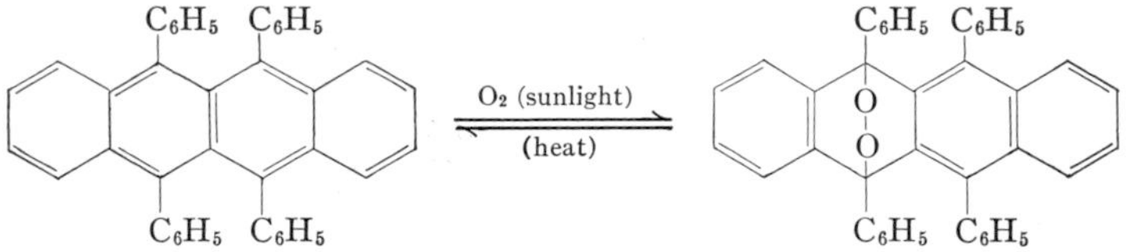

sociates with liberation of oxygen and reformation of the red hydrocarbon. The reaction resembles the reversible oxygenation of hemoglobin to oxy-

[5] Charles F. H. Allen, b. 1895 Milford, N. H.; Ph.D. Harvard (Kohler); Eastman Kodak Co.

hemoglobin but does not proceed with the ease or efficiency of the respiratory process, and the cycle cannot be completed without appreciable destruction of material. After the structure of rubrene was established, the parent hydrocarbon naphthacene was found capable of absorbing oxygen in the light to form a colorless peroxide; the reaction is shown also by anthracene derivatives, particularly by those substituted in both *meso* positions by aryl or alkyl groups.

Pentacene; Heptacene. — Pentacene, or 2,3,6,7-dibenzanthracene, has been isolated as deep blue crystals (Clar,[6] 1930); the next two benzologs are

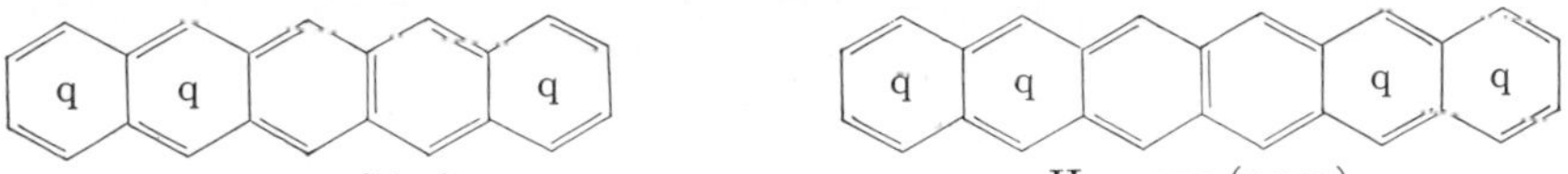

Pentacene (blue)   Hexacene (green)

also known. The hydrocarbons are sparingly soluble in organic solvents and highly reactive. Thus they add maleic anhydride rapidly and are highly sensitive to air oxidation in the presence of light. Even the most stable possible arrangement of the double bonds in terms of ordinary Kekulé formulations gives a pentacyclic system with three quinonoid rings and a hexacyclic structure with four quinonoid rings. Progressive deepening in color is apparent in the series:

Anthracene	<	Naphthacene	<	Pentacene	<	Hexacene	<	Heptacene
(colorless)		(orange)		(blue)		(green)		(ultragreen)

The effect seems attributable to accumulation of conjugated double bonds, particularly in the quinonoid rings, analogous to the diphenylpolyenes (p. 881). Another interesting comparison is with the bicyclic hydrocarbon azulene. This substance is a blue solid and has the same characteristic

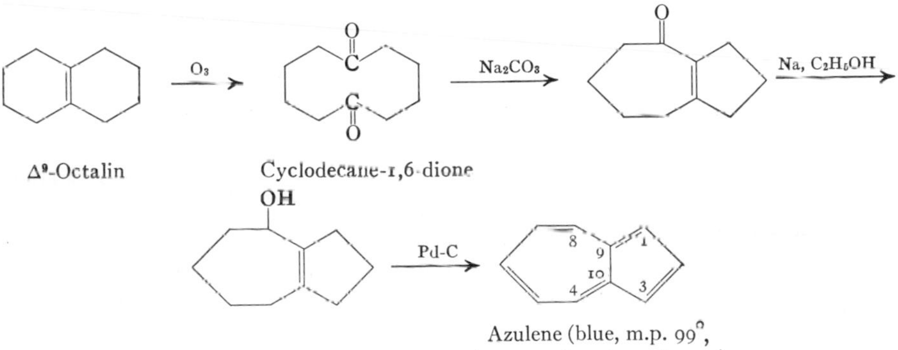

Δ⁹-Octalin   Cyclodecane-1,6-dione

Azulene (blue, m.p. 99°, abs. max. 699, 633, 580 mμ)

odor and crystalline form as its isomer naphthalene. Likewise it forms complexes with picric acid and trinitrobenzene. It is much more reactive than the aromatic hydrocarbon, and the fully conjugated system of reactive double bonds gives rise to marked color. Azulene, prepared by

[6] Erich Clar, b. 1902, Herrnskretschen/Elbe, Sudetenland; Ph.D. Dresden (Scholl); Glasgow

synthesis from Δ^9-octalin (Plattner and Pfau, 1937), is the parent substance of a group of coloring matters obtained from certain essential oils by oxidation or dehydrogenation (see also pp. 533-534).

HYDROCARBONS OF ANGULAR STRUCTURE

Chrysene. — Chrysene can be formulated with four benzenoid rings, and it is less reactive than the isomeric naphthacene or than anthracene. The

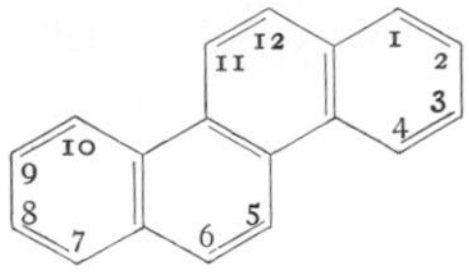

Chrysene

hydrocarbon occurs in small amounts in coal tar, and can be produced in 60% yield by pyrolysis of indene. Several syntheses are available for the preparation of chrysene and derivatives; a few typical intermediates are

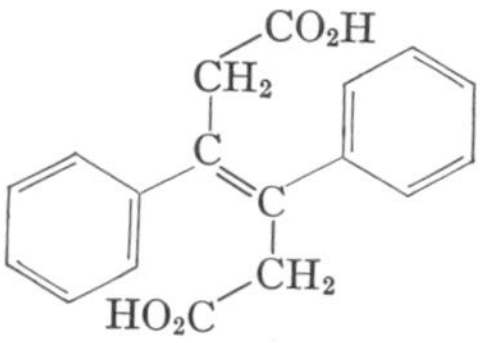

I 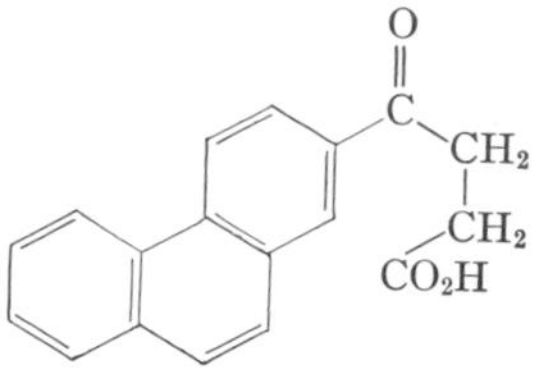 II 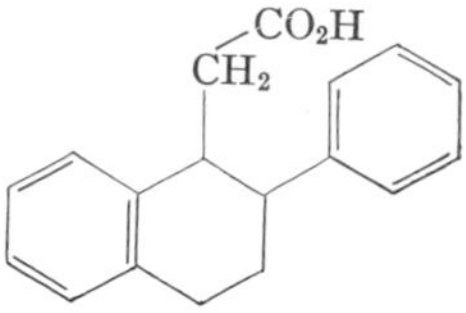 III

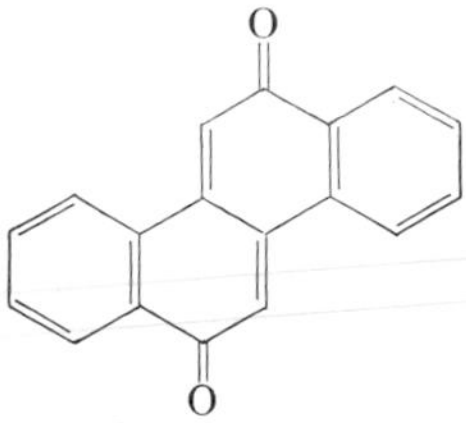

amphi-Chrysenequinone, IV
(m.p. 290° dec., E_0 alc. 0.392 v.)

indicated in formulas I–III. The hydrocarbon is somewhat less susceptible to attack by substituting agents than phenanthrene, and the chief point of attack is the 6-position. 6,12-Dihydroxychrysene, prepared by double ring closure of the intermediate I, is converted by oxidation into *amphi*-chrysenequinone (IV). The *amphi*- or 2,6-quinone derived from naphthalene is known as such and as the 1,5-dichloro derivative.

1,2-Benzanthracene. — This isomer of naphthacene and of chrysene is less reactive than the former hydrocarbon and more reactive than the latter. Specific properties of hydrocarbons of this series are discussed later.

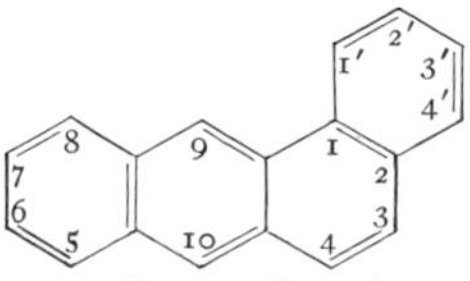

1,2-Benzanthracene
(m.p. 160°)

CONDENSED-RING HYDROCARBONS

Pyrene. — This tetracyclic hydrocarbon was discovered as a constituent of coal tar (Graebe, 1871), and is now available in limited amounts from this source. The material employed in early studies was obtained from stupp, a sooty deposit resulting as a by-product in an early process for the production of mercury by smelting of a bituminous cinnabar ore found in the Idrian district of Italy. When the ore was heated in contact with air, pyrene, phenanthrene, fluoranthene, and other aromatic hydrocarbons were liberated and volatilized by a process of mercury distillation, akin to steam distillation. The soot or stupp collecting on the walls of the condensing chambers consisted of a mixture of mercury and higher aromatic hydrocarbons, and when it was heated in a muffle furnace for recovery of mercury the organic portion collected as an oily mass containing as much as 20% of pyrene.

The most stable bond arrangement of pyrene appears to be the one shown in formula Ia, which contains three benzenoid rings; formula Ib,

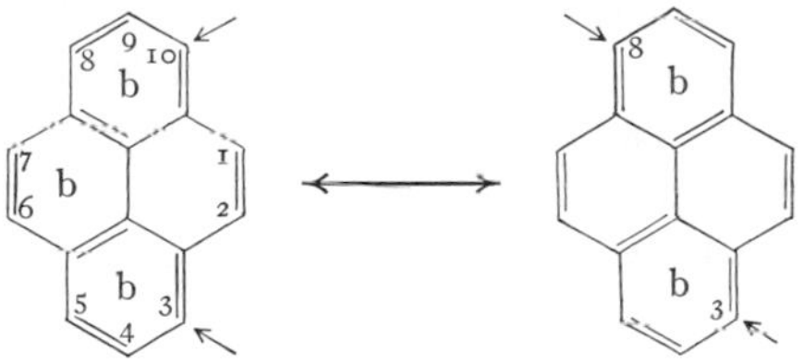

Ia   Ib

containing two such rings, contributes to the structure to a lesser extent. In all substitutions pyrene is attacked initially at the 3-position, and the 3-chloro, 3-nitro, 3-sulfonate, 3-acyl, and 3-aldehydo derivatives are obtainable in good yield. The susceptibility to substitution is about the same as that of anthracene; for example both hydrocarbons afford aldehydic derivatives on condensation with N-methylformanilide. The second terminal ring is attacked nearly as readily as the first, and disubstitution gives a mixture of the 3,10- and 3,8-isomers, with the former predominating. The 3- and 10-positions apparently are reactive because they are the ends of a conjugated system extending from the nonbenzenoid ring of structure Ia and resembling a 1,4-naphthoquinonoid unit; the 3- and 8 positions

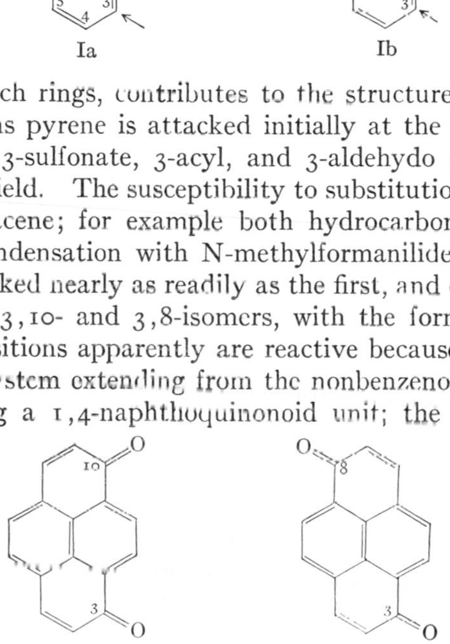

3,10-Pyrenequinone
(dark red, m.p. 270°)

3,8-Pyrenequinone
(golden yellow, m.p. 309°)

possess a comparable relationship in structure Ib (1,5-naphthoquinonoid system). Oxidation of pyrene similarly gives a mixture of which about two thirds is the 3,10-quinone and one third the 3,8-quinone. Separation is accomplished by partial vatting with aqueous-alcoholic hydrosulfite solution, which preferentially extracts the more soluble 3,10-quinone.

Bond fixation is indicated by the fact that 3-hydroxypyrene does not couple with diazotized amines. The 3,10- and 3,8-dihydroxy compounds likewise fail to enter into the diazo coupling reaction, and hence appear to

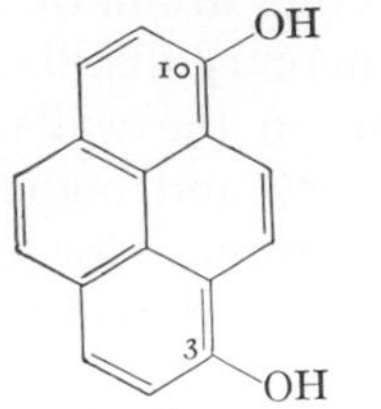

3,10-Dihydroxypyrene 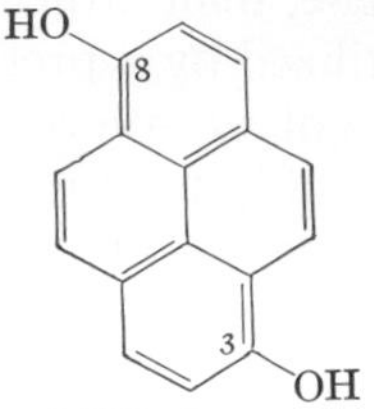   3,8-Dihydroxypyrene
(m.p. 330°)

be derived from the structures Ia and Ib, respectively. The hydroxyl groups apparently stabilize a quinonoid system of linkages to which they are attached, probably because of resonance associated with charge separation (see formulation on page 736).

Indirect methods for the preparation of pyrene derivatives substituted at positions other than the accessible position 3 are of interest. One route to compounds of the 4-series is rearrangement of the sulfate of 3-aminopyrene

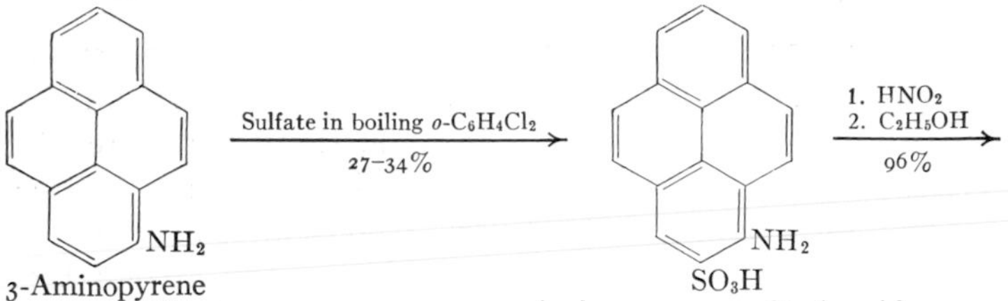

Sulfate in boiling o-C₆H₄Cl₂
27–34%

1. HNO₂
2. C₂H₅OH
96%

3-Aminopyrene
(m.p. 118°)

3-Aminopyrene-4-sulfonic acid 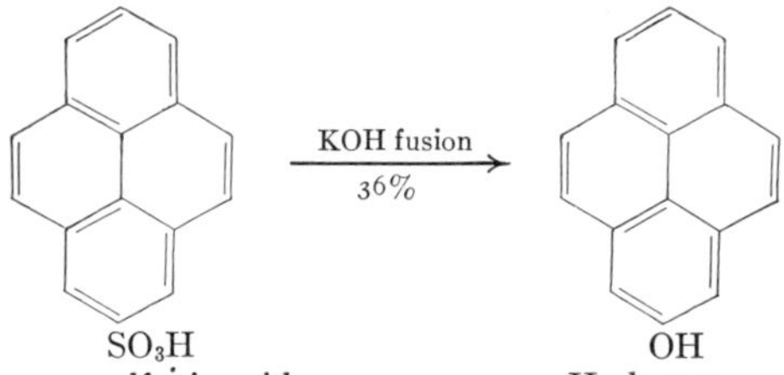
SO₃H

KOH fusion
36%

SO₃H
Pyrene-4-sulfonic acid

OH
4-Hydroxypyrene
(m.p. 207°; couples)

at the boiling point of o-dichlorobenzene to the 3-amino-4-sulfonic acid, followed by elimination of the amino group; 4-hydroxypyrene is obtained by alkali fusion of the sulfonate. The isomeric 1-hydroxypyrene, which, like the 4-isomer and in contrast with 3-hydroxypyrene. couples readily with diazonium salts, is obtained by a novel process starting with ozonization of the hydrocarbon in suspension in acetic acid. Apparently ozone adds to the central phenanthrenoid double bond at C_1–C_2 and the ozonide undergoes rearrangement, for the product is an aldehyde-acid derived from phenan-

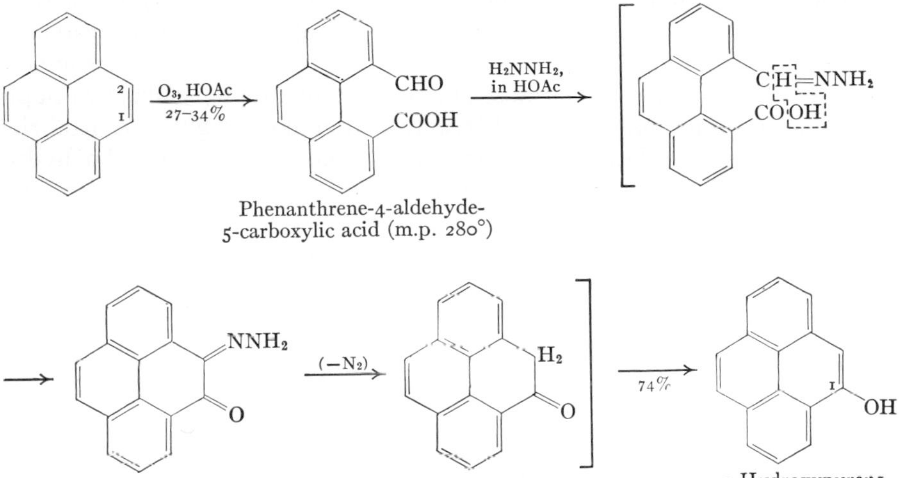

Phenanthrene-4-aldehyde-
5-carboxylic acid (m.p. 280°)

1-Hydroxypyrene
(m.p. 202°; couples)

threne. This substance when treated with hydrazine undergoes cyclization with reformation of the pyrene ring system and production of 1-hydroxy-pyrene in good yield. A possible reaction sequence, indicated in the chart, consists in formation of a hydrazone and cyclization to a substance that loses nitrogen in a reaction parallel to one step in the Wolff-Kishner method for reduction of carbonyl compounds.

Perylene. — This hydrocarbon, whose structure consists of two naphthalene units joined at the *peri* positions, was first obtained by the action of aluminum chloride on naphthalene or 1,1'-dinaphthyl, but a better starting material is di-β-naphthol, which results in high yield on oxidation of β naphthol with ferric chloride (p. 838). An efficient procedure consists in heating di-β-naphthol with a mixture of phosphorus pentachloride and

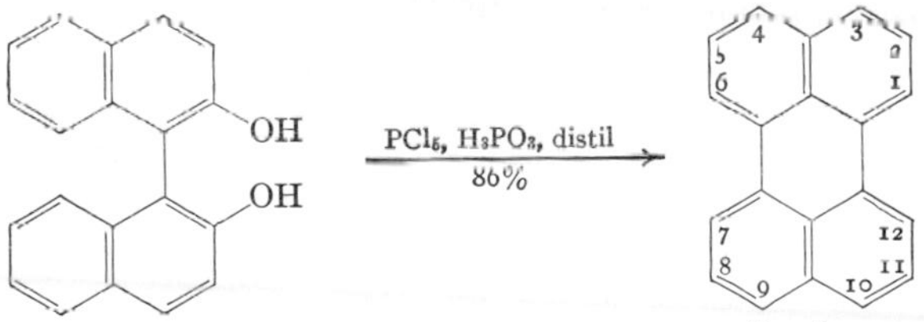

Di-β-naphthol

Perylene
(yellow, m.p. 265°)

phosphorous acid and eventually distilling the hydrocarbon from the mixture at 500–600°. The combination of phosphorus oxychloride and zinc can be used also. In another procedure di-β-naphthol dimethyl ether is heated at 150° with aluminum chloride, which effects cyclization and demethylation to give 1,12-dihydroxyperylene; this is distilled with zinc dust to remove the hydroxyl groups.

The structure of perylene embraces the structural units found in naphthalene, phenanthrene, and anthracene, but perylene differs from all these substances in being colored, as a consequence of the extended system of conjugated double bonds. The bond structure shown in the formula is regarded as representing the most stable state of the molecule; two naphthalene units of normal benzenoid structure are linked to give a central ring corresponding to a hexaketocyclohexane. Like naphthalene, the hydrocarbon is substituted most readily at the α-position 3. Disubstitution gives the 3,10-isomer as the chief product and a lesser amount of the 3,9-derivative. The 3,10-quinone is made by stirring a suspension of the finely divided hydrocarbon in aqueous chromic acid solution at the reflux temperature (83% yield), and is crystallized from nitrobenzene and from pyridine. One of a series of related pigments isolated from aphids is a 4,9-dihydroxyperylenequinone of the structure shown (Todd, 1955).

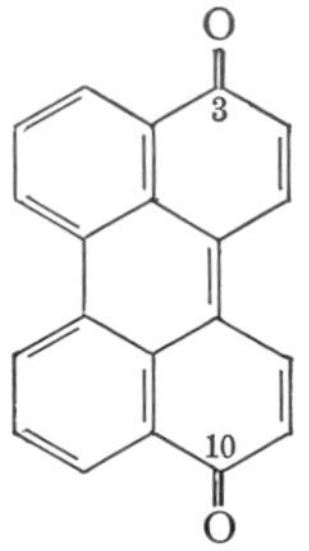

3,10-Perylenequinone
(yellow, dec. 350°)

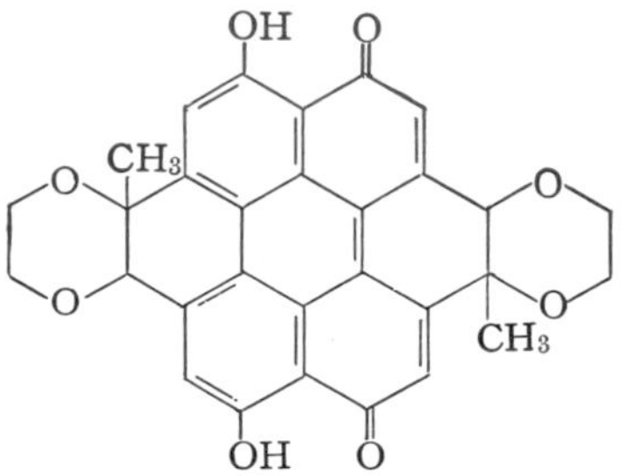

Erythroaphin-fb

Although the hydrocarbon does not ordinarily form an addition product with maleic anhydride, a reaction product is formed on heating the reagents in nitrobenzene solution, apparently as the result of addition of maleic anhydride to the diene system extending between positions 1 and 12 and displacement of the equilibrium by dehydrogenation of the addition product by nitrobenzene:

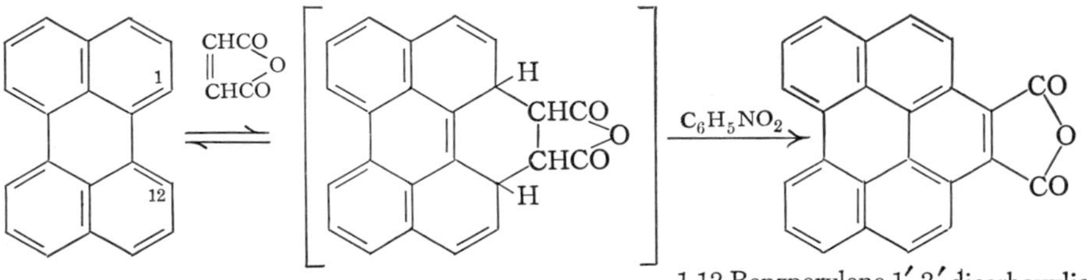

1,12-Benzperylene-1′,2′-dicarboxylic
anhydride (orange, dec. 470°)

Coronene. — This interesting hydrocarbon consists of a ring, or crown, of six benzene rings. In the bond arrangement shown in the formula, each peripheral ring has the normal structure of a Kekulé ring, and the central nucleus corresponds to that in perylene. The hydrocarbon, which is pale yellow and shows blue fluorescence in benzene solution, is very high melting and extremely stable and inert. The first synthesis, achieved by Scholl[7] (1932) after many initial trials, proceeded from the chloride of anthraquinone-1,5-dicarboxylic acid. In the Friedel-Crafts condensation with *m*-xylene, the diacid chloride reacts in the tautomeric form I to give the dilactone II. The methyl groups are then converted into carboxyl groups by oxidation, and the lactone rings opened by reduction (III). Fuming sulfuric acid then effects double ring closure to IV, and when this substance is heated with hydriodic acid and red phosphorus the carbonyl groups are first reduced; closure of two more rings is then possible, and the two newly developed carbonyl groups are reduced, with conversion into a tetrahydro derivative of V. This substance when heated with soda lime and copper powder at 2 mm. pressure undergoes decarboxylation and dehydrogenation to give 2,3,8,9-dibenzcoronene (VI).

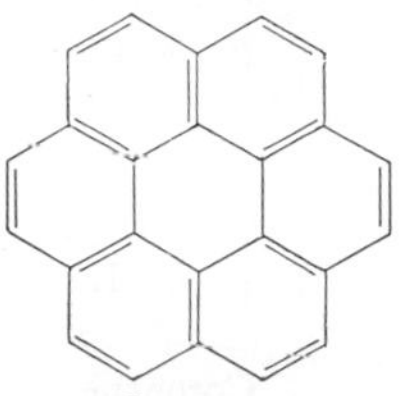

Coronene
(pale yellow, m.p. 440°)

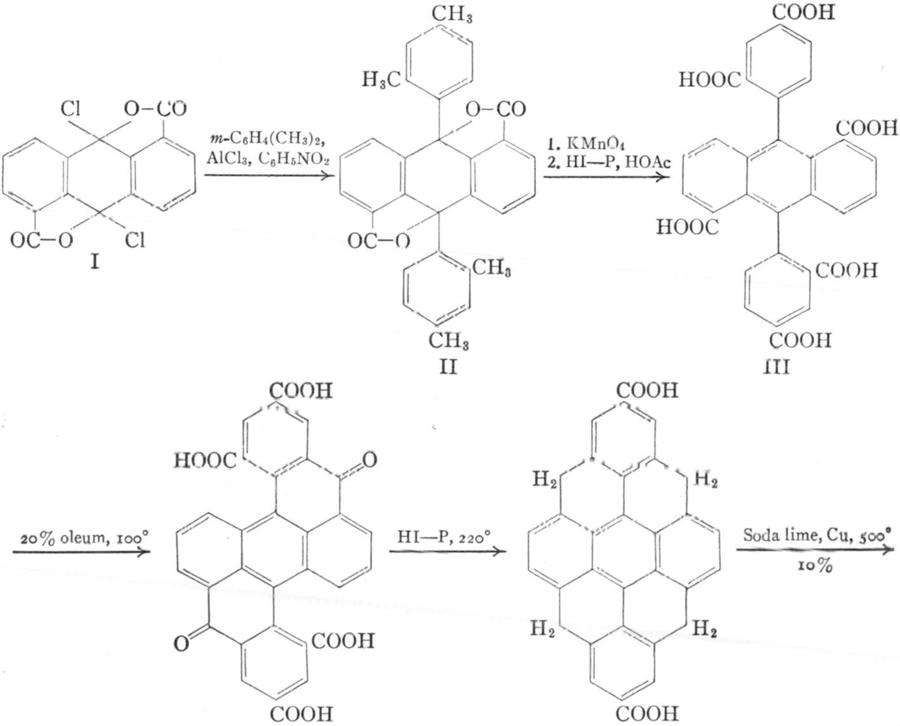

[7] Roland Scholl, b. 1865 Zürich; Ph.D. Basel; Dresden

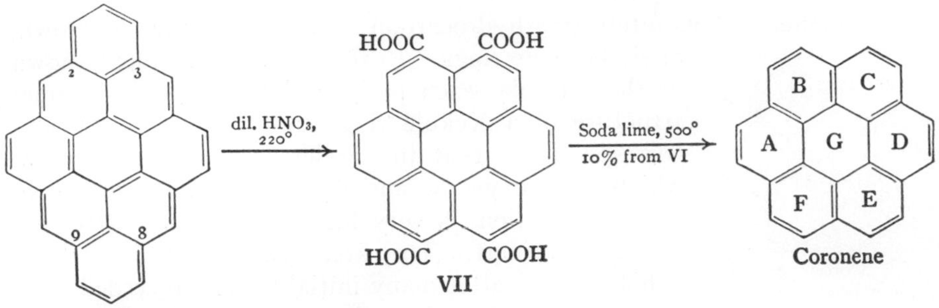

This greenish red hydrocarbon is sensitive to oxidizing agents, even to air in boiling xylene solution (several quinonoid rings), and is degraded by nitric acid oxidation and decarboxylation of the intermediate VII to coronene. Yields are good except in the terminal stages. In the Scholl synthesis the starting material provides rings A, G, and D. In a second synthesis by Newman (1940) 7-methyltetralone is reduced to a pinacol that provides the B,C-unit linked to the F,E-unit. A similar but even shorter synthesis starts with 2,7-dimethylnaphthalene (W. Baker, 1951–52). It involves allylic bromination with N-bromosuccinimide to 2,7-di-(bromomethyl)naphthalene, which undergoes Wurtz coupling, done more efficiently with phenyl-

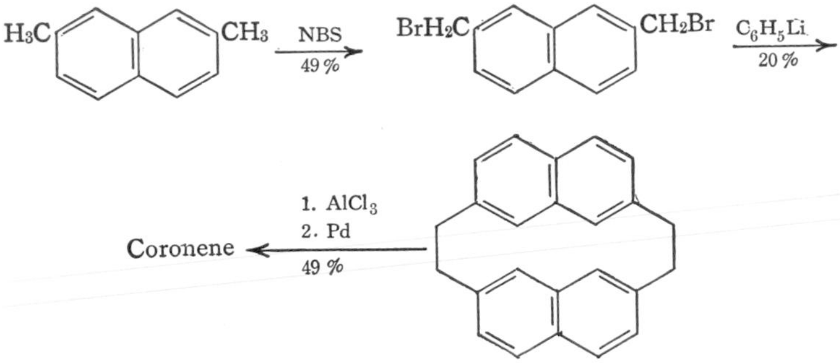

lithium than with sodium, to give an appreciable amount of the hydrocarbon formed by closure of a fourteen-carbon ring. Cyclodehydration with aluminum chloride gives a mixture of coronene and its 1,2-dihydro derivative, and the mixture on dehydrogenation is converted into coronene.

CARCINOGENIC HYDROCARBONS

Discovery that certain polynuclear hydrocarbons can evoke malignant tumors in animal tissues opened a new field for investigation of the incidence and control of cancer. The discovery was the outcome of the realization, at the early part of the present century, that individuals in specific occupations involving prolonged exposure to coal-tar products tended to show an abnormally high incidence of skin cancer, which sometimes developed only several years after the period of exposure.   Production of cancer in experimental animals by a specific coal-tar fraction was achieved by Yamagiwa and Ichikawa in 1915, and in 1930 Kennaway and Cook at the Royal Cancer Hospital in London discovered that synthetic 1,2,5,6-dibenzanthracene (I) possesses marked carcinogenic activity.   The hydrocarbon was not a known constituent of coal tar but was selected for trial on the basis of the boiling

1,2,5,6-Dibenzanthracene, I
(colorless, m.p. 266°)

3,4-Benzpyrene, II
(light yellow, m.p. 179°)

point range of carcinogenic coal-tar fractions and of a rough similarity to a type of fluorescence spectrum associated with these fractions.   In 1933 Cook and co-workers, with guidance of fluorescence spectroscopy, isolated from two tons of pitch a substance characterized by synthesis as 3,4-benzpyrene (II); it is now known that coal tar contains about 1.5% of the carcinogen. Benzpyrene bears a structural relationship to dibenzanthracene, for both pentacyclic hydrocarbons contain the ring system of 1,2-benzanthracene.

In 1933 Wieland[8] and Dane effected the stepwise degradation of desoxycholic acid (III), one of the normal constituents of human bile, into an aromatic hydrocarbon called methylcholanthrene (VI) because of its origin and characterization as an anthracene derivative.   Cook soon adduced completing evidence of the structure, and reported that the hydrocarbon is a very potent carcinogen (1934).   When the formula is arranged as in VIb, it is seen that methylcholanthrene is a derivative of 1,2-benzanthracene that resembles dibenzanthracene (I) in having carbon substituents at the 5- and 6-positions, and resembles benzpyrene (II) in containing a carbocyclic ring linked to one of the *meso* carbon atoms.   The hydrocarbon subsequently was obtained by degradation of a still more abundant bile acid, cholic acid (IV), involving, like the degradation of desoxycholic acid, an intramolecular Perkin condensation between a 12-keto group and the α-position of the acid side chain.   Methylcholanthrene also has been produced by an unusual pyrolytic degradation of a derivative of cholesterol (V), a substance present in all tissues of the human body.   The bile acids and cholesterol belong to the group of steroids (p. 961), which also includes hormones secreted by the gonads and by the adrenal cortex.   The fact that three natural steroids have been transformed by chemical processing into an actively carcinogenic hydrocarbon suggested the hypothesis that cancer may originate through abnormal metabolism of a sterol or bile acid to methylcholanthrene.   How-

⁸ Heinrich Wieland, b. 1877 Pforzheim, Germany; Ph.D. Munich (Thiele); Munich; Nobel Prize 1927

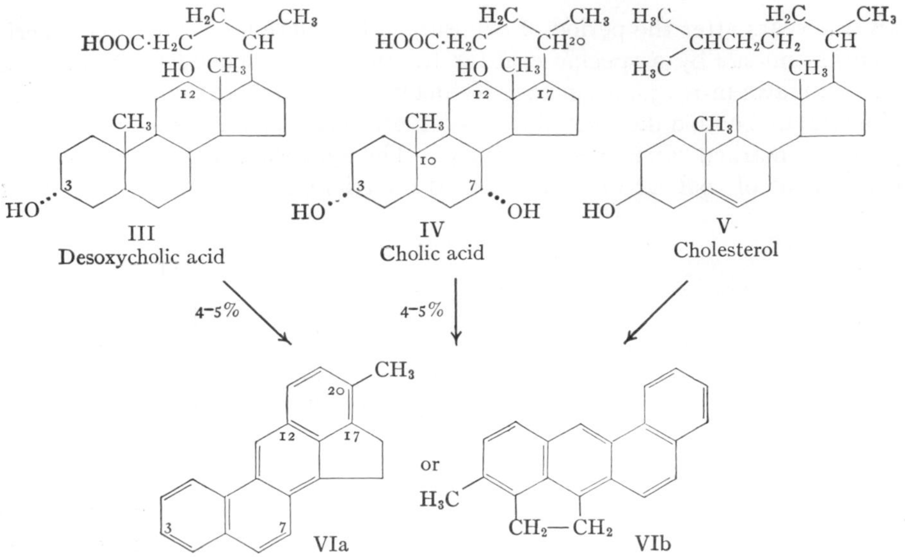

III
Desoxycholic acid

IV
Cholic acid

V
Cholesterol

VIa   or   VIb

Methylcholanthrene
(light yellow, m.p. 180°)

ever, all attempts to demonstrate the *in vivo* conversion of a natural steroid to the hydrocarbon have failed, as have many attempts to isolate methylcholanthrene from cancerous tissue, and the accumulated evidence strongly discounts the possibility of a causative relationship.

Carcinogenic Activity and Structure. — Even though polynuclear hydrocarbons probably play no part in the incidence of spontaneous cancer, the study of hydrocarbon carcinogenesis in experimental animals is justified on the ground that an even partial understanding of the mode of action of carcinogens may suggest methods of forestalling or inhibiting the effect. One search for a clue to the mode of action of carcinogens has consisted in the synthesis and assay of various hydrocarbons in the attempt to discover some correlation between structure and biological activity. Accurate, though inevitably slow, test methods are available, usually employing mice or rats. Mice of pure strains, developed by selection followed by inbreeding throughout twenty or more generations, are particularly suitable, for the animals of a given strain have very much the same genetic constitution and show nearly the same susceptibility to hydrocarbon carcinogenesis, though susceptibility varies considerably from strain to strain. In one test method the hydrocarbon is applied in benzene solution to the skin of the mouse, usually twice weekly for a period of several weeks, and a positive effect is attended with the appearance of cancerous growths of the skin (epitheliomas) or of benign tumors (papillomas), sometimes after an induction period of as much as one year, or toward the end of the life span of the animal. Another method is to administer the hydrocarbon in solution in pure synthetic tricaprylin by a single subcutaneous injection. An active agent in this case usually gives rise to a sarcoma (tumor of the connective tissue) at the site of injection. An experienced operator can determine within a day or two the time at which a palpable thickening of the tissue is indicative of development of a tumor, and the fact of tumor formation can be established later by pathological examination or transplantation experiments. In comparative tests conducted by U.S. Public Health Service workers with mice of the C3H strain, dibenzanthracene injected subcutaneously in tricaprylin solution was observed to produce tumors in 80% of the test animals at the low dosage of 0.25 mg. per mouse. At this level the tumors appeared, on the average, after a latent period of 23.1 weeks. The average induction time dropped to 21.7 weeks at a dosage of 1 mg. per mouse and reached a minimum value of 16.8 weeks at a dosage of 2–3 mg. Benzpyrene, in parallel experiments, produced tumors in C3H mice in a minimum average latent period of 12.4 weeks at a dosage of only 1 mg. Methylcholanthrene gave rise to tumors in every one of eighty mice in an average time of 9.7 weeks, and acted as rapidly at a dosage of 0.25 mg. as at a 2-mg. level. Thus methylcholanthrene not only is the most rapidly acting of the three carcinogens but exerts its maximum effect at a lower dosage. These three hydrocarbons stand in very nearly the same order of potency with respect to the production of skin cancers, in which case the induction time is longer: about 30 weeks for dibenzanthracene and 18 weeks for methylcholanthrene. In some other instances to be noted below, potency varies considerably with the test tissue.

As judged by all available data for the production of skin and subcutaneous tumors in rats and mice, methylcholanthrene probably is the most potent known chemical carcinogen. Systematic studies of synthetic model compounds have shown that the methyl group is of no importance to the activity; that much, if not all, of the efficacy of cholanthrene (VII) is retained in the analogous hydrocarbon 5,10-dimethyl-1,2-benzanthracene (VIII); and that the most significant structural feature of cholanthrene or methylcholanthrene is the 1,2-benzanthracene ring system with a carbon

CH₂—CH₂
Cholanthrene, VII
(m.p. 173°)

CH₃   CH₃
5,10-Dimethyl-1,2-benz-
anthracene, VIII (m.p. 147°)

CH₃
10-Methyl-1,2-benz-
anthracene, IX (m.p. 174°)

substituent at the *meso* position 10. 10-Methyl-1,2-benzanthracene (IX) evokes sarcomas in mice nearly as rapidly as methylcholanthrene, and, though it is less effective in production of skin cancer, it constitutes the nearest approach in a simple model compound to simulation of the biological properties of the hydrocarbon of more complicated structure. The activity falls rapidly in the series methyl, ethyl, propyl. All twelve possible monomethyl derivatives of the inactive 1,2-benzanthracene have been synthesized and tested for carcinogenic activity, and of these the 10-isomer is the most potent. The *meso*-substituted 9-methyl compound stands next in order of potency, followed closely by the 5-methyl derivative, which produces sarcomas in mice with a latent period about twice as long as that observed with 10-methyl-1,2-benzanthracene. Methylcholanthrene and benzpyrene can be regarded as 1,2-benzanthracenes substituted at the *meso* positions 10 and 9, respectively, and in model compounds combination of the two types of substitution is particularly favorable. 9,10-Dimethyl-1,2-benzanthracene (X) produces skin tumors in mice with remarkable rapidity and in this test surpasses methylcholanthrene in speed of action, though it is less effective when administered by subcutaneous injection. The thiophene isolog of the

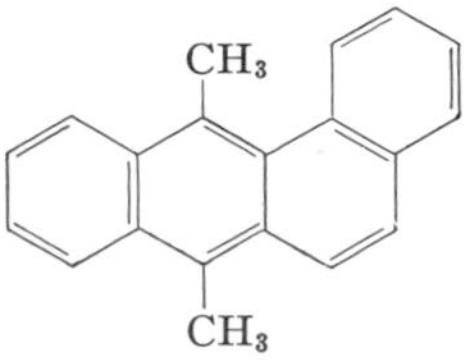

9,10-Dimethyl-1,2-benz-
anthracene, X (m.p. 123°)

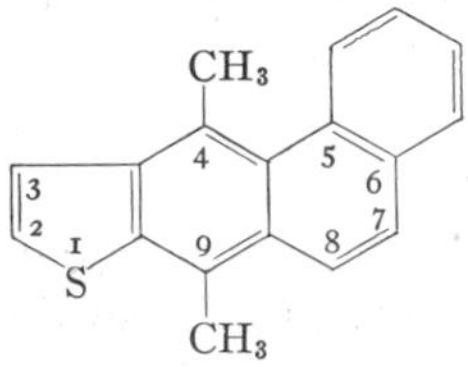

4,9-Dimethyl-5,6-benzthio-
phanthrene, XI (m.p. 159°)

hydrocarbon (XI) has comparable properties. The nitrogen isologs of the acridine series, XII and XIII, are also carcinogenic; XIII approaches methylcholanthrene in potency. Contraction of the central ring of dibenzanthracene or its isolog, as in XIV and XV, decreases activity.

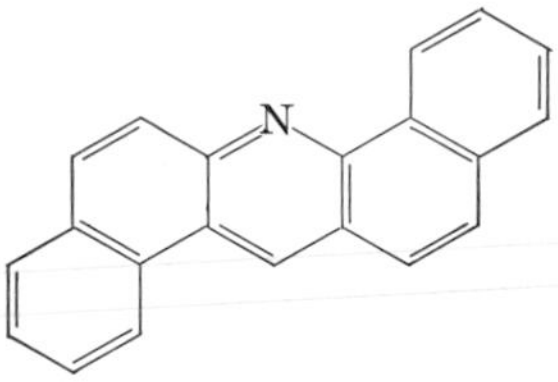

1,2,5,6-Dibenzacridine, XII

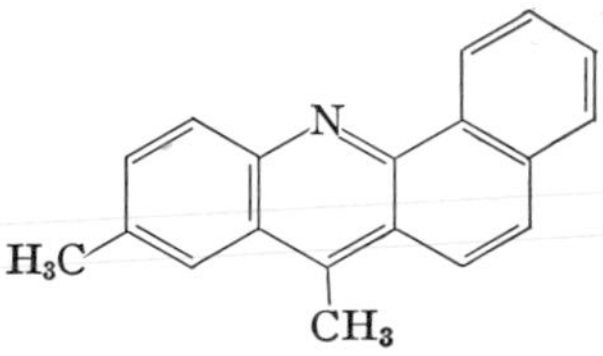

7,9-Dimethyl-3,4-benzacridine, XIII

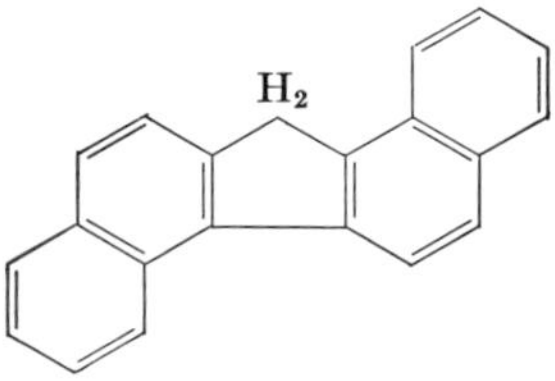

1,2,5,6-Dibenzfluorene, XIV

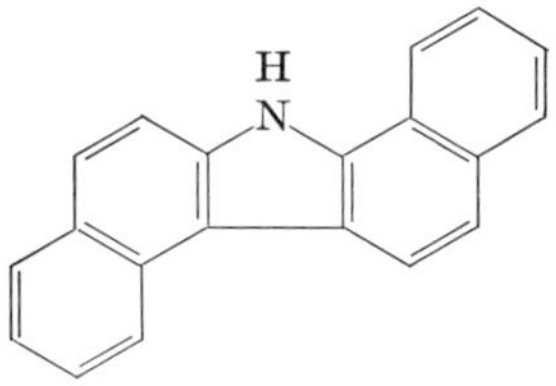

1,2,5,6-Dibenzcarbazole, XV

Carcinogens of another type are derivatives of phenanthrene substituted with methyl or benz groups at at least three of the positions 1, 2, 3, and 4. Thus the hydrocarbons XVI, XVII, and XVIII are carcinogenic. Car-

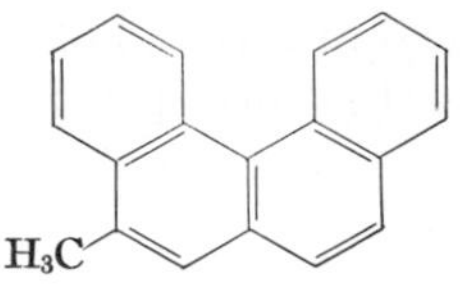

2-Methyl-3,4-benz-
phenanthrene, XVI

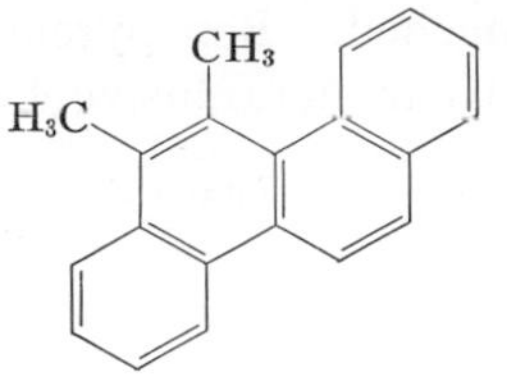

5,6-Dimethylchrysene,
XVII

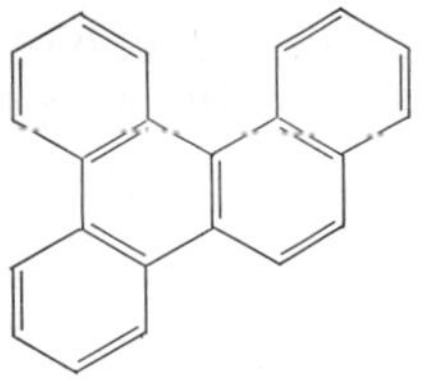

1,2,3,4-Dibenz-
phenanthrene, XVIII

cinogens of the 1,2-benzanthracene group can be regarded as 2,3- or 1,2,3-substituted phenanthrenes.

Correlation with Chemical Reactivity. — The active carcinogens of the 1,2-benzanthracene group show no special tendency to enter into addition reactions. Some, for example methylcholanthrene and 10-methyl-1,2-benzanthracene, add hydrogen only sluggishly at positions other than the hindered though reactive *meso* centers, and are attacked in exposed positions, as shown in Chart 2. Others, notably benzpyrene, are so resistant to this type of reaction that they are not convertible into maleic anhydride-addition products. On the other hand, the most potent carcinogens are endowed with remarkable susceptibility to substitution reactions, and indeed surpass all other aromatic hydrocarbons in this special manifestation of chemical reactivity. A striking instance is the diazo coupling of benzpyrene and of methylcholanthrene. The only other exception to the rule that an activating amino or hydroxyl substituent is required to promote this form

CHART 2. ADDITION OF HYDROGEN

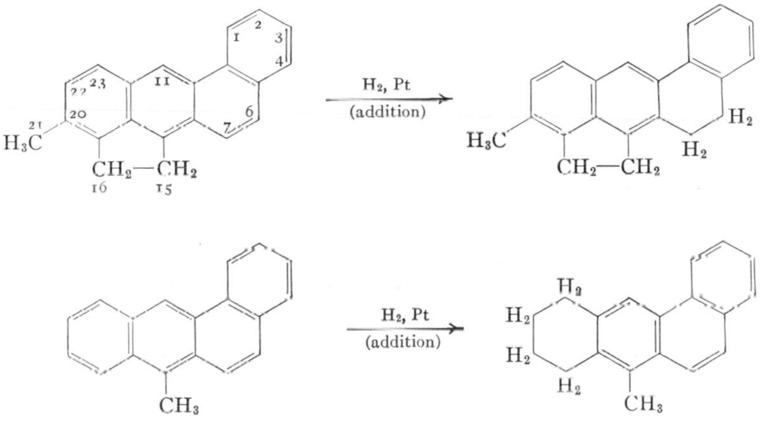

of substitution in the benzene ring is that mesitylene and a few related polyalkylbenzenes couple with the specially reactive diazonium salt from picramide. Benzpyrene and methylcholanthrene couple readily even with the only moderately reactive *p*-nitrobenzenediazonium chloride, which leaves mesitylene practically untouched.   Benzpyrene is attacked in this and other substitutions, as shown in Chart 3, exclusively at a point (C$_5$) corresponding

CHART 3.   SUBSTITUTION REACTIONS OF 3,4-BENZPYRENE

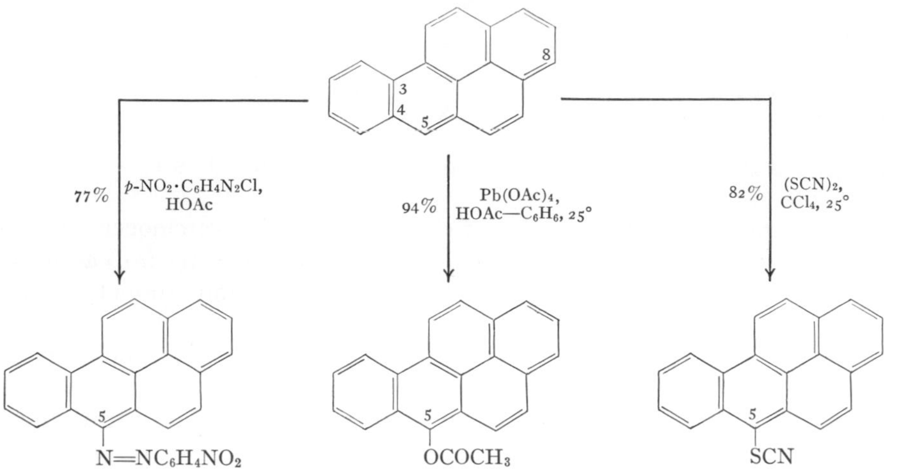

77% | p-NO$_2$·C$_6$H$_4$N$_2$Cl, HOAc

94% | Pb(OAc)$_4$, HOAc—C$_6$H$_6$, 25°

82% | (SCN)$_2$, CCl$_4$, 25°

N=NC$_6$H$_4$NO$_2$
5-p-Nitrobenzeneazo-3,4-benzpyrene (m.p. 246°)

OCOCH$_3$
5-Acetoxy-3,4-benzpyrene (m.p. 210°)

SCN
5-Thiocyano-3,4-benzpyrene (m.p. 241°)

to the *meso* position 10 in the benzanthracene ring system; the carcinogenically inactive parent substance, 1,2-benzanthracene, does not couple. The second substitution illustrated in the chart is acetoxylation by lead tetraacetate, which proceeds at room temperature.   The third reaction, thiocyanation with a solution of thiocyanogen (prepared by the action of bromine on a suspension of lead thiocyanate in carbon tetrachloride solution), is in the same category, for anthracene derivatives less reactive than benzpyrene are substituted by the reagent, but less readily than benzpyrene.

Methylcholanthrene, though differing considerably in structural characteristics from benzpyrene, enters into the same special substitution reactions with comparable readiness.   It couples rapidly with p-nitrobenzene-diazonium chloride in acetic acid solution, but a homogeneous reaction product has not been isolated from the resulting deep red solution.   Rapid reactions occur with lead tetraacetate and with thiocyanogen; the resulting mixtures are not easily processed, but the initial products have been characterized as 15-derivatives (Chart 4).   The point of attack is thus not at a nuclear position, as in benzpyrene, but at the methylene group joined to the 1,2-benzanthracene ring system at the 10-*meso* position.   The two hydrocarbons thus exhibit comparable susceptibility to the special substitutions even though one is substituted in the nucleus and the other in a methylene group.

The correlation of high carcinogenic potency with unusual sensitivity to specific reagents, particularly to diazo components, suggests a possible association between the two phenomena, though comparative results for a

CHART 4. SUBSTITUTIONS OF METHYLCHOLANTHRENE

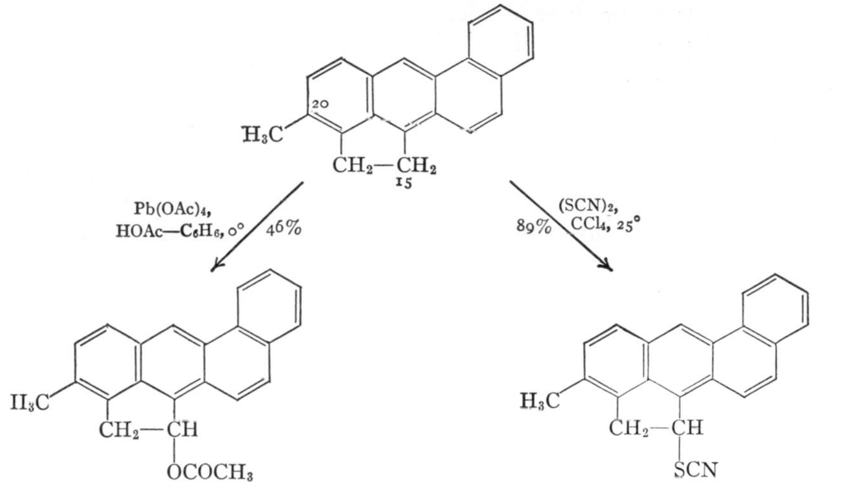

15-Acetoxy-20-methylcholanthrene
(m.p. 180°)

15-Thiocyano-20-methylcholanthrene
(m.p. 132° dec.)

series of carcinogenic and noncarcinogenic hydrocarbons indicate that the relationship is merely approximate and not without exceptions. However the likelihood of a causative relationship is strengthened by the fact that the chemical substitutions occur at that part of the molecule which is recognized from the data surveyed in the preceding section as being particularly important for carcinogenic potency.

Administered carcinogens are metabolized in part to phenolic derivatives that are noncarcinogenic. Since the metabolic reaction represents a process of detoxication by which the carcinogen is converted into a harmless form, an understanding of the reaction might suggest methods for increasing the

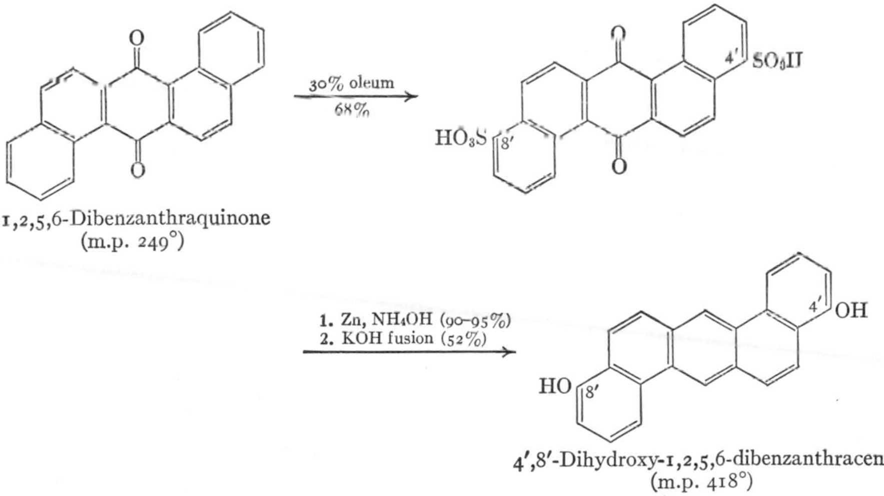

1,2,5,6-Dibenzanthraquinone
(m.p. 249°)

4',8'-Dihydroxy-1,2,5,6-dibenzanthracene
(m.p. 418°)

power of the organism to effect such detoxications. The metabolite excreted in the urine and feces of mice and rats injected with dibenzanthracene
is 4',8'-dihydroxy-1,2,5,6-dibenzanthracene. The appearance of hydroxyl
groups at exposed positions of the molecule rather than at the more reactive
meso centers suggests that the metabolic detoxication product may arise
through an intermediate product of the addition of hydrogen peroxide, in a
reaction comparable to the observed additions of hydrogen. 3,4-Benzpy-
rene undergoes metabolic hydroxylation not at the center most susceptible
to chemical substitution, position 5, but at the exposed position 8 (see
formula, Chart 3).

Methods of Synthesis. — 1,2,5,6-Dibenzanthracene is prepared by the
process illustrated. β-Naphthoic acid is converted into the chloride by

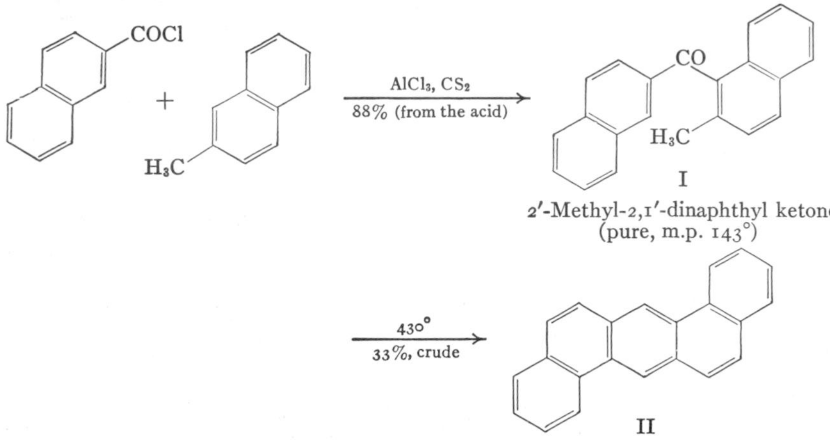

2'-Methyl-2,1'-dinaphthyl ketone
(pure, m.p. 143°)

II
1,2,5,6-Dibenzanthracene

phosphorus pentachloride, and the crude product is treated in carbon
disulfide solution with β-methylnaphthalene and aluminum chloride   The
ketonic product, consisting largely of the substance I but containing isomeric
ketones, is then pyrolysed, which results in elimination of water and formation of an anthracene ring system.   This step is an application of the Elbs[9]
reaction (1884) for the preparation of anthracenes by pyrolysis of diaryl
ketones having a methyl substituent adjacent to the carbonyl group.   The
reaction proceeds poorly with *o*-methylbenzophenones, and the anthracenes
are obtained in about 10% yield after refluxing for periods of several days.
The results are better with ketones such as I, where ring closure involves
substitution into a more reactive naphthalene system.   The dibenzanthracene resulting from the pyrolysis contains a trace of 1,2,6,7-dibenzanthra-
cene as a persistent yellow contaminant that cannot be eliminated by
repeated recrystallization.   A convenient method of purification consists in

---

[9] Karl Elbs, 1858–1933; b. Breisach, Germany; Ph.D. Freiburg (Claus); Giessen; *Ber.*, **66A**,
74 (1933)

preferential oxidation with lead tetraacetate, which attacks the more reactive yellow linear hydrocarbon and leaves the bis-angular isomer II untouched.

Methylcholanthrene is prepared by a synthesis also utilizing the Elbs reaction (Fieser and Seligman, 1935). In the procedure illustrated, p-chlorotoluene (III) is condensed with β-chloropropionyl chloride (Friedel-Crafts

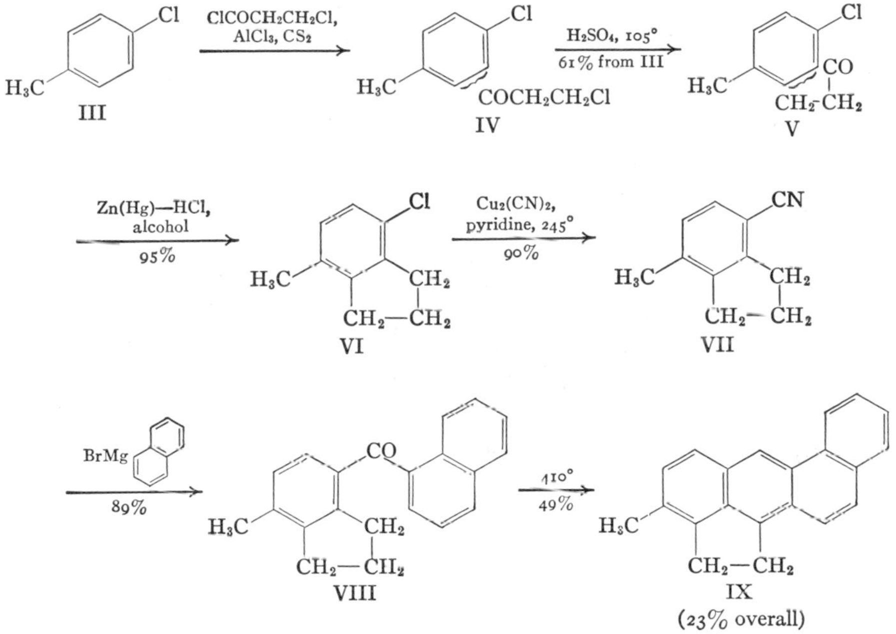

condensation). Substitution occurs at both available positions, but no separation of the isomers (IV) is required, for after cyclization to a mixture of hydrindones (V), Clemmensen reduction of both isomers affords a single product, 4-methyl-7-chlorohydrindene (VI). This is converted into the nitrile VII, which is condensed with α naphthylmagnesium bromide to give the ketone VIII. The ketone undergoes unusually smooth pyrolysis, with condensation of the o-methylene group of the five-membered ring into the second aromatic nucleus. Pure methylcholanthrene is obtainable in overall yield from p-chlorotoluene of 23%. A number of alkyl, alkoxyl, halo, and benzo derivatives of cholanthrene have been synthesized by pyrolysis of suitably substituted α-naphthyl 7-hydrindyl ketones related to VIII.

One route to benzpyrene is the succinic anhydride synthesis, illustrated in Chart 5. The reactions are conducted in the usual manner, except that in the intramolecular Friedel-Crafts ring closure the mild reagent stannic chloride is employed in order to avoid destructive attack of the sensitive

CHART 5. SUCCINIC ANHYDRIDE SYNTHESIS OF 3,4-BENZPYRENE

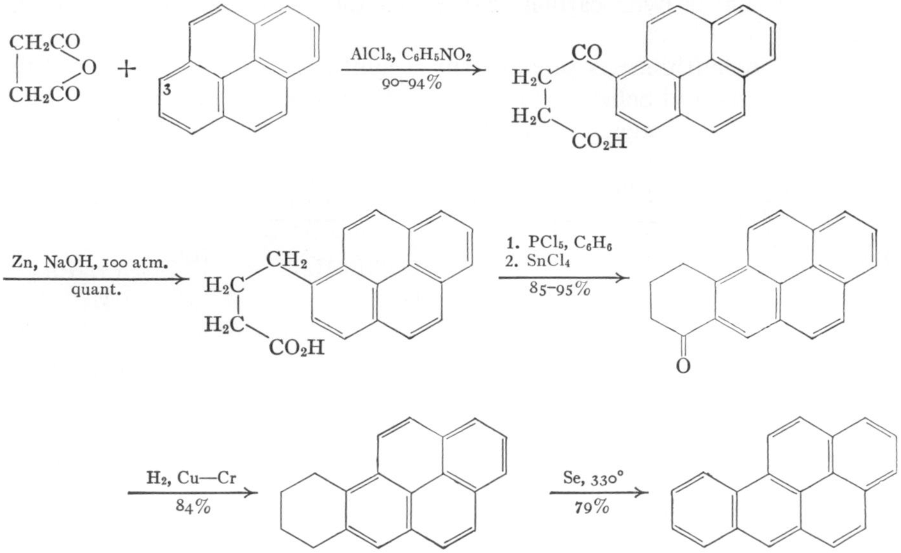

pyrene nucleus. A second synthesis (Chart 6) is based on a reaction introduced by Scholl for the preparation of benzanthrones (p. 915); this involves

CHART 6. 3,4-BENZPYRENE FROM PERINAPHTHANE (X)

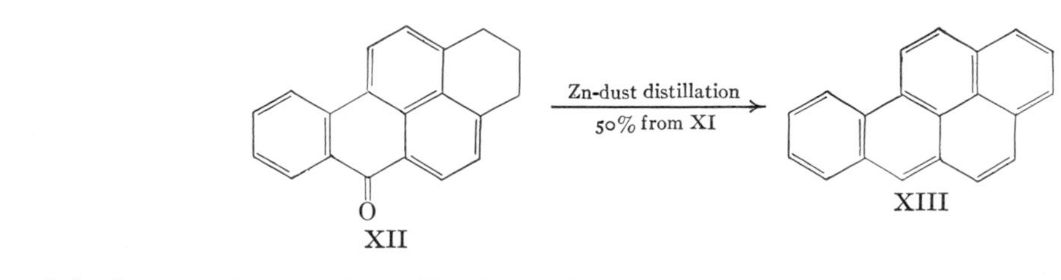

a dehydrogenative *peri* cyclization of an α-benzoylnaphthalene. The starting hydrocarbon perinaphthane (X) is available from β-naphthol in 19% yield, and the overall yield of the carcinogen from β-naphthol is 9%.

Some of the methods developed for the synthesis of interesting *meso-*substituted 1,2-benzanthracenes are indicated briefly as follows. In one process the keto acid XIV, resulting as the chief product of the addition of phenylmagnesium bromide to 1,2-naphthalic anhydride, is condensed with a Grignard reagent, and the resulting lactone (XV) is converted by reduction into the saturated acid XVI, which affords 10-methyl-1,2-benzanthra-

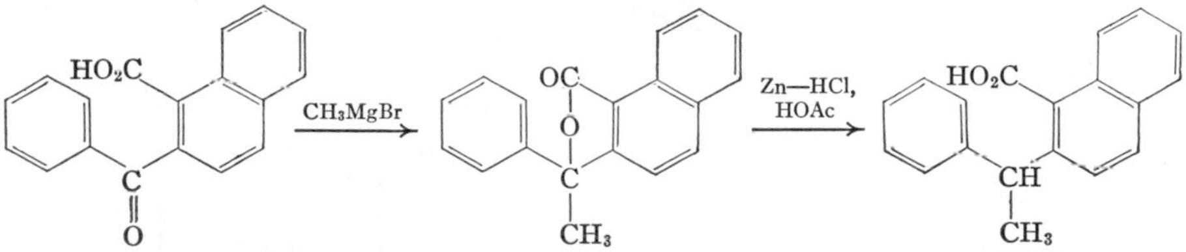

cene on cyclization and reduction. Another synthesis consists in the preparation of 1,2-benzanthrone-10 (XVII) by a process of cyclization with hydrogen fluoride already described (p. 768) and introduction of a methyl substituent by Grignard addition; water is easily eliminated from the reaction product, with the production of a hydrocarbon (XVIII). 10-Methyl-

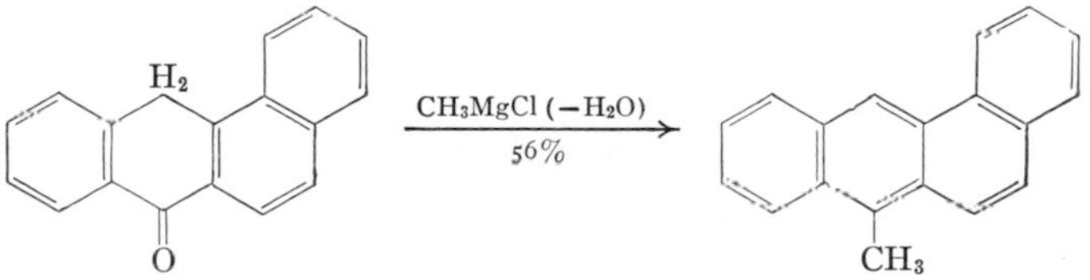

1,2-benzanthracene can be synthesized also by conversion of 1,2-benzanthracene into the 10-aldehyde by the N-methylformanilide reaction and reduction of the aldehyde by heating the hydrazone with sodium ethoxide (Wolff-Kishner reaction; 54% yield from the hydrocarbon). Another synthesis is accomplished by ring closure effected by refluxing 1-(o-acetobenzyl)-naphthalene (XIX) with acetic acid containing hydrobromic acid (Bradsher,[10] 1940).

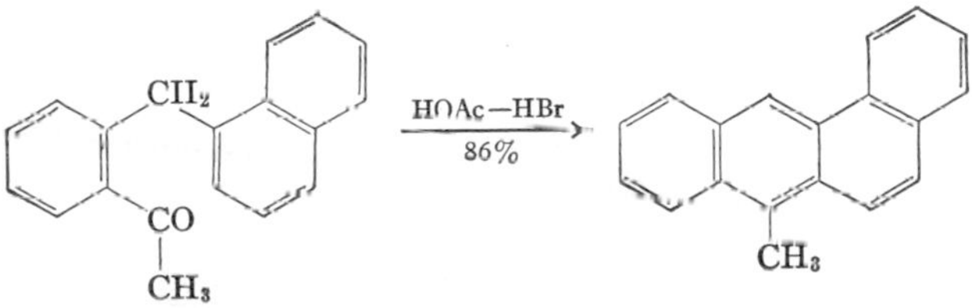

The potent carcinogen 9,10-dimethyl-1,2-benzanthracene has been prepared by two syntheses starting with the reaction of methyl Grignard reagent on 1,2-benzanthraquinone to give a diol represented by the partial formula XX. In one process the diol is converted by treatment with methanol and hydrogen chloride into the dimethyl ether XXI, which is re-

[10] Charles K. Bradsher, b. 1912 Petersburg, Va.; Ph.D. Harvard (Fieser); Duke Univ.

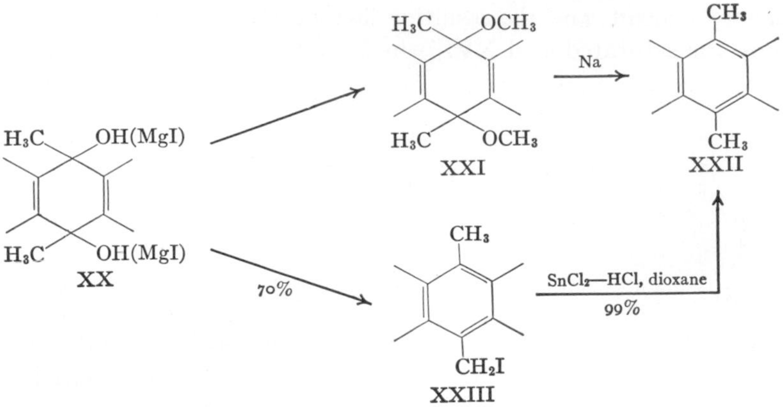

duced to the hydrocarbon (XXII) by interaction with sodium (Bachmann, 1938). In the second process the Grignard reaction mixture containing the magnesiohalide derivative of the diol XX is treated with hydriodic acid, which converts the material into the iodo compound XXIII; the halo derivative is reduced readily by stannous chloride in dioxan solution to 9,10-dimethyl-1,2-benzanthracene (XXII), which is produced by this method in 69% overall yield from the quinone (Sandin[11] and Fieser, 1940).

PROBLEMS

1. Formulate the synthesis of:
   (a) 9-Methylphenanthrene from phenanthrene
   (b) 4-Methylphenanthrene from γ-(2-naphthyl)-butyric acid

2. Sulfonation of retene (p. 757) gives two monosulfonic acids that on alkali fusion afford two isomeric retenols, m.p. 162° and 202°. The structure of the higher-melting isomer was inferred from the observation that it fails to couple with diazonium salts. What is the structure?

3. The structure of one of the disulfonic acids resulting from sulfonation of phenanthrene was established by alkali fusion, methylation of the dihydroxyphenanthrene, oxidation to a dimethoxy-9,10-phenanthrenequinone, and oxidation of the quinone with hydrogen peroxide to a dibasic acid that proved identical with an acid synthesized by the action of cuprous ammonium hydroxide on the diazonium salt derived from 4-methoxy-2-aminobenzoic acid.

   (a) What is the structure of the disulfonic acid?
   (b) The 4-methoxy-2-aminobenzoic acid was prepared by a five-step synthesis starting with the nitration of p-toluidine in sulfuric acid solution; formulate the process.

4. Formulate a synthesis of β-aminoanthraquinone starting with phthalic anhydride and chlorobenzene.

5. Formulate a synthesis of 3-methyl-1,2-benzanthracene starting with α-methylnaphthalene.

6. How can 1-anthranol be prepared starting with anthraquinone?

7. Suggest a synthesis of 9-methylanthracene.

[11] Reuben B. Sandin, b. 1897 Forest Lake, Minn.; Ph.D. Chicago, (Nicolet); Univ. Alberta, Canada

READING REFERENCES

A. E. Everest, "The Higher Coal-Tar Hydrocarbons," Longmans, Green, New York (1927)

L. F. Fieser, "The Elbs Reaction," in R. Adams, "Organic Reactions," I, 129–154, Wiley, New York (1942)

G. M. Badger, "The Carcinogenic Hydrocarbons: Chemical Constitution and Carcinogenic Activity," *British Journal of Cancer*, **2**, 309 (1948)

W. Baker, "Non-Benzenoid Aromatic Hydrocarbons," *J. Chem. Soc.*, 258 (1945)

J. W. Cook, "Polycyclic Aromatic Hydrocarbons," *J. Chem. Soc.*, 1210 (1950)

G. Wolf, "Chemical Induction of Cancer," Harvard Univ. Press (1952)

CHAPTER 33

HETEROCYCLES

A number of known unsaturated five- and six-membered ring systems contain one or more atoms other than carbon as ring members, and these heterocycles possess, to a greater or lesser extent, the distinguishing stability found in benzene and roughly defined as aromaticity. The names and formulas of some parent heterocycles are given in the formulation, which also indicates the approximate order of aromaticity. All these compounds share to some extent the qualities that distinguish benzene from aliphatic unsaturated compounds, namely, stability to oxidation, tendency to undergo substitutions rather than additions, ease of formation. Pyridine is less

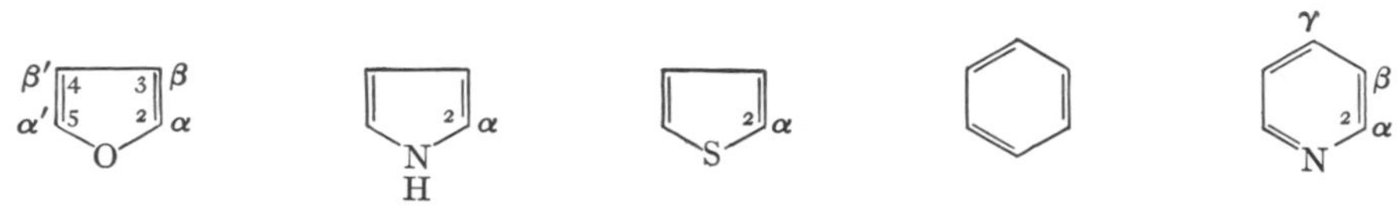

Furan
b.p. 31.5°

Pyrrole
b.p. 131°

Thiophene
b.p. 84°

Benzene
b.p. 80°

Pyridine
b.p. 115°

Increasing aromaticity

easily substituted than benzene and in general surpasses the carbocyclic analog in aromatic character; thiophene is subject to more ready substitution, and is less stable and endowed with less pronounced aromaticity than benzene. The aromatic character is still weaker in pyrrole and in furan; the latter is a borderline case since it is almost as susceptible to additions as an aliphatic diene.

The simple heterocycles can be fused to a benzene ring or to another heterocycle to give a bicyclic system comparable to naphthalene, and repetition of the process leads to tricycles; hence polynuclear heterocyclic compounds exist in a wide variety of types, which will only be exemplified in the following survey.

FIVE-MEMBERED HETEROCYCLES

Preparation of Furan, Pyrrole, and Thiophene. — Derivatives of all three types can be made from γ-dialdehydes or γ-diketones by reactions that apparently involve a dienolic form. The yields are often in the order of 80–90%, and the method is valuable when the required starting material is readily available; thus the 2,5-dimethyl derivatives of the three heterocycles are prepared from acetonylacetone ($CH_3COCH_2CH_2COCH_3$), available as a by-product of the manufacture of acetic acid from acetylene.

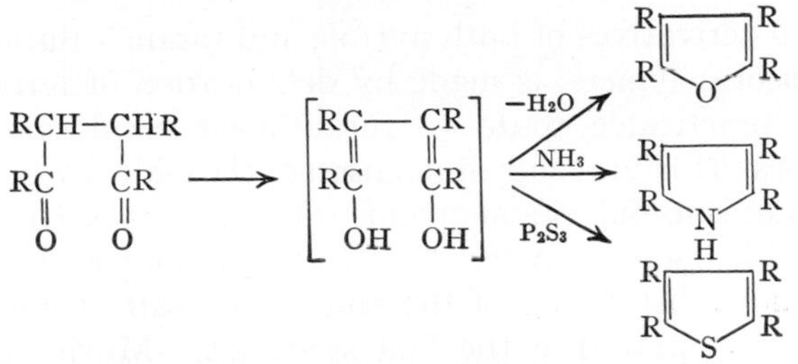

The parent substances can be prepared from succindialdehyde, obtainable as the diacetate in over 70% yield by hydroformylation of the commercially available acrolein diacetate (Adkins and Krsek, 1949); saponification in alcohol or water affords the free dialdehyde.   An early laboratory prepara-

$$(CH_3CO_2)_2CHCH=CH_2 \ + \ CO \ + \ H_2 \ \xrightarrow[125°, \ 200 \ atm.]{[Co(CO)_4]_2}$$

$$(CH_3CO_2)_2CHCH_2CH_2CHO \ \xrightarrow{HCl} \ O=CHCH_2CH_2CH=O$$
$$\text{Succindialdehyde}$$

tion of thiophene involved the high-temperature reaction of sodium succinate with phosphorus trisulfide (25–30% yield).

A variety of heterocycles, as well as butadiene, are manufactured from butyne-2-diol-1,4, made by condensation of acetylene with formaldehyde in

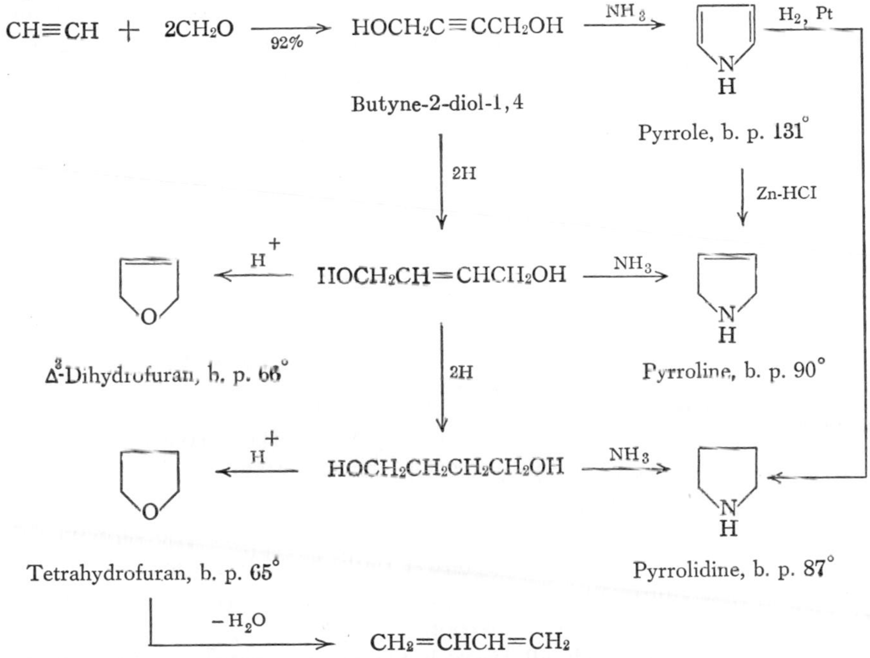

the presence of copper acetylide catalyst (Reppe).   The acetylenic diol reacts with ammonia under pressure to give pyrrole, and the diols resulting from partial and from complete hydrogenation serve for production of di and tetrahydro derivatives of both pyrrole and furan. Butadiene, required for production of polymers, is made by dehydration of tetrahydrofuran.

The most practicable route to furan itself involves dehydration of natural pentoses to furfural and elimination of the α-aldehydo group (p. 549). Tetrahydrofuran is useful as a supplementary solvent in Grignard reactions because of its high solvent power for Grignard complexes. A practicable route to pyrrole is distillation of the ammonium salt of mucic acid, which was the method employed in the first synthesis. Mucic acid is available

$$CO_2NH_4$$
$$|$$
$$HCOH$$
$$|$$
$$HOCH$$
$$|$$ $\xrightarrow[\text{37-40\%}]{\text{Distil}}$ $\quad$ $\boxed{}$ NH
$$HOCH$$
$$|$$
$$HCOH$$ $\quad\quad\quad$ Pyrrole
$$|$$
$$CO_2NH_4$$
Ammonium mucate

commercially by the hydrolytic oxidation of galactan, a hemicellulose composed of galactose units present in various woods. The reaction may involve intermediate formation of a furan derivative, since furans are convertible into pyrroles by the action of ammonia at a high temperature. The reaction does not stop at the stage of the 2,5-dicarboxylic acid, since pyrrolecarboxylic acids undergo ready decarboxylation. A useful general synthesis of substituted pyrroles (Knorr[1]) involves condensation of an α-amino ketone with ethyl acetoacetate or related component, as illustrated

$$CH_3CO$$ $$CH_3CO$$ $$CH_3CO$$
$$|$$ $\xrightarrow{\text{HONO}}$ $\quad$ $$|$$ $\xrightarrow{\text{Zn, HOAc}}$ $\quad$ $$|$$
$$C_2H_5O_2CCH_2$$ $$C_2H_5O_2CC{=}NOH$$ $$C_2H_5O_2CCHNH_2$$

$$H_2CCO_2C_2H_5$$
$$|$$
$$OCCH_3$$ $\quad\xrightarrow[\text{57-64\%}]{}$ $\quad$ CH$_3$ ⬠ CO$_2$C$_2$H$_5$ $\xrightarrow[\text{57-63\%}]{\text{KOH}}$ CH$_3$ ⬠
$\quad\quad\quad\quad$ C$_2$H$_5$O$_2$C — N — CH$_3$ $\quad\quad\quad\quad$ N — CH$_3$
$\quad\quad\quad\quad\quad\quad\quad$ H $\quad\quad\quad\quad\quad\quad\quad\quad\quad$ H
$\quad\quad\quad\quad\quad\quad\quad\quad\quad\quad\quad\quad\quad\quad\quad\quad\quad\quad$ 2,4-Dimethylpyrrole

for the preparation of 2,4-dimethylpyrrole. The yields are very low unless activating groups such as carbethoxyl are present; the activating groups are subsequently removed readily by treatment with alkali.

Thiophene was made commercially available by a process involving reaction of n-butane with sulfur at a high temperature (Socony-Vacuum, 1940). The paraffin is dehydrogenated (sulfur) to butadiene, which then combines with sulfur to form thiophene. Alkylthiophenes are obtained similarly from C_5- and C_6-hydrocarbons.

Reactions. — Although all three heterocycles contain a diene system, only furan enters readily into Diels-Alder reaction, for example, with

---

[1] Ludwig Knorr, 1859–1921; b. Munich; Ph.D. Erlangen; Würzburg, Jena

maleic anhydride (p. 312) and with dimethyl acetylenedicarboxylate. The adduct from the latter reaction can be used for preparation of dimethyl furan-3,4-dicarboxylate: partial hydrogenation reduces the less hindered double bond, and on pyrolysis of the dihydride ethylene is extruded with

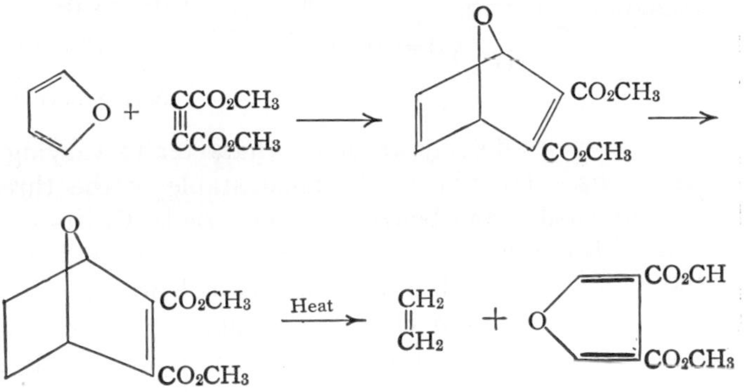

formation of the furan derivative. α-Methylpyrrole reacts with maleic anhydride, but the product results from addition at one end of the conjugated system. Pyrrole itself reacts under more drastic conditions and gives secondary products. In the presence of acids, pyrroles undergo a type of polymerization that apparently proceeds by the diene reaction. Dimers have been isolated in the case of some of the alkylated pyrroles.

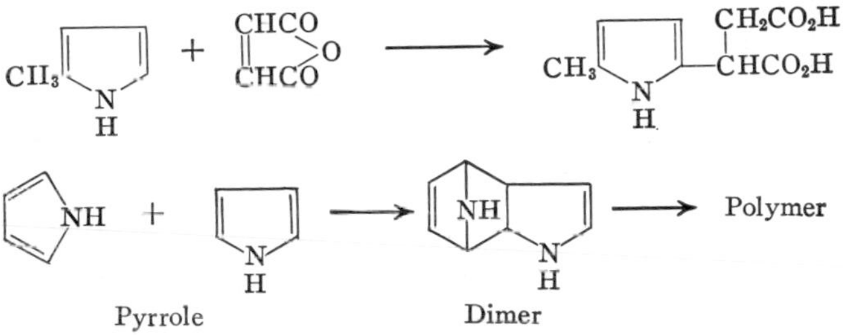

A further property that distinguishes furan and pyrrole from aromatic hydrocarbons is the facility with which the ring is opened, particularly in the furan series. The product from furan itself, succindialdehyde, suffers resinification under the conditions of ring fission. 2,5-Dimethylfuran (pyrolysis of carbohydrates), however, affords acetonylacetone in 88% yield by hydrolysis in aqueous acetic acid in the presence of a little sulfuric acid. The fission reaction can also be conducted in the presence of a carbonyl reagent such as hydroxylamine, when both furan and pyrrole yield the oxime of succindialdehyde. The conversion of furfuryl alcohol into levulinic acid by very dilute hydrochloric acid involves ring fission followed by a disproportionation in which the ketol group becomes reduced and the aldehydic group becomes oxidized. The reaction is general and forms the basis for an interesting process for the preparation of acetonyllevulinic acid.

$$\underset{\text{Furfuryl alcohol}}{\left[\bigcirc\hspace{-0.5em}CH_2OH\right]} \xrightarrow{H^+} \left[\begin{array}{cc} CH_2-CH_2 \\ | \hspace{1em} | \\ CH \hspace{0.5em} CCH_2OH \\ \| \hspace{1em} \| \\ O \hspace{1em} O \end{array}\right] \xrightarrow[40-50\%]{} \underset{\text{Levulinic acid}}{\begin{array}{c} CH_2-CH_2 \\ | \hspace{1em} | \\ HO_2C \hspace{0.5em} COCH_3 \end{array}}$$

$$\underset{\text{Furfural}}{\bigcirc\hspace{-0.5em}CHO} \xrightarrow{CH_3COCH_3} \bigcirc\hspace{-0.5em}CH=CHCOCH_3 \xrightarrow{H^+} \underset{\text{Acetonyllevulinic acid}}{\begin{array}{c} CH_2-CH_2 \\ | \hspace{1em} | \\ CO_2H \hspace{0.5em} COCH_2CH_2COCH_3 \end{array}}$$

The three heterocycles display aromatic character to varying degree in substitution reactions. Thiophene, the most stable of the three, is substituted much more easily than benzene in the Friedel-Crafts reaction and can be acylated with anhydrides, acid chlorides, and even free carboxylic acids under the influence of such mild catalysts as zinc chloride, iodine, or orthophosphoric acid; aluminum chloride is liable to cause resinification. In this and other substitutions the point of attack is invariably the α-position

$$\bigcirc\hspace{-0.5em}S \xrightarrow[94\%]{(CH_3CO)_2O,\ H_3PO_4} \underset{\text{2-Acetothiophene}}{\bigcirc\hspace{-0.5em}S\hspace{-0.5em}COCH_3}$$

unless both α-positions are occupied, in which case substitution can occur β to the hetero atom. The high reactivity of the α-position is shown further by the fact that thiophene can be iodinated (α) with iodine and nitric acid (73% yield) and that it undergoes the Mannich reaction. The product is the hydrochloride of a base known both as 2-thenylamine and 2-thienyl-methylamine.

$$\bigcirc\hspace{-0.5em}S \xrightarrow[45\%]{CH_2O,\ NH_4Cl,\ CH_3OH} \bigcirc\hspace{-0.5em}S\hspace{-0.5em}CH_2NH_2\cdot HCl$$

Pyrrole has only feeble basic properties (pK$_b$ about 13.6); it is dissolved only slightly by dilute acids and is resinified by concentrated acids. Indeed pyrrole actually is best characterized as a weak acid resembling phenol in many respects. Thus it forms a sodium and a potassium salt; it couples with benzenediazonium chloride (predominately α); it reacts with a Grignard reagent to form a pyrrylmagnesium halide (C_4H_4NMgBr); and it undergoes the Reimer-Tiemann reaction. The yield of pyrrole-2-aldehyde

$$\underset{H}{\overset{}{\bigcirc\hspace{-0.5em}N}} + CHCl_3 \xrightarrow[23\%]{KOH} \underset{\underset{(a)}{H}}{\overset{}{\bigcirc\hspace{-0.5em}N}}\hspace{-0.5em}CHO$$

$$\downarrow NaOC_2H_5$$

$$\left[\underset{N}{\overset{H}{\bigcirc}}\hspace{-0.5em}CHCl_2 \ \text{or} \ \underset{N}{\overset{H}{\bigcirc}}\hspace{-0.5em}CHCl_2\right] \xrightarrow{-HCl} \underset{\underset{(b)}{N}}{\overset{}{\bigcirc}}\hspace{-0.5em}Cl$$

is low and a part of the loss undoubtedly results from a concurrent ring-enlargement reaction leading to β-chloropyridine, for this was isolated from the reaction of pyrrole with chloroform and sodium ethoxide. The latter reaction is regarded as analogous to the abnormal Reimer-Tiemann reaction (p. 682). Similar reactions with methylene iodide and with benzal chloride afford pyridine and β-phenylpyridine, respectively.

Alkylated pyrroles are often convertible into aldehydic derivatives in excellent yield by the Gattermann reaction. Thiophene undergoes the Gattermann reaction in only low yield.

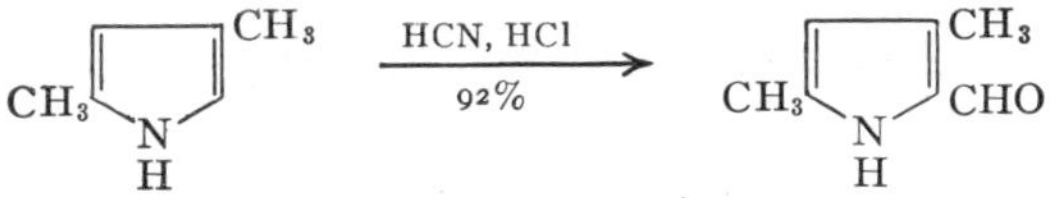

Resonance Stabilization. — In furan, pyrrole, and thiophene stabilization cannot be achieved as in benzene by resonance involving chiefly two equivalent Kekulé structures. Yet the difference between the calculated and observed heats of combustion points to a resonance stabilization of 23, 31, and 31 kg.-cal./mole for furan, pyrrole, and thiophene, respectively, as compared with 39 kg.-cal./mole for benzene. Furthermore the interatomic distance between the carbon and the hetero atom is somewhat less than normal and hence indicative of a certain degree of double-bond character. Actually the hetero atom is responsible for a resonance effect by virtue of displacement of a pair of its unshared electrons. Thus five resonance structures can be written for thiophene (or for furan or pyrrole). Structures (b) to (e) involve a formal separation of charge, and resonance stabilization in such a system is not so great as that acquired from resonance involving exactly equivalent structures, as in benzene. Structures

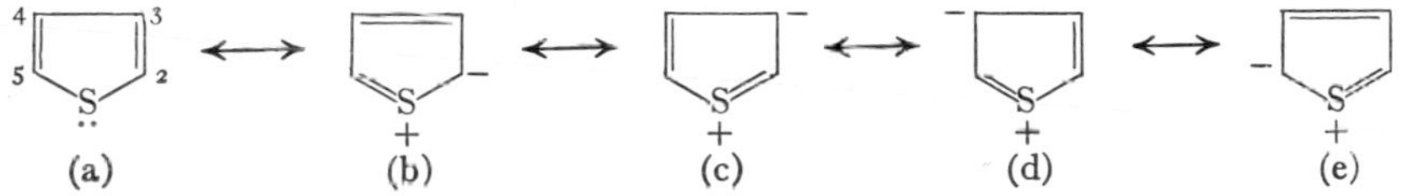

(c) and (d) probably represent excited states of minor contribution, since they possess cross conjugated unsaturated systems, which usually possess less stability (absorption of ultraviolet light of shorter wave length) than systems of extended conjugation such as those of (b) and (e), where the conjugation extends between the two ionic charges. That (b) and (e) are indeed prominent contributors is suggested further by the preponderance of α-substitutions in electrophilic reactions, for the centers of high electron density are at the α- and α'-positions in these structures.

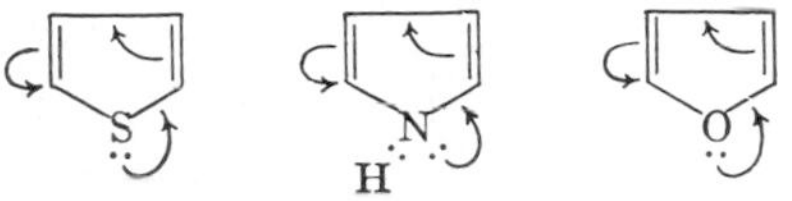

The Ingold formulation for the three heterocycles expresses the same interpretation of α-substitution more simply. Displacement of an electron pair from the hetero atom toward C_2 initiates a succession of displacements resulting in high electron density at C_5.

The feeble basicity of pyrrole can be described as due to the fact that the nitrogen atom bears a fractional positive charge or is deficient in electrons and therefore has little tendency to accept a proton. When pyrrole is treated with acid sufficiently strong to form a salt the originally unshared pair of electrons is no longer free to shift to other positions in the ring, and hence pyrrole in acid solution exhibits high reactivity characteristic of dienes. Tetrahydropyrrole, or pyrrolidine, has the typical basic properties of a secondary amine.

Other Types. — A few of the many ring systems derivable from the simple five-membered heterocycles by introduction of one or two additional hetero atoms are listed in Table 33.1. Azole is the generic name for five-

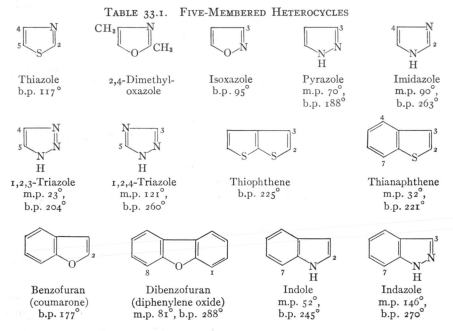

TABLE 33.1.   FIVE-MEMBERED HETEROCYCLES

Thiazole
b.p. 117°

2,4-Dimethyl-
oxazole

Isoxazole
b.p. 95°

Pyrazole
m.p. 70°,
b.p. 188°

Imidazole
m.p. 90°,
b.p. 263°

1,2,3-Triazole
m.p. 23°,
b.p. 204°

1,2,4-Triazole
m.p. 121°,
b.p. 260°

Thiophthene
b.p. 225°

Thianaphthene
m.p. 32°,
b.p. 221°

Benzofuran
(coumarone)
b.p. 177°

Dibenzofuran
(diphenylene oxide)
m.p. 81°, b.p. 288°

Indole
m.p. 52°,
b.p. 245°

Indazole
m.p. 146°,
b.p. 270°

membered heterocycles containing a nitrogen atom and one or more other hetero atoms. Thiazoles and oxazoles thus are azoles containing sulfur and oxygen. The systematic names for pyrazole and for imidazole are 1,2- and 1,3-diazole, respectively.

Whereas pyrrole is but feebly basic, imidazole is a strong base (pK_b 7.0). The marked difference is attributable to the fact that the ion from imidazole is stabilized by resonance between two equivalent structures. The isomeric

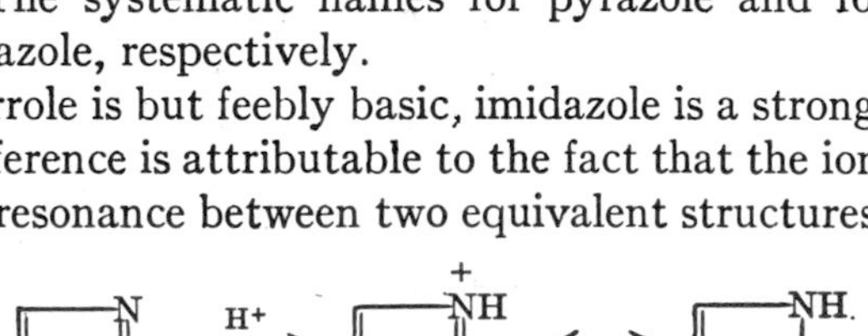

Imidazole

pyrazole (pK_b 11.5) is a much weaker base than imidazole, although still stronger than pyrrole. A resonant ion hybrid is possible in this case as well and the lower basicity as compared with that of imidazole may be associated

(a)   (b)

Pyrazole

with hydrogen bonding in the nonionized molecule (b). The very high boiling point of imidazole suggests that it is highly associated. Simple chelation is not possible in this case, but possibly four rings are associated in a porphyrin-like structure.

Indole. — The most important route to indole derivatives was developed by E. Fischer (1883) as a result of the observation that the phenylhydrazone

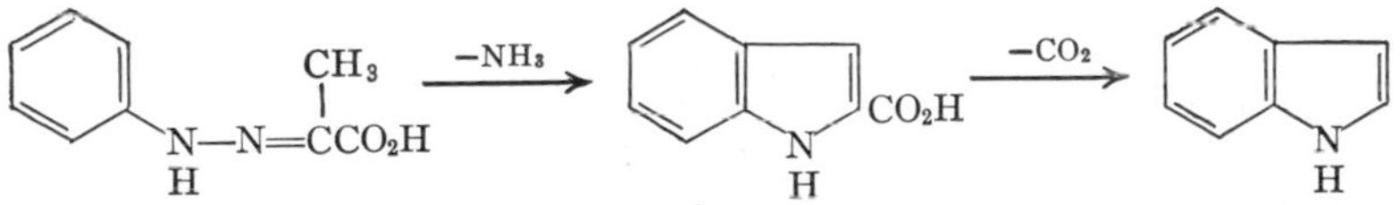

Indole

of pyruvic acid is converted by acid (or, better, zinc chloride) into indole-2-carboxylic acid. The reaction was originally thought to proceed through an intermediate rearrangement of the o-benzidine type but at present the exact mechanism of the rearrangement is in question. The Fischer indole synthesis is very general, with the exception that the phenylhydrazone of acetaldehyde does not yield indole itself. Indole is available from coal tar or can be made by decarboxylation of the 2-carboxylic acid. Indole resembles pyrrole in properties with the exception that the β-position is substituted more readily than the α-position; the β-position is thus activated by the adjacent benzene ring just as the α-position of naphthalene is activated.

Benzofurans. — Benzofuran itself is more generally known as coumarone, since it is made readily from coumarin (p. 690) by the reaction sequence formulated (a). Another synthesis (b) involves treatment of sodium

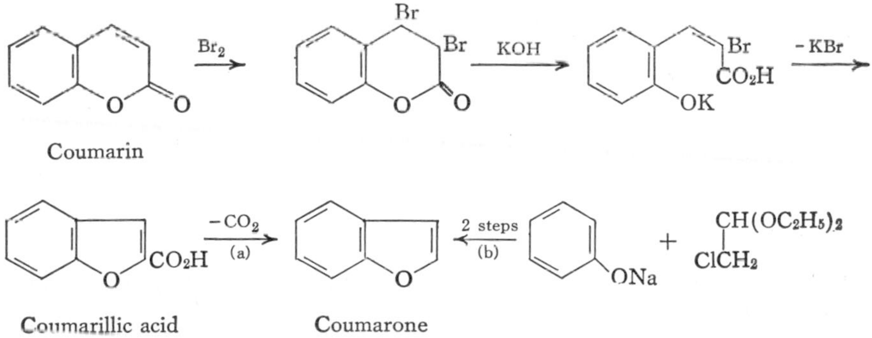

Coumarin

Coumarillic acid   Coumarone

phenolate with chloroacetal and cyclization of the resulting ether with zinc chloride in acetic acid solution.

Usnic acid, a yellow antibiotic pigment of lichens, is a complicated benzofuran derivative which has been studied by many investigators. The formula of Robertson[2] (1937) provided the most satisfactory explanation of many degradative experiments but was held inconsistent with the ready racemization (both d- and l-forms occur in nature). Stork (1955) has sug-

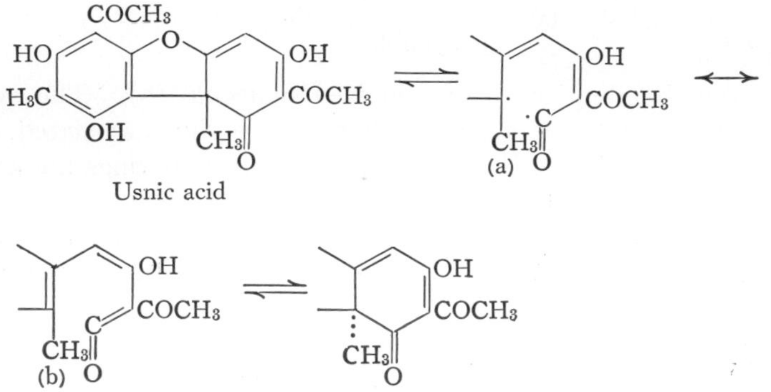

Usnic acid

(a)

(b)

Epimer

gested that epimerization occurs by homolysis to the diradical (a), one of the resonance forms of which is the ketene (b).

Another substance characterized as a benzofuran is griseofulvin, a colorless, neutral product isolated from *Penicillium griseofulvum* (Oxford, Raistrick, 1939). The mold product is of interest because it has antibiotic properties. Griseofulvin is the enol ether of a 1,3-diketone (ring C) and is readily hydrolyzed to the free enol, originally mistaken for a carboxylic

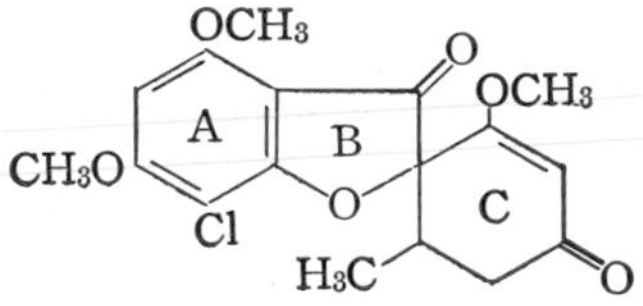

Griseofulvin
M.p. 219°, αD + 337°

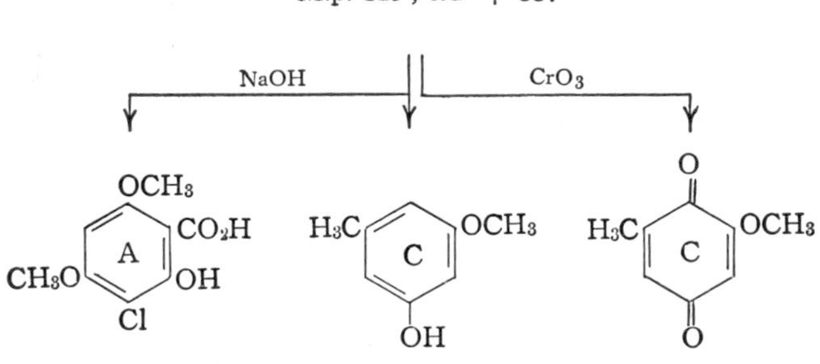

NaOH   CrO₃

(a)   (b)   (c)

acid ("griseofulvic acid"); reetherification gives a mixture of griseofulvin and the isomeric enol ether. Rings B and C have a single carbon atom in common to form a spiro grouping. Structure elucidation (Grove,[3] 1952) was based in part on permanganate oxidation to the hydroxy acid (a) and chromic acid oxidation to 2-methyl-6-methoxy-1,4-benzoquinone (c), two fragments that account for all of the original carbon atoms. That they represent different rings is shown by the fact that alkaline cleavage yields the same carboxylic acid (a) together with the methyl resorcinol ether (b).

Triaryltetrazolium Salts. — These salts are colorless substances that on reduction, for example by a reducing sugar, yield intensely colored, sparingly soluble products known as formazans. They are thus valuable reagents for visualization of biological reduction processes (Kuhn and Jerchel,[4] 1941). The preparation involves synthesis of the formazan and oxidation. Thus triphenyltetrazolium chloride (TTC) is made by alkaline coupling of benzenediazonium chloride with benzalphenylhydrazone, followed by oxidative

$$[C_6H_5\overset{+}{N}{\equiv}N]Cl^-$$

$$+$$

$$C_6H_5NHN{=}CHC_6H_5$$

$$\xrightarrow{-HCl}$$

$$\begin{array}{c} C_6H_5N{=}N \\ \diagdown \\ CC_6H_5 \\ \diagup\diagup \\ C_6H_5N{\cdot}N{\cdot}H \end{array}$$

Formazan (red)

$$\underset{2H}{\overset{HgO,\ HCl}{\rightleftharpoons}}$$

$$\left[\begin{array}{c} C_6H_5\overset{+}{N}{=}N \\ | \diagdown \\ | CC_6H_5 \\ | \diagup\diagup \\ C_6H_5N{-}N \end{array}\right] Cl^-$$

TTC (colorless)

ring closure. The test for reducing action, conducted in weakly alkaline solution, involves reversal of the oxidation and appearance of the red formazan. A reagent preferred because it gives a blue pigment well adapted to colorimetry is 3,3'-dianisole bis-4,4(3,4-diphenyl)-tetrazolium chloride (called BT = blue tetrazolium).

Butenolides. — Butenolides, or unsaturated γ-lactones, can be regarded as α-ketodihydrofurans. Dehydration of a γ-keto acid gives a β,γ-unsaturated butenolide, which is largely isomerized by alkali to the α,β-unsaturated

$$\begin{array}{c} CH_2{-}CH_2 \\ | | \\ RCO CO_2H \end{array} \xrightarrow{-H_2O} \underset{R}{\overset{\beta}{\underset{\gamma}{\diagdown}}}\!\!\overset{}{\underset{O}{\diagup}}\!\!O \quad \overset{OH^-}{\rightleftharpoons} \quad \underset{R}{\overset{\beta}{\diagdown}}\!\!\overset{\alpha}{\underset{O}{\diagup}}\!\!O$$

isomer, the position of equilibrium depending upon the substituent groups. The isomers are distinguishable by ultraviolet spectroscopy, since the conjugated ketone alone shows absorption at 220 mμ. An efficient synthesis of Δ^{α}-butenolides involves addition of sodium acetylide to a ketone in liquid ammonia solution, carboxylation of the ethynyl group through the Grignard derivative, partial hydrogenation, and spontaneous ring closure (E. R. H. Jones; Raphael[5]).

[3] John Frederick Grove, b. 1921 Sheffield, England; stud. Kings Coll. (Allmand); Imperial Chem. Ind.

[4] Dietrich Jerchel, b. 1913 Seiferdau, Schlesien; Ph.D. Munich (H. Wieland); Mainz

[5] Ralph Alexander Raphael, b. 1921 London; Ph.D. and D.Sc. London, Imperial Coll. (Heilbron, E. R. H. Jones); Queen's Univ., Belfast, Ireland

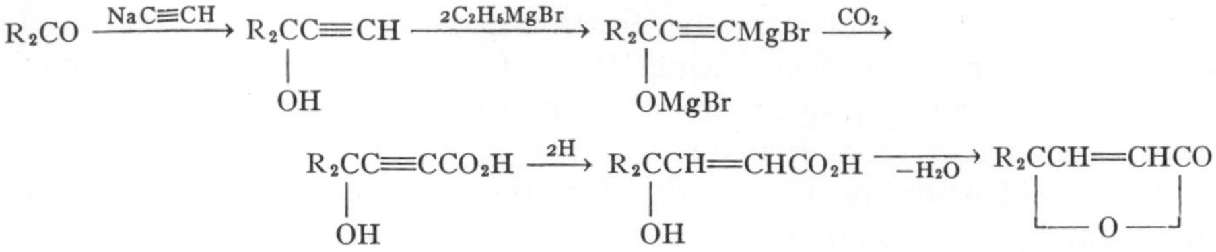

$$R_2CO \xrightarrow{\text{NaC}\equiv\text{CH}} R_2\underset{\underset{OH}{|}}{C}C\equiv CH \xrightarrow{\text{2C}_2\text{H}_5\text{MgBr}} R_2\underset{\underset{OMgBr}{|}}{C}C\equiv CMgBr \xrightarrow{\text{CO}_2}$$

$$R_2\underset{\underset{OH}{|}}{C}C\equiv CCO_2H \xrightarrow{\text{2H}} R_2\underset{\underset{OH}{|}}{C}CH=CHCO_2H \xrightarrow{-H_2O} R_2CCH=CHCO$$

The butenolide structure occurs in many natural products. The angelica lactones are γ-methyl Δ^α-and Δ^β-butenolide. A number of antibiotics are relatively simple derivatives of this type: penicillic acid (a metabolite of various strains of *Penicillium*), protoanemonin (*Anemone pulsatilla*), and patulin (or clavacin, a metabolite of various molds). Vulpinic acid and

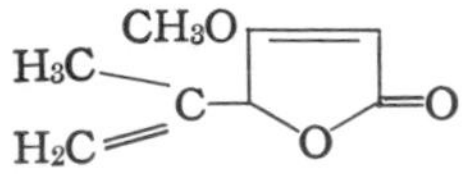

Penicillic acid 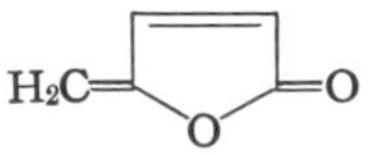   Protoanemonin 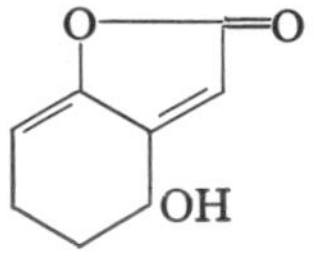   Patulin (λ_{max} 277mµ)

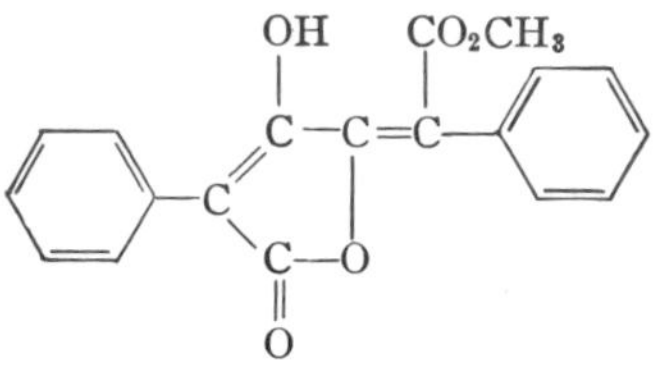

Vulpinic acid 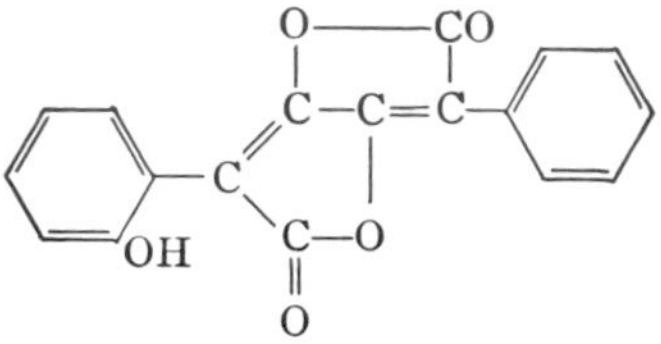   Calycin

calycin, yellow and orange-red pigments isolated from lichens, are butenolide derivatives.

SIX-MEMBERED HETEROCYCLES

Pyridine. — Coal tar is a practicable source of pyridine, and also affords the three monomethyl derivatives known as α-, β-, and γ-picoline, the di-methylpyridines or lutidines, a fraction containing trimethyl- and methyl-ethyl pyridines, known as collidines, and α-vinylpyridine. β-Picoline is currently manufactured by condensation of two molecules of acrolein with ammonia. 2-Methyl-5-ethylpyridine is made by condensation of paralde-hyde with ammonia and ammonium hydroxide and is called aldehyde col-lidine.

The pyridine ring has stability surpassing that of benzene. Thus oxi-dation of quinoline results in preferential destruction of the benzene, rather than of the pyridine ring. The initially formed quinolinic acid suffers ready

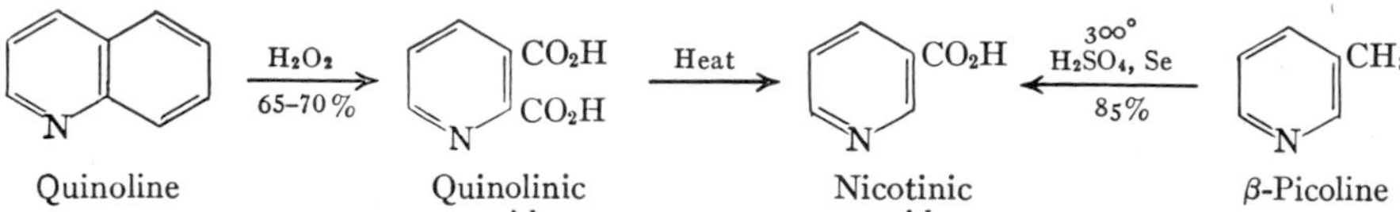

Quinoline   Quinolinic acid   Nicotinic acid   β-Picoline

decarboxylation to nicotinic acid; α- and γ-carboxylic acid derivatives of pyridine generally lose carbon dioxide readily, whereas β-carboxylic acids are much more stable. Nicotinic acid is also obtained in high yield by oxidation of β-picoline with concentrated sulfuric acid at 300° in the presence of selenium as catalyst.

Pyridine also is more resistant than benzene to the usual aromatic substitutions. Bromination can be accomplished only in the vapor phase at a temperature of about 300°, and sulfonation and nitration can be effected only under forcing conditions; substitutions, where realized, always occur in the β-position. Attempted Friedel-Crafts reactions are invariably negative. Thus pyridine corresponds in degree of reactivity to nitrobenzene rather than to benzene. Furthermore, a halogen atom in the 2- or 4-position, but not one at position 3, is readily replaceable by hydrogen or by an amino group; the halopyridines are thus analogous to the halonitrobenzenes.

The facts noted find satisfactory interpretation in terms of the resonance theory. In pyridine the possibility for resonance extends beyond the two identical Kekulé structures (a) and (b) to three additional structures (c-e),

(a)   (b)   (c)   (d)   (c)

in which the relatively electron-attracting nitrogen atom acquires an additional pair of electrons from a carbon atom in the α- or γ-position, which thereby becomes positively charged. Reactions with electrophilic reagents involve the pyridinium ion, and this offers the same opportunity for resonance. Thus electrophilic substitution, if realizable, occurs only at the β-position. An electron-attracting halogen atom in the α- or γ-position is incompatible with the positive resonance polarization at these positions and hence is subject to ready displacement.

In the resonance structures (c) to (e) the nitrogen atom is linked to each of the two carbon atoms by a single bond. Actually, physical measurements have shown that the C—N bond distance is somewhat greater (1.37Å) than the bond distance (1.33)Å calculated for a hybrid of the two Kekulé structures (a, b). The resonance energy of pyridine is 43 kg.-cal./mole, significantly higher than that of benzene.

The resonance structures (c) to (e) account for the fact that pyridine is substituted by anionic fragments (OH^-, NH_2^-) at the 2- and 4-positions. Thus pyridine, unlike benzene, reacts with sodamide to form 2-amino-pyridine (Chichibabin,[6] 1914). The two components are heated in dimethylaniline until hydrogen is no longer evolved; the 2-amino derivative is obtained in excellent yield on hydrolysis. A second amino group can be

[6] Alexei E. Chichibabin, 1871–1945; b. Gouv. Poltowa, Russia; Ph.D. St. Petersburg; Moscow, Paris; *J. Chem. Soc.*, 760 (1946)

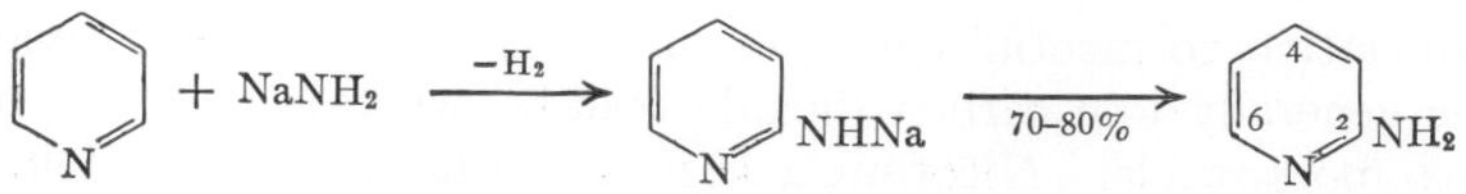

introduced in the 6-position (82–90% yield); if both the 2- and 6-positions are blocked, the amino group enters position 4. In contrast with the parent heterocycle, 2-aminopyridine undergoes usual aromatic substitutions, usually with attack at positions 3 and 5, *ortho* and *para* to the amino group. 2-Aminopyridine affords a route to 3-substituted pyridines through an interesting reaction sequence in which the two products of mononitration

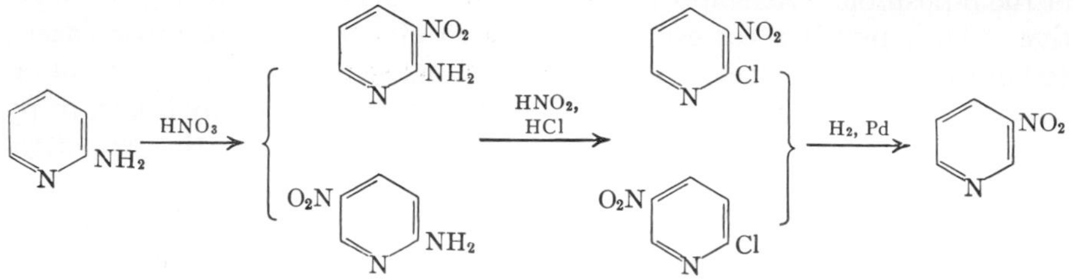

are converted by diazotization in the presence of hydrochloric acid into nitrochloro derivatives in which the chloro group is activated and hence readily removed by selective hydrogenation. 3-Aminopyridine is obtained most readily by the action of sodium hypobromite on nicotinamide (67% yield).

The reaction of pyridine with Grignard reagents and with alkyl- and aryllithium compounds also results in substitution at the 2-position. A

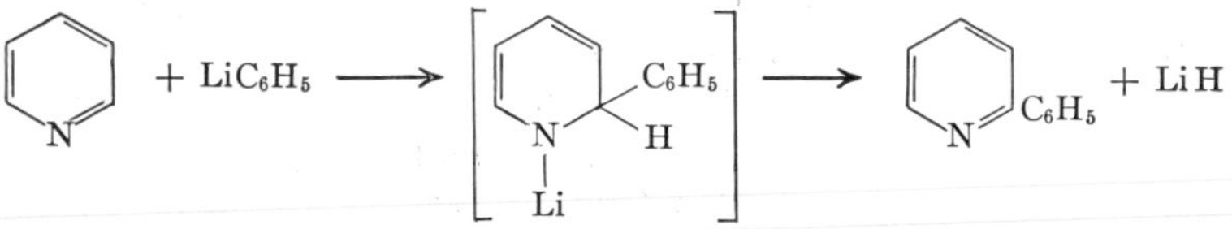

methyl group in the α- or γ-position, but not in the β-position, shows reactivity comparable to that of a methyl ketone. Thus α-picoline readily condenses with benzaldehyde; the activation is analogous to that encountered in 2,4-dinitrotoluene.

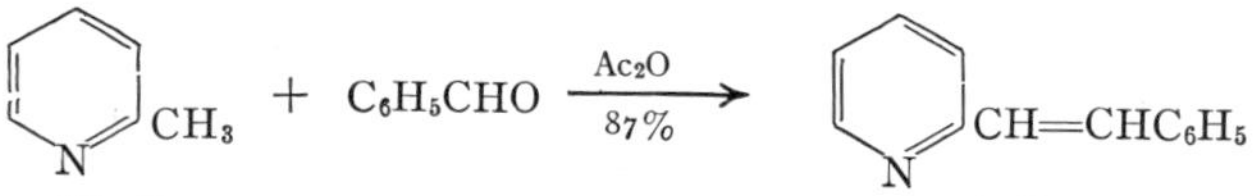

α-Picoline   α-Stilbazole

That pyridine (pK_b 8.8) is a much weaker base than trimethylamine (pK_b 4 2) is not fully understood. The heterocycle otherwise exhibits properties typical of a tertiary amine: it yields an amine oxide (m.p. 66°) on reaction with perbenzoic acid, and forms quaternary salts that behave as strong electrolytes. The quaternary hydroxides, however, exhibit special properties. Thus N-methylpyridinium hydroxide (a) responds to oxidation with potassium ferricyanide as though it has the structure (b). The product, N-methylpyridone-2, is formulated as a hybrid of the amide (c) and the inner salt (d); it reacts with phosphorus pentachloride to give 2-chloropyridine. The quaternary hydroxide (a) thus appears capable of

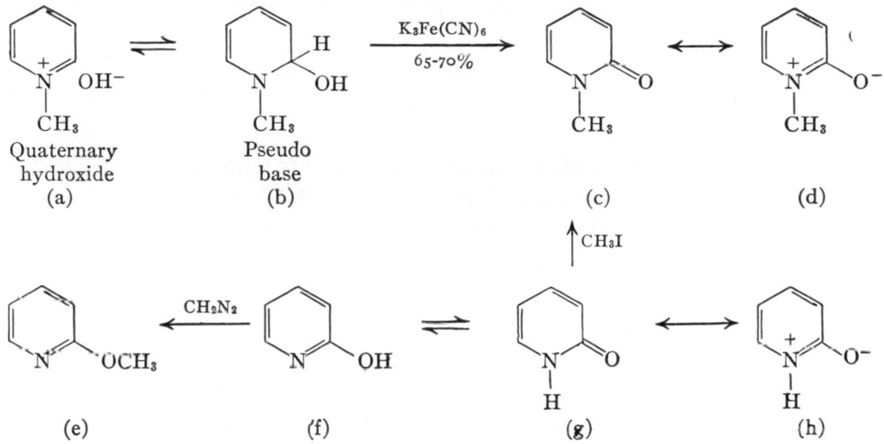

reacting in the form of the pseudo base (b). Various reactions lead to a substance that can be formulated as 2-hydroxypyridine (f), pyridone-2 (g), or the corresponding inner salt (h). The substance does not exhibit the phenolic properties expected for formula (f), although etherification with diazomethane yields the O-methyl ether (e). Methylation with methyl iodide, on the other hand, gives N-methylpyridone-2 (c). The inner-salt structures (d) and (h) are the most plausible formulations for the pyridones, for the substances are devoid of carbonyl characteristics and are readily soluble in water and sparingly soluble in benzene.

A new route to substituted pyridines was opened by the observation, made independently by Ochiai in Japan (1941) and by den Hertog in Holland (1950) that pyridine oxide is more susceptible to electrophilic attack than pyridine. The positions substituted are α and γ, with γ-derivatives predominating, and this orientation is accounted for by consideration of the resonance structures possible for the oxide. After the substitution reaction

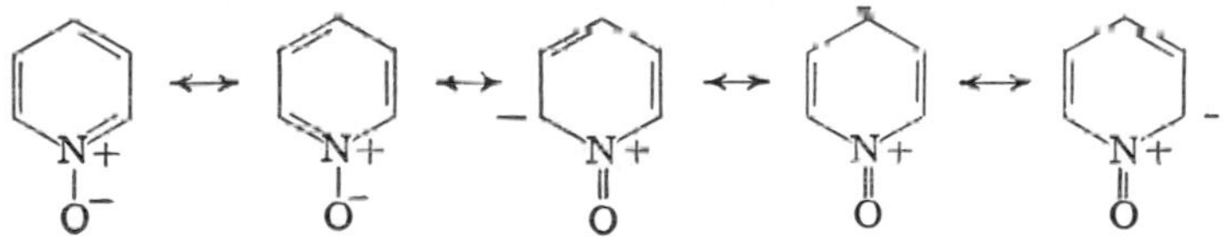

has been carried out, for example, nitration to α- and γ-nitropyridine oxide, reaction with phosphorus trichloride in chloroform removes the N-oxide group and gives the substituted pyridine.

2,4-Dinitrochlorobenzene contains a halogen atom of sufficiently enhanced reactivity to condense with pyridine to form the pyridinium chloride. This substance is converted by alkali into a water-insoluble product

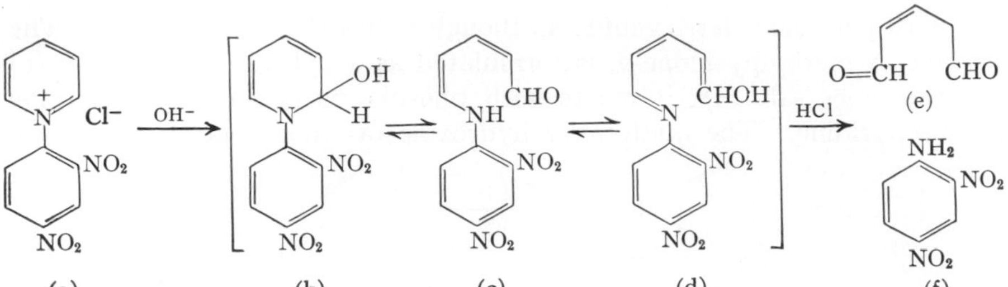

(a)   (b)   (c)   (d)   (f)

that on acid hydrolysis yields glutaconic aldehyde (e) and 2,4-dinitroaniline
(f).   The reaction is believed to proceed through a pseudo base (b) to a
Schiff base (d), which undergoes hydrolysis to the final products (e) and (f).

   Quinoline and Isoquinoline. — The isomeric benzpyridines, quinoline
and isoquinoline, occur in coal tar and are also available by synthesis.   A
particularly general and useful route to quinoline and many of its derivatives
is the synthesis discovered by Skraup[7] (1880) in which, for example, aniline
is treated with glycerol, sulfuric acid, and an oxidizing agent (nitrobenzene,
arsenic pentoxide, ferric oxide, or picric acid).   The reaction is exothermic
and may proceed with violence unless controlled by moderators such as

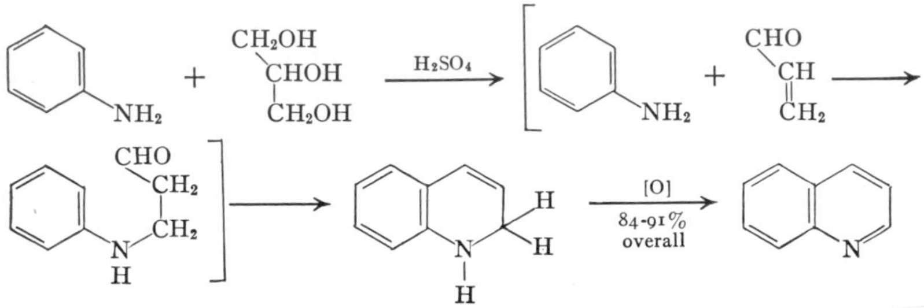

ferrous sulfate or boric acid.   The functional intermediate is acrolein, but
oddly enough, the yield is often negligible if preformed acrolein is employed.
The reaction proceeds by 1,4-addition of the amine to the α,β-unsaturated
carbonyl intermediate or component, as demonstrated by the reaction of
aniline with methyl vinyl ketone to yield 4-methylquinoline, or lepidine.

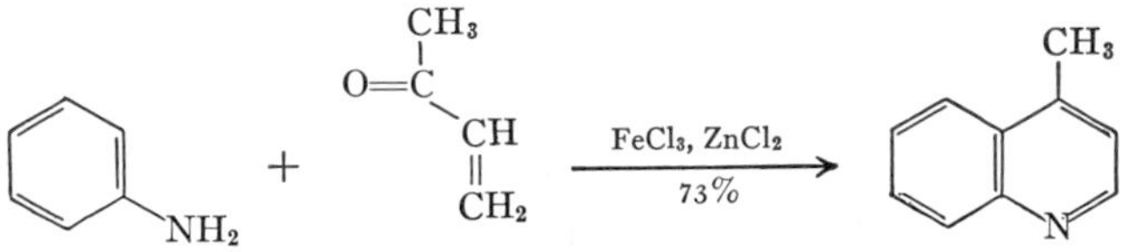

Lepidine

   Another route to lepidine derivatives involves condensation of an aromatic amine with diketene to an acetoacetanilide capable of undergoing
ring closure to an α-hydroxylepidine; as in the pyridine series, a hydroxyl

---

[7] Zdenko Hans Skraup, 1850–1910; b. Prague; Ph.D. Giessen; Graz, Austria; *Ber.*, **43**, 3683
(1910)

group in the α- (or γ-) position is readily eliminated by conversion into the chloro derivative and hydrogenation.

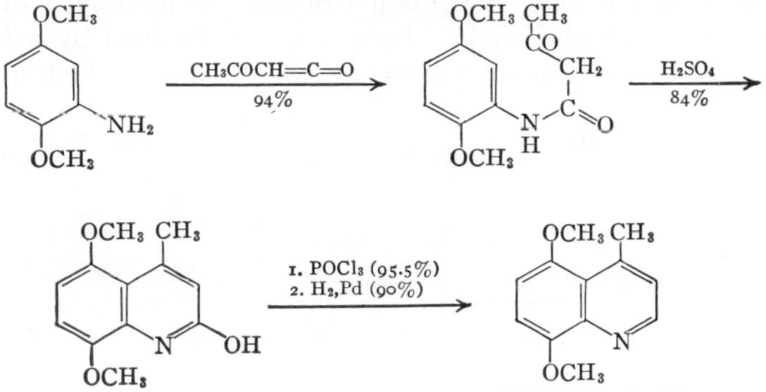

5,8-Dimethoxylepidine

One advantage of the Skraup reaction is that almost any desired quinoline derivative can be obtained by variation in the aldehyde component or in the aniline moiety. One complication in the latter case is that the directive influence of a substituent group may augment or compete with that of the amino group. In the Skraup reaction of m-toluidine, for example,

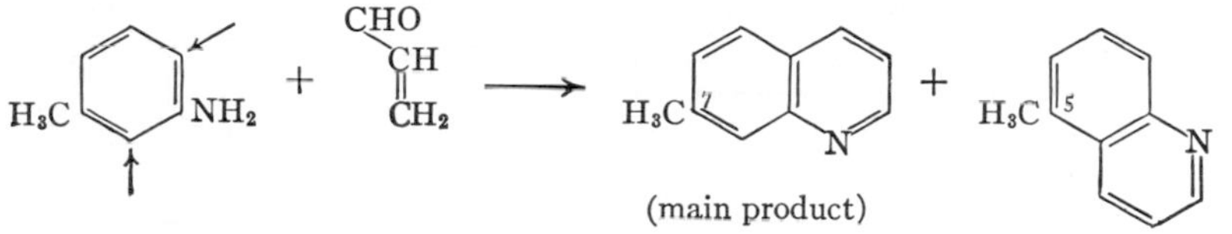

(main product)

ring closure takes place at both positions *ortho* to the amino group, but the predominant product is 7-methylquinoline, in which ring closure has occurred *para* to the methyl group. Ring closure at a single position can be effected by blocking one of the positions *ortho* to the amino group by a nitro group, which can be eliminated after formation of the quinoline ring system by reduction, diazotization, and deamination.

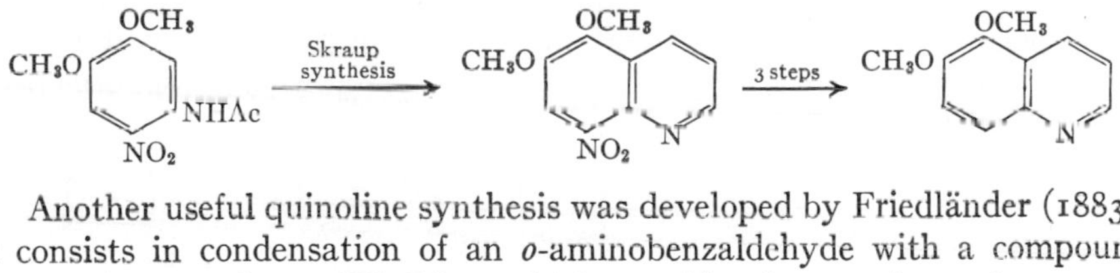

Another useful quinoline synthesis was developed by Friedländer (1883); it consists in condensation of an *o*-aminobenzaldehyde with a compound having the grouping —CH_2CO—, which provides the 2- and 3-carbon atoms in the resulting quinoline. Thus quinaldine (2-methylquinoline) is obtained by condensation with acetone (Schöpf, 1932). The Friedländer synthesis

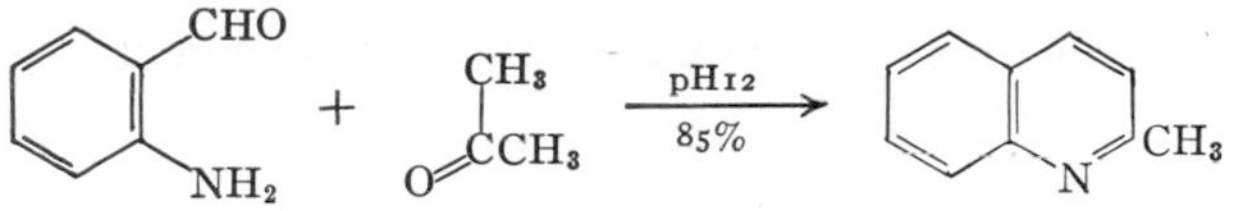

Quinaldine

suffers from the disadvantage that o-aminobenzaldehydes are not readily available. In a modification introduced by Pfitzinger (1902), the benzenoid component is isatinic acid, the product of alkaline hydrolysis of isatin, a derivative of 2,3-dihydroindole. Isatin can be obtained by oxidation of the dye indigo (p. 905) or by various syntheses, one of which utilizes the

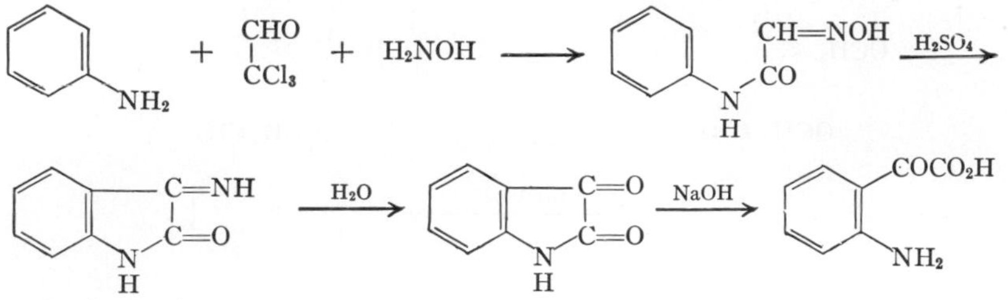

| Isatin-β-imide | Isatin | Isatinic acid |

condensation of aniline, chloral, and hydroxylamine. The Friedländer synthesis with isatinic acid results in a quinoline-4-carboxylic acid. As in the pyridine series a carboxyl group in a position γ (or α) to the nitrogen atom is readily eliminated.

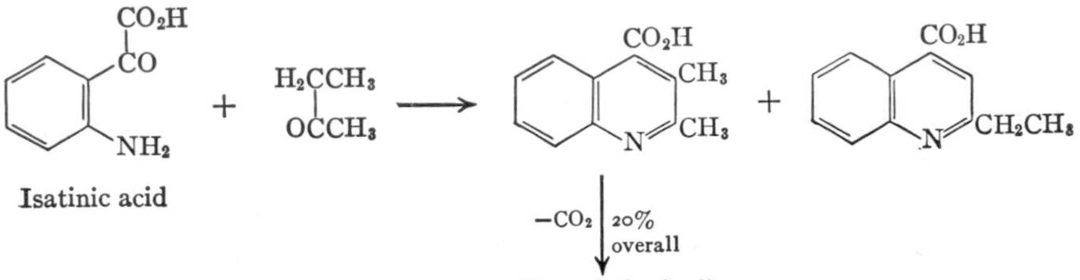

2,3-Dimethylquinoline

A useful synthesis of isoquinoline derivatives is that of Bischler and Napieralski (1893), in which an acyl derivative of a β-phenylethylamine undergoes intramolecular condensation to a 3,4-dihydroisoquinoline, convertible into an isoquinoline by oxidation (KMnO$_4$) or by dehydrogenation with palladium. In the preparation of 1-methylisoquinoline illustrated (Späth, 1930), N-acetylphenylethylamine is cyclized with phosphorus pent-

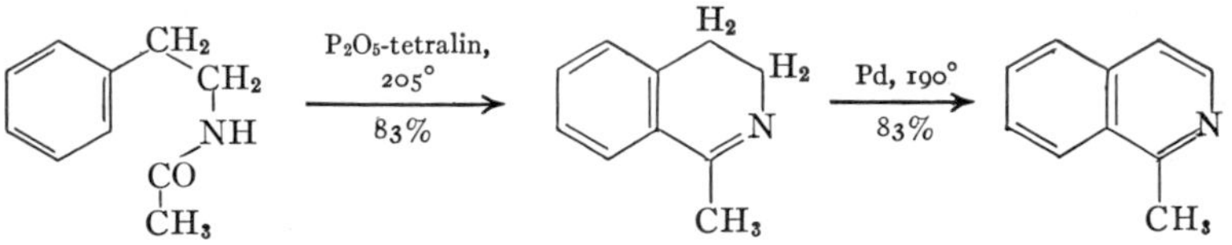

oxide; phosphorus oxychloride is also a favored reagent. Isoquinoline derivatives can be obtained directly by cyclization of an N-acyl derivative of a vinylamine (Krabbe, 1941), as shown for the preparation of 1,4-dimethylisoquinoline.

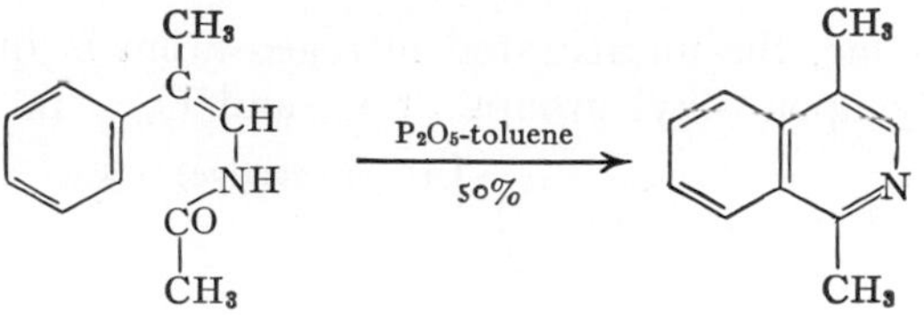

Another useful method which leads directly to isoquinolines substituted either at the 1-position or in the benzene ring involves condensation of a

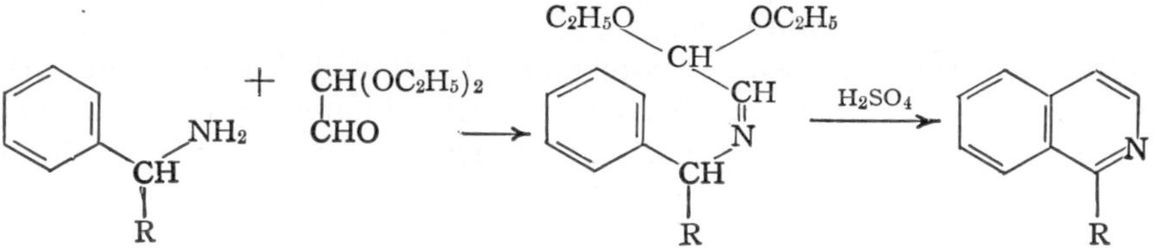

benzylamine with glyoxal semiacetal to form a Schiff base, which on treatment with sulfuric acid undergoes ring closure (modified Pomeranz-Fritsch procedure). The yields are about 50%.

Quinoline and isoquinoline behave as would be expected from the properties of pyridine. Electrophilic substitutions, like oxidation, involve attack of the benzene ring; thus nitration of quinoline affords the 5- and 8-nitro derivatives in yields of 37% and 27%, respectively. Amination, hydroxylation by potassium hydroxide, and reaction with Grignard reagents result in substitution α to the nitrogen atom: at C_2 in quinoline, and at C_1 in isoquinoline. The pyridine ring in quinoline or isoquinoline is more susceptible to reduction than the benzene ring, tetrahydro derivatives being readily formed by catalytic hydrogenation or by reduction with tin and hydrochloric acid. A process akin to reduction is involved in the first stage of the interesting process for preparation of the 4-cyano derivative formu-

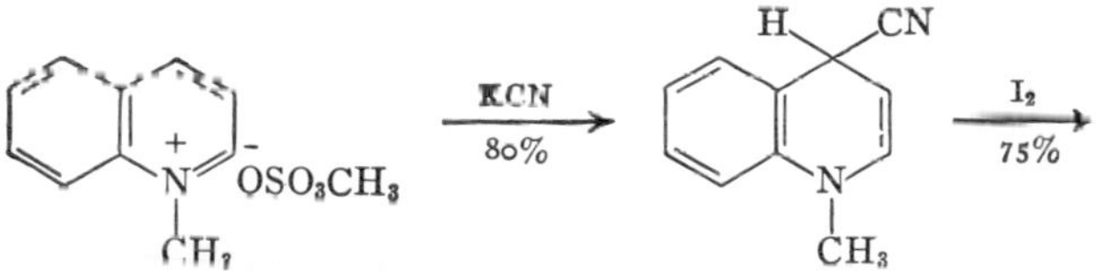

N-Methylquinoline methosulfate   4-Cyano-N-methyldihydroquinoline

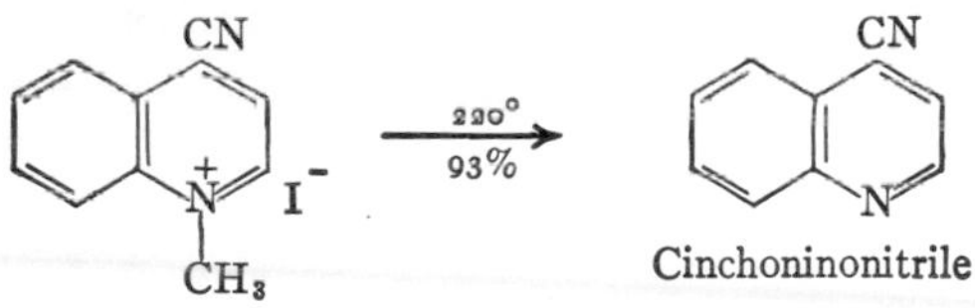

Cinchoninonitrile

lated (Kaufmann, 1909); the reaction doubtless initiates in an attack by cyanide ion at a position bearing a fractional positive charge due to resonance.

As with pyridine, the unsaturated nitrogen atom in quinoline bestows special reactivity upon alkyl groups at C_2 and C_4. In the case of iso-

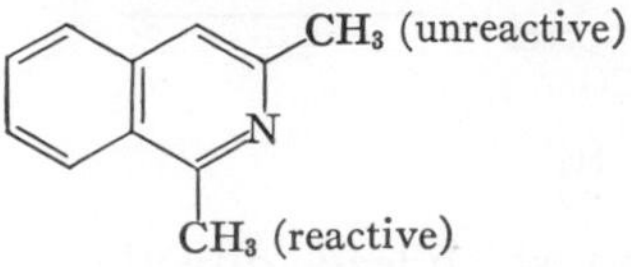

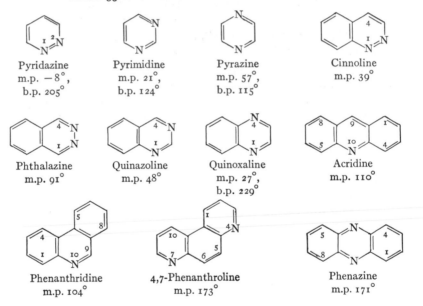

CH₃ (unreactive)

CH₃ (reactive)

quinoline this activation is manifested only on an alkyl group located at C_1; the lack of activation of a group at C_3 is evidence of fixation of the double bonds, as in naphthalene.

Other N-Heterocycles. — Six-membered heterocycles containing two nitrogen atoms are known as diazines; the trivial names of the monocyclic bases are derived from combination of the name pyridine with -azine or -imid-. Examples are listed in Table 33.2.

TABLE 33.2. HETEROCYCLES CONTAINING NITROGEN

Pyridazine m.p. −8°, b.p. 205°	Pyrimidine m.p. 21°, b.p. 124°	Pyrazine m.p. 57°, b.p. 115°	Cinnoline m.p. 39°
Phthalazine m.p. 91°	Quinazoline m.p. 48°	Quinoxaline m.p. 27°, b.p. 229°	Acridine m.p. 110°
Phenanthridine m.p. 104°	4,7-Phenanthroline m.p. 173°	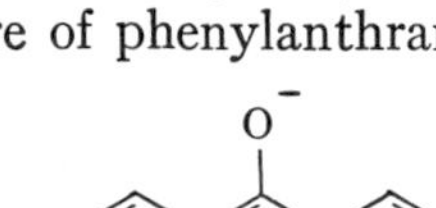	Phenazine m.p. 171°

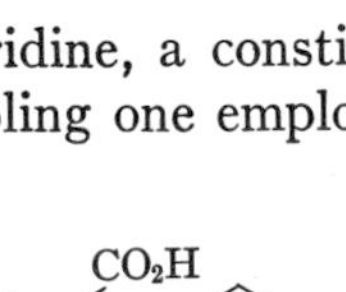

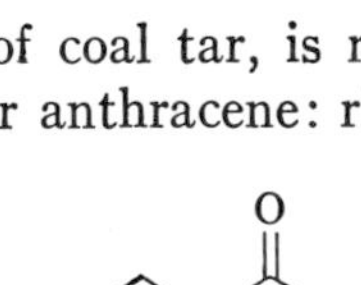

Acridine, a constituent of coal tar, is readily available by a synthesis resembling one employed for anthracene: ring-closure of phenylanthranilic

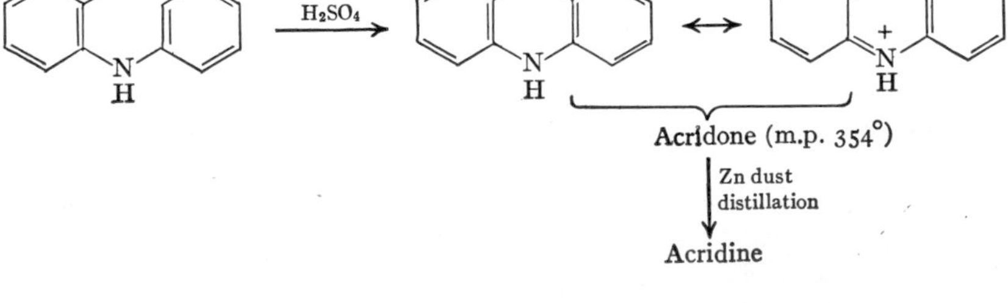

Acridone (m.p. 354°)

Zn dust distillation

Acridine

acid to acridone and zinc dust reduction. Acridone is a stable, high-melting substance that shows neither ketonic nor phenolic properties, and it probably exists as an inner salt. Important derivatives of acridine include dyes, bactericides, and the antimalarial drug atabrine (p. 1027). The isomeric angular dibenzpyridine is named phenanthridine. It is obtained by pyrolysis of N-benzylideneaniline (a) or of N-methylcarbazole (b).

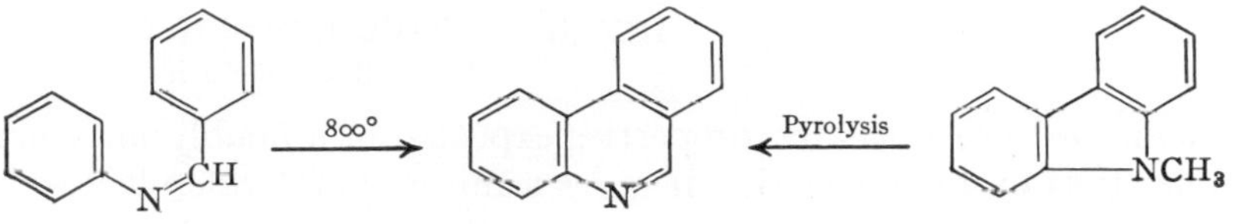

(a)   Phenanthridine   (b)

SIX-MEMBERED O-HETEROCYCLES

The pyrans, α- and γ-, are not known as such but are the parent substances of the corresponding pyrones, of dihydropyran, and of the benzene-like, stable pyrylium salts.

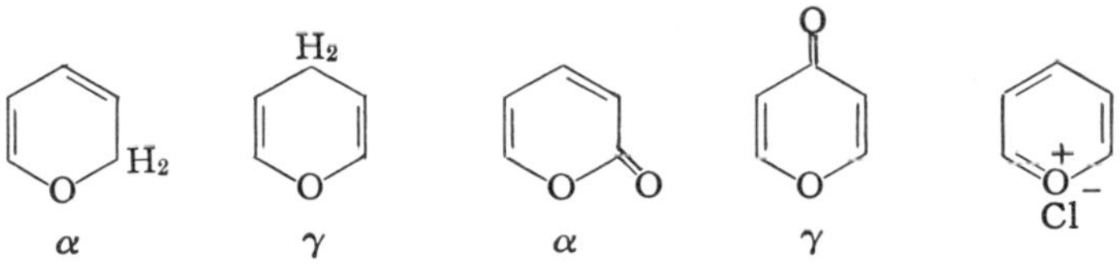

α γ α γ

Pyrans   Pyrones   Pyrylium chloride

Dihydropyran. — This cyclic vinyl ether, prepared by dehydration of tetrahydrofurfuryl alcohol (Paul,[8] 1933) is used for protection of alcoholic

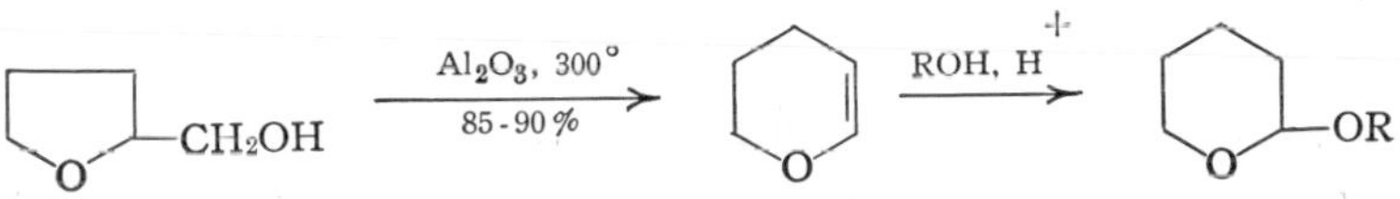

Dihydropyran
(b.p. 86°)

hydroxyl groups. It adds an alcohol under acid catalysis to give an acetal derivative stable to bases and neutral reagents, from which the alcohol can be regenerated by mild acid hydrolysis.

Pyrones. — α-Pyrone has been prepared by decarboxylation of coumalic acid, the product of the action of concentrated sulfuric acid on malic acid. Possibly malic acid is first converted by loss of carbon monoxide and water into formylacetic acid, two molecules of which (in the enol form) condense to give coumalic acid. In a reaction characteristic of 5-carboxy-α-pyrones, coumalic acid undergoes smooth cleavage by alkali to formic acid and gluta-

---

[8] Raymond-Etienne Paul, b. 1907 Angers, France; Ph.D. Paris (Blanchard. Lespieaux); Univ. Angers, Rhône-Poulenc.

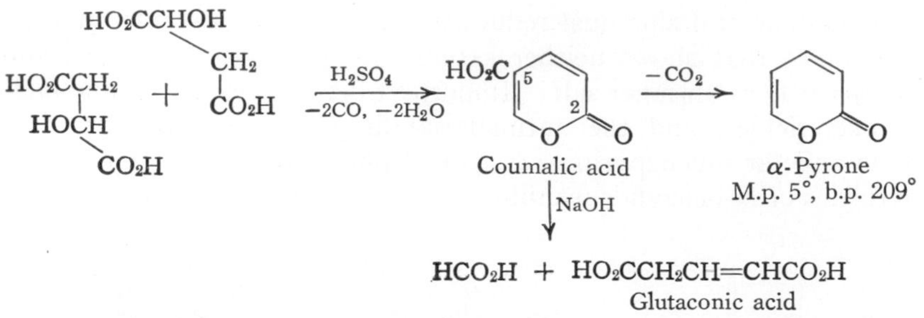
HO2CCHOH
CH2
CO2H
HO2CCH2
HOCH
CO2H
H2SO4
−2CO, −2H2O
HO2C
Coumalic acid
NaOH
−CO2
α-Pyrone
M.p. 5°, b.p. 209°
HCO2H + HO2CCH2CH=CHCO2H
Glutaconic acid

conic acid. α-Pyrone has the properties expected of a doubly unsaturated δ-lactone; thus on hydrogenation it gives a mixture of δ-valerolactone and valeric acid. The diene system reacts normally in the Diels-Alder reaction.

The most readily accessible γ-pyrone is the 2,6-dimethyl derivative, obtainable from dehydracetic acid, which is formed by self-condensation of ethyl acetoacetate. Dehydracetic acid is isomerized by sulfuric acid

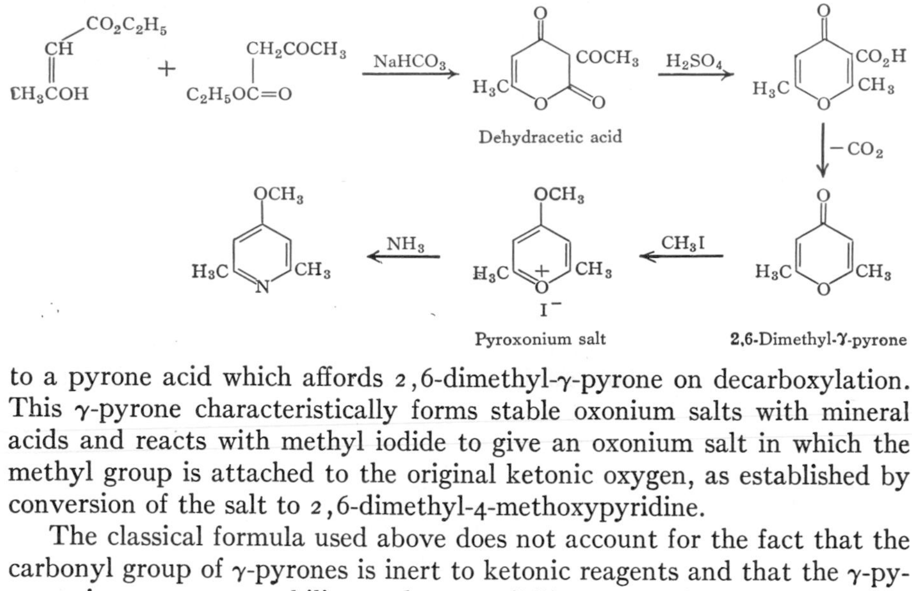
NaHCO3
Dehydracetic acid
H2SO4
−CO2
CH3I
NH3
Pyroxonium salt
2,6-Dimethyl-γ-pyrone

to a pyrone acid which affords 2,6-dimethyl-γ-pyrone on decarboxylation. This γ-pyrone characteristically forms stable oxonium salts with mineral acids and reacts with methyl iodide to give an oxonium salt in which the methyl group is attached to the original ketonic oxygen, as established by conversion of the salt to 2,6-dimethyl-4-methoxypyridine.

The classical formula used above does not account for the fact that the carbonyl group of γ-pyrones is inert to ketonic reagents and that the γ-pyrone ring possesses stability and susceptibility to catalyzed electrophylic substitutions (bromination, nitration) comparable to benzene. These

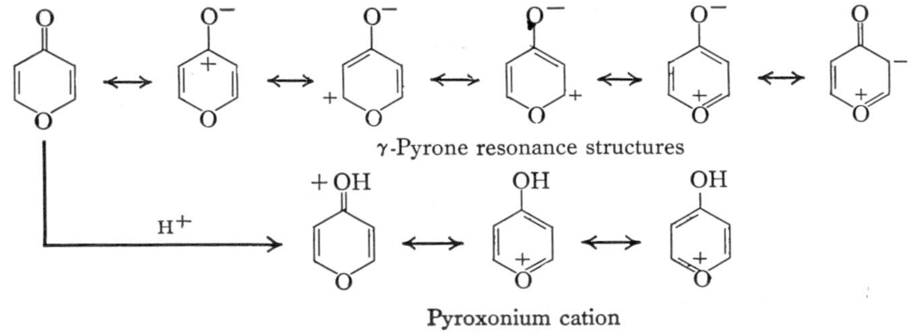
γ-Pyrone resonance structures
H+
Pyroxonium cation

properties are understandable on the postulate of stabilization by resonance between several structures, some of which are formulated. The pyroxonium cation is also stabilized by resonance. Comparable resonance is not possible in α-pyrones, and these substances do not form oxonium salts or undergo aromatic substitutions.

Representative natural γ-pyrones are kojic acid, formed by bacterial fermentation of carbohydrates; maltol, isolated from the bark of the larch tree; and yangonin, from the roots of the kava shrub (South Sea Islands).

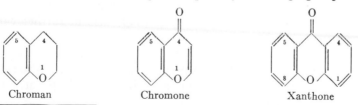

Kojic acid   Maltol   Yangonin

Coumarins. — Coumarin (benzo-α-pyrone) itself is readily available from salicylaldehyde by the Perkin synthesis. Routes to substituted derivatives, particularly to hydroxylated types that occur in nature, developed by v. Pechmann[9] and by v. Pechmann and Duisberg, involve

condensation of a phenol with (a) malic acid and concentrated sulfuric acid or (b) ethyl acetoacetate and a dehydrating agent.

Examples of natural coumarins are umbelliferone, which occurs free in the bark of spurge-laurel; aesculetin, present as the 6-glucoside in horse

Umbelliferone   Aesculetin   Daphnetin

chestnut bark; and daphnetin, which occurs as the 7-glucoside in species of *Daphne*. Both dihydroxycoumarins are fluorescent in aqueous solution. An interesting coumarin derivative used in medicine is dicoumarol (p. 1019).

Chroman, Chromone, Xanthone. — Chroman (benzodihydropyran) is the parent ring system of α-tocopherol (p. 1015). A large group of natural

Chroman   Chromone   Xanthone

[9] Hans Frh. von Pechmann, 1850–1902; b. Nuremberg; Ph.D. Greiswald; Munich, Tübingen.

pigments are derived from the 4-keto derivative, chromone (benzo-γ-pyrone). Most of these have a 2-phenyl substitutent and are called flavones (p. 821). A few natural products contain the xanthone system. Thus euxanthone is 1,7-dihydroxyxanthone, ravenillin is 1,4,8-trihydroxy-3-methylxanthone.

Khellin, a furanochromone isolated from the Mediterranean plant *Ammi visnaga*, and used for centuries in folk medicine, has attracted interest owing to its ability to increase coronary flow. The structure was deduced

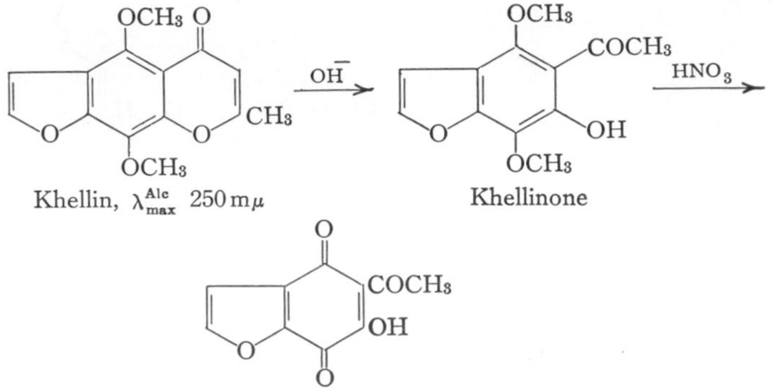

Khellin, λ_{max}^{Alc} 250 mμ $\xrightarrow{\text{OH}^-}$ Khellinone $\xrightarrow{\text{HNO}_3}$

from various degradations (Späth,[10] 1938). Thus treatment with dilute alkali hydrolyzes khellin to khellinone, which on oxidation yields a *p*-quinone. Evidence of the presence of the furan ring is furnished by formation of furan-2,3-dicarboxylic acid on oxidation of khellin with hydrogen peroxide. Khellin has been resynthesized from khellinone by several methods, one of which involves rearrangement of O-acetyl khellinone to the C-acetyl derivative ($-COCH_2COCH_3$) by treatment with sodium hydride, followed by cyclization with a mineral acid. Companions of khellin are visnagin, which lacks the methoxyl group adjacent to the two oxide linkages, and khellol (as glucoside), in which the C-methyl group of khellin is hydroxylated.

Anthocyanins. — This group includes a large number of pigments of flowers and fruits (Gr. *antho-*, flower + Gr. *kyanos*, blue). The anthocyanins are glycosides and on hydrolysis yield sugars and colored aglycones known as anthocyanidins. Modern investigations of these pigments were initiated by Willstätter in 1914 and extended by Karrer, R. Robinson, G. M. Robinson, and others. The substances are glycosides of hydroxylated benzopyrylium (or flavylium) salts. The structure of the parent cation can be regarded as a resonance hybrid of the oxonium forms (a) and (b) and the carbonium forms (c) and (d), and perhaps also of further carbonium structures carrying the positive charge in the benzenoid ring. Since oxygen has a greater tendency than carbon to assume a positive charge, the carbonium structures (c) and (d) probably make less contribution to the ground state than the oxonium structures (a) and (b); of the latter structures (a)

---

[10] Ernst Späth, 1886–1946; b. Bärn, Nordmähren; Ph.D. Vienna; Vienna

1.

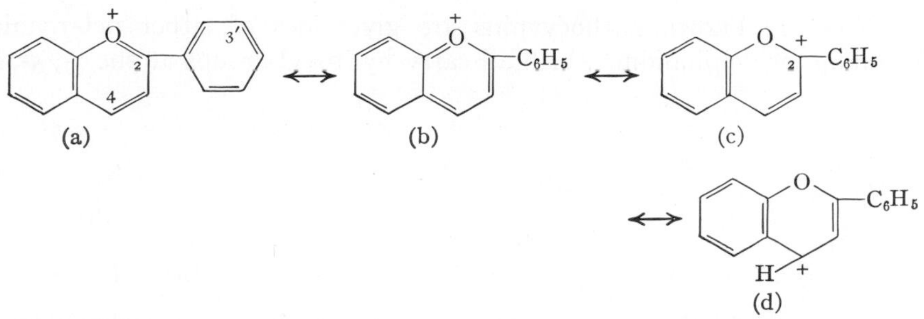

(a)   (b)   (c)

(d)

should be the more stable, since it contains a naphthalenoid system of linkages whereas (b) contains a quinonoid system. Consequently, in the discussion that follows anthocyanidins are formulated as oxonium salts of the type (a). However, significant contribution by the carbonium structure (c) is indicated by the fact that the 2-phenyl group suffers nitration at the 3'-position, that is *meta* to the 2-carbon atom, which thus must carry a fractional positive charge.

Anthocyanidins are commonly isolated as the chlorides after hydrolytic fission of the glycosides with hydrochloric acid. The glycosides probably exist in the plant as salts of organic acids. Willstätter made the striking observation that the same pigment can give rise to different colors. Thus acid hydrolysis of the pigment of either the blue cornflower or the red rose affords cyanidin chloride. The actual color in the plant appears to be determined by the acidity of the cell sap, since either color can be developed *in vitro* by suitable adjustment of the pH. An acidic solution of cyanin chloride is red (2a); on neutralization the color changes to violet, and on further addition of alkali the blue color appears. The violet form is known as the color base and is assigned the quinonoid formula 2b (Willstätter). The blue color presumably is associated with ionization of the hydroxyl group on the quinonoid ring (2c).

2.

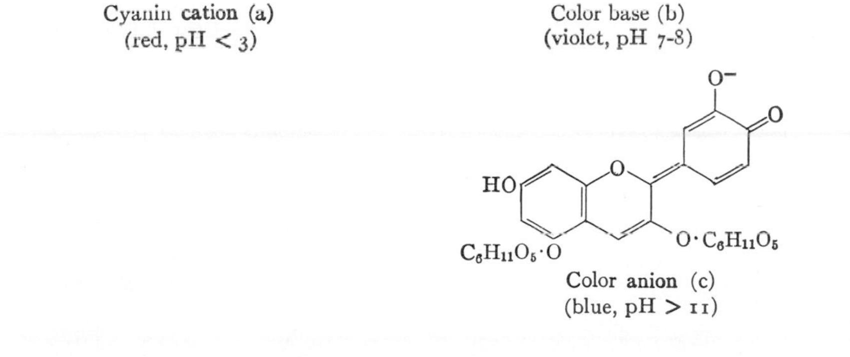

Cyanin cation (a)
(red, pH < 3)

Color base (b)
(violet, pH 7-8)

Color anion (c)
(blue, pH > 11)

Nineteen known anthocyanins are glycosides of either pelargonidin, cyanidin, or delphinidin, which all carry hydroxyl groups at the 3-, 5-, and

3.

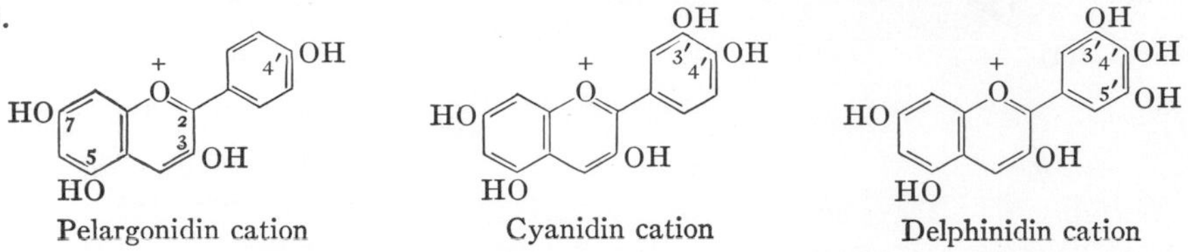

Pelargonidin cation   Cyanidin cation   Delphinidin cation

7-positions and differ merely in the number of hydroxyl or methoxyl groups in the 2-phenyl nucleus. The sugar residues are linked to the 3- or 5-hydroxyl group or to both; the majority of anthocyanins are 3,5-diglycosides.

The constitution of an anthocyanidin can be determined by alkali fusion into a phenolic component and a phenolcarboxylic acid (Willstätter), as in example 4. Aglycones of all three types yield phloroglucinol (a) as the first component, and the presence of one, two, or three hydroxyl functions in the carboxylic acid (b) establishes a relationship to pelargonidin, cyanidin,

4.

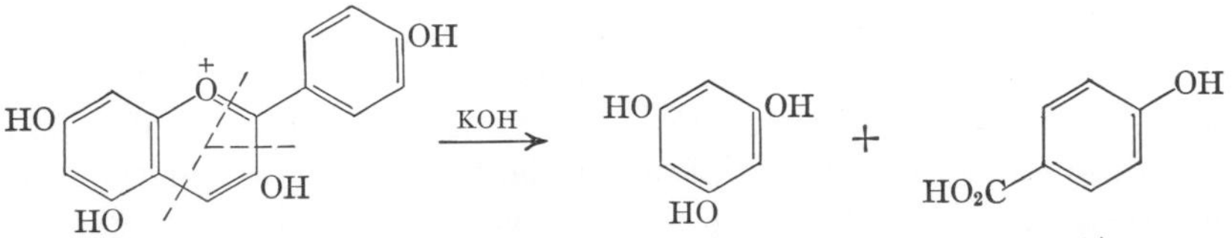

(a)   (b)

or delphinidin. An anthocyanidin containing methoxyl groups can be degraded with dilute alkali without cleavage of the methoxyl residues (Karrer). One method of determining the position of attachment of the sugar residues in an anthocyanin consists in methylation of all free hydroxyl groups, hydrolytic fission of the glycosidic groups, and degradation with dilute alkali to locate the free hydroxyl groups and hence those originally linked to sugars.

5.

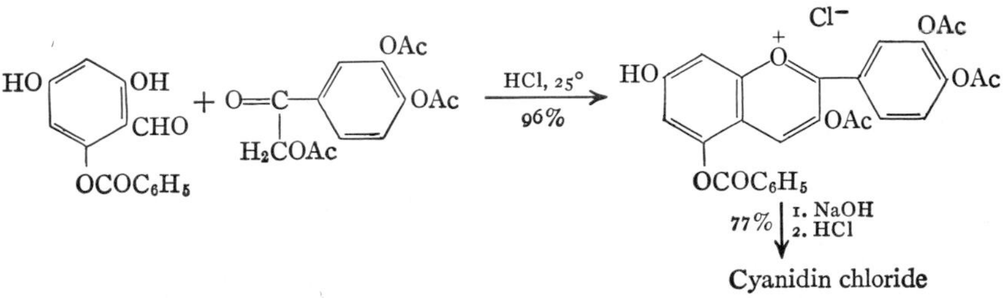

Cyanidin chloride

6.

Cyanin chloride

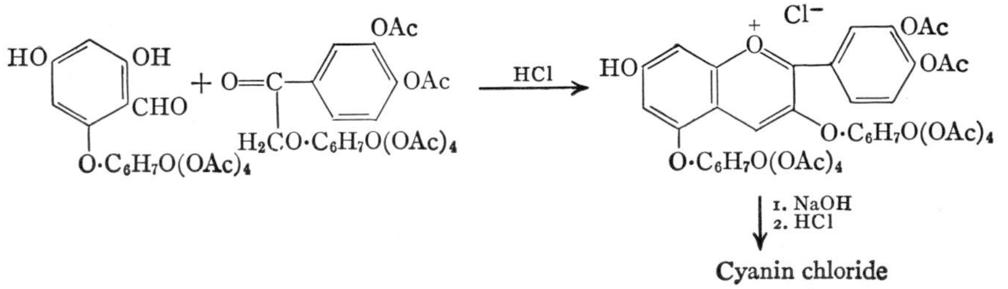

Of several syntheses that have been devised, one developed by Robinson is the most general and has been used for the synthesis of anthocyanidins of various types and also of several of the natural glycosides. The method involves condensation of a suitably substituted o-hydroxybenzaldehyde with a derivative of ω-hydroxyacetophenone, as illustrated for the synthesis of cyanidin chloride (5) and cyanin chloride (6).

Flavones. — The flavones are widely distributed yellow pigments derived from flavone (L. *flavus*, yellow) or isoflavone and carrying from two to six hydroxyl or alkoxyl substituents. Flavone itself is a colorless substance, m.p. 97°, and is described as 2-phenylbenzopyrone or 2-phenylchromone;

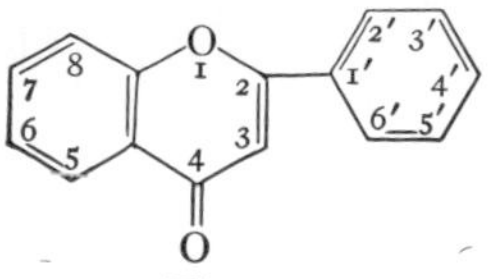

Flavone 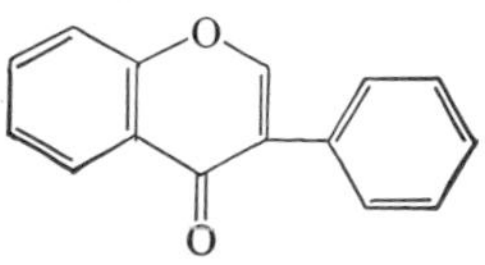   Isoflavone

it has been isolated from the primrose (1915). The majority of the yellow pigments are derivatives of hydroxyl- and methoxyl-substituted flavones and isoflavones that occur in the plant as glycosides or as esters of tannic acid   The structures have been elucidated largely by alkaline degradation (a). On gentle treatment with alkali a flavone suffers ring fission to an o-hydroxydibenzoylmethane, which can undergo further cleavage in two different ways to give rise to four simple products. The manner of cleavage depends to some extent upon the nature and positions of substituent groups.

One general method of synthesis employs in the key step a cyclization reaction that is the reversal of the ring fission just described (a). Thus o-hydroxydibenzoylmethane is cyclized to flavone in 77% yield by concentrated sulfuric acid; the required 1,3-diketone can be obtained by the action of pulverized potassium hydroxide in pyridine on the O-benzoate of o-hydroxyacetophenone (77% yield). An application of the same method in which the intermediate 1,3-diketone is obtained by intermolecular ester condensation is illustrated by the synthesis of chrysin (5,7-dihydroxyfla-

(a)

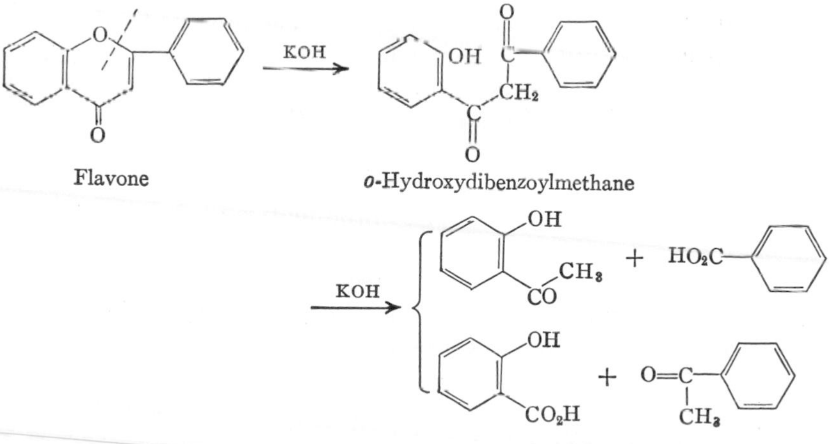

Flavone o-Hydroxydibenzoylmethane

(b)

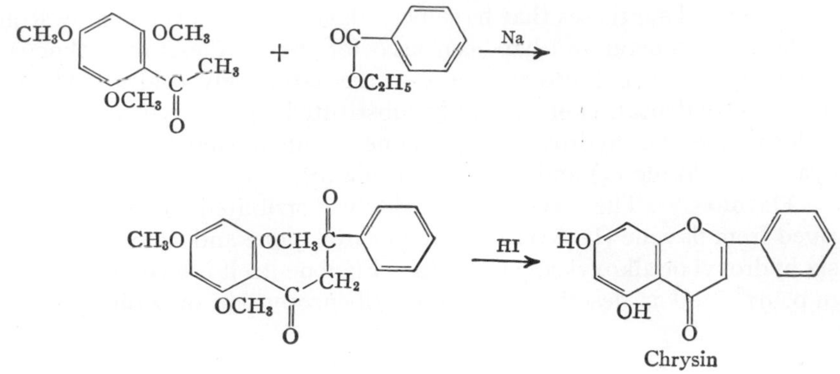

Chrysin

(c)

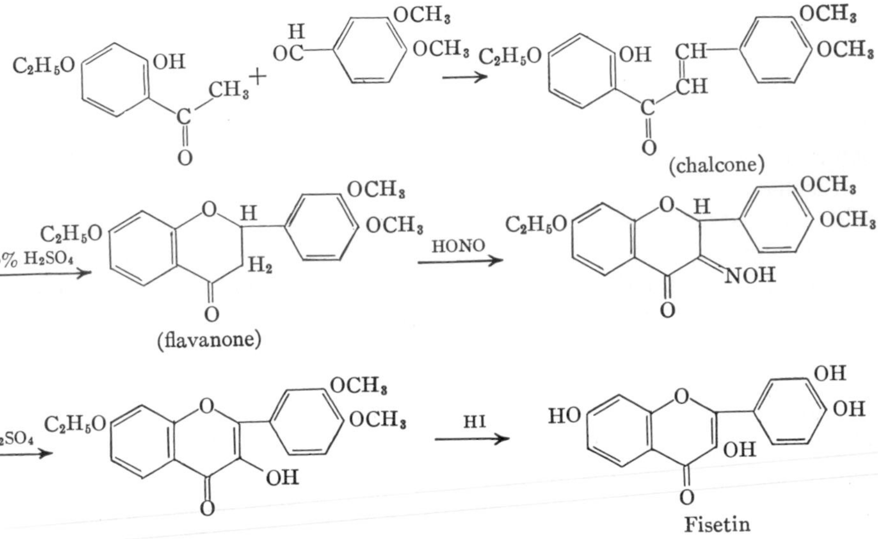

(chalcone)

(flavanone)

Fisetin

vone, pigment of poplar buds) formulated in (b). Another general method is illustrated by the synthesis (c) of fisetin (3,7,3',4'-tetrahydroxyflavone, a pigment of yellow cedar and of sumac). The intermediate submitted to cyclization in this case is an *o*-cinnamoylphenol known as a chalcone, and the product of cyclization is a 2,3-dihydroflavone or flavanone. Conversion into a 3-hydroxyflavone can be effected through the oximino compound in the manner illustrated in the example. In other instances dehydrogenation of a flavanone to a C_3-hydroxyl-free flavone is accomplished by treatment with selenium dioxide or by bromination at C_3 and dehydrobromination.

About seventeen flavone and three isoflavone pigments are known. The course of the alkaline degradation of an isoflavone is illustrated for the case of genistein, a pigment of broom (*Genista tinctoria*).

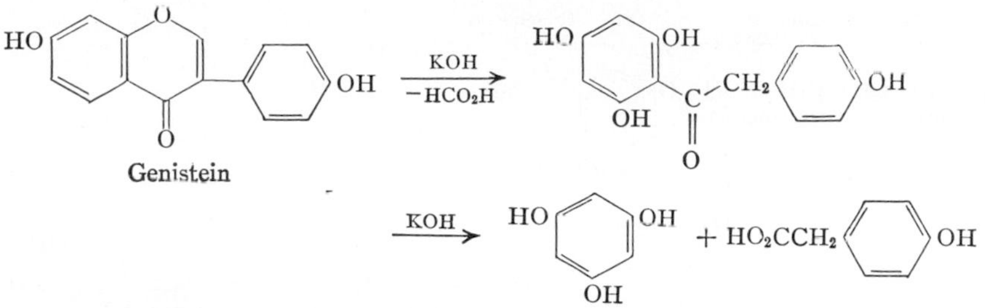

Genistein

Two closely related pigments of the osage orange are isoflavones substituted by two isoprene units (Wolfrom, 1938–46). One is osajin; the other, pomiferin, is the 3'-hydroxy derivative of osajin.

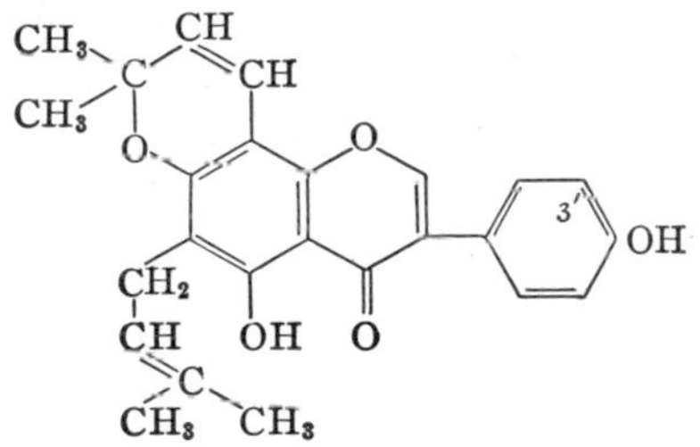

Osajin

The close structural similarity of the flavones to the anthocyanidins suggests the possibility of a biogenetic relationship between the two groups of pigments, and indeed Willstätter (1914) converted quercetin by chemical reduction into cyanidin. At present there is no evidence for a similar reaction *in vivo*.

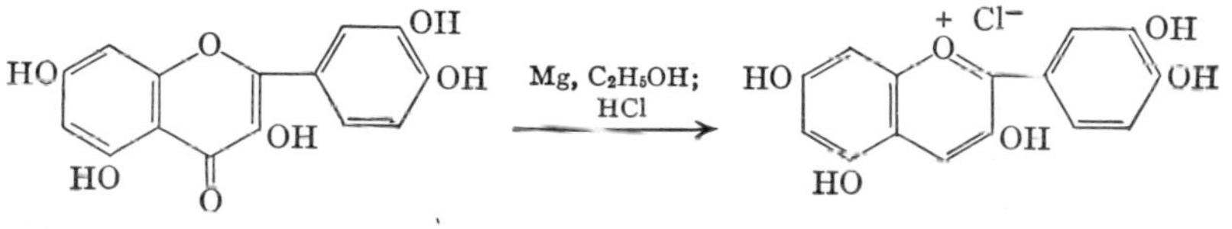

Quercetin   Cyanidin chloride

Certain flavone glycosides have been found to exert an effect on the permeability of capillary walls similar to the effect of crude water-soluble extracts of citrus fruit peels containing an active principle designated vitamin P or citrin (Szent-Györgyi, 1936). These include hesperidin, isolated from citrus fruit, and rutin, a glycoside in common rue and in other flowers and vegetables. Hesperidin is the 7-rutinoside of the flavanone hesperitin; rutin is the 3-rutinoside of quercetin. The pure substances, however, are much less active than crude concentrates from various fruits, particularly grapes, and hence neither should be designated vitamin P.

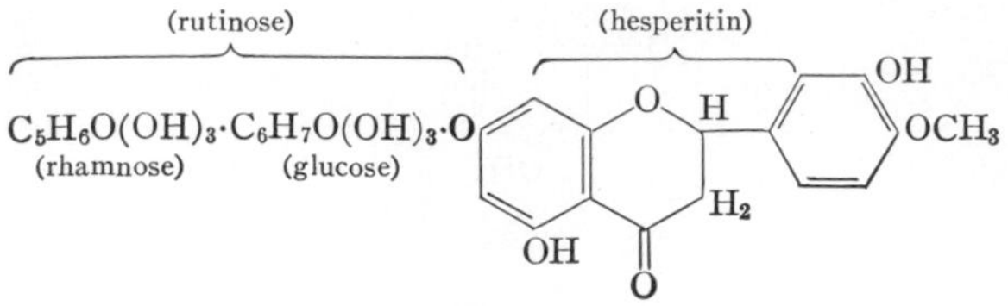

(rutinose)   (hesperitin)

$C_5H_6O(OH)_3 \cdot C_6H_7O(OH)_3 \cdot O$
(rhamnose)   (glucose)

OH
OCH₃

OH
O

Hesperidin

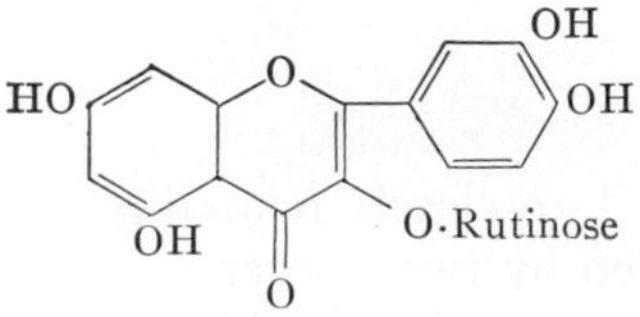

OH
OH

HO
OH
O·Rutinose
O

Rutin

Miscellaneous Pigments. — Dragon's blood, the resin of the tree *Dracaena draco*, contains two pigments related to the anthocyanidins

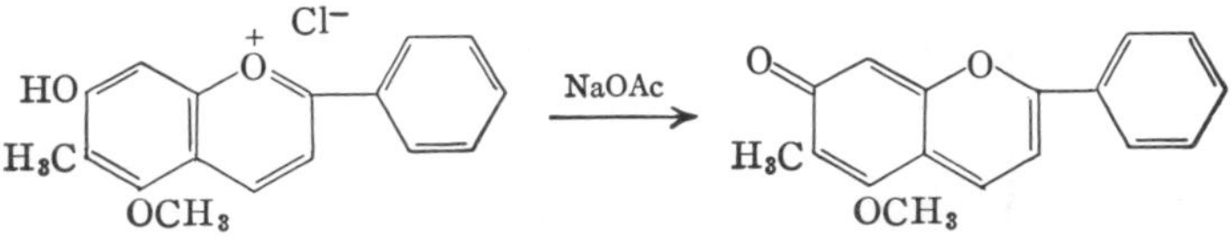

HO
H₃C
OCH₃
$C_{17}H_{15}O_3Cl$
(yellow-red)

NaOAc →

H₃C
OCH₃
Dracorhodin
(bright red)

(Brockmann, 1942). The simpler one, dracorhodin, carries a methyl at C_6 and is devoid of hydroxyl functions in the 2-phenyl group and at position 3. The chloride is yellow-red and the color base (anhydro base) is bright red. The structure was inferred from the formation on alkaline fusion of acetophenone and 4-methyl-5-methoxyresorcinol, and confirmed by synthesis. The second pigment, dracorubin, is a bis derivative of the first.

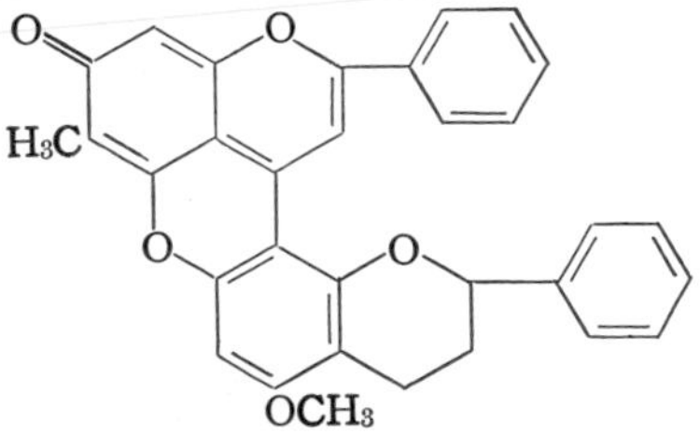

H₃C
OCH₃

Dracorubin

CH₃
OH
CH₃
HO
CH₃

3 Steps →

OCH₃
OH
CH₃
CH₃O
O

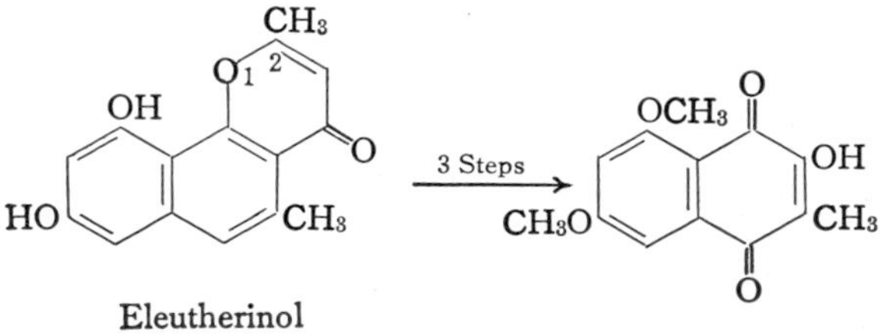

Eleutherinol

Eleutherinol (*Eleutherine bulbosa*) has been characterized as a naphtho-pyrone of the structure shown by degradations conducted with 500 mg. of material (H. Schmid,[11] 1952). One of two C-methyl groups present (Kuhn-Roth determination) was characterized as a reactive 2-methyl group by formation of a piperonylidine derivative. The dimethyl ether, prepared by reaction with diazomethane, on alkali cleavage gave a naphthalene deriva-tive and the corresponding 2-acetonaphthalene, and the former product on oxidation with lead tetraacetate gave a naphthoquinone identified by syn-thesis.

Citrinin, a yellow metabolite of *Penicillium citrinin* Thom isolated in 1931 (Raistrick), is potent against Gram-positive bacteria. It is a highly labile substance and on treatment with acid and then with base is degraded to 4-methyl-5-ethylresorcinol. This degradation coupled with a synthesis

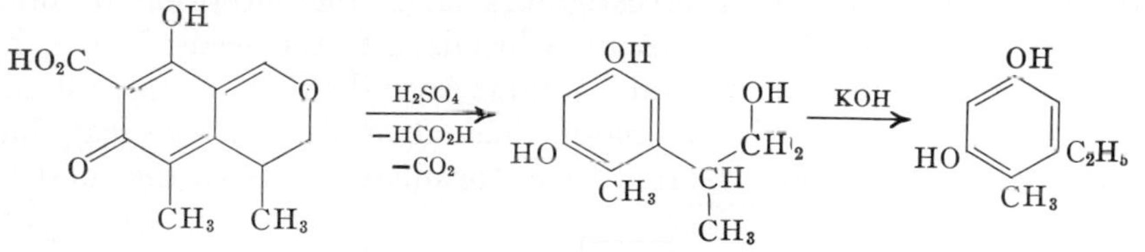

Citrinin   Phenol

of citrinin from the resorcinol (Robertson, 1949) completed the evidence for the structure.

READING REFERENCES

N. V. Sidgwick, "The Organic Chemistry of Nitrogen," 474–573, Oxford, Clarendon Press (1937)
K. P. Link, "The Anthocyanins and the Flavones," in H. Gilman, "Organic Chemistry," 2nd Ed., II, 1315, Wiley, New York (1943)
R. C. Elderfield, "Heterocyclic Compounds," Vols. 1–4, Wiley, New York (1950–52)
I. P. Wibaut, "Some Recent Developments in Pyridine Chemistry," *Prog. Org. Chem.*, **2**, 156 (1953)

[11] Hans Schmid, b. 1917 Austria; Ph.D. Vienna (Späth, Karrer); Univ. Zurich

CHAPTER 34

ALKALOIDS

Occurrence and Isolation. — Alkaloids (alkali-like) are nitrogenous bases that occur in plants, particularly those of the families *Papaveraceae* (poppies), *Papilionaceae* (lupines), *Ranunculaceae* (aconite), and *Solanaceae* (tobacco, potato). Some have characteristic physiological actions, either toxic or curative to the animal organism, and hence the group as a whole has attracted attention of investigators since the inception of organic chemistry. Usually the occurrence is localized to the seeds, leaves, bark, or root of the plant, and each site contains several closely related alkaloids. For example, nicotine 1 is the major alkaloid of the tobacco leaf, but is accompanied by the three related bases formulated. Both the total alka-

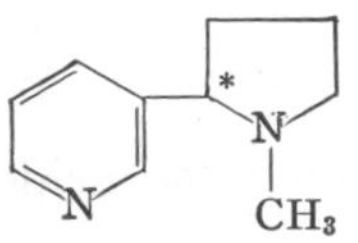

Nicotine
b.p. 247°, $[\alpha]$ − 169°

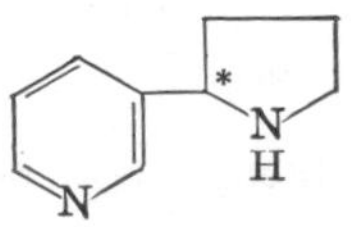

Nornicotine
d-, $[\alpha]_D$ = + 38°
l-, $[\alpha]_D$ = − 18°

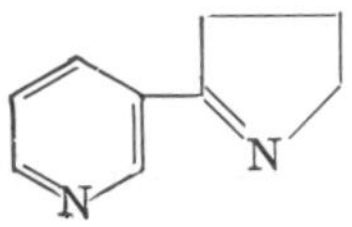

Myosmine

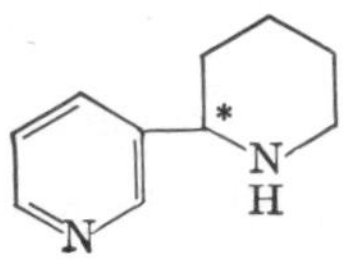

Nicotimine
(anabasine)
l , $[\alpha]_D$ = − 73°

loid content and the relative proportion of the component bases may vary considerably with the stage of growth of the plant. The bases occur largely as salts of common plant acids (acetic, oxalic, lactic, malic, tartaric, citric) or of special acids (fumaric in *Fumaria officinalis*, veratric = 3,4-dimethyl-benzoic in *Veratrum sabadilla*, aconitic (p. 483) in *Aconitum sabadilla*). If the plant material is rich in fats (seeds) it is first extracted with petroleum ether for their removal. In a general procedure recommended by Manske,[1] the material is then extracted with methanol and the dark solution containing suspended solids is separated from cellulosic and other insoluble material and evaporated. Water is added and the mixture is acidified to pH 2 and steam distilled to remove residual methanol. The dark aqueous solution contains considerable suspended material, which if let stand for several days in a refrigerator may settle and leave a clear solution that can be decanted; if not, heating with molten paraffin may entrap suspended particles. Extraction with ether or chloroform for removal of water-soluble nonbasic organic material is followed by steam distillation, since a few alkaloids are steam-volatile and can be separated by this operation. The aqueous solution of alkaloid salts is then basified and extracted with ether

---

[1] Richard H. F. Manske, b. 1901 Berlin; Ph.D. Manchester (Robinson, Lapworth), D.Sc. Manchester; Dominion Rubber Co., Canada

or chloroform. Evaporation of the solvent gives a solid, or more frequently, a resinous mass consisting of a mixture of alkaloid bases, and the investigator is ready to try the techniques of fractional crystallization, either as free base or as the salt of an organic or inorganic acid.

Structural Types. — Some idea of the extraordinary variety in the types of bases resulting from plant biosynthesis can be gained from inspection of

CHART 1. SOME ALKALOID TYPES

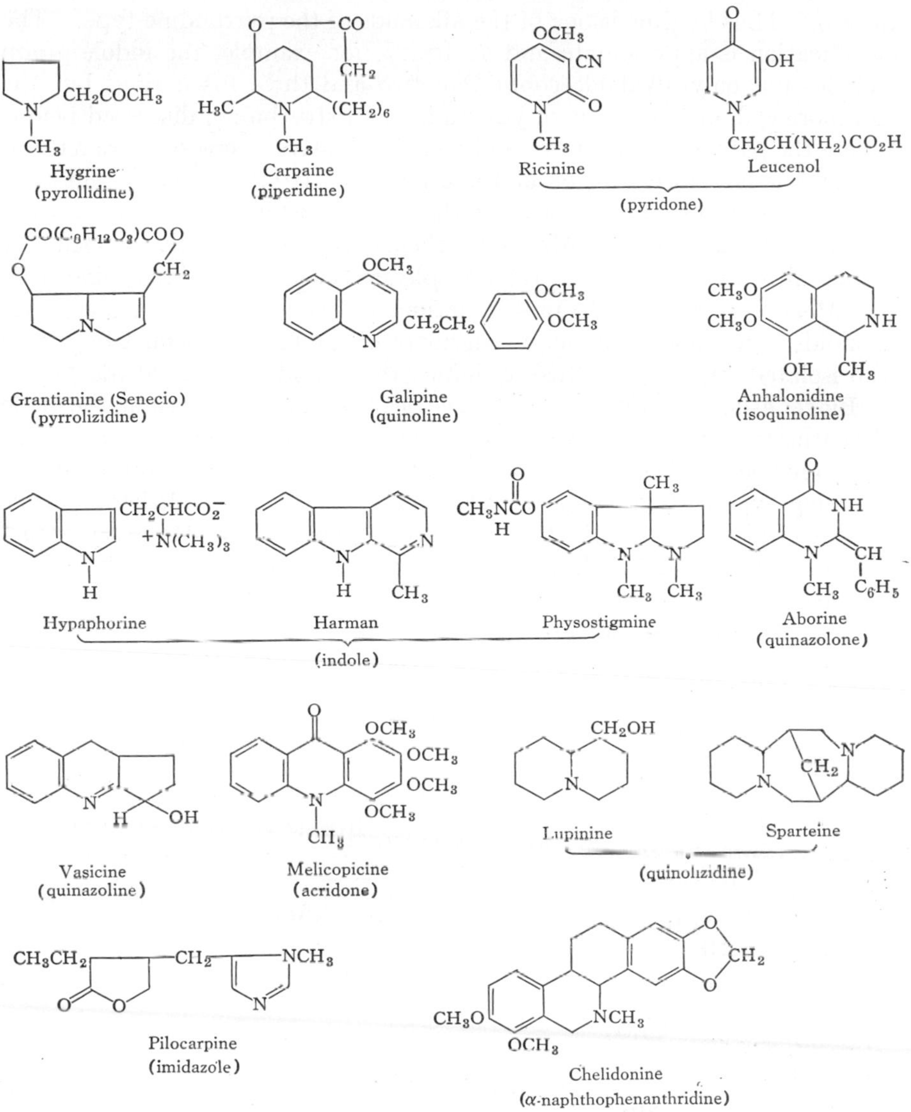

Hygrine
(pyrrolidine)

Carpaine
(piperidine)

Ricinine

Leucenol

(pyridone)

Grantianine (Senecio)
(pyrrolizidine)

Galipine
(quinoline)

Anhalonidine
(isoquinoline)

Hypaphorine

Harman

Physostigmine

Aborine
(quinazolone)

(indole)

Vasicine
(quinazoline)

Melicopicine
(acridone)

Lupinine

Sparteine

(quinolizidine)

Pilocarpine
(imidazole)

Chelidonine
(α-naphthophenanthridine)

Chart 1, which lists representatives of alkaloid types other than those selected for discussion in subsequent sections of this chapter. Almost all known nitrogen-containing ring systems are present in alkaloids; in fact, some were encountered first in alkaloids (pyrrolizidine, quinolizidine). The 5-membered pyrrole and pyrrolidine rings and the 6-membered pyridine and piperidine rings occur both singly and fused to one or more 5- or 6-membered rings. The nitrogen atom sometimes forms a bridgehead between two rings, as in grantianine, one of many *Senecio* alkaloids. The type to which an alkaloid belongs is designated by the name of a common nitrogen-containing ring system present (written, in Chart 1, in parentheses). Thus hygrine is one of the alkaloids of the pyrrolidine type. The classification is approximate and arbitrary; for example, the indole group includes not only alkaloids containing two and three fused rings but the still more elaborate systems of yohimbine and strychnine, discussed below. Where the parent base is known only as a derivative of one or more natural products it is named for one of these alkaloids (tropane, the parent base of atropine and of cocaine) or after the plant in which the alkaloids occur (pomgranate alkaloids). Alkaloids themselves are usually named for plants, although some names refer to physiological effects (morphine from Gr. *Morpheus*, god of dreams; emetine, an emetic). The pomgranate alkaloids were named pelletierines in honor of the French chemist Pelletier,[2] who isolated strychnine (1818), quinine (1820), and other alkaloids.

Biogenesis. — Various theories have been advanced concerning the mode of synthesis of the complex structures in plants, particularly from amino acid precursors   The tryptophan skeleton is present in several alkaloids, including hypaphorine (Chart 1), yohimbine, strychnine; and the imidazole nucleus of histidine is present in a few, e.g. pilocarpine. However, structural analogies can be misleading.   Thus nicotinic acid was postulated as a precursor of pyridine-type alkaloids such as nicotine, but experiments with labeled nicotinic acid indicate that this transformation does not occur, at least in the tobacco plant.   Whatever their ultimate validity, theories of

(a)
$$CH_2-CH_2 \quad CH_2 \quad CHO \quad NH \quad CH_3 \quad + \quad CO_2C_2H_5 \quad CH_2COCH_3 \quad \xrightarrow{pH\ 7} \quad CH_2COCH_3$$
Hygrine

(b)
$$CH_2-CH_2 \quad CH_2 \quad CHO \quad NH \quad CH_3 \quad + \quad CO_2H \quad CO_2H \quad CH_2COCH_2 \quad \xrightarrow{pH\ 7} \quad CH_2COCH_2$$
Cuscohygrine

(c)
$$CHO \quad NH_2 \quad + \quad CH_2CO_2H \quad CO(CH_2)_4CH_3 \quad \xrightarrow[70-75\%]{pH\ 9} \quad (CH_2)_4CH_3$$
2-*n*-Amylquinoline

[2] P. Joseph Pelletier, 1788–1842; b. Paris; Paris

biogenesis have often prompted synthetic approaches that proved successful. Thus hygrine and a companion alkaloid, cuscohygrine, have been prepared by reaction of γ-methylaminobutyraldehyde with acetoacetic ester (a) and with acetonedicarboxylic acid (b), respectively, under physiological conditions. 2-n-Amylquinoline, an alkaloid of angostura bark, has been synthesized (c) by Friedländer condensation of o-aminobenzaldehyde with β-ketocaprylic acid. The former component has not been found in nature, but the corresponding acid, anthranilic acid, is a known product of degradation of tryptophan. Tryptophan could be the precursor of harman, and indeed the synthesis from this amino acid has been accomplished.

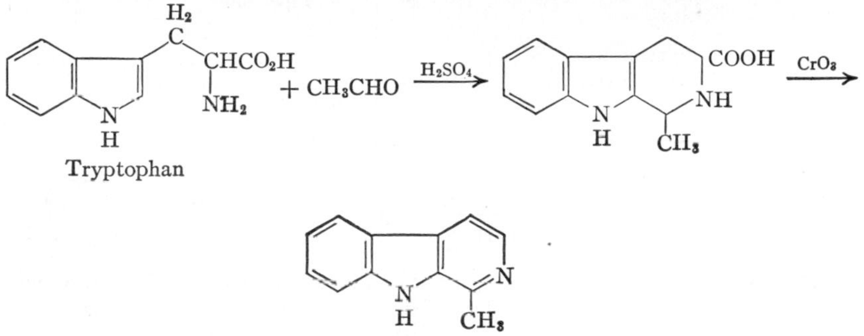

Tryptophan

Harman

Methods of Degradation. — As might be expected the Hofmann degradation has been a useful tool in structural investigations. Thus the correct structure of the lobelia alkaloids, of which lobelanine is typical, was first deduced from the result of Hofmann degradation of the quaternary hydroxide, which led to ring scission with formation of trimethylamine and

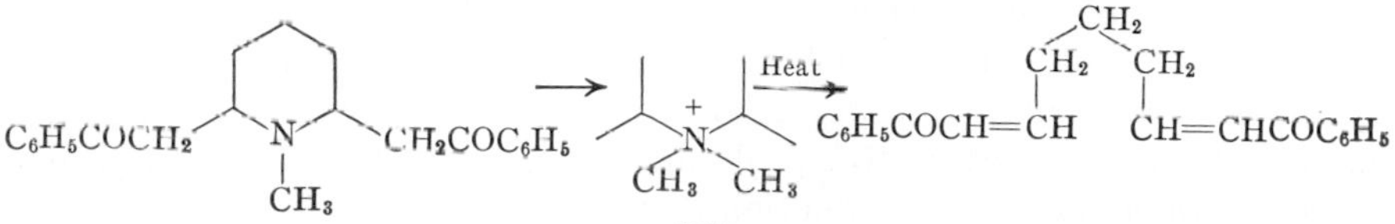

Lobelanine

a diunsaturated compound which on hydrogenation yielded 1,7-dibenzoylheptane. The Hofmann degradation is unsuccessful in many instances in which the nitrogen atom is incorporated into a ring system. Thus the reaction fails in the case of derivatives of 1,2,3,4-tetrahydrodimethyl-

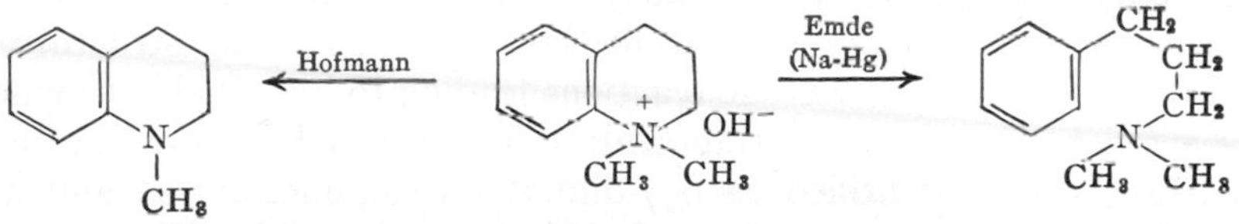

quinolinium hydroxide, which on pyrolysis merely loses methanol without fission of the ring. A similar reversal occurs to some extent in successful degradations. In some cases reduction of the hydroxide or chloride with sodium amalgam (Emde[3] degradation) results in ring fission.

Since many of the alkaloids contain ester or amide linkages, hydrolytic fission in these cases leads to smaller, more easily identifiable units. Piperine, an alkaloid of the fruit of *Piper nigrum* (black pepper), is an amide and on hydrolysis is converted into fragments that were named piperic acid and piperidine because of their relationship to the alkaloid. The acid

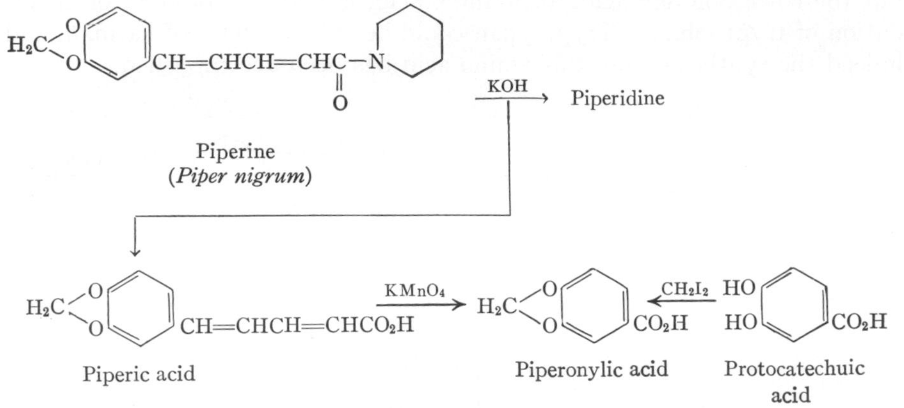

Piperine
(*Piper nigrum*)

KOH → Piperidine

Piperic acid

$KMnO_4$

Piperonylic acid   Protocatechuic acid

CH_2I_2

component was found to have two reactive olefinic double bonds, and these were located between the benzene ring and the carboxyl group by oxidation to piperonylic acid, the structure of which was established by synthesis from protocatechuic acid. Resynthesis of piperine by the reaction of the acid chloride of piperic acid with piperidine (Ladenburg, 1894) completed evidence for the structure of the alkaloid.

Where more vigorous conditions are required to effect degradation, pyrolysis or zinc dust distillation often produces aromatic ring systems. Thus pyrolysis of leucenol (Chart 1) gives 3,4-dihydroxypyridine. The useful method of oxidative degradation is illustrated by oxidation of leucenol with bromine water to α,β-diaminopropionic acid. These two degradations alone suffice for deduction of the structure.

Benzylisoquinoline and Related Alkaloids. — The alkaloids discussed in this section are representative of seven structural types. Six of them occur in opium along with morphine and codeine. One of the opium constituents, papaverine (m.p. 147°, pK 8.07), has been studied particularly intensively because it has some clinical use as an antispasmodic. Analysis indicated the formula $C_{20}H_{21}O_4N$, and methoxyl determination established that all four oxygen atoms are present as methoxyl groups. The structure was further elucidated from cleavage reactions leading to identifiable fragments. Thus alkali fusion gives two fragments that account for all of the carbon atoms: a C_{11}-base identified as 6,7-dimethoxyisoquinoline (a) and a C_9-ether identified as 4-methylcatechol dimethyl ether (b). The two frag-

---

[3] Herman Emde, 1880–1935; b. Opladen; Ph.D. Marburg; Königsberg; *Ber.*, **68A**, 164 (1935)

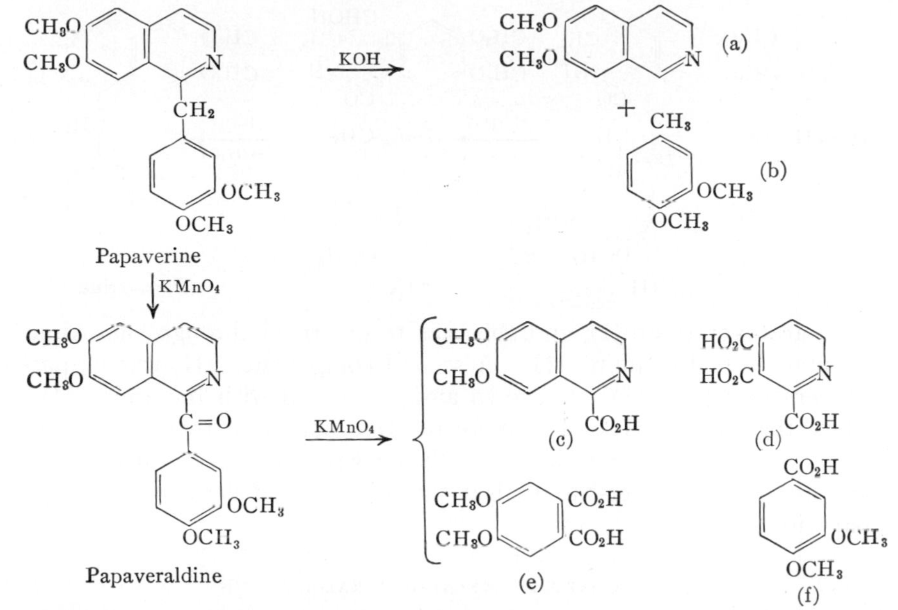

ments cannot be linked through a carbon atom of one of the ether groups, for then Zeisel determination would have revealed three and not four methoxyls, and the most likely site in the fragment (b) is the ring-methyl group. The point of linkage in the isoquinoline fragment was revealed by permanganate oxidation, which results in attack at the methylene group to give the secondary alcohol papaverinol, then the ketone papaveraldine, and then the four products (c) to (f). The position of the carboxyl group in products (c) and (d) shows that the isoquinoline unit is linked at the 1-position.

The first synthesis of papaverine was achieved (Pictet[4] and Gams, 1909) by the reactions shown. Veratrole was converted by Friedel-Crafts reac-

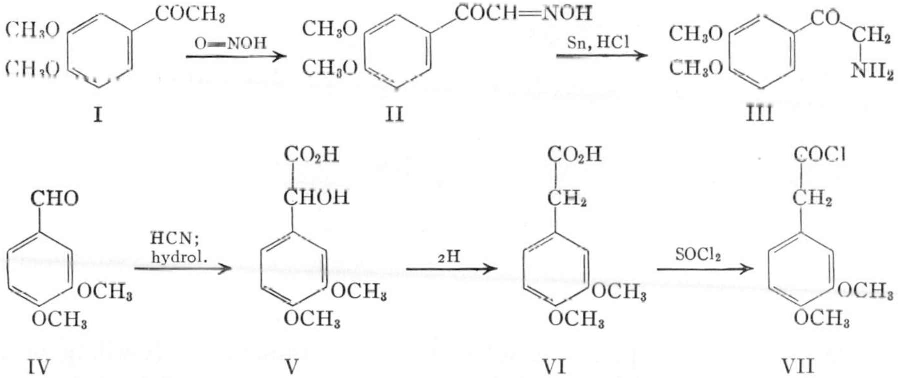

[4] Amé Pictet, 1857–1937; b. Geneva; Ph.D. Geneva; Geneva

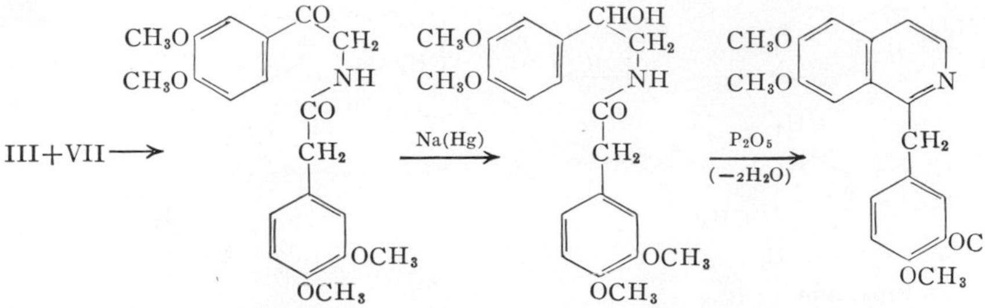

$$\text{III} + \text{VII} \longrightarrow \text{VIII} \xrightarrow{\text{Na(Hg)}} \text{IX} \xrightarrow[(-2H_2O)]{P_2O_5} \text{Papaverine}$$

VIII   IX   Papaverine

tion to acetoveratrone (I), and this was transformed through the oximino compound II to the amine III. A second component, VII, was prepared from veratraldehyde (IV) as shown and condensed with the amine III to produce the amide VIII The more reactive ketonic carbonyl group was reduced and the alcohol-amide IX refluxed with phosphorus pentoxide in xylene to effect Bischler-Napieralski ring closure and dehydration to give papaverine.

CHART 2. RELATED ALKALOIDS

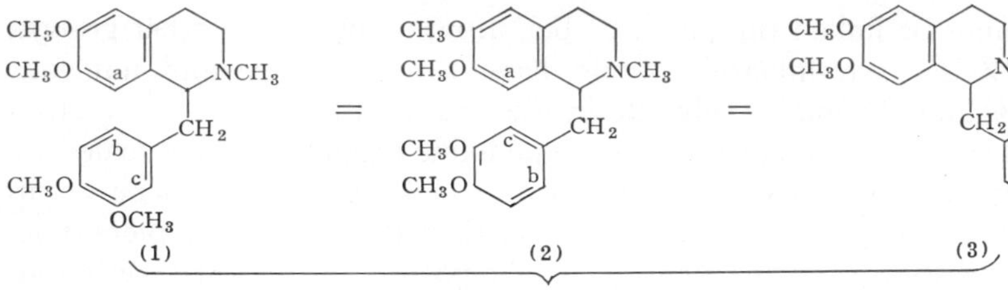

Laudanosine, m.p. 89,° αD +106°

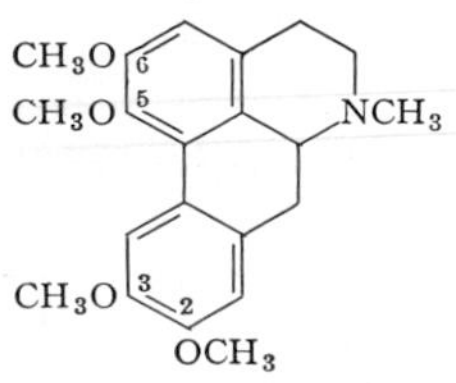

Glaucine 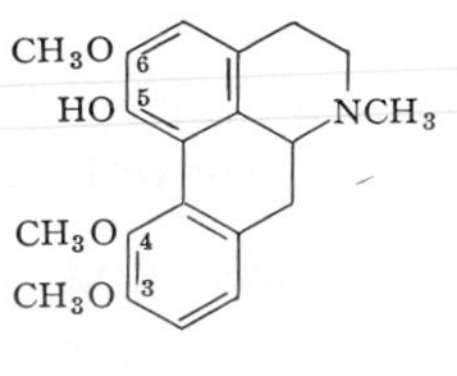   Corydine 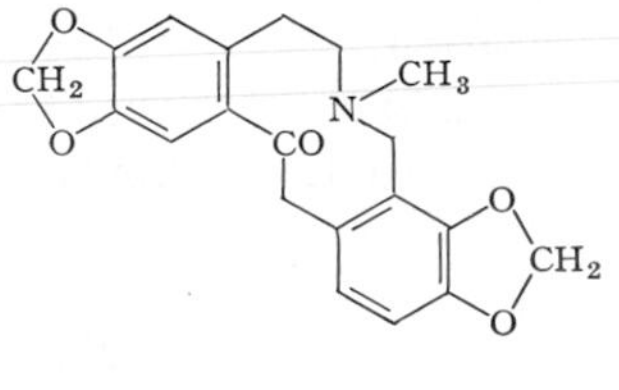   Protopine

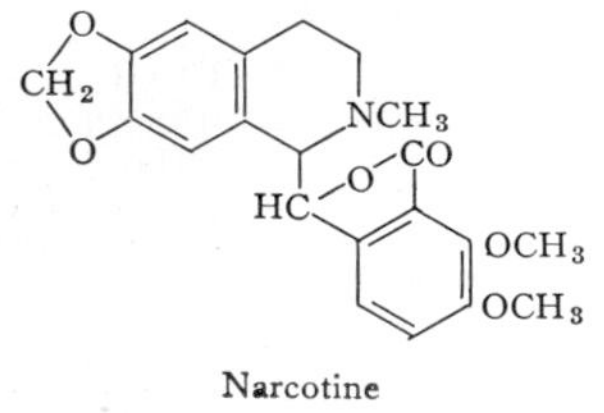

Narcotine 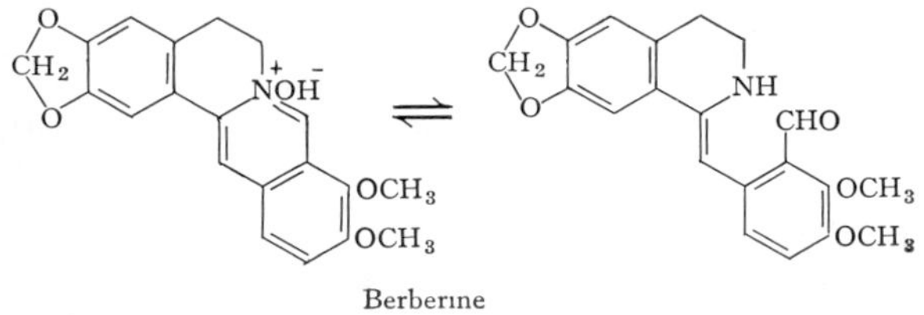   Berberine

Papaverine is an optically inactive 1-benzylisoquinoline. It will be seen from Chart 2 (second formula) that laudanosine, an optically active base isolated from opium, is N-methyltetrahydropapaverine. Since reactions of methylation-demethylation and of hydrogenation-dehydrogenation occur biologically, alkaloids of the benzylisoquinoline and benzyltetrahydroisoquinoline series may be related biogenetically as well as chemically. Laudanosine is related also to the series of aporphine alkaloids. The majority of these have oxygen functions, present as hydroxyl, methyl ether, or methylene ether groups at either the 2,3,5,6-positions, as in glaucine, or at the 3,4,5,6-positions, as in corydine (these two are the only alkaloids of Chart 2 that are not found in opium). When the formula of laudanosine is written as in (1), it is seen that dehydrogenative coupling at positions (a) and (b) would lead to glaucine, and that rotation of the phenyl group as in (2) prior to coupling would lead to the location of oxygen functions in corydine. Actually, the structure of glaucine was established by synthesis of the alkaloid from papaverine (Gadamer, 1911). Arrangement of the formula of laudanosine as in (3) brings out relationships to the opium alkaloids protopine (the keto form of a carbinolamine), narcotine, and berberine (first formula). Thus coupling between position (c) and the N-methyl group (d) forms a new 6-membered ring corresponding to that of berberine; protopine and narcotine could yield the berberine ring system by cyclization. As the formulas show, berberine can react both as a quaternary ammonium hydroxide and as an amino aldehyde.

The close structural relationship between these alkaloids and papaverine suggests that they are all intermediates in a general pathway of biosynthesis. It is possible that laudanosine comes from an amine and an aldehyde component both derived from 3,4-dihydroxyphenylalanine, and in fact Schöpf[5] (1934) effected such a condensation:

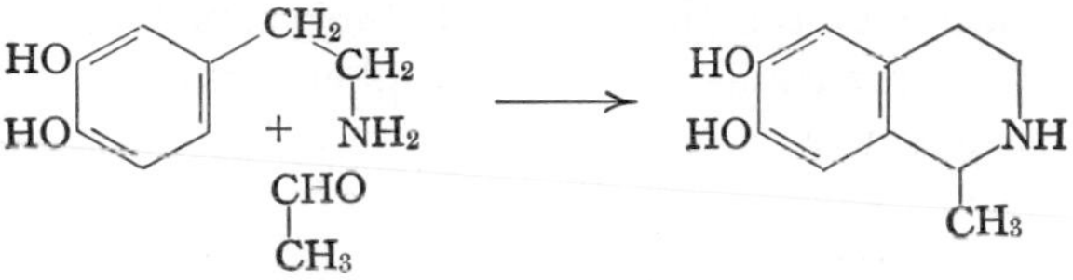

Morphine. — The most prominent of some twenty-three alkaloids isolated from opium are morphine, its phenolic methyl ether, codeine, and thebaine, the enol methyl ether of codeinone. By virtue of its powerful analgesic properties, morphine has been indispensible in medical practice in spite of its habit-forming character. Codeine has considerably less addiction liability and is used widely as a local anesthetic; since it is present in opium in smaller amount (0.5%) than morphine (7–15%), it is made by methylation of morphine with phenyltrimethylammonium hydroxide (which does not attack the nitrogen). Morphine was isolated in 1803 (Sertürner), and elucidation of its structure became the goal of extended researches in many laboratories. A formula advanced by Gulland and R. Robinson in 1925 was secure in all points except the position of anchoring of the ethanamine bridge extending from C_9. Finally, total synthesis of a degradation

---

[5] Clemens Schöpf, b. 1899 Gersfeld/Rhone; Ph.D. Munich (Wieland); Darmstadt

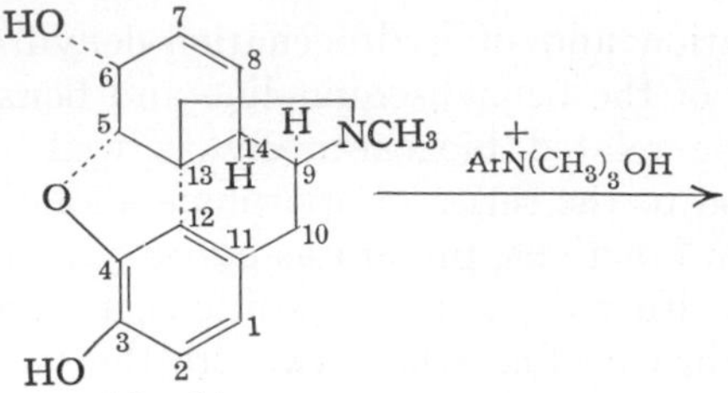

Morphine

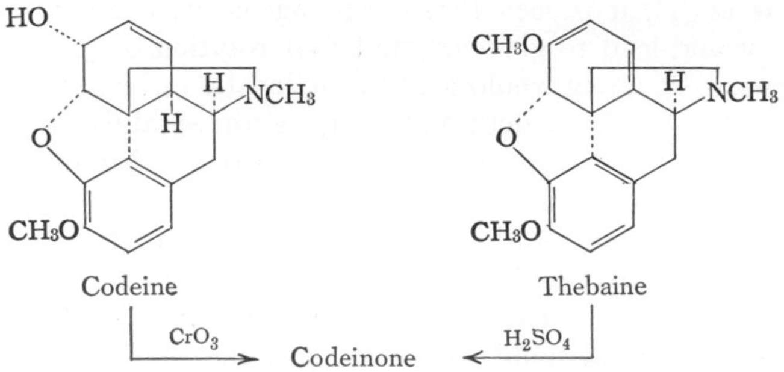

Codeine

Thebaine

Codeinone

product (Grewe, 1949) and of morphine itself (Gates, 1952) established that the chain is indeed linked at C_{13} and completed the evidence of structure. The stereochemistry was inferred by Schöpf (1930) and the writers (1949), and the mechanisms of many interesting replacements were elucidated by Stork (see third reading ref.).

The presence of a hydrophenanthrene ring system was suggested in 1881 by isolation of phenanthrene as a product of zinc dust distillation of morphine. The location of the three oxygen functions was established by a combination of degradations leading to phenanthrene derivatives oxygenated at positions 3, 4, 5, and 6. An example is a stepwise Hofmann

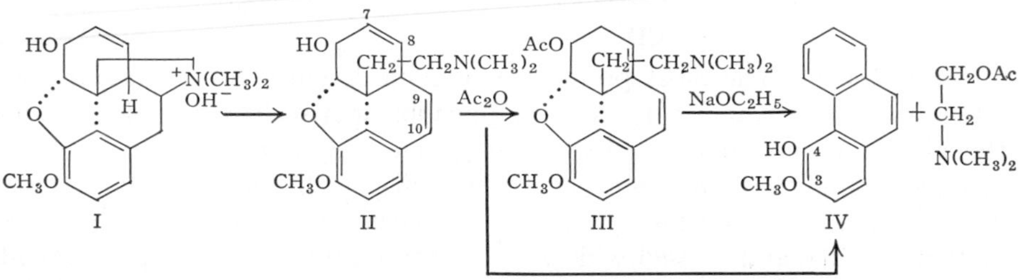

degradation of codeine methohydroxide (I). When this is heated the ethanamine bridge is ruptured with production of a 9,10-double bond and the product is the nonconjugated diene α-methylmorphimethine (II)   On acetolysis of II a part of the material is converted by bond migration to the more stable conjugated isomer, isolated as β-methylmorphimethine acetate (III), and a part suffers expulsion of the side chain as ethanoldimethylamine with aromatization to the acetate of 3,4-dihydroxyphenanthrene (morphol) 3-methyl ether (IV). The β-methine can be converted into IV by vigorous treatment with sodium ethoxide. The hydroxy-methoxyphenanthrenes resulting from this and other degradations were at the time unknown and their structures were established by synthesis by a general method developed by Pschorr in 1896.

The synthetic method was useful also in proof of structure of apomorphine (V), formed by heating morphine with hydrochloric acid. The substance presented a puzzling problem because there was no initial indication

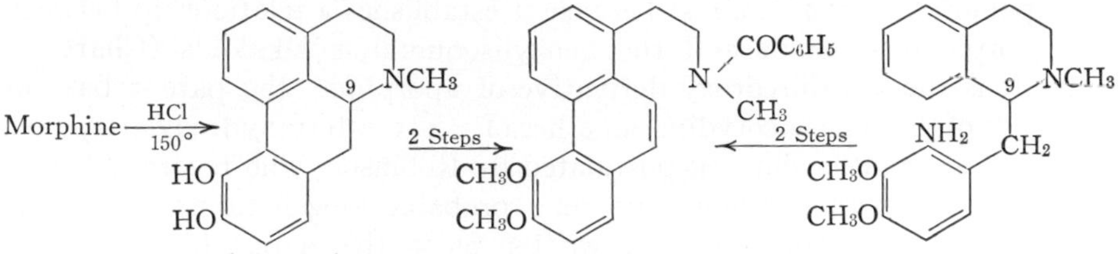

Morphine $\xrightarrow[150°]{\text{HCl}}$

Apomorphine
V (*l*)   VI (±0°)   VII (*dl*)

that it is formed by a rearrangement. Pschorr elucidated the structure through a series of degradations (1902–07) and drew the erroneous conclusion that morphine has the ring system of apomorphine. Structure V was later verified by synthesis (Späth and Hromatka, 1929). Pschorr ring closure of the *dl*-intermediate VII by treatment of the diazonium salt with copper powder gave *dl*-apomorphine methyl ether, and since attempts to obtain a comparison sample by racemization of *l*-apomorphine were unsuccessful the *dl*- and *l*-bases were benzoylated to open the heterocyclic ring and destroy the center of asymmetry at C_9 ; the two reactions gave an identical product (VI).

The morphine-apomorphine rearrangement was clarified by Small.[6] It can be envisioned as an attack by a proton with displacement of the allylic hydroxyl group (a), migration of hydrogen from C_{14} to open the oxide ring

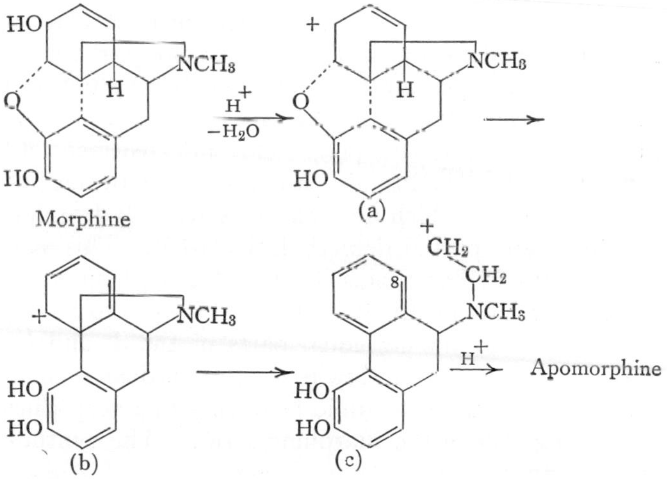

Morphine   (a)

(b)   (c) $\xrightarrow{\overset{+}{H}}$ Apomorphine

[6] Lyndon F. Small, b. 1897 Allston, Mass.; Ph.D. Harvard (Conant); Nat. Inst. Health

and give another carbonium ion (b), in which one ring now has two double bonds. Aromatization of this ring is achieved by detachment of the ethanamine bridge at C_{13} (c) and reattachment at the available position C_8 by expulsion of a proton. A more spectacular rearrangement leading to four isomeric phenyldihydrothebaines containing a nine-membered ring incorporating the ethanamine bridge was investigated extensively by Small and interpreted by Robinson.

Apomorphine is of interest because it establishes a relationship between the morphine alkaloids and the benzylisoquinoline alkaloids (Chart 2), since it is the 3,4-dihydroxy derivative of aporphine, the parent base of alkaloids of the type of corydine, an ether of 3,4,5,6-tetrahydroxyaporphine. A still closer relationship was postulated by Robinson, who regarded laudanosine, a companion of morphine, as a probable biogenetic precursor. If the formula of laudanosine (a) is written as in (b), a possible biogenetic

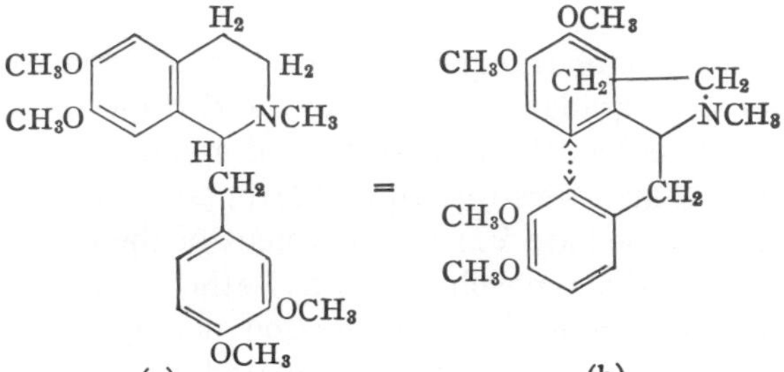

(a)

Laudanosine

(b)

route to morphine can be envisioned which involves ring closure (indicated by the dotted arrow), reduction, demethylation, and dehydration. Grewe[7] (1946–49) discovered a means of realizing the type of ring closure indicated and achieved the first total synthesis of a degradation product having the complete carbon-nitrogen skeleton of the morphine molecule. Bz-Tetrahydroisoquinoline (I), available by an efficient five-step synthesis from 2-carbethoxycyclohexanone, was aminated and the amine converted into the corresponding bromide (II) by the improved process of L. C. Craig (1933–34): reaction with bromine to form the perbromide and treatment of this derivative with nitrous acid. The bromide was converted through III into the octahydroisoquinoline IV, which on treatment with hydrochloric acid underwent cyclization and partial demethylation to V. This substance contains three asymmetric carbon atoms (C_9, C_{13}, C_{14}) and the synthetic material was of course optically inactive; however, it proved to be identical with a *dl*-product obtained by mixing equal parts of the *d*- and *l*-degradation products of the structure V resulting from degradations of morphine (VI) and of sinomenine (VII), a rare alkaloid belonging to a stereochemical series that is the exact opposite of the morphine series. The synthesis supplied

---

[7] Rudolf Grewe, b. 1910 Münster, Germany; Ph.D. Göttingen (Windaus); Kiel

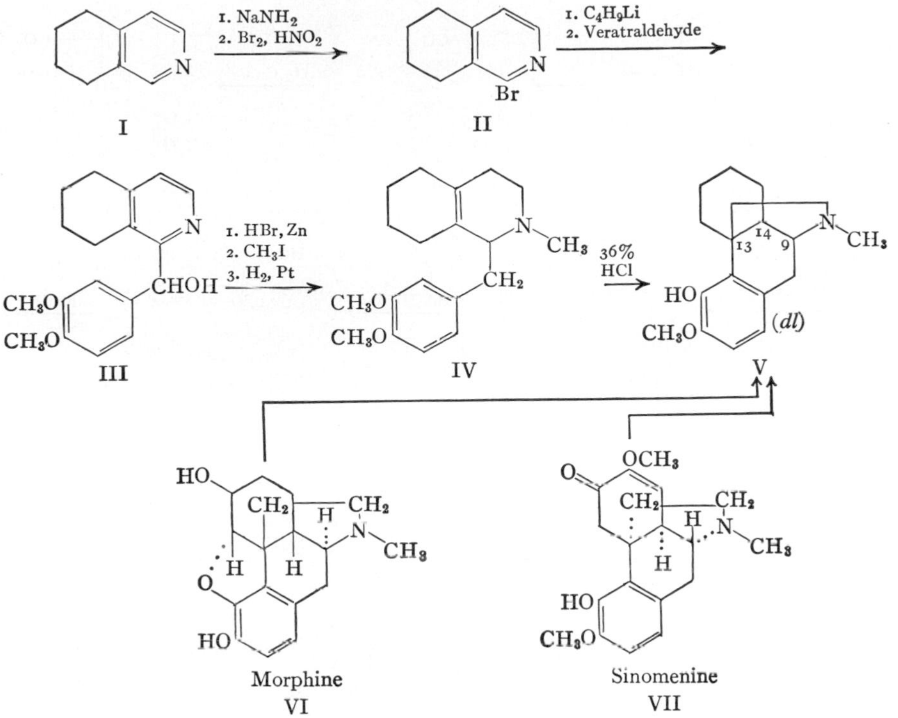

Morphine
VI

Sinomenine
VII

long missing evidence that the ethanamine chain of morphine and of sino-menine is linked at position 13.

The key step in the morphine synthesis of Gates[8] (1952) is a Diels-Alder addition of butadiene to 4-cyanomethyl-1,2-naphthoquinone (I). On cata-lytic hydrogenation the adduct II undergoes ring closure to a keto lactam III, the carbonyl group of which was removed by Wolff-Kishner reduction and the amide carbonyl by reduction with lithium aluminum hydride N-Methylation then gave the product IV, which proved to have the cor-rect ring structure but the unnatural configuration at C_{14}, a fault, however, which was corrected by a fortunate rearrangement discovered near the end of the synthetic sequence. The double bond of IV was hydrated (V), the ether group at C_6 selectively demethylated (VI), and the product oxidized to the 6-ketone, which was brominated. Bromine is introduced first at C_7 and C_1 (VII), and a further mole of bromine then closes the oxide bridge (VIII). In the course of dehydrobromination of VIII with 2,4-dinitro-phenylhydrazine to produce the α,β-unsaturated ketone structure of codein-one, inversion occurs at the center adjacent to the conjugated system to produce the natural orientation at C_{14}. Since resolution had been effected at an intermediate stage (IV), reductive removal of the 1-bromine atom gave codeine, convertible into morphine by cleavage of the ether group.

Tropane Alkaloids. — Cocaine, atropine, and scopolamine, the most

---

[8] Marshall Gates, b. 1915 Boyne City, Mich.; Ph.D. Harvard (Fieser); Univ. Rochester

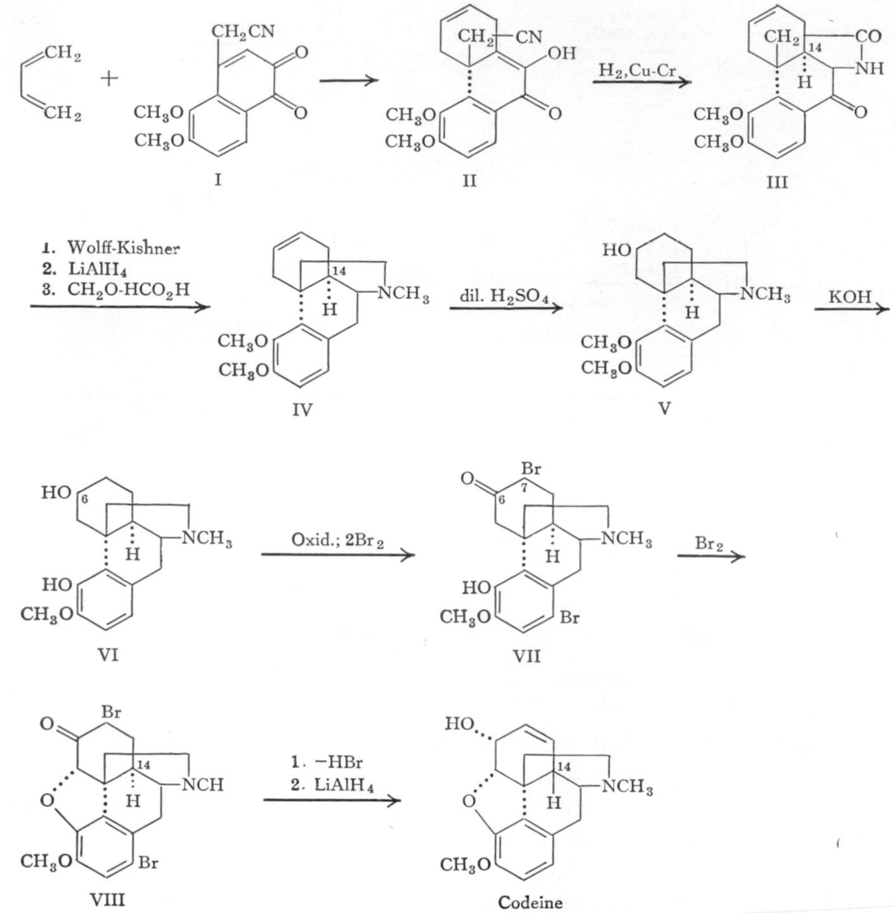

I   II   III

1. Wolff-Kishner
2. LiAlH$_4$
3. CH$_2$O-HCO$_2$H

IV   V

VI   VII

VIII   Codeine

prominent members of the group, are derivatives of the parent base tropane, which has a seven-carbon ring with an endo nitrogen bridge that locks the

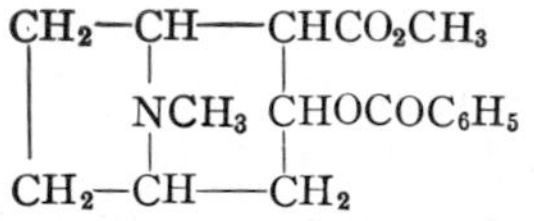

$$CH_2\!-\!CH\!-\!\!-CHCO_2CH_3$$
$$\qquad NCH_3\ \ CHOCOC_6H_5$$
$$CH_2\!-\!CH\!-\!\!-CH_2$$

Cocaine
(*Erythroxylon coca*)

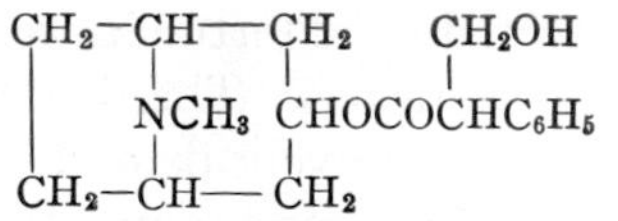

$$CH_2\!-\!CH\!-\!\!-CH_2 \qquad CH_2OH$$
$$\qquad NCH_3\ \ CHOCOCHC_6H_5$$
$$CH_2\!-\!CH\!-\! CH_2$$

Atropine
(*Atropa belladonna*)

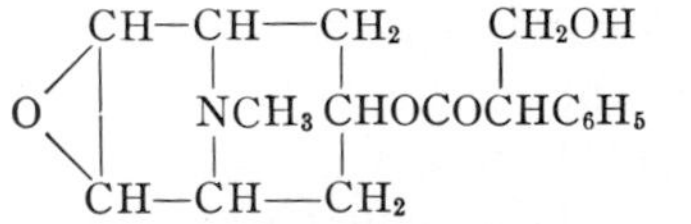

$$CH\!-\!CH\!-\!\!-CH_2 \qquad CH_2OH$$
$$O\qquad\ \ NCH_3\ CHOCOCHC_6H_5$$
$$CH\!-\!CH\!-\!\!-CH_2$$

Scopolamine
(*Scopolia* spp.)

skeleton into a cage shaped like a baseball mask. Atropine is optically inactive, since on hydrolysis it affords *dl*-tropic acid. $C_6H_5CH(CH_2OH)CO_2H$.

and the secondary alcohol tropine, which has a plane of symmetry and therefore is inactive. Cocaine on hydrolysis yields a β-hydroxy acid convertible by oxidation and decarboxylation into the ketone tropinone, which results from oxidation of tropine. Reduction of tropinone affords both tropine and the epimer pseudotropine, which is also formed by isomerization of tropine with boiling sodium amylate solution. The latter reaction indicates that tropine is less stable than pseudotropine and hence that the hydroxyl group is axial in the former and equatorial in the latter, as shown

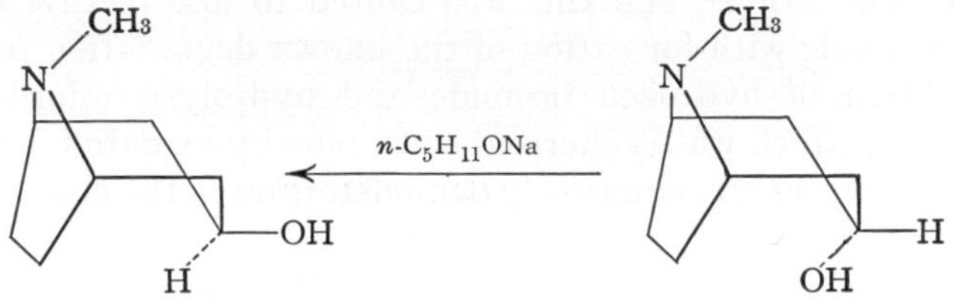

Pseudotropine   Tropine

in the formulas These configurations have been established by the method of acyl migrations (G. Fodor; A. Nickon, 1952). Thus N-acyl derivatives of norpseudotropine undergo smooth, reversible N → O migration, whereas, under comparable conditions, corresponding amides of the nortropine series are inert. Scopolamine, m.p. 59°, α_D − 33°, on enzymatic hydrolysis yields

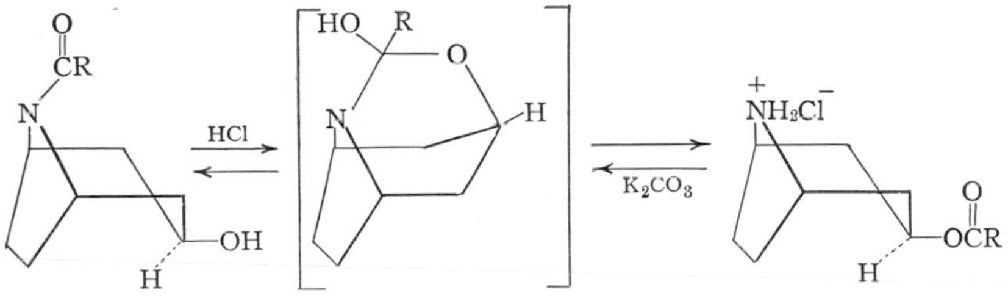

l-tropic acid and the oxido alcohol scopine, which is considered to have the structure shown because of its ready rearrangement to scopoline, in which

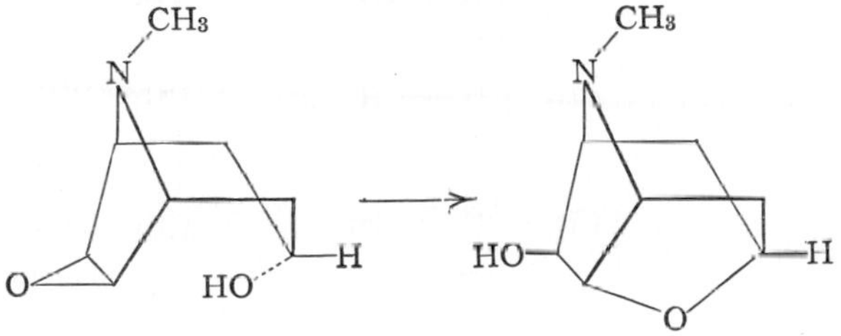

Scopine   Scopoline

the new oxide bridge must be on the opposite side of the molecule from the nitrogen bridge.

The first synthesis of tropinone and tropine was accomplished by Willstätter (1901–03) by the systematic stepwise process formulated. Suberone was converted into cycloheptene either through the iodide or by reduction of the oxime and exhaustive methylation and pyrolysis. Cycloheptene dibromide was converted by two elimination reactions into the diene, and this afforded the triene by 1,4-addition of one mole of bromine and dehydrobromination with boiling quinoline. The triene formed a hydrobromide, probably by 1,6-addition, and this reacted with dimethylamine with replacement of halogen. The product of saturation of one of the two double bonds formed a dibromide that could be rearranged to a quaternary salt having the desired nitrogen bridge, and this was caused to lose methyl bromide and hydrogen bromide with formation of the known degradation product tropidine. Addition of hydrogen bromide and hydrolysis afforded synthetic pseudotropine, which was isomerized to tropine by oxidation and reduction. The synthesis represents a masterly demonstration of the classical method of approach.

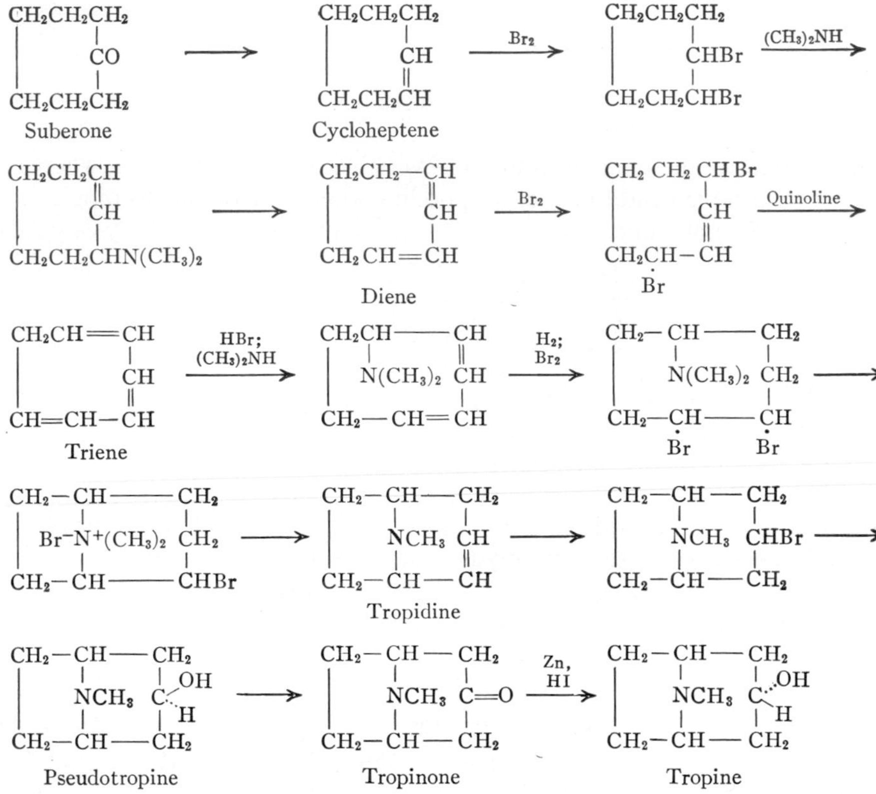

$$CH_2CH_2CH_2 \quad \text{(with } CO \text{) } CH_2CH_2CH_2 \xrightarrow{} CH_2CH_2CH_2 \text{(with CH=CH)} \xrightarrow{Br_2} CH_2CH_2CH_2 \text{(CHBr)} \xrightarrow{(CH_3)_2NH}$$

Suberone — Cycloheptene

(chemical scheme continues)

$$CH_2CH_2CH \text{ (CH, } CH_2CH_2CHN(CH_3)_2) \xrightarrow{} CH_2CH_2-CH \text{ Diene} \xrightarrow{Br_2} CH_2\,CH_2\,CHBr \xrightarrow{Quinoline}$$

$$CH_2CH=CH \text{ Triene} \xrightarrow{HBr;\ (CH_3)_2NH} CH_2CH----CH \xrightarrow{H_2;\ Br_2} CH_2-CH----CH_2$$

$$CH_2-CH----CH_2 \text{ (Br}^-\text{N}^+(CH_3)_2) \xrightarrow{} CH_2-CH----CH_2 \text{ NCH}_3 \text{ Tropidine} \xrightarrow{} CH_2-CH----CH_2 \text{ NCH}_3 CHBr \xrightarrow{}$$

$$CH_2-CH----CH_2 \text{ NCH}_3 \text{ C(OH)H Pseudotropine} \xrightarrow{} CH_2-CH----CH_2 \text{ NCH}_3 C=O \text{ Tropinone} \xrightarrow{Zn,\ HI} CH_2-CH----CH_2 \text{ NCH}_3 \text{ C(OH)H Tropine}$$

Consideration of possible routes of biosynthesis led R. Robinson (1917) to introduce a synthesis remarkable for its simplicity. The fused piperidine-pyrrolidine ring system of the coca and belladonna alkaloids can conceivably arise from a Mannich-type condensation of succindialdehyde, methylamine, and a derivative of acetone; indeed Robinson achieved the synthesis of tropinone by such a condensation utilizing acetonedicarboxylic acid.

The yield in the initial work was low, but Schöpf (1935) later carried out the same reaction in buffered solution at room temperature and found that

$$
\begin{array}{c}
\text{CH}_2\text{—CHO}\\
|\\
\\
|\\
\text{CH}_2\text{—CHO}
\end{array}
+\; \text{H}_2\text{NCH}_3 +
\begin{array}{c}
\text{CH}_2\text{CO}_2\text{H}\\
|\\
\text{CO}\\
|\\
\text{CH}_2\text{CO}_2\text{H}
\end{array}
\longrightarrow
\begin{array}{c}
\text{CH}_2\text{—CH—-CHCO}_2\text{H}\\
|\quad\quad|\\
\text{NCH}_3\; \text{CO}\\
|\quad\quad|\\
\text{CH}_2\text{—CH——CHCO}_2\text{H}
\end{array}
\xrightarrow{-2\text{CO}_2}
\begin{array}{c}
\text{CH}_2\text{—CH——CH}_2\\
|\quad\quad|\\
\text{NCH}_3\; \text{CO}\\
|\quad\quad|\\
\text{CH}_2\text{—CH——CH}_2
\end{array}
$$

Tropinone

under these simulated physiological conditions the intermediate dicarboxylic-acid loses carbon dioxide spontaneously and that tropinone can be obtained in yields as high as 90%. The optimum acidity is pH 5. Succindialdehyde can conceivably arise in nature from degradation of ornithine. Willstätter (1923) achieved the synthesis of cocaine starting with condensation of succindialdehyde, methylamine, and the monomethyl ester of acetonedicarboxylic acid. He also synthesized pseudopelletierine by analogous reactions starting with glutardialdehyde.

$$
\begin{array}{c}
\text{CH}_2\text{—CH——CH}_2\\
|\quad\quad\quad\quad|\\
\text{CH}_2\;\; \text{NCH}_3\; \text{CO}\\
|\quad\quad\quad\quad|\\
\text{CH}_2\text{—CH——CH}_2
\end{array}
$$

Pseu lopelletierine
(*Punica granatum*)

Ergot Alkaloids. — Ergot is a parasitic fungus that grows on cereal grasses, particularly rye. The alkaloid components are responsible for the oxytocic effect of ergot, of clinical value, as well as for a disease known as ergotism, characterized in its acute form by gangrene and convulsions. Chemical investigations of the active principles have been conducted mainly by W. A. Jacobs[9] and by the research group of A. Stoll.[10] All known ergot alkaloids are amides of lysergic acid. The structure deduced by these investigators for lysergic acid has since been confirmed by synthesis (E. C. Kornfeld, *et al.*, 1954). Lysergic acid contains asymmetric centers at C_5 and C_8 and is readily isomerized by acids to the 8-epimer, isolysergic acid, amides of which have no physiological activity. The double bond in ring D is readily hydrogenable, with production of another asymmetric center. Isolysergic acid gives a mixture of two dihydrides, but only one dihydride is formed from lysergic acid.

Lysergic acid

The simplest ergot alkaloid, ergonovine, is the lysergic acid amide of L-2-aminopropanol; the substance possesses marked uterotonic activity. Ergotamine, the dihydride of which is useful in treatment of migraine, contains a cyclic tripeptide moiety with no free amino or carboxyl groups. The components of this portion of the molecule were found to be L-proline (a), L-phenylalanine (b), and L-α-hydroxyalanine (c), which cannot exist as such in the free form. The three units are joined together and to lysergic

[9] Walter A. Jacobs, b. 1883 New York, N. Y.; Ph.D. Berlin (E. Fischer, Levene); Rockefeller Inst.

[10] Arthur Stoll, b. 1887 Schinznach, Switz.; Ph.D. Zurich ETH (Willstätter); Sandoz AG, Basel

acid as shown in the formula. Other known ergot alkaloids contain similar tripeptide units. L-Proline is an invariable constituent. In three the

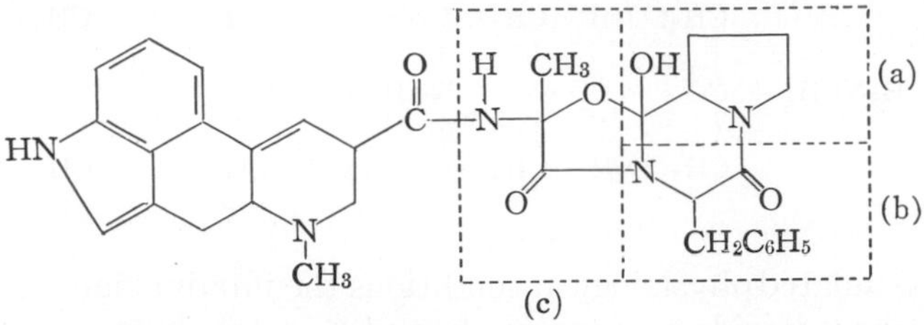

Ergotamine

α-hydroxyalanine unit is replaced by one of α-hydroxyvaline. The third component, L-phenylalanine, is replaced in other members of the series by L-leucine and by L-valine.

As the constitution of the natural alkaloids was being unraveled, Stoll and A. Hoffman (1943) prepared a series of synthetic amide derivatives of lysergic acid and found that some are even more active than the natural alkaloids. The most interesting is lysergic acid diethylamide, which when administered to normal subjects in extremely small doses produces symptoms like those of schizophrenia.

Yohimbe Alkaloids. — Evidence of the structure of yohimbine (I), the major alkaloid of the bark of *Corynanthe yohimbe*, is based mainly upon dehydrogenation to the products II, III, and IV, whose structures were established by synthesis. Products II and III result from rupture of the 4,21- and 4,5-C–N bonds. Sempervirine, an alkaloid of *Gelsemium sempervirens*,

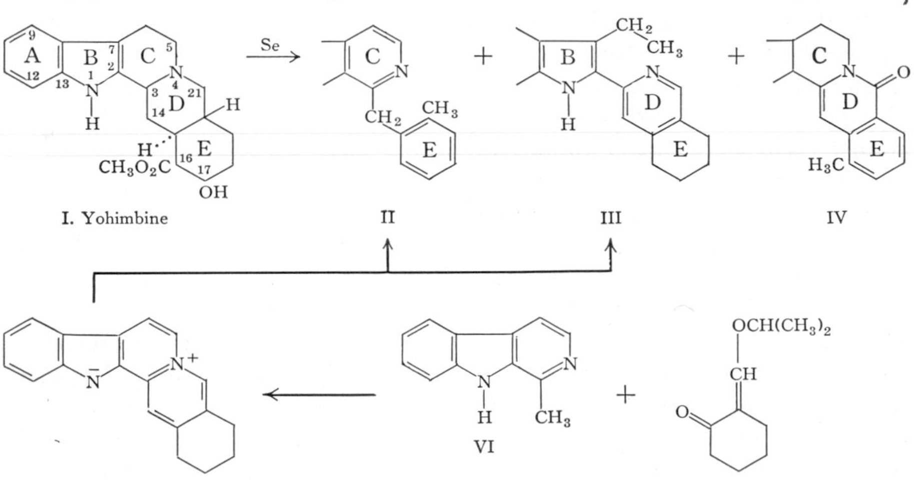

I. Yohimbine   II   III   IV

V. Sempervirine   VI   VII

is related since it yields II on selenium dehydrogenation and III when refluxed in xylene with Raney nickel. The alkaloid is colored, in consequence of the extensive conjugated system and resonance forms, and is strongly basic. The anhydronium base structure V has been verified by synthesis

BASSETT. Peter.
ph. 3015.

WEST SUSSEX COUNTY COUNCIL
LIBRARY SERVICE

LIBRARY
.... CHICHESTER 777350

THIS ITEM IS NOW AVAILABLE
AND WILL BE RESERVED FOR
YOU UNTIL THE LIBRARY CLOSES
ON ....

....
**PLEASE BRING THIS CARD AND
YOUR MEMBERSHIP TICKET**

MR / MRS / MISS / MS
NAME
.... PETER BASSETT

ADDRESS
.... MILL LANE COTTAGE
.... AMBERLEY.
.... ARUNDEL
.... BN18 9LZ
....

TELEPHONE NO.
.... 01798 831346

REQUEST CARD

MEMBERSHIP NUMBER 02 210 5389

DATE 19.4.96 INITIALS CW

URGENT?

AUTHOR / COMPOSER / PERFORMER FIESER, LF + FIESER, May

CLASS

FORMAT

TITLE ORGANIC CHEMISTRY

CONTROL. NO.

PUBLISHER HARRAP

MANF. NO.

EDITION 2nd.

DATE 1950

PRICE 42/-

ALTERNATIVE YES/NO

BIB SOURCES B50-8867

LASER YES/NO

PLEASE ADDRESS CARD ON REVERSE

FOR STAFF USE	ACTION	LOCATION	DATE DUE	MESSAGE
LOLI	X			
GALAXY	X			
POT REQ.				
ON ORDER				
TRAP				
LIB 139	19/4			
STANDARD LETTER				

NOTES

225879

R.2293A SY9
LIB 135a

by condensation of the lithium derivative of harmane (VI) with 2-isopropoxymethylenecyclohexanone, VII (Woodward, 1953).

Although sempervirine has some hypertensive activity, the ester alkaloid reserpine, of different *Rauwolfia* species, is superior in this respect and is useful in the treatment of hypertension and of various mental disorders. The structure was established (Schlittler,[11] 1953) by characterization of the acid component as 3,4,5-trimethoxybenzoic acid and by reactions relating the other product of hydrolysis, reserpic acid, to yohimbine derivatives. The configuration (Schlittler; Diassi, Wintersteiner et al.; Huebner; van Tamelen, 1955) was established partly by ring formation between N_4 and C_{22}. When the derivative obtained by reduction of the carbomethoxyl group (C_{22}) is treated with tosyl chloride in pyridine a spontaneous quaternization occurs by reaction of the C_{22} tosylate group with N_4. This inner quaternary tosic acid salt can only be formed if the hydrogens at C_{15}, C_{16}, and C_{20} are *cis* and α. The substituents at C_{16} and C_{18} were shown to be *cis* by the fact that reserpic acid readily forms a γ-lactone without inversion, and application of Hudson's lactone rule to the change in molecular rotation involved related the orientation at C_{18} to that of D-glyceraldehyde and fixed the absolute configuration as that formulated rather than its mirror image. The orientation of the methoxyl at C_{17} is most probably α (Wenkert, 1955) Similar physiological actions are exhibited by deserpidine, which lacks the 11-methoxyl group, and rescinnamine. in which the acyl group esterified with the C_{18}-hydroxyl is 3,4,5-trimethoxycinnamoyl.

Reserpine

Strychnine, $C_{21}H_{22}O_2N_2$. — Strychnine (m.p. about 290°) occurs along with brucine and minor companion alkaloids in the seeds of *Strychnos nux vomica*. It is easily isolated from the seeds and, being very poisonous, is used for extermination of rodents and for trapping fur-bearing animals. Th strychnos alkaloids have found no significant application in medicine. Although the empirical formula is relatively simple, elucidation of structure presented a particularly challenging problem because of the intricate system of seven fused rings, and strychnine has been studied extensively since 1891 in several laboratories, particularly those of H. Leuchs[12] and H Wieland. The correct formula was eventually deduced by Robinson in 1946 and has been verified by synthesis (Woodward, 1954).

---

[11] Emil Schlittler, b. 1906 Schwanden, Switz.; Ph.D. ETH Zurich and Edinburgh (Barger, Robinson, Karrer); Ciba Ltd., Univ. Basel

[12] Hermann Leuchs, 1879–1945; b. Nürnberg, Germany; Ph.D. Berlin (E. Fischer); Berlin; *Ber.*, **85**, Lv (1952)

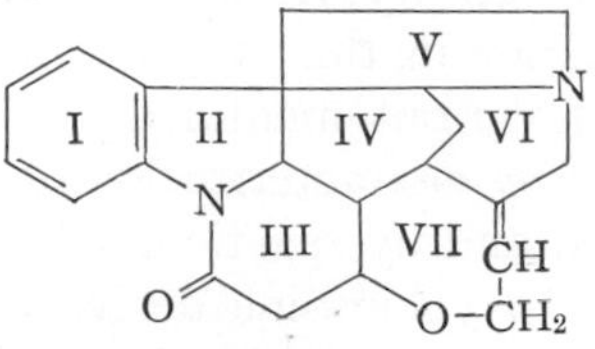

Strychnine

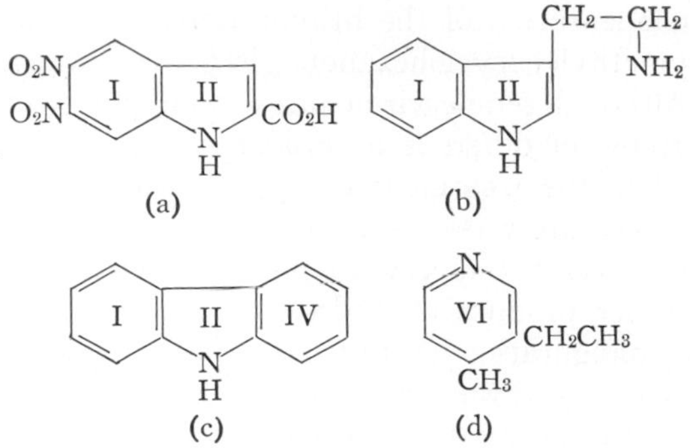

(a)

(b)

(c)

(d)

Degradation Products

The character of the functional groups was deduced readily. Thus one nitrogen was recognized as tertiary (formation of quaternary salts) and the other as present as an amide group. Since strychnine is not ketonic or hydroxylic, the second oxygen atom was recognized as forming on oxide linkage in a ring. An ethylenic double bond was identified by hydrogenation to dihydro derivatives and a benzene ring from the absorption spectrum. Reaction with benzaldehyde to form a benzylidine derivative revealed the presence of an active methylene group adjacent to the double bond. Important evidence was obtained by drastic degradations to fragments containing only one, two, or three of the original rings. Thus 5,6-dinitroindole-2-carboxylic acid (a), derived from rings I and II, results from exhaustive nitric acid oxidation. Among products of alkali fusion are: tryptamine (b), which discloses the relative positions of the two nitrogen atoms, and carbazole (c), which contains three of the seven original rings. β-Collidine (d) evidently arises from the ring containing the tertiary nitrogen atom. The final deduction of structure was based on consideration of many other complicated degradations involving a series of oxidation products.

Febrifugin and Isofebrifugin. — Reports during World War II that the Chinese drug Ch'ang San, the powdered root of *Dichroa febrifuga*, showed antimalarial activity stimulated chemical investigation of the active principle. Febrifugin, one of two alkaloids isolated from this source by Koepfli[13] (1947), has high antimalarial activity in chickens, ducks, and monkeys, but

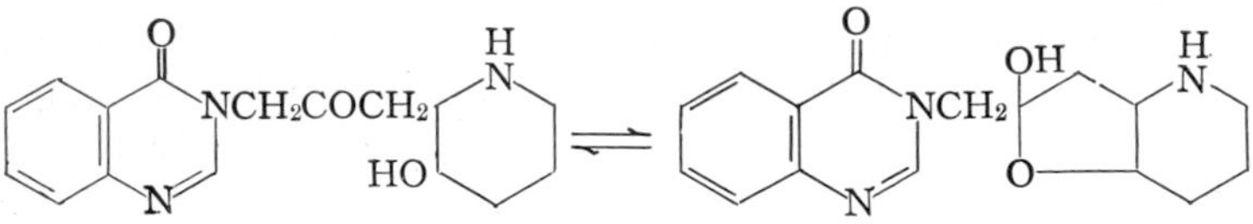

Febrifugin   Isofebrifugin

clinical trials have been discouraging. The companion substance, isofebrifugin, is interconvertible with febrifugin by heating; it has no antimalarial activity. The one substance is merely the cyclic ketal of the other. The

¹³ Joseph B. Koepfli, b. 1904 Los Angeles; Ph.D. Oxford; Calif. Inst. Techn.

quinazoline structures formulated have been established by degradation and synthesis. This ring system is found only rarely in alkaloids.

Ipecac Alkaloids. — Ipecac root, of a South American creeping plant (*Cephaelis ipecachuanha*), has long been used as an emetic and expectorant, and the principal alkaloid emetine has important use in the treatment of amebic dysentery. Rings A and B of emetine correspond to the tetrahydro-

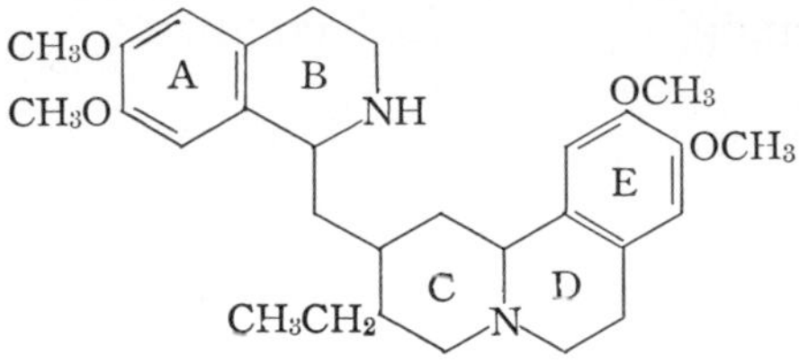

CH₃O / A / B / NH — structure

OCH₃ / OCH₃ / E

CH₃CH₂ / C / D / N

Emetine

HO / A / CH₃O — HO / A / B / NH

CH₃O / CH₃O

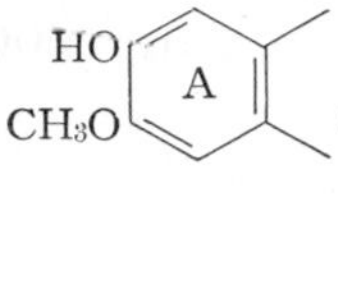

Cephaeline 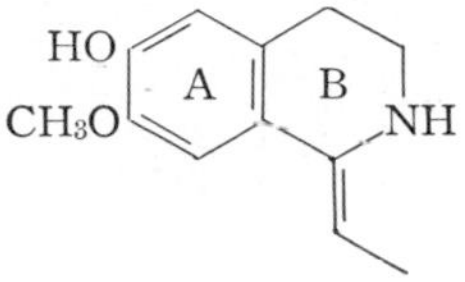   Psychotrine

isoquinoline system of papaverine. As in the case of the aporphine alkaloids, companion alkaloids differ only in having some free phenolic hydroxyl groups. Cephaeline, of the partial structure shown, is converted by methylation into N-methylemetine. Another companion, psychotrine, has a free hydroxyl group at the same position and contains a double bond conjugated with ring A. On hydrogenation and methylation it gives the N-methyl derivatives of emetine and isoemetine. Emetine ($C_{29}H_{40}O_4N_2$) on catalytic dehydrogenation loses four atoms of hydrogen and yields a substance known as emetamine ($C_{29}H_{36}O_4N_2$), and on oxidation with bromine, ferric chloride, or mercuric acetate it affords rubremetine chloride ($C_{29}H_{32}O_4N_2 \cdot HCl$, yellow). The latter substance is regarded as having a pyrrole ring formed by cyclization between rings B and C.

Alkaloid Substitutes. — Alkaloids of the tropane group dilate the pupil of the eye; atropine is used for this purpose in ophthalmic practice. They also have a paralyzing effect on sensory nerve endings and hence are useful local anesthetics. Cocaine is the most valuable in the respect but it also produces an undesirable effect on the central nervous system (euphoria). Consequently many synthetic products bearing some structural relationship to cocaine have been examined as substitutes. The only one commonly used is procaine (also called novocain), which has about one half the anesthetic potency of cocaine and is about one fourth as toxic. It is an

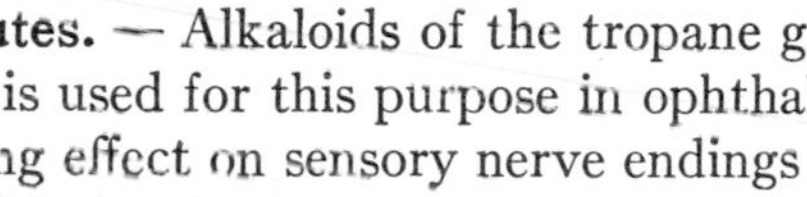

H_2N—⟨ ⟩—$COOCH_2CH_2N(C_2H_5)_2$

Procaine

ester prepared by the reaction of ethylene chlorohydrin and diethylamine with *p*-aminobenzoic acid.

Morphine is the most efficacious remedy known for the relief of pain and is indispensable in medical practice. Unfortunately the beneficial analgesic effect is accompanied by the undesirable property of producing addiction. A few derivatives of morphine having less addiction liability but still com-

parable analgesic action have been introduced and have certain value; but
again, as in the case of cocaine, investigation of simple substitutes of un-
related structure has proved fruitful. A simple morphine substitute introduced in 1939 in Germany is known as demerol. The substance is less
potent than morphine as an analgesic, but is also less toxic. The drugs

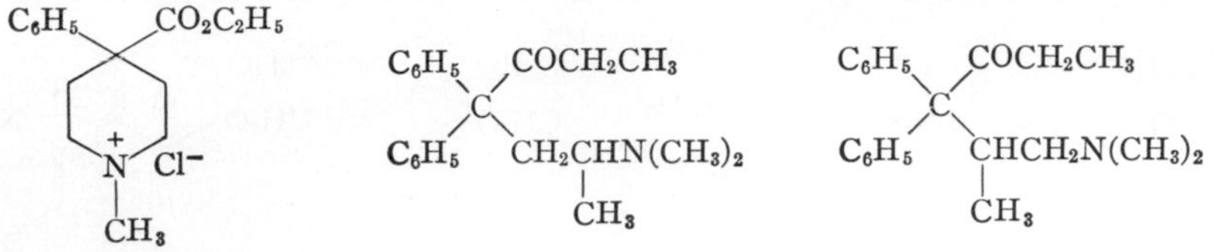

| Demerol | Amidone | Isoamidone |

amidone and isoamidone are as potent analgesics as morphine and less toxic,
but they appear to possess undesirable side reactions. The development of
substitutes for quinine, a useful antimalarial, has been particularly successful
(p. 1025).

READING REFERENCES

L. F. Small, "Alkaloids," in H. Gilman, "Organic Chemistry," 2nd Ed., II, 1166 Wiley, New
   York (1943)
T. A. Henry, "The Plant Alkaloids," 4th Ed., Churchill Ltd., London (1949)
R. H. F. Manske and H. L. Holmes, "The Alkaloids," I–V, Academic Press, New York (1950–55)
R. H. F. Manske, "The Isoquinoline Alkaloids," *J. Chem. Soc.*, 2987 (1954)
A. Stoll, "Recent Investigations of Ergot Alkaloids," *Prog. Chem. Nat. Prod.*, **9**, 115 (1952)

POLYMERS

The term polymer is usually applied to substances composed of at least 100 repeating units, that is, high polymers, for only substances of such high molecular weight exhibit unique physical properties: high tensile strength, elasticity, ability to form fibers. Carothers[1] classified polymers into two types: condensation and addition polymers. The former are formed from a single monomer by elimination of water or the equivalent, as exemplified by the natural polymers cellulose, starch, glycogen. Proteins are products of condensation polymerization of units of the same general type but having varying side chains. Other condensation polymers are derived from two monomeric starting materials; for example, a diacid (A) and a diol (B) condense to form a polyester having the repeating unit AB An addition polymer is derived from multiple condensation of an unsaturated monomer and has the same percentage composition as the monomer. Natural rubber is a typical addition polymer.

RUBBER, NATURAL AND SYNTHETIC

Raw Rubber. — Rubber, a polyterprene of the formula $(C_5H_8)_n$, occurs in many tropical plants; the commercial supply comes almost entirely from the tree *Hevea brasiliensis*, largely cultivated in plantations. When an incision is made through the outer bark of a rubber tree, a milky fluid called latex oozes out. This is a colloidal dispersion of rubber particles in water, and addition of dilute acetic or formic acid causes coagulation of the rubber in a cheeselike mass. In one common process this is passed through rollers with water washing to produce thin, kinky sheets of light-colored "pale crepe rubber"; in another, it is milled into sheets and smoked to form amber-colored "smoked sheet rubber." These two forms of "raw rubber" of commerce contain over 95% of rubber hydrocarbon (sometimes called caoutchouc, from the South American *caa*, tears, and *ochu*, of wood).

Early investigators identified products of destructive distillation of rubber as isoprene, C_5H_8, and its dimer dipentene, $C_{10}H_{16}$, and found that under certain conditions isoprene undergoes self-condensation to give rubberlike material. More specific evidence of structure was obtained by ozonization of rubber in chloroform or ethyl acetate solution (Harries,[2] 1905–12;

---

[1] Wallace H. Carothers, 1896–1937; b. Burlington, Iowa; Ph.D. Illinois (Adams); du Pont Co.; *J. Chem. Soc.*, 100 (1940)

[2] Carl Dietrich Harries, 1866–1923; b. Luckenwalde; Ph.D. Berlin; Berlin; *Ber.*, **59A**, 123 (1926)

Pummerer,[3] 1931), which affords levulinic aldehyde (with some of the acid) in up to 90% yield. This result must mean that the isoprene units are linked head-to-tail.

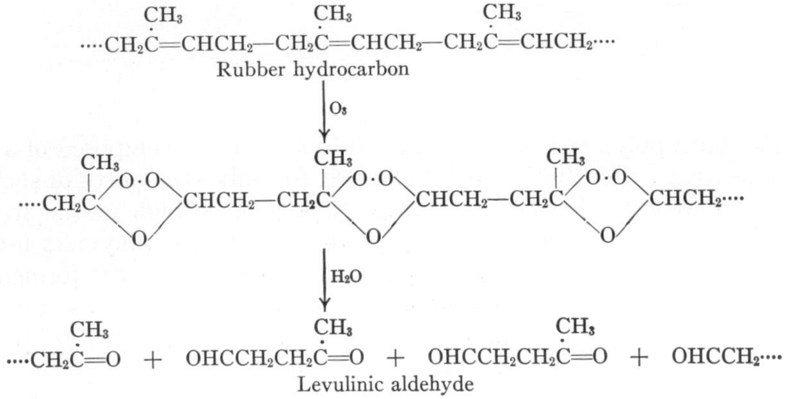

$$\text{....CH}_2\text{C}\underset{\overset{|}{\text{CH}_3}}{=}\text{CHCH}_2\text{---CH}_2\text{C}\underset{\overset{|}{\text{CH}_3}}{=}\text{CHCH}_2\text{---CH}_2\text{C}\underset{\overset{|}{\text{CH}_3}}{=}\text{CHCH}_2\text{....}$$

Rubber hydrocarbon

$$\downarrow O_3$$

$$\downarrow H_2O$$

$$\text{....CH}_2\overset{\overset{\text{CH}_3}{|}}{\dot{\text{C}}}\text{=O} \; + \; \text{OHCCH}_2\text{CH}_2\overset{\overset{\text{CH}_3}{|}}{\text{C}}\text{=O} \; + \; \text{OHCCH}_2\text{CH}_2\overset{\overset{\text{CH}_3}{|}}{\dot{\text{C}}}\text{=O} \; + \; \text{OHCCH}_2\text{....}$$

Levulinic aldehyde

Rubber is characterized particularly by its elasticity, a property not shared by the isomeric natural polymers gutta-percha and balata (probably identical). Even rubber becomes nonelastic and crystalline at $-80°$. At ordinary temperature unstretched rubber shows no regular X-ray diffraction pattern and is, therefore, amorphous, but stretched rubber exhibits the characteristics of an oriented, ordered structure, and analysis of the pattern leads to the conclusion that rubber has the all *cis* configuration. In contrast, the nonelastic gutta-percha has the all *trans* form.

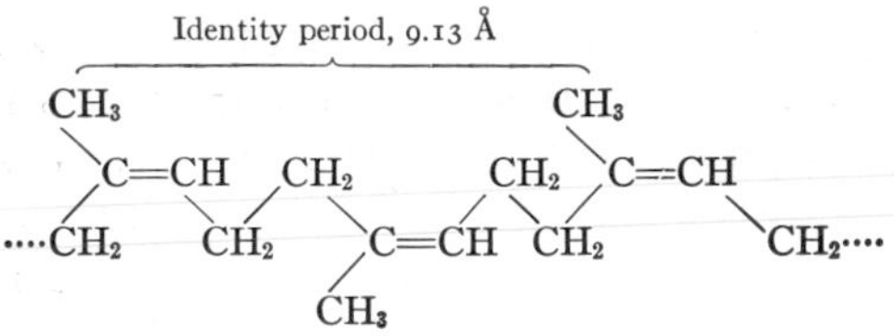

Identity period, 9.13 Å

cis Form

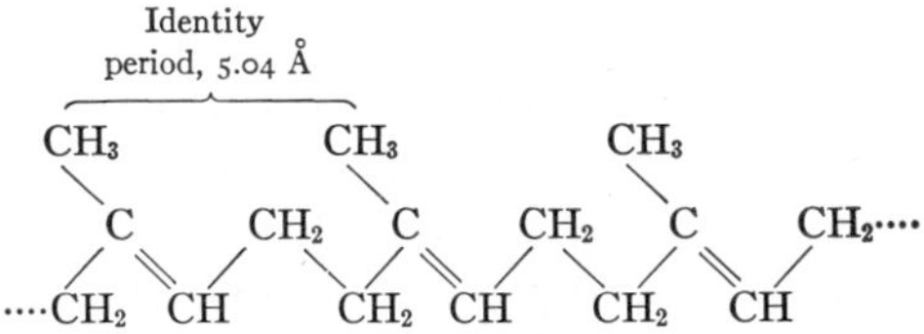

Identity period, 5.04 Å

trans Form

Vulcanized Rubber. — Raw rubber is tacky and soft and becomes even more so in hot weather. The tensile strength and resistance to abrasion are low, and elasticity is maintained over only a limited range of temperature. All these properties are improved markedly by the process of vulcanization (Charles Goodyear, 1838), which consists in heating rubber with sulfur,

[3] Rudolf Pummerer, b. 1882 Wels, Austria; Ph.D. Munich: Erlangen

usually 5–8%. One development in the technology of vulcanization is use of accelerators to decrease the time required for chemical combination of rubber and sulfur or to lower the temperature of reaction. Another was

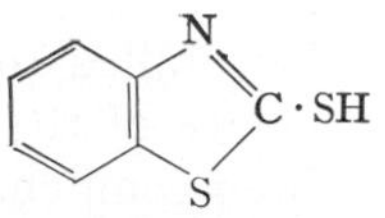

Mercaptobenzothiazole
(medium accelerator)

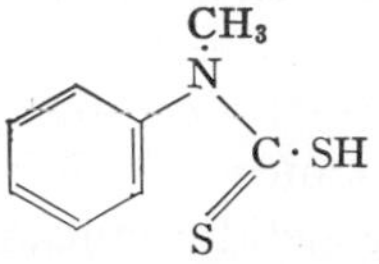

Phenylmethyldithiocarbamic acid
(medium accelerator)

$$(CH_3)_2NC\!-\!SS\!-\!CN(CH_3)_2$$
Tetramethylthiuram disulfide
(powerful accelerator)

$$(CH_3)_2NC\!-\!S\!-\!Zn\!-\!S\!-\!CN(CH_3)_2$$
Zinc dimethyldithiocarbamate
(ultra-accelerator)

the discovery that addition of an inert powder as filler to the rubber–sulfur mix increases the effectiveness of the accelerator and gives a vulcanizate of superior physical properties. Zinc oxide is the usual reinforcing filler for production of light-colored stock and carbon black is the preferred filler for tire rubber. If the sulfur content is increased to 30–50%, the product, which is hard and of high tensile strength, is known as ebonite; this material retains some 15% of the original unsaturation. The nature of the vulcanization process is still uncertain, although it undoubtedly involves establishment of sulfur cross links between parallel hydrocarbon chains. The initial attack by sulfur is probably not at double bonds of the polyisoprenoid chain but at activated allylic positions. Similar allylic oxidation to a hydroperoxide is probably the first step in the aging of rubber due to air oxidation,

$$\cdots CH_2C\!=\!CHCH_2\cdots \xrightarrow{O_2} \cdots CH\!-\!C\!=\!CHCH_2\cdots$$
$$\;\;\;\;\;\;\;| \;| \;\;\;\;|$$
$$\;\;\;\;CH_3 \;\;\;\;\;\;\;\;\;\;\;\;\;\;\;\;\;OOH \; CH_3$$

with eventual clipping of the chains with lowering of the average molecular weight and decrease in strength and elasticity. Various aromatic amines, phenols, and quinones incorporated in the stock function as antioxidants and materially prolong the life of the rubber articles.

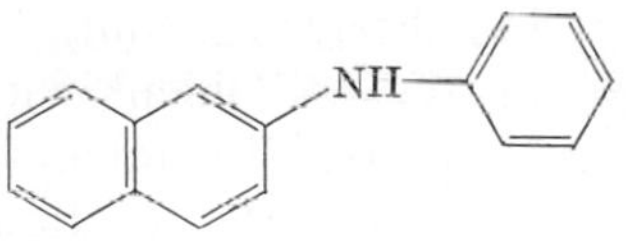

Phenyl-β-naphthylamine

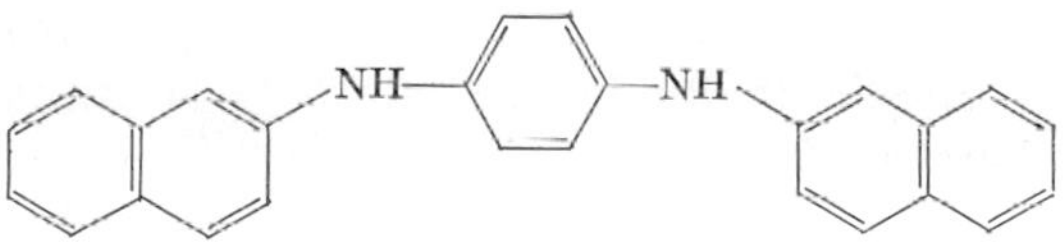

Di-β-naphthyl-p-phenylenediamine

Antioxidants for rubber

Latex. — Although the bulk of the latex produced in plantations is converted into pale crepe or smoked sheet stock that is later vulcanized, a portion is reserved for special uses. Latex contains emulsoid particles consisting of hydrocarbon aggregates inclosed in protein envelopes, together with fatty acids (2.5–3%), sugars, resins, and a natural antioxidant removable by extraction with acetone. The emulsion is preserved from putrefaction by addition of ammonia and shipped at its original concentration (35–38%) or concentrated to 60–70% by centrifugation, evaporation, or creaming.

Latex rubber is stronger and more extensible than milled rubber and has remarkable resistance to aging owing to the presence of the natural antioxidant. It is generally vulcanized after it has been compounded by addition of a paste of sulfur, an accelerator, and an antioxidant, reduced to colloidal dimensions in the presence of a protective colloid, for example, a solution of casein in dilute ammonia. Balloons, gloves, shoes, bathing caps are made by the dipping process. A mold is introduced into the compounded latex, the adhering film is coagulated on the form by drying at a temperature below that at which vulcanization occurs, then cured while still on the form. Sponge rubber is made by whipping air into compounded latex and subsequently coagulating the whipped mass by the action of a dormant coagulant (e.g. zinc ammonium chloride) that becomes effective at a critical temperature; further heat treatment completes the process of vulcanization. Rubber thread is made by extruding latex through tiny orifices into a coagulating and dehydrating bath of acetic acid and ammonium acetate; the thread is then washed, dried, and vulcanized. Lastex is latex thread wrapped with cotton or silk. Textiles are impregnated with latex to produce flexible and resistant finishes.

Rubber Derivatives. — Rubber cements are made by dissolving crepe rubber in benzene or carbon tetrachloride. Smoked sheet rubber gives solutions of lower viscosity, probably because the milling and smoking operations by which it is made effect some depolymerization. Vulcanized rubber swells in organic solvents but does not dissolve.

When raw rubber is heated with an aromatic sulfonic acid, the properties change progressively and the material resembles balata (*trans*-form). One commercial preparation known as Thermoprene is used for making special adhesives. Another, Pliolite, is a molding resin. Chlorination of rubber gives hard, brittle products soluble in common solvents and used in chemical-resistant paints and varnishes (Parlon, Raolin). Rubber hydrochloride, prepared by passing hydrogen chloride into a benzene solution of raw rubber, is produced in the form of transparent films and in sheets (Pliofilm).

Synthetic Rubbers. — Both G. Bouchardat[4] and W. A. Tilden[5] had observed (1879–84) that isoprene (b.p. 34.3°) is polymerized by mineral acids to give products that resemble rubber superficially, but the reaction never found practical application. The first synthetic rubber (**methyl rubber**), produced on a small scale in Germany during World War I, was made by polymerization of 2,3-dimethylbutadiene, available from acetone

[4] Gustave Bouchardat, 1842–1918; b. Paris; Ph.D. Paris (Wurtz, Berthelot); Paris

[5] Sir William A. Tilden, 1842–1926; b. St. Pancras, England; D.Sc. London; London; *J. Chem. Soc.*, **129**, 3190 (1927)

via pinacol. The polymer, however, had poor physical properties and never attained any importance.

Discovery of the first American synthetic rubber, **Neoprene** (1932), was an outcome of fundamental studies of Nieuwland[6] on the chemistry of acetylene. Nieuwland had developed a satisfactory method for preparation of the trimer divinylacetylene by polymerization of acetylene in the pres-

$$CH \equiv CH \ + \ CH \equiv CH \ + \ CH \equiv CH \ \longrightarrow \ CH_2 = CH - C \equiv C - CH = CH_2$$

Divinylacetylene

ence of cuprous chloride and ammonium chloride. du Pont chemists headed by Carothers investigated the further polymerization of divinylacetylene with unpromising results and then found that the initial polymerization of acetylene can be modified in such a way as to yield the dimer, vinylacetylene, and that this adds hydrogen chloride to form chloroprene, of structure analogous to that of isoprene. Chloroprene polymerizes very readily (700

$$CH \equiv CH \ + \ CH \equiv CH \ \xrightarrow{Cu_2Cl_2, NH_4Cl} \ \overset{4}{C}H_2 = \overset{3}{C}H\overset{2}{C} \equiv \overset{1}{C}H \ \xrightarrow[\text{(1,4-addition)}]{HCl}$$

Vinylacetylene

$$\underset{\underset{Cl}{|}}{CH_2CH} = C = CH_2 \ \xrightarrow{\text{Isomerization}} \ CH_2 = CH - \underset{\underset{Cl}{|}}{C} = CH_2$$

Chloroprene

times as fast as isoprene); no specific catalysts are added, but the polymerization is slower in the absence of oxygen. A comparison of the speed of polymerization for various butadienes (referred to that of isoprene) is shown in Table 35.1.

The polymer from chloroprene is analogous to unvulcanized rubber. Although it can be vulcanized by treatment with sulfur, metallic oxides (of zinc, magnesium) are commonly used. The chains are formed by a process of 1,4-addition, for oxidation gives succinic acid as the main product. In

$$\cdots CH_2\underset{\underset{Cl}{|}}{C} = CHCH_2 - CH_2\underset{\underset{Cl}{|}}{C} = CHCH_2 - CH_2\underset{\underset{Cl}{|}}{C} = CHCH_2 \cdots$$

$$\downarrow O_2$$

$$\cdots CH_2COOH \ + \ HOOCCH_2CH_2COOH \ + \ HOOCCH_2CH_2COOH \ + \ HOOCCH_2 \cdots$$

X-ray diffraction studies of polychloroprene the identity period is found to be almost the same as that of gutta-percha, an indication that the polymer has the *trans* configuration. Although in the hydrocarbon series this configuration corresponds to the nonelastic gutta type, the presence of the chlorine atom introduces two additional factors. The distance between linked chlorine and carbon atoms (1.77 Å) is longer than the distance be-

---

[6] Julius A. Nieuwland, 1878–1936; b. Hansbeke, Belgium; Univ. Notre Dame

TABLE 35.1.   ESTIMATED SPEED OF POLYMERIZATION OF DIENES AT 25°

DIENE	SPEED	CHARACTER OF POLYMER
$H_2C=CH-CH=CH_2$	0.8	fair rubber
$H_2C=C-CH=CH_2$ $\quad\ \ CH_3$	1	fair rubber
$H_2C=C----C=CH_2$ $\quad\ \ CH_3\ \ CH_3$	3	fair rubber, low extensibility
$HC=CH-CH=CH_2$ $\ \ Cl$	7	soft, sticky
$HC===C-CH=CH_2$ $\ \ CH_3\ \ Cl$	30	soft
$H_2C=C-C=CH_2$ $\quad\ \ Cl\ \ CH_3$	500	fair rubber, low extensibility
$H_2C=C-CH=CH_2$ $\quad\ \ Cl$	700	excellent rubber
$H_2C=C-CH=CH_2$ $\quad\ \ Br$	1000	good rubber
$H_2C=C-CH=CH_2$ $\quad\ \ I$	1500	rubberlike under certain conditions
$H_2C=C-C=CH_2$ $\quad\ \ Cl\ \ Cl$	2000	hard rubber, no extensibility

tween linked carbon atoms (1.53 Å); therefore the chlorine atom lies farther from the chain than the methyl groups of gutta-percha and offers less obstruction to molecular wriggling.   Moreover the external radius of a chlorine atom is slightly less than that of a methyl group.

Although Neoprene is too expensive to compete with natural rubber for the production of tires, the synthetic rubber has many special uses because of its superior resistance to organic solvents, stability to air oxidation, and general resistance to chemicals.

The first high polymers of butadiene, developed in Germany in 1927, are known as **Buna rubbers** because sodium was originally used as polymerization catalyst (butadiene–Natrium, sodium).   Fundamental investigations by Ziegler (1928–34) indicate that sodium polymerization involves, first, reaction between sodium and the diene, followed by 1,4-addition of the organometallic compound to a second molecule of diene:

$$CH_2=CHCH=CH_2\ +\ 2Na\ \longrightarrow\ NaCH_2CH=CHCH_2Na\ +\ CH_2=CHCH=CH_2\ \longrightarrow$$

$$NaCH_2CH=CHCH_2-CH_2CH=CHCH_2Na\ \longrightarrow\ etc.$$

Normal 1,4-addition is not the only reaction involved; in fact 1,2-addition may predominate to give a polymer of the partial structure (a). A certain amount of cyclization, or cross-linking, also occurs, for the total unsaturation

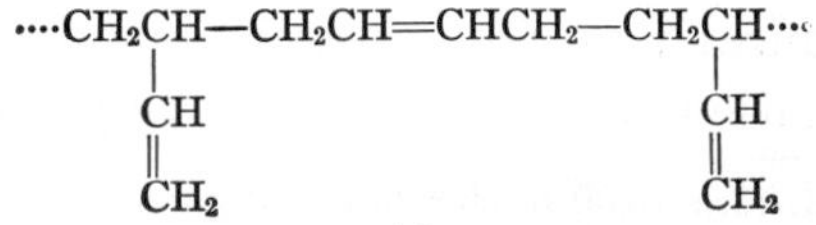

$$\cdots CH_2CH-CH_2CH=CHCH_2-CH_2CH\cdots$$
$$\qquad\quad |\qquad\qquad\qquad\qquad\qquad\quad |$$
$$\qquad\quad CH\qquad\qquad\qquad\qquad\qquad\ CH$$
$$\qquad\quad ||\qquad\qquad\qquad\qquad\qquad\quad ||$$
$$\qquad\quad CH_2\qquad\qquad\qquad\qquad\qquad CH_2$$

(a)

of the polymer is only 90–95% of the theory (one double bond per butadiene residue).

A major advance that contributed to the further development of synthetic rubbers was introduction of the technique of **emulsion polymerization,** suggested by the fact that natural rubber occurs as an emulsion. The monomer is dispersed in 2–4 parts of water with the aid of an emulsifying agent (salt of a fatty acid or of naphthenic acid) and a protective colloid (glue, gelatin), and polymerization is maintained at a suitable rate by addition of a suitable polymerization catalyst. Emulsion polymerization is easier to control than massive polymerization, it is more rapid, it allows easier control of the degree of polymerization, and it lends itself well to incorporation of modifying agents. The process is well adapted to polymerization of butadiene and of chloroprene, but it has the particular advantage of permitting copolymerization, that is, use of more than one building unit. The product of emulsion polymerization of a mixture of two monomers consists of chains containing both units, the distribution of which depends upon the ratio in the initial mixture and upon the relative reactivities of the monomers.

The most important rubber substitute is a copolymer of butadiene and styrene ($C_6H_5CH\!\!=\!\!CH_2$), known as **Buna S** or **GRS** (Government Rubber Styrene). The ratio of butadiene to styrene is about 3:1 in the usual commercial product used in manufacture of tires. The copolymer is represented in the formula as a long chain molecule but actually the chains appear to be cross-linked; chain modifiers are used to regulate the extent of cross

$$\cdots CH_2CH\!\!=\!\!CHCH_2\!-\!CH_2CH\!\!=\!\!CHCH_2\!-\!CH_2CH\!-\!CH_2CH\!\!=\!\!CHCH_2\cdots$$
$$\underset{\textstyle C_6H_5}{|}$$

Buna S or GRS rubber

linking. Buna S is vulcanized with sulfur and accelerators similarly to natural rubber.

An early German process for **production of butadiene** (1) involved aldolization of acetaldehyde derived from acetylene. A later German

$$1.\ 2CH\!\!\equiv\!\!CH \xrightarrow[69.4\%]{H_2O} 2CH_3CHO \xrightarrow[57.6\%]{} \underset{\textstyle OH}{CH_3CHCH_2CHO}|\xrightarrow{H_2}$$

$$CH_3CH(OH)CH_2CH_2OH \xrightarrow{-H_2O} CH_2\!\!=\!\!CHCH\!\!=\!\!CH_2$$

process (2) developed by Reppe utilizes acetylene and formaldehyde as starting materials. The overall yield is high and the process was operated

$$CH\!\!\equiv\!\!CH + 2CH_2O \longrightarrow HOCH_2C\!\!\equiv\!\!CCH_2OH \xrightarrow{2H_2}$$

$$2.\quad HOCH_2CH_2CH_2CH_2OH \xrightarrow{-H_2O} \underset{\substack{CH_2\ CH_2 \\ \diagdown\ \diagup \\ O}}{\overset{CH_2-CH_2}{|\qquad|}} \xrightarrow{-H_2O} CH_2\!\!=\!\!CHCH\!\!=\!\!CH_2$$

Tetrahydrofuran

on a large scale during the latter part of World War II.   A Russian process (3) employing ethanol afforded butadiene in only 30–35% yield, but a modification (4) in which a mixture of ethanol and acetaldehyde is used

3. $2C_2H_5OH \rightarrow CH_2{=}CHCH{=}CH_2 + 2H_2O + H_2$

4. $C_2H_5OH + CH_3CHO \rightarrow CH_2{=}CHCH{=}CH_2 + H_2O$

raises the yield to 70% and is used on a large scale (Carbon and Carbide Chemicals Corp.)   Petroleum is an equally important raw material.   Butadiene can be obtained directly by cracking naphtha and light oil, but the catalytic dehydrogenation of butene or of butene–butane mixtures is more important (p. 106).   Another process involves dehydration of 2,3-butylene glycol, made by fermentation of grain:

$$CH_3CH{-}CHCH_3 \xrightarrow{95\%} CH_3CH{-}CHCH_3 \xrightarrow[85\%]{585°} CH_2{=}CHCH{=}CH_2$$
$$\quad\;\; |\quad\;\; | \qquad\qquad\qquad |\quad\;\; |$$
$$\quad\;\; OH\;\; OH \qquad\qquad\quad OAc\;\; OAc$$

2,3-Butylene glycol

Direct dehydration of the free glycol is unsatisfactory because of formation of considerable amounts of methyl ethyl ketone:

$$CH_3CH{-}CHCH_3 \longrightarrow CH_3CH{=}CCH_3 \longrightarrow CH_3CH_2CCH_3$$
$$\quad\;\; |\quad\;\; | \qquad\qquad\qquad | \qquad\qquad\qquad \|$$
$$\quad\;\; OH\;\; OH \qquad\qquad\quad OH \qquad\qquad\qquad O$$

Copolymers of butadiene and acrylonitrile are manufactured as synthetic rubbers under the names Perbunan, Hycar (Ameripol), and Chemigum.   Perbunan contains about 25% of the nitrile; it is vulcanized in the

$$\cdots CH_2CH{=}CHCH_2{-}CH_2CH{=}CHCH_2{-}CH_2CH{-}CH_2CH{=}CHCH_2\cdots$$
$$\qquad\qquad\qquad\qquad\qquad\qquad\qquad\qquad\qquad\qquad |$$
$$\qquad\qquad\qquad\qquad\qquad\qquad\qquad\qquad\qquad\quad CN$$

Perbunan

usual way and shows good resistance to oils and withstands aging, abrasion, and heat better than natural rubber.   The nitrile is prepared from acetylene and hydrogen cyanide (p. 89) or from ethylene chlorohydrin:

$$HOCH_2CH_2Cl \xrightarrow{NaCN} CH_2{=}CHC{\equiv}N$$

Development of the above synthetic products shows that rubberlike properties can be attained with unsaturated carbon chains differing considerably in both structure and configuration from the natural rubber hydrocarbon.   Indeed, even a carbon chain is not essential.   **Polysulfide rubbers** known as Perdurens (Germany) and Thiokols (U. S. A.), although not of superior quality, can be manufactured at low cost by condensation of an organic dichloride with an inorganic polysulfide, for example:

$$n\ ClCH_2CH_2Cl + Na_2S_4 \rightarrow [{-}CH_2CH_2{-}S_4{-}]_n + 2n\ NaCl$$

The components are mixed in the presence of a dispersing agent and the resulting latexlike suspension is washed, coagulated with acid, and cured by milling.   Heating with zinc oxide effects a change comparable to vulcanization and gives material that is nonplastic and elastic. Although the polysulfide rubbers are of low tensile strength, superior resistance to swelling by solvents and to abrasion make them useful as coating to conserve tire tread.

When the polysulfide rubber from ethylene dichloride (Thiokol A) is warmed at 80° with sodium hydroxide, approximately two atoms of sulfur are lost per ethylene unit and the product is a white granular powder, $[-CH_2CH_2-S_2-]_n$. A similar product is formed from ethylene dichloride and sodium disulfide, and when this is heated with sulfur combination occurs to give a rubbery material. The structure postulated on this evidence is: $-C_2H_4-S(=S)-S(=S)-C_2H_4-$.

That the elasticity of rubber is not dependent upon the presence of double bonds is demonstrated particularly strikingly by the elasticity of the **polybutene rubbers** (1940). These are derived essentially from isobutene, prepared commercially from isobutane containing various percentages of n-butane. The polymerization is catalyzed by aluminum chloride or

$$\underset{\text{Isobutane}}{\overset{\displaystyle CH_3}{\underset{\displaystyle CH_3}{H_3C-\overset{|}{\underset{|}{C}H}}}} \longrightarrow \underset{\text{Isobutene}}{\overset{\displaystyle CH_3}{\underset{\displaystyle CH_3}{H_2C=\overset{|}{\underset{|}{C}}}}} \longrightarrow \underset{\text{Polybutene}}{\overset{\displaystyle CH_3 \qquad CH_3}{\underset{\displaystyle CH_3 \qquad CH_3}{\cdots CH_2-\overset{|}{\underset{|}{C}}-CH_2-\overset{|}{\underset{|}{C}}\cdots}}}$$

boron fluoride and is rapid. The polymer is obtained in a wide range of molecular weights depending on the temperature of polymerization. At $-10°$, the molecular weight (viscosity method) is 10,000; at $-95°$, it is 250,000. The latter polymer exhibits a high degree of elasticity. The polybutenes cannot be vulcanized, but they are useful because they are chemically inert. They are added to rubber to improve resistance to ozone and acids, and to motor oils, greases, and lubricants to increase the viscosity. The material is sold in this country under the trade name of Vistanex or Polybutene and in Germany as Oppanol.

Development of **Butyl rubber** is a result of attempts to vulcanize the polybutenes. Since a certain amount of unsaturation is necessary, the possibility of introducing the double bonds in a copolymer component was investigated. This synthetic rubber is a copolymer of isobutene and isoprene, differing from Buna S in that the amount of diolefin is relatively small. Only an amount of unsaturation necessary for curing is provided, and the chemical inertness of the polybutenes is regained after cure. A typical formula for vulcanization includes zinc oxide (5%), stearic acid (3%), sulfur (1.5%), and accelerator (1%). The vulcanizates show good resistance to aging and chemical action; the tensile strength and elongation are high. Reinforcement with carbon black improves abrasion and cutting resistance, and also toughness. The largest commercial use is for inner tubes, since this rubber provides a very efficacious barrier to passage of gases.

Mechanism of Polymerization. — Addition polymerization of olefins and dienes is a typical chain reaction. Thus lower species such as trimers and tetramers have never been detected and, indeed, are incapable of polymerization. At intermediate stages monomer is still present together with polymers comparable in size to those present in the final stages. Evidently the growing polymer chain is formed by consecutive addition of monomer units. Moreover, polymerization of the monomer is strongly catalyzed by free radicals, for example, the radicals formed on decomposition of benzoyl peroxide:

$$C_6H_5COO—OOCC_6H_5 \rightarrow C_6H_5COO\cdot \rightarrow C_6H_5\cdot \rightarrow C_6H_5—C_6H_5 + C_6H_5COOC_6H_5 + C_6H_5COOH$$

The chain reaction proceeds by the stages of initiation, propagation, and termination. The first involves reaction of a free radical $(A\cdot)$ with a monomer to give a new radical, which grows by successive addition of monomer. The chain is terminated when two chain radicals react with each other (a) or by disproportionation (b).

Initiation $\qquad\qquad A\cdot + CH_2{=}CHR \rightarrow A\overset{\cdot}{C}H_2CHR$

Propagation

$$A\overset{\cdot}{C}H_2CHR + CH_2{=}CHR \rightarrow A\underset{\underset{R}{|}}{C}H_2CH\overset{\cdot}{C}H_2CHR \xrightarrow{\ CH_2{=}CHR\ } A\underset{\underset{R}{|}}{C}H_2CH\underset{\underset{R}{|}}{C}H_2CH\overset{\cdot}{C}H_2CHR$$

Termination

(a) $\quad A(CH_2CHR)_m\overset{\cdot}{C}H_2CHR + \overset{\cdot}{R}CHCH_2(CHRCH_2)_nA \rightarrow$

$$A(CH_2CHR)_mCH_2CH(R)—CH(R)CH_2(CHRCH_2)_nA$$

(b) $\quad 2A(CH_2CHR)_n\overset{\cdot}{C}H_2CHR \rightarrow A(CH_2CHR)_nCH_2CH_2R + A(CH_2CHR)_nCH{=}CHR$

Proof that the initiator is actually incorporated into the final polymer has been obtained in several instances by use of radicals containing an identifying label such as halogen. The mode of addition of radicals to unsymmetrical dienes shown in the formulation leads to head-to-tail polymers, whereas addition in the alternative direction, for example to give $ACH(R)\overset{\cdot}{C}H_2$ in the first step, would give a head-to-head arrangement. Actually all vinyl polymers investigated are predominantly of the head-to-tail type.

The reaction of a radical initiator with a 1,3-diene gives a resonance-stabilized radical, which on addition of another monomer unit can give rise to a product of either 1,4- or 1,2-addition. In general the 1,4-unit pre-

$$R\cdot + CH_2{=}CHCH{=}CH_2 \rightarrow R\overset{\cdot}{C}H_2CH{=}CHCH_2 \leftrightarrow RCH_2CHCH{=}CH_2$$

with $CH_2{=}CHCH{=}CH_2$ leading down to:

$$RCH_2CH{=}CHCH_2CH_2CH{=}\overset{\cdot}{C}HCH_2 \qquad R\overset{\cdot}{C}H_2CHCH_2CH{=}CHCH_2$$

$$\underset{CH{=}CH_2}{|}$$

dominates in polybutadienes. Both *cis* and *trans* forms are invariably present in synthetic polymers. That unsymmetrical dienes of the types of both isoprene and chloroprene undergo head-to-tail polymerization is attributable to electron displacements with partial charge separation. The electron-repelling and electron-attracting groups produce polarization in

$$
\begin{array}{cc}
\overset{\displaystyle CH_3}{\underset{\displaystyle \updownarrow}{CH_2{=}C{-}CH{=}CH_2}} & \overset{\displaystyle Cl}{\underset{\displaystyle \updownarrow}{CH_2{=}C{-}CH{=}CH_2}} \\
\underset{\text{I} \qquad\qquad\qquad 4}{\overset{\displaystyle CH_3}{\overset{-}{CH_2}{-}C{=}CH{-}\overset{+}{CH_2}}} & \underset{\text{I} \qquad\qquad\qquad 4}{\overset{\displaystyle Cl}{\overset{+}{CH_2}{-}C{=}CH{-}\overset{-}{CH_2}}}
\end{array}
$$

opposite directions, but in each case attraction between incipient poles of opposite sign leads to a C_1–C_4-orientation.

Polymerization is also promoted by sodium and other reagents. Typical Friedel-Crafts catalysts are very effective: aluminum chloride, boron fluoride, stannic chloride. In this case the initiation step involves formation of a carbonium ion, usually by transfer of a proton; propagation proceeds as in the peroxide-induced polymerization. The termination reaction then involves loss of a proton with production of an unsaturated terminal unit. Such units have indeed been detected by ultraviolet absorption spectroscopy.

$$
CH_2{=}CHR \xrightarrow{H^+} CH_3\overset{+}{C}HR \xrightarrow{CH_2{=}CHR} CH_3CH\underset{R}{CH_2}\overset{+}{\underset{R}{C}H} \xrightarrow{n\ CH_2{=}CHR}
$$

$$
CH_3CH\underset{R}{(CH_2}\underset{R}{CH)_n}CH_2\overset{+}{\underset{R}{C}H} \xrightarrow{-H^+} CH_3CH\underset{R}{(CH_2}\underset{R}{CH)_n}CH{=}\underset{R}{CH}
$$

SYNTHETIC FIBERS

The natural textile fibers cotton and linen are cellulosic products of plant biosynthesis, and wool is a protein resulting from animal biosynthesis. Silk fiber, however, is formed in a process that can be simulated artificially. The silkworm, which exists on a diet consisting very largely of cellulose from mulberry leaves, produces a viscous solution of the protein fibroin. This protein solution is secreted from two large glands that communicate by ducts with tiny orifices known as spinnerets located near the lip. After drops are attached to an object, the silkworm draws threads by moving its head and forefeet. The two filaments are cemented by a sticky protein known as sericin, or silk glue. Artificial silks and synthetic fibers are made from cellulose or from synthetic polymers by conversion to derivatives that can be brought into solution and so formed into fibers by passage through the capillary orifices of a mechanical spinning device known as a spinerette into a coagulating bath. The fibers prepared in this way from cellulose are known as rayons.

Cellulose Nitrate (Nitrocellulose) Process. — The discovery of the nitrates of cellulose, some of which, in contrast with cellulose, are soluble in organic solvents, was soon followed by a patent (1855) for the manufacture of artificial threads from nitrated cellulose derived from mulberry twigs. The threads were drawn originally from the solution with a needle; later filaments for electric lamps were prepared by squeezing an alcohol–ether solution of cellulose nitrate (collodion) through fine orifices. The nitrocellulose process for making rayon was established commercially by Count Hilaire de Chardonnet, who had studied the diseases of the silkworm as a student of Pasteur and who had later worked for the French government on guncotton.

Fully nitrated cellulose, or guncotton, was first prepared in 1846 by Schönbein. The nitration is a sensitive equilibrium reaction, and by adjustment of the conditions the nitrate content of the product can be varied considerably. Sulfuric acid is used in relatively large amounts as catalyst.

$$[C_6H_7O_2(OH)_3]_n \xrightleftharpoons{HNO_3,\ H_2SO_4} [C_6H_7O_2(ONO_2)_3]_n + 3nH_2O$$
$$\text{Cellulose trinitrate}$$

The temperature must be carefully controlled; at elevated temperatures considerable depolymerization occurs. Guncotton has a nitrogen content of 12.2–13.8% and thus corresponds nearly to cellulose trinitrate, for which the theoretical nitrogen content is 14.16%. Less highly nitrated material containing 10.5–12% nitrogen and corresponding approximately to a dinitrate (11.13% nitrogen) is known as pyroxylin and is the intermediate in the Chardonnet process. X-ray studies indicate that the nitro groups are probably distributed statistically along the chains.

Collodion solution, prepared by dissolving pyroxylin in alcohol–ether, is filtered several times, then forced through a spinnerette; the solvents are evaporated by warm air. Since cellulose nitrate is flammable and hence unsatisfactory for a fiber, the nitrate groups are removed by treatment with sodium or ammonium hydrosulfide. The denitrated thread resembles silk, but the process has never been widely used in this country and was discontinued in 1934.

Cuprammonium Process. — The cuprammonium process (1890) utilizes the solubility of cellulose in an ammoniacal solution of copper hydroxide (Schweitzer's reagent). The filtered solution is forced through the orifices of the spinnerette into a stream of water, which stretches the plastic filaments, and these are then passed through a dilute solution of sulfuric acid, which destroys the cuprammonium complex and precipitates cellulose. By this stretch spinning process filaments are produced that are at least twice as fine as those of silk.

Viscose Process. — This process (1892) is based on the reaction of carbon disulfide with the sodium salt of cellulose to yield a xanthate, which forms a viscous colloidal solution in dilute aqueous alkali. The xanthate solution must be ripened for some time before use. Certain complex reactions occur during this period, as evidenced by a change in the ratio of

$$[C_6H_{10}O_5]_n \xrightarrow{\text{NaOH}} \underset{\text{Alkali cellulose}}{[(C_6H_{10}O_5)_2 \cdot NaOH]_n} \xrightarrow{CS_2} \underset{\text{Cellulose xanthate}}{\left[(C_6H_9O_4)_2 \cdot OH \cdot OC \underset{SNa}{\overset{S}{\diagup}} \right]_n} + \; n\,H_2O$$

sodium and sulfur to cellulose. Ripening is followed by introduction of enough sodium chloride solution to initiate coagulation of the viscose. After filtration filaments are extruded in the usual manner into a solution containing dilute sulfuric acid and various salts. The acid regenerates the cellulose with precipitation of some free sulfur, which is removed by treatment with sodium sulfide; the rayon yarn is then bleached and dried. Purified wood pulp containing 80–90% cellulose can be utilized in this process, since the hemicelluloses (mainly pentosans) are soluble in alkali and are removed in the production of alkali cellulose.

About 65% of the total rayon produced in the United States is made by this process. If the viscose sirup is forced through long narrow slits, the regenerated cellulose is obtained in sheets. After washing and bleaching the films are passed through a solution of glycerol, which imparts softness and pliability. The film (Cellophane) is widely used as a protective and artistic wrapping material.

Acetate Process. — This process involves conversion of cellulose into a solvent-soluble acetyl derivative permitting formation of fiber and removal of solvent by evaporation. The fiber thus consists of cellulose acetate rather than regenerated cellulose, and this has certain advantages. The material used in manufacture corresponds approximately to a diacetate and is made by partial hydrolysis of the triacetate. The triacetate itself is not suitable because it is soluble only in expensive chlorinated solvents and even so gives threads and films that are too brittle. The discovery that the diacetate formed on partial hydrolysis is soluble in acetone and gives a rayon of satisfactory textile properties was empirical (1903). It has not been found possible to produce diacetate of satisfactory properties by partial acetylation, probably because material produced in this way is different in structural type from that formed on hydrolysis. In the product of acetylation the most highly hindered hydroxyl groups are free, whereas in the product of partial hydrolysis the hindered groups are acetylated.

The formation of the triacetate requires pretreatment with acetic acid and sulfuric acid catalyst to effect swelling, and then treatment with acetic anhydride and more catalyst. After the product is fully acetylated a certain amount of water is added and hydrolysis is allowed to proceed to the desired extent, when the diacetate is precipitated by drowning with water. Since individual preparations vary somewhat in acetyl content, batches are blended appropriately before spinning. Acetone is used as the solvent for spinning and the filaments are dried by extrusion into warm air and twisted to threads. The mineral acid used to catalyze both acetylation and hydrolysis catalyzes also hydrolytic cleavage of cellulose with the result that commercial cellulose acetate (di-) contains only 200–300 glucose units per chain.

It is thus more degraded than pyroxylin, and fibers and films are a little weaker and more brittle. Acetate rayon is also more expensive than the nitrate, because acetic anhydride is costly and because the acetic acid has to be diluted so extensively that recovery of solvent is a major operation. However the cost is partially compensated by a 40% gain in weight. Furthermore, acetate rayon has certain advantages over regenerated cellulose rayon and its production has steadily increased. The material absorbs only half as much moisture and loses a smaller percentage of its strength when wetted. Acetate fibers are more extensible and hence less susceptible to wrinkling. The specific gravity (1.3) is close to that of silk (1.36), whereas that of viscose rayon is higher (1.5).

Fibers Derived from Proteins (Azlons). — Use of modified proteins as fibers was initiated in Italy (Lanital, 1936). A water solution of a globular protein together with various salts is forced through a die; and the extended filaments, which are weak and brittle, are then hardened by treatment with formaldehyde, which reacts with free amino groups. Hardening improves flexibility and resistance to water, and further increase in stability can be accomplished by partial acetylation. Since the final stretched fibers have an X-ray pattern similar to that of stretched fibrous proteins, conversion of the globular-type structure into the long-chain structure characteristic of fibrous proteins (denaturation) is involved. Only two protein fibers are now made commercially. Vicara is made from zein, the protein of corn; the fiber Caslen is made from casein. These proteinoid fibers are similar to wool and can be blended with wool.

Nylon. — In the preceding materials, the long-chain structure essential for fiber formation is of natural origin. Nylon is the first synthetic fiber to be made chemically by condensation of small units. Nylon was produced commercially in 1940, only five years after the polymer was obtained by Carothers. In 1930 Carothers began his brilliant studies of polymerization that eventually led not only to a synthetic silk but to the synthetic rubber neoprene. He first studied the polymer obtained by condensing dibasic acids and glycols; later he prepared the polyamide of ϵ-aminocaproic acid, $NH_2(CH_2)_5COOH$. Both the polyesters and the polyamides obtained by usual heat treatment were of relatively low molecular weight (2500–5000), but after heating (12 days) in a molecular still at elevated temperatures (200°), superpolymers were obtained of much higher molecular weight

$$\underset{\text{HO}}{}\overset{\text{O}}{\underset{\|}{C}}(CH_2)_4\overset{\text{O}}{\underset{\|}{C}}-OH \;+\; H_2N(CH_2)_6NH_2 \;\xrightarrow{-H_2O}$$

$$\cdots\overset{\text{O}}{\underset{\|}{C}}(CH_2)_4\overset{\text{O}}{\underset{\|}{C}}NH(CH_2)_6NH\overset{\text{O}}{\underset{\|}{C}}(CH_2)_4\overset{\text{O}}{\underset{\|}{C}}NH(CH_2)_6NH\overset{\text{O}}{\underset{\|}{C}}(CH_2)_4\overset{\text{O}}{\underset{\|}{C}}NH(CH_2)_6NH\cdots$$

(10,000–25,000). Filaments drawn from the molten polymers could be further extended on cooling. Eventually in 1935 a supermolecule suitable for use as a textile was synthesized from hexamethylenediamine and adipic acid (called polymer 6–6, since both substituents contain 6 carbon atoms). The polymer, with its multiple peptide linkages, bears a marked structural resemblance to proteins.

Originally the starting material for both components was benzene, which can be converted through cyclohexanol into cyclohexanone and then on oxidation into adipic acid, a part of which is converted into the desired

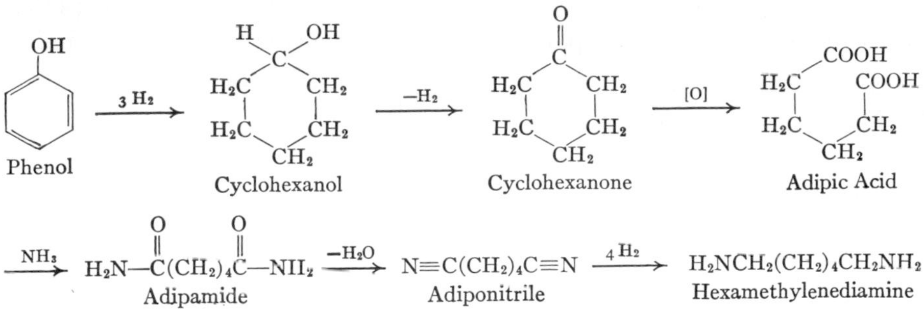

Phenol   Cyclohexanol   Cyclohexanone   Adipic Acid

$$\xrightarrow{NH_3} \quad H_2N{-}\overset{\overset{O}{\|}}{C}(CH_2)_4\overset{\overset{O}{\|}}{C}{-}NH_2 \xrightarrow{-H_2O} N{\equiv}C(CH_2)_4C{\equiv}N \xrightarrow{4\,H_2} H_2NCH_2(CH_2)_4CH_2NH_2$$

Adipamide   Adiponitrile   Hexamethylenediamine

diamine. Adipic acid is now made also from cyclohexane, and furfural is an alternative starting material for the diamine. The condensation polymerization is effected in an autoclave. The polymer melts at about 263°, and filaments are obtained by extruding the molten material (blanketed with an inert gas to prevent oxidation) through fine orifices of spinnerettes. The filaments are frozen in a current of air. Subsequent stretching increases the tensile strength and elasticity. A considerable degree of orientation results from stretching, for the X-ray pattern of the final fiber is similar to that of natural silk fibers. Nylon is higher in tensile strength than any natural fiber, but silk and wool recover more rapidly from mild deformation. Nylon is tough and of good chemical stability and excels in abrasion resistance. Large monofilaments suitable for bristles are also prepared.

Perlon L or 6-Nylon. — A polyamide closely related to Nylon, known as Perlon L (Germany) or as 6-Nylon (U. S. A.), is prepared by prolonged heating of ε-aminocaprolactam at 260–270°. The monomer is prepared by

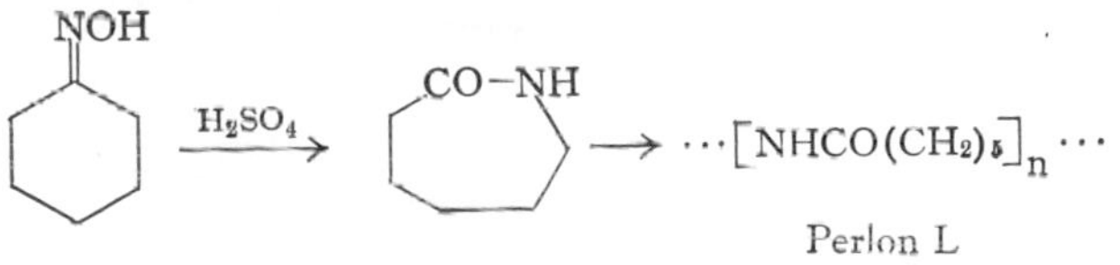

Perlon L

Beckmann rearrangement of cyclohexanone oxime. The fiber is practically identical to Nylon in properties.

Polyester Fiber (Terylene; Dacron). — This fiber, introduced by Imperial Chemical Industries (English name: Terylene), is made from terephthalic acid and ethylene glycol either by direct esterification or by catalyzed ester-interchange. The fiber has high tensile strength and resiliency

$$n\ HO_2CC_6H_4CO_2H + n\ HOCH_2CH_2OH \xrightarrow{-H_2O} \cdots (COC_6H_4CO{-}OCH_2CH_2O)_n\cdots$$

and is surprisingly stable to fairly severe hydrolytic treatment.   Garments made of it are markedly crease-resistant.

Vinyl Fibers. — Polymers derived from vinyl monomers, particularly vinyl chloride and vinyl acetate, were initially developed as plastics and resins, but later the technique of emulsion copolymerization was found applicable to the production of a variety of vinyl copolymers useful as fibers. The first developed was Vinyon (1939), a copolymer of vinyl chloride (88%) and vinyl acetate (12%; preparation from acetylene, p. 89).   The spinning

$$CH_2{=}CHCl \ + \ CH_2{=}CHOCOCH_3 \ \longrightarrow \ \left[\cdots CH_2CH{-}CH_2CH{-}CH_2CH\cdots \atop \quad\quad\quad Cl \quad\quad\quad OCOCH_3 \ Cl \right]_n$$

Vinyl chloride   Vinyl acetate

Vinyon

dope is a solution of the fluffy polymer (mol. wt. about 20,000) in acetone. Vinyon is highly resistant to chemicals, but the low softening point of 65° limits its usefulness.

Saran (1940) is a copolymer of vinylidene chloride (85%) and vinyl chloride (15%).   The molecular weight (20,000) is comparable to that of Vinyon but the softening point is considerably higher (120–140°).   Fibers

$$CH_2{=}CH_2 \ \xrightarrow{\ Cl_2\ } \ CH_2ClCH_2Cl \ \xrightarrow{\ Cl_2\ } \ CH_2ClCHCl_2$$

$$\downarrow {-}HCl \qquad\qquad\qquad\qquad\qquad\qquad \downarrow {-}HCl$$

$$CH_2{=}CHCl \qquad\qquad\qquad\qquad\qquad CH_2{=}CCl_2$$

Vinyl chloride   Vinylidene chloride

$$\cdots[CH_2CHCl{-}CH_2CCl_2]_n\cdots$$

Saran

suitable for dress material are made by melt spinning, immersion in hot water to prevent crystallization, and mechanical stretching.   Saran has certain uses as a plastic.   The flexible tubing made for laboratory use is resistant to acids, solvents, and alkalis other than ammonium hydroxide.

Orlon fiber (U. S. A., 1950) is made from polyacrylonitrile.   The polymer was known for many years but not considered as a fiber material because of lack of solubility in common solvents.   It is, however, soluble

$$2n \ CH_2{=}CHCN \ \longrightarrow \ \cdots\left[CH_2CH{-}CH_2CH \atop \quad CN \quad\quad CN \right]_n\cdots$$

in special solvents: dimethylformamide, dimethylmethoxyacetamide, nitro-phenols.   Solutions are spun into multifilaments in a dry-spinning process. The fiber has unusual dimension stability in the dry and wet states and excellent resistance to sunlight, outdoor exposure, microorganisms, acids, and solvents.   It can be made to resemble either silk or wool; the textiles feel warm to the hand.   **Dynel** (originally Vinyon N) is a copolymer of acrylonitrile and vinyl chloride.   **Acrilan** is a polyacrylonitrile modified with vinyl acetate.

Polyethylene, $\cdots(CH_2{-}CH_2)_n\cdots$. — Polymerization of liquid ethylene at high temperatures and pressures gives a resin which has a low softening point ($110°$) and can be melt spun or molded. The plastic is tough and flexible and possesses excellent electrical insulation characteristics and high water resistance. Polyethylene is unique in having a low specific gravity (0.92).

PLASTICS AND RESINS

Resins are amorphous organic solids or semisolids which usually have a typical luster and are often transparent or translucent. Natural resins of vegetable origin occur as exudates from pine or fir trees, either alone or as fluid mixtures (oleoresins) with turpentine or other essential oil; examples are pine oleoresin and rosin, derived from it by steam distillation of the essential oil; copal; damar; sandarac. Shellac, a common resin of non-vegetable origin, is a substance secreted by the lac insect. The major uses are in finishing compositions, varnishes, low grade soaps, paints, inks, and linoleums. The synthetic resins made available by modern research have found much wider application.

In the true meaning of the terms a plastic is a substance capable of being molded, whereas a resin lacks this property. Typical plastics on heating become soft enough to be formed under pressure without affording mobile melts, whereas resins on heating give melts of relatively low viscosity. Plastics usually have much higher molecular weights than resins. However, the differentiation is not too distinct and the terms plastic and resin are to a certain extent used interchangeably. In industrial terminology the unfabricated material is sometimes called a resin and the fabricated article a plastic.

Cellulose Nitrate Plastic. — The oldest synthetic plastic is made from pyroxylin, or cellulose dinitrate (12% N). Pyroxylin itself is brittle and cannot be molded, but camphor incorporated in the material acts as an efficient plasticizer. Parkes, an Englishman, reported the discovery in 1865, and in 1869 the American inventor Hyatt developed an improved camphor-plasticized pyroxylin in a prize competition for a substitute for ivory for billiard balls and coined the name celluloid.

Celluloid, now marketed under various trade names, is manufactured by first gelatinizing pyroxylin with camphor ($20{-}50\%$) and ethanol; neither substance alone leads to sufficient softening of the mass. The alcohol promotes plastic flow during molding and is removed by evaporation in a curing operation. The thermoplastic mixture is molded into desired shapes by application of heat ($100°$) and pressure (compression molding). Rods, tubes, or strips are produced by extrusion molding, in which the plastic is fed into a heated cylinder and extruded through fairly long nozzles, when it cools and hardens. The molded article must then be cured by heating at a slightly elevated temperature until the solvent alcohol, but not the non-volatile plasticizer, has been expelled. Finished celluloid sheeting, rods, or other stock lends itself admirably to the construction of laboratory devices, models, etc. It is easily cut or machined on a lathe, and pieces can be cemented firmly by immersion in acetone for a few seconds followed by application of pressure. A cylinder can be made by softening a thick sheet of celluloid under hot water, forming it on a mandrel, and butt-welding the edges together after moistening them with acetone. A thick cement can be made by dissolving scrap celluloid in acetone or in a mixture of ethyl and butyl acetate.

Celluloid finds many uses in the manufacture of spectacle frames, containers, piano keys, and photographic film. It is light in weight (sp. gr. 1.35–1.40), resistant to water and to hydrocarbon oils, and possesses considerable toughness, but it has the disadvantage of being highly flammable and of giving rise to toxic combustion gases. Pigments can be incorporated into the colorless transparent plastic to simulate tortoise shell, amber, malachite, etc.

Plasticizers are used also to increase the flexibility of cellulose nitrate film. Camphor is unsuitable because it volatilizes in the drying process sufficiently to give a dull finish. Dibutyl phthalate and tricresyl phosphate, $(CH_3C_6H_4O)_3PO$, are widely used as plasticizers.

Cellulose nitrate lacquers were introduced as quick-drying finishes for automobiles in 1924. Pyroxylin itself is unsuitable as a coating material because the viscosity of solutions in organic solvents is so high that a solution thin enough to be spread over a surface leaves an inadequate film on evaporation of the solvent. The material can be modified in the desired direction, however, by partial depolymerization, effected by heating pyroxylin under pressure in contact with very dilute acid. The modified pyroxylin, containing molecules of 100–600 glucose units as compared to original molecules of 1000–1200 units, is more soluble than before and gives solutions of adequate concentration that are thin enough to flow freely when applied with a brush or as a spray. Finishes of the modified pyroxylin type dry as the result of evaporation of the organic solvent and do not require for setting the slow process of oxidation characteristic of the oleoresin drying oils.

The lacquer solvent must not be too volatile, for the cooling effect of rapid evaporation may produce blushing. Butyl acetate (b.p. 127°) is a good solvent for modified pyroxylin and evaporates at a satisfactory rate, and fortunately became available at a time when a rapid expansion of the automobile industry created a special demand for quick-drying lacquer paints. The *n*-butanol required for producing the ester is obtained abundantly and cheaply by the Weizmann fermentation process (p. 121), which had been developed originally with the idea of employing the alcohol as a starting material for the synthesis of rubber but which had been operated during World War I as a source of the second product, acetone, required for smokeless powder. After the war, the same process was operated for supplying butyl acetate to the lacquer industry.

Cellulose Acetate. The cellulose acetate (di-) used for making textile fibers is less suited to compression molding than cellulose nitrate because an uneconomical chilling period is required. On the other hand, the acetate can be subjected to heat and pressure without hazard for longer periods than the nitrate, and these properties led to the development of the technique of injection molding. The acetate, plasticized with dimethyl or diethyl phthalate or with triphenyl phosphate, is softened by heat (135–170°) and forced under pressure (2000–5000 lbs./sq. in.) through branching channels into molds, where the plastic is cooled. Injection molding has the advantage over compression molding of much greater speed; two discharges per minute is not unusual. Some 200 parts used in an automobile are made from acetate.

Cellulose Mixed Esters. — As the molecular weight of the acid used for esterification of cellulose increases, the solubility of the ester in organic solvents increases, and the tensile strength and softening temperature decrease. An advantageous combination of properties can be obtained through the mixed esters, for example cellulose acetate propionate and cellulose acetate butyrate. The esterifications can be carried out simultaneously or in two steps. Cellulose acetate butyrate has replaced the acetate for uses in which increased resistance to weathering and warping is desirable, for instance in airplane dopes.

Cellulose Ethers. — The cellulose derivatives most stable to alkali and to acid are the ethers, of which three are made commercially, namely, the methyl (Methocel, 1939), ethyl (Ethocel, 1935), and benzyl ethers. The ethers are less stable to light than the esters. They are prepared by treating alkali cellulose with the appropriate alkyl chloride. Ethers that contain less than one alkyl group for each glucose unit are soluble in alkali and are used as sizes and finishing agents for textiles. The more completely alkylated celluloses are soluble in a variety of organic solvents, and are readily compatible with many resins and plasticizers; they are used for the fabrication of films and molded or extruded objects.

Casein Plastic. — Casein plastic was manufactured in Europe in 1897, before the development of any of the cellulose derivatives other than pyroxylin. Casein is the principal protein of cow's milk, and is prepared commercially by precipitation with acid or by coagulation with the enzyme rennin from rennet (membrane of the cow's stomach), which is capable of clotting 400,000 times its weight of casein. In the usual manufacturing process casein granules containing approximately 10% of water are masticated under the influence of heat and pressure with plasticizers (glycerol, tricresyl phosphate) and dyes, and finally extruded as rods, sheets, or tubes. These are then hardened in 4% formaldehyde solutions at pH 4–7 and at 18-24°. The hardening step is the most important and also the most expensive part of the entire process. The thickness of the mass governs the length of time required, which in any case is never less than one week and may be as long as six months. After hardening, the material is dried to a moisture content of 8–12%, an operation that is likewise slow.

Hardened casein is far less hygroscopic than untreated protein, but is subject to some warping and cracking under extreme variations in relative humidity. The chief use in this country is for buttons and buckles; about four thousand tons are made annually. In the most economical process for making buttons, the casein is mixed with alum before extrusion and this partially hardened product is turned in automatic screw machines to form the desired shape. The final formaldehyde hardening of the small objects requires only a few days; scrap material from the cutting operation is not wasted, for it is still unhardened and thermoplastic, and hence can be reprocessed.

Polytetrafluoroethylene (Teflon). — Tetrafluoroethylene is made by pyrolysis of chlorodifluoromethane, and on emulsion polymerization catalyzed by oxygen it affords a plastic of unusual properties (du Pont). Teflon possesses unrivaled resistance to solvents and to boiling acids, even aqua regia, and is stable at temperatures up to about 325°. A mixture with

$$2CHClF_2 \xrightarrow{600-750°} CF_2{=}CF_2 + 2HCl$$

$$nCF_2{=}CF_2 \rightarrow -(CF_2CF_2)_n- \quad (n = about\ 1000)$$

graphite is cold-pressed into special-service gaskets by powder metallurgy technique. Tape cut from a block with a microtome is used for wrapping wire (excellent electrical insulation).

Phenol-Formaldehyde Resins. — Cellulose derivatives are examples of resins of the thermoplastic group, which are rigid at normal temperatures but which can be deformed or remolded by heat and pressure. A second broad group of plastics includes thermosetting materials, which are fusible at some stage of their production but become permanently hard and infusible under the influence of heat and pressure. In the first type the change from fluid to solid is reversible; in the second, irreversible. Phenol-formaldehyde resins were the first thermosetting resins produced commercially.

Baeyer observed in 1872 that the reaction between various phenols and aldehydes leads to resinous masses, but was interested chiefly in the crystalline products initially formed. A technical application of the reaction was worked out later by Baekeland,[7] who modified the procedure in various ways and patented processes for production of the useful resin Bakelite (1909). Baekeland recognized three distinct stages in the reaction of phenol with formaldehyde in alkaline solution. The initial product, Bakelite A, a liquid or semisolid, is converted by continued heating into an intermediate, Bakelite B, a relatively insoluble, fusible solid; this, when subjected to heat and pressure, is converted into Bakelite C, an insoluble and infusible resin. Acid conditions favor production of a noncurable type of resin known as Novolak, with consumption of a high percentage of phenol. In an alkaline medium more formaldehyde is utilized, even though an excess of phenol is employed, and the product is of the Bakelite rather than Novolak type. However, if phenol is replaced by a substituted phenol containing only one

---

[7] Leo Hendrik Baekeland, 1863–1944; b. Ghent, Belg.; Ph.D. Ghent; Univ. Brussels, Columbia Univ.: president, Gen. Bakelite Corp.; *Chem. Eng. News*, **23**, 228 (1945)

free active position, for example 2,4-xylenol, only a noncurable Novolak type is obtained. If the phenol has two free active positions, for example o- or p-cresol, partially or slowly curable resins are obtained. Apparently three reactive positions must be available for formation of truly thermosetting resins.

Isolation of a pure crystalline compound from the condensation of phenol with formaldehyde was accomplished in 1894. The product, isolated earlier (1843) from a natural source, is saligenin, or o-hydroxybenzyl alcohol. Formation of the corresponding p-hydroxybenzyl alcohol is favored in an alkaline medium. Saligenin is easily dehydrated by acid catalysts or by

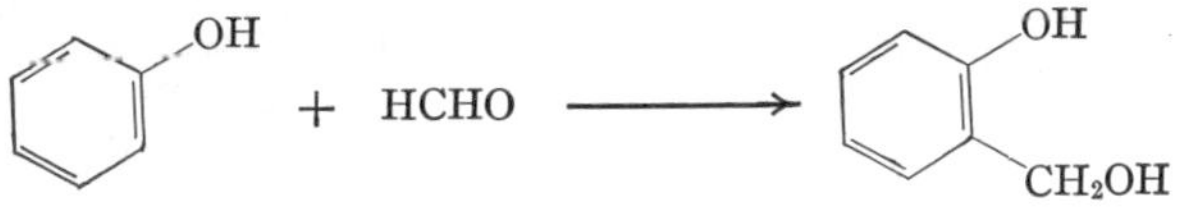

Saligenin

heat, with formation of a resinous product. Evidence has been obtained that the following dialcohols are formed also in the alkaline condensation:

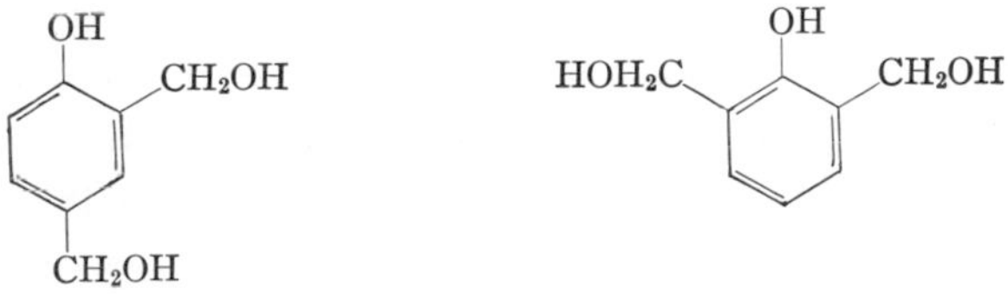

Compounds of the dihydroxydiarylmethane type have been isolated in acidic condensations; this mode of combination of phenols and aldehydes has many applications and is known as the Baeyer reaction:

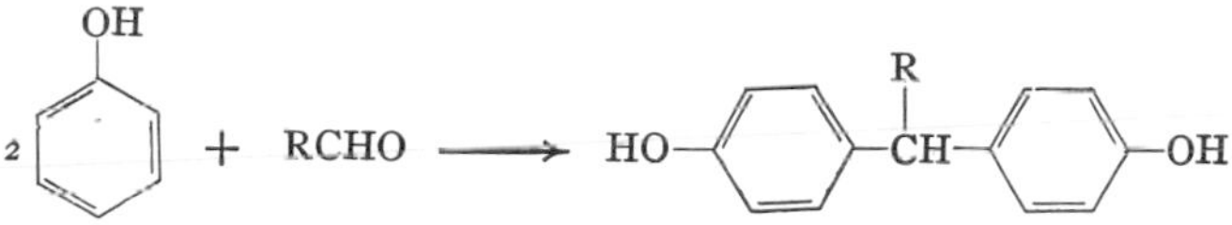

Two diarylmethanes have been isolated as intermediates in the Novolak type of condensation, namely 4,4'-dihydroxydiphenylmethane (I) and

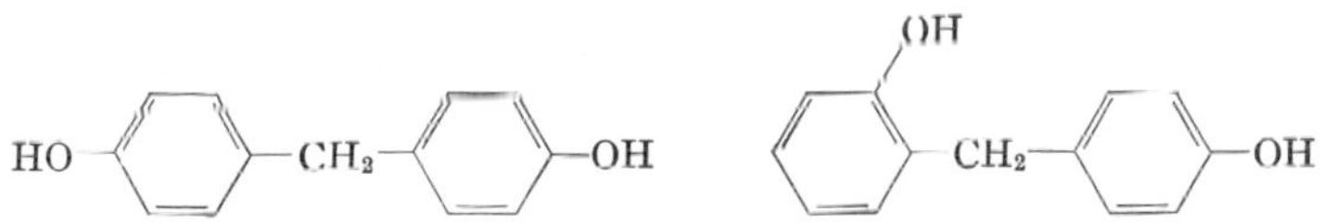

I

II

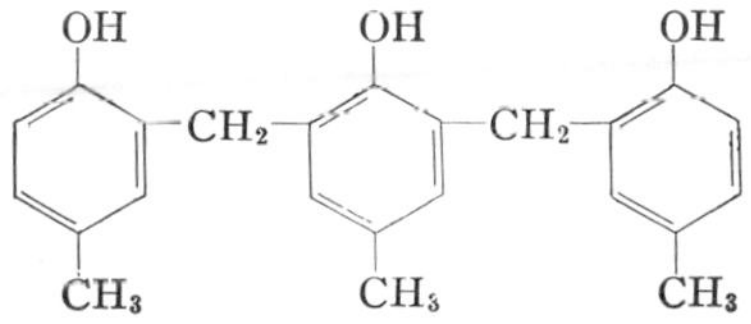

III

2,4'-dihydroxydiphenylmethane (II).   A reaction product containing three benzene nuclei (probable structure, III) has been obtained from the acid condensation of *p*-cresol.   Novolaks probably are mixtures of polynuclear compounds of the diphenylmethane type of structure.

Although the alkaline condensation is far more rapid than the acid reaction and the isolation of intermediates is more difficult, a few initial products have been identified.   Formulas IV and V represent the probable structure of intermediates from phenol and *o*-cresol, respectively.   In view

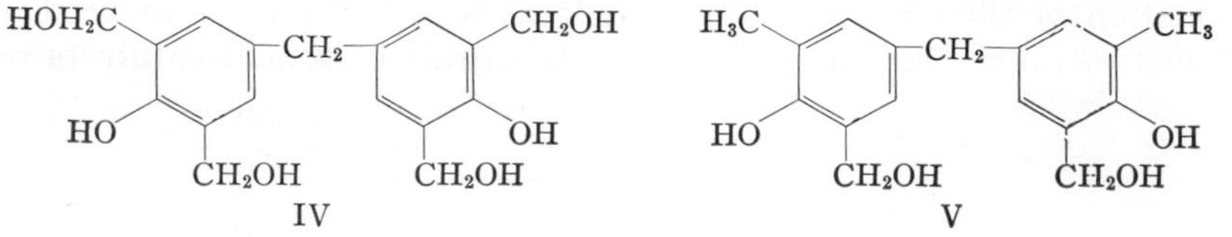

of this evidence and the fact that in commercial practice the ratio of form-aldehyde to phenol is usually 2.5–3:1, Bakelite A probably is similar in structure to Novolak but more highly substituted.   Such a multifunctional chain polymer could readily undergo condensation to a three-dimensional structure, which accounts for the physical characteristics of Bakelite C (sp. gr. 1.3).   Of several formulations that have been suggested for the polymerization, two that conform satisfactorily with the experimental evidence are shown in Chart 1.   The free phenolic groups postulated in both

CHART 1.   POSSIBLE PATHS OF POLYMERIZATION TO BAKELITE C

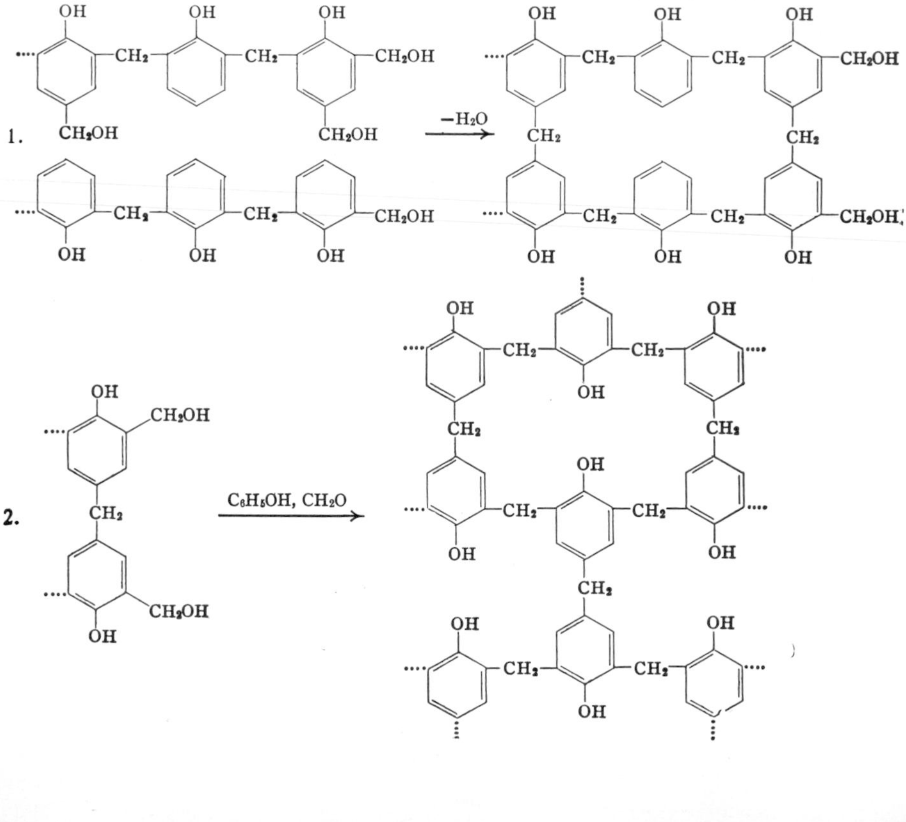

formulas are presumably responsible for the base-exchange properties of Bakelite resins. Since Bakelite C is completely insoluble in all solvents, determination of the molecular weight is not possible.

Bakelite was first developed for molding and is still used in this way in large amounts. The molding powder consists of the B-stage resin (40–50%), a filler to improve strength and shock resistance (35–50%), occasionally a plasticizer (5%), and small amounts of a lubricant and pigments. The powder is cured in a mold at 120–185° under a pressure of 2000 lbs. per sq. in. or more. In the standard one-stage process for the manufacture of resins for laminated materials and for lacquers, 1 mole of phenol and 1.5 moles of formaldehyde (usually 40% solution) and a basic catalyst are heated; after a few hours the mixture settles into two layers. After removal of the upper water layer, more water is eliminated by heating in vacuum. Then the sirup is poured into shallow pans to cool (B stage, soluble in alcohol). Molding powders are usually made by the two-stage process. A Novolak is first made using 1 mole of phenol and about 0.8 mole of formaldehyde in the presence of an acidic catalyst. The Novolak is mixed with fillers and 12–14% of hexamethylenetetramine, $(CH_2)_6N_4$, on heated rollers. The "hexa" acts both as a formaldehyde (methylene bridge) donor and as catalyst (ammonia is liberated). No water is produced when the mixture is heated, since Novolak contains no methylol groups. This dry process is often advantageous, for the presence of water in molded resins lowers the electrical insulating properties. If the presence of water is not undesirable, formalin and a basic catalyst can be employed in the second step.

An important modification is replacement of formaldehyde by furfural This aldehyde is produced on a large scale from oathulls (10% yield), obtained as a by-product in the manufacture of Quaker Oats. Furfural is reactive and resinifies readily in hot alkali. The largest commercial application is in the manufacture of a furfural-phenol molding resin. Curing is rapid at 175–190°, and moldings can be made with great accuracy.

The production of cast phenolic resins introduced in 1928 has increased substantially. The phenol (1 mole), formaldehyde (1.5–2.5 moles), and catalyst, usually sodium or potassium hydroxide, are heated, and the water that separates is removed. The hot liquid, after acidification with a weak acid (lactic acid), is vacuum distilled to a thick sirup, which is mixed with glycerol and then cast into molds and cured at 60–80° for three to fourteen days. Cast phenolics can be fashioned by standard machining operations, and are used mainly for fabrication of decorative articles.

Laminated sheets and tubes are made from Bakelite and paper, canvas, or fibers. Silent gears are often made of laminated canvas. Phenolic resins find use as adhesives for plywood. Phenol and formaldehyde are condensed in an alkaline medium, and after the water is separated the resin (type A) is impregnated on tissue paper 0.001 inch thick. The film is cut to size and slipped between veneers (8–10% water content); the whole is pressed (125–250 lbs. per sq. in.) at elevated temperatures for five to twenty minutes.

Ion-Exchange Resins. — A further important use of the insoluble phenol-formaldehyde resins was introduced in 1935, when it was noted that the constituent phenolic hydroxyl groups react with cations of salts: $-OH + NaCl \rightarrow -ONa + HCl$. Further developments have utilized synthetic resins capable of cation exchange by virtue of the groups $-SO_3H$, $-CH_2CO_2H$, and $-COOH$. The resin can be regenerated by treatment with dilute mineral acids. A further extension of the ion-exchange reaction consists in use of resins containing a basic group such as $-NH_2$ and $=NH$. These resins can absorb acids by formation of salts, $-NH_3Cl$ and $=NH_2Cl$. Efficient exchangers of this type are prepared by the condensation of formaldehyde with amines such as *m*-phenylenediamine and urea. These resins are regenerated by treatment with sodium carbonate or sodium hydroxide. The exchange resins were introduced for use in the purification of water. Thus water after passage over a cationic exchanger contains no salts, but free mineral acids and carbonic acid. The latter can be removed by degassing, the former by passage over an anionic exchanger. Further uses include removal of inorganic impurities from organic substances, neutralization of amine hydrochlorides, and separation of amino acids. Thus only the basic amino acids are absorbed on cationic exchangers containing carboxyl groups, and the acidic amino acids are absorbed on exchangers containing sulfonic acid groups.

Urea-Formaldehyde Resins. — Thermosetting molding powders are produced by the condensation of two moles of urea and three of formaldehyde (40% solution) in the presence of pyridine, ammonia, or hexamethylenetetramine. The sirupy intermediate condensation product is mixed with cellulose and a dye, and molded under pressure at elevated temperatures to a desired shape. The resins are also available in solutions suitable for laminating and for treating textiles. The production of urea resins is about one fourth the production of phenolic resins.

Two crystalline compounds, monomethylolurea and dimethylolurea, have been isolated from the reaction of urea with formaldehyde in an alkaline solution. In the presence of an acidic catalyst the initial product is

Monomethylolurea (m.p. 111°)   Dimethylolurea (m.p. 126°)

methyleneurea, which is regarded as either a ring compound or an azomethine, or an equilibrium mixture of the two. Dimethylolurea on being

Methyleneurea

melted is converted into the crystalline methylolmethyleneurea; a crystalline trimeric form of this substance has been isolated from the condensation of two moles of formaldehyde with one of urea in the presence of ammonia.

$$\underset{C=O}{\overset{NHCH_2OH}{\diagup}}\underset{}{\overset{NHCH_2OH}{\diagdown}} \quad \xrightarrow{-H_2O} \quad \underset{C=O}{\overset{N=CH_2}{\diagup}}\underset{}{\overset{NHCH_2OH}{\diagdown}}$$

Methylolmethyleneurea

$$3\,\underset{NH_2}{\overset{NH_2}{\diagup}}C=O \;+\; 6\,HCHO \quad \xrightarrow{OH^-} \quad$$

$$\begin{array}{c} CONHCH_2OH \\ | \\ N \\ H_2C \diagup \quad \diagdown CH_2 \\ HOCH_2NHCO-N \qquad N-CONHCH_2OH \\ \diagdown CH_2 \diagup \end{array}$$

Trimer

Polymerization can occur through mono- or dimethylolurea, or possibly through both, with formation of long chains. Originally it was considered that the two ends became joined during the curing process. This is now recognized as unlikely, and a better knowledge of the chemistry of Bakelite and other thermosetting resins indicates that the hard infusible state is associated with a three-dimensional structure. A formula based on further condensation of the cyclic trimer above is one possibility; another possible structure is built up from dimethylolurea or methylolmethyleneurea units.

Until 1937 urea resins were not used in paints and varnishes because they are soluble only in special solvents and even so do not give solutions of satisfactory stability. Modified resins suitable for films

$$\begin{array}{ccccc} & & \cdots N-CH_2 \cdots & & \\ & & | & & \\ & & C=O & & \\ \cdots N-CH_2-N-CH_2-N\cdots & & \\ | & & | & \\ C=O & & C=O & \\ \cdots N-CH_2-N-CH_2-N-CH_2-N\cdots & \\ | & & | & \\ C=O & & C=O & \\ \cdots N-CH_2-N-CH_2-N-CH_2-N\cdots & \\ | & & | & \\ C=O & & C=O & \\ \cdots N-CH_2-N-CH_2-N\cdots & & \\ \vdots & & & \end{array}$$

are prepared by condensing urea and formaldehyde in the presence of monohydric or complex polyhydric alcohols, obtained by the condensation of phthalic anhydride with varying amounts of ethylene glycol or glycerol and represented by the type formula HO—X—OH (I). The polyhydric alcohol presumably condenses with urea and formaldehyde to give an intermediate (II) similar to mono- or dimethylolurea that polymerizes by loss of water between successive molecules.

$$\underset{NH_2}{\overset{NH_2}{\diagup}}C=O \;+\; CH_2O \;+\; HO-X-OH \quad \longrightarrow \quad \underset{NHCH_2O\,H}{\overset{NHCH_1\,O-X-O\,H\;HO}{\diagup}}C=O \quad \longrightarrow \; Polymer$$

I   II

Melamine-Formaldehyde Resins. — The chemistry and use of the melamine resins are entirely similar to those of the urea resins. Although melamine was prepared in 1834 by Liebig, it became available commercially only in 1940. It is prepared usually by heating dicyandiamide under pressure. The mechanism is still obscure, though the tendency to form an unsaturated six-membered ring similar to that of benzene doubtless sup-

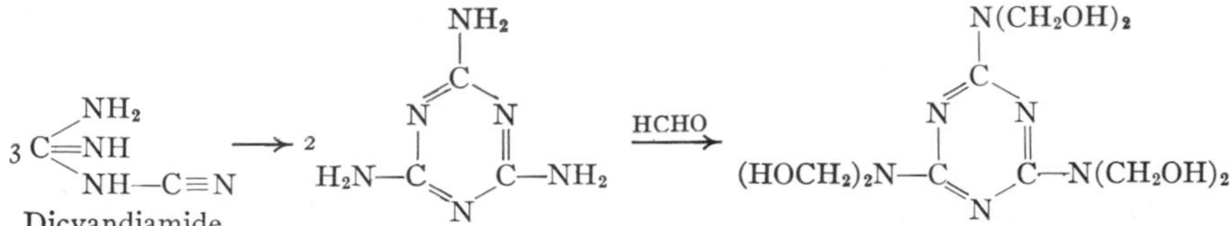

Dicyandiamide

Melamine
(2,4,6-triamino-1,3,5-triazine)

Hexamethylolmelamine

plies the driving force. Hexamethylol derivatives are obtained on treatment with formaldehyde, and such compounds are presumably the intermediates in the resinification process. Molding compositions are also available that are prepared by condensing formaldehyde with mixtures of melamine and phenol or urea.

Alkyd Resins. — Alkyd resins are formed by the condensation of polybasic acids or anhydrides with polyhydric alcohols (alcohol + acid = alkyd). Since the most common member of the group is a glycerol-phthalic acid polymer, the specific name glyptal is frequently conferred on the whole group. Development of these resins was slow until a relatively cheap method for the production of phthalic anhydride was developed (1918). Alkyd resins are used primarily as coating materials, the largest single outlet of synthetic resins, but are also valuable as cements and binders.

By varying the acid and alcohol both thermoplastic and thermosetting alkyd resins of a wide variety of types can be prepared. Investigation of the resinification process (Kienle[8]) has shown that if both the acid and the alcohol have only two functional groups, long-chain molecules are obtained (unless the primary product can form a 5- or 6-membered ring). For example, the product of the esterification of ethylene glycol and phthalic anhydride is a long-chain polymer (I) that cannot be converted to an infusible resin (gel) on heating.

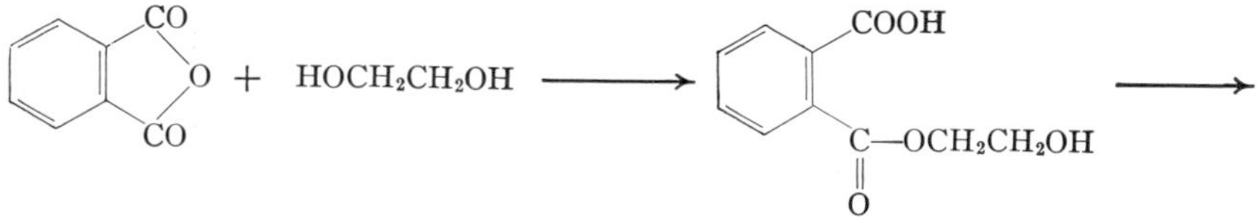

$$HOCH_2CH_2O(COC_6H_4COOCH_2CH_2O)_nCOC_6H_4COOH$$
I

From the study of other alcohols and acids it has become apparent that one of the reactants must have more than two functional groups and the other at least two, if a heat-convertible resin is to be obtained. Thus glycerol has three centers of reactivity and gives heat-convertible resins if the acid component has two or more functional groups. If phthalic an-

---

[8] Roy H. Kienle, b. 1896 Easthampton, Mass.; Ph.D. Rutgers; American Cyanamid Co.

hydride is the constant component the alcohol must have three or more groups in order to yield convertible resins. This functionality relationship is understandable in terms of the structures assigned to the polymers. When phthalic acid (3 moles) is esterified with glycerol (2 moles), esterification proceeds very rapidly, and at a point corresponding to 50% esterification the mixture consists of the monobasic glyceride (II) and the dibasic glyceride (III). The esterification then proceeds quite slowly. Carothers

$$
\begin{array}{ll}
\text{CH}_2\text{OH} & \text{CH}_2\text{OCOC}_6\text{H}_4\text{COOH} \\
| & | \\
\text{CHOH} & \text{CHOH} \\
| & | \\
\text{CH}_2\text{OCOC}_6\text{H}_4\text{COOH} & \text{CH}_2\text{OCOC}_6\text{H}_4\text{COOH} \\
\text{II} & \text{III}
\end{array}
$$

suggested that the reaction can be formulated in two stages; a linear polymer is formed first after esterification of the α-hydroxy groups of glycerol. In the second stage the chains are cross-linked to form a three-dimensional structure (IV) through esterification of the β-hydroxy group of glycerol with phthalic anhydride.

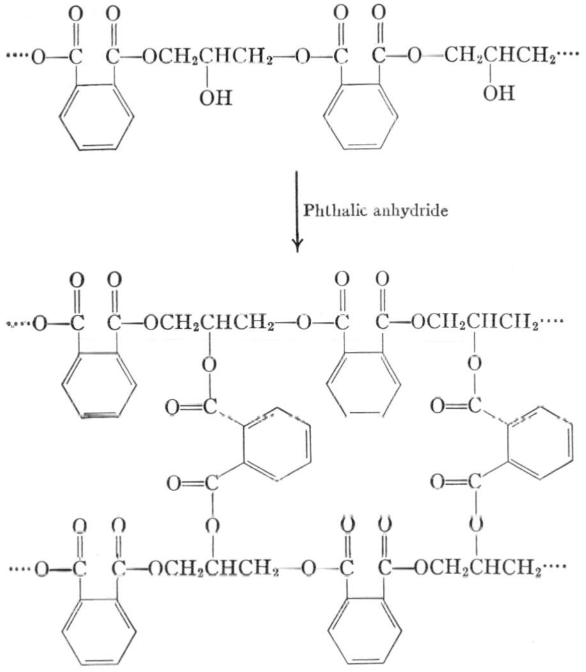

IV

Simple glyptal resins for surface coatings are used as stoving varnishes. The intermediate condensation product is dissolved in a suitable solvent and the film left on evaporation is set by baking. Such a film is tough but not flexible. Since flexibility generally is associated with chain polymers, Kienle investigated the possibility of rendering the glyptal resins more flexible by the introduction of varying amounts of polyglycol succinate,

$H—(OCH_2CH_2OCOCH_2CH_2CO)_n—OCH_2CH_2OH$. The desired result was achieved, for flexible, heat-convertible resins were obtained that appear to be made up of three-dimensional glyptal units linked through long chains of polyglycol succinate. Mixed alkyd resins can be produced by condensing together the four component ingredients; the product is a true copolymer and not a mechanical mixture.

Vinyl Resins. — The monomers vinyl chloride, vinyl acetate, and vinylidene chloride are used for production not only of fibers but also of rubberlike to brittle resins. That the resins are thermoplastic is in agreement with Kienle's functionality theory, since the monomers are bifunctional in that the double bond of the vinyl group gives rise to polymer growth in two directions. Pure vinyl acetate polymerizes only slowly in the dark at ordinary temperatures, but the rate of polymerization increases with temperature. The reaction is catalyzed by ultraviolet light or by peroxides, ozone, or tetraethyllead. Polymerization in emulsion can lead to higher-viscosity polymers. By control of the various factors, polymers can be obtained ranging in average molecular weight from 4300 to 100,000. The tensile and impact strengths, resistance to abrasion, and viscosity in solution increase with increase in molecular weight. The hardness, refractive index, and electrical properties remain fairly constant. The polymers are com-

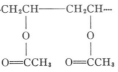
Polyvinyl acetate

patible with many solvents; depending on the degree of polymerization, they soften at relatively low temperatures. They are not particularly suitable for molding compositions, but are used to some extent in lacquers and adhesives. A thin surface film of a vinyl polymer, particularly of a polymer containing halogen, renders even celluloid somewhat fire-resistant. The evidence is fairly conclusive that the monomers are linked head-to-tail. Polymerization of the chloride is analogous to that of the acetate. The polymers are unusually strong and resistant to water. They are thermoplastic, but soften so slowly that the molding process is accompanied by considerable decomposition unless plasticizers are added. Solutions of the resin are used for certain varnishes.

Simultaneous polymerization of vinyl acetate and vinyl chloride yields resins of desirable properties. Films of polyvinyl acetate are adhesive, but too soft and soluble; films of polyvinyl chloride are strong, but not adhesive. Copolymers containing a major proportion of vinyl chloride are both strong and adhesive, and are suitable for molding compositions and for surface coatings. The copolymers resemble cellulose derivatives in molding characteristics, mechanical strength, and apperance.

Polyvinyl acetate is readily hydrolyzed by acids or alkalis. If hydrolysis is complete, the product is polyvinyl alcohol, which finds limited use in sizing formulations and in the production of resists (preparations that prevent dyes from adhering to fabrics). If polyvinyl alcohol is treated with sulfur or sulfur monochloride, a reaction takes place that closely resembles vulcanization of rubber. The extent of hydrolysis is easily controlled to give products containing both acetyl and hydroxyl groups, and polymers containing free hydroxyl groups can react with aldehydes to form acetals. Properties of the polyvinyl acetal resins depend on the original ester selected, the extent of hydrolysis, the aldehyde employed, and the extent of reaction between the alcoholic groups and the aldehyde. A typical polyvinyl acetal resin made by partial hydrolysis of polyvinyl acetate followed by condensation with formaldehyde is shown in the formula. The

$$\cdots CH_2CH-CH_2CH-CH_2CH-CH_2CH\cdots$$
$$\underset{\underset{O=CCH_3}{|}}{\overset{|}{O}} \quad \overset{|}{O}-CH_2-\overset{|}{O} \quad \overset{|}{OH}$$

acetals are tougher, more resistant to water, but less resistant to weathering than the corresponding acetates. Some are suitable for lacquers and for injection molding. Polyvinyl butyral is the most widely used resin for the interlayer in safety glass and has displaced cellulose nitrate and acetate almost entirely. It is not discolored by light and retains its toughness even at low temperatures.

Polystyrene. — The monomer required for polystyrene resin is made by condensing ethylene with benzene to ethylbenzene, which is then cracked to styrene. The conditions and catalysts for polymerization are similar to

$$\bigcirc + CH_2=CH_2 \xrightarrow{AlCl_3} \overset{CH_2CH_3}{\bigcirc} \xrightarrow{Heat} \overset{CH=CH_2}{\bigcirc}$$
$$\text{Styrene}$$

those for the other vinyl compounds just discussed. Polymerization proceeds rapidly in an emulsion of 5% sodium oleate solution and results in high-molecular weight polymers. Evidence that polymerization follows the radical-initiated chain mechanism described for the general case (p. 855) is that, when the reaction is conducted in the presence of p-bromobenzoyl peroxide, p-bromobenzoate and p-bromophenyl end groups appear in the polymer; hence the radicals $BrC_6H_4COO\cdot$ and $BrC_6H_4\cdot$ both function as chain initiators. The head-to-tail structure of polystyrene is deduced from identification of fragments produced on pyrolysis.

Polystyrene is thermoplastic, but the polymer produced when only a

$$\overset{CH=CH_2}{\bigcirc} + \begin{matrix} \overset{C_6H_5}{|} \overset{C_6H_5}{|} \\ \cdots CHCH_2-CHCH_2\cdots \\ \\ \cdots CHCH_2-CHCH_2\cdots \\ \overset{|}{C_6H_5} \overset{|}{C_6H_5} \end{matrix} \longrightarrow \begin{matrix} \overset{C_6H_5}{|} \overset{C_6H_5}{|} \\ \cdots CHCH_2-CHCH_2-CHCH_2\cdots \\ \bigcirc \\ \cdots CHCH_2-CHCH_2-CHCH_2-CHCH_2\cdots \\ \overset{|}{C_6H_5} \overset{|}{C_6H_5} \bigcirc \\ \cdots CHCH_2\cdots \end{matrix}$$

small amount (0.01%) of divinylbenzene is added is relatively nonthermo-plastic as the result of cross-linking in the manner shown.

Directed Polymerization. — This method of polymerization resulted from an extensive study of aluminum trialkyls by Ziegler (1952–54). One of several procedures for preparation of the alkyls, for example triethylalu-

1. $LiAlH_4 + 4CH_2=CH_2 \longrightarrow LiAl(CH_2CH_3)_4$

2. $3LiAl(CH_2CH_3)_4 + AlCl_3 \longrightarrow 3LiCl + 4Al(CH_2CH_3)_3$

3. $Al(CH_2CH_3)_3 + 3CH_2=CH_2 \longrightarrow (CH_3CH_2{-}CH_2CH_2)_3Al$

4. $\Big\lvert$ 5. $\Big\lvert nCH_2=CH_2$ 6. $\Big\lvert CH_2=CH_2$

$CH_3CH_2CH=CH_2$ $[CH_3CH_2(CH_2CH_2)_{n-1}]_3Al$ $CH_3CH_2CH_2CH_2CH=CH_2$
$+ Al(CH_2CH_3)_3$

minum, involves addition of lithium aluminum hydride to ethylene at high temperature and pressure to form lithium aluminum tetraethyl (1), and reaction of this with aluminum chloride (2). The aluminum alkyl adds stepwise to an olefin (3), and the process can be controlled to give the product of the first addition, butene-1 in example (4), in high yield. Alternatively, the dimeric alkyl can be caused to react with more monomer to produce a polymer (5), or to undergo the displacement reaction (6). Higher α-olefins are preparable in this way. The method is generally applicable to the polymerization of α-olefins and, surprisingly, leads to a sterically oriented polymer. Thus polystyrene produced in this way is crystalline, and all the asymmetric carbon atoms have the same configuration (G. Natta, 1955).

Acryloid Plastics. — Methyl, ethyl, and higher alkyl acrylates, $CH_2=CHCO_2R$, and methacrylates, $CH_2=C(CH_3)CO_2R$, are useful monomers that polymerize much as other vinyl monomers do. In contrast, β-substituted acrylates such as methyl crotonate, $CH_3CH=CHCO_2CH_3$, show no tendency to polymerize. Lower acrylate esters are prepared from ethylene chlorohydrin and the higher esters by transesterification or by

$$CH_2OHCH_2Cl \xrightarrow{\text{NaCN}} CH_2OHCH_2CN \xrightarrow{\text{CH}_3\text{OH, H}_2\text{SO}_4} CH_2=CHCO_2CH_3$$

esterification of acrylic acid. Another process utilizing waste lactic acid of the dairy industry involves pyrolysis of the methyl ester acetate (84% yield). Methacrylate esters are prepared efficiently from acetone cyanohydrin.

$$CH_3{-}C(OH)CN \xrightarrow{\text{ROH, H}_2\text{SO}_4} CH_2=CCO_2R + (NH_4)_2SO_4$$
$$\qquad\quad | \qquad\qquad\qquad\qquad\qquad |$$
$$\qquad\quad CH_3 \qquad\qquad\qquad\qquad\quad CH_3$$

Polymerization occurs under usual conditions; it can be conducted in solution for preparation of dopes. Methyl methacrylate sheets (Plexiglas, Lucite), distinguished by colorless transparency, represent the nearest approach known to an organic glass. Polyacrylates as a class are adhesive, stable to light and to moderate heat (200°), and a low specific gravity (1.0–1.2) is favorable since the cost is based on weight. They are suitable for compression and injection molding and are used also as protective coatings, adhesives, impregnating agents for textiles, and finishes for leather.

Modified Rosin. — Rosin, of which the major constituent is abietic acid, is cheap and abundant but suffers from the defects of being soft and tacky, of low melting point (80°) and high acid number (160), and of undergoing rapid aging due to air oxidation. One type of modified rosin, known as **ester gum**, is made by partial esterification with a polyhydric alcohol, particularly glycerol. Some polymerization to polyester occurs, the acidity is reduced, and stability is increased. Ester gum is used as substitute for tung oil in varnishes and is incorporated into cellulose nitrate lacquers for improvement of adhesion and gloss.

Another scheme of modification is to decrease unsaturation and so stabilize the material against air oxidation. This can be done by direct **hydrogenation** or, more simply by heat treatment, which causes abietic acid to undergo **disproportionation** to a pyroabietic acid mixture of the aroma-

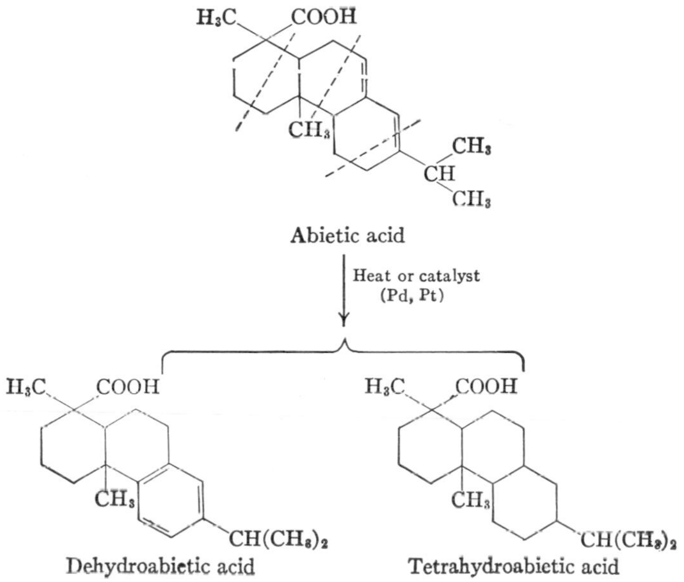

Abietic acid

Heat or catalyst
(Pd, Pt)

Dehydroabietic acid   Tetrahydroabietic acid

tized dehydroabietic acid and tetrahydroabietic acid, both of which are inert chemically and resistant to oxidation.

In the modified material known as **Poly-pale Resin** decrease in unsaturation is accomplished by partial polymerization of dienic abietic acid units. The material, which contains about 40% of dimer, has a higher melting point (98–130°) than rosin, and gives solutions of distinctly higher viscosity. Utilization of double bonds to establish links between monomer units greatly increases stability to oxidation. The material is used for preparation of ester gums and modified alkyd resins.

Organosilicon Polymers. — Early observations by Friedel and Ladenburg (1866, 1874) indicated that complex products are obtained by heating alkylsilanediols, $R_2Si(OH)_2$, and alkylsilanetriols, $RSi(OH)_3$, but Kipping[9] was the first to realize that these substances are intermolecular condensation products of the silanols (1908). Utilization of the polymerization for the preparation of useful products has been developed only recently by both Russian and American companies. Dehydration of a dialkylsilanediol leads to long-chain anhydrides as well as cyclic polymers, particularly the trimer and tetramer:

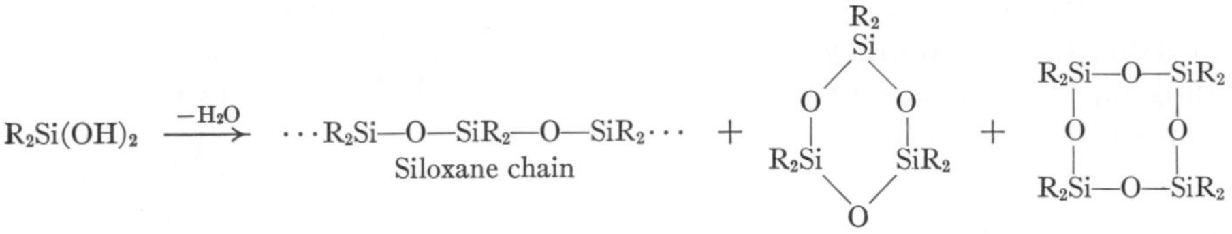

$$R_2Si(OH)_2 \xrightarrow{-H_2O} \cdots R_2Si-O-SiR_2-O-SiR_2 \cdots \; + \; \begin{array}{c} R_2 \\ Si \\ O \quad O \\ R_2Si \quad SiR_2 \\ O \end{array} \; + \; \begin{array}{c} R_2Si-O-SiR_2 \\ O \qquad O \\ R_2Si-O-SiR_2 \end{array}$$

Siloxane chain

Three-dimensional polymers are obtained from polymerization of an alkylsilanetriol; each silicon atom is bound into a completely cross-linked rigid structure resembling that of silica. Intermediate polymers containing occasional cross links, as in the siloxane resin formulated, are obtained by copolymerization of an alkylsilanetriol and a dialkylsilanediol. When R

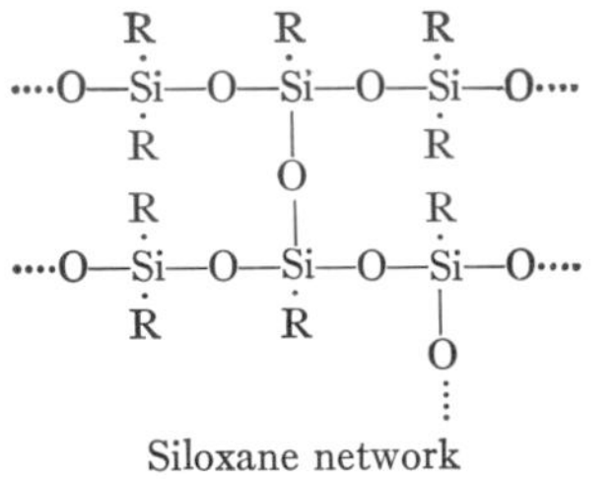

Siloxane network 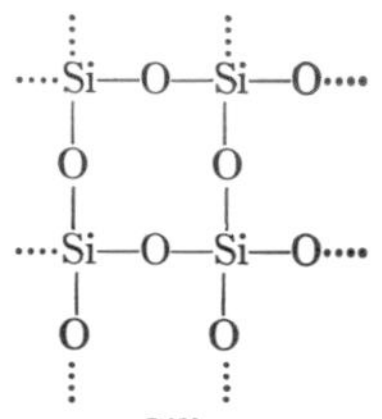   Silica

represents methyl or phenyl, the resins are highly stable to heat and to oxygen; they are particularly well suited for use in electrical insulation.

Silicone rubber is made from the long-chain polymer of dimethylsilanediol; cross links are introduced during curing, probably by controlled oxidation. Methylsilicone rubber has the advantage over natural rubber and the other synthetics in that it is more stable to heat and to chemical reagents and remains flexible at very low temperatures. Linear polymers of dimethylsiloxane with terminal trimethylsilyl groups are valuable oils because they change in viscosity much more slowly with temperature than hydrocarbon oils do.

The most readily available starting materials for preparation of the monomer are the silicon tetrahalides. Kipping introduced the use of the Grignard reagent for preparation of the desired alkylsilanols; the reaction

$$SiCl_4 \; + \; RMgX \longrightarrow RSiCl_3 \xrightarrow{H_2O} RSi(OH)_3$$

$$RSiCl_3 \; + \; RMgX \longrightarrow R_2SiCl_2 \xrightarrow{H_2O} R_2Si(OH)_2$$

---

[9] Frederic Stanley Kipping, 1863–1949; b. Manchester; Ph.D. Munich; Nottingham; *J. Chem. Soc.*, 849 (1951)

cannot be controlled to one particular stage, and the product is a mixture of substances containing from one to four alkyl groups. A direct synthesis has since been achieved (Rochow,[10] 1940) by the vapor-phase reaction of alkyl halides with silicon at high temperatures under the catalytic action of copper or silver: $Si + 2RCl \rightarrow R_2SiCl_2$. Again a mixture of related organosilicon halides is obtained and separation by distillation is required.

READING REFERENCES

Am. Chem. Society, Rubber Div., "One Hundred Years of Vulcanized Rubber," 98th Meeting (1939)

H. L. Fisher, "Natural and Synthetic Rubbers," Edgar Marburg Lecture, Am. Soc. for Testing Materials (1941)

P. J. Flory, "Principles of Polymer Chemistry," Cornell University Press, New York (1953)

H. Barron, "Modern Synthetic Rubbers," Van Nostrand (1944)

Institute of Plastics Research, "The Plastics Industry" (1941)

U. S. Tariff Commission, "Synthetic Resins and Their Raw Materials" (1938)

F. Sproxton, "The Rise of the Plastics Industry," Chem. Ind., 16, 607 (1938)

H. A. Neville, "Synthetic Resins and Plastics," J. Chem. Ed., 19, 9 (1942)

C. A. Redfarn, "The Chemical Structure of Plastics," Chem. Ind. 20, 201 (1942)

R. H. Kienle, "Structural Chemistry of Synthetic Polymerides and Their Films," J. Soc. Chem. Ind., 55, 229T (1936)

E. R. Weidlein, "History and Development of Laminated Safety Glass," Ind. Eng. Chem., 31, 563 (1939)

S. D. Douglas, "Vinyl Resins," ibid., 32, 315 (1940)

E. Ott, "Cellulose Derivatives as Basic Materials for Plastics," ibid., 32, 1641 (1940)

C. S. Marvel and E. C. Horning, "Synthetic Polymers," in H. Gilman, "Organic Chemistry," 2nd Ed., I, 701–778, Wiley, New York (1943)

E. G. Rochow, "Chemistry of the Silicones," 2nd Ed., Wiley, New York (1950)

"Modern Plastics Encyclopedia," Plastics Catalogue Corp., New York (1942–)

---

[10] Eugene G. Rochow; b. 1909 Newark, N. J.; Ph.D. Cornell; General Electric Co., Harvard Univ.

CHAPTER 36

DYES

COLOR AND CONSTITUTION

Light is composed of rays of varying wave length, and that visible to the eye includes waves of length between 4000 and 8000 Ångstrom units ($\text{Å} = 1 \times 10^{-8}$ cm.). Light composed of rays of a selected region of wave length produces the sensation of color; for instance, that of wave length 4000–4250Å appears violet. All organic molecules absorb light to some extent, but the majority absorb in the ultraviolet region of the spectrum, that is, below 4000Å, and appear colorless. The phenomenon of absorption is associated with vibrations of electrons in the molecule responsive to stimulation by light rays of specific oscillation frequency. If the electrons are firmly bound, they will respond to, and absorb, light of short wave length and high frequency. As the electrons become more mobile, usually with accumulation of conjugated centers of unsaturation in the molecule, they become capable of being set in vibration by light of longer wave length, with resulting utilization of radiant energy and absorption in the visible region of the spectrum. If a substance absorbs all visible light except that corresponding, for instance, to violet, it will reflect only violet light, and hence be seen as that particular color. Colors of the various regions of the visible spectrum and their complementary colors are shown in Table 36.1.

TABLE 36.1. ABSORPTION OF VISIBLE LIGHT

LIGHT ABSORBED		COLOR OBSERVED
Wave length, Å	Corresponding color	
4000	violet	greenish yellow
4250	indigo blue	yellow
4500	blue	orange
4900	blue-green	red
5100	green	purple
5300	yellow-green	violet
5500	yellow	indigo blue
5900	orange	blue
6400	red	bluish green
7300	purple	green

Unsaturation is essential for light absorption. Compounds containing only one such center absorb light in a single, narrowly limited region of the spectrum, and thus are described as having an absorption band of maximal intensity at a specified wave length. Groups responsible for selective absorption of light of wave length 2500–10,000Å are called chromophores (Gr. *chroma*, color + *phoros*, bearer). The chromophores encountered in organic compounds are listed in Table 36.2. Both the wave length and

TABLE 36.2. CHROMOPHORIC GROUPS

GROUP	EXAMPLE	λ_{max}, Å	INTENSITY, E
C=C	Ethylene	1930	10,000
C≡C	Acetylene	1730	6000
C=N	Acetoxime	1900	5000
C≡N	Acetonitrile	<1600	
C=O	Acetone	2706	15.8
CHO	Acetaldehyde	2934	11.8
CO₂H	Acetic acid	2040	40
CONH₂	Acetamide	2080	
N=N	Diazomethane	4100	1200
N=O	Nitrosobutane	3000, 6650	100, 20
NO₂	Nitromethane	2710	18.6
ONO	Octyl nitrite	2300, 3700	2200, 55
ONO₂	Ethyl nitrate	2700	12

intensity of absorption vary over a wide range, and hence absorption characteristics are of invaluable aid in structural studies. Only two of the chromophores listed, azo (—N=N—) and nitroso (—N=O), are sufficient in themselves to give rise to visible color. Conjugation of two or more chromophores produces a marked shift to longer wave length, an effect demonstrated clearly in the series of diphenylpolyenes listed in Table 36.3 (Kuhn, 1928–29).

TABLE 36.3. DIPHENYLPOLYENES, $C_6H_5(CH=CH)_nC_6H_5$

VALUE OF n	COLOR	ABSORPTION MAXIMA OF CHARACTERISTIC BANDS, Å [1]		
		A	B	C
1	none	3190	3060	2940
2	none	3520	3340	3160
3	pale yellow	3770	3580	3430
4	greenish yellow	4040	3840	3630
5	orange	4240	4030	3870
6	brownish orange	4450	4200	4000
7	copper-bronze	4650	4350	4130
11	violet-black	5300	4930	4620
15	greenish black	5700	5320	. . . .

[1] In benzene solution.

The diphenylpolyenes show three characteristic absorption maxima, and these are all shifted to longer wave length by addition of another ene group, though the effect diminishes somewhat with increasing chain length. The color is not due to the ethylenic groups alone, for the conjugated unsaturation of the benzene rings also contributes. Diphenyldecatetraene, which is formed as the initial product of reduction of the colored diphenyl-decapentaene, is colorless. Substances having several adjacent double

$$C_6H_5(CH{=}CH)_5C_6H_5 \xrightarrow{\ 2H\ } C_6H_5CH_2(CH{=}CH)_4CH_2C_6H_5$$

Diphenyldecapentaene   Diphenyldecatetraene

(orange)   (colorless)

bonds are known as cumulenes, and the effect of cumulation on selective absorption is similar to that of conjugation (Kuhn and Zahn, 1951). Thus in the series of tetraphenylcumulenes, $(C_6H_5)_2C{=}(C{=}C)_n{=}C(C_6H_5)_2$, the color and λ_{max} are as follows: $n = 1$, yellow, 4200Å; $n = 2$, orange red, 4890Å; $n = 3$, violet, 5570Å.

Displacements to longer wave length are known as bathochromic effects; displacements to shorter wave length are hypsochromic. Structural changes that increase intensity of absorption are said to be hyperchromic, those decreasing the intensity are hypochromic.

Absorption characteristics of some simple conjugated systems are shown in Table 36.4. Conjugation of a double bond with a second one or with a

TABLE 36.4. CONJUGATED CHROMOPHORES

SYSTEM	EXAMPLE	λ_{max}, Å	E
C=C—C=C	Butadiene	2170	20,900
C=C—CH=O	Crotonaldehyde	2170; 3210	16,000; 19.5
C=C—CO$_2$H	Crotonic acid	2000; 2500	10,000; 100
C=C—NO$_2$	3-Nitropropene-2	2290	9500
Aromatic ring	Benzene	2550	230
C$_6$H$_5$CH=CH$_2$	Styrene	2440	12,000
C=C—C=C—C=C	Octatrienol	265	53,000
C=C—C=C—CH=O	Sorbaldehyde	263	27,000

triple bond, carbonyl, carboxyl, or nitro group gives rise to high intensity bands in the region 2000–2300Å, representing a bathochromic displacement of 150–450Å with respect to the ethylene bond. Two distinct bands are often observed; for example, α,β-unsaturated ketones have one maximum of high intensity at 2300–2700Å and another of low intensity at 3000–3300Å. The former is ascribed to the transition $C{=}C{-}C{=}O \rightarrow \overset{+}{C}{-}C{=}C{-}\overset{-}{O}$ and, since it is associated with a conjugated system, it is referred to as a K-band (K from the German "konjugiert"). The low-intensity band is due to electronic transitions of an individual chromophore, in this case the carbonyl group. Similar low-intensity bands are also noted in the case of free radicals, where they are associated with unpaired electrons, and hence are called R-bands (radical). The spectrum of benzene differs significantly from those of aliphatic compounds. Bands of intensity about 8000 occur in the region near 2000Å, not susceptible to measurement in commercial spectrophotometers, and probably correspond to K-bands. The measurable maximum at 2550Å is resolvable into multiple narrow bands, which probably are R-bands but which are usually referred to as B-bands (benzene). The maximum is similar in position to that of open-chain dienes but of much lower intensity.

O. N. Witt (1867) recognized that certain substituents augment the color due to chromophoric systems and named them auxochromes. The main auxochromes, which exert both bathochromic and hyperchromic effects, are listed in the order of decreasing effectiveness: —NR$_2$, —NHR, —NH$_2$, —OH, halogen, —OCH$_3$. Auxochromic effects of low order are also noted for alkyl groups. Bathochromic displacements caused by substituents roughly follow the order of electron-repelling potency.

Color is now considered as associated with a highly unsaturated system in which resonance confers adequate mobility on the electrons. Early interpretations of color can be seen, in retrospect, to have been vague expressions of the resonance concept. Thus Baeyer (1907) suggested that the intense color of Doebner's Violet, which is structurally related to the

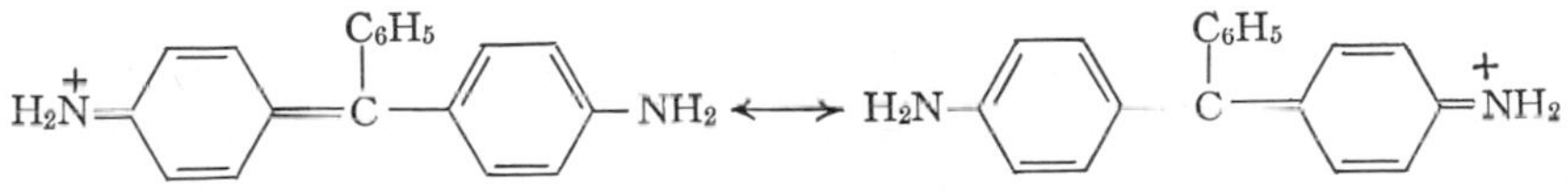

Doebner's Violet cation

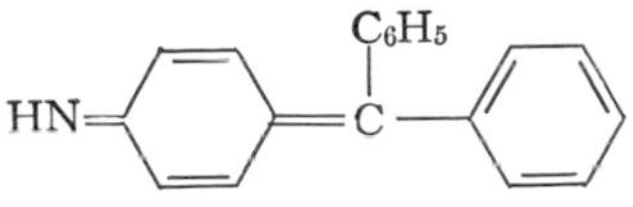

Fuchsonimine

colorless fuchsonimine, is due to oscillation of the quinonoid structure between two rings; his postulated structures are, in reality, identical resonance structures. The resonance concept explains also why the dihydrochloride of Doebner's Violet is only feebly colored, since in this salt resonance is no longer possible. Kuhn (1932) pointed out that color is often associated with heteropolar forms. He pointed out that the intense color of indigo cannot be due to the enedione system, since quinones containing this system

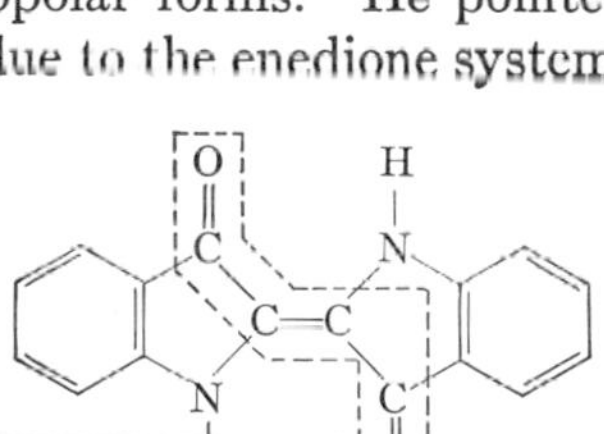

Indigo (deep blue; abs. max. in xylene, 5900 Å)

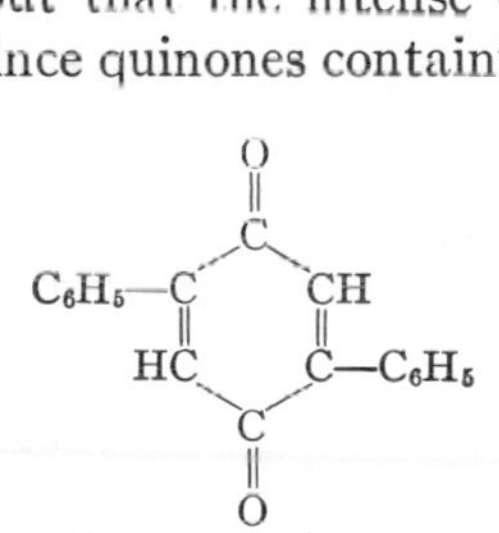

2,5-Diphenyl-1,4-benzoquinone (orange-yellow)

are only weakly colored, and proposed for indigo the heteropolar formula (a). This is one of several possible resonance structures, such as (b), and a form

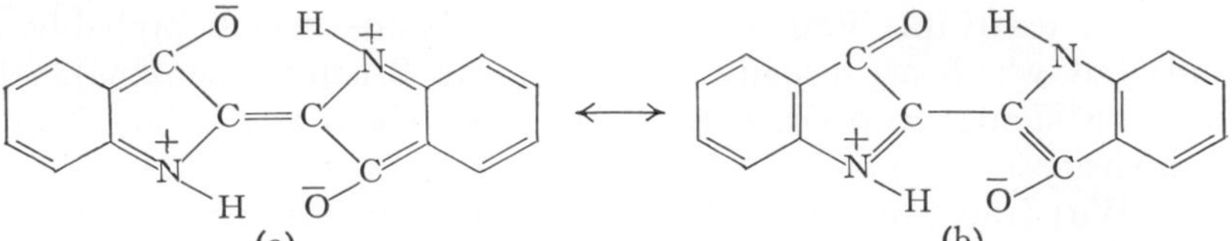

Indigo

in which the oxygens are hydrogen bonded. The extensive conjugated systems account for the color, and the heteropolar representation is consistent with the high melting point (390–392°) and the fact that only the *trans* form is known (configuration from X-ray analysis), since oppositely charged oxygen and nitrogen attract one another.

APPLICATION OF DYES

A colored substance is useful as a dye only if it can be attached to a fiber. The method of applying a dye depends not only on the type and nature of the dye but on the type of fiber. Wool and silk are amphoteric proteins and have a natural affinity for substances containing acidic or basic groups with which they combine by salt formation. Thus wool and silk have similar dyeing properties and can be dyed directly by introduction into a solution of either an acidic or a basic dye. Typical dyes for proteinic fibers are shown in Chart 1.

CHART 1. DIRECT DYES TO WOOL OR SILK[a]

Basic:

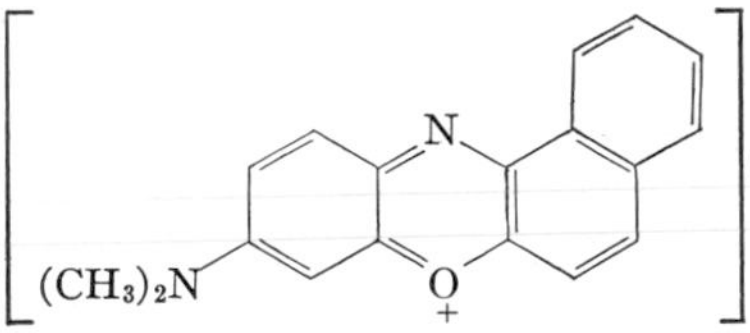

Meldolas Blue
(abs. max. 6223, 5737, 5334 Å)

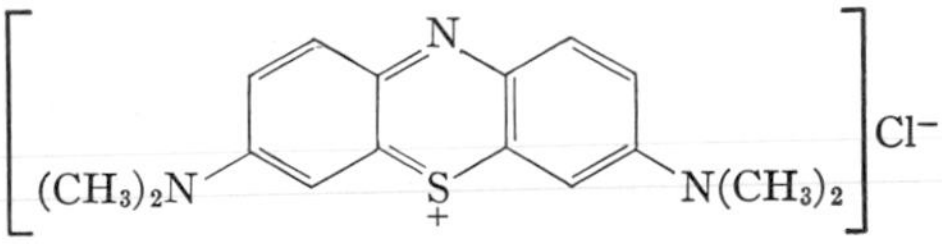

Methylene Blue
(abs. max. 6678, 6093 Å)

Acidic:

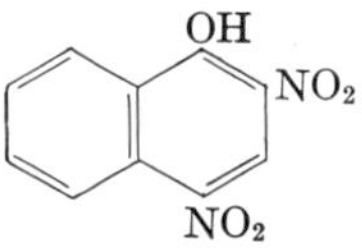

Martius Yellow

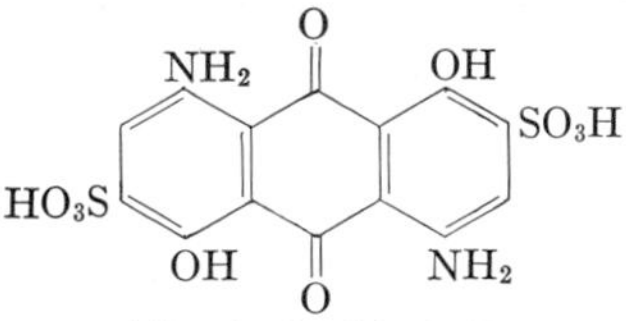

Alizarin Saphirole B
(blue, abs. max. 6490 Å)

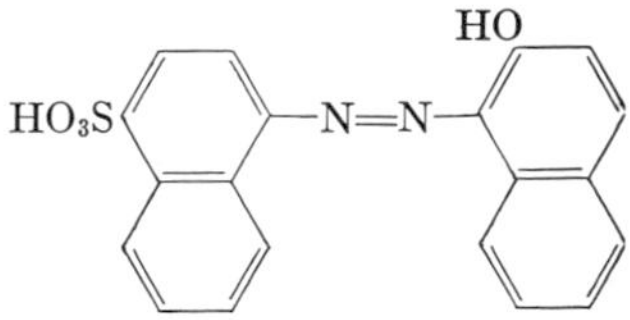

Fast Red A

[a] Trade names of the various dyestuffs generally include one or more alphabetical letters and often a number. The number refers to the shade. The alphabetical designations are not uniform; they may refer to the color: G = yellow (*gelb*), R = red (*rot*); to specific properties: SWE = fast to perspiration (*schweissecht*), WE = fast to washing (*waschecht*); to the company: A = General Aniline, By = Friedrich Bayer; or they may have been used originally to conceal the identity of the product.

Cotton, linen, and rayons of the regenerated cellulose type are composed of neutral cellulose molecules and show no affinity for many dyes direct to wool and silk. They do combine with substances known as substantive dyes, which they bind by adsorption or hydrogen bonding to an extent determined in part by compatibility of the dye molecule with space groupings in the fiber. Cellulosic fabrics can also be dyed by processes of vatting, mordanting, and formation of dye on the fiber as described below. The vat process and one process for indirect application of azo dyes are conducted in alkaline solution and cannot be used for dyeing wool and silk, which are sensitive to alkali. Cellulose acetate and nylon are neutral or substantially neutral substances but they differ from cellulose in having no hydroxyl groups available for hydrogen bonding, and these hydrophobic fibers are resistant to the usual cotton dyes. They are best dyed from an aqueous dispersion of a water-insoluble azo or anthraquinone dye in the presence of a dispersing agent (soap), when the dye enters the fiber in the form of a solid solution. Dyes that have affinity for hydrophobic fibers under these conditions contain free amino and hydroxyl groups.

Vat Dyeing. — A method of dyeing cotton with the very insoluble natural dye indigo, obtained from species of the Indian plant *Indigofera*, was known to the ancients. The process depends upon the fact that indigo is reduced to a colorless dihydro, or leuco derivative, which is soluble in dilute alkali. If fabric is immersed in the alkaline solution of a reduced dye (vat), the leuco compound is adsorbed and on withdrawal and exposure to the air is oxidized to the dye, which remains fixed to the cloth. A dye is satisfactory only if its leuco compound, or anion, has adequate affinity for the fiber (hydrogen bonding). In the early process, reduction was accomplished by fermentation; in the modern process (1871), sodium hydrosulfite ($Na_2S_2O_4$) is used as the reducing agent. Dyes that are applied in this way are known as vat dyes. Synthetic vat dyes other than indigo and its derivatives were discovered only in 1901 but now include several hundred members. Vat dyes are all quinonoid substances that are readily reduced to hydroquinonoid compounds reoxidizable by air.

Vat dyeing is carried out partly by a continuous process in which cotton cloth from a roll is conveyed over a system of rollers into a solution of the reduced dye, where the cloth is padded (impregnated) with vat liquor, then into a chamber where proper fixation of the leuco compound to the padded fabric is accomplished by steaming, next into an oxidizing bath containing chromate and acetic acid or perborate, and finally into soaping, rinsing, and drying baths. A method favored for dyes of high molecular weight and limited vat solubility involves passage of the cloth through an aqueous suspension of highly dispersed dye in the pigment form followed by repeated treatment with alkaline hydrosulfite to effect reduction and fixation of the leuco compound *in situ*, prior to eventual oxidation. Cellulosic fiber in the form of yarn or skeins is placed in a stationary compartment of a dyeing apparatus, and the caustic hydrosulfite solution of the dye is pumped through the material. Dyes of the type known as sulfur colors are applied by vatting with sodium sulfide, a reagent of insufficient potential to reduce any but a few dyes of the indigo and anthraquinone types.

Mordant Dyeing. — This method consists in processing cotton in such a way as to affix to it either acidic or basic groups capable of combining with a basic or an acidic dye. The processing agent, or binding link between cloth and dye, is known as a mordant (L. *mordere*, to bite).

A complicated process of mordant dyeing known in the ancient world was used for applying alizarin (Chart 2), the principal coloring material of

CHART 2. METAL OXIDE MORDANT DYES

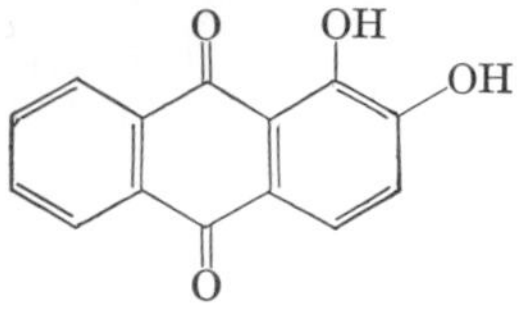

Alizarin

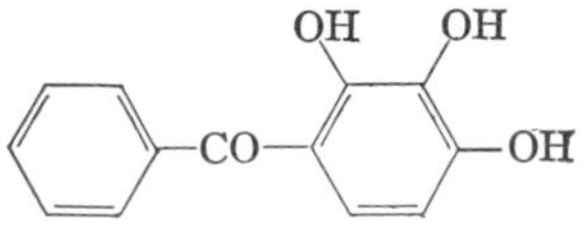

Alizarin Yellow A

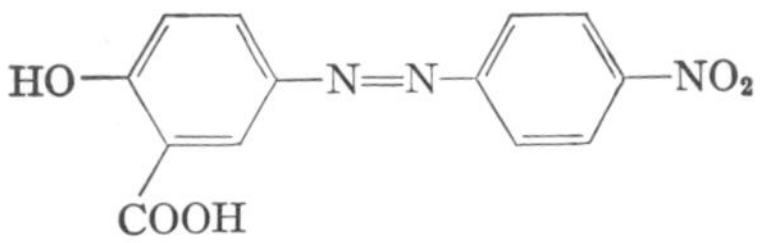

Alizarin Yellow R

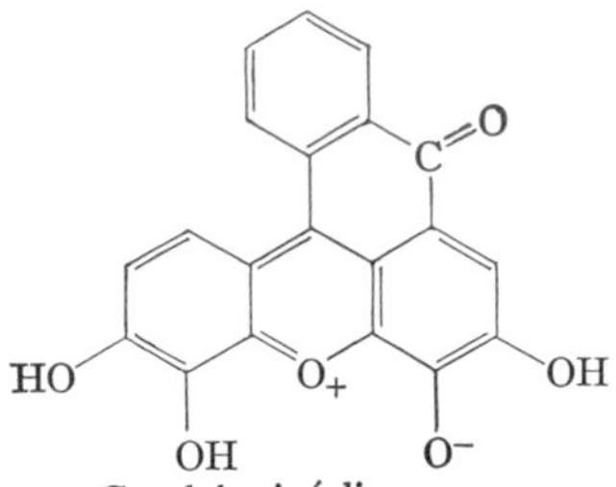

Cerulein A (olive green, chromium mordant)

madder, a rubiaceous plant, *Rubia tinctorum.* For centuries madder and indigo were the two leading dyes of the world. In early formulas for production of the color known as Turkey red, cotton was impregnated first with rancid olive oil containing lime and then with a solution of aluminum sulfate, and finally steamed. The mordanted cloth was then treated with the dye in the form of a fine aqueous suspension. The colloidal metal hydroxide adheres to the fiber and the dye molecule combines with the metallic mordant to form a complex salt, or lake. The early process of dyeing with Turkey red involved a complicated series of operations requiring as much as four months for completion. More modern methods using sulfonated castor oil (Turkey-red oil, p. 412) in place of olive oil require only about five days. The color can be varied by using other metals; for instance violet colors are obtained with an iron mordant, brownish red with a chromium mordant. Wool and silk also can be dyed by the same method. Dyes that can be applied in this way contain hydroxyl or carboxyl groups, which are evidently concerned in formation of the lake. Dyes of widely varied chemical types can be applied to cloth mordanted with metal oxides. The metal oxides provide basic groups on the fiber. Acidic groups suitable for binding basic dyes can be affixed to cotton by a mordanting process in which cloth is impregnated with tannic acid, which is fixed on the fiber with potassium antimonyl tartrate (tartar emetic). Tannic acid, a polymeric glycoside derivative of gallic acid, contains a number of acidic groups, some of which are bound as antimonyl groups in the process of fixation whereas others are free to bind basic dyes, for example the triphenylmethane dyes.

Substantive Dyes. — The first synthetic compound found capable of dyeing cotton directly, Congo Red (Böttiger, 1884), is a substantive dye. Congo Red is made from diazotized benzidine and naphthionic acid, and owing to its ready application the new dye was very popular for a time, in

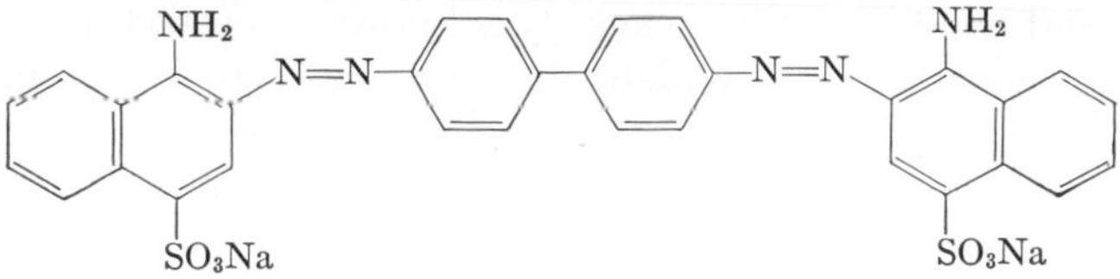

Congo Red
(abs. max. 4970 Å)

spite of the fact that it is fugitive (not fast) and so sensitive to acids that it is used as an indicator. Better substantive dyes, mainly other azo dyes derived from benzidine, were subsequently introduced. The substantive dyes are substances of rather high molecular weight showing colloidal properties, and they probably become fixed on the fiber by hydrogen bonding. The amount of dye taken up is increased by assistants (e.g., sodium chloride), which decrease the solubility of the dye.

Formation of Dye on the Fiber. — A superior method of applying azo dyes to cotton, patented in England in 1880, consists in soaking cotton in an alkaline solution of a phenol and then in an ice-cold solution of a diazonium salt; the azo dye is developed directly on the fiber. Azo dyes applied in this way are known as ice colors. The earliest of these dyes is a blue-red substance known as Vacanceine Red. The reverse process (ingrain dyeing)

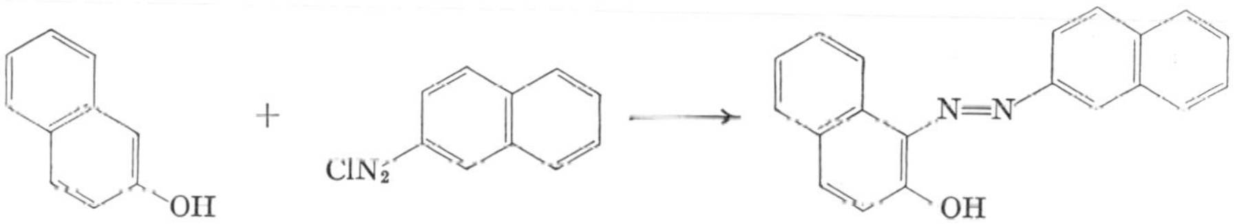

Vacanceine Red

of impregnating cotton with an amine, which is then diazotized and developed by immersion in a solution of the phenol, was introduced in 1887. The first ingrain dye was Primulin Red, obtained by coupling the fugitive sulfur dye Primulin, after application to the cloth and diazotization, with β-naphthol. Primulin (substantive to cotton) is a complex thiazole, prepared by heating p-toluidine with sulfur and then introducing a solubilizing sulfonic acid group; the position of the acid group is uncertain.

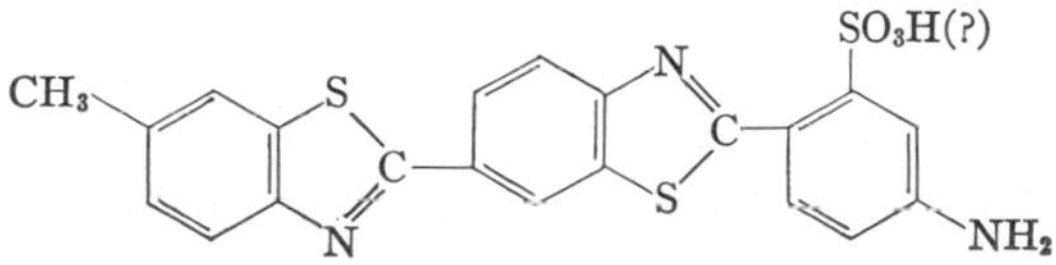

Primulin

A limited group of dyes are produced on the fiber by oxidation of aromatic amines. The first member of this class, Aniline Black (Lightfoot, 1862), is made by padding cotton with a solution of aniline hydrochloride, an oxidizing agent (sodium chlorate), an oxygen carrier (copper sulfate or vanadium chloride), and a hygroscopic salt (ammonium chloride). The cloth is dried at 35° until the color is dark bottle-green, and then immersed in a bath containing aniline, dichromate, and dilute sulfuric acid, and dried at 80°, when the final jet-black color is obtained. Aniline Black is one of the fastest and most beautiful black dyes known even today. The constitution is not established. Willstätter considered that the intermediate dark green dye (pernigraniline) is a complex quinonediimine containing eight aromatic rings. A phenylphenazonium inner salt structure has been

Pernigraniline

Aniline Black

suggested for the final black dye. Paramine Brown, prepared in a similar manner from p-phenylenediamine (1904), is an important dye for fur.

Methods of Printing. — One of the earliest methods of printing a color on fabric is known as resist printing (batik dyeing) and consists in covering a portion of the cloth with wax, which is removed after the dyeing operation by application of heat. Direct printing with a vat dye can be accomplished by stamping the cloth in the required pattern with a paste of alkaline hydrosulfite and the reduced dye and then passing the cloth through an oxidizing bath that develops the color. Another important printing process utilizes a leucosulfuric acid ester sodium salt prepared from the reduced form of an anthraquinone or indigoid vat dye. A paste of the salt is printed on the fabric and the dye is regenerated by treatment with aqueous nitrous acid, which effects hydrolysis and oxidation of the two ester groups ($-OSO_2ONa$). The sulfate ester is more soluble in water and hence better absorbed than the sodium salt of the leuco compound, and the same process is favored for dyeing fabric in pastel shades, since level dyeings of excellent fastness can be obtained even with dyes of high molecular weight and low vat solubility.

Prints of developed dyes can be made by impregnating cloth with the naphthol component and then applying the diazotized amine in the desired pattern, or by printing cloth with the naphthol component and then passing it through a solution of the diazotized amine. Mordant colors can be applied in a somewhat analogous manner by printing with a mixture of the dye and the mordant and developing the color by steaming. A further

method, discharge printing, involves localized reduction of an azo dye. It
consists in printing the dyed fabric from an engraved printing roll with a
paste of alkaline hydrosulfite; the colorless amines produced by reductive
cleavage are removed by soaping and rinsing, and the result is a white discharge. Colored discharge effects are obtained by addition of a vat dye
and additional hydrosulfite to the discharge printing paste. A method of
pigment printing (Aridye process) utilizes a water- and oil-insoluble phthalocyanine pigment (p. 933) or an anthraquinone of similar properties (vat
dye pigment). The pigment is incorporated into a water-in-oil printing
emulsion in which the oil phase is a hydrocarbon lacquer solvent containing
a heat-hardening resin (urea-formaldehyde plus a glyptal resin as plasticizer,
Chapter 35). Simple heat treatment after printing hardens the resin, which
serves as binder for the pigment.

BASIC DYES OF TRIARYLAMINE, TRIARYLMETHANE, AND METHINE TYPES

Mauveine. — The first synthetic dye was discovered in 1856 by an
eighteen-year-old chemist, William Henry Perkin. Three years earlier, Perkin had entered the Royal College of Chemistry as a student of Hofmann,
and within two years progressed to the title of honorary assistant to the
great teacher. As his first research problem, Perkin was assigned the task of
preparing nitro and amino derivatives of the coal-tar hydrocarbon anthracene, for which Dumas's incorrect empirical formula $C_{14}H_{12}$ was still accepted. The problem was unsuccessful, for the hydrocarbon was not nitrated on treatment with nitric acid but oxidized to the quinone. His next
problem resulted in a publication, and Perkin, at the age of seventeen, was
promoted to the rank of an assistant. At the time, chemists were particularly interested in synthesizing natural substances, and Perkin picked the
synthesis of quinine as a research problem of his own conception for investigation during evening and vacation hours in a laboratory in his home. Although the existence of isomers was recognized, the structures of even the
simplest compounds were unknown and empirical formulas constituted essentially the only characterization of complex molecules. Hofmann sometime earlier had discussed in a lecture the possibility of obtaining quinine
from an aromatic amine, and Perkin, reasoning on the basis of empirical
formulas alone, decided to attempt a synthesis as follows:

$$2 C_{10}H_{13}N \; + \; 3[O] \; \xrightarrow{\;?\;} \; C_{20}H_{24}N_2O_2 \; + \; H_2O$$

Allyltoluidine   Quinine

He obtained only a dirty reddish brown precipitate, but in spite of this unpromising result, decided to investigate the oxidation of the simpler amine
aniline. Treatment of the acid sulfate with potassium dichromate gave a
black precipitate that contained a small amount (5%) of a purple dye, which
was soon to become famous as Aniline Purple or mauveine (mauve), the
first of a vast number of synthetic dyes derived from coal tar. Perkin

sent his purple product to a dyeing establishment, and on receiving a report that the color and fastness to light were promising, decided to drop his scientific studies for the time in order to manufacture the new dye, a decision made in spite of Hofmann's advice to apply his talents to research. The manufacturing project was a courageous undertaking, for the benzene required was extracted from coal tar only in small amounts, since it was used only to a slight extent as a solvent and an illuminant, and the nitration process had to be worked out on a technical scale. Fortunately an excellent method of reducing nitrobenzene to aniline with iron and acetic acid had been discovered three years earlier by Béchamp, and Perkin states that, "had it not been for this discovery, the coal-tar colour industry could not have started." The new dye was on the market in 1857, and was soon accepted by French dyers, who introduced the name mauve. Although the new dye was priced the same as platinum, on a weight basis, it enjoyed considerable popularity for a decade. The color has striking brilliance not matched by any of the known natural dyes. It is a basic dye for wool or silk or for tannin-mordanted cotton.

Since the constitution of benzene was unknown, the structure could not be determined and presented a difficult problem solved only some years later by O. Fischer[1] (1888–90). Perkin had found that the commercial product contains two dyes, one derived from aniline and known as pseudomauveine, and one from aniline and o- and p-toluidine, impurities in early commercial aniline. He showed that the former is a C_{24}-compound built up from four molecules of aniline. Fischer established the skeletal structure

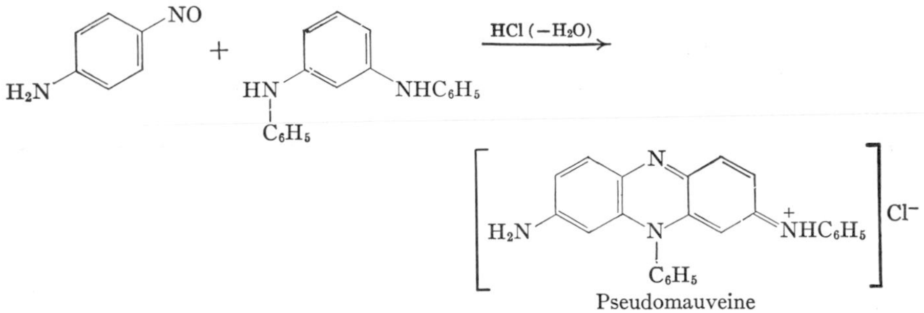

Pseudomauveine

by the synthesis of pseudomauveine from p-nitrosoaniline and diphenyl-m-phenylenediamine, and formulated both dyes as p-quinonediimines.

These two dyes belong to a rather small group of dyes known as phenyl-phenazonium salts, a few of which are still used. One useful member, a vivid pink dye known as safranine T (tolusafranine) and discovered by Williams in 1859, is prepared by oxidizing a mixture of p-toluylenediamine, o-toluidine, and aniline.

---

[1] Otto Fischer, 1852–1932; b. Euskirchen, Germany (cousin of Emil Fischer); Ph.D. Strasbourg (Baeyer); Erlangen

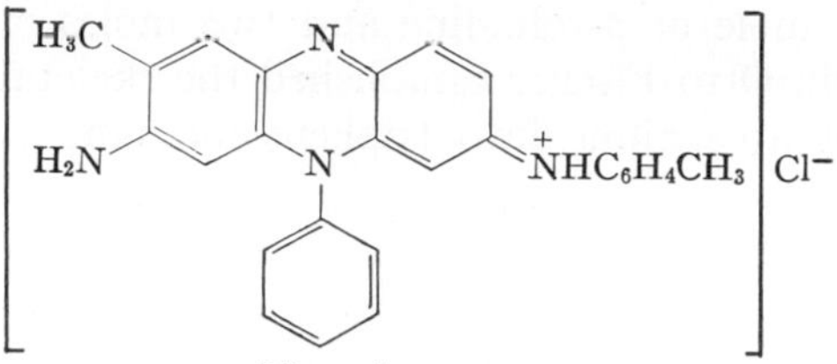

Mauveine
(abs. max., 5438, 5373 Å)

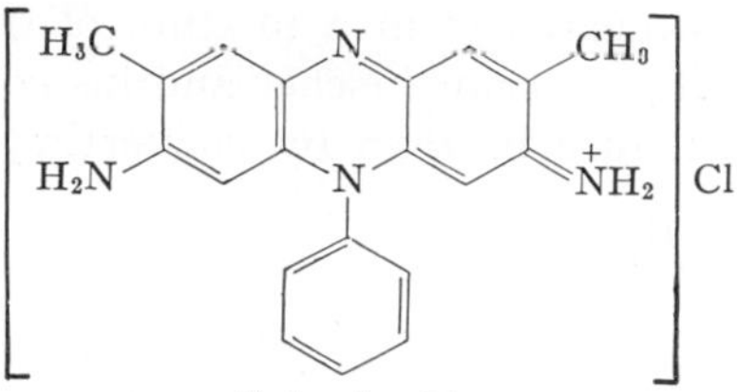

Safranine T
(abs. max., 5390 Å)

Rosaniline Dyes. — In 1859, Verguin (Lyons) obtained a red dye, which he named fuchsin, by oxidizing aniline with stannic chloride. The discovery must have been accidental, since it is surprising that two different dyes should result from oxidation of aniline, depending on the oxidizing agent. Hofmann had obtained the same substance a year earlier by treating aniline with carbon tetrachloride, but initiated studies on the product, which he named rosaniline, only after the use as a dye had been noted. This represented Hofmann's entry into the field of dyes, in which he subsequently played a prominent role. Hofmann showed that the dye is not formed from pure aniline, but only from mixtures containing toluidine. The ordinary commercial product is made by oxidation of equimolecular amounts of aniline, *p*-, and *o*-toluidine. Oxidizing agents other than stannic chloride

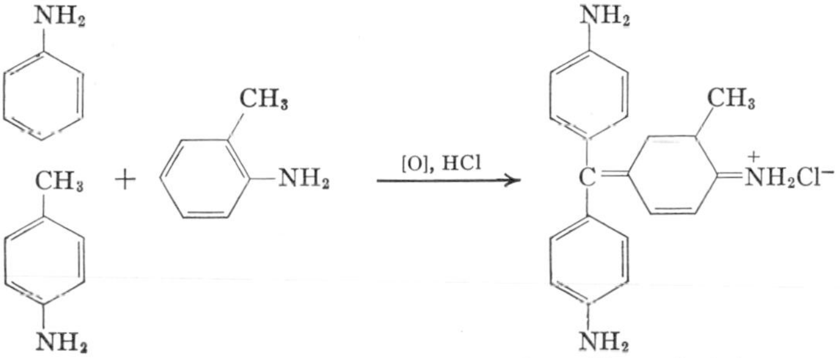

Rosaniline or fuchsin
(abs. max. 5465, 4990 Å)

can be used; mercuric nitrate was favored in early commercial processes, but nitrobenzene is now commonly employed.

Hofmann was the first to note that the color salt is reduced to a colorless dihydro derivative, leucorosaniline; but rosaniline is not a vat dye, since the leuco compound shows no affinity to fiber and is not oxidized to the dye by exposure to air. The salt is basic and is a direct dye to wool or silk and to tannin-mordanted cotton. A blue dye, Blue de Lyons or Aniline Blue (abs. max. 5975Å), introduced in 1860, was shown to be triphenyl-rosaniline by Hofmann, who prepared it by heating rosaniline hydrochloride with aniline. Hofmann shortly obtained the first violet dye of this class by treating rosaniline with ethyl iodide (Hofmanns Violet, abs. max. 5850Å).

The parent member of the rosaniline dyes, pararosaniline or parafuchsin, is prepared from a mixture of one mole of *p*-toluidine and two moles of aniline. Emil Fischer and his cousin Otto Fischer established the skeletal structure in 1880 by converting pararosaniline into triphenylmethane, a

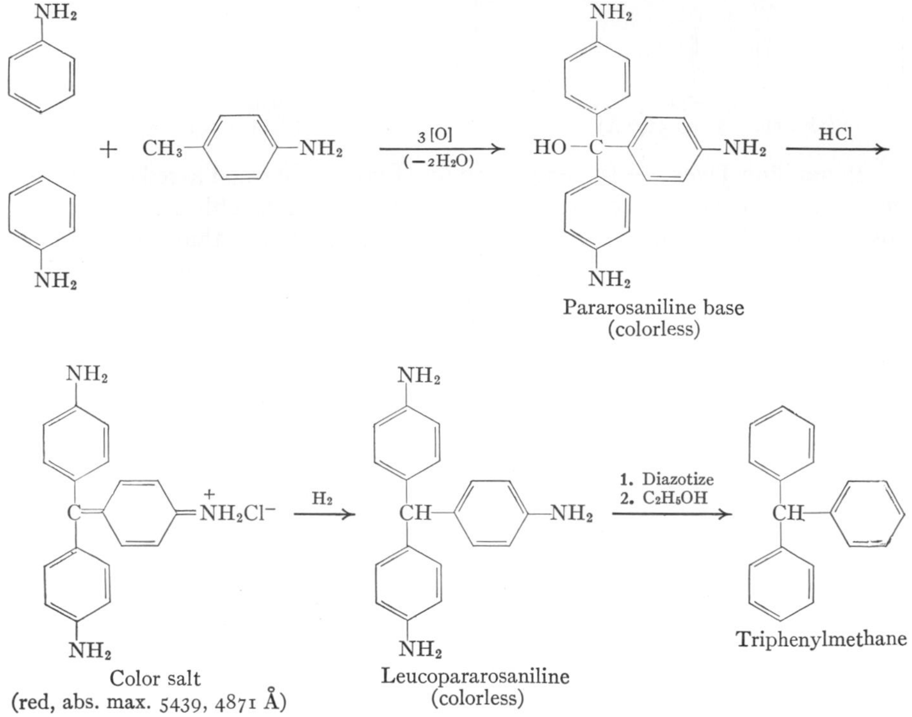

Pararosaniline base
(colorless)

Color salt
(red, abs. max. 5439, 4871 Å)

Leucopararosaniline
(colorless)

Triphenylmethane

hydrocarbon that had been prepared six years earlier by Kekulé. The position of the amino groups was established by degradation and synthesis.

Triphenylmethane dyes are very brilliant, and gradually displaced mauveine, even though they are not so fast to light. Conversion of an insoluble dye into a useful water-soluble acidic dye by sulfonation was first employed in 1862 when Aniline Blue was treated with concentrated sulfuric acid. The product, Nicholson Blue or Alkali Blue, is direct to wool or silk. The sulfonate of fuchsin itself, Acid Fuchsin (abs. max. 5450Å), was prepared only in 1877, since fuming sulfuric acid is required in this case and became available commercially only in 1875. Acid Fuchsin was valued at the time since it was the first violet acidic dye.

The usual preparation of Crystal Violet (discovered by Kern and by Caro[2]), the hexamethyl derivative of pararosaniline, illustrates another method for the preparation of triphenylmethane dyes. Hexaalkyl derivatives are more valuable than less highly substituted derivatives because their color is more intense.

[2] Heinrich Caro, 1834–1910; b. Posen, Germany; BASF Ludwigshafen

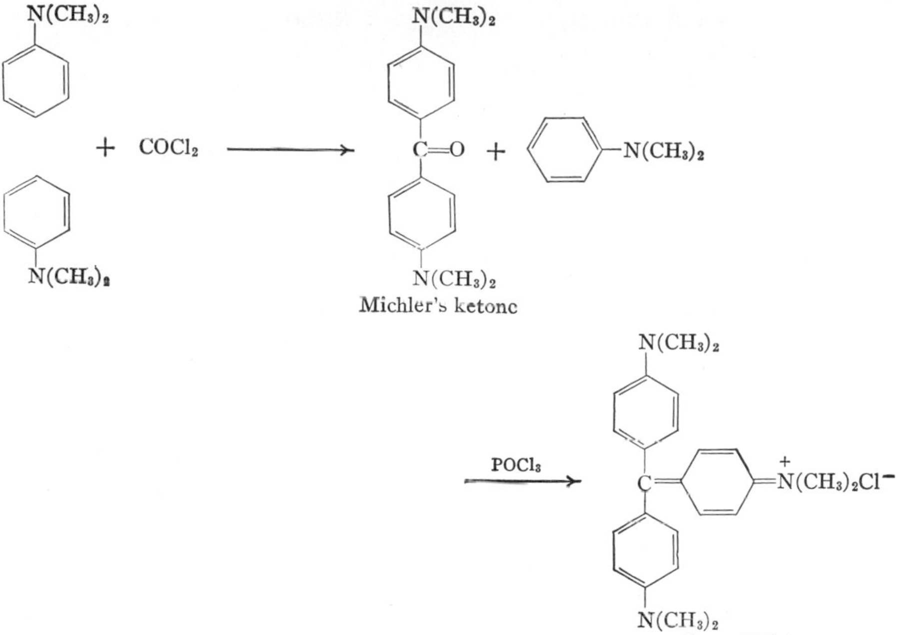

Michler's ketone

Crystal Violet
(abs. max. 5910, 5405 Å)

Another class of triphenylmethane dyes, in which one of the three amino groups characteristic of the rosaniline type is missing, is represented by the

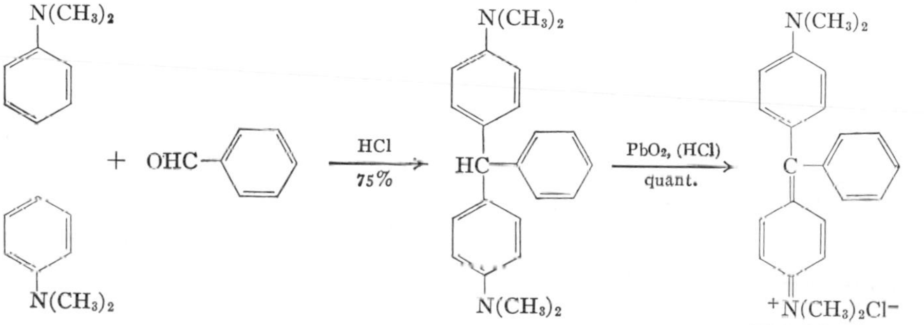

Malachite Green
(abs. max. 6169 Å)

bluish green dye Malachite Green (O. Fischer, 1877). Brilliant Green (abs. max. 6230Å) is the corresponding tetraethyl derivative. The so-called Patent Blues, which are sulfonated derivatives of dyes formed by condensation of *m*-hydroxybenzaldehyde with a dialkylaniline (Hermann, 1888), are more stable to light and to alkali.

Victoria Blue B, from Michler's ketone and phenyl-α-naphthylamine, is

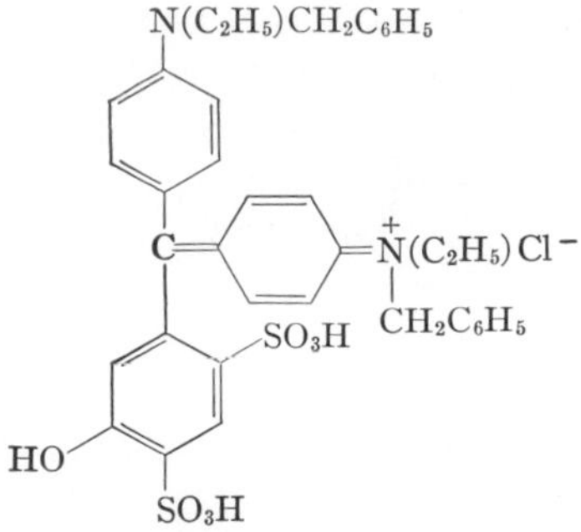

Patent Blue A
(abs. max. 6364 Å)

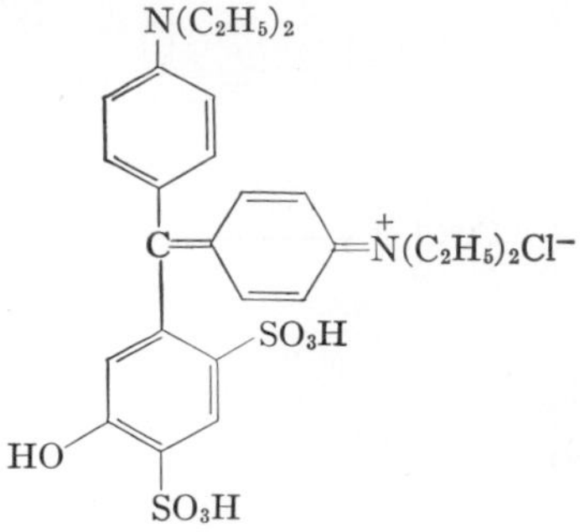

Patent Blue V
(abs. max. 6380 Å)

much used in the form of the phosphomolybdic (or tungstic) acid complex or lake (water-insoluble) for tinting high quality writing paper and as a pigment for inks. The poor light fastness generally characteristic of these basic dyes is improved considerably by complex formation. The dye

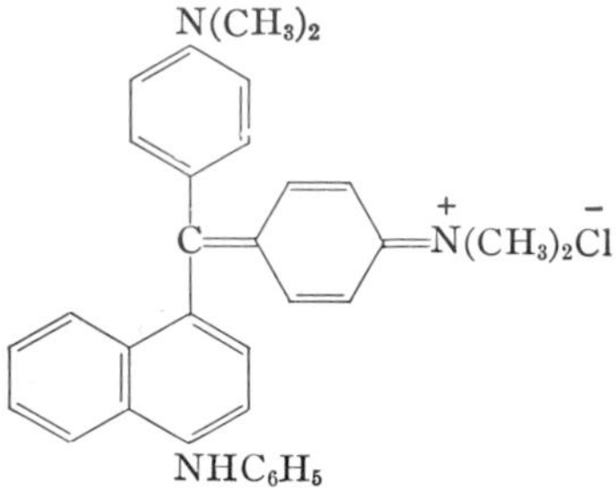

Victoria Blue B

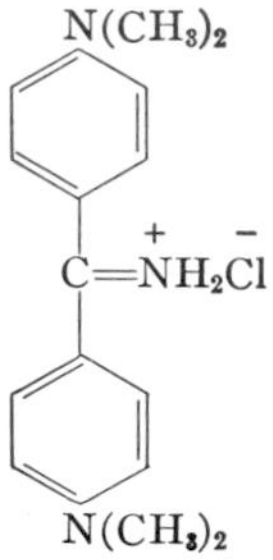

Auramine

Auramine, prepared by the action of sulfur and ammonium chloride on Michler's ketone, is still used for dyeing paper in strong, bright yellow shades, though its fastness to light and stability leave much to be desired.

Aurin. — Aurin (rosolic acid) is one of the earliest known synthetic coloring matters, having been obtained in 1834 (Runge) by oxidation of

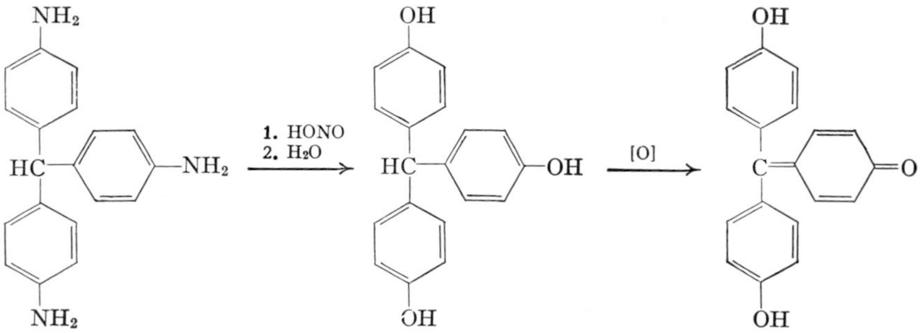

Leucopararosaniline

1. HONO
2. H_2O

Leucoaurin

[O]

Aurin (yellow; abs. max. in KOH, 5346, 4795 Å)

phenol. Kolbe (1861) prepared the same substance by heating phenol with oxalic acid and concentrated sulfuric acid. The constitution as a triphenyl-methane derivative was established by O. and E. Fischer when they obtained aurin by treating diazotized leucopararosaniline with water. The Kolbe synthesis is considered to involve condensation of three molecules of phenol with formic acid (from decarboxylation of oxalic acid). Formaldehyde can also be used to supply the central carbon atom, and several dyes are made commercially by condensing formaldehyde with substituted phenols in the presence of nitrite-containing sulfuric acid, as illustrated by the synthesis of aurintricarboxylic acid (Chrome Violet Gy). Aurin is not used

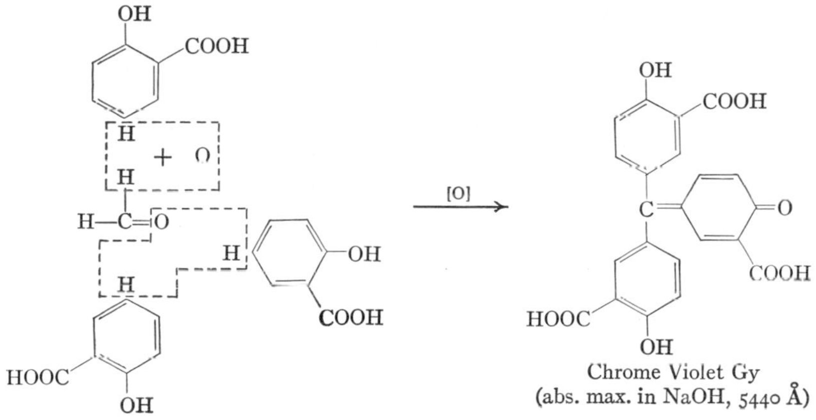

Chrome Violet Gy
(abs. max. in NaOH, 5440 Å)

as a dye since it is not highly colored, lacks solubility in water, and contains no anchoring groups. Aurins containing a carboxyl group *ortho* to a hydroxyl group, e.g., Chrome Violet, are useful mordant dyes.

The Phthaleins. — Baeyer in 1871 discovered a new class of dyes when he heated pyrogallol with phthalic anhydride at 195–200° and obtained a red substance to which he gave the name gallein. On replacing pyrogallol with resorcinol Baeyer obtained a yellow product whose solutions in water showed an intense yellow fluorescence and which he accordingly named fluorescein. Baeyer next prepared the parent member of the group by condensing phthalic anhydride with phenol in the presence of dehydrating agents (sulfuric acid, zinc chloride). The product, phenolphthalein, is colorless, though it forms vivid red solutions in alkali, from which the colorless material is recovered on acidification. Baeyer's next publication on the phthaleins was nine years later when he presented two papers totaling one hundred and thirty-three pages in the *Annalen* (1880) entitled "The Compounds of Phthalic Acid with Phenols," in which he describes the preparation of fifty derivatives and degradation products of the phthaleins. Baeyer arrived at the structure on the basis of the degradation of phthalophenone to triphenylmethane illustrated in the formulas. Conversion of phthalophenone to phenolphthalein (by nitration, reduction, diazotization, and hydrolysis) showed that phenolphthalein is a dihydroxy derivative of

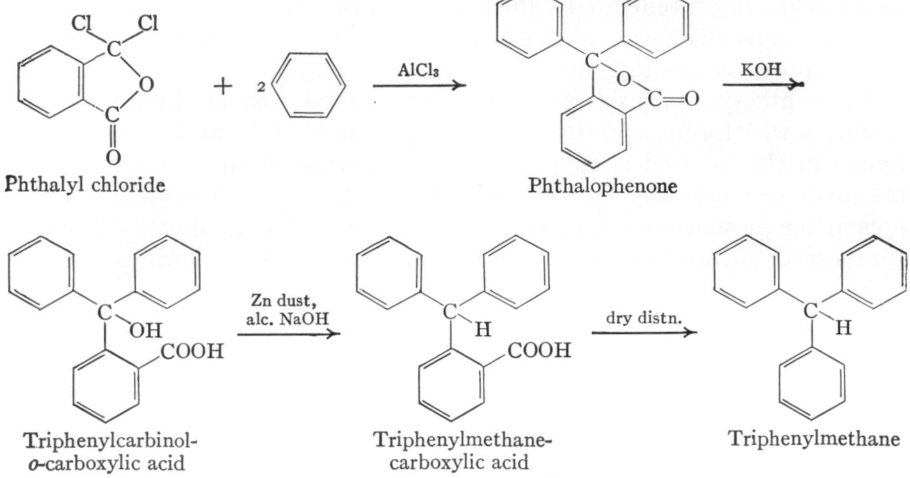
Cl
Cl
C
O
C
O
Phthalyl chloride
+ 2
AlCl₃
C
O
C=O
Phthalophenone
KOH
C
OH
COOH
Triphenylcarbinol-
o-carboxylic acid
Zn dust,
alc. NaOH
C
H
COOH
Triphenylmethane-
carboxylic acid
dry distn.
C
H
Triphenylmethane

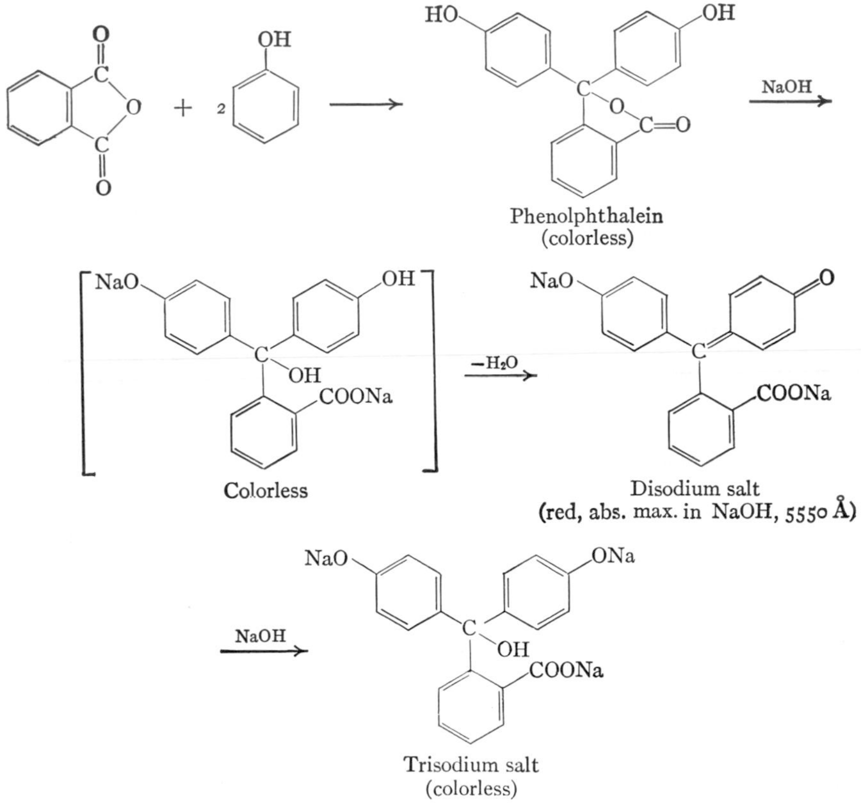
O
C
O
C
O
+ 2
OH
HO
OH
C
O
C=O
Phenolphthalein
(colorless)
NaOH
NaO
OH
C
OH
COONa
Colorless
−H₂O
NaO
O
C
COONa
Disodium salt
(red, abs. max. in NaOH, 5550 Å)
NaOH
NaO
ONa
C
OH
COONa
Trisodium salt
(colorless)

phthalophenone. When alkali is added to an alcoholic solution of phenol-phthalein, an intense red color is obtained as a disodium salt is formed, but disappears if more alkali is added.

In analogy with phenolphthalein, fluorescein was originally considered to have the structure shown in formula I. However, such a formula does

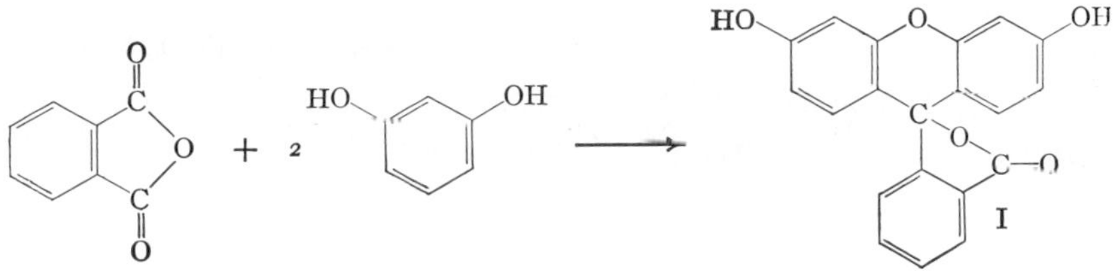

not account for the color. Consequently formula IIa or IIb (and resonance forms) are more likely. Fluorescein dyes wool and silk direct from an acid

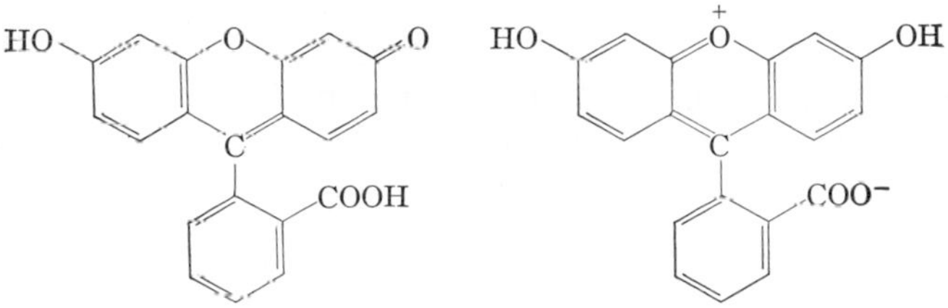

Fluorescein
(abs. max. 4935, 4600 Å)

bath but the yellow color is not fast. A tetrabromo derivative known as Eosin A (yellowish red, Gr. *eos*, dawn), is used as a direct dye to wool and to silk.

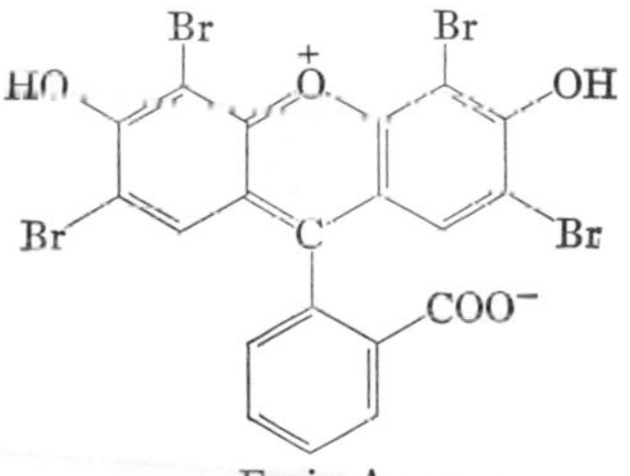

Eosin A
(abs. max. 5160, 4835 Å)

Similar dyes, known as rhodamines, are obtained by heating phthalic anhydride with *m*-monoalkyl- or *m*-dialkylaminophenols. The preparation of the ethyl ester of diethylrhodamine (Rhodamine 6G) is shown in the formulas (next page).

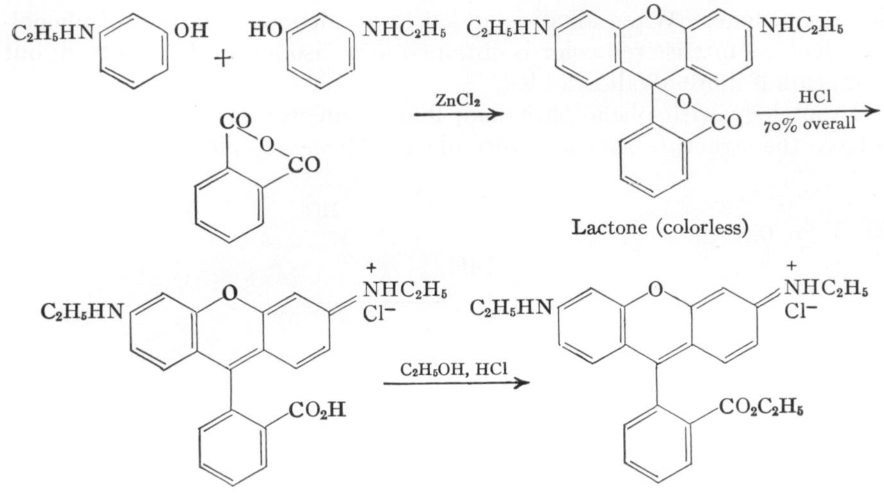

Lactone (colorless)

Diethylrhodamine

Rhodamine 6G
(red, abs. max. 5250, 4970 Å)

Cyanine Dyes. — Cyanine dyes are prepared by a reaction discovered by Greville Williams in 1856, which consists in heating a mixture of the alkyl halide derivatives of quinoline and lepidine in an alkaline medium, as shown for the preparation of Cyanine Blue (1,1′ diethyl-4,4′-cyanine iodide):

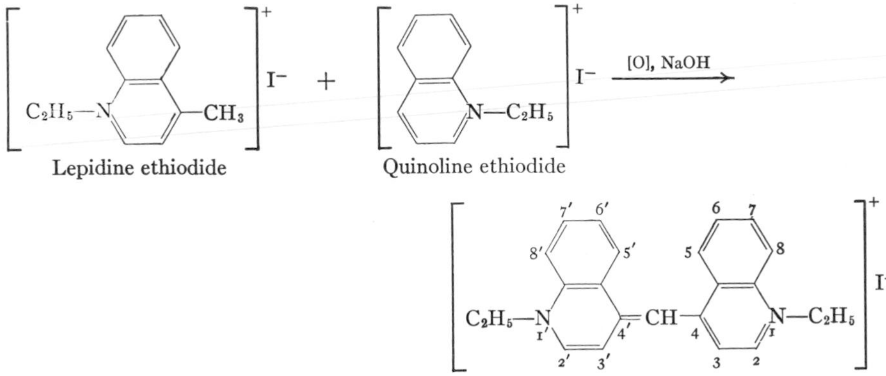

Lepidine ethiodide   Quinoline ethiodide

Cyanine Blue
(abs. max. in alc., 5922, 5537 Å)

The isocyanines, of which Ethyl Red is a typical example, are obtained by similar condensation of the ethiodides of quinaldine and quinoline (1883). Another important dye of this type, 1,1′,6-trimethylisocyanine iodide (abs. max. 5621Å), is known as Sensitive Green or Pinaverdol. The pseudocyanines are formed by the action of alcoholic potassium hydroxide on the quaternary ammonium salts of 2-iodoquinoline and quinaldine (1912).

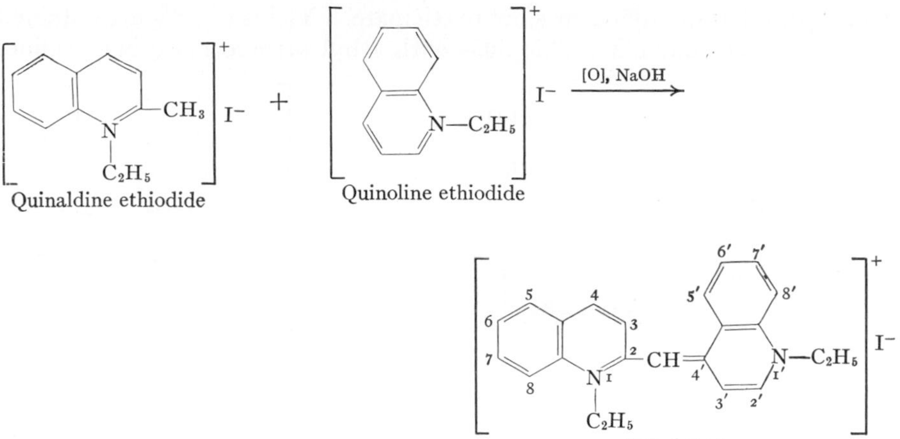

Quinaldine ethiodide + Quinoline ethiodide →[O], NaOH

Ethyl Red
(bluish red; abs. max. in alc., 5602 Å[b])

Cyanines are of no value as dyes since they are expensive and extraordinarily sensitive to light and to acids. Their great value lies in their

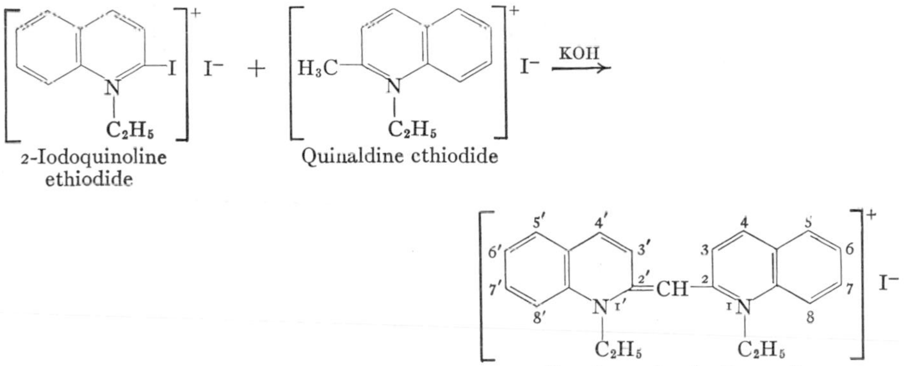

2-Iodoquinoline ethiodide + Quinaldine ethiodide →KOH

Pseudocyanine (yellow-red)

ability to sensitize silver halide photographic plates (Miethe, 1903), which are sensitive ordinarily only to light of wave length 4000–4500Å. Certain other dyes have been used since 1873 for this purpose; for instance, eosin is a sensitizer for green and yellow light (5100–5500Å) and rosaniline for red light; but the cyanines sensitize over a far wider region of the spectrum and are more potent. The isocyanines are particularly useful; Ethyl Red sensitizes photographic plates to light from ultraviolet to orange (5900Å); Sensitive Green is even more powerful.

König (1915) found that if the isocyanine condensation is carried out in the presence of formaldehyde, blue dyes (carbocyanines) are obtained that sensitize to light of longer wave length than the isocyanines, that is, yellow to infrared. Pope and Mills established that the reaction involves condensation of formaldehyde with two molecules of the quinaldine com-

---

[b] The isocyanines also absorb weakly in the green region of the spectrum.

ponent and that quinoline does not participate. Yields of 70% are obtained by condensing quinaldine alkiodides with ethyl orthoformate in pyridine:

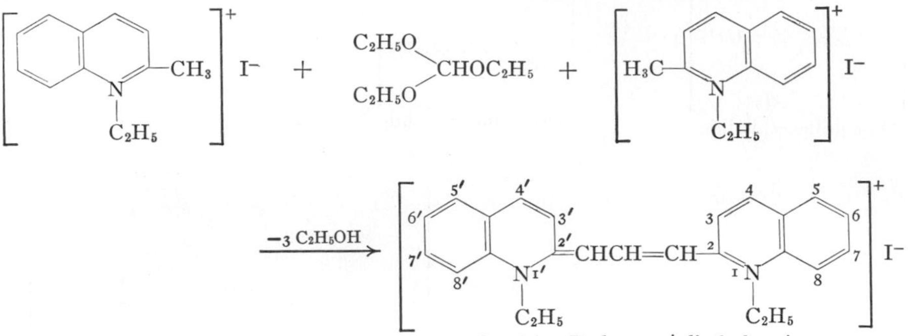

Sensitive Red or 1,1'-diethyl-2,2'-
carbocyanine iodide (blue; abs. max. in alc., 6081 Å•)

The isomeric 4,4'-carbocyanines or kryptocyanines (1920) are prepared from lepidine ethiodide. Kryptocyanine is a potent sensitizer to red and

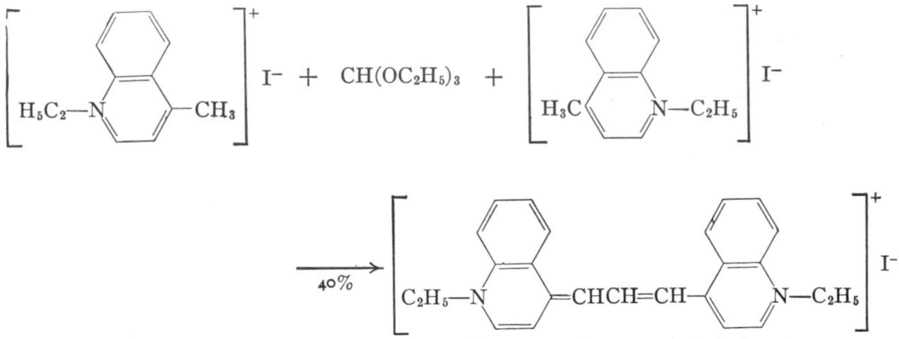

Kryptocyanine or 1,1'-diethyl-4,4'-
carbocyanine iodide (purple-black)

infrared. It is accompanied by a by-product, neocyanine (uncertain struc-

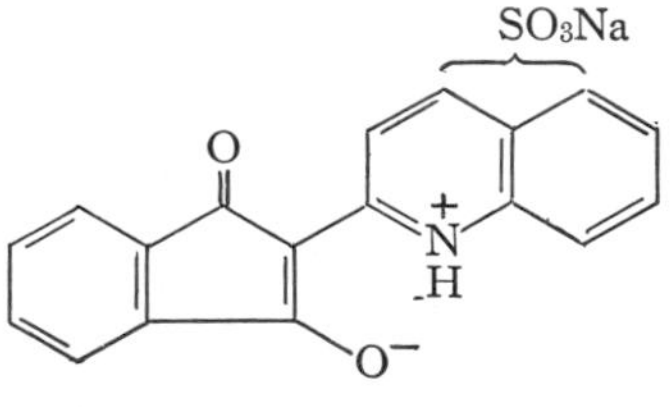

Quinoline Yellow extra 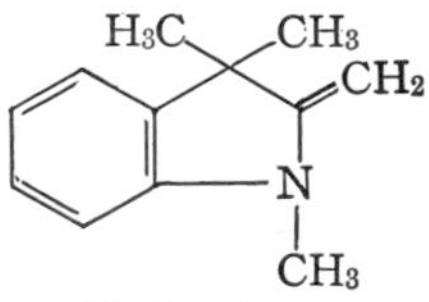   Fischer base

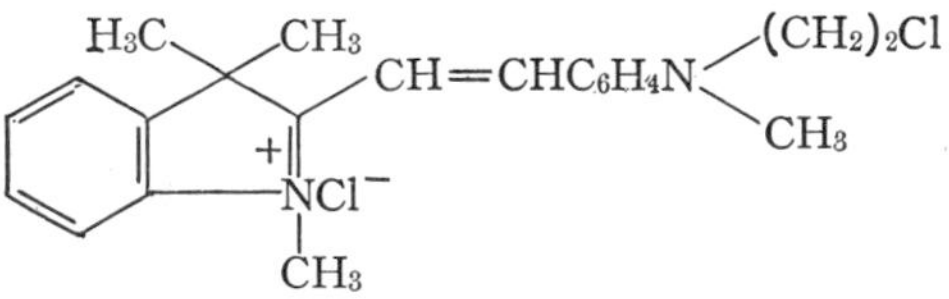

Astrazone Pink FG

• The carbocyanines absorb weakly in the yellow and green regions also.

ture; abs. max. 8300Å), which sensitizes even further in the infrared. Such substances are valuable particularly for long-distance (aerial) photography.

Related Methine Dyes. — Sulfonated Quinoline Yellow (Jacobsen, 1882) is a related basic dye that is still manufactured for dyeing paper in canary yellow shades. Another series of methine-type dyes, the Astrazones, was developed in Germany shortly before World War II. They are made by condensation of an aromatic aldehyde with a substance known as the Fischer base (1,3,3-trimethyl-2-methylenedihydroindole); a typical member is Astrazone Pink FG.

ANTHRAQUINONOID AND INDIGOID DYES

Synthetic Alizarin. — The discovery of the early synthetic aniline dyes was necessarily the result of intuitive following of clues derived from fortuitous experiments, since the constitution of even benzene was unknown. In 1865, Kekulé published his theory of the structure of benzene, and thus paved the way for elucidation of structures of aromatic compounds and for development of the dye industry on a rational basis. Carl Graebe, a young chemist in Baeyer's laboratory, applied the new theory to quinones, and was able to show (1868) that they contain a cyclic system rather than an open-chain structure, as proposed by Kekulé. The investigation was extended by Graebe in collaboration with Carl Liebermann, another young chemist in the same laboratory, to the dye alizarin (Ar. *asara*, to press out), considered at the time to be a naphthoquinone. Graebe and Liebermann applied the method of zinc dust distillation discovered one year earlier by Baeyer during the investigation of indigo. The reaction proceeded with unusual efficiency with production of anthracene, a coal-tar hydrocarbon that at the time had been characterized merely as containing three aromatic rings in either the linear or the angular arrangement. Quinonoid characteristics were recognized both in alizarin and in a little studied oxygenated derivative of anthracene designated by Graebe and Liebermann as anthraquinone. Alizarin was inferred to be a dihydroxyanthraquinone, and though evidence was lacking concerning the structure of the parent substance and the relative positions of the substituents, an attempt was made at this early stage to synthesize the dye. The method was based on a crude

Chloranil   Boiling aq. NaOH   Chloranilic acid

analogy to the behavior of chloranil, which was known to react readily with aqueous alkali with replacement of two of the four halogens by hydroxyl groups. The scheme was to introduce two halogen atoms into anthraquinone with the expectation that these might assume the proper positions and that the substance subsequently could be hydrolyzed.   Anthraquinone was brominated and the dibromo compound, since it failed to react with aqueous alkali at ordinary temperatures, was eventually fused with alkali. The product was found to be identical with natural alizarin (1869)!   It was recognized only many years later that this spectacular first synthesis of a natural dye is remarkable not only because one specific member of a series of possible isomers is obtained, but also because the dibromo compound does not correspond in structure to the dye but suffers rearrangement during alkali fusion, probably involving fission of the quinone ring and ring closure in an alternate position:

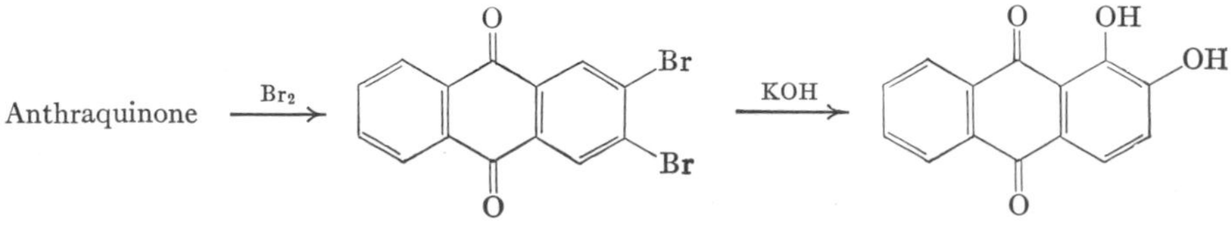

Anthraquinone $\xrightarrow{Br_2}$ 2,3-Dibromoanthraquinone $\xrightarrow{KOH}$ Alizarin
(abs. max. in KOH,
6108, 5665, 5276 Å)

   The first synthesis of a naturally occurring dye was hailed as a remarkable achievement, but it was not suitable for commercial exploitation owing to the great expense of bromine and the difficulty in carrying out the fusion on a technical scale.   A patent assigned to the Badische Anilin- und Soda-Fabrik was found inoperable.   Attempts were then made by Graebe and Liebermann, in collaboration with Heinrich Caro of the Badische company, to apply the method of introducing phenolic hydroxyl groups through the sulfonates, discovered independently in 1867 by Kekulé, by Wurtz, and by Dusart.   Initial attempts failed, for anthraquinone proved to be much more resistant to sulfonation than any compound previously investigated, but Caro eventually discovered, through an unintentional experiment, that if anthraquinone is heated with concentrated sulfuric acid to a sufficiently high temperature it is converted into a water-soluble sulfur-containing derivative. Before this sulfonic acid derivative had been fully characterized, it was found by the three collaborators to afford alizarin in high yield on fusion with alkali (1869).   The substance was at first supposed to be a disulfonic acid corresponding to alizarin in structure, but an *ortho* orientation of *meta* directing groups would be abnormal; it is now known that a second sulfonic acid substituent enters the second benzenoid ring.   In due course, it was established that the intermediate is the 2-monosulfonic acid and that conversion of this substance into alizarin results from nucleophilic hydroxylation in the α-position with oxidation by air (or an added oxidant such as sodium chlorate).   The same synthesis was discovered independently and simultaneously by W. H. Perkin. Synthetic alizarin was placed on the market in 1871, only two years after the initial discovery, and within a short time supplanted the natural product.

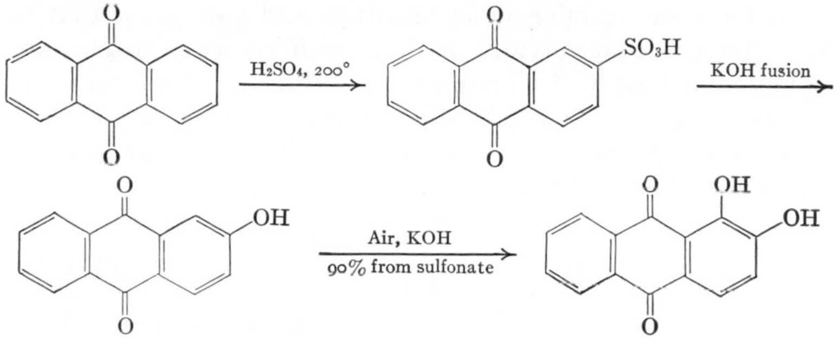

Polyhydroxyanthraquinones. — The discovery of synthetic alizarin did not lead immediately to similar dyes as in the case of rosaniline, partly because alizarin is the only one of the nine dihydroxy derivatives of anthraquinone that forms colored lakes with mordants and also because simple derivatives of alizarin are not valuable dyes. The first important derivative, Alizarin Blue, was discovered by Prud'homme (1877) and shown by Graebe to be a pyridine derivative. The reaction by which Alizarin Blue

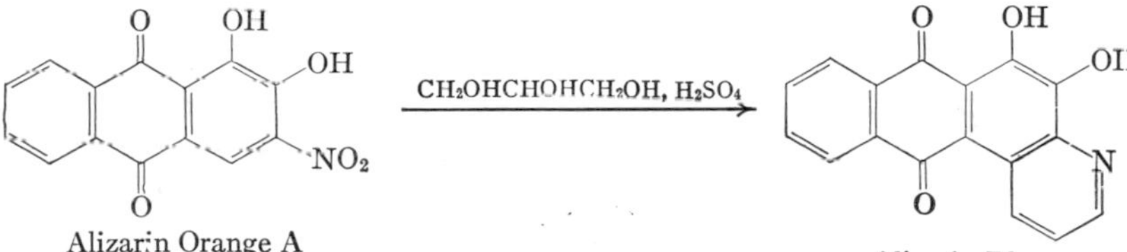

Alizarin Orange A
(Al lake, orange-yellow; Fe lake,
violet-red; abs. max. in KOH,
5785, 5340, 4955 Å)

Alizarin Blue
(abs. max. 6021, 5580, 5227, 4952 Å)

is formed was later studied by Skraup, and is known as the Skraup quinoline synthesis (p. 810).

After the introduction of Alizarin Blue, advances in alizarin dyes lapsed till Bohn[3] (Badische Company, 1888) discovered that hydroxyl groups can be introduced into anthraquinones by fuming sulfuric acid (nucleophilic substitution). The reaction was discovered in connection with Alizarin Blue, and led to several valuable new dyes containing one or more hydroxyl (and sulfonate) groups. Alizarin Indigo Blue is a trihydroxy derivative prepared by treating Alizarin Blue with 80% fuming sulfuric acid at room temperature for several days. R. E. Schmidt, at the rival dye firm of Friedrich Bayer,

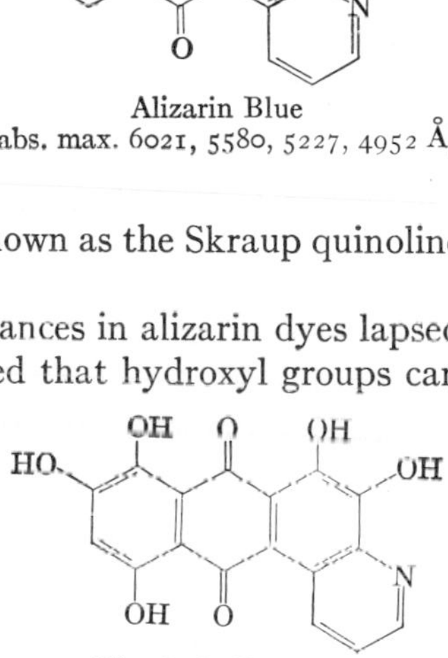

Alizarin Indigo Blue

[3] René Bohn, 1862–1922; b. Dornach/Mühlhausen, Alsace; Ph.D. Zurich (Heumann); BASF Ludwigshafen

discovered the same reaction independently, and also found that addition of boric acid is advantageous and that a trace of mercury or selenium, often present in commercial acid, is required as catalyst. The process is applicable to alizarin itself and also to other anthraquinones, as in (1) and (2); the product of the second reaction on desulfonation yields 1,2,4,5,6,8-hexahydroxyanthraquinone (Alizarin Blue WR).

1. $\xrightarrow{\text{MnO}_2,\ \text{H}_2\text{SO}_4}$

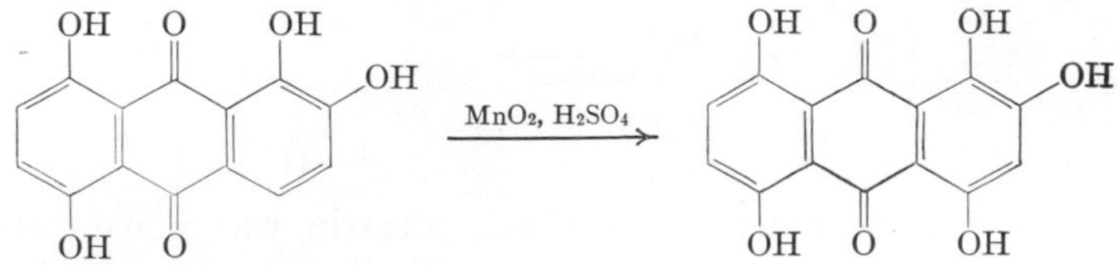

Alizarin Bordeaux or quinalizarin
(violet-blue, Cr mordant; abs. max. in
KOH, 5870, 5435 Å; in alc., 4902 Å)

Alizarin Cyanin R
(blue, Cr mordant; abs. max. in KOH,
5817, 5387, 5024 Å; in alc., 5590, 5202 Å)

2. $\xrightarrow{\text{H}_2\text{SO}_4,\ \text{SO}_3}$

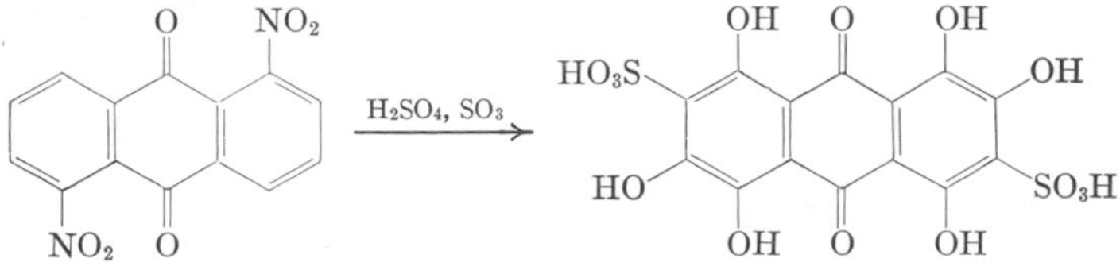

1,5-Dinitroanthraquinone

Anthracene Blue WSR
(blue, Cr mordant; abs. max. 5490,
5355, 5100, 4990, 4760 Å)

Anthraquinone Dyes for Wool and for Hydrophobic Fibers. — Sulfonated amino- or hydroxyanthraquinones are important direct dyes for wool, giving green or blue shades of outstanding brightness and good fastness. Representative commercial standards are Alizarin Saphirol B (from 1,5-dihydroxyanthraquinone by disulfonation, dinitration, and reduction); Alizarin Sky Blue BS (condensation of 1-amino-2,4-dibromoanthraquinone with *p*-toluidine, followed by sulfonation); Alizarin Cyanine Green G

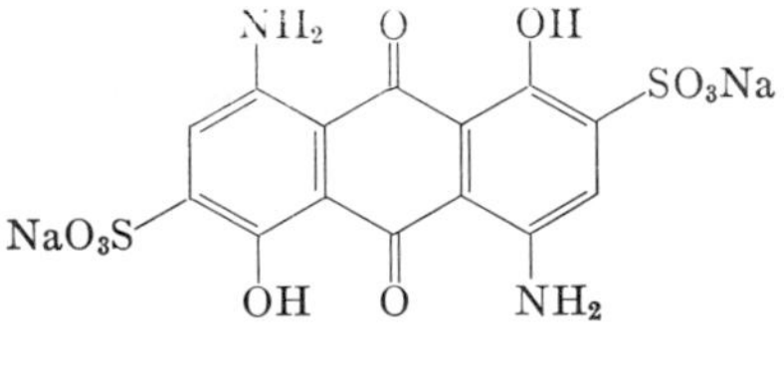

Alizarin Saphirol B

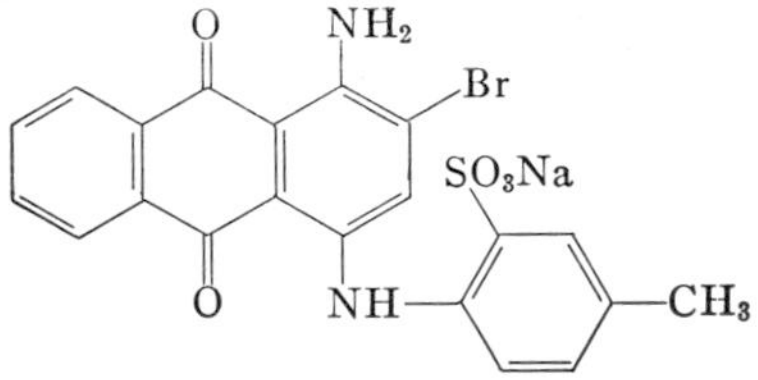

Alizarin Sky Blue BS

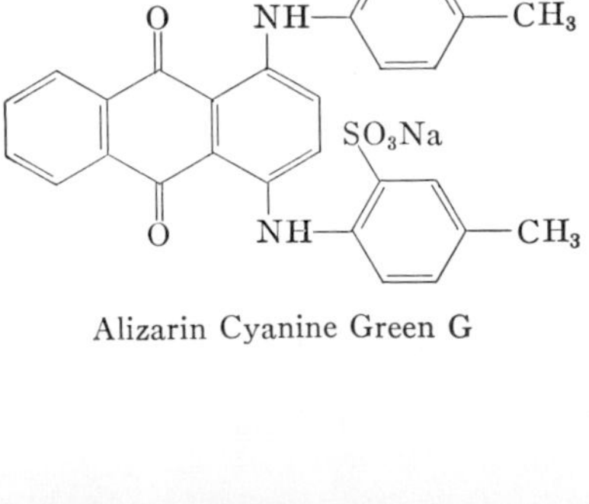

Alizarin Cyanine Green G

(condensation of quinizarin = 1,4-dihydroxyanthraquinone with *p*-toluidine, followed by sulfonation).

Celliton Fast Blue B and Celliton Fast Pink B are typical dyes that serve in dispersible form as direct (unsulfonated) dyes for acetate rayon. Related dyes are used for nylon and other hydrophobic fibers.

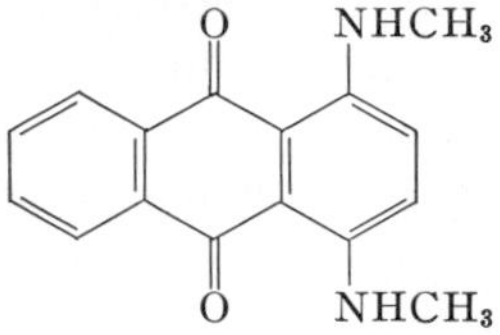
O
$NHCH_3$
O
$NHCH_3$
Celliton Fast Blue B

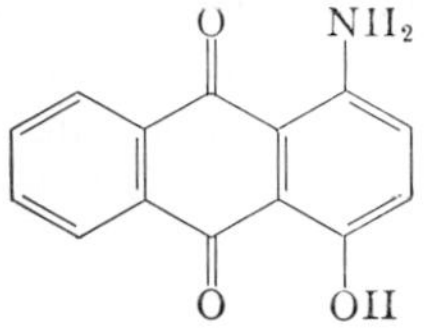
O
NH_2
O
OH
Celliton Fast Pink B

Synthetic Indigo. — Indigo does not occur as such in the indigo plant but is derived from the colorless glucoside indican. On extraction of the crushed plant with water the glucoside is hydrolyzed by enzymes to glucose

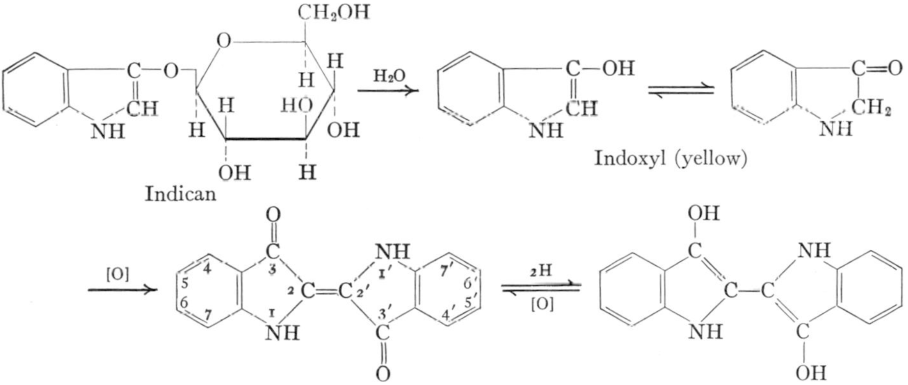
CH_2OH
H_2O
Indican
Indoxyl (yellow)
[O]
2H
[O]
Indigo
(blue; abs. max. in xylene, 5900 Å)

Leucoindigo (white)

and indoxyl, and the latter is oxidized by air to the blue dye. Since indigo, together with alizarin, had maintained a position of prominence throughout

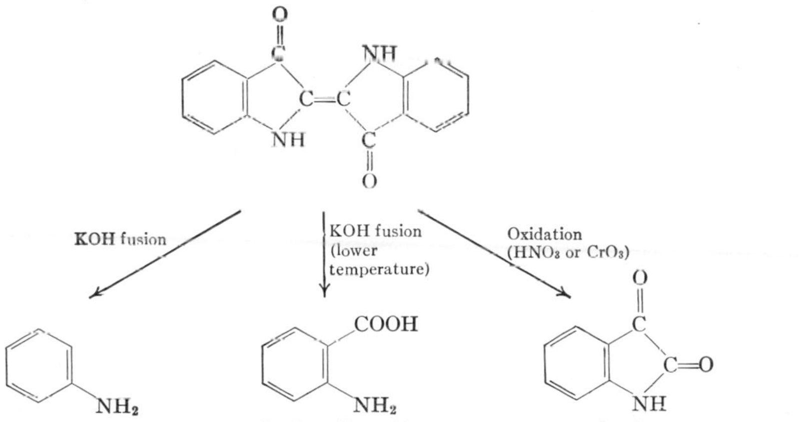
KOH fusion
KOH fusion
(lower
temperature)
Oxidation
(HNO_3 or CrO_3)
NH_2
COOH
NH_2
Aniline
Anthranilic acid
Isatin

the Middle Ages as an important natural dye, chemical characterization attracted the attention of many early chemists. The degradations formulated were worked out during the period 1826–41, though an interpretation of the reactions became possible only several years later. The structure finally was settled by Baeyer in 1883 as a result of researches extending over eighteen years. Baeyer first attempted (1865) to reconvert isatin into indigo by reduction, but obtained instead a series of reduction products, of which the oxygen-free indole represented the final stage. The desired conversion was achieved in 1878 by use of phosphorus trichloride, phosphorus,

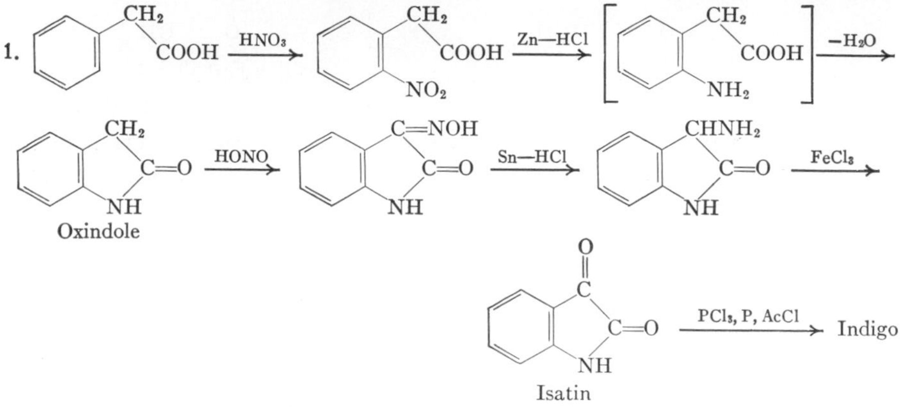

1. $\overset{CH_2}{\underset{COOH}{\bigcirc}}$ $\xrightarrow{HNO_3}$ $\overset{CH_2}{\underset{NO_2 \; COOH}{\bigcirc}}$ $\xrightarrow{Zn—HCl}$ $\left[\overset{CH_2}{\underset{NH_2 \; COOH}{\bigcirc}} \right]$ $\xrightarrow{-H_2O}$

$\overset{CH_2}{\underset{NH}{\bigcirc}} C{=}O$ $\xrightarrow{HONO}$ $\overset{C=NOH}{\underset{NH}{\bigcirc}} C{=}O$ $\xrightarrow{Sn—HCl}$ $\overset{CHNH_2}{\underset{NH}{\bigcirc}} C{=}O$ $\xrightarrow{FeCl_3}$

Oxindole

Isatin $\xrightarrow{PCl_3, P, AcCl}$ Indigo

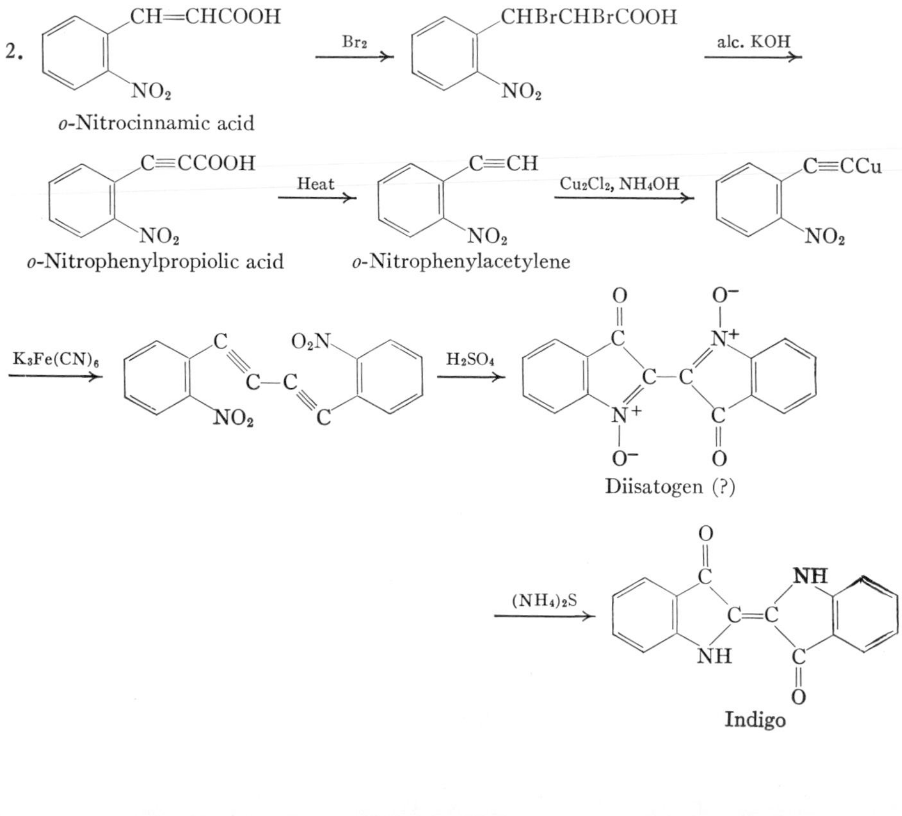

2. $\overset{CH=CHCOOH}{\underset{NO_2}{\bigcirc}}$ $\xrightarrow{Br_2}$ $\overset{CHBrCHBrCOOH}{\underset{NO_2}{\bigcirc}}$ $\xrightarrow{alc. KOH}$

o-Nitrocinnamic acid

$\overset{C\equiv CCOOH}{\underset{NO_2}{\bigcirc}}$ $\xrightarrow{Heat}$ $\overset{C\equiv CH}{\underset{NO_2}{\bigcirc}}$ $\xrightarrow{Cu_2Cl_2, NH_4OH}$ $\overset{C\equiv CCu}{\underset{NO_2}{\bigcirc}}$

o-Nitrophenylpropiolic acid   o-Nitrophenylacetylene

$\xrightarrow{K_3Fe(CN)_6}$ Diisatogen (?) $\xrightarrow{H_2SO_4}$

Diisatogen (?)

$\xrightarrow{(NH_4)_2S}$ Indigo

and acetyl chloride (1); this synthesis had no commercial value since many steps are involved and the yield is low, but was of theoretical importance since isatin was produced by a synthesis that established its structure. The second synthesis (2) utilized *o*-nitrocinnamic acid as the starting material (1882), and showed that the two benzene nuclei in indigo are joined by a chain of four carbon atoms. Baeyer then for the first time proposed a formula for the dye, which he abandoned the following year in favor of a formula which is the *cis* form of the present accepted structure. The Baeyer formula was not disputed until 1928, when X-ray measurements showed that the dye must have the symmetrical *trans* configuration.

Baeyer developed two alternate syntheses from *o*-nitrocinnamic acid as well as one from *o*-nitrobenzaldehyde; the one starting with the aldehyde was tried commercially, but abandoned, since synthetic material could not compete with the natural product in price. The first successful commercial synthesis was developed in 1890 by Heumann.[4] Phenylglycine, prepared by condensation of aniline and chloroacetic acid, was cyclized by fusion with alkali to indoxyl, which was oxidized by air in alkaline solution to indigo. The original synthesis suffered from the disadvantage that cyclization of phenylglycine with alkali could be accomplished only at a destructively high temperature (300°). The successful use of phenylglycine as an intermediate was later made possible by the discovery (Deutsche Gold- und Silberscheidanstalt, 1901) that cyclization can be effected with sodamide in good yield at a temperature of only 180–200°; sodamide was available to Degussa as a by-product of the manufacture of sodium cyanide for extraction of noble metals.

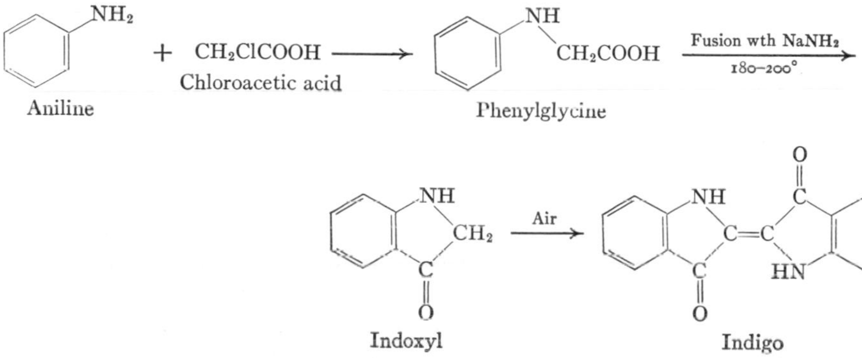

Heumann developed a second synthesis in 1893 utilizing as starting material naphthalene, which at the time was practically a waste product of the coal-tar industry. The hydrocarbon was converted through phthalic anhydride and phthalimide into anthranilic acid, the effective starting material. Condensation of anthranilic acid with chloroacetic acid gives phenylglycine-*o*-carboxylic acid, which is cyclized by alkali at a moderate

4 Karl Heumann, 1850–93; b. Darmstadt, Germany; Ph.D. Heidelberg; Zurich ETH; *Ber.* 27, 2653 (1894)

temperature to indoxylcarboxylic acid, and this β-keto acid readily loses
carbon dioxide to yield indoxyl. Synthetic indigo, made by Heumann's

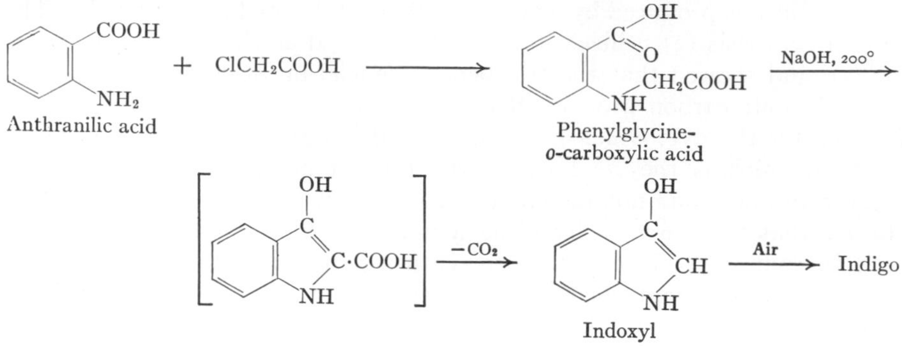

Anthranilic acid

Phenylglycine-
o-carboxylic acid

Indoxyl

second process, could be sold at a price less than that of the natural dye,
and consequently soon controlled the market. The dye is still manufactured on a large scale. Heumann's first synthesis, as modified by use of
sodamide, is now preferred because phenylglycine is cheaper than anthranilic
acid.

Tyrian Purple. — The dye Tyrian (or Phoenician) purple, obtained
from the purple snail (*Murex brandaris*), was prized so highly in ancient
times that it was used as an emblem of royalty and in connection with
religious ceremonies. Dyeing with Tyrian purple became a lost art with the
advent of the Dark Ages, but the species of mollusk containing the rare
pigment was rediscovered in Ireland in 1684. The dye is obtained by air
oxidation of a colorless fluid expressed from the glands of the snail. A crystalline preparation was prepared by Schunck in 1879, who isolated 7 mg. from
400 mollusks. Later Friedländer (1909-11) isolated 1.4 g. on dissecting
12,000 mollusks, and concluded that the dye is a dibromo derivative of

Tyrian purple

indigo, of which there are sixteen possible isomers. Only four have a symmetrical arrangement, which appeared
likely in analogy to the formation of
indigo by oxidative condensation of
two similar parts. Friedländer synthesized 4,4'-, and 5,5'-, and finally
6,6'-dibromoindigo, and found the last
of these identical with Tyrian purple. The dye has no commercial importance, since cheaper dyes of similar color are available.

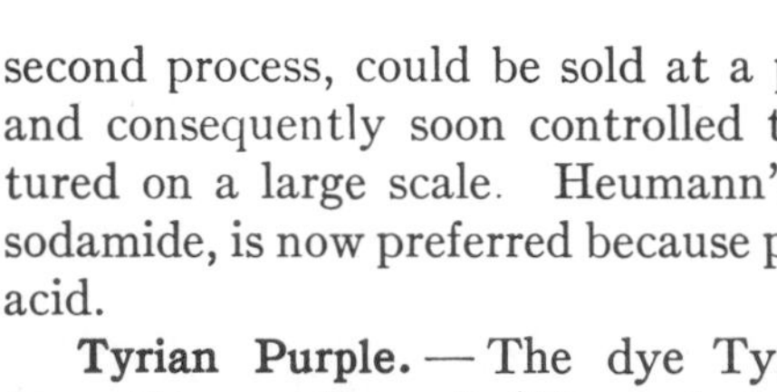

Other Indigoid Dyes. — Because of the beautiful color effects obtained
with indigo and the remarkable fastness and durability of the dye, many
derived and related substances were prepared. The first derivative differing in color from the parent substance was introduced in 1883 under the
name Indigo (or Ciba) Yellow 3G. The dye has no commercial importance,
but the reaction by which it is formed is interesting. It is obtained by

heating indigo at 150° with benzoyl chloride in the presence of copper powder; a rearrangement occurs, with enlargement of the five-membered heterocyclic rings and production of a condensed system of six-membered rings, as shown in the formula.

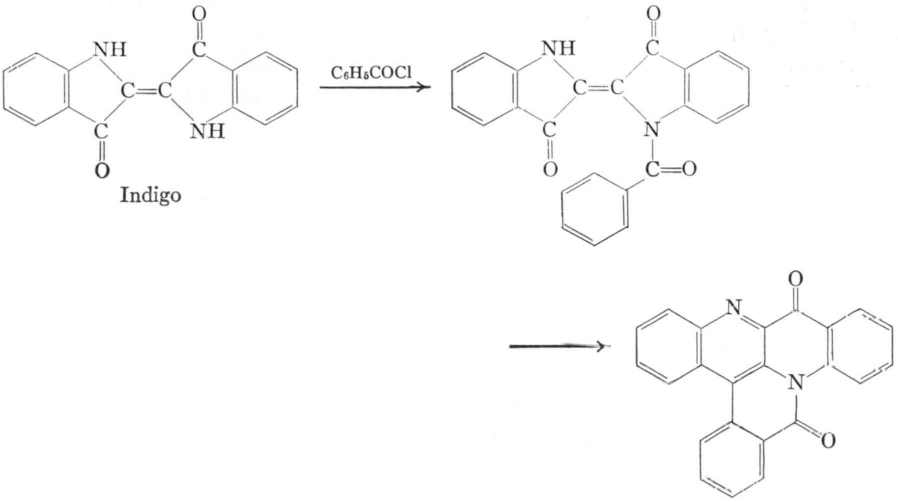

Indigo

Indigo Yellow 3G
(blue-red vat)

Bromine or chlorine atoms can be introduced in the 5-, 7-, 5'-, and 7'-positions of indigo by direct halogenation (1901). Tetrabromoindigo (Brilliant Indigo 4B) is still important; it is not noticeably different from indigo in shade but is considerably brighter.

Various naphthindigos have been prepared but are not valuable since the colors (green) are not fast. A dibromo derivative of 2,1,2',1'-naphthindigo is used to some extent under the name Ciba Green G.

Friedländer (1905) introduced a useful variant in structure by synthesis of thioindigo by the Heumann method from thiosalicylic acid, made by interaction of diazotized anthranilic acid with sodium hydrogen sulfide. This dye is even faster than indigo, but the color is a dull bluish red and

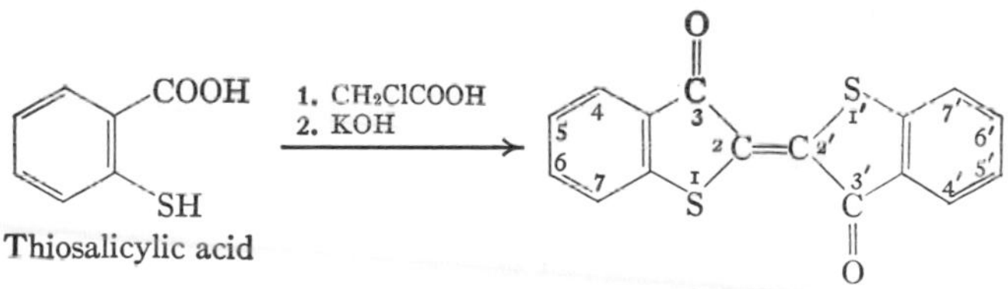

Thiosalicylic acid

Thioindigo or Helindon Red 2B
(yellow vat; abs. max. in xylene, 5440, 5020 Å)

thioindigo itself is not a satisfactory dye. Friedländer (1908) also synthesized the compound known as Ciba Violet A, containing half of the indigo molecule combined with half of the thioindigo molecule, but this likewise found only limited use. However, four derivatives of thioindigo formulated below are important for printing rayon in strong shades of excellent brightness and fairly good fastness to light. They are used to some extent as their leucosulfuric acid ester salts for textile printing. Such an ester derivative is made by treatment of the reduced dye with chlorosulfonic acid and pyridine in the presence of copper or iron. One is Helindon Orange R; the ethoxyl groups in the 6- and 6'-positions produce a hypsochromic shift of the absorption bands. Indanthrene Red Violet RH is made from

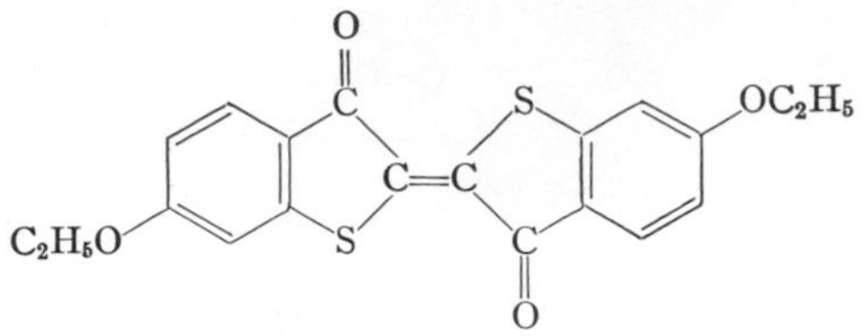

Helindon Orange R
(abs. max. 5775, 5320, 4905 Å)

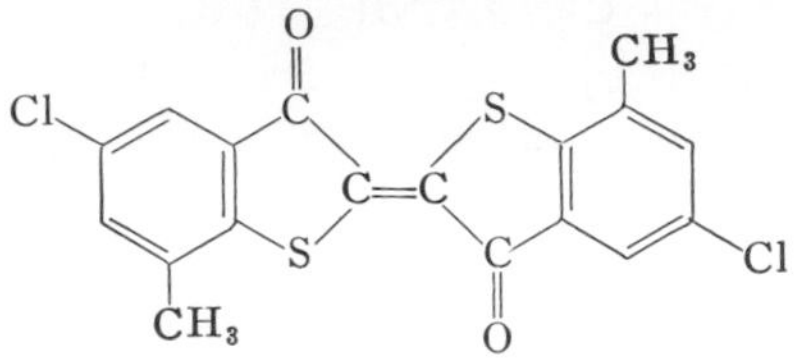

Indanthrene Red Violet RH

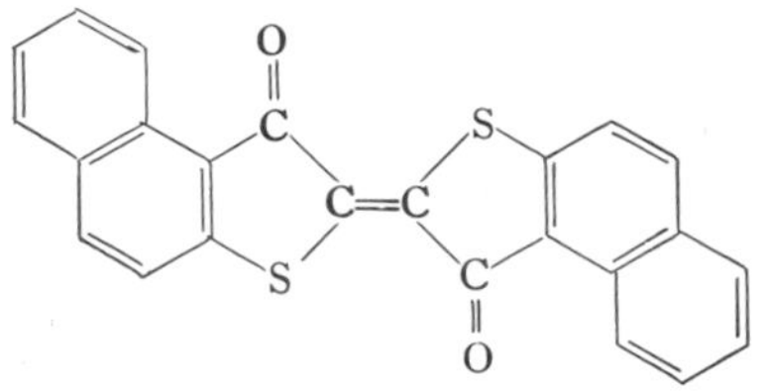

Indanthrene Brown RRD

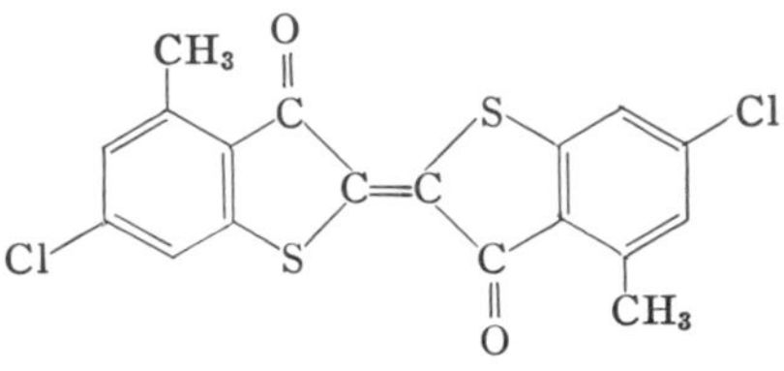

Vat Pink FFR

5-chloro-2-aminotoluene by diazotization, conversion into the mercaptan, condensation with chloroacetic acid to the thioglycolic acid derivative, ring closure with sodamide to the thioindoxyl, and air oxidation. Indanthrene Brown RRD is made similarly from thio-β-naphthol.

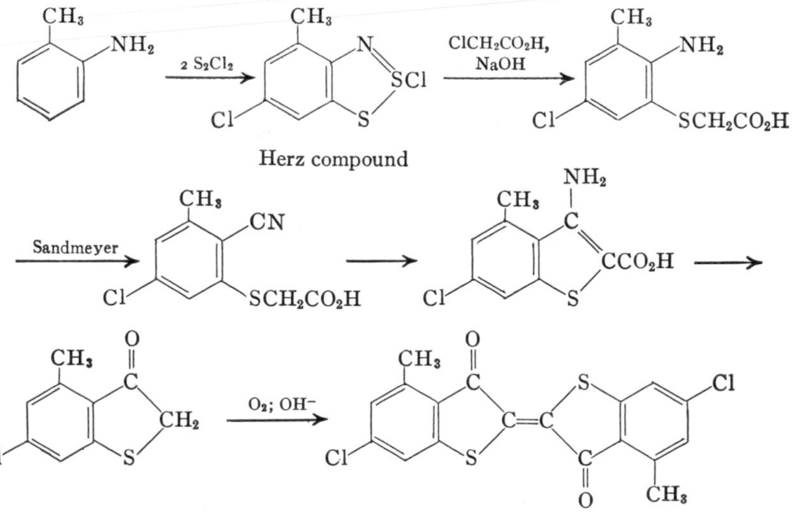

Herz compound

Vat Pink FFR

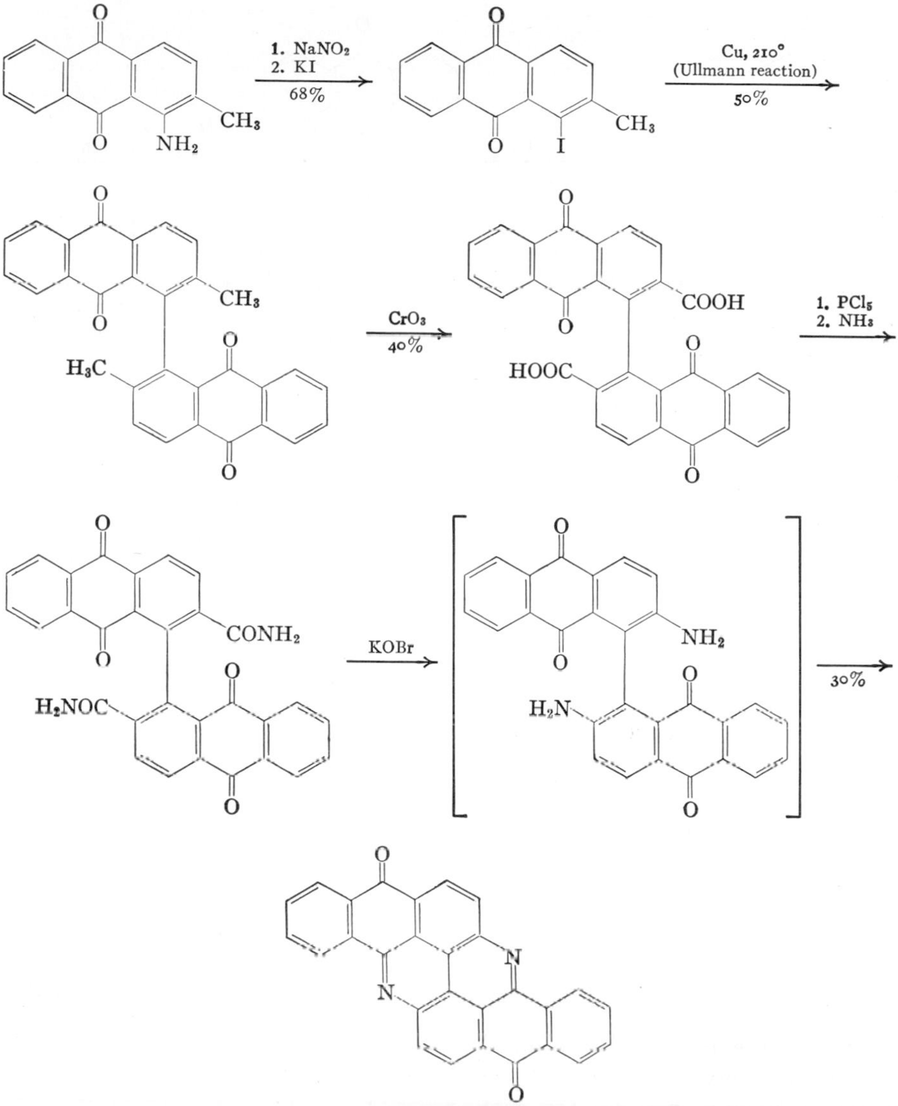

1. NaNO₂
2. KI
68%

Cu, 210°
(Ullmann reaction)
50%

CH₃

O I CH₃

CH₃

H₃C

CrO₃
40%

COOH

HOOC

1. PCl₅
2. NH₃

CONH₂

H₂NOC

KOBr

NH₂

H₂N

30%

Flavanthrone
(ultramarine blue vat; abs. max.
in H₂SO₄, 5114, 4810 Å)

trade name Indanthrene Golden Orange G. It is exceedingly fast and, unlike flavanthrone, is stable to strong irradiation. A dibrominated pyran-throne, Indanthrene Scarlet G, is a valuable dye of beautiful bright orange-red shade and excellent fastness.

Benzanthrone Dyes. — Bally (1904, Badische Anilin- und Soda-Fabrik), in an investigation of anthraquinones, was interested in preparing anthra-quinolinequinone, which Graebe had isolated in small yield during his investigation of Alizarin Blue (1880). In the meantime the Skraup reaction

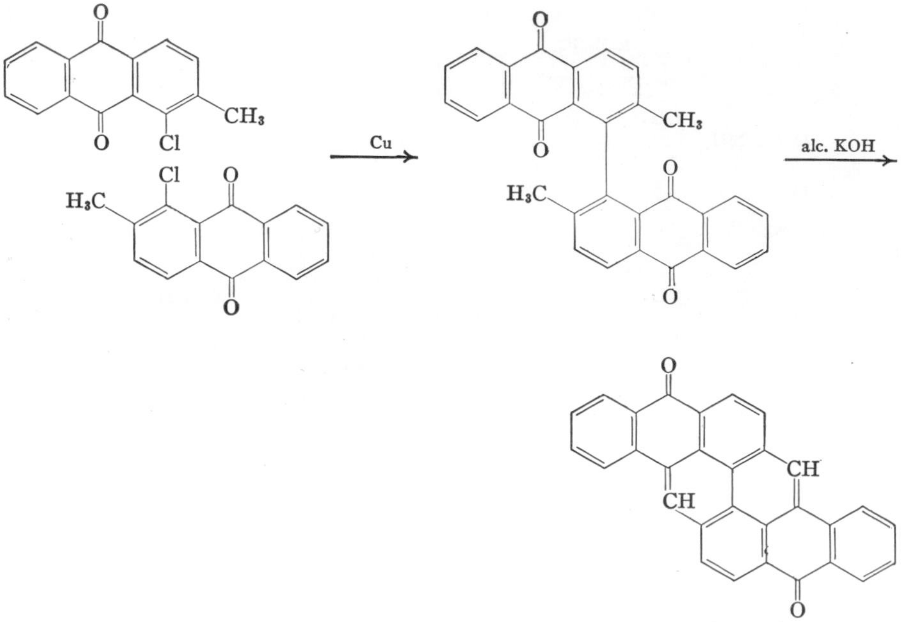

Pyranthrone
(cherry red vat; abs. max.
in H$_2$SO$_4$, 6227, 5456 Å)

had become an important method for the synthesis of quinoline compounds,
and Bally investigated this route to the desired quinone. The product of

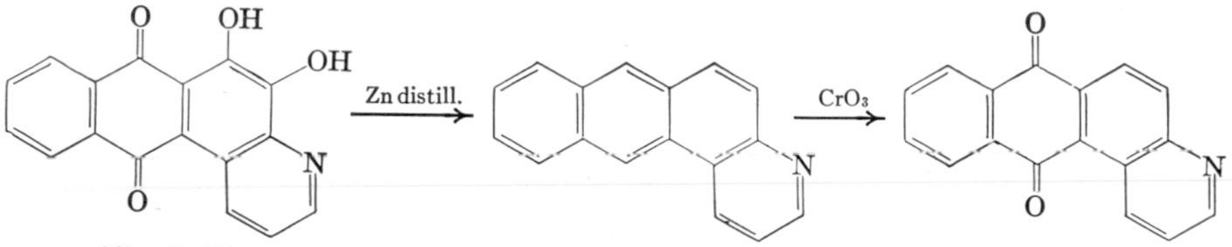

Alizarin Blue   Anthraquinoline   Anthraquinolinequinone

the reaction of β-aminoanthraquinone and glycerol in the presence of sulfuric
acid did not have the expected properties, and analyses indicated that two
moles of glycerol had reacted with one mole of the quinone. Bally concluded that the reaction had proceeded as formulated.   The same product

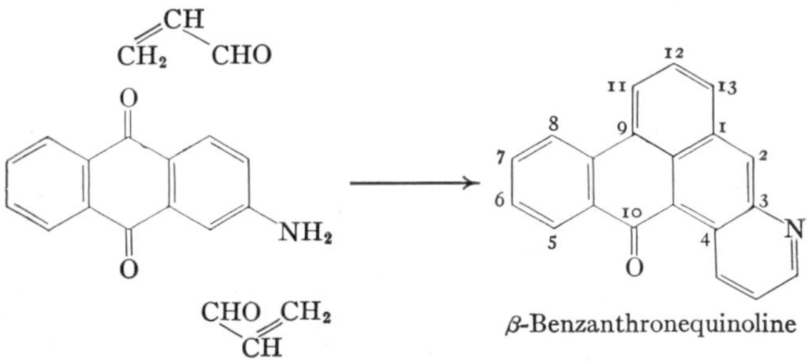

β-Benzanthronequinoline

is obtained by applying the reaction (Bally-Scholl reaction) to anthra-quinolinequinone, so Bally then tried anthraquinone or its reduction product, anthrone, and obtained the parent member of the series, benzanthrone. Benzanthrone is also formed by the dehydrogenating action of aluminum

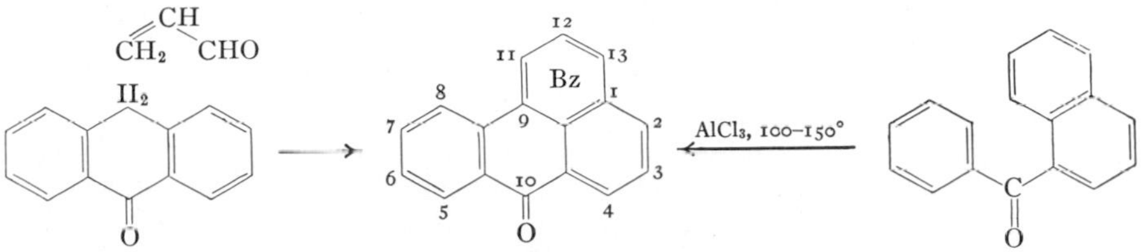

Anthrone   Benzanthrone (yellow, m.p. 170°)   1-Benzoylnaphthalene

chloride on 1-benzoylnaphthalene. This latter synthesis is of no commercial significance, but confirms the structure assigned. Although benz-anthrone itself is valueless as a dye, Bally subjected the substance to fusion with alkali after the manner of Bohn's spectacular syntheses and obtained a dark violet-blue vat dye of excellent fastness, violanthrone. When used in conjunction with indanthrone, excellent navy blue colors are obtained. The structure assigned to violanthrone is based on an alternate synthesis (Scholl) from 4,4'-dibenzoyl-1,1'-dinaphthyl. It is surprising that ring

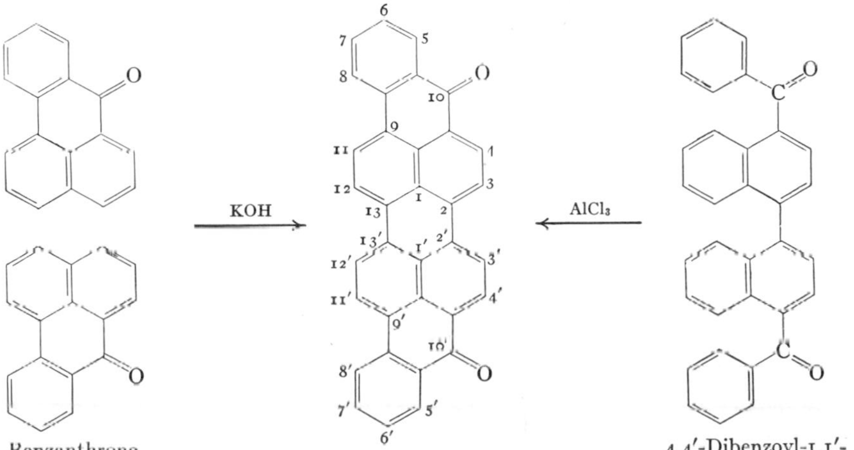

Benzanthrone   Violanthrone (red-violet vat; abs. max. in xylene, 5865, 5300, 4970 Å)   4,4'-Dibenzoyl-1,1'-dinaphthyl

closure in the potassium hydroxide fusion occurs in only one direction and does not give in addition the symmetrical product. This isomer is made by a synthesis in which the position of ring closure is directed by loss of hydro-gen chloride between two molecules of 13-chlorobenzanthrone. The chloro derivative is made by direct chlorination of benzanthrone; the naphthalene nucleus is a more vulnerable site for attack than the benzenoid ring, and

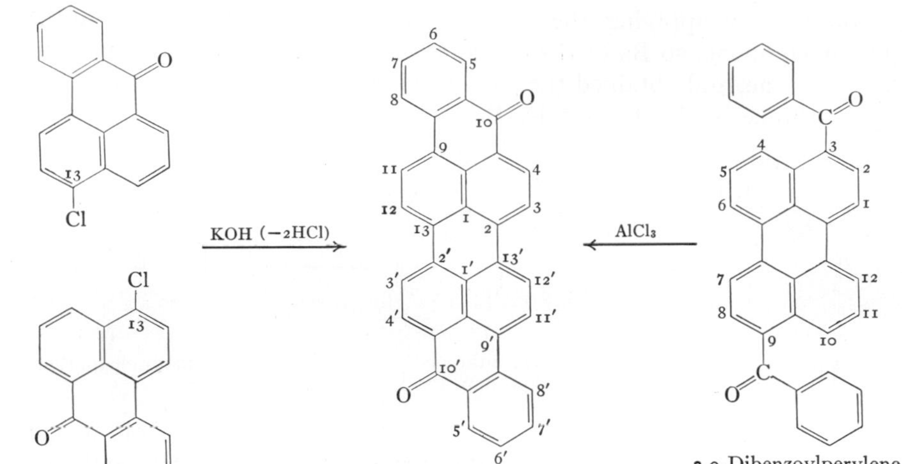

13-Chlorobenzanthrone

Isoviolanthrone
(violet vat; abs. max. in xylene,
5845, 5440, 5045 Å)

3,9-Dibenzoylperylene

chlorine enters the α-position of that half of the naphthalene nucleus which is not deactivated by the attached carbonyl group. The isomer is known as isoviolanthrone; it is an excellent violet dye, but is less important than a dichloro derivative, Indanthrene Brilliant Violet 2R, which gives a very attractive dyeing shade and is also used as a pigment.

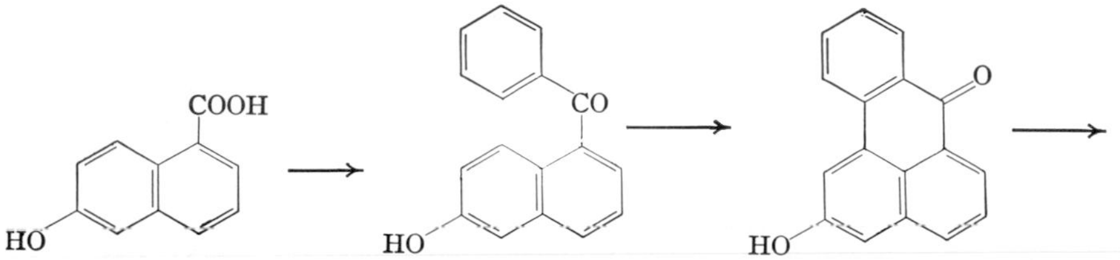

12-Hydroxybenzanthrone

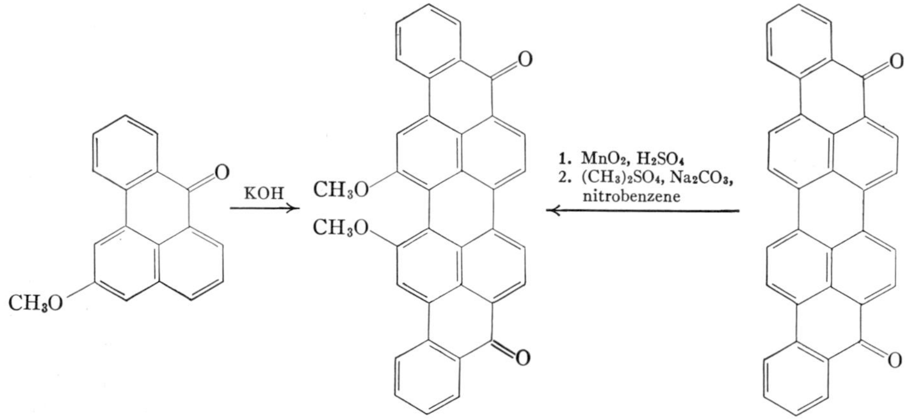

Indanthrene Brilliant Green B
(Caledon Jade Green)

Violanthrone

After the success of violanthrone numerous derivatives were prepared. An excellent black dye, Indanthrene Black BB, is prepared by nitration of violanthrone, followed by reduction of the nitro group to give a green dye which is not useful itself, but which yields the black dye when oxidized on the fiber. The 12,12'-dihydroxy derivative was prepared in 1912 but was valueless, since the color is yellowish green. Ten years later Scottish Dyes prepared the O,O-dimethyl derivative, which is a green dye, the first really good vat dye of this color; the vat is blue. A newer process of manufacture consists in oxidation of violanthrone with manganese dioxide in concentrated sulfuric acid to the 10,12,10',12'-tetraketone and reduction of this with aqueous sulfite to 12,12'-dihydroxyviolanthrone, which is then methylated. The selective reduction with sulfite can be attributed to the high reactivity (potential) of the o,o'-diphenoquinone system between C_{12} and C_{12}'.

Algol Colors. — Prior to Bohn's discovery that dyes other than indigo and its relatives can be applied by vatting, several highly colored anthraquinones had been prepared but tested, as the sulfonic acid derivatives, only as direct dyes. After Bohn's discovery R. E. Schmidt reinvestigated a series of such substances and found various aroylaminoanthraquinones to be promising vat dyes. Several were initially marketed as Algol Colors, but the fastest members of the series now bear the name Indanthrene. The only Algol-type vat dye that still has significance and is manufactured in this country is 1,5-dibenzoylaminoanthraquinone, or Indanthrene Yellow GK. The related Helio Fast Yellow 6GL, which has an o-hydroxybenzoyl-

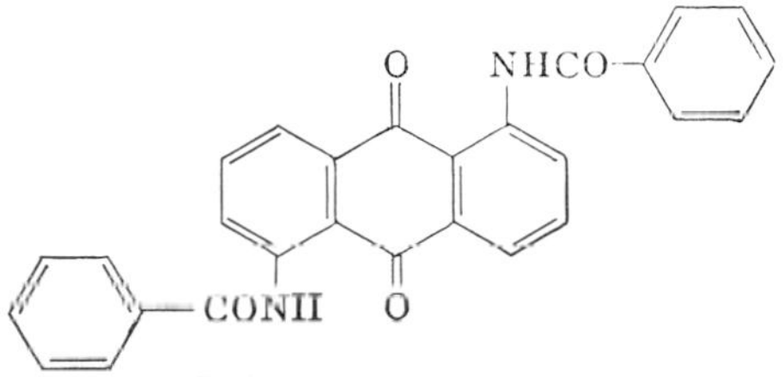

Indanthrene Yellow GK

Helio Fast Yellow 6GL

amino group, is used for paper dyeing and as a pigment. It gives bright, greenish yellow shades of good light fastness.

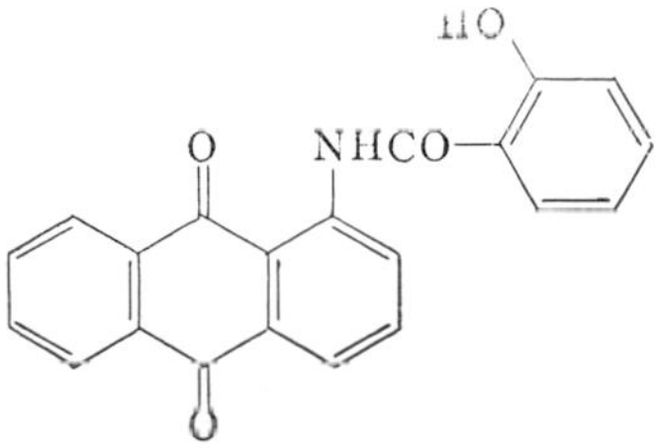

Carbazole Types. — Dyes of this group are made from intermediate dianthrimides obtained by condensation of an aminoanthraquinone with an α-haloanthraquinone. Thus the intermediate for Indanthrene Brown R is made from the condensation either of 1-benzoylamino-4-chloroanthraqui-

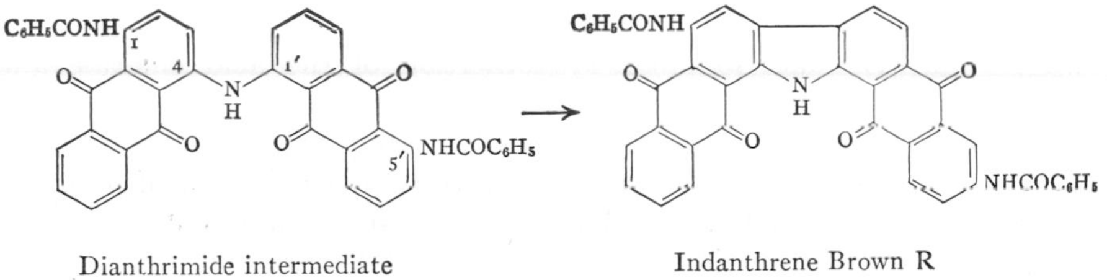

Dianthrimide intermediate

Indanthrene Brown R

none with 1-amino-5-benzoylaminoanthraquinone or of the 1-benzoylamino-4-amino and 5-benzoylamino-1-chloro compounds. Closure of the carbazole ring is accomplished with concentrated sulfuric acid.

Indanthrene Khaki 2G is a related anthraquinone carbazole vat dye that was used during World War II in large quantities for dyeing military fabrics. It is made by condensation of 1,4,5,8-tetrachloroanthraquinone with four equivalents of α-aminoanthraquinone and treatment of the resulting anthrimide with aluminum chloride.

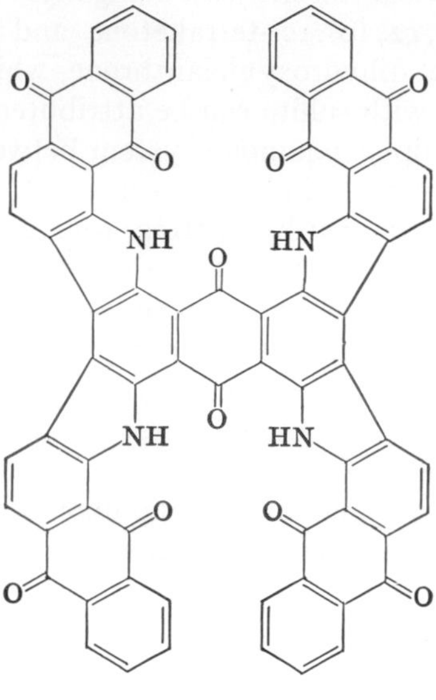

Indanthrene Khaki 2G

Acridone Dyes. — A representative acridone vat dye is Indanthrene Red RK, made by condensation of 1-chloroanthraquinone-2-carboxylic acid

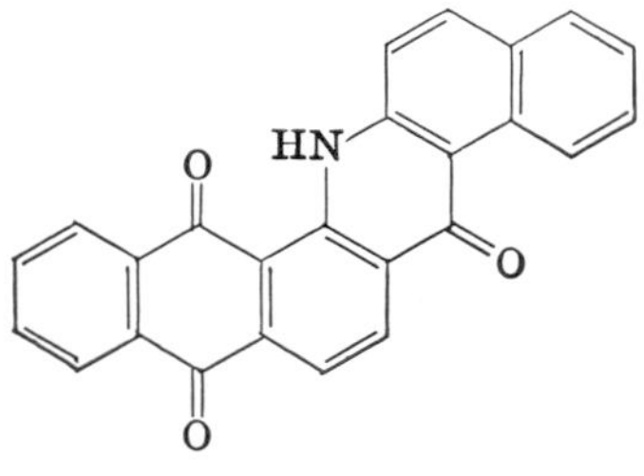

Indanthrene Red RK

with β-naphthylamine, followed by formation of the acid chloride and cyclization with aluminum chloride.

Dialkyl Dipyrazolanthrones. — These dyes are prepared from the starting material pyrazolanthrone, which is made by diazotization of α-amino-anthraquinone, reduction of the diazonium salt to the hydrazine, and ring

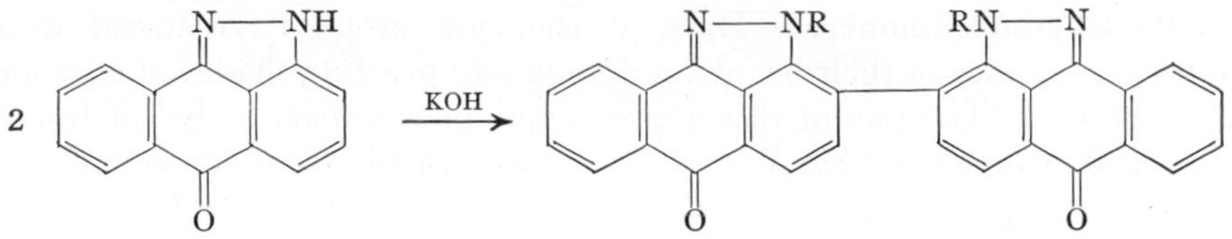

Pyrazolanthrone

R = H: Dipyrazolanthronyl
R = C₂H₅: Indanthrene Rubine R

closure with sulfuric acid. Fusion of the pyrazole derivative with alcoholic potassium hydroxide gives dipyrazolanthronyl, which is then converted into a useful dye by alkylation. The N,N-diethyl derivative, Indanthrene Rubine R, is the best known member of the series.

Dithiazolanthraquinone Dyes. — The only important dye of this class is Algol Yellow GC, made by condensation of 2,6-diaminoanthraquinone

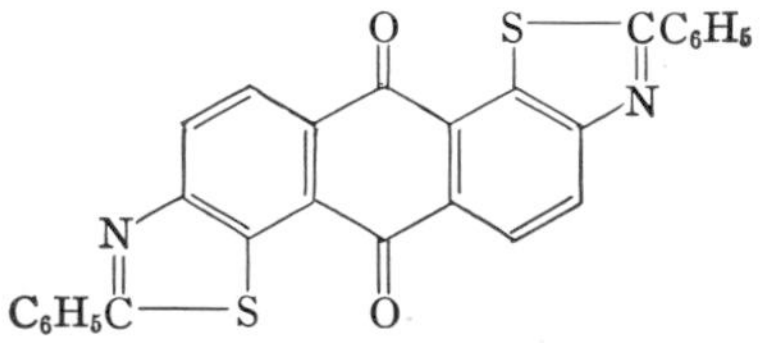

Algol Yellow GC

with benzotrichloride and sulfur. The dye is only moderately fast to light but is nevertheless much used in printing; a combination with Jade Green gives attractive yellowish-green printing shades of good light fastness.

Anthanthrone Dyes. — The parent substance of this group is made by a synthesis starting with Peri acid, which is converted through the nitrile

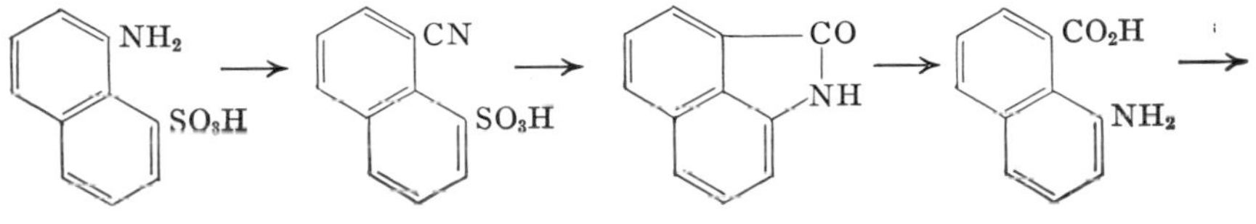

Peri acid   Naphthostyril

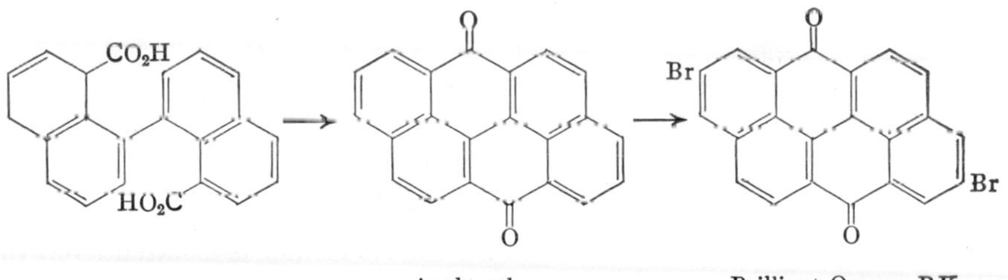

Anthanthrone   Brilliant Orange RK

and naphthostyril into 1,1'-dinaphthyl-8,8'-dicarboxylic acid, which is cyclized to anthanthrone. The most important dye of the group is the dibromo compound formulated.

Dibenzpyrenequinones. — Dyes of this new group have found widespread use because of their beautiful dyeing and printing shades of excellent light fastness. The parent dibenzpyrenequinone is itself a dye of importance (Indanthrene Golden Yellow GK) and is made by dibenzoylation of

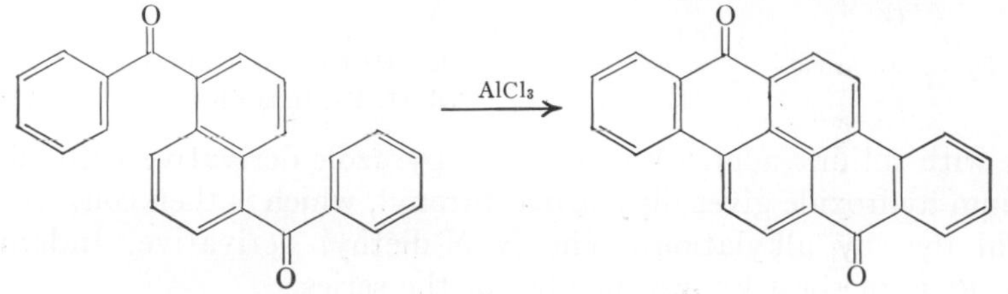

Indanthrene Golden Yellow GK

naphthalene and double ring closure. The product of dibromination, Indanthrene Golden Yellow RK, also finds commercial use.

Tetracarboxyimide Dyes. — The process by which these dyes are made is illustrated by the condensation of naphthalene-1,4,5,8-tetracarboxylic acid with two equivalents of o-phenylenediamine. The resulting mixture of "*cis*" and "*trans*" isomers is marketed as Indanthrene Scarlet GG Base.

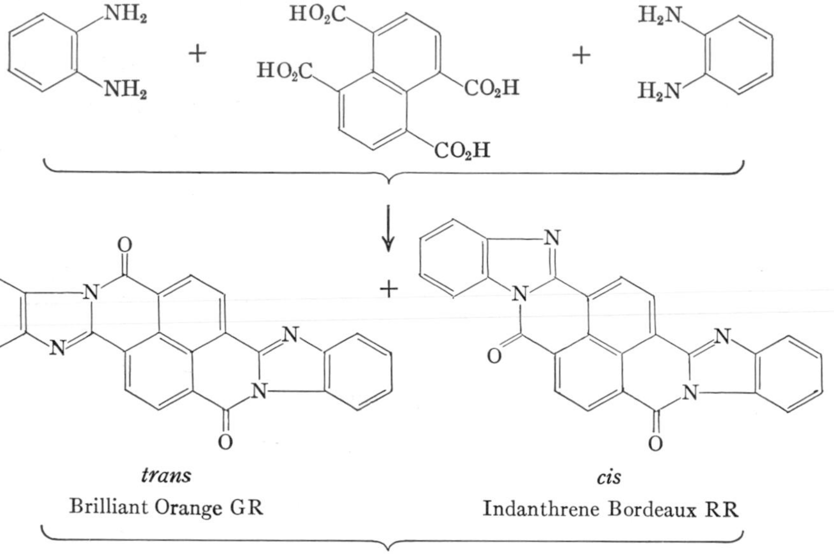

trans	*cis*
Brilliant Orange GR	Indanthrene Bordeaux RR

Indanthrene Scarlet GG Base

A separation is effected by repeated treatment with alcoholic potassium hydroxide; the *trans* isomer is insoluble and the *cis* isomer is isolated from the filtrate. Although these bisimidazoles are not actually anthraquinones, the *trans* isomer is closely analogous in structure to anthanthrones and dibenzpyrenequinones, and both isomers contain the 4,9-diazapyrene structural unit. Related dyes are obtained by condensation of the tetracarboxylic acids of naphthalene and of perylene with various o-diamines.

SULFUR DYES

Dyes of this group are water-insoluble polymeric substances often obtainable merely by heating a simple aromatic starting material with sodium polysulfide (thionation). They are more easily reducible than the anthraquinonoid and indigoid dyes and are applied by vatting with sodium sulfide rather than sodium hydrosulfite. Generally low production costs and excellent fastness to washing have led to the widespread use of sulfur dyes, though they are notoriously inferior in fastness to bleach and to light. The first known member of the group was a greenish yellow dye known as Cachou de Laval, obtained by Croissant and Bretonnière (1873) by heating materials such as cellulose, sawdust, or hide with sodium polysulfide at 350°. The development of the field was stimulated by Vidal's discovery (1893) that useful black sulfur dyes can be obtained by melting aminophenols with sulfur and solid sodium hydroxide at 200°. Modern processes of thionation use aqueous sodium polysulfide containing varying amounts of excess sulfur at much lower temperatures. Cheap Sulfur Blacks, used for example for dyeing cotton stockings, are made by thionation of 2,4-dinitronaphthol, sometimes with addition of nitrophenol or picric acid to vary the shade. More valuable black and blue dyes are made from derivatives of *p*-hydroxydiphenylamine, the leuco form of indophenol.

It is likely that indophenols are involved as intermediates to sulfur dyes derived from both aminophenols and nitrophenols. Thus the dye Immedial Pure Blue, made by thionation of a mixture of *p*-aminodimethylaniline and phenol, has been synthesized through an intermediate indophenol in the manner shown. The intermediate Herz compound is hydrolyzed to an

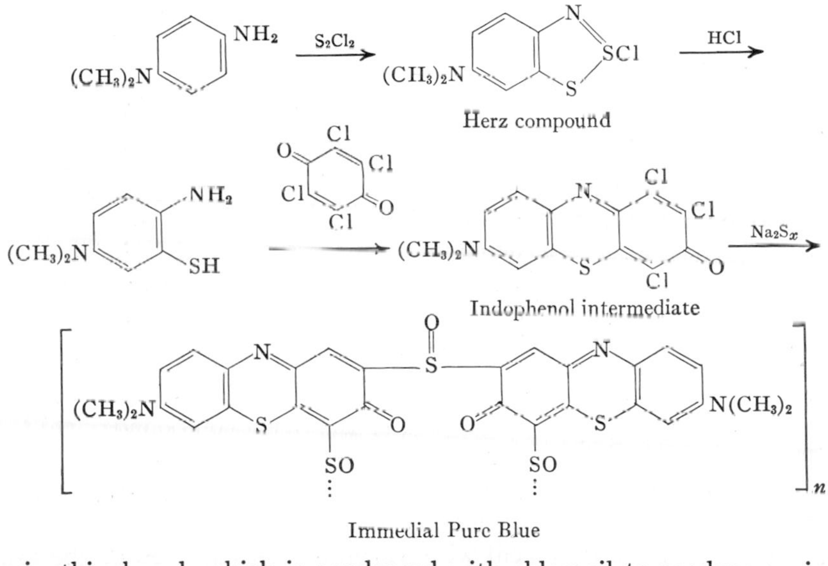

Herz compound

Indophenol intermediate

Immedial Pure Blue

o-aminothiophenol, which is condensed with chloranil to produce an indophenol, and in the final treatment with polysulfide some of the halogen

atoms are replaced in establishment of sulfoxide links and some are replaced
by hydrogen. When the dye, of the probable structure shown, is formed by
thionation, an unsubstituted indophenol is probably formed, as can be
done by oxidation of a mixture of *p*-aminodimethylamine with phenol, and
sulfhydryl groups are introduced by hydrogen sulfide addition to reactive
positions in the quinonoid nucleus. The important Hydron Blue R is made
by thionation in alcoholic solution of preformed carbazole indophenol. The

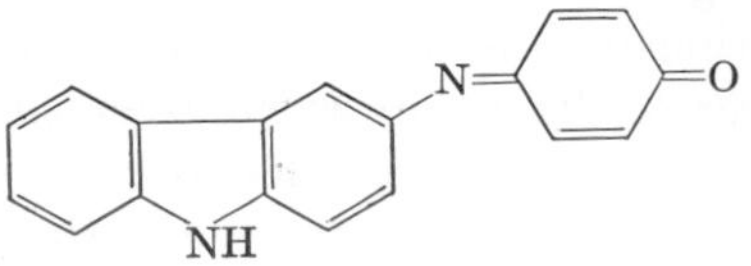

Carbazole indophenol

likewise important Indocarbon CL derived from *p*-hydroxyphenyl-β-naph-
thylamine is formulated by Fierz-David (1946) in the manner shown; the
two *p*-aminophenol groups may, in the pigment form, be oxidized. Green

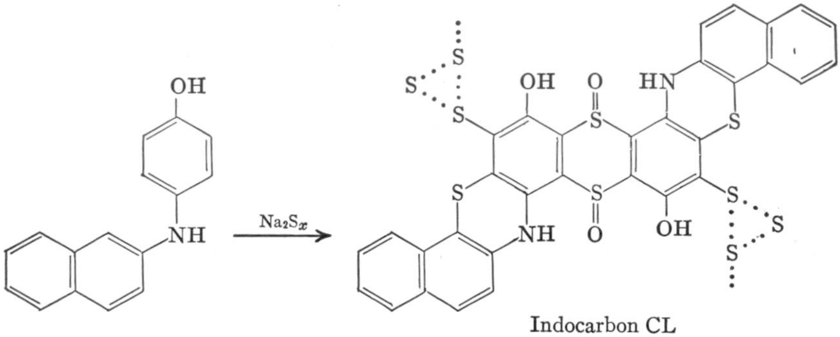

Indocarbon CL

sulfur dyes are made by thionation of naphthol- or naphthylaminesulfonic
acids in the presence of copper salts.

The high potential of the sulfur colors (reducible with sulfide) suggests
that vatting may involve reduction of quinonimine groups if present.
However some of the dyes, such as Immedial Yellow GG, obtained by
condensation of an intermediate primulin-type base (p. 887) with benzidine
and sulfur, appear to consist merely of chains of some ten heterocyclic rings
joined by disulfide linkages, which are believed to suffer fission in vatting.

AZO DYES

Acidic and Basic Azo Dyes. — In 1858 Peter Griess, a young student in
Kolbe's laboratory, discovered the first of the diazo compounds, which he
described as "a new class of organic compound in which hydrogen is replaced by nitrogen." The discovery was a result of an investigation of a
known reaction by which an amino group in an aromatic compound is replaced by hydroxyl on treatment with warm nitrous acid. At Kolbe's suggestion, Griess applied the reaction to picramic acid; the reaction proceeded

without application of heat, but the properties of the product did not correspond to those of a phenol. Analysis showed that the product had the same number of oxygen atoms but one more nitrogen atom than the starting material. Actually, as Kekulé soon showed, the product is a diazo anhydride, or diazo oxide. Griess soon applied the reaction to aniline itself, and

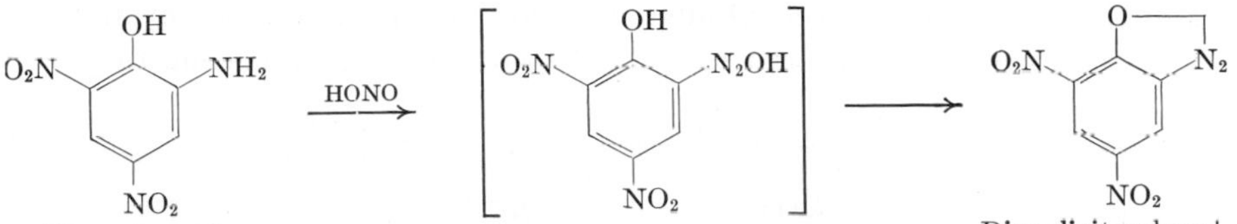

Picramic acid

Diazodinitrophenol
anhydride

unknowingly prepared the first of the azo dyes, Aniline Yellow, introduced commercially four years later (1863). Martius and Griess (1866) showed that Aniline Yellow is p-aminoazobenzene, formed by coupling of the intermediate benzenediazonium hydroxide with unchanged aniline followed by rearrangement. A similar coupling of diazo compounds with phenols was

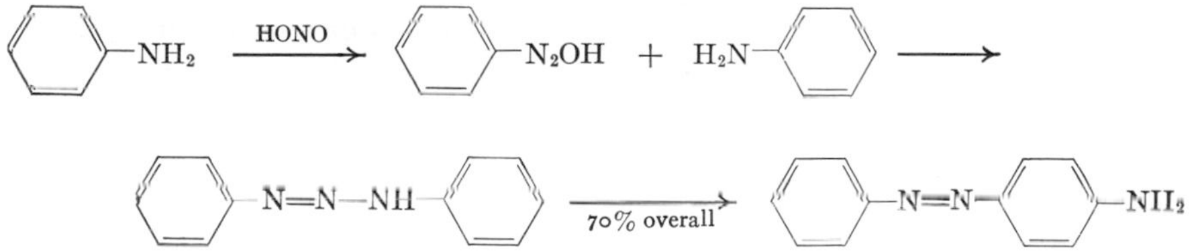

p-Aminoazobenzene or Aniline Yellow
(abs. max. in HCl, 4910 Å)

observed in 1870 by Kekulé, and thus the preparation of a large number of azo dyes became possible. Aniline Yellow itself is of little value since it is sensitive to acids; Chrysoidine (Witt, 1876) is a more important basic dye. Oil Yellow is an important oil-soluble dye.

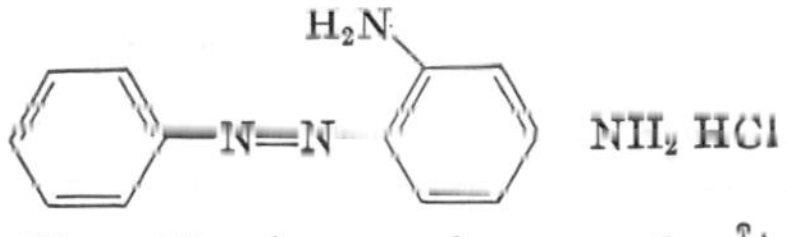

Chrysoidine (orange, abs. max. 4610 Å)

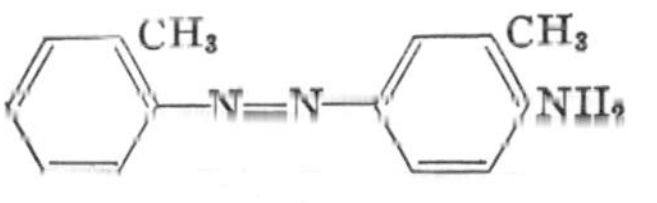

Oil Yellow
(3,2'-dimethyl-4-aminoazobenzene)

The first acidic azo dyes were marketed (1876) as Orange I and Orange II. They are prepared by coupling diazotized sulfanilic acid with α- and

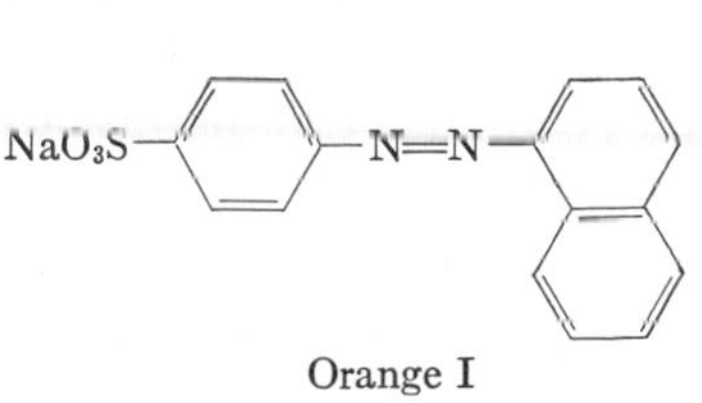

Orange I

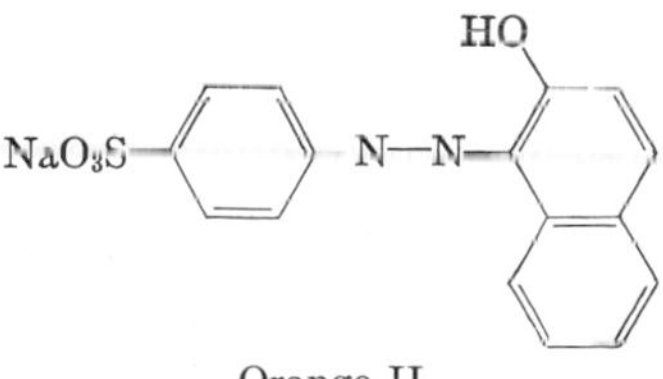

Orange II
(abs. max. 4844 Å)

β-naphthol, respectively.   The presence of the sulfonic acid group has no effect on the color, but renders the dye water-soluble and capable of dyeing wool and silk.   Orange II is still one of the most commonly used dyes.   The first red acidic azo dye, Fast Red A (Caro), was introduced in 1878.   It is prepared by coupling diazotized naphthionic acid with β-naphthol.   The difference in color between Orange II and Fast Red A is an example of the frequently noted observation that replacement of a benzene ring by a

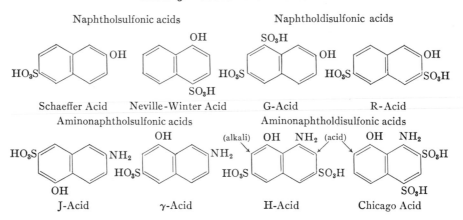

Fast Red A
(abs. max. 5045 Å)

naphthalene nucleus has a bathochromic effect.   The sulfonic acid grouping can also be situated in the naphthol component (Caro), and a host of dyes are made from the naphthol- and aminonaphtholsulfonic acids prepared by methods that have been described (pp. 746–751).   The most important of these components are listed in Chart 3.   R-Acid has one of the sulfonic acid

CHART 3.   COUPLING COMPONENTS

Naphtholsulfonic acids   Naphtholdisulfonic acids

Schaeffer Acid   Neville-Winter Acid   G-Acid   R-Acid

Aminonaphtholsulfonic acids   Aminonaphtholdisulfonic acids

J-Acid   γ-Acid   H-Acid   Chicago Acid

groups in the ring involved in coupling, and G-Acid differs only in that this group is transposed to the other ring; Chart 4 shows that this change produces only a subtle difference in shade.   Blue azo dyes are obtainable from an aminonaphtholsulfonic acid, principally H-Acid or Chicago Acid (Chart 3).   H-Acid couples *ortho* to the amino group in acid solution and *ortho* to the hydroxyl group in alkaline solution.   Two different azo groups can be introduced, in either order desired, by coupling with one component in acid

CHART 4. AZO DYES DERIVED FROM R-ACID AND G-ACID

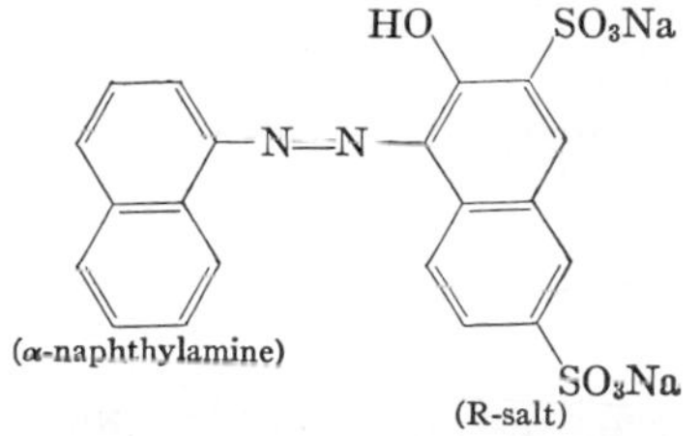

(α-naphthylamine)
(R-salt)

Fast Red B or Bordeaux B
(rosaniline red, abs. max. 5230 Å)

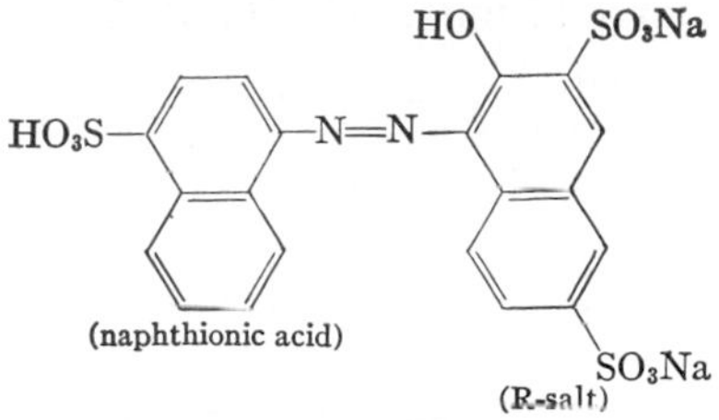

(naphthionic acid)
(R-salt)

Amaranth
(rosaniline red, abs. max. 5225 Å)

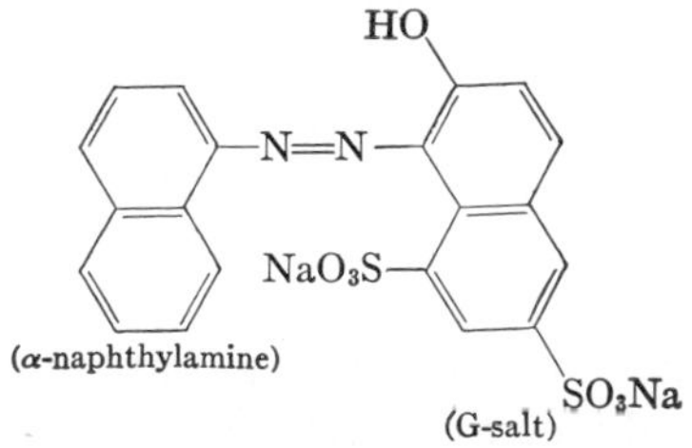

(α-naphthylamine)
(G-salt)

Crystal Ponceau 6R
(scarlet red)

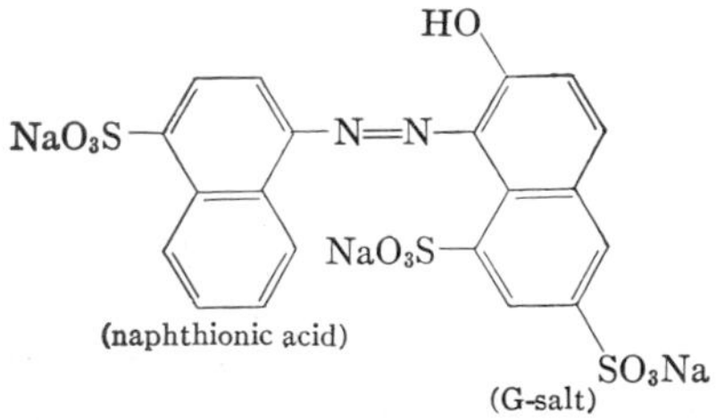

(naphthionic acid)
(G-salt)

Cochineal Red A
(scarlet red)

solution and with the other after alkalinization.   Naphthol Blue Black B is an example.

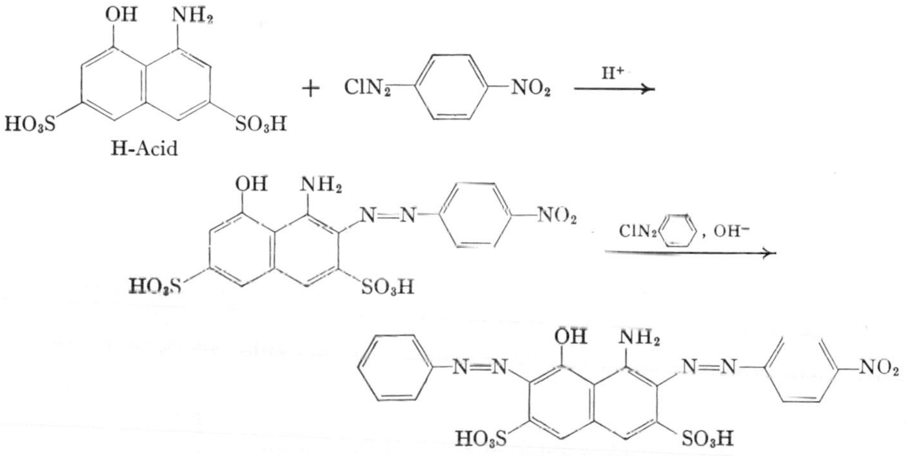

H-Acid

Naphthol Blue Black B

Substantive Azo Dyes. — Congo Red, a bisazo dye derived from benzidine and naphthionic acid, was the first azo dye found to have direct affinity for cotton, probably as a result of its colloidal properties.   Molecular weight measurements of Congo Red give values of about 8000, which shows that the molecules are highly associated.   Congo Red suffers from the disadvantage that it changes color from red to blue in the presence of mineral acids. The color change is considered to be due to formation of a blue quinonoid inner salt (Pauli, 1938):

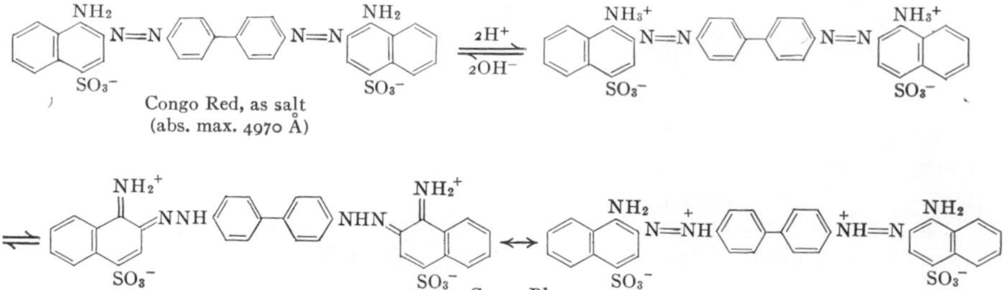

Congo Red, as salt
(abs. max. 4970 Å)

$$\rightleftharpoons \overset{2H^+}{\underset{2OH^-}{\rightleftharpoons}}$$

Congo Blue
(abs. max. in H₂SO₄, 6470, 5895 Å)

If only one mole of the secondary component is used, an intermediate can be isolated containing a free diazo group which can be coupled with a different amine or phenol. Congo Corinth is a mixed dye derived from benzidine coupled with naphthionic acid and with Neville-Winter acid.

Many other azo dyes derived from benzidine and derivatives containing substituent groups in *ortho* positions are also direct to cotton; for example the following diamines yield substantive dyes:

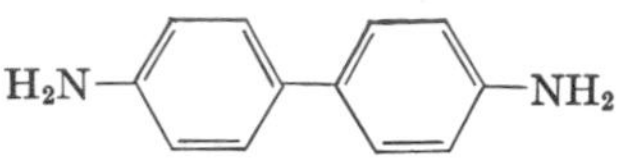

Benzidine

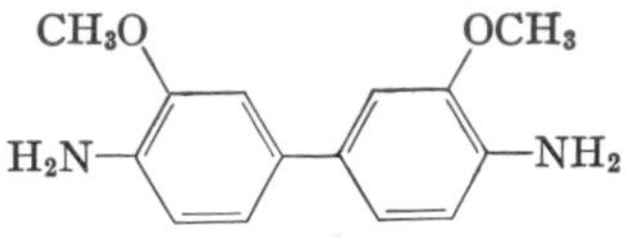

Dianisidine

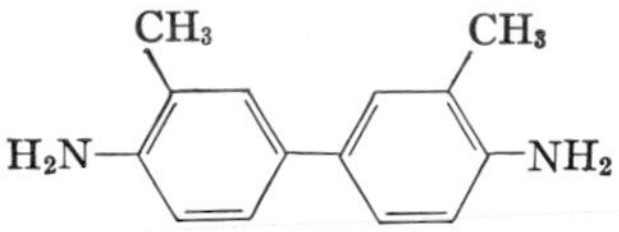

Tolidine

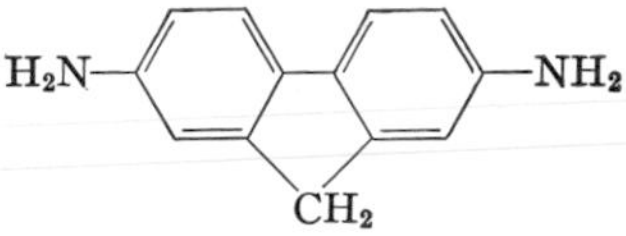

Diaminofluorene

If the substituents are *meta* to the amino groups or if the amino groups are not *para* to each other, the resultant azo dyes are not direct to cotton. Diaminofluorene is an apparent exception to this rule, since it does yield substantive dyes, but this structure is not directly comparable to a *meta* disubstituted benzidine. Direct azo dyes can also be obtained from other diamines, all of which bear some analogy to benzidine:

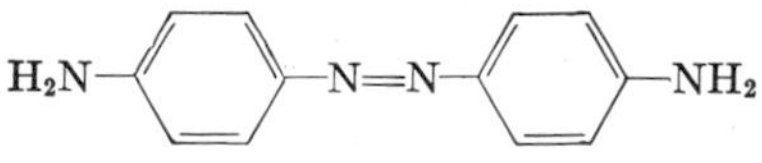

4,4'-Diaminoazobenzene

4,4'-Diaminodiphenylurea

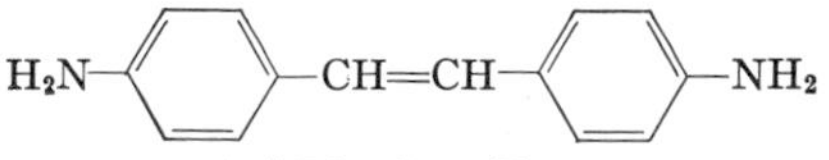

4,4'-Diaminostilbene

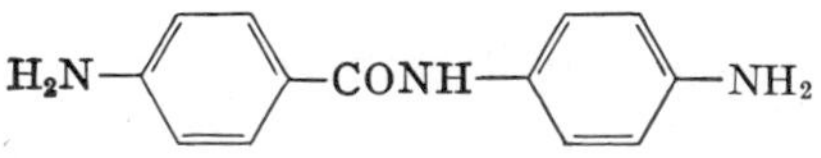

N-*p*-Aminobenzoyl-*p*-phenylenediamine

Azo dyes derived from J-acid (I) are also substantive to cotton, even if they do not contain any of the favorable groupings shown above. Excellent dyes

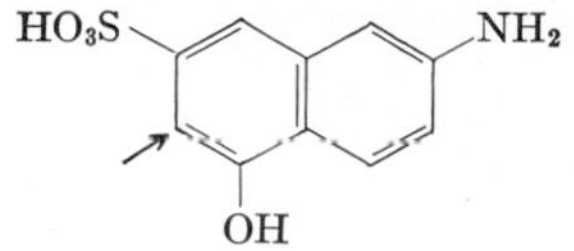

J-Acid
I

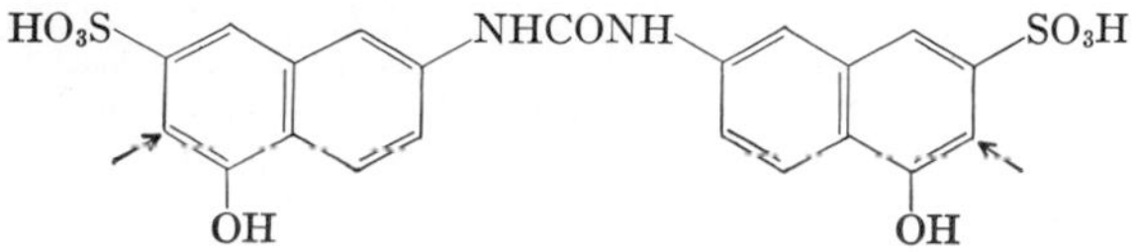

II

are derived from the derivative II, prepared by heating J-acid with phosgene.

The color change noted in the case of Congo Red is not common to all the bisazo dyes, but is dependent on the nature of the secondary component. The diamine can be coupled with a wide variety of amines and phenols, for example with two molecules of salicylic acid or of naphthionic acid.

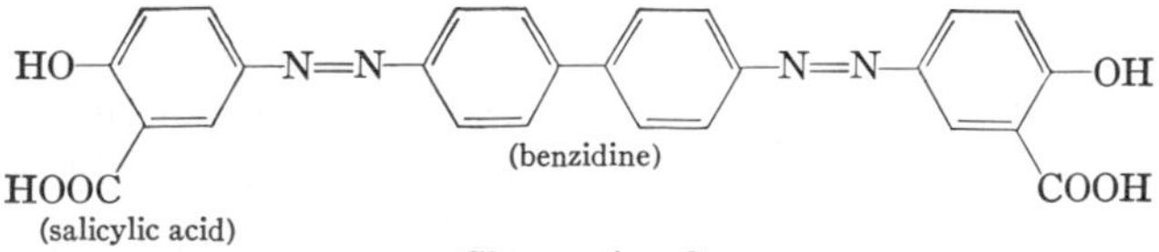

(benzidine)
(salicylic acid)

Chrysamine G
(yellow; abs. max. in H_2SO_4, 5430 Å)

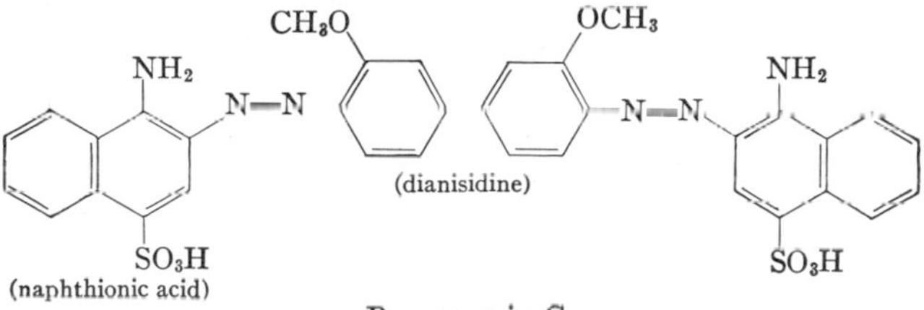

(naphthionic acid)
(dianisidine)

Benzoazurin G
(violet-blue; abs. max. 5690 Å)

Another variation is use of two secondary components; the dye obtained by coupling benzidine with one molecule of salicylic acid and one molecule of naphthionic acid is known as Benzoorange R (reddish yellow in water).

Direct blue azo dyes are obtained by coupling benzidine or, better, dianisidine with H-acid or Chicago acid. The first of this type to be discovered (Direct Blue BB) is surpassed in brightness by Sky Blue 6B. One

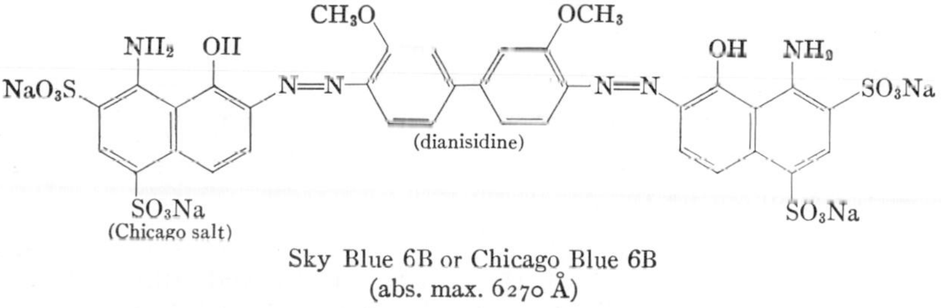

(Chicago salt)
(dianisidine)

Sky Blue 6B or Chicago Blue 6B
(abs. max. 6270 Å)

of the most important direct yellow dyes, Chrysophenine G, is derived from diaminostilbene. The intermediate dye, Brilliant Yellow, has two

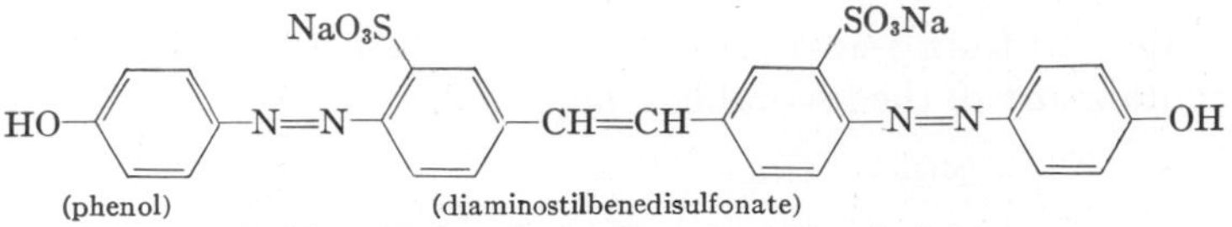

(phenol)   (diaminostilbenedisulfonate)
Brilliant Yellow (red-yellow; in acid, red-violet;
abs. max. in NH_3, 4932 Å; in H_2SO_4, 5430 Å)

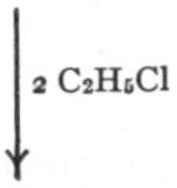

$\downarrow$ 2 C_2H_5Cl

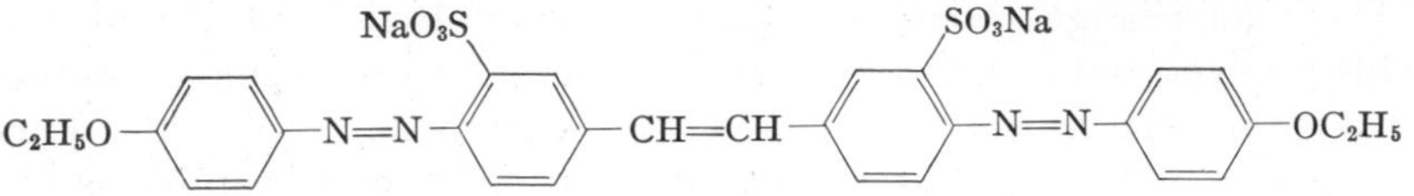

Chrysophenine G
(orange-yellow; abs. max. in H_2SO_4, 5550 Å)

free phenolic hydroxyl groups and shows a marked shade change to red in the presence of alkali; nevertheless it is used extensively for coloration of paper. In other instances where free phenolic groups are objectionable they are often masked by conversion into the *p*-toluenesulfonyl esters. Substantive azo dyes containing three or four azo groups are also used. The first-known green azo dye, Diamine Green B (1891), is of this type. Di-

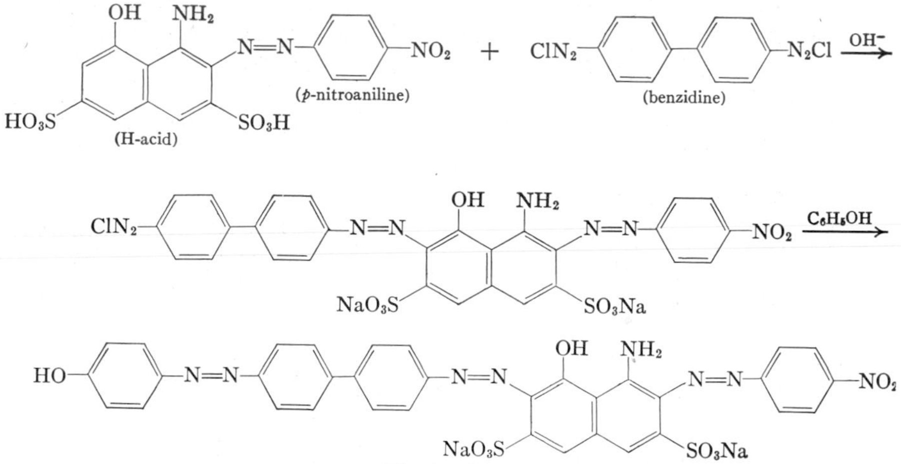

(*p*-nitroaniline)   (benzidine)
(H-acid)

Diamine Green B
(abs. max. 6730 Å)

amine Green G (abs. max. 6655Å) is a similar dye made by coupling benzidine with an azo component derived from H-acid and *o*-nitroaniline and then with salicylic acid.

Trypan Blue and Trypan Red have been useful as chemotherapeutic agents for protozoan diseases (p. 1022). Improved substantive dyes are available of the primulin type (p. 887), that is, having a free amino

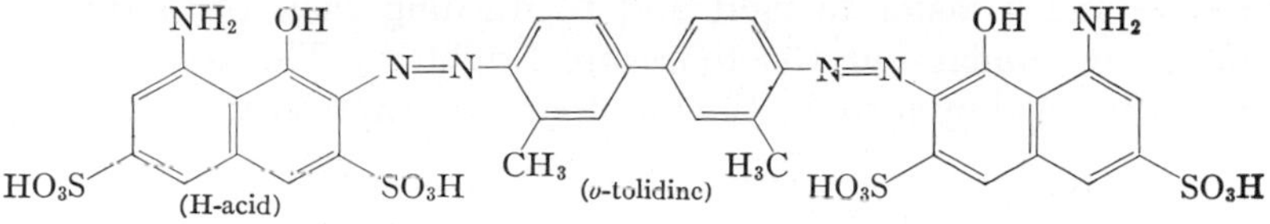

Trypan Blue or Diamine Blue 3B

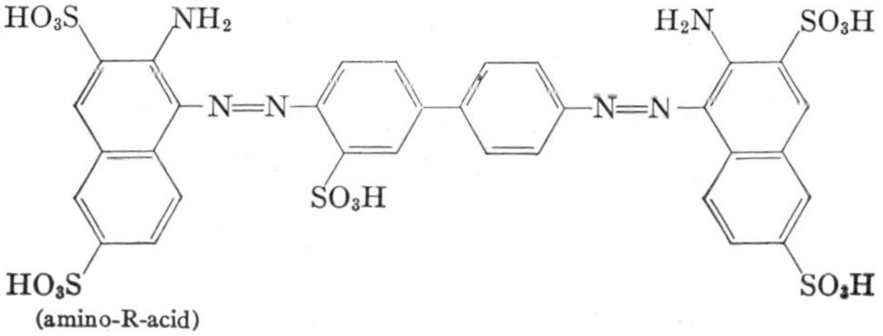

Trypan Red

group available for diazotization and further coupling on the fiber. An example is Rosanthrene Pink: aniline → N-(*m*-aminobenzoyl)-J-Acid; this is substantive to cotton and on diazotization and coupling with β-naphthol gives a bright pink that is very fast to washing and capable of giving good discharges. Substantive ureide dyes are usually made by phosgenation of aminoazo compounds. Thus Benzo Fast Yellow 5GL, $[2,3\text{-}(OH)(CO_2H)C_6H_3N=NC_6H_4NH]_2CO$, is prepared by coupling diazotized *p*-nitroaniline with salicylic acid, reduction of the nitro groups with alkali sulfide, and treatment of the aminoazo compound with phosgene.

Ingrain or Developed Azo Dyes. — The first important dye of this type, Para Red (Nitraniline Red), is made by impregnating fabric with an alkaline solution of β-naphthol containing Turkey-red oil (wetting agent), and then developing the dye on the dried cloth by immersion in an ice-cold bath of diazotized *p*-nitroaniline. Para Red was the first synthetic dye comparable in color to alizarin, and since it is considerably cheaper it was used extensively at one time as

Para Red

a substitute for alizarin, in spite of the disadvantage that it is not particularly fast to light and sublimes from the fiber when subjected to heat. Colors ranging from orange to blue can be obtained by variation of the primary component:

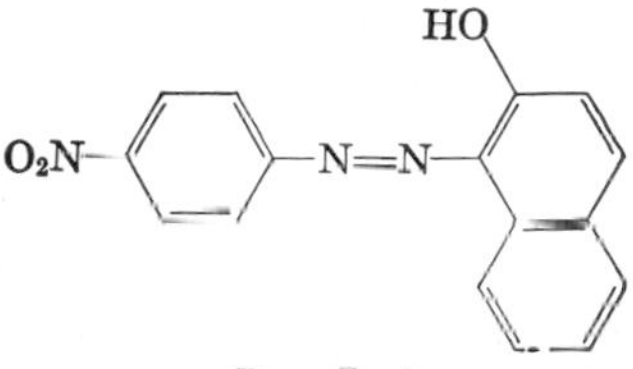

Typical Para Colors	β-naphthol	+	*m*-nitroaniline	⟶ Nitraniline Orange
	β-naphthol	+	2,4-dinitroaniline	⟶ Permanent Red 2G
	β-naphthol	+	α-naphthylamine	⟶ Ice Bordeaux (claret)
	β-naphthol	+	dianisidine	$\xrightarrow{CuCl_2}$ Dianisidine Blue

Naphthol-AS (Anilid Säure) was introduced in 1911 as a substitute for β-naphthol. In the presence of formaldehyde this more complex naphthol itself has some affinity for cellulose fibers, and the dyes obtained on developing are much faster to light and to washing than the Para Colors. The colors are similar but the tones are brighter. The color range has since been extended by introduction of other naphthol derivatives. Yellow

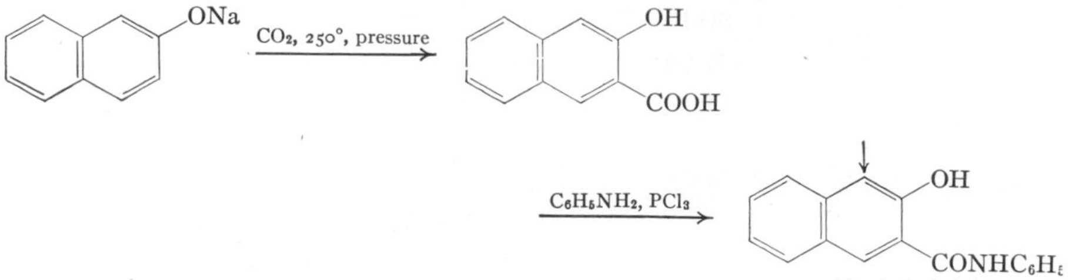

shades are obtainable from Naphthol-ASG, brown shades from Naphthol AS-LB, but some colors are still lacking.

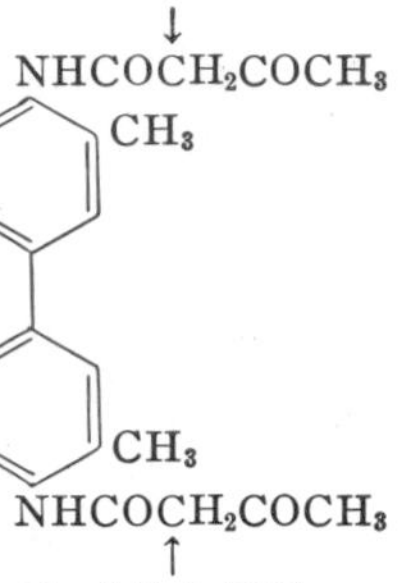

Naphthol ASG
(couples as enol)

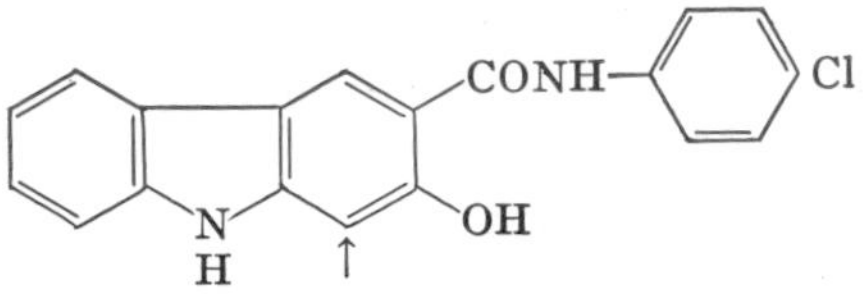

Naphthol AS-LB

An important method of printing cotton in bright, fast shades involves application of a printing paste containing a Naphthol AS and a triazene,

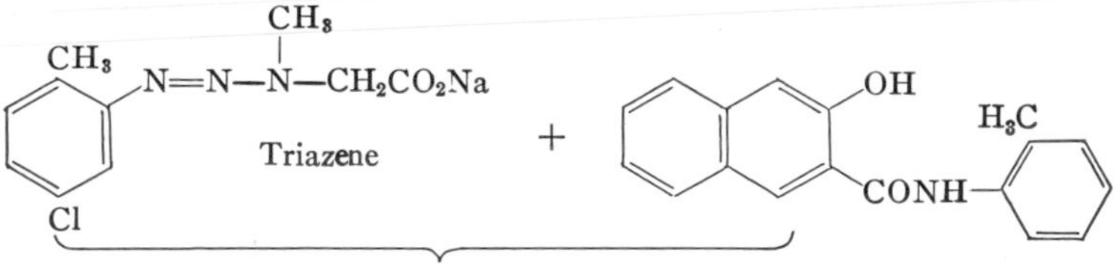

Triazene

Printing Paste

prepared by coupling a diazotized amine with a primary or a secondary alkylamine containing a solubilizing group. On acidification of the printed material the triazene is hydrolyzed to the diazonium component and coupling occurs on the fiber. The components are so chosen that the final pigment is devoid of solubilizing groups and hence fast to washing.

The introduction in 1894 of a stable ice-color base, Nitrosamine Red, represented an important advance from the dyer's point of view, since the necessity of preparing and storing the diazonium salts was eliminated. Nitrosamine Red is the *trans*-diazotate of *p*-nitroaniline. The diazonium

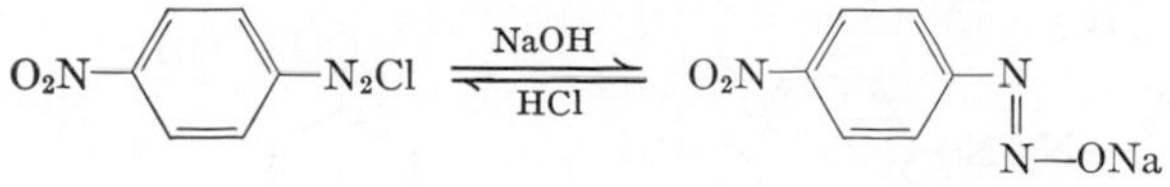

Nitrosamine Red

salt is readily obtained merely by addition of hydrochloric acid to a solution of Nitrosamine Red. Another stabilized form of this diazo component, marketed as Azophor Red PN, is prepared by evaporating an acidic solution of the diazonium chloride under vacuum at moderate temperature (45°), and then adding anhydrous aluminum or sodium sulfate to bind the remaining water and form a solid mass that can be ground to a powder. The diazonium salt is obtained immediately on addition of water. Many diazonium compounds can be stabilized by formation of a complex with stannic chloride, naphthalenedisulfonic acid, or zinc chloride. No one method of stabilization is applicable to all diazonium salts. Approximately fifty stabilized Fast Color Bases are on the market.

Chrome Colors. — Azo dyes can form complex lakes with metallic salts if they contain one of the groupings (a); the complex salts formed with metals are considered to be of the types (b). Aluminum and iron are used

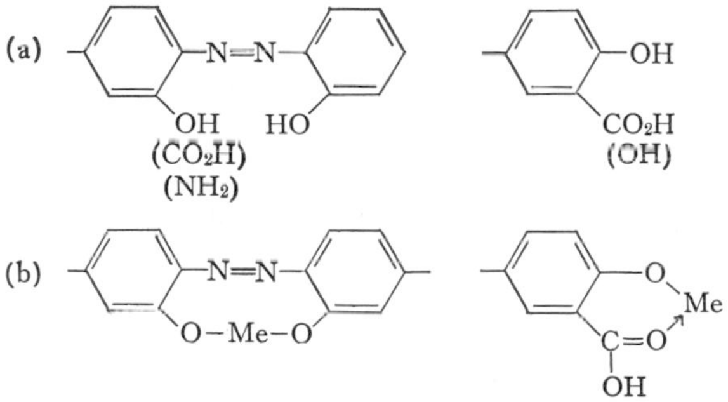

sometimes as mordants, but chromium is more important. The fiber is impregnated with the metal by boiling with sodium dichromate solution for several hours with or without an assistant, or reducing agent (lactic acid, oxalic acid, formic acid), which reduces the dichromate to chromic hydroxide, $Cr(OH)_3$. More often the azo dye is applied first and then chromed on the fiber by boiling with dichromate and an assistant. Chroming may only deepen the color or may change the color. The chrome colors have superior fastness to light and to washing.

The first-known chrome color, Diamond Black F, is prepared by coupling α-naphthylamine with diazotized aminosalicylic acid, followed by diazotization and coupling with 1-naphthol-5-sulfonic acid. Diamond Black PV, of structure shown in the formula, is still faster, probably because it has two neighboring hydroxyl groups available for complexing. Other dyes that are chromed on the fiber are derived from chromotropic acid, for example Chromotrope 2R (see formula) and Victoria Violet 4BS, which has an amino group *para* to the azo linkage.

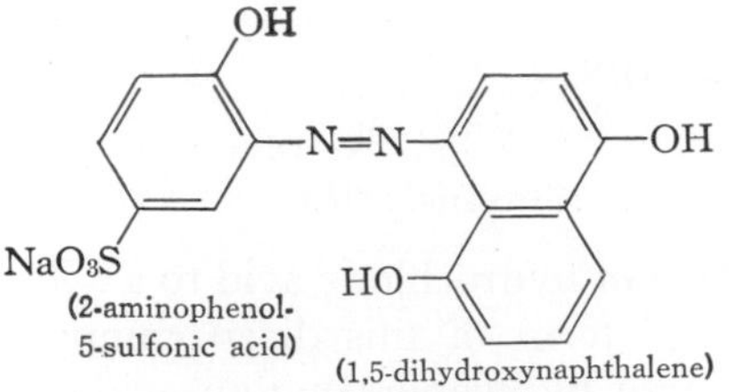

OH

—N=N— —OH

NaO$_3$S   HO—

(2-aminophenol-
5-sulfonic acid)

(1,5-dihydroxynaphthalene)

Diamond Black PV
(cherry red, black chrome lake)

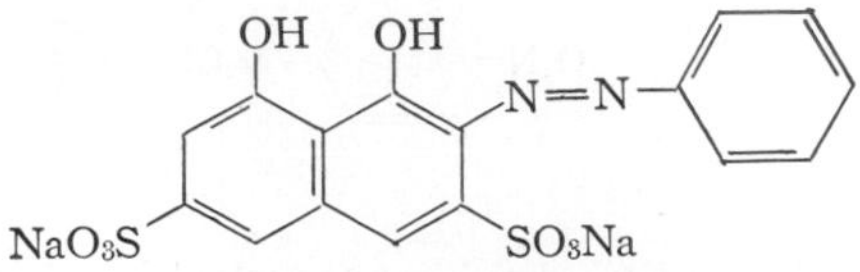

OH   OH

N=N—

NaO$_3$S   SO$_3$Na

Chromotrope 2R
(red; blue-black chrome lake;
abs. max. 5295, 5048 Å)

Dyes of a second group can be applied to wool in the presence of the chroming agent (metachrome process), for example Metachrome Brown B, derived from picramic acid. Dyes of a third type, exemplified by Neolan

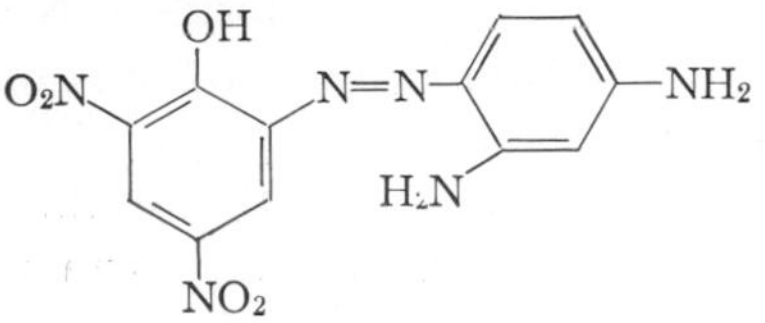

OH

O$_2$N— —N=N— —NH$_2$

H$_2$N

NO$_2$

Metachrome Brown B
(orange-red, brown chrome lake)

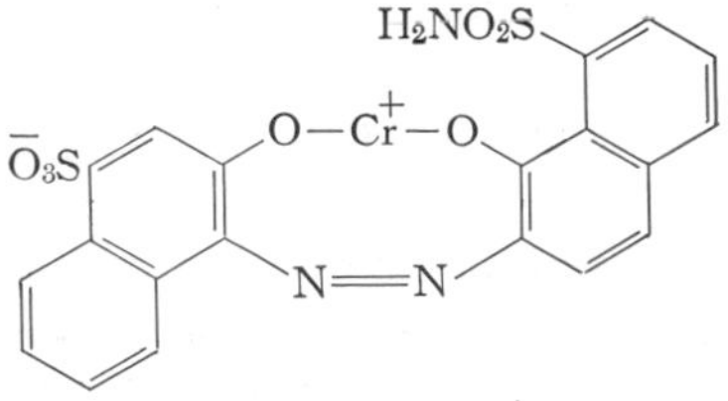

H$_2$NO$_2$S

$\overline{O}_3$S   O—Cr$^+$—O

N=N

Neolan Blue 2G

Blue 2G, are water-soluble chromium complexes that can be applied to wool directly from an acid dye bath.

Dyes for Hydrophobic Fibers. — Typical water-insoluble hydroxy- or aminoazo dyes that can be applied as dispersions in a dyebath containing a

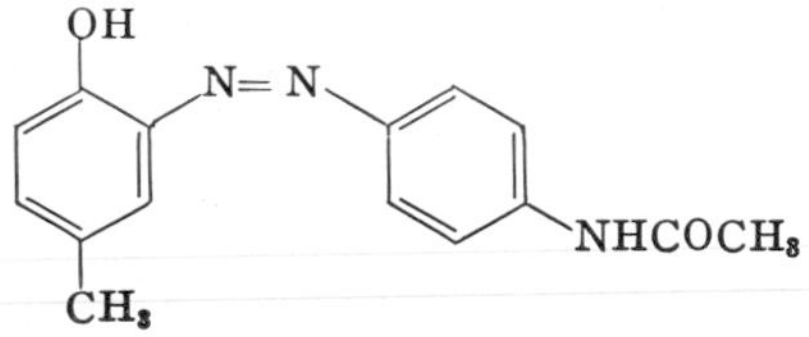

OH

N=N—

NHCOCH$_3$

CH$_3$

I (yellow)

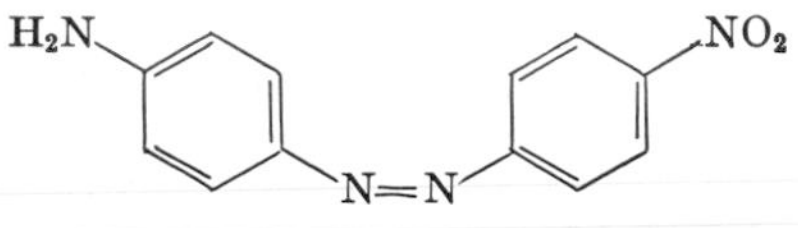

H$_2$N— —NO$_2$

N=N

II (orange)

O$_2$N— —N(CH$_2$CH$_2$OH)$_2$

N=N

Cl   CH$_3$

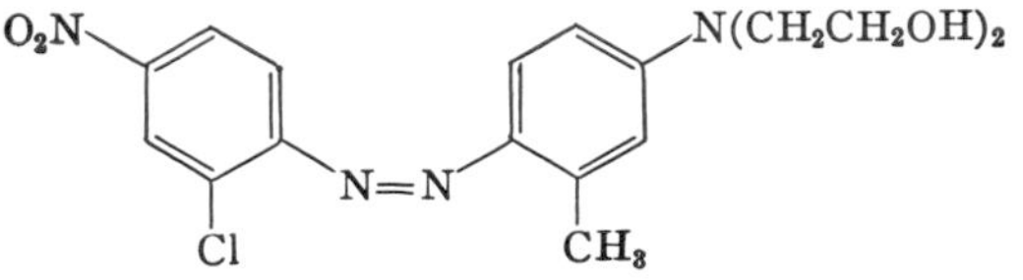

III (blue-red)

surface-active agent for dyeing of acetate rayon or nylon are shown in the formulas (I–III).

PIGMENTS

Certain organic dyes are also used as pigments for paints and as oil-soluble dyes for lacquers, fats, oils, plastics, and nonaqueous inks. Vat dyes originally developed for textile use only, when finished by special methods as pigments, are preferred for automotive finishes because of excellent durability and freedom from limitations in intensity and range of shade encountered with inorganic pigments. Halogenated indanthrone, for example, met the need for a nonbronzing deep blue pigment. Helio Fast Yellow 6GL (p. 917), a simple aroylaminoanthraquinone is used in part as a pigment. Representative water-insoluble azo compounds that serve as low-cost pigments are Toluidine Toner (red) and Hansa Yellow G.

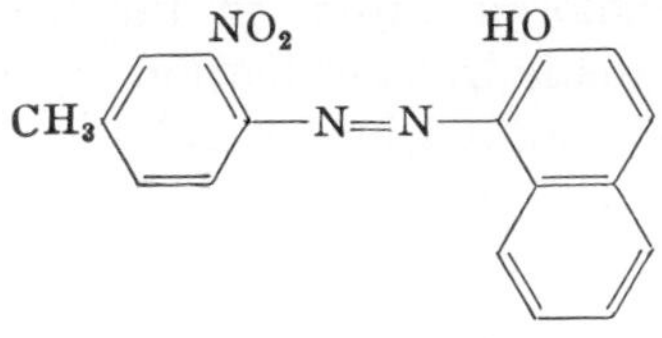

Toluidine Toner

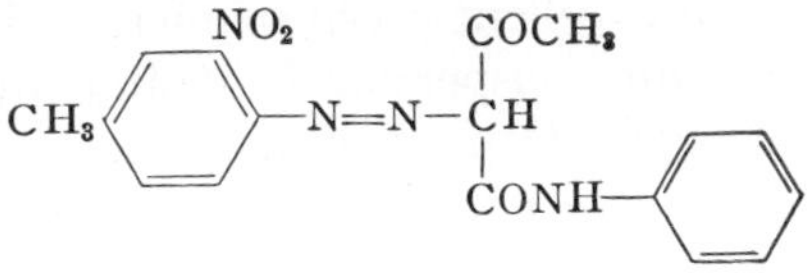

Hansa Yellow G

Phthalocyanines. — In 1927 de Diesbach and von der Weid observed the formation of a deep blue pigment containing copper when o-dibromobenzene or phthalonitrile was heated with cuprous cyanide in pyridine at 200°, but they did not characterize the substance. The following year it was observed at Scottish Dyes that some lots of phthalimide, prepared by treating molten phthalic anhydride with ammonia in an open vessel, are contaminated with a dark blue pigment containing iron. British chemists saw the commercial possibilities in such pigments and, under the leadership of Linstead, elucidated the structure and mode of formation of the important group now known as phthalocyanines. Copper phthalocyanine is readily made by the reaction of the metal with phthalonitrile. The structure is closely analogous to that of the porphyrin nucleus present in chlorophyll and hemin. Copper phthalocyanine (Monastral Blue) is a deep blue pigment that is exceedingly close to a pure blue; that is, it absorbs almost completely the red and yellow portions of the spectrum. It is the best available blue pigment for the three color process used in color printing.

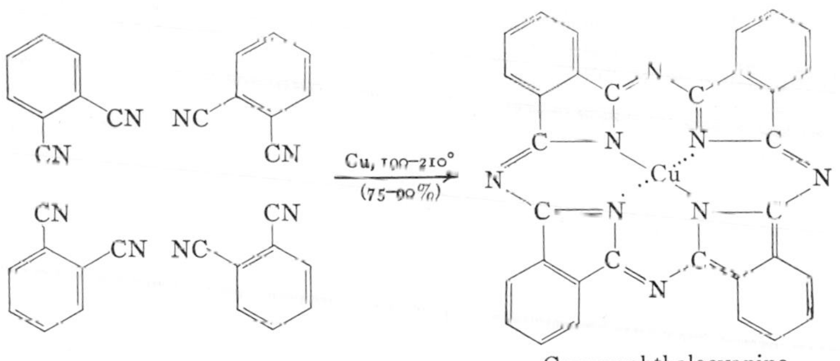

Copper phthalocyanine

Copper phthalocyanine is exceedingly stable: it is not affected by molten alkali or boiling hydrochloric acid. It can be purified by sublimation in vacuum (500°) or by dissolving in concentrated sulfuric acid, from which it is recovered unchanged on dilution. It is completely insoluble in all the usual organic solvents. The metal-free phthalocyanine can be obtained by acid treatment of magnesium or lead phthalocyanine. It is a brilliant, greenish blue pigment of stability comparable to copper phthalocyanine. The color is somewhat dependent upon both the crystalline form and the nature of the metal; thus lead phthalocyanine is yellowish green, whereas the nickel, cobalt, and copper derivatives are of similar shade of blue. Copper phthalocyanine containing 14–16 chlorine atoms in the benzene nuclei is an excellent green pigment. It is made by chlorination of copper phthalocyanine suspended in molten phthalic anhydride or sodium aluminum chloride. Copper phthalocyanine and the chlorinated derivative are used in pigment printing (p. 889), in printing inks, artists' colors, paints, and lacquers; they can be used as coloring matter for cellulose viscose and acetate fibers by incorporation into the spinning bath. Phthalocyanine pigments are used in the form of water-dispersible powders for dyeing of paper pulp and of wallpaper in strong, bright blue or green shades of unsurpassed fastness. Soluble salts, obtained by sulfonation, can be used as direct and mordant dyes.

READING REFERENCES

H. E. Fierz-David and L. Blangey, "Fundamental Processes of Dye Chemistry", Interscience New York (1949)

L. Pauling, "A Theory of the Color of Dyes," *Proc. Nat. Acad. Sciences*, **25**, 577 (1939)

L. G. S. Brooker, *et al.*, "Color and Constitution," *J. Am. Chem. Soc.*, **62**, 1116 (1940); **63**, 3192 3203, 3214 (1941); **64**, 199 (1942)

W. H. Perkin, "Origin of the Coal-Tar Colour Industry," *J. Chem. Soc.*, **69**, 596 (1896)

L. F. Fieser, "The Discovery of Synthetic Alizarin," *J. Chem. Ed.*, **7**, 2609 (1930)

H. W. Grimmel, "Organic Dyes," in H. Gilman, "Organic Chemistry," Vol III, 243 (1953)

K. Venkataraman, "Chemistry of Synthetic Dyes," Academic Press, New York (1950)

H. A. Lubs, "The Chemistry of Synthetic Dyes and Pigments," Reinhold, New York (1955)

F. M. Rowe, "The Development of the Chemistry of Commercial Synthetic Dyes, (1856–1938)," Institute of Chemistry, London (1938)

R. P. Linstead, "Discoveries Among Conjugated Macrocyclic Molecules," *J. Chem. Soc.*, 2873 (1953)

F. M. Hamer, "The Cyanine Dyes," *Quart. Rev.*, **4**, 327 (1950)

H. Caro, "Über die Entwickelung der Theerfarben-Industrie," Ber., **25** (Referate), 954 (1892)

ISOPRENOIDS

A large number of plant products have been found to be related in that they are built up of one or more units of isoprene. For example, the terpene dipentene, the racemic form of limonene, can be made by heating isoprene

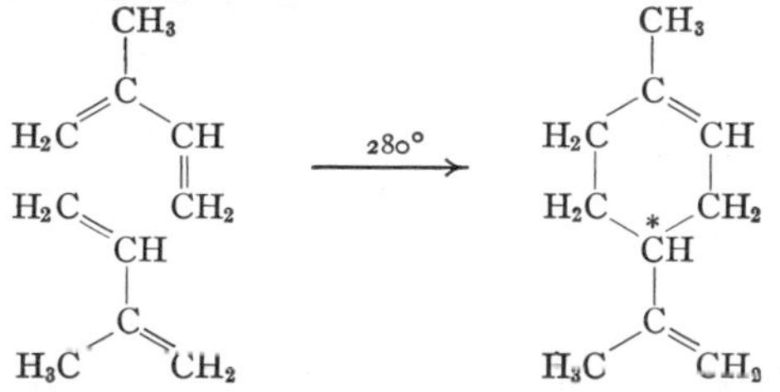

Isoprene   dl-Limonene = dipentene

derived from pyrolysis of rubber; the dimerization is a form of Diels-Alder reaction involving 1,4-addition of one molecule of diene to the 1,2-position of another. So many known compounds are isoprenoid that the postulate of an isoprenoid structure, the isoprene rule, has been a useful guide in structural studies of natural products where the carbon content is an even multiple of 5. Isoprene itself has never been encountered in nature, but iso-valeric acid is a natural product. Terpenes (C_{10}), sesquiterpenes (C_{15}), and diterpenes (C_{20}) are common constituents of volatile (essential) oils. No terpenes containing 5 or 7 isoprene units have been discovered, but many triterpenes (C_{30}) and tetraterpenes (C_{40}) are known.

TERPENES (C_{10})

Isolation and Characterization. — Isolation and elucidation of structure of terpenes and their oxygenated derivatives is beset by special difficulties because these substances are usually liquids and occur in mixtures with closely related compounds. Systematic preparation of pure individual terpenes was first achieved by Wallach[1] who found that certain reagents, particularly nitrosyl chloride (NOCl), form solid addition compounds suitable for characterization. Bromine, hydrogen chloride and bromide, and dinitrogen tetroxide (N_2O_4) were also used. A difficulty not realized in the

[1] Otto Wallach, 1847–1931; b. Königsberg; Ph.D. Göttingen; Göttingen; Nobel Prize 1910; J. Chem. Soc., 1582 (1932)

early work is that addition reactions conducted under acidic conditions are sometimes attended with rearrangement of the carbon skeleton. Ozonization, introduced by Harries, proved of value in establishing the positions of double bonds. Also useful is the general scheme of conversion of a cyclic terpene into an aromatic hydrocarbon amenable to synthesis if not already known. Thus Dumas and Peligot converted camphor into *p*-cymene by dehydration with phosphorus pentoxide. Sulfur is often used for dehydrogenation of sesqui- and diterpenes to aromatic hydrocarbons. Aromatization sometimes can be effected by catalytic disproportionation, as illustrated for the case of dipentene.

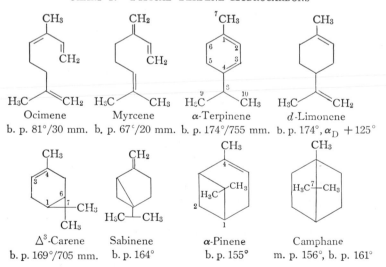

Hydrocarbons. — The principal structural variations found in terpenes of natural occurrence are illustrated by the formulas of Chart 1. Camphane,

CHART 1. TYPICAL TERPENE HYDROCARBONS

Ocimene   b. p. 81°/30 mm.   Myrcene   b. p. 67°/20 mm.   α-Terpinene   b. p. 174°/755 mm.   d-Limonene   b. p. 174°, α_D +125°

Δ^3-Carene   b. p. 169°/705 mm.   Sabinene   b. p. 164°   α-Pinene   b. p. 155°   Camphane   m. p. 156°, b. p. 161°

$C_{10}H_{18}$, itself is not a natural product but the ketone camphor is; the seven unsaturated hydrocarbons in the chart all have the formula $C_{10}H_{16}$. Ocimine (basil) and myrcene (bayberry) are triunsaturated acyclic hydrocarbons that differ only in the positions of two of the double bonds. Both contain a conjugated diene system, and both can be pictured as built from two isoprene units joined head-to-tail. The next two hydrocarbons, α-terpinene and d-limonene, are monocyclic dienes, one conjugated and the other nonconjugated; they have the p-menthane skeleton, that is, the skeleton of the fully saturated hydrocarbon formulated on p. 936. The three natural terpenes Δ^3-carene, sabinene, and α-pinene are monounsaturated bicyclic hydrocarbons; the carbon skeleton is that of p-menthane modified by closure of a bridging cyclopropane or cyclobutane ring. In camphane the six-ring is spanned by a bridge containing a gem-dimethyl group that forms two five-membered rings; camphane is a highly volatile solid of melting point almost as high as the boiling point. A few terpenes are known belonging to the m-menthane series, but no o-menthane derivatives are known, which accords with expectations from the isoprene rule.

Alcohols and Aldehydes. — Alcoholic and aldehydic derivatives of acyclic terpenes occur abundantly in essential oils and have more fragrant odors than the hydrocarbons. For example, rose oil (*Rosa damascena*), a valued flower essence, contains 40–60% of a diunsaturated terpene alcohol, geraniol, 20–40% of the monounsaturated *l*-citronellol, and an odorless mixture of paraffin hydrocarbons. The yield of rose oil from 4000–5000 kg. of rose petals is 1 kg. Geraniol is a mixture of the allylic alcohols I and II, in which I predominates. In both forms the allylic bond has the *cis*-con-

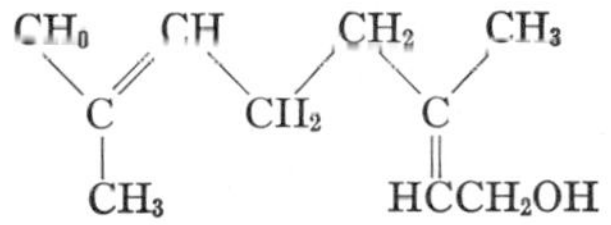

I 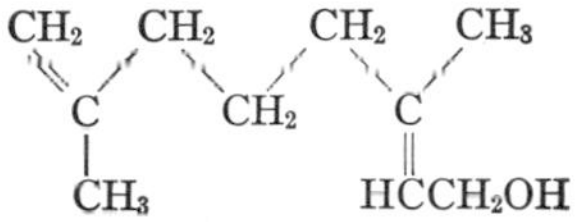   II

Geraniol

figuration; the second double bond forms part of either an isopropylidene (I) or an isopropenyl (II) group. The allylic *trans* isomer mixture nerol occurs in bergamot and cyclamen. *l*-Citronellol is a mixture of the dihydrogeraniols III and IV, in which IV predominates. The aldehyde cor-

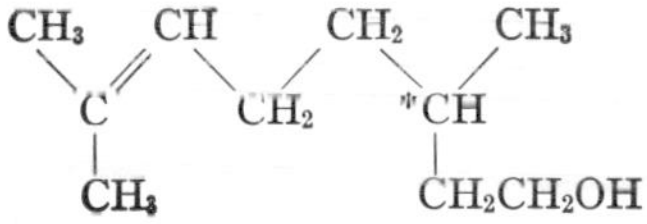

III 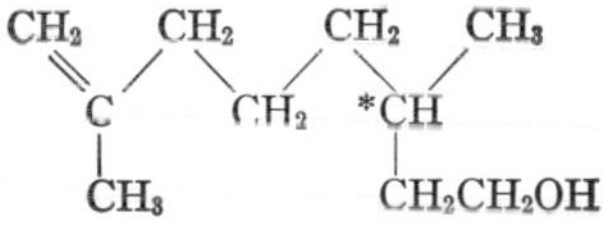   IV

Citronellol

responding to geraniol-I, known as citral-a, is the main constituent (70%) of lemon grass oil, which also contains a small amount of the *trans*-isomer citral-b, corresponding to nerol.

Acyclic terpenes have been cyclized to natural cyclic terpenes. For example, citronellal undergoes ring closure to isopulegol, a terpene alcohol that occurs with citronellal, and the reaction can be reversed. Both geraniol and nerol are cyclized to α-terpineol.

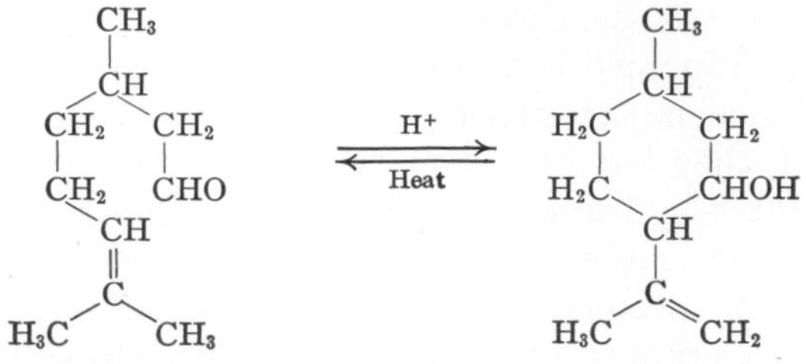

CH$_3$
CH
CH$_2$ CH$_2$
CH$_2$ CHO
CH
C
H$_3$C   CH$_3$
Citronellal

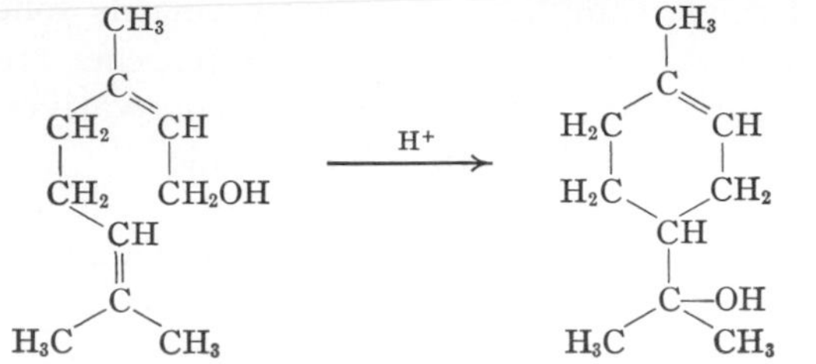

H$^+$ ⇌ Heat

CH$_3$
CH
H$_2$C   CH$_2$
H$_2$C   CHOH
CH
C
H$_3$C   CH$_2$
Isopulegol

CH$_3$
C
CH$_2$ CH
CH$_2$ CH$_2$OH
CH
C
H$_3$C   CH$_3$
Geraniol or nerol

H$^+$ →

CH$_3$
C
H$_2$C   CH
H$_2$C   CH$_2$
CH
C—OH
H$_3$C   CH$_3$
α-Terpineol

Ionones and Irones. — At a time when irone, the fragrant principle of the violet, was thought to have the formula $C_{13}H_{20}O$ (1893–98), Tiemann sought to synthesize the material by aldol condensation of citral with acetone: $C_{10}H_{16}O + C_3H_6O \rightarrow C_{13}H_{20}O + H_2O$. The product, after acid treatment, was not irone but a mixture of ionones. The synthesis was later perfected (Chart 2) to afford pure β-ionone in good yield, since this

CHART 2. SYNTHESIS OF β-IONONE

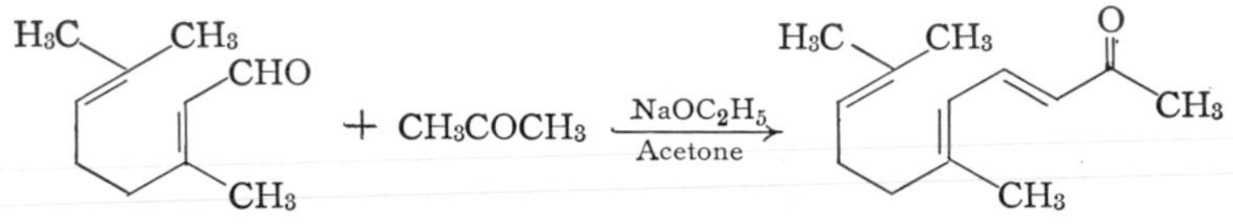

H$_3$C   CH$_3$
CHO
CH$_3$
Citral
λ$_{max}$ 2380 Å

+ CH$_3$COCH$_3$ → $\xrightarrow[\text{Acetone}]{\text{NaOC}_2\text{H}_5}$

H$_3$C   CH$_3$ O
CH$_3$
CH$_3$
Pseudoionone
λ$_{max}$ 2910 Å

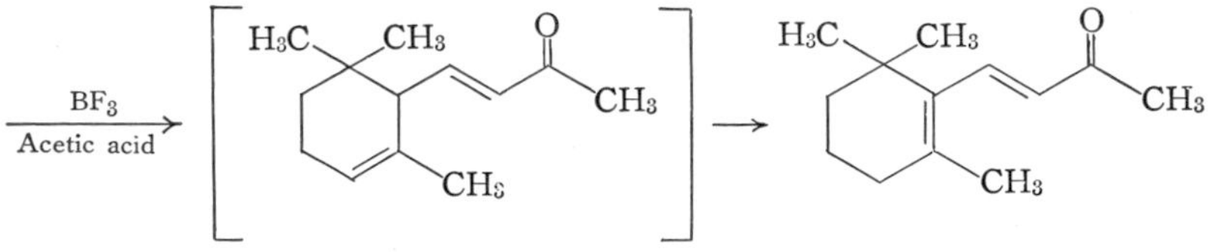

$\xrightarrow[\text{Acetic acid}]{\text{BF}_3}$

[H$_3$C   CH$_3$ O
CH$_3$
CH$_3$
α-Ionone
λ$_{max}$ 2280 Å]

→

H$_3$C   CH$_3$ O
CH$_3$
CH$_3$
β-Ionone
λ$_{max}$ 2960 Å

substance became a key intermediate for the commercial synthesis of vitamin A (p. 956). The base-catalyzed aldol condensation affords pseudoionone, which has two double bonds conjugated with the carbonyl group, in contrast to one in citral, and which in consequence absorbs ultraviolet light of longer wave length and gives a 2,4-dinitrophenylhydrazone that is deep red, whereas that of citral is yellow.   Sulfuric acid, or better boron fluoride in acetic acid, cyclizes pseudoionone to α-ionone, in which, as indicated by the position of the absorption band, only one of the two double bonds is in a position of conjugation.   Under the influence of the catalyst, the ring double bond migrates to a position of conjugation to give β-ionone, a conjugated dienone whose DNP derivative is red.   In contrast to citral, which has a strong lemon odor, the ionones have pleasant violet odors and are used for production of synthetic perfumes in combination with a small amount of 1-carbomethoxyheptyne, $CH_3(CH_2)_4C\equiv CCO_2CH_3$, which has an odor reminiscent of violet leaves; the total effect is an approximate duplication of the odor of the complete plant.   Both α- and β-ionone have been isolated from essential oils and are classified as terpenes even though they contain only 13 carbon atoms.

Irene, the odoriferous principle of the violet, is isolated most readily from the rhizomes of iris.   Actually the formula is $C_{14}H_{22}O$ and the substance differs from ionone in having an additional methyl group at the 6-position. Irone as isolated is a mixture of isomers, five of which have been separated (Y-R. Naves[2]).   Three, α, β, and γ-irone, differ in the location of the double

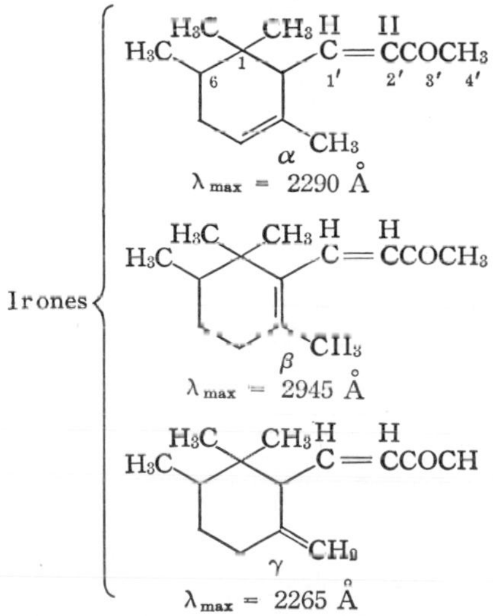

bond.   The difference in absorption of the dienone (β) and monoenone systems (α, γ) is the same as noted above.   The 1',2'-double bond in all three isomers has the *cis* configuration.   One of two stereoisomers of α-irone isolated from iris differs in the configuration at C_6, the other in that the

[2] Yves-René Naves, b. 1902 Auch, France; D.Sc. Tolouse (Sabatier); L. Givaudan et Cie., Vernier-Geneva

1′,2′-double bond is *trans*. Two degradations of γ-irone illustrate the evidence adduced in determination of structure (Ruzicka). Ozonization gave formaldehyde (35% yield) and β,β,γ-trimethylpimelic acid; reduction, followed by selenium dehydrogenation, gave 1,2,6-trimethylnaphthalene.

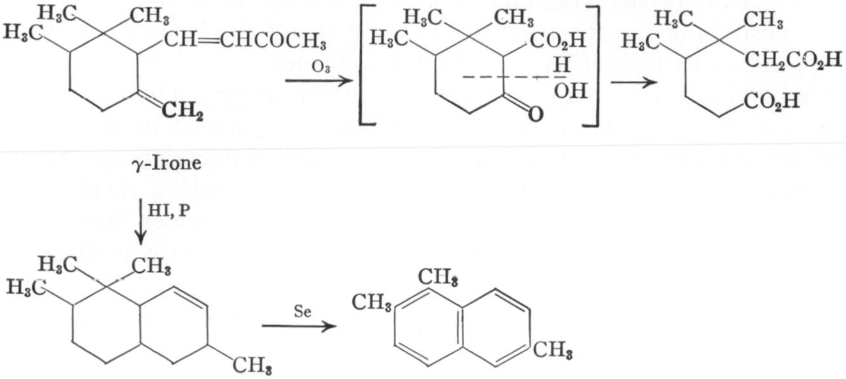

γ-Irene

Irene

Rearrangement of Bicyclic C₁₀-Terpenes. — Elucidation of the structures of derivatives of pinane and camphane presented a particularly difficult problem because under certain conditions the carbon skeleton suffers rearrangement of a type not fully appreciated before the classical studies of Wagner and of Meerwein in 1890. The pinacol–pinacolone rearrangement is one of many examples now known of Wagner-Meerwein type rearrangements in which formation of a carbonium ion with an open sextet of electrons promotes migration from an adjacent position of an alkyl group with its pair of electrons. Rearrangements of bicyclic terpenes are similar. When treated with hydrogen chloride at temperatures below 0°, both α- and β-pinene react normally to give the same product, pinene hydrochloride. At higher temperatures, however, the product is bornyl chloride, which has the 1,4-bridge of a camphane, rather than the original 1,3-bridge. The

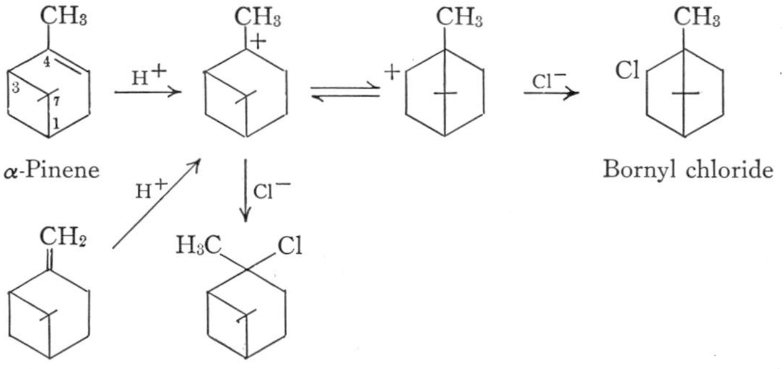

α-Pinene

β-Pinene   Pinene hydrochloride

Bornyl chloride

nature of the rearrangement and the stereochemistry involved are easier to appreciate when projection formulas are used. The six-membered ring of

α-Pinene   Bornyl chloride

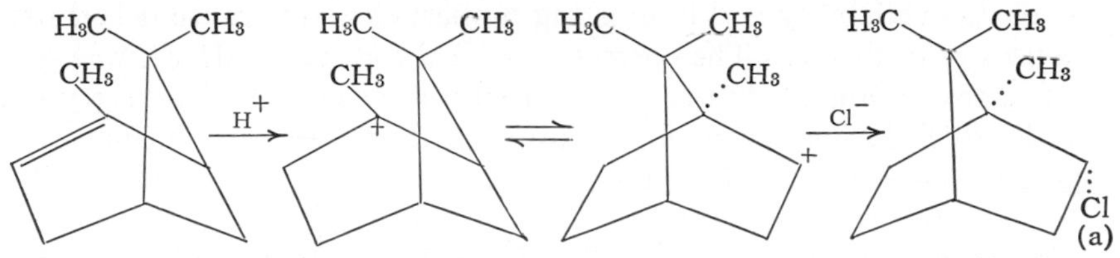

necessity has the boat conformation, because of the presence of a 1,3- or
1,4-bridge. In bornyl chloride the C_4-methyl group and the C_3-chlorine
atom are oriented with respect to the ring in the direction opposite to the
orientation of the bridge, as indicated by dotted-line bonds; a model corresponding to the projection formula shows that the methyl group is equatorial (e) and the chlorine atom axial (a).

Elimination of hydrogen chloride from bornyl chloride by treatment with
base is attended with another rearrangement to produce a monounsaturated

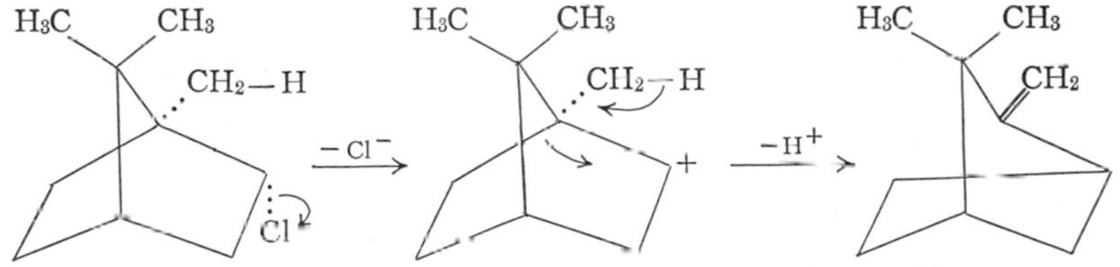

Bornyl chloride   Camphene

hydrocarbon having two five-membered rings. The substance is named
camphene, but actually the carbon skeleton is that of isocamphane rather
than of camphane. Curved arrows in the formulation show the direction of
electron displacements involved in the Wagner-Meerwein rearrangement.
The hydrochloride of camphene like that of pinene is unstable and rearranges readily to isobornyl chloride, the C_3-epimer of bornyl chloride.

Camphor. — Natural, dextrorotatory camphor forms prismatic, translucent crystals and is characterized by its fragrant, penetrating odor. The

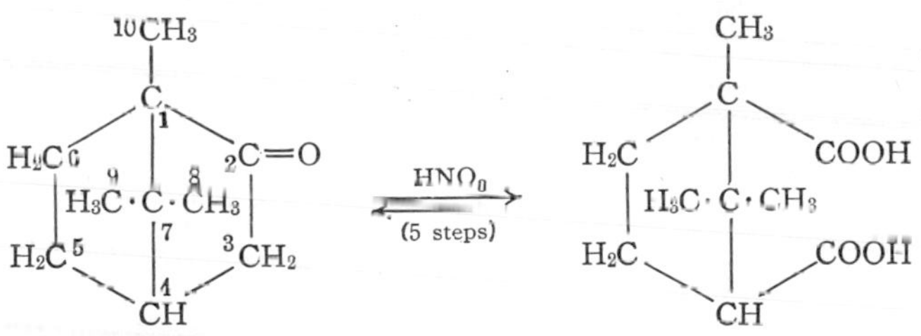

d-Camphor   Camphoric acid
(m.p. 179°, $[\alpha]_D +44°$)

sole commercial source is the camphor tree (*Cinnamomum camphora*), in-
digenous to the island of Formosa. It is obtained by steam distillation of
comminuted trees. Camphor attracted the attention of early chemists be-

cause of its availability and interesting properties and because it had found some uses in medicine. The correct empirical formula $C_{10}H_{16}O$, was determined in 1833 (Dumas), but the true structure was only deduced sixty years later (Bredt[3]), during which time more than thirty different formulas were proposed. Even the nature of the oxygen function, which would have been evident at once from the infrared spectrum, was not known until 1883 when an oxime was prepared. The carbonyl group is rather hindered and unreactive, but reduction to camphane was accomplished (1911–12) by the now classical Wolff-Kishner method. The fact that the hydrocarbon is optically inactive indicated that it has a symmetrical structure. Dehydration of camphor to p-cymene provided a rather misleading suggestion of the nature of the carbon skeleton, since the reaction involves rupture of a carbon–carbon bond of the bridge. The true nature of the skeleton was revealed in a series of degradations starting with nitric acid oxidation of camphor to camphoric acid (formula above, $\alpha_D + 50°$), which contains one hindered tertiary carboxyl group and a more reactive secondary carboxyl group, and which readily forms an anhydride. Successive further oxidations afforded camphoronic acid and finally trimethylsuccinic acid.

Camphoric acid →

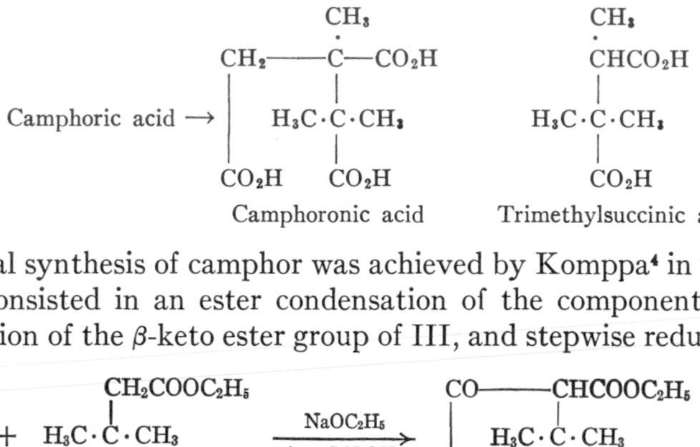

Camphoronic acid   Trimethylsuccinic acid

The total synthesis of camphor was achieved by Komppa[4] in 1903. The synthesis consisted in an ester condensation of the components I and II, C-methylation of the β-keto ester group of III, and stepwise reduction of the

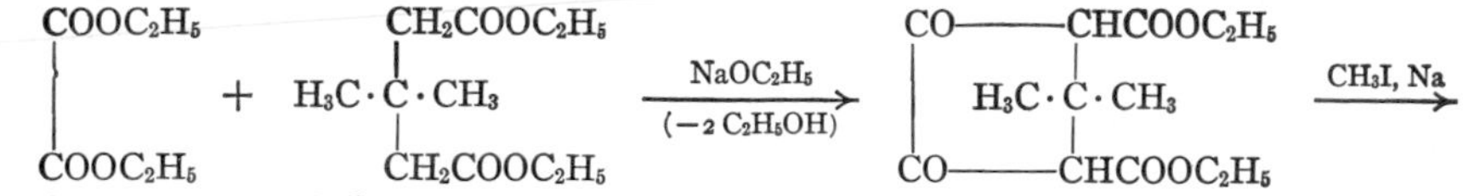

Ethyl oxalate   Diethyl β,β-dimethyl   Diketoapocamphoric ester
I   glutarate   III
                 II

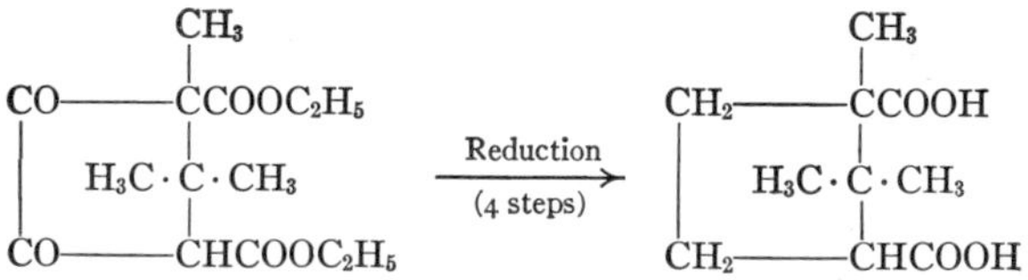

Diketocamphoric ester   dl-Camphoric acid
IV   V

[3] Julius Bredt, 1855–1937; b. Berlin; Ph.D. Strasbourg (Fittig); Aachen
[4] Gustav Komppa, 1867–1949; b. Wiborg, Finland; Ph.D. Helsingfors; Helsingfors: *J. Chem. Soc.*, 2912 (1950); *Ber.*, **85A**, 1 (1952)

carbonyl groups of IV. Synthetic *dl*-camphoric acid was then transformed into *dl*-camphor by a procedure already known (Haller) for reconversion of *d*-camphoric acid to *d*-camphor starting with reduction of the less hindered of the two carbonyl groups of camphoric anhydride:

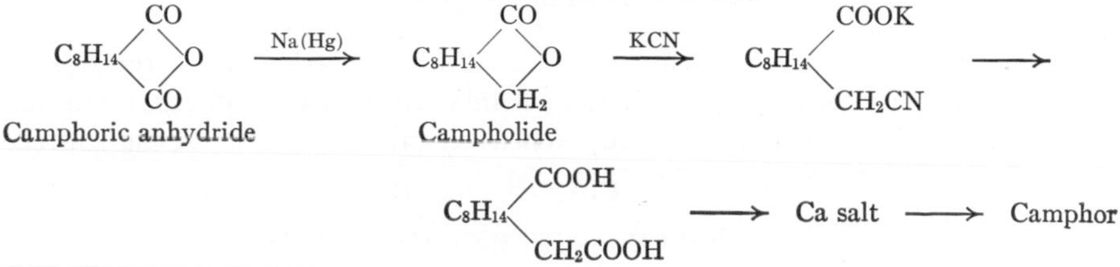

Camphoric anhydride   Campholide

Large-scale use of camphor as plasticizer for cellulose nitrate (celluloid) provided the incentive for development of a commercial synthesis from inexpensive starting materials, and a practical process was developed in Germany during the English blockade of World War I. Optically inactive synthetic camphor effectively replaces the natural material in all technical uses. The synthesis utilizes α- or β-pinene, or the mixture of the two iso-mers that accounts for 80–90% of gum turpentine, the steam volatile portion of pine oleoresin (the residue is rosin). The first two steps, conversion of pinene to bornyl chloride and of this chloride to camphene are formulated in the preceding section. Sulfuric acid-catalyzed addition of acetic acid to

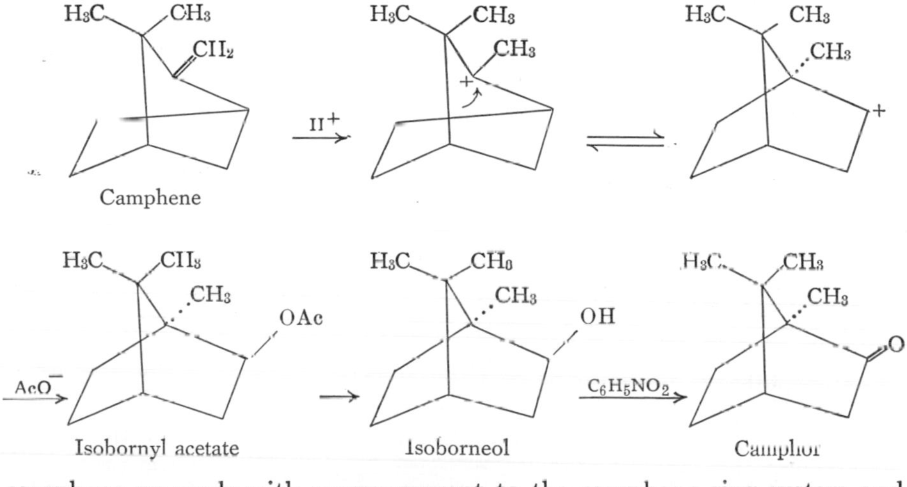

Camphene

Isobornyl acetate   Isoborneol   Camphor

camphene proceeds with rearrangement to the camphane ring system and affords isobornyl acetate; this is hydrolyzed and the alcohol is oxidized to camphor.

Camphor on sulfonation is attacked in the bridge-head methyl group to give camphor-10-sulfonic acid. Bromination affords the 3-bromo deriva-tive. Reaction with amyl nitrite catalyzed by sodium ethoxide gives the 3-isonitroso derivative ($>C{=}NOH$), which on hydrolysis affords the 2,3-dione, a substance known as camphorquinone although it lacks quinonoid properties.   The same substance is formed smoothly on oxidation of camphor with selenium dioxide.   Dogs fed camphor excrete in the urine glucuronides of 3-, 5-, 8-, and 9-hydroxycamphor.

SESQUITERPENES (C_{15})

Farnesol is a widely distributed but rare C_{15}-alcohol; it is related to geraniol (C_{10}), and similarly consists of a mixture of two isomers, formulas I and II.   Farnesol occurs in many essential oils, but in the best source,

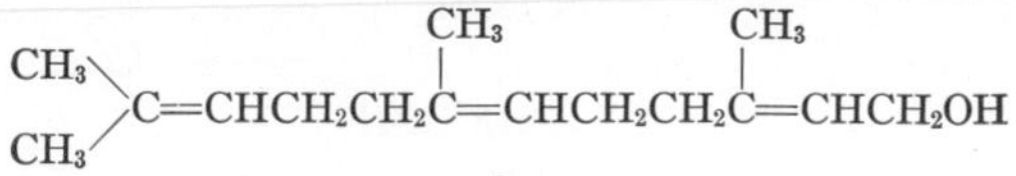

$$CH_3 \diagdown \atop CH_3 \diagup C{=}CHCH_2CH_2\underset{\underset{CH_3}{|}}{C}{=}CHCH_2CH_2\underset{\underset{CH_3}{|}}{C}{=}CHCH_2OH$$

I

$$CH_2 \diagdown \atop CH_3 \diagup CCH_2CH_2CH_2\underset{\underset{CH_3}{|}}{C}{=}CHCH_2CH_2\underset{\underset{CH_3}{|}}{C}{=}CHCH_2OH$$

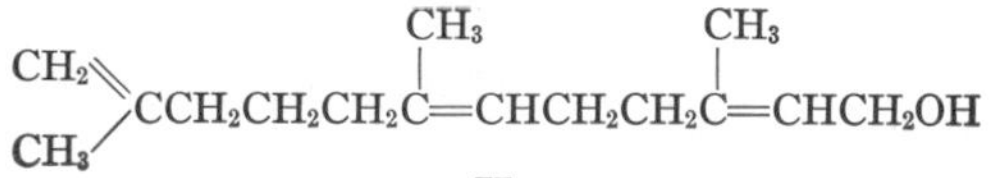

II

Farnesol

ambrette-seed oil, the amount present is only about 0.1%.   The scent is that of lily-of-the-valley.   Farnesol may be the precursor of one of the widely distributed sesquiterpene hydrocarbons, bisabolene, since the conversion can be effected readily in the laboratory.   Bisabolene has been converted into a dicyclic sesquiterpene, isocadinene, which is probably a

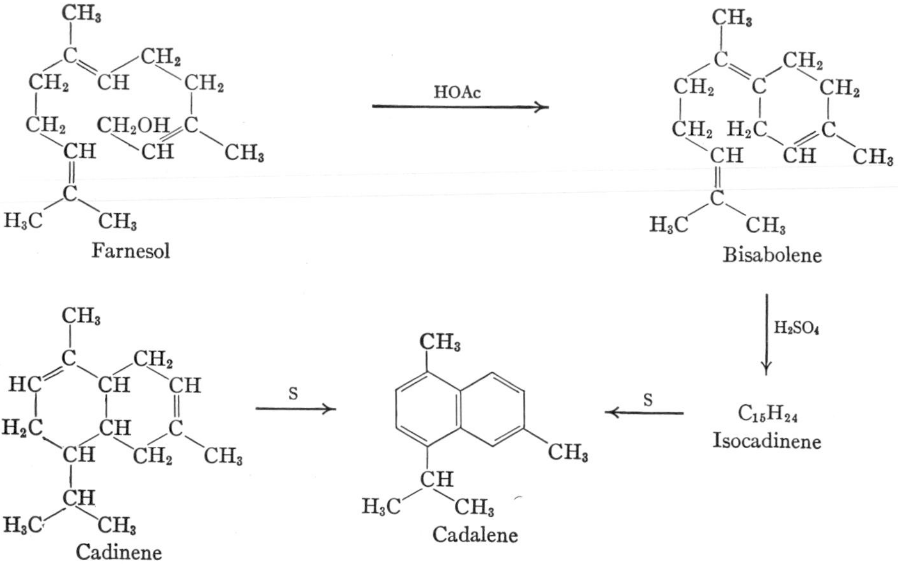

Farnesol

HOAc

Bisabolene

H_2SO_4

$C_{15}H_{24}$
Isocadinene

Cadinene

S

Cadalene

S

double-bond isomer of the widely distributed cadinene (structure: W. P. Campbell, M. D. Soffer, 1944), since both compounds on dehydrogenation yield cadalene.

Farnesol also may be the precursor of selinene (oil of celery), though this conversion has not been demonstrated.   The structure of selinene is

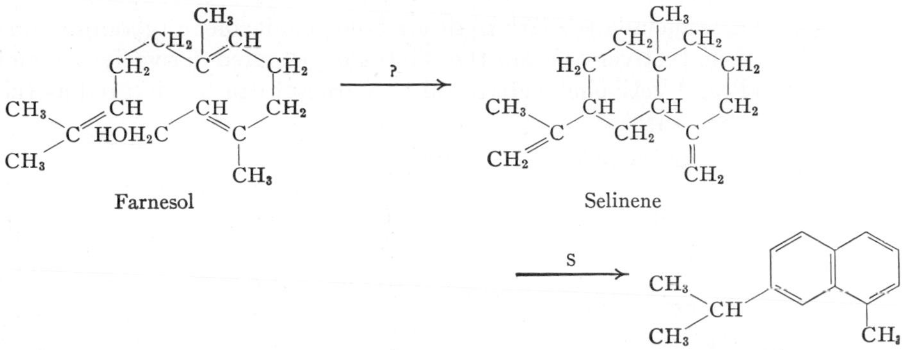

Farnesol

?

Selinene

S

Eudalene

deduced from dehydrogenation to eudalene. The reaction establishes the position of all but one carbon atom, which must be present as an angular methyl group and which is inferred to be at the position indicated on the basis of the isoprene rule.

Farnesol and the three cyclic sesquiterpenes related to it are head-to-tail isoprenoids. Carotol has a combination head-to-tail and tail-to-head arrangement of isoprene units; it is $1,7$-dimethyl-4-dimethylhydroxymethyl-$\Delta^{1(9)}$-octalin.

An interesting sesquiterpene containing the eudalene skeleton is the ketolactone santonin, an anthelmintic isolated from various species of *Artemisia* (structure: Ruzicka, Clemo,[b] R. D. Haworth, 1930). Under acid catalysis santonin very readily undergoes Wagner-Meerwein rearrangement, formulated as proceeding by protonation to the conjugate acid (a, b), methyl

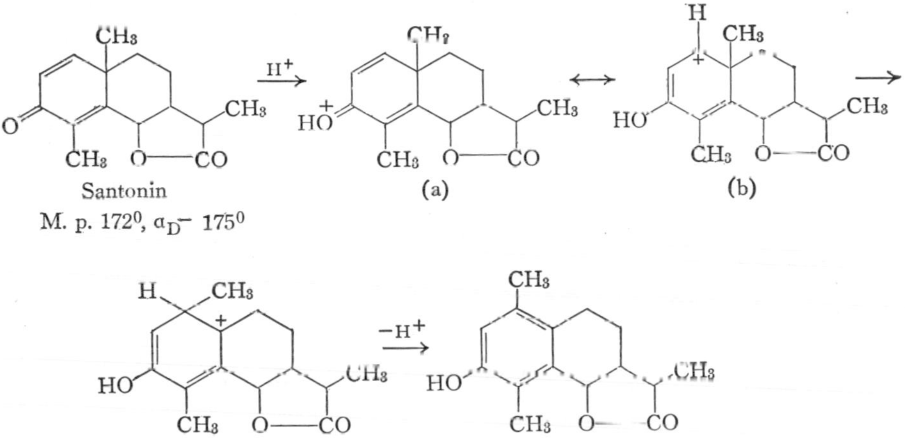

Santonin

M. p. 172^0, $a_D^- 175^0$

(a)

(b)

(c)

Desmotroposantonin

migration (c), and elimination of a proton to give the phenol desmotroposantonin.

Bicyclic sesquiterpenes of an interesting type are derivatives of azulene

---

[b] George Roger Clemo, b. 1889 Devon, England; Ph.D. and D.Sc. Univ. London (Perkin Jr., Chattaway); King's Coll., Durham

(p. 775). These include the two hydrocarbons, guaiazulene (geranium oil) and vetivazulene (vetiver oil) and the related oxygenated derivatives guaiol (guaiac wood) and vetivone (vetiver oil). Farnesol can be pictured as the

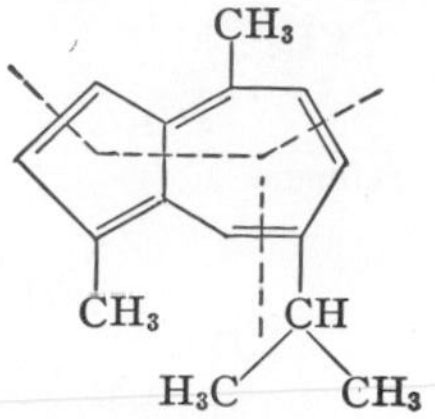

Guaiazulene
(blue-violet)

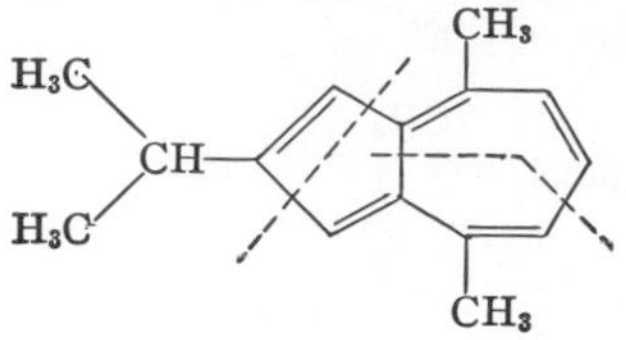

Vetivazulene
(violet)

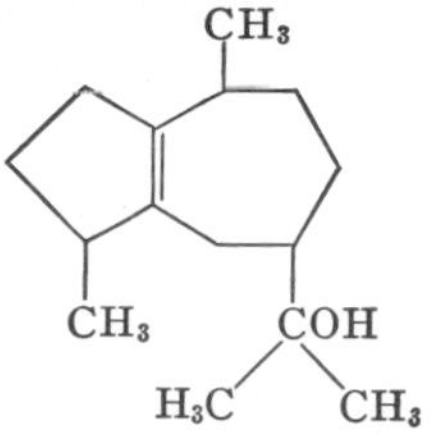

Guaiol

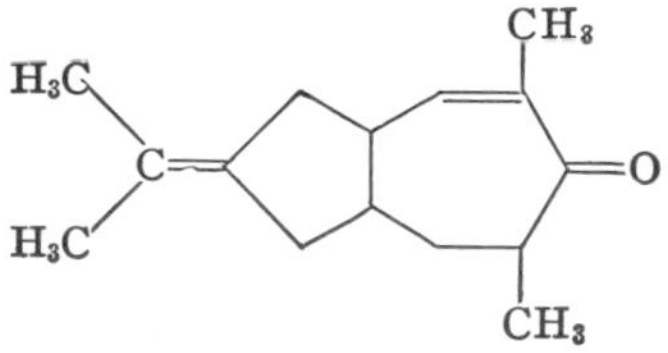

β-Vetivone

precursor of these four azulenes. Several general schemes of synthesis have been developed for the synthesis of polyalkylazulenes. One depends upon a reaction discovered by Buchner (1901) for conversion of a benzene ring into a triunsaturated seven-membered ring. The starting material is a suitably substituted indane derivative, and the reactions are illustrated for the synthesis of vetivazulene (Plattner,[6] 1939). Diazoacetic ester on reaction with the indane (I) yields a cyclopropane derivative (II), which is unstable and undergoes intramolecular rearrangement to the dicyclic ester III. After

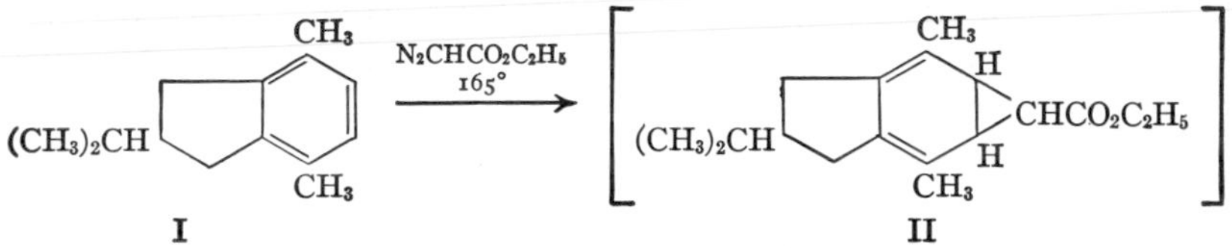

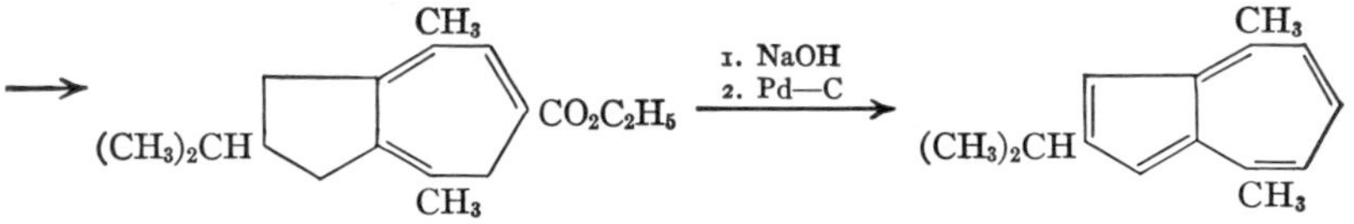

hydrolysis of the ester grouping, treatment with palladium charcoal effects decarboxylation and dehydrogenation.

Another unusual ring system is encountered in caryophyllene ($C_{15}H_{24}$), a

[6] Placidus Andreas Plattner, b. 1904 Chur, Switzerland; Ph.D. Zurich ETH (Ruzicka, Cherbuliez); Zurich, Hofmann La Roche, Basel

hydrocarbon constituent of oil of cloves. It contains two double bonds and therefore two rings: a four-membered ring fused to a nine-membered ring. The three isoprene units are linked head-to-tail. The presence of the cyclobutane ring was established mainly by oxidative degradation to a dimethylcyclobutanedicarboxylic acid, norcaryophyllenic acid. The size of the other ring was deduced by Barton (1953). A difficulty encountered in structural studies is that caryophyllene very readily undergoes isomerization and cyclization. Thus it forms a beautiful blue addition product with nitrous

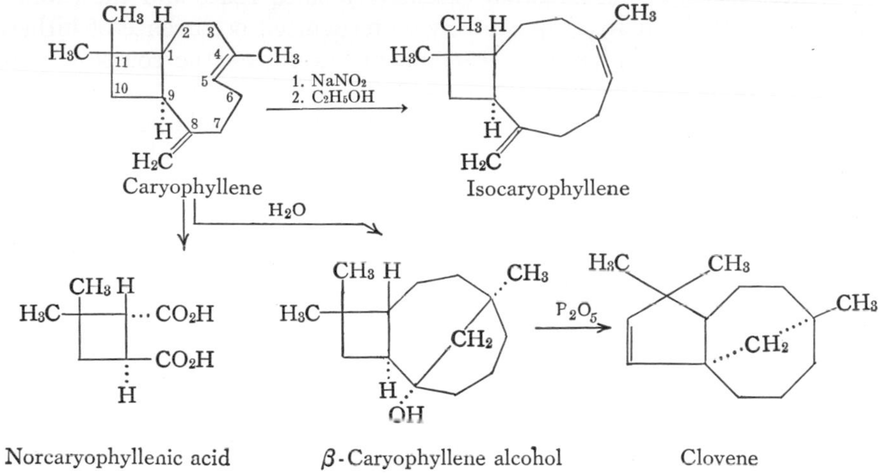

Caryophyllene   1. NaNO₂ 2. C₂H₅OH → Isocaryophyllene

Norcaryophyllenic acid   β-Caryophyllene alcohol   Clovene

acid (known to add preferentially to more highly substituted double bonds), but the hydrocarbon obtained on regeneration is an isomer, eventually shown to differ only in the stereochemistry of the endocyclic (4,5) double bond. The configurations shown in the formulas, *trans* in caryophyllene and *cis* in the isomer, were deduced from the relative reactivity of the double bond to peracids as compared with the reactivity of *cis* and *trans* cyclononene and cyclooctene, where the strained *trans* double bond is the more reactive. The striking ease with which caryophyllene is converted into tricyclic derivatives is illustrated by acid-catalyzed hydration, which gives as one product the saturated tertiary alcohol β-caryophyllene alcohol. Dehydration of the alcohol gives a tricyclic monounsaturated hydrocarbon, clovene, with still a different carbon skeleton.

Humulene ($C_{15}H_{24}$), isomeric with caryophyllene but containing three nonconjugated double bonds, also occurs in oil of cloves. The hydrocarbon

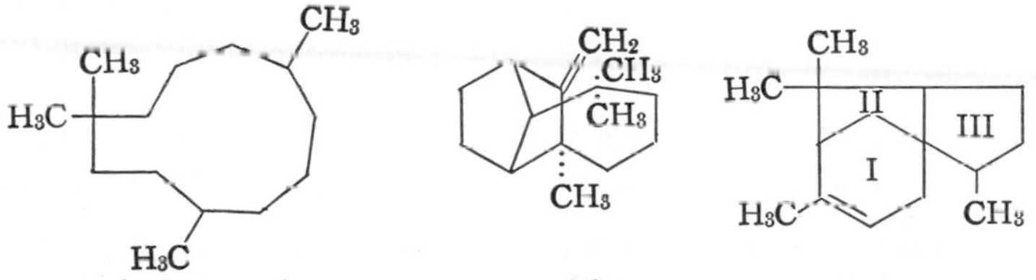

Hexahydrohumulene   Longifolene   Cedrene

has been characterized as a 1,5,5,8-tetramethylcycloundecatriene related to caryophyllene (R. W. Fawcett and J. O. Harris, 1953). Longifoline, $C_{15}H_{24}$, has been isolated from *Pinus longifolia* and other oleoresins (Simonsen[7]). The structure shown in the formula was suggested on the basis of X-ray analysis (R. H. Moffett and D. Rogers) and of molecular rotation data and chemical evidence (G. Ourisson, 1955). Cedar wood oil contains both the crystalline tertiary alcohol cedrol ($C_{15}H_{26}O$, m. p. 86°) and the liquid hydrocarbon cedrene derived from it by dehydration. The constitution of these substances has been investigated extensively since 1841, and the problem was finally solved in 1953 by Stork, who recognized occurrence of hitherto unsuspected Wagner-Meerwein rearrangements during the course of some of the reactions (synthesis: Stork, 1955).

Resin Acids ($C_{20}H_{30}O_2$). — Rosin, the nonsteam-volatile fraction of pine oleoresin, is a mixture of five isomeric diterpene acids. The most abundant component is abietic acid, a heteroannular diene (double bonds distributed between two rings). The homoannular diene system of levo-

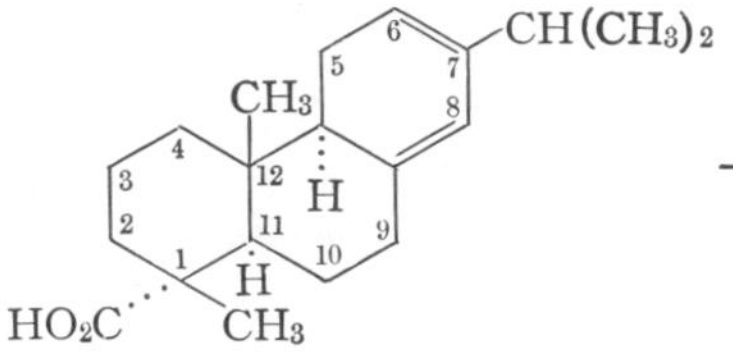

Levopimaric acid
M. p. 152°, α_D −275°, λ_{max} 2725 Å

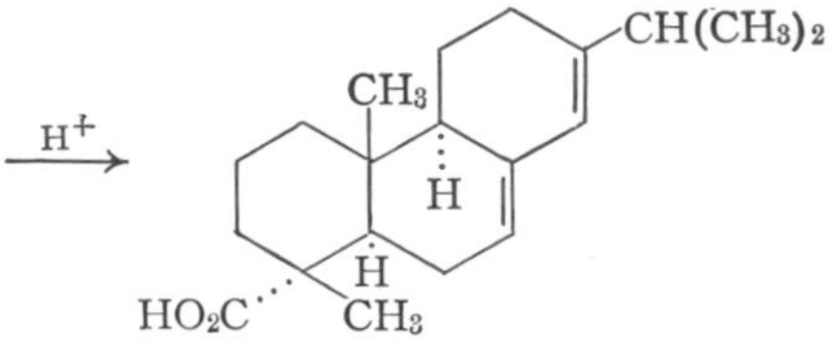

Abietic acid
M. p. 174°, α_D −104°, λ_{max} 2375 Å

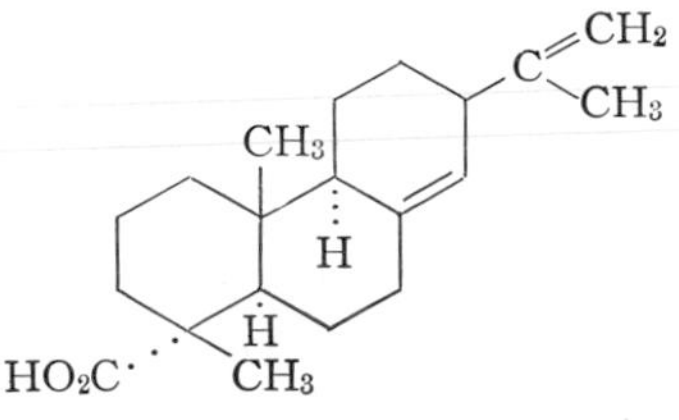

d-Pimaric acid
M. p 219°, α_D + 73°

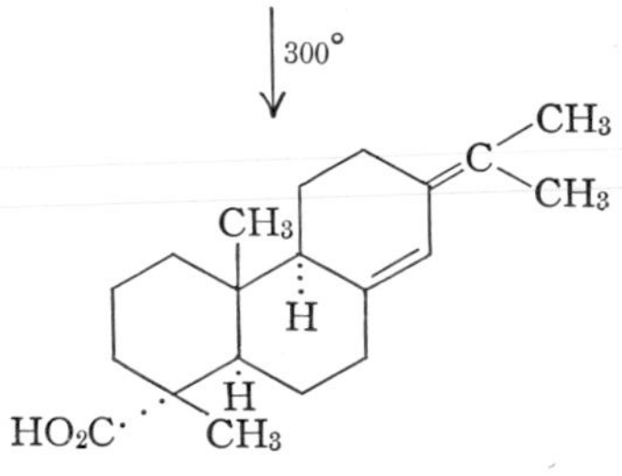

Neoabietic acid
M. p 169°, α_D + 159°, λ_{max} 2500 Å

pimaric acid gives rise to absorption at longer wave length and to less stability, and levopimaric acid is readily isomerized by acid to abietic acid. Abietic acid when heated rearranges to another conjugated isomer, neoabietic acid. *d*-Pimaric acid, a primary rosin constituent, is a nonconjugated diene which is stable to acid.

The nature of the ring system was established by dehydrogenation with sulfur to retene, identified as 1-methyl-7-isopropylphenanthrene by oxidative

[7] Sir John Lionel Simonsen, b. 1884 Manchester; D.Sc. Manchester (Perkin, Jr.); Madras Presidency Coll., and Indian Inst. Sci., India; Coll. North Wales

degradation (Bamberger and Hooker; Bucher) and by synthesis (R. D. Haworth; Bardhan and Sengupta, 1932). The positions of the angular

Retene (m. p. 99°) C_{11}-Acid

methyl and carboxyl groups eliminated in the dehydrogenation were deduced mainly from study of a C_{11}-tricarboxylic acid formed on vigorous oxidation of abietic acid and of d-pimaric acid (Ruzicka). The stereochemistry shown in the formulas was deduced from further characterization of the C_{11}-acid (Barton, 1948). Since this acid is optically inactive it must possess a plane of symmetry, possible only if the C_1 and C_3 carboxyl groups bear a *cis* relationship. The C_2-carboxyl group is probably trans. The configuration at C_{13} is not fully sure.

Phytol $(C_{20}H_{40}O)$. — Willstätter (1909) found that chlorophyll on saponification affords a nitrogen-containing substance, phaeophytin, and phytol, a viscous oil characterized as a monounsaturated primary alcohol of the formula $C_{20}H_{39}OH$. Elucidation of the structure of the substance as a β,γ-unsaturated, or allylic diterpene alcohol was accomplished by F. G. Fischer[8] in 1928. The products of ozonization were characterized as a methyl ketone of the formula $C_{18}H_{36}O$ (6,10,14-trimethylpentadecanone-2) and glycolic aldehyde:

$$\underset{\text{CH}_3}{C_{16}H_{33}\overset{\overset{\displaystyle CH_3}{|}}{C}=CHCH_2OH} \xrightarrow{O_3} C_{16}H_{33}\overset{\overset{\displaystyle CH_3}{|}}{C}=O + O=CHCH_2OH$$

Fischer suspected a relationship to geraniol and farnesol, and succeeded in synthesizing the C_{18}-ketone and finally phytol from the latter substance, as follows:

$$CH_3\overset{\overset{\displaystyle CH_3}{|}}{C}=CHCH_2CH_2\overset{\overset{\displaystyle CH_3}{|}}{C}=CHCH_2CH_2\overset{\overset{\displaystyle CH_3}{|}}{C}=CHCH_2OH \xrightarrow{6H} C_{14}H_{29}CH_2OH \xrightarrow{PBr_3}$$

Farnesol   Hexahydrofarnesol

$$C_{14}H_{29}CH_2Br \xrightarrow{CH_3COCH_2CO_2C_2H_5, Na} \underset{CH_3}{C_{14}H_{29}CH_2\overset{\overset{\displaystyle CO_2C_2H_5}{|}}{CH}COCH_3} \rightarrow C_{14}H_{29}CH_2CH_2COCH_3$$

$$\xrightarrow{CH\equiv CH, NaNH_2} C_{14}H_{29}CH_2CH_2\overset{\overset{\displaystyle CH_3}{\bullet}}{\underset{\underset{\displaystyle OH}{|}}{C}}C\equiv CH \xrightarrow{H_2, Pd} C_{14}H_{29}CH_2CH_2\overset{\overset{\displaystyle CH_3}{\bullet}}{\underset{\underset{\displaystyle OH}{|}}{C}}CH=CH_2$$

$$\xrightarrow{Ac_2O; hydrol.} CH_3\overset{\overset{\displaystyle CH_3}{\bullet}}{CH}CH_2CH_2CH_2\overset{\overset{\displaystyle CH_3}{\bullet}}{CH}CH_2CH_2CH_2\overset{\overset{\displaystyle CH_3}{\bullet}}{CH}CH_2CH_2CH_2\overset{\overset{\displaystyle CH_3}{\bullet}}{C}=CHCH_2OH$$

Phytol

[8] F. Gottwald Fischer, b. 1902 Florence; Ph.D. Freiburg (Wieland); Freiburg, Würzburg

TRITERPENES (C_{30})

Squalene $(C_{30}H_{50})$. — In 1906 Tsujimoto isolated the unsaturated hydrocarbon squalene from the unsaponifiable fraction of liver oils of various sharks, and ten years later he established the composition $C_{30}H_{50}$. Heilbron[9] (1926–29) characterized the compound as an acyclic dihydrotriterpene; Karrer (1931) established the structure by synthesis from farnesyl bromide:

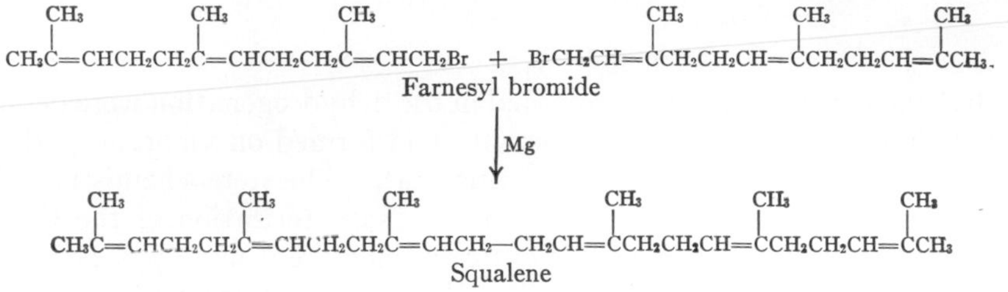

$$CH_3C{=}CHCH_2CH_2C{=}CHCH_2CH_2C{=}CHCH_2Br \; + \; BrCH_2CH{=}CCH_2CH_2CH{=}CCH_2CH_2CH{=}CCH_3.$$

Farnesyl bromide

$$\downarrow Mg$$

$$CH_3C{=}CHCH_2CH_2C{=}CHCH_2CH_2C{=}CHCH_2{-}CH_2CH{=}CCH_2CH_2CH{=}CCH_2CH_2CH{=}CCH_3$$

Squalene

This was the first evidence of the occurrence of an isoprenoid substance in the animal kingdom. The structure of squalene departs from the usual type in that it is symmetrical around the center; the union at this position is head-to-head, whereas within the two halves the isoprene units are joined head-to-tail.

Ambrein $(C_{30}H_{52}O)$. — This interesting doubly unsaturated tertiary alcohol occurs in ambergris. The structure was deduced (Lederer,[10] Ru-

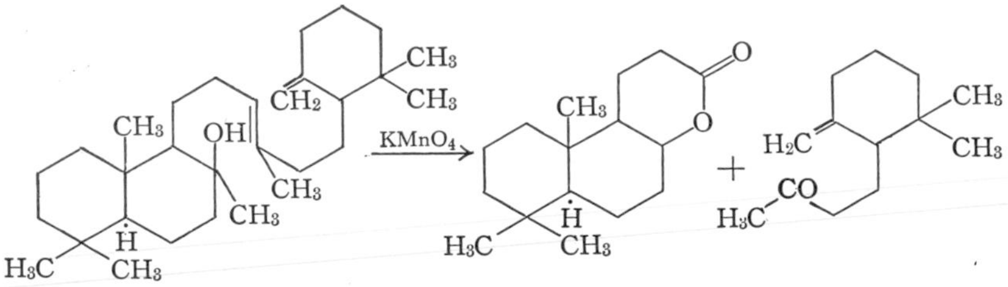

Ambrein   Ambreinolide   Dihydro-γ-ionone

zicka) mainly from characterization of various oxidation products. Thus permanganate cleaves the molecule at the more highly substituted double bond to give the lactone ambreinolide and dihydro-γ-ionone.

Lanosterol $(C_{30}H_{50}O)$ **and Agnosterol** $(C_{30}H_{48}O)$. — These two alcohols occur in the nonsaponifiable fraction of wool fat along with cholesterol, and the names reflect similarity in properties to sterols. Lanosterol contains two double bonds, one (in the side chain) showing normal reactivity and the other (in the nucleus) inert to hydrogenation. Agnosterol is a dehydro derivative of lanosterol and contains a conjugated diene system. One interesting feature of these triterpenes is that the structures do not obey the

---

[9] Sir Ian Morris Heilbron, b. 1886 Glasgow; Ph.D. Leipzig (Hantzsch), D.Sc. Glasgow (Henderson); Manchester, Imperial Coll. Sci. Techn., Brewing Ind. Res. Found.

[10] Edgar Lederer, b. 1908 Vienna; Ph.D. Univ. Vienna (Späth, Kuhn, Fromageot); Sorbonne, Paris

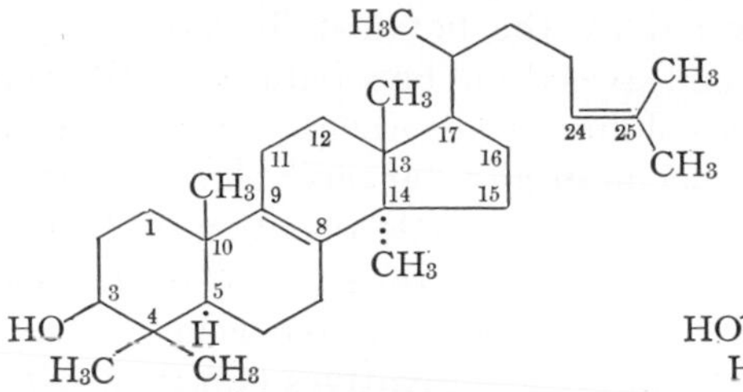

Lanosterol
M. p. 139°, α_D+61°

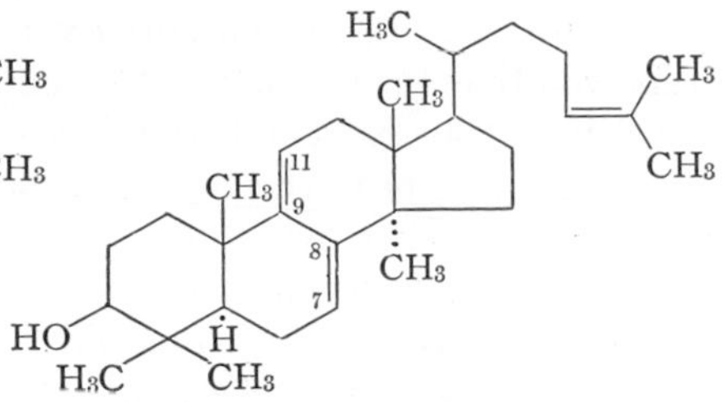

Agnosterol
M. p. 165°. α_D+66°, λ_{max} 2400 Å

isoprene rule; the substances can be regarded as 4,4,14-trimethyl substituted C_{27}-sterols.

Pentacyclic Sapogenins (C_{30}). — The majority of the triterpenoid sapogenins are pentacyclic and fall into three groups, exemplified by α- and

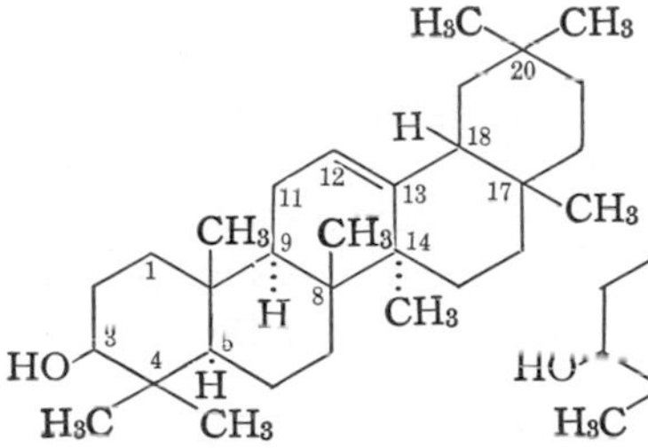

β-Amyrin α-Amyrin   Lupeol

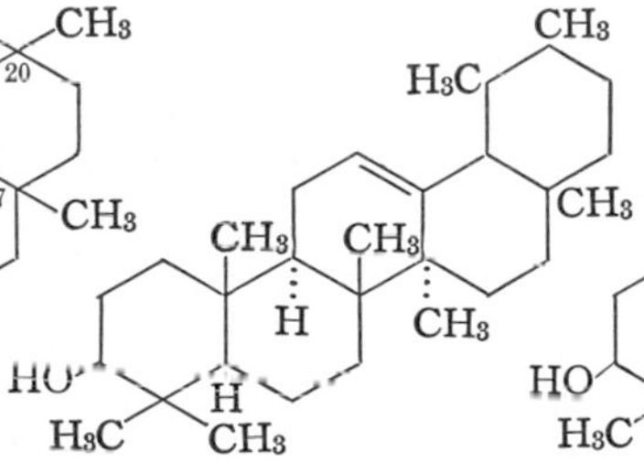

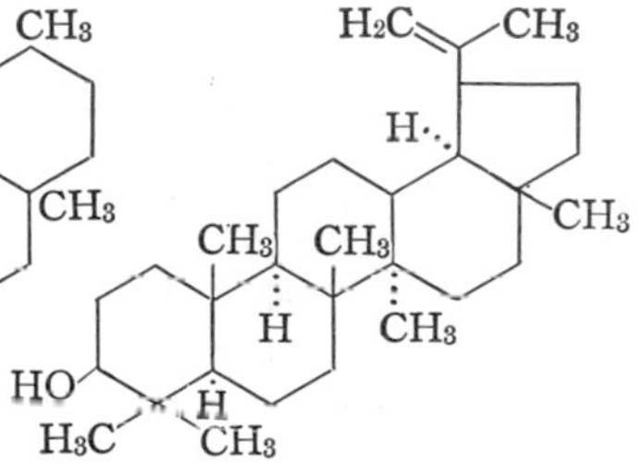

β-amyrin and lupeol. The structures shown are based mainly on investigations of the Zurich School (Ruzicka, Jeger[11]). The double bond in lupeol shows normal reactivity, that in β-amyrin is somewhat hindered, and that in α-amyrin is markedly inert. Triterpenoid acids are derivatives of one of the three structures shown in which a carboxyl group replaces an angular methyl group at C_4, C_{17}, or C_{20}.

CAROTENOIDS (C_{20}, C_{40})

Carotenoids are pigments that occur in many plant and animal fats (lipochrome pigments). The hydrocarbon carotene, the first member of the series to be isolated, was obtained by Wackenroder in 1831 from the common carrot as ruby red crystals, and later was isolated from green leaves, but the identity of the two preparations was established only in 1907 by Willstätter. Carotene, m.p. 168°, $C_{40}H_{56}$, was considered to be a single individual till Kuhn (1931–33) was able to separate it into three isomers, α-carotene, m.p. 188°, β-carotene, m.p. 184°, and γ-carotene, m.p. 178°. Ordinary carotene contains about 15% of α-carotene, 85% of β-carotene, and only a trace (0.1%) of the γ-isomer. Kuhn effected separation by

---

[11] Oskar Jeger, b. 1917 Lwow, Poland; D.Sc. ETH Zurich (Ruzicka, Prelog); ETH Zurich

chromatographic adsorption, discovered by the botanist Tswett in 1906, who showed that the pigments of green leaves could be separated by filtering a petroleum ether extract through a column of adsorbent chalk. Chlorophyll is adsorbed near the top of the column and various yellow pigments form distinct zones below. The method attracted little attention till Kuhn's spectacular reintroduction. It has been used since then for separation and purification of over sixty carotenoids. They belong to four general types: hydrocarbons (carotenes), ketonic or hydroxylic derivatives (xanthophylls), carotenoid acids, and xanthophyll esters. The carotenoids occur in a complex mixture, and preliminary separation is effected by partition between two immiscible solvents, usually petroleum ether and 90% methanol. The carotenes and xanthophyll esters are soluble in the upper layer (epiphase), the xanthophylls and carotenoid acids in the lower layer (hypophase). The epiphase pigments can be separated by a similar partition after saponification; the hypophase pigments are separated by extraction of the carotenoid acids with aqueous alkali.

Structure. — Zechmeister[12] in 1928 found that carotene absorbs eleven moles of hydrogen; since perhydrocarotene has the formula $C_{40}H_{78}$, it evidently contains two rings as well as an extended system of conjugated double bonds responsible for the color. Although earlier workers had noted that carotene is readily oxidized by air, with the appearance of the odor of violets, Karrer first demonstrated the presence of the β-ionone ring; he established the structure of β-carotene in 1931, largely by identification of a series of oxidation products. The dibasic acids are evidently further

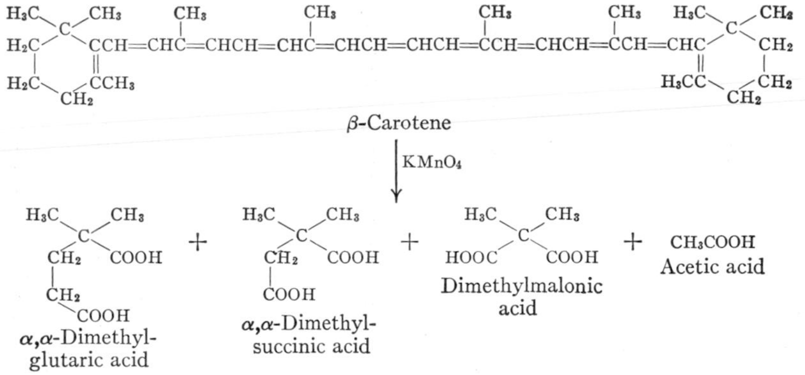

β-Carotene

KMnO₄

α,α-Dimethyl-glutaric acid   +   α,α-Dimethyl-succinic acid   +   Dimethylmalonic acid   +   CH₃COOH Acetic acid

oxidation products of geronic acid, which is obtained on ozonization in an amount that corresponds to the presence of two β-ionone residues. The amount of acetic acid corresponds to six moles per mole of β-carotene oxidized. It is formed by oxidation of the grouping —C(CH₃)=, and consequently the reaction can be used as a diagnostic method for determination of the number of C-methyl groups (Kuhn-Roth

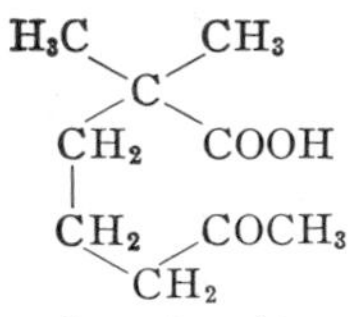

Geronic acid

¹² Laszlo Zechmeister, b. 1889 Györ, Hungary; Ph.D. Zurich ETH (Willstätter); Univ. Pécs (Hungary), Calif. Inst. Techn.

method, 1933). The Kuhn-Roth oxidation is accomplished by chromic anhydride in concentrated sulfuric acid (sp. gr. 1.84); the excess reagent is reduced by hydrazine hydrate; after neutralization with alkali, phosphoric acid is added, and the acetic acid is distilled. The amount of acetic acid is determined by titration with standard alkali.

α-Carotene contains one β-ionone ring and one α-ionone ring, since on ozonization equal amounts of the corresponding ozonization products, geronic acid and isogeronic acid, are obtained. α-Carotene, unlike the other

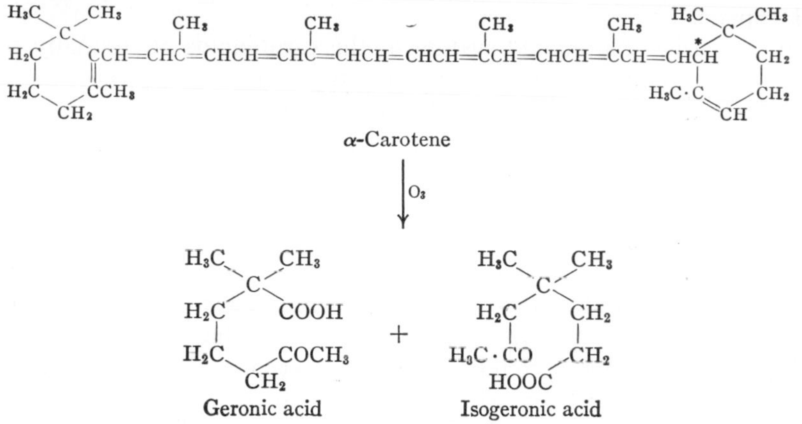

α-Carotene

Geronic acid $\qquad$ Isogeronic acid

two isomers, is optically active; the formula contains one asymmetric carbon atom

γ-Carotene has the same empirical formula as the other carotenes, $C_{40}H_{56}$, but it contains twelve double bonds and only one ring. The structure is based on physical and biological properties and the formation of acetone on ozonolysis (Kuhn):

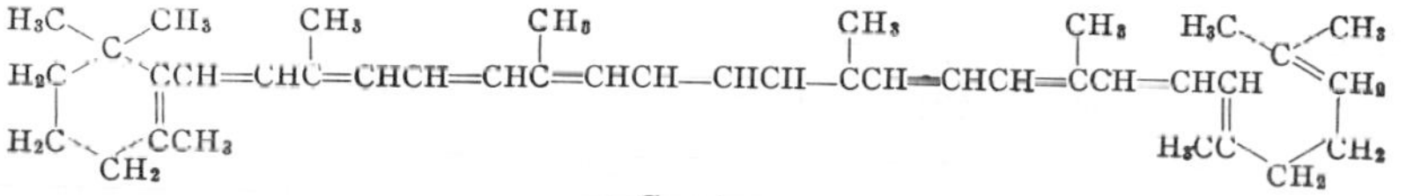

γ-Carotene

Lycopene. — The carotenes are closely related to lycopene, $C_{40}H_{56}$, the red coloring matter of the tomato and many other fruits. Lycopene on catalytic hydrogenation yields the paraffin hydrocarbon $C_{40}H_{82}$, and hence

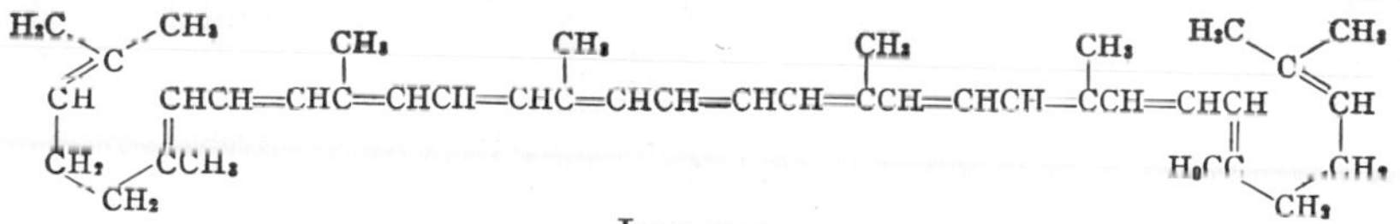

Lycopene

contains no rings. Karrer deduced the structure in 1930 on the basis of oxidation experiments and from consideration of the probable relation to β-carotene, and in 1931 established the skeletal structure by the synthesis of perhydrolycopene from dihydrophytyl bromide:

$$\text{(H}_3\text{C, CH}_3)\text{CH–CH}_2\text{–CH}_2\text{–CHCH}_3\text{–CH}_2 \quad \text{CH}_2\text{CH}_2\text{CH}_2\text{CHCH}_2\text{CH}_2\text{CH}_2\text{CHCH}_2\text{CH}_2\text{Br} \xrightarrow{\text{K}} \text{Perhydrolycopene}$$

β-Carotene can be considered as a derivative of lycopene in which cyclization has occurred at each end; γ-carotene is intermediate between β-carotene and lycopene.

The extensive conjugated system of the carotenoids offers many possibilities for *cis-trans* isomerism. The majority of natural polyenes have the all-*trans* configuration, which is not unexpected in view of the greater stability associated with the *trans* structure. However a few carotenoids containing one or more *cis* linkages have been isolated; partial isomerization of *trans*-carotenoids can be accomplished by iodine or acid catalysis and by thermal or photochemical isomerization.

Vitamin A. — The existence of a fat-soluble growth factor, vitamin A, in butter, egg fat, and cod-liver oil, was established in 1913–15 by feeding experiments; shortly afterwards Steenbock found that rats suffering from a deficiency of vitamin A could be cured by extracts of green plants whose activity could be correlated with the amount of carotene present. Carotene, however, is not identical with vitamin A, since Karrer (1931) found that a concentrate of the vitamin from liver oils of the halibut is more active than carotene. In spite of the fact that the concentrate was impure, Karrer was able to deduce the correct structure, mainly from the observation that geronic acid is obtained on ozonization in amount indicating the presence of one β-ionone ring. The skeletal structure was established conclusively two years later by the synthesis from β-ionone of perhydrovitamin A (eleven steps).

Vitamin A ($C_{20}H_{30}O$), yellow, m.p. 64°, λ_{max} 326 (EtOH), 332 mμ (CHCl$_3$)

The carotenoids are converted into vitamin A in the liver. While theoretically one molecule of β-carotene could give rise to two molecules of the vitamin, quantitative measurements of the potency of β-carotene indicate that the relationship is more nearly 1:1. The α- and γ-isomers have only about half the activity of β-carotene, in agreement with the fact that only half of the molecule can give rise to the vitamin. Vitamin A has not been observed in plants. It occurs most abundantly in the liver oils of marine fish, from which it is extracted commercially.

Isolation of pure crystalline vitamin A from natural sources is difficult and was only accomplished in 1937–40 (H. N. Holmes; C. D. Baxter and J. G. Robeson). Impure vitamin A preparations, particularly those obtained from fresh-water fish, show, in addition to the absorption bands of the pure vitamin, bands in the region of longer wave length due to a companion, vitamin A_2. Separation of A_2 from A (also called A_1) is extremely dif-

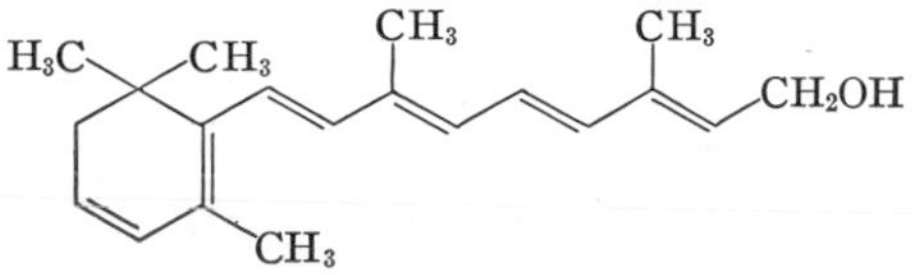

Vitamin A_2 (λ_{max}^{alc} 351 mμ)

ficult, but Shantz (1948) isolated pure A_2 from pike livers selected on the basis of examination under an ultraviolet lamp; those that showed the brilliant yellow fluorescence of A were discarded, and those that showed a brownish orange fluorescence were processed. After successive enrichments the vitamin was converted into the phenylazobenzoate (orange), which was purified by chromatography and finally obtained crystalline; hydrolysis afforded noncrystalline but homogeneous vitamin A_2, with an absorption maximum at 351 mμ. Vitamin A_2 thus absorbs at a wave length much longer than that observed for A (326 mμ). The substance was eventually shown by partial synthesis to be a dehydrovitamin A_1 of the structure given (E. R. H. Jones,[13] 1951): allylic bromination of vitamin A_1 acid methyl ester followed by dehydrobromination introduced a second double bond in the ring, and reduction of the ester with lithium aluminum hydride gave the corresponding alcohol, identical with A_2. A_2 is only 40% as active as A_1.

A further isomer that accompanies A_1 is neovitamin A_1 (Robeson and Baxter, 1947), characterized as the Δ^2-cis-isomer of A_1. It is somewhat less

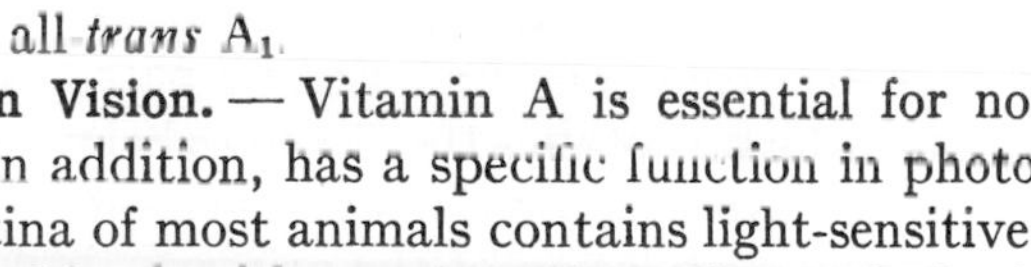

Neovitamin A

M. p. 58-60°, λ_{max}^{alc} 328 mμ

potent than the all-trans A_1.

Vitamin A in Vision. — Vitamin A is essential for normal growth of mammals and, in addition, has a specific function in photoreception in the retina. The retina of most animals contains light-sensitive pigments which are proteins combined with carotenoids. The typical pigment of vertebrates is known as rhodopsin (bright red); on exposure to light it bleaches, with liberation of the protein opsin and the carotenoid, which has been

[13] Ewart Ray Herbert Jones, b. 1911 Wrexham, Denbighshire; Ph.D. Univ. Wales (Simonsen); D.Sc. Manchester (Heilbron); Manchester, Oxford

identified as vitamin A aldehyde (Ball, Goodwin and Morton,[14] 1948). It was originally assumed that vitamin A is the prosthetic group of rhodopsin and that on exposure to light it is dehydrogenated to retinene, the corresponding aldehyde. However, pure all-*trans* A is inactive in formation of rhodopsin but becomes an effective precursor on isomerization to a mixture containing *cis* isomers; the same is true of pure all-*trans* retinene. The system is now formulated as shown in the chart (Wald,[15] 1952–53). Synthe-

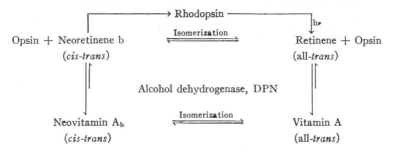

sis of rhodopsin from vitamin A requires oxidation to the aldehyde and isomerization of one (or more) double bonds to the *cis*-configuration to give neoretinene b, which combines with the specific protein opsin to form the pigment. On exposure to light, the prosthetic group is isomerized to the all-*trans* isomer, which must be isomerized to the neo form before it can reenter the cycle.

The light-sensitive pigment of fresh water fishes is porphyropsin (purple). The protein moiety is apparently the same, but the prosthetic group is the aldehyde of vitamin A_2 (Wald, 1938–39).

Synthesis. — Syntheses of compounds structurally similar to, but possibly stereoisomeric with vitamin A were announced in 1946. Pure, synthetic vitamin A was prepared in 1947 by Isler of the Hoffmann-La Roche laboratories in Switzerland. β-Ionone is a logical starting material, but it behaves abnormally in most condensation reactions, probably because of a steric effect. It can be converted however into the C_{14}-aldehyde (III), which behaves normally in Grignard reactions. The aldehyde is prepared from β-ionone (a) by condensation with ethyl chloroacetate (sodium ethoxide, liquid ammonia) to a glycide ester (Darzens reaction); the corresponding acid on decarboxylation yields an aldehydic group, and at the same time the double bond moves into conjugation with the carbonyl group. The C_{14}-aldehyde is condensed with the C_6-unit VII, prepared by the process (b), to give the diol VIII, which contains the carbon skeleton of the vitamin. The remaining steps involve preferential hydrogenation of the acetylenic bond (97% yield), partial acetylation of the primary alcoholic group (98% yield), allylic rearrangement of the secondary alcoholic group followed by

[14] Richard Alan Morton, b. 1899 Liverpool; Ph.D. and D.Sc. Liverpool (Baly, Heilbron); Dept. Biochem. Univ. Liverpool

[15] George Wald, b. 1906 New York, N. Y.; Ph.D. Columbia (Hecht); Dept. Biol. Harvard Univ.

(a)

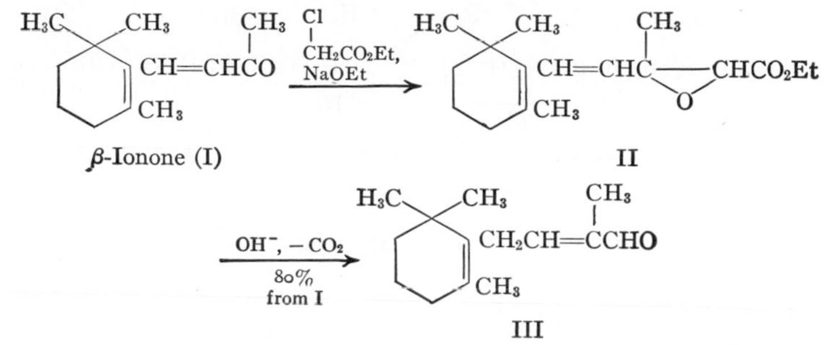

β-Ionone (I)
$\xrightarrow[\text{NaOEt}]{\text{CH}_2\text{CO}_2\text{Et,}}$
II

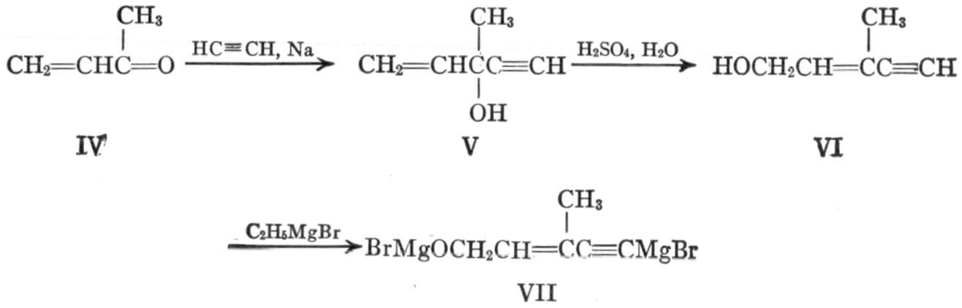

$\xrightarrow[\substack{80\% \\ \text{from I}}]{\text{OH}^-, -\text{CO}_2}$
III

(b) $\text{CH}_2=\text{CHC}=\text{O}$ $\xrightarrow{\text{HC}\equiv\text{CH, Na}}$ $\underset{\text{OH}}{\text{CH}_2=\text{CHCC}\equiv\text{CH}}$ $\xrightarrow{\text{H}_2\text{SO}_4,\ \text{H}_2\text{O}}$ $\text{HOCH}_2\text{CH}=\text{CC}\equiv\text{CH}$

IV V VI

$\xrightarrow{\text{C}_2\text{H}_5\text{MgBr}}$ $\text{BrMgOCH}_2\text{CH}=\text{CC}\equiv\text{CMgBr}$

VII

(c) III + VII $\xrightarrow{81\%}$ VIII $\xrightarrow[\substack{\text{1. H}_2 \\ \text{2. Ac}_2\text{O} \\ \text{3. I}_2}]{}$

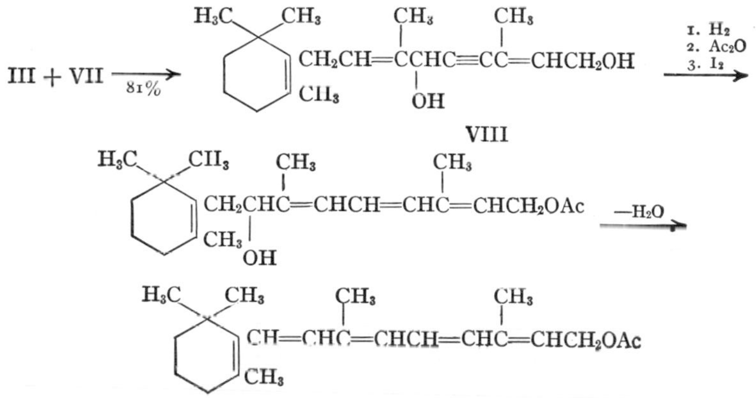

Vitamin A acetate

dehydration (induced by iodine in a neutral medium, poor yield). Vitamin A alcohol was obtained on saponification of the acetate.

The carboxylic acid corresponding to vitamin A has been synthesized by van Dorp and Arens (Organon); vitamin A acid is one half as active as the vitamin. The initial step in the synthesis involves a Reformatsky condensation of β-ionone with γ-bromocrotonate and proceeds in very low yield. The resulting hydroxy ester (IX) is dehydrated and saponified (X) and

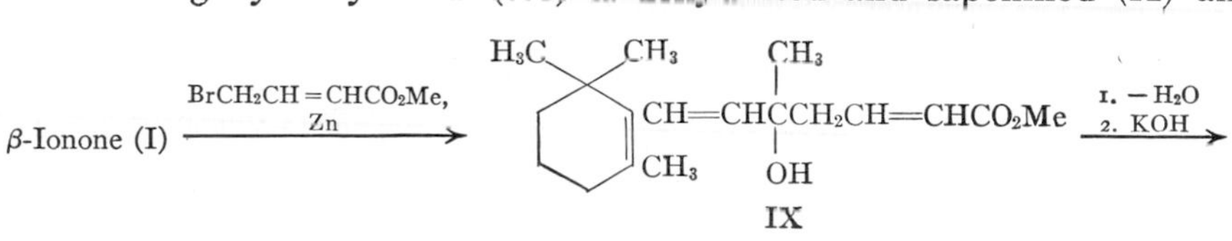

β-Ionone (I) $\xrightarrow[\text{Zn}]{\text{BrCH}_2\text{CH}=\text{CHCO}_2\text{Me,}}$ IX $\xrightarrow[\text{2. KOH}]{\text{1. }-\text{H}_2\text{O}}$

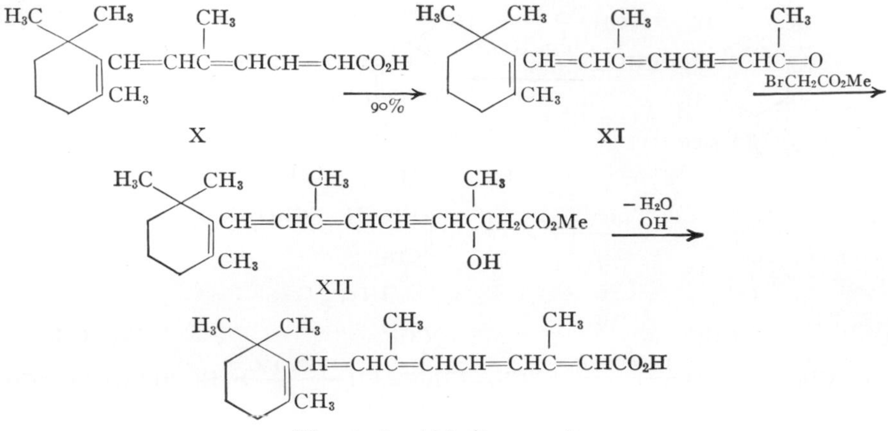

H_3C, CH_3 CH_3
$CH=CHC=CHCH=CHCO_2H$
CH_3

X $\xrightarrow{90\%}$

H_3C, CH_3 CH_3 CH_3
$CH=CHC=CHCH=CHC=O$
CH_3 $\xrightarrow{BrCH_2CO_2Me}$

XI

H_3C, CH_3 CH_3 CH_3
$CH=CHC=CHCH=CHCCH_2CO_2Me$ $\xrightarrow[OH^-]{-H_2O}$
CH_3 OH

XII

H_3C, CH_3 CH_3 CH_3
$CH=CHC=CHCH=CHC=CHCO_2H$
CH_3

Vitamin A acid (λ_{max}^{alc} 350 mμ)

converted into the C_{18}-ketone **XI** by reaction of the acid chloride with methyllithium. A second Reformatsky reaction yielded the hydroxy acid **XII**, which on dehydration (oxalic acid) and hydrolysis was converted into vitamin A acid. Synthesis of vitamin A by reduction of vitamin A acid or

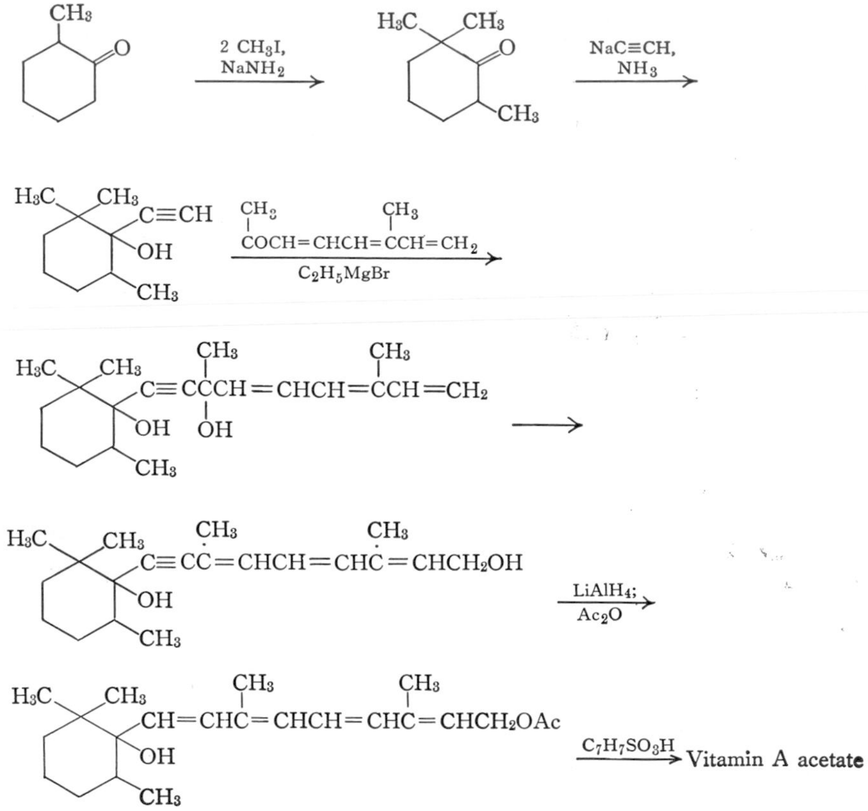

CH_3
⬡=O $\xrightarrow[NaNH_2]{2\ CH_3I,}$

H_3C, CH_3
⬡=O $\xrightarrow[NH_3]{NaC\equiv CH,}$
CH_3

H_3C, CH_3
$C\equiv CH$ CH_2 CH_3
OH $\xrightarrow[C_2H_5MgBr]{COCH=CHCH=CCH=CH_2}$
CH_3

H_3C, CH_3 CH_3 CH_3
$C\equiv CCH=CHCH=CCH=CH_2$
OH OH $\longrightarrow$
CH_3

H_3C, CH_3 CH_3 CH_3
$C\equiv CC=CHCH=CHC=CHCH_2OH$
OH $\xrightarrow[Ac_2O]{LiAlH_4;}$
CH_3

H_3C, CH_3 CH_3 CH_3
$CH=CHC=CHCH=CHC=CHCH_2OAc$
OH $\xrightarrow{C_7H_7SO_3H}$ Vitamin A acetate
CH_3

ester with lithium aluminum hydride was reported in 1949 by Swiss and American groups (Schwartzkopf; Tishler).

One of several other syntheses reported starts from 2-methylcyclohexanone rather than β-ionone (J. Altenburrow, et al., Glaxo Laboratories, 1952). Dimethylation gives 1,1,3-trimethylcyclohexanone, which is condensed with sodium acetylide in liquid ammonia. The Grignard derivative of the acetylene is then added to the C_9-ketone to give a ditertiary glycol, which in an acidic medium rearranges to give a fully conjugated primary-tertiary glycol. The next step, selective reduction of the triple bond, is accomplished with use of lithium aluminum hydride; the adjacent (allylic) hydroxyl group is essential for this reaction. The remaining steps are selective acetylation of the primary hydroxyl group and acid-catalyzed dehydration of the tertiary alcoholic grouping.

The synthesis of β-carotene was achieved by Karrer and by Inhoffen.[16] Three schemes for construction of the C_{40} skeleton employed the following fragments: $2\ C_{19} + C_2$ (Inhoffen, 1950); $2\ C_{16} + C_8$ (Karrer, Inhoffen, 1950); $2\ C_{18} + C_4$ (Inhoffen, 1951). Some of the intermediates of the vitamin A synthesis were employed, for example, the C_{14}-aldehyde III, and the reactions followed much the same general pattern.

Crocin and Crocetin. — Crocetin, $C_{20}H_{24}O_4$, has been isolated from saffron (*Crocus sativus*), where it occurs as the digentiobiose ester, crocin. The structure shown in the formula is based on the following experimental

$$\underset{\text{HOOC}}{\overset{\overset{\displaystyle CH_3}{|}}{C}}{=}CHCH{=}CH\overset{\overset{\displaystyle CH_3}{|}}{C}{=}CHCH{=}CHCH{=}\overset{\overset{\displaystyle CH_3}{|}}{C}CH{=}CHCH{=}\overset{\overset{\displaystyle CH_3}{|}}{C}COOH$$

Crocetin (red needles, m.p. 285°)

observations: the substance is a dibasic acid; it takes up seven moles of hydrogen on catalytic hydrogenation; oxidation with chromic acid gives three to four moles of acetic acid per mole of pigment. The structure has been confirmed by synthesis of perhydrocrocetin.

Crocetin is accompanied in nature by picrocrocin, $C_{16}H_{26}O_7$, the glucoside of an aldehyde, safranal, $C_{10}H_{14}O$, which is formed on hydrolysis:

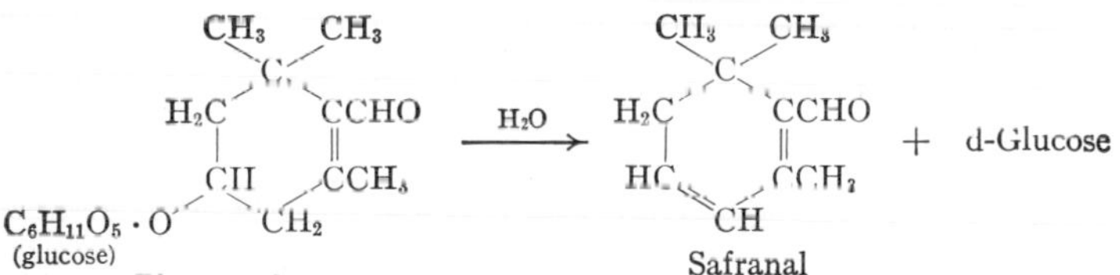

Picrocrocin $\xrightarrow{H_2O}$ Safranal + d-Glucose

Kuhn suggests that crocin and picrocrocin arise in nature from a hypothetical precursor, protocrocin, of the β-carotene type of structure.

---

[16] Hans Herloff Inhoffen, b. 1906 Hannover-Döhren; Ph.D. Göttingen (Windaus); Göttingen, Braunschweig

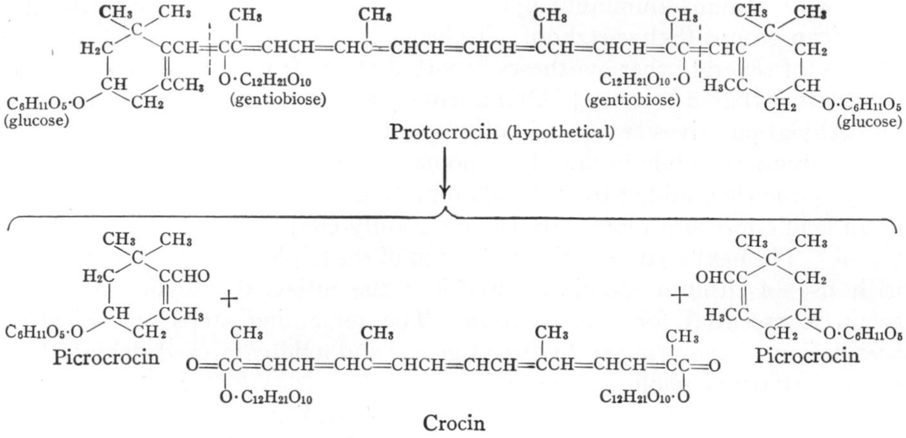

Protocrocin (hypothetical)

Picrocrocin + $O=CC=CHCH=CHC=CHCH=CHCH=CCH=CHCH=CC=O$ + Picrocrocin

Crocin

READING REFERENCES

L. Ruzicka, "The Life and Work of Otto Wallach," *J. Chem. Soc.*, 1582–1597 (1932)

M. T. Bogert, "Recent Isoprene Chemistry," *Chem. Rev.*, **10**, 265–294 (1932); "Carotenoids: The Polyene Pigments of Plants and Animals," in H. Gilman, "Organic Chemistry," 1st Ed., I, 1138–1219, Wiley, New York (1938)

F. Mayer, "The Chemistry of Natural Coloring Matters," 11–95, Reinhold, New York (1943)

D. H. R. Barton, "The Chemistry of the Diterpenes," *Quart. Rev.*, **3**, 36 (1949)

L. Ruzicka, "The Isoprene Rule and the Biosynthesis of Terpenic Compounds," *Experientia*, 357 (1953)

E. H. Rodd, "Chemistry of Carbon Compounds," **2**, Chapters XII–XXI, by D. H. R. Barton, Elsvier (1953)

STEROIDS

Sterols are crystalline alcohols (Gr. *stereos*, solid, + ol) found in the nonsaponifiable matter of plants and animals and characterized structurally by the presence of a saturated phenanthrene ring system having an additional, five-membered ring fused at the 1,2-position; thus they are hydroxylated perhydro-1,2-cyclopentenophenanthrene derivatives. Cholesterol (I), the principal sterol of the animal organism, has this ring system with an attached eight-carbon side chain and two angular methyl groups, and on dehydrogenation with selenium it yields, among other products, the aromatic substance II, the Diels hydrocarbon (1927), which possesses the identifying structural unit. The secondary alcoholic group at C_3 is elimi

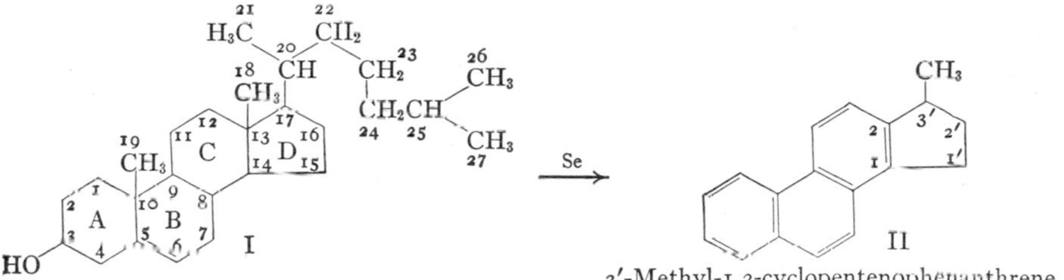

Cholesterol
(m.p. 150°, $[\alpha]_D$ −39°)

3'-Methyl-1,2-cyclopentenophenanthrene,
or Diels hydrocarbon

nated as water, the angular methyl group at C_{10} is expelled as methane in the aromatization of the six-membered rings A and B, and the second angular methyl group at C_{13} migrates to the adjacent 17-position with expulsion of the side chain. The Diels hydrocarbon results also from selenium dehydrogenation of other sterols and of bile acids; in addition a number of other natural products were first recognized by this reaction as steroids.

Sterols. — Cholesterol (Gr. *chole*, bile) occurs in all tissues of the animal body, particularly abundantly in the spinal cord, the brain, and gallstones; the total cholesterol content of a man weighing 140 lbs. is about 210 g. Tissue cholesterol contains small amounts of companion sterols, one of which is the saturated alcohol cholestanol, the sole product of hydrogenation of cholesterol. Coprostanol (IV) is excreted in the feces. These two saturated substances differ in the configuration of the asymmetric center C_5 at the juncture of rings A and B, as shown in the formulas. In cholestanol rings A and B are *trans*, and correspond to *trans*-decalin; the formula written with a full line connecting the C_{10}-methyl group and a dotted line

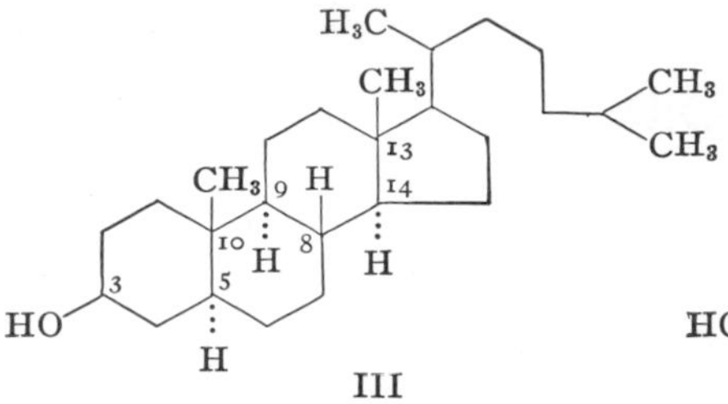

III
Cholestanol
A/B *trans,* allo series

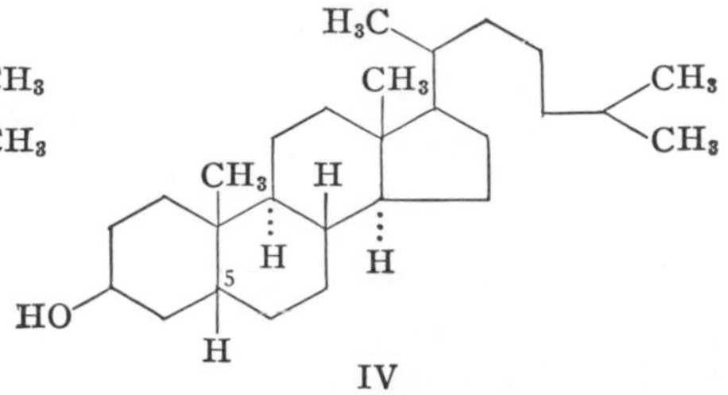

IV
Coprostanol
A/B *cis,* normal series

connecting the C_5-hydrogen indicates that these substituents lie on opposite sides of the molecule. By convention, the 3-hydroxyl group of cholestanol is regarded as projecting in front of the plane of the ring system and is described as β-oriented (full-line bond); the hydrogen at C_5 projects to the rear and is α-oriented (dotted-line bond). The two angular methyl groups and the side chain at C_{17} all extend from the front side of the molecule (β), and this orientation is characteristic of all natural steroids. Coprostanol is the 5β-epimer of cholestanol, and since the hydrogen at C_5 and the methyl at C_{10} are both β-oriented, rings A and B constitute a *cis*-decalin unit. The A/B *cis* type is called the normal series merely from the circumstance that it is normal to bile acids. Naturally occurring saturated sterols (stanols) other than coprostanol belong to the 5α or allo series. Since the reduced cholesterol structure contains nine centers of asymmetry, no less than 512 stereoisomers are possible, and yet cholestanol and coprostanol are the only isomers known to occur in nature. Configurations at the bridgehead positions are 8β, 9α, 14α, as shown in the formulas; in cholestanol all three ring junctures are *trans*.

A second common stereochemical variation concerns the configuration at C_3, or the steric orientation of the secondary alcoholic hydroxyl group. The orientation is β in cholesterol, cholestanol, coprostanol and in most natural sterols. Cholestanol is thus 3β-hydroxycholestane, or cholestanol-3β. The 3α-epimer, described by the trivial name epicholestanol (VI) or by the systematic name cholestanol-3α, is obtained by oxidation of cholestanol to cholestanone (V) and catalytic hydrogenation in the presence of hydro-

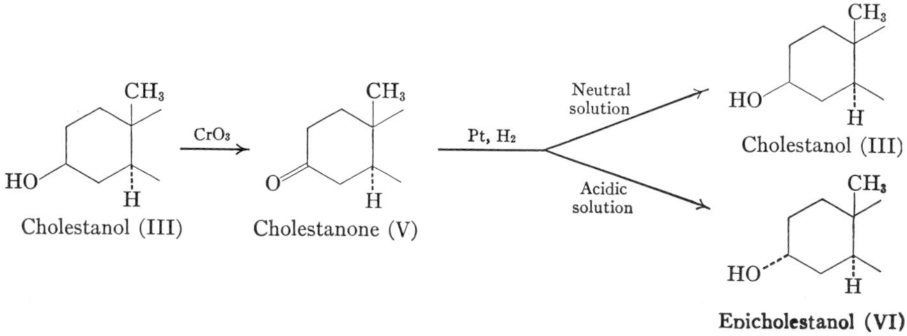

Cholestanol (III)   Cholestanone (V)

Cholestanol (III)

Epicholestanol (VI)

chloric acid; epicholestanol is the chief product, but is accompanied by some cholestanol. When the hydrogenation is conducted in neutral solution the situation is reversed and cholestanol is the chief product.

Mixtures of the 3-hydroxy epimers can be separated quantitatively by a remarkably specific precipitation reaction utilizing digitonin (Windaus,[1] 1909). Digitonin is a rare glycoside found in digitalis seeds along with digitalis drugs; it contains a pentasaccharide unit linked to a steroid sapogenin nucleus (p. 993) and has the empirical formula $C_{56}H_{92}O_{29}$ (mol. wt. 1229). The highly hydroxylic substance is soluble in water and insoluble in ether. Addition of a solution of the reagent in 90% alcohol to a solution of cholesterol precipitates a 1:1 complex, cholesterol digitonide. The digitonide can be split by boiling pyridine, which effects complete dissociation of the components; digitonin is precipitated on addition of ether, and the sterol is isolated by washing the mother liquor with acid to remove pyridine and evaporating the dried ethereal solution. Digitonin usually precipitates 3β-hydroxysteroids but not 3α-hydroxysteroids; the latter form much more soluble complexes. Thus the cholestanol resulting as the chief product of neutral hydrogenation of cholestanone can be freed from any isomer by precipitation with digitonin and recovery from the washed precipitate. The mixture resulting on acidic hydrogenation is treated with enough digitonin to precipitate the cholestanol present, and pure epicholestanol is obtained by processing the filtrate.

Digitonin precipitation is employed in a micromethod for determination of cholesterol in blood plasma, where it occurs partly free and partly as the palmitate or related ester. Since these cholesteryl esters are not precipitated by digitonin, both free and combined cholesterol can be determined. A 0.2-ml. sample of plasma is extracted with acetone–alcohol and the free cholesterol is precipitated from a portion of the solution with digitonin. Another portion is submitted to saponification and the total cholesterol is precipitated. The cholesterol content of the two digitonin precipitates is then determined by a colorimetric method based on the Liebermann-Burchard color reaction of cholesterol with sulfuric acid and acetic anhydride in chloroform solution; the color test is specific to unsaturated sterols. Blood plasma contains 0.15–0.25 g. of total cholesterol per 100 ml., and of this amount about 27% is present in the free form.

The C_5-epimers of cholestanol and coprostanol can be made as follows. When cholesterol is oxidized with aluminum *t*-butoxide and acetone (Oppenauer reaction), the double bond at the 5,6-position migrates to a position of conjugation with the carbonyl group to give cholestenone, (Δ^4-cholestenone, VII). This substance on partial hydrogenation affords coprostanone, of the A/B *cis* configuration, and on further hydrogenation gives either coprostanol or its C_3-epimer, according to the acidity. Coprostanol (3β) is precipitated by digitonin and epicoprostanol (3α) is not.

[1] Adolf Windaus; b. 1876 Berlin; Ph.D. Freiburg; Göttingen; Nobel Prize 1928

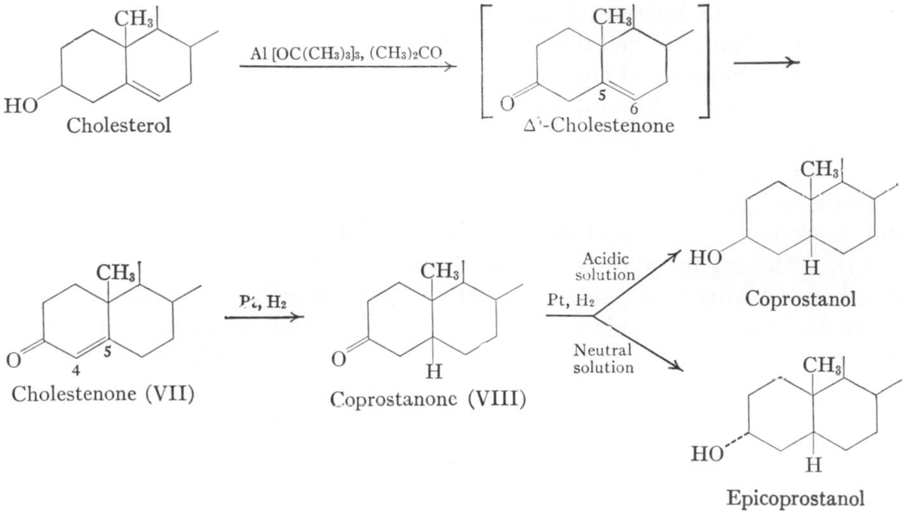

Cholesterol   Al [OC(CH₃)₃]₃, (CH₃)₂CO →   [Δ⁵-Cholestenone] →

Cholestenone (VII)   Pt, H₂ →   Coprostanone (VIII)

Acidic solution → HO H Coprostanol

Pt, H₂   Neutral solution → HO H Epicoprostanol

Sterols of the animal organism, cholesterol, β-cholestanol, and coprostanol, all have the same skeletal structure of twenty-seven carbon atoms. The principal plant sterols, typified by ergosterol and stigmasterol, are either C_{28}- or C_{29}-compounds. These substances have both the 3β-hydroxyl group and the 5,6-double bond characteristic of cholesterol; they differ

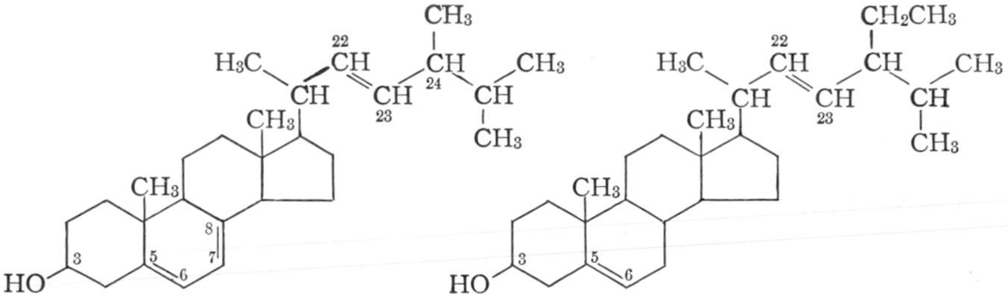

Ergosterol
(m.p. 163°, $[\alpha]_D$ −133°,
abs. max. 2800 Å)

Stigmasterol
(m.p. 170°, $[\alpha]_D$ −45°)

from cholesterol in having a side chain with a double bond at C_{22}–C_{23} (*trans*) and an extra alkyl group, methyl and ethyl respectively, at C_{24}. Ergosterol possesses a second nuclear double bond conjugated with the first; the diene system gives rise to a characteristic ultraviolet absorption spectrum, and ergosterol is thereby differentiated from cholesterol and stigmasterol. Ergosterol is found in the nonsaponifiable fraction from yeast, and stigmasterol in that from calabar bean and soybean oil. The amounts present are small and the substances are accompanied by related sterols, and hence preparation of pure materials is tedious and costly. Mixtures of sitosterols (Gr. *sitos*, grain) are widely distributed in the plant world, but individual constituents are secured only with difficulty; those that are fully characterized have the stigmasterol skeleton but lack the C_{22}–C_{23} double bond.

Steric Course of Reactions. — Application to steroid chemistry of Hassel's concept of axial and equatorial bonds (Barton, 1950) immediately accounted for a number of previously obscure phenomena and permitted

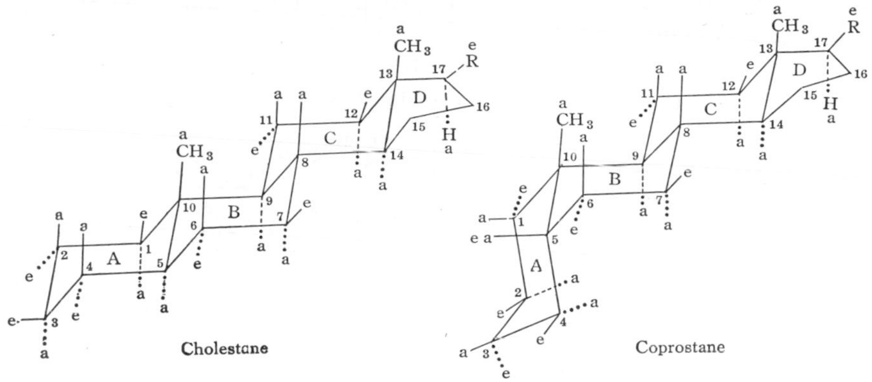

Cholestane   Coprostane

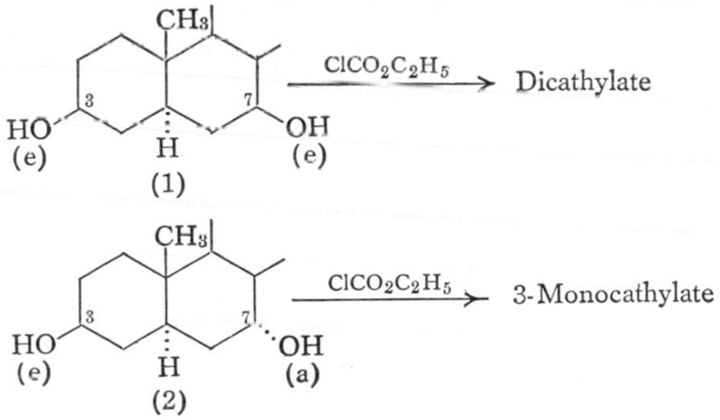

accurate predictions concerning the steric course of unexplored reactions. The most stable conformations of cholestane and coprostane are shown in the formulas; both contain three chair-form cyclohexane rings. In the cholestane series a 3β-hydroxyl group is equatorial and hence is thermodynamically more stable than an axial 3α-hydroxyl; hence an explanation is at hand for the long-known fact that if either cholestanol or epicholesterol is heated with sodium ethoxide at $180°$ until equilibrium is established the mixture consists preponderantly of the β-epimer. The reaction involves oxidation-reduction and requires the presence of a trace of ketone; reduction of cholestanone with sodium and alcohol also provides for equilibration and gives cholestanol as the chief product. Similar experiments have shown that a 4α(e) hydroxyl is more stable than a 4β(a) hydroxyl; 6α(e) > 6β(a); 7β(e) > 7α(a). Conformational analysis also explains differences in ease of acylation of secondary hydroxyl groups, revealed particularly in the reaction of steroid alcohols with excess ethyl chloroformate in pyridine solution to form cathyl (carbethoxy) derivatives: $ROH + ClCO_2C_2H_5 + Py \rightarrow ROCO_2C_2H_5 + Py \cdot HCl$. Only very accessible hydroxyl groups respond to this particular acylation reaction. Cholestane-$3\beta,7\beta$-diol (1) and cholestane-3β,7α-diol (2) both form diacetates and dibenzoates, but only the isomer in which both hydroxyl groups are equatorial (1) forms a dicathylate; (2), even with excess reagent, forms only the 3-monocathylate. As in the cyclohexanol series, an axial alcoholic group is more vulnerable than an equatorial one to chromic acid oxidation, since the reaction involves attack of the C—H bond. The specificity is often evident in oxidation with other reagents, for example, in oxidation of a bile acid 3α,7α-diol with N-bromo-

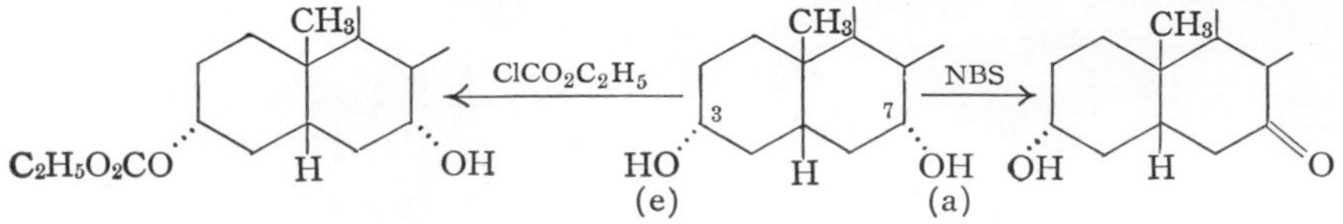

succinimide (NBS). The product is the 7-ketone; the product of cathyla-tion is the 3-acyl derivative.

It should be emphasized that the axial or equatorial orientation of groups determines the relative stability of the structures under equilibrium condi-tions but does not control the orientation assumed in addition reactions. Thus the initial product of bromination of cholesterol is the diaxial 5α,6β-

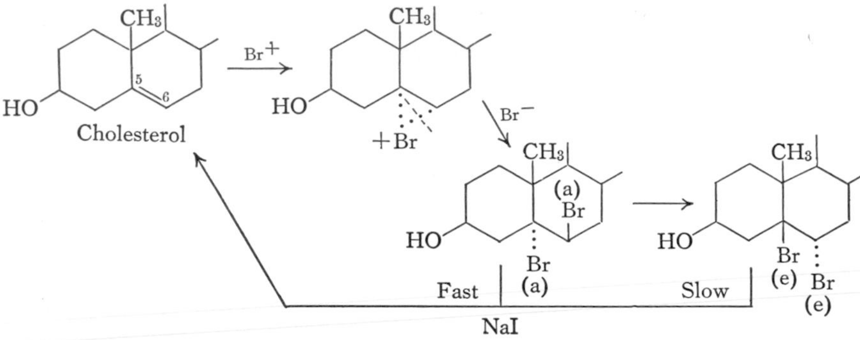

dibromide which, as anticipated, is labile (αD −44°) and readily rearranges (with mutarotation) to the stable diequatorial 5β,6α-dibromide (αD +47°) Both dibromides when treated with sodium iodide in acetone undergo *trans* elimination with regeneration of cholesterol, but the labile 5α,6β-dibromide reacts much faster because the bromine and carbon atoms concerned all lie in a plane and hence are ideally oriented for a four-center transition state (a) requiring minimum activation energy.

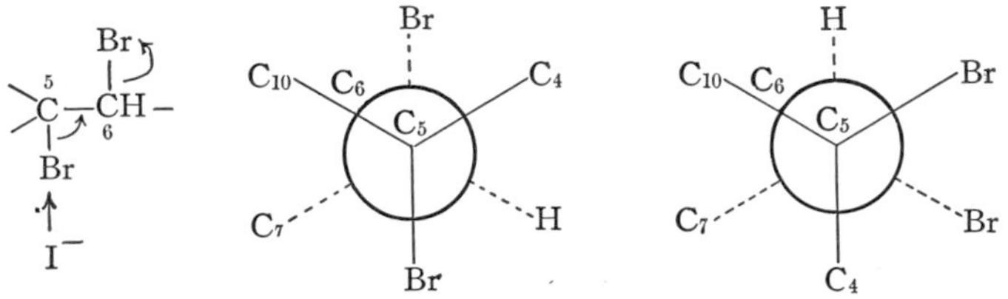

Formulations (b) and (c) depict the views obtained on looking along the C_5–C_6 axis from C_5 to C_6 in the labile (b) and in the stable (c) dibromide; the planarity of the bromines and carbons in the first and lack of planarity in the second is evident. A similar planar transition state in the reverse reaction of bromination accounts for the formation of the diaxial $5\alpha,6\beta$-dibromide. At some stage bromination appears to involve an α-oriented bromonium ion which suffers fission of the three-membered ring with inversion at C_6, a mechanism supported by the fact that the chief product of the reaction of cholesterol with peracids is cholesterol-α-oxide, which on fission with water and with acid yields the $5\alpha,6\beta$-substituted products shown. In both reactions, as well as in hydrogenation, the α-orientation at

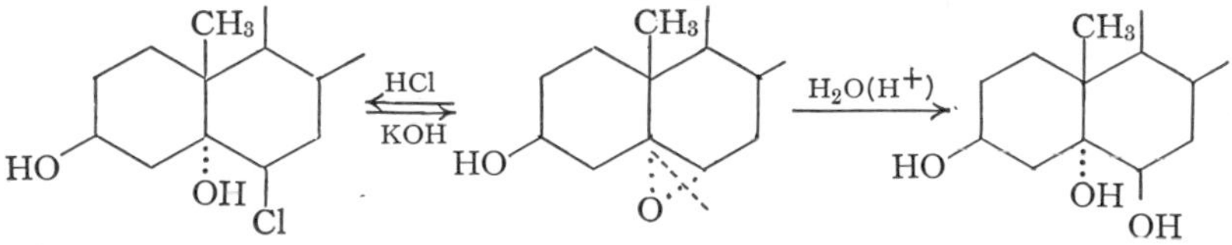

α-Oxide

C_5 in the products shows that the attack is from the rear. Indeed rear attack is the rule at all positions of the steroid structure, and it can be attributed to the shielding of the front side of the molecule by the β-oriented angular methyl groups and side chain. The fact that fission of cholesterol-α-oxide gives the diaxial diol and chlorohydrin may be stressed, because this rule applies to all oxides. The rule of rear attack is also sufficiently general for purposes of prediction, although a few exceptions are known.

Bile Acids. — Saponification of bile splits the glyco- and taurocholic acid components and gives a mixture of bile acids, the most abundant of which, from human or ox bile, is cholic acid. The carbon skeleton has the

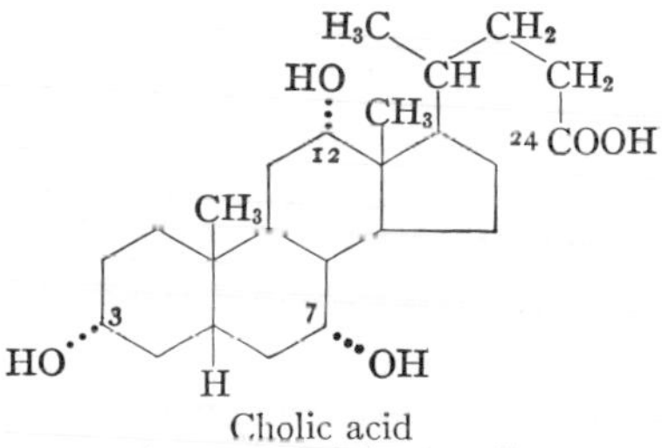

Cholic acid
(m.p. 195°, $[\alpha]_D + 37°$)

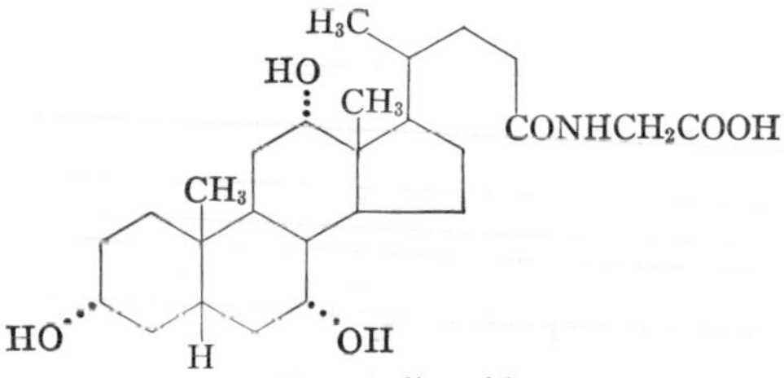

Glycocholic acid

same structure and configuration as coprostanol except that the side chain terminates in a C_{24}-carboxyl group. All three hydroxyl groups are α-oriented; all the bile acids have a 3α-hydroxyl group and are not precipitated by digitonin. The 3α-hydroxyl group is equatorial, while the 7α- and 12α-hydroxyls are in the less vulnerable axial orientation, and hence cholic acid and its esters can be selectively acylated at C_3; the 3-cathylate is obtainable in particularly high yield. The order of decreasing susceptibility to oxidation is $C_7 > C_{12} > C_3$. That the equatorial β-hydrogen at C_{12} is less vulnerable than that at C_7 is attributable to hindrance from the β-oriented angular methyl group at C_{13}.

The parent acid, cholanic acid, is obtained by pyrolytic dehydration of cholic acid and hydrogenation of the resulting mixture of cholatrienic acids. It is the product of similar treatment of desoxycholic acid, of the isomeric chenodesoxycholic acid, which is $3\alpha,7\alpha$-dihydroxycholic acid, and of lithocholic acid (isolated first from gall stones). The yields obtainable from

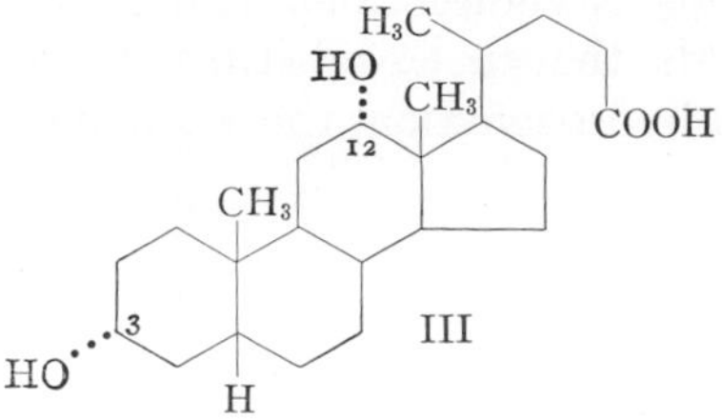

Desoxycholic acid   Lithocholic acid
(m.p. 176°, [α]$_D$ + 55°)   (m.p. 186°, [α]$_D$ + 32°)

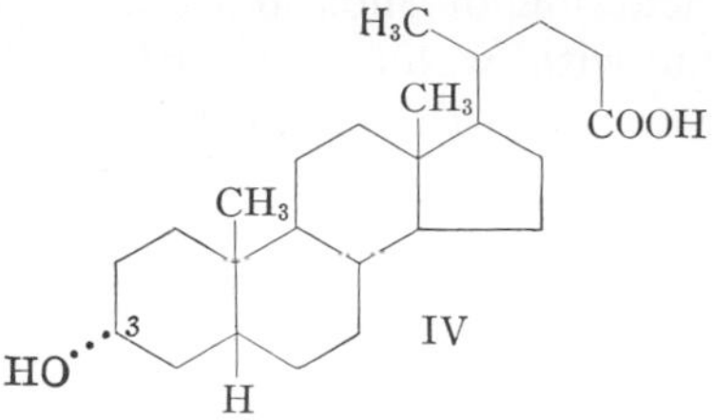

bile are: cholic acid, 5–6%; desoxycholic acid, 0.6–8%; lithocholic acid, 0.02%; chenodesoxycholic acid, trace. Hyodesoxycholic acid, one of the acids of pig bile (Gr. *hys*, swine), is the $3\alpha,6\alpha$-dihydroxy isomer. When the hydroxyl group at C_6 is oxidized to a carbonyl group, isomerization at C_5 is possible through the enol, and treatment of the ketone with alkali converts the A/B *cis* cholanic acid derivative largely into the more stable *trans* epimer

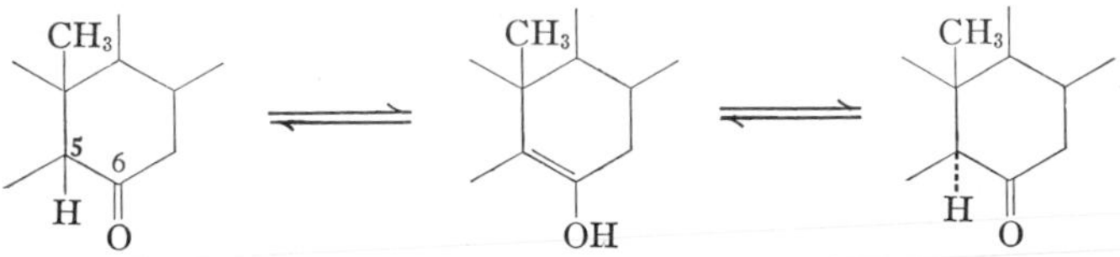

Cholanic acid series   Allocholanic acid series

of the allocholanic acid series. Thus hyodesoxycholic acid is convertible by oxidation, isomerization, and degradation into allocholanic acid, which has the A/B *trans* configuration characteristic of cholestanol. Correlation of the sterols with the bile acids was established by Windaus's discovery (1919) that on oxidation with chromic acid cholestane is degraded in part into acetone and allocholanic acid; the 5-epimer, coprostane, yields cholanic acid.

SEX HORMONES

Sex hormones are steroids secreted by the gonads under stimulation from proteinic hormones of the anterior lobe of the pituitary gland which are carried to the gonads through the blood stream. Thus removal of the anterior lobe (hypophysectomy) results in dysfunction and atrophy of the gonads, and implantation of pituitary tissue or administration of cell-free extracts in hypophysectomized animals brings about regeneration of the reproductive organs. Experiments of a similar nature with castrated and immature animals established that the testes and ovaries normally secrete chemical agents of a hormonic character that control sexual processes and secondary sex characteristics but are significant in the broader sense that they are growth substances of importance to health and well-being. Estrone, the first-known member of the sex hormone group, was isolated in 1929 (Butenandt[2]; Doisy). Androsterone, typical of a series of male sex hormones or androgens, was isolated in 1931 (Butenandt), and isolation of the pregnancy hormone progesterone was accomplished in 1934 in four laboratories (Butenandt; Slotta[3]; Allen and Wintersteiner[4]; Hartmann and Wettstein[5]). Chemical characterization of these substances and of members of the respective groups was assisted greatly by the fundamental knowledge of steroid chemistry derived from the extensive researches in the field of sterols and bile acids conducted by Windaus, Wieland, and others over many years. These investigations culminated in establishment of the structures of cholesterol and of cholic acid in 1932 (Rosenheim[6] and King[7]; Wieland and Dane), and with this enormously difficult classical problem solved, structures of the steroid hormones were elucidated shortly after their isolation.

Estrogens. — This group includes the related C_{18}-compounds: estradiol estrone, and estriol, whose formulas are shown. Configurations at C_8, C_9

Estradiol   Estrone   Estriol

C_{13}, and C_{14} (shown for estradiol) are the same for all three and correspond to the arrangement in cholesterol. The sterol side chain is replaced by an oxygen function, and in estradiol and estriol this is a hydroxyl group in the β-orientation, projecting to the front. In estriol the second alcoholic hydroxyl is α (extends to the rear). Estriol on distillation from potassium bisulfate yields estrone (dehydration; ketonization of enol). The 17-keto group of estrone is represented in the formula by one full and one dotted

[2] Adolf Butenandt; b. 1903 Wesermünde-Lehe; Ph.D. Göttingen (Windaus); Göttingen, Danzig, KWI Biochem. Berlin, Tübingen; Nobel Prize 1939

[3] Karl H. Slotta, b. 1895 Breslau, Germany; Ph.D. Breslau; São Paulo, Brazil

[4] Oskar Wintersteiner, b. 1898 Bruck, Austria; Ph.D. Graz (Pregl); Coll. Phys. and Surg. Columbia, Squibb Inst. Med. Res.

[5] Albert Wettstein, b. 1907 Frauenfeld, Switz.; Ph.D. Zurich (Karrer); Ciba Ltd., Basel

[6] Otto Rosenheim, 1871–1953; b. Germany; stud. Würzburg, Bonn, Geneva, Manchester; Nat. Inst. Med. Res.

[7] Harold King, b. 1887 Carnarvonshire, Wales; D.Sc. Wales (Barger, Ewins, Pyman); Nat. Inst. Med. Res.

line, for the bonds lie in a plane perpendicular to that of ring D. The front side of C_{17} is adjacent to the front-facing methyl group and appears to be more hindered than the rear side. Thus a carbonyl reagent such as RMgX attacks a 17-ketosteroid from the less hindered rear side, opens the rear member of the double bond (dotted), and gives a product with a β-oriented hydroxyl group. Addition of hydrogen proceeds similarly, and hence estrone on hydrogenation or on lithium aluminum hydride reduction affords estradiol and not its 17-epimer. The fact that the 17β-hydroxyl group has the stable equatorial orientation has no influence in determining the course of the reduction of estrone but this feature does influence the reactivity of 17-ester groups. Thus a 17-equatorial ester of type (a) is invariably hydrolyzed faster than the axial epimer (b).

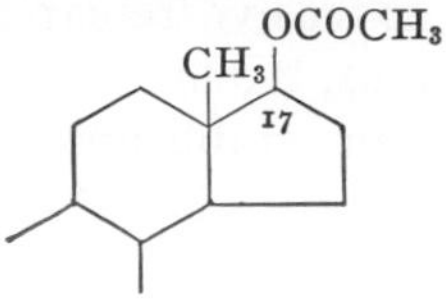

(a) 17β-ol acetate 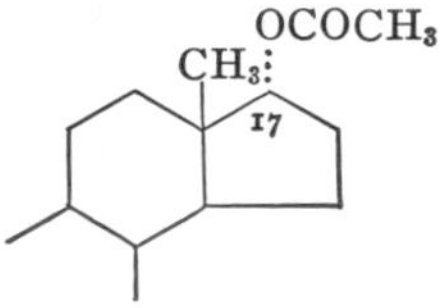　　　　　(b) 17α-ol acetate

The most distinctive structural feature of the estrogens is that the usual angular methyl group at C_{10} is missing and ring A is aromatic; the 3-hydroxyl group is therefore phenolic. Equilenin, a weakly estrogenic companion steroid of mare's urine, has two aromatic rings.

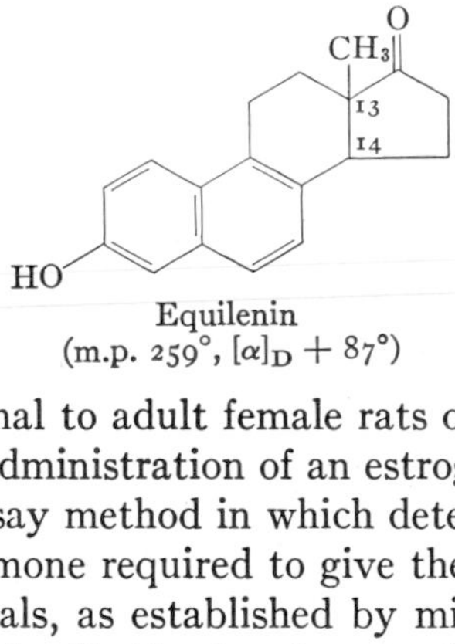

Equilenin
(m.p. 259°, $[\alpha]_D + 87°$)

The sexual cycle normal to adult female rats or mice ceases on ovariectomy but is restored on administration of an estrogen. E. Allen and Doisy (1923) developed a bioassay method in which determination is made of the minimum amount of hormone required to give the typical estrous response in castrated female animals, as established by microscopic examination of vaginal smears. Estrone is effective in mice at a dosage of 0.1γ (1γ = 0.001 mg.), defined as one international mouse unit. The rat unit is 5–7 times greater than the mouse unit. Application of this assay method led to the discovery that estrogenic material is excreted in the urine (B. Zondek, 1930), and this is the source from which estrone, estriol, and equilenin were eventually isolated. The hormones are present as glucuronides and sulfate

esters, and hence urine is submitted to acid hydrolysis prior to extraction with solvent.   The 17-ketosteroids present in the crude lipid fraction are separated most readily by use of Girard's reagent, trimethylaminoaceto-hydrazide chloride.   The reagent combines with ketonic substances to form

$$(CH_3)_3N \;+\; ClCH_2COOC_2H_5 \;+\; H_2NNH_2 \xrightarrow[83-89\%]{C_2H_5OH,\ HCl,\ o-60^\circ} [(CH_3)_3\overset{+}{N}CH_2CONHNH_2]Cl^-$$

Girard's reagent

hydrazone derivatives having a polar group that renders the substances soluble in water; after separation from nonketonic materials, the ketones are easily regenerated by hydrolysis of the Girard derivatives with mineral acid:

17-Ketosteroid   Girard derivative

Thus the alkali-soluble fraction of a urinary extract is refluxed briefly with Girard's reagent in alcoholic solution containing 10% of acetic acid; the mixture is then diluted with water, partially neutralized, and extracted with ether to remove water-insoluble products and tars; the aqueous solution after acidification with mineral acid is warmed, and the liberated ketonic fraction is recovered by extraction with ether.   In processing human urines some use has been made of a partial separation of estrone and estriol based on the fact that the latter, with an additional hydroxyl function, is more hydrophilic than the former.

Estrone soon proved to have various uses in therapy and was initially produced commercially by extraction from mare's pregnancy urine and from human pregnancy urine.   The latter source affords less estrone than the former, only about 0.3 mg./l., but affords also estriol (1.3 mg./l.).   The triol is only half as active as estrone by subcutaneous injection, but is valued in therapy because, unlike the other estrogens (less hydrophilic), it is nearly as active when given orally as when injected.   As soon as the primary estrogens became available in adequate quantity, numerous derivatives were prepared and assayed.   By far the most potent was estradiol, the reduction product of estrone, which is no less than nine times as active as estrone. The diol was introduced into therapy before it was isolated as a natural product.   This feat was accomplished by the Doisy group in 1935.   Processing of 1.5 tons of hog ovaries led to isolation, as the di-α-naphthoate, of 12 mg. of material identical with estradiol.

Estradiol, initially produced by reduction of estrone from urine, is now manufactured by partial synthesis from natural steroids.   In a process developed in Germany (Inhoffen, 1948), cholesterol from spinal cord and brain of cattle or from wool fat is converted in a number of steps into $\Delta^{1,4}$-androstadiene-17β-ol-3-one, which on pyrolysis suffers aromatization with elimination of methane (see next page).

Estrogenic activity is displayed not only by a number of derivatives of the natural estrogens but also by synthetic substances differing considerably

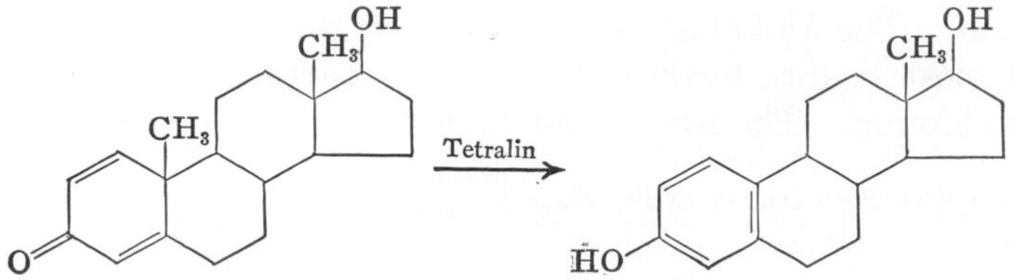

Δ^{1,4}-Androstadiene-   Estradiol
17β-ol-3-one

in structure from the hormones. Among synthetic estrogens that have found a place in therapy are stilbestrol (rat dose 0.4γ) and hexestrol (rat dose 0.2γ).

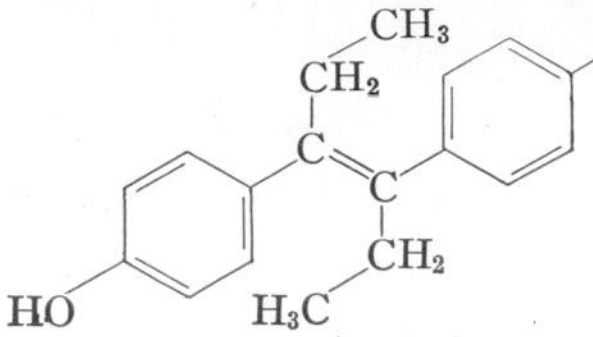

Stilbestrol   Hexestrol
(*trans*, m.p. 171°)   (*meso*, m.p. 186°)

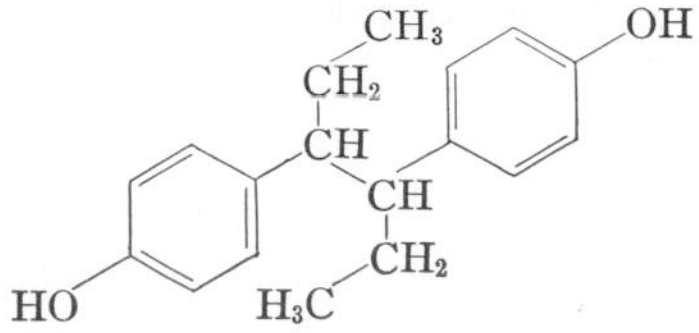

Androgens. — The most prominent members of the male sex hormone or androgen group are testosterone and androsterone, I and II. The oxygen substituents at C_{17} correspond to those of estradiol and estrone, respectively, but no aromatic ring is present and both angular methyl groups character-

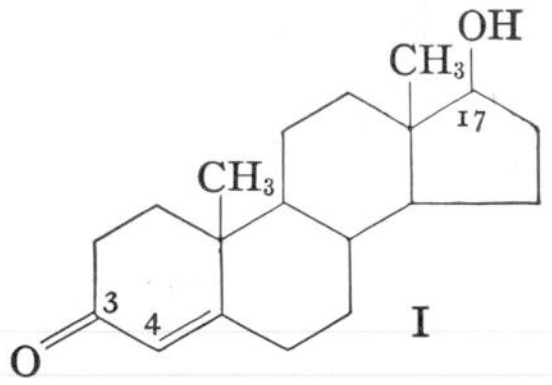

Testosterone   Androsterone
(m.p. 154°, [α]_D + 109°)   (m.p. 184°, [α]_D + 94.5°)

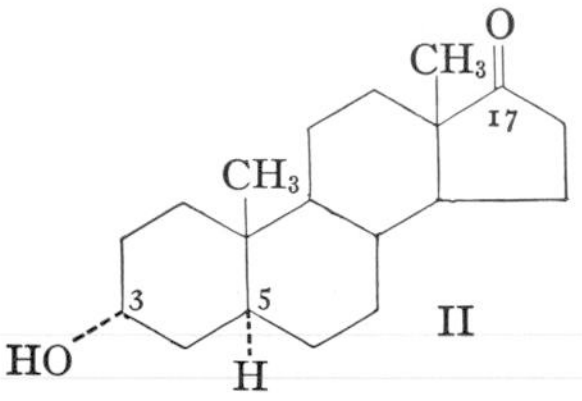

istic of the sterols are intact. Testosterone has an α,β-unsaturated ketonic grouping in ring A, which renders the substance sensitive to alkali and gives rise to an ultraviolet absorption band at 2380Å. Androsterone belongs to the A/B *trans* series of cholestane, and the alcoholic group at C_3 is α-oriented; thus it is not precipitated by digitonin. Testosterone has been isolated in small amounts from testis tissue (Laqueur, 1935[8]), and is regarded as a true hormone. Androsterone is found only in urine and it is one of three principal urinary steroids regarded as excretory products of hormone metabolism; the other two are 5-isoandrosterone (III) and dehydroepiandrosterone (IV). Androsterone displays male sex hormone activity of the same type as testosterone but is less potent, and its companion substances are inactive and weakly ineffective, respectively; the activity or lack of activity of the metabolites appears to be incidental and without physiological significance.

---

[8] Ernst Laqueur, 1880–1947; b. Obernigk, Netherlands; Ph.D. Breslau, Amsterdam

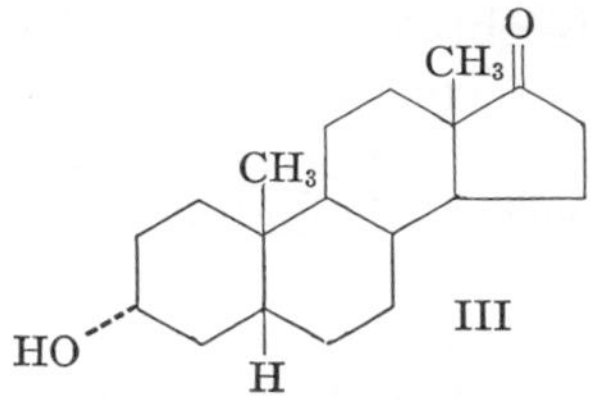

5-Isoandrosterone 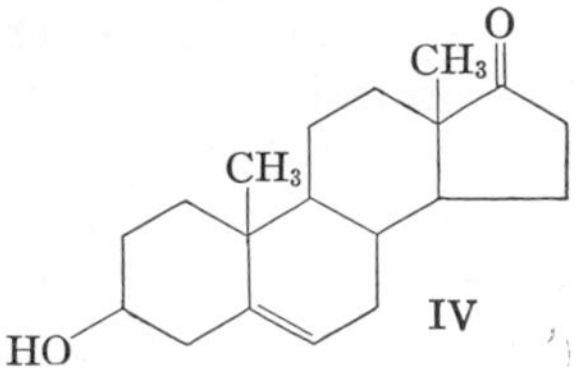   Dehydroepiandrosterone

Some physiological actions of the androgens are indicated by the nature of assay methods that led to their discovery. One is based on the ability of a hormone to promote comb growth in capons (Gallagher[9] and Koch,[10] 1929). Castration of a cock results in general regression of the characteristic head furnishings, and the comb and wattles soon atrophy and almost disappear. Administration of testosterone or androsterone to such a prepared test animal causes regeneration of these secondary sex characteristics. In one technique a capon unit (c.u.) is defined as the amount of substance that, when injected into each of three capons on two successive days, produces on the third or fourth day an average increase of 20% in the area of the comb, as measured on a shadowgraph. In one test procedure (Butenandt) androsterone produces this biological response at a dosage of 150–200γ. The comb-growth test established the presence of an active principle in cell-free extracts of testicular tissue and urine, and guided Butenandt in his isolation in 1931 of the first known androgen from the latter source. The extensive processing of several thousand liters of urine afforded a few milligrams of a pure, active crystallizate, characterized by analysis and by formation of an oxime and of an acetate as a C_{17}-hydroxy ketone containing four reduced rings. Butenandt divined a relationship to the sterols, and in 1932 proposed a tentative formula that Ruzicka established (1934) by production of an identical substance by oxidative degradation of epicholestanol. The acetate of this substance was oxidized with chromic acid in acetic acid solution according to the technique introduced by Windaus for partial degradation of the cholesterol side chain, and the ketonic material present in the neutral fraction of the saponified reaction mixture was isolated through the semicarbazone and found to have the biological and other properties of

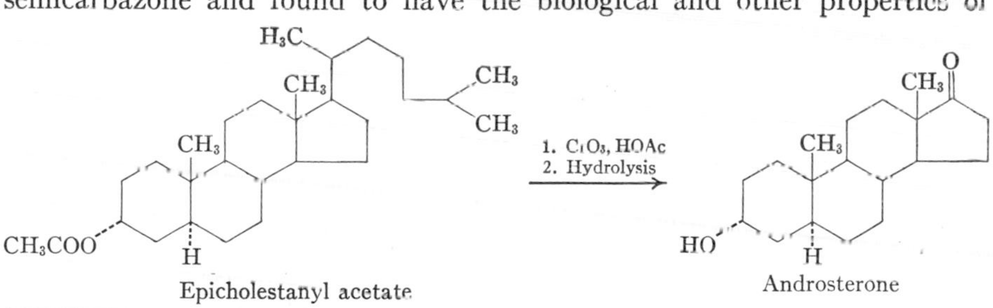

Epicholestanyl acetate   1. C_rO_3, HOAc   Androsterone
                                2. Hydrolysis

---

[9] Thomas F. Gallagher, b. 1905 Chicago; Ph.D. Chicago (Koch); Sloan Kettering Inst. Cancer Res.

[10] Fred C. Koch; b. 1876 Chicago; Ph.D. Chicago; Dept. Physiolog. Chem. Chicago, Armour and Co.

androsterone. The starting material is obtained from cholesterol by the following transformations: cholesterol → cholestanol → cholestanone → epicholestanol → epicholestanyl acetate. These reactions can be conducted with relatively little loss, but the oxidative elimination of the side chain proceeds so poorly that under the most favorable conditions the overall yield of androsterone from cholesterol is only about 0.2%.

A second test for androgenic activity is that of Loewe and Moore, based on the ability of a hormonic substance to stimulate growth of the seminal vesicles of castrated male rodents. Laqueur recognized first that a significant differential exists between the two test methods (1935). When castrated rats were treated with amounts of urinary and testicular extracts of equivalent potency in capon units, the average weights of the seminal vesicles of the controls, of the animals receiving urinary extracts, and of those receiving testicular extracts, were in the ratio of 1:14:67. Material from testes has about five times the activity per capon unit in promoting growth of the seminal vesicles as androsterone; testicular extracts differ also from urinary extracts in showing a decided decrease in activity when boiled with alkali. While Laqueur pursued his ultimately successful attempts to isolate the active hormone, to which he applied the name testosterone, other workers sought to discover in the androstane series a substance of high potency in the rat test and of comparable sensitivity to alkali. Thus only a few months after Laqueur announced the isolation of testosterone, both Butenandt and Ruzicka achieved the synthetic preparation of an identical product by methods establishing the structure as that of Δ^4-androstene-17β-ol-3-one. Pure testosterone is about seven times as powerful as androsterone in promoting comb growth; the capon unit is 15γ. The activity in the rat test per capon unit is approximately seven times that of androsterone.

The key intermediate for the preparation of testosterone is dehydroepi-

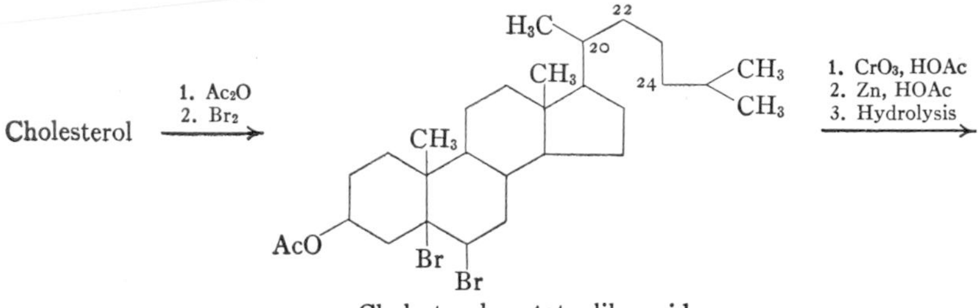

Cholesteryl acetate dibromide

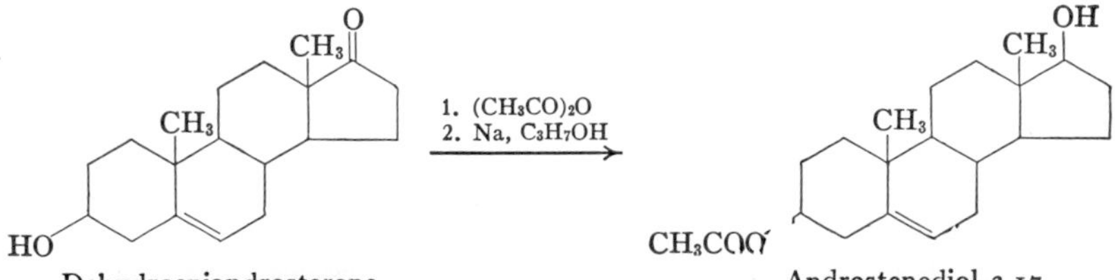

Dehydroepiandrosterone

Androstenediol-3,17
3-monoacetate

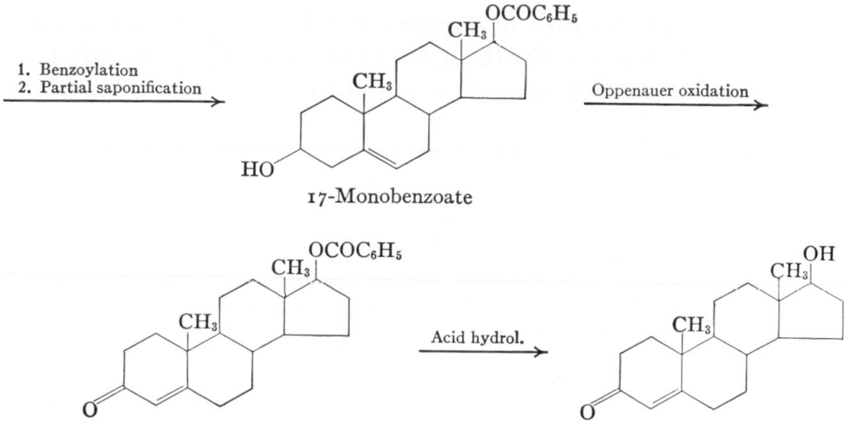

OCOC₆H₅

1. Benzoylation
2. Partial saponification

Oppenauer oxidation

17-Monobenzoate

Acid hydrol.

Testosterone

androsterone (IV), a 17-ketosteroid accompanying androsterone in urine. The substance is prepared from cholesterol by protecting the alcoholic group by acetylation and the double bond by bromination and submitting the derivative to Ruzicka oxidation. The reaction mixture is debrominated with zinc and acetic acid, and the ketone isolated from the neutral fraction through the sparingly soluble semicarbazone. The overall yield from cholesterol is 6.5% on a technical scale. The transformation of dehydroepi-androsterone into testosterone requires reduction of the 17-carbonyl group and oxidation at C_3. The hydroxy ketone is acetylated and the product reduced to the 3-acetate of androstenediol-3,17; this is benzoylated and then submitted to partial saponification, when the more reactive C_3-function is attacked preferentially, since the 17-monobenzoate is obtained. Oxidation of this substance is accomplished by the Oppenauer reaction, and testosterone is obtained on hydrolysis. The intermediate androstene-$3\beta,17\beta$-diol is also an intermediate in the partial synthesis of estradiol. This diol is some three to four times as active in the comb-growth test as androsterone; thus in both the estrogen and androgen series biological activity is enhanced by reduction of the 17-keto group. Since esters of testosterone have protracted action and consequent advantages in therapy, the hormone is largely employed in medicine in the form of testosterone propionate (m.p. 123°).

Progesterone. — This substance (I) has been identified as the hormone secreted by the corpus luteum, a tissue of the ovary colored yellow by carotene. The main functions of the corpus luteum are associated with prepa-

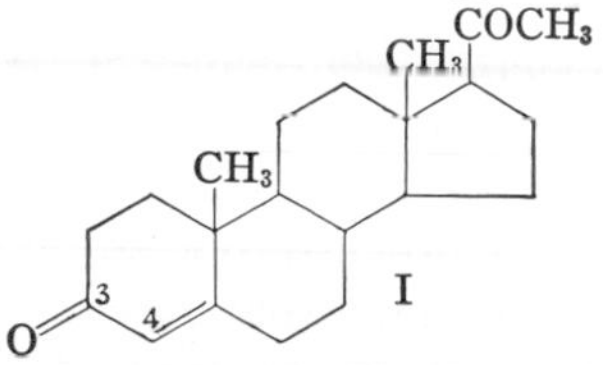

Progesterone
(m.p. 121°, 128°; $[\alpha]_D$ + 192°; abs. max. 2400 Å)

ration for and maintenance of pregnancy. The uterine mucosa, which grows to a certain extent under the influence of estradiol, proliferates further under stimulation of the progesterone secreted by the corpus luteum and so is prepared for reception of the fertilized ovum. Corner and W. M. Allen paved the way for isolation of the hormone by development of a test method based on the discovery that after progestational changes have been stopped by extirpation of the corpus luteum, activity can be restored by adminis-tration of extracts of this gland. In the Corner-Allen assay method utilizing castrated rabbits, pure progesterone gives a positive response at a dosage of 1.0 mg. The substance is thus effective only at a level vastly higher than that observed with estrogenic and androgenic hormones.

Progesterone has the same skeletal structure as a biologically inactive C_{21}-alcohol that Marrian had isolated in 1929 from human pregnancy urine and named pregnanediol ($3\alpha,20\alpha$). Pregnanediol (II) is the principal metabolite of progesterone and is excreted in urine as the glucuronide. The diol, which has a two-carbon side chain and a ring system of the cholanic

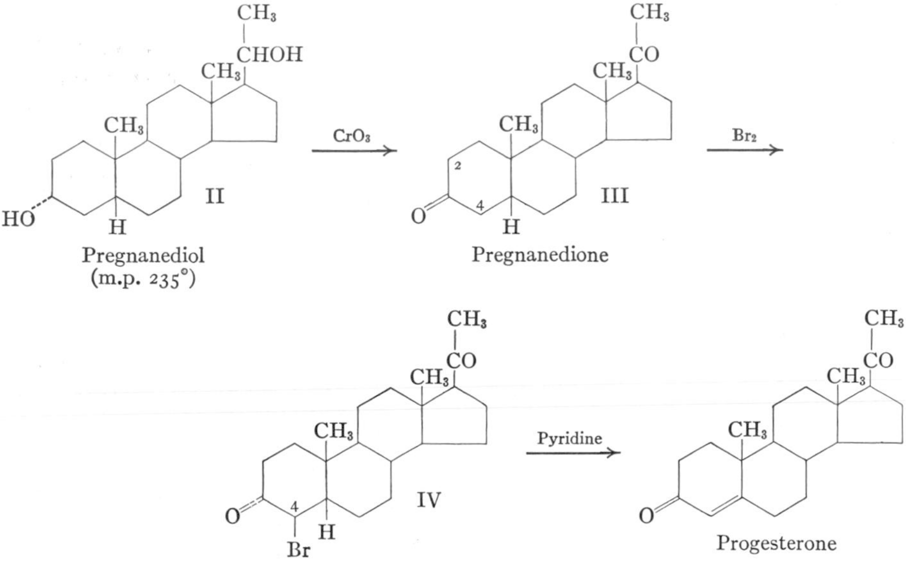

II Pregnanediol (m.p. 235°) — CrO₃ → III Pregnanedione — Br₂ → IV — Pyridine → Progesterone

acid type, was employed as starting material for one of the first syntheses of the pregnancy hormone. The diol is oxidized to pregnanedione (III); this is brominated, and hydrogen bromide is eliminated.

Progesterone has been produced commercially by several processes utiliz-ing steroid starting materials: stigmasterol, cholesterol, cholic acid, and the sapogenin diosgenin (p. 994). The shortest partial synthesis is from diosgenin via Δ⁵-pregnene-3β-ol-20-one, which affords progesterone on Oppenauer oxidation.

The physiological action of progesterone is highly specific, and only a few of the many related compounds that have been examined possess pro-gestational activity comparable to that of the hormone. One is 17α-ethinyltestosterone, prepared by addition of acetylene to the carbonyl group of dehydroepiandrosterone and Oppenauer oxidation; it is only one third as active as progesterone by subcutaneous injection but is more active

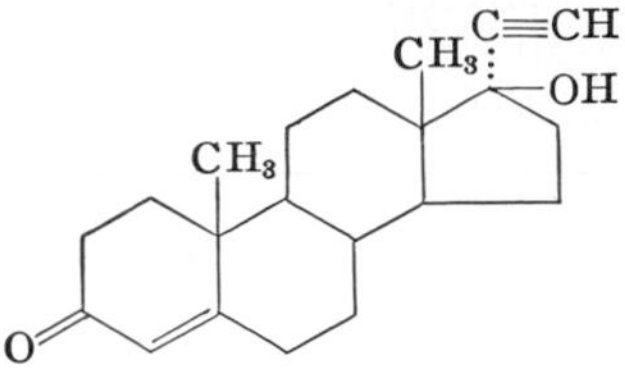

17α-Ethinyltestosterone 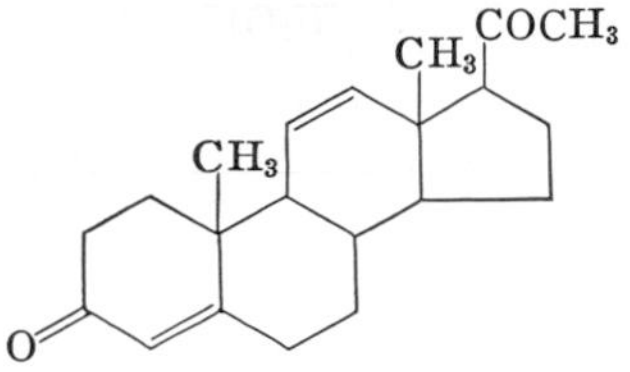   11-Dehydroprogesterone

than the hormone when given orally.   Another is 11-dehydroprogesterone, which is no less than three times as potent as progesterone.   19-Norprogesterone, surprisingly, is as active as progesterone.   It is prepared from the methyl ether of an estrone derivative by reduction with sodium or lithium

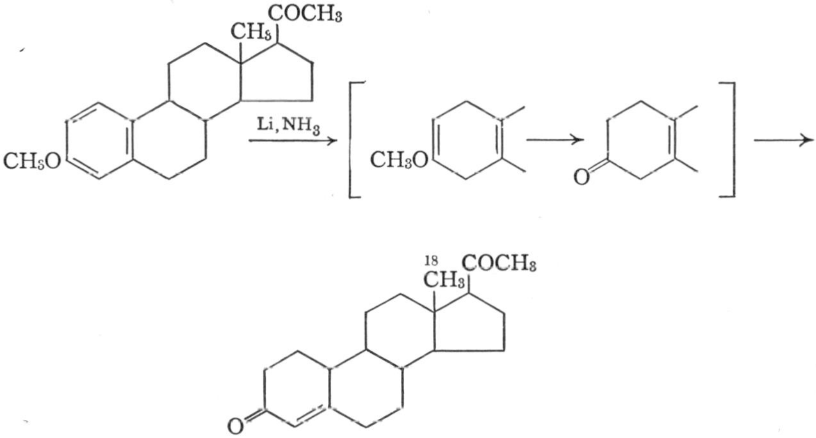

19-Norprogesterone

in liquid ammonia (method of Birch[11]).   The reaction involves 1,4-addition of hydrogen to give an enol methyl ether, which undergoes hydrolysis to a β,γ-ketone; in the alkaline medium the double bond migrates to the α,β-position.

Adrenal Cortical Hormones. — Discovery in 1929 that the life span of adrenalectomized animals is prolonged by administration of extracts of the adrenal cortex prompted extensive chemical investigation initiated about 1933 in Switzerland by Reichstein and in the United States by Kendall,[12] Wintersteiner and Pfiffner, and Kuisenga and Cartland.   Within a few years twenty-eight individual steroids were isolated from glandular extracts. The structures and configurations were soon elucidated, largely by the Reichstein group.   The additional component aldosterone was isolated and characterized in 1953 (S. A. Simpson, J. F. Tait, Wettstein, Reichstein, and

---

[11] Arthur John Birch, b. 1915 Sydney, Australia; Ph.D. Oxford (Robinson); Sydney, Manchester

[12] Edward C. Kendall, b. 1886 South Norwalk, Conn.; Ph.D. Columbia (Sherman, Bogert, Chambers); Mayo Clinic, Rochester, Minn.; Nobel Prize 1950

others).   Seven of the twenty-nine steroids exhibit cortical hormonal activity.   These are the first seven substances formulated in the chart; they

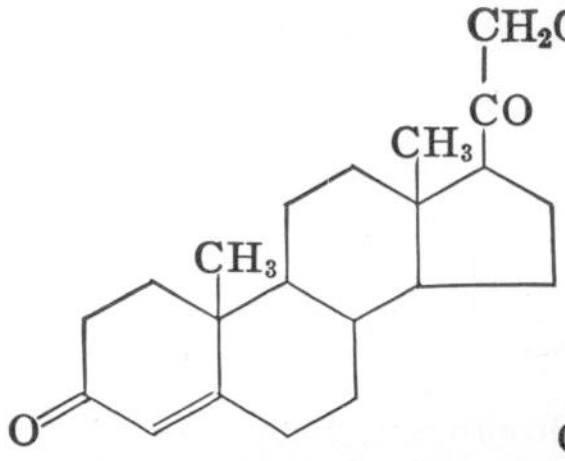

Desoxycorticosterone
$M_D + 588$

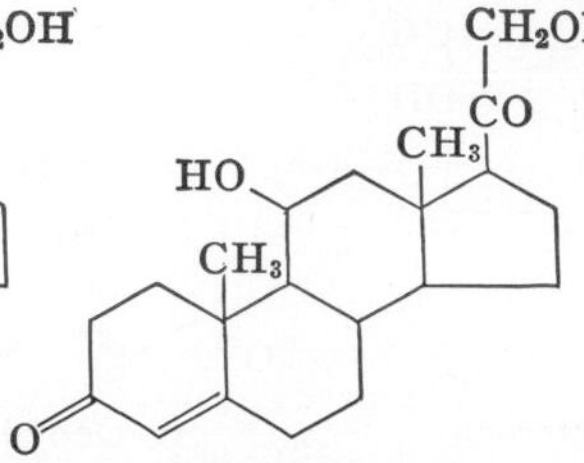

Corticosterone
$M_D + 773$

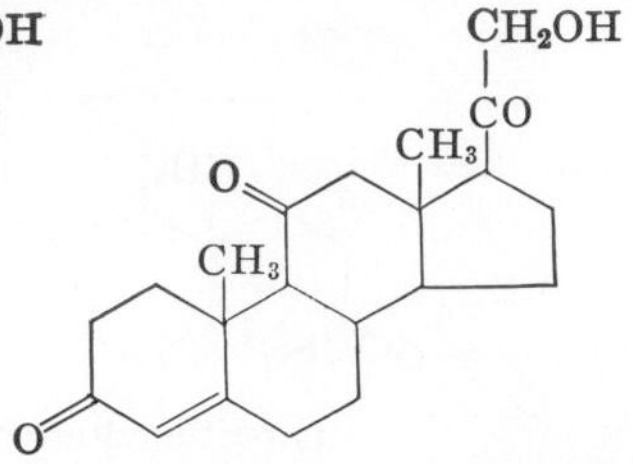

11-Dehydrocorticosterone
$M_D + 1030$

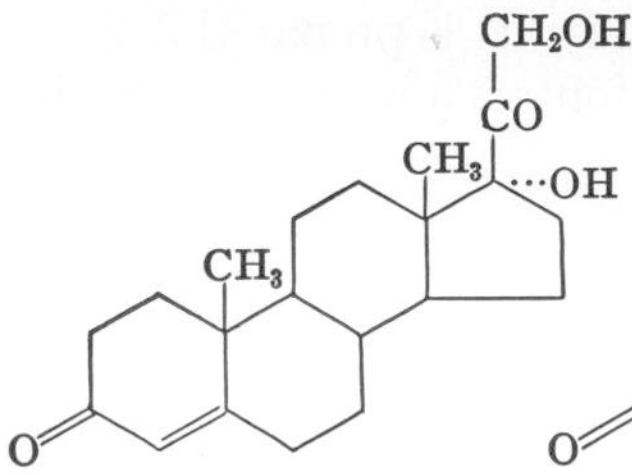

17-Hydroxydesoxycortico-
sterone; acetate, $M_D + 451$

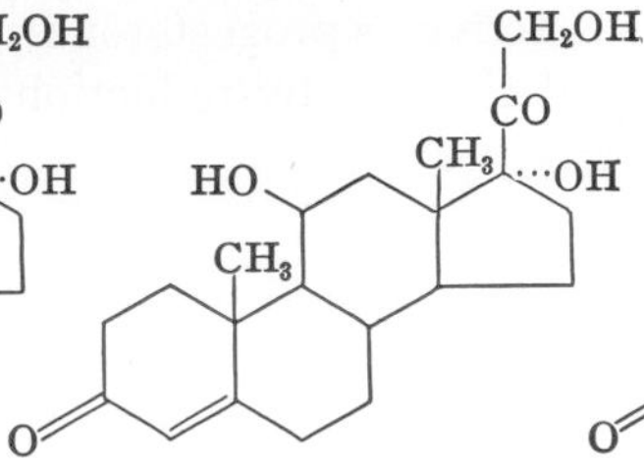

17-Hydroxycorticosterone
$M_D + 605$

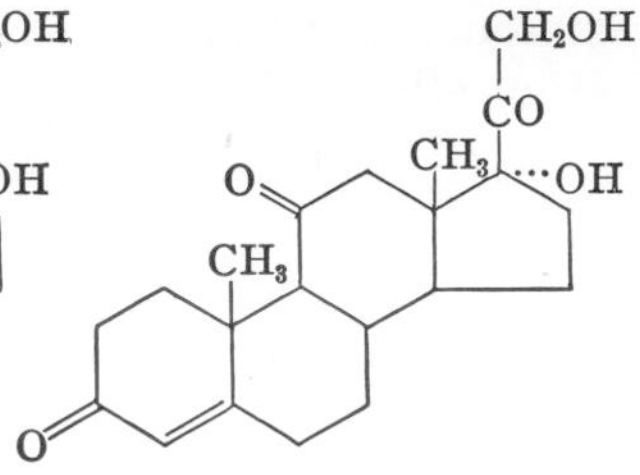

Cortisone
$M_D + 753$

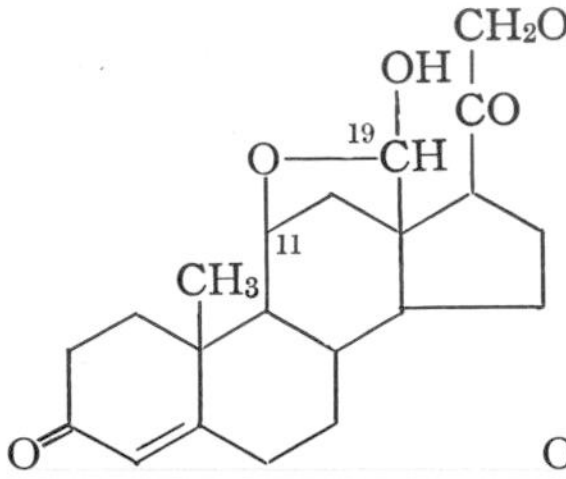

Aldosterone

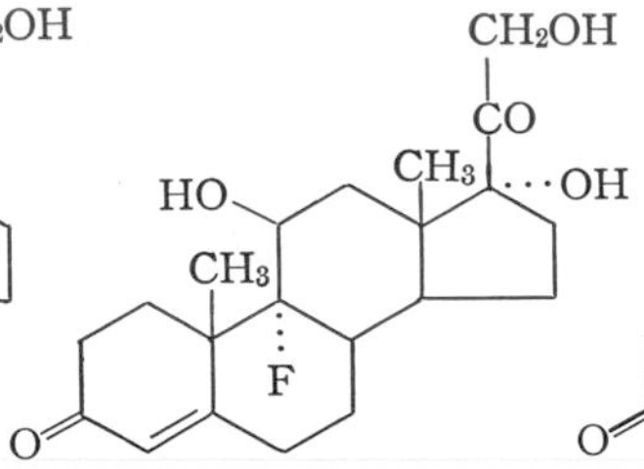

9α-Fluorohydrocortisone

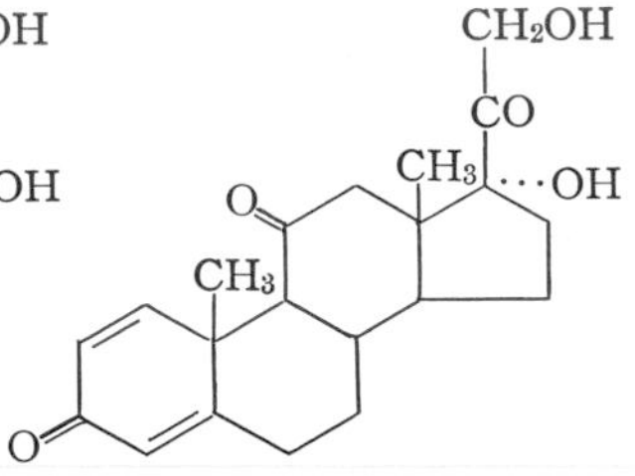

1-Dehydrocortisone

all have the α,β-unsaturated ketonic grouping in ring A characteristic of
testosterone and progesterone, and they all possess a ketol side chain; they
differ in the degree of oxygenation at C_{11}, C_{17}, and C_{19}.   The inactive
companion steroids lack one or both of these structural features and appear
to be reduction products of the hormones.   The last two compounds formulated in the chart are active, synthetic substances to be discussed presently.

Of the seven active natural hormones desoxycorticosterone (cortexone)
and aldosterone are the most active in bioassays that measure life maintenance or control of electrolyte balance in adrenalectomized animals; the
former, which is readily available by partial synthesis, promotes retention
of sodium by the kidney and is used clinically for treatment of Addison's
disease, which is associated with hypofunction of the adrenal cortex.   Cortisone and hydrocortisone are the most active in control of carbohydrate
metabolism, that is metabolic formation of carbohydrate from protein, as
measured by the extent of deposition of glycogen in the liver of adrenalectomized rats.   In this respect desoxycorticosterone and 17-hydroxydesoxy-

corticosterone, which lack a C_{11}-oxygen function, are inactive. A further activity of cortisone and hydrocortisone, discovered by Hench and Kendall in 1949, is the ability to relieve the symptoms of rheumatoid arthritis. Cortisone has also been found to have beneficial effects for such diseases as rheumatic fever, asthma, and many skin disorders.

The study of related substances became possible only when commercial production of cortisone made available adequate supplies of intermediates. Hydrocortisone is a glandular product but its biological activity could only be assessed adequately when it became available by lithium aluminum hydride reduction of an intermediate (I) in which carbonyl groups other than

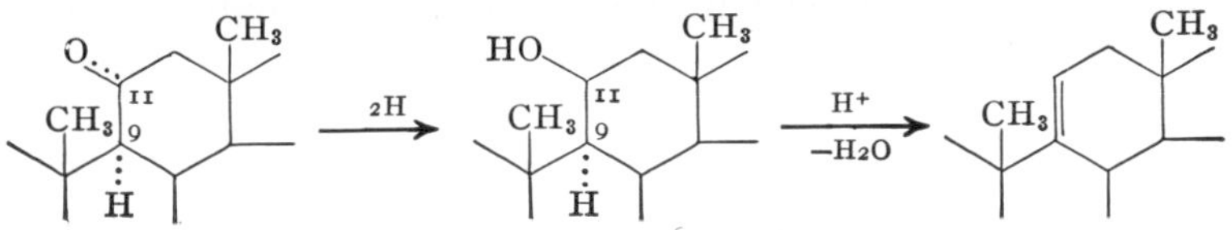

the one at C_{11} are protected. The 11-keto group is highly hindered on the front side of the molecule by the two angular methyl groups and does not respond to ordinary carbonyl reagents. It is, however, susceptible to rear attack by a reducing agent with opening of the rear member of the double bond (dotted line) and production of an 11β-hydroxyl group. This group is hindered and axial and it resists acetylation by acetic anhydride in pyridine, under which conditions an 11α-hydroxyl (equatorial, rear) is readily acetylated. Acid catalysis cannot be employed because the 11β-OH is *trans* to the tertiary hydrogen at C_9 and is readily eliminated. The second active derivative to be discovered in 9α-fluorohydrocortisone, formulated in the chart above (Fried[13] and E. F. Sabo, 1954). This possesses about 10 times the glucocorticoid activity of hydrocortisone but is also more active in undesirable side effects (for example, edema); it has found use for dermatological disorders where only small amounts of drug are required. 9α-Halo derivatives were obtained by cleavage of the $9\beta,11\beta$-oxide, with the appropriate acid; the oxide was obtained from the $\Delta^{9,11}$-ethylene via the bromohydrin. In this series biological activity is inversely proportional to the

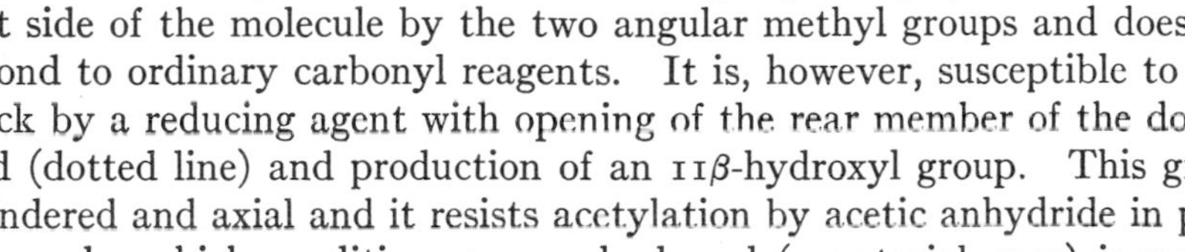

size of the halogen atom. A further advance was the discovery that the 1-dehydro derivatives of cortisone and hydrocortisone are considerably more active than the parent hormones (Hershberg,[14] *et al.*, 1955).

---

[13] Josef Fried, b. 1914 Przemysl, Poland; Ph.D. Columbia (Elderfield); Squibb Inst. Med. Res.

[14] Emanuel B. Hershberg, b. 1908 Lynn, Mass.; Ph.D. Mass. Inst. Tech. (Huntress); Schering Corp.

The cortisone used by Hench and Kendall in the initial demonstration of the efficacy of the hormone in treatment of rheumatoid arthritis, some 100–150 g., had been prepared at great effort by a developmental research team of Merck and Co. utilizing a 32-step synthesis starting with desoxycholic acid from ox bile. The synthetic method was based on extended researches in several laboratories. One key operation, introduction of oxygen at C_{11}, was done by a method discovered by Kendall (1946). Methyl desoxycholate is selectively benzoylated at the 3-position (equatorial-OH; C_{12}-α-OH is axial) and the product oxidized to the 12-ketone (1). Oxidation with selenium dioxide introduces a 9,11-double bond (2), and the allylic chloride (3) is obtained by reduction and reaction with hydrogen

chloride. The next reaction, elimination of hydrogen chloride, produces an oxide structure of novel type (4), with migration of the double bond to the 11,12-position. Addition of bromine (5) and hydrolytic oxidation gives the bromoketone (6), from which bromine is removed by reduction to give (7). The 3α,9α-oxide ring is now cleaved by reaction with hydrogen bromide to give (8); a hydroxyl group is restored to the 3-position but bromine, instead of appearing at C_9, migrates to the 12 position, from which it can be eliminated by reduction. By these operations, the oxygen function originally at C_{12} has been transposed to C_{11}.

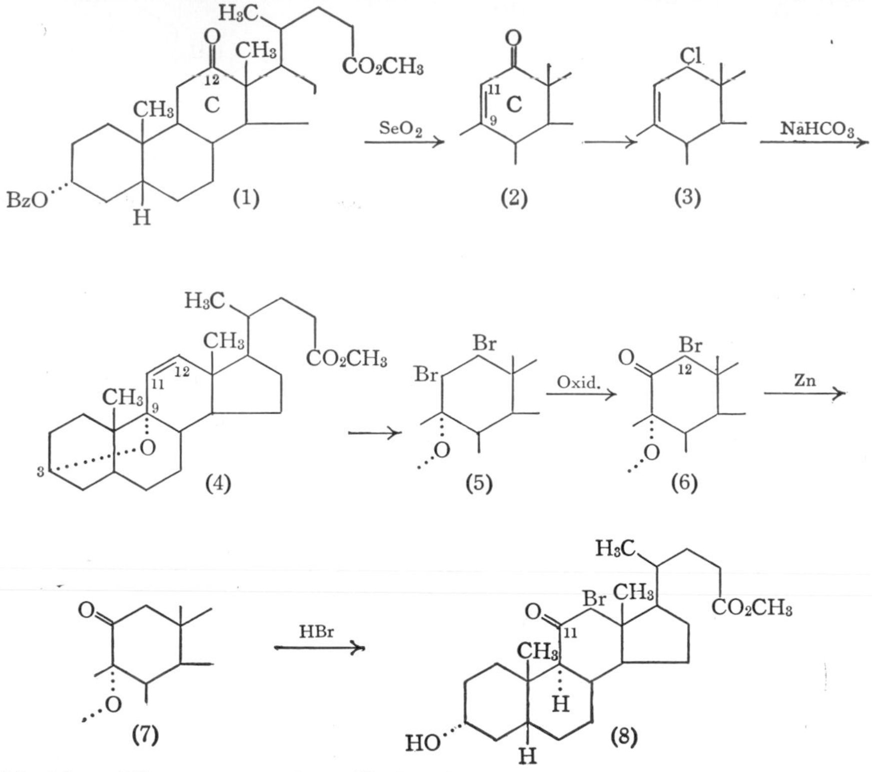

The next task, degradation of the bile acid side chain to the ketol structure —COCH$_2$OH, is accomplished efficiently by a method due to Meystre and Miescher[15] (1947). The product (9) of debromination of the 12-bromo-11-ketone (8) is converted by a Grignard reaction into the carbinol (10), which is dehydrated to the diphenylethylene (11). The latter reacts with

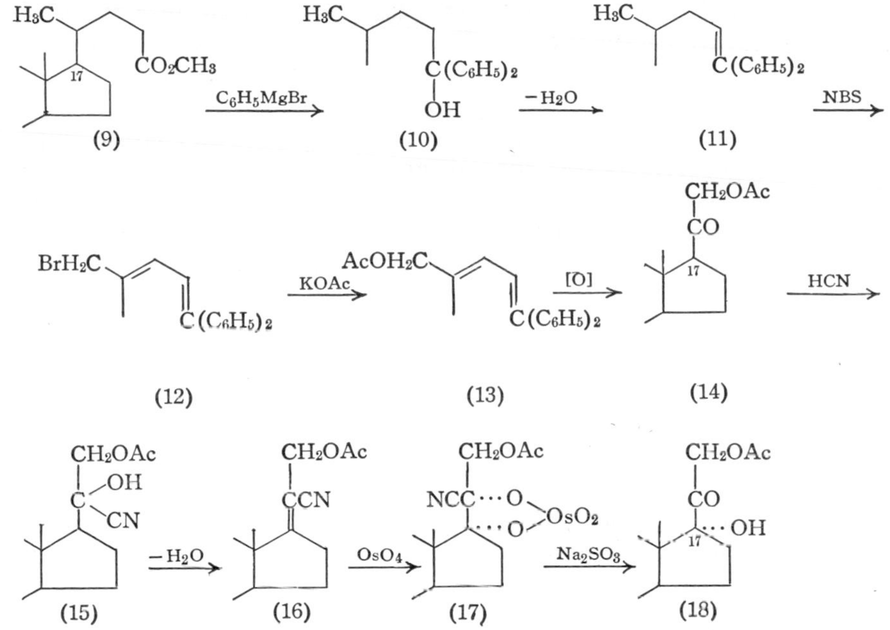

H$_3$C (9) CO$_2$CH$_3$ $\xrightarrow{C_6H_5MgBr}$ H$_3$C (10) C(C$_6$H$_5$)$_2$ OH $\xrightarrow{-H_2O}$ H$_3$C (11) C(C$_6$H$_5$)$_2$ $\xrightarrow{NBS}$

BrH$_2$C (12) C(C$_6$H$_5$)$_2$ $\xrightarrow{KOAc}$ AcOH$_2$C (13) C(C$_6$H$_5$)$_2$ $\xrightarrow{[O]}$ CH$_2$OAc CO (14) $\xrightarrow{HCN}$

CH$_2$OAc C—OH CN (15) $\xrightarrow{-H_2O}$ CH$_2$OAc CCN (16) $\xrightarrow{OsO_4}$ CH$_2$OAc NCC···O ···O OsO$_2$ (17) $\xrightarrow{Na_2SO_3}$ CH$_2$OAc CO ···OH (18)

one mole of N-bromosuccinimide to form the allylic bromide; this need not be isolated, and can be caused to lose hydrogen bromide to form a diphenyl-diene, which reacts with another mole of NBS to form the allylic bromide (12). After replacement of bromine by an acetoxy group, oxidation removes the diene grouping to produce the ketol acetate (14). An α-hydroxyl group is then introduced at C$_{17}$ by the method of Sarett.[16] Hydrogen cyanide is added to the 20-keto group (15), the cyanohydrin is dehydrated (16), and the unsaturated nitrile treated with osmium tetroxide. The reagent attacks from the rear to give the osmic ester (17), and when this is cleaved the cyanohydrin group at C$_{20}$ spontaneously loses hydrogen cyanide to give the 17α-hydroxy-20-ketone (18). Completion of the synthesis of cortisone requires oxidation to a 3-ketone (actually done with the ester 17), bromination at C$_4$, and dehydrohalogenation.

The above lengthy synthesis was adapted to plant scale operation by Merck chemists under the leadership of Tishler[17] and used in the first commercial production of the drug. For a time it appeared likely that the bile available would be inadequate, and many research groups investigated other possible steroid starting materials. Only sarmentogenin and a few other rare heart poisons carry an oxygen function at C$_{11}$, and only a few natural

[15] Karl Miescher, b. 1892 Naples (Swiss parent.); Ph.D. ETH Zurich (Staudinger); Ciba Ltd., Basel

[16] Lewis H. Sarett, b. 1917 Champaign, Ill.; Ph.D. Princeton (Wallis); Merck and Co.

[17] Max Tishler, b. 1906 Boston; Ph.D. Harvard (Kohler); Merck and Co.

steroids (e.g., hecogenin) are oxygenated at the alternate position 12 in ring C. To start with a sterol having a double bond at the 5,6-position in ring B means that a succession of synthetic operations have to be performed to build in functional groups extending to C_{11}. These problems were solved, and routes to cortisone were mapped out starting with ergosterol, stigmasterol, hecogenin, sarmentogenin. However, all previous methods of partial synthesis were overtaken by a new approach, that of microbiological oxidation. First O. Hechter, et al., (1949) found that certain steroids on perfusion through surviving beef adrenals are oxygenated at C_{11}; for example, desoxycorticosterone → corticosterone. Although this method was not adapted to production, a practical method of microbiological oxidation was soon reported by the Upjohn group (D. H. Peterson and H. C. Murray, 1952). Thus various species of *Rhizopus* convert progesterone into 11α-hydroxyprogesterone in yields as high as 90%. Progesterone is readily obtainable from diosgenin, and the 11α-hydroxy derivative is convertible into cortisone in 10 high-yield steps. By microbiological oxidation with selected organisms, it is now possible to introduce hydroxyl groups at positions 6, 7, 11, 14, 15, 16, 17, and 21 of the pregnane molecule. It is also possible to effect microbiological dehydrogenation of Δ^4-3-ketones to $\Delta^{1,4}$-3-ketones, possibly as the result of hydroxylation at C_1 and dehydration. The last reaction has significance for production of 1-dehydrocortisone.

TOTAL SYNTHESIS

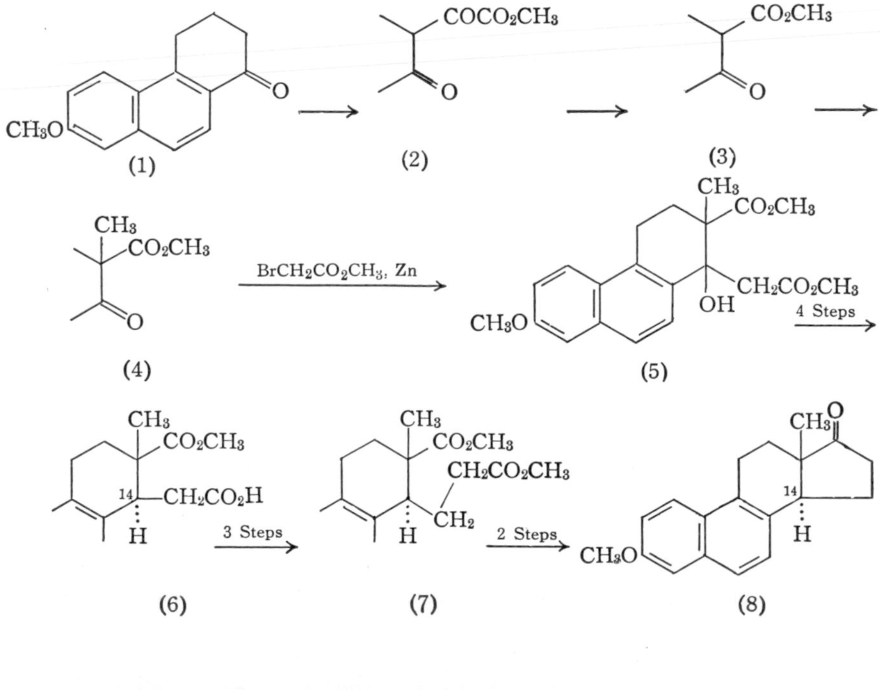

Total synthesis of steroids has been the goal of many investigators. Equilenin presents the simplest problem, since only two asymmetric centers are involved, and this was the first one solved. Synthesis of the estrogen was achieved in 1939 by Bachmann,[18] Cole,[19] and Wilds[20] starting with the tricyclic ketone (1), prepared by conventional methods from β-naphthol. The ketone was condensed with dimethyl oxalate (NaOCH₃) to give the glyoxylate (2), which when heated at 180° lost carbon monoxide to give the β-keto ester (3). An angular methyl group (C₁₈) was introduced by the action of methyl iodide on the sodio derivative of (3) and the product submitted to Reformatsky reaction to attach a two-carbon chain for construction of ring D. The hydroxyl group of the product (5) was then replaced by hydrogen and the diester partially hydrolyzed to liberate the less hindered acid group and give (6). Two dl-half-esters were obtained at this point, one of which proved to have the natural configuration at the position corresponding to C₁₄. The free carboxyl group offered opportunity for lengthening the chain by the Arndt-Eistert reaction, and finally Dieckmann cyclization of the diester (7), hydrolysis, and decarboxylation gave dl-equilenin, resolved through the l-menthoxyacetic acid ester.

The first total synthesis of estrone by Anner[21] and Miescher in 1948 utilized a similar sequence of reactions starting with a tricyclic ketone (9)

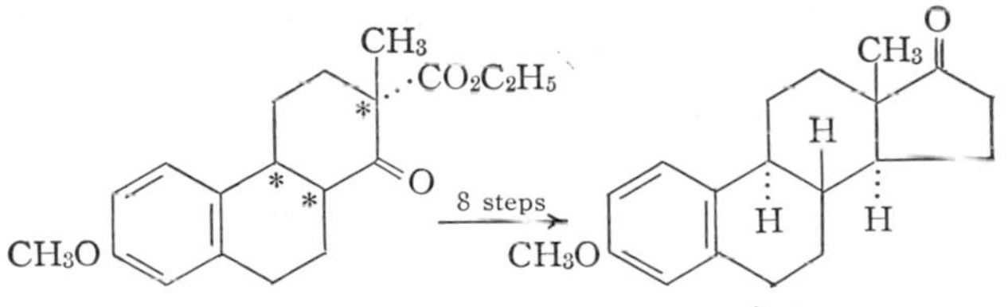

(9)   (10)

previously synthesized by Robinson (1938). This starting material contains three asymmetric centers, and the Swiss workers were able to isolate three of the four possible racemates and by application of Bachmann's synthetic sequence for addition of ring D to the individual isomers prepared not only estrone itself but some of the stereoisomers. Thanks to this work, and to another estrone synthesis developed by Johnson, all stereoisomers of estrone are now known.

The more difficult synthesis of nonaromatic steroids has been achieved by several groups of investigators. The first one was that of Cornforth[22] and Robinson (1951), who employed what is known as the BC → ABC → ABCD route. That is, 1,6-dimethoxynaphthalene, the starting material, ultimately provided rings B and C; as in previous syntheses, the D ring was added last. These workers also used the scheme of synthesis through relay intermediates which could be drawn on in large quantity from degradation of natural steroids. The first objective was synthesis of the tricyclic diketone (f), which H. Reich had obtained in very low yield from desoxycholic acid. The chart shows only some of the key intermediates. The first step,

[18] Werner E. Bachmann, 1901–51; Detroit; Ph.D. Michigan (Gomberg); Univ. Michigan
[19] Wayne Cole, b. 1913 Indianapolis; Ph.D. Illinois (Fuson); Glidden Co.
[20] Alfred L. Wilds, b. 1915 Kansas City; Ph.D. Michigan (Bachmann); Univ. Wisconsin
[21] Georg Anner, b. 1917 Madras, India; Ph.D. Zurich ETH (Ruzicka); Ciba Ltd. Basel
[22] John Warcup Cornforth, b. 1917 Australia; Ph.D. Oxford (Robinson); Nat. Inst. Med. Res.

a Birch reduction of (a) to a methoxytetralone, was followed by introduction of the angular methyl group to give (b). Ring A was added by a combined Michael-aldol condensation of (b) with methyl vinyl ketone (as the Mannich

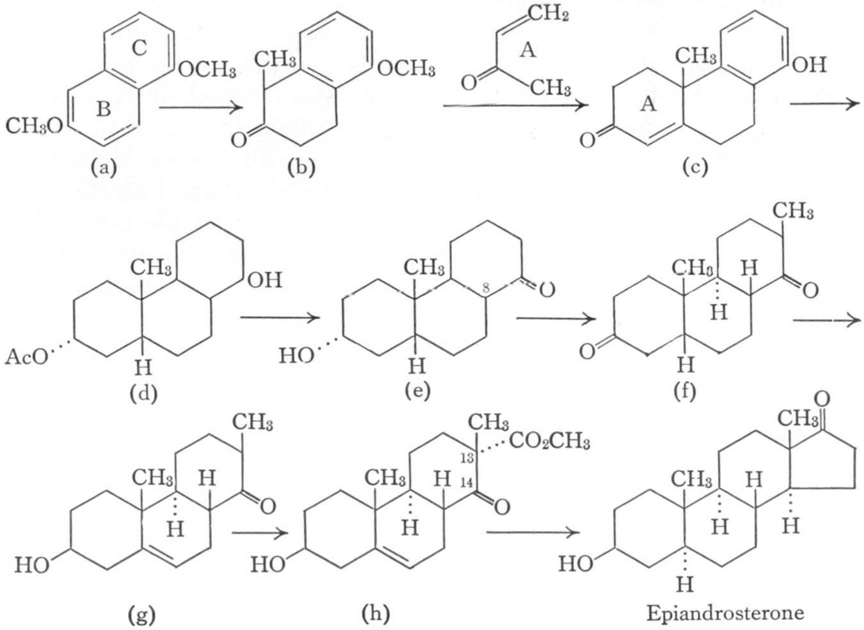

(a) (b) (c)

(d) (e) (f)

(g) (h) Epiandrosterone

base $\bar{I}(C_2H_5)_2\overset{+}{N}CH_2CH_2COCH_3)$ and the ether was hydrolyzed to (c). On catalytic hydrogenation the α,β-unsaturated ketone group was reduced first with formation of an A/B *cis* ring junction and a 3α-hydroxyl group. After selective acetylation of the alcoholic group, further hydrogenation gave a mixture of all four *dl*-diol monoacetates (d); two B/C *cis* and two B/C *trans*. The number of isomers was then decreased by oxidation of the hydroxyl group in ring C and equilibration of the ketone with dilute alkali; by inversion at C_8 through the enol, the B/C *cis* forms of (e) were isomerized to *trans* forms, and the two *trans* *dl*-forms could be separated and resolved. Each optically active form of (e) was methylated and oxidized and the product having the natural configuration (f) was recognized from its identity with Reich's diketone. This part of the synthesis was completed in 1947. The configuration at C_5 of the Reich ketone is the opposite of that of the natural androstane derivatives, and hence the next objective was introduction at C_5–C_6 of a double bond hydrogenable to a 5α-steroid. Furthermore, the unsaturated hydroxy ketone (g) had been characterized by Köster and Logemann (1940) and was available as a by-product in the commercial production of dehydroepiandrosterone and so could serve as a relay point. The desired transformation was effected by bromination of (f) at C_4, dehydrohalogenation to the Δ^4-3-ketone, conversion to the doubly unsaturated enol acetate, in which one of the double bonds is at the 5,6-position, and reduction with lithium aluminum hydride (method of Dauben,[23] 1950). Carbonation of the Köster-Logemann ketone (g) gave a mixture of (h) and the C_{13}-epimer, and Reformatsky reaction of (h) gave the two C_{14}-epimers. These were separated, and one of them on Arndt-Eistert reaction and Blanc distillation of the anhydride acetate afforded epiandrosterone.

A synthesis of epiandrosterone by Johnson (1953) also starts with 5-methoxytetralone-2 (2), but this is used to form the CD-unit. Ring B

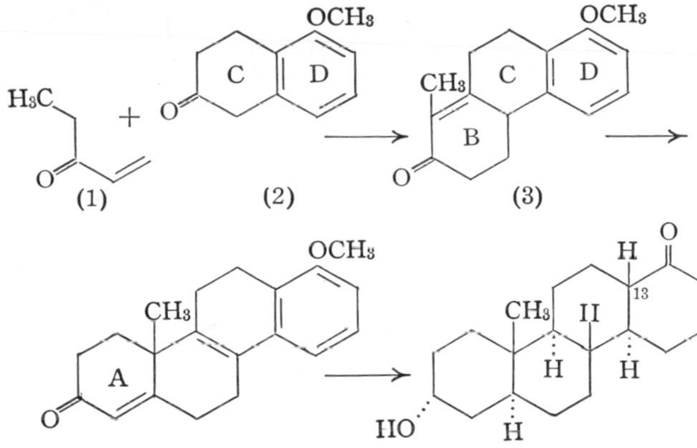

(1) (2) (3)

(4) (5)

was added by condensation with ethyl vinyl ketone (1) to give (3), and ring A by reaction with methyl vinyl ketone to give a tetracyclic ketone with an aromatic ring D (4). This was reduced by the Birch procedure to a di-α,β-unsaturated ketone which on hydrogenation gave the saturated hydroxy ketone (5). Although six asymmetric centers are introduced in this sequence, only one dl-product was obtained. The α-methylene group in ring D was then protected by conversion to the furfurylidine derivative, and the angular methyl group was introduced at C_{13} by methylation. Two dl-products are produced in this reaction and unfortunately the desired one

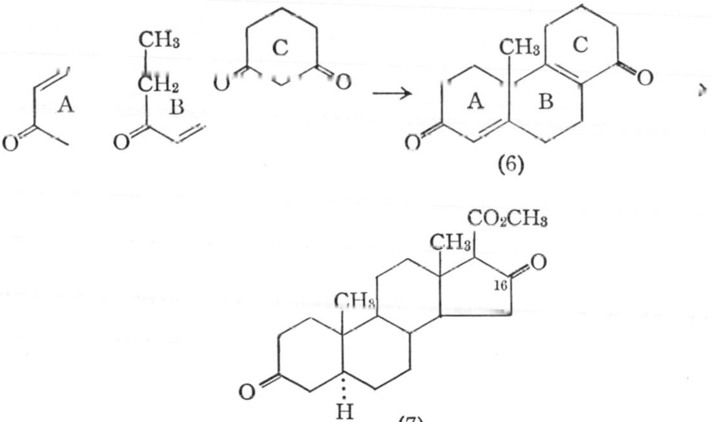

(6)

(7)

is the minor product. It was, however, put through completing steps involving the opening of homo-D, resolution, and formation of the five-membered D ring to give epiandrosterone.

Wilds (1953) developed a synthesis in which the key intermediate is a tricyclic diketone (6). This was obtained by condensing dihydroresorcinol (to form ring C) with ethyl vinyl ketone (B) and adding ring A by reaction with methyl vinyl ketone. A number of succeeding steps led to the unsaturated diketone ester (7), which afforded a route to a steroid, methyl dl-3-ketoetiocholanate, and to 16-substituted steroids.

A total synthesis of cortisone achieved by the Woodward[24] group in 1951 starts with construction of the CD part of the nucleus by Diels-Alder addition of 2-methyl-5-methoxy-1,4-quinone (I) to butadiene to give a cis adduct, which was equilibrated with base to produce the more stable trans isomer, and this was reduced to the diol II. Acid dehydration of II gave

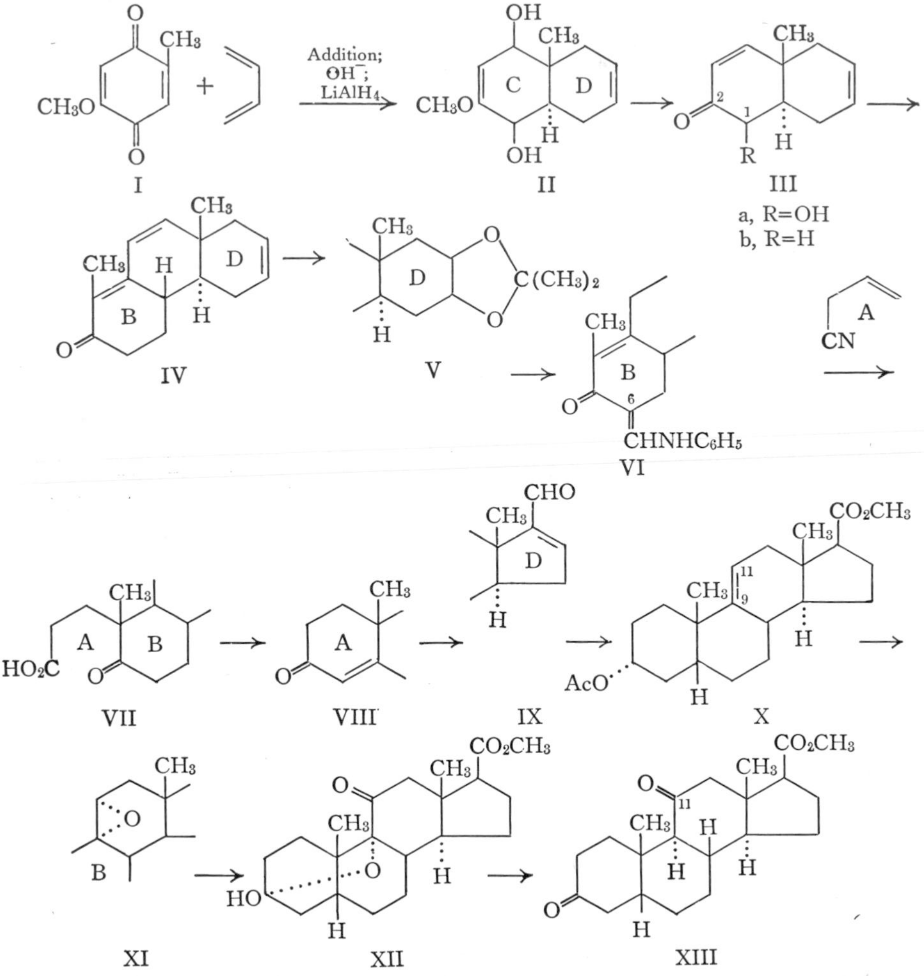

[24] Robert B. Woodward, b. 1917 Boston; Ph.D. Mass. Inst. Techn.; Harvard Univ.

the α-hydroxy ketone IIIa, and reduction with zinc and acetic acid eliminated the hydroxyl group and gave IIIb.   Ring B was added by condensation of the 1-formyl derivative of IIIb with ethyl vinyl ketone (IV) and the double bond in ring D was protected by osmylation and conversion of the more abundant of two *cis* glycols formed into the acetonide V.   Reduction of the double bond in ring C and protection of the future position 6 (VI) permitted addition of acrylonitrile to give, after hydrolysis, two isomeric keto acids of the formula VII.   A method developed by Turner (1947) for the synthesis of radioactive Δ^4-3-ketones was used for conversion of one isomer via the enol acetate into VIII, a tetracyclic ketone.   The protective acetonide group attached to ring D was then eliminated, the *cis* glycol was cleaved with periodic acid to the dialdehyde, which was cyclized to IX, in which ring D is of the proper size. Conversion of the aldehyde IX to the corresponding acid ester and resolution gave an ester identical with the degradation product of one of the cortical steroids.   The triply unsaturated keto ester was transformed into $\Delta^{9(11)}$-etiolithocholenic acid methyl ester acetate (X), a known compound which H. Heymann (1951) converted via the $9\alpha,11\alpha$-oxide XI and the 3,9-epoxyhemiketal XII into methyl 3,11-diketo-etiocholanate (XIII), which can be converted by reactions reported by Reichstein[25] and by Sarett into cortisone.   This formal total synthesis was followed by total synthesis of the hormone by the Monsanto group (Barkley, *et al.*).

A total synthesis of cortisone by Sarett and co-workers also starts with a Diels-Alder reaction, but for construction of the BC unit.   The adduct (1) from ethoxypiperylene and benzoquinone was converted into (2) by hydrogenation (Ni), reduction (LiAlH₄), and acid hydrolysis of the enol ether.   In the condensation of (2) with methyl vinyl ketone for addition of ring A, blocking of future position 6 was unnecessary because the *cis* configuration of the decalin system makes C_{10} the preferential point of attack. The condensation was followed by formation of a protective ethylene ketal group at C_3, which causes migration of the double bond to C_5–C_6; by avoidance of acidic reaction conditions during subsequent operations, the ketal group was kept intact until the last step in the synthesis.   Oppenauer oxidation of the diol attacked the C_{14}-hydroxyl group exclusively and the corresponding keto group promoted epimerization at C_8 to the required B/C *trans* configuration.   Methylation then gave (4).   A carbon chain that supplies C_{17} of ring D and also the side chain was introduced by alkylation of (4) with methallyl iodide, and oxidation at C_{11} then gave (5).   Ethoxyacetylenemagnesium bromide was added to the 14-carbonyl group and the ethynyl group was hydrated and dehydrated to the α,β-unsaturated ester (6): $>C(OH)C\equiv COEt \rightarrow\ >C(OH)CH_2CO_2Et \rightarrow\ >C=CHCO_2Et$. Reduction of the C_{11}-keto group (NaBH₄) and of the exocyclic double bond (K–NH₃) gave (7), and reduction of the ester group (LiAlH₄), tosylation, and oxidation (CrO₃) of the methylene group in the methallyl unit afforded

[25] Tadeus Reichstein, b. 1897 Wloclawek, Poland; Ph.D. Zurich ETH (Staudinger); ETH Zurich, Basel; Nobel Prize 1950

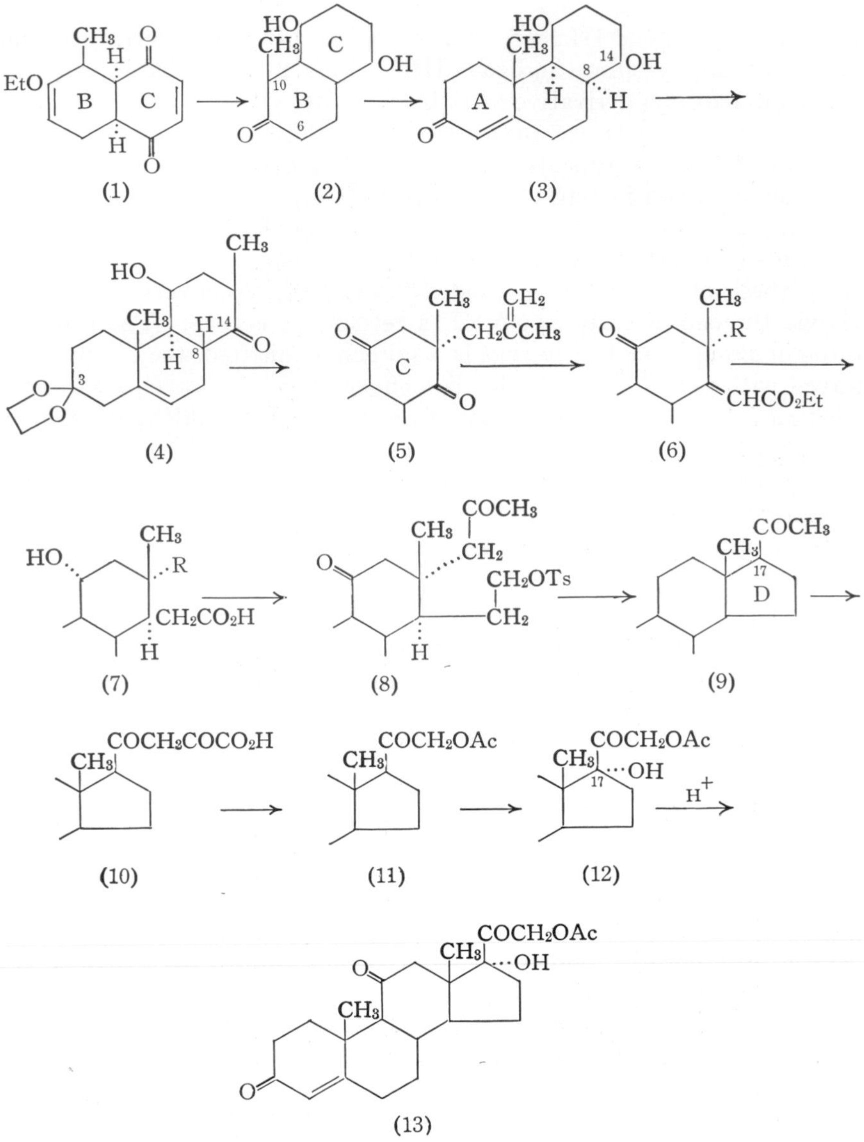

CH₃ O
EtO B C
H
O
(1)

HO CH₃ C OH
10 B
6 O
(2)

HO CH₃ 14 OH
8
A H H
O
(3)

CH₃
HO
CH₃ H 14
H 8
O
3 O
O
(4)

CH₃ CH₂
O ‥CH₂CCH₃
C
O
(5)

CH₃
O ‥R
CHCO₂Et
(6)

HO‥ CH₃ ‥R
CH₂CO₂H
H
(7)

COCH₃
CH₃ CH₂
O CH₂OTs
CH₂
H
(8)

COCH₃
CH₃
17
D
(9)

COCH₂COCO₂H
CH₃
(10)

COCH₂OAc
CH₃
(11)

COCH₂OAc
CH₃ ‥OH
17 H⁺
(12)

COCH₂OAc
CH₃ ‥OH
CH₃
O
O
(13)

(8), which underwent internal alkylation to form ring D with a C_{17}-acetyl group (9). The side chain was initially α-oriented but epimerization at the activated center (C_{17}) occurred readily to give the more stable natural β-orientation. Substance (9) was then converted into the 21-oxalyl derivative (10), a *dl*-product, which was resolved through the strychnine salts. The *d*-form of (10) was then transformed by α-iodination, replacement of iodine by an acetoxyl group, and cleavage, into the desired ketol acetate (11). Hydroxylation at C_{17} to (12) was accomplished by dehydration of the 20-cyanohydrin to the 17, 20-ethylene, and *cis*-hydroxylation of the double bond with permanganate in acetone. Finally, acid hydrolysis removed the protective ketal group at C_3. The product (13) was identical with natural cortisone. One remarkable feature of the synthesis is its high degree of stereospecificity; the ratio of desired to undesired product is 8 to 1 or better for all steps concerned.

Wettstein later (1955) achieved the synthesis of aldosterone starting with one of the Sarett intermediates, namely the immediate precursor

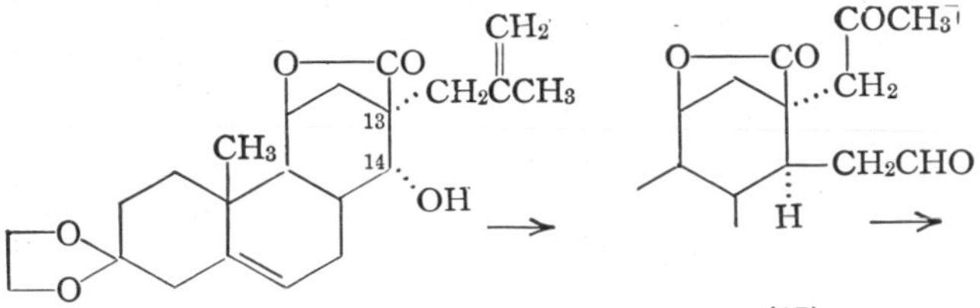

(14)   (15)

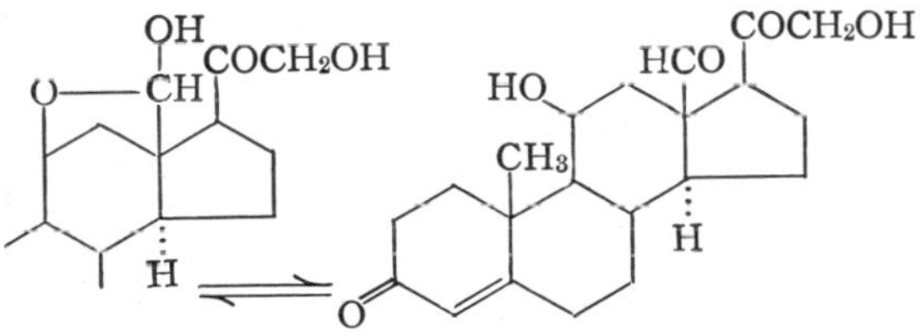

(16)   (17)

(unmethylated) of the ketone (4). A carboxyl function was introduced at C_{13} and used for formation of a protective lactone ring extending to C_{11}, and the methallyl group was introduced at C_{13} to give (14). Oxidation at C_{14}, condensation with ethoxyacetylenemagnesium bromide, hydrogenation, and rearrangement, introduced —CH_2CHO at C_{14}, and degradation of the methallyl group (15), cyclization and hydrogenation formed ring D. Introduction of hydroxyl at C_{21} and reduction of the lactone gave dl-aldosterone, an equilibrium mixture of the hemiketal (16) and hydroxyaldehyde (17) forms.

BIOSYNTHESIS

Present knowledge of the biosynthesis of cholesterol is based mainly on researches initiated by Schoenheimer (1933) and continued by his pupils Bloch and Rittenberg. Early balance studies showed that the amount of cholesterol excreted by an animal can exceed that consumed in the diet and hence that the animal organism can effect synthesis of the sterol. With advent of tracer techniques, Rittenberg and Schoenheimer (1937) demonstrated that the cholesterol of animals maintained on drinking water enriched with deuterium oxide has a high deuterium content and concluded that biosynthesis must involve condensation of several small molecules. In the same year R. Sonderhoff and H. Thomas noted that deuterium acetate is utilized by yeast for sterol synthesis, and the same conversion was later established in animal tissues (Bloch and Rittenberg, 1942). In view of the manifold metabolic reactions of acetic acid, these initial experiments did not establish a direct synthesis from acetate. More important evidence resulted from determination of the distribution of labeled carbon in cholesterol from acetate labeled in the carboxyl group, $CH_3C^{14}O_2H$, or, alternatively, in the methyl group, $C^{14}H_3CO_2H$. Comparison of the radioactivity of various degradation products from biosynthetic cholesterol (Bloch, Cornforth) established the origin of 20 of the 27 carbon atoms (Fig. 38.1a). In

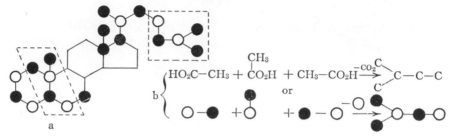

FIG. 38.1. — Distribution of C^{14} in Cholesterol (a) and in Isoprene (b): ● = Acetate Methyl, ○ = Acetate Carboxyl

addition, the results indicated that 15 of the carbon atoms are derived from methyl and 12 from carboxyl groups of acetate. The latter finding suggests that acetate is transformed into cholesterol by way of isoprenoid intermediates, in which the branched C_5-chain is formed by condensation of three C_2-units with concomitant loss of one carboxyl carbon atom, as in Fig. 38.1b, for such building would give a CH_3/CO_2H ratio of 3:2. Indeed two isoprene units of the construction of Fig. 38.1b are discernible in Fig. 38.1a.

As early as 1926 the C_{30}-isoprenoid hydrocarbon squalene (p. 950) was tentatively postulated as a precursor of cholesterol, but the suggestion had been largely discounted, mainly because squalene had been isolated only from elasmobranch fish liver oil and was not known to occur in animal tissues. With the clue that the triterpene might be involved, Langdon and Bloch (1952) looked for squalene as a metabolite of labeled acetate in mammalian tissues and by using natural material as carrier were able to isolate

Squalene   Lanosterol

labeled squalene. This biosynthetically labeled squalene was then tested as a cholesterol precursor and found to be 30–50 times more efficient than acetate. A further link in the chain of evidence was demonstration that acetate is a precursor for squalene. The hypothesis is further supported by evidence that the distribution of labeled carbon in biosynthetic cholesterol corresponds, as far as is known, to the pattern expected if cyclization occurs as indicated in the formula. This suggests that the angular methyl group at C_{13} is derived by migration of the methyl-labeled group (c). Actually any one of the methyl-labeled groups (a), (b), (c), or (d) may migrate; the other three are eliminated. Squalene is also a likely precursor of lanosterol, which could result merely by migration of methyl group (c) and cyclization. This would account for nonconformance to the isoprene rule.

OTHER STEROIDS

Cardiac Glycosides. — Digitalis, a pharmaceutical preparation made from seeds or leaves of *Digitalis purpurea* (purple foxglove), has inestimable value for treatment of heart diseases. It is a mixture of glycosides, and affords on hydrolysis a mixture of the aglycones digitoxigenin, digoxigenin, and gitoxigenin. These substances conform in skeletal structure and con-

Digitoxigenin   Digoxigenin   Gitoxigenin

figuration, with the exception of one detail, to the bile acid pattern to the extent of the twenty three carbon atoms present. They are of the *cis*-decalin type, the angular methyl groups and side chain are β-oriented, the B/C ring juncture is *trans,* and the only difference is that the C/D juncture is *cis*, since C_{14} has the β-configuration, or the opposite of that in the bile acids and sterols. Distinguishing structural features are the β-oriented hydroxyl group at C_{14} and the five-membered α,β-unsaturated lactone ring (butenolide ring). The aglycones retain little of the physiological activity of the natural glycosides, in which one or more sugar residues are linked to the 3-hydroxyl group. The various natural glycosidic derivatives of these genins all have comparable activity in the standard cat assay on a molar basis (mean lethal dose, LD_{50}, = 0.2–0.5 micromoles/kg. of cat body weight); hence the presence or absence of hydroxyl groups at C_{12} or C_{16} and the orientation of the 3-hydroxyl group, α or β, is relatively unimportant. The unsaturated lactone ring is necessary for activity, since the dihydro derivatives are inactive. The 14β-hydroxyl substituent also is a necessary feature. The *cis* configuration of rings A and B (5β) is also important, for the glycoside uzarin has all the essential features except that it is an A/B *trans* compound, and it is practically devoid of activity.

Cardiac glycosides are the active constituents of many preparations from rare plants used as early remedies, medieval ordeal drugs, and arrow poisons. A typical glycoside is strophanthin, which occurs in the seed of *Strophanthus kombé*; 0.07 mg. of strophanthin suffices to kill a 20-g. mouse

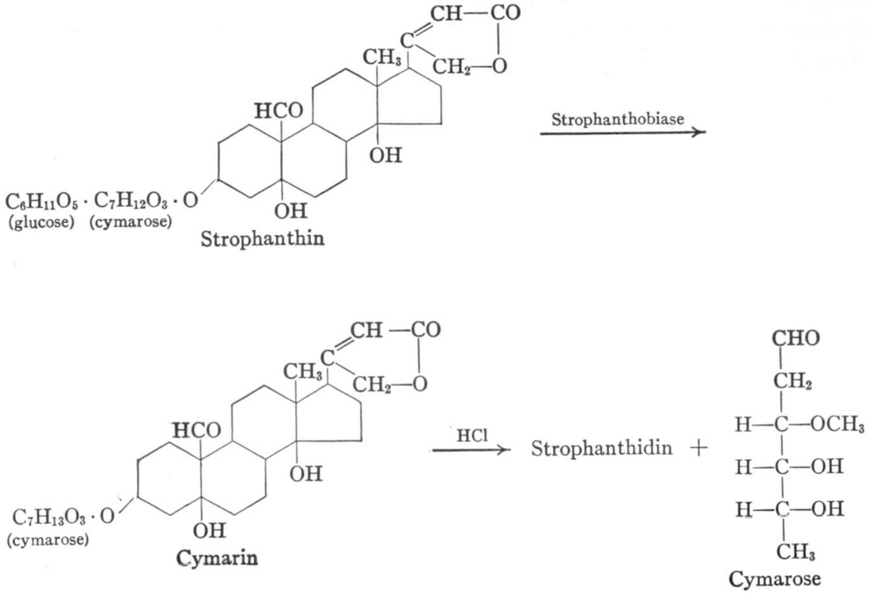

$C_6H_{11}O_5 \cdot C_7H_{12}O_3 \cdot O$
(glucose) (cymarose)
Strophanthin

Strophanthobiase

$C_7H_{13}O_3 \cdot O$
(cymarose)
Cymarin

HCl → Strophanthidin +

CHO
|
CH₂
|
H—C—OCH₃
|
H—C—OH
|
H—C—OH
|
CH₃
Cymarose

within a few minutes. It is a bioside, and can be hydrolyzed by an enzyme isolated from *Strophanthus courmanti* seeds (strophanthobiase) to glucose and the monoside cymarin, which occurs in Canadian hemp. Cymarin is hydrolyzed by acid to the aglycone strophanthidin and the rare sugar cymarose. Strophanthidin has an aldehydic group at C_{10} in place of the usual steroid methyl group, but this difference does not interfere with high cardiotonic potency; the corresponding methyl derivative is also known (periplogenin), and its glycosides are as active as the strophanthidin glycosides.

The red variety of squill (sea onion) contains a glycoside, scilliroside, of specific toxicity to rats and used as a rat poison. The morphologically similar white squill is practically nontoxic to rats but contains a potent cardiac-active glycoside, scillaren A. The glycosides are both derived from C_{24}-aglycones that contain a doubly unsaturated six-membered lactone ring similar to that of gamabufotalin, formulated below; the nuclear structures are not fully elucidated.

Sarmentogenin, isolated from the glycoside of a rare seed of uncertain origin, was found by Katz (1948) to have the rare feature of an oxygen

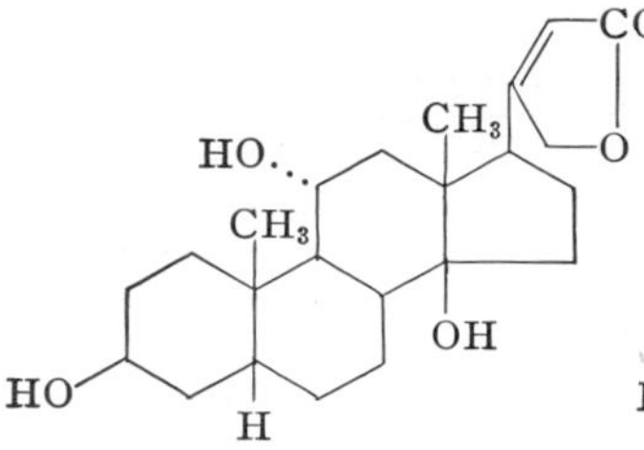

Sarmentogenin 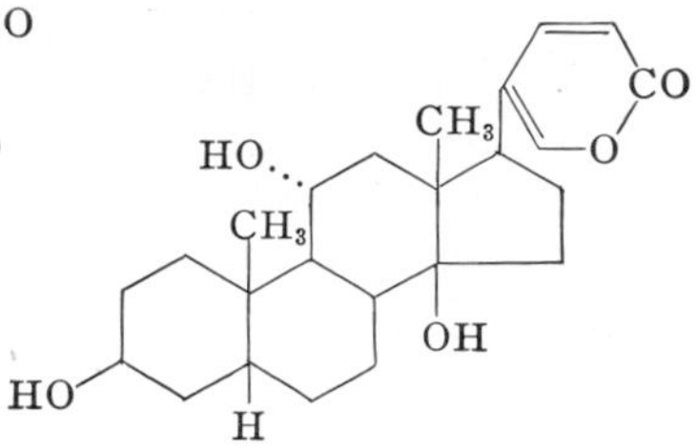   Gamabufotalin

function at C_{11}, as in cortisone. The same is true of gamabufotalin, characterized (Kuno Meyer, 1949) as a member of a series of cardiotonic principles secreted as conjugates in parotid glands of toads. The toad poison differs from the plant heart poison in containing a doubly unsaturated six-membered lactone ring. The 11α-hydroxyl group is acylable, and on oxidation of the diacetates with permanganate in acetone both genins give the same product, a 17-carboxylic acid (etio acid). The toxins of toad venoms are not glycosides but ester conjugates of an alcoholic aglycone with suberyl-arginine. Thus bufotoxin, isolated from the common European toad *Bufo vulgaris* by Wieland, is the ester of the genin bufotalin:

$$\overset{\overset{\text{CO}_2\text{H}}{|}}{} \quad \overset{\overset{\text{NH}_2}{|}}{}$$

$$C_{26}H_{35}O_5\text{—OCO(CH}_2)_6\text{CONHCH(CH}_2)_3\text{NHC=NH·H}_2\text{O} \longrightarrow$$

$$\overset{\overset{\text{CO}_2\text{H}}{|}}{} \quad \overset{\overset{\text{NH}_2}{|}}{}$$

$$C_{26}H_{35}\text{OH} \quad + \quad \text{HO}_2\text{C(CH}_2)_6\text{CONHCH(CH}_2)_3\text{NHC=NH}$$

Bufotalin   Suberylarginine

Saponins and Sapogenins. — The term saponin (L. *sapo*, soap) is applied to two groups of plant glycosides that form colloidal, soapy solutions in water. They can effect hemolysis of red blood cells at high dilution. Saponins have been used as fish poisons; fish are dazed by maceration of a suitable plant in the water, but are not rendered inedible. One group of saponins is that of the abundantly occurring triterpenoid glycosides (p. 951). A second group, the steroid saponins, is exemplified by the rare glycosides digitonin, gitonin, and tigonin, which occur in digitalis seeds as companions of the cardiac glycosides digitoxin, gitoxin, and digoxin. The three saponins are tetrosides and pentosides that on hydrolysis yield various sugars (galactose, xylose, glucose) and the aglycones digitogenin, gitogenin, and tigogenin.

Tigogenin and its glycoside have the structures shown; gitogenin has an additional 2α hydroxyl group and digitogenin is the 2α,3β,15β-triol. Tigogenin corresponds to cholestanol in the structure of the eight-carbon side chain and of the nucleus, and in the configuration at C_3 and C_5. It is remarkable that these plant products have the C_{27}-framework of cholesterol rather than that of the C_{29}-sitosterols. The sapogenin side chain differs in having two oxidic bridges linked at C_{22} in a ketospiroacetal grouping, which is subject to a number of transformations (R. E. Marker, 1940–49).

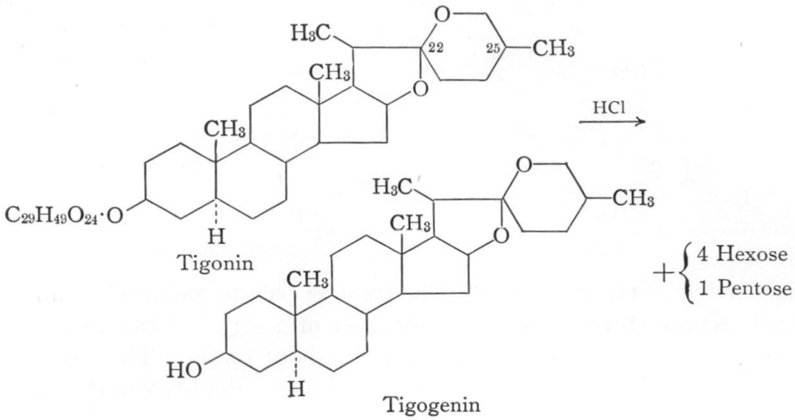

Tigonin

Tigogenin

$+\begin{cases} 4 \text{ Hexose} \\ 1 \text{ Pentose} \end{cases}$

Smilagenin, from smilax, belongs to the coprostane series and is the 5β-epimer of tigogenin. Another isomer, sarsasapogenin from sarsaparilla root, is the 25-epimer of smilagenin and is isomerized to this substance by prolonged treatment with alcoholic hydrocholoric acid.

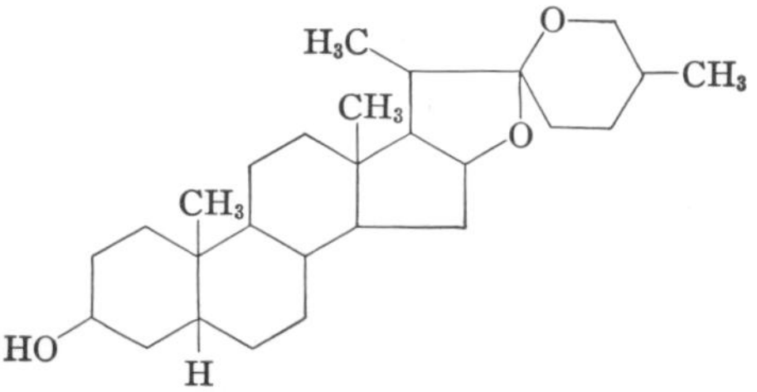

Chlorogenin, isolated from a California soap plant (C. R. Noller, 1935) once used by Mexicans as a soap substitute and by Californian Indians as a fish poison, is a 3β,6α-dihydroxyisosapogenin of the cholestane series. Diosgenin (I), isolated by Japanese workers and characterized by Marker (1940), has a 5,6-double bond, and material extracted from the

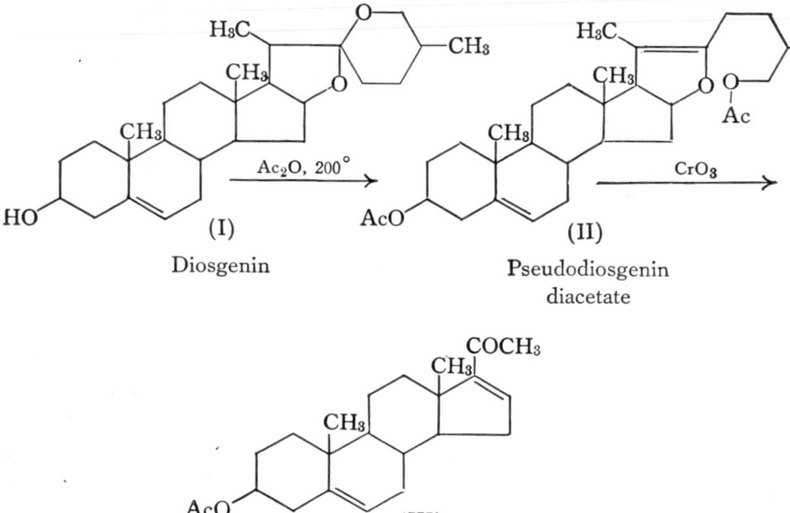

Sarsasapogenin

(I)
Diosgenin

Ac₂O, 200°

(II)
Pseudodiosgenin
diacetate

CrO₃

(III)

rhizomes of Mexican *Dioscorea* is employed for production of progesterone. Acetolysis gives the unsaturated derivative II, which on oxidation yields the substance III with a two-carbon side chain.   The double bond conjugated with the carbonyl group can be selectively hydrogenated, and the product resulting after hydrolysis (pregnenolone) yields progesterone on Oppenauer oxidation.   Nologenin and some of the many other sapogenins discovered by Marker (1943) in an investigation of hundreds of plants found in Mexico and southern parts of the United States can also be degraded to progesterone.   The new substances vary with respect to the configurations at C_5 and C_{25} and in the number and positions of the hydroxyl groups.   Two have been found with oxygen at C_{11} .

Alkaloids. — Three groups of alkaloids are known in which nitrogen is incorporated into the sterol framework.   One is exemplified by solanidine isolated from potato shoots and other species of *Solanum*.   Solanidine occurs in the plant as a glycoside (solanine); it is precipitated by digitonin and yields the Diels hydrocarbon on selenium dehydrogenation.   F. C. Uhle and W. A. Jacobs (1945) established the structure by transforming sarsasapogenin into dihydrosolanidine.   The veratrum alkaloids,

Solanidine

highly toxic glycosides occurring in roots and rhizomes of liliaceous plants of the United States, Canada, and Mexico, have the sterol skeleton as shown by Y. Sato and Jacobs (1949), who eliminated one of two hydroxyl groups from one member (rubijervine) and obtained a product identical with solanidine.   Connesine, a member of a third group, has the formula $C_{24}H_{40}N_2$ (one double bond; no oxygen!).   It has been degraded to allopregnane.

PROBLEMS

1. Predict the chief products of :
   (a) Reduction of coprostanone with sodium and alcohol.
   (b) Cathylation of methyl cholate.
   (c) Partial oxidation (removal of 2 H) of cholestane-$3\beta,5\alpha,6\beta$-triol.
   (d) Equilibration of coprostane-4-one with alkali.
   (e) Hydrolytic fission of cholesterol-β-oxide.
   (f) Reaction of cholesterol β-oxide with HCl.
   (g) Reaction of Δ^8-cholestenol with perbenzoic acid.
   (h) Reaction of cholesterol with osmium tetroxide.

2. The orientation of the substituent in the 2-monobromo derivative obtained on bromination of cholestanone was established by the following observations.   Reduction of the bromoketone with sodium borohydride gave two epimeric bromohydrins, A and B.   A on hydrogenation gave cholestanol, and on treatment with base gave an oxide. On similar treatment, B gave epicholestanol and cholestanone.   What is the configuration of the bromo ketone?   Is it the product expected on the assumption that bromination involves equilibration?

3. How would you expect HCl to add to cholesterol?   Can the bromination of cholesterol be explained on the assumption of an intermediate carbonium ion rather than a
   bromonium ion?
4. How could estriol be distinguished from 16-epiestriol?
5. Rationalize the dienone–phenol rearrangement (p. 972) and cite a related reaction.
6. Devise a synthesis of ketone I, p. 982.

READING REFERENCES

L. F. Fieser and M. Fieser, "Natural Products Related to Phenanthrene," 3rd Ed., Reinhold,
   New York (1949)
E. H. Rodd, "Chemistry of the Carbon Compounds," IIB, 764–1049, Elsevier (1953)
K. Bloch, "Biological Synthesis of Cholesterol," Harvey Lectures, **47**, 68 (1952–53)

CHAPTER 39

VITAMINS

The realization that animals require small amounts of specific organic substances in addition to carbohydrates, fats, proteins, and inorganic salts is comparatively recent. The fact that lack of such substances can cause diseases in man was accepted only about 1920 as applied to a characteristic eye disease (ophthalmia), to beriberi, and to scurvy, though the latter two diseases had been shown sometime previously to be curable by certain foods. For instance, the incidence of beriberi, a widespread Asiatic disease, was substantially decreased in the Japanese navy when a portion of the polished rice customary in the diet was replaced by wheat or barley (Takaki, 1885).

Experimental proof of the necessity of specific dietary factors for animals was obtained by Lunin, who reported in 1881 that mice were unable to grow normally on experimental diets containing only inorganic salts and the three types of organic food materials known to be required at that time, proteins, fats, and carbohydrates, but were able to grow on such a diet if small quantities of milk were added. This effect of milk was substantiated in 1906 by F. G. Hopkins,[1] who showed in addition that the active fraction containing substances that he named accessory factors could be extracted with alcohol. At the same time two American groups, McCollum and Davis, and Osborne and Mendel, commenced nutritional studies that showed that the activity of the alcohol extract is due to two factors, a fat-soluble A and a water-soluble B, both of which are soluble in alcohol. The activity of both factors was measurable on the basis of growth of young rats, and in this way the fat-soluble substance was shown to be present also in butter and cod-liver oil. Osborne and Mendel in 1913 reported that experimental animals on fat-free diets develop a characteristic eye disease, and the relation of A to human xerophthalmia and nyctalopia (night blindness) was accepted shortly. Credit for the first experimental production of a disease in animals by specific diets belongs to Eijkman,[2] who found in 1897 that fowls kept on a diet containing polished rice develop polyneuritis, which is effectively cured by an aqueous extract of rice polishings. The disease is similar to human beriberi. Eijkman interpreted his results on the basis of a specific nutritional factor in rice polishings only in 1906. These significant results stimulated interest in isolation of the essential fac-

[1] Sir Frederick G. Hopkins, 1861–1947, b. Eastbourne, Sussex; D.Sc. London (Stevenson); Nobel Prize 1929; *J. Chem. Soc.*, 713 (1948)

[2] Christiaan Eijkman, 1858–1930; b. Nykerk, Netherlands; Ph.D. Amsterdam; Utrecht; Nobel Prize 1929

tor. Funk[3] (1911) succeeded in obtaining an active fraction showing basic properties, and proposed the general name vitamine (L. *vita*, life, + amine) because he believed the antiberiberi substance to be an amine required for life. Later the final "e" was dropped to remove the implication that the active substances are amines, and the various vitamins were distinguished by the alphabetical designation introduced earlier. Hence the fat-soluble factor was named vitamin A, and the water-soluble factor vitamin B. This terminology has led to a certain awkwardness, however, for these earlier extracts soon were found to contain two or even more factors, identified by the names vitamin B_1, vitamin B_2, etc. The name vitamin, however, was useful in the period when the chemical constitution of a given factor was unknown. Most of the vitamins have been given more descriptive names with establishment of the structures. Thus the antiberiberi vitamin (B_1) is now known as thiamine, and B_2 as riboflavin.

The period following 1920 was marked by the recognition, based on nutritional requirements of experimental animals, of several additional dietary factors. Scurvy was shown to be curable by a substance named C, present in fruit juice. The active fat-soluble A was shown to consist of two factors, the eye factor for which the name A was retained and a rickets-preventive factor, D. The necessity of two additional fat-soluble factors, E and K, was established. The E factor is required for normal reproduction of rats, and K is required by chicks, which otherwise develop a hemorrhagic condition. A few letters of the alphabet were skipped in this latter case in order to denote the relation to coagulation (Danish, *Koagulation*).

During this same period many laboratories were engaged in isolation of the curative substances. Oddly enough, the first pure vitamin to be isolated, nicotinic acid, was not recognized as such. It was obtained by Funk when attempting to isolate the antiberiberi substance from rice polishings, but was ignored when found ineffective in curing beriberi. Its vitamin character was recognized only in 1937 when it was found to cure blacktongue in dogs and pellagra in man. Highly potent concentrates of the antiscorbutic substance of lemons were available in 1924 (Zilva). Two years later Jansen and Donath in Java isolated a minute amount of a crystalline hydrochloride from rice polishings that was highly potent in curing avian polyneuritis, but the procedure required was so sensitive that other workers were unable for several years to reproduce the result. Karrer obtained a highly potent concentrate of A in 1931, and succeeded for the first time in determining the constitution of a vitamin. The structures of the various factors were gradually determined: C in 1933, riboflavin (B_2) in 1935, thiamine (B_1) in 1936. The antirachitic factor D was finally isolated in 1936 (Brockmann) and found to be identical with a cholesterol derivative that had just been prepared (Windaus). The constitution of the reproductive factor E

---

[3] Casimir Funk, b. 1884 Warsaw, Poland; Ph.D. Bern (Kostanecki); Funk Found. Res. Lab.

was unraveled in 1937–38, shortly after the isolation in 1936.   The isolation and synthesis of K were achieved in 1939; B_{12} was isolated in 1948.

It is not easy to produce deficiency diseases in animals, and it is only with the more obvious deficiency diseases that the existence of specific vitamins can be demonstrated by use of restricted diets.   Furthermore some animals are evidently able to synthesize some of the required substances; for example, scurvy cannot be induced in animals other than primates and the guinea pig.   Early workers were favored by the circumstance that growth in animals can be used as an index of the activity of some of the essential factors.   The need of the animal organism for additional factors has been established by more recent research directed to the determination of the nutritional requirements of microorganisms.   The earliest experiment of this nature was performed by Liebig, who postulated that yeasts require factors present in extracts of living tissue (bios).   Inositol, isolated from bios in 1928, was found to be one of several factors for yeast, and in 1935 another factor, biotin, was isolated.   The isolation in 1938 by R. J. Williams[4] of pantothenic acid (Gr. *pan*, every, + *thena*, place) was a direct outcome of studies initiated in 1933 of the nutritional requirements of the yeast *Saccharomyces cerevisiae*.   It was not suspected immediately that these bios constituents, required by yeasts and other lower forms of plant life, might play a role in the animal organism.   Then in 1939 pantothenic acid was identified as an antidermatitis factor for chicks, and in 1940 inositol was recognized as essential for mice, and biotin as identical with vitamin H, required by a wide variety of animals, including man. Another practical application of the microbiological approach has been the development of useful methods of bioassay.   Microbiological methods alone are available at the present time for the quantitative determination of biotin.   Physical methods are available for the determination of riboflavin, but a microbiological assay, based on the essential nature of the substance for *Lactobacillus casei*, is more generally employed.   As little as 0.01 γ (1 γ = 0.001 mg.) of thiamine can be detected by the stimulating effect upon the growth of *Phycomyces Blakesleeanus*.

The remarkably successful work of elucidating the structures of the vitamins did not provide an answer to the interesting question of the function in the animal organism.   The fact that the requirement can be slight, for instance the minimum daily requirement for normal adults of thiamine is only 1.0 mg., points to a subtle function.   They are obviously not required as building units or as a source of energy.   One of the first clues was furnished in the case of the colored factor of the B complex, riboflavin, isolated in 1933 by Kuhn, György, and Wagner-Jauregg,[5] who pointed out that riboflavin is closely related to the prosthetic group of Warburg's yellow enzyme obtained from yeast.   The identity was shortly established,

[4] Roger J. Williams, b. 1893 India; Ph.D. Chicago; Univ. Texas
[5] Theodor Wagner-Jauregg, b. 1903 Vienna; Ph.D. Munich; Frankfurt, Edgewood Arsenal

and riboflavin was also recognized as a component of a number of enzymes (p. 464). The interesting hint that dietary factors are essential owing to their incorporation into enzyme systems was strengthened in 1937 when two more B factors, thiamine and nicotinic acid, were related to enzymes. Thiamine was found by Lohmann and Schuster to be present in carboxylase, an enzyme involved in metabolism of carbohydrates (p. 467). Nicotinamide was isolated from hydrolyzates of TPN (Warburg, 1934) and DPN (von Euler,[6] 1935) and shown to be involved in hydrogen transport. Its importance in animal nutrition was shown shortly afterward when Elvehjem (1937) found that the free acid or the amide cures canine blacktongue and human pellagra. Simultaneously nicotinic acid was found to be an essential growth factor for a variety of bacteria. The reversible oxidation and reduction of ascorbic acid (C) suggests a role in biological oxidations. Ascorbic acid oxidase is widely distributed in plant tissue, and dehydroascorbic acid is reduced by the sulfhydryl form of glutathione (G—SH) in the presence of a reductase:

$$\text{Ascorbic acid} \;+\; \tfrac{1}{2}O_2 \;\xrightarrow{\;\text{Oxidase}\;}\; \text{Dehydroascorbic acid} \;+\; H_2O$$

$$\text{Dehydroascorbic acid} \;+\; 2\,G\text{—}SH \;\xrightarrow{\;\text{Reductase}\;}\; \text{Ascorbic acid} \;+\; GS\text{—}SG$$

Ascorbic acid is probably involved in plant metabolism but its role in animal metabolism is not established; for although dehydroascorbic acid is readily reduced by animal tissues, an ascorbic acid oxidase system in animals has not been demonstrated. The role of vitamin A in ocular diseases is understandable since this substance is the prosthetic group of the rose-colored protein rhodopsin, which is concerned with photoreception in the retina (p. 955). Pantothenic acid occurs in coenzyme A (p. 467), essential in carbohydrate and fat metabolism. Pyridoxal phosphate (the aldehyde corresponding to B_6) is the prosthetic group of at least several amino acid decarboxylases (Umbreit, 1944) and of glutamic acid-aspartic acid transaminase. Pyridoxal is probably the active form of the vitamin, rather than pyridoxine, from which it can be derived by dehydrogenation.

Vitamins are of widely different chemical structure. Vitamin A is a carotenoid (p. 954); C and inositol are related to sugars (p. 394). Choline (p. 488) and some of the amino acids (p. 498) and fatty acids (p. 495) have been found to be essential for animals. If they are not synthesized by the organism, they must be supplied in the diet. Although they are thus essential dietary factors, they usually are not classed as vitamins, since they may be utilized as structural building units. The distinction perhaps is not justified. Although specific deficiency diseases (other than impaired growth) have not been definitely demonstrated for the amino acids, lack of certain of the fatty acids and of choline leads to definite syndromes that can be cured by administration of the essential nutrilite.

---

[6] Hans von Euler, b. 1873 Augsburg, Germany; Ph.D. Berlin (Landolt); Stockholm; Nobel Prize 1929

Thiamine (Vitamin B₁).— The water-soluble B fraction of yeast, rice polishings, etc., was found to cure avian polyneuritis and to be required for normal growth of young rats. Both effects initially were thought to be due to one factor, but in 1926 the B fraction was separated into two components, a thermostable one showing the growth effect and a thermolabile one containing the antiberiberi factor (B₁). R. R. Williams[7] and collaborators developed a method for large-scale production of the active crystalline hydrochloride in 1934, based on the original process of Jansen and Donath but including various improvements. The yield was about 25% of the amount originally present in rice polishings, or 5–10 g. from one ton of polishings. Jansen (1935) proposed the name aneurin for the antipolyneuritis vitamin; this is used widely abroad, but since the American Medical Association preferred a name which did not imply therapeutic utility, that adopted in the United States is thiamine, which indicates the presence of sulfur, first demonstrated by Windaus (1932).

The structure was established and verified by synthesis in 1936 by R. R. Williams in collaboration with the Merck laboratory. The structure, shown in formula I, is based largely on cleavage into two fragments on treatment with sodium sulfite (Chart 1). The character of fragment II was shown by conversion into a pyrimidine derivative (IV), whose constitution was established by synthesis. The other fragment (III) yielded a known thiazole derivative on oxidation. The point of attachment in thiamine of the pyrimidine nucleus is marked by the sulfonic acid group of II; the position at which the methylene bridge is linked in the thiazole nucleus was suggested by the resemblance of thiamine to known quaternary ammonium salts in behavior on potentiometric analysis. Final proof of the structure was furnished by synthesis (1936), which involved condensation of suitable thiazole and pyrimidine derivatives. The thiazole half is compound III, and the pyrimidine half is a bromo derivative of IV. The compo-

CHART 1. DEGRADATION OF THIAMINE

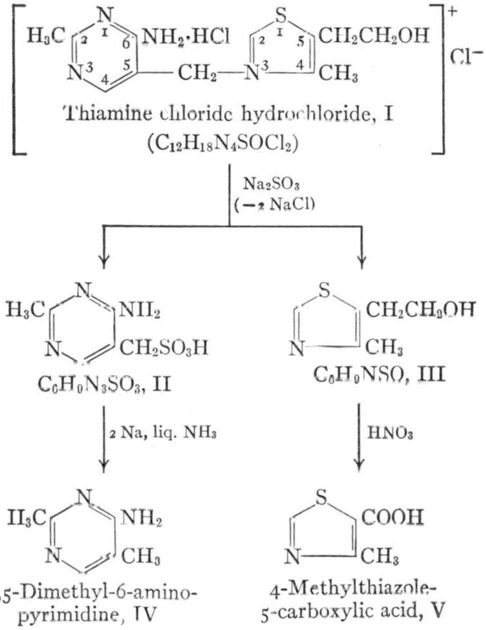

Thiamine chloride hydrochloride, I
(C₁₂H₁₈N₄SOCl₂)

Na₂SO₃
(−2 NaCl)

C₆H₉N₃SO₃, II

2 Na, liq. NH₃

C₆H₉NSO, III

HNO₃

2,5-Dimethyl-6-aminopyrimidine, IV

4-Methylthiazole-5-carboxylic acid, V

---

[7] Robert R. Williams, b. 1886 India; stud. Chicago; Bell Telephone Labs., Research Corp.

nent III was prepared in yields of 8–12 g. from 100 g. of ethyl acetoacetate:

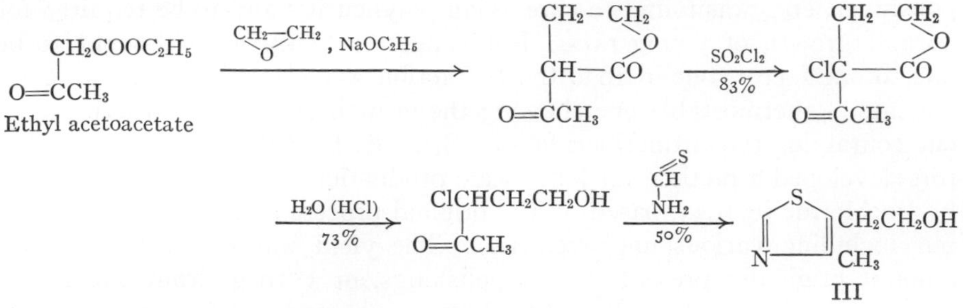

$$CH_2COOC_2H_5,\ O{=}CCH_3 \text{ (Ethyl acetoacetate)} \xrightarrow{CH_2{-}CH_2\,O,\ NaOC_2H_5} \quad \text{(CH}_2{-}CH_2, O, CH{-}CO, O{=}CCH_3) \xrightarrow[83\%]{SO_2Cl_2} \text{(CH}_2{-}CH_2, O, ClC{-}CO, O{=}CCH_3)$$

$$\xrightarrow[73\%]{H_2O\ (HCl)} \text{ClCHCH}_2CH_2OH,\ O{=}CCH_3 \xrightarrow[50\%]{\text{(CH}{=}S, NH_2)} \text{III (thiazole: S, CH}_2CH_2OH, N, CH_3)}$$

III

The more difficult preparation of the pyrimidine half (VI) and the condensation of the two components are shown in Chart 2.

CHART 2. SYNTHESIS OF THIAMINE CHLORIDE HYDROCHLORIDE

$$HCO[OC_2H_5] + [H]CHCH_2OC_2H_5 \xrightarrow{Na} \begin{bmatrix} COOC_2H_5 \\ CHCH_2OC_2H_5 \\ CHO \end{bmatrix}$$

Ethyl formate   Ethyl β-ethoxy-propionate

Formyl ester (as sodio derivative)

$$\begin{matrix} H_3CC, NH_2 \\ NH \end{matrix} \text{ (Acetamidine)} + \begin{bmatrix} O{=}, COC_2H_5 \\ CCH_2OC_2H_5 \\ HOCH \end{bmatrix} \xrightarrow[3\text{-}5\%\ \text{overall}]{Na} \text{(H}_3C, N, OH, N, CH_2OC_2H_5) \xrightarrow[70\%]{POCl_3}$$

Formyl ester (enol)

$$\text{(H}_3C, N, Cl, N, CH_2OC_2H_5) \xrightarrow[70\%]{\text{alc. NH}_3} \text{(H}_3C, N, NH_2, N, CH_2OC_2H_5) \xrightarrow[90\%]{HBr}$$

$$\text{(H}_3C, N, NH_2{\cdot}HBr, N, CH_2Br) \text{ VI} \quad + \quad \text{(S, CH}_2CH_2OH, N, CH_3) \text{ III}$$

$$\downarrow 45\%$$

$$\begin{bmatrix} \text{H}_3C, N, NH_2{\cdot}HBr, \ S, CH_2CH_2OH \\ CH_2{-}N, CH_3 \end{bmatrix}^+ Br^- \xrightarrow[90\%]{AgCl,\ C_2H_5OH} \text{Thiamine chloride hydrochloride}$$

Thiamine bromide hydrobromide

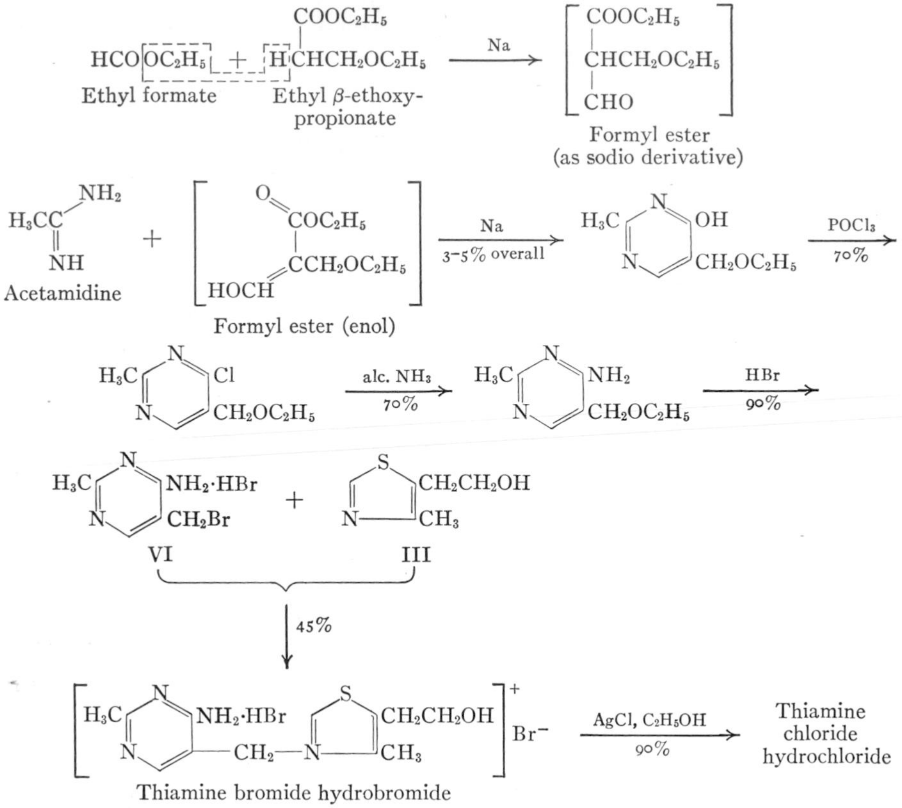

Thiamine is manufactured on a large scale; the annual U.S.A. production is about 25–30 tons. Very little is isolated from natural sources since the process cannot compete with synthesis. Although beriberi, a disease of extreme thiamine deficiency, is observed only occasionally in the United States, it has become increasingly evident since 1936 that milder diseases resulting from B_1 deficiency and usually characterized by changes in the nervous system are fairly common. Polyneuritis is frequently observed in chronic alcoholics and pregnant women. Since many diets are deficient in thiamine, a large percentage of flour and of white bread is enriched with thiamine. Cereal grains contain thiamine, but most is lost in milling. The standard for enriched flour set by the Food and Drug Administration also includes nicotinic acid and riboflavin.

Riboflavin (Vitamin B₂). — The heat-stable, water-soluble fraction of B was originally named the B_2, G, and also P-P (pellagra-preventive) factor, since lack of the substance in rats is marked by impaired growth and a form of dermatitis originally described as rat pellagra but now known as rat acrodynia, for it is not related to human pellagra. Although the presence of two factors was suggested in 1931, this fact was established only in 1935 after isolation of a pure factor that showed the growth but not the antiacrodynia effect, and for which the name B_2 was retained. The name B_6 was proposed for the second factor, since the subscripts 3, 4, and 5 had already been proposed for suspected factors that have not been authenticated. B_2 was first isolated from milk, and since it is a flavin (isoalloxazine) derivative, was named lactoflavin. Active flavins from egg white and from liver were originally named ovoflavin and hepatoflavin, but since all flavins of biological activity are identical, the names indicating the origin have been dropped and the name riboflavin, chosen because the factor contains a D-ribitol unit, has been adopted.

The structure of riboflavin was established by synthesis by both Kuhn and Karrer (1935). A later improved method (Karrer, 1936), which gives an overall yield of 39% based on ribose, is shown in Chart 3. In the

CHART 3. SYNTHESIS OF RIBOFLAVIN

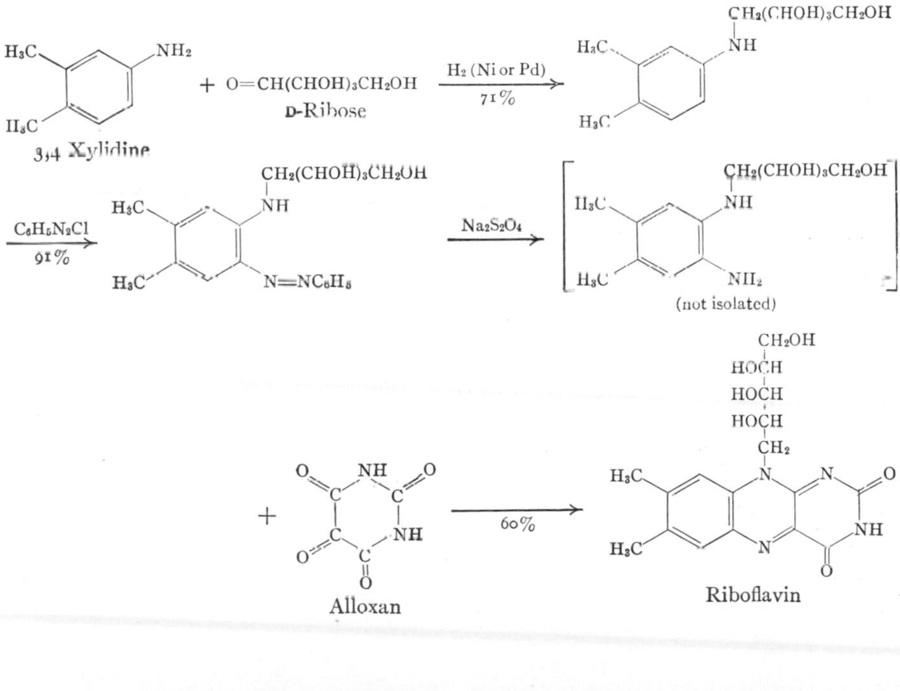

initial step the aldose is condensed with an aniline derivative to give a product containing a double linkage, which is then saturated by hydrogenation. In a more convenient synthesis alloxan is replaced by the more readily available barbituric acid (Tishler, 1947).

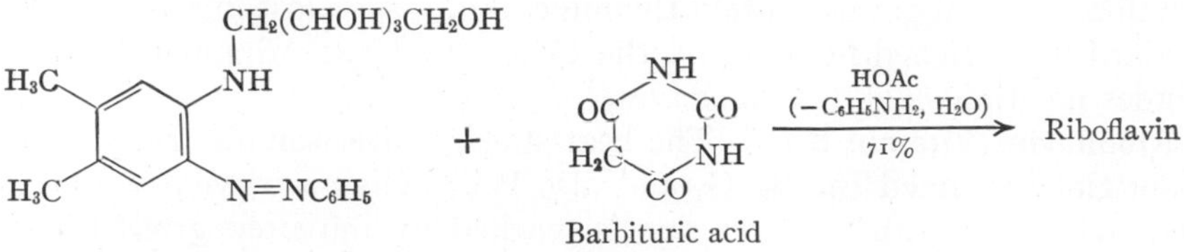

Barbituric acid

The effects of riboflavin deficiency have been studied most extensively in rats, where it is manifested in impairment not only of normal growth but of the ectodermal organs, particularly the skin and the eye. Effects due to riboflavin deficiency in humans have been recognized only since 1938–39. A syndrome that is similar to pellagra, and therefore named (1795) "pellagra sine pellagra," is due to riboflavin deficiency. The disorder is characterized particularly by lesions on the lip (cheilosis). Apparently ariboflavinosis is rather prevalent, since the average diet does not supply the daily requirement (about 3 mg. for an adult). The best natural sources of riboflavin are liver, heart, and kidney.

Pyridoxine (Vitamin B₆). — The rat acrodynia factor of the B complex was isolated in a pure crystalline form in 1938 in five different laboratories. The structure (I) was determined the following year by Kuhn and by the Merck laboratory, and was deduced mainly from that of an oxidation product (II). Interestingly enough, B₆ turned out to be identical with a substance isolated by a Japanese worker in 1921 from rice polishings. Kuhn

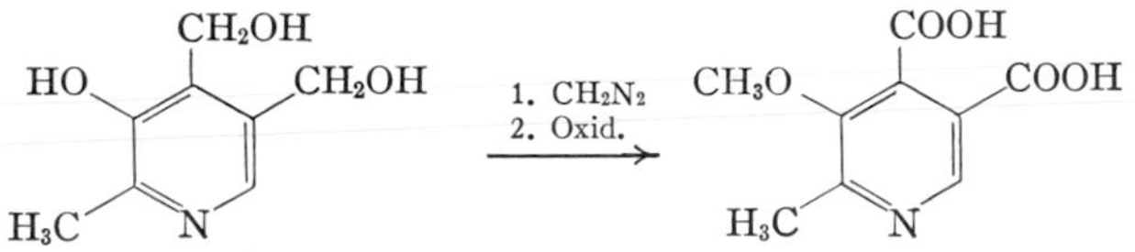

Pyridoxine, I
(m.p. 160°)

II

proposed the name adermin for B_6; the factor is now known as pyridoxine, since it is a pyridine derivative containing hydroxyl and hydroxymethyl groups.

Pyridoxine was synthesized in the Merck laboratory (1939) and shortly afterward by Kuhn and co-workers. The synthesis by the first group, including certain improvements introduced later, is shown in Chart 4. Kuhn's method utilized the degradation product II, obtained synthetically by oxidation of the isoquinoline derivative III; the acid II was converted in a five-step process into the vitamin. Kuhn's method has become useful with the advent of lithium aluminum hydride, since reduction of the carboxyl groups to hydroxymethyl groups can now be effected in one step in yield in the order of 80%.

CHART 4. SYNTHESIS OF PYRIDOXINE

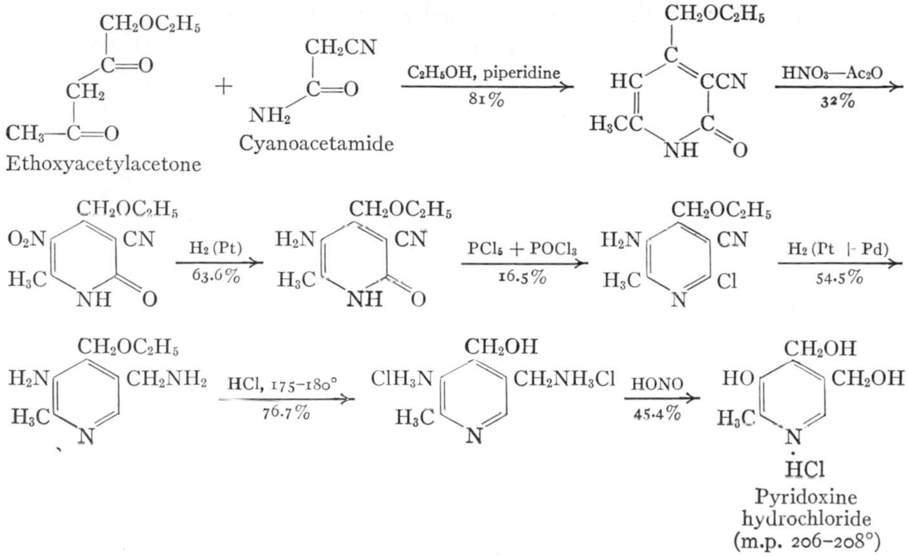

CH₂OC₂H₅ ... Ethoxyacetylacetone + Cyanoacetamide → (C₂H₅OH, piperidine, 81%) → ... HNO₃—Ac₂O 32%

O₂N ... H₂ (Pt) 63.6% → H₂N ... PCl₅ + POCl₃ 16.5% → H₂N ... Cl H₂ (Pt + Pd) 54.5%

CH₂OC₂H₅ H₂N CH₂NH₂ HCl, 175–180° 76.7% → ClH₃N CH₂NH₃Cl HONO 45.4% → HO CH₂OH

Pyridoxine hydrochloride (m.p. 206–208°)

No clinical disorders have been associated with a deficiency of pyridoxine Even the production of acrodynia in rats apparently involves deficiency of

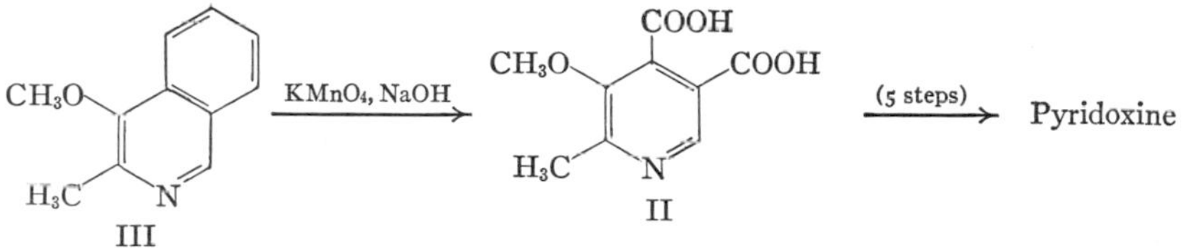

III KMnO₄, NaOH → II (5 steps) → Pyridoxine

more than pyridoxine, for several workers have reported that rats on a B₆-deficient diet do not invariably develop acrodynia. There is some indication that pantothenic acid and the essential fatty acids are also involved in the production and cure of the syndrome. Rats on a pyridoxine-deficient diet often become abnormally excitable and subject to convulsions. In the dog lack of pyridoxine is manifested by a form of anemia that is characterized by decrease in hemoglobin and red cells and is responsive to the addition of pyridoxine to the diet, though there is some evidence that another factor of liver is required for complete cure. Necessity of pyridoxine has been demonstrated for the rat, chick, and dog, and also for certain yeasts and bacteria. The mode of action of pyridoxine is discussed on p. 499.

Nicotinic Acid (Antipellagra Factor). — A syndrome of humans, described as early as 1755 and named pellagra (Ital. *pelle agra*, rough skin), since it is characterized particularly by skin lesions and inflammation of the tongue, was shown to be a deficiency disease in 1915 when Goldberger induced pellagra in six of eleven convicts fed on a limited diet suspected to be the cause of the disease. Goldberger's later experiments indicated that blacktongue in dogs is similar to pellagra, since foods curative for pellagrins are often effective in treating blacktongue. Liver, yeast, red meats, and kidney were found effective, in the order named, and the active principle was located in the thermostable B component. After the discovery of Whipple and Minot that liver can cure pernicious anemia, liver extracts became available commercially and were used successfully in treating pellagrins (1934–36). After long and intensive research the antiblacktongue factor was isolated from liver by Elvehjem (1937) and identified as nicotinic acid amide. The free acid was found to be equally effective. Within a few months nicotinic acid was shown to be effective as well for pellagra. The name niacin has been adopted officially as a synonym for nicotinic acid, which might be confused by the layman with nicotine.

Nicotinic acid was prepared first in 1867 by oxidation of nicotine, the principal alkaloid of the leaves of *Nicotiana tabacum*. The reaction is preferably carried out with concentrated nitric acid. It is also obtained

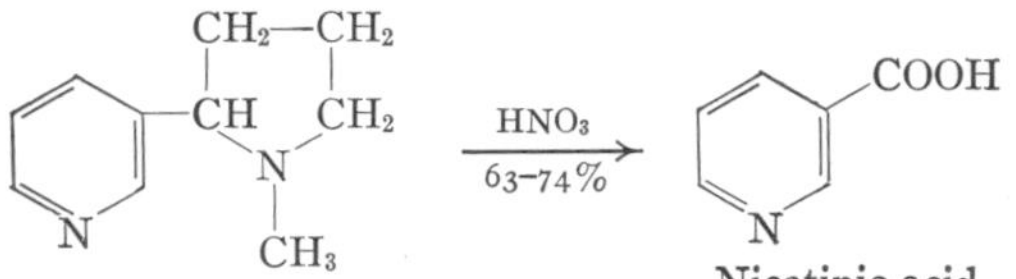

Nicotine

Nicotinic acid (m.p. 232°)

by oxidation of β-picoline or of quinoline (p. 806). Pyridine has also been used as a starting material:

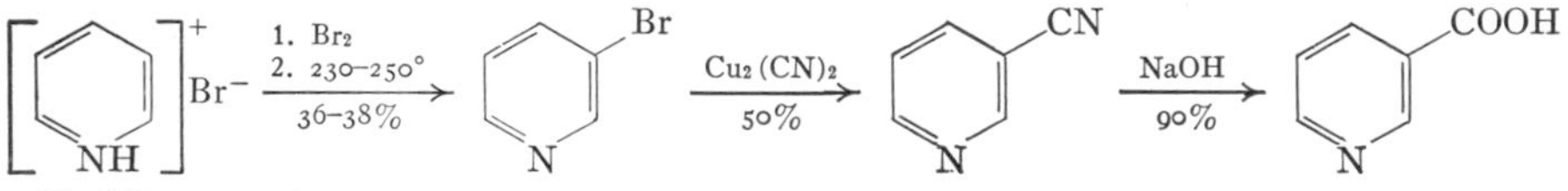

Pyridine hydrobromide

Nicotinic acid is stored in highest amounts in the liver. For a water-soluble factor it is excreted rather slowly, as such, as the betaine trigonelline (a), the 6-pyridone of N-methylnicotinic acid (b), and as the dipeptide

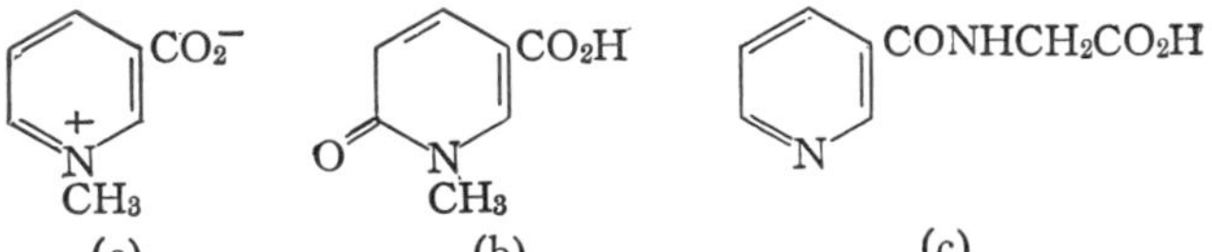

(a) (b) (c)

nicotinuric acid (c). β-Picoline and coramine (N,N-diethylnicotinic acid amide) are also effective in curing blacktongue, though only the latter is effective for pellagra.

Since a single vitamin deficiency in man is rather rare, nicotinic acid treatment alone usually is not sufficient for cure of typical pellagra, and inclusion of the other B factors and of A and C is necessary. The daily allowance of nicotinic acid recommended for adults is 12–23 mg.

Pteroic Acid Factors. — A number of growth factors contain the hetero-bicyclic sytems of pteridine (λ_{max} 2980, 3090 Å), derivatives of which were first encountered in nature as pigments of butterfly wings and insects. These pigments were studied particularly by Wieland (1925–40), who elucidated the structures of xanthopterin and leucopterin. Leucopterin can

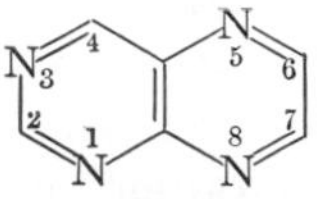

Pteridine 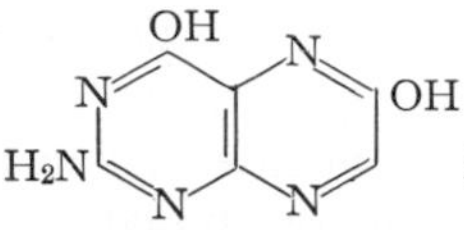   Xanthopterin 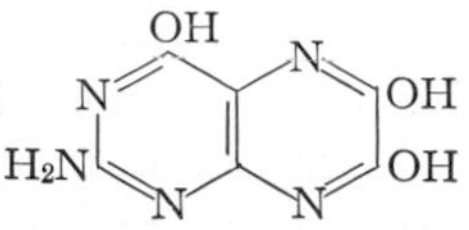   Leucopterin

be synthesized in 90% yield by condensation of 2,5,6-triamino-4-hydroxy-pyrimidine with oxalic acid at 140°. Sodium amalgam reduction of leucopterin gives 7,8-dihydroxanthopterin, which on oxidation gives xanthopterin All known natural pteridines, about a dozen, are 2-amino-4-hydroxy derivatives.

A number of growth factors are derivatives of pteroic acid, so named because of its relationship to the butterfly pigments, the pterins. The simplest, pteroylglutamic acid (PGA, I), is a conjugate of pteroic acid and

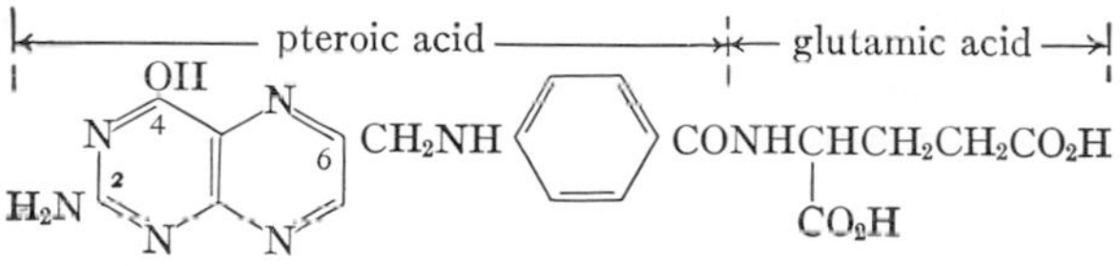

Pteroylglutamic acid (I)

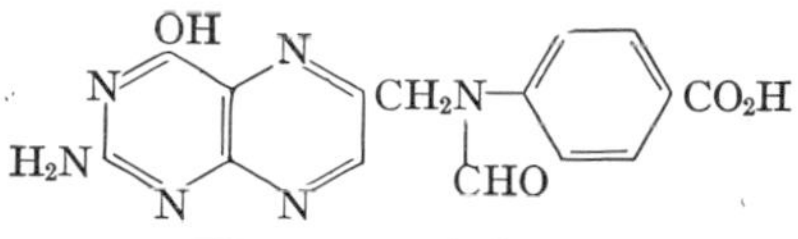

Rhizopterin (II)

glutamic acid. It has been isolated from liver and from yeast; since the same or a very similar factor is present in spinach, PGA is often referred to as folic acid (*L. folium*, leaf). Conjugates of pteroic acid with as many as seven units of glutamic acid have also been isolated. Pteroic acid itself has not been isolated as a natural product, but the N-formyl derivative rhizopterin (II) is a fermentation product of *Rhizopus nigricans*. These pteroic acids are all growth factors but differ in their effect on various organisms. Thus rhizopterin is highly active for *S. faecalis* and relatively inactive for *L. casei*, whereas PGA is strongly active for both. The most recently discovered member of the group is known as the citrovorum factor (formula, p. 505) because it is highly active toward the bacterium *Leuconostoc citrovorum*, which responds only weakly to other pteroic acid factors. This substance, 5-formyl-5,6,7,8-tetrahydro-PGA, is probably the true vitamin, since it has been shown to be involved in various enzyme systems. Elucidation of the structures of the pteroic acid factors explained observations noted previously (1941) that *p*-aminobenzoic acid itself is a growth factor for several microorganisms. Given this portion of the vitamin, the organisms can synthesize the more complex factor.

Vitamin B_{12} . — Although rhizopterin has certain value in pernicious anemia, it was soon found to lack the completely curative qualities of whole liver extract, shown by Minot and Murphy (1926) to be effective in clinical treatment of human pernicious anemia. The long and arduous concentration of active liver fractions finally culminated in isolation of crystalline material with extraordinarily high antipernicious anemia activity in 1948 at the Merck laboratories and of similar, though not crystalline, material by E. L. Smith at the Glaxo Laboratories (England). The substance, now known as vitamin B_{12}, has also been isolated from the mold *Streptomyces griseus*. Vitamin B_{12} is one of the most potent of the accessory factors, for dosages of only 3–6 micrograms are effective in human anemia. It appears however that rhizopterin is also required for complete cure. Vitamin B_{12} is probably identical with the "animal protein factor," originally associated with the protein casein and later with liver extracts and shown to be required for rats and for poultry, and with the LLD factor required by *Lactobacillus lactis* Dorner. Vitamin B_{12} is probably involved in purine metabolism, for thymidine (the desoxyriboside of thymine) can replace B_{12} in stimulating growth of *L. lactis* Dorner. Since thymine is inactive, it has been suggested that B_{12} acts as a coenzyme in the enzymatic conversion of thymine into thymidine.

Vitamin B_{12}, the first natural product found to contain cobalt, is a deep red substance of the formula $C_{63}H_{90}O_{14}N_{14}PCo$. A cyanide group is coordinately bound to the metal atom and can be removed or substituted by other groups or ions; hence the name cyanocobalamin has been used. A whole family of natural or semisynthetic cobalamins are known that differ in the group replacing CN. The porphyrin-like structure shown in the formula is based in part upon degradative evidence adduced by Todd and co-workers at Cambridge University and by the Folkers group of Merck. One degradation product is 1-aminopropane-2-ol, $CH_3CHOHCH_2NH_2$, the configuration of which is that of D-glyceraldehyde and not that of the natural amino acids. Another is the 3-phosphate ester of a ribofuranosyl-5,6-dimethylbenzimidazole (rings E, F, G). A further product, isolated by chromic acid oxidation of a crude B_{12}-hydrolyzate (Folkers, 1955), is the succinimide derivative III, which reveals the structure of ring C. The largest degradation product isolated is the nucleotide-free hexacarboxylic acid II, isolated in crystalline form from the crude hydrolyzate by the Todd group (1954). X-ray studies of II by Dorothy Crowfoot Hodgkin and her group at Oxford and analysis of the data on a SWAC computer by K. N. Trueblood and associates at the University of California at Los Angeles revealed the general nature of the cyclic system and a combination of X-ray and chemical evidence led to full elucidation of the structures of both II and B_{12}. A scheme of biogenesis from δ-aminovaleric acid can be developed along the lines of the porphyrin synthesis (p. 506).

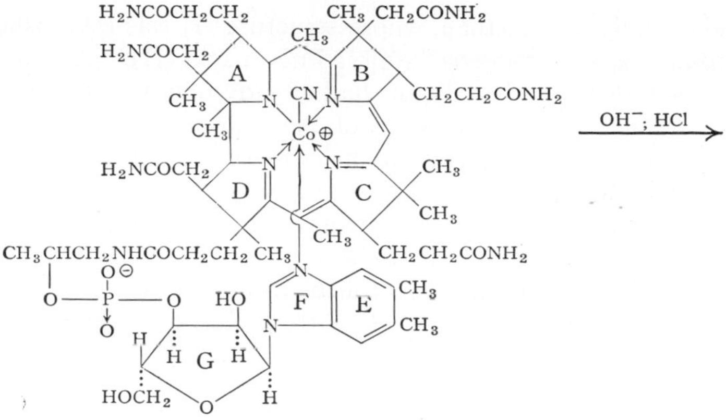

$H_2NCOCH_2CH_2$ CH_3 CH_2CONH_2

H_2NCOCH_2 CH_3

CH_3 A   B

CH_3 N   CN   N $CH_2CH_2CONH_2$

CH_3 Co⊕

H_2NCOCH_2 N   N CH_3

D   C CH_3

CH_3

$CH_3CHCH_2NHCOCH_2CH_2$ CH_3 N CH_3

$O⊖$ F   E CH_3

O—P—O   HO   N

O   H   H

H G H

$HOCH_2$ O   H

OH⁻; HCl →

Vitamin B₁₂ (I)

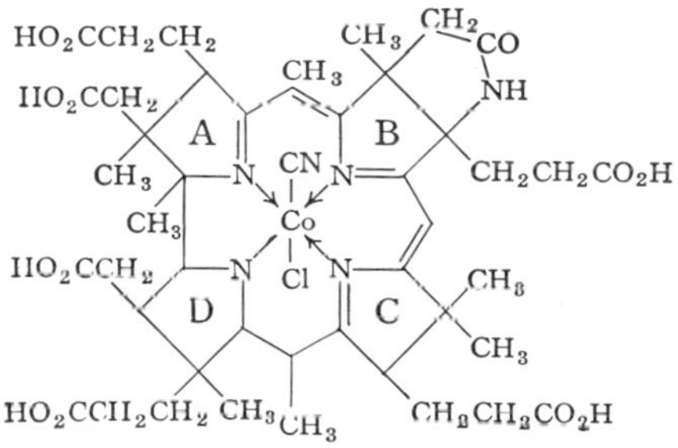

$HO_2CCH_2CH_2$ CH_3 CH_2 CO

HO_2CCH_2 CH_3 NH

A   B

CH_3 N   CN   N $CH_2CH_2CO_2H$

CH_3 Co

HO_2CCH_2 N   Cl   N CH_3

D   C CH_3

$HO_2CCH_2CH_2$ CH_3 CH_3 $CH_2CH_2CO_2H$

II

CrO₃ ↓ →   NH

O   O

C CH_3

$HO_2CCH_2CH_2$ CH_3

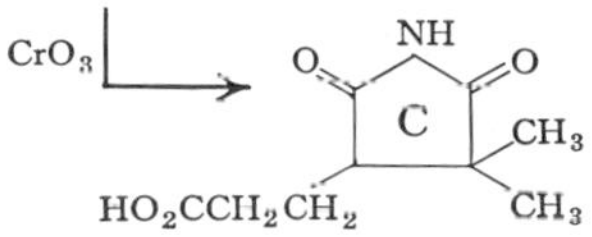

III

Panthothenic Acid. — The structure of pantothenic acid, a growth factor of yeasts first recognized by R. J. Williams in 1933, was not established until 1940. This slow development was due mainly to the great difficulty of obtaining pure material; indeed the empirical formula was determined only after preparation of pure synthetic material. Williams showed in 1938 that pantothenic acid is a dipeptide made up of β-alanine and of a hydroxy

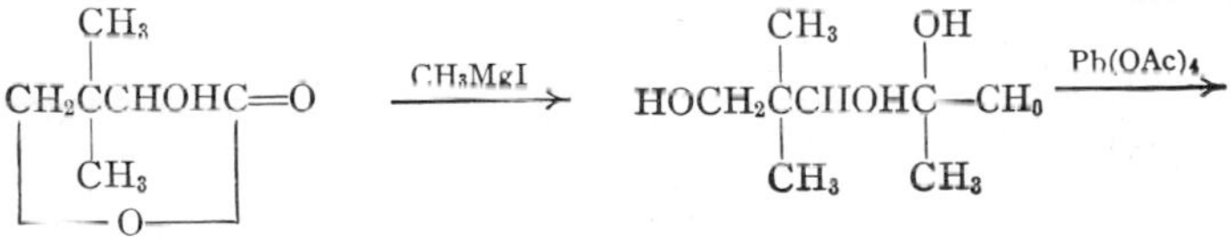

CH_3

$CH_2CCHOHC=O$ CH₃MgI → CH_3 OH

CH_3 $HOCH_2CCHOHC—CH_3$ Pb(OAc)₄ →

—O— CH_3 CH_3

α-Hydroxy-β, β-dimethyl-
γ-butyrolactone, I ([α]_D −50.7°)

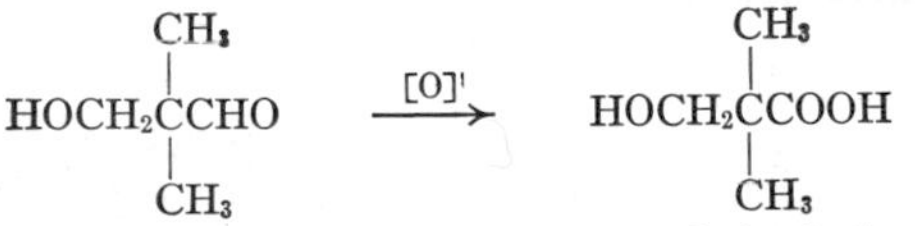

CH_3 CH_3

$HOCH_2CCHO$ [O]' → $HOCH_2CCOOH$

CH_3 CH_3

α,α-Dimethyl-β-hydroxy-
propionic acid, II

acid obtained only as a lactone, whose structure (I) was established by the Merck group (1940) by conversion into a known acid (II). A total synthesis was achieved shortly, since Williams had already found that active material could be obtained by recombination of the lactone and amino acid. The synthesis of the levorotatory lactone is discussed on page 274.

Pantothenic acid was identified in 1939 as the "chick antidermatitis factor" and as one factor involved in nutritional achromotrichia (graying of hair) of rats and silver foxes. The importance of pantothenic acid in the diet of humans has not been established.

The peptide of pantothenic acid with β-mercaptoethylamine, panto-

$$\underset{\text{Pantotheine}}{\overset{\overset{\displaystyle CH_3}{\displaystyle |}}{\underset{\underset{\displaystyle CH_3}{\displaystyle |}}{HOCH_2\overset{4'}{C}CHOHCO-NHCH_2CH_2CO-NHCH_2CH_2SH}}}$$

theine, is a growth factor for *Lactobacillus bulgaricus* (Snell, 1950). Pantothine is the corresponding disulfide. Pantotheine represents a large portion of the coenzyme A molecule (p. 467). 4'-Phosphopantotheine is a factor for *Acetobacter suboxydans*.

Biotin. — Bios, the material necessary for growth of yeast and synthesized by many strains though not in adequate amounts, was separated into two factors in 1924. The first was shortly identified as *meso*-inositol (p. 394); the second factor was subsequently shown to contain at least two growth substances, one of which, bios IIb, is adsorbable on charcoal. Kögl in 1935 isolated from this fraction a minute amount of a substance that he named biotin. Richer sources of biotin were shortly found, and the following year Kögl described a process for the isolation of 1.1 mg. of the crystalline methyl ester of biotin from 250 kg. of dried yolks of ducks' eggs. The empirical formula $C_{11}H_{18}O_3N_2S$ was assigned to the ester, which was found to be highly active in promoting growth of yeast.

A few years earlier, Allison, Hoover, and Burk had found that various species of *Rhizobium* (legume nodule bacteria) require a factor that, since it stimulates respiration, was named coenzyme R. The factor was found in yeast, molasses, and liver. Identity of coenzyme R and biotin was established by American and Swedish groups in 1939–1940. Biotin promotes growth not only of some yeasts but also of several genera of bacteria: *Staphylococcus, Streptococcus, Clostridium, Lactobacillus, Pasteurella,* and *Fusarium.* On the other hand, a wide variety of bacteria and several molds have been shown by microbiological assay to synthesize biotin in varying degrees.* Biotin is involved in the metabolic fixation of carbon dioxide by microorganisms.

---

* The biosynthesis of biotin by the mold *Aspergillus niger* is greatly increased by addition to the culture medium of pimelic acid, $HOOC(CH_2)_5COOH$; the effect is further enhanced by addition of cysteine or cystine. Pimelic acid is a growth factor for the diphtheria bacillus, probably because it is required by the bacillus for synthesis of biotin, since biotin itself can support growth in the absence of pimelic acid.

Biotin was identified in 1940 by György, du Vigneaud, *et al.*, with a factor required by higher animals including man, vitamin H (György). In 1927, Boas described a syndrome that appeared in rats fed on a diet containing egg white as the protein constituent. Since the syndrome of egg-white injury involves particularly a typical dermatitis, the protective factor was named vitamin H (Ger. *Haut*, skin). The factor was shown to be in liver though it can be extracted only after drastic hydrolysis, preferably by acids. Recognition that crude liver extracts possess biotin activity facilitated isolation of the pure H factor, since procedures useful in the isolation of biotin were found applicable also to vitamin H, and, in 1941, pure crystalline material was available to the American group for chemical studies and direct comparison with biotin. Biotin deficiency in yeasts can be induced by adding egg white to the medium, and R. J. Williams (1940–42) has shown that the effect is due to a protein constituent that is named avidin because of the avidity with which the protein combines with biotin to form an inactive complex. Egg-white injury therefore is a deficiency disease induced by avidin.

After characterization and degradation of biotin by Kögl and by du Vigneaud, the complete structure was established by the latter investigator in 1942, and the structure was confirmed by total synthesis (Merck Research Laboratory, 1943). A urea grouping is established by formation of the degradation product I, which contains two primary amino groups,

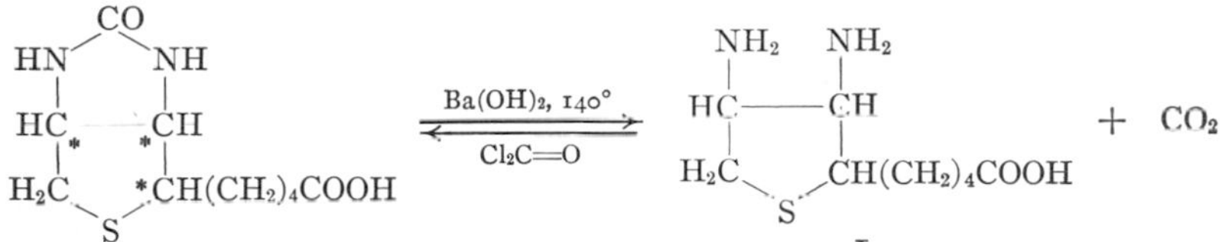

Biotin ($C_{10}H_{16}O_3N_2S$,
m.p. 230–232°, $[\alpha]_D + 92°$)

and from which biotin can be resynthesized by the action of phosgene. Evidence of the nature of the sulfur-containing ring is furnished by degradation of I to a thiophene derivative II, whose structure was established by synthesis. Additional evidence for the structure of biotin is derived

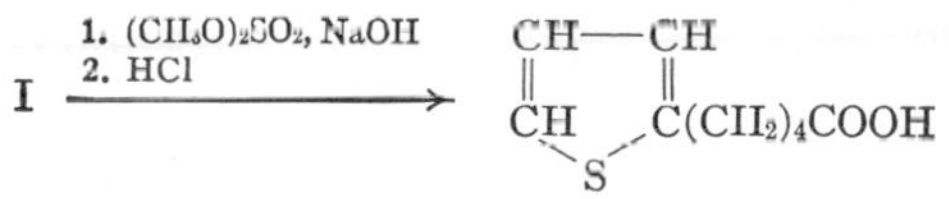

II (m.p. 40–41°)

from a reaction, given prominence by Mozingo, by which sulfides undergo an unexpected reductive cleavage when treated with Raney nickel catalyst (without added hydrogen). When the reaction is applied to biotin, a desthio derivative (III) is obtained that can be further degraded to a diaminopelargonic acid (IV). This substance contains two of the three asymmetric carbon atoms of biotin, but comparison with a synthetic racemic diamino acid was made by conversion of both samples into the quinoxaline derivative V, in which the centers of asymmetry are eliminated. The prod-

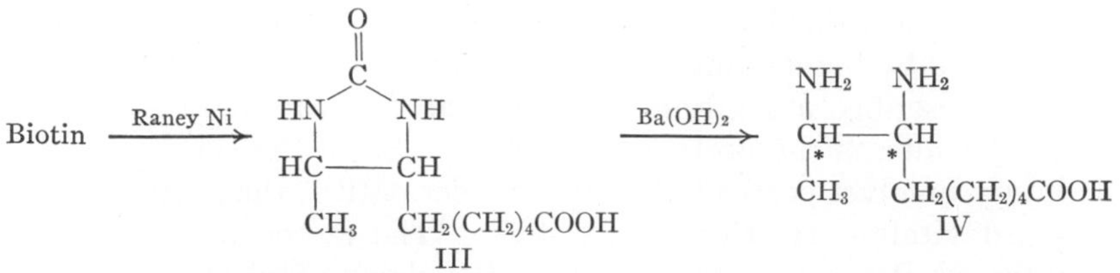

Biotin $\xrightarrow{\text{Raney Ni}}$ III $\xrightarrow{\text{Ba(OH)}_2}$ IV

uct of initial condensation contains a dihydride ring and undergoes de-hydrogenation at the expense of the quinonoid component, with aromatization of the heterocyclic nucleus.

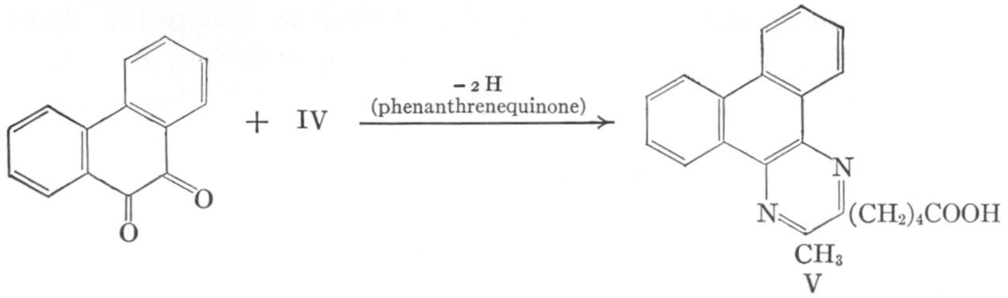

+ IV $\xrightarrow[\text{(phenanthrenequinone)}]{-2\,\text{H}}$ V

Biotin occurs mainly bound to protein or polypeptides. A simple derivative isolated from yeast, biocytin, is a peptide of biotin linked to the ε-amino group of L-lysine. Biotin has been implicated in various biochemical systems (fixation of carbon dioxide, decarboxylation of malic and oxalacetic acid), but it has not been identified as a component of a coenzyme.

Vitamin D. — Rickets is a disease of infancy or early childhood characterized by faulty deposition of calcium phosphate, with the result that the bones do not grow normally. Rickets was shown to be a deficiency disease by feeding experiments (1918–22). An antirachitic factor was found to occur along with A in various oils, particularly fish oils, but was shown to differ from the eye factor, since the oils retain their antirachitic activity after destruction of vitamin A. The antirachitic activity was found to be associated with the unsaponifiable sterol fraction.

A second line of attack was furnished by the observation that irradiation of a person suffering from rickets or even administration of irradiated foodstuffs (Hess, Steenbock, 1924) resulted in a rapid cure. The activity of irradiated oils likewise was traced to the sterol fraction, and the effect of irradiation on cholesterol, the common animal sterol, was investigated. Although some samples of cholesterol were found capable of being activated, this effect was soon found to be due to an impurity present in small amounts (1926), and the evident steroidal character of the activatable material suggested examination of other known sterols as possible provitamins. Ultraviolet absorption spectroscopy provided a particularly significant clue, for preparations acquiring antirachitic activity on irradiation showed characteristic absorption not observed with cholesterol, which contains one double bond, or with other known sterols that are either saturated or contain isolated double bonds. Ergosterol, from yeast, has a conjugated diene system (ring B, see formula) and gives an absorption band in the ultraviolet region very similar to that tentatively attributed to the provitamin, and it was shortly announced from two laboratories that ergosterol can be irradiated to give highly active material. An active crystalline product of the irradiation of ergosterol was isolated in 1930–1931 by a group at the National Institute for Medical Research in London and by Windaus and co-workers in Germany, and named calciferol and vitamin D_1, respectively. The initial preparations, however, proved to be mixtures, but isolation of a pure active product was achieved by both groups in 1932. Windaus named the pure material vitamin D_2; the English group retained the earlier name calciferol. Two more isomeric, inactive products have since been obtained after shorter periods of irradiation, as well as two stable substances that result from overirradiation of D_2. The irradiation process is now known to lead to a succession of products, shown in part in the chart. The first transformation

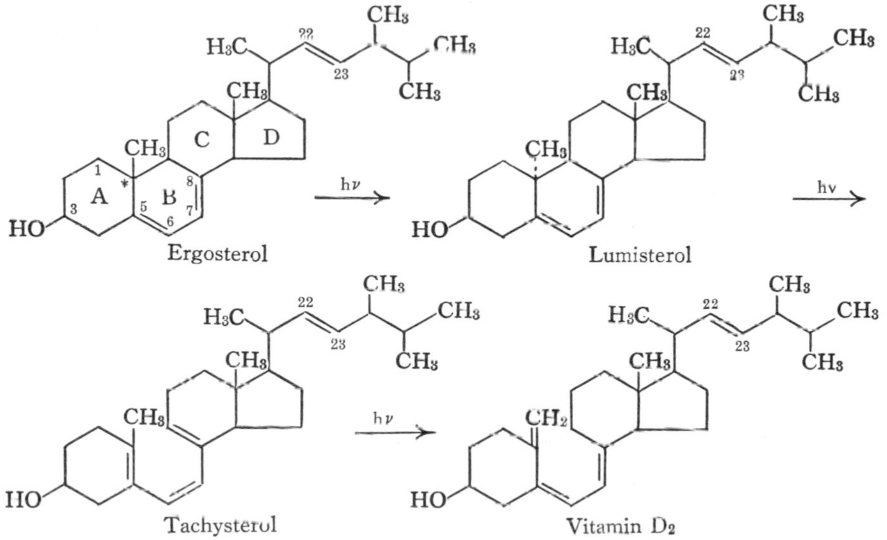

Ergosterol

Lumisterol

Tachysterol

Vitamin D_2

consists in an inversion of an activated asymmetric carbon atom carrying one of the angular methyl groups, and the next step consists in rupture of ring B. The ruptured linkage is adjacent to both ends of the diene system and hence is activated, particularly when this system acquires added energy by light absorption. The stage affording antirachitic material is reached by a progression of the bonds in the resulting triene system. The difficult problem of establishing the structure of D_2 was solved by the work of Windaus and of Heilbron. Vitamin D_2 shows high potency; it was originally assumed to be identical with the natural factor and was soon introduced into human therapy. However biological differences were noted as early as 1930, for quantities of cod-liver oil and of irradiated ergosterol that produce an equivalent response in one species of animal may show widely different efficacies in another test animal. Then in 1933 Windaus prepared a similar substance by irradiation of 22-dihydroergosterol, which differs from ergosterol in that the side chain is saturated. The biological activity of this product is comparable to that of D_2 and actually even greater. Sterols other than ergosterol can function therefore as provitamins, and Windaus next prepared the cholesterol derivative in which ring B has the same bond structure as in ergosterol. This sterol, 7-dehydrocholesterol, on

Cholesterol   7-Dehydrocholesterol

irradiation yielded a potent antirachitic substance, named vitamin D_3. The structure is entirely analogous to D_2; the only difference is in the side chain. In the same year Brockmann isolated the active principle of tunny-liver oil, following the hypothesis that the natural vitamin would correspond closely to vitamin D_2. The fish-oil factor was recognized as D_3, just prepared by Windaus. The substance has been isolated since from the halibut and the blue tunny.

Windaus (1937) isolated 7-dehydrocholesterol, or provitamin D_3, from the external layers of hog skin, but it is not known whether this is the exclusive precursor in animals. The origin of the large amounts of D in fish oils is puzzling since it seems hardly possible that it is formed in this case by irradiation of a provitamin. Another unsettled problem is the exact role of D in the organism. Vitamin D apparently prevents excessive loss of calcium and phosphate from the blood. A condition resembling rickets can be induced in rats by feeding a diet deficient in D and either low in calcium and high in phosphorus or low in phosphorus and high in calcium. Either type can be cured by administration of D. The standard unit for vitamin D potency is based on the formation of new deposits of calcium phosphate after administration of the factor to rachitic rats. The rat requirement is rather low in comparison with that of the chick and other animals. Moreover animals show a marked difference in their response to a specific D. Thus D_2 and D_3 show the same potency when tested in rats, but D_3 is much more effective than D_2 when tested in chicks. Vitamin D_2, from irradiated ergosterol, is considered satisfactory for human therapy, but is greatly inferior to D_3 or fish-liver oil concentrates for application to poultry husbandry. The names ergocalciferol (D_2) and cholecalciferol (D_3) are gaining acceptance.

Tocopherols (Vitamin E). — Evans (1922) observed that young rats on a restricted diet ceased to grow and lost the function of reproduction. At the time, only four essential dietary factors were recognized, A, B, C, and D; Evans demonstrated that no deficiency of any one of these substances is

involved. The new factor E was found in certain vegetables and particularly in seed-germ oils. In the ten years following 1925, active concentrates
of the factor were obtained, as measured on the basis of the cure of resorption
sterility in rats. This method of bioassay is based on the fact that a vitamin
E-deficient female rat conceives in the normal manner but pregnancy proceeds normally for only about ten days, after which the fetus is resorbed.
Administration of the factor after the next conception results in normal
birth of living young. The isolation of two pure factors from wheat-germ
oil concentrates in 1936 was simplified by the discovery of crystalline derivatives, allophanates, resulting from esterification of the factors with
cyanic acid. This reaction substantiates the presence of a hydroxyl group

$$HN{=}C{=}O \;+\; HOR \longrightarrow \left[H_2N{-}\overset{\displaystyle O}{\overset{\|}{C}}{-}OR \right]$$

Cyanic acid

$$HN{=}C{=}O \;+\; \left[H_2N{-}\overset{\displaystyle O}{\overset{\|}{C}}{-}OR \right] \longrightarrow H_2N\overset{\displaystyle O}{\overset{\|}{C}}{-}NH\overset{\displaystyle O}{\overset{\|}{C}}{-}OR$$

Allophanate

in E. On hydrolysis of the derivatives, the two pure active factors were
obtained as highly active, pale yellow oils, named α- and β-tocopherol (Gr.
tokos, childbirth, + Gr. *pherein*, to bear). The two forms were found to be
almost identical in chemical and physical properties, and the empirical
formulas indicated that α-tocopherol, $C_{29}H_{50}O_2$, differed from β-tocopherol,
$C_{28}H_{48}O_2$, only in the presence of an additional methyl group. A third
active form, γ-tocopherol, isomeric with β-tocopherol, was isolated shortly
afterward from cottonseed oil.

The correct structure of α-tocopherol was deduced by Fernholz in 1938
on the basis of thermal decomposition to durohydroquinone and of formation
of various oxidation products. The structure is that of a chroman (dihy-

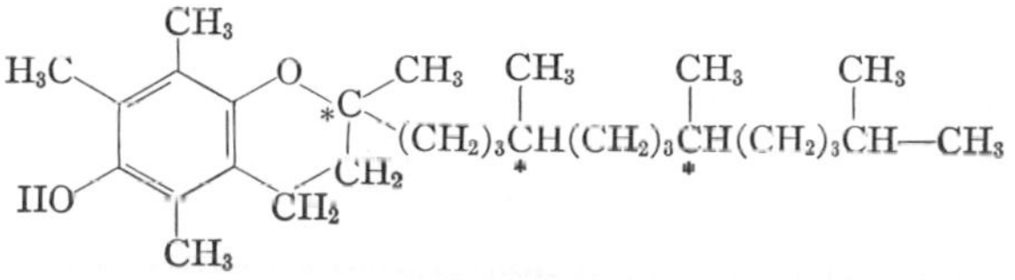

α-Tocopherol

drobenzo-γ-pyran) containing an isoprenoid side chain. *dl*-α-Tocopherol
was synthesized (Karrer, 1938) by condensation of trimethylhydroquinone
with the bromide of phytol, a natural isoprenoid alcohol of plants (p. 949).

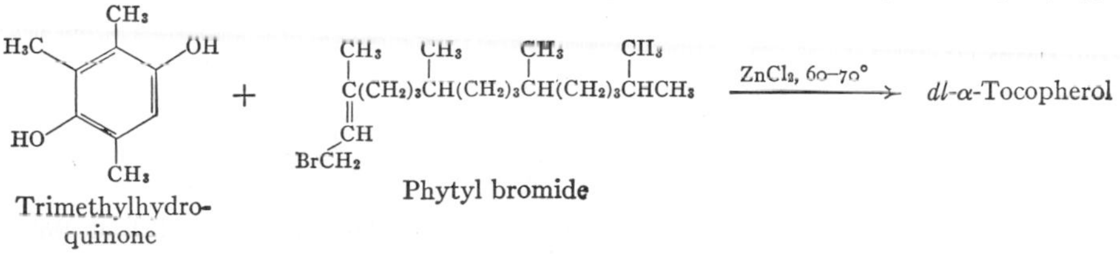

Trimethylhydro-
quinone

Phytyl bromide

$\xrightarrow{\text{ZnCl}_2,\ 60{-}70°}$ *dl*-α-Tocopherol

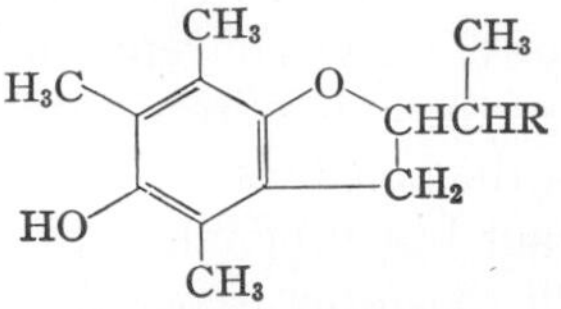

Coumaran derivative

The synthesis could also result in formation of a coumaran; however such a structure for α-tocopherol is ruled out by oxidation to a quinone, α-tocopherylquinone (inactive), by auric or ferric chloride. The hydroxyl group of the quinone is tertiary (stable to oxidation), whereas the quinone obtained from a coumaran type would have a secondary alcoholic group. The chemistry of the tocopherols has been extensively investigated by L. I. Smith.

The other known tocopherols differ only in the number and location of methyl substituents in the phenolic ring. The β- and γ-factors are 5,8- and 7,8-dimethyl derivatives; they are half as active as the α-factor. δ-To-

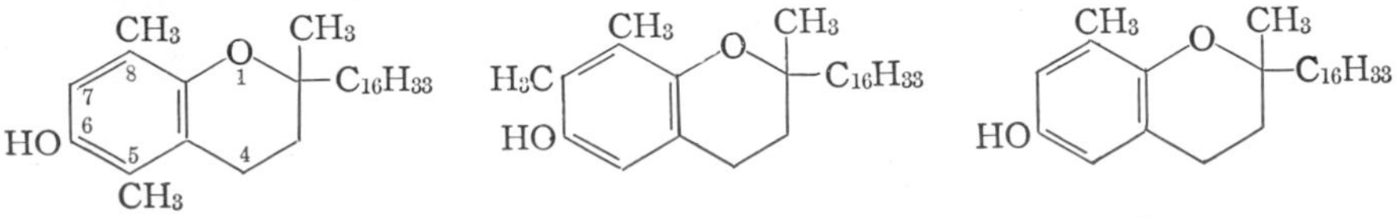

Tocopherols

copherol, the principal tocopherol of soybean oil isolated in 1947, has a lone methyl group at C_8 and is only 1/100 as active as α-tocopherol. The tocopherols are powerful antioxidants and are used to protect foods from oxidation. For therapeutic uses α-tocopherol is marketed as the acetate, since this is stable to oxidation but, in the organism, is the biological equivalent of the free phenol. The tocopherols are believed to function in the organism as antioxidants for fats.

The relation of the tocopherols to normal reproduction has been extensively investigated only in certain rodents. The factor is required by both the male and female mouse and rat. In the male, deficiency results in degeneration of the spermatozoa. E may not be required by humans, though successful deliveries have been reported after administration of E to pregnant women with previous histories of miscarriages. Effects noted in tocopherol-deficient animals, other than those involved in reproduction, include muscular dystrophy, generalized edema, and pathological changes in the central nervous system.

Vitamin K. — The existence of an antihemorrhagic factor in green plants was discovered in 1929 by Dam at Copenhagen. The substance was isolated from alfalfa by Dam and Karrer at Zurich in 1939 as a water-insoluble yellow oil characterized by a distinctive ultraviolet absorption spectrum and by the appearance of a transient purple color on treatment with alcoholic alkali. Independent isolation of the alfalfa principle was soon reported by Doisy,[8] who also isolated a second antihemorrhagic principle, vitamin K_2 (m.p. 54°), from putrefied fish meal. The lipoid substances were

---

[8] Edward A. Doisy, b. 1893 Hume, Ill.; Ph.D. Harvard; St. Louis Univ. Med. School; Nobel Prize 1943

found to be highly sensitive to light, alkali, and excessive heat, and the initial isolations were accomplished by extraction with petroleum ether followed by extensive chromatographic fractionation. The processing was guided by a procedure of bioassay based on the fact that blood of K-deficient chicks shows a prolonged clotting time (over 1 hr.) that is restored to the normal value (4–6 min.) by administration of active material (1 γ of vitamin K_1). Doisy characterized the K factors as $C_{31}O_2$- and $C_{41}O_2$-substances having closely analogous spectra and possessing properties characteristic of quinones (reversible reduction to colorless dihydro derivatives). Vitamin K_1 was shown to be 2-methyl-3-phytyl-1,4-naphthoquinone (IV) in 1939 by degradation (Doisy) and by synthesis (Fieser). The original synthesis, involving acid condensation of 2-methyl-1,4-naphthohydroquinone with phytol, precipitation of K_1-hydroquinone with petroleum ether, and oxidation with silver oxide suffered from the fact that the hydroquinone II was accompanied by an isomeric by-product III, which decreased the yield

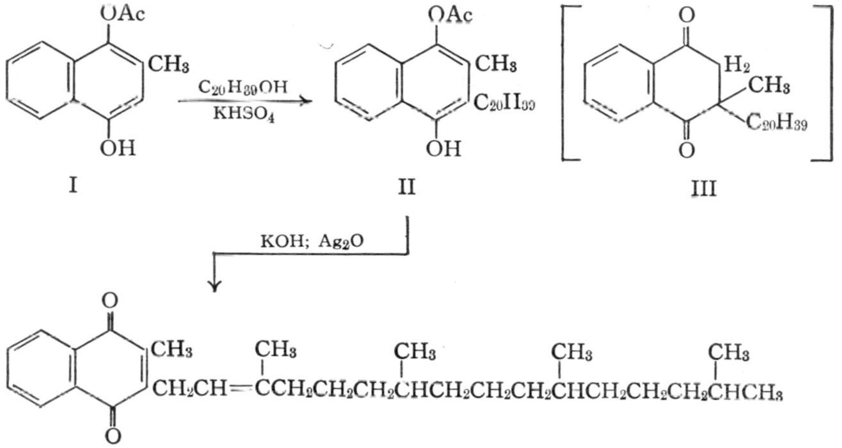

I   II   III

IV, Vitamin K_1

This fault is corrected in a modification (R. Hirschmann, 1954) utilizing the 1-acetate, I. The condensation is conducted in dioxan at 76°, unchanged I is precipitated with petroleum ether (in which II, unlike hydro-K, is soluble), and II is extracted with Claisen's alkali ($KOH-MeOH-H_2O$), which effects hydrolysis, and oxidized to K_1 (yield 65%). K_1-Hydroquinone, like II, is a cryptophenol (phenolic properties hidden). Thus K_1 is easily extracted from alfalfa concentrates by hydrosulfite reduction, removal of acids and ordinary phenols by extraction with aqueous alkali, and extraction of K_1-hydroquinone from neutral material with Claisen's alkali.

The degradative methods used by Doisy were employed also for elucidation of the structure of K_2, as illustrated in Chart 6. This substance was found to differ from the K_1 factor only in the nature of the side chain, which is a C_{30}-isoprenoid group having six double bonds, the difarnesyl group.

The structure is based mainly on characterization of degradation products obtained on ozonolysis of the hydroquinone diacetate.

CHART 6. DEGRADATION OF VITAMIN K_2

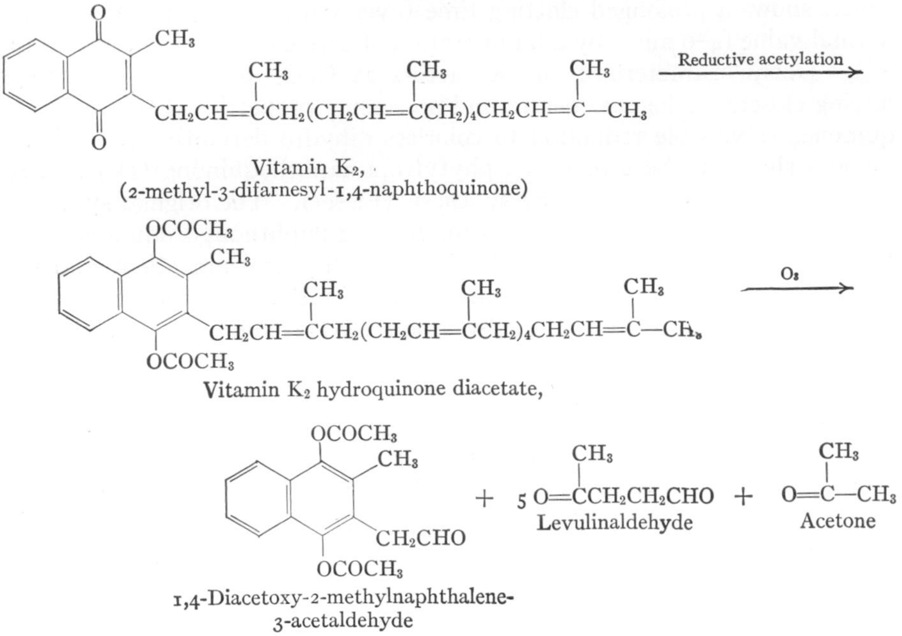

Vitamin K_2,
(2-methyl-3-difarnesyl-1,4-naphthoquinone)

Reductive acetylation →

Vitamin K_2 hydroquinone diacetate,

O_3 →

$+ \; 5 \; O=CCH_2CH_2CHO \; + \; O=C-CH_3$

Levulinaldehyde   Acetone

1,4-Diacetoxy-2-methylnaphthalene-
3-acetaldehyde

The K_2 factor, which has ten carbon atoms more in the side chain than the K_1, is slightly less potent than K_1. Among a large number of synthetic model compounds, a certain number of 3-alkyl and 3-alkenyl derivatives of 2-methyl-1,4-naphthoquinone exhibit antihemorrhagic activity, but invariably of a lower order than the natural factors. Such a slight change as the addition of two hydrogen atoms, results in a 4- to 8-fold loss; replacement of the 2-methyl group by ethyl practically deactivates the molecule. It is therefore a remarkable fact, discovered by Ansbacher and Fernholz (1939), that the simple parent substance 2-methyl-1,4-naphthoquinone (menadione) is highly potent. Indeed in the chick assay (but not necessarily in humans) the simple quinone is three times as potent as vitamin K_1 on a weight basis and about equal to the vitamin in terms of molecular equivalents. A possible explanation is that administered methylnaphthoquinone furnishes one component for biosynthesis in the organism of an active compound of the true vitamin type. A considerable amount of K-active material found by bioassay in the feces very probably arises from a synthesis by microorganisms in the intestines.

Clotting of blood is a complicated and not fully understood process that is known to involve several factors. It is considered that fibrin, the insoluble protein that constitutes the clot, is formed from a soluble proteinic precursor, fibrinogen, by the action of the enzyme thrombin. Thrombin is not present as such in blood but is formed in the presence of calcium ions from a precursor, prothrombin, when tissue cells or blood corpuscles are damaged. The prothrombin level is low in K-deficient animals; the manner in which K influences the prothrombin concentration is unknown.

Vitamin K occurs widely and the average diet supplies adequate amounts. However, absorption of the lipoid substance from the intestines is dependent on the emulsifying action of bile salts, and an impairment in the flow of bile into the intestines is attended with K deficiency and a consequent bleeding tendency. Thus a condition of hypoprothrombinemia, or prothrombin deficiency, usually is encountered in obstructive jaundice and ulcerative colitis. Operation for the relief of the biliary obstruction may be attended with dangerous bleeding unless, prior to operation, the prothrombin level is restored to normal, and the blood clotting time thereby reduced, by therapy with synthetic vitamin K_1 or with the substitute compound methylnaphthoquinone. In cases of complete biliary obstruction or fistula, oral therapy with these lipid quinones necessitates administration of bile salts and is rendered uncertain and sometimes impossible by nausea and vomiting. An alternative is intravenous injection of an aqueous solution of a phosphate or sulfate ester of vitamin K_1 hydroquinone or methylnaphthohydroquinone. Oral therapy is adequate in the treatment of the hemorrhagic disease of the newborn. Infants in the first few days after birth do not derive vitamin K from milk or through the synthetic activity of intestinal bacteria and may be subject to a dangerously low prothrombin level. It is therefore considered desirable to administer the factor routinely either to the mother during the last few days of pregnancy or to the infant. Bleeding diseases not associated with the prothrombin content of the blood, such as congenital hemophilia, do not respond to K therapy.

One therapeutic use of vitamin K is connected with the administration of a hemorrhagic principle dicoumarol, 3,3'-methylenebis-(4-hydroxycoumarin), first isolated from spoiled sweet clover hay and responsible for the hemorrhagic sweet clover disease of bovine, characterized by hypoprothrombinemia (Link, 1941). The action of dicoumarol on blood pro-

Dicoumarol

thrombin is therefore opposite to that of vitamin K_1. Dicoumarol is now employed as an anticoagulant in diseases where there is a tendency to thrombosis, but since there is no satisfactory method for controlling the dosage, a dangerously low prothrombin level may be induced. The resulting hypoprothrombinemia can be corrected by administration of the innocuous vitamin K_1 in massive doses; the more toxic methylnaphthoquinone is unsatisfactory.

READING REFERENCES

E. A. Evans, Jr., "The Biological Action of the Vitamins," University of Chicago Press, Chicago (1942)

H. R. Rosenberg, "Chemistry and Physiology of the Vitamins," Interscience, New York (1942)

L. I. Smith, "The Chemistry of Vitamin E," *Chem. Rev.*, **27**, 287–329 (1940)

R. R. Williams and T. D. Spies, "Vitamin B₁ and Its Use in Medicine," Macmillan, New York (1938)

W. H. Sebrell, Jr. and R. S. Harris, "The Vitamins," Academic Press, New York (1954)

CHEMOTHERAPY

Chemotherapy may be defined as the selective destruction of pathogenic organisms within a host by chemical agents. This definition excludes disinfectants, which act externally, and the many drugs having physiological effects on various organs in the body. From earliest times countless natural substances have been tested for ability to cure infectious diseases, but at the beginning of the present century only three specific remedies were known: mercury for syphilis (introduced about 1500), cinchona bark for malaria, and ipecacuanha for dysentery (both introduced into Europe in the seventeenth century).

Although Pasteur suspected that contagious diseases and putrefaction, like fermentation, are due to microorganisms, this important fact was first established by Robert Koch, who succeeded in isolating the microscopic rods (*Bacillus anthracis*) present in blood of cattle afflicted with anthrax (splenic fever), in growing them in a synthetic medium, and in showing that they produce the disease when inoculated into healthy animals (1876). Shortly afterward (1881) Pasteur discovered that animals acquire immunity against anthrax after subcutaneous injection of attenuated (weakened) bacilli. A somewhat similar prophylactic inoculation had been demonstrated eighty-four years earlier by Jenner, who protected a child against smallpox infection by vaccination with lymph from a cowpox or vaccinia lesion (L. *vacca*, cow). In 1890 von Behring found that diphtheria can be cured by serum prepared by injecting bacteria or bacterial products into a healthy animal and, after the induced disease has abated, collecting serum from the immunized animal. Serum treatment and vaccination are forms of biotherapy, and these early striking successes encouraged the hope that all contagious diseases could be combated in this way. Disappointing results, however, were obtained shortly (1891) in attempted biotherapy of tuberculosis. At the present time it appears that immunization with vaccines is successful only in diseases in which, in case of recovery, an attack is followed naturally by more or less lasting immunity. Prophylactic vaccination (active immunization) has been shown to be highly effective in human therapy only against smallpox, typhoid fever, scarlet fever, pertussis, tetanus, paratyphoid fever, rabies, and diphtheria. Serum therapy (passive immunization) is of established value for only a few diseases of man: diphtheria, erysipelas, scarlet fever, bacillary dysentery, and snake bite. Since approximately two hundred and fifty microorganisms are known to produce diseases in man, biotherapy has found limited use.

Organic Arsenicals. — Paul Ehrlich[1] devoted the major part of his scientific career to the principle that a molecule can be constructed which can act as a specific agent against a parasite without untoward injury to the host.   As a medical student, he was particularly impressed with the ability of dyes to stain tissue selectively, which he assumed to be the result of a chemical reaction.   His thesis for the doctorate was entitled "Contributions to the Theory and Practice of Histological Staining."   Ehrlich thought that it might be possible to find a dye with selective affinity for a parasitic organism and to render the dye lethal to the microorganism by incorporating some active grouping that alone could not be affixed to the parasite.   An early promising lead was the observation that Methylene Blue (p. 884) selectively stains certain parasites in preference to tissue of the host.   From later experiments with a dye that was named Trypan Red (I) because it showed some activity against trypanosomes in infected mice, Ehrlich conceived the idea that the curative property of the dye is invested in the azo grouping.   He then initiated investigations of comparable substances containing arsenic, the periodic neighbor of nitrogen.   A relatively simple

Trypan Red (I)

arsenic compound, atoxyl, had already been shown to have some trypanosomicidal activity.   The name is based on the early view that the substance is relatively nontoxic.   Ehrlich established the correct structure (II) and confirmed previous observations of activity, but found that the compound is too toxic for practical use, even when modified in the form of derivatives.   During these investigations, an experimental method became available for testing spirochetal activity when the

Atoxyl (II)

rabbit was found to develop a mild form of syphilis when infected intratesticularly with *Treponema pallidum*, the protozoan shown in 1905 to be responsible for syphilis in man.   Following the lead that trivalent arsenic compounds are more active than pentavalent ones, Ehrlich in 1909 found that 3,3'-diamino-4,4'-dihydroxyarsenobenzene (III) effectively cured rabbit syphilis at a dosage level lower than the maximum tolerated dose. The drug was patented in Germany as Salvarsan, reflecting the high hopes placed upon its curative powers.   When the patent was taken over in the United Sates during World War I, the name was changed to arsphenamine.

Although the drug is not entirely specific for the pathogenic organism, Ehrlich's discovery represents a triumph in the field of chemotherapy,

[1] Paul Ehrlich, 1854–1915; b. Strehlen, Germany; M.D. Leipzig; Frankfurt; Nobel Prize 1908

particularly so because it was the result of planned research. Actually no chemotherapeutic agent is known even today that does not have some toxic

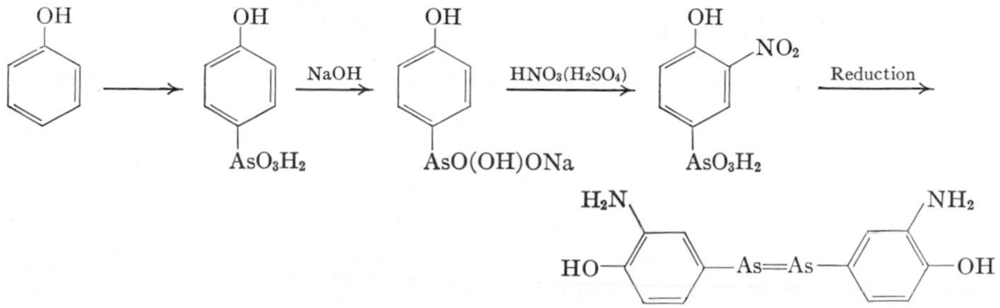

Arsphenamine (III)

effect on the host as well, but this toxicity is not surprising since parasites inevitably possess some protoplasmic characteristics in common with higher forms of animals. Fortunately, toxicity and therapeutic activity are not necessarily changed to the same extent by modifications in the structure. Low toxicity is obviously desirable, but is not the sole criterion since it may be accompanied by low parasiticidal activity. The margin of safety is usually expressed as the chemotherapeutic index, which is the ratio of the maximum tolerated dose to the minimum curative dose, both expressed in milligrams per kilogram of body weight. Before clinical use a new drug must be tested extensively for toxicity in small animals. Toxicity unfortunately varies widely for different animals in an unpredictable manner. Chemotherapy is handicapped in another respect: many parasites develop an increased resistance to a chemical, known as drug fastness. Ehrlich observed this phenomenon early in his work, and suggested that the solution lay in administering a few large doses of a drug (*"therapia sterilisans magna"*). In clinical practice this solution has not been successful and in the early days of arsphenamine therapy resulted in considerable harm, since patients were dismissed as cured after a few treatments.

Arsphenamine is unstable in the free form and is marketed as the stable dihydrochloride, which cannot be used directly but must be converted into the mono- or disodium salt within thirty minutes before intravenous injection. Ehrlich later prepared (1912) a stable soluble derivative, neoarsphenamine (IV), which can be used as such. Although a tremendous number of aromatic arsenicals have been tested for spirochetal activity,

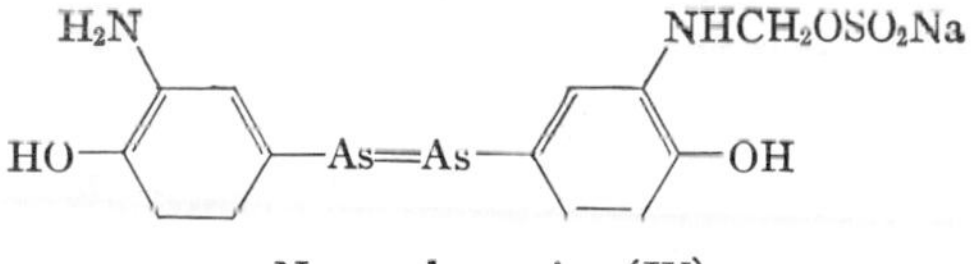

Neoarsphenamine (IV)

arsphenamine and neoarsphenamine are still used for treatment of syphilis, often in conjunction with bismuth compounds, which have largely replaced mercury. Tryparsamide (V), a derivative of atoxyl, has proved of value in neurosyphilis and in African sleeping sickness (trypanosomiasis), and the

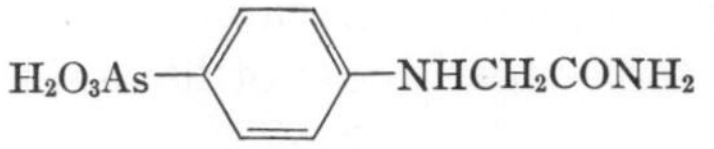

$$H_2O_3As\text{—}\langle\bigcirc\rangle\text{—}NHCH_2CONH_2 \qquad H_2O_3As\text{—}\langle\bigcirc\rangle\text{—}NHCONH_2$$

Tryparsamide (V) 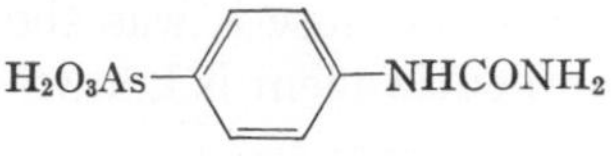   Carbarsone (VI)

closely related compound, carbarsone (VI), is a useful amebicide. Penta-valent arsenicals are usually more active than trivalent arsenicals against more highly developed protozoan organisms.

Germanin. — In 1920 the German Bayer company introduced Germanin or Bayer 205, a potent drug against African sleeping sickness (*Trypanosoma gambiense* and *T. rhodesiense*) with the very high therapeutic index in animals of 100. Within four years Fourneau[2] at the Pasteur Institute deduced the formula, which was not disclosed by the Germans, by examining a large number of substances of the type indicated by German patents.

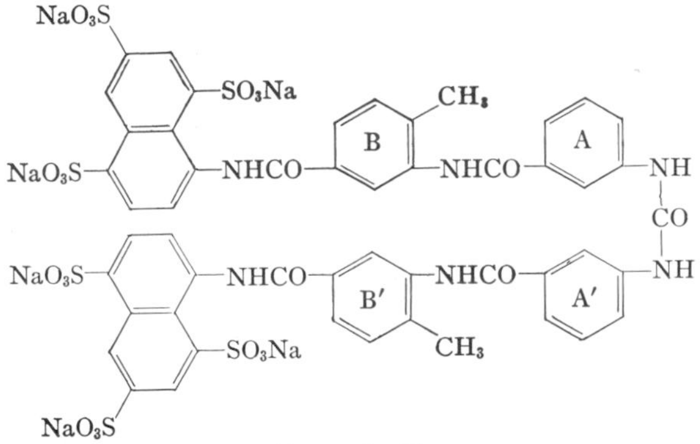

Germanin (I)

Fourneau 309 (I) is regarded as identical with Bayer 205. Germanin is a valuable drug for the early stages of trypanosomiasis, but is not preferable to tryparsamide. An interesting feature of Germanin is that it represents a departure from the arsenical drugs, whose therapeutic activity is undoubt-edly due to the presence of a specifically poisonous metal, though the drug obviously stems from Ehrlich's early Trypan Red clue. In addition the structure is remarkably specific, for the slightest deviation from the parent substance greatly lessens activity. When the methyl groups are shifted from rings B and B' to the corresponding position in rings A and A', only one sixtieth of the activity is retained and the toxicity is doubled.

Amebicidal Drugs. — Amebiasis (amebic enteritis and amebic dysen-tery) is a disease that results from invasion of the intestinal mucosa by a protozoan parasite (*Endameba histolytica*). It is transmitted by a cyst form of the parasite that gives rise to the motile form (trophozoite) in the large intestine. A human in apparent good health can harbor the cysts and hence serve as a potential source of infection. The curative effect of ipecac or ipecacuanha (Tupi, *ipe-caa-goéne*, small roadside emetic plant), an extract

---

[2] Ernest Fourneau, 1872–1949; b. Biarritz, France; Pasteur Inst., Paris; *J. Chem. Soc.*, 261 (1952)

from roots of a semitropical plant, is due to one of the alkaloids present, emetine (Gr. *emetikos*, vomit).   Since emetine (formula, p. 845) has accumulative toxic effects and has value only in acute amebiasis, considerable interest has been attached to suitable synthetic drugs.   Three of these are particularly active against the cyst form and have replaced emetine for treatment of asymptomatic carriers and of chronic amebiasis.   Two of these, chiniofon (I) and vioform (II), are quinoline compounds that owe their therapeutic value to the iodine content.   The other important amebicide is an arsenical prepared by Ehrlich, carbarsone.

SO_3Na Cl

I OH N I OH N

Chiniofon (I)   Vioform (II)

Antimalarials. — Human malaria is caused by four species of the protozoan *Plasmodium*, which are transmitted by females of the *Anopheles* mosquito (definitive host) to man (intermediary host), and back again.   The parasites transmitted from the salivary gland of the mosquito are sporozoites; they undergo transformation in the human body and appear in red blood cells as trophozoites, which develop to schizonts.   The regular bouts of chills and fever occur in an asexual cycle in which the schizonts divide into merozoites, a few of which develop into sexual forms, gametocytes, which, in a mosquito that acquires infected blood, undergo a cycle of sexual reproduction and produce sporozoites.   No test animal is known that can be infected with the *Plasmodia* responsible for human malaria, but compounds can be screened for antimalarial activity by assays in certain animals infected with other species, particularly *P. lophurae* (duck), *P. gallinaceum* (chicken), *P. knowlesi* and *P. cynomolgi* (monkey).   A particularly prevalent form of malaria in man caused by the species *P. vivax*, benign tertian or vivax malaria, is not fatal but involves regular relapses of fever that may continue for years.   Between relapses the blood is completely free of trophozoites, and yet a tissue form of parasite appears to persist and lead to eventual relapse; in *P. gallinaceum* infection in the chicken a tissue form (exoerythrocytic) is easily demonstrated.   In malarial therapy of paretics, the infection is transmitted by injection of blood, and termination of fever is not followed by relapse, evidently because the tissue form is absent. The ideal drug for vivax malaria would be capable of destroying sporozoites (prophylaxis), trophozoites (suppression), and tissue parasites (cure).   Falciparum, or malignant tertian, malaria is deadly but less prevalent, and it presents an easier problem in chemotherapy.

Bark of the cinchona tree contains more than twenty-five alkaloids, of which two predominate: quinine, $C_{20}H_{24}N_2O_2$ (I), and its desmethoxy derivative, cinchonine, $C_{19}H_{22}N_2O$, both isolated by Pelletier and Caventou in 1820.   Use of the bark in treatment of fever was introduced into Europe

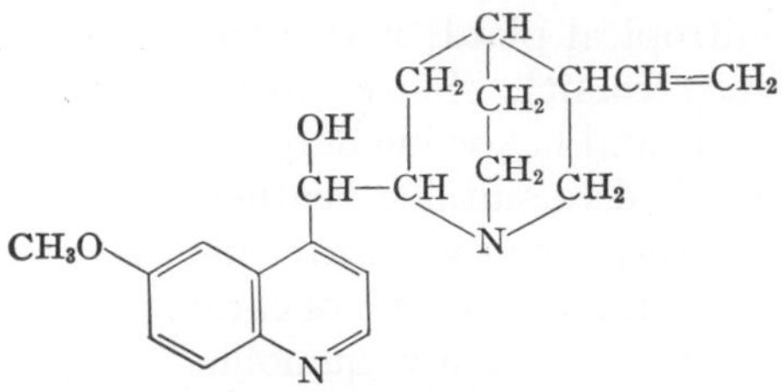

Quinine (I)

in 1639, shortly after the material had been employed successfully in treating the Countess de Chinchón, the wife of the Spanish Viceroy to Peru. The main source of quinine in recent times has been plantations in the Dutch East Indies, and a shortage of quinine during World War I led to an active interest, particularly in Germany, in a substitute. A further impetus to research was the fact that quinine, though curative to falciparum malaria, suppresses but fails to cure, or provide prophylaxis against, vivax malaria. Quinine administered to a chicken infected with *P. gallinaceum* destroys the trophozoites but allows the exoerythrocytic parasites to increase and eventually cause death. There is no reason to suppose that a particular product of plant biosynthesis is ideally suited to use in therapy of a given disease of man. When assay methods in avian infections were developed, antiplasmodial activity was found not to be specific to the quinine structure. Thus cinchonine is one-fifth as active as quinine; dihydroquinine is twice as active as the natural alkaloid.

Schulemann of the I. G. Farbenindustrie reported in 1926 the striking antimalarial activity of the synthetic substance plasmochin (II), which is about sixty times as effective as quinine in avian malaria. Plasmochin (also known as pamaquin) suffers from high toxicity. It exerts more of a curative than suppressive effect, and in combination with quinine appeared for a time to offer some promise; but the therapeutic dose is too close to the toxic dose for practicable use. The I. G. Farbenindustrie (Mauss and

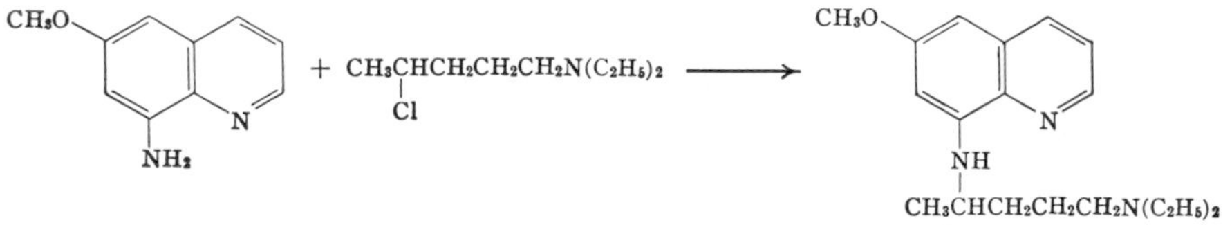

Plasmochin (II)

Mietzsch) announced development of another antimalarial, atabrine (mepacrine) in 1930. The structure was disclosed in 1933, a few months after a Russian group announced the synthesis of an antimalarial claimed to be identical with atabrine. Atabrine (V) has the same side chain as plasmochin, incorporated in this case into an acridine rather than a quinoline nucleus. The complete synthesis involves the steps formulated.

$$CH_3COCH_2COOC_2H_5 + ClCH_2CH_2N(C_2H_5)_2 \cdot HCl \longrightarrow CH_3COCHCH_2CH_2N(C_2H_5)_2 \longrightarrow$$
$$\underset{COOC_2H_5}{|}$$

$$CH_3COCH_2CH_2CH_2N(C_2H_5)_2 \xrightarrow[\text{(Raney Ni)}]{NH_3,\ H_2} CH_3CHCH_2CH_2CH_2N(C_2H_5)_2$$
$$\underset{NH_2}{|}$$
$$III$$

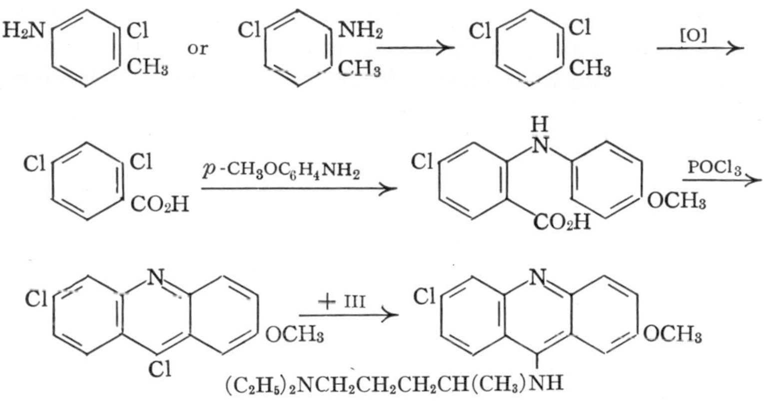

IV   Atabrine (V)

Atabrine had made little headway in competition with the established natural drug quinine at the time of the Japanese attack on Pearl Harbor. The East Indies quinine plantations soon fell to the Japanese and the United States was faced with the prospect of conducting combat in malaria-indigenous regions without adequate means of coping with the disease. The Committee on Medical Research promptly organized an extensive program of antimalarial research for evaluation of all existing candidate drugs and discovery of better drugs. Extensive clinical studies showed, unexpectedly, that atabrine can be used with safety and is actually a somewhat better suppressive drug than quinine. Thus this easily synthesized drug was adopted for use by the U. S. Armed Forces and gave excellent service, particularly in the vivax-infected Pacific theater. The drug must be taken on a steady regime, it produces an objectionable yellow pigmentation of the skin, and exposed individuals on discontinuation of drug are often subject to long-continuing relapses, but atabrine nevertheless adequately replaced the inaccessible natural drug. Practical therapy thus was not influenced by the achievement of Woodward and Doering (1944) in effecting total synthesis of quinine.

Wartime research in England resulted in the discovery of paludrine, a biguanidine derivative prepared by condensation of p-chlorophenyldicyano-

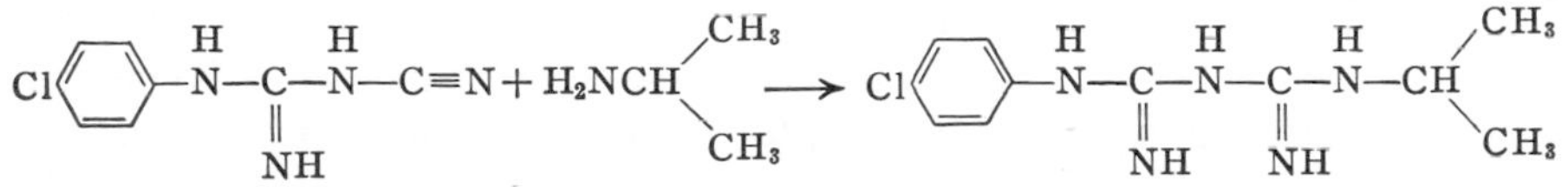

Paludrine

diamide with isopropylamine.   Paludrine has the advantage over atabrine of being effective at a lower dosage; it is less toxic and does not color the skin.   Like quinine and atabrine, it is a suppressive for vivax malaria but is not curative.

Of some 14,000 substances screened in the American wartime program, one of the most promising is pentaquine, a close relative of plasmochin.   It is prepared in 70% yield by condensation of 6-methoxy-8-aminoquinoline with 5-chloro-N-isopropylamylamine.   Pentaquine is less toxic than plasmochin.   Administered with quinine, it effects a drop in the relapse rate of

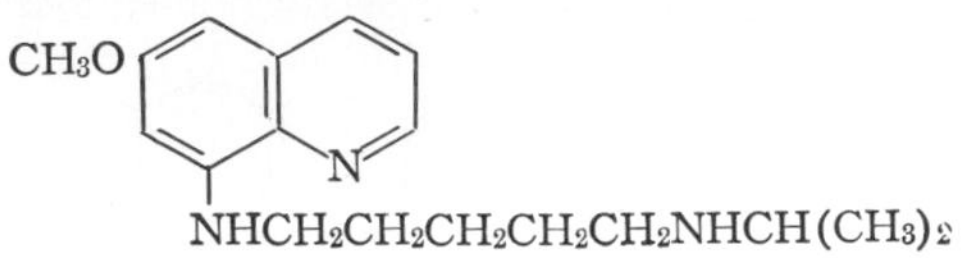

CH_3O

NHCH$_2$CH$_2$CH$_2$CH$_2$CH$_2$NHCH(CH$_3$)$_2$

Pentaquine

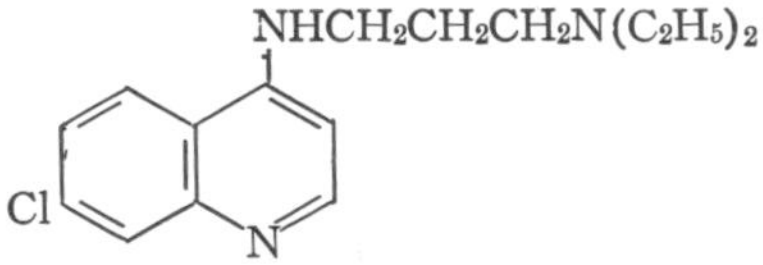

NHCH$_2$CH$_2$CH$_2$N(C$_2$H$_5$)$_2$

Cl

Chloroquine

recurring vivax infection.   Chloroquine, a related quinoline derivative, is also an effective suppressive agent and it is useful in terminating acute attacks of vivax malaria.   In addition it is a useful amebicidal drug.

Sulfonamides. — Considerable progress had been made before 1930 in development of external bactericides, but practically all bactericides that could be administered internally with safety lost activity in the presence of blood serum.   A few drugs, including the two acridine derivatives trypaflavine (I) and flavicide (II), had found limited use as systemic bactericides, but on the whole chemotherapy had shown its worth only against diseases

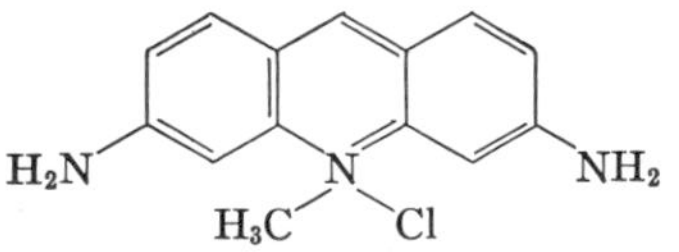

H$_2$N   NH$_2$
            H$_3$C   Cl
        Trypaflavine (I)

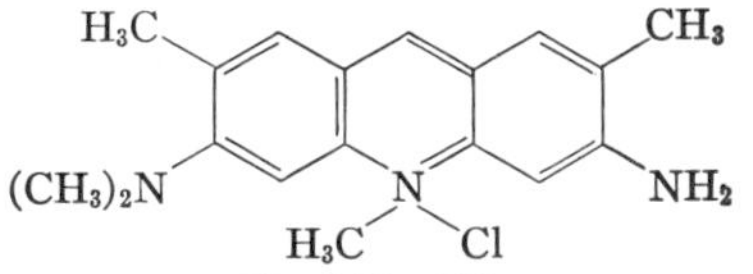

H$_3$C   CH$_3$
(CH$_3$)$_2$N   NH$_2$
            H$_3$C   Cl
        Flavicide (II)

caused by protozoa.   In 1933 a German physician successfully cured a child with staphylococcal septicemia (infection of the blood) by injection of a new drug "streptozon," which had been patented the previous year by the I. G. Fabenindustrie as Prontosil.   The report passed almost unnoticed till 1934, when G. Domagk announced the remarkable effectiveness of Prontosil in curing experimental streptococcal and staphylococcal infections in test animals.   This discovery was honored in 1939 by the award of the Nobel Prize in Medicine.   Prontosil is an azo dye containing a sulfonamido substituent (III).   It was originally prepared in the course of investigation of dyes, but was tested for chemotherapeutic activity when particular affinity was noted for protein fiber.   In 1935 Tréfouëls (Pasteur Institute)

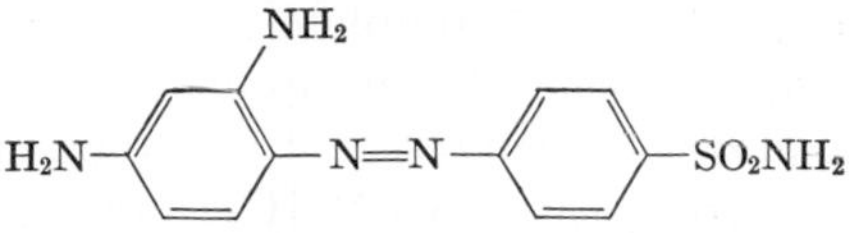

4-Sulfonamido-2',4'-diaminoazobenzene (III)

found that Prontosil breaks down in the tissues to *p*-aminobenzenesulfonamide, now commonly called sulfanilamide (V), and Fourneau in the same year showed that the split product is as effective as Prontosil in cure of infections.   This result explains the earlier German observations that Prontosil is inactive in experiments *in vitro*.   Since sulfanilamide had been

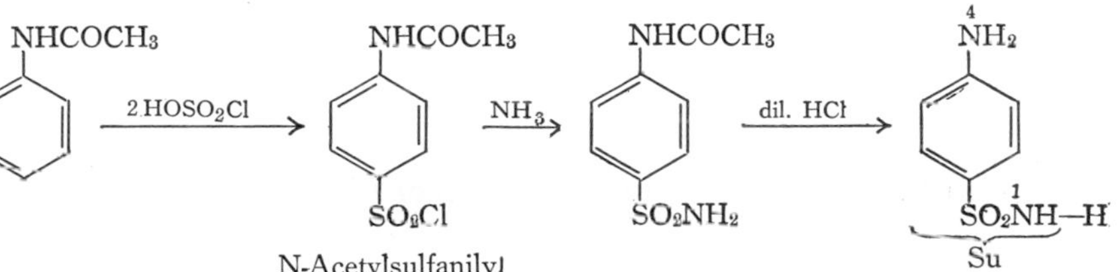

N-Acetylsulfanilyl chloride (IV)

Sulfanilamide (V)

made by Glemo in 1908, the manufacture could not be protected by patents, which probably contributed to the rapid development and use of the new drug.   In the five years following Fourneau's discovery, more than one thousand sulfa compounds were synthesized, but only a few showed outstanding promise.   Six of these contain the structural unit designated Su in formula (V) for sulfanilamide and are represented with abbreviated formulas.   These (VI–XI) and the further active compounds XII–XIV,

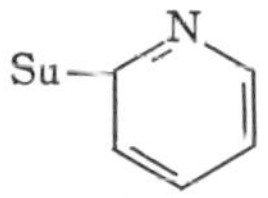

VI. Sulfa-pyridine

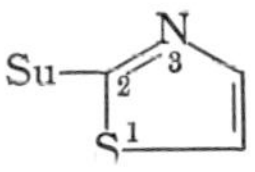

VII. Sulfa-thiazole

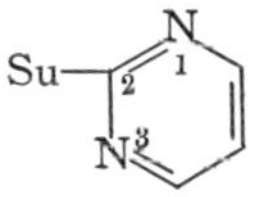

VIII. Sulfa-diazine

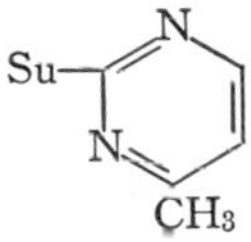

IX. Sulfa-merazine

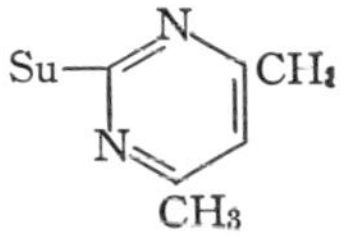

X. Sulfa-methazine

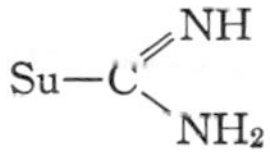

XI. Sulfa-guanidine

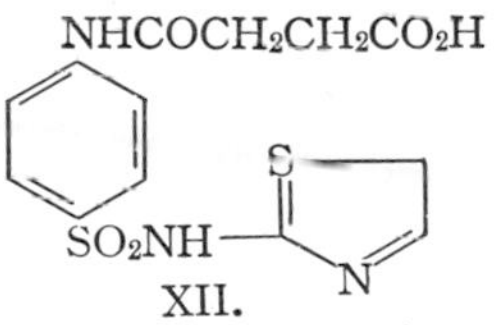

XII. Succinoylsulfathiazole

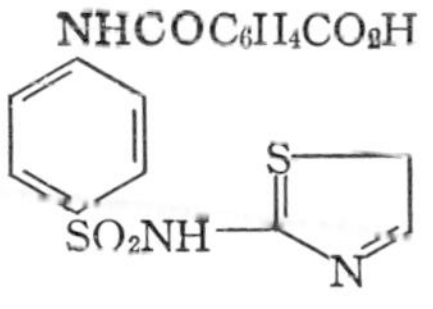

XIII Phthalysulfathiazole

Su—COCH$_3$

XIV. Sulfacetamide

all contain substituent groups on the amide nitrogen, designated N^1. If the amino nitrogen (N^4) is substituted by a group that cannot be removed in the body, activity is entirely lost. All nuclear substitution products of sulfanilamide tested to date are completely inactive; thus the structure exhibits remarkable specificity. The grouping —$SO_2NHCR{=}N$— is present in eight of the nine particularly active compounds and the ninth (XIV) has the related grouping —$SO_2NHCR{=}O$. These derivatives are made by condensation of N-acetylsulfanilyl chloride (IV) with the appropriate amine, followed by hydrolysis of the acetyl group. 2-Aminopyridine (XV), used for making sulfapyridine, is produced in 70–80% yield by the Chichibabin reaction (1914), in which pyridine is treated with sodamide in dimethylaniline at 90–115°. 2-Aminothiazole (XVI) is made by

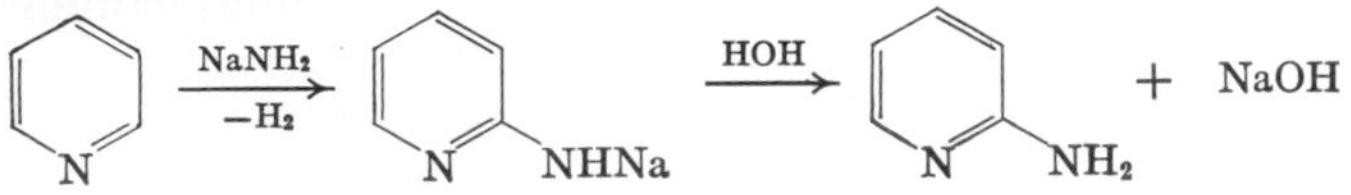

XV

treating thiourea with α,β-dichloroethyl ether (Traumann, 1888). 2-Ami-

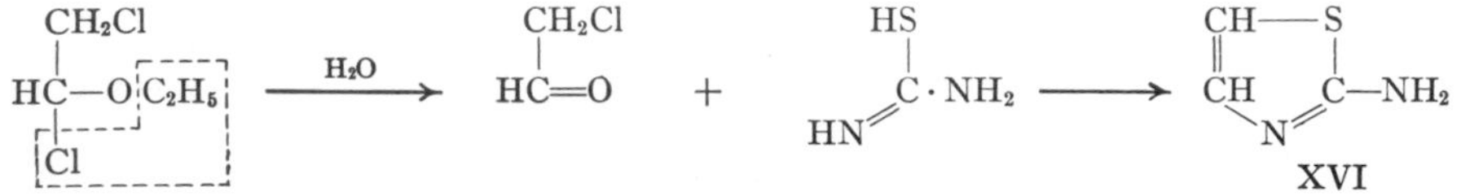

XVI

nopyrimidine (aminodiazine, XVII) is prepared by condensation of guanidine and formylacetic acid (made from malic acid). 2-Amino-4-methyl-

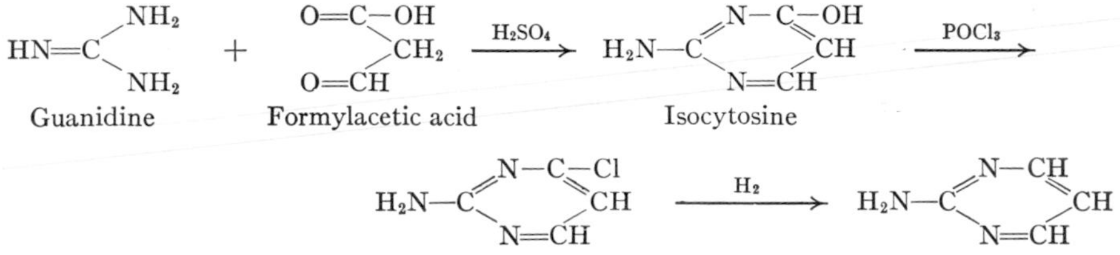

Guanidine   Formylacetic acid   Isocytosine

XVII

pyrimidine (XVIII), used in the preparation of sulfamerazine, is made by the reaction of the sodio derivative of formylacetone (product of condensation of acetone with ethyl formate) with guanidine. The 4,6-dimethyl

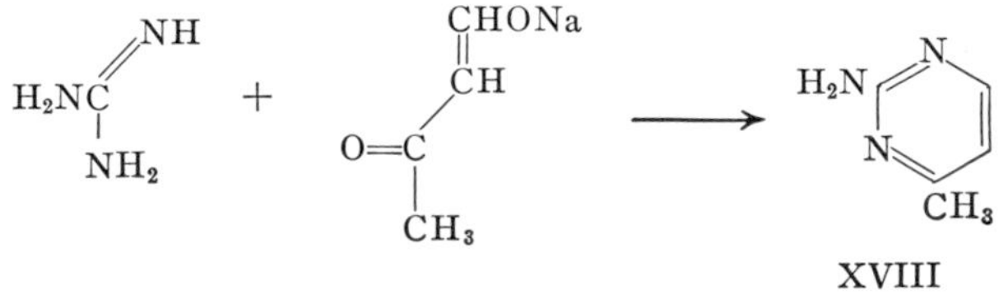

XVIII

derivative can be prepared similarly by condensation of guanidine with acetylacetone (sodium). Sulfaguanidine is prepared by condensation of guanidine with N-acetylsulfanilyl chloride or by addition of ammonia to the corresponding cyanamide derivative (XIX). N⁴-Succinoylsulfathiazole

$$\text{AcHN}-\langle\!\!\!\bigcirc\!\!\!\rangle-\text{SO}_2\text{Cl} + \text{Ca}=\text{NC}\equiv\text{N} \xrightarrow[\text{2. Hydrolysis}]{\text{1. Condensation}} \text{H}_2\text{N}-\langle\!\!\!\bigcirc\!\!\!\rangle-\text{SO}_2\text{NHC}\equiv\text{N}$$

XIX

$$\xrightarrow{\text{NH}_3} \text{H}_2\text{N}-\langle\!\!\!\bigcirc\!\!\!\rangle-\text{SO}_2\text{NHC}\!\!<\!\!^{\text{NH}}_{\text{NH}_2}$$

XI

(sulfasuxidine, XII) can be prepared by refluxing sulfathiazole and succinic anhydride in absolute ethyl alcohol:

$$\begin{array}{c}\text{CH}_2\text{CO}\\|\qquad\quad\rangle\text{O}\\\text{CH}_2\text{CO}\end{array} + \text{NH}_2\text{C}_6\text{H}_4\text{SO}_2\text{NH}\!\!\begin{array}{c}\text{N}\\\diagdown\\\text{S}\end{array} \xrightarrow{77\%} \text{HOOCCH}_2\text{CH}_2\text{CONHC}_6\text{H}_4\text{SO}_2\text{NH}\!\!\begin{array}{c}\text{N}\\\diagdown\\\text{S}\end{array}$$

XII

The sulfanilamide derivatives can also be prepared by condensation of the appropriate amine with p-nitrobenzenesulfonyl chloride followed by reduction of the nitro group to an amino group. The condensation is usually rapid and smooth, and the troublesome hydrolysis of the acetyl group is avoided. p-Nitrobenzenesulfonyl chloride is not readily available, however, and is probably not used in the large-scale production of sulfa drugs. It is made by oxidation of 4,4'-dinitrodiphenyl disulfide, prepared by route (1) or (2); conversion of the disulfide into the sulfonyl chloride (1) can be effected in one step with concentrated nitric and hydrochloric acids (1948–49).

1. $\text{Cl-C}_6\text{H}_4\text{-NO}_2 \xrightarrow[75\%]{\text{Na}_2\text{S}_2} (\text{S-C}_6\text{H}_4\text{-NO}_2)_2 \xrightarrow[90\text{-}95\%]{\text{Oxid.}} \text{HO}_3\text{S-C}_6\text{H}_4\text{-NO}_2 \xrightarrow[90\%]{\substack{\text{1. KOH}\\\text{2. PCl}_5}} \text{ClO}_2\text{S-C}_6\text{H}_4\text{-NO}_2$

2. $\text{H}_2\text{N-C}_6\text{H}_4\text{-NO}_2 \xrightarrow{\text{Diazotize}} \text{ClN}_2\text{-C}_6\text{H}_4\text{-NO}_2 \xrightarrow{\text{KSCSOC}_2\text{H}_5} \text{C}_2\text{H}_5\text{OCSSN}_2\text{-C}_6\text{H}_4\text{-NO}_2 \xrightarrow{\text{KOH}} (\text{S-C}_6\text{H}_4\text{-NO}_2)_2$

Substitution in the sulfonamide group (N¹) modifies the antibacterial activity but has little effect on the specificity toward organisms. The heterocyclic sulfa drugs have found the widest clinical use. Sulfapyridine was introduced in 1938 but was soon replaced by sulfathiazole (1940) and sulfadiazine (1941). Sulfadiazine is more readily absorbed than the other two heterocyclic derivatives and hence can be given at lower dosage levels, with the advantage that undesirable toxic effects are reduced. The mono-methyl and dimethyl derivatives of sulfadiazine have been in use since 1943 and are apparently less toxic. Sulfaguanidine was introduced in 1940 for treatment of intestinal infections, since it is not absorbed readily from the gastrointestinal tract. Succinoylsulfathiazole (1942) and phthalylsulfathiazole (1942) are now the drugs of choice for this purpose. These substituted amides of dicarboxylic acids presumably are slowly hydrolyzed to sulfathiazole, the active agent. Sulfacetamide is used primarily for chemotherapy of urinary tract infections (1941).

At one time the sulfonamides were the preferred drugs for many bacterial diseases. Although in many cases newer drugs have been found more effective, sulfonamides are still widely used, particularly in chemotherapy of meningitis, chancroid, lobar pneumonia, cholera, and certain virus diseases (trachoma, psittacosis).

Most of the sulfa drugs that are active, with the exception of Prontosil noted above, are active *in vitro* as well as *in vivo*.* The drugs are bacteriostatic (growth inhibiting) at low concentrations, but are bactericidal at higher levels. In 1940 Woods and Fildes observed that *p*-aminobenzoic acid inhibits the effect of sulfanilamide *in vitro*. They suggested as a likely interpretation of the inhibition that *p*-aminobenzoic acid is essential for an enzyme system in bacteria, and that the structurally related sulfa drug when administered in large amounts is accepted in place of *p*-aminobenzoic acid but cannot perform a comparable function. This suggestive hypothesis has been strengthened by the observation that *p*-aminobenzoic acid is a growth factor for several bacteria, and that it is a component of the pteroic acid group of growth factors. Analogous competitions between essential factors and related substances have since been noted frequently. Thus nicotinamide is inhibited by pyridine-3-sulfonic acid and thiamine by pyrithiamine, the pyridine analog of thiamine. Organisms that do not require

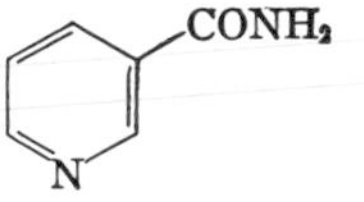

Nicotinamide 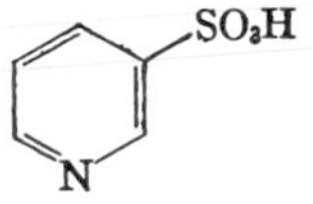   Pyridine-3-sulfonic acid

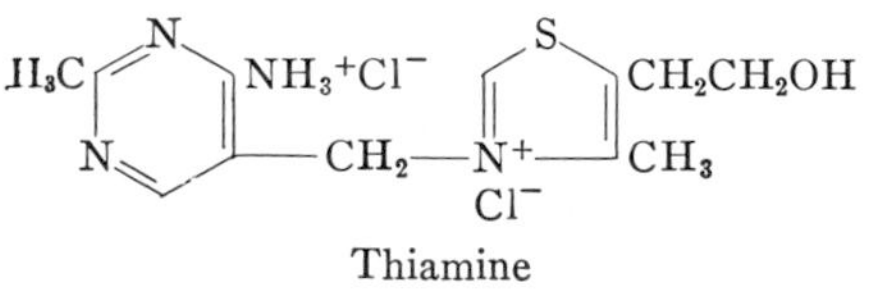

Thiamine 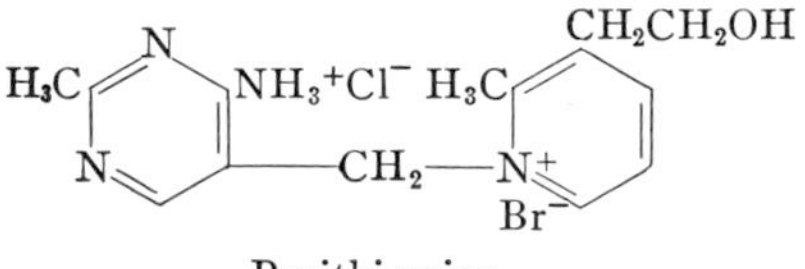   Pyrithiamine

pteroylglutamic acid are not sensitive to sulfonamides. These results suggest a new approach to chemotherapeutic research, namely, the synthesis of compounds that are related in structure to an essential metabolite of a pathogenic organism closely enough to permit competition with an enzyme

* 4-Sulfanilamidodiazine, isomeric with sulfadiazine (2-sulfanilamidodiazine, VIII) is as active as sulfadiazine *in vitro*, but completely inactive *in vivo*. This same difference has been noted with several other sulfa drugs.

system. Of course, the success of such an agent de-
pends upon ability of the more robust host organism H_2NCH_2 ⟨☐⟩ SO_2NH_2
to survive the deficiency.

Marfanil

A homolog of sulfanilamide known as marfanil
(benzylamino-p-sulfonamide) is effective in treatment of gas gangrene. Its
mode of action is apparently different from that of the sulfa drugs, for it
is not inhibited by p-aminobenzoic acid. Moreover bacteria that have
developed resistance to the sulfonamides are still susceptible to marfanil.

Antibacterials of Microbial Origin. — It has often been noted that in
mixed cultures of microorganisms one type may be suppressed by another.
One example was reported in 1929, when it was found that a certain strain
of the mold *Penicillium notatum* Westling produces the bacteriostatic agent
penicillin (Fleming). The observation passed almost unnoticed. About
ten years later Florey and Chain at Oxford began investigation of the antibiotic agent and succeeded in obtaining crude preparations which had remarkably high activity against many Gram-positive organisms. The first
clinical results (1941) were highly successful. One advantage of penicillin
over previous chemotherapeutic agents is its remarkably low toxicity; disadvantages are that it loses much of its activity when given orally and that
it is excreted rapidly. It is active only against Gram-positive organisms
(including staphylococci, streptococci, pneumococci, meningococci, gono-
cocci) and against spirochetes; certain strains are less sensitive than others.
Moreover organisms sometimes develop fastness to penicillin. Although
it has a broad chemotherapeutic spectrum, penicillin is relatively ineffective against Gram-negative bacteria. Commercial preparations contain
mainly or only penicillin G; *P. chrysogenum* is the preferred organism. Addition of phenylacetic acid to the fermentation increases the yield of the G
type. Various derivatives of penicillin have been prepared with the view
to producing agents that persist in the organism. The most useful are
amine salts, particularly that formed with procaine.

The remarkable chemotherapeutic properties stimulated intensive Anglo-
American investigation during the war; eventually pure crystalline material was obtained, the structure was established, and problems of manufacture of the highly labile substance on a large scale were solved. The mold

$$\begin{array}{c} S \\ \diagup \;\; \diagdown \\ RCONHCH\text{—}CH \qquad C(CH_3)_2 \\ | \qquad\quad | \qquad\qquad | \\ O{=}C\text{——}N\text{———}CHCOOH \end{array}$$

Penicillin

F, R = —CH_2CH=$CHCH_2CH_3$ G, R = —$CH_2C_6H_5$
K, R = —$CH_2(CH_2)_5CH_3$ X, R = —$CH_2C_6H_4OH(p)$

produces several closely related substances, differing only in the nature
of the group R, shown in the formula for four of the known penicillins.

Some of the many known degradations that led to elucidation of the structure are shown in the formulas. Acid hydrolysis cleaves the molecule into an amino acid (β-thiol-D-valine), identical in all penicillins, and a penaldic acid, which is unstable and readily loses carbon dioxide to give a penilloaldehyde. Penicillamine is the β,β-dimethyl derivative of D-cysteine.

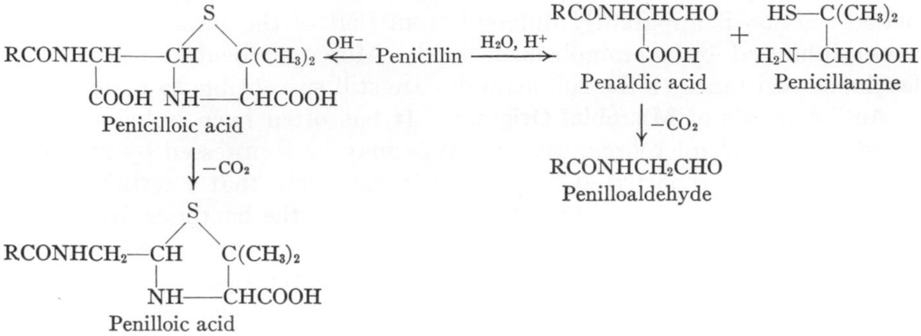

$$\begin{array}{c} \overset{S}{\diagup\diagdown} \\ \underset{\underset{\text{Penicilloic acid}}{\overset{\mid}{\text{COOH}}\ \ \overset{\mid}{\underset{\mid}{\text{NH}}}\text{---}\overset{\mid}{\text{CHCOOH}}}{\text{RCONHCH---CH}\quad\text{C(CH}_3)_2} \end{array} \overset{OH^-}{\longleftarrow} \text{Penicillin} \overset{H_2O,\ H^+}{\longrightarrow} \begin{array}{c}\text{RCONHCHCHO}\\ \mid \\ \text{COOH}\\ \text{Penaldic acid}\end{array} \ + \ \begin{array}{c}\text{HS---C(CH}_3)_2\\ \mid \\ \text{H}_2\text{N---CHCOOH}\\ \text{Penicillamine}\end{array}$$

$\downarrow -CO_2$ (left branch)

$\downarrow -CO_2$ (right branch)

$$\begin{array}{c} \overset{S}{\diagup\diagdown} \\ \underset{\underset{\text{Penilloic acid}}{\overset{\mid}{\text{NH}}\text{---}\overset{\mid}{\text{CHCOOH}}}{\text{RCONHCH}_2\text{---CH}\quad\text{C(CH}_3)_2} \end{array}$$

$$\begin{array}{c}\text{RCONHCH}_2\text{CHO}\\ \text{Penilloaldehyde}\end{array}$$

The structures assigned to the amino acid and to the penilloaldehydes have been verified by synthesis. Alkaline hydrolysis opens the β-lactam ring with liberation of one new basic and one new acidic function. The product, penicilloic acid, readily loses carbon dioxide even at room temperature to yield a penilloic acid. The penicilloic acids are also cleaved by acid to penicillamine and a penaldic acid.

The remarkable therapeutic properties of penicillin stimulated investigation of other biologically produced bactericidal substances. A large number of substances have been isolated, such as gramicidine and tyrocidine (p. 450), but one of the more useful of the newer antibiotics is **streptomycin,**

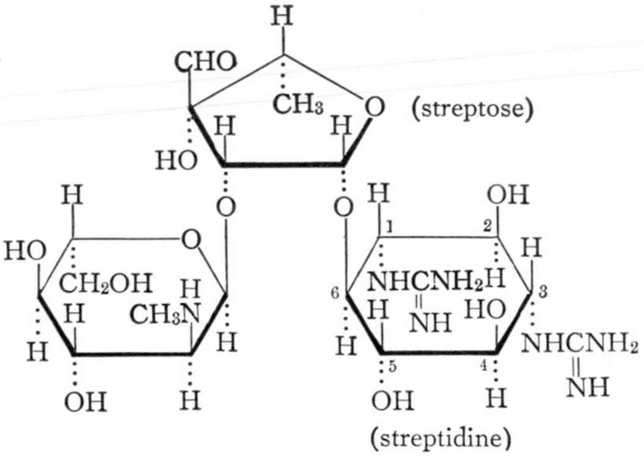

Streptomycin

isolated from the strain *Streptomyces griseus* (Waksman,[3] 1942–44). The formula shown is based largely on work by the groups of Folkers[4] (1948) and of Wolfrom (1947–). Mild acid hydrolysis cleaves the molecule into the

---

[3] Selman A. Waksman, b. 1888 Priluka, Russia; Ph.D. Calif.; Rutgers Inst. Microbiol.; Nobel Prize 1952

[4] Karl A. Folkers, b. 1906 Decatur, Ill.; Ph.D. Wisconsin (Adkins); Merck and Co.

base streptidine and the bioside streptobiosamine. Streptidine, the diguanidino derivative of an inositol, has the all-*trans* configuration. One component of streptobiosamine, streptose, is an unusual 3-methylpentose; the other is N-methyl-L-glucosamine (unnatural configuration). It is still uncertain whether the streptidine unit is joined through the C_6-OH, as shown, or through the C_4-OH. The dihydro derivative, prepared by hydrogenation of the streptose aldehydic group to —CH_2OH, is also used clinically.

Streptomycin is more toxic than penicillin and also provokes emergence of resistant strains. It is particularly useful in treatment of infections caused by Gram-negative bacteria (tularemia, bacteremia, plague). It is also effective against acid-fast organisms and has important uses in tuberculosis therapy. The only other drug of comparable importance in this respect is **isoniazid**, the hydrazide of isonicotinic acid.

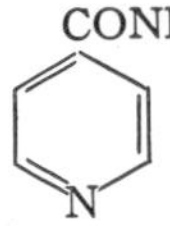

CONHNH₂

Isoniazid

Tetracyclines. — The success of streptomycin in therapy stimulated search for other antibiotics and led to isolation of **aureomycin** from *Streptomyces aureofaciens* (Lederle) and of terramycin from *S. rimosus* (Pfizer). The empirical formulas and general properties, including the antibacterial spectra, suggested a close relationship, which structural studies established (1953–54). Both are derivatives of a highly complex substance containing four fused rings, named for this reason **tetracycline**. This parent metabo-

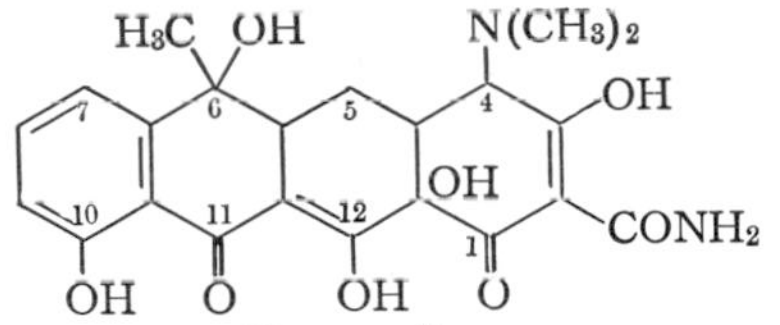

H₃C OH N(CH₃)₂

OH

OH

CONH₂

OH O OH O

Tetracycline

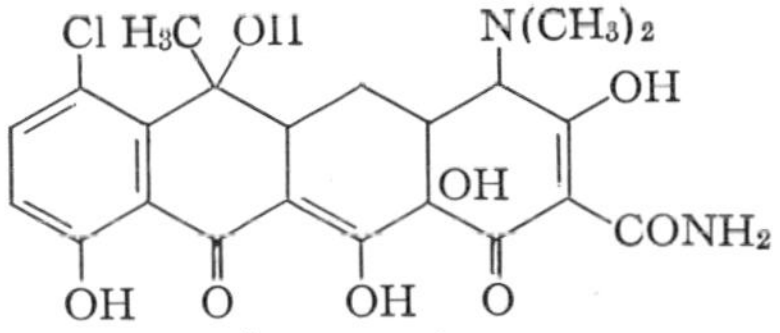

Cl H₃C OH N(CH₃)₂

OH

OH

CONH₂

OH O OH O

Aureomycin

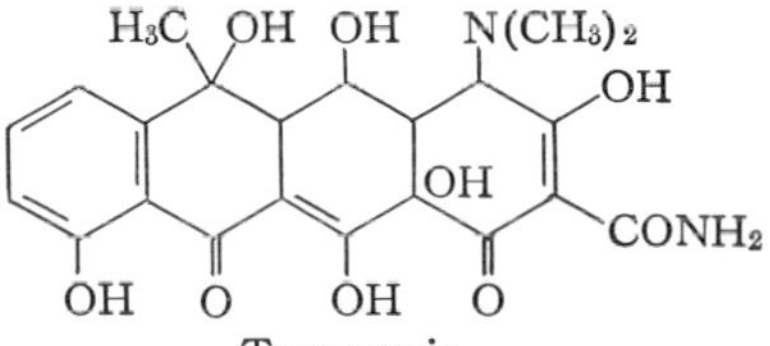

H₃C OH OH N(CH₃)₂

OH

OH

CONH₂

OH O OH O

Terramycin

lite has since been isolated from a natural source. Aureomycin and terramycin are the 7-chloro- and 5-hydroxy derivatives of tetracycline. The structures are exceedingly intricate and probably contain more functional groups than any other natural products (short of a protein). These antibiotics are used widely in various diseases, bacterial, viral, and rickettsial.

Chloramphenicol. — The chlorine containing antibiotic chloramphenicol was isolated (Parke, Davis, 1947) from a *Streptomyces* sp. found in a soil sample collected in Venezuela and named *S. venezuelae*. Particular interest is attached to this antibiotic, orginally named chloromycetin, because of its activity in experimental rickettsial and viral infections. The toxicity is similar to that of streptomycin. After elucidation of the structure, the name was changed to the more accurate chloramphenicol, although chloromycetin is retained as a trade name. The Geneva name is D-(−)-threo-2-dichloroacetamido-1-p-nitrophenyl-1,3-propanediol (I). Alkaline or acid hydrolysis yields dichloroacetic acid and an optically active base (II) showing the properties of a primary amine. Periodic acid oxidation of II yielded

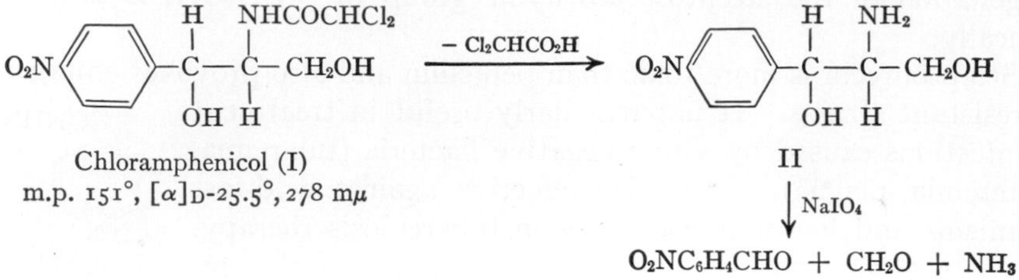

Chloramphenicol (I)
m.p. 151°, [α]D-25.5°, 278 mμ

II

$$O_2NC_6H_4CHO + CH_2O + NH_3$$

the three products shown and thus furnished evidence for the structure, which was confirmed by synthesis (1949). The stereochemical classification rests upon analogies to ephedrine bases.

READING REFERENCES

E. H. Northey, "Structure and Chemotherapeutic Activities of Sulfanilamide Derivatives," *Chem. Rev.*, **27**, 85 (1940)

E. K. Marshall, J. S. Lockwood, and R. J. Dubos, "Chemotherapy," University of Pennsylvania Bicentennial Conference (1941)

F. Mietzsch and H. Mauss, *Angew. Chem.*, **47**, 633 (1934)

L. Goodman and A. Gilman, "The Pharmacological Basis of Therapeutics," Macmillan, New York (1955)

A. Goldstein, "Antibacterial Chemotherapy," *New England Journal of Medicine*, **240**, 98 (1949)

F. L. Rose, "A Chemotherapeutic Search in Retrospect," *J. Chem. Soc.*, 2770 (1951)

Answers to Problems

ANSWERS TO PROBLEMS

CHAPTER 1. INTRODUCTION (*questions: p. 22*)

1.

Hydrazine: H_2NNH_2. Formic acid: H—C̈=O with OH above

2. CH_3CHBr_2 and $BrCH_2CH_2Br$; CH_3CBr_3 and $BrCH_2CHBr_2$

3. $H:\overset{H}{\underset{H}{\overset{..}{N}:}} + H:\overset{..}{\underset{..}{Cl}}: \rightarrow \left[H:\overset{H}{\underset{H}{\overset{..+}{N}:}}H \right]^{+} :\overset{..}{\underset{..}{Cl}}:^{-}$

4. $H:\overset{:Br:}{\underset{:Br:}{\overset{..}{C}:Br:}}$ $H:\overset{H}{\underset{H}{\overset{..}{C}:O:}}H$ $H:\overset{H}{\underset{H}{C::C}}:H$

5. 65.47% C, 6.73% H

6. (a) $C_6H_6O_2$; (b) $C_{11}H_8O_3$

7. Possible formulas: $C_{10}H_{22}O$, $C_{14}H_8O_4$, $C_{21}H_{31}O_3N$, $C_{20}H_{32}OSN_2$

8. $C_5H_{12} = (CH_3)_4C$, b.p. 9.5°

9. $C_{15}H_{14}O_3$ (lapachol, p. 722); 74.36% C, 5.82% H

10. $C_{31}H_{46}O_2$ (vitamin K_1, p. 1017; analysis at the Merck Research Laboratories of a sample isolated by L. F. Fieser)

11. $C_{18}H_{21}O_3N$ (codeine)

CHAPTER 2. ALKANES (*questions: p. 47*)

1. Dibromoisobutanes:
$(CH_3)_2CHCHBr_2$ (1,1-),
$(CH_3)_2CBrCH_2Br$ (1,2-),
$BrCH_2CH(CH_3)CH_2Br$ (1,3-)
Dibromo-*n*-butanes:
$CH_3CH_2CH_2CHBr_2$ (1,1-),
$CH_3CH_2CHBrCH_2Br$ (1,2-),
$CH_3CHBrCH_2CH_2Br$ (1,3-),
$BrCH_2CH_2CH_2CH_2Br$ (1,4-),
$CH_3CH_2CBr_2CH_3$ (2,2-),
$CH_3CHBrCHBrCH_3$ (2,3-)

2. Dimethyl-*n*-butylmethane,
$(CH_3)_2CHCH_2CH_2CH_2CH_3$
Diisopropylmethane, $(CH_3)_2CHCH_2CH(CH_3)_2$
Methylethylisopropylmethane,
$(CH_3)_2CHCH(CH_3)CH_2CH_3$
Methylethyl-*n*-propylmethane,
$CH_3CH_2CH(CH_3)CH_2CH_2CH_3$
Trimethyl-*n*-propylmethane,
$(CH_3)_3CCH_2CH_2CH_3$

3.
(a) $CH_3CH_2CH_2CH_2CH_2CH_2CH_2CHClCH_2Br$
(b) $CH_3CH_2CH_2CH_2CHClCCl_2CH_3$
(c) $CH_3CH_2C(OH)(CH_3)_2$
(d) $(CH_3)_2CHCH(CH_3)_2$

(e) $(CH_3CH_2)_4C$
(f) $CH_3CH_2CH_2CH_2CH_2CH_2MgI$

4. (a) Dichlorodifluoromethane
(b) Dimethyldiethylmethane
(c) Trimethyl-*n*-butylmethane
(d) Di-(*n*-propyl)-isopropylmethane

5. (a) 2,5-Dimethylheptane
(b) 2-Methylpropane
(c) 3-Methylhexane
(d) 2,5-Dimethyl-3-ethylhexane

6. 2,2-Dimethylhexane,
$CH_3CH_2CH_2CH_2C(CH_3)_3$
3,3-Dimethylhexane,
$CH_3CH_2CH_2C(CH_3)_2CH_2CH_3$
2,2,3-Trimethylpentane,
$CH_3CH_2CH(CH_3)C(CH_3)_3$
2,2,4-Trimethylpentane,
$(CH_3)_2CHCH_2C(CH_3)_3$

CHAPTER 3. ALKENES (*questions: p. 82*)

2. $H:\overset{..}{\underset{..}{O}}:\overset{:\overset{..}{O}:^{-}}{\underset{:\overset{..}{O}:}{S^+}}:\overset{..}{\underset{..}{O}}:H$

Alternate structure: $H:\overset{..}{\underset{..}{O}}:\overset{:\overset{..}{O}:}{\underset{:\overset{..}{O}:^{-}}{S^+}}:\overset{..}{\underset{..}{O}}:H$

3. (a) Propanediol-1,2
(b) 2,3-Dimethylbutane
(c) 3,7-Dimethyloctene-6-ol-1
(d) 2-Methyl-3-isopropylhexene-5-ol-1
(e) 1,2-Dimethyl-4-ethylcyclohexane
(f) 2,5-Dimethylhexadiene-2,4
(g) Cyclohexatriene-1,3,5

4.
(a) $CH_3CH_2CH(CH_2CH_3)CH(CH_3)CH_2OH$
(b) $C_6H_5CH=CHCH=CHC_6H_5$
(c) $(CH_3)_2C=CHCH_3$
(d) $CH_3CH(OH)CH(OH)CH_3$
(e) $ClCH_2CH(CH_3)CH_2CH=CH_2$
(f) $CH_3CH_2CH—CH_2$ with O bridge

5. (a) Wash with concentrated sulfuric acid and discard the lower layer of acid containing $ROSO_2OH$ formed by addition to the olefin.
(b) Same as in (a).
(c) Prepare the dibromide, separate it from *n*-hexane by fractionation, debrominate with zinc.

6. On drastic oxidation the first hydrocarbon gives a C_3-acid and a C_4-ketone and the second gives a C_2-acid and a C_4-ketone.

7. 1,4-Dimethylcyclopentadiene-1,3

8. Hexene-2

9. Dehydration to cyclohexene and oxidation; actually adipic acid is formed on direct oxidation of cyclohexanol with nitric acid.

10.
$CH_3CH_2C(CH_3)=CH(CH_2)_2CH=CHCH_2CH_3$

11. (a) 2 rings; (b) 4 rings

12. $CH_2CH_2CCH_2CH_2$
$\quad\ |\qquad\ ||\qquad\ |$
$\quad CH_2CH_2CCH_2CH_2$

CHAPTER 4. ALKYNES (questions: p. 93)

1. (a) Reaction with PBr_3 to give CH_3-CBr_2CH_3; dehydrohalogenation with alcoholic potassium hydroxide.
(b) Dehydration to pentene-2; addition of bromine; dehydrohalogenation.
(c) Reaction of the sodio derivative with methyl iodide.
(d) Dimerization of acetylene to vinylacetylene; exhaustive catalytic hydrogenation.

2. $CH_2=CHCOCH_3$ (the triple bond has greater additive power than the double bond).

3. $CH_3C\equiv CCH(CH_3)_2$

4. Benzene forms no silver or copper derivative.

CHAPTER 6. ALCOHOLS (questions: p. 143)

1. (a) 3-Methylpentene-2
(b) $(CH_3)_2C=CHCH_2CH(CH_3)_2$
(c) $(CH_3)_2C=CHCH_2CH_2OH$
(d) $CH_3CH_2CO_2H + O=C(CH_3)_2$ [initial dehydration to $CH_3CH_2CH=C(CH_3)_2$]
(e) Adipic aldehyde, $OHC(CH_2)_4CHO$
(f) n-$C_5H_{11}OCH_2CH_2OH$
(g) Ethanolamine, $HOCH_2CH_2NH_2$

2. (a) $CH_3CH_2CH_2MgBr + (CH_3)_2CO$
(b) $2CH_3CH_2CH_2MgBr + CH_3CO_2C_2H_5$
(c) $CH_3CH_2CH_2MgBr + CH_2O$
(d) $CH_3CH_2CH_2MgBr +$ ethylene oxide
(e) $CH_3CH_2CH_2MgBr + CH_3COCH_2CH_3$

3. (a) $(CH_3)_2CHMgBr + CH_2O$
(b) $(CH_3)_2CO + BrMgCH_2CH_3$
(c) $CH_3CH_2CO_2CH_3 + 2CH_3CH_2MgI$
(d) $CH_3CH_2CH_2MgBr +$ ethylene oxide
(e) $CH_3CH_2MgCl + OC(CH_3)_2$; dehydration
(f) $(CH_3)_2CHMgBr +$ ethylene oxide $\rightarrow$ $(CH_3)_2CHCH_2CH_2OH$; $(CH_3)_2CHCH_2CH_2MgBr + CH_2O$; dehydration
(g) $(CH_3)_2CHMgI + OC(CH_3)_2$; dehydration
(h) $(CH_3)_2CO + CH_3MgCl$; dehydration; hydrogenation
(i) $CH_3CH_2CH_2MgBr + OC(CH_3)_2$; dehydration; hydrogenation
(j) $2(CH_3)_2CHMgBr + CH_3CO_2C_2H_5$; dehydration; hydrogenation

4. (a) $2CH_3CH_2CH_2MgBr + CH_3CH_2CO_2CH_3$; dehydration; hydrogenation
(b) $CH_2=CHCH_2MgBr + OC(CH_3)_2$; dehydration
(c) $(CH_3)_2CO + CH_3MgI \rightarrow (CH_3)_3COH$; $(CH_3)_3COH \rightarrow (CH_3)_3CBr \rightarrow (CH_3)_3CMgBr$; $(CH_3)_3CMgBr + CH_2O \rightarrow (CH_3)_3CCH_2OH$

5. (a) $(CH_3)_2CHCH_2MgCl + OC(CH_3)_2$; dehydration
(b) $CH_3CH_2CH(OH)CH_3 \rightarrow$ $CH_3CH_2COCH_3$; reaction with $CH_3CH_2CH_2MgBr$
(c) $(CH_3)_2CO + CH_3CH_2CH_2CH_2MgCl$; dehydration; hydrogenation
(d) $(CH_3)_3CMgCl + CH_3CH_2CHO$; conversion to $(CH_3)_3CCHBrCH_2CH_3$; formation of RMgBr; decomposition with water

6. $(CH_3)_2CHCH=CH_2$

7. $(CH_3)_2CHCHOHCH_3$

8. Cyclohexene + $H_2O_2 \rightarrow$ cyclohexanediol-1,2; glycol cleavage with HIO_4 gives the dialdehyde, $OHCCH_2CH_2CH_2CH_2CHO$, which on condensation with CH_3MgCl yields $CH_3CHOHCH_2CH_2CH_2CH_2CHOHCH_3$; dehydration affords $CH_3CH=CHCH_2CH_2CH=CHCH_3$.

9. On dehydration to a diene, followed by chromic acid oxidation, the first diol would give a C_6-diketone and the second would give a C_6-diacid.

10. From ricinoleic acid by hydroxylation of the double bond (H_2O_2–HOAc) and reduction with $LiAlH_4$.

CHAPTER 7. HALOGEN COMPOUNDS (questions: p. 160)

1. (a) Treat stearyl alcohol with thionyl chloride and remove excess by evaporation in vacuum; or use PCl_5 and remove $POCl_3$ by distillation.
(b) Shake t-amyl alcohol with 36% hydrochloric acid in a separatory funnel; separate and wash the upper layer, dry, and distil.
(c) Treat the alcohol with PBr_3; decant the bromide from phosphorous acid.
(d) Heat the alcohol with constant-boiling hydriodic acid.

2. $d > b > a > c$

3. Positive: b, e, g

4. (a) $(CH_3)_2CHMgBr + BrCH_2CH=CH_2$
(b) $CH_2=CHCH_2Br + Br_2$
(c) $CH_2=CHCH_2Br + HBr$
(d) $CH_2BrCHBrCH_2Br$ (b) + alc. KOH

5. $CH_2=CHCHO$ (see p. 198).

CHAPTER 8. CARBOXYLIC ACIDS (questions: p. 189)

1. Acidic strength increases in the order $CH_3CH_2CO_2H$, $HOCH_2CO_2H$, ICH_2CO_2H, $ClCH_2CO_2H$. The order of relative electronegativity, as indicated by the position in the periodic table, is: C < O < I < Cl (p. 1052).

2. Malonic acid is the more strongly acidic; the electron-attracting inductive effect of the second carboxylic acid group decreases with increasing distance from the first group.

3. (a) $(CH_2)_2CHCH_2CO_2H$
(b) $CH_3CHBrCHBrCO_2H$
(c) $(CH_3CH_2)_3CCOOH$
(d) $CH_3CH_2CH_2CH_2CH_2CH_2CH_2CO_2H$

4. (a) Grignard (KCN probably would eliminate HBr).
(b) Nitrile synthesis (the hydroxyl group would prevent formation of a Grignard reagent).

5. $CH_3CH_2OH \rightarrow CH_2{=}CH_2 \rightarrow BrCH_2CH_2Br \rightarrow NCCH_2CH_2CN \rightarrow HO_2CCH_2CH_2CO_2H$

6. By sodium hypochlorite oxidation.

7. Dissolve the mixture in ether, extract the acidic component with sodium bicarbonate solution, acidify the extract, extract with ether, dry the solution and evaporate the solvent.

8. On chlorination in the presence of iodine as catalyst, (a) would give a monochloro derivative, (b) would give a dichloro derivative, and (c) would remain unchanged. Rates of esterification would also distinguish between the three acids.

9. :O ::C: O: ⟷ :O:C::O:
       :O: :O:

10. H:C::C:C:H ⟶ (with :Br: and -:Br:)
    H H H

H:C::C:C:H ⟷ H:C:C::C:H
H H H   H H H

(Note that the departing bromide ion takes along one electron that originally belonged to carbon, with the result that carbon is left with a positive charge.)

11. (a) H.C ..C: D.: ( ) H:C:C::Br:
       H H   H H

(b) The initially uncharged bromine atom shares an additional pair of electrons with the adjacent carbon atom, and this atom in turn donates to the terminal carbon atom a pair of shared electrons in which each atom originally had an equal stake of one electron. Hence bromine, in effect, has donated one electron to the terminal carbon atom.

(c) The electronic formulation of $\overset{+}{C}H_2{-}CH{=}Br^-$ represents more electrons (10)

H:C:C::Br:
H H

than bromine can accommodate.

12. No; a requirement for resonance is that the structures involved do not differ in the position of the atomic nuclei.

13. H:C:N:::N: ⟷ H:C::N::N:
    H   H

14. (a) Fischer esterification with HCl, H_2SO_4, or BF_3 as catalyst.
(b) Diazomethane or silver salt method.
(c) Fischer esterification with BF_3 as catalyst (HCl or H_2SO_4 might add to the double bond).
(d) Reflux the n-propyl ester with excess methanol containing 3% sulfuric acid.

15. R   F   R
    C:O:H + B:F → C:O:H
    ‖   F   ‖ BF₃
    O   O

    R   R
    CH₃OH + C:O:H → CH₃O:C + H:O:H
            ‖ BF₃   ‖   BF₃
            O   O

16. $(CH_3)_2CHCO_2H \rightarrow (CH_3)_2CHCOCl$ (reaction with $SOCl_2$); $(CH_3)_2CHCOCl + CH_3CdCl$

17. $CH_3COOH + Br_2$ (I_2 catalyst) $\rightarrow CH_2BrCOOH$; $CH_2BrCOOH + PCl_3 \rightarrow CH_2BrCOCl$

18. Acetic acid and ethyl acetate.

19. Dehydration with acetic anhydride to succinic anhydride; action of boiling methanol on the anhydride to produce the half ester; reaction with thionyl chloride.

20. Replacement of hydrogen by acetyl involves a net gain of C_2H_2O, hence four hydroxyl groups must have been acetylated. The substance contains only four carbon atoms and each can carry only one hydroxyl group (gem-diols are unstable), hence the structure must be $HOCH_2CHOHCHOHCH_2OH$. Note that the structure $(HOCH_2)_3COH$ is ruled out because the tertiary alcoholic group would not be acylated on treatment with acetic anhydride.

21. Prepare the diester, $CH_3OCOCH_2CH_2COOCH_3$, and treat it with four moles of CH_3MgCl; dehydrate the diol, $(CH_3)_2C(OH)CH_2CH_2C(OH)(CH_3)_2$.

22. $RCOCl > (RCO)_2O > RCOOCH_3 > ROR$

23. (a) Conversion to capryl alcohol; hypochlorite oxidation. (b) Conversion to n-heptaldehyde; oxidation with dichromate solution.

CHAPTER 9. ALDEHYDES AND KETONES
(questions: p. 222)

1. (a) Pentanol-2-one-3
(b) 3,7-Dimethyloctene-2-ol-1
(c) 2,6-Dimethyloctatriene-2,4,6-dial-1,8

2. (a) Oxidation with chromic acid
(b) Oxidation with chromic acid
(c) Grignard reaction of allylmagnesium bromide with acetaldehyde to give $CH_2=CHCH_2CH(OH)CH_3$; Oppenauer oxidation (chromic acid would attack the double bond).
(d) Hydroxylation of the double bond with H_2O_2 in acetic acid and cleavage of the glycol, $HOCH_2CHOH(CH_2)_8COOH$, with lead tetraacetate.
(e) Conversion to the acid chloride (e.g. with $SOCl_2$); Rosenmund reduction.

3. Cyclohexanone on nitric acid oxidation gives adipic acid, $HO_2C(CH_2)_4CO_2H$; pyrolysis of the calcium salt of this acid affords cyclopentanone. To effect the reverse transformation, oxidize cyclopentanone with nitric acid to glutaric acid, $HO_2C(CH_2)_3CO_2H$, reduce the diethyl ester with sodium and alcohol (Bouveault-Blanc method) to produce pentamethyleneglycol, $HO(CH_2)_5OH$, replace both hydroxyl groups by bromine, replace the bromine atoms by nitrile groups (aqueous-alcoholic KCN), hydrolyze to $HO_2C(CH_2)_5CO_2H$, pyrolyze the calcium salt of the diacid.

4. Aldehydes, but not ketones: give the Ag-mirror test and reduce Fehling's solution, polymerize under acid catalysis or in aqueous solution, give a positive Schiff test; aldehydes with no α-hydrogen atom undergo the Cannizzaro reaction. Aldehydes react to a greater extent than ketones: with $NaHSO_3$, with HCN, in aldol condensations, and with alcohols (acetal formation).

5. Chloral is the most reactive of the compounds because it alone forms stable addition products with water and with hydroxylamine. The bisulfite reaction (Table 9.3) establishes the order acetaldehyde > acetone > diethyl ketone. The failure of diisopropyl ketone to add isopropylmagnesium bromide (p. 204) shows it to be the least reactive compound listed.

6. By reduction with aluminum isopropoxide and isopropyl alcohol (Meerwein-Ponndorf method).

7. $(CH_3)_2CHCH(OH)C(CH_3)_2CHO$

8. $(CH_3)_3CCH_2OH + (CH_3)_3CCO_2H$

9. Preparation of diacetone alcohol by aldol condensation; oxidation with sodium hypochlorite.

10. $CH_3COCH_2CH_2CHO + 2C_2H_5OH$ (dry HCl) $\rightarrow$ $CH_3COCH_2CH_2CH(OC_2H_5)_2$; oxidation with alkaline hypochlorite to $HO_2CCH_2CH_2CH(OC_2H_5)_2$; hydrolysis of the acetal with dilute aqueous hydrochloric acid.

11. $2CH_3CHO \rightarrow CH_3CH(OH)CH_2CHO$ $\rightarrow CH_3CH=CHCHO \rightarrow CH_3(CH_2)_2CH_2OH$

12. Methyl ketones add $NaHSO_3$ and HCN; none of the esters add these reagents. Ketones react with hydrazine with replacement of the carbonyl oxygen, whereas an ester reacts with hydrazine to form a hydrazide ($RCONHNH_2$, p. 179), in which the carbonyl group is still intact.

13. $(CH_3)_2CHCH(OH)CH_3$

14. $CH_3COCH_2CH_2CHO$

15. (a) $HOCH_2CH_2CN$ (compare action of RMgX on ethylene oxide and on carbonyl compounds).
(b) $(CH_3)_3CCH(OH)CH_2COCH_3$ (trimethylacetaldehyde cannot undergo self-condensation but has a more reactive carbonyl group than acetone).

16. (a) Pyrolysis of $(CH_3CH_2COO)_2Ca$
(b) $CH_3CH_2CH_2MgBr + CH_3CH_2CHO$; oxidation of the resulting secondary alcohol
(c) Acetone $\rightarrow$ diacetone alcohol $\rightarrow$ mesityl oxide $\rightarrow$ $(CH_3)_2C=CHCO_2H$ (NaOCl) $\rightarrow$ $(CH_3)_2CHCH_2CO_2H$ (hydrogenation)

17. Vinylcyclopentane

18. The formation of a monoacetate indicates the presence of a primary or secondary alcoholic group; resistance to phenylhydrazine shows that the second oxygen atom is not present as a carbonyl group. The reaction with lead tetraacetate is evidently a glycol cleavage producing two carbonyl groups; since these are in the same molecule, III, the glycol group must be part of a ring. The positive Fehling's test indicates that at least one carbonyl must be present as an aldehydic group, and the formation of iodoform reveals the presence of a methyl ketone group. The acid $HOOC(CH_2)_4COOH$ must, then, have come from the keto aldehyde $CH_3CO(CH_2)_4$-CHO, and the glycol I must have the structure:

$$\begin{array}{c} CH_3 \\ | \\ CH_2CH_2COH \\ | \quad\quad | \\ CH_2CH_2CHOH \end{array}$$

19. Attack of carbon by the anionic fragment of $\overset{-}{R}\overset{+}{Mg}Br$.

20. Condensation with ethanedithiol and desulfurization with Raney Ni.

21. $C_6H_5CHOHCOOH$ (mandelic acid).

22. (a) $(CH_3)_2CHBr + Na^+[CH(CO_2C_2H_5)_2]^-$ $\rightarrow$ $(CH_3)_2CHCH(CO_2C_2H_5)_2$; hydrolysis and decarboxylation
(b) $CH_3I + Na^+[CH(CO_2C_2H_5)_2]^-$ $\rightarrow$ $CH_3CH(CO_2C_2H_5)_2$; conversion to sodio derivative; reaction with CH_3CH_2I; hydrolysis and decarboxylation.
(c) Condensation of $Br(CH_2)_4Br$ with two moles of sodiomalonic ester, etc.

23. The second compound, the C-acetyl derivative, has three carbonyl groups in a position to activate the central hydrogen atom and hence this substance exists to the greater extent in the enolic form.

$\subset$

CHAPTER 10. AMINES (*questions: p. 248*)

1. (*a*) *sec*-Butylamine (primary)
(*b*) Diethylisopropylamine (tertiary)
(*c*) *t*-Amylamine (primary)
(*d*) Methylisobutylamine (secondary)
(*e*) Methyldi-*n*-propylamine hydrochloride (salt of tertiary amine)
(*f*) Tetraisopropylammonium bromide (quaternary ammonium salt)
(*g*) N-Nitrosoethyl-*n*-propylamine (nitroso derivative of a secondary amine)
(*h*) N-Ethylacetamide (secondary amide)
(*i*) Trimethylacetamide (primary amide)

2. Weakly acidic: phthalimide (pK$_a$ 8.3), succinimide (pK$_a$ 10.5). Substantially neutral: acetamide, acetylmethylamine; inner salt: β-alanine. Feebly basic: urea. Basic: methylamine (pK$_b$ 3.4), tetramethylammonium hydroxide (pK$_b$ nearly zero).

3. (*a*) Treat with a little acetic anhydride, extract an ethereal solution of the resulting mixture with portions of dilute hydrochloric acid until no more amine is removed, neutralize the acid solution, extract with ether, distil the ether and then the triethylamine.
(*b*) Treat with NaNO$_2$ + HCl, extract an ethereal solution of the resulting mixture with dilute HCl to remove the triethylamine, heat the neutral fraction with HCl to hydrolyze the (CH$_2$CH$_2$)$_2$NNO, extract the acidic solution with ether, recover the diethylamine from the acid liquor by neutralization and ether extraction.
(*c*) Treat with benzenesulfonyl chloride, separate the alkali-soluble CH$_3$CH$_2$NHSO$_2$C$_6$H$_5$ from the alkali-insoluble (CH$_2$CH$_2$)$_2$NSO$_2$C$_6$H$_5$ and (CH$_3$CH$_2$)$_3$N, hydrolyze the alkali-soluble derivative.

4. (*a*) CH$_3$CH$_2$CH$_2$CH$_2$OH → CH$_3$CH$_2$CH$_2$CO$_2$H → chloride → amide → CH$_3$CH$_2$CH$_2$NH$_2$ (NaOBr).
(*b*) CH$_3$CH$_2$CH$_2$CH$_2$OH → bromide → nitrile → CH$_3$CH$_2$CH$_2$CH$_2$CH$_2$NH$_2$ (LiAlH$_4$).

5. CH$_3$CH$_2$CHOHCH$_3$ → CH$_3$CH$_2$COCH$_3$ → oxime → CH$_3$CH$_2$CHNH$_2$CH$_3$ (H$_2$, Pt).

6. The Gabriel synthesis would give a pure product, whereas reaction with ammonia would give some secondary amine. The route through the aldehyde and oxime suffers from some difficulty in avoiding overoxidation in the preparation of the aldehyde.

7. RCN → RCONH$_2$ → RCOOH. RCOOH → RCOCl → RCONH$_2$ → RCN (Ac$_2$O). Yes, the reaction RCH=NOH → RC≡N is realizable (action of Ac$_2$O).

8. Exhaustive methylation, conversion to the quaternary ammonium hydroxide, and pyrolysis affords cyclohexene.

9. Exhaustive methylation, conversion to the quaternary ammonium hydroxide, and pyrolysis opens the ring and gives a vinyl derivative.

A second degradation eliminates nitrogen as (CH$_3$)$_3$N and gives a divinyl derivative. The latter could be oxidized to (CH$_3$)$_2$C(COOH)$_2$.

10. Yes, they both contain an electron sextet (they are described as isoelectronic):

$$R:\overset{\cdot\cdot}{\underset{R}{B}}:R \qquad R:\overset{\cdot\cdot}{\underset{R}{C}}{}^{+}:R$$

11.

12. In an alkyl bromide (*a*) the bromine atom is described as negative because it separates with the pair of shared electrons and accepts a proton.

(*a*)

$$R:\overset{\cdot\cdot}{\underset{\cdot\cdot}{O}}:H + H:\overset{\cdot\cdot}{\underset{\cdot\cdot}{Br}}:$$

In N-bromosuccinimide (*b*) the two electron-attracting carbonyl groups prevent separation

(*b*)

$$\text{>N:H} + \text{H:}\overset{\cdot\cdot}{\underset{\cdot\cdot}{O}}:\overset{\cdot\cdot}{\underset{\cdot\cdot}{Br}}:$$

of the electron pair shared between nitrogen and bromine, and hence bromine departs with only an electron sextet and combines with hydroxide ion to form HOBr.

13. Cracking; methane (CH$_4$ → HC≡CH); alkanes (CH$_3$CH$_3$ → CH$_2$=CH$_2$); alkenes (CH$_3$CH$_2$CH=CH$_2$ → CH$_2$=CHCH=CH$_2$); aromatization (*n*-heptane → toluene). Thermal dehydration of alcohols over alumina. Alkenes from alkylsulfuric acids. Formation of calcium carbide (electric furnace). Pyrolysis of castor oil to *n*-heptaldehyde and undecylenic acid. Decarboxylation of formic acid at 160°. Thermal chlorination of propylene to allyl chloride (formed instead of the saturated addition product). Pyrolysis of acetone to ketene. Catalytic dehydrogenation of secondary alcohols to ketones. Thermal depolymerization of aldehyde polymers. Aldol → crotonaldehyde. Thermal decomposition of quaternary ammonium hydroxides.

CHAPTER 11. STEREOCHEMISTRY
(questions: p. 292)

1. No, there is equal chance for the opening of either member of the double bond, and the product resulting after hydrolysis would be the *dl*-alcohol.

2.

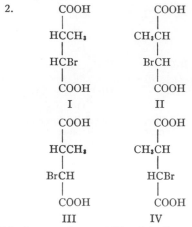

COOH	COOH
HCCH₃	CH₃CH
HCBr	BrCH
COOH	COOH
I	II

2. COOH / HCCH₃ / HCBr / COOH (I)   COOH / CH₃CH / BrCH / COOH (II)   COOH / HCCH₃ / BrCH / COOH (III)   COOH / CH₃CH / HCBr / COOH (IV)

I is the enantiomer of II and is diastereoisomeric with III and IV; III and IV are enantiomers.

3. (*a*) 4; (*b*) 2; (*c*) 8; (*d*) 16

4. CH₃CH₂CH(CH₃)COOH

5. Monomethyl ester of mesotartaric acid

6. (*a*) *d-*, *l-*, *dl-*
(*b*) No stereoisomers
(*c*) *cis* and *trans*
(*d*) *d-*, *l-*, *dl-*
(*e*) *d-*, *l-*, *dl-*, *d'-*, *l'-*, *d'l'-*
(*f*) No stereoisomers
(*g*) *d-*, *l-*, *dl-*, *meso-*
(*h*) Eight optically active isomers; four *dl-* forms

7. Partial epimerization at the asymmetric carbon atom adjacent to the carbonyl group (through enol form).

8. Hydrogenation to *n*-butyric acid would establish the nature of the carbon chain; isolation of acetic acid as a product of permanganate oxidation would establish the position of the double bond.

9. The 1,2-acid can exist in an optically inactive *cis* form and in *d-* and *l-trans* forms; the 1,3-acid can exist only in one *cis* and one *trans* form.

10. Butene-2: *cis* and *trans* forms. Ricinoleic acid: *d-* and *l-cis* and *d-* and *l-trans* forms. Menthol: 3 dissimilar asymmetric carbon atoms, 8 optically active forms possible. Menthone: 4 optically active forms.

11. It must be tetrahedral.

12. Since the two double bonds lie in planes perpendicular to each other, an allene with four different substituents should exhibit molecular asymmetry and hence be resolvable into optically active components. Even an allene of the type R₁R₂C=C=CR₁R₂ should be resolvable. Allenes are very reactive and very easily isomerized to acetylenes, and it was not until 1935 (Mills, England; Kohler, U.S.A.) that the predictions were verified.

13. The fluorescent agent originally has the *trans* configuration but on absorption of light it may change in part to the *cis* form, which probably is less powerfully fluorescent.

14. Both forms are enolic; they are the hydroxy derivatives of maleic and fumaric acid:

$$HO-C-CO_2H \qquad\qquad HO-C-CO_2H$$
$$\parallel \qquad\qquad\qquad\qquad\qquad \parallel$$
$$H-C-CO_2H \qquad\qquad HO_2C-C-H$$
m.p. 152°   m.p. 184°

CHAPTER 12. RING FORMATION
(questions: p. 325)

1. Pentene-2 and 1,2-dimethylcyclopropane would decolorize bromine solution whereas cyclopentane would not. Pentene-2, but not 1,2-dimethylcyclopropane, would give a test for unsaturation with permanganate.

2. In muscone the carbon atom carrying the methyl group is asymmetric because the part of the ring joined to it on one side contains a β-keto group and the part joined on the other side does not; reduction of the carbonyl group destroys the asymmetry.

3. Condensation of butadiene with maleic anhydride; saturation of the double bond by catalytic hydrogenation; hydrolysis of the anhydride group. (Note that the Diels-Alder reaction gives *cis* addition products.)

4. The reactions are all analogous to those illustrated on page 310.

5. CH₂=O + 2CH₂(CO₂C₂H₅)₂ →
CH₂[CH(CO₂C₂H₅)₂]₂ (elimination of H₂O); hydrolysis to CH₂[CH(CO₂H)₂]₂; decarboxylation to CH₂(CH₂CO₂H)₂.

6. (*a*) O=C=C=C=O + 2H₂O →
(HO)₂C=C=C(OH)₂ →
HOOCCH₂COOH
(*b*) Malonamide: H₂NCOCH₂CONH₂

7. In 9β-methyl-*trans*-decalin the methyl group is axial to both rings and hence its hydrogen atoms are repelled by 1,3-interactions with the two axial hydrogens in each ring; the increase in strain energy can be estimated as equivalent to four skew interactions, or 3.2 kg.-cal. In the *cis* isomer the angular methyl is axial to one ring but equatorial to the other and hence the energy increase is only half as great. Hence the energy difference is reduced from 2.4 to 0.8 kg.-cal.

CHAPTER 13. REACTION MECHANISMS
(questions: p. 349)

1. Meisenheimer and Beutter, *Ann.*, **508**, 58 (1934).

2. See p. 941.

3. Schjånberg, *Ber.*, **70**, 2385 (1937).
5. Kharasch, et al., *J. Org. Chem.*, **2**, 288 (1937).
6. Winstein and Buckels, *J. Am. Chem. Soc.*, **64**, 2780 (1942).
7. Kharasch and Cooper, *J. Org. Chem.*, **10**, 47 (1945).
8. Whitmore, et al., *J. Am. Chem. Soc.*, **64**, 2970 (1942).
9. Olivier and Weber, *Rec. trav. chim.*, **53**, 1087, 1093 (1934).

CHAPTER 14. CARBOHYDRATES
(questions: p. 397)

1. 2-Ketopentose

2. On oxidation with nitric acid (a) would give a C_6-monobasic acid and (b) would give a C_6-dibasic acid.

3. On reaction with excess phenylhydrazine (a) would give a phenylhydrazone and (b) would give an osazone.

4. Isomer (a) would not react with phenylhydrazine until after it had been hydrolyzed with dilute acid and then it would give an osazone; (b) would react directly to give a methoxyl-containing phenylhydrazone; isomer (c) would react directly to give a methoxyl-containing osazone.

5. A D-4-ketohexose corresponding in configuration to glucose and galactose at C_2, C_3, and C_5.

6.

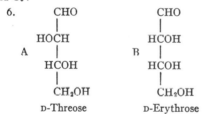

D-Threose   D-Erythrose

7. On oxidation with nitric acid, only ribose and xylose give optically inactive C_5-dibasic acids. Of these, only ribose gives an inactive C_4-dibasic acid when submitted to Wohl degradation followed by nitric acid oxidation.

8 The β-form should be the more stable because the C_1-OH is equatorial rather than axial. The equilibrated solution is closer in rotation ($+52°$) to the β-form ($+19°$) than to the α-form ($+113°$); hence the β-form is indeed the more stable.

9. C_5 (equatorial hydroxyl).

CHAPTER 20. STRUCTURE OF BENZENE
(questions: p. 926)

1. The 1,3-dicarboxylic acid could be obtained by condensation of trimethylene bromide with methylenebismalonic ester, $CH_2[CH(CO_2C_2H_5)_2]_2$, followed by hydrolysis and decarboxylation of the tetrabasic acid. The ester $(C_2H_5O_2C)_2CHCH_2CH_2CH(CO_2C_2H_5)_2$,

required for the synthesis of the 1,4-isomer, is obtainable by condensation of $BrCH_2CH_2Br$ with two moles of sodiomalonic ester; the preparation of methylenebismalonic ester by condensation of formaldehyde with diethyl malonate is mentioned in answer 5, Chapt. 12.

2. Yes; 1,2,3-trimethylbenzene can afford two monosubstitution products, three are derivable from 1,2,4-trimethylbenzene, and one from the 1,3,5-isomer.

3. This numbering is required because a 1,2-di derivative would then give two substitution products (3- or 4-, 5- or 6-), the 1,3-isomer would afford three (2- or 4-, 5-, 6-), and the 1,4-isomer (fully symmetrical) only one.

4. The answer will be obvious from the formulas.

5. Nine geometrical isomers, two of which are optically active enantiomers (see p. 655).

6. The molecular ratio of glyoxal to diacetyl to methylglyoxal should be 1:1:4.

CHAPTER 21. AROMATIC HYDROCARBONS
(questions: p. 555)

1. (a) Benzene, t-butyl chloride, with 0.4 mole $AlCl_3$.
(b) Condensation of t-butyl chloride with t-butylbenzene in the presence of BF_3 at 25°.

2. $(CH_3)_3CCl + C_6H_5CH_3 (+ BF_3) \rightarrow$ p-$(CH_3)_3CC_6H_4CH_3$; the t-butyl group is resistant to oxidation, and hence the hydrocarbon can be oxidized to the acid desired.

3. Isopropylbenzene could be obtained by Friedel-Crafts condensation of benzene with $(CH_3)_2CHCl$, CH_3CH_2CHCl, $CH_3CH=CH_2$, or $(CH_3)_2CHOH$; condensation of $(CH_3)_2CHC_6H_5$ with CH_3COCl in the presence of $AlCl_3$ would give p-$(CH_3)_2CHC_6H_4COCH_3$, which could be converted by the haloform reaction with NaOCl into p-$(CH_3)_2CHC_6H_4CO_2H$ (the usual oxidizing agents would attack the isopropyl group).

4. (a) $C_6H_5C(CH_3)_3$
(b) p-$(CH_3)_2CHC_6H_4CH_2CH_3$
(c) 1,3,5-Triethylbenzene
(d) p-$CH_3C_6H_4COCH_3$

5. (a) $CH_3CH_2CH_2COCl + C_6H_6 (AlCl_3) \rightarrow$ $CH_3CH_2CH_2COC_6H_5$; Clemmensen or Wolff-Kishner reduction.
(b) $CH_3CH_2CH_2CH_2Br + C_6H_5Br + 2Na$
(c) $C_6H_5CH=O + BrMgCH_2CH_2CH_3$ (decompose reaction mixture with H_2O) $\rightarrow$ $C_6H_5CH(OH)CH_2CH_2CH_3$; dehydrate to $C_6H_5CH=CHCH_2CH_3$; hydrogenate.

6. Friedel-Crafts succinoylation of benzene $\rightarrow$ $C_6H_5COCH_2CH_2CO_2H$; Clemmensen reduction to $C_6H_5CH_2CH_2CH_2CO_2H$; cyclization to α-tetralone with HF (or by the action of $AlCl_3$ on the acid chloride); reaction with C_6H_5MgBr; dehydration of the resulting carbinol; dehydrogenation with Se (or S, or Pd—C).

7. Friedel-Crafts condensation to p-$CH_3C_6H_4COCH_2CH_2CO_2H$; Clemmensen or

Wolff-Kishner reduction; cyclization with HF to the tetralone; reduction to the tetralin; dehydrogenation.

8. (a) Wurtz-Fittig reaction of α-bromonaphthalene with methyl bromide (+2Na); (b) conversion to α-naphthylmagnesium bromide and reaction of the latter with (CH₃)₂SO₄.

9. Condensation of cyclohexanone with C₆H₅MgBr to give 1-phenylcyclohexanol-1; dehydration to 1-phenylcyclohexene-1; permanganate oxidation to cleave the hydrocarbon at the position of the double bond to give C₆H₅CO(CH₂)₄CO₂H; Clemmensen or Wolff-Kishner reduction to C₆H₅(CH₂)₅CO₂H (see page 669 for a shorter method).

CHAPTER 22. AROMATIC SUBSTITUTIONS
(questions: p. 569)

(a) 4-Nitro-1,3-dimethoxybenzene
(b) Substitution *ortho* to the acetylamino group (more potent)
(c) Substitution *ortho* to the methyl group (smaller)
(d) Substitution *ortho* to the methyl group and *meta* to —COCH₃
(e) Mild conditions: 2-nitrophenol-4-sulfonic acid; more drastic conditions: 2,4-dinitrophenol, picric acid
(f) 2,4,5-Trimethylacetophenone
(g) 2,4-Dichloronitrobenzene
(h) C₆H₅COCH₂C₆H₄(p)-COCH₂CH₂CO₂H
(i) o- and p-NO₂C₆H₄CH₂C₆H₄CO₂H(p)
(j) 4-ClC₆H₄CH₂C₆H₄CH₃-4′
(k) 4-Methyl-3′-nitro-4′-hydroxydiphenyl
(l) m-Nitro derivative

CHAPTER 23. NITRO COMPOUNDS
(questions: p. 587)

1. Dinitration of chlorobenzene gives 2,4-dinitrochlorobenzene, in which the halogen is labile; condensation with methylamine and reduction gives the product desired.

2. (a) Disproportionation of nitrobenzene in the presence of alkali to give a reduction product (azoxybenzene) and products of hydroxylation in the o- and p-positions (o- and p-nitrophenol). Attack by the negative ion occurs at centers rendered relatively positive by resonance in nitrobenzene (see structures on p. 569); the nitro group is *meta* directing only for electrophilic substitution.
(b) Action of KOH or alkaline ferricyanide on m-dinitrobenzene with hydroxylation o- or p- to both nitro groups.

3. (a) Reaction of o- or p-dinitrobenzene with OH⁻, CH₃O⁻, or NH₃ with displacement of one nitro group by OH, OCH₃, or NH₂.
(b) Similar displacement of chlorine in o-chloronitrobenzene.
(c) Low temperature reactions of 2,4-dinitrochlorobenzene with aniline, with ammonia, and with sodium carbonate (preparation of picric acid).
(d) Reaction of β- and γ-TNT with sodium sulfite and with alkali.

4. (a) 5-Nitro-1-tetralone
(b) Mixture of 2,2′-, 2,4′-, 4,4′-derivatives.
(c) 3-Chloro-4-methoxynitrobenzene. (d) C₆H₅CH=C(NO₂)C₆H₅ (note analogy to the vinylog TNT, in which the effect of nitro groups is relayed through the aromatic ring).

5. Trinitro-m-xylene

CHAPTER 25. ARYL AMINES
(questions: p. 622)

2. Oxidation of a primary amine can abstract a hydrogen atom from the amino group (transient free radical) and can also result in attack at the reactive p-position (formation of quinone). Stabilization is achieved by salt formation (e.g. nitration in a solution in concentrated sulfuric acid), when the nitrogen function becomes ionic and weakly *meta* directing. Stabilization by formation of the N-acetyl derivative decreases the substitution-facilitating effect and makes possible the preparation of mono o- or p-derivatives.

3. Aniline sulfate → phenylsulfamic acid → orthanilic acid → sulfanilic acid. N-Methylaniline → N-nitroso derivative → p-nitroso-N-methylaniline. Benzenediazonium chloride + aniline → diazoaminobenzene → p-aminoazobenzene. Similar rearrangements (p. 585): phenylhydroxylamine → p-aminophenol; hydrazobenzene → benzidine.

4. Brominate, hydrolyze to p-bromoaniline, diazotize, hydrolyze diazonium salt.

5. Diazotize, run Sandmeyer with Cu₂(CN)₂, hydrolyze the nitrile to 2-methylbenzoic acid, oxidize with permanganate in alkaline solution.

6. (a) Diazotize, Sandmeyer to give p-bromotoluene, oxidize.
(b) Diazotize, reduce with sodium sulfite.
(c) Brominate (e.g. with bromine water), with introduction of Br at both positions *ortho* to the amino group, diazotize, deaminate by reduction with H₃PO₂.
(d) Diazotize, run Gattermann condensation with toluene in the presence of copper powder.
(e) Acetylate, nitrate adjacent to the acetylamino group, deacetylate, diazotize, hydrolyze —N₂Cl to —OH, reduce the nitro group.
(f) Treat with benzenesulfonyl chloride to produce the Hinsberg derivative, methylate this in alkaline solution, and remove the benzenesulfonyl group by hydrolysis.

7. Make the N-nitroso derivative, rearrange to 4-nitroso-N-methylaniline, reduce.

8. (a) Diazotize m-nitroaniline, run a Sandmeyer reaction to form m-chloronitrobenzene, reduce.
(b) From m-toluidine (available from p-toluidine, p. 617) by diazotization and hydrolysis.
(c) Convert m-nitroaniline into m-chloronitrobenzene as in (a), reduce, replace NH₂ by Br by the Sandmeyer method.

9. (a) From mesitylene by mononitration, reduction, diazotization, and hydrolysis.
(b) From p-xylene by nitration, reduction,

diazotization, and Sandmeyer reaction with $Cu_2(CN)_2$. Another route: reaction of p-xylene with $CH_3COCl + AlCl_3$, hypochlorite oxidation to p-xylenecarboxylic acid, conversion through the acid chloride to the amide, dehydration with acetic anhydride. The route from p-xylene through the sulfonate to the nitrile would be limited by a poor yield.

(c) Monochlorination of m-xylene (or nitration, reduction, replacement of NH_2 by Cl) and oxidation.

(d) From p-xylene by sulfonation, alkali fusion, coupling with diazotized sulfanilic acid, and reduction.

(e) From toluene by Friedel-Crafts acetylation in the 4-position, nitration, and reduction.

CHAPTER 26. PHENOLS (questions: p. 643)

1. A *meta* nitro group decreases pK_a of phenol by 2.0 units and increases pK_b of aniline by 2.1 units; for a *para* group the effects are -2.8 and $+2.7$ units. The *ortho* series is irregular: -2.8 units for phenol and $+4.5$ units for aniline.

2. Instances in this chapter: steam-volatility of o-nitrophenol; greater steam-volatility, lower boiling points, greater solubility in ligroin of o-hydroxyacetophenones as compared with p-isomers. Instances cited earlier: separation of o-(chelated) from p-nitroaniline by steam distillation; chelation of o-hydroxy azo compounds accounts for insolubility in alkali, steam volatility and low m.p. as compared with p-isomers.

3. Saligenin is not soluble in bicarbonate solution but dissolves in aqueous alkali and, unless the solution is very dilute, precipitates on acidification; hence at least one phenolic hydroxyl group is present. On treatment with HBr one hydroxyl group is replaced by bromine, and hence this must be an alcoholic and not a phenolic group.

4. Prepare the dimethyl ether (dimethyl sulfate and alkali) and condense it with $CH_3COCl + AlCl_3$. Reflux the product in benzene with $AlCl_3$ to remove the methoxyl groups, and reduce the ketonic group with amalgamated zinc and HCl.

5. (a) $C_6H_6 \rightarrow C_6H_5SO_3H \rightarrow$ $C_6H_5SO_2Na \rightarrow C_6H_5OH \rightarrow$ $C_6H_5OCH_3$ (dimethyl sulfate and alkali)
(b) $C_6H_5OH \rightarrow 2,4$-disulfonate $\rightarrow$ catechol-4-sulfonate $\rightarrow$ catechol
(c) $C_6H_5OH \rightarrow o,p\text{-}NO_2C_6H_4OH$; separate o-nitrophenol by steam distillation; reduce
(d) $C_6H_5OH + N_2^+C_6H_4SO_3^-(p) + $ alkali $\rightarrow$ $NaO_3SC_6H_4N=NC_6H_4OH(p) \rightarrow$ sulfanilic acid Na salt + p-aminophenol. (Alternates: $C_6H_5OCH_3 \rightarrow p$-nitrosophenol; reduction; $C_6H_5NO_2 \rightarrow C_6H_5NHOH \rightarrow p$-aminophenol.)
(e) Preparation and alkali fusion of m-benzenedisulfonic acid to give resorcinol; condensation with caproic acid $(ZnCl_2)$; Clemmensen reduction.

6. The acid is soluble in bicarbonate solution; the phenol is insoluble in bicarbonate but soluble in alkali solution; the ester is insoluble in cold alkali but dissolves when the mixture is warmed or allowed to stand; the last compound, a ketol, is neutral and nonhydrolyzable and it could be identified by formation of an osazone.

7. α-Naphthol: $C_6H_6 +$ succinic anhydride ($+ AlCl_3$) $\rightarrow C_6H_5COCH_2CH_2CO_2H$; reduce to $C_6H_5CH_2CH_2CH_2CO_2H$; cyclize with HF to α-tetralone, dehydrogenate. β-Naphthol: $CH_3OC_6H_5 \rightarrow CH_3OC_6H_4COCH_2CH_2CO_2H \rightarrow$ 7-methoxy-1-tetralone (with HF); Clemmensen reduction of keto group; dehydrogenation; demethylation.

8. In either p-aminophenol or its diacetate the N-function has a stronger directive influence than the O-function. However, acetylation in aqueous solution gives p-HOC_6H_4NHCOCH_3$, in which a free hydroxyl group competes for a substituting agent with the weaker acetylamino group. Hence controlled bromination gives 2-bromo-4-acetylaminophenol, which affords the desired product on hydrolysis.

CHAPTER 27. ARYL HALIDES COMPOUNDS (questions: p. 655)

1. $C_6H_5NH_2 \rightarrow C_6H_5NHCOCH_3 \rightarrow$ $p\text{-}BrC_6H_4NHCOCH_3 \rightarrow p\text{-}BrC_6H_4NH_2 \rightarrow$ $p\text{-}BrC_6H_4N_2^+Cl^-(+ KI) \rightarrow p\text{-}BrC_6H_4I$.

2. $C_6H_5CH_2Cl \rightarrow C_6H_5CH_2OH$. $C_6H_5CHCl_2 \rightarrow [C_6H_5CH(OH)_2] \rightarrow$ C_6H_5CHO. $C_6H_5CCl_3 \rightarrow [C_6H_5C(OH)Cl_2] \rightarrow$ $C_6H_5COCl] \rightarrow C_6H_5COOH$.

3. (a) $CH_3C_6H_5 + CH_2O + HCl(ZnCl_2) \rightarrow$ $p\text{-}CH_3C_6H_4CH_2Cl$; hydrolysis (expect mixture in which p-isomer predominates).
(b) $p\text{-}ClC_6H_4Br \rightarrow p\text{-}ClC_6H_4MgBr$ $[+ (CH_3)_2SO_4] \rightarrow p\text{-}ClC_6H_4CH_3 (+ 2 Li) \rightarrow$ $p\text{-}LiC_6H_4CH_3 (+ CH_2=O) \rightarrow$ $p\text{-}HOCH_2C_6H_4CH_3$.

4. Chloromethylation of p-xylene.

5. $C_6H_5OCH_3 + Br_2 \rightarrow p\text{-}BrC_6H_4OCH_3 \rightarrow$ 2-nitro-4-bromoanisole $\rightarrow$ 2-amino-4-bromoanisole.

6. Conversion to the nitrile, hydrolysis, decarboxylation. Catalytic hydrogenation is also applicable.

7. Preparation of the 4-bromo derivative, formation and carbonation of the Grignard reagent; chlorination, formation, and carbonation of the lithium derivative; conversion of either the bromide or chloride to the nitrile (cuprous cyanide in pyridine) and hydrolysis.

CHAPTER 28. AROMATIC CARBOXYLIC ACIDS (questions: p. 673)

1. From m- and p-xylene by Friedel-Crafts acetylation and hypohalite oxidation.

2. Naphthalene $\rightarrow$ phthalic anhydride $\rightarrow$ phthalimide $\rightarrow$ phthalamidic acid $\rightarrow$ anthranilic acid.

3. Toluene nitrated and o- and p-isomers separated by fractionation; p-nitrotoluene → p-toluidine → N-acetyl-p-toluidine; bromination *ortho* to acetylamino group, hydrolysis, diazotization, deamination to m-bromotoluene (see p. 645); preparation and carbonation of the Grignard reagent.

4. The esters melt at much lower temperatures and more sharply than the acids; a high melting acid often suffers decarboxylation or dehydration to an anhydride when heated.

5. In analogy with the behavior of acetanilide, the N-acetyl derivative of anthranilic acid would be expected on bromination to yield 2-acetylamino-5-bromobenzoic acid. This could be deacetylated, diazotized, and the diazonium salt treated with $Cu(NH_3)_2OH$ (compare p. 667).

6. (a) Friedel-Crafts succinoylation of toluene and Clemmensen reduction.
(b) $C_6H_5(CH_2)_4COCl + C_6H_6$ $(AlCl_3)$ → $C_6H_5(CH_2)_4COC_6H_5$; Clemmensen reduction → $C_6H_5(CH_2)_5C_6H_5$. The required δ-phenylvaleric acid is available from cinnamaldehyde and malonic acid or from phenylmagnesium bromide and cyclopentanone (p. 669).
(c) Pyrolysis of the calcium salt of the diacid o-HOOCCH$_2$C$_6$H$_4$CH$_2$CH$_2$COOH or Dieckmann condensation (p. 220) of the diester.

CHAPTER 29. AROMATIC ALDEHYDES AND KETONES (*questions: p. 708*)

1. (a) Oxidation of p-bromotoluene (available from p-toluidine) with MnO_2—H_2SO_4.
(b) p-Xylene + CO, HCl, $ZnCl_2$—Cu_2Cl_2 (Gattermann-Koch).
(c) Resorcinol dimethyl ether + HCl, $Zn(CN)_2$ in ether (Gattermann-Adams).
(d) Side-chain bromination of p-xylene to p-Br$_2$CHC$_6$H$_4$CHBr$_2$ and hydrolysis.

2. The chart should include all methods specifically covered.

3. The groups CH_3, CN, CHO, and $COCH_3$ are ordinarily convertible to COOH, which can be eliminated by decarboxylation. The nitro group is convertible to NH_2, which can be eliminated by the deamination reaction. The SO_3H group can be removed by hydrolysis. The only general method of eliminating OH, zinc dust distillation, is subject to limitations. A halo substituent can be replaced by CN, the nitrile hydrolyzed, and the acid decarboxylated; an iodide can be reduced directly with HI; a bromo substituent is removable by catalytic hydrogenation.

4. (a) $C_6H_5CH=C(C_2H_5)CHO$ (10% alkali)
(b) $C_6H_5CH=CHCH=CHCOC_6H_5$ (10% alkali)
(c) $C_6H_5CH=CHCH=CHCHO$ (condensation in 70% alcohol with piperidine acetate as catalyst affords the phenylpentadienal in 50% yield).

5. Oxidation with MnO_2—H_2SO_4 to o-bromo-**benzaldehyde**; condensation of the aldehyde

with $(CH_3CO)_2O$—CH_3CO_2Na or with $CH_2(CO_2H)_2$ in pyridine-piperidine.

6. $C_6H_5COCH_3 + BrCH_2CO_2C_2H_5 + Zn →$ $C_6H_5C(OH)(CH_3)CH_2CO_2C_2H_5$; dehydration to $C_6H_5C(CH_3)=CHCO_2C_2H_5$ (or bond isomer); hydrogenation; hydrolysis.

7. Reimer-Tiemann synthesis of aldehydic phenols; Fries synthesis of ketonic phenols; acylation of resorcinol-type phenols (very reactive) with RCOOH + $ZnCl_2$; condensation of dimethylaniline with phosgene to give Michler's ketone.

CHAPTER 31. NAPHTHALENE (*questions: p. 752*)

1. (a) β-Acetonaphthalene → β-COOH → β-COCl; Friedel-Crafts condensation with benzene.
(b) α-Bromonaphthalene → α-MgBr → α-COOH → α-COCl → α-CHO (Rosenmund or Sonn-Müller reaction).
(c) Naphthalene-β-sulfonic acid → β-naphthol → β-naphthylamine → diazonium salt → β-iodonaphthalene (Sandmeyer).
(d) β-Acetonaphthalene + CH_3MgBr → β-C(OH)(CH$_3$)$_2$ → β-C(=CH$_2$)CH$_3$ → β-CH(CH$_3$)$_2$.

2. (a) Sulfonation to Schaeffer acid (p. 747) and alkali fusion.
(b) See page 715.
(c) Nitrosation
(d) Methyl ether + CH_3COCl $(AlCl_3$ in $C_6H_5NO_2)$ → 6-aceto-2-methoxynaphthalene; Clemmensen reduction and demethylation.
(e) Claisen rearrangement of β-naphthol allyl ether and hydrogenation of the double bond in the side chain.

3. (a) Nitration and reduction
(b) Friedel-Crafts reaction with acetyl chloride in nitrobenzene solution and hypochlorite oxidation of the 6-aceto derivative.
(c) Sulfonation to 2-methylnaphthalene-6-sulfonic acid, alkali fusion to the naphthol, Bucherer reaction with ammonium bisulfite.

4. (a) Nitration of α-nitronaphthalene gives a mixture from which the high-melting 1,5-dinitro compound is easily separated; this on reduction gives the 1,5-diamine.
(b) Dibromination of α-naphthylamine gives the 2,4-dibromo compound (compare dinitration of α-naphthol); this on diazotization and deamination gives 1,3-dibromonaphthalene.
(c) α-Naphthylamine → α-naphthol → 2,4-disulfonic acid → 2,4-dinitro-1-naphthol (Martius Yellow) → 2,4-diamino-1-naphthol.

5. Succinoylation of naphthalene gives a mixture of 1- and 2-naphthoylpropionic acids that need not be separated. Clemmensen reduction gives a mixture of two naphthylbutyric acids, each of which on cyclization with liquid HF yields a ketotetrahydrophenanthrene. Both isomers on reduction afford tetrahydrophenanthrene, and phenanthrene is obtained on dehydrogenation (Se or Pd—C).

CHAPTER 32. POLYNUCLEAR HYDROCARBONS
(questions: p. 794)

1. (a) Bromination to the 9-bromo compound; RMgBr + (CH₃)₂SO₄. (b) Cyclization, condensation with CH₃MgI, dehydration, dehydrogenation.

2. 2-Retenol (2-hydroxyretene)

3. (a) The dibasic acid obtained as a degradation product is 5,5'-dimethoxydiphenic acid (for synthetic method, see p. 667), and the sulfonation product is phenanthrene-3,6-disulfonic acid.
(b) Nitration of p-toluidine in sulfuric acid solution results in substitution meta to the amino group. Diazotization, hydrolysis, and methylation gives 4-methoxy-2-nitrotoluene, and permanganate oxidation of the methyl group and reduction of the nitro group gives the required intermediate.

4. Friedel-Crafts condensation → o-(4-chlorobenzoyl)-benzoic acid; cyclization to β-chloroanthraquinone; reaction with ammonia.

5. Condensation of phthalic anhydride with α-methylnaphthalene effects substitution in the 4-position and cyclization of the product with H₂SO₄ gives 3-methyl-1,2-benzanthraquinone, which affords the desired hydrocarbon on reduction with zinc and ammonia.

6. Monosulfonation in the presence of mercuric sulfate, reduction with zinc and ammonia, alkali fusion.

7. Reaction of anthrone with CH₃MgI and dehydration of the resulting carbinol (1,4-elimination of water).

CHAPTER 38. STEROIDS
(questions: p. 995)

1. (a) Epicoprostanol. (b) 3-Monocathylate. (c) Cholestane-3β,5α-diol-6-one. (d) Cholestane-4-one (trans-decalin more stable than cis; epimerization through the enol). (e) Cholestane-3β,5α,6β-triol. (f) 5α-Chlorocholestane-3β,6β-diol. (g) The 8α,9α-oxide. (h) Choestane-3β,5α,6α-triol.

2. Since bromohydrin A on elimination of HBr gave an oxide, it must be trans, and since hydrogenation shows the 3-OH to be β, the 2-Br must be α. Conversion of B to a ketone rather than an oxide shows that the hydrogen eliminated is the C₃-β-H trans to the bromine, which therefore is α. The 2α-bromine is equatorial and hence this is the expected product of bromination. Bromination of coprostanone gives the 4β-bromoketone, also equatorial.

3. According to the Markownikoff rule (attack by a proton at C₆) to give the 5-chloro derivative (configuration unknown). If bromination involved a rear attack by Br⁺ at C₆, the product would be the 5β,6α-dibromide.

4. The latter forms an acetonide, estriol does not.

5. The bond linking the angular methyl group is activated by both double bonds and hence easily severed. Hydrogen derived from tetralin affords methane and the keto form of the phenol. Related reaction: see santonin.

6. See "Nat. Prod. Rel. to Phenanthrene," pp. 337–339.

AUTHOR INDEX

Biographies are indicated by bold-face type and literature citations by parentheses

Abel, J. J., 458
Adams, R., **65,** (294), 407, 495, 679, 724
Adkins, H., **66,** (83), 197, (223), 797
Alder, K., **310**
Alexander, P., 722
Allen, C. F. H., (223), **774**
Allen, E., 970
Allen, W. M., 969, 976
Allison, F. E., 1010
Altenburrow, J., 959
Amadori, M., 353
Anderson, G. W., 446
Anderson, R. J., **407**
Anner, G., **983**
Anschütz, R., **285**
Anson, M. L., (471)
Arago, D. F., 249
Ardao, M. I., 723
Arens, J. F., 957
Armstrong, E. F., **362**
Armstrong, H. E., **521**
Arnaud, A., 405
Arndt, F., **184**
Auwers, K. v., **217,** 283, 682
Avery, O. T., 396–397
Avison, A. W. D., (487)

Bachmann, W. E., 214, (555), (708), 794, **983**
Backer, H. J., 177
Baddiley, J., **467,** 470
Badger, G. M., (526), (795)
Baekeland, L. H., **866**
Baer, E., **489**
Baeyer, A. von. 245–247, **296**–297, 325, 485,
  516, 517, 521, 529, 895, 906–907
Bailey, J. R., 99
Bailey, K., (471)
Baker, J. W., **333**
Baker, W., 782, (795)
Balbiano, L., 435
Ball, S., 956
Bally, O., 913–915
Bamberger, E., 510, **585,** 603, 949
Banting, F. G., **458**
Bardhan, J. C., 949
Barger, G., 433
Barkley, L. B., 987
Barltrop, J. A., 641
Barron, P. J., (879)
Bart, H. E., 615
Bartlett, P. D., **330**–331, 335, (349), (570),
  619, 760

Barton, D. H. R., **306,** 347, 947, 949, (960),
  965
Baumann, C. A., 529
Baumann, E., 627
Baur, A., 583
Baxter, C. D., 955
Beadle, G. W., **508**
Béchamp, A., 890
Beckmann, E., **701**
Behring, E. von, 1021
Bell, D. J., (487)
Bell, P. H., 460
Bennett, G. M., (325)
Bergius, F., **108**
Bergmann, E. D., (93), **534**
Bergmann, M., **442,** 462, (471), 497, (513)
Berthelot, M., 533
Berzelius, J., **3,** 16, 252, 255
Biilmann, E., **284**
Biot, J. B., **249,** 250
Birch, A. J., **977**
Birch, S. F., (110)
Bischler, A., 812
Black, H. K., 405
Blackman, F. F., 485
Blanc, G., 177, 318, 647
Blangey, L., 739, (752)
Blatt, A. H., (223), (643)
Blicke, F. F., (708)
Bloch, K. E., **494,** 989, 990, (996)
Block, R. J., (471)
Blodgett, K. B., 411
Blomquist, T., 321
Boer, Th. J. de, 177
Böeseken, J., **299**
Bogert, M. T., (960)
Bohn, R., 766, **903,** 911, 912
Boissonnas, R. A., 445
Bond, A. C., Jr., 116
Bonner, D. M., 509
Böttiger, P., 887
Bouchardat, G., **850**
Bougault, J., 216, 544
Bouveault, L., **177,** 440
Boyd, T. A., 100
Braconnot, H., 419
Bradsher, C. K., **793**
Bragg, W. H., 517
Bragg, W. L., 517
Braun, J. von, **97,** 158

Bredt, J., **942**
Bretonnière, 921
Brewster, R. Q., 616
Brockmann, H., **729,** 824, 1013
Brockway, L. O., 159
Brooker, L. G. S., (934)
Brooks, B. T., (110)
Brown, H. C., 226
Brown, J. B., 399, 404
Brown, W. G., 116
Bruyn, L. de, **360**
Buchanan, J. M., **507**
Bucherer, H. Th., 432, **741**
Buchner, E., **472,** 946
Bunnett, J. F., (570)
Bunsen, R. W., 551
Burk, D., 1010
Burr, G. O., 495–496
Burr, M. M., 495–496
Butenandt, A., 13, **969,** 973, 974
Butleroff, A. M., **367**

Cairns, R. W., (144)
Calcott, W. S., 537
Calingaert, G., (48)
Calvin, M., **485,** 681
Cameron, M. E., (555)
Campbell, W. P., 944
Cannizzaro, S., **210**
Carmack, M., (708)
Caro, H., **892,** 902, 924
Carothers, W. H., 317, **847,** 851, 860
Carter, H. E., 274, 437, **490**
Caventou, J. B., 2, 15, 1025
Celmer, W. D., 406
Chevreul, M. E., **2,** 15
Chain, E., 1033
Chardonnet, H. de, 858
Chibnall, A. C., 409, 493
Chichibabin, A. E., **807**
Christie, G. H., 292
Claisen, L., **639,** 688, 692, 704
Clar, E., **775**
Claus, A., 521
Clemo, G. R., **945**
Cleve, P. T., 749
Cohn, E. J., 454–455, (471)
Cole, A. G., 520
Cole, W., **983**
Cook, J. W., **642,** (643), 783, (795)
Cooke, R. G., 731
Cookson, R. C., 630
Cooley, L. C., (223)
Cope, A. C., **524**

Cori, C., **474–**475, (487)
Cori, G., **474–**475
Corner, G. W., 976
Cornforth, J. W., 704, **983**
Coulson, C. A., (83), (327)
Crafts, J. M., **535–**536
Craig, L. C., **450,** 836
Craig, L. E., (325)
Cramer, D. L., 404
Criegee, R., **129**
Croissant, 921
Crombie, L., 405
Curtius, Th., 233, 434, **442**

Dakin, H. D., 626
Dam, H., 1016
Dane, E., 783, 969
Darzens, G., **700**
Dauben, W. G., **985**
Davis, B. D., **508**
Davis, M., 997
Davy, Sir Humphrey, 135
Davy, J., 184
Debye, P., 516
Dewar, J., 521
Dewar, M. J. S., 640, 641
Diassi, P. A., 843
Dieckmann, W., **220**
Diels, O., **310,** 316, 545
Diesbach, H. de, 933
Dimroth, O., **769,** 771
Dippy, J. F. G., (190)
Dochez, A. R., 396
Doebner, O., 883
Doering, W. von E., **642,** 1027
Doisy, E. A., 969, 970, 971, **1016,** 1017
Domagk, G., 1028
Donath, W. F., 998
Dorp, D. A van, 957
Douglas, S. D., (879)
Drake, N. L., (752)
DuBois, A. S., (708)
Dubos, R., 450
Dufraisse, C., **773**
Duisberg, C., 817
Dumas, J. B. A., **15,** 579, 936, 942
Dunn, M. S., **433–**434, 435
Duppa, B. F., 431
Dusart, L., 902

Edgar, G., (48)
Edman, P., 447
Edsall, J. T., 454–455, (471)
Eggleston, P., 477
Egloff, G., (83), (110)

Ehrlich, F., 481
Ehrlich, P., 1022-102;
Eijkman, C., 997
Eistert, B., 184
Ekenstein, W. A. van, 360, 361
Elbs, K., 790
Elderfield, R. C., (825)
Elliot, D. F., 439
Elvehjem, C. A., 1000, 1006
Embden, G., 470, 479, 494
Emde, H., 830
Engelhardt, H., 255
Entemann, C. E., Jr., (190)
Erlenmeyer, E., Jr., 436, 692
Erlenmeyer, E., Sen., 113, 280, 732
Estable, C., 723
Étard, A. L., 676
Euler, H. von, 464, 479, 1000
Evans, E. A., Jr., 483, (1020)
Evans, H. M., 1014
Everest, A. E., (795)

Faraday, M., 514
Fawcett, R. W., 948
Feofilaktov, V. V., 440
Fernholz, E., 1015
Fierz-David, H. E., 739, 746, (752), 922, (934)
Fieser, L. F., 98, (526), 669, 713, 715, 721, 723,
    729 734, 767, 791, 794, (795), (934),
    (996), 1017
Fieser, M., 713, 729, (996)
Fildes, P., 1032
Finholt, A. E., 116
Fischer, E., 245-246, 262, 350, 351 352, 354
    356, 358-359, 361-362, 367 370, 426-427,
    432, 440-442, 803, 892, 895
Fischer, F., 108
Fischer, F. G., 949
Fischer, H., 456-458, 486
Fischer, H. O. L., 394, 508
Fischer, O., 890, 892, 893, 895, 901
Fisher, H. L., (879)
Fiske, C. H., 477
Fittig, R., 534
Fleming, A., 1033
Florey, H. W., 1033
Flory, P. J., (879)
Fodor, G., 839
Folch, J., 488
Folkers, K. A., 1008, 1034
Fourneau, E., 1024, 1029
Francis, F., 330
Frankland, E., 551
Frankland, P., (294)

Franzen, V., 645
Freudenberg, K., 423
Freund, M., 309
Fried, J., 979
Friedel, C., 535-536, 877
Friedländer, P., 616, 811, 908, 909
Fries, K., 634, 733, 735, 745
Fritsch, P., 813
Fritsche, C. J., 595
Fruton, J. S., (471), 497
Funk, C., 998
Fuson, R. C., (325), (655)

Gabriel, S., 233, 431, 691
Gadamer, J. G., 311, 381, 833
Gallagher, T. F., 973
Gams, A., 831
Gates, M., 834, 837
Gattermann, L., 614, 677, 678
Gay-Lussac, L. J., 551
Gerhardt, C. F., 3
Gibbs, H. D., 659
Gilbert, E. E., (48)
Gilman, A., (1036)
Gilman, H., 182, 649, 650
Girard, A., 971
Glass, N. B., (513)
Glemo, P., 1029
Goepp, R. M., Jr., (398)
Goldberger, J., 1005
Goldschmidt, S., 637
Goldstein, A., (1036)
Gomberg, M., 551-553, (555)
Goodman, L., (1036)
Goodwin, T. W., 956
Goodyear, C., 848
Goudsmit, S. A., 74
Graebe, C., 732, 777, 901-903, 913
Greenstein, J. P., 431
Gresham, W. F., 373
Grewe, R., 834, 836
Griess, P., 519, 611, 615, 922, 923
Grignard, V., 37
Grimmel, H. W., (934)
Grove, J. F., 805
Gulland, J. M., 833
Gunstone, F. D., 405, (416)
Günther, F., 721
Gustavson, G., 309, 539
György, P., 999, 1011

Haber, F., 585
Hamer, F. M., (934)
Hammett, L. P., 336. (349)

Handrick, G. R., (587)
Hanes, C. S., 475
Hantzsch, A., 171, **611**
Harden, A., **464,** 472
Harfenist, M., 431
Harington, C. R., 459
Harries, C. D., 520, **587**
Harris, J. O., 948
Harris, R. S., (1020)
Hartmann, M., 969
Hartung, W. H., 704
Hass, H. B., 45, 309
Hassel, O., **305**
Hassid, W. Z., **382**
Haurowitz, F., (471)
Hauser, C. R., (223)
Haüy, R. J., 249
Hawkins, J. D., (487)
Haworth, R. D., **641,** 642, 745, 753, 945, 949
Haworth, W. N., **363,** 364, 366, 367, 375–377, 381, 382, 386–387, 392, (398), (487)
Hechter, O., 982
Heidelberger, M., **396,** 524
Heilbron, I. M., **950,** 1013
Hell, C., 170
Hench, P. S., 979
Henne, A. L., **159,** (160)
Henry, T. A., (846)
Hermann, A., 893
Herschel, J., 250
Hershberg, E. B., 65, 98, **979**
Hertog, H. J. den, 809
Herz, R., 911
Hess, A. F., 1012
Hesse, G., 394
Heumann, K., 907
Hey, D. H., (48)
Heymann, H., 987
Hilditch, T. P., **402,** (416)
Hill, J. W., 317
Hinsberg, O., 236
Hirschberger, J., 354
Hirschmann, R., 1017
Hirst, E. L., **363,** 390, 392, (398)
Hodgkin, D. C., 1008
Hoesch, K., **695**
Hoff, J. H. van't, **256**–257, 278–280, 287, (294), 371
Hoffmann, A., 842
Hofmann, A. W. v., (23), **225,** 228, 231, 237, 238, 515, 610, 638, 671, 891
Hofmann, K. A., **296**
Holleman, A. F., **558,** (570)
Holmes, H. L., (846)

Honeyman, J., (398)
Hooker, S. C., **727**–728, 729, 949
Hoover, S. R., 1010
Hopkins, F. G., **997**
Horning, E. C., (879)
Houdry, E. J., 103
Hromatka, O., 835
Huang-Minlon, 214
Huber, G., 382–383
Hückel, E., **554**
Hückel, W., **299**
Hudson, B. E., Jr., (223)
Hudson, C. S., 262, 364–365, 373, **374**–378, (398)
Huebner, C. F., 843
Hughes, E. D., 149, **337**–339, 341, (349), 565
Huisgen, R., **612**
Hunsdiecker, H., 320
Huntress, E. H., (160)
Huston, R. C., (83)
Hyatt, 863

Ichikawa, K., 783
Iljinsky, M., 764–765
Inhoffen, H. H., **959,** 971
Ing, H. R., 445
Ingold, C. K., 149, **327,** 337–339, 341, 343–347, (349), 554, 565, 801
Ipatieff, V. N., **66,** 104
Isler, O., 956
Ittner, M. H., 410

Jackson, E. L., 364–365
Jacobs, W. A., **841,** 995
Jacobsen, O., **664**
Jacobsen, O. G. F., 901
Jansen, B., 323
Jansen, B. C. P., 998
Japp, F. R., (23), (526)
Jeger, O., **951**
Jenner, E., 1020
Jerchel, D., **805**
Jones, E. R. H., 805, **955**
Johnson, A. W., **642,** (643)
Johnson, J. R., **183,** (190), 549, (708)
Johnson, W. S., **306,** 699, (708), 983, 955

Karrer, P., 325, **465,** 818, 820, 950, 952, 953, 954, 959, 998, 1003, 1015, 1016
Karrer, W., 722
Katz, A., 992
Kaufmann, A., 813
Kekulé, A., **17,** 18–22, 285, 514–516, 519–523, 902

Kendall, E. C., 459, **977**, 979, 980
Kennaway, E. L., 783
Kenner, J., 292
Kern, A., 892
Kerschbaum, M., 302
Kharasch, M. S., **42**, 62, 646
Kidd, D. A., 445
Kienle, R. H., **872**–874, (879)
Kiliani, H., **350**–351, 356, 487
Kimball, R. H., 329
King, C. G., **391**
King, F. E., 445
King, H., **969**
Kipping, F. S., **878**
Kishner, N. M., **214**
Kistiakowsky, G. B., 523
Kjeldahl, J., **15**
Klenk, E., **490**, (496)
Kloetzel, M. C., (325)
Kluyver, A. J., 479
Klyne, W., (294), (325)
Knoevenagel, E., **692**
Knoop, F., **492**–494
Knorr, L., 217, **798**
Knox, W. E., 510
Koch, A., 749
Koch, F. C., **973**
Koch, J. A., 677
Koch, R., 1021
Koepfli, J. B., **844**
Kögl, F., **723**, 724, 1010, 1011
Kohler, E. P., **205**, 541
Kolbe, H., **40**, 45, 257, 661, 895
Komppa, G., **942**
König, W., 899
Kornblum, N., 45
Körner, W., **518**–519
Kornfeld, E. C., 841
Köster, H., 984
Kovács, K., 450
Krabbe, W., 812
Krebs, H. A., **481**–484, 490, 502
Krsek, G., 797
Kuhn, R., 267, 415, 464–**465**, 523, 689, 691,
    726, 805, 881, 882, 883, 951, 952, 959,
    1003, 1004
Kuhn, W., **387**
Küster, W., 456

Ladenburg, A., **517**, 520, 521, 830, 877
Landsteiner, K., 596
Langdon, R. G., 990
Langmuir, I., 411
Lapworth, A., **326**, 603

Laqueur, E., **972**, 974
Lauer, W. M., 205
Laurent, A., **514**, 579
Lavoisier, A., **2**
Le Bel, J. A., **256**–257
Lederer, E., **950**
Leloir, L. F., **475**
Lemieux, R. U., **382**–383
Leuchs, H., **843**
Leuckart, R., 600
Levene, P. A., 379, **468**
Levine, A. A., 520
Lewis, G. N., **138**, 163, 326, 522
Liebermann, C., **284**, 769, 901–903
Liebig, J. von, 2, **9**, 10–15, 244–247, 255, 280,
    380, 394, 514, 693, 872, 999
Lightfoot, J., 888
Link, K. P., (825), 1019
Linstead, R. P., **401**, 404, 545, 933, (934)
Lipmann, F., **467**, 478–479, 494–495, (496)
Loconti, J. R., 723
Loew, O., 368
Loewe, S., 974
Logemann, W., 984
Lohmann, K., 470, 1000
Lonsdale, K., 517
Lothrop, W. C., (587), 734, 772
Loudon, J. D., 643
Lovell, W. G., (110)
Lovern, J. A., (496)
Lubs, H. A., (934)
Lundsgaard, E., 477, 478
Lunin, G., 997
Lüttringhaus, A., **322**
Lynen, F., **467**, 494, (496)

Macbeth, A. K., 726
Macleod, J. J. R., **458**
Magerlein, B. J., (708)
Mai, J., 616
Major, R. T., 135, 270
Malus, E. L., 249
Mannich, C., **704**
Manske, R. H. F., 445, **826**, 846
Marckwald, W., 733
Mark, H., **453**
Marker, R. E., (48), 993, 994, 995
Markley, K. S., (416)
Markownikoff, V. W., **61**, 97
Marrian, G. F., 976
Martin, A. J. P., **428**
Martin, E. L., 544, (555)
Martius, K. A. von, 923
Marvel, C. S., (294), (879)

Mauss, H., 1026, (1036)
Maxwell, W. R., 667
Mayer, F., (731), (960)
Mayo, F. R., (83)
McCollum, E. V., 997
McElroy, W. D., (513)
McElvain, S. M., **218**
McFadyen, J. S., 687
McKay, A. F., 176
McKeever, C. H., (655)
McKenzie, A., **276**
Meerwein, H., **126,** 207
Meisenheimer, J., **240**
Mendel, L. B., 997
Mering, J. von, 246
Mester, L., 353
Meyer, K., **395**
Meyer, K. H., **217,** 218, 390, (398), 453
Meyer, Kuno, 993
Meyer, V., **45,** 518, 520, 528–529, 654, 671
Meyerhof, O., **473,** 478, (487)
Meystre, Ch., 980
Michael, A., **286**–287, 379, 690, 699
Michaelis, L., 694
Micheel, F., **392,** (398)
Michler, W., 696
Midgley, T., 100, 159
Miescher, K., **981**
Miethe, A., 899
Mietzsch, F., 1026, (1036)
Miller, J. A., 529
Miller, W. von, 769
Minot, G. R., 1006
Mitscherlich, E. A., **252,** 514
Moffett, R. H., 948
Mohr, E., **298**
Moore, C. R., 974
Moore, F. J., (23)
Moore, S., **429**
Mörner, K. A. H., 420
Morton, R. A., **956**
Moureu, C., **773**
Mozingo, R., 216, 544, 1011
Müller, E., 686
Munch, J. C., 704
Murphy, W. P., 1008
Murray, H. C., 982

Nakanishi, K., 493
Napieralski, B., 812
Natta, G., 876
Naves, Y.-R., **939**
Nencki, M. von, 456
Neuberg, C., **472**

Neurath, H., (471)
Neville, H. A., (879)
Neville, R. H. C., 746
Newman, M. S., **672,** (708), 739, 762, 782
Nicholson, E. C., 892
Nicholson, J. S., 641
Nickon, A., 839
Nicol, W., 249
Niel, C. B. van, **486**
Nieuwland, J. A., **851**
Nilsson, R., 479
Nobel, A., 131, 132
Noller, C. R., 994
Norris, J. F., **538**
Nozoe, T., 640
Nunn, J. R., 296
Nystrom, R. F., 166

Ochiai, E., 809
Ochoa, S., (487), **494,** (496)
Oppenauer, R. V., 194
Orchin, M., 586
Osborne, T. B., 997
Ott, E., (879)
Ourisson, G., 948
Oxford, A., 722, 804

Parkes, 863
Parnas, J., 478, 479
Partington, J. R., (23), 667
Pasteur, L., **251**–255, 270, 273, (294), 394
    473, 476, 1021
Paul, R.-E., **815**
Pauli, W., 74
Pauling, L., (83), 114, (144), **327,** 523, (526),
    554, (934)
Peat, S., 475
Pechmann, H. Frh. von, **817**
Peligot, E. M., 936
Pelletier, P. J., 2, 15, **828,** 1025
Perkin, A. G., 641
Perkin, W. H., 431, **515,** 689–690, 889–891,
    903, (934)
Perkin, W. H. Jr., (325), **516,** (526)
Perrier, G., 738
Peters, R. A., (93)
Peterson, D. H., 982
Pfau, A. St., 776
Pfeiffer, P., 681
Pfitzinger, W., 812
Pictet, A., **831**
Pigman, W. W., (398)
Piloty, O., 456
Pitzer, K. S., **305**

Plattner, Pl. A., 776, **946**
Polgar, N., 407
Pomeranz, C., 813
Ponndorf, W., 207
Pope, W. J., **273,** 899
Posternak, T., 394
Pregl, F., **13**
Prelog, V., **320,** (325)
Prey, V., 627
Price, C. C., **563**
Price, J. R., 730
Priestley, J., **2**
Provostaye, M. de la, 252
Prud'homme, M., 903
Pschorr, R., 835
Pummerer, R., 638, **848**
Purdie, T., **364**

Raistrick, H., **393,** 722, 804, 825
Ralston, A. W., (416)
Raper, H. S., 511
Raphael, R. A., (93), (325), **805**
Rast, K., 11
Ratner, S., 502, (513)
Redfarn, C. A., (879)
Reeves, R. E., 366
Reformatsky, S., **692**
Reich, H., 983
Reichstein, T., 392–393, 977, **987**
Reimer, C., **680**
Remick, A. E., (160), (349)
Remsen, I., **591**
Rennie, E. H., 726, 729
Reppe, W., **91,** 524, 797, 853
Rittenberg, D., **429,** 494, 989
Roberts, I., **329**
Robertson, A., **804,** 825
Robertson, J. M., 735
Robeson, J. G., 955
Robinson, G. M., 818
Robinson, R., **326,** 704, 730, 818, 821, 833, 836, 840, 843, 983
Robiquet, P. J., 15
Rochow, E. G., **879**
Rodd, E. H., (325)
Rogers, D., 948
Roozeboom, H. W. B., **269**
Rosanoff, M. A., 262
Rose, F. L., (1036)
Rose, W. C., **498,** (513)
Rosenberg, H. R., (1020)
Rosenheim, O., **969**
Rosenmund, K., 196
Rossini, F. D., **95**

Rouelle, G. F., 2
Rowe, F. M., (934)
Ruben, S., 485
Ruff, O., **358**
Ruggli, P., **319**
Ruigh, W., 135
Runge, F. F., 595, 894
Ruzicka, L., **299**–302, 318, (325), 940, 945, 949, 950, 951, (960), 973, 974
Rydon, H. N., 147

Sabatier, P., **66,** 516
Sabo, E. F., 979
Sachse, H., 298
Sanderhoff, R., 989
Sandin, R. B., **794**
Sandmeyer, T., **613**
Sanger, F., **446**–447, 459
Sarett, L. H., **981,** 987
Sato, Y., 995
Saussure, N. Th. de, 367
Saytzeff, A. M., **126**
Schaeffer, L., 747
Scheele, C. W., **1,** 2, 124, 244, 255, 663
Scherrer, P., 516
Schiemann, G., 615
Schiff, H., 361
Schlatter, M. J., 539
Schlenk, F., 464
Schlesinger, H. I., **116**
Schlittler, E., **843**
Schmid, H., 825
Schmidt, C. L. A., 233, (471)
Schmidt, J. G., 688
Schmidt, K. E., **764,** 766, 903, 917
Schmitt, J., 689
Schmitt, R., **661**
Schneider, E., 486
Schoenheimer, R., **491**–492, (496), 497, 499, 502, (513), 989
Scholl, R., **781,** 911, 912, 915
Schönbein, C. F., 858
Schöpf, C., 811, **833,** 834, 841
Schorlemmer, C., (23)
Schotten, C., **627**
Schunck, E., 908
Schuster, P., 1000
Schwartzkopf, O., 959
Schwenk, E., 705
Sebrell, W. H., Jr., (1020)
Seligman, A., 791
Senderens, J. B., 516
Sengupta, S. C., 949
Sertürner, F. W., 2, **833**

Shantz, E. M., 955
Sheehan, J. C., 214, **445**
Shemin, D., 506
Sherman, C. S., 544
Shreve, R. N., 659
Shriner, R. L., (294), (708)
Sidgwick, N. V., (825)
Simons, J. H., 537
Simonsen, J. L., **948**
Simpson, S. A., 977
Skraup, Z. H., **810,** 903
Slotta, K. H., **969**
Small, L. F., **835,** 836, (846)
Smart, C. L., (398)
Smith, E. L., 1008
Smith, J. C., 405
Smith, L. I., **536,** 664, 1016, (1020)
Snell, E. E., **429,** 499
Snell, F. D., (416)
Soffer, M. D., 214, 944
Solomons, I. A., 406
Sommelet, M., 677
Sonn, A., 686
Sörensen, N. A., 406
Späth, E., 812, **818,** 835
Spielman, M. A., (708)
Spies, T. D., (1020)
Spoerri, P. E., (708)
Sprengel, 579
Sproxton, F., (879)
Stanley, W. M., **470,** (471)
Staudinger, H., **387**
Steenbock, H., 954, 1012
Stein, W. H., 429
Stephen, H., 687
Stevens, T. S., 687
Stobbe, H., 699
Stoll, A., **841,** (846)
Stoll, M., 321
Stork, G., **311,** 804, 834, 948
Stotz, E. H., **490**
Strecker, A., **432**
Strong, F. M., 404
Struve, W. S., (708)
Stuart, H. A., 258
Subbarow, Y., 477
Sullivan, M. X., 428
Sumner, J. B., 460–**461**
Svedberg, T., 387, 452
Swietoslawski, W., 11
Synge, R. L. M., **428**
Szent-Györgyi, A., 391, **481,** 823
Szmuszkovicz, J., 534, 669

Tafel, J., 368
Tait, J. F., 977
Takaki, K., 997
Tamelen, E. E. van, 843
Tanret, C., **362**
Tarbell, D. S., 330–331, **642,** (643)
Tatum, E. L., **508**
Theorell, H., **464,** 466, 493
Thiele, J., **521,** 706, 717
Thomas, C. A., (144)
Thomas, H., 989
Thompson, R. H., 726
Tiemann, F., **680**
Tiffeneau, M., **649**
Tilden, W. A., **850**
Tiselius, A., **451,** 454, (471)
Tishler, M., 432, 438, 959, **981,** 1004
Tobias, G., 748
Todd, A. R., **469,** 470, 723, 780, 1008
Tollens, B., **361**
Tréfouël, J., 1029
Tropsch, H., **108**
Trueblood, K. N., 1008
Tschugaeff, L. A., **348**
Tsujimoto, M., 950
Tuppy, H., 448
Turner, R. B., **306,** 987
Turpeinen, O., 496

Uhle, F. C., 995
Uhlenbeck, G. E., 74
Ullmann, F., **580,** 600, 652
Umbreit, W. W., 1000
Unverdorben, 595
Urey, H. C., 491

Van Slyke, D. D., 427
Vaughan, J. R., 445
Venkataraman, K., (934)
Verguin, 891
Verkade, P. E., **493,** 592
Vesterberg, A., 545
Vickery, H. B., (471)
Vidal, R., 921
Vigneaud, V. du, 439, **448**–449, 503, 1011
Volhard, J., 170

Wackenroder, H. W. F., 951
Wagner, G., **126**
Wagner-Jauregg, Th., 267, **999**
Wahlbaum, H., 299
Waksman, S., **1034**
Wald, G., **956**
Walden, P. v., **277**

Wallach, O., **935**
Wallenfels, K., 726
Walling, C., (83)
Wallis, E. S., (708)
Warburg, O., **464,** 479, 485, 1000
Waser, E., 524
Waters, W. A., (48), (555)
Watson, H. B., (570)
Weedon, B. C. L., 405
Weermann, R. A., 358
Weid, E. von der, 933
Weidlein, E. R., (879)
Weinhouse, S., **493**
Weissberger, A., 694
Weizmann, C., 91, **121,** 531
Wenkert, E., 843
Went, F. W., 513
Wessely, F., **442**
Wettstein, A., **969,** 977, 989
Weygand, F., **352,** 358
Wheland, G. W., (83)
Whipple, G. H., 1006
Whistler, R. L., (398)
Whitmore, F. C., 214, **339,** 701
Wibaut, J. P., **521,** 558. (825)
Wieland, H., 127, 604, **783,** 843, 969, 993, 1007
Wieland, T., 445
Wildiers, E., 394
Wilds, A. L., 184, **983,** 986
Willgerodt, C., **652,** 705
Williams, G., 890, 898
Williams, R. J., **999,** 1009, 1010
Williams, R. R., **1001,** (1020)
Williamson, A. W., **136**
Willstätter, R., **456,** 484, 485, 524, 641, 716, 818, 819, 820, 823, 839, 841, 888, 949, 951

Windaus, A., 641, **963,** 973, 998, 1001, 1013, 1014
Winstein, S., **341**
Winter, A., 746
Wintersteiner, O., 843, **969**
Winzor, F. L., 726
Wislicenus, J., **255**–256, 280, 670
Witt, O. N., 883, 923
Wittig, G., **650,** 651
Wohl, A., **357**
Wöhler, F., **3,** 16, 244–247, 380, 693
Wolff, G., (795)
Wolff, L., 184, **214**
Wolfrom, M. L., 216, **395,** (398), 544, 823, 1034
Woods, D. D., 1032
Woodward, R. B., 683, 843, **986,** 1027
Woolley, D. W., 395
Woskresensky, 709
Wurtz, A., **35,** 224, 534, 902

Yamagiwa, K., 783
Young, W. J., 464, 472

Zahler, R. E., (570)
Zahn, H., 882
Zechmeister, L., **952**
Zeidler, F., 654
Zeisel, S., 137, 641
Zelikow, J., 126
Zelinsky, N. D., 107, 126, 171, **545**
Zemplén, G., **358**
Zerewitinoff, Th., 205
Ziegler, K., **151,** 243, 852
Zilva, S. S., 998
Zincke, Th., **733,** 735, 745
Zinin, N., 595
Zondek, B., 970

SUBJECT INDEX

Abietic acid, 877, 948–949
Aborine, 827
Acenaphthene, 528,* 534,† 680
  oxidation, 664
  polynitro complexes, 586*
  succinoylation, 665
β-1-Acenaphthoylpropionic acid, 665
β-3-Acenaphthoylpropionic acid, 665
1-Acenaphthylacetic acid, 705
Acetal, 215*
Acetaldehyde, 89,† 150, 192,* 193,† 194,† 211,
    213, 215, 334
  addition reactions, 202, 349
  aldol condensation, 207–208, 209, 336
  dimedone derivative, 480
  fermentation intermediate, 472, 476, 477
  oxidation, 89, 90, 127
  phenylhydrazone, 212, 213
  polymerization, 199–200
  reaction with PCl₅, 157
  semicarbazone, 212
Acetaldoxime, 211
Acetals, 215
Acetamide, 179,* 241,*† 881*
Acetaminomalonic acid, 434
Acetanilide, 231, 560, 599,*† 601, 702
Acethydrazide, 179,*† 213†
Acetic acid, 90,† 127, 163,* 165–166,† 181, 881*
  from pyroligneous acid, 120, 166
  metabolism, 494–495
  pyrolysis of salts, 39–40
Acetic anhydride, 186,*† 541
1-Acetoacenaphthene, 705
Acetoacetic acid, 321,† 494
Acetoacetic ester (ethyl), 218–219,† 816
  synthesis, 218–220, 320
  tautomerism, 217–218
1-(o-Acetobenzyl)-naphthalene, 793
Acetobromogentiobiose, 381
Acetobromoglucose, 379
2-Aceto-9, 10-dihydrophenanthrene, 756
Acetoin, 353, 694
Acetomesitylene, 697
1-Aceto-2-methoxynaphthalene, 746
6-Aceto-2-methoxynaphthalene, 746
α-Acetonaphthalene, 705, 737*†
β-Acetonaphthalene, 737,*† 738†
Acetone, 90,† 121, 128, 192,* 194,† 195,† 881*
  addition reactions, 202, 349
  aldol condensation, 208–209, 534
  biological formation, see metabolism
  haloform reaction, 154–156

  metabolism, 494
  pyrolysis, 186–187
  reduction, 121, 206
Acetone bodies, 494
Acetone cyanohydrin, 203, 876
Acetonides, 375–376
Acetonitrile, 167, 881*
Acetonylacetone, 117, 797, 799†
Acetonyllevulinic acid, 800
2-Acetophenanthrene, 756
3-Acetophenanthrene, 756
9-Acetophenanthrene, 755
Acetophenone, 540–541,* 543, 695*
  bisulfite addition, 202, 203
  condensation, 699, 700, 703, 704
  halogenation, 647, 697–698
  nitration, 697
  oxidation, 698
  oxime, 702, 703
  reduction, 543
Acetophenone-o-carboxylic acid, 691
Acetopseudocumene, 666
2-Acetothiophene, 800
Acetoxime, 211, 881*
9-Acetoxyanthracene, 760
5-Acetoxy-3, 4-benzpyrene, 788
γ-Acetoxybutyradlehyde, 197
Acetoxylation, 788–789
15-Acetoxy-20-methylcholanthrene, 789
2-Acetoxy-1, 4-naphthoquinone, 712
Acetylacetone, 191, 192,* 218
2-Acetylamino-1, 4-naphthoquinone, 712
p-Acetylamino-p'-nitrodiphenyl sulfone, 596
p-Acetylaminophenol, 632
Acetylating agents, see Acetyl chloride, Acetic
    anhydride, and Ketene
Acetylation, alcohols, 187, 188
  amines, 187, 235–236, 599, 632
  phenols, 627
  reductive, 707
Acetyl bromide, 180*
Acetyl chloride, 180,* 181,† 188, 189, 235
Acetylcholine, 461
Acetylcoenzyme A, 482–483
N-Acetylcolchiceine, 641
Acetylcoumaric acid, 690
Acetyl determination, 189
Acetyldiisopropylamine, 235* †
Acetylene, 85,* 87–88,† 103, 881*
  polymerization, 90, 524, 533, 581
  purification, 87
  reactions, 88–92, 157, 286, 797
Acetylenedicarboxylic acid, 286–287
Acetylene dichloride, see s-Dichloroethylene

---

* Physical constants   † Preparation

Acetylenemagnesium bromide, 87
Acetylene tetrachloride, see s Tetrachloro-
ethane
Acetylenic hydrocarbons, see Alkynes
Acetylesterase, 461
Acetyl fluoride, 180*
N-Acetylglucosamine, 389, 396
Acetylides, 86, 87, 91–92
Acetyl iodide, 180*
Acetylisobutylamine, 235* †
Acetyl mercaptans, 139
Acetyl nitrate, 556
Acetyl peroxide, 721–722
N-Acetylphenylethylamine, 812
Acetylsalicylic acid, 662
N-Acetylsulfanilyl chloride, 1029, 1031
3-Acetyl-2-thiohydantoin, 435
N-Acetyl-p-toluidine, 599*
γ-Acid, 748, 924
Acid anhydrides, 185–189, 540–541, 664, 666,
667
Acid-base equilibria, 424–426
Acid chlorides, carboxylic acids, 180–185, 196,
233, 442
sulfonic acids, 589–590
Acid Fuchsin, 892
Acid hydrazides, 179, 233, 442
Acids, see Carboxylic acids and Fatty acids
cis-Aconitic acid, 483, 484, 826
Acridine, 530,* 814*–815†
Acridone, 813*–814*
Acridone dyes, 918
Acrilan, 862
α-Acritol, 369
Acrolein, 192,* 198,† 209,† 311, 331–332, 797
Acrolein diacetate, 797
Acrolein dibromide, 368
Acrosazone (α- and β-), 369
Acrose, 368–369
α Acrosone, 369
Acrylic acid, 61, 163,* 323,† 331, 332–333
Acrylic esters, 876†
Acryloid plastics, 876–877
Acrylonitrile, 89,† 222, 314, 854,† 862
ACTH, 430
Active amyl alcohol, see d-Amyl alcohol
Acyl halides, 180*–185
reduction, 196
Acyloin condensation, 321–322, 693
Adams catalyst, 65
cis- and trans-Addition, 285–289, 335–336
Adenine, 462, 468, 473
Adenosine, 463, 468
diphosphate, 463, 473
triphosphate, 463, 468, 473

Adenosine-5'-monophosphoric acid, see Ad-
enylic acid
S-Adenosylhomocysteine, 504
S-Adenosylmethionine, 504
Adenylic acid, muscle, 470, 473
yeast, 468
Adermin, see Pyridoxine
Adipamide, 861
Adipic acid, 199,† 312,* 314,† 861†
pyrolysis of salts, 196, 318
Adipic anhydride, 317
Adiponitrile, 861
Adkins catalyst, 66
Adrenal cortical hormones, 977–982
Adrenaline, 500
Adrenocorticotropic hormone, 460
Aerosol OT, 413
Aesculetin, 817
Affinin, 405
Agnosterol, 950–951
L-Alanine, 229,† 419,* 424,* 430, 431,† 432,†
434,† 440†
configuration, 423
metabolism, 476, 482, 483, 486, 498, 512–513
β-Alanine, 243,*† 324,† 422, 1009
Albumins, 417
egg, 417, 418, 429, 430, 452*
plasma, 430, 452,* 454, 455
Alcohol dehydrogenase, 461
Alcohols, 63,† 111–144, 210†
acetylation, 188–189
from amines, 236–237
dehydration, 53–57, 66, 125–127
dehydrogenation, 194
derivatives, 608–609, 663
esterification, 174–177
nomenclature, 52, 111
occurrence, 111–113
oxidation, 127–129, 193, 194
reaction with HX, 35, 145–147
Alcoholysis, acids, 130, 174–175
acyl halides, 181, 185
anhydrides, 188–189
esters, 178, 876
oxides, 123
Aldehydes, 69, 192,* 193–194,† 198–199, 675–
684†
acetals, 215
addition reactions, 201–206
aldol condensation, 207–210, 688–690
Cannizzaro reaction, 210–211
condensations, 211–214, 434–437, 688–694
Grignard reaction, 118–119, 204
hydrates, 216
oxidation, 166, 198, 694–695

polymerization, 199–201
reaction with PX$_3$, 86
reduction, 116–117, 209
α,β-unsaturated, 208, 688–691
Aldol, 207,*† 853
Aldolase, 477
Aldol condensation, 207–210, 336, 688–690
  examples, 275–276
Aldomedone, 480
Aldosterone, 977, 978, 989
Aleuritic acid, 320
Algol Colors, 917
Algol Yellow GC, 919
Alicyclic hydrocarbons, see Cycloalkanes
Alizarin, 550, 886, 901–903, 911
Alizarin Blue, 903, 913, 914
Alizarin Bordeaux, 904
Alizarin Cyanin Green G, 904
Alizarin Cyanin R, 904
Alizarin Indigo Blue, 903
Alizarin Orange A, 903
Alizarin Saphirole B, 884, 904
Alizarin Sky Blue BS, 904
Alizarin Yellow A, 886
Alizarin Yellow R, 886
Alkali Blue, 892
Alkali cellulose, 859
Alkaloids, 826–846, 995, 1026
Alkanes, 24–48, 31,* 35–41,† 64–66,† 197†
  aromatization, 107
  chlorination, 41–43
  chlorosulfonation, 42–43
  dehydrogenation, 107
  isomerization, 106
  nitration, 45–46
  occurrence, 33–34, 94–95
  oxidation, 45–46
  pyrolysis, 43, 101–103
  reaction with alkenes, 105–106
  tertiary, 45, 105
  urea complexes, 46
Alkannin, 729
Alkaptonuria, 510
Alkenes, 49–83, 53,* 53–59,† 152,† 238†
  addition reactions, 59–70, 329–335
  alkylation, 105–106
  halogenation, 59–61, 151, 153, 243
  hydration, 63, 115
  hydrogenation, 64–67
  oxidation, 67–69
  ozonization, 67–69
  polymerization, 104–105, 851–853, 855–857,
    876

pyrolysis, 101–103
titration, 659
Alkyd resins, 872–875
Alkylation, acetoacetic ester, 218–220
  acetylene, 86
  alkenes, 105–106, 107
  amines, 228–229, 599–600
  aromatic hydrocarbons, 534–540
  malonic ester, 220–221, 432–434
  phthalimide, 234, 431
  quinones, 718, 721–722, 727
  sodium alkoxides, see Williamson synthesis
Alkyl bromides, 146,* 147,† 148
Alkylcadmium halides, 182
Alkyl chlorides, 41–42,† 148
  hydrolysis, 115, 122
Alkyl cyanides, see Nitriles
Alkyl fluorides, 159–160
Alkyl halides, 35,† 41,† 61–63,† 145–160
  dehydrohalogenation, 57–58
  hydrolysis, 115, 122
  isomerization, 539
  physical constants, 146*
  reaction with AgNO$_2$, 45
  reaction with CH$_3$COSK, 139
  reaction with Mg, see Grignard reagents
  reaction with Na, 35–37
  reaction with NaOR, see Williamson syn-
    thesis
  reaction with NaSCH$_3$, 140
  reaction with NaSH, 139
  reaction with Na$_2$S, 140
  reaction with NH$_3$, 228–229
  reactivity, 147–153
  reduction, 37–39
Alkyl iodides, 36–37, 115, 145–146*†
Alkylmagnesium halides, 37–39,† 141, see also
    Grignard reagents
Alkyl nitrates, 130–131
Alkyl nitrites, 130–131
Alkylsulfonic acids, 139
Alkylsulfuric acids, 130
s-Alkylthiuronium salts, 139
Alkynes, 84–93, 85*
  coupling, 406
  hydrogenation, 289
Allantoin, 245, 246, 506–507
Allene, 85
Allocholanic acid, 968
Allocinnamic acid, 284*
Allocinnamic acid dibromide, 265*
Allocolchiceine, 641
Allodunnione, 731
Alloisoleucine, 424*
Allophanates, 1015

* Physical constants   † Preparation

Allose, 356, 359, 372*
Allothreonine, 423, 437–439†
Allothreo-oxazoline, 439
Alloxan, 244–245, 247, 1003
Alloxazine, 462
Allylacetic acid, 324
Allyl alcohol, 91,† 112,* 123†
  acetate, 197
  reaction with HCl, 147
Allylamine, 224*
Allylbenzene, 532*
Allyl bromide, 145,† 146,* 150, 333
Allyl chloride, 123, 146,* 147,† 150
Allyl halides, 146,* 150–152, 338
Allylic bromination, 151, 243, 545, 981
Allylic oxidation, 405, 849
Allylic rearrangements, 343, 639–640, 649,
  729, 734–735, 949, 956–957
Allyl iodide, 146*
Allyl isothiocyanate, 381, 609
α-Allylnaphthalene, 546†
1-Allyl-2-naphthol, 734
1-Allyl-2-phenanthrol, 753
o-Allylphenol, 639
Altrose, 356, 359, 372*
Aluminum t-butoxide, 125, 194
Aluminum isopropoxide, 125, 207
Aluminum naphthenate, 98
Aluminum trialkyls, 876
Amadori reaction, 353
Amaranth, 925
Ambrein, 950
Ambreinolide, 950
Ambrettolide, 302
Amidases, 461
Amides, 178–179,*† 220–224, 241†–242
  reduction, 230–231
Amidone, 846
Amination,
  alkyl halides, 228 229
  anthraquinones, 765
  chlorobenzene, 599
  α-halo acids, 229, 431, 441
  naphthols, see Bucherer reaction
  nitro compounds, 573, 575, 580
  pyridine, 807–808
  quinonoid compounds, 716, 717, 718
Amine oxides, 239–240
Amines, aliphatic, 224*–241
  alkylation, 228–229, 599–600
  aromatic, 595–622, 597*
  coupling, 618–619
  derivatives, 235, 239, 241–244, 599–600, 602,
    608

nitrous acid reaction, 236–237, 605–607
  oxidation, 239, 604, 605, 709–710
  salts, 226–227
o-Aminoacetanilide, 596
Amino acids, 418–440
  essential, 498
  metabolism, 497–513
α-Aminoanthraquinone, 765–766
β-Aminoanthraquinone, 765, 911, 912
p-Aminoazobenzene, 620,*† 923*†
o-Aminobenzaldehyde, 675,* 688†
p-Aminobenzaldehyde, 675,* 688†
m-Aminobenzoic acid, 656*
p-Aminobenzoic acid, 656,* 1032
N-p-Aminobenzoyl-p-phenylenediamine, 926
1-Amino-2-bromoanthraquinone, 911
L-α-Aminobutyric acid, 422, 424,* 440†
γ-Aminobutyric acid, 422
ε-Aminocaproic acid, 860
ε-Aminocaprolactam, 861
2-Amino-p-cymene, 596
2-Aminodiazine, see 2-Aminopyrimidine
2-Aminogalactose, 395
2-Aminoglucose, see Glucosamine
2-Amino-1-hydroxyhydrindene, 271*
2-Amino-6-hydroxypurine, see Guanine
5-Amino-4-imidazolecarboxamide, 507
δ-Aminolevulinic acid, 506
Aminomalonic ester, 433–434
1-Amino-2-methylanthraquinone, 766
2-Amino-4-methylpyrimidine, 1030
1-Amino-2-naphthol, 715
1-Amino-8-naphthol-2,4-disulfonic acid, 751
1-Amino-8-naphthol-3,6-disulfonic acid, 749-
  750
1-Amino-2-naphthol-4-sulfonic acid, 717
2-Amino-5-naphthol-7-sulfonic acid, 748–749
2-Amino-8-naphthol-6-sulfonic acid, 748
2-Amino-1,4-naphthoquinone, 714*–715, 718†
4-Amino-1,2-naphthoquinone, 714
m-Aminophenol, 624*, 631†
o-Aminophenol, 624,* 631†
p-Aminophenol, 572, 585, 621,† 624,* 631–632†
  oxidation, 715
Aminopropanols, 841, 1008
2-Amino-1-n-propoxy-4-nitrobenzene, 592
6-Aminopurine, see Adenine
3-Aminopyrene, 778
3-Aminopyrene-4-sulfonic acid, 778
2-Aminopyridine, 807–808,† 1030†
3-Aminopyridine, 808
2-Aminopyrimidine, 1030
2-Aminothiazole, 1030†
Ammonium mucate, 798

Ammonium picrate, 581, 582, 583
Ammonium rhodanilate, 427
Ammonolysis, acyl halides, 181
    anhydrides, 188
    esters, 178–179
    phosgene, 184
Amygdalin, 380–381
n-Amyl acetate, 174*
d-Amyl alcohol (active, sec-butylcarbinol), 112, 122,*† 257, 481†
n-Amyl alcohol, 111,* 112,* 122†
t-Amyl alcohol, 112*
Amyl alcohols, 111–112,* 121–122†
n-Amylamine, 224,* 233†
N-n-Amylaniline, 600
Amylase, 384, 389, 390, 461, 473
n-Amyl bromide, 146,* 345
 -Amyl bromide, 146,* 347
n-Amyl chloride, 122
Amyl chlorides, see Chloropentanes
n-Amyl cyanide, see Capronitrile
Amylopectin, 389–390, 476
Amylose, 384, 389, 475, 476
2-n-Amylquinoline, 828, 829
α-Amyrin, 951
β-Amyrin, 951
Anabasine, 865
Analysis, combustion, 9–15
    carbon-hydrogen, 9–15
    fats, 407–408
    methoxyl determination (Zeisel), 137
    micro and semimicro, 13–15
    nitrogen, 15
Androgens, 972–975
Δ1,4-Androstadiene-17β-ol-3-one, 972
Androstenediol-3, 17, 974–975
Androsterone, 968, 972,* 973–974
Anesthetics, 134–135, 145
Anethole, 632–633, 681
Aneurine, see Thiamine
Angelic acid, 284–285*
Angelica lactone, 806
Anhalonidine, 827
Anhydroalkannin, 778
1, 2-Anhydroglucose, 382
Aniline, 480, 595, 597,* 599,† 890
    acid salts, 227,* 598,* 602
    alkylation, 599–600
    halogenation, 602
    oxidation, 604–605, 709–710
    reactions, 602, 605, 608, 609, 610
Aniline Black, 888

Aniline Blue, 891, 892
Aniline point, 96
Aniline Yellow, 923
2-Anilino-1,4-naphthohydroquinone, 716
2-Anilino-1,4-naphthoquinone, 716
4-Anilino-1,2-naphthoquinone, 717
Anisaldehyde, 675,* 679,† 681†
Anisalhydantion, 435
Anisanilide, 702
Anisic acid, 656,* 663†
o-Anisidine, 597,* 598, 604†
p-Anisidine, 597,* 598, 604†
Anisole, 133,* 136,† 626–627, 634, 679
p-Anisoylphenylcarbinol, 694
Anisylhydantoin, 435
Anol, 624,* 632†
Ansa compounds, 322
Anthanthrone, 919
Anthocyanidins, 818–821
Anthocyanins, 818–821
Anthracene, 528,* 758–760, 769†
    coal tar, 529
    formylation, 680
    oxidation, 759
    polynitro complexes, 586*
Anthracene Blue WR, 904
Anthracene Blue WSR, 904
endo-Anthracene—maleic anhydride, 760
Anthracene-α-sulfonic acid, 769
Anthracene-β-sulfonic acid, 769
Anthrahydroquinone, 712, 767, 769
9-Anthraldehyde, 679,*† 680,*† 760
Anthranilic acid, 512–513, 656,* 666–667, 905, 908
Anthranol, 768, 769
Anthraquinoline, 914
Anthraquinolinequinone, 914
Anthraquinone, 712,* 719,† 758, 761–765
    bromination, 902
    sulfonation, 763–765, 902–903
Anthraquinone-α-carboxylic acid, 761
Anthraquinone-β-carboxylic acid, 761
Anthraquinone-1, 5-dicarboxylic acid, 781
Anthraquinonedisulfonic acids, 764
Anthraquinones, 760–769
Anthraquinone-α-sulfonic acid, 764–765, 766
Anthraquinone-β-sulfonic acid, 763, 765
Anthraquinonoid vat dyes, 901–905
Anthrasol Blue IBC, 912
α-Anthrol, 769
β-Anthrol, 769
Anthrone, 767,*† 768, 915
Antibodies, 396–397, 455
Antigens, 396, 455

* Physical constants   † Preparation

Antimalarials, 1025–1028
Antioxidants for: aldehydes, 695
 divinyl ether, 135
 ether, 134
 rubber, 849
Apiose, 351
Apomorphine, 835–836
Aporphine, 836
D-Arabinose, 264, 357–358, 360
L-Arabinose, 356, 375,* 377*
Arachidic acid, 400,* 408, 409, 415, 670†
Arachidonic acid, 401,* 404
Arbutin, 378, 379
Arctostaphylos uva-ursi, iv, 378
Arginase, 461
L-Arginine, 271,* 420,* 422, 424,* 430, 461
 determination, 427, 429
 indispensability, 498
 metabolism, 476, 498, 502–503
Arginosuccinic acid, 502
Arndt-Eistert reaction, 184
Aromatic hydrocarbons, 527–555, 528,* 532,*
  see also Naphthalene and Polynuclear
  hydrocarbons
 coal-tar, 527–529
 petroleum, 96, 97, 531
Arsenicals, 1022–1025
Arsphenamine, 1022–1023
Aryl halides, 644*–654
Aryllithium compounds, 650–651
Ascorbic acid, 390–393,† 510, 1000
Ascorbic acid dehydrogenase, 461
Asparagine, 257, 421, 427, 444–445†
L-Aspartic acid, 257, 419,* 421, 424,* 426, 430,
  433,† 440,† 444
 metabolism, 476, 482, 483, 486, 498
Aspirin, see Acetylsalicylic acid
Astrazone Pink FG, 900, 901
Asymmetric synthesis, 276, 277, 369
Atabrine, 1026–1027
Atomic dimensions, 183
Atoxyl, 1022
Atrolactic acid, 274
Atromentin, 724
Atropine, 837, 838
Auramine, 894
Aureomycin, 1035
Aurin, 894–895
Aurintricarboxylic acid, 895
Autoxidation, aldehydes, 694–695
 benzoin, 694
 ether, 134
 rubber, 849
 unsaturated acids, 405

Auxochromic groups, 883
Avidin, 1011
Azelaic acid, 300, 301, 312,* 315,† 402, 493
Azelaic half-aldehyde, 402
Azeotropic distillation, 121
Azides, 233, 434, 442
Azines, 212
Azlactone synthesis, 436–437
Azlons, 860
Azobenzene, 584, 585*†
Azo dyes, 922–932
Azophor Red PN, 931
Azoxybenzene, 572, 584, 585*†
Azulene, 533–534, 775

Babassu oil, 400, 408,*
Bacitracin-A, 450
Bacteriochlorophyll, 486
Bayer reaction, 867
Baeyer strain theory, 296 297
Bakelite A, 866, 868
Bakelite B, 866, 869
Bakelite C, see Phenol-formaldehyde resins
Baker-Nathan effect, 333–334, 345–346
BAL, 92–93
Balata, 848
Bally-Scholl reaction, 915
Barbital, 246
Barbiturate drugs, 246
Barbituric acid, 245,* 246,*† 1004
Bart reaction, 615
Baur musk, 583
Bayer 205, see Germanin
Bayer acid, see Crocein acid
Beckmann rearrangement 701–703, 756, 861
Behenic acid, 400,*
Benzacetoin, 694
Benzalacetone, 689
Benzalacetophenone, 689,*† 699
p-Benzalaminophenol, 632
Benzal chloride, 568, 646, 647,* 674
Benzaldehyde, 192,* 203, 210, 349, 674,† 675,*
  676,† 687,† 689–690
 autoxidation, 694
 condensation, 577, 693
 nitration, 687
 phenylhydrazone, 212
 reduction, 116, 206, 480
Benzaldoximes, 701
Benzamide, 241,* 658
Benzanilide, 658, 702
Benz-p-anisidide, 702
1,2-Benzanthracene, 759, 776*
1,2 Benz-10-anthraldehyde, 793

1,2-Benz-10-anthranol, 768
1,2-Benzanthranyl-10-acetate, 768
1,2-Benzanthraquinone, 762
1,2-Benz-10-anthrone, 793
1,9-Benz-10-anthrone, 761, 913–915†
2,3-Benz-9-anthrone, 773
β-Benzanthronequinoline, 914
Benzedrine, 500–501
Benzene, 532,* 796*
    coal tar, 527–528
    halogenation, 519–520, 645–646, 654
    hydrogenation, 516, 519
    metabolism, 510
    nitration, 572
    oxidation, 283
    ozonolysis, 520–521
    petroleum, 96, 103
    structure, 514–526
    succinoylation, 542
    sulfonation, 625
    ultraviolet absorption, 882–883
Benzeneazo-p-cresol, 619
1-Benzeneazo-2-naphthol, 622
4-Benzeneazo-1-naphthol, 622
p-Benzeneazophenol, see p-Hydroxyazobenzene
Benzenediazoic acid, 611
Benzenediazonium chloride, 610–611
    reactions, 440, 613, 615, 617, 618–620
Benzenediazotates, 611–612
Benzene-m-disulfonic acid, 588,*† 630
Benzene hexabromide, 519
Benzene hexachloride, 520, 654–655
Benzenepentacarboxylic acid, 666,*† 668*
Benzenesulfinic acid, 593,*† 615†
Benzenesulfonamide, 590
Benzenesulfonic acid, 588*
Benzenesulfonyl chloride, 236, 589–590,*† 594, 600
Benzenetetracarboxylic acid 1,2,3,4-, see Prehnitic acid
    1,2,3,5-, see Mellophanic acid
    1,2,4,5-, see Pyromellitic acid
Benzenetricarboxylic acid 1,2,3-, see Hemimellitic acid
    1,2,4-, see Trimellitic acid
    1,3,5-, see Trimesic acid
Benzhydrazide, 658
Benzhydrol, 116
2,3-Benz-9-hydroxy-10-anthrone, 773
Benzhydrylamine, 600
Benzidine, 585,† 597,* 926
Benzil, 694, 706,*† 707

Benzilic acid, 707–708
Benzilic acid rearrangement, 707, 731, 757
Benzoazurin G, 927
Benzo Fast Yellow 5GL, 929
Benzofuran (coumarone), 802,* 803–804†
Benzoic acid, 181, 656,* 657–658†
    esterification, 658, 672
    nitration, 559
Benzoic anhydride, 186,* 188,† 658*†
Benzoin, 353, 693,*† 694
Benzoin condensation, 693–694, 706, 707
Benzonitrile, 230, 593, 701
Benzoorange R, 927
Benzophenone, 192,* 540,† 600, 695*
    hydrazone, 720
    oxime, 702
    reduction, 116, 700
Benzopinacol, 700
Benzopinacolone, 700
o-Benzoquinone, 709, 712,* 716†
p-Benzoquinone, 605, 630, 709*–710,† 712,* 716, 719, 721
Benzotrichloride, 568, 646, 647,* 658
Benzoylaminomalonic ester, 434
Benzoyl-p-anisylcarbinol, 694
o-Benzoylbenzoic acid, 542,† 761, 762, 767
Benzoyl chloride, 180,* 181,† 236, 540, 658*
Benzoylleucine, 497
Benzoylleucine anilide, 497
1-Benzoylnaphthalene, 738,*† 792, 915
2-Benzoylnaphthalene, 738–739
Benzoyl peroxide, 42, 658
1-Benzoylphenanthrene, 756–757
Benzoylpiperidine, 158
β-Benzoylpropionic acid, 117, 542,† 544
Benzoyl radical, 694
1,12-Benzperylene-1′,2′-dicarboxylic anhydride, 780
3,4-Benzpyrene, 586,* 783,* 785, 787–788, 791–792†
Benzyl alcohol, 112,* 117,† 210,† 442, 480
Benzylamine, 230†
p-Benzylaminophenol, 632
Benzyl benzoate, 658
o-Benzylbenzoic acid, 767
Benzyl bromide, 647
Benzyl chloride, 568, 646, 647,* 676
Benzyl cyanide, 230, 501, 576
S-Benzyl-DL-cysteine, 439
N-Benzylideneaniline, 815
Benzyl iodide, 647
Benzylmagnesium halides, 649
Benzyl mercaptan, 439
o-Benzyloxyacetophenone, 706

* Physical constants   † Preparation

o-Benzyloxyphenylacetic acid, 706
o-Benzyloxyphenylthioacetmorpholide, 706
Benzylthiolmethyl chloride, 443
S-Benzylthiolmethylphthalimidomalonic ester,
    439
Berberine, 832, 833
Bergius hydrogenation process, 108
Betaine, 503
Betaines, 503–504
Bile acids, 967–968
Bile salts, 491
Bios, 394–395, 999
Biotin, 1010–1012
Biphenyl, see Diphenyl
Biphenylene, 772
Bisabolene, 944
Bischler-Napieralski synthesis, 812–813, 832
Bisulfite addition, 201–203, 718, 757
Blanc reaction, 647
Blanc rule, 318
Blasting gelatin, 132
Blue de Lyons, 891
Blue tetrazolium, 805
Bohn-Schmidt reaction, 766, 903
Boiling point comparisons,
    acid chlorides, 180
    alcohols, 113–115
    aldehydes and ketones, 191
    alkanes, 32
    alkyl halides, 145
    amides, 179
    amines, 225
    anhydrides, 185–6
    carboxylic acids, esters, amides, 164–165,
        173, 179
    ethers, 133
    hydrocarbons, 32, 47, 53, 85, 528–529
    mercaptans, 139
    nitro compounds, 571–572
Boosters (explosives), 581–582
Bordeaux B, 925
Boric acid complexes, 363, 470
Bornyl chloride, 940 941
Boron fluoride, 130, 138, 174, 537, 538, 540
Bouveault-Blanc reduction, 177
Brassidic acid, 403
Brassylic acid, 403
von Braun reaction, 158
Brillaint Green, 893
Brilliant Indigo 4B, 909
Brilliant Orange GR, 920
Brilliant Orange RK, 919
Brilliant Yellow, 927–928
Bromination, acids, 170–171, 260–261

acid salts, 147
alkenes, 59–61, 151, 243, 287, 329–332
allylic, 980–981
amides, 232, 242
amines, 640
aromatic hydrocarbons, 519–520, 563–564,
    645–646, 654
ketones, 199
succinimide, 243
p-Bromoacetanilide, 602
Bromoacetic acid, 163
ω-Bromoacetophenone, see Phenacyl bromide
Bromoacetyl bromide, 180*
Bromoamides, 233
p-Bromoaniline, 597
o-Bromoanisole, 644
p-Bromoanisole, 644
o-Bromobenzaldehyde, 676
Bromobenzene, 153, 644*
m-Bromobenzoic acid, 656
o-Bromobenzoic acid, 656
p-Bromobenzoic acid, 656
α-Bromobutyric acid, 260–261*†
α-Bromocamphor-π-sulfonic acid, 271*
α-Bromocaproic acid, 170
o-Bromochlorobenzene, 644,* 645†
p Bromochlorobenzene, 644,* 645†
1-Bromo-1-chloro-2-keto-1, 2-dihydronaphtha-
    lene, 735
Bromococcin, 771
α-Bromocyclohexanone, 199
3-Bromocyclohexene 1, 151
Bromodifluoromethane, 159
p-Bromodimethylaniline, 644,* 645†
Bromoform, 154,* 156,† 157
Bromohydrins, 64
o-Bromoiodobenzene, 644
p-Bromoiodobenzene, 644
1-Bromo-8-iodonaphthalene, 547
α-Bromoisobutyric acid, 58
α-Bromoisocaproic acid, 433
α Bromoisocaproyl chloride, 441
α-Bromoisocaproylglycylglycine ethyl ester,
    441
2-Bromomesitylene, 657
α-Bromo-β-methoxy-n-butyric acid, 437, 438
1 Bromo-4-methylnaphthalene, 743
1-Bromo-8-methylnaphthalene, 547
α-Bromonaphthalene, 546, 652, 736, 740,† 741*
β-Bromonaphthalene, 741,* 742†
1-Bromo-2-naphthol, 745
6-Bromo-2-naphthol, 745
3-Bromo-1, 2-naphthoquinone, 721
6-Bromo-1, 2-naphthoquinone, 720

5-Bromo-2-nitronaphthalene, 743
Bromonium ion, 60, 329
9-Bromophenanthrene, 564,† 755*
o-Bromophenol, 549,† 628†
p-Bromophenol, 624,* 628†
α-Bromopropionic acid, 229, 340, 341
β-Bromopropionic acid, 332–333
N-Bromosuccinimide, 151, 243,† 545
m-Bromotoluene, 644,* 645†
o-Bromotoluene, 644,* 676
p-Bromotoluene, 614,† 644*
Brucine, 2, 271, 272*
Bucherer reaction, 741–742
Bufotalin, 993
Bufotoxin, 993
Buna rubbers, 852–854
Bushy stunt virus, 452*
Butadiene-1,3, 91,† 106–107,† 121, 797,† 853–854†
    addition reactions, 70–72, 310, 312, 314, 334, 852
    electronic structure, 78–79
    resonance, 70–72
n-Butane, 31,* 37, 95, 102, 798
Butane-1,1,4,4-tetracarboxylic acid ethyl ester, 517
Butanol, see Butyl alcohol
Butene-1, 53,* 102, 103, 876†
    dehydrogenation, 106–107
    isomerization, 106
    oxidation, 68
Butene-2, 53,* 106
Butenes (-1 and -2), 121
Butenolides, 805–806
Butenylbenzene, see Phenylbutene
Butter, 409
n-Butyl acetate, 955, 174,* 864
t-Butyl acetate, 174
n-Butyl alcohol (butanol-1) 111,* 112,* 121,† 174, 210†
sec-Butyl alcohol (butanol-2), 112,* 117,† 121†
t-Butyl alcohol, 112,* 115, 147, 174
Butyl alcohols, 111, 112*
n-Butylamine, 224*
sec-Butylamine, 231†
n-Butylbenzene, 532,* 535†
t-Butylbenzene, 532,* 539,† 561
n-Butyl bromide, 146,* 147,† 345
sec-Butyl bromide, 146,* 147,† 148†
t-Butyl bromide, 146,* 147,† 149, 337, 338, 346
sec-Butylcarbinol, 122*†
n-Butyl cellosolve, 123

n-Butyl chloride, 146*
sec-Butyl chloride, 146*
t-Butyl chloride, 146*
2,3-Butylene glycol, 854
t-Butylethylene, 126
t-Butyl iodide, 61
n-Butylmalonic acid, 221*†
Butyl oleate, 177
n-Butyl palmitate, 117
Butyl rubber, 855
Butyne-2-diol-1,4, 91,† 797†
n-Butyraldehyde, 192*
Butyramide, 179
n-Butyric acid, 163,* 166, 174, 181, 261, 400,* 409
Butyric anhydride, 186*
β-Butyrolactone, 321†
γ-Butyrolactone, 324*†
n-Butyryl chloride, 180,* 181†

Cachou de Laval, 921
Cacodyl, 551
Cacodyl chloride, 551
Cadalene, 944
Cadaverine, 502
Cadinene, 944
Caffeine, 247
Calciferol, see Vitamin D₂
Calcium carbide, 87
Caledon Jade Green, 916
Calycin, 806
Camphane, 936
Camphene, 941, 943
Campholide, 943
Camphonanic acid, 98
Camphor, 533, 863, 941–944
Camphoric acid, 942–943
Camphoronic acid, 942
d-Camphorsulfonic acid, 271*
Canavanine, 422
Cannizzaro reaction, 210–211, 549
Cantharidin, 311–312
Capric acid, 400,* 408, 409
n-Caproaldehyde, 192*
n-Caproamide, 179,* 233
Caproic acid, 163,* 169, 221,† 400*
    bromination, 170
    occurrence, 166, 409
Caproic anhydride, 188*†
Capronitrile, 168,* 230
n-Caproyl chloride, 180*
Capryl alcohol (octanol-2), 112,* 113†
    resolution, 272–273
Capryl chloride, 180*

* Physical constants   † Preparation

Caprylic acid, 147, 163,* 400,* 408, 409
Capsaicin, 405
Carbanilide, see s-Diphenylurea
Carbanion, 554
Carbarsone, 1024
Carbazole, 529, 530
Carbazole dyes, 917–918
Carbazole indophenol, 922
2-Carbethoxycyclopentanone, 220
Carbethoxy group, 185, 442
Carbinol, see Methanol
Carbobenzoxy chloride, 442†
Carbobenzoxyglutamic acid, 443
Carbobenzoxy synthesis, 442–445
Carbocyanines, 899–900
Carbodiphenylimide, 609
Carbohydrates, 350–398
    metabolism, 472–487
Carbohydrases, 461
1-Carbomethoxyheptyne, 939
Carbona, 157
Carbonation, Grignard reagents, 167, 657, 740
Carbon blacks, 44–45, 94, 102
Carbon disulfide, 157
Carbonic acid, 161, 162, 184
Carbon monoxide, 169,† 458
    chlorination, 184
    hydrogenation, 108–109
    reaction with acetylene, 91
    reaction with alkenes, 197
    reaction with NaOH, 165
Carbon suboxide, 316*†
Carbon tetrabromide, 154*
Carbon tetrachloride, 41, 154,* 157†
Carbon tetrafluoride, 154*
Carbonyl chloride, see Phosgene
Carbonyl group, see Aldehydes and Ketones
Carbonyl reagents, 211–212, 618
o-Carboxybenzoylacetic acid 691
Carboxylase, 467, 477, 481–482
Carboxylic acids, 39–40, 161–190, 221–222,†
        656–673
    decarboxylation, 39, 549
    from petroleum, 97
    reduction, 117
Carboxypeptidase, 461, 462
o-Carboxyphenylacetonitrile, 670
Carcinogenic hydrocarbons, 782–794
Cardiac glycosides, 991–993
Δ³-Carene, 936
Carlic acid, 393
Carlosic acid, 393
Carminazarin, 770
Carminic acid, 769–771

Carolic acid, 393
Carolinic acid 393
α-Carotene, 951,* 953
β-Carotene, 951,* 952, 959
γ-Carotene, 951,*, 953
Carotol, 945
Carpaine, 827
Carvacrol, 624,* 632†
Caryophyllene, 947
Caryophyllene alcohol, 947
Casein, 417, 430, 452,* 461
    fiber, 860
    plastic, 865–866
Casing-head gasoline, see Gasoline, natural
Caslon, 860
Castor oil, 113, 116, 404, 408*
Catalase, 461, 466, 467
Catechol, 624,* 629†
    oxidation, 716
Cedrene, 947–948
Cedriret, see Cerulignone
Cedrol, 948
Celliton Fast Blue B, 905
Celliton Fast Pink B, 905
Cellobiose, 381, 385
Cellobiuronic acid, 397
Cellophane, 859
Cellosolves, 123
Cellotetrose, 386
Cellotriose, 386
Celluloid, 863
Cellulose, 385–388
Cellulose acetate, fiber, 859–860
    plastic, 864–865
Cellulose acetate butyrate, 865
Cellulose acetate propionate, 865
Cellulose ethers, 865
Cellulose nitrate, see Nitrocellulose
Cellulose xanthate, 858–859
Cephaeline, 845
Cephalins, 488, 489–490†
Cerane, 37
Cerebronic acid, 490
Cerebrosides, 490
Cerotic acid, 400*
Cerulein A, 886
Cerulignone, 638
Ceryl iodide, 37
Cetane, see n-Hexadecane
Cetane number, 100
Cetoleic acid, 401,* 403
Cetyl alcohol, 112,* 113, 409*
Cetyl iodide, 36
Cetyl palmitate, 113

Chain reactions, 42, 694–695, 855–856
Chalcones, 822
Chardonnet process, 858
Chaulmoogric acid, 406–407*
Chavicol, 632
Chelation, see also Hydrogen bonding
  acetoacetic ester enol, 218
  amine oxide salts, 607
  o-hydroxy aldehydes, 681
  o-hydroxyazo compounds, 622
  o-hydroxy ketones, 636
  indigo, 884
  o-nitrophenols, 628
  osazones, 353
  pyrazole, 803
Chelidonine, 827
Chemigum, 854
Chemotherapy, 1019–1036
Chicago acid (1-amino-8-naphthol-2,4-disul-
  fonic acid) 751,† 924, 927
Chicago Blue 6B, 927
Chiniofon, 1025
Chitin, 388–389
Chloral, 170, 192,* 197–198,† 213
Chloral ammonia, 213
Chloral hydrate, 216
Chloral hydroxylamine, 213
Chloramine-T, 590–591
Chloramphenicol, 1035–1036
Chloranil, 901
Chloranilic acid, 901
Chlorination, acetylene, 157
  alkanes, 41–42
  benzene, 626, 645, 646
  carbon disulfide, 157
  carbon monoxide, 184
  carboxylic acids, 170–171
  diethyl ether, 137
  ethyl alcohol, 197
  ethylene, 157
  methane, 41
  pentanes, 121–122
  phenols, 628, 735, 745, 758
  propylene, 123
  rubber, 850
Chloroacetamide, 179
Chloroacetic acid, 163,* 164, 170,† 313
Chloroacetone, 192*
ω-Chloroacetophenone, 647
Chloroacetyl chloride, 180,* 441
Chloroacetylglycylglycine, 441
Chloroacid chloride synthesis, 441–442

Chloroamides, 590–591
6-Chloro-2-aminotoluene, 675
m-Chloroaniline, 597,* 598
o-Chloroaniline, 597,* 598
p-Chloroaniline, 597,* 598
α-Chloroanthraquinone, 766
β-Chloroanthraquinone, 765
o-Chlorobenzaldehyde, 675
p-Chlorobenzaldehyde, 675
13-Chlorobenzanthrone, 916
Chlorobenzene, 625–626, 644*
  hydrolysis, 625–626
  resonance, 567
  substitution, 560, 561, 579
m-Chlorobenzoic acid, 656,* 662†
o-Chlorobenzoic acid, 656,* 662†
p-Chlorobenzoic acid, 656,* 662†
o-Chlorobromobenzene, 614
1-Chloro-8-bromonaphthalene, 651
m-Chlorocinnamic acid, 690
o-Chlorocinnamic acid, 690
p-Chlorocinnamic acid, 690
Chlorodifluoromethane, 866
β-Chloroethyl methyl sulfide, 433
Chloroform, 41, 154*-155†
  anesthetic, 135
Chlorogenin, 994
1-Chloroheptane, 42
2-Chloroheptane, 42
Chlorohydrins, 64, 876
Chlorohydroquinone, 716
o-Chloroiodobenzene, 644
p-Chloroiodobenzene, 644,* 653
β-Chloro-α-iodo-n-butyric acid, 333
Chloromalic acids, 266–267
o-Chloromercuriphenol, 633
Chloromethylation, 647–648
Chloromethyl ether, 152, 647
α-Chloromethylnaphthalene, 648, 741*
1-Chloro-8-methylnaphthalene, 651
Chloromycetin, 1035
α-Chloronaphthalene, 740–741*
1-Chloro-2-naphthol, 735
3-Chloro-1,2-naphthoquinone, 720
2-Chloro-1,4-naphthoquinone, 712
o-Chloronitrobenzene, see o-nitrochlorobenzene
Chloropentanes, 122
9-Chloro-10-phenanthrol, 637
m-Chlorophenol, 624*
o-Chlorophenol, 624,* 627–628,† 629
p-Chlorophenol, 624,* 627–628,† 766
Chlorophyll, 456, 484, 485, 949
Chloroprene, 524, 851–852
Chloroprene rubber, 851–852

* Physical constants   † Preparation

α-Chloropropionic acid, 163,* 164
β-Chloropropionic acid, 163,* 164, 166,† 324†
3-Chloropyrene, 777
β-Chloropyridine, 800–801
Chloroquine, 1028
d- and l-Chlorosuccinic acid, 277, 278
Chlorosulfonation, 42–43
Chlorotoluenes, 614,† 644*
β-Chlorovinylarsine oxide, 92
β-Chlorovinyldichloroarsine, see Lewisite
Cholanic acid, 968
Cholanthrene, 785
Cholestane, 965, 968
Cholestanediols, 965–966
Cholestanol, 962, 963–964, 965
Cholestanone, 962
Δ⁴-Cholestenone, 963–964
Δ⁵-Cholestenone, 963–964
Cholesterol, 2, 454, 783, 784, 961,* 962,
    963–964, 1014
  biosynthesis, 989–991
  dibromide, 966, 974
  digitonide, 963
  oxide, 967
Cholic acid, 783, 784, 967*
Choline, 488, 489, 503
Cholinesterase, 461
Chondroitin sulfate, 395
Chondrosamine, 395
Chondrosine, 395
Chroman, 817
Chromatography, 428, 429, 952
Chrome Violet GY, 895
Chromone, 817, 818
Chromophoric groups, 881
Chromotrope 2R, 931–932
Chromotropic acid, 749–750, 931–932
Chrysamine G, 927
Chrysene, 528,* 529, 776
amphi-Chrysenequinone, 776
Chrysin, 822
Chrysoidine, 923
Chrysophenine G, 927–928
Ciba Green G, 909
Ciba Violet A, 909
Ciba Yellow 3G, 908
Cinchonidine, 270, 271*
Cinchonine, 2, 270, 271,* 1026
d-Cinchonine d- and l-mandelate, 272
Cinchoninonitrile, 813
Cinnamalacrylic acid, 690–691*†
Cinnamaldehyde, 547, 651, 669, 688,*† 689,
    691
Cinnamalmalonic acid, 669

Cinnamic acid, 284,* 668,* 690†
  decarboxylation, 549
  dibromide, 265*
  stereochemistry, 284
Cinnamyl acetate, 151
Cinnamyl bromide, 151
Cinnoline, 814
Citraconic acid, 283
Citral, 191, 938
Citric acid, 476, 481–483
Citrin, 823
Citrinin, 825
Citronellal, 938
Citronellol, 937
Citrovorum factor, 505
Citrulline, 422, 498, 502
Civetane, 300
Civetone, 299–302, 320,† 321†
Claisen condensation, 692
Claisen rearrangement, 639–640, 734, 735
Claisen-Schmidt condensation, 688–689
Clavacin, 806
Clemmensen reduction, 543–544
  examples: 300, 301, 546, 669, 754, 791
Cleve's acid-1,6, 749
Cleve's acid-1,7, 749
Clostridium botulinum toxins, 471
Clovine, 947
Coal, 527
  hydrogenation, 108–109
  tar, 527
Cobalt carbide, 109
Cocaine, 837, 838, 839, 841,† 845
Cocarboxylase, 467, 481, 482
Cocceryl alcohol, 409
Coccinin, 770
Coccinone, 770, 771
Cochenillic acid, 771
Cochineal, 769
Cochineal Red A, 925
Coconut oil, 400, 408*
Codeine, 833, 834, 838|
Codeinone, 834
Coenzyme A, 467–468, 494–495
Coenzyme I, see Diphosphopyridine nucleotide
Coenzyme II, see Triphosphopyridine nucleo-
    tide
Coenzymes, 463
Cogalactowaldenase, 475
Colchiceine, 641
Colchicine, 641–642
Collagen, 417, 429, 430, 453, 454, see also
    Gelatin
Collidines, 806

Combustion analysis, 9–15
Condensing enzyme, 482
Conformation, 302–309
Congo Blue, 926
Congo Corinth, 926
Congo Red, 887,* 925–926*
Connesine, 995
Coordinate covalent bond, 38, 51, 240, 557, 653
Copal, 863
Copolymerization, 583, 584–585
Copper-chromium oxide catalyst, 66
Copper naphthenate, 98
Copper phthalocyanine, 933–934
Coprostane, 965, 968
Coprostanol, 962, 963–964†
Coprostanone, 963–964
Coramine, 1006
Cordite, 132
Corn oil, 415
Coronene, 781–782
Cortical steroids, 977–982
Corticosterone, 978*
Cortisone, 978*–982, 986–988†
Corydine, 832, 833
Cottonseed oil, 415*
Coumalic acid, 815–816
Coumaric acid, 690
Coumarillic acid, 803
Coumarin, 690,*† 803, 817†
Coumarinic acid, 690
Coumarone, 802,* 803–804†
Coupling, see also Diazo coupling
    diazonium salts, 666–667, 721
    Grignard reagents, 152
Covalent bonds, 8, 9, 50–51
Cozymase, see Diphosphopyridine nucleotide
Cracking, see also Pyrolysis
    hydrocarbons, 43, 101–104
Creatine, 502–503
Creatinine, 502–503
m-Cresol, 530,* 632
o-Cresol, 530,* 632, 682
p-Cresol, 530,* 592†
    oxidation, 510
    Reimer-Tiemann reaction, 682–683
m-Cresyl acetate, 635
Crocein acid, 747
Crocetin, 959
Crocin, 959–960
Crotonaldehyde, 117, 192,* 207, 208,† 692, 882*
Crotonic acid, 283,*† 331, 333, 437, 438, 882*

Crotyl alcohol, 117,† 207†
Crotyl chloride, 334
Cryptopyrrole, 456
Crystal Ponceau 6R, 925
Crystal Violet, 892–893
Cucumber mosaic virus, 471
Cumene (isopropylbenzene), 96, 105, 532,* 538, 539,* 626
Cumulenes, 882
Cupferron, 606–607
Cuprammonium process, 858
Cuprous acetylide, 91–92
Curtius reaction, 233, 442
Cuscohygrine, 828–829
Cyanamide, 244
Cyanidin, 819, 820, 823
Cyanin, 819–820
Cyanine Blue, 898
Cyanine dyes, 898–901
Cyanoacetic acid, 163,* 313†
Cyanoethylation, 222
Cyanoethylmalonate, 222
Cyanohydrins, 203–204, 876
Cyanohydrin synthesis, 203–204, 335–336
    examples: 167–168, 260, 275, 277, 313, 356–357, 432
4-Cyano-N-methyldihydroquinoline, 813
4-Cyanomethyl-1,2-naphthoquinone, 837, 838
9-Cyanophenanthrene, 755
Cyanophoric glycosides, 380–381
Cyclic anhydrides, 188, 316–317
Cyclic ketones, 196,† 220, 299–302, 319–322,† 543†
    oxidation, 199
Cyclic ureides, 244–247
Cyclitol, 394
Cyclization, see Ring closure
Cycloalkanes, 46–47,* 295–299, 304–310
    see also Naphthenes
Cycloalkannin, 730
Cyclobutane, 47,* 296, 297*
Cyclodecane, 533–534
Cyclodecane-1,6-dione, 775
Cycloheptadecanone, 320,† see also Dihydro-civetone
Cycloheptane, 47,* 297*
Cycloheptanone, 320†
Cyclohexane, 47,* 296, 297,* 309†
    reaction with phosgene, 43
    steric forms, 298, 204–306
Cyclohexane-1,2-dicarboxylic acids, 292
Cyclohexane-1,4-dicarboxylic acids, cis- and trans-, 292,* 517†
Cyclohexane-1,3,5-trione, trioxime, 631

---

* **Physical constants**	† **Preparation**

Cyclohexanol, 112,* 540, 861
dehydration, 54, 56
dehydrogenation, 194, 861
oxidation, 199, 314
Cyclohexanone, 192,* 194,† 534, 861†
addition reactions, 202, 203, 349
oxidation, 199, 861
oxime, 861
Cyclohexanone-2-carboxylic acid, 314
Cyclohexene, 54,† 56,† 151, 539
Cyclohexenecarboxylic acids, 314
Cyclohexylbenzene, 539,† 540†
Cyclohexylcarbinol, 119
o-Cyclohexylphenol, 624
p-Cyclohexylphenol, 624
3-Cyclohexylpropyne-1, 153
Cyclonite, 214
Cyclononane, 533–534
Cyclooctane, 47,* 524*
Cyclooctanone, 301, 320†
Cyclootatetraene, 524–525
Cyclooctene, 524
Cyclopentadecanone, 301, 302, 320,† 321†
Cyclopentadiene, 311, 528
Cyclopentane, 47,* 103, 296, 297*
Cyclopentanecarboxylic acid, 97
Cyclopentanone, 196,*† 220,*† 318†
oxidation, 199, 314
oxime, 231
Cyclopentene, 197
Cyclopentylacetic acid, 97
Cyclopentylamine, 231†
Cyclopropane, 47,* 297,* 309†
anesthetic, 135
hydrogenation, 295
Cyclopropanedicarboxylic acids, 290–291
Cyclopropene, 296*†
Cymarin, 992
Cymarose, 992
p-Cymene, 532,* 533, 547, 936
2-sulfonic acid, 632
Cystathionine, 504
Cysteic acid, 448, 502
L-Cysteine, 419,* 421, 424,† 430, 433,† 439†
metabolism, 502, 504
Cysteinylglycine ethyl ester, 443
L-Cystine, 419,* 420, 421, 430, 439,† 476, 498
determination, 428
Cystosine, 468
Cytidylic acid, 469
Cytochrome c, 466
Cytosine, 468

Dacron, 861–862

Dakin reaction, 629
Damar, 863
Daphnetin, 817
Darzens condensation, 700, 956–957
DDT, 654
Deamination, amines, 615–617, 645, 745
amino acids, 499
Debromination, 58–59, 304
Decahydronaphthalene, see Decalin
cis-Decalin, 298–299,* 308
trans-Decalin, 298–299,* 308
Decamethylene glycol, 177
n-Decane, 31*
Decanediol-1,10, 117
Decarboxylation, 34, 39–40, 147, 170, 172, 549
amino acids, 500
carboxyamines, 232
formic acid, 169
gallic acid, 630–631, 663
β-keto acids, 219, 319, 320, 691
malonic acids, 221–222
oxalic acid, 315
pyrrolecarboxylic acids, 806–807
2,4,6-triaminobenzoic acid, 631
trichloroacetic acid, 315
2,4,6-trinitrobenzoic acid, 578
α,β-unsaturated acids, 549, 908
1-Decene-1,10-dicarboxylic acid, 315
n-Decyl alcohol, 112
Δ9,10-Decylenic acid, 401*
Decyne-9-oic acid, 89
Dehalogenation, 58–59, 84–85, 158, 304
Dehydracetic acid, 816
Dehydration, alcohols, 54–57, 125–126, 198
289–290, 314
aldols, 208
amides, 242
ammonium acetate, 241
benzaldoxime, 701
2,3-butylene glycol, 854
carboxylic acids, 185–188
dibasic acids, 188, 281
hydroxy acids, 322–325
pinacol, 54, 126–127
stereochemistry, 307–308, 347–348
Dehydroabietic acid, 877
Dehydroascorbic acid, 391, 461, 1000
7-Dehydrocholesterol, 1014
11-Dehydrocorticosterone, 978
Dehydrocortisone, 978, 979
Dehydroepiandrosterone, 972, 973, 974, 975
Dehydrogenases, 461, 463–467
Dehydrogenation, alcohols, 194
alkanes, 106

alkenes, 106–107
hydroaromatic compounds, 544–545, 624–625, 772
isoprenoids, 936, 940, 944, 945, 946
steroids, 961
Dehydrohalogenation, 57–58, 85, 86, 152, 289–290, 345–347, 625, 669
Dehydroiso-β-lapachone, 729
Dehydro-β-naphthol, 637–638
11-Dehydroprogesterone, 977
Delphinidin, 820
Demerol, 846
Denaturation of proteins, 418, 450–451
Deserpidine, 843
Desmotroposantonin, 945
Desoxybenzoin, 707
Desoxybenzoin-2'-carboxylic acid, 670
Desoxycarminic acid, 770, 771
Desoxycholic acid, 783, 784, 968,* 980
Desoxycorticosterone, 978
2-Desoxyribose, 379, 468
Desulfurization, 216
Detergents, 410–414
Deuteroporphyrin, 457
Diacetone alcohol, 208*–209†
Diacetone-sorbose, 393
Diacetyl, 192,* 520
Diacetyl peroxide, see Acetyl peroxide
N,N'-Diacetyl-p-phenylenediamine, 599*
Diallyl ether, 133*
Diamine Blue 2B, 927
Diamine Blue 3B, 929
Diamine Green B, 928
Diamine Green G, 928
2,6-Diaminoanthraquinone, 919
Diaminoazobenzene, 926
L-α,γ-Diaminobutyric acid, 422, 450
1,10-Diaminodecane, 230†
3,3'-Diamino-4,4'-dihydroxyarsenobenzene, see Arsphenamine
p,p'-Diaminodiphenyl sulfone 596
Diaminodiphenylurea, 926
4,4'-Diaminofluorene, 926
β,ε-Diaminopimelic acid, 426
2,6-Diaminopyridine, 808
Diaminostilbene, 926
2,4-Diaminotoluene, 595†
Diamond Black F, 931
Diamond Black PV, 931–932
Di-n-amyl ether, 133*
Di-n-amyl ketone, 192*
Dianisidine, 597,* 926

Dianisidine Blue, 929
3,3'-Dianisole-bis-4,4(3,4-diphenyl)-tetrazolium chloride, 805
Diastereoisomers, 265
1,3-Diazine, see Pyrimidine
Diazoaminobenzene, 619
p-Diazobenzenesulfonic acid, 612
Diazo coupling, amines and phenols, 618–622, 666–667, 715, 733–734, 887, 922–931
hydrazones, 805
hydrocarbons, 620–621, 787–788
pyrrole, 800
quinones, 721
Diazodinitrophenol anhydride, 923
Diazoketones, 184
Diazomethane, 177–178,† 184, 881*
reactions, 184, 720
Diazonium salts, 605, 610–622, 721
Diazotates, cis and trans, 611–612
1,2,5,6-Dibenzacridine, 786
1,2,5,6-Dibenzanthracene, 783,* 790–791†
carcinogenic activity, 783, 785
1,2,5,6-Dibenzanthraquinone, 789, 790
1,2,5,6-Dibenzanthraquinone-4',8'-disulfonic acid, 789
Di-benzanthrone, see Violanthrone
1,2,5,6-Dibenzcarbazole, 786
2,3,8,9-Dibenzcoronene, 781, 782
1,2,5,6-Dibenzfluorene, 786
Dibenzofuran, 802
1,5-Dibenzoylaminoanthraquinone, 917
4,4'-Dibenzoyl-1,1'-dinaphthyl, 915
1,7-Dibenzoylheptane, 829
Dibenzoylmethane, 699
Dibenzoyl peroxide, see Benzoyl peroxide
3,9-Dibenzoylperylene, 916
1,2,3,4-Dibenzphenanthrene, 787
Dibenzpyrenequinone, 920
Dibenzyl, 545, 707
Dibenzyl ketone, 196
ω,ω-Dibromoacetophenone, 698
9,10-Dibromoanthracene, 759
2,3-Dibromoanthraquinone, 902
p-Dibromobenzene, 644,* 645†
2,6-Dibromobenzoic acid, 672
3,4-Dibromobutene-1, 71
1,4-Dibromobutene-2, 71
α,β-Dibromocinnamic acids, 284*
5,5'-Dibromo-3,3'-di-β-carboxyethyl-4,4'-dimethylpyrro-2,2'-methene hydro bromide, 457
1,5-Dibromo-2,6-dihydroxyanthracene, 758
2,2'-Dibromodiphenyl, 772
1,1-Dibromoethane, 62

* Physical constants   † Preparation

1,2-Dibromoethane, 62
Dibromofumaric acid, 287
6,6'-Dibromoindigo, see Tyrian purple
1,1-Dibromo-2-keto-1,2-dihydronaphthalene, 745
Dibromomaleic acid, 287
2,4-Dibromomenthone, 625
2,7-Di-(bromomethyl)naphthalene, 782
1,6-Dibromonaphthalene, 745
1,6-Dibromo-2-naphthol, 745
1,6-Dibromo-2-naphthylamine, 745
1,1-Dibromopropane, 86
1,2-Dibromopropane, 333
dl-Dibromosuccinic acid, 286
meso-Dibromosuccinic acid, 286
Dibromo-o-toluidine, 602
Dibromo-p-toluidine, 602
Di-n-butyl ether, 133*
Di-t-butyl ketone, 204
Dicarboxylic acids, 312*-322
Dichloramine-T, 591
Dichloroacetic acid, 163,* 170†
s-Dichloroacetone, 192*
2,6-Dichlorobenzal chloride, 675
2,6-Dichlorobenzaldehyde, 675
o-Dichlorobenzene, 573, 629, 644,* 645†
p-Dichlorobenzene, 644,* 645†
3,4-Dichlorobenzenesulfonic acid, 427
2,4-Dichlorobenzoic acid, 662
2,5-Dichlorobenzoic acid, 662
3,4-Dichlorobenzoic acid, 662
Dichlorodifluoromethane, 154,* 159 160†
Dichlorodiphenyltrichloroethane, see DDT
1,2-Dichloroethane, 303 304
s-Dichloroethylene (acetylene dichloride), 88, 154,* 158†
Di-(β-chloroethyl) ether, 133,* 135†
β,β'-Dichloroethyl ether, see Di-(β-chloro-ethyl) ether
α,β-Dichloroethyl ethyl ether, 133,* 137†
β,β'-Dichloroethyl sulfide, see Mustard gas
3,3'-Dichloroindanthrone, 912
1,1-Dichloro-2-keto-1,2-dihydronaphthalene, 735
Dichloromethane (methylene chloride), 41, 153,† 154*
N-(Dichloromethylene)-aniline, 610
s-Di-(chloromethyl) ether, 133*
10-Dichloromethyl-2-keto-Δ¹,⁹; ³,⁴-hexahydro-naphthalene, 683
3,3-Dichloropentane, 86
2,4-Dichlorophenoxyacetic acid (2,4-D), 513
1,2-Dichloropropane, 42†
1,3-Dichloropropane, 42,† 309

4,6-Dichlororesorcinol, 630
d-Dichlorosuccinic acid, 267
2,4-Dichlorotoluene, 662
2,6-Dichlorotoluene, 675
Dicobalt octacarbonyl, 197
Dicoumarol, 817, 1019
Dicrotolic acid, 495
Dicyandiamide, 872
p-Dicyclohexylbenzene, 540
Dicyclopentylamine, 231
Dieckmann reaction, 220, 319, 320
Diels-Alder reaction, 310-312
    examples: 314, 531, 630, 719-720, 726, 760, 763, 780, 798-799, 837, 838, 986, 987
Diels hydrocarbon, 961, 995
Diene synthesis, see Diels-Alder reaction
Dienes, conjugated, 70-72, 85
Diesel fuels, 100
Diethanolamine, 224,* 225, 235†
Diethylacetic acid, 222
Diethyl adipate, 177, 220
Diethylamine, 224,* 226,* 229†
    hydrochloride, 227*
Diethylaminobutanone methiodide, 704 705
N,N-Diethylaniline, 597*
Diethylbarbituric acid, 246
Diethyl n-butylmalonate, 221
Diethylcarbinol, 122,*† 128
1,1'-Diethyl-2,2'-carbocyanine iodide, see Sensitive Red
1,1'-Diethyl-4,4'-carbocyanine iodide, see Kryptocyanine
1,1'-Diethyl-4,4'-cyanine iodide, see Cyanine Blue
Diethyl diethylmalonate, 222
Diethyl ether, 55,† 133*-134, 135†
    anesthetic, 134-135
    peroxide, 134
Diethyl α-formylsuccinate, 197
Diethyl fumarate, 197
Diethyl ketone, 86, 128,† 192,* 202, 203
Diethyl malonate, see Malonic ester
Diethylmalonic acid, 222
Diethyl α-naphthylmethylmalonate, 648
Diethylrhodamine, 697, 698
Diethyl sebacate, 177
Diethyl succinate, 177
Diethyl sulfate, 55-56†
Diethyl sulfide, 140*†
as-Difluoroethylene, 159
Digitalis glycosides, 991-992
Digitogenin, 993
Digitonin, 963, 993
    precipitation of steroids, 963

Digitoxigenin, 991
Diglycylglycine, 441
  methyl ester, 441
Digoxigenin, 991
gem-Dihalides, 86, 153, 158
vic-Dihalides, 58–59, 85
Di-n-heptylamine, 231
Di-n-hexyl ether, 133*
9,10-Dihydroanthracene, 759
N,N - Dihydro - 1,2,1',2' - anthraquinonean-
  thrahydroquinoneazine, 912
N,N-Dihydro-1,2,1',2'-anthraquinoneazine,
  see Indanthrone
N,N-Dihydro-1,2,2',3'-anthraquinoneazine,
  912
1,2-Dihydrobenzene, 523
Dihydrocivetone, 300, 320†
Δ³-Dihydrofuran, 797
Dihydro-γ-ionone, 950
1,4-Dihydronaphthalene, 737
9,10-Dihydrophenanthrene, 755,*† 756
Dihydrophytyl bromide, 36, 954
Dihydropyran, 815
Dihydroquinine, 1026
Dihydroxyacetone, 124, 476
  phosphate, 476, 477
2,6-Dihydroxyanthracene, 758
1,2-Dihydroxybenzene, see Catechol
1,3-Dihydroxybenzene, see Resorcinol
1,4-Dihydroxybenzene, see Hydroquinone
2,6-Dihydroxychrysene, 776
4',8'- Dihydroxy - 1,2,5,6 - dibenzanthracene,
  789, 790
4,4'-Dihydroxy-α,β-diethylstilbene, see Stilbestrol
5,6 - Dihydroxydihydroindole - α - carboxylic
  acid, 512
2,2'-Dihydroxydinaphthyl, see Di-β-naphthol
3,6 - Dihydroxy - 2,5 - diphenyl - 1,4 - benzoquinone, see Polyporic acid
2,4'-Dihydroxydiphenylmethane, 867–868
4,4'-Dihydroxydiphenylmethane, 867–868
Dihydroxyethyl peroxide, 134
β,β'-Dihydroxyethyl sulfide, see β-Thiodiglycol
2,6-Dihydroxy-8-methyl-1,4-naphthoquinone-
  3,5-dicarboxylic acid, 770
1,5-Dihydroxynaphthalene, 725
2,6-Dihydroxynaphthalene, 747
2,7 Dihydroxynaphthalene, 734
1,8 - Dihydroxynaphthalene - 3,6 - disulfonic
  acid, 750
1,12-Dihydroxyperylene, 780

2,5-Dihydroxyphenylacetic acid, see Homogentisic acid
L-3,4-Dihydroxyphenylalanine, 511–512, 833
2,5-Dihydroxyphenylpyruvic acid, 510–511
3,8-Dihydroxypyrene, 778
3,10-Dihydroxypyrene, 778
9,10-Dihydroxystearic acids, 402
12,12'-Dihydroxyviolanthrone, 917
Diiodoacetylene, 645
3,5-Diiodo-4-(4'-methoxyphenoxy)-benzalde-
  hyde, 437
L-Diiodotyrosine, 422, 423, 430, 459
Diisatogen, 906
Diisoamyl ether, 133,* 135–136†
Diisobutyl ketone, 192*
Diisopropylamine, 235
p-Diisopropylbenzene, 538
Diisopropylcarbinol, 204
Diisopropyl ether, 133,* 136†
Diisopropyl ketone, 192,* 204
Diketene, 321
Diketoapocamphoric acid, 942
Diketocamphoric acid, 942
2,5-Diketopiperazine, 435,† 436
Dilaurylamine, 231
Dimedone, 480
2,3-Dimercaptopropanol-1, 93
3,4-Dimethoxyacetophenone, 704
3,4-Dimethoxy-ω-aminoacetophenone hydrochloride, 704
2,3-Dimethoxybenzaldehyde, 685
3,4-Dimethoxybenzaldehyde, see Veratraldehyde
2,6-Dimethoxy-1,4-benzoquinone, 722
5,6-Dimethoxylepidine, 811
5,8-Dimethoxylepidine, 811
3,4-Dimethoxy-ω-oximinoacetophenone, 704
d-Dimethoxysuccinic acid, 364, 367
12,12'-Dimethoxyviolanthrone, 916, 917
2,4-Dimethylacetophenone, 698
Dimethylacetylene, 85*
Dimethyl acetylenedicarboxylate, 799
β,β-Dimethylacrylic acid, 209
Dimethylamine, 224,* 226*
p-Dimethylaminoazobenzene, 618
3,2'-Dimethyl-4-aminoazobenzene, 923
p-Dimethylaminobenzaldehyde, 428, 675,*
  680†
p-Dimethylaminobenzophenone, 697
p,p'-Dimethylaminobenzophenone, see Michler's ketone
ω-Dimethylaminopropiophenone hydrochloride, 704
2,5-Dimhetyl-6-aminopyrimidine, 1001

---

* Physical constants   † Preparation

N,N-Dimethylaniline, 597,* 599,† 607, 618, 680, 696, 697
  acid salts, 598*
1,4-Dimethylanthraquinone, 762
2,3-Dimethylanthraquinone, 763
7,9-Dimethyl-3,4-benzacridine, 786
5,10-Dimethyl-1,2-benzanthracene, 785
9,10-Dimethyl - 1,2 - benzanthracene, 786,* 793–794
Dimethylbenzenes, see Xylenes
5,6-Dimethylbenzimidazole, 1008, 1009
2,3-Dimethylbenzoquinone, 723
2,5-Dimethylbenzoquinone, 723
4,9-Dimethyl-5,6-benzthiophanthrene, 786
2,3-Dimethylbutadiene-1,3, 54,† 310, 311, 850
2,2-Dimethylbutane, 28*
2,3-Dimethylbutane, 28*
2,4-Dimethyl-8-sec-butylquinoline, 99
Dimethyl-t-butylsulfonium iodide, 344
3,3-Dimethylbutyne-1, 85*
5,6-Dimethylchrysene, 787
1,2-Dimethylcyclohexane, 107
5,5-Dimethylcyclohexanedione-1,3, see Dimedone
1,1-Dimethylcyclopentane, 96*
1,3-Dimethylcyclopentane, 96*
1,1-Dimethylcyclopropane-2-carboxylic acid, 296
1,5-Dimethyl-2,6-dihydroxyanthracene, 758
3,3'-Dimethyldiphenyl (m-ditolyl), 616
3,4'-Dimethyldiphenyl, 652
4,4'-Dimethyldiphenyl, 652
Dimethyl 3,6 - epoxy - 3,4,5,6 - tetrahydrophthalate, 312
Dimethyl ether, 20, 133,* 135,† 316*
as-Dimethylethylene, 331
Dimethylethylmethane, 27
Dimethylethyl n-propylammonium hydroxide, 343–344
2,3 Dimethyl-4-ethylpyrrole, see Hemopyrrole
2,4-Dimethyl-3-ethylpyrrole, see Cryptopyrrole
Dimethylformamide, 179, 680
2,5-Dimethylfuran, 799
Dimethylfuran-2,3-dicarboxylate, 799
2,3-Dimethylglucose, 389
α,α-Dimethyl-β-hydroxypropionaldehyde, 275
α,α-Dimethyl-β-hydroxypropionic acid, 1009
1,1-Dimethyl-2-isobutenylcyclopropane, 296
1,6 - Dimethyl - 4 - isopropylnaphthalene, see Cadinene
1,4-Dimethylisoquinoline, 812–813
Dimethylmaleic acid, 331
Dimethylmaleic anhydride, 311

2,4-Dimethylmandelic acid, 698
1,6-Dimethylnaphthalene, 529
2,3-Dimethylnaphthalene, 529
2,6-Dimethylnaphthalene, 529, 744
2,7-Dimethylnaphthalene, 529, 782
2,6-Dimethylnaphthalene-3-sulfonic acid, 744
2,6-Dimethylnaphthalene-8-sulfonic acid, 744
2,3-Dimethyl-1,4-naphthoquinone, 721–722
2,6-Dimethyl-1,4-naphthoquinone, 719
Dimethylolurea, 870
2,4-Dimethyloxazole, 802
2,2-Dimethylpentane, 29,* 105
Dimethylpentanes, 29*
Dimethylphenols, see Xylenols
N,N-Dimethyl-p-phenylenediamine, 607
Dimethylpriothetin, 503–504
2,6-Dimethylpyrone, 816
2,4-Dimethylpyrrole, 798
2,3-Dimethylquinoline, 812
Dimethyl sulfate, 136, 146
3,4-Dimethyl-Δ²-tetrahydrobenzaldehyde, 311
Dimethylthetin, 503
3,4-Dimethyl-L-threonamide, 391, 392
Di-β-naphthol, 637–638,*† 779, 780
1,1'-Dinaphthyl, 779
Di-β-naphthyl-p-phenylenediamine, 849
2,4-Dinitroaniline, 597,* 598
1,5-Dinitroanthraquinone, 763,† 904
1,8-Dinitroanthraquinone, 763
m-Dinitrobenzene, 557,† 571,* 574, 596
o-Dinitrobenzene, 571,* 573,† 574
p-Dinitrobenzene, 571,* 573†
2,4-Dinitrobenzenediazonium chloride, 620
2,4-Dinitrobenzoic acid, 559
3,5-Dinitrobenzoic acid, 656,* 663†
3,5-Dinitrobenzoyl chloride, 663
2,4-Dinitrochlorobenzene, 571,* 575, 579, 581, 809
6,6'-Dinitrodiphenic acid, 271,* 292
2,2'-Dinitrodiphenyl, 652
2,4'-Dinitrodiphenyl, 559
4,4'-Dinitrodiphenyl, 559
2,4-Dinitrodiphenylamine, 575
2,2'-Dinitrodiphenyl disulfide, 603*†
4,4'-Dinitrodiphenyl disulfide, 1031
2,4-Dinitrofluorobenzene, 358, 446–447
2,4-Dinitro-N-methylaniline, 581
1,5-Dinitronaphthalene, 743
1,8-Dinitronaphthalene, 743
2,4-Dinitro-1-naphthol, 743, see also Martius Yellow
2,4-Dinitrophenol, 574, 579,† 624*
2,6-Dinitrophenol, 574
2,4-Dinitrophenylhydrazine, 618

2,4-Dinitroresorcinol, 630
2,4-Dinitrostilbene, 577
4,4'-Dinitrostilbene, 573
2,4-Dinitrotoluene, 571,* 576, 595
2,6-Dinitrotoluene, 576
Dioctyl sodium sulfosuccinate, 413
Diosgenin, 994–995
Dioxan, 123*†
Dipentene, 847, 935, 936
Diphenic acid, 666–667 *†, 757
Diphenic anhydride, 667
Diphenoquinone, 711–712
Diphenyl, 528,* 532,* 546,† 615
    derivatives, 652†
Diphenylamine, 597,* 598, 604†
2,5-Diphenyl-1,4-benzoquinone, 721†
1,4-Diphenylbutadiene-1,3, 691,*† 737, 881
Diphenyldecapentaene, 881, 882
Diphenyldecatetraene, 881–882
Diphenyldiazomethane, 720
Diphenyl disulfide, 594
Diphenylene oxide, 530,* 802*
Diphenyl ether, 133*
Di-β-phenylethylamine, 230†
α,α-Diphenylethylene, 546
1,6-Diphenylhexadiene-2,4, 523
1,6-Diphenylhexatriene-1,3,5, 523, 881
Diphenylguanidine, 609
Diphenyliodonium hydroxide, 654
Diphenyliodonium iodide, 654
Diphenyl isomerism, 292
Diphenylmethane, 532,* 536†
Diphenyl-α-naphthylmethyl, 553
Diphenyl-β-naphthylmethyl, 553
Diphenylnitrogen, 604–605
1,8-Diphenyloctatetraene, 691,*† 881
Diphenyl oxide, 546, 626
Diphenylpolyenes, 671,† 881–882
    reduction, 882
2,3-Diphenylquinoxaline, 707
Diphenyl sulfide, 594
Diphenyl sulfone, 594
Diphenyl sulfoxide, 594
s-Diphenylthiourea, 609
s-Diphenylurea, 608*†
Diphosgene, 185
1,3-Diphosphoglyceraldehyde, 477
1,3-Diphosphoglyceric acid, 476, 477
Diphosphoinositide, 488
Diphosphopyridine nucleotide, 464, 476, 477,
    480
Diphtheria toxin, 471

Dipole moments, 326–327, 566–567
Di-n-propylamine, 224*
Di-n-propyl ether, 133,* 135†
Di-n-propyl ketone, 192*
Dipyrazolanthronyl, 919
Direct Blue BB, 927
Directive influence, 556–570
Disaccharides, 381–385
Dismutation, see Disproportionation
Disproportionation, 210–211, 549
    examples: 661, 688, 716–717, 772, 877, 936
Dissociation constants, aliphatic amines, 224
    aliphatic carboxylic acids, 163, 283–285, 312
    amino acids, 425–426
    aromatic amines, 596–598
    aromatic carboxylic acids, 656, 668
    aryl-substituted paraffinic acids, 668
    benzenesulfinic acid, 593
    heterocycles, 802–803, 808
    ionizing groups of proteins, 453
    phenols, 623, 624
Disulfides, 139
m-Ditolyl, see 3,3'-Dimethyldiphenyl
Divinylacetylene, 851
Divinyl ether, 133,* 135†
Djenkolic acid, 422
n-Docosane, 31,* 40†
Dodecahydrotriphenylene, 534*†
n-Dodecane, 31,* 97
Δ⁹,¹⁰-Dodecylenic acid, 401*
Doebners Violet, 883
n-Dohexacontane, 31*
n-Dotriacontane, 36†
Dracorhodin, 824
Dracorubin, 824
Droserone, 726
Drying oils, 415–416
Dumas nitrogen determination, 15
Dunnione, 730–731
Duprene, see Neoprene
Durene (1,2,4,5-tetramethylbenzene), 532,
    536–537,† 666
Dynamite, 131
Dynel, 862
Dypnone, 698–699

Echinochrome A, 726–727
Eclipsed interactions, 304
Edestin, 430, 451, 452*
Ehrlich's reagent, 428
n-Eicosane, 31,* 44*
Elaidic acid, 284,* 403
Elastin, 417
Elbs reaction, 790, 791

* Physical constants   † Preparation

Electrolysis of carboxylic acids, 40, 401
Electrophilic attack, 59–64, 88, 328–329
Electrophoresis, 451
α-Eleostearic acid, 401,* 403, 415
β-Eleostearic acid, 403
Eleutherinol, 824–825
Embelin, 723 .
Emde degradation, 829, 830
Emetamine, 845
Emetine, 845, 1025
Emulsin, 378, 380, 385
Enanthol, see n-Heptaldehyde
Enantiomers, 259
Enantiomorphs, 256, see Enantiomers
End group analysis, 446
3,6-Endomethylene-Δ⁴-tetrahydrophthalic an-
    hydride, 311
Enol acetylation, 199
Enolase, 477, 480
Enols, 80, 89, see also Tautomerism, keto-enol
Enzymes, 378, 427, 460–468
Eosin, 897, 899
Ephedrine, 500
Epiandrosterone, 983–985
Epicholestanol, 962, 963, 965, 973, 974
Epicoprostanol, 963–964
Epimerization, 275, 276, 356, 360
Epinephrine, see Adrenaline
Equilenin, 970, 982 983
Ergonovine, 841
Ergosterol, 964
    irradiation, 1013
Ergot alkaloids, 841–842
Ergotamine, 841–842
Ergothioneine, 503
Erlenmeyer rule, 113
Erucic acid, 401,* 403, 408
Erythritol, 113*
    fatty acid esters, 414
Erythroaphin-fb, 780
Erythrogenic acid, 405–406*†
D-Erythrose, 164, 360
Esterases, 461
Ester-condensation, 219, 441, 699
Ester gum, 877
Esterification, 130–131, 174–176, 671–673
    diazomethane, 176–177
    Fischer, 130, 174–176, 658
    silver salt method, 176
    sulfonic acids, 590
Ester interchange, see Alcoholysis of esters
Esters, 130–132, 173–179, 213
    in Grignard reaction, 118–119, 177
    hydrolysis, 178

Estradiol, 969, 971–972
Estriol, 969
    glucuronide, 970
Estrogens, 969–972
    synthetic, 972
Estrone, 969–971, 983
    sulfate ester, 970
Étard reaction, 676
Ethane, 31,* 44,* 102
    conformation, 303
Ethanol, see Ethyl alcohol
Ethanolamine, 224,* 234–235,† 502
Ether, see Diethyl ether
Etherification, 136, 626–627, 718
Ethers, 132–138
Ethoxyacetaldehyde, 432
2-Ethoxy-1-naphthaldehyde, 680*†
β-Ethoxynaphthalene, 680
9-Ethoxy-10-phenanthrol, 637
Ethyl acetate, 130,† 174*
Ethyl acetoacetate, see Acetoacetic ester
Ethylacetylene, 85*
Ethylal, 215
Ethyl alcohol, 55, 111, 112,* 115,* 120–121†
    absolute, 101
    dehydration, 55, 57, 135
    by fermentation, 476, 477, 479–481†
    oxidation, 127, 155, 166, 193, 194
    reactions, 20, 197
Ethylamine, 224,* 226,* 229†
    hydrohalide salts, 227*
Ethyl p-aminobenzoate, 596
N-Ethylaniline, 231†
p-Ethylbenzaldehyde, 679
Ethylbenzene, 532,* 533,* 543,† 875
Ethyl benzoate, 117, 658
Ethyl bromide, 145,† 146,* 149, 337, 339, 345
2-Ethylbutanol-1, 210
Ethyl n butylacetoacetate, 220
Ethyl n-butyl ether, 57, 133,* 136†
Ethyl n-butyrate, 174
Ethyl carbamate, see Urethan
Ethyl carbonate, 185*†
Ethyl chloride, 100, 145, 146*
Ethyl chloroacetate, 179
Ethyl chlorocarbonate, 185*†
Ethyl chloroformate, see Ethyl chlorocarbonate
Ethyl cinnamate, 692
Ethyl crotonate, 236
Ethyl cyanide, see Propionitrile
Ethylcyclohexane, 96*
Ethyldimethylsulfonium salts, 343
Ethylene, 53,* 54–55,† 102,† 106,† 297,* 881*
    addition reactions, 59–70, 121, 157, 330, 331

alkylation, 105
anesthetic, 134–135
electronic structure, 77–78
oxidation, 67
polymerization, 863
pyrolysis, 103
reaction with S_2Cl_2, 70
Ethylene chlorohydrin, 63–64, 70, 122–123, 135, 167, 854
Ethylene cyanohydrin, 167
Ethylenediamine, 224*
Ethylene dibromide, 59 101,† 152, 154*
Ethylene dichloride, 101, 122, 154,* 157†
Ethylene glycol, 67, 113, 122*–123,† 189
dimethyl ether, 133*
monoethyl ether, 432
Ethyleneketals, 215
Ethylene oxide, 64, 123†
reactions, 119–120, 123, 235, 240
Ethylenesemithioketals, 216
Ethylenethioketals, 215–216
Ethyl ether, see Diethyl ether
Ethyl fluoride, 159
Ethyl formate, 174*
Ethyl D-glucofuranosides, 376–377
Ethyl glucoside, 374
Ethyl n-heptylate, 174*
2-Ethylhexanol-1, 210
Ethyl hydantoa e, 435
Ethyl hydracrylate, 323
Ethylidene bromide, 154*
Ethylidene chloride, 154,* 157†
Ethylidene iodide, 88
Ethylidene peroxide polymer, 134
Ethyl iodide, 35,† 146*†
Ethyl mercaptan, 139
Ethyl nitrate, 130–131, 881*
Ethyl nitrite, 130–131
Ethyl p-nitrobenzoate, 596
Ethyl orthoformate, 215
Ethyl pelargonate, 174*
3-Ethylpentane, 29*
Ethyl N-phenylcarbonate, see Phenylurethan
Ethyl β-phenyl-β-hydroxypropionate, 693
Ethyl propionate, 174*
Ethyl-n-propylcarbinol, 66, 118†
Ethyl n-propyl ether, 57, 136*
Ethylquinone, 722
Ethyl Red, 898, 899
Ethylsulfuric acid, 55, 63
Ethyl n-valerate, 174*
Ethyl vinyl ketone, 985

17α-Ethynyltestosterone, 976–977
Etioporphyrin, 456
Eudalene, 945
Eugenol, 624,* 633, 684–685
Euxanthone, 818
Exaltone, 302
Explosives, 92, 131–132, 214, 581–583

Farnesol, 944, 945, 949
Farnesyl bromide, 949, 950
Fast Red A, 884, 924*
Fast Red B, 925
Fats, 166, 399–416
metabolism, 488–496
Fatty acids, 399–407
biosynthesis, 491–493
essential, 495–496
Febrifugin, 844–845
Fehling's solution, 198, 351
Fermentation, 472
Ferric chloride color test for phenols, 633
Fibers, synthetic, 857–863
Fibrin, 418, 1018
Fibrinogen, 418, 430, 1018
Fibroin, 417, 429, 430, 452,* 453, 454,* 657
Fibrous proteins, 417, 453–454
Fieser's solution, 767
Fischer base, 900, 901
Fischer conventions, 262–264, 365–366
esterification, 130, 174–176
Fischer-Tropsch process, 108–109
Fisetin, 822
Flavanthrone, 921–913
Flavicide, 1028
Flavin, mononucleotide, 465
Flavone, 821
Flavones, 821–824
Fluoranthene, 528*
Fluorene, 528*
Fluorenone, 667,*† 757
Fluorenone-4-carboxylic acid, 667*†
Fluorescein, 895, 897
Fluoroacetic acid, 163
Fluorobenzene, 614,† 644*
Fluoroform, 159
Fluorohydrocortisone, 978*, 979
Folic acid, 1007
Formal charge, 51
Formaldehyde, 153-154,† 192,* 194†
hydrate, 201
polymerization, 200–201
reactions, 90–91, 119, 128, 209, 211, 213, 215, 234, 275, 323, 368, 865, 867–868, 870
Formalin, 194

* Physical constants   † Preparation

Formamide, 189
Formazans, 805
Formic acid, 162, 163,* 128, 162, 163,* 165,† 168–169, 600
  anhydrous, 169†
  metabolism, 507
  pyrolysis of salt, 313
Formimino chloride, 678
Formose, 368
Formylation, 197, 677–680, 773, 793
Formylcycylopentane, 197
Formyl fluoride, 677
8 Formyltetrahydropteroylglutamic acid, 505, 508
Fourneau 309, see Germanin
Fractional distillation, 32, 33, 34
Free radical reactions, 328
  alkylation, arylation, 721–722
  bromination, 151
  cracking, 43
  halogenation, 42, 151, 243
  hydrobromination, 62–63
  miscellaneous, 40, 42–43
  oxidation, 604–605, 637–638, 694–695, 710
  polymerization, 855–857, 875
Freons, 160
Friedel-Crafts hydrocarbon synthesis, 535–540, 560–561, 565
Friedel-Crafts ketone synthesis, 540–543
Fries reaction, 634–637
Fries rule, 733, 753, 758, 772
Fructose, 351, 353, 355, 366
  fermentation, 379–381
  metabolism, 372–379
  photosynthesis, 486
  synthesis, 367–370
Fructose cyanohydrin, 351
Fructose-1,6-diphosphoric acid, 472, 474, 475, 476
Fructose-6-phosphoric acid, 474, 475
FSH, 460
Fuchsin, see Rosaniline
Fuchsonimine, 883
Fulminates, 581, 582
Fumaric acid, 280,† 283*
  biosynthesis, 461, 481, 482, 483
  bromination, 286
  hydroxylation, 285–286
  metabolism, 502
  stereochemistry, 281–282*
Fumarylacetoacetic acid, 511
Fumigatin, 722
Fungus pigments, 723–724
Furan, 311, 363, 549,*† 796,* 798,† 801–802

Furan-2,3-dicarboxylic acid, 818
Furanoside, 363
Furfural, 192,* 549, 800, 861, 869†
  -phenol resins, 869
Furfuryl alcohol, 549, 799, 800
2-Furoic acid, 549*†
Fusel oil, 481

Gabriel synthesis, 233–234, 431
G-Acid, 747,† 924
Gadoleic acid, 401,* 403
Galactan, 798
Galactose, 355, 356, 359, 372,* 373,* 377,* 475, 481, 490, 491
α-D-Galactose diacetonide, 376
Galactowaldenase, 475
Galipine, 827
Gallacetophenone, 695
Gallein, 895
Gallic acid, 656,* 663
  decarboxylation, 630, 663
Gamabufotalin, 993
Gammexane, 655
Gangliosides, 490–491
Gas oil, 94
Gasoline, cracked, 101
  high-octane, 100–108
  natural, 94–95
  polymer, 104–105
  straight-run, 100
  synthetic, 108–109
Gattermann, aldehyde synthesis, 678–679, 685, 801
  reaction, 614–615
Gattermann-Koch aldehyde synthesis, 677–678
Gelatin, 417, 419, 427, 451, 452,* 453
Geneva system of nomenclature, 52, 79–82, 162, 191
Genistein, 823, 824
Gentiobiose, 380, 381
Gentisaldehyde, 686
Geometrical isomerism, 277–292, 611–612, 701–702
Geraniol, 937, 938
Germanin, 1024
Geronic acid, 952, 953
Girard's reagent, 971
Gitogenin, 993
Gitonin, 993
Gitoxigenin, 991
Glacial acetic acid, 166*†
Glaucine, 832, 833
Gliadin, 427

Globin, 455, 458
Globular proteins, 417, 454
Globulins, 417
  plasma, 430, 454, 455, 491
Glucolactone, see Gluconolactone
4-Glucomannose, 373*†
Gluconamide, 358
D-Gluconic acid, 357,† 369–370,† 377*
  degradation, 357, 358
  γ lactone, see Gluconolactone
L-Gluconic acid, 356
Gluconolactone, 358, 370, 377,* 378
Glucoproteins, 454
Glucosamine, 389, 395
Glucosazone, 352, 353
Glucose, 350–351, 354–356, 359, 372*
  conformation, 366
  derivatives, 351, 352–353, 357, 379
  fermentation, 479–481
  α- and β-forms, 361–363
  γ-form, 367
  hydrogenation, 355, 392, 393
  from lipids, 490, 491
  oxidation, 357
  oxide structure, 361–367
  photosynthesis, 485–486
  reduction, 354–355
  synthesis, 367–370
Glucose acetonide, 376
Glucose-1, 2-anhydride-3, 4, 6-triacetate, 363
Glucose-5, 6-carbonate, 376
Glucose cyanohydrin, 351
Glucose diacetonide, 376
Glucose oxime, 357
Glucose phenylhydrazone, 352
Glucose-1-phosphate, 382, 474, 475, 476
Glucose-6-phosphate, 474, 475, 476
Glucosides, 378–380
Glucosone, 370
Glucuronic acid, 395, 396, 397
Glutaconic acid, 816
Glutaconic aldehyde, 810
D-Glutamic acid, 450
L-Glutamic acid, 419,* 421, 424,* 430, 433,†
  434,† 440,† 443, 498
  carbobenzoxy derivative, 443
  metabolism, 476, 481, 482, 483, 486, 505
Glutamine, 421, 427
Glutamylglutamic acid, 442–443
Glutardialdehyde, 841
Glutaric acid, 167,† 199,† 312,* 314†
Glutaric anhydride, 316,*† 318†

Glutathione, 443–444,† 447, 511
Glutelins, 418
Glyceraldehyde, 124, 355, 476
  configuration, 260–264
3-Glyceraldehyde phosphate, 476, 477
Glyceric acid, 124,† 263, 365†
Glycerides, see Fats
Glycerol, 113, 123,† 124,* 177, 178, 189, 410. 476
  dehydration, 208
  fermentation, 124, 480
  monochlorohydrin, 124
  nitration, 131–132
  oxidation, 124, 368
Glycerol trinitrate, see Nitroglycerin
Glycerosazone, 368
Glycerose, 368
Glycine, 418–419,* 426,* 430, 431,† 432,† 434, 498
  betaines, see Betaine and Sarcosine
  metabolism, 476, 486, 504–505, 507, 532
Glycine anhydride, see Diketopiperazine
Glycocholic acid, 491, 967
Glycocoll, see Glycine
Glycogen, 390, 474, 476
Glycogenic substances, 476
Glycogenolysis, 473–476
Glycoaldehyde, 432
Glycolic acid, 163,* 322, 486
Glycolide, 322
vic-Glycols, 67,† 122–123, 288–289,† 363
  acetonides, 375–376, 392, 393
  cleavage, 129, 195, 402
Glycolysis, 473
Glycosides, 378–381
Glycosphingosides, 490
Glycylalanine, 497
Glycylcysteine, 445
Glycylglycine, 426,* 441†
Glycylphenylalanine, 445
Glyoxal, 192,* 520
  hydrate, 216
Glyoxylic acid, 163* 216, 486
Glyptal, 872
Goitrogens, 459–460
Gorlic acid, 406–407*
Gramicidin, 450
Gramine, 434
Grantianine, 827
Graphite, 516
Greases, 110
Green bacteria, 486
Grenzdextrin, 390
Grignard machine, 205

* Physical constants † Preparation

Grignard reagents, 37–38, 87, 153, 650, 793
 cleavage of acetates by, 768
 coupling, 152
 dietherate, 38
 limitations, 141, 152, 153, 204, 650
 reaction with quinones, 718, 773, 774, 793–794
Grignard synthesis of: alcohols, 177, 182, 204–205
 alkanes, 37–39
 alkenes, 152
 alkylsilicanediols, 878–879
 alkynes, 87
 aromatic hydrocarbons, 546–548, 651, 794
 o-aroylbenzoic acids, 762, 792–793
 carboxylic acids, 167, 657, 755
 keto acids, 669
 ketones, 182, 791
 lactones, 793
 metal alkyls, 100
 sulfinic acids, 593
 thiophenols, 594
Griseofulvic acid, 805
Griseofulvin, 804–805
Growth hormone, 430
GRS, see Buna S
Guaiacol, 624,* 685
Guaiazulene, 946
Guaiol, 946
Guanidine, 453
Guanidylacetic acid, 502–503
Guanine, 468
Guanylic acid, 469
Gulose, 356, 359, 372*
Guncotton, 132, 858
Gutta-percha, see Balata

H-acid, 749,† 924, 927
Haloform reaction, 154–156
α-Halogen acids, 170–171, 229, 260–261, 431
Halozone, 591
Hansa Yellow G, 933
Haptens, 396, 397
Harman, 827, 829, 842–843
Hecogenin, 982
Helindon Orange R, 910
Helindon Red 2B, see Thioindigo
Helio Fast Yellow 6GL, 917
Heliotropine, 683
Hell-Volhard-Zelinsky reaction, 170–171, 260
Hematinic acid, 457
Heme, 417, 456
Hemiacetals, 215

Hemicelluloses, 368, 388, 859
Hemimellitene (1,2,3-trimethylbenzene), 532,* 537,† 538
Hemimellitic acid (benzene-1,2,3-tricarboxylic acid), 664,*† 668*
Hemin, 455–457
Hemin chloride, see Hemin
Hemin hydroxide, see Heme
Hemocyanin, 451
Hemoglobin, 417, 430, 451, 452,* 455–458, 572
Hemoproteins, 466
Hemopyrrole, 456
n-Heneicosane, 33*
Hentriacontane, 35
Heparin, 395
Heptacene, 775
n-Heptacontane, 31*
Heptacosane, 35
n-Heptadecane, 31,* 40,† 197†
Heptadecylamine, 233
n-Heptaldehyde, 116,† 166, 192,* 197†
n-Heptaldoxime, 231
n-Heptane, 31,* 34, 42
 aromatization, 107
Heptanes, 29–30
o-Heptanoylphenol, 636
p-Heptanoylphenol, 636
Heptene-1, 53*
n-Heptoic acid, see n-Heptylic acid
n-Heptyl alcohol, 116
n-Heptylamine, 231†
n-Heptyl bromide, 147†
n-Heptylic acid, 163,* 166, 402
Herz reaction, 910, 911, 921
Hesperidin, 823, 824
Hesperitin, 823, 824
Heterocyclic compounds, 796–825
Hexacene, 775
Hexachlorobenzene, 644*
Hexachloroethane, 154,* 157†
n-Hexacontane, 31*
Hexacosanol, 409
n-Hexadecane (cetane), 31,* 100
n-Hexadecanol, 117
Hexadiene 2,4, 335
Hexaethylbenzene, 532*
Hexahydrofarnesol, 949
Hexahydrohumulene, 947
Hexahydrophthalic acids, see Cyclohexane-1,-2 dicarboxylic acids
Hexahydrosalicylic acid, 315
Hexamethylbenzene, 517, 532,* 537,† 666

Hexamethylene bromide, 154,* 158,† 309
Hexamethylenediamine, 224,* 860, 861†
Hexamethylene glycol, 113,* 158, 177*†
Hexamethylenetetramine, 213†–214, 677, 869
Hexamethylolmelamine, 872
n-Hexane, 31,* 40, 45,* 66†
Hexanediol-2,5, 117
Hexanes, 28–29
Hexanol-3, 66, 118
Hexanone (-2 and -3), 192*
Hexaphenylethane, 552–554
Hexene-1, 53,* 197
Hexene-2, 66
Hexene-3, 66
Hexestrol, 972
Hexokinase, 474, 475
Hexuronic acid, see Ascorbic acid
n-Hexyl alcohol, 111,* 112,* 120,† 210†
n-Hexylamine, 224* 230,†
n-Hexyl bromide, 146
4-n-Hexylresorcinol, 633,*† 695
Hexynes (-1, -2, and -3), 85*
Hinokitiol, 640
Hinsberg test, 236, 590
Hippuric acid, 2, 493
    azlactone, 436, 437
Hippuryl-ε-carbobenzoxylysine methyl ester,
    444
Hippuryllsyine methyl ester, 444
Histamine, 501
L-Histidine, 420,* 422, 424,* 430, 436†
    betaine, 503
    biological transformations, 476, 501
    determination, 427–428
    indispensability, 498
    isolation, 427
Histones, 418, 430
Hoesch ketone synthesis, 695–696
Hofmann alkylation, 228–229
    degradation, 237–239, 296, 343–345, 808, 829,
    834–835
    reaction, 231–233, 358, 661
Hofmanns Violet, 891
Homocysteine, 421, 503, 504
Homogentisic acid, 510–511
Homophthalic acid, 670*†
Homosalicylaldehyde, 682
Honey, 382
Hooker oxidation, 728–729
Houdry process, 103–104

Hudson's rules, 373–378, 843
Humulene, 947
Hund rule, 75
Hyaluronic acid, 395–396
Hyaluronidase, 396
Hybridization, 75
Hycar, 854
Hydantoin, 245, 246, 432, 434–435
Hydnocarpic acid, 406–407
Hydration, alkenes, 63
    alkynes, 89–90
Hydrazine, 179–211
Hydrazines, 212
Hydrazobenzene, 584, 585*†
Hydrazones, 212, 214
Hydride ion, 210
Hydrindane, 308–309
1,3-Hydrindanedione, see Indane-1,3-dione
Hydrindene (indane), 544*†
α-Hydrindone, 309, 543,*† 544
β-Hydrindone, 325
Hydrobenzoin, 707
Hydrocinnamic acid, 543, 668*–669†
Hydroforming, 107–108
Hydroformylation, 197
Hydrogenation, acid chlorides (Rosenmund),
    196, 686, 755
    aldehydes, 116, 206
    alkenes, 64–66, 289
    alkynes, 90, 404
    amides, 231
    aromatic hydrocarbons, 519, 755, 787
    carbon monoxide, 108, 120
    coal, 108
    cycloalkanes, 295–296
    esters, 177
    fats, 409–410
    ketones, 116, 121, 206, 544
    nitriles, 229–230
    nitro compounds, 596
    oximes, 231
    ozonides, 69
    petroleum, 107
Hydrogen bonding, 113–115, 165, 218, 225, 454,
    803, 885, 887
Hydrogen cyanide, addition to alkynes, 89
    addition to carbonyl group, 203, 336, 351, 357
    condensation with aromatic hydrocarbons,
    678
    condensation with phenols, 679
Hydrogen halides, reactivity, 61

---

* Physical constants   † Preparation

Hydrohalogenation, 61–63, 88, 287, 332–335
α-Hydrojuglone, 725
Hydrolapachol, 729
Hydrolases, 461
Hydrolomatiol, 729
Hydrolysis, acyl halides, 181
  alkyl halides, 115, 122, 337
  amides, 242
  anhydrides, 188
  arylamines, 742
  aryl halides, 575, 579, 580, 625–626
  benzotrichloride, 658
  cyanamide, 244
  diazonium salts, 613
  esters, 178
  fats, 410–411
  α-halo acids, 261
  imides, 243
  isocyanates, 232
  methylene halides, 153
  nitriles, 167, 242
  oxides, 123
  proteins, 427
  sulfonates, 592
Hydron Blue, 922
Hydronium ion, 4–5
Hydroperoxides, 405, 849
Hydroquinone, 322, 378, 624,* 630†
  antioxidant, 695
  methyl ethers, 630*
o-Hydroxyacetophenone, 634–635†
p-Hydroxyacetophenone, 624,* 634–635†
α-Hydroxyalanine, 841, 842
3-Hydroxyanthranilic acid, 512–513
2-Hydroxyanthraquinone, 903
o-Hydroxyazobenzene, 618, 622
p-Hydroxyazobenzene, 618,*† 621
m-Hydroxybenzaldehyde, 675,* 687†
p-Hydroxybenzaldehyde, 675,* 681†
12-Hydroxybenzanthrone, 916
m-Hydroxybenzoic acid, 656,* 663†
p-Hydroxybenzoic acid, 656*
o-Hydroxybenzyl alcohol, see Saligenin
p-Hydroxybenzyl alcohol, 867
α-Hydroxybutyric acid, 260–261*†
β-Hydroxybutyric acid, 494
γ-Hydroxybutyric acid, 324
17-Hydroxycorticosterone, 978
9-Hydroxydecanoic acid, 493
17-Hydroxydesoxycorticosterone, 978
x-Hydroxy-β,β-dimethylbutyrolactone, 275,*†
  1009
2-Hydroxy-3-(β,β-dimethylvinyl)-1,4-naphtho-
  quinone, 728

o-Hydroxydiphenyl, 624,* 626†
p-Hydroxydiphenyl, 624,* 626†
p-Hydroxydiphenylamine, 632
Hydroxydroserone, 726
Hydroxyhydroquinone, 624*
2-Hydroxykynurenine, 512–513
Hydroxylamine, 211
Hydroxyl group, determination, 205
α-Hydroxylignoceric acid, 490
Hydroxylysine, 422, 423, 430
2-Hydroxy-3-methoxybenzaldehyde, 685
o-(Hydroxymethyl)-phenylacetic acid, 325
2-Hydroxy-1,4-naphthohydroquinone triacetate, 717
2-Hydroxy-3-naphthoic acid, 671, 930
2-Hydroxy-1,4-naphthoquinone, 713*–714,
  717,† 718
  reactions, 718, 721
  tautomerism, 713
α-Hydroxynervonic acid, 490
2-Hydroxy-5-nitrobenzyl chloride, 648
10-Hydroxypalmitone, 409
15-Hydroxypentadecylic acid, lactone, 302
Hydroxyperezone, 723
p-Hydroxyphenyl-β-naphthylamine, 922
p-Hydroxyphenylpyruvic acid, 510–511
Hydroxyproline, 419,* 420, 430, 440,† 498, 505
  isolation, 427
β-Hydroxypropionic acid, 167
o-Hydroxypropiophenone, 636
p-Hydroxypropiophenone, 636
1-Hydroxypyrene, 779
3-Hydroxypyrene, 378–379
4-Hydroxypyrene, 778
2-Hydroxypyridine, 809
2-Hydroxy-3,5,6-trimethylbenzaldehyde, 682
Hydroxytryptophane, 501
α-Hydroxyvaline, 842
Hygrine, 827, 828–829
Hyodesoxycholic acid, 968
Hypaphorine, 827
Hyperconjugation, 333–334, 345–346
Hypnone (acetophenone), 699
Hypohalite oxidation, 154–156, 167, 657, 755
  addition, 63–64, 330
Hypoxanthine, 507

Ice Bordeaux, 929
Ice colors, 887
Idose, 356, 359, 372*
Igepon A and T, 413
Imidazole, 453, 462, 802*
Imides, 242–243
Immedial Pure Blue, 921–922

Immedial Yellow GG, 922
Impregnite, 591
Indamine, 715
Indane-1,3-dione, 691
Indane (hydrindene), 544
Indanthrene Black BB, 917; Blue BCS, 912; Blue GCD, 912; Blue RS, 912; Bordeaux RR, 920; Brilliant Green B, 916; Brilliant Violet 2R, 916; Brown R, 917; Brown RRD, 910; Golden Orange G, 913; Golden Yellow GK, 920; Golden Yellow RK, 920; Green B, 916; Khaki 2G, 918; Red RK, 918; Red Violet RH, 910; Rubine R, 919; Scarlet G, 913; Scarlet GG Base, 920; Yellow G, 912; Yellow GK, 917
Indanthrone, 911–912
Indazole, 802,* 803
Indene, 528,* 776
Indican, 905
Indigo, 579, 883*–884, 905*–908†
  dyeing process, 885
  halo derivatives, 908, 909
Indigo Yellow 3G, 908–909
Indocarbon CL, 922
Indole, 434, 509, 530,* 802,* 803†
Indole-β-acetic acid, 513
Indoleacetonitrile, 513
Indole-β-aldehyde, 437, 513
Indole-2-carboxylic acid, 803
Indophenin reaction, 529
Indophenol, 715–922
Indoxyl, 905, 907,† 908†
Inductive effect, 62, 163–165, 216, 226, 326, 338, 344, 565–567, 712–713, 883
Ingrain dyes, 929–931
Inosinic acid, 507–508
meso-Inositol, 394–395, 993
Insect dyes, 769–771
Insulin, 430, 431, 447, 451, 452,* 458–459
Inulin, 390
Invertase, 381
Invert soaps, 414
Invert sugar, 382
Iodine number, 408
Iodoacetic acid, 480
Iodobenzene, 613, 644,* 645,† 653, 654
Iodobenzene dichloride, 653
o-Iodobenzoic acid, 662
α-Iodocarboxylic acids, 171
Iodoform, 154,* 156,† 157
  reduction, 153

o-Iodophenol, 633–634
2-Iodoquinoline, 898
Iodosobenzene, 653, 654
Iodosobenzene diacetate, 653
Iodoxybenzene, 653–654
Ion-exchange resins, 241–242, 445, 870
α-Ionone, 938
β-Ionone, 938, 956–957
Ipecac, 845
Irone, 939–940
Isatin, 812, 905, 906†
Isatinic acid, 812
Isatin-β-imide, 812
Isethionic acid, 413
Isoalloxazine, 462, 465
Isoamidone, 846
Isoamyl acetate, 174*
Isoamylacetic acid, 97
Isoamyl alcohol, 112,* 122,*† 481†
Isoamyl bromide, 146,* 147†
Isoamyl n-butyrate, 174
Isoamyl chloride, 122
Isoamyl isovalerate, 174
5-Isoandrosterone, 972, 973
Isoborneol, 943
Isobornyl acetate, 943
Isobutane, 27,* 95, 106†
  alkylation, 105–106
  nitration, 45
  occurrence, 95
  pyrolysis, 102
Isobutene (isobutylene), 53,* 57,† 61, 63, 102,† 105, 106†
  oxidation, 68
  polymerization, 104, 855
Isobutyl alcohol, 112*
  acetate, 174*
Isobutyl bromide, 146,* 339, 345, 433
Isobutyl chloride, 146*
Isobutylene, see Isobutene
Isobutyl mercaptan, 98
Isobutyraldehyde, 192,* 274, 275
Isobutyric acid, 163,* 166
Isobutyryl chloride, 180*
Isocadinene, 944
Isocaproic acid, 162
Isocaryophyllene, 947
Isocitric acid, 482, 483
Isocrotonic acid, 283
Isocyanates, 232, 233, 608
Isocyanines, 898–899
Isocytosine, 1030
Isodurene (1,2,3,5-tetramethylbenzene), 532*

---

* Physical constants † Preparation

Isoelectric point, 425, 452
Isoeugenol, 624,* 633
Isofebrifugin, 844
Isoflavone, 821–823
Isogeronic acid, 953
3-Isohexylnaphthazarin (alkannan), 730
L-Isoleucine, 419,* 424,* 430, 440†
    biological transformations, 481
    indispensability, 498
Isolomatiol, 729
Isolysergic acid, 841
Isomerase, 474
Isomerism, 16
    diphenyl, 292
    geometrical, 278–292
    optical, 249–279, 406
Isomerization, see also Bond migration, Racemization, and Rearrangements
    alkanes and alkenes, 106
    alkyl halides, 539
    cis-trans, 281–284, 292, 293, 403, 406
Isomycomycin, 406
Isooctane, 99, 104–105†
Isooctene, 104†
Isopentane (2-methylbutane), 27,* 58, 95,* 105†
    chlorination, 121–122
Isophthalic acid, 663,†* 668†
Isoprene, 91†, 847, 855
Isoprene rule, 935
Isoprenoids, 351, 399, 495, 723, 727, 935–960
Isopropenyl acetate, 199
Isopropyl alcohol, 63, 112,* 121,† 206
    from n-propylamine, 237
Isopropylbenzene, see Cumene
Isopropyl bromide, 35, 146,*† 149, 337, 539
Isopropyl chloride, 146*
Isopropyl fluoride, 159
Isopropyl iodide, 57, 146*
2-Isopropylmethoxycyclohexanone, 842, 843
Isopulegol, 938
Isoquinoline, 530,* 810–814
Isosafrole, 685
Isotope dilution method, 429
Isovaleraldehyde, 192*
Isovaleric acid, 162, 166, 399, 400*
Isovaleryl chloride, 180*
Isoviolanthrone, 916
Isoxazole, 802

J-Acid, 748,† 924, 927
Jacobsen reaction, 664
Juglone, 725

Kendall's Compound E, see Cortisone
Keratin, 417, 429, 430, 439, 453–454
Kermes, 771
Kermesic acid, 771
Kerosene, 94, 97
Ketene, 186*–187, 199, 323
    dimer, 321,*† 323, 810–811
Ketenes, 184
Keto-enol tautomerism, 124, 170, 199, 217–222, 244–245, 274, 275, 360–361, 631, 768, 773
α-Ketoglutaric acid, 481, 482, 483, 505
2-Ketogulonic acid, 392, 393
Ketone bodies, 494
4-Ketostearic acid, 405
1-Keto-1,2,3,4-tetrahydrophenanthrene, 625
Khellin, 818
Khellinone, 818
Khellol, 818
Kjeldahl determination, 15
Knocking, 99
Knoevenagel reaction, 692
Koch acid, 749, 750
Kogasin, 108, 109
Kojic acid, 817
Kolbe reaction, 661
    synthesis, 40–41
Körner's orientation method, 518–519
Kryptocyanine, 900
Kuhn-Roth determination, 952–953
Kynurenic acid, 512
Kynurenin, 512–513

Laccaic acid, 771
Lac dye, 771
Lactase, 384, 461, 473
Lactic acid, 163,* 255, 256,† 257, 258, 276,† 365,† 461, 876
    dehydration, 323
    by fermentation, 476, 477
    metabolism, 476, 477
    stereochemistry, 255–256, 257–260, 263
Lactic acid dehydrogenase, 461, 477
Lactide, 322
Lactobacillic acid, 296
β-Lactoglobulin, 430, 452†
Lactones, β-, 323–324
    γ-, 324
    δ-, 325
    sugar, 358, 370, 377–378
Lactose, 373,* 381, 384, 473
Lampblack, 44
Lanital, 860
Lanosterol, 950–951, 990, 991
Lanthionine, 421, 422, 450

Lapachol, 727–729
α-Lapachone, 727, 728
β-Lapachone, 727, 728
Lard, 408,* 409
Lastex, 850
Latex, 847, 849–850
Laudanosine, 832–833, 836
Lauramide, 231
Lauric acid, 147, 400*
    electrolysis, 40
    occurrence, 400, 408, 409
    reduction, 113
Lauroleic acid, 409
Lauronitrile, 230
Lauryl alcohol, 112,* 113,† 177,† 178,† 410†
n-Laurylamine, 224,* 230,† 231†
n-Lauryl bromide, 145†
1-Lauryl-3-ethylbenzotrazolium bromide, 415
Lawsone, 725, see also 2-Hydroxy-1,4-naphtho-
    quinone
Lead azide, 581, 582
Lead naphthenate, 98
Lead phthalocyanin, 934
Lead tetraacetate, alkylation with, 721–722
    oxidation with, 12 , 402, 771, 788, 789
Lecithins, 488, 489†
Lepidine, 810†
    ethiodide, 898, 899
Leucenol, 827, 830
L-Leucine, 419,* 420, 424,* 430, 432–433,†
    437,† 440,† 842
    biological transformations, 481, 500
    indispensability, 498
Leuckart reaction, 600
Leuco bases, 892
Leuco form of vat dyes, 885, 888, 892, 894, 905,
    911–912
Leucopterin, 1007
Leucyltriglycylleucyltriglycylleucyloctaglycyl-
    glycine, 440
Levopimaric acid, 948
Levulinic acid, 799, 800, 848
Levulinic aldehyde, 848
Lewis acids, 138, 225–226, 537, 541
Lewis bases, 138, 225–226
Lewisite, 92–93
Licanic acid, 401,* 405, 415
Lignin, 386, 684
Lignoceric acid, 400,* 408, 415, 490
Ligroin, 94
Limonene, 935, 936*
Lindlar catalyst, 90
Linelaidic acid, 403

9,11-Linoleic acid, 416
9,12-Linoleic acid, 401,* 404, 416
    indispensability, 496
    occurrence, 403, 404, 408, 409, 415, 489
Linolenic acid, 401,* 404, 416
    indispensability, 496
    occurrence, 403, 404, 415, 489
Linoleum, 415
Linseed oil, 403, 415
Lipases, 461
Lipids, see Fats and Waxes
Lipoic acid, 139–140
Lipoproteins, 417, 454, 455
Lithium aluminum hydride, 116–117, 177–178,
    230–231
Lithium borohydride, 117
Lithium ethylanilide, 319
Lithocholic acid, 968
Lobelanine, 829
Lobry de Bruyn-van Eckenstein rearrange-
    ment, 124, 360–361
Lomatiol, 729
Longifoline, 497–498
Lubricating oils, 94, 109–110
Lucite, 876
Lumisterol, 1013
Lupeol, 951
Lupinine, 827
Lutidines, 806
Lycopene, 953–954
Lysergic acid, 841, 842
    diethylamide, 842
L-Lysine, 420,* 422, 424,* 426,* 430, 431
    decarboxylation, 502
    indispensability, 498
Lyxose, 360, 375,* 377*

Madder, see Alizarin
Malachite Green, 893
Maleic acid, 280, 282,* 314
    additions, 285–286
    reduction, 281
    stereochemistry, 281–282
Maleic anhydride, 281–283,† see Diels-Alder
    reaction
Maleylacetoacetic acid, 510
D-(−)-Malic acid, 263, 271,* 277, 355, 486,
    815–816
    dehydration, 280
    metabolism, 313–314, 481, 482, 483
    oxidation, 313
L-(+)-Malic acid, 277
Malonic acid, 163,* 312,* 313,† 482
    condensation with aldehydes, 669, 692

---

decarboxylation, 221
dehydration, 316
Malonic ester (ethyl), 218, 220†
  synthesis, 220–222, 432–434, 439, 648, 669, 754
Malonylurea, see Barbituric acid
Maltase, 378, 382, 384, 461, 473
Maltol, 817
Maltose, 381, 384–385, 461, 473
Mandelic acid, 203–204,† 259,* 271,* 274, 698
d-Mandelic acid, 259*
l-Mandelic acid, 256,* 259,* 271*
Mandelonitrile, 203
Mandelonitrile glucoside (prunasin), 380
Mannich reaction, 704, 800, 840–841
Mannitol, 254, 369
Mannonic acid, 356, 369, 378*
  γ- and δ-lactone, 378
Mannose, 354, 355, 359
  optical rotation, 372, 373
  phenylhydrazone, 354
  synthesis, 369–370
Marfanil, 1033
Margaric acid, 400
Markownikoff rule, 61, 63–64, 88, 90, 295
Martius Yellow (2,4-dinitro-1-naphthol), 743,† 884
Matricaria methyl ester, 406
Mauveine, 889–891
McFadyen and Stevens aldehyde synthesis, 687
Meerwein-Ponndorf reduction, 207
Melamine, 872
Melamine-formaldehyde resins, 871–872
Melanin, 461, 463, 511–512
Meldolas Blue, 884
Melicopicine, 827
Mellitic acid, 516, 666,*† 668*
Mellophanic acid (benzene-1,2,3,5-tetracar-boxylic acid), 665* 666,† 668*
Melting point comparisons, amides, 179
  amines, 596
  aromatic isomers, 533
  carboxylic acids, 400–401
  diacids, 312
  cis-trans isomers, 282, 283, 284
  phenols, 623
p-Menthane, 936
Δ³-p-Menthene, 348
l-Menthol, 193,* 276, 348
l-Menthone, 193,*† 625
l-Menthylamine, 271*
  mesotartrate, 272
  d- and l-tartrate, 272

l-Menthyl d-lactate, 276
l-Menthyl l-lactate, 276
l-Menthylpyruvate, 276
Mercaptans, 139–140
Mercaptobenzothiazole, 849
β-Mercaptoethanolamine, 468
β-Mercaptopropionic acid, 324
Mercuration, phenols, 633
Mercury fulminate, 581, 582
Mesaconic acid, 283
Mesitylaldehyde, 679, 755
Mesitylene, 517, 532,* 534,† 537–538,† 562
  coupling, 621
  oxidation, 550, 664
Mesityleneacetic acid, 672
Mesitylenecarboxylic acid, 657,* 666, 672
Mesityl oxide, 192,* 209†
Mesomerism, 327
Mesotartaric acid, 269*
Mesoxalic acid, 216
Metachrome Brown B, 932
Metal acetylides, 86, 91–92
Metaldehyde, 200
Metanilic acid, 604
Methacrylic acid, 58†
  esters, 876*
Methane, 31*
  formation, 38
  halogenation, 41
  nitration, 46
  occurrence, 34, 94, 95
  pyrolysis, 87, 102
Methanol, 111, 112,* 120†
  dehydrogenation, 194
  oxidation, 128
  reaction with sodium, 124–125
Methemoglobin (ferrihemoglobin), 458, 572
L-Methionine, 419,* 421, 424,* 430, 432,† 433†
  indispensability, 498
  methyl donor, 503–504
Methoxyacetic acid, 163*
2-Methoxy 4 allylphenol, see Eugenol
o-Methoxybenzaldehyde, 675*
p-Methoxybenzoic acid, see Anisic acid
p-Methoxybenzophenone oximes, 702
Methoxybenzoquinone, 722
β-4-Methoxybenzoylpropionic acid, 634
Methoxy determination, 137
β-Methoxynaphthalene, 743, 746
4-Methoxy-1,2-naphthoquinone, 713
2-Methoxy-1,4-naphthoquinone, 713,* 714†
9-Methoxy 10 phenanthrol, 637
β-Methoxypropionic acid, 324
N-Methylacetanilide, 231

Methyl acetate, 174*
Methylacetylcarbinol, see Acetoin
Methyl 6-acetyldehydroabietate, 703
Methylacetylene, 85,*† 86–87,† 90
Methyl acrylate, 437, 876†
  polymers, 876
Methylal, 215,* 647
Methyl alcohol, see Methanol
α-Methylallyl chloride, 334, 343
γ-Methylallyl chloride, 343
Methylamine, 224,* 225, 226*
  hydrochloride, 227*
Methyl α-amino-β-chloropropionate, 439
Methyl 6-aminodehydroabietate, 704
N-Methylaniline, 597,* 600,† 610
  hydrochloride, 598*
Methyl anthranilate, 661
β-Methylanthraquinone, 762
Methyl arabinofuranoside, 365
Methylarbutin, 379
Methylation, see also Alkylation
  acetyl peroxide, 721–722
  diazomethane, 176
  dimethyl sulfate, 136, 364, 547, 590, 600
  lead tetraacetate, 721–722
  Methyl halides, 136, 363–364, 536–537, 713–
    714
  sugars, 363–364
Methyl azide, 723
5-Methyl-1, 2-benzanthracene, 786
9-Methyl-1, 2-benzanthracene, 786
10-Methyl-1, 2-benzanthracene, 785, 786, 793†
Methyl benzenesulfonate, 590
Methyl benzoate, 658,*† 663
2-Methyl-3, 4-benzphenanthrene, 787
p-Methylbenzyl chloride, 677
Methyl benzyl ketone, 195–196
Methyl bromide, 145, 146,* 149, 337
Methyl γ-bromocrotonate, 243,† 693
Methyl α-bromo-β-methoxypropionate, 437
2-Methylbutane, see Isopentane
2-Methylbutanol-1, see Amyl alcohol, active
2-Methylbutanol-2, 56
3-Methylbutanol-1, see Isoamyl alcohol
2-Methylbutene-1, 53*
3-Methylbutene-1, 53*
2-Methylbutene-2, 56†
γ-Methylbutenolides, 806
Methyl-n-butylacetic acid, 351
Methyl-t-butylcarbinol, 126
Methyl n-butyl ether, 133*
Methyl t-butyl ketone, see Pinacolone

3-Methylbutyne-1, 85*
Methylbutyne-1-ol-3, 91†
Methyl n-butyrate, 174*
N-Methylcarbazole, 815
Methyl Cellosolve, 123
Methyl chloride, 41, 145, 146*
  dipole moment, 326
Methyl chloroformate, 185
Methylcholanthrene, 783–784,*† 791†
  carcinogenic activity, 783, 785
  polynitro complexes, 586*
  reactions, 787–789
o-Methylcinnamic acid, 690
Methyl crotonate, 243
Methyl cyanide, see Acetonitrile
Methylcyclohexane, 306
4-Methylcyclohexanecarboxylic acid, 98
Methylcyclohexanol, 306–308
Methylcyclopentadecane, 301
3-Methylcyclopentylacetic acid, 97
3'-Methyl-1, 2-cyclopentenophenanthrene, see
  Diels hydrocarbon
10-Methyldecalone-2, 683
Methyl dehydroabietate, 703
Methyl α,β-diaminopropionate, 441
4-Methyldiazoaminobenzene, 620
4-Methyl-4-dichloromethyl-Δ²,⁵-cyclohexa-
  dienone-1, 682
Methyldiethylmethane, see 3-Methylpentane
2-Methyldodecene-2-yne-11, 89
2-Methyl-3-difarnesyl-1, 4-naphthoquinone, see
  Vitamin K₂
1-Methyl-5, 8-dihydroxyanthraquinone,   see
  1-Methylquinizarin
2'-Methyl-2, 1'-dinaphthyl ketone, 790
N-Methylemetine, 845
3, 3'-Methylenebis(4-hydroxycoumarin), 1019
Methylene Blue, 884,* 1022
Methylene bromide (dibromomethane), 153,†
  154*
Methylene chloride (dichloromethane), 41,
  153,† 154*
γ-Methyleneglutamic acid, 422
Methylene halides, 153–158
Methylene iodide, 154*
Methyleneurea, 870
N, N-Methylethylaniline, 231†
Methyl ethyl ether, 133*
Methyl ethyl ketone, 192,* 854
3-Methyl-4-ethylpyrrole, see Opsopyrrole
Methylethylpyruvic ester, 440
Methyl ethyl sulfide, 98, 140*†
N-Methylformanilide reaction, 679–680, 777,
  793

---

* Physical constants   † Preparation

Methyl formate, 174*
Methyl fructopyranosides, 375*
Methylgentiobiose, 380
α-Methylglucoside, 361, 374*
β-Methylglucoside, 361, 363
  -3,4,6-triacetate, 363
γ-Methylglucoside, 367
Methylglyoxal, 520–521
Methyl n-heptyl ketone, 493
2-Methylhexane, 29,* 105
3-Methylhexane, 29*
Methyl hydracrylate, 324
Methyl hydrogen succinate, 188*†
Methylhydroquinone, 510
2-Methyl-4-hydroxyacetophenone, 635–636
4-Methyl-2-hydroxyacetophenone, 635–636
Methyl iodide, 36, 146*†
Methyl isobutyl ether, 136†
1-Methyl-4-isopropylbenzene, see p-Cymene
1-Methyl-4-isopropylbenzene-2-sulfonic acid,
  632
Methyl isopropyl ketone, 202
1-Methyl-7-isopropylnaphthalene, see Eudalene
1-Methyl-7-isopropylphenanthrene, see Retene
1-Methylisoquinoline, 812
Methyl isovalerate, 174
Methyl ketones, 202, 540–541,† 705, 737, 746
  oxidation, 154, 167, 657, 698, 756
Methyl laurate, 178*†
Methyl mannopyranoside, 365
Methyl mercaptan, 139
Methyl methacrylate, 876†
  polymer, 876
2-Methyl-5-methoxybenzoquinone, 986
2-Methyl-6-methoxybenzoquinone, 805
Methylmorphimethines, α and β, 834
α-Methylnaphthalene, 528,* 546†
  petroleum, 97
β-Methylnaphthalene, 528,* 744, 745, 751–752
  petroleum, 97
1-Methylnaphthalene-4-sulfonic acid, 743
2-Methylnaphthalene-6-sulfonic acid, 744
α-Methyl-β-naphthocinchonic acid, 480
4-Methyl-1-naphthol, 733
1-Methyl-2-naphthol, 733, 735
2-Methyl-1,4-naphthoquinone, 718, 751–752†
  antihemorrhagic activity, 1018
  oxide, 719
S-(2-Methyl-1,4-naphthoquinonyl-3)-gluta-
  thione, 718
1-Methyl-lin-naphthotriazole-4,9-quinone, 720
β-6-Methylnaphthoylpropionic acid, 745
Methyl β-naphthyl ketone, 657

N-Methyl-N-nitroso-N′-nitroguanidine, 176
Methyl n-nonyl ketone, 493
6-Methyloctanoic acid, 450
Methyl n-octyl ketone, 407
Methylolmethyleneurea, 871
Methyl palmitoleate, 402
2-Methylpentane, 28*
3-Methylpentane, 28*
2-Methylpentanol-3, 125–126
2-Methylpentene-2, 126
Methylphenanthrene (1-, 2-, 3-, 4-, 9-), 753*
Methylphenanthrenequinone (1-, 2-, 3-, 4-),
  753*
Methylphenylcarbamyl chloride, 680
α-Methylphenylhydrazine, 606
Methylphenylnitrosoamine, see N-Nitroso-N-
  methylaniline
2-Methyl-3-phytyl-1,4-naphthoquinone, see
  Vitamin K₁
N-Methylpicramide, 581
Methyl propionate, 174*
Methyl-n-propylcarbinol, 122*†
Methyl n-propyl ketone, 192,* 202
N-Methylpyridinium hydroxide, 808–809
N-Methylpyridone, 809
α-Methylpyrrole, 799
1-Methylquinizarin, 730
2-Methylquinoline, see Quinaldine
4-Methylquinoline, see Lepidine
5-Methylquinoline, 811
7-Methylquinoline, 811
N-Methylquinoline methosulfate, 813
Methylreductinic acid, 394
Methyl rubber, 850–851
Methyl salicylate, 662, 672
Methylsilicone rubber, 878
Methylsodium, 36
10-Methylstearic acid, see Tuberculostearic
  acid
Methylsuccinic anhydride, 754
1-Methyl-5,6,7,8-tetrahydronaphthalene, 97*
2-Methyl-5,6,7,8-tetrahydronaphthalene, 97*
2-Methyl-5,8,9,10-tetrahydro-1,4-naphtho-
  quinone, 310
7-Methyltetralone, 782
3-Methyltetryl, 577
4-Methylthiazole-5-carboxylic acid, 1001
Methyl 2-thienyl ketone, 542
Methyl p-toluenesulfonate, 590
1-Methyl-3,5,8-trihydroxyanthraquinone, 771
Methyl-2,4,6-trinitrophenylnitramine, see
  Tetryl
Methyl undecyl ketone, 493
5-Methyluracil, see Thymine

Methyl *n*-valerate, 174*
Methyl vinyl ether, 89
Methyl vinyl ketone, 705, 810, 984
Michael reaction, 699
Michler's ketone, 696,*† 893
Milk sugar, *see* Lactose
Mixed anhydride synthesis, 445–446
Molecular rotations, 371, 372–378, 423–424
Molecular weight determination, 11
  end-group assay method, 386–387
  osmotic pressure determination, 387, 451
  proteins, 451–452
  Rast, 11
  ultracentrifuge determination, 387, 451, 452
  viscosity determination, 387
Monastral Blue, 933
Monomethylolurea, 870
Monoperphthalic acid, *see* Perphthalic acid
Mordant dyes, 886–887
Morphine, 2, 271,* 550, 833–837, 845
Morpholine, 705, 706
Mucic acid, 848
Mucoitin sulfate, 395
Muconic acid, 510
Muscarufin, 724
Muscone, 299–302, 321
Musk ambrette, *see* Ambrettolide
Musk ketone, 583
Mustard gas, 70, 591
Mustard oil, *see* Allyl isothiocyanate
Mustard-oil glycosides, 381
Mutarotation, 362
Mycoceranic acid, 407
Mycolipenic acid, 407
Mycomycin, 406
Myelin, 454
Myosin, 381
Myosmine, 826
Myrcene, 936*
Myristic acid, 400,* 408, 409
Myristoleic acid, 409
Myristyl alcohol, 112*

Napalm, 98
Naphthacene, 529,* 772†–773, 775
  peroxide, 775
Naphthacenehydroquinone, 773
Naphthacenequinone, 772*–773
β-Naphthaldehyde, 196,† 687†
Naphthalene, 97, 528,* 529, 545, 751–752
  chloromethylation, 648

  oxidation, 659, 752
  polynitro complexes, 586*
  reduction, 737, 751
Naphthalene-1,4-dicarboxylic acid, 665
Naphthalene-α-sulfonic acid, 737,† 741,* 750
Naphthalene-β-sulfonic acid, 592, 737,† 741,* 749, 750
Naphthalene-1,4,5,8-tetracarboxylic acid, 920
Naphthalene-1,3,6-trisulfonic acid, 749–750
Naphthalic anhydride, 534, 664, 792
Naphthazarin, 729–730
Naphthenes, 95–96
Naphthenic acids, 97–98
lin-Naphthindazole-4,9-quinone, 720
Naphthionic acid, 746†
α-Naphthoic acid, 740,† 741*
β-Naphthoic acid, 657,† 741*
α-Naphthol, 530,* 741,*† 743
β-Naphthol, 530,* 592,† 740†–741,* 743–744
  amination, 741–742
  coupling, 715, 733, 887
  halogenation, 735, 745
  oxidation, 637–638
  sulfonation, 747
β-Naphthol allyl ether, 734
Naphthol-AS, 929–930
Naphthol-ASG, 930
Naphthol-AS-LB, 930
Naphthol Blue Black B, 925
2-Naphthol-1,6-disulfonic acid, 747
2-Naphthol-3,6-disulfonic acid, *see* R-Acid
2-Naphthol-6,8-disulfonic acid, *see* G-Acid
1-Naphthol-4-sulfonic acid (Neville-Winter acid), 746
2-Naphthol-1-sulfonic acid, 747
2-Naphthol-6-sulfonic acid (Schaeffer acid), 747†
2-Naphthol-8-sulfonic acid, 747
2-Naphthol-1,3,6-trisulfonic acid, 747
α-Naphthonitrile, 652,† 741*
β-Naphthonitrile, 741,* 742†
α-Naphthoquinone, 659, 712,* 719†
  addition reactions, 716, 717, 718, 720
β-Naphthoquinone, 712,* 715,† 717, 721
amphi-Naphthoquinone, 776
1,2-Naphthoquinone-4-sulfonic acid, 428, 717†
Naphthostyril, 919
2-α-Naphthoylbenzoic acid, 738,*† 768
β-Naphthoyl chloride, 196
β-1-Naphthoylpropionic acid, 738,*† 754
β-2-Naphthoylpropionic acid, 738,*† 754
1,8-Naphthsultam-2,4-disulfonic acid, 751
α-Naphthylamine, 732, 741*
β-Naphthylamine, 480, 741*–742†

α-Naphthylamine acid sulfate, 746
β-Naphthylamine acid sulfate, 748
2-Naphthylamine-5,7-disulfonic acid, 749
2-Naphthylamine-6,8-disulfonic acid, 748, 749
1-Naphthylamine-4-sulfonic acid (naphthionic acid), 746
1-Naphthylamine-5-sulfonic acid, 750
1-Naphthylamine-6-sulfonic acid (Cleve's acid), 749
1-Naphthylamine-7-sulfonic acid, 750
1-Naphthylamine-8-sulfonic acid, 750, 751
2-Naphthylamine-1-sulfonic acid (Tobias acid), 747
1-Naphthylamine-3,6,8-trisulfonic acid (Koch acid), 750
2-Naphthylamine-1,5,7-trisulfonic acid, 748
γ-2-Naphthylbutyric acid, 739
2-α-Naphthylmethylbenzoic acid, 768
β-1-Naphthylpropionic acid, 648
γ-2-Naphthylvaleric acid, 699
Narcotine, 832
Neoabietic acid, 948
Neoarsphenamine, 1023
Neocyanine, 900–901
Neoherculin, 405
Neohexane (2,2-dimethylbutane), 28*
Neolan Blue 2G, 932
Neopentane, 95,* 102
Neopentyl alcohol, 117
Neopentyl–t–amyl rearangement, 342–343
Neopentyl bromide, 339–340, 342–343
Neopentyl ethyl ether, 342
Neoprene, 851–852
Neovitamin A, 955
Nerol, 938
Nervonic acid (selacholeic acid), 401,* 403, 490
Neuraminic acid, 491
Neville-Winter acid, 746,† 924
Niacin, see Nicotinic acid
Nicholson Blue, 892
Nicotimine, 826
Nicotinamide, 242,† 463–464, 808, 1032
Nicotine, 826,* 1006
Nicotinic acid, 806–807,† 1005 1006
    biosynthesis, 512–513
Nicotinonitrile, 242, 1006
Nicotinuric acid, 1006
Ninhydrin, 428
Nitraniline Orange, 929
Nitraniline Red, see Para Red
Nitric acid, structure, 51, 161–162
Nitriles, 167–168, 592–593, 614,† 652,† 755, 1006
    hydrolysis, examples: 167–168, 241–242, 256, 670, 755, 1006
    reduction, 229–230
o-Nitroacetanilide, 596, 601
p-Nitroacetanilide, 601
m-Nitroacetophenone, 697
Nitroalkanes, 45–46,† 231
m-Nitroaniline, 596,† 597,* 613
o-Nitroaniline, 573, 595, 597,* 601†
p-Nitroaniline, 597,* 601,† 608
o-Nitroaniline-p-sulfonic acid, 601
o-Nitroanisole, 573, 575
p-Nitroanisole, 604
α-Nitroanthraquinone, 763, 766
m-Nitrobenzaldehyde, 675,* 687†
o-Nitrobenzaldehyde, 675,* 667–668,† 688†
p-Nitrobenzaldehyde, 675,* 677†
Nitrobenzene, 571,* 572,† 605
    dipole moment, 566
    nitration, 557, 558
    reduction, 480, 583–585, 595, 599
    resonance, 569, 577
    sulfonation, 572
5-p-Nitrobenzeneazo-3,4-benzpyrene, 788
p-Nitrobenzenediazonium chloride, 621, 788
m-Nitrobenzenesulfonic acid, 572,† 766
o-Nitrobenzenesulfonyl chloride, 603
p-Nitrobenzenesulfonyl chloride, 1031
m-Nitrobenzoic acid, 656,* 662†–663
    methyl ester, 663
o-Nitrobenzoic acid, 656,* 662†
p-Nitrobenzoic acid, 559, 656,* 662†
p-Nitrobenzyl chloride, 677
2-Nitrobutane, 231
Nitrocellulose, see also Pyroxylin
    fiber, 857–858
    plastic, 863–864
m-Nitrochlorobenzene, 571,* 574,† 614†
o-Nitrochlorobenzene, 571,* 574, 575, 652
p-Nitrochlorobenzene, 571,* 574, 1031
2-Nitro-6-chlorotoluene, 675
m-Nitrocinnamic acid, 690†
o-Nitrocinnamic acid, 688, 690,† 906
p-Nitrocinnamic acid, 690†
Nitro compounds, 45–46, 571–587
    reduction, 583–585, 595–596
    ultraviolet absorption, 881
2-Nitro-p-cymene, 596
p-Nitrodimethylaniline, 607
o-Nitrodiphenyl, 571*
p-Nitrodiphenyl, 571*
Nitroethane, 46
Nitrogen, determination, 15
Nitrogen mustards, 240–241

Nitroglycerin, 131–132
Nitro group, resonance, 557, 569
Nitroguanidine, 176
Nitromethane, 45–46, 881*
o-Nitro-N-methylaniline, 575
1-Nitro-2-methylanthraquinone, 766
1-Nitro-1-methyl-2-keto-1, 2-dihydronaphthalene, 735
1-Nitro-2-methylnaphthalene, 744
1-Nitro-4-methylnaphthalene, 743
2-Nitro-2-methylpropane, 45
Nitro musks, 583
α-Nitronaphthalene, 732, 739–740,† 741,* 743
β-Nitronaphthalene, 741,* 742,† 743
1-Nitronaphthalene-5-sulfonic acid, 750
5-Nitronaphthalene-2-sulfonic acid, 749
8-Nitronaphthalene-2-sulfonic acid, 749
1-Nitronaphthalene-3,6,8-trisulfonic acid, 750
3-Nitro-1, 2-naphthoquinone, 721
o-Nitronitrosobenzene, 573
Nitronium ion, 565
Nitroparaffins, 45–46
m-Nitrophenol, 580, 613,† 624,* 628–629†
o-Nitrophenol, 557,† 571,* 573, 575, 601, 624,* 628
p-Nitrophenol, 557,† 571,* 624,* 628, 631, 648
o-Nitrophenylacetic acid, 906
o-Nitrophenylacetylene, 906
p-Nitrophenylcarbamyl chloride, 608
α-(m-Nitrophenyl)-ethanol, 117
p-Nitrophenylhydrazine, 617
p-Nitrophenyl isocyanate, 608
o-Nitrophenylpropiolic acid, 906
3-Nitrophthalic acid, 732
Nitropropanes, 46
3-Nitropropene-2, 882*
3-Nitropyrene, 777
3-Nitropyridine, 808
5-Nitroquinoline, 813
8-Nitroquinoline, 813
Nitrosamine Red, 930–931
N-Nitrosoamines, 237, 605–606
Nitrosobenzene, 584–585*†
Nitrosobutane, 881*
C-Nitroso compounds, 607–608
N-Nitrosodiisopropylamine, 237*
N-Nitrosodimethylamine, 237*
p-Nitrosodimethylaniline, 607*† 608
N-Nitrosodiphenylamine, 606
N-Nitroso-N-methylaniline, 605*†–606
p-Nitroso-N-methylaniline, 606
N-Nitroso-N-methyl-p-toluidine, 606

1-Nitroso-2-naphthol, 717
p-Nitrosophenol, 607, 628
N-Nitrosophenylhydrazine, 609
N-Nitrosophenylhydroxylamine, 606–607
Nitrosylsulfuric acid, 440
m-Nitrotoluene, 571,* 573,† 617
o-Nitrotoluene, 571,* 573,† 576†, 662, 675
p-Nitrotoluene, 571,* 573,† 576,† 662
  detoxication, 572
m-Nitro-p-toluidine, 617
Nitrous acid, 161–162
  reaction with amides, 242, 427
  reaction with amines, 236–237
Nitrous oxide, 135
No-bond resonance, see Hyperconjugation
n-Nonacosane, 34*
n-Nonadecane, 31*
n-Nonane, 31*
Nondecylic acid, 400
Norcaryophyllenic acid, 947
Norleucine, 440,† 498
Nornicotine, 826
19-Norprogesterone, 977
L-Norvaline, 440†
Novocain (procaine), 845
Novolaks, 866, 867, 868, 869
Nucleic acids, 468–470
Nucleophilic attack, 89–90, 328–329, 337–342
Nucleoproteins, 468–471
Nucleotides, 468–471
Nylon, 860–861

Ocimene, 936
Octaacetylsucrose, 371
Octacosanol, 400
n-Octadecane, 31*
8, 10, 12-Octadecatrienoic acid, 416
9, 11, 13-Octadecatrienoic acid, 416
10, 12, 14-Octadecatrienoic acid, see Pseudoeleostearic acid
n-Octadecyl bromide, 146*
Octadecyene-1, 85*
Δ9-Octalin, 775
Octamethyllactose, 384
Octamethylmaltose, 385
Octamethylsucrose, 382
n-Octane, 31*
Octane number, 99–100
Octanol-2, see Capryl alcohol
Octastearylsucrose, 371
Octatrienol, 882*
Octene-1, 53*
n-Octyl acetate, 174*
n-Octyl alcohol, 112

* Physical constants † Preparation

Octyl nitrite, 881*
Oenanthic acid, see n-Heptylic acid
Oenanthol, see n-Heptaldehyde
Oil of bitter almonds, see Benzaldehyde
Oil of mirbane, see Nitrobenzene
Oil of wintergreen, see Methyl salicylate
Oil Yellow, 923
Oiticica oil, 415–416
Olefins, see Alkenes
Oleic acid, 284,* 401,* 413
  biosynthesis, 492
  esters, 413
  isomerization, 284, 403
  occurrence, 403, 404, 408, 409, 415, 489
  oxidation, 315, 402
Oleyl alcohol, 177,† 409,* 410†
β-Oleylethanesulfonic acid, 413
Oligosaccharides, 350
Olive oil, 408*
Oppanol, 855
Oppenauer oxidation, 194, 963–964, 994–995
Opsopyrrole, 456
Optical isomerism, 249–278
Orange I, 923–924
Orange II, 715,† 923–924
Orbitals, atomic, 73–75
  molecular, 75–79, 525–526
Organosilicon polymers, 877–879
Orlon, 862
L-Ornithine, 422, 424,* 450
  metabolism, 502–503, 505
Orthanilic acid, 603†
Osajin, 823
Osazones, 351 354, 694
Osmium tetroxide hydroxylation, 287–288, 402
Oxalacetic acid, 313*†
  biosynthesis, 481, 482, 483
Oxalic acid, 244, 312,* 313,† 365, 367
  dehydrating agent, 57
  properties, 315
Oxalosuccinic acid, 482, 483
Oxaluric acid, 247
Oxalyl chloride, 43
Oxidation, see also Autoxidation, Dehydrogenation, and Glycol cleavage
  aceto compounds, see methyl ketones
  alcohols, 127–129, 166–167, 193, 194
  aldehydes, 90, 166–167, 170, 198
  alkanes, 44–45
  alkenes, 67–69, 166
  alkylaromatic hydrocarbons to acids, 550, 578, 657, 662, 663, 666, 761
  alkylaromatic hydrocarbons to aldehydes, 676

  allylic, 405, 849
  amines, 239, 573, 604–605, 630, 709–710, 715
  aminophenols, 715
  aromatic hydrocarbons, 282–283, 659, 664, 665, 761
  aromatic hydrocarbons to quinones, 751–752, 757, 758, 770, 780
  biological, 982
  t-carbinols, 129, 669–670
  cyclic ketones, 199, 300, 301
  Dakin reaction, 629
  diphenylmethane, 551
  diphenyl sulfide, 594
  ethers, 134
  Hooker reaction, 728–729
  hydroquinones, 710–711, 716
  α-hydroxy ketones, 706–707
  ketones, 198–199
  mercaptans, 139, 594
  methyl ketones, 154, 167, 657, 698, 756
  nitroso compounds, 573, 668
  Oppenauer reaction, see Oppenauer oxidation
  phenanthrenequinone, 757
  phenols, 637–638
  sulfinic acids, 594
  triphenylmethane, 551
  unsaturated acids, 401–402
β-Oxidation, 493
ω-Oxidation, 493–494
Oxidation-reduction systems, ascorbic acid, 391, 1000
  cysteine-cystine, 421
  isoalloxazine, 465
  nicotinamide, 463–464
  quinones-hydroquinones, 630, 710 714
Oxides, 64, 123, 288, 363, 658–659
  1, 2-anhydroglucose, 382–383
  of amines, 239–240
  cholesterol α oxide, 967
  of quinones, 715
Oximes, 211–212
  Beckmann rearrangement, 701–703
  isomerism, 701
  reduction to amines, 231, 433, 440–441, 703
Oximinomalonic ester, 433
Oximinopropiophenone, 704
Oxindole, 906
Oxonium ion intermediates, 88, 175, 341, 342, 658–659
Oxonium salts, 39, 137–138, 709, 815, 816–817, 818–819
Oxo process, 197
Oxyhemoglobin, 455, 458

Oxytocin, 447–449
Ozonization, 68–69, 195, 402
    aromatic hydrocarbons, 520–521, 779
    rubber, 847–848

Palmitic acid, 400*
    metabolism, 492
    occurrence, 97, 398–400, 408, 409, 415, 490
Palmitoleic acid, 401*
    occurrence, 403, 408, 409
    oxidation, 401
Palmitone, 409
Palm-kernel oil, 408*
Palm oil, 400, 408*
Paludrine, 1027–1028
Pantotheine, 1010
Pantothenic acid, 468, 999, 1009–1010
Pantothine, 1010
Papain, 497
Papaveraldine, 831
Papaverine, 139, 830–833
Papaverinol, 831
Paper strip chromatography, 428–429
Parabanic acid, 244, 245, 246
Paracasein, 461
Paraffin hydrocarbons, see Alkanes
Paraformaldehyde, 201
Parafuchsin, see Pararosaniline
Paraldehyde, 199–200
Paramine Brown, 888
Para Red, 929
Pararosaniline, 891–892
Parinaric acid, 401,* 403
Parlon, 850
Patent Blues, 893, 894
Patulin, 806
Pauli exclusion principle, 74, 77
Peanut oil, 408*
Pelargonic acid, 163,* 400
Pelargonic aldehyde, 402
Pellargonidin, 820
Pelletierines, 828
Penaldic acid, 1034
Penicillamine, 1034
Penicillic acid, 806
Penicillin, 1033–1034
Penicilloic acid, 1034
Penilloaldehyde, 1034
Penilloic acid, 1034
Pentacene, 775
5-Pentacetylglucose, 379
n-Pentacontane, 31*

n-Pentacosane, 31*
n-Pentadecane, 31*
n-Pentadecane-1,15-dicarboxylic acid, 300
Pentadecylic acid, 400
Pentaerythritol, 132, 211,*† 414
Pentaerythritol monalaurate, 414
Pentaerythritol monostearate, 414
Pentaerythritol tetranitrate, 132, 582
Pentaglycylglycine methyl ester, 441
Pentamethylbenzene, 532,* 537,† 664
Pentamethylene bromide, 154,* 158†
Pentamethylenediamine, 224,* 225
Pentamethylene sulfide, 98
Pentamethylglucose, 364
n-Pentane, 31,* 95,* 105†
    chlorination, 121–122
Pentanes, 27–28, 94, 95
Pentanol-2, 56, 122, 125
Pentanol-3, 122
Pentaphenylphosphorus, 651
Pentaquine, 1028
n-Pentatriacontane, 31*
Pentene-1, 53,* 122, 346
Pentene-2, 56,† 122, 346
Pentene-1-yne-4, 88
Pentosans, 388
Pentyne-1, 85*
Pentyne-2, 85*
Pepsin, 452,* 461, 462
Peptidases, 461
Peracetic acid, 289
Perbenzoic acid, 67, 88, 289, 325, 658–659†
Perbunan, 854
Perdurans, 854
Perezinone, 723
Perezone, 723
Performic acid, 289, 402, 448
Perhydrocarotene, 952
Perhydrolycopene, 36,† 954
Peri acid, 750,† 919
Perilla oil, 415,* 416
Perinaphthane, 792
Perinaphthanone-7, 648
Periodic acid oxidation, 129, 364–365, 428
Periplogenin, 992
Perkin reaction, 689–691, 817
Perlon, 861
Permanent Red 2G, 929
Pernigraniline, 888
Peroxidase, 466, 467
Peroxide catalysis, 42, 43, 62–63, 243, 851, 875
Peroxides, of acids, 658–659
    acyl, 658, 721–722
    of ethers, 134, 136

---

* Physical constants   † Preparation

of naphthacenes, 774–775
of rubber, 849
Perphthalic acid, 660–661
Perrier procedure, 738, 756–757
Perylene, 779–780
3,10-Perylenequinone, 780
PETN, see Pentaerythritol tetranitrate
Petroleum, 94–110
Petroleum ether, 94
Petroselinic acid, 401,* 405
Phaeophytin, 949
Phenacyl bromide, 698
Phenacyl chloride, 647
1-Phenanthraldehyde, 687
2-Phenanthraldehyde, 687
3-Phenanthraldehyde, 687
9-Phenanthraldehyde, 687, 755*†
Phenanthrene, 528,* 753–757
  bromination, 563–564
  polynitro complexes, 586*
Phenanthrene-4-aldehyde-5-carboxylic   acid,
  779
Phenanthrene-9,10-dibromide, 563–564
Phenanthrenedisulfonic acids, 755–756
Phenanthrenemonosulfonic acids, 755–756
9,10-Phenanthrenequinone, 757
Phenanthridine, 814,* 815†
3-Phenanthroic acid, 756
9-Phenanthroic acid, 755
1-Phenanthrol, 625,† 753,* 754†
2-Phenanthrol, 753,* 756†
3-Phenanthrol, 753,* 756†
4-Phenanthrol, 753,* 754†
9-Phenanthrol, 753,* 754†
Phenanthroline, 814
β-3-Phenanthroylpropionic acid, 756
β-9-Phenanthroylpropionic acid, 669
1-Phenanthrylamine, 757
2-Phenanthrylamine, 757
3-Phenanthrylamine, 756, 757
4-Phenanthrylamine, 757
9-Phenanthrylamine, 757
Phenazine, 814
p-Phenetidine, 597*
Phenetole, 626
Phenol, 530,* 624,* 625–626†
  C-alkylation, 540
  carboxylation, 661
  coupling, 618
  ethers, 136,† 626–627
  halogenation, 627–628
  hydrogenation, 861
  mercuration, 633
  nitration, 447, 560, 578, 628–629

C-nitrosation, 607, 628
Reimer-Tiemann reaction, 680–684
resonance, 568
sulfonation, 578
Phenol allyl ether, 639
Phenol-2,4-disulfonic acid, 578, 629
Phenol-formaldehyde resins, 866–870
Phenolphthalein, 895–897
Phenols, 592,† 613,† 624,* 625–633†
  aldehyde condensation, 638–639, 866–870
  Bucherer reaction, 741–742
  carboxylation, 661
  coupling, 618–622
  ethers, 136,† 621, 626, 629, 634, 679
  C-nitrosation, 607
  oxidation, 637–638
  zinc dist distillation, 550
Phenoxide ion, 568, 619, 680
Phenoxyacetic acid, 627
γ-Phenoxypropyl bromide, 158
Phenylacetaldehyde, 524
Phenyl acetate, 627,* 635
Phenylacetic acid, 163,* 195, 501, 668,*† 1033
Phenylacetone, 501
Phenylaceturic acid, 493
Phenylacetylcarbinol, see Benzacetoin
L-Phenylalanine, 419,* 424,* 430, 433,† 434,†
  437,† 440,† 841, 842
  indispensability, 498
  metabolism, 476, 500, 510–511
Phenylarsonic acid, 615
Phenyl azide, 609
Phenyl benzoate, 627,*† 658
2-Phenyl-1,4-benzoquinone, 721
1-Phenylbutadiene-1,3, 547,*† 651
1-Phenylbutene-1, 547,*† 548†
1-Phenylbutene-2, 547*†
γ-Phenylbutyric acid, 543, 544,† 668,* 669†
ε-Phenyl-n-caproic acid, 668,* 669,† 670†
Phenyldithiocarbamic acid, 609
o-Phenyleneacetic-β-propionic acid, 668,* 671†
m-Phenylenediacetic acid, 668*
o-Phenylenediacetic acid, 670–671*†
p-Phenylenediacetic acid, 668*
o-Phenylenediacetonitrile, 671
m-Phenylenediamine, 597,* 602†
o-Phenylenediamine, 595,† 597,* 707
p-Phenylenediamine, 597,* 601–602, 715
  diacetate, 599*
α-Phenylethylamine, 271,* 272, 703†
β-Phenylethylamine, 230†
α-Phenylethylformamide, 703
Phenylglycine, 907
Phenylglycine-o-carboxylic acid, 908

Phenylglyoxal, 698
7-Phenylheptatrienal, 689
Phenylhydrazine, 212, 609, 617†
  reaction with carbohydrates, 351–354
Phenylhydrazones, see also Osazones, 212, 440
Phenylhydroxylamine, 584,*† 585, 606, 631
Phenyliodochloride, see Iodobenzene dichloride
Phenyliodoso acetate, see Iodosobenzene di-
  acetate
Phenylisocyanate, 608,*† 609
Phenylisocyanide, 610
β-Phenylisopropylamine, see Benzedrine
Phenyl isothiocyanate, 447, 610
Phenyllithium, 650–651
Phenylmagnesium bromide, 119, 153
Phenylmethyldithiocarbamic acid, 849
Phenyl mustard oil, see Phenyl isothiocyanate
Phenyl-α-naphthylamine, 135
Phenyl-β-naphthylamine, 849
β-Phenylnitroethane, 568
Phenylnitromethane, 575–576
Phenylpentadecaheptaenal, 689
5-Phenylpentadienal, 689
Phenylphenazonium dyes, 890–891
Phenylphosphoryl dichloride, 489
Phenylpolyenals, 689
Phenylpropanolamine, 704
Phenylpropiolic acid, 668,* 669†
Phenyl propionate, 636
ω-Phenyl-n-propylmalonic acid, 669
2-Phenylpyridine, 808
3-Phenylpyridine, 801
Phenylsulfamic acid, 603
Phenylthiohydantoins, 447
Phenyl p-toluenesulfonate, 627
Phenyltrimethylammonium nitrate, 557–558,
  569
11-Phenylundecapentaenal, 689
Phenylurea, 608
Phenylurethan, 608–609
δ-Phenyl-n-valeric acid, 668,* 669†
Phenylvinylcarbinol acetate, 151
Phloroacetophenone, 696
Phloroglucinol, 624,* 631,† 696
Phoenician purple, see Tyrian purple
Phoenicin, 722
Phorone, 192,* 209†
Phosgene, 43, 156, 184*–185†
  condensation with alcohols, 442
  condensation with amines, 232, 608, 696
  condensation with ammonia, 244
Phosphatases, 461

Phosphatides, 488–491
Phosphatidylethanolamine, 488
Phosphatidylserine, 488
Phosphoarginine, 478
Phosphocreatine, 478
Phosphoenolpyruvic acid, 476, 477
Phosphoglucomutase, 474, 475
Phosphoglyceraldehyde dehydrogenase, 477
Phosphoglyceric acid (2- and 3-), 476, 477, 485,
  486
Phosphohomoserine, 504
Phospholipids, 488–491
Phosphonium iodide, 444
Phosphoribitol, 469
Phosphoribose, 469
Phosphorylases, 461, 462, 474, 275
Phosphosphingosides, 490–491
Phosphotungstic acid, 427
Photosynthesis, 367, 484–487
Phthalazine, 814
Phthalamidic acid, 660
Phthaleins, 895–897
Phthalic acid, 659*†
  esters, 660*†
Phthalic anhydride, 186,* 273–274, 542, 659–
  660,*† 872
Phthalic anhydride synthesis, 761–762, 766
Phthalide, 660–661, 670
Phthalimide, 234,* 431, 433, 660, 661
Phthalimidomalonic ester synthesis, 432
Phthalocyanines, 933–934
Phthalonitrile, 933
Phthalophenone, 895, 896
Phthaloyl chloride, 660
Phthalylacetic acid, 691
as-Phthalyl chloride, 660
Phthalylglycyl chloride, 445
Phthalylhydrazide, 445
Phthalylsulfathiazole, 1029, 1032
Phthalyl synthesis, 445
Phthiocol, 719,*† 725
Phthioic acid, 407
Phyllopyrrole, 456
Physostigmine, 827
Phytol, 949
Picein, 380
α-Picoline, 530,* 806, 807
β-Picoline, 530,† 806, 807, 1006
γ-Picoline, 530,* 806
Picramic acid, 580,*† 922–923
Picramide, 580,*† 586, 598
Picrates, amines, 579, 598
  polynuclear hydrocarbons, see Picric acid
  complexes

Picric acid, 571,* 578–579†
  complexes, 97, 585–586, 753
  explosive, 581–583
  reactions, 580
Picrocrocin, 959–960
Picryl acetate, 580
Picryl chloride, 580,*† 586
Pilocarpine, 827
d-Pimaric acid, 948, 949
Pimelic acid, 312,* 314,† 493–494, 1010
Pinacol, 54, 206,*†
Pinacol hydrate, 206*
Pinacolone (methyl t-butyl ketone), 167, 192*
  addition reactions, 202, 349
Pinacol rearrangement, 700–701
Pinacol reduction, see Dimolecular reduction
Pinaverdol, 898
α-Pinene, 936,* 940–941
β-Pinene, 940–941
Pinene hydrochloride, 940
Piperic acid, 830
Piperidine, 830
Piperine, 830
Piperonal, 685,*† 686, 692
β-Piperonylacrylic acid, 692
Piperonylic acid, 830
Piperylene, 310
Plasma proteins, 417–418, 454–455
Plasmochin, 1026
Plexiglas, 876
Pliofilm, 850
Pliolite, 850
Plumbagin, 725
Poison gases, Lewisite, 92–93
  mustard gas, 70, 571
  nitrogen mustards, 240–241
  phosgene, 184–185
Polarimeter, 250–251
Polarization of light, 249–250
Polyacrylates, 876–877
Polyacrylonitrile, 862
Polybutenes, 855
Polychloroprene, 851–852
Polyester fiber, 861–862
Polyethylene (polythene), 863
Polyglucuronic acid, 386, 388
Poly-D-glutamic acid, 397, 450
Polyglycerol, 414
Polyglycolide, 322
Polymers, 847–879
Polymethylene halides, 158
Polymixins, 450
Polynuclear hydrocarbons, 753–795
Poly-pale resin, 877

Polypeptides, 440–446†
Polyporic acid, 724
Polysaccharides, 350, 385–390, 395–396
  immunologically active, 396–397
Polystyrene, 875–876
Polysulfide rubbers, 854–855
Polytetrafluoroethylene, 866
Polyvalent iodine compounds, 652–654
Polyvinyl acetals, 875
Polyvinyl acetate, 874
Polyvinyl alcohol, 874
Polyvinyl butyral, 875
Polyvinyl chloride, 874
Pomeranz-Fritsch synthesis, 813
Porphyrin c, 466
Porphyrins, 456–458, 506
Porphyropsin, 956
Potato X virus, 471
Pregnanediol, 976
Pregnanedione, 976
Δ^5-Pregnenol-3-one-20, 976, 994, 995
Prehnitene (1,2,3,4-tetramethylbenzene),
  532,* 644†
Prehnitenesulfonic acid, 664
Prehnitic acid (benzene-1,2,3,4-tetracarbox-
  ylic acid), 664†–665,* 668*
Primacord, 132
Primulin, 887
Primulin Red, 887
Procaine, 845
Progesterone, 969, 975*–976
Prolamines, 418
L-Proline, 419,* 420, 424,* 433,† 438, 498, 841,
  842
  biological formation, 505
  isolation, 427
Prontosil, 1028, 1029
Propane, 31,* 105, 295
  nitration, 46
  pyrolysis, 102
Propargyl alcohol, 91†
Propellants, 132
β-Propiolactone, 323*†–324
Propionaldehyde, 86, 192,* 207
Propionamide, 179,* 241*
Propionic acid, 163,* 164, 476
Propionic anhydride, 186*
Propionitrile, 167
Propionyl chloride, 180*
Propiophenone, 214, 695,* 704
1-n-Propoxy-2-amino-4-nitrobenzene, 592
n-Propyl acetate, 174*
n-Propyl alcohol, 63, 112,*
n-Propylamine, 224,* 237

n-Propylbenzene, 214,† 532*
n-Propyl bromide, 62,† 146,* 339, 345, 539
n-Propyl chloride, 42, 146,* 147†
Propylene, 53,* 57,† 102,† 105
  addition reactions, 61, 62, 64, 123, 159, 331, 332
  chlorination, 123
Propylene chlorohydrin, 64, 123
Propylene glycol, 67, 123,† 476
Propylene oxide, 123
n-Propyl iodide, 57, 146*†
n-Propyl mercaptan, 139
Protamines, 418
Proteases, 461, 462
Proteins, 417–471
  metabolism, 498–513
Prothrombin, 418, 1019
Protoanemonin, 806
Protocatechualdehyde, 685–686*†
Protocatechuic acid, 830
Protocrocin, 959–960
Protopine, 832
Protoporphyrin, 506
Prunasin, 380
Pschorr synthesis, 835
Pseudocumene   (1,2,4-trimethylbenzene), 532,* 538
  occurrence, 96
  oxidation, 664
  ozonization, 521
Pseudocumenol, 682*
Pseudocyanine, 898, 899
Pseudodiosgenin, 994
Pseudoeleostearic acid, 416
Pseudoionone, 938
Pseudomauveine, 890
Pseudopelletierine, 841
Pseudotropine, 839, 840
Psychotrine, 845
Pteridine, 1007
Pteroic acid, 1007
Pteroylglutamic acid, 1007
Pteroylheptaglutamic acid, 1007
Purine, 247,* 462
Purines, 506–508
Purpurogallin, 641
Putrescine, 502
Pyolipic acid, 493
α-Pyran, 815
γ-Pyran, 363, 815
Pyranoside, 363
Pyranthrone, 912–913

Pyrazine, 462, 814*
Pyrazolanthrone, 918, 919
Pyrazole, 802,† 803*
Pyrene 528,* 680, 777–779
3,8-Pyrenequinone, 778–779
3,10-Pyrenequinone, 778–779
Pyrene-4-sulfonic acid, 778
Pyridazine, 814
Pyridine, 530,* 796,* 801, 806–810, 1006
Pyridine-β-carboxylic acid amide, see Nicotinamide
Pyridine oxide, 809
Pyridine-3-sulfonic acid, 1032
Pyridone-2, 809
Pyridoxal, 499, 500
Pyridoxamine, 499
Pyridoxine, 499, 500, 1004, 1005
Pyrimidine, 247,* 462, 814*
Pyrithiamine, 1032
Pyroabietic acid, 877
Pyrogallol, 624,* 630–631,† 640–641
  1,3-dimethyl ether, 631,† 638
Pyroligneous acid, 120, 166
Pyrolysis, see also Cracking, Decarboxylation, and Elbs reaction
  acetone, 186–187
  alcohols (benzoates), 289–290, 347–348
  acids, 195–196, 318
  ethylbenzene, 875
  indene, 776
  polymeric anhydrides, 317
  quaternary ammonium hydroxides, 237–240
  ricinoleic acid, 113, 116
  wood, 120
Pyromellitic acid, 656,*† 668*
Pyrones, 815–817
Pyroxonium salts, 816, 817
Pyroxylin, 858, 863
Pyrrole, 797,*† 798,† 799, 800*–802
Pyrrole-2-aldehyde, 800–801
Pyrrolidine, 797,† 802
Pyrroline, 797†
Δ^1-Pyrroline-5-carboxylic acid, 505
Pyrrolizidine, 828
Pyruvic acid, isolation, 480
  metabolism, 476, 477, 481–483, 486
  phenylhydrazone, 803
Pyrylium chloride, 815

Q-enzyme, 475–476
Quantum mechanics, 73
Quaternary ammonium compounds, 228–229
  decomposition, 237–240
Quaterphenyl, 532,* 615

* Physical constants   † Preparation

Quercetin, 823
Quinaldine, 530,* 811†
Quinalizarin, 904
Quinazoline, 814
Quinhydrone, 710
Quinic acid, 271,* 709*
Quinidine, 270, 271*
Quinine, 2, 270, 271,* 1025, 1026
    methohydroxide, 270
Quinizarin, 766
Quinoline, 530,* 806, 810-814
Quinoline yellow, 900-901
Quinolinic acid, 806
Quinolizidine, 828
Quinone, see o- and p- Benzoquinone
p-Quinonediimine, 715
Quinones, 709-731
p-Quinonimine, 715
Quinoxaline, 814
Quinquiphenyl, 615

Racemic acid, see dl-Tartaric acid
Racemization, 274-276
R-Acid, 747,† 924
Radicals (free), acyl, 721-722
    alkyl, 41-42
    benzoyl, 694
    hydrocarbon, 551-554
    nitrogen, 604-605, 709, 710
    phenoxyl, 637-638
Raney nickel catalyst, 66
Raolin, 850
Rapanone, 723
Rape oil, 408*
Raschig process, 626
Rast method, 11
Ravenillin, 818
Rayons, see Fibers
RDX, see Cyclonite
Rearrangements, acyl migration, 612
    allylaryl derivatives, 632, 633, 684, 685
    allylic, see Allylic rearrangements
    amine sulfates, 603, 746, 778
    Beckmann, 701-703, 756
    benzilic acid, 707, 757
    bond migration, 106, 416, 547, see also
        allylaryl derivatives
    bromoamides, 232
    camphor–p-cymene, 533
    Claisen, 639-640, 734-735, 753
    Curtius, 233
    diazoamino compounds, 619
    Fries, 634-635
    hydrazobenzene, 585

cis-trans isomers, 281-282, 403, 956
Jacobsen, 664
ketoximes, see Beckmann rearrangement
Lobry de Bruyn–van Eckenstein, 124, 360-
    361
naphthalenesulfonic acids, 737, 744, 746, 747
N-nitroso compounds, 606
phenylhydroxylamine 585, 631
phthaloyl chloride–as-phthalyl chloride, 660
pinacol, 700-701
terpenes, 940-943, 945
Wagner-Meerwein, 126-127
Wolff, 184
Reduction, see also Hydrogenation
    alkaloids, 835-836
    alkyl halides, 37, 153
    alkynes, 90
    azo compounds, 584, 621
    benzil and benzoin, 706-707
    benzyl chlorides, 647
    bimolecular, 206-207, 700, 741, 833
    Bouveault-Blanc, 177
    carbonyl group, 116-117, 206-207, 276, 543-
        544
    Clemmensen, 543-544
    diazonium salts, 617-618
    esters, 177
    Meerwein-Ponndorf, 207
    microbiological, 480
    naphthalene, 736-737, 751
    nitriles, 229-230
    nitro compounds, 583-585, 595-596, 749,
        750, 766
    C-nitrosoamines, 607
    N-nitrosoamines, 606
    oximes, 231, 433, 440-441, 703
    phenylhydrazones, 440
    quinones, 710-713, 766-768
    sulfinic acids, 593-594
    Wolff Kishner, 214, 544, 770, 703
Reductone, 394
Reformatsky reaction, 692
Reforming, 104
Reichert-Meissl value, 408
Reimer-Tiemann reaction, 680-684, 800-801
Reinecke's salt, 427
Rennin, 461
Resacetophenone, 695
Rescinnamine, 843
Reserpic acid, 843
Reserpine, 843
Resin acids, 948-949
Resins, 863

Resolution of racemic forms, 269–274, 275, 369–370, 431
Resonance, 70–72, 328
  allyl compounds, 151
  aniline, 597
  anthracene, 759
  azide group, 176, 609
  benzene, 522–525
  bromonium ion, 73
  carboxylic acids, 171–172
  dienes, 70–72
  dyes, 883–884
  free radicals, 554
  halides, 150–153, 567
  heterocycles, 801–803, 807, 816–817, 818–819
  naphthalene, 735–736
  nitro compounds, 569
  phenol, 568
  sulfonate ion, 593
Resorcinol, 624,* 629–630, 633
Resorcinol-4,6-disulfonic acid, 580
β-Resorcylaldehyde, 686
Retene, 757
Retenequinone, 757
Retinene, 956
Rhamnase, 379
Rhamnonic acid, 378
  γ- and δ-lactone, 378
Rhamnose, 375,* 377,* 379
Rhizopterin, 1007
Rhodamine 6G, 897, 898
Rhodamines, 897
Rhodanates, see Thiocyanates
Rhodanine, 437
Rhodopsin, 955–956
Ribitol, 463
Riboflavin, 464, 465, 998, 1003–1004
Riboflavin adenine dinucleotide, 465
Riboflavin-5′-phosphoric acid, 464–465
Ribonuclease, 430
Ribose, 360, 379, 462, 463, 468, 1003
Ricinine, 827
Ricinoleic acid, 401,* 404–405, 408
  dehydration, 416
  pyrolysis, 113, 116
Ricinstearolic acid, 405
Ring closure, aroylbenzoic acids, 763
  arylbutyric acids, 543, 546, 754, 767, 776, 792
  o-arylmethylbenzoic acids, 768, 793
  arylpropionic acids, 543, 648
  Blanc rule, 318
  camphors, 937–938

peri-cyclization, 779–780, 781, 792, 915, 916
  dibasic acids, 318–322
  hydroxy acids, 322–325
  o-methyl diaryl ketones, see Elbs reaction
  polymethylene dihalides, 309
Ring formation, 309–310, see also Diels-Alder reaction and Ring closure
Rosaniline, 203, 891,*† 899
Rosanthrene Pink, 929
Rosenmund reduction, 196, 686, 755
Rosin, 863, 948
  modified, 877
Rosolic acid, see Aurin
Rubber, 847–857
Rubber hydrochloride, 850
Rubijervine, 995
Rubremetine chloride, 845
Rubrene, 773–775
  peroxide, 774–775
Ruff degradation, 357, 358
Rutin, 823, 824
Rutinose, 824

Sabinene, 936
Saccharin, 591
Safranal, 959
Safranine T, 891
Safrole, 685
Salcomine, 681
Salicin, 380, 633
Salicylaldehyde, 675,* 680–681,† 690
  Dakin oxidation, 629
  potassium persulfate oxidation, 686
Salicylic acid, 579, 656,* 661†
  esters, 662
  reductive cleavage, 314
Saligenin, 624,* 633, 867
Salmin, 430
Salol, 662
Salvarsan, see Arsphenamine
Sandarac, 863
Sandmeyer reaction, 613–615
  examples: 613, 614, 645, 662, 675, 742
Santonin, 945
Sapamines, 414
Sapogenins, steroid, 993–995
  triterpenoid, 951
Saponification value, 408–409
Saponins, steroid, 993–995
  triterpenoid, 951
Saran, 862
Sarmentogenin, 982, 992, 993
Sarsasapogenin, 994, 995
Saytzeff rule, 126, 346, 347

* Physical constants　　　　† Preparation

Schaeffer acid, 747, 924
Schiff bases, 600, 810
Schiff test, 203
Schmidt reaction, 233
Schotten-Baumann reaction, 442, 627
Schweitzer's reagent, 387, 858
Scillaren A, 992
Scilliroside, 992
Scopine, 839
Scopolamine, 837, 838
Scopoline, 839
Sebacic acid, 113,† 117, 312*
Sebaconitrile, 230
Selacholeic acid (nervonic acid), 401,* 403, 490
Selenium dehydrogenation, 545, 625
    of sterols, 961, 995
Selinene, 945
Semicarbazide, 212
Semicarbazones, 212, 336
Semipolar bond, see Coordinate covalent bond
Sempervirine, 842–843
Senecio alkaloids, 828
Sensitive Green, 898, 899
Sensitive Red, 900
Sericin, 857
L-Serine, 419, 424,* 430, 432,† 433,† 437,† 439
    determination, 428
    dispensability, 498
    metabolism, 486, 504, 505
Serotonin, 501
Serum albumins, 417, 454–455
Serum globulins, 417, 454–455
Sesquiterpenes, 944–948
Sex hormones, 968–977
Shellac, 863
Shikonin, 730
Silica, structure, 878
Silicone rubber, 878
Silk fibroin, see Fibroin
Silk glue, see Sericin
Siloxane, 878
Silver acetylides, 92
Silver mirror test, 198
Silver salt degradation, 147
Silver salt method of esterification, 176
Sinigrin, 381
Sinomenine, 836, 837
Sitosterols, 964
Skatole, 502
Skew interactions, 304
Skraup quinoline synthesis, 810, 811, 903, 913–914
Sky Blue 6B, 927
Smilagenin, 994

Soaps, 399, 410–412
    synthetic, 412–415
Sodium acetylides, 86–87, 404
Sodium alkoxides, 124–125, 136
Sodium alkylates, see Sodium alkoxides
Sodium-ammonia reduction, 90
Sodium borohydride, 117
Sodium ethoxide, 124–125
Sodium formate, 313
Sodium glyceryl monolaurate sulfate, 413
Sodium methoxide, 124–125
Solanidine, 995
Solanine, 995
Sommelet reaction, 677
Sonn and Müller reaction, 686–687
Sorbaldehyde, 882*
Sorbic acid, 310, 692†
Sorbitol, 392,† 393
Sorbose, 392,† 393
Soybean oil, 415*
Sparteine, 827
Sphingomyelins, 490
Sphingosine, 490, 491
Spinulosin, 722
Spreading factor, see Hyaluronidase
Squalene, 950, 990–991
Staggered interactions, 304
Starch, 389–390, 461, 475–476
Stearaldehyde, 192*
Stearamide, 179,* 241*
Stearic acid, 233, 400*
    decarboxylation, 40
    occurrence, 400, 408, 409, 415, 489, 490
Stearic anhydride, 186*
Stearone, 192*
Stearoyl chloride, 180*
Stearyl alcohol, 112,* 197
Stephen reaction, 687
Sterculic acid, 296
Stereochemistry, 249–294
    amino acids, 423–424
    diazole acids, 611–612
    oximes, 701
    sugars, 371–378
Steric hindrance, 61, 174, 183, 203, 204, 292, 554, 561, 671–672, 697, 736, 744, 745, 746, 755
Steroids, 961–996
Stigmasterol, 964,* 970
α-Stilbazole, 808
Stilbene, 330, 532,* 545, 707†
    dibromides, 303,* 304
Stilbenediol diacetate (α- and β-), 706
Stilbestrol, 972

Stillingic acid, 401*
Stipitatic acid, 640, 642–643
Stobbe reaction, 699
Strain theory (Baeyer), 296–297
Strecker cyanohydrin synthesis, 432
Streptomycin, 1034–1035
Strophanthidin, 992
Strophanthin, 992
Strophanthobiase, 992
Strychnine, 2, 272,* 843–844
Stuart models, 258, 259
Styphnic acid, see 2,4,6-Trinitroresorcinol
Styrene, 532,* 549,† 669, 875,† 882*
    addition reactions, 331, 332
    polymerization, 875–876
Suberic acid, 312,* 315, 524†
Suberone, 839, 840
Suberylarginine, 993
Substantive dyes, 887
Subtilin, 450
Succinamic acid, 188,*† 243
Succinamide, 242–243*
Succindialdehyde, 797,† 799, 840, 841
Succinic acid, 281, 312,* 313–314,† 481, 797
    metabolism, 481, 482, 483, 506
Succinic anhydride, 186,* 198,† 281, 316
Succinic anhydride synthesis, 542, 753–754,
    792–793
Succinic dehydrogenase, 461, 482
Succinimide, 242–243*†
Succinoylation, acenaphthene, 665
    anisole, 634
    benzene, 542, 669
    Grignard reagent, 669
    β-methylnaphthalene, 745
    naphthalene, 738, 754
    phenanthrene, 753–754
    pyrene, 792
    tetralin, 739
    veratrole, 634
Succinoylsulfathiazole, 1029, 1031, 1032
Sucrase, 473
Sucrose, 350, 381–383, 473
Sugar, see Sucrose
Sugars, see Carbohydrates
Sulfacetamide, 1029, 1032
Sulfadiazine, 1029, 1031
Sulfa drugs, 1028–1033
Sulfaguanidine, 1029, 1032
Sulfamerazine, 1029
Sulfamethazine, 1029
Sulfanilamide, 1029

2-Sulfanilamidodiazine, see Sulfadiazine
4-Sulfanilamidodiazine, 1032
Sulfanilic acid, 598–599,* 602–603,† 612
Sulfapyridine, 1029
Sulfasuxidine, see Succinoylsulfathiazole
Sulfathiazole, 1029
Sulfides, 140
Sulfinic acids, 593
o-Sulfobenzoic acid imide, see Saccharin
Sulfonamides, 590
4-Sulfonamido-2′,4′-diaminoazobenzene,   see
    Prontosil
Sulfonation, acetanilide, 601
    anthraquinone, 763, 764
    benzene and alkylbenzenes, 515, 556, 561,
        588–589
    mechanism, 565
    naphthalene, 737, 740
    naphthalenesulfonic acids, 749–751
    β-naphthol, 746–748
    phenanthrene, 755–756
Sulfonic acids, 139,† 588–594
    desulfonation, 548–549; examples: 601, 747,
        748
    fusion, 592–593; examples: 623, 625, 629,
        632, 663, 740, 747, 748, 749, 769, 778, 789
Sulfonium salts, 140
Sulfur dyes, 886, 921–922
Sulfuric acid, 162
Sulfurous acid, 162
Sullivan color reaction, 428
Surface-active compounds, 411–415
Sympathomimetric bases, 500
Syntex M, 412–413
Syringic acid, 656,* 663

Tachysterol, 1013
Tallows, 408*
D-Talolactone, 377,* 378
D-Talonic acid, 377
Talose, 356, 359, 372,* 373*
Tannic acid, 887
Tariric acid, 405*
Tartaric acid, stereochemistry, 252–255, 263,
    267–269*
d-Tartaric acid, 269,* 271*
dl-Tartaric acid, 269,* 271,* 285, 313
l-Tartaric acid (D-series), 263, 269*
Taurine, 413, 502
Taurocholic acid, 491, 967
Tautomerism aminonaphthoquinones, 714–715
    hydroxyquinones, 713–714, 726–727
    keto-enol, see Keto-enol tautomerism
    nitrosohydroxylamine oxide, 606–607

---

* Physical constants   † Preparation

Teflon, 866
Terephthalaldehyde, 524
Terephthalic acid, 517, 663,*† 668,* 861
Terpenes, 935–944
p-Terphenyl (1,4-diphenylbenzene), 532,* 615
α-Terpinene, 936
α-Terpineol, 938
Terramycin, 1035
Terylene, 861–862
Testosterone, 972,* 974, 975
Tetraacetylfructopyranose, 383
Tetrabromostearic acid, 403
Tetracarboxyimide dyes, 920
1,2,3,4-Tetrachlorobenzene, 644*
1,2,4,5-Tetrachlorobenzene, 644,* 645–646†
Tetrachloro-p-benzoquinone, see Chloranil
s-Tetrachloroethane, 88, 154,* 157†
n-Tetracontane, 31*
n-Tetracosane, 31*
Tetracycline, 1035
n-Tetradecane, 31*
Tetraethylammonium hydroxide, 238
Tetraethyllead, 100–101
Tetraethylpyrophosphite, 446, 449
Tetrafluoroethylene, 866
n-Tetrahexacontane, 31*
Tetrahydroabietic acid, 877
Tetrahydrodimethylquinolinium hydroxide, 829
Tetrahydrofuran, 133,* 134, 797,† 798
Tetrahydrofurfuryl alcohol, 815
5,6,7,8-Tetrahydro-10-methyl-1,2-benzanthracene, 787
cis-Δ⁴-Tetrahydrophthalic anhydride, 310
Tetrahydropyrrole, see Pyrrolidine
2,3-Tetralanthraquinone, 772
Tetralin (1,2,3,4-tetrahydronaphthalene), 97,* 545, 546, 739, 751†
ar-2-Tetralol, 683
α-Tetralone, 543,*† 544, 546†
Tetramethylammonium bromide, 227
Tetramethylammonium hydroxide, 228, 238*
Tetramethylammonium iodide, 228
Tetramethylene bromide, 154,* 158†
Tetramethylenediamine, 224*
Tetramethylene glycol, 177*†
Tetramethylethylene, 126, 331
1,3,4,6-Tetramethylfructose, 382
2,3,4,6-Tetramethylgalactose, 384
Tetramethyl-γ-gluconolactone, 367
2,3,4,6-Tetramethylglucose, 364†
    formation, 382, 385, 389, 390
Tetramethyl-γ-glucose, 367
Tetramethylmethane, 27*

4,5,3',5'-Tetramethylpyrro-2,2'-methene hydrobomide, 457
Tetramethylthiuram disulfide, 849
Tetranitromethane, 70, 89, 295
N,2,4,6-Tetranitro-N-methylaniline, see Tetryl
2,3,4,6-Tetranitrophenol, 580
Tetraphenyl-1,4-benzoquinone, 721
Tetraphenylcumulenes, 882
Tetraphenylethylene, 59
    dichloride, 59
Tetraphenylhydrazine, 604–605
Tetraphenylmethane, 532,* 551
5,6,11,12-Tetraphenylnaphtacene, see Rubrene
Tetronic acid, 393
Tetryl, 571,* 581†
    explosive, 581–583
o-(2-Tetroyl)-benzoic acid, 739
β-2-Tetroylpropionic acid, 739
Thapsic acid chloride, 321
Thebaine, 833, 834
Thelephoric acid, 724
2-Thenylamine, 800
Theobromine, 247
Theophylline, 247
Thermal decomposition, see Pyrolysis
Thermoprene, 850
Thiamine (vitamin B₁), 393, 467, 998, 1001–1003, 1032
Thiamine hydrochloride pyrophosphate, see Cocarboxylase
Thianaphthene, 802
Thiazole, 802
Thiele reaction, 717–718, 722, 770, 771
2-Thienylmethylamine, 800
Thiocarbanilide, see s-Diphenylthiourea
Thio-o-cresol, 594
Thio-p-cresol, 594
Thioctic acid, 139–140, 482
Thiocyanates, 615
Thiocyanation, 788, 789
5-Thiocyano-3,4-benzpyrene, 788
15-Thiocyano-20-methylcholanthrene, 789
β-Thiodiglycol, 70
Thioglycolic acid, 163*
Thiohydantoin, 435
Thioindigo, 909–910
Thiokols, 854
Thiolacetic acid, 139, 494
Thiolvaline, 422
Thionaphthene, 529
Thio-β-naphthol, 594
Thionyl chloride, 147, 180, 181, 341–342

Thiophene, 98, 528*-529, 542, 796,† 797,† 798,† 800, 801–802
Thiophenol, 594
Thiophthene, 802
Thiosalicylic acid, 909
Thiourea, 46, 139
Thiouracil, 459–460
L-Threonine, 419,* 421, 430, 437–439,† 476
    configuration, 423
    determination, 438
    indispensability, 498
Threo-oxazoline, 438, 439
D-Threose, 360, 423
Thrombin, 1018–1019
Thymidine, 1008
Thymine, 468, 1008
Thymol, 624,* 625, 632, 679
p-Thymol-aldehyde, 679
Thyroglobulin, 430, 431, 459
L-Thyroxine, 422, 423, 430, 437,† 459, 511
Tiglic acid, 284–285*
Tigogenin, 993
Tigonin, 993
TNB, see 1,3,5-Trinitrobenzene
TNT, see 2,4,6-Trinitrotoluene
TNX, see 2,4,6-Trinitro-m-xylene
Tobacco mosaic virus, 452,* 470–471
Tobacco ringspot virus, 471
Tobias acid (2-naphthylamine-1-sulfonic acid), 747
α-Tocopherol, 1015
β-Tocopherol, 1016
γ-Tocopherol, 1016
α-Tocopherylquinone, 1016
o-Tolidine, 597,* 616, 926
m-Tolualdehyde, 675,* 676†
o-Tolualdehyde, 687
p-Tolualdehyde, 675,* 677,† 678,† 679†
Toluene, 532,* 533,* 535
    formylation, 678, 679
    halogenation, 550, 646, 674
    nitration, 560, 676
    oxidation, 550, 657, 658, 675
    petroleum, 96, 107†
    sulfonation, 561
2,4-Toluenediamine, 595
p-Toluenesulfinic acid, 593
o-Toluenesulfonamide, 590
p-Toluenesulfonic acid, 588,* 592
p-Toluenesulfonyl chloride, 590,* 593
Toluic acids, 656,* 662†

m-Toluidine, 597,* 616–617†
    hydrochloride, 598*
o-Toluidine, 597,* 600,† 614, 910, 911
    hydrochloride, 598*
p-Toluidine, 597,* 600,† 614, 615, 616–617
    acetate, 594,* 617
    substitutions, 645
    sulfonic acid salts, 589
Toluidine Toner, 933
o-Tolunitrile, 614†
p-Tolunitrile, 614†
Toluquinone, 310, 732
o-Tolylcarbinol, 649
p-Tolyl methyl ketone, 547
p-Tolylsulfonylmethylnitrosoamide, 176
Tomato bushy stunt virus, 471
Toxins, 396, 471
Transamination, 498–499
Transesterification, see Alcoholysis of esters
Transition state, 278, 337–338, 339–340, 343, 345, 346, 966–967
Transmethylation, 503–504
Transthiolation, 504
Traumatic acid, 315
n-Triacontane, 31*
n-Triacontanol, 409*
s-Triaminobenzoic acid, 631
Tri-o-anisylmethyl, 553
Triaryltetrazolium salts, 805
1,2,3-Triazole, 802
1,2,4-Triazole, 802
Tri-p-biphenylmethyl, 553
2,4,6-Tribromoaniline, 597,* 602,† 616
s-Tribromobenzene, 616
2,4,6-Tribromophenol, 624,* 628†
Tribromo-m-toluidine, 602
Tricaprin, 409
Trichloroacetic acid, 163,* 170†
Trichloroacetone, 154
Trichloroacetonitrile, 696
2,4,6-Trichloroaniline, 597*
1,2,4-Trichlorobenzene, 644,* 645–646†
γ,γ,γ-Trichlorocrotonic acid, 283
Trichloroethylene, 154,* 158†
Trichlorofluoromethane, 160
Trichloromethyl chloroformate, 185
2,4,6-Trichlorophenol, 624,* 628
n-Tricosane, 31*
n-Tridecane, 31*
Tridecylic acid, 400
Triethanolamine, 224,* 235†
    soaps, 414
Triethylamine, 224,* 226,* 229,† 238
    hydrochloride, 227*

1,3,5-Triethylbenzene, 532,* 538†
Trifluoromethane, 159*
Trigonelline, 1006
1,2,3-Trihydroxybenzene, see Pyrogallol
1,2,4-Trihydroxybenzene, see Hydroxyhydro-
    quinone
1,3,5-Trihydroxybenzene, see Phloroglucinol
3,5,8-Trihydroxy-1-methylanthraquinone, 771
2,6,8-Trihydroxypurine, see Uric acid
2,4,6-Triisopropylphenol, 540
Trilaurin, 178,* 409
Trilinolein, 409
Trilinolenin, 409
Trimellitic acid (benzene-1,2,4-tricarboxylic
    acid), 664,*† 668,* 733
Trimesic acid (benzene-1,3,5-tricarboxylic
    acid), 664,*† 668*
  trimethyl ester, 664*
3,4,5-Trimethoxybenzoic acid, 843
Trimethylacetic acid, 117, 163,* 167,† 174
Trimethylacetophenone, see Acetopseudocu-
    mene
Trimethylamine, 224,* 225, 226,* 229,† 234,†
    238
  hydrobromide, 227
  hydrochloride, 234†
  oxide, 239
  trimethylboron, 225
Trimethylammonium bromide, 227, 229
Trimethylammonium methylide, 650
Trimethylanilinium nitrate, 559
1,2,3-Trimethylbenzene, see Hemimellitene
1,2,4-Trimethylbenzene, see Pseudocumene
1,3,5-Trimethylbenzene, see Mesitylene
2,4,6-Trimethylbenzoic acid, 672
2,3,5-Trimethylbenzoquinone, 723
Trimethylboron, 225, 335
2,2,3-Trimethylbutane, 29,* 105
Trimethylcellulose, 386
1,2,4-Trimethylcyclohexane, 96*
2,2,6-Trimethylcyclohexanecarboxylic acid,
    98
Trimethylcyclopropylammonium hydroxide,
    286
2,4,5-Trimethyl-4-dichloromethyl-Δ²,⁶-cyclo-
    hexadienone-1, 682
Trimethylene bromide, 154,* 158,† 167, 309
Trimethylene chlorohydrin, 166
Trimethylene cyanide, 167
Trimethylenediamine, 224*
Trimethylene glycol, 124,*† 158, 166, 314
Trimethylene oxide, 120*
  dibromide, 58*-59
Trimethylethylene, 58*-59

2,3,4-Trimethylglucose, 380
2,3,6-Trimethylglucose, 384, 385, 389, 390
Trimethylhydroquinone, 1015
Trimethylmethane, see Isobutane
1,3,3-Trimethyl-2-methylenedihydroindole,
    901
1,2,6-Trimethylnaphthalene, 940
2,2,4-Trimethylpentane, see Isooctane
β,β,γ-Trimethylpimelic acid, 940
2,3,8-Trimethylquinoline, 99
2,4,8-Trimethylquinoline, 99
Trimethylsuccinic acid, 942
Trimyristin, 409
1,3,5-Trinitrobenzene, 571,* 578†
  complexes, 586,* 598
  explosive properties, 581-582
2,4,6-Trinitrobenzeneazomesitylene, 620
2,4,6-Trinitrobenzenediazonium chloride, 620
2,4,6-Trinitrobenzoic acid, 578,† 631
2,4,6-Trinitrochlorobenzene, see Picryl chlo-
    ride
Trinitrofluorenone, complexes, 586*
2,4,6-Trinitrophenol, see Picric acid
2,4,6-Trinitroresorcinol, 571,* 580†
  complexes, 586
2,4,6-Trinitrostilbene, 577
2,3,4-Trinitrotoluene, 577
2,4,5-Trinitrotoluene, 577
2,4,6-Trinitrotoluene, 571,* 576-577,† 631
  complexes, 586
  explosive properties, 581-583
  oxidation, 578
2,4,6-Trinitro-m-xylene, 571,* 578†
Triolein, 409, 410
Triose mutase, 477
Trioxan, 200-201
Tripalmitin, 399, 409*
Triphenylamine, 597,* 604†
s-Triphenylbenzene, 532,* 699†
Triphenylcarbinol, 119,† 128, 168, 551,*† 554
Triphenylcarbinol-o-carboxylic acid, 896
Triphenylchloromethane, 552
Triphenylene, 545-546
Triphenylmethane, 168, 532,* 536†
  oxidation, 128, 557
Triphenylmethanecarboxylic acid, 896
Triphenylmethane dyes, 891-895
Triphenylmethyl, 551, 554, 603
Triphenylphosphinemethylene, 651
Triphenylphosphite, 147
Triphenylphosphonium bromide, 651
Triphenylrosaniline, 891
Triphenyltetrazolium chloride, 805

Triphosphopyridine nucleotide (coenzyme II), 464
Tri-*n*-propylamine, 224*
Triptane, 106
Triptycene, 335, 760*
Tristearin, 399, 409*
Triterpenes, 850–851
Triundecylin, 493
Trivalent carbon, *see* Radicals
Tropane alkaloids, 837–841
Tropic acid, 838
Tropidine, 840
Tropine, 839, 840
Tropinone, 839, 840, 841†
Tropolones, 640–643
Trypaflavine, 1028
Trypan Blue, 928, 929
Trypan Red, 928, 929, 1022
Tryparsamide, 1023–1024
Trypsin, 462
Tryptamine, 844
L-Tryptophan, 419,* 420, 424,* 427, 430, 434,† 435,† 437,† 829
  betaine, *see* Hypaphorine
  determination, 428
  indispensability, 498
  metabolism, 501, 512–513
Tschugaeff dehydration, 348
Tuberculostearic acid, 407
Tung oil, 403, 415,* 416
Turkey Red, 886, *see also* Alizarin
Turkey-red oil, 412, 886
Tyramine, 500
Tyrian purple, 908
Tyrocidine, 450
Tyrosinase, 461, 463
L-Tyrosine, 419,* 420, 424,* 430, 433,† 435,† 440†
  biosyntheses, 508–509
  dispensability, 498
  metabolism, 461, 463, 476, 481, 508–509, 510–511
  nitration, 579
Tyrosol, 481

Ullmann reaction, 652
  examples: 913, 914
Umbelliferone, 817
n-Undecane, 31*
Undecanedioic acid, 493
Undecyl bromide, 147
Undecylenic acid, 116

Undecylic acid, 400
Uracil, 468
Urea, 2, 3, 184,† 243*–244,† 246, 461
  complexes, 46, 399
  -formaldehyde resins, 870–871
  metabolism, 502–503
  mononitrate, 244
Urease, 460, 461, 462
Ureides, 244–247, 608
Urethan, 185*†
Urethans, 608–609
Uric acid, 244–246, 506–507
Uridylic acid, 469
Uridylribosidodiphosphatoglucoside (UDPG), 475
Urotropin, *see* Hexamethylenetetramine
Usnic acid, 804

Vacanceine Red, 887
Vaccenic acid, 401,† 404†
n-Valeraldehyde, 192*
n-Valeramide, 179,* 241*
n-Valeric acid, 163,* 166, 816
n-Valeric anhydride, 186*
γ-Valerolactone, 304, 816
n-Valeryl chloride, 180*
L-Valine, 419,* 424,* 430, 431,† 434,† 440,† 476, 842
  indispensability, 498
  isolation, 427
Vanillin, 684,* 685†
Van Slyke nitrogen determination, 427–428
Vaseline, 110
Vasicine, 827
Vasopressin, 447, 448, 449
Vat dyes, 885–886
Vat Pink FFR, 910–911
Venetian scarlet, 771
Veratraldehyde, 685
Veratric acid, 826
Veratrole, 629,*† 685
Veratrum alkaloids, 995
Vernolic acid, 405
Veronal, 246
Vetivazulene, 946
β-Vetivone, 946
Vicara, 860
Victoria Blue B, 893–894
Victoria Violet 4BS, 931
Vinethene, 135
Vinyl acetate, 89†
  polymerization, 862, 874
Vinylacetic acid, 163
Vinylacetylene, 90,† 851

---

* Physical constants   † Preparation

Vinyl alcohol, 89, 150
Vinylation, 89
Vinylbenzene, see Styrene
Vinyl bromide, 62, 146,* 152†
  addition reactions, 331, 333
  polymerization, 862
Vinyl chloride, 146,* 157, 862†
  polymerization, 862, 874
Vinyl halides, 146,* 152–153
  polymerization, 862, 874
  resonance, 152–153, 327–328
Vinylidene chloride, 862, 874
Vinyl iodide, 88,† 152
Vinyl polymers, 862, 874–875
α-Vinylpyridine, 806
Vinyon, 862
Vioform, 1025
Violanthrone, 915–916
Virus proteins, 470–471
Viscose process, 858–859
Visnagin, 818
Vitamin A, 954*–959, 998
Vitamin A acid, 958
Vitamin A aldehyde (retinene), 956
Vitamin A_2, 955
Vitamin B_1, see Thiamine
Vitamin B_2, see Riboflavin
Vitamin B_6, see Pyridoxine
Vitamin B_{12}, 999, 1008–1009
Vitamin C, see Ascorbic acid
Vitamin D, 998, 1012–1014
Vitamin D_1, 1013
Vitamin D_2, 1013
Vitamin D_3, 1014
Vitamin E, 998, 1014–1016
Vitamin G, see Riboflavin
Vitamin H, see Biotin
Vitamin K_1, 998, 1016–1018
  alkali cleavage, 725
Vitamin K_2, 1017–1018
Vitamin P, 823
Vitamins, 997–1020
Vulcanization, 848–849, 851
Vulpinic acid, 806

Wagner-Meerwein rearrangement, 126–127, 940–941
Walden inversion, 277–278, 288, 363, 379
Weermann degradation, 358
Wetting agents, see Surface-active agents
Whale blubber, 408*
Wieland dehydrogenation theory, 127–128

Willgerodt reaction, 705–706
Williamson ether synthesis, 136
Wohl degradation, 357, 358
Wolff-Kishner reduction, 214, 544, 779, 793
Wool, see Keratin
Wurtz-Fittig synthesis, 534–535, 650
Wurtz reaction, 35–36, 552, 782, 950

Xanthine, 247
Xanthone, 817, 818
Xanthophylls, 952
Xanthopterine, 1007
Xanthurenic acid, 512–513
Ximenynic acid, 405
Xylan, 388
m-Xylene, 81, 532,* 562
  oxidation, 657, 662, 663, 676
  sulfonation, 548–549
o-Xylene, 81, 107,† 532,* 562
  ozonization, 520–521
  sulfonation, 548–549
p-Xylene, 81, 532,* 535,† 562
  oxidation, 657, 663
  sulfonation, 548–549
"Xylene musk," 583
Xylenes, coal tar, 528, 529, 548
  methylation, 536–537
  separation, 548–549
m-Xylene-4-sulfonic acid, 548–549
o-Xylene-4-sulfonic acid, 548–549
p-Xylene-2-sulfonic acid, 548–549
Xylenols, 530*
3,4-Xylidine, 1003
D-Xylose, 360, 375,* 377*
Xylotrimethoxyglutaric acid, 364
o-Xylylene dibromide, 671–672
p-Xylylene dichloride, 647

Yangonin, 817
Yeast adenylic acid, 468
Yeast nucleic acid, 469–470
Yohimbe alkaloids, 842–843
Yohimbine, 842

Zein, 418, 860
Zeisel methoxy determination, 137
Zephiran, 414
Zerewitinoff determination, 205–206
Zinc dimethyldithiocarbamate, 849
Zinc dust distillation 550, 830, 901
Zwitterion, see Dipolar ion

Bond Distances (* designates hybrid bond)

Bond	Type	Distance, Å	Bond	Type	Distance, Å
C—C	R—R	1.54	C—N	$(CH_3)_3N$	1.47
C—C	Ar—R	1.54	C—N	$CH_3—NO_2$	1.46
C—C	Cyclopropane	1.53	C—N*	Trinitrobenzene	1.4
C—C	$CH_3CH{=}CHCH_3$	1.54	C—N	$H_2N—CHRCO_2H$	1.47
C—C*	$CH_3C{\equiv}N$	1.49	C≡N	$HC{\equiv}N$	1.15
C—C*	$CH_3C{\equiv}CCH_3$	1.47	$C\overset{\cdots}{-}\overset{+}{N}$*	Diazomethane	1.34
C—C*	$C_6H_5—C_6H_5$	1.48			
C—C*	$CH_2{=}CH—CH{=}CH_2$ (2,3-bond)	1.46	$C\overset{\cdots}{-}\overset{+}{N}$*	Urea	1.37
			$C\overset{\cdots}{-}N$*	Pyridine	1.37
C—C*	Furan (β,β-bond)	1.46	C—S	CH_3SCH_3	1.82
C—C*	Thiophene (β,β-bond)	1.44	C=S*	CS_2	1.54
C—C*	$O{=}CH—CH{=}O$	1.47	C—F	CH_3F	1.42
C—C*	$N{\equiv}C—C{\equiv}N$	1.37	C—F	CCl_2F_2	1.35
C—C*	$HC{\equiv}C—C{\equiv}CH$	1.36	C—Cl	CH_3Cl	1.77
C=C	$R_2C{=}CR_2$	1.33	C—Cl	$(CH_3)_3CCl$	1.78
C=C	$CH_2{=}C{=}CH_2$	1.33	C—Cl*	$CH_2{=}CHCl$	1.69
$C\overset{\cdots}{-}C$*	Benzene	1.40	C—Cl*	C_6H_5Cl	1.70
$C\overset{\cdots}{-}C$*	Naphthalene	1.36, 1.39	C—Cl	$HC{\equiv}CCl$	1.68
C≡C	$RC{\equiv}CR$	1.20	C—Cl	$N{\equiv}CCl$	1.67
C≡C	$C_6H_5C{\equiv}CC_6H_5$	1.19	C—Br	CH_3Br	1.91
C—H	CH_4	1.09	C—Br*	$CH_2{=}CHBr$	1.86
C—H	$CH_2{=}CH_2$	1.09	C—I	CHI_3	2.12
C—H*	$HC{\equiv}CH$	1.06	C—I*	$CH_2{=}CHI$	2.03
C—H*	$HC{\equiv}N$	1.06	O—H	H_2O	0.96
C—O	CH_3OCH_3	1.42	N—H	NH_3	1.01
C—O	$CH_3—ONO_2$	1.43	N—O	$CH_3O—NO_2$	1.36
C—O	Dioxan	1.46	N—N	Calculated	1.40
C=O	$CH_2{=}O$	1.21	N=N	$C_6H_5N{=}NC_6H_5$ (*cis* and *trans*)	1.23
C=O*	CCl_3CHO	1.15			
C=O*	Carbon dioxide	1.16	$\overset{+}{N}\overset{\cdots}{\equiv}N$*	Diazomethane	1.13
$C\overset{\cdots}{-}O^{-}$*	Carbonate ion	1.30	S—H	H_2S	1.35
:C≡O:*	Carbon monoxide	1.13	S—S	CH_3SSCH_3	2.04
C=O*	Carbon suboxide	1.20			

BOND ENERGIES (kg.-cal./mole)

BOND	ENERGY	BOND	ENERGY	BOND	ENERGY
C—H	87.3	C—F	107.0	N—N	20.0
C—C	58.6	C—Cl	66.5	N≡N	170.0
C=C	100.0	C—Br	54.0	N—Cl	38.4
C≡C	123.0	C—I	45.5	S—H	87.5
C—O	70.0	H—H	103.4	S—S	63.8
C=O (CH$_2$O)	142.0	H-bond	5.0	F—F	63.5
C=O (RCHO)	149.0	H—F	147.5	Cl—Cl	57.8
C=O (R$_2$CO)	152.0	H—Cl	102.7	Br—Br	46.1
C—N	48.6	H—Br	87.3	I—I	36.2
C=N	94.0	H—I	71.4	Cl—F	86.4
C≡N (HCN)	144.0	O—H	110.2	Br—Cl	52.7
C≡N (RCN)	150.0	O—O	34.9	I—Cl	51.0
C—S	54.5	O=O	96.0	I—Br	42.9
C=S	103.0	N—H	83.7	Na—Na	18.5

RESONANCE ENERGIES (kg.-cal./mole)

COMPOUND	ENERGY	COMPOUND	ENERGY
Acetamide	25	Furan	23
Acetic acid	25	Indole	54
Acetic anhydride	41	Naphthalene	75
Acetophenone	46	Phenanthrene	110
Aniline	45	Phenol	46
Anthracene	105	Phenylacetylene	49
Benzene	39	Pyridine	43
Butadiene-1,3	3.5	Pyrrole	31
Carbon dioxide	33	Quinoline	69
Crotonaldehyde	2.4	Stilbene	93
Cyclohexadiene-1,3	1.8	Styrene	46
Cyclopentadiene-1,3	2.9	Thiophene	31
2,3-Dimethylbutadiene-1,3	2.9	Toluene	39
Diphenyl	86[a]	1,3,5-Triphenylbenzene	64
Ethyl acetate	25	Urea	41

[a] 2 × 39 (benzene) + 8

PROPERTIES OF SOLVENTS

SOLVENT	DIELECTRIC CONSTANT	SOLY. IN $H_2O^{20°}$, %	SOLVENT	DIELECTRIC CONSTANT	SOLY. IN $H_2O^{20°}$, %
HCN (liq.)	95	∝	Pyridine	12.5	∝
Water	81.1		Aniline	7.2	3.49
Formic acid	47.9	∝	Acetic acid	7.1	∝
Nitromethane	39.4	sl. sol.	Ethylamine	6.3	∝
Acetonitrile	38.8	∝	Chlorobenzene	5.9	insol.
Nitrobenzene	36.1	0.19	Chloroform	5.0	0.82
Methanol	33.7	∝	Ether	4.3	7.5
Ethanol	25.7	∝	Triethylamine	3.1	∝ < 19°
Ammonia (liq.)	21	∝	Dioxan	2.3	∝
Acetone	21.4	∝	Benzene	2.3	0.06
Acetic anhydride	20.5	12	Carbon tetrachloride	2.2	0.1
n-Butanol	17.8	8.3	Pentane	1.8	insol.

INDUCTIVE EFFECTS (ALIPHATIC SERIES)

Electron-attracting groups: $Cl > Br > I > OCH_3 > OH > C_6H_5 > CH{=}CH_2 > H$

Electron-releasing groups: $(CH_3)_3C > (CH_3)_2CH > CH_3CH_2 > CH_3 > H$

ELECTRONEGATIVITY VALUES

F	4.0	S	2.5	B	2.0
O	3.5	C	2.5	Sn	1.7
N	3.0	I	2.4	Al	1.5
Cl	3.0	P	2.1	Mg	1.2
Br	2.8	H	2.1	Na	0.9